S. CHAND'S SUCCESS GUIDE
(Questions and Answers)

REFRESHER COURSE SERIES

PHYSICS

VOLUME–I

S. CHAND'S SUCCESS GUIDE
(Questions and Answers)

REFRESHER COURSE IN
PHYSICS

For B. Sc. Students

(Revised as per new UGC Model Syllabus)

VOLUME–I

INCLUDING :
I. MECHANICS AND PROPERTIES OF MATTER
II. WAVES, VIBRATIONS AND E.M. THEORY
III. ELECTRICITY AND MAGNETISM

(Including : Solved Long Answer Type, Short Answer Type, Objective Type, Multiple Choice and Numerical Problems)

C.L. ARORA

Former Principal
DAV College, Jalandhar
and Dean Colleges
GNDU, Amritsar

S. CHAND
PUBLISHING
empowering minds

S.CHAND & COMPANY PVT. LTD.
(AN ISO 9001 : 2008 COMPANY)
RAM NAGAR, NEW DELHI - 110055

S. CHAND & COMPANY PVT. LTD.
(An ISO 9001:2008 Company)

Head Office: 7361, RAM NAGAR, NEW DELHI - 110 055
Phone: 23672080-81-82, 9899107446, 9911310888 Fax: 91-11-23677446
www.schandpublishing.com; e-mail: helpdesk@schandpublishing.com

Branches

Ahmedabad	:	Ph: 27541965, 27542369, ahmedabad@schandpublishing.com
Bengaluru	:	Ph: 22268048, 22354008, bangalore@schandpublishing.com
Bhopal	:	Ph: 4274723, 4209587, bhopal@schandpublishing.com
Chandigarh	:	Ph: 2625356, 2625546, chandigarh@schandpublishing.com
Chennai	:	Ph: 28410027, 28410058, chennai@schandpublishing.com
Coimbatore	:	Ph: 2323620, 4217136, coimbatore@schandpublishing.com (Marketing Office)
Cuttack	:	Ph: 2332580, 2332581, cuttack@schandpublishing.com
Dehradun	:	Ph: 2711101, 2710861, dehradun@schandpublishing.com
Guwahati	:	Ph: 2738811, 2735640, guwahati@schandpublishing.com
Hyderabad	:	Ph: 27550194, 27550195, hyderabad@schandpublishing.com
Jaipur	:	Ph: 2219175, 2219176, jaipur@schandpublishing.com
Jalandhar	:	Ph: 2401630, 5000630, jalandhar@schandpublishing.com
Kochi	:	Ph: 2378740, 2378207-08, cochin@schandpublishing.com
Kolkata	:	Ph: 22367459, 22373914, kolkata@schandpublishing.com
Lucknow	:	Ph: 4026791, 4065646, lucknow@schandpublishing.com
Mumbai	:	Ph: 22690881, 22610885, mumbai@schandpublishing.com
Nagpur	:	Ph: 6451311, 2720523, 2777666, nagpur@schandpublishing.com
Patna	:	Ph: 2300489, 2302100, patna@schandpublishing.com
Pune	:	Ph: 64017298, pune@schandpublishing.com
Raipur	:	Ph: 2443142, raipur@schandpublishing.com (Marketing Office)
Ranchi	:	Ph: 2361178, ranchi@schandpublishing.com
Siliguri	:	Ph: 2520750, siliguri@schandpublishing.com (Marketing Office)
Visakhapatnam	:	Ph: 2782609, visakhapatnam@schandpublishing.com (Marketing Office)

First Edition 1957
Subsequent Editions and Reprints 1995, 98, 99, 2001, 2003, 2005, 2006, 2008, 2010, 2011
Revised Edition 2014; Reprints 2014 (Twice); Reprint 2015
Reprint 2016 (Twice)

ISBN: 978-81-219-0465-0   **Code: 1016D 072**

PRINTED IN INDIA
By Nirja Publishers & Printers Pvt. Ltd., 54/3/2, Jindal Paddy Compound, Kashipur Road, Rudrapur-263153, Uttarakhand and published by S. Chand & Company Pvt. Ltd., 7361, Ram Nagar, New Delhi -110 055.

Preface to the Revised Edition

The University Grants Commission has recently issued 'UGC Model Curriculum' and most of the Indian Universities have adopted the same with minor modifications.

This book is Volume-I of the 'Question Answer Bank' series in B.Sc. Physics. It has three parts:

(i) Mechanics and Properties of Matter

(ii) Waves, Vibrations and E.M. Theory

(iii) Electricity and Magnetism

It has been revised and brought up-to-date in accordance with the latest syllabi, to meet the needs of the students and teachers alike. The book is unique in the respect that it has adopted a new style in the form of 'questions and answers'. For this purpose questions set in the latest B.Sc. examination of various prominent Indian Universities only during the last few years have been selected and arranged chapterwise to cover almost the entire syllabus. No attempt has been made to pick and choose the material to reduce the volume of the book.

My experience of over fifty years as a teacher in some of the biggest colleges has revealed that some times even the best students are unable to make out what and how much they have to write in answer to a question set in the examination.

This book has been prepared to enable the students to give a correct and to the point answer to questions set in the examination. The answers have been arranged under various heads and subheads to facilitate the students to remember various steps. In accordance with the modern style of question papers, long answer type, short answer type, objective type and multiple choice type questions have been included to cover the entire syllabus. In Physics, numerical problems form a very important part of the questions paper. A very large number of solved problems have been included in each chapter at the proper place, so that the students can easily understand the theory used in solving the problem.

The students generally feel shy of solving additional unsolved problem given at the end of each chapter. In this edition, therefore, new unsolved problems have been given as exercise alongwith the solved problems with brief useful hints to encourage the students to attempt the same.

Vector treatment has been used through out and S.I. units have been encouraged.

Mechanics and Properties of Matter includes topics like 'Vectors', 'Co-ordinate Systems' 'Conservation of Momentum and Energy', 'Moment of Inertia and Rigid Body Dynamics', Frames of Reference', 'Gravitation', 'Motion under a Central Force', 'Rockets and Satellites', 'Elastic and Inelastic Collisions', and Special Theory of Relativity under 'Mechanics' and 'Elasticity', 'Surface Tension' and 'Viscosity' under 'Properties of Matter'. A new chapter 'Classical Mechanics (Lagrangian and Hamiltonian Formulation)' has been added to cover the latest syllabus.

Waves, Vibrations and E.M. Theory includes topics like 'Simple Harmonic Motion', 'Damped Simple Harmonic Motion', 'Forced Oscillator and Resonance', 'Coupled Oscillators', 'Transverse and Logitudinal Waves', 'Interference, Beats, Stationary waves, Doppler Effects and Ultrasonics', 'Electromagnetic Waves' and 'Fourier Analysis'.

Electricity and Magnetism includes topics like 'Vector Calculus', Gauss's Divergence Theorem', 'Stokes Law and Green's Theorem', 'Electric Intensity', 'Gauss's Theorem and its Applications', 'Electric Potential', 'Electric Fields in Matter', 'Electric Currents', 'Fields of charges in Motion', 'The magnetic Field', 'Magnetism in Matter—Diamagnetism, Paramagnetism, Ferromagnetism and Ferrites,' 'Electromagnetic Induction' and 'Alternating Currents'.

Some universities have recently adopted the **semester system** and have included some additional topics.

The additional topics included in this edition are :

(*i*) Reflection and transmission of electromagnetic waves for normal and oblique incidence.

(*ii*) Laplace's equation in cartesian and spherical co-ordinates and their complete solution.

I am thankful to the management and the editorial team of S.Chand & Company Pvt. Ltd. for all help and support in the publication of this edition.

It is hoped that the present edition will be found all the more useful.

Author

Contents

SECTION–III
ELECTRICITY AND MAGNETISM

SECTION–I
MECHANICS AND PROPERTIES OF MATTER

1

Vectors

1.1. Scalars and Vectors. All physical quantities, in general, can be divided into two classes *i.e.,* (*i*) scalar quantities and (*ii*) vector quantities.

(*i*) **Scalar quantities or Scalars.** *Physical quantities which have only a magnitude but no direction* are called **scalar quantities** or simply **scalars.** Examples of these are mass, volume, density, temperature, speed, work, heat etc. These quantities can be added according to ordinary laws of algebra.

(*ii*) **Vector quantities or Vectors.** *Physical quantities which are completely known by their magnitude as well as direction* are called **vector quantities** or simply **vectors.** Examples of these are displacement, velocity, acceleration, force, momentum, electric field intensity etc.

Graphical representation. In a diagram, a vector is represented by a straight line with an arrow head whose direction gives the direction of the vector and whose length gives the magnitude of the vector on some suitable scale. *The magnitude of the vector in itself is a scalar quantity.*

A vector is usually represented by a capital letter with an arrow head on its top. Thus vector A is represented as $\vec{A}$.

The absolute value of the vector is indicated by A. The magnitude of the vector is always taken as *positive*. A negative sign before the vector indicates that a vector has merely changed the sense of direction *i.e.*, it interchanges the *arrow head and tail* without changing the length.

Some laws of Vector Algebra. (*i*) *Equal vectors.* Two vectors are considered equal if their magnitude and directions are the same.

As shown in Fig. 1.1 vectors $\vec{A}, \vec{B}$ and $\vec{C}$ are equal. A given vector can be moved around at will provided its length and direction are not changed.

Thus $\vec{A} = \vec{B} = \vec{C}$.

Fig. 1.1

This equation means that the vectors have the same magnitude and same direction.

(*ii*) *Negative vector.* A vector having the same magnitude as that of the given vector $\vec{A}$, but directed in the opposite sense is called a negative of the given vector. Symbolically the negative of vector $\vec{A}$ is represented by $-\vec{A}$ (Fig. 1.2).

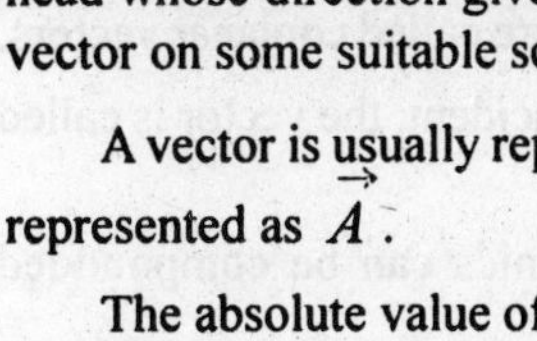

(*iii*) *Scalar multiple of a vector.* The product of a vector $\vec{A}$ and a real number m is a vector $m\vec{A}$. This means that length is m times the

Fig. 1.2

3

magnitude of $\vec{A}$. The direction of the vector is the same or opposite, according as m is positive or negative. Thus

$$m\,(-\vec{A}) = -m\,\vec{A} \text{ and } -m\,(-\vec{A}) = m\,\vec{A}$$

(*iv*) *Position vector.* The position of a point with respect to an arbitrary origin can be represented by a vector called the position vector. If O is an arbitrary origin and P a point in space, then the position vector of P with respect to O is represented by $\vec{OP}$ (Fig 1.3).

(*v*) *Co-initial vectors.* Vectors are said to be co-initial if they have a common initial point.

(*vi*) *Collinear or parallel vectors.* Vectors acting along the same line or along parallel lines are called collinear vectors.

If two vectors $\vec{A}$ and $\vec{B}$ are parallel and act in the same direction as shown in Fig. 1.4 (*a*) the resultant vector $\vec{R}$ is given by $\vec{R} = \vec{A} + \vec{B}$.

Fig. 1.3

When the two vectors have opposite directions as shown in Fig. 1.4 (*b*) the resultant vector $\vec{R}$ is given by, $\vec{R} = \vec{A} - \vec{B}$

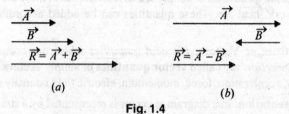

(*a*)   (*b*)

Fig. 1.4

(*vii*) *Coplanar vectors.* Vectors which are confined to the same plane are called coplanar vectors.

(*viii*) *Null vector.* If the initial and terminal points of a vector are coincident, the vector is called a null vector and has a *zero magnitude* and no direction.

1.2. (*i*) Composition of vectors. The vector quantities in mechanics can be compounded together by **parallelogram and triangle** *law of additions.*

The parallelogram law states that the sum of the two vectors $\vec{A}$ and $\vec{B}$ is the vector $\vec{R}$ determined by the diagonal oc of the parallelogram of which the adjacent sides oa and ab represent the two vectors.

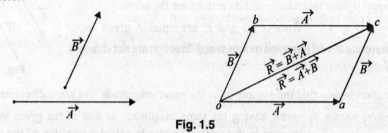

Fig. 1.5

Consider two vectors $\vec{A}$ and $\vec{B}$ acting in different directions as shown in Fig. 1.5 (*a*). On a diagram to a scale lay out draw oa representing the vector $\vec{A}$ and ac representing the vector $\vec{B}$ such that its tail is at the head of vector $\vec{A}$. Draw a line oc from the tail of $\vec{A}$ to the head of $\vec{B}$ to get the vector sum $\vec{R}$. This is a vector equivalent in length and direction to the successive vectors $\vec{A}$ and $\vec{B}$. Thus

$$\vec{R} = \vec{A} + \vec{B}$$

If we represent vector $\vec{B}$ along *ob* and draw the vector $\vec{A}$ along *bc* such that its tail is at the head of vector $\vec{B}$, the line *oc* again represents the vector sum $\vec{R}$. Then $\vec{R} = \vec{B} + \vec{A}$

Hence the two vector sums are mathematically equal *i.e.,* $\vec{A} + \vec{B} = \vec{B} + \vec{A}$

This shows that the vector sum is **commutative**.

(*ii*) **Associative law.** Suppose the point O is acted upon by a number of vectors $\vec{A}$, $\vec{B}$, $\vec{C}$ and $\vec{D}$ as shown in Fig. 1.6 (*a*). From a point O, draw a line *oa* to a scale layout representing the vector $\vec{A}$ in magnitude and direction. Draw a line *ab* on the same scale representing the vector $\vec{B}$ such that the tail of $\vec{B}$ coincides with the head of $\vec{A}$, then the line *ob* represents the vector sum $\vec{E}$. Hence $\vec{E} =$ $\vec{A} + \vec{B}$. Similarly draw *bc* representing the vector $\vec{C}$ and *cd* representing the vector $\vec{D}$ and join *od* representing the vector $\vec{R}$.

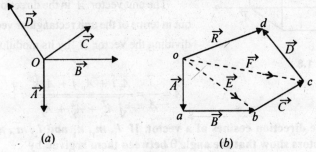

(*a*)   (*b*)

Fig. 1.6

Now $\vec{F}$ is the vector sum of $\vec{E}$ and $\vec{C}$ $\therefore \vec{F} = \vec{C} + \vec{E} = \vec{A} + \vec{B} + \vec{C}$

Again $\vec{R}$ is the vector sum of $\vec{F}$ and $\vec{D}$ $\therefore \vec{R} = \vec{F} + \vec{D} = \vec{A} + \vec{B} + \vec{C} + \vec{D}$

This law holds good for any number of vectors. Hence the vector addition is **associative**.

(*iii*) **Vector subtraction.** The negative of a vector is a vector of the same magnitude but opposite in direction. Hence subtraction of vector $\vec{B}$ from vector $\vec{A}$ is the same as addition of vector $-\vec{B}$ to vector $\vec{A}$. Thus $\vec{A} - \vec{B} = \vec{A} + (-\vec{B})$

1.3. Rectangular or orthogonal unit vectors. The vectors can be resolved into component vectors along the three orthogonal axes of the cartesian co-ordinate system in which the three axes *OX, OY* and *OZ* are mutually perpendicular to each other. The unit vectors along the *X, Y* and *Z* axes are represented by $\hat{i}, \hat{j},$ and $\hat{k}$ respectively. The rectangular system such as shown in Fig. 1.7 is called the right handed coordinate system. The word right handed has been derived from the fact that a right handed screw when rotated from *X* to *Y*-axis through a small angle will move the screw in the positive direction of *Z*-axis.

A vector $\vec{A}$ taken along *X*- axis can be written as $\vec{A} = \hat{i} A$ where A is the magnitude of $\vec{A}$.

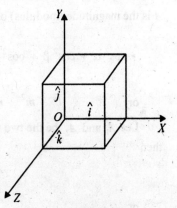

Fig. 1.7

1.4. Orthogonal resolution of vectors and direction cosines. Let the vector $\vec{A} = \vec{OP}$ in a rectangular co-ordinate system be resolved into its component vectors in the directions of X, Y and Z axes. Let the initial point of the vector A be at the origin O of the co-ordinate system. Draw a rectangular parallelopiped with its three edges at O and lying along the three cartesian axes such that the vector $\vec{A}$ becomes the diagonal through the solid figure.

Let $\vec{A_x}$, $\vec{A_y}$ and $\vec{A_z}$ be the vector intercepts along X, Y and Z axes respectively and A_x, A_y and A_z be their magnitudes respectively, then $\vec{A_x} = A_x\,\hat{i}$, $\vec{A_y} = A_y\,\hat{j}$ and $\vec{A_z} = A_z\,\hat{k}$.

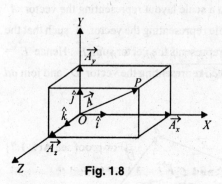

Fig. 1.8

$$\therefore\ \vec{A} = \vec{A_x} + \vec{A_y} + \vec{A_z} = A_x\,\hat{i} + A_y\,\hat{j} + A_z\,\hat{k}$$

By Pythagoras theorem in three dimensions we have,

$$A^2 = A_x^2 + A_y^2 + A_z^2$$

or

$$A = \sqrt{A_x^2 + A_y^2 + A_z^2}$$

The unit vector $\hat{A}$ in the direction of $\vec{A}$ can be found out in terms of the unit rectangular vectors $\hat{i}$, $\hat{j}$, and $\hat{k}$ by dividing the vector $\vec{A}$ by its modulus A.

$$\therefore\quad \hat{A} = \frac{\vec{A}}{A} = \frac{A_x\,\hat{i} + A_y\,\hat{j} + A_z\,\hat{k}}{\sqrt{A_x^2 + A_y^2 + A_z^2}}$$

Q. 1.1. Define direction cosines of a vector. If l_1, m_1, n_1 and l_2, m_2, n_2 are the direction cosines of two vectors show that the angle θ between them is given by

$$\cos\theta = l_1 l_2 + m_1 m_2 + n_1 n_2.$$ (A. U., 1993; K.U., 1994)

Ans. Direction cosines. The cosine of the angles which the vector $\vec{A}$ makes with the X- axis, Y-axis and Z-axis are known as X- direction cosine, Y-direction cosine and Z-direction cosine respectively. These are denoted by l, m and n respectively.

Suppose the vector $\vec{A}$ makes angle α, β and γ with X, Y and Z axes respectively, then

$$l = \cos\alpha = \frac{A_x}{A}\,;\ m = \cos\beta = \frac{A_y}{A}\,;\ n = \cos\gamma = \frac{A_z}{A}$$

where A_x, A_y and A_z are the intercepts of the vector $\vec{A}$ along the X, Y and Z axes respectively and A is the magnitude (modulus) of the vector $\vec{A}$. Squaring and adding the cosines, we get

$$\cos^2\alpha + \cos^2\beta + \cos^2\gamma = \left(\frac{A_x}{A}\right)^2 + \left(\frac{A_y}{A}\right)^2 + \left(\frac{A_z}{A}\right)^2 = \frac{A_x^2 + A_y^2 + A_z^2}{A^2}$$

or

$$l^2 + m^2 + n^2 = \frac{A_x^2 + A_y^2 + A_z^2}{A^2} = \frac{A^2}{A^2} = 1$$

Let $\vec{A_1}$ and $\vec{A_2}$ be the two vectors, whose magnitudes are represented by A_1 and A_2 respectively, then

$$\vec{A_1} = A_{1x}\,\hat{i} + A_{1y}\,\hat{j} + A_{1z}\,\hat{k}$$

or

$$\frac{\vec{A_1}}{A_1} = \frac{A_{1x}}{A_1}\,\hat{i} + \frac{A_{1y}}{A_1}\,\hat{j} + \frac{A_{1z}}{A_1}\,\hat{k}$$

But
$$\frac{A_{1x}}{A_1} = l_1 \; ; \; \frac{A_{1y}}{A_1} = m_1 \; ; \; \frac{A_{1z}}{A_1} = n_1$$

$\therefore$
$$\vec{A_1} = A_1 \, (l_1 \hat{i} + m_1 \hat{j} + n_1 \hat{k})$$

Similarly
$$\vec{A_2} = A_2 \, (l_2 \hat{i} + m_2 \hat{j} + n_2 \hat{k})$$

Now $\vec{A_1} \cdot \vec{A_2} = A_1 \, A_2 \cos\theta$ where θ is the angle between the vectors $\vec{A_1}$ and $\vec{A_2}$ [For proof see Q. 1.4]

$\therefore$
$$\cos\theta = \frac{\vec{A_1} \cdot \vec{A_2}}{A_1 A_2}$$

$$= \frac{A_1 (l_1 \hat{i} + m_1 \hat{j} + n_1 \hat{k}) \cdot A_2 (l_2 \hat{i} + m_2 \hat{j} + n_2 \hat{k})}{A_1 A_2}$$

$$= l_1 l_2 + m_1 m_2 + n_1 n_2$$

as $\hat{i} \cdot \hat{i} = \hat{j} \cdot \hat{j} = \hat{k} \cdot \hat{k} = 1$ and $\hat{i} \cdot \hat{j} = \hat{j} \cdot \hat{k} = \hat{k} \cdot \hat{i} = 0$

[For proof see **Art. 1.7**]

Q. 1.2. If vector $\vec{A} = \hat{i} + 2\hat{j} - 2\hat{k}$, $\vec{B} = 2\hat{i} + \hat{j} + \hat{k}$ and $\vec{C} = \hat{i} - 3\hat{j} - 2\hat{k}$ find the magnitude and direction cosines of the vector $(\vec{A} + \vec{B} + \vec{C})$.

Ans. Vector sum
$$\vec{R} = \vec{A} + \vec{B} + \vec{C}$$

$$= \hat{i} + 2\hat{j} - 2\hat{k} + 2\hat{i} + \hat{j} + \hat{k} + \hat{i} - 3\hat{j} - 2\hat{k} = 4\hat{i} - 3\hat{k}$$

$\therefore$ $R_x = 4\hat{i}$, $R_y = 0$ and $R_z = -3k$

Hence magnitude of $\vec{R} = |\vec{R}| = \sqrt{4^2 + 0^2 + 3^2} = 5$

Direction cosines of $\vec{R}$

$$l = \frac{R_x}{R} = \frac{4}{5} \; ; \; m = \frac{R_y}{R} = \frac{0}{5} = 0 \; ; \; n = \frac{R_z}{R} = \frac{-3}{5}$$

Q. 1.3. Prove that $\hat{A} = \hat{i} \cos(\vec{A}, x), + \hat{j} \cos(\vec{A}, y) + \hat{k} \cos(\vec{A}, z)$ where $\hat{A}$ is a unit vector and $\cos(\vec{A}, x)$, $\cos(\vec{A}, y)$ and $\cos(\vec{A}, z)$ are the direction cosines of $\vec{A}$.   (*A. U.*, 1994)

Ans. $\cos(\vec{A}, x) = \frac{A_x}{A}$, $\cos(\vec{A}, y) = \frac{A_y}{A}$, $\cos(\vec{A}, z) = \frac{A_z}{A}$

$$\hat{i} \cos(\vec{A}, x) + \hat{j} \cos(\vec{A}, y) + \hat{k} \cos(\vec{A}, z) = \frac{A_x \hat{i}}{A} + \frac{A_y \hat{j}}{A} + \frac{A_z}{A} \hat{k}$$

$$= \frac{\vec{A}}{A} = \hat{A}$$

1.5. Position vector and displacement vector. If the co-ordinates of a point are (x, y, z) then the vector $\vec{r}$ joining the origin to this point is expressed as $(x\hat{i} + y\hat{j} + z\hat{k})$.

This vector is known as the **position vector** of this point.

If a particle P having co-ordinates (x_1, y_1, z_1) is represented by position vector $\vec{r_1}$, then in Fig. 1.9,
$$\vec{r_1} = x_1 \hat{i} + y_1 \hat{j} + z_1 \hat{k}$$

If this particle moves to another point Q which has a position vector $\vec{r_2}$ given by

$$\vec{r_2} = x_2\,\hat{i} + y_2\,\hat{j} + z_2\,\hat{k}$$

where $(x_2,\ y_2,\ z_2)$ are the coordinates of Q, then the displacement from P to Q is represented by vector $\vec{r}$ given by

$$\vec{r} = \vec{r_2} - \vec{r_1} \qquad \because \vec{r_2} = \vec{r_1} + \vec{r}$$

or $\qquad \vec{r} = (x_2 - x_1)\,\hat{i} + (y_2 - y_1)\,\hat{j} + (z_2 - z_1)\,\hat{k}$

If PQ represents a small vectorial change $d\vec{r} = \vec{r_2} - \vec{r_1}$ and $x_2 - x_1 = dx$, $y_2 - y_1 = dy$ and $z_2 - z_1 = dz$, then $d\vec{r} = dx\,\hat{i} + dy\,\hat{j} + dz\,\hat{k}$

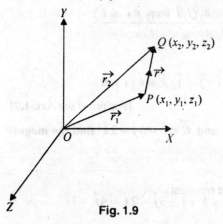

Fig. 1.9

$\vec{r_2} - \vec{r_1} = \vec{r}$ represents a **line element** and $d\vec{r}$ represents an infinitesimally small line element.

1.6. Product of vectors. Owing to different ways in which vectors occurs in various physical problems, the product of two vectors $\vec{A}$ and $\vec{B}$ is defined as,

(*i*) **Scalar product** or dot product $\vec{A}\,.\,\vec{B}$ (read as $\vec{A}$ dot $\vec{B}$)

(*ii*) **Vector or cross product** $\vec{A} \times \vec{B}$ (read as $\vec{A}$ cross $\vec{B}$)

The dot product $\vec{A}\,.\,\vec{B}$ gives a **scalar result**, while the cross product $\vec{A} \times \vec{B}$ gives a **vector result**.

Q. 1.4. Define scalar (dot) product of two vectors.   *(K. U., 1991)*

Ans. Scalar (or dot) product of two vectors. *The scalar product of two vectors $\vec{A}$ and $\vec{B}$ is defined as a scalar quantity which is equal to the product of the magnitudes of the given two vectors and the cosine of the angle between their directions.* Thus if θ is the given angle between the directions of the two vectors $\vec{A}$ and $\vec{B}$ (Fig. 1.10) then

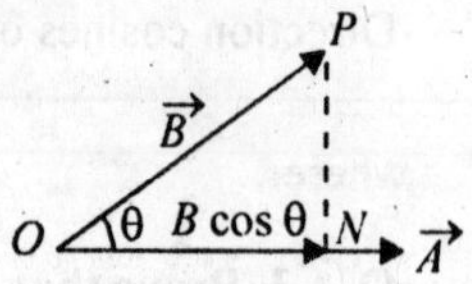

$$\vec{A}\,.\,\vec{B} = AB \cos\theta$$

$$= A\,(B \cos\theta) = A\,(ON)$$

Fig. 1.10

It is thus clear that the scalar product of two vectors is equivalent to the product of the *magnitude* (modulus) of one vector and the component of the other vector in the direction of the former.

1.7. Properties of scalar product of two vectors

(*a*) **Condition for two perpendicular vectors.** When the two vectors are mutually perpendicular, then $\theta = 90°$ and $\cos\theta = 0$

$\therefore \qquad\qquad\qquad \vec{A}\,.\,\vec{B} = AB \cos\theta = 0$

Thus if $\hat{i},\ \hat{j}$ and $\hat{k}$ are unit vectors along the three co-ordinate axes mutually perpendicular to each other, then

$$\hat{i}\,.\,\hat{j} = \hat{j}\,.\,\hat{k} = \hat{k}\,.\,\hat{i} = 0$$

Hence the two non-zero vectors are orthogonal vectors if and only if

$$\vec{A}\,.\,\vec{B} = 0$$

(b) **Condition for two collinear vectors.** The two vectors are collinear if $\theta = 0$ or π.

(i) If $\theta = 0$ $\cos \theta = 1$

$\therefore \qquad\qquad \vec{A} \cdot \vec{B} = AB \cos \theta = AB$

In other words, scalar product of two like vectors is positive and equal to the product of their moduli.

(ii) If the two vectors are antiparallel, then

$$\theta = \pi \text{ and } \cos \theta = -1 \qquad \therefore \ \vec{A} \cdot \vec{B} = AB \cos \pi = -AB$$

This shows that the scalar product of two antiparallel vectors is negative and is equal to the product of their moduli.

(c) **Scalar product of two equal vectors.** If $\vec{A} = \vec{B}$ and $\theta = 0$, then $\vec{A} \cdot \vec{A} = AA \cos \theta = A^2$

Thus the square of any vector is equal to the square of its magnitude (modulus).

If $\hat{i}, \hat{j}$, and $\hat{k}$ are unit vectors along three axes, then

$$\hat{i} \cdot \hat{i} = \hat{j} \cdot \hat{j} = \hat{k} \cdot \hat{k} = 1$$

(d) **Scalar product is distributive i.e,**

$$\vec{A} \cdot (\vec{B} + \vec{C}) = \vec{A} \cdot \vec{B} + \vec{A} \cdot \vec{C}$$

Q. 1.5. Prove that $\vec{A} \cdot (\vec{B} + \vec{C}) = \vec{A} \cdot \vec{B} + \vec{A} \cdot \vec{C}$.   (K. U., 1991)

Ans. Consider three vectors A, B and C as shown in Fig. 1.11. Let the angle between the vectors $\vec{A}$ and $\vec{B}$ be α, and between $\vec{A}$ and $\vec{C}$ be β. Let $\vec{R}$ be the resultant of $\vec{B}$ and $\vec{C}$ making an angle θ with $\vec{A}$

Now $\qquad\qquad\qquad \vec{R} = \vec{B} + \vec{C}$

and $\qquad\qquad \vec{A} \cdot (\vec{B} + \vec{C}) = \vec{A} \cdot \vec{R}$

$\qquad\qquad\qquad\qquad = AR \cos \theta = A \,(OM)$

where $\qquad\qquad OM = R \cos \theta$ is the component of $\vec{R}$ along the vector $\vec{A}$.

Again $\qquad\qquad \vec{A} \cdot \vec{B} = AB \cos\alpha = A(OL)$

Similarly $\qquad\qquad \vec{A} \cdot \vec{C} = AC \cos\beta = A\,(LM)$

Now $\qquad A\,(OM) = A\,(OL + LM) = A\,(OL) + A\,(LM)$

$\therefore \qquad\qquad \vec{A} \cdot (\vec{B} + \vec{C}) = \vec{A} \cdot \vec{B} + \vec{A} \cdot \vec{C}$

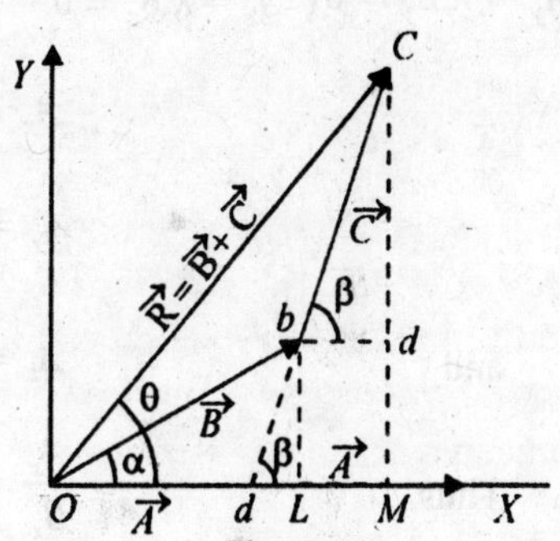

Fig. 1.11

Q. 1.6. (a) **Deduce the expression for the scalar product of two vectors in terms of their rectangular components.**

(b) **Hence derive an expression for the angle between two vectors.**

Ans. (a) **Scalar product in terms of rectangular components.** The vectors $\vec{A}$ and $\vec{B}$ in terms of their components can be written as

$$\vec{A} = A_x \hat{i} + A_y \hat{j} + A_z \hat{k} \text{ and } \vec{B} = B_x \hat{i} + B_y \hat{j} + B_z \hat{k}$$

$\therefore \qquad \vec{A} \cdot \vec{B} = (A_x \hat{i} + A_y \hat{j} + A_z \hat{k}) \cdot (B_x \hat{i} + B_y \hat{j} + B_z \hat{k})$

$$= A_x B_x (\hat{i} . \hat{i}) + A_x B_y (\hat{i} . \hat{j}) + A_x B_z (\hat{i} . \hat{k}) + A_y B_x (\hat{j} . \hat{i})$$
$$+ A_y B_y (\hat{j} . \hat{j}) + A_y B_z (\hat{j} . \hat{k}) + A_z B_x (\hat{k} . \hat{i}) + A_z B_y (\hat{k} . \hat{j}) + A_z B_z (\hat{k} . \hat{k})$$
$$= A_x B_x + A_y B_y + A_z B_z$$

$\because$ $\qquad\qquad\qquad \hat{i} . \hat{j} = \hat{i} . \hat{k} = \hat{j} . \hat{i} = \hat{j} . \hat{k} = \hat{k} . \hat{i} = \hat{k} . \hat{j} = 0$

and $\qquad\qquad\qquad \hat{i} . \hat{i} = \hat{j} . \hat{j} = \hat{k} . \hat{k} = 1$

(b) **Angle between two vectors.** We know that

$$\vec{A} . \vec{B} = AB \cos\theta$$

or $\qquad\qquad \cos\theta = \dfrac{\vec{A} . \vec{B}}{AB} = \dfrac{A_x B_x + A_y B_y + A_z B_z}{\sqrt{A_x^2 + A_y^2 + A_z^2} \ \sqrt{B_x^2 + B_y^2 + B_z^2}}$

Q. 1.7. If $\vec{A} = \lambda\vec{B}$ **prove that** $\dfrac{A_x}{B_x} = \dfrac{A_y}{B_y} = \dfrac{A_z}{B_z}$. $\qquad\qquad$ (A. U., 1995)

Ans. $\qquad\qquad\qquad \vec{A} = \lambda\vec{B}$

or $\qquad (A_x \hat{i} + A_y \hat{j} + A_z \hat{k}) = \lambda(B_x \hat{i} + B_y \hat{j} + B_z \hat{k})$

or $\qquad (A_x - \lambda B_x)\hat{i} + (A_y - \lambda B_y)\hat{j} + (A_z - \lambda B_z)\hat{k} = 0$

As $\hat{i}, \hat{j}, \hat{k}$ are non-co-planer vectors, the equation is satisfied only if $A_x - \lambda B_x = 0$; $A_y - \lambda B_y = 0$; $A_z - \lambda B_z = 0$.

$\therefore$ $\qquad\qquad\qquad A_x = \lambda B_x$ or $\dfrac{A_x}{B_x} = \lambda$

$$A_y = \lambda B_y \text{ or } \dfrac{A_y}{B_y} = \lambda$$

and $\qquad\qquad\qquad A_z = \lambda B_z$ or $\dfrac{A_z}{B_z} = \lambda$

Thus $\qquad\qquad\qquad \dfrac{A_x}{B_x} = \dfrac{A_y}{B_y} = \dfrac{A_z}{B_z}$

Q. 1.8. If $|\vec{A}| = |\vec{B}|$ **prove that** $(\vec{A} + \vec{B})$ **is perpendicular to** $(\vec{A} - \vec{B})$. $\qquad$ (A. U., 1994)

Ans. $\qquad\qquad\qquad |\vec{A}| = |\vec{B}|$

$$|\vec{A}|^2 = |\vec{B}|^2 \text{ or } \vec{A} . \vec{A} = \vec{B} . \vec{B}$$

Now $\qquad (\vec{A} + \vec{B}) . (\vec{A} - \vec{B}) = \vec{A} . \vec{A} - \vec{A} . \vec{B} + \vec{B} . \vec{A} - \vec{B} . \vec{B} = 0$

As $\qquad\qquad\qquad \vec{A} . \vec{B} = \vec{B} . \vec{A}$

As the scalar product of the vectors $(\vec{A} + \vec{B})$ and $(\vec{A} - \vec{B})$ is zero, the vectors $(\vec{A} + \vec{B})$ is perpendicular to $(\vec{A} - \vec{B})$.

Q. 1.9. Two sides of a triangle are formed by the vectors $\vec{A} = 3\hat{i} + 6\hat{j} - 2\hat{k}$ **and** $\vec{B} = 4\hat{i} - \hat{j} + 3\hat{k}$. **Determine all the angles of the triangle.**

Ans. Let $\vec{C}$ be the third side of the triangle, then

$$\vec{A} + \vec{C} = \vec{B}$$
$$\vec{C} = \vec{B} - \vec{A}$$
$$= (4\hat{i} - \hat{j} + 3\hat{k}) - (3\hat{i} + 6\hat{j} - 2\hat{k})$$

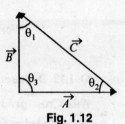

Fig. 1.12

$$\therefore \qquad \vec{C} = \hat{i} - 7\hat{j} + 5\hat{k}$$

Angle between the vectors $\vec{A}$ and $\vec{B}$ is given by

$$\cos\theta_3 = \frac{\vec{A}.\vec{B}}{AB} = \frac{A_x B_x + A_y B_y + A_z B_z}{\sqrt{A_x^2 + A_y^2 + A_z^2}\sqrt{B_x^2 + B_y^2 + B_z^2}}$$

$$= \frac{12 - 6 - 6}{\sqrt{A_x^2 + A_y^2 + A_z^2}\sqrt{B_x^2 + B_y^2 + B_z^2}} = 0$$

$$\therefore \qquad \theta_3 = 90°$$

Angle between vectors $\vec{A}$ and $\vec{C}$ is given by

$$\cos(\pi - \theta_2) = \frac{\vec{A}.\vec{C}}{AC} = \frac{A_x C_x + A_y C_y + A_z C_z}{\sqrt{A_x^2 + A_y^2 + A_z^2}\sqrt{C_y^2 + C_y^2 + C_z^2}} = \frac{-49}{\sqrt{49}\sqrt{75}}$$

$$\therefore \qquad \cos\theta_2 = \frac{7}{5\sqrt{3}} = 0.8083$$

or $\qquad\qquad \theta_2 = 36°4' \qquad\qquad\qquad$ Hence $\theta_1 = 53°56'$

Q. 1.10. Show that the vectors $\vec{A} = 3\hat{i} - 2\hat{j} + \hat{k}$, $\vec{B} = \hat{i} - 3\hat{j} + 5\hat{k}$ and $\vec{C} = 2\hat{i} + \hat{j} - 4\hat{k}$ form a right angled triangle.

Ans. The vectors $\vec{A}$, $\vec{B}$ and $\vec{C}$ will form a triangle if one of the vectors is equal to the vector sum of the remaining two vectors.

Now $\qquad\qquad \vec{B} + \vec{C} = \hat{i} - 3\hat{j} + 5\hat{k} + 2\hat{i} + \hat{j} - 4\hat{k} = 3\hat{i} - 2\hat{j} + \hat{k} = \vec{A}$

Hence the three vectors form a triangle.

Again $\qquad\qquad \vec{A}.\vec{B} = (3\hat{i} - 2\hat{j} + \hat{k}).(\hat{i} - 3\hat{j} + 5\hat{k}) = 14$

$$\vec{A}.\vec{C} = (3\hat{i} - 2\hat{j} + \hat{k}).(2\hat{i} + \hat{j} - 4\hat{k}) = 0$$

$$\vec{B}.\vec{C} = (\hat{i} - 3\hat{j} + 5\hat{k}).(2\hat{i} + \hat{j} - 4\hat{k}) = -21$$

As $\vec{A}.\vec{C} = 0$, the vectors $\vec{A}$ and $\vec{C}$ are orthogonal and triangle formed is a right angled triangle.

Q. 1.11. A particle moves from a point $(3, -4, -2)$ m to a point $(-2, 3, 5)$ m under the influence of a force $\vec{F} = (-2\hat{i} + 3\hat{j} + 4\hat{k})$ Newton. Calculate the work done by the force.

(*A. U.*, 1993)

Ans. Displacement of the particle

$$\vec{r} = (-2 - 3)\hat{i} + (3 + 4)\hat{j} + (5 + 2)\hat{k}$$
$$= (5\hat{i} + 7\hat{j} + 7\hat{k}) \text{ m}$$

$$\vec{F} = (-2\hat{i} + 3\hat{j} + 4\hat{k})\ N$$

∴   Work done $W = \vec{F}.\vec{r} = (-2\hat{i} + 3\hat{j} + 4\hat{k}).(-5\hat{i} + 7\hat{j} + 7\hat{k})$

$$= (10 + 21 + 28)\ \text{Joules} = 59\ J$$

Q. 1.12. Define cross-product of two vectors.

Ans. Cross-product or Vector product. The cross product of two vectors $\vec{A}$ and $\vec{B}$ denoted as $\vec{A} \times \vec{B}$ and read as ($\vec{A}$ cross $\vec{B}$) whose directions are inclined at an angle θ is the vector whose magnitude is $AB \sin θ$ and direction is perpendicular to the plane containing $\vec{A}$ and $\vec{B}$. It is **positive** if the rotation from $\vec{A}$ to $\vec{B}$ is anti-clockwise [Fig. 1.13 (a)] and negative if the rotation from $\vec{A}$ to $\vec{B}$ is clockwise [Fig 1.13 (b)].

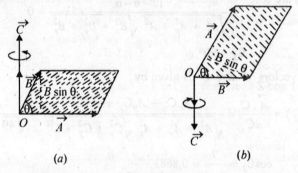

(a)   (b)

Fig. 1.13

Thus $\vec{A} \times \vec{B} = AB \sin θ\ \hat{n} = \vec{C}$

where $\hat{n}$ is a unit vector perpendicular to the vectors $\vec{A}$ and $\vec{B}$.

The unit vector $\hat{n}$ is called *unit normal.*

1.8. Properties of vector product of two vectors.

(i) Commutative law is not obeyed. From the definition of the vector product it is evident that the change in the order of vectors in a cross product reverses the direction of the product as sin (− θ) = − sin θ

$$\vec{B} \times \vec{A} = - AB \sin θ\ \hat{n} = -\vec{A} \times \vec{B}$$

Hence the vector product of the two vectors is not commutative and the order of the terms should be strictly maintained. However **distributive** law shall hold good *i.e.,*

$$\vec{A} \times (\vec{B} + \vec{C}) = \vec{A} \times \vec{B} + \vec{A} \times \vec{C}$$

(ii) Area of a parallelogram. The magnitude of the vector product $\vec{A} \times \vec{B}$ gives the area of the parallelogram formed by the two vectors as adjacent sides. Referring to Fig. 1.13, we find that

Height of parallelogram $h = B \sin θ$

Now $\vec{A} \times \vec{B} = AB \sin θ = Ah = $ Base × height of parallelogram

$$= \text{Area of the parallelogram}$$

Since $\vec{A} \times \vec{B}$ is a vector whose direction is perpendicular to the plane containing $\vec{A}$ and $\vec{B}$, the area is a vector quantity. In the case of an **open** surface, the direction of the area is taken along $\hat{n}$ which is normal to the plane containing the parallelogram. The area is taken as **positive** if the direction of $\hat{n}$ coincides with the direction of advance of a right handed screw when rotated so as to describe the boundary of the (open) surface in a positive sense *i.e.*, **anticlockwise** direction.

In the case of a **closed** surface the direction of the area vector is normal to the surface pointing **outwards** *i.e.*, away from the closed surface of which the area forms a part. The advantage of representing an area by a vector is that the cross product of the two vectors $\vec{A}$ and $\vec{B}$ representing the sides being equal to $AB \sin \theta$ where θ is the angle contained between the two vectors automatically gives the magnitude of the area and the direction of the resultant vector gives the direction of the area as a vector.

(*iii*) **Collinear vectors.** If two vectors are collinear, then $\theta = 0$ or π, *i.e.*, $\sin \theta = 0$

$$\therefore \qquad \vec{A} \times \vec{B} = AB \sin \theta \; \hat{n} = 0$$

Thus two vectors are collinear (parallel, or antiparallel) if the vector product $\vec{A} \times \vec{B} = 0$.

(*iv*) **Equal vectors.** If two vectors are equal then $\theta = 0$, and vector product

$$\vec{A} \times \vec{A} = AA \sin \theta \; \hat{n} = 0$$

Hence vector product of two equal vectors is always zero. In a particular case if $\hat{i}$, $\hat{j}$ and $\hat{k}$ are unit vectors along X, Y and Z axes, then $\hat{i} \times \hat{i} = \hat{j} \times \hat{j} = \hat{k} \times \hat{k} = 0$.

(*v*) **Vector product of two unit vectors.** We know

$$\vec{A} \times \vec{B} = AB \sin \theta \; \hat{n} \qquad \text{or} \qquad \frac{\vec{A}}{A} \times \frac{\vec{B}}{B} = \sin \theta \; \hat{n}$$

or $\qquad\qquad \hat{A} \times \hat{B} = \sin \theta \; \hat{n}$

Hence vector product of two unit vectors is a vector whose magnitude is equal to the sine of the angle between their directions and whose direction is perpendicular to the plane containing the given vectors. The direction is determined by the right hand rule.

(*vi*) **Vector product of two perpendicular vectors.** In this case $\theta = \pi/2$ and $\sin \theta = 1$

$$\vec{A} \times \vec{B} = AB \sin \frac{\pi}{2} \; \hat{n} = AB \hat{n}$$

Hence vector product of two perpendicular vectors is a vector whose magnitude is equal to the product of the magnitudes of the given vectors and whose direction is along $\hat{n}$ such $\vec{A} \times \vec{B}$ and $\hat{n}$ form a right handed system.

If $\hat{i}$, $\hat{j}$ and $\hat{k}$ are the unit vectors along the three axes X, Y and Z respectively, then

$$\hat{i} \times \hat{j} = \hat{k}, \; \hat{j} \times \hat{k} = \hat{i} \text{ and } \hat{k} \times \hat{i} = \hat{j}$$

Also $\qquad\qquad \hat{j} \times \hat{i} = -\hat{k}, \hat{k} \times \hat{j} = -\hat{i} \text{ and } \hat{i} \times \hat{k} = -\hat{j}$

Q. 1.13 (*a*) Deduce the expression for vector product of two vectors in terms of their components.

(*b*) Hence derive an expression for the angle between two vectors.

Ans. (*a*) Vector product in terms of components. Let (A_x, A_y, A_z) and (B_x, B_y, B_z) be the orthogonal projections of the vectors $\vec{A}$ and $\vec{B}$ along X, Y and Z axes respectively, then

$$A = \hat{i} A_x + \hat{j} A_y + \hat{k} A_z \text{ and } \vec{B} = \hat{i} B_x + \hat{j} B_y + \hat{k} B_z$$

$$\therefore \qquad \vec{A} \times \vec{B} = (\hat{i} A_x + \hat{j} A_y + \hat{k} A_z) \times (\hat{i} B_x + \hat{j} B_y + \hat{k} B_z)$$

$$= A_x B_y \hat{k} - A_x B_z \hat{j} - A_y B_x \hat{k} + A_y B_z \hat{i} + A_z B_x \hat{j} - A_z B_y \hat{i}$$

$$= \hat{i}(A_y B_z - A_z B_y) + \hat{j}(A_z B_x - A_x B_z) + \hat{k}(A_x B_y - A_y B_x)$$

$$= \begin{vmatrix} \hat{i} & \hat{j} & \hat{k} \\ A_x & A_y & A_z \\ B_x & B_y & B_z \end{vmatrix}$$

(b) Determination of sin θ from vector product.

We know $\vec{A} \times \vec{B} = AB \sin \theta \, \hat{n}$

Also $\qquad \vec{A} \times \vec{B} = (A_y B_z - A_z B_y)\hat{i} + (A_z B_x - A_x B_z)\hat{j} + (A_x B_y - A_y B_x)\hat{k}$

$$= AB \sin \theta \, \hat{n}$$

Squaring both sides and taking self-product on either side, we have

$$A^2 B^2 \sin^2 \theta = (A_y B_z - A_z B_y)^2 + (A_z B_x - A_x B_z)^2 + (A_x B_y - A_y B_x)^2$$

$\because \qquad \hat{n}.\hat{n} = 1$ and $\hat{i}.\hat{i} = \hat{j}.\hat{j} = \hat{k}.\hat{k} = 1$

As $\qquad A^2 = A_x^{\,2} + A_y^{\,2} + A_z^{\,2}$ and $B^2 = B_x^{\,2} + B_y^{\,2} + B_z^{\,2}$

$$\therefore \qquad \sin \theta = \left\{ \frac{(A_y B_z - A_z B_y)^2 + (A_z B_x - A_x B_z)^2 + (A_x B_y - A_y B_z)^2}{(A_x^{\,2} + A_y^{\,2} + A_z^{\,2})(B_x^{\,2} + B_y^{\,2} + B_z^{\,2})} \right\}^{\frac{1}{2}}$$

Q. 1.14. The position and velocity vectors of two particles at any instant are $\vec{r_1}$, $\vec{r_2}$ and $\vec{v_1}$, $\vec{v_2}$ respectively. Prove that they will collide if

$$(\vec{r_1} - \vec{r_2}) \times (\vec{v_1} - \vec{v_2}) = 0 .$$

Ans. Let the two particles P and Q have position vectors $\vec{r_1}$ and $\vec{r_2}$ as shown in Fig. 1.14.

The velocity vectors of P and Q are $\vec{v_1}$ and $\vec{v_2}$ at that instant as shown. Let the two particles collide at a point C after a time interval t, then

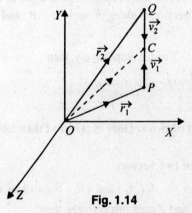

Fig. 1.14

Position vector of particle P at C

$$\overrightarrow{OC} = \overrightarrow{OP} + \overrightarrow{PC}$$

$$= \vec{r_1} + \vec{v_1} t$$

as $\vec{v_1} t$ is the distance travelled by the particle in time t.

Position vector of particle Q at C

$$\overrightarrow{OC} = \overrightarrow{OQ} + \overrightarrow{QC} = \vec{r_2} + \vec{v_2} t$$

The particles P and Q will collide if

$$\vec{r_1} + \vec{v_1} t = \vec{r_2} + \vec{v_2} t$$

or $\qquad (\vec{r_1} - \vec{r_2}) = -(\vec{v_1} - \vec{v_2}) t$

For this condition to be satisfied

$$(\vec{r_1} - \vec{r_2}) \times (\vec{v_1} - \vec{v_2}) = -t[(\vec{v_1} - \vec{v_2}) \times (\vec{v_1} - \vec{v_2})]$$

$$= 0$$

As vector product of two equal vectors is zero.

Q. 1.15. What is the unit vector perpendicular to both $\vec{A}$ and $\vec{B}$ where $\vec{A} = 2\hat{i} - \hat{j} + \hat{k}$ and $\vec{B} = (3\hat{i} + 4\hat{j} - \hat{k})$? Calculate the sine of the angle between them.   *(K. U., 1991)*

Ans. The vector $\vec{C}$ perpendicular to both the vectors $\vec{A}$ and $\vec{B}$ is given by the vector product of the two vectors

$$\vec{A} = (2\hat{i} - \hat{j} + \hat{k}) \text{ and } \vec{B} = (3\hat{i} + 4\hat{j} - \hat{k})$$

$\therefore$
$$\vec{C} = \vec{A} \times \vec{B} = (2\hat{i} - \hat{j} + \hat{k}) \times (3\hat{i} + 4\hat{j} - \hat{k})$$

$$= \begin{vmatrix} i & j & k \\ 2 & -1 & 1 \\ 3 & 4 & -1 \end{vmatrix} = -3\hat{i} + 5\hat{j} + 11\hat{k}$$

The magnitude of vector $\vec{C} = -3\hat{i} + 5\hat{j} + 11\hat{k}$

$$|\vec{C}| = \sqrt{3^2 + 5^2 + 11^2} = \sqrt{155}$$

$\therefore$ Unit vector in the direction of $\vec{C}$ is given by

$$\hat{C} = \frac{\vec{C}}{|\vec{C}|} = \frac{-3\hat{i} + 5\hat{j} + 11\hat{k}}{\sqrt{155}}$$

Again magnitude of
$$\vec{A} = |\vec{A}| = \sqrt{2^2 + 1^2 + 1^2} = \sqrt{6}$$

and magnitude of
$$\vec{B} = |\vec{B}| = \sqrt{3^2 + 4^2 + 1^2} = \sqrt{26}$$

If θ is the angle between the two vectors, then

$$|\vec{C}| = |\vec{A}||\vec{B}| \sin\theta$$

$$\sin\theta = \frac{|\vec{C}|}{|\vec{A}||\vec{B}|} = \frac{\sqrt{155}}{\sqrt{6}\sqrt{26}} = \sqrt{\frac{155}{156}} = 0.997$$

Exercise. *Find the Cartesian components of a vector $\vec{C}$ which is perpendicular to the vectors*

$$\vec{A} = 2\hat{i} - \hat{j} - 4\hat{k} \text{ and } \vec{B} = 3\hat{i} - \hat{j} - \hat{k}. \qquad (Gauhati\ U.\ 2000;\ Luck.\ U.\ 2001)$$

Hint.
$$\vec{C} = \vec{A} \times \vec{B} = (2\hat{i} - \hat{j} - 4\hat{k}) \times (3\hat{i} - \hat{j} - \hat{k})$$

$$= \begin{vmatrix} \hat{i} & \hat{j} & \hat{k} \\ 2 & -1 & -4 \\ 3 & -1 & -1 \end{vmatrix} = -(3\hat{i} + 10\hat{j} - \hat{k})$$

Q. 1.16. The diagonals of a parallelogram are given by vectors $(3\hat{i} + \hat{j} + 2\hat{k})$ and $(\hat{i} - 3\hat{j} + 4\hat{k})$. Find the area of the parallelogram.

Ans. Consider a parallelogram *PQRS* such that the diagonal *PR* is represented by the vector $\vec{A} = 3\hat{i} + \hat{j} + 2\hat{k}$ and the diagonal *SQ* by the vector $\vec{B} = \hat{i} - 3\hat{j} + 4\hat{k}$.

Now the diagonal *PR* and *SQ* bisect each other at *O*. Hence

$$\vec{PO} = \frac{1}{2}\vec{A} = \frac{1}{2}(3\hat{i} + \hat{j} + \hat{k})$$

and $\vec{OQ} = \frac{1}{2}\vec{B} = \frac{1}{2}(\hat{i} - 3\hat{j} + 4\hat{k})$

Area of parallelogram $PQRS$ = 4 × area of $\triangle POQ$

$$= 4 \times \frac{1}{2}\ \vec{PO} \times \vec{OQ}$$

$$= 2\left[\frac{1}{2}(3\hat{i} + \hat{j} + 2\hat{k}) \times \frac{1}{2}(\hat{i} - 3\hat{j} + 4\hat{k})\right]$$

$$= \frac{1}{2}(3\hat{i} + \hat{j} + 2\hat{k}) \times (\hat{i} - 3\hat{j} + 4\hat{k})$$

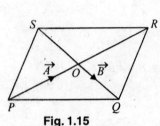

Fig. 1.15

$$= \frac{1}{2}\begin{vmatrix} \hat{i} & \hat{j} & \hat{k} \\ 3 & 1 & 2 \\ 1 & -3 & 4 \end{vmatrix} = \frac{1}{2}(10\hat{i} - 10\hat{j} - 10\hat{k})$$

$$= \frac{1}{2}(10\hat{i} - 10\hat{j} - 10\hat{k}) = (5\hat{i} - 5\hat{j} - 5\hat{k})$$

$$= \sqrt{5^2 + 5^2 + 5^2} = \sqrt{75} = 8.66\ sq.\ \text{units.}$$

Q. 1.17. If $\vec{A} + \vec{B} + \vec{C} = 0$**, prove that** $\vec{A} \times \vec{B} = \vec{B} \times \vec{C} = \vec{C} \times \vec{A}$.   (A. U., 1995)

Ans. In rectangular component form

$$\vec{A} = A_x\hat{i} + A_y\hat{j} + A_z\hat{k}$$

$$\vec{B} = B_x\hat{i} + B_y\hat{j} + B_z\hat{k}$$

and

$$\vec{C} = C_x\hat{i} + C_y\hat{j} + C_z\hat{k}$$

Given $\vec{A} + \vec{B} + \vec{C} = 0$

∴ $\vec{A} = -(\vec{B} + \vec{C})$

or $A_x\hat{i} + A_y\hat{j} + A_z\hat{k} = -(B_x + C_x)\hat{i} - (B_y + C_y)\hat{j} - (B_z + C_z)\hat{k}$

Hence $A_x = -(B_x + C_x);\ A_y = -(B_y + C_y);\ A_z = -(B_z + C_z)$

Now $\vec{A} \times \vec{B} = (A_x\hat{i} + A_y\hat{j} + A_z\hat{k}) \times (B_x\hat{i} + B_y\hat{j} + B_z\hat{k})$

$$= \begin{vmatrix} \hat{i} & \hat{j} & \hat{k} \\ A_x & A_y & A_z \\ B_x & B_y & B_z \end{vmatrix}$$

$$= (A_yB_z - A_zB_y)\hat{i} + (A_zB_x - A_xB_z)\hat{j} + (A_xB_y - A_yB_x)\hat{k}$$

Substituting the values of $A_x,\ A_y$ and A_z in terms of $B_x,\ B_y,\ B_z$ and $C_x,\ C_y,\ C_z$, we have

$$\vec{A} \times \vec{B} = \left\{-(B_y + C_y)B_z - \left[-(B_z + C_z)B_y\right]\right\}\hat{i}$$

$$+ \left\{-(B_z + C_z)B_x - \left[-(B_x + C_x)B_z\right]\right\}\hat{j}$$

$$+ \left\{-(B_x + C_x)B_y - \left[-(B_y + C_y)B_x\right]\right\}\hat{k}$$

Now $-(B_y + C_y)B_z - [-(B_z + C_z)B_y]$

$$= -B_yB_z - C_yB_z + B_zB_y + C_zB_y = B_yC_z - B_zC_y$$

and $-(B_z + C_z)B_x - [-(B_x + C_x)B_z]$

$$= -B_z B_x - C_z B_x + B_x B_z + C_x B_z = B_z C_x - C_z B_x$$

Also $-(B_x + C_x)B_y - [-(B_y + C_y)B_x]$

$$= -B_x B_y - C_x B_y + B_y B_x + C_y B_x = B_x C_y - B_y C_x$$

$\therefore$

$$\vec{A} \times \vec{B} = (B_y C_z - B_z C_y)\hat{i} + (B_z C_x - B_x C_z)\hat{j} + (B_x C_y - B_y C_x)\hat{k}$$

$$= \vec{B} \times \vec{C}$$

Similarly

$$\vec{A} \times \vec{B} = \vec{C} \times \vec{A}$$

Hence

$$\vec{A} \times \vec{B} = \vec{B} \times \vec{C} = \vec{C} \times \vec{A}$$

Q. 1.18. (*a*) **Define torque. Show that torque can be written as** $\vec{\tau} = \vec{r} \times \vec{F}$. (*K. U., 1991*)

(*b*) **Derive a relation between angular momentum of a particle, its mass and angular velocity. Which property of vector is used in deriving this relation?** (*K. U., 1992*)

Ans. (*a*) **Torque.** Let QR represent the force vector $\vec{F}$ in magnitude and direction as shown in

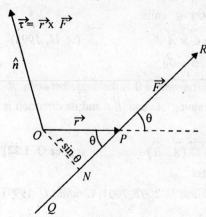

Fig. 1.16

Fig. 1.16. Let O be an arbitray point and $\vec{r}$ the position vector of any point P on the line of action of the force QR. Let θ be the angle between $\vec{r}$ and $\vec{F}$ and $\hat{n}$ a unit vector perpendicular to the plane containing $\vec{r}$ and $\vec{F}$. From O draw ON perpendicular to QR the line of action of the force, then

$$ON = r \sin \theta$$

The moment of the force $\vec{F}$ about the point O is defined as the vector quantity torque whose magnitude is equal to the product of the magnitude of the force and the perpendicular distance of the point O from the line of action of the force and whose direction is perpendicular to the plane containing $\vec{r}$ and $\vec{F}$

Magnitude of the torque = Moment of the force = $(F)(ON) = Fr \sin \theta$

$\therefore$ Torque $\vec{\tau} = rF \sin \theta \, \hat{n} = \vec{r} \times \vec{F}$

where $\hat{n}$ is a unit vector along $\vec{\tau}$. The direction of $\hat{n}$ is such that $\vec{r}, \vec{F}$ and $\hat{n}$ form a right handed system. Thus

$$\vec{\tau} = \vec{r} \times \vec{F}$$

Thus torque is a vector which gives the moment of the force $\vec{F}$ about O.

(*b*) **Angular momentum.** Consider a particle of mass m which at a particular instant of time is at the point P and has a linear velocity vector $\vec{v}$, then linear momentum of the particle $\vec{p} = m\vec{v}$, its direction is the same as that of $\vec{v}$.

Let O be an arbitrary point and $\vec{r}$ the position vector of the moving particle P relative to the fixed point O. The angular momentum of the particle about O is the moment of

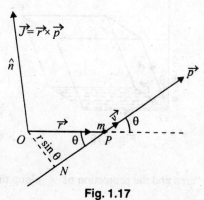

Fig. 1.17

its momentum about O and is thus a vector quantity whose magnitude is equal to the product of the magnitude of the linear momentum vector and its perpendicular distance from the point O and whose direction is perpendicular to the plane containing $\vec{r}$ and $\vec{p}$. Hence the angular momentum $\vec{J}$ of the particle about O is given by

$$|\vec{J}| = ON|\vec{p}| = rp \sin \theta$$

or
$$\vec{J} = rp \sin \theta \, \hat{n} = \vec{r} \times \vec{p}$$

Where $\hat{n}$ is a unit vector along $\vec{J}$. The direction of $\hat{n}$ is such that $\vec{r}, \vec{p}$ and $\hat{n}$ form a right handed system.

$$\therefore \qquad \vec{J} = \vec{r} \times \vec{p} = \vec{r} \times m\vec{v} = m(\vec{r} \times \vec{v})$$

Relation between angular momentum, mass and angular velocity. If $\vec{\omega}$ is the angular velocity, then $\vec{v} = \vec{\omega} \times \vec{r}$

$$\therefore \qquad \vec{J} = m(\vec{r} \times \vec{v}) = m\{\vec{r} \times (\vec{\omega} \times \vec{r})\}$$
$$= m\{\vec{\omega}(\vec{r} \cdot \vec{r}) - \vec{r}(\vec{r} \cdot \vec{\omega})\}$$
$$= mr^2 \vec{\omega}$$

[If $\vec{r}$ and $\vec{\omega}$ are perpendicular to each other so that $\vec{r} \cdot \vec{\omega} = 0$]

Property of vector product used. (*i*) $\vec{A} \times \vec{B} = AB \sin \theta \, \hat{n}$ where θ is the angle between $\vec{A}$ and $\vec{B}$ and $\hat{n}$ a unit vector perpendicular to the plane containing $\vec{A}$ and $\vec{B}$ and its direction is given by right hand screw rule.

(*ii*) **Vector triple product** $\vec{A} \times (\vec{B} \times \vec{C}) = \vec{B}(\vec{A} \cdot \vec{C}) - \vec{C}(\vec{A} \cdot \vec{B})$ [See Q. 1.22]

Q. 1.19 (*a*) What are scalar and vector triple products?

(Meerut U. 2002, 2001; *Gauhati U.* 1999)

(*b*) Show that $\vec{A} \cdot (\vec{B} \times \vec{C}) = \vec{B} \times (\vec{C} \cdot \vec{A}) = \vec{C} \cdot (\vec{A} \times \vec{B})$.

Ans. (*a*) Triple product of vectors. The vector product of two vectors $\vec{B}$ and $\vec{C}$ is a vector which can give both scalar and vector product with a third vector $\vec{A}$. There are, therefore, two triple products

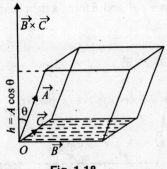

Fig. 1.18

$$\vec{A} \cdot (\vec{B} \times \vec{C})$$

This is known as **scalar triple product** and

$$\vec{A} \times (\vec{B} \times \vec{C})$$

This is known as **vector triple product.**

Scalar triple product. $\vec{A} \cdot (\vec{B} \times \vec{C})$. We have proved that $\vec{B} \times \vec{C}$ is a vector normal to the plane of $\vec{B}$ and $\vec{C}$ and its magnitude is equal to the area of a parallelogram having the sides represented by $\vec{B}$ and $\vec{C}$ shown shaded in Fig. 1.18.

The scalar product of $\vec{A}$ and $(\vec{B} \times \vec{C})$ is a product of this area and the projection of $\vec{A}$ along the vector $(\vec{B} \times \vec{C})$ which is equal to $h = A \cos \theta$.

$$\therefore \qquad \vec{A}.(\vec{B} \times \vec{C}) = \text{Area of base} \times \text{height } h$$

This is the volume of the parallelopiped enclosed by the vectors $\vec{A}, \vec{B}$ and $\vec{C}$ as its edges.

As any face of the parallelogram enclosed can be taken as its base, three equivalent expressions for volume are

Volume $\quad V = \vec{A}.(\vec{B} \times \vec{C}) = \vec{B}.(\vec{C} \times \vec{A}) = \vec{C}.(\vec{A} \times \vec{B})$

The scalar triple product is **positive** if the angle θ as shown in Fig. 1.18. is **acute** *i.e.*, if $\vec{A}, \vec{B}$ and $\vec{C}$ are **right handed** system of vectors and **negative** if θ is obtuse *i.e.*, if $\vec{A}, \vec{B}$ and $\vec{C}$ form a **left handed** system of vectors. Also in the scalar triple product, the final result is the same even if the position of dot and cross may be interchanged. The above expression, therefore can be written as

Volume $\quad V = (\vec{A} \times \vec{B}).\vec{C} = (\vec{B} \times \vec{C}).\vec{A} = (\vec{C} \times \vec{A}).\vec{B}$

We can also write the scalar triple product of $\vec{A}, \vec{B}, \vec{C}$ as $[\vec{A}\vec{B}\vec{C}]$.

Thus in scalar triple product the position of dot and cross may be interchanged without changing the value of the product provided the **cyclic order** of vectors is maintained.

Again $\qquad\qquad \vec{C} \times \vec{B} = -\vec{B} \times \vec{C}$

$\therefore \qquad\qquad \vec{A}.(\vec{C} \times \vec{B}) = -\vec{A}.(\vec{B} \times \vec{C})$

For vector triple product see Q. 1.22.

Q. 1.20. Express the scalar triple product in terms of rectangular components.

Ans. Scalar triple product in terms of rectangular components. The scalar triple product in terms of rectangular components of vectors may be written in the form of a determinant. Now,

$$\vec{A}.(\vec{B} \times \vec{C}) = (A_x \hat{i} + A_y \hat{j} + A_z \hat{k}). \begin{vmatrix} \hat{i} & \hat{j} & \hat{k} \\ B_x & B_y & B_z \\ C_x & C_y & C_z \end{vmatrix}$$

$$= (A_x \hat{i} + A_y \hat{j} + A_z \hat{k}).[(B_y C_z - B_z C_y)\hat{i} + (B_z C_x - B_x C_z)\hat{j} + (B_x C_y - B_y C_x)\hat{k}]$$

$$= A_x (B_y C_z - B_z C_y) + A_y (B_z C_x - B_x C_z) + A_z (B_x C_y - B_y C_x)$$

$$= \begin{vmatrix} A_x & A_y & A_z \\ B_x & B_y & B_z \\ C_x & C_y & C_z \end{vmatrix}$$

The scalar triple product of three unit vectors $\hat{i}, \hat{j}, \hat{k}$

$$[\hat{i}\,\hat{j}\,\hat{k}] = [\hat{j}\,\hat{k}\,\hat{i}] = [\hat{k}\,\hat{i}\,\hat{j}] = 1$$

Q. 1.21. (a) Prove that if the scalar triple product vanishes the vectors are co-planar.

(Meerut U., 1995)

(b) Prove that the vectors $2\hat{i} - \hat{j} + \hat{k}, \hat{i} + 2\hat{j} + 3\hat{k}, 3\hat{i} - 4\hat{j} + 5\hat{k}$ **are co-planar.**

(Meerut U., 2001)

Ans. (a) condition for co-planar vectors. The condition that the three vectors may be co-planar is that their scalar triple product should vanish. In other words,

$$\vec{A}.(\vec{B} \times \vec{C}) = 0$$

In such a case the volume of the parallelopiped formed by the three vectors = 0. Hence these lie in one plane. The above condition is satisfied if two of the vectors are **parallel** or **equal**.

(b) Let $\vec{A} = 2\hat{i} - \hat{j} + \hat{k}$; $\vec{B} = \hat{i} + 2\hat{j} - 3\hat{k}$; $\vec{C} = 3\hat{i} - 4\hat{j} + 5\hat{k}$. The three vectors $\vec{A}, \vec{B}$ and $\vec{C}$ are co-planar if $\vec{A} \cdot (\vec{B} \times \vec{C}) = 0$

Now
$$\vec{A} \cdot (\vec{B} \times \vec{C}) = \begin{vmatrix} A_x & A_y & A_z \\ B_x & B_y & B_z \\ C_x & C_y & C_z \end{vmatrix} = \begin{vmatrix} +2 & -1 & +1 \\ +1 & +2 & -3 \\ +3 & -4 & +5 \end{vmatrix}$$
$$= 2(10-12) - 1(-9-5) + 1(-4-6)$$
$$= -4 + 14 - 10 = 0$$

As $\vec{A} \cdot (\vec{B} \times \vec{C}) = 0$, the three vectors are co-planar.

Q. 1.22. Show that the vector triple product

$$\vec{A} \times (\vec{B} \times \vec{C}) = \vec{B}(\vec{A} \cdot \vec{C}) - \vec{C}(\vec{A} \cdot \vec{B}).$$ *(Meerut U., 2002)*

Ans. Vector triple product $\vec{A} \times (\vec{B} \times \vec{C})$. To evaluate this expression we shall first find the value of $\vec{B} \times \vec{C}$ which in terms of rectangular components is given by

$$\vec{B} \times \vec{C} = \begin{vmatrix} \hat{i} & \hat{j} & \hat{k} \\ B_x & B_y & B_z \\ C_x & C_y & C_z \end{vmatrix}$$
$$= (B_y C_z - B_z C_y)\hat{i} + (B_z C_x - B_x C_z)\hat{j} + (B_x C_y - B_y C_x)\hat{k}$$

Now
$$\vec{A} \times (\vec{B} \times \vec{C}) = (A_x\hat{i} + A_y\hat{j} + A_z\hat{k}) \times [(B_y C_z - B_z C_y)\hat{i}$$
$$+ (B_z C_x - B_x C_z)\hat{j} + (B_x C_y - B_y C_x)\hat{k}]$$

$$= \begin{vmatrix} \hat{i} & \hat{j} & \hat{k} \\ A_x & A_y & A_z \\ (B_y C_z - B_z C_y) & (B_z C_x - B_x C_z) & (B_x C_y - B_y C_x) \end{vmatrix}$$

The first term of the above determinant
$$= [A_y(B_x C_y - B_y C_x) - A_z(B_z C_x - B_x C_z)]\hat{i}$$
$$= [A_y B_x C_y - A_y B_y C_x - A_z B_z C_x + A_z B_x C_z]\hat{i}$$

Add and subtract $A_x B_x C_x$, collect positive terms and negative terms and arrange, then we get

First term $= [(A_y B_x C_y + A_z B_x C_z + A_x B_x C_x) - (A_y B_y C_x + A_z B_z C_x + A_x B_x C_x]\hat{i}$
$$= [B_x(A_x C_x + A_y C_y + A_z C_z) - C_x(A_x B_x + A_y B_y + A_z B_z)]\hat{i}$$
$$= B_x(\vec{A} \cdot \vec{C})\hat{i} - C_x(\vec{A} \cdot \vec{B})\hat{i}$$

Similarly the second and third terms of the determinant are
$$\text{2nd term} = B_y(\vec{A} \cdot \vec{C})\hat{j} - C_y(\vec{A} \cdot \vec{B})\hat{j}$$
$$\text{3nd term} = B_z(\vec{A} \cdot \vec{C})\hat{k} - C_z(\vec{A} \cdot \vec{B})\hat{k}$$

Adding all these terms, we get

$$\vec{A} \times (\vec{B} \times \vec{C}) = (B_x \hat{i} + B_y \hat{j} + B_z \hat{k})(\vec{A} . \vec{C}) - (C_x \hat{i} + C_y \hat{j} + C_z \hat{k})(\vec{A} . \vec{B})$$

$$= \vec{B}(\vec{A} . \vec{C}) - \vec{C}(\vec{A} . \vec{B})$$

As the vector $\vec{B} \times \vec{C}$ is perpendicular to the plain containing $\vec{B}$ and $\vec{C}$, the vector $\vec{A} \times (\vec{B} \times \vec{C})$ will be perpendicular to the plane containing $\vec{A}$ and $(\vec{B} \times \vec{C})$ i.e., it will be in the plane of $\vec{B}$ and $\vec{C}$, the vectors inside the brackets. This is also clear from the result $(\vec{A} . \vec{C})$ and $(\vec{A} . \vec{B})$ being scalar quantities the resultant lies in the plane of $\vec{B}$ and $\vec{C}$.

Also $\vec{A} \times (\vec{B} \times \vec{C}) = -(\vec{B} \times \vec{C}) \times \vec{A}$

Q. 1.23. Prove that $\vec{A} \times (\vec{B} \times \vec{C}) + \vec{B} \times (\vec{C} \times \vec{A}) + \vec{C} \times (\vec{A} \times \vec{B}) = 0.$

(K. U. 1992; Gauhati U. 2000; Meerut U. 2002)

Ans. According to triple vector product

$$\vec{A} \times (\vec{B} \times \vec{C}) = \vec{B}(\vec{A} . \vec{C}) - \vec{C}(\vec{A} . \vec{B})$$

$$\vec{B} \times (\vec{C} \times \vec{A}) = \vec{C}(\vec{B} . \vec{A}) - \vec{A}(\vec{B} . \vec{C})$$

$$\vec{C} \times (\vec{A} \times \vec{B}) = \vec{A}(\vec{C} . \vec{B}) - \vec{B}(\vec{C} . \vec{A})$$

Now $\vec{A} . \vec{C} = \vec{C} . \vec{A}, \ \vec{A} . \vec{B} = \vec{B} . \vec{A}, \vec{B} . \vec{C} = \vec{C} . \vec{B}$

$\therefore \ \vec{A} \times (\vec{B} \times \vec{C}) + \vec{B} \times (\vec{C} \times \vec{A}) + \vec{C} \times (\vec{A} \times \vec{B}) = 0$

Q. 1.24. Prove that $(\vec{A} + \vec{B}) . [(\vec{B} + \vec{C}) \times (\vec{C} + \vec{A})] = 2\vec{A} . (\vec{B} \times \vec{C})$

Ans. $(\vec{A} + \vec{B}) . [(\vec{B} + \vec{C}) \times (\vec{C} + \vec{A})]$

$$= (\vec{A} + \vec{B}) . [(\vec{B} \times \vec{C}) + (\vec{B} \times \vec{A}) + (\vec{C} \times \vec{C}) + (\vec{C} \times \vec{A})]$$

$$= \vec{A} . (\vec{B} \times \vec{C}) + \vec{A} . (\vec{B} \times \vec{A}) + \vec{A} . (\vec{C} \times \vec{C}) + \vec{A} . (\vec{C} \times \vec{A})$$

$$+ \vec{B} . (\vec{B} \times \vec{C}) + \vec{B} . (\vec{B} \times \vec{A}) + \vec{B} . (\vec{C} \times \vec{C}) + \vec{B} . (\vec{C} \times \vec{A})$$

Now $\vec{A} . (\vec{B} \times \vec{A}) = 0; \ \vec{A} . (\vec{C} \times \vec{C}) = 0; \ \vec{A} . (\vec{C} \times \vec{A}) = 0$

$$\vec{B} . (\vec{B} \times \vec{C}) = 0; \ \vec{B} . (\vec{B} \times \vec{A}) = 0; \ \vec{B} . (\vec{C} \times \vec{C}) = 0$$

$\therefore \ (\vec{A} + \vec{B}) . [(\vec{B} + \vec{C}) \times (\vec{C} + \vec{A})] = \vec{A} . (\vec{B} \times \vec{C}) + \vec{B} . (\vec{C} \times \vec{A}) = 2\vec{A} . (\vec{B} \times \vec{C})$

Q. 1.25. If $\vec{A}$ **and** $\vec{B}$ **are two vectors, show that the component of** $\vec{A}$ **perpendicular to** $\vec{B}$

is given by $\dfrac{\vec{B} \times (\vec{A} \times \vec{B})}{B^2}$.   *(A. U., 1995)*

Ans. Suppose the vectors $\vec{A}$ and $\vec{B}$ lie in the X-Y plane with the vector $\vec{B}$ coinciding with the X-axis, then

$$\vec{A} \times \vec{B} = AB \sin \theta \, \hat{n}$$

where $\hat{n}$ is a unit vector perpendicular to the plane containing the vectors $\vec{A}$ and $\vec{B}$ i.e., in the direction of –Z-axis.

or $\hat{n} = -\hat{k}$

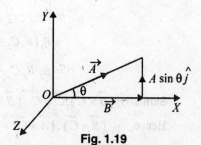

Fig. 1.19

$\therefore$ $\qquad \vec{A} \times \vec{B} = - AB \sin\theta \, \hat{k}$

Hence $\qquad \vec{B} \times (\vec{A} \times \vec{B}) = - AB \sin\theta \, \vec{B} \times \hat{k}$

$\qquad\qquad\qquad\qquad = - AB \sin\theta \, B \, (\hat{i} \times \hat{k})$ $\qquad\qquad$ $[\because \vec{B} = B\hat{i}\,]$

$\qquad\qquad\qquad\qquad = - AB^2 \sin\theta \, (\hat{i} \times \hat{k})$

$\qquad\qquad\qquad\qquad = AB^2 \sin\theta \, \hat{j}$ $\qquad\qquad\qquad$ $[\because \hat{i} \times \hat{k} = -\hat{j}\,]$

or $\qquad\qquad A \sin\theta \, \hat{j} = \dfrac{\vec{B} \times (\vec{A} \times \vec{B})}{B^2}$

where $A \sin\theta \, \hat{j}$ is the component of $\vec{A}$ perpendicular to $\vec{B}$ and lies along the Y-axis as shown in Fig. 1.19.

Q. 1.26. Prove that $\hat{i} \times (\vec{A} \times \hat{i}) + \hat{j} \times (\vec{A} \times \hat{j}) + \hat{k} \times (\vec{A} \times \hat{k}) = 2\vec{A}$. $\qquad$ *(A. U., 1994)*

Ans. Applying the relation $\vec{A} \times (\vec{B} \times \vec{C}) = \vec{B} (\vec{A}.\vec{C}) - \vec{C} (\vec{A}.\vec{B})$ we have

$\qquad\qquad \hat{i} \times (\vec{A} \times \hat{i}) = \vec{A}(\hat{i}.\hat{i}) - \hat{i}\,(\hat{i}.\vec{A})$

$\qquad\qquad\qquad\qquad = \vec{A} - \hat{i}\,(\hat{i}.\vec{A})$

$\qquad\qquad \hat{j} \times (\vec{A} \times \hat{j}) = \vec{A} - \hat{j}(\hat{j}.\vec{A})$

$\qquad\qquad \hat{k} \times (\vec{A} \times \hat{k}) = \vec{A} - \hat{k}(\hat{k}.\vec{A})$

$\therefore \qquad\qquad \hat{i} \times (\vec{A} \times \hat{i}) + \hat{j} \times (\vec{A} \times \hat{j}) + \hat{k} \times (\vec{A} \times \hat{k})$

$\qquad\qquad\qquad\qquad = 3\vec{A} - \hat{i}\,(\hat{i}.\vec{A}) - \hat{j}\,(\hat{j}.\vec{A}) - \hat{k}\,(\hat{k}.\vec{A})$

Now $\qquad\qquad \hat{i}.\vec{A} = \hat{i}.(A_x\hat{i} + A_y\hat{j} + A_z\,\hat{k}) = A_x$

Similarly $\qquad\qquad \hat{j}.\vec{A} = A_y$ and $\hat{k}.\vec{A} = A_z$

$\therefore \qquad\qquad 3\vec{A} - \hat{i}\,(\hat{i}.\vec{A}) - \hat{j}\,(\hat{j}.\vec{A}) - \hat{k}\,(\hat{k}.\vec{A})$

$\qquad\qquad\qquad\qquad = 3\vec{A} - [A_x\hat{i} + A_y\hat{j} + A_z\hat{k}]$

$\qquad\qquad\qquad\qquad = 3\vec{A} - \vec{A} = 2\vec{A}$

Q. 1.27. Prove that $(\vec{B} \times \vec{C}).\{\vec{A} \times (\vec{B} \times \vec{C})\} = 0$. $\qquad$ *(A. U. 1995)*

Ans. $\qquad \vec{A} \times (\vec{B} \times \vec{C}) = \vec{B} (\vec{A}.\vec{C}) - \vec{C} (\vec{A}.\vec{B})$

$\therefore (\vec{B} \times \vec{C}).\{\vec{A} \times (\vec{B} \times \vec{C})\} = (\vec{B} \times \vec{C}).\vec{B} (\vec{A}.\vec{C}) - (\vec{B} \times \vec{C}).\vec{C} (\vec{A}.\vec{B})$

Now $(\vec{B} \times \vec{C}).\vec{B} = \vec{B}.(\vec{B} \times \vec{C})$

$\qquad\qquad = \begin{vmatrix} B_x & B_y & B_z \\ B_x & B_y & B_z \\ C_x & C_y & C_z \end{vmatrix}$

$\qquad = B_x (B_y C_z - C_y B_z) + B_y (B_z C_x - B_x C_z) + B_z (B_x C_y - B_y C_x)$

$\qquad = B_x B_y C_z - B_x C_y B_z + B_y B_z C_x - B_y B_x C_z + B_z B_x C_y - B_z B_y C_x = 0$

Similarly $(\vec{B} \times \vec{C}).\vec{C} = \vec{C}.(\vec{B} \times \vec{C}) = 0$

Hence $\qquad (\vec{B} \times \vec{C}).[\vec{A} \times (\vec{B} \times \vec{C})] = 0$.

1.9. Differentiation of a vector with respect to a scalar. In ordinary differential calculus $y = f(x)$ means y is a function of variable x. Similarly if a vector undergoes a continuous change in magnitude and direction with respect to some scalar variable then it is said to be a vector function of the scalar variable. Thus $\vec{A} = \vec{A}(t)$ denotes a vector which is a function of scalar variable t.

Consider a particle which moves form P to Q along a curved path in time δt. Let the position vector of P with respect to the origin O be $\vec{r}(t)$ and of Q be $\vec{r}(t + \delta t)$. The average rate of change of the vector $\vec{r}$ with time is given by,

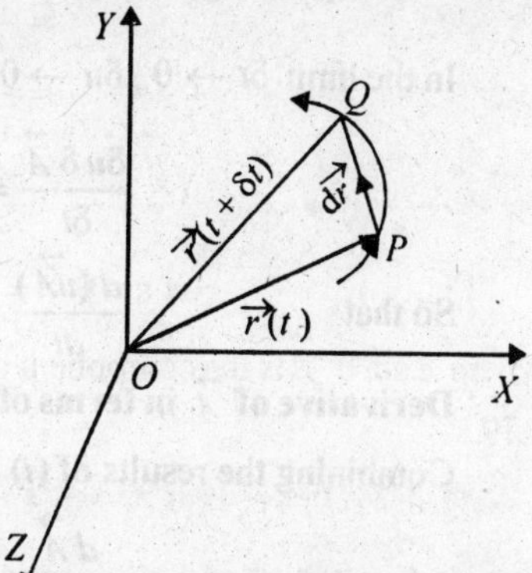

$$\frac{\vec{r}(t + \delta t) - \vec{r}(t)}{\delta t} = \frac{\delta \vec{r}}{\delta t}$$

because if PQ is small it can be taken to be a straight line so that

$$\vec{r}(t + \delta t) - \vec{r}(t) = \delta \vec{r}$$

Fig. 1.20

The derivative of the function $\vec{r}(t)$ with respect to the scalar (t) is defined as

$$\frac{d\vec{r}}{dt} = \underset{\delta t \to 0}{\text{Lt}} \frac{\delta \vec{r}}{\delta t}$$

provided the limit exists. The derivative $\dfrac{d\vec{r}}{dt}$ is also a vector since its numerator is a vector and denominator a scalar quantity. In general the derivative of any vector $\vec{A}$ which is the function of a scalar t is defined as

$$\frac{d\vec{A}}{dt} = \underset{\delta t \to 0}{\text{Lt}} \frac{\vec{A}(t + \delta t) - \vec{A}(t)}{\delta t}$$

Differentiation of sum of vectors. Let $\vec{A}$ and $\vec{B}$ be two vectors which are functions of scalar variable t. If $\delta \vec{A}$ and $\delta \vec{B}$ are the increments in these vector functions due to an increment δt, then

$$\frac{d}{dt}(\vec{A} + \vec{B}) = \underset{\delta t \to 0}{\text{Lt}} \frac{[\{(\vec{A} + \delta A) + (\vec{B} + \delta \vec{B})\} - (\vec{A} + \vec{B})]}{\delta t}$$

$$= \underset{\delta t \to 0}{\text{Lt}} \frac{\delta \vec{A}}{\delta t} + \underset{\delta t \to 0}{\text{Lt}} \frac{\delta \vec{B}}{\delta t}$$

$$= \frac{d\vec{A}}{dt} + \frac{d\vec{B}}{dt} \qquad \qquad ...(i)$$

Thus the derivative of the sum of two differentiable vector functions is equal to the sum of their derivatives. The result is true for any number of vectors. Further, if $\vec{A}$ is a vector function of a scalar s and s is a scalar differentiable function of another scalar variable t, then

$$\frac{d\vec{A}}{dt} = \frac{d\vec{A}}{ds} \frac{ds}{dt} \qquad \qquad ...(ii)$$

Differentiation of product of vectors. (a) Product of a scalar and a vector. Let u be a scalar quantity and $\vec{A}$ a vector quantity both differentiable functions of a scalar variable t. If δu and $\delta \vec{A}$ are the increments in u and $\vec{A}$ due to an increment δt, then the increment $\delta (u \vec{A})$ is given by

$$\delta(u\vec{A}) = (u+\delta u)(\vec{A}+\delta\vec{A}) - u\vec{A} = \delta u\vec{A} + u\delta\vec{A} + \delta u\,\delta\vec{A}$$

Dividing throughout by δt, we have $\dfrac{\delta(u\vec{A})}{\delta t} = \dfrac{\delta u}{\delta t}\vec{A} + u\dfrac{\delta\vec{A}}{\delta t} + \dfrac{\delta u\,\delta\vec{A}}{\delta t}$

In the limit $\delta t \to 0$, $\delta u \to 0$ and $\delta A \to 0$

$$\therefore \qquad \frac{\delta u\,\delta\vec{A}}{\delta t} = 0$$

So that $\qquad \dfrac{d(u\vec{A})}{dt} = \dfrac{du}{dt}\vec{A} + u\dfrac{d\vec{A}}{dt}$ ...(iii)

Derivative of $\vec{A}$ in terms of unit vectors. The vector $\vec{A} = A_x\,\hat{i} + A_y\,\hat{j} + A_z\,\hat{k}$

Combining the results of (i) and (iii), we have

$$\frac{d\vec{A}}{dt} = \frac{dA_x}{dt}\hat{i} + \frac{dA_y}{dt}\hat{j} + \frac{dA_z}{dt}\hat{k}$$

$\hat{i}$, $\hat{j}$ and $\hat{k}$ being unit vectors along X, Y and Z axes respectively have a constant direction and magnitude and hence $\dfrac{d\hat{i}}{dt} = \dfrac{d\hat{j}}{dt} = \dfrac{d\hat{k}}{dt} = 0$.

(b) Scalar product of two vectors. If $\vec{A}$ and $\vec{B}$ are two vector functions of a scalar variable t, then increment δt in t causes an increment $\delta\vec{A}$ in $\vec{A}$ and $\delta\vec{B}$ in $\vec{B}$.

$$\therefore \qquad \delta(\vec{A}.\vec{B}) = (\vec{A}+\delta\vec{A}).(B+\delta\vec{A}) - \vec{A}.\vec{B} = \delta\vec{A}.\vec{B} + \vec{A}.\delta\vec{B} + \delta\vec{A}.\delta\vec{B}$$

Dividing throughout by δt, we have

$$\frac{\delta(\vec{A}.\vec{B})}{\delta t} = \frac{\delta\vec{A}}{\delta t}.\vec{B} + \vec{A}.\frac{\delta\vec{B}}{\delta t} + \frac{\delta\vec{A}.\delta\vec{B}}{\delta t}$$

In the limit $\delta t \to 0$, $\delta\vec{A} \to 0$; $\delta\vec{B} \to 0$

$$\therefore \qquad \frac{\delta\vec{A}.\delta\vec{B}}{\delta t} = 0$$

Hence $\qquad \dfrac{d(\vec{A}.\vec{B})}{dt} = \dfrac{d\vec{A}}{dt}.\vec{B} + \vec{A}.\dfrac{d\vec{B}}{dt}$ ...(iv)

(c) Vector product of two vectors. If $\vec{A}$ and $\vec{B}$ are two vector functions of a scalar variable t, then increment δt in t causes an increment $\delta\vec{A}$ in $\vec{A}$ and $\delta\vec{B}$ in $\vec{B}$.

$$\therefore \qquad \delta(\vec{A}\times\vec{B}) = (\vec{A}+\delta\vec{A})\times(\vec{B}+\delta\vec{B}) - (\vec{A}\times\vec{B})$$

$$= \vec{A}\times\delta\vec{B} + \delta\vec{A}\times\vec{B} + \delta\vec{A}\times\delta\vec{B}$$

Dividing throughout by δt, we have

$$\frac{\delta(\vec{A}\times\vec{B})}{\delta t} = \vec{A}\times\frac{\delta\vec{B}}{\delta t} + \frac{\delta\vec{A}}{\delta t}\times\vec{B} + \frac{\delta\vec{A}\times\delta\vec{B}}{\delta t}$$

In the limit $\delta t \to 0$, $\delta\vec{A} \to 0$; $\delta\vec{B} \to 0$

$$\therefore \qquad \frac{\delta\vec{A}\times\delta\vec{B}}{\delta t} = 0$$

Hence $\dfrac{d(\vec{A} \times \vec{B})}{dt} = \vec{A} \times \dfrac{d\vec{B}}{dt} + \dfrac{d\vec{A}}{dt} \times \vec{B}$ ...(v)

Thus the derivative of any product of vectors is found in the same way as for an algebraic product. It is equal to the sum of the quantities obtained by differentiating a single factor and leaving the other unchanged. In the case of the differentiation of a vector product the order of the vectors should also be not changed.

If $\vec{B} = \dfrac{d\vec{A}}{dt}$, then $\dfrac{d}{dt}\left(\vec{A} \times \dfrac{d\vec{A}}{dt} \right) = \vec{A} \times \dfrac{d^2\vec{A}}{dt^2} + \dfrac{d\vec{A}}{dt} \times \dfrac{d\vec{A}}{dt}$

but $\dfrac{d\vec{A}}{dt} \times \dfrac{d\vec{A}}{dt} = 0$

$\therefore$ $\dfrac{d}{dt}\left(\vec{A} \times \dfrac{d\vec{A}}{dt} \right) = \vec{A} \times \dfrac{d^2 A}{dt^2}$ ...(vi)

Q. 1.28. Show that if $\dfrac{d|\vec{A}|}{dt} = 0$, then $\vec{A}$ is perpendicular to $\dfrac{d\vec{A}}{dt}$.

Ans. We know that

$$\dfrac{d(\vec{A} \cdot \vec{B})}{dt} = \dfrac{d\vec{A}}{dt} \cdot \vec{B} + \vec{A} \cdot \dfrac{d\vec{B}}{dt}$$

If $\vec{A} = \vec{B}$, then

$$\dfrac{d(\vec{A} \cdot \vec{A})}{dt} = \dfrac{d(A^2)}{dt} = \dfrac{d(\vec{A})}{dt} \cdot \vec{A} + \vec{A} \cdot \dfrac{d\vec{A}}{dt} = 2\vec{A} \cdot \dfrac{d\vec{A}}{dt} = 2A\dfrac{dA}{dt}$$

where A is the magnitude of vector $\vec{A}$ *i.e.*, $A = |\vec{A}|$.

As $\dfrac{d|\vec{A}|}{dt} = 0$, $\vec{A}$ is a vector of constant magnitude. Thus

$$\dfrac{d|\vec{A}|}{dt} = \dfrac{dA}{dt} = 0$$

$\therefore$ $A\dfrac{dA}{dt} = \vec{A} \cdot \dfrac{d\vec{A}}{dt} = 0$

i.e., $\vec{A}$ and $\dfrac{d\vec{A}}{dt}$ are perpendicular to each other.

Thus the derivative of a vector of constant magnitude is perpendicular to the vector itself.

Q. 1.29. Show that the derivative of a vector of constant direction is parallel to that vector.

Ans. Let $\vec{r}$ be a vector whose magnitude is r and $\hat{r}$ is a unit vector along $\vec{r}$. Then $\vec{r} = r\hat{r}$.

$\therefore$ $\dfrac{d\vec{r}}{dt} = r\dfrac{d\hat{r}}{dt} + \dfrac{dr}{dt}\hat{r}$

$\therefore$ $\vec{r} \times \dfrac{d\vec{r}}{dt} = \vec{r} \times \left[r\dfrac{d\hat{r}}{dt} + \dfrac{dr}{dt}\hat{r} \right] = r\hat{r} \times \left[r\dfrac{d\hat{r}}{dt} + \dfrac{dr}{dt}\hat{r} \right] = r\hat{r} \times r\dfrac{d\hat{r}}{dt} + r\hat{r} \times \dfrac{dr}{dt}\hat{r}$

$$= r^2\hat{r} \times \dfrac{d\hat{r}}{dt}   [\because \hat{r} \times \hat{r} = 0]$$

If $\vec{r}$ has a constant direction then $\hat{r}$ is a constant vector and therefore $\dfrac{d\hat{r}}{dt} = 0$.

$\therefore \qquad \vec{r} \times \dfrac{d\vec{r}}{dt} = 0$ or $\vec{r}$ and $\dfrac{d\vec{r}}{dt}$ are parallel to each other.

Hence the derivative of a vector of constant direction is parallel to that vector.

Q. 1.30. (*a*) **Calculate the angular velocity of a rigid body about a fixed axis.**

(*b*) **Derive vector relation between linear acceleration and angular acceleration**

$$\vec{a} = \vec{\alpha} \times \vec{r} + \vec{\omega} \times \vec{v}$$
(K. U., 1991)

Ans. (*a*) **Angular velocity of a rigid body about a fixed axis.** Consider a rigid body rotating about a fixed axis *OM* at the rate of $\vec{\omega}$ radian/sec. The angular velocity is specified by the vector ω whose direction is parallel to the axis and in the positive sense relative to the rotation. When the body rotates all the particles constituting the body rotate along circular paths whose centre lies on the axis *OM* (Fig. 1.21)

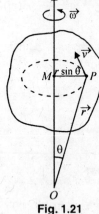

Fig. 1.21

Consider any point *P* on the body and *O* any point on the axis such that $\vec{r}$ is the position vector of *P* with respect to *O*. Draw *PM* perpendicular to the axis of rotation. The particle at *P* is moving in a circular path of radius $r \sin \theta$ where θ is the angle between the direction of $\vec{r}$ and $\vec{\omega}$. The linear velocity $\vec{v}$ of the point *P* is perpendicular to the plane of $\vec{\omega}$ and $\vec{r}$.

If $\hat{n}$ is the unit vector normal to the plane containing $\vec{r}$ and $\vec{\omega}$, then

$$\vec{v} = \vec{\omega} \times \vec{r} = (\omega r \sin \theta)\,\hat{n} = (\omega\, MP)\hat{n}$$

Thus magnitude of $\vec{v} = |\vec{\omega} \times \vec{r}| = \omega\, MP$

and direction of $\vec{v} = \vec{\omega} \times \vec{r}$ *i.e.,* $\hat{n}$

is the direction of the velocity of the point *P* about *O*. Hence $\vec{v} = \vec{\omega} \times \vec{r}$ ...(*i*)

In this case all the three vectors are perpendicular to each other.

(*b*) According to relation (*i*) $\vec{v} = \vec{\omega} \times \vec{r}$

Differentiating both sides with respect to *t*, we have

$$\frac{d\vec{v}}{dt} = \frac{d}{dt}(\vec{\omega} \times \vec{r}) = \frac{d\vec{\omega}}{dt} \times \vec{r} + \vec{\omega} \times \frac{d\vec{r}}{dt}$$

But $\dfrac{d\vec{v}}{dt} = \vec{a}$ The linear acceleration;

$\dfrac{d\vec{\omega}}{dt} = \vec{\alpha}$ The angular acceleration and $\dfrac{d\vec{r}}{dt} = \vec{v}$ The linear velocity

$\therefore \qquad\qquad \vec{a} = \vec{\alpha} \times \vec{r} + \vec{\omega} \times \vec{v}$

Q. 1.31. A vector $\vec{a} = \vec{a}\,(t)$ has a constant magnitude. Show that $\vec{a} \cdot \dfrac{d\vec{a}}{dt} = 0$.

(Cal. Univ., 1991)

Ans. $\vec{a} \cdot \dfrac{d\vec{a}}{dt} = a\,\dfrac{da}{dt}$ where *a* is the magnitude of vector $\vec{a}$.

Since vector $\vec{a}$ has a constant magnitude $\dfrac{da}{dt} = 0$ $\quad \therefore \quad \dfrac{da}{dt} = 0$ or $\vec{a} \cdot \dfrac{d\vec{a}}{dt} = 0$

Q. 1.32. A particle moves in a plane with constant speed but continuously changing direction. Show that the acceleration is always perpendicular to velocity vector. (*P. U. 1999, 1995*)

Ans. As the speed *i.e.*, the magnitude of velocity is constant

$$\frac{d|\vec{v}|}{dt} = 0 \text{ or } \frac{dv}{dt} = 0 \text{ where } |\vec{v}| = v$$

Also

$$\frac{d}{dt}(\vec{v} \cdot \vec{v}) = \frac{d\vec{v}}{dt} \cdot \vec{v} + \vec{v} \cdot \frac{d\vec{v}}{dt} = 2\vec{v} \cdot \frac{d\vec{v}}{dt}$$

$$\therefore \qquad 2\vec{v} \cdot \frac{d\vec{v}}{dt} = 0 \quad \text{But} \quad \frac{d\vec{v}}{dt} = \vec{a} \text{ (The acceleration)}$$

Hence $\vec{v} \cdot \vec{a} = 0$; As the dot product of $\vec{v}$ and $\vec{a}$ is zero, the acceleration $\vec{a}$ is perpendicular to $\vec{v}$.

Q. 1.33. If $\vec{V} = \vec{a} \cos \omega t + \vec{b} \sin \omega t$, then show that

$$\vec{V} \times \frac{d\vec{V}}{dt} = \omega (\vec{a} \times \vec{b}).$$

(*Gharwal U., 2000*)

Ans. $\vec{V} = \vec{a} \cos \omega t + \vec{b} \sin \omega t$

$$\therefore \qquad \frac{d\vec{V}}{dt} = -\vec{a} \omega \sin \omega t + \vec{b} \omega \cos \omega t$$

and

$$\vec{V} \times \frac{d\vec{V}}{dt} = (\vec{a} \cos \omega t + \vec{b} \sin \omega t) \times (-\vec{a} \sin \omega t + \vec{b} \cos \omega t)$$

$$= \vec{a} \cos \omega t \times (-\vec{a} \omega \sin \omega t + \vec{b} \omega \cos \omega t) + \vec{b} \sin \omega t \times (-\vec{a} \omega \sin \omega t + \vec{b} \omega \cos \omega t)$$

$$= \vec{a} \times \vec{b} (\omega \cos^2 \omega t) - \vec{b} \times \vec{a} (\omega \sin^2 \omega t) \qquad [\because \vec{a} \times \vec{a} = \vec{b} \times \vec{b} = 0]$$

$$= \vec{a} \times \vec{b} (\omega \cos^2 \omega t) + \vec{a} \times \vec{b} (\omega \sin^2 \omega t) \qquad [\because \vec{a} \times \vec{b} = -\vec{b} \times \vec{a}]$$

$$= \omega (\vec{a} \times \vec{b})$$

Q. 1.34. Mark the correct answer

(*i*) If *l, m, n* are the direction cosines of a vector, then

   (*a*) $l^2 + m^2 + n^2 = 0$ (*b*) $l^2 + m^2 + n^2 = 1$ (*c*) $l^2 + m^2 + n^2 > 0$ (*d*) $l^2 + m^2 + n^2 < 1$

(*ii*) Two vector $\vec{A}$ and $\vec{B}$ are perpendicular to each other if

   (*a*) $\vec{A} \cdot \vec{B} = 0$ (*b*) $\vec{A} \times \vec{B} = 0$ (*c*) $\vec{A} \cdot \vec{B} = 1$ (*d*) $\vec{A} \times \vec{B} = 1$

(*iii*) Two vectors $\vec{A}$ and $\vec{B}$ are collinear if

   (*a*) $\vec{A} \cdot \vec{B} = 0$ (*b*) $\vec{A} \times \vec{B} = 0$ (*c*) $\vec{A} \cdot \vec{B} = 1$ (*d*) $\vec{A} \times \vec{B} = 1$

(*iv*) Three vectors $\vec{A}, \vec{B}$ and $\vec{C}$ will form a triangle if

   (*a*) $\vec{A} + \vec{B} > \vec{C}$ (*b*) $\vec{A} + \vec{B} < \vec{C}$

   (*c*) $\vec{A} + \vec{B} = \vec{C}$ (*d*) $\vec{A} + \vec{B} + \vec{C} = 0$

(*v*) Volume of a paralloelopiped formed by $\vec{A}, \vec{B}$ and $\vec{C}$ is

   (*a*) $\vec{A} \times (\vec{B} \cdot \vec{C})$ (*b*) $\vec{A} (\vec{B} \times \vec{C})$ (*c*) $\vec{A} \cdot (\vec{B} \cdot \vec{C})$ (*d*) $\vec{A} \cdot (\vec{B} \times \vec{C})$

(*P.U., 1994, 1993*)

Ans.   (*i*) *b*   (*ii*) *a*   (*iii*) *b*   (*iv*) *c*

(*v*) *d*

Note. For further questions on vector calculus involving grad., divergence and curl of a vector see 'Electricity and Magnetism' by the same author.

$$\boxed{\textbf{EXERCISES}}$$

1. Under a force $10\hat{i} - 3\hat{j} + 6\hat{k}$ Newton a body of mass 5 kg moves from position $6\hat{i} + 5\hat{j} - 3\hat{k}$ metre to position $10\hat{i} - 2\hat{j} + 7\hat{k}$ metre. Calculate the work done.

[**Ans.** 21 Joules]

2. If $\vec{A} = \hat{i} - 3\hat{j} + \hat{k}$ and $\vec{B} = 3\hat{i} - 2\hat{j} + \hat{k}$ find $\vec{A} \times \vec{B}$.   [**Ans.** $5\hat{i} - 4\hat{j} + 7\hat{k}$]

3. Two constant forces $\vec{F_1}(2\hat{i} + 3\hat{j} + 3\hat{k})$ Newton and $\vec{F_2}(5\hat{i} + 6\hat{j} + 2\hat{k})$ Newton are acting simultaneously on a particle. If the particle is displaced from the point $(4, -3, -5)$ metre to the point $(-1, 4, 3)$ metre under these forces, then calculate the amount of work done on the particle.   (*Gharwal U.* 1999)

Hint. $\vec{F} = \vec{F_1} + \vec{F_2} = (2\hat{i} + 3\hat{j} + 3\hat{k}) + (5\hat{i} - 6\hat{j} - 2\hat{k}) = (7\hat{i} - 3\hat{j} + \hat{k})N$

Displacement $\vec{S} = (x_2 - x_1) = (-1\hat{i} + 4\hat{j} + 3\hat{k}) - (4\hat{i} - 3\hat{j} - 5\hat{k}) = (-5\hat{i} + 7\hat{j} + 8\hat{k})$

∴   Work done $W = \vec{F} \cdot \vec{S} = (7\hat{i} - 3\hat{j} + \hat{k}) \cdot (-5\hat{i} + 7\hat{j} + 8\hat{k}) = -48$ Joule.

2 Co-ordinate System

Q. 2.1. (*a*) **What is rectangular cartesian co-ordinate system?**

(Pbi.U. 2007, 2003, 2001, 1999;
P.U. 2000 1991 ; H.P.U. 2000, 1994)

(*b*) **Find the value of position vector, velocity and acceleration in two dimensional and three dimensional cartesian co-ordinate system.** *(Pbi. U. 2007)*

Ans. (*a*) **Rectangular cartesian co-ordinate system.** In classical mechanics *space* is considered to have *three* dimensions. In the cartesian co-ordinate system the three dimensions are represented by *three axes X, Y* and *Z* mutually perpendicular to each other. The fixed point at which the three axes meet is known as the *origin*. A point in space is represented by three co-ordinates *x, y, z*. These co-ordinates represent the distance of the point from the origin along the *X*, *Y* and *Z* axes respectively. There are two types of cartesian co-ordinate systems:

(*i*) *Right handed* and (*ii*) *Left handed*.

(*i*) **Right handed system.** In this system the three axes are taken in such a way that a right handed screw will move forward in the direction of *Z*-axis when its head is rotated in the anti-clockwise direction through a small angle from *X* to *Y* axis.

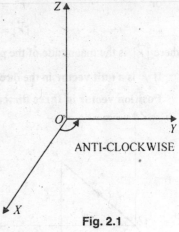

ANTI-CLOCKWISE

Fig. 2.1

One way of representing the right handed cartesian co-ordinate system is shown in Fig. 2.1. *Y* and *Z* axes are taken in the plane of the paper and *X*-axis perpendicular to the plane of the paper pointing outwards.

Moreover, if we stretch the *middle* finger, the *thumb* and the *first* finger of the right hand so that these are mutually at right angles, then if the middle finger points along the *X*-axis, the thumb along *Y*-axis the first finger will point along the *Z*-axis.

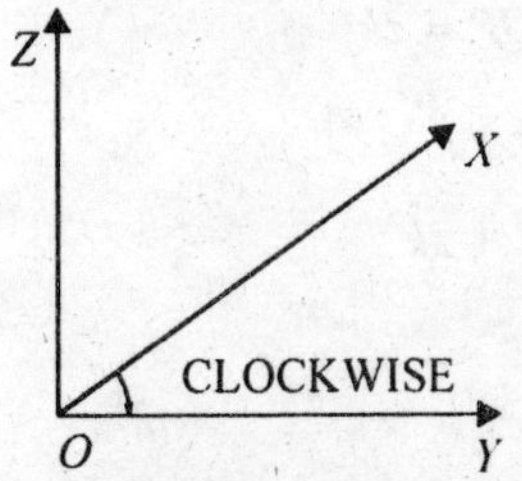

(*ii*) **Left handed system.** This system can be obtained by the mirror reflection of the right handed system or by changing the direction of one of the co-ordinate axes of the right handed system as shown in Fig. 2.2 where the direction of *X*-axis has been reversed by obtaining a mirror reflection by placing the mirror parallel to the *YZ* plane *i.e.*, the plane of the paper.

CLOCKWISE

Fig. 2.2

In this system the three axes are taken in such a way that a left handed screw will move forward in the direction of Z-axis when its head is rotated in the clockwise direction through a small angle from X to Y axis. Moreover, if we stretch the *middle* finger, the *thumb* and the *first* finger of the left hand so that these are mutually at right angles, then if the middle finger points along the X-axis, the thumb along the Y-axis, the first finger will point along the Z-axis.

One way of representing the left handed cartesian co-ordinate system is shown in Fig. 2.2. Y and Z axes are taken in the plane of the paper and X-axis perpendicular to the plane of the paper pointing inward.

(b) Position vector in two dimensional cartesian co-ordinate system. When motion of a particle takes place in a plane, we make use of two dimensional co-ordinate system. Normally we consider the motion in X-Y plane.

Consider a particle P in the X-Y plane having cartesian co-ordinates x and y at any time, then

Position vector of the point $P = \overrightarrow{OP} = \overrightarrow{r}$

Now $$\overrightarrow{OP} = \overrightarrow{OQ} + \overrightarrow{QP}$$

or $$\overrightarrow{r} = x\hat{i} + y\hat{j}$$

where $\hat{i}$ and $\hat{j}$ are *unit vectors* in the x and y directions respectively.

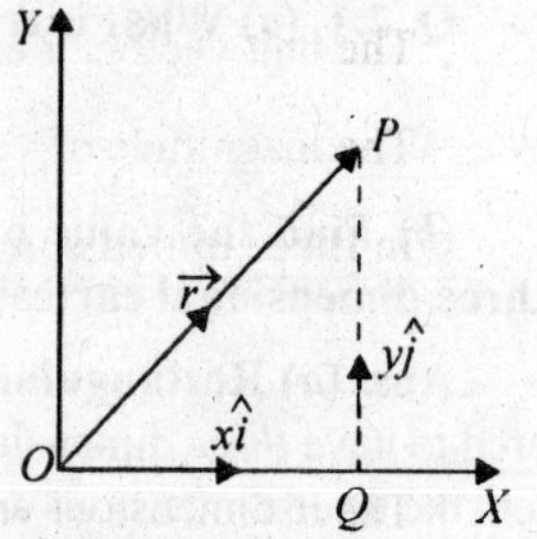

Again $$\overrightarrow{r} \cdot \overrightarrow{r} = (x\hat{i} + y\hat{j}) \cdot (x\hat{i} + y\hat{j})$$

or $$r^2 = x^2 + y^2$$

$$\therefore \quad |\overrightarrow{r}| = \sqrt{x^2 + y^2}$$

Fig. 2.3

where $|\overrightarrow{r}|$ is the magnitude of the position vector.

If $\hat{r}$ is a **unit vector** in the direction of $\overrightarrow{r}$, then $\overrightarrow{r} = r\hat{r}$.

Position vector in three dimensional cartesian co-ordinate system. Consider a particle P in space and OX, OY, OZ, the three mutually perpendicular axes of cartesian co-ordinate system. The position vector of the point $P = \overrightarrow{OP} = \overrightarrow{r}$. From P draw PQ perpendicular on the x-y plane meeting the plane at Q. Draw QR parallel to Y-axis meeting the X-axis at R and QS parallel to X-axis meeting the Y-axis at S. *The distances OR, OS and QP are the x, y and z co-ordinates respectively of the point P.* If $\hat{i}$, $\hat{j}$ and $\hat{k}$ are the *unit vectors* along the X, Y and Z axes respectively, then

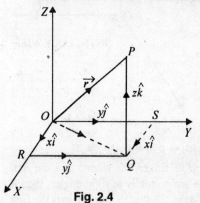

Fig. 2.4

$$\overrightarrow{OR} = x\hat{i}; \quad \overrightarrow{OS} = y\hat{j}; \quad \overrightarrow{QP} = z\hat{k}$$

Now $$\overrightarrow{OQ} = \overrightarrow{OR} + \overrightarrow{OS} = x\hat{i} + y\hat{j}$$

and $$\overrightarrow{OP} = \overrightarrow{OQ} + \overrightarrow{QP} = \overrightarrow{OR} + \overrightarrow{OS} + \overrightarrow{QP} = x\hat{i} + y\hat{j} + z\hat{k}$$

$$\therefore \quad \overrightarrow{r} = x\hat{i} + y\hat{j} + z\hat{k}$$

Again $$\overrightarrow{r} \cdot \overrightarrow{r} = (x\hat{i} + y\hat{j} + z\hat{k}) \cdot (x\hat{i} + y\hat{j} + z\hat{k})$$

or $$r^2 = x^2 + y^2 + z^2$$

or $$r = |\overrightarrow{r}| = (x^2 + y^2 + z^2)^{\frac{1}{2}}$$

where $r = |\vec{r}|$ is the magnitude of the position vector. If $\hat{r}$ is a *unit vector* in the direction of $\vec{r}$, then

$$\vec{r} = r\hat{r}$$

Velocity. *The velocity of a particle is defined as the time rate of change of position vector.*

$$\vec{v} = \frac{d\vec{r}}{dt}$$

In **two dimensional** cartesian co-ordinate system, Position vector $\vec{r} = x\hat{i} + y\hat{j}$

∴ Velocity $\qquad \vec{v} = \frac{d\vec{r}}{dt} = \frac{dx}{dt}\hat{i} + \frac{dy}{dt}\hat{j} = \dot{x}\hat{i} + \dot{y}\hat{j}$

where $\qquad \frac{dx}{dt} = \dot{x}$ and $\frac{dy}{dt} = \dot{y}$

The unit vectors $\hat{i}$ and $\hat{j}$ have *constant* magnitude and direction and do not depend upon time.

The magnitude of velocity (speed) $|\vec{v}| = [\dot{x}^2 + \dot{y}^2]^{1/2}$

In **three dimensional** cartesian co-ordinate system, Position vector $\vec{r} = x\hat{i} + y\hat{j} + z\hat{k}$

∴ Velocity $\qquad \vec{v} = \frac{d\vec{r}}{dt} = \frac{dx}{dt}\hat{i} + \frac{dy}{dt}\hat{j} + \frac{dz}{dt}\hat{k} = \dot{x}\hat{i} + \dot{y}\hat{j} + \dot{z}\hat{k}$

The magnitude of velocity (speed) $|\vec{v}| = [\dot{x}^2 + \dot{y}^2 + \dot{z}^2]^{1/2}$

Acceleration. *Acceleration is defined as the time rate of change of velocity.* In **two dimensional** Cartesian co-ordinate system, velocity $\vec{v} = \dot{x}\hat{i} + \dot{y}\hat{j}$

∴ Acceleration $\qquad \vec{a} = \frac{d}{dt}(\dot{x}\hat{i} + \dot{y}\hat{j}) = \ddot{x}\hat{i} + \ddot{y}\hat{j}$

where $\qquad \ddot{x} = \frac{d^2x}{dt^2}$ and $\ddot{y} = \frac{d^2y}{dt^2}$

The magnitude of acceleration $|\vec{a}| = [\ddot{x}^2 + \ddot{y}^2]^{1/2} = [a_x^2 + a_y^2]^{1/2}$

where a_x and a_y are the x and y components of acceleration respectively.

In **three dimensional** cartesian co-ordinate system, velocity $\vec{v} = \dot{x}\hat{i} + \dot{y}\hat{j} + \dot{z}\hat{k}$

∴ Acceleration $\qquad \vec{a} = \frac{d}{dt}(\dot{x}\hat{i} + \dot{y}\hat{j} + \dot{z}\hat{k}) = \ddot{x}\hat{i} + \ddot{y}\hat{j} + \ddot{z}\hat{k}$

where $\qquad \ddot{x} = \frac{d^2x}{dt^2}$; $\ddot{y} = \frac{d^2y}{dt^2}$; $\ddot{z} = \frac{d^2z}{dt^2}$

The magnitude of acceleration $|\vec{a}| = [\ddot{x}^2 + \ddot{y}^2 + \ddot{z}^2]^{1/2} = [a_x^2 + a_y^2 + a_z^2]^{1/2}$

where a_x, a_y, a_z are the x, y and z components of acceleration $\vec{a}$ respectively.

Q. 2.2. (a) The position vector of a point is given by

$$\vec{r} = \left(\frac{4}{3}t^3 - 2t\right)\hat{i} + t^2\hat{j}.$$

Find the velocity and acceleration of the point at $t = 3$ sec. The distance is measured in metres. *(P.U., 1993)*

(b) The motion of a particle is described by the equation $x = 4 \sin 2t$, $y = 4 \cos 2t$, $z = 6t$. **Find equation of velocity and acceleration of the particle.**

(P.U. 2006, Pbi. U. 2006, H.P.U. 2001, G.N.D.U. 1992)

Ans. (a) Given
$$\vec{r} = \left(\frac{4}{3}t^3 - 2t\right)\hat{i} + t^2\hat{j}$$

Velocity
$$\vec{v} = \frac{d\vec{r}}{dt} = \dot{x}\hat{i} + \dot{y}\hat{j}$$

Now
$$x = \frac{4}{3}t^3 - 2t \quad \therefore \dot{x} = \frac{dx}{dt} = \frac{4}{3}\cdot 3t^2 - 2 = 4t^2 - 2$$

$$y = t^2 \quad \therefore \dot{y} = \frac{dy}{dt} = 2t$$

$$\therefore \qquad \vec{v} = (4t^2 - 2)\hat{i} + 2t\hat{j} = 2(2t^2 - 1)\hat{i} + 2t\hat{j}$$

At
$$t = 3 \text{ sec} ; \quad \vec{v} = 34\hat{i} + 6\hat{j} \quad \therefore |\vec{v}| = \sqrt{34^2 + 6^2} = 34.5 \text{ ms}^{-1}$$

Acceleration
$$\vec{a} = \frac{d\vec{v}}{dt} = \ddot{x}\hat{i} + \ddot{y}\hat{j}$$

$$\ddot{x} = \frac{d}{dt}\dot{x} = 8t ; \quad \ddot{y} = \frac{d}{dt}\dot{y} = 2$$

$\therefore$ Acceleration $\vec{a} = 8t\hat{i} + 2\hat{j}$

At $t = 3$ sec $\vec{a} = 24\hat{i} + 2\hat{j}$ $\therefore |\vec{a}| = \sqrt{24^2 + 2^2} = 24.1 \text{ ms}^{-2}$

(b) Given $x = 4 \sin 2t$ $y = 4 \cos 2t$ $z = 6t$

$\therefore$ Displacement $\vec{r} = x\hat{i} + y\hat{j} + z\hat{k} = 4 \sin 2t \, \hat{i} + 4\cos 2t \, \hat{j} + 6t \, \hat{k}$

Velocity
$$\vec{v} = \frac{d\vec{r}}{dt} = \dot{x}\hat{i} + \dot{y}\hat{j} + \dot{z}\hat{k}$$

Now $x = 4 \sin 2t$ $\therefore \dot{x} = \frac{dx}{dt} = 8 \cos 2t$

$y = 4 \cos 2t$ $\therefore \dot{y} = \frac{dy}{dt} = -8 \sin 2t$

$z = 6t$ $\therefore \dot{z} = \frac{dz}{dt} = 6$

$\therefore$ $\vec{v} = 8 \cos 2t \, \hat{i} - 8 \sin 2t \, \hat{j} + 6\hat{k}$

and $|\vec{v}| = \sqrt{8^2 \cos^2 2t + 8^2 \sin^2 2t + 6^2}$

$\qquad\qquad = \sqrt{100} = 10 \text{ ms}^{-1}$

Acceleration
$$\vec{a} = \frac{d\vec{v}}{dt} = \ddot{x}\hat{i} + \ddot{y}\hat{j} + \ddot{z}\hat{k}$$

Now $\ddot{x} = \frac{d^2x}{dt^2} = -16 \sin 2t$ $\ddot{y} = \frac{d^2y}{dt^2} = -16 \cos 2t$ $\ddot{z} = \frac{d^2z}{dr^2} = 0$

$\therefore$ Acceleration $\vec{a} = -16 \sin 2t \, \hat{i} - 16 \cos 2t \, \hat{j}$

$$|\vec{a}| = \sqrt{256 \sin^2 2t + 256 \cos^2 2t} = \sqrt{256} = 16 \text{ ms}^{-2}$$

Exercise. *A particle moves along a curve $x = 2 \sin 3t$; $y = 2 \cos 3t$, $z = 8t$. At any time $t > 0$ find its velocity and acceleration and their magnitudes.* *(Gharwal U. 1999)*

Hint.
$$x = 2 \sin 3t; \ y = 2 \cos 3t; \ z = 8t$$

$\therefore$
$$\vec{r} = 2 \sin 3t \, \hat{i} + 2 \cos 3t \, \hat{j} + 8t \, \hat{k}$$

and
$$\vec{v} = \frac{d\vec{r}}{dt} = 6 \cos 3t \, \hat{i} - 6 \sin 3t \, \hat{j} + 8\hat{k}$$

$\therefore$
$$|\vec{v}| = \sqrt{6^2 \cos^2 3t + 6^2 \sin^2 3t + 64} = 10 \ \text{ms}^{-1}$$

Hence
$$\vec{a} = \frac{d\vec{v}}{dt} = -18 \sin 3t \, \hat{i} - 18 \cos 3t \, \hat{j}$$

or
$$|\vec{a}| = 18 \, \text{ms}^{-2}$$

Q. 2.3. The velocity of a moving particle at any instant is given by

$$\vec{v} = 2\hat{i} + 5t\hat{j} + \frac{1}{t}\hat{k}.$$

Find the position vector of the particle at that instant. *(P.U. 2008)*

Ans. Here
$$\vec{v} = 2\hat{i} + 5t\hat{j} + \frac{1}{t}\hat{k}$$

But
$$\vec{v} = \frac{d\vec{r}}{dt}$$

$\therefore$
$$\frac{d\vec{r}}{dt} = 2\hat{i} + 5t\hat{j} + \frac{1}{t}\hat{k}$$

or
$$d\vec{r} = 2dt\,\hat{i} + 5tdt\,\hat{j} + \frac{1}{t}dt\,\hat{k}$$

or
$$\vec{r} = \int d\vec{r} = \hat{i}\int 2dt + \hat{j}\int 5tdt + \hat{k}\int\frac{1}{t}dt$$

$$= 2t\hat{i} + \frac{5t^2}{2}\hat{j} + \ln t\,\hat{k} + \vec{r_0}$$

where $\vec{r_0}$ is a vector representing the initial position vector of the particle.

Q. 2.4. (*a*) What is plane polar co-ordinate system?

(*b*) Give the relation of plane polar co-ordinates with cartesian co-ordinates.

Ans. (*a*) Plane polar co-ordinates. In a two dimensional case the motion takes place in a plane. For this purpose plane polar co-ordinates are sometimes very suitable. The two co-ordinates for a point P, in this system, are :

(*i*) The *radial distance* of the point from the origin $O = r$. It is always positive and r can take any value between zero and infinity.

(*ii*) The angle which the radius vector $\vec{r}$ makes with the positive direction of x-axis $= \theta$. It is always measured in anti-clockwise direction with respect to the line OX and can take any value between 0 and 2π.

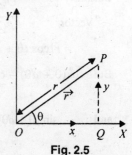

Fig. 2.5

(*b*) **Relation with cartesian co-ordinates.** If x and y are cartesian co-ordinates of the point P, then as shown in Fig. 2.5,

$$x = OQ = r \cos \theta \text{ and } y = PQ = r \sin \theta$$

Conversely $\qquad\qquad r = (x^2 + y^2)^{½} \text{ and } \theta = \tan^{-1} \dfrac{y}{x}$

Q. 2.5. Define unit vectors $\hat{r}$ and $\hat{\theta}$ in planar motion in terms of their cartesian counterparts $\hat{i}$ and $\hat{j}$.

Ans. Unit vectors in plane polar co-ordinates. In a two dimensional case of cartesian co-ordinate system (planar motion) two unit vectors are $\hat{i}$ along x-axis and $\hat{j}$ along y-axis.

In a similar way the two unit vectors in the two dimensional plane polar co-ordinate system are

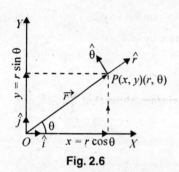

Fig. 2.6

Radial unit vector $\hat{r}$ along the direction of increasing radius vector $\vec{r}$

and Unit vector $\hat{\theta}$ along the direction of increasing θ.

The directions of $\hat{r}$ and $\hat{\theta}$ are, therefore, perpendicular to each other.

Unit vector $\hat{r}$ in terms of $\hat{i}$ and $\hat{j}$. If P is a point having cartesian co-ordinates (x, y) and polar co-ordinates (r, θ), then

$$\overrightarrow{OP} = \vec{r}.$$

The unit vector $\hat{r}$ will be be along OP and the unit vector $\hat{\theta}$ will be perpendicular to OP, as shown in Fig. 2.6.

Now $\qquad\qquad \vec{r} = x\hat{i} + y\hat{j}$

But $\qquad\qquad x = r \cos \theta \text{ and } y = r \sin \theta$

$\therefore \qquad\qquad \vec{r} = r \cos \theta \hat{i} + r\sin \theta \hat{j}$

or $\qquad\qquad \hat{r} = \dfrac{\vec{r}}{r} = \cos \theta \hat{i} + \sin \theta \hat{j} \qquad\qquad\qquad …(i)$

Unit vector $\hat{\theta}$ in terms of $\hat{i}$ and $\hat{j}$. Consider a point P having polar co-ordinates (r, θ) and a point Q having polar co-ordinates $(r, \theta + d\theta)$ as shown in Fig. 2.7.

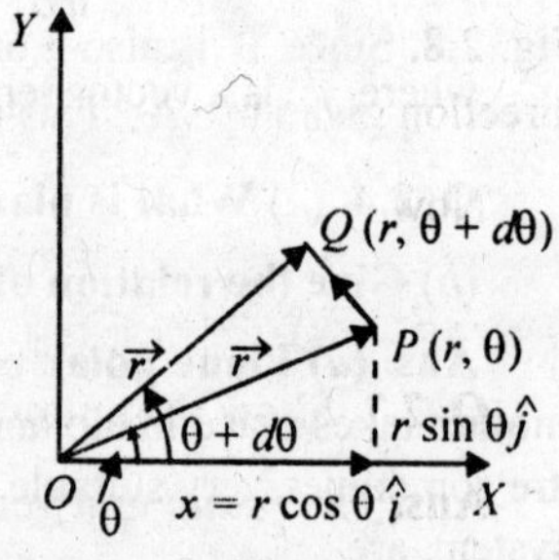

Now $\qquad\qquad \overrightarrow{OP} = r\cos \theta \hat{i} + r \sin \theta \hat{j}$

Similarly $\qquad\qquad \overrightarrow{OQ} = r \cos (\theta + d\theta) \, \hat{i} + r\sin (\theta + d\theta) \, \hat{j}$

$\therefore$ Vector $\qquad\qquad \overrightarrow{PQ} = \overrightarrow{OQ} - \overrightarrow{OP}$

$\qquad\qquad = r[\cos (\theta + d\theta) - \cos \theta] \, \hat{i} + r \, [\sin (\theta + d\theta) - \sin \theta] \hat{j}$

But $\cos (\theta + d\theta) - \cos \theta = \cos \theta \cos d\theta - \sin \theta \sin d\theta - \cos \theta$

$\qquad\qquad\qquad = - \sin \theta \; d\theta \qquad\qquad [\because \cos d\theta = \cos 0 = 1 \text{ and } \sin d\theta = d\theta]$

and $\qquad \sin (\theta + d\theta) - \sin \theta = \sin \theta \cos d\theta - \cos \theta \sin d\theta - \sin \theta = \cos \theta \; d\theta$

$\therefore \qquad\qquad \overrightarrow{PQ} = -r \sin \theta \; d\theta \hat{i} + r \cos \theta \; d\theta \hat{j}$

Fig. 2.7

The vector $\vec{PQ}$ points in the direction of increasing θ. The magnitude of

$$|\vec{PQ}| = rd\theta(\sin^2\theta + \cos^2\theta)^{1/2} = rd\theta$$

∴ Unit vector $\quad \hat{\theta} = \dfrac{\vec{PQ}}{|\vec{PQ}|} = \dfrac{-r\sin\theta\, d\theta\,\hat{i} + r\cos\theta\, d\theta\,\hat{j}}{r\, d\theta}$

or $\quad\quad\quad\quad \hat{\theta} = -\sin\theta\,\hat{i} + \cos\theta\,\hat{j}$

Alternative method. As unit vector $\hat{\theta}$ is perpendicular to unit vector $\hat{r}$ it can be obtained from

relation (*i*) by replacing θ by $\left(\theta + \dfrac{\pi}{2}\right)$.

∴ $\quad\quad\quad \hat{\theta} = \cos\left(\theta + \dfrac{\pi}{2}\right)\hat{i} + \sin\left(\theta + \dfrac{\pi}{2}\right)\hat{j} = -\sin\theta\,\hat{i} + \cos\theta\,\hat{j} \quad\quad\quad …(ii)$

The polar unit vectors $\hat{r}$ and $\hat{\theta}$ are *not fixed* like $\hat{i}$ and $\hat{j}$ but vary from point to point. Thus for a moving point the polar unit vectors are themselves functions of time.

Q. 2.6. If $\hat{r}$ and $\hat{\theta}$ are unit vectors in plane polar co-ordinate system, show that $\dfrac{d\hat{r}}{d\theta} = \hat{\theta}$ and $\dfrac{d\hat{\theta}}{d\theta} = -\hat{r}$.

Ans. Relation between $\dfrac{d\hat{r}}{d\theta}$ and $\hat{\theta}$. Unit radial vector $\hat{r}$ for

angles θ and θ + *d*θ is shown in Fig. 2.8. Since $\hat{r}$ is a unit vector its magnitude remains constant and there is only a change in direction given by $d\hat{r}$. This change in direction is along the unit vector $\hat{\theta}$.

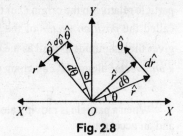

Fig. 2.8

Now $\quad\quad\quad\quad \hat{r} = \cos\theta\,\hat{i} + \sin\theta\,\hat{j}$

∴ $\quad\quad\quad\quad \dfrac{d\hat{r}}{d\theta} = -\sin\theta\,\hat{i} + \cos\theta\,\hat{j} = \hat{\theta}$

Relation between $\dfrac{d\hat{\theta}}{d\theta}$ and $\hat{r}$. Unit angular vector $\hat{\theta}$ for angles θ and θ + *d*θ is also shown in Fig. 2.8. Since $\hat{\theta}$ is also a unit vector its magnitude remains constant and there is only a change in direction given by $d\hat{\theta}$. This change in direction is along the unit vector $-\hat{r}$ as shown.

Now $\quad\quad\quad\quad \hat{\theta} = -\sin\theta\,\hat{i} + \cos\theta\,\hat{j}$

∴ $\quad\quad\quad\quad \dfrac{d\hat{\theta}}{d\theta} = -\cos\theta\,\hat{i} - \sin\theta\,\hat{j} = -\hat{r}$

Q. 2.7. Show that plane polar co-ordinates are orthogonal. $\quad\quad$ (*G.N.D.U. 2009*)

Ans. The *radial* unit vector $\hat{r}$ in plane polar co-ordinates, in terms of cartesian unit vectors $\hat{i}$ and $\hat{j}$ is given by

$$\hat{r} = \cos\theta\,\hat{i} + \sin\theta\,\hat{j}$$

The *angular* unit vector $\hat{\theta}$ in the direction of increasing θ is given by

$$\hat{\theta} = -\sin\theta\,\hat{i} + \cos\theta\,\hat{j}$$

Taking the *scalar product* $\hat{r}.\hat{\theta}$, we have

$$\hat{r}.\hat{\theta} = (\cos\theta\,\hat{i} + \sin\theta\,\hat{j}).(-\sin\theta\,\hat{i} + \cos\theta\,\hat{j})$$

$$= -\sin\theta\cos\theta + \sin\theta\cos\theta = 0$$

As the dot product of unit vectors $\hat{r}$ and $\hat{\theta} = 0$, the two unit vectors are *perpendicular* to each other. This implies that the plane polar co-ordinate system is *orthogonal*.

Q. 2.8. (*a*) **A particle is moving along a curve in a plane. Derive expression for the displacement, radial and transverse component of velocity and acceleration. Prove that for the motion of a particle in a plane**

$$\vec{v} = \dot{r}\hat{r} + r\dot{\theta}\hat{\theta} \quad \text{and} \quad \vec{a} = (\ddot{r} - r\dot{\theta}^2)\hat{r} + (r\ddot{\theta} + 2\dot{r}\dot{\theta})\hat{\theta}$$

where the letters have their usual meaning.   (*Pbi. U.* 2008; *Cal. U.* 2003;

Bangalore U. 1993, 1990; *P.U.* 2006, 1991)

(*b*) **The trajectory of particle moving in a plane is a straight line passing through the origin. What is transverse component of velocity ?**   (*P.U.* 2007)

(*c*) **A particle moves in a plane in such a way that its distance from the origin remains constant. What is the radial component of velocity ?**   (*Pbi. U.* 2005)

Ans. (*a*) **Displacement.** The position of a point P in a co-ordinate system can be specified by a single vector *i.e.*, the displacement of the particle relative to the origin O of the co-ordinate system. This vector is called the *position vector* of the point and denoted by $\overrightarrow{OP} = \vec{r}$. It gives the magnitude as well as the direction of the *displacement*. If $\hat{r}$ is a *unit vector* along OP *i.e.*, along the direction of $\vec{r}$, then

$$\vec{r} = r\hat{r}$$

When a particle is moving along a curve in a plane it has a velocity and an acceleration.

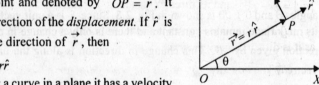

Fig. 2.9

Velocity. *The velocity is the derivative of displacment $\vec{r}$ with respect to time t.*

$\therefore$ Velocity $\vec{v} = \dfrac{d}{dt}(\vec{r}) = \dfrac{d}{dt}(r\hat{r}) = \dfrac{dr}{dt}\hat{r} + r\dfrac{d\hat{r}}{dt} = \dfrac{dr}{dt}\hat{r} + r\dfrac{d\hat{r}}{d\theta}\dfrac{d\theta}{dt}$

But $\dfrac{d\hat{r}}{d\theta} = \hat{\theta}$

$\therefore$ Velocity $\vec{v} = \dfrac{d\vec{r}}{dt} = \dot{r}\hat{r} + r\dot{\theta}\hat{\theta}$ ...(*i*)

where $\dot{r} = \dfrac{dr}{dt}$ and $\dot{\theta} = \dfrac{d\theta}{dt}$

or $\vec{v} = \vec{v}_r + \vec{v}_\theta$ ...(*ii*)

Components of velocity. The quantity $v_r = \dot{r}\hat{r}$ is known as the *radial component of velocity* and is due to the change in magnitude of r, θ remaining constant and $v_\theta = r\dot{\theta}\hat{\theta}$ is known as *transverse component of velocity* and is due to the change in θ, r remaining constant.

The magnitude of radial velocity $|\vec{v}_r| = \dot{r}$

and the magnitude of transverse velocity $|\vec{v}_\theta| = r\dot{\theta}$

If $\dot\theta$ = a constant = ω the angular velocity, then $|\vec{v_\theta}| = r\omega$

The magnitude of velocity $\vec{v}$ is

$$|\vec{v}| = [|\vec{v_r}|^2 + |\vec{v_\theta}|^2] = [\dot{r}^2 + r^2\,\dot\theta^2]^{\frac{1}{2}}$$

Acceleration. *Acceleration is the derivative of velocity $\vec{v}$ with respect to time t.*

$$\therefore \qquad \text{Acceleration } \vec{a} = \frac{d\vec{v}}{dt} = \frac{d}{dt}(\dot{r}\hat{r} + r\dot\theta\hat\theta)$$

$$= \ddot{r}\hat{r} + \dot{r}\left(\frac{d\hat{r}}{dt}\right) + \dot{r}\,\dot\theta\hat\theta + r\ddot\theta\,\hat\theta + r\,\dot\theta\left(\frac{d\hat\theta}{dt}\right)$$

$$= \ddot{r}\hat{r} + \dot{r}\left(\frac{d\hat{r}}{d\theta}\cdot\frac{d\theta}{dt}\right) + \dot{r}\,\dot\theta\hat\theta + r\ddot\theta\hat\theta + r\,\dot\theta\left(\frac{d\hat\theta}{d\theta}\cdot\frac{d\theta}{dt}\right)$$

But
$$\frac{d\hat{r}}{d\theta} = \hat\theta \text{ and } \frac{d\hat\theta}{d\theta} = -\hat{r}$$

$$\therefore \qquad \vec{a} = \ddot{r}\hat{r} + \dot{r}\,\dot\theta\hat\theta + \dot{r}\,\dot\theta\hat\theta + r\ddot\theta\hat\theta - r\dot\theta^2\,\hat{r}$$

$$= (\ddot{r} - r\dot\theta^2)\,\hat{r} + (r\ddot\theta + 2\dot{r}\dot\theta)\,\hat\theta$$

or
$$\vec{a} = \vec{a_r} + \vec{a_\theta} = a_r\hat{r} + a_\theta\hat\theta$$

Components of acceleration. The quantity $\vec{a_r}$ is known as *radial acceleration.* Its magnitude $|\vec{a_r}| = \ddot{r} - r\dot\theta^2$ and its direction is along $\hat{r}$. It consists of two parts.

(*i*) The quantity $\ddot{r}$ gives the acceleration due to change in magnitude of $\dot{r}$. It has a positive sign as it is directed *away from* the centre.

(*ii*) The quantity $r\dot\theta^2$ gives the *centripetal acceleration* (if $\dot\theta$ = a constant = ω, $r\dot\theta^2 = r\omega^2$) due to change in θ. It has a negative sign as it is directed *towards* the centre.

The quantity $\vec{a_\theta}$ is known as *transverse acceleration.* Its magnitude $|\vec{a_\theta}| = r\ddot\theta + 2\dot{r}\dot\theta$ and its direction is along θ. This also consists of two parts.

(*i*) The quantity $r\ddot\theta$ gives the angular acceleration due to change in $\dot\theta$.

(*ii*) The quantity $2\dot{r}\dot\theta$ arises due to the interaction of linear and angular velocities due to changes in r and θ respectively. This is similar to *coriolis acceleration.*

$\vec{a_r}$ and $\vec{a_\theta}$ are perpendicular to each other. The magnitude of $|\vec{a}|$ is given by

$$|\vec{a}| = \left[|\vec{a_r}|^2 + |\vec{a_\theta}|^2\right]^{\frac{1}{2}}$$

(*b*) When the trajectory of a particle moving in a plane is a straight line passing through the origin, only the co-ordinate r varies, but the co-ordinate θ remains constant,

As $\theta = a$ constant; $\dfrac{d\theta}{dt} = \dot\theta = 0$

As $\dot\theta = 0$, $v_\theta = 0$

Thus, the transverse component of velocity of the particle is zero.

(*c*) The particle moves in a plane and its distance from the origin remains constant.

$$\therefore \qquad\qquad r = \text{constant}$$

∴ The radial component of velocity $v_r = \dot{r} = \dfrac{dr}{dt} = 0$

Thus the radial component of velocity is zero.

Q.2.9. The path of a projectile is defined by the equation $r = 3t - t^2/30$ and $\theta^2 = 1600 - t^2$. Find its velocity and acceleration after 30 sec. (*P.U. 2008; G.N.D.U. 1991*)

Ans. Given $\qquad\qquad r = 3t - \dfrac{t^2}{30}$

At $\qquad\qquad t = 30\ s\ ;\ r = 3 \times 30 - \dfrac{30^2}{30} = 60\ m$

∴ $\qquad\qquad r = 60\ m$

$\qquad\qquad \dot{r} = \dfrac{dr}{dt} = 3 - \dfrac{t}{15}$

At $\qquad\qquad t = 30 s;\ \dot{r} = 3 - \dfrac{30}{15} = 1\ ms^{-1}$

∴ $\qquad\qquad \dot{r} = 1\ ms^{-1}$

$\qquad\qquad \ddot{r} = \dfrac{d(\dot{r})}{dt} = -\dfrac{1}{15}$

∴ $\qquad\qquad \ddot{r} = -\dfrac{1}{15}\ ms^{-2}$

Given $\qquad\qquad \theta^2 = 1600 - t^2$

At $\qquad\qquad t = 30\ s \quad \theta^2 = 1600 - 900 = 700$

∴ $\qquad\qquad \theta^2 = 700$

and $\qquad\qquad \theta = \sqrt{1600 - t^2}$

At $\qquad\qquad t = 30\ s;\ \theta = \sqrt{1600 - 900} = 10\sqrt{7}$

∴ $\qquad\qquad \theta = 10\sqrt{7}\ rad$

Differentiating $\qquad \theta^2 = 1600 - t^2$

we get $\qquad\qquad 2\theta\dot\theta = -2t$

∴ $\qquad\qquad \dot\theta = -\dfrac{t}{\theta}$

At $\qquad\qquad t = 30\ s;\ \dot\theta = -\dfrac{30}{10\sqrt{7}} = -\dfrac{3}{\sqrt{7}}$

∴ $\qquad\qquad \dot\theta = -\dfrac{3}{\sqrt{7}}\ rad\ sec^{-1}$

Differentiating $\qquad \dot\theta = -\dfrac{t}{\theta}$, we get

$$\ddot\theta = -t \times -1\theta^{-2}\ \dot\theta - \dfrac{1}{\theta} = \dfrac{t}{\theta^2}\dot\theta - \dfrac{1}{\theta}$$

At $\qquad\qquad t = 30\ s,\ \ddot\theta = -\dfrac{30}{700} \times \dfrac{3}{\sqrt{7}} - \dfrac{1}{10\sqrt{7}}$

$$= -\dfrac{9}{70\sqrt{7}} - \dfrac{1}{10\sqrt{7}} = -\dfrac{16}{70\sqrt{7}}$$

$$\therefore \qquad \ddot{\theta} = -\frac{16}{70\sqrt{7}} \text{ rad sec}^{-2}$$

Now velocity $\vec{v} = \dot{r}\hat{r} + r\dot{\theta}\hat{\theta}$

$$= \hat{r} + 60 \times \frac{-3}{\sqrt{7}}\hat{\theta} = \hat{r} - \frac{180}{\sqrt{7}}\hat{\theta}$$

Also acceleration $\vec{a} = (\ddot{r} - r\dot{\theta}^2)\hat{r} + (r\ddot{\theta} + 2\dot{r}\dot{\theta})\hat{\theta}$

or
$$\vec{a} = \left(-\frac{1}{15} - 60 \times \frac{9}{7}\right)\hat{r} + \left(60 \times \frac{-16}{70\sqrt{7}} + 2 \times 1 \times \frac{-3}{\sqrt{7}}\right)\hat{\theta}$$

$$= -\left(\frac{8107}{105}\right)\hat{r} - \left(\frac{96}{7\sqrt{7}} + \frac{6}{\sqrt{7}}\right)\hat{\theta}$$

$$= -\left(\frac{8107}{105}\right)\hat{r} - \left(\frac{138}{7\sqrt{7}}\right)\hat{\theta} = -\left[\frac{8107}{105}\hat{r} + \frac{138}{7\sqrt{7}}\hat{\theta}\right]$$

Q. 2.10. For planar motion $x = r \cos\theta$; $y = r \sin\theta$. Prove that
$$\dot{r} = \frac{x\dot{x} + y\dot{y}}{r} \text{ and } r\dot{\theta} = \frac{x\dot{y} - y\dot{x}}{r}. \qquad (G.N.D.U. 2009; P.U. 1999, 1991; Pbi. U., 1991)$$

Ans. Relation between velocity as expressed in Cartesian and Polar co-ordinates. If x and y are cartesian co-ordinates of the point P having polar co-ordinates (r, θ) in a two dimensional system, then

$$x = r \cos\theta \text{ and } y = r \sin\theta$$

$$\therefore \qquad \cos\theta = \frac{x}{r}; \sin\theta = \frac{y}{r} \text{ and } r = (x^2 + y^2)^{\frac{1}{2}}$$

Differentiating $x = r \cos\theta$ and $y = r \sin\theta$ with respect to t we have

$$\dot{x} = \dot{r}\cos\theta - r\sin\theta\dot{\theta} \qquad \qquad ...(i) \text{ where } \dot{x} = \frac{dx}{dt}$$

and
$$\dot{y} = \dot{r}\sin\theta + r\cos\theta\dot{\theta} \qquad \qquad ...(ii) \text{ where } \dot{y} = \frac{dy}{dt}$$

Multiplying (i) by $\cos\theta$, (ii) by $\sin\theta$ and adding, we get

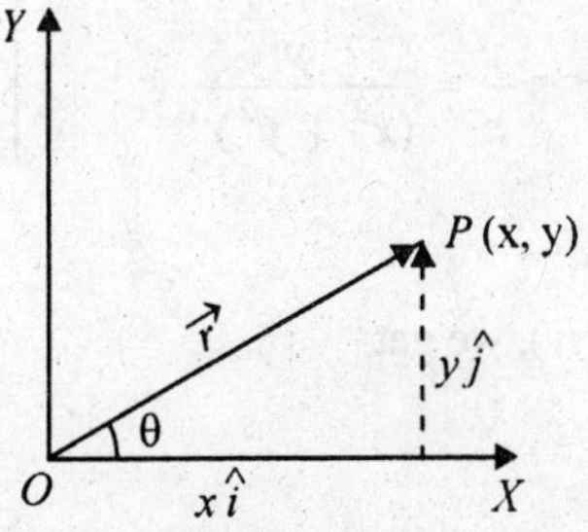

$$\dot{x}\cos\theta + \dot{y}\sin\theta = \dot{r}(\cos^2\theta + \sin^2\theta) = \dot{r}$$

$$\therefore \qquad \dot{r} = \dot{x}\cos\theta + \dot{y}\sin\theta = \frac{x\dot{x} + y\dot{y}}{r} = \frac{x\dot{x} + y\dot{y}}{(x^2 + y^2)^{\frac{1}{2}}}$$

Fig. 2.10

or $\qquad |\vec{v_r}| = \frac{x\dot{x} + y\dot{y}}{(x^2 + y^2)^{\frac{1}{2}}}$

Multiplying (i) by $\sin\theta$, (ii) by $\cos\theta$ and subtracting (i) from (ii) we have

$$\dot{y}\cos\theta - \dot{x}\sin\theta = r(\cos^2\theta + \sin^2\theta)\dot{\theta}$$

$$\therefore \qquad \dot{\theta} = \frac{\dot{y}\cos\theta - \dot{x}\sin\theta}{r} = \frac{\dot{y}x - \dot{x}y}{r^2} = \frac{\dot{y}x - \dot{x}y}{x^2 + y^2}$$

$$\therefore \qquad |\vec{v_\theta}| = r\dot{\theta} = \frac{\dot{y}x - \dot{x}y}{r}$$

Q. 2.11. A point moving in a plane has co-ordinates $x = 3$, $y = 4$ and has components of speed $\dot{x} = 5$ m/sec, $\dot{y} = 8$ m/sec at some instant of time. Find the components of speed in polar co-ordinates r, θ along directions $\hat{r}$ and $\hat{\theta}$.

Ans. Component of speed along $\hat{r}$

$$|\vec{v_r}| = \frac{\dot{x}x + \dot{y}y}{(x^2 + y^2)^{\frac{1}{2}}} = \frac{5 \times 3 + 8 \times 4}{(9 + 16)^{\frac{1}{2}}} = 9.4 \text{ m/s}$$

Component of speed along $\hat{\theta}$

$$|\vec{v_\theta}| = \frac{\dot{y}x - \dot{x}y}{(x^2 + y^2)^{\frac{1}{2}}} = \frac{8 \times 3 - 5 \times 4}{(9 + 16)^{\frac{1}{2}}} = 0.8 \text{ m/s}$$

Q. 2.12. For planar motion derive a relationship between acceleration as expressed in cartesian and polar co-ordinates.   (*H.P.U.* 2001, 2000; *P.U.* 1991)

Ans. Relation between acceleration as expressed in cartesian and polar co-ordinates. If x and y are the cartesian co-ordinates of a point having polar co-ordinates r, θ, then

$$x = r \cos \theta \quad \text{and} \quad y = r \sin \theta$$

∴ $\dot{x} = \dot{r} \cos\theta - r \sin \theta \dot{\theta}$ ...(*i*)

and $\dot{y} = \dot{r} \sin \theta + r \cos \theta \dot{\theta}$ ...(*ii*)

Differentiating equation (*i*) with respect to *t*, we have

$$\ddot{x} = \ddot{r} \cos \theta - \dot{r} \sin \theta \dot{\theta} - \dot{r} \sin \theta \dot{\theta} - r \cos \theta \dot{\theta}^2 - r \sin \theta \ddot{\theta}$$

$$= (\ddot{r} - r\dot{\theta}^2) \cos \theta - (r \ddot{\theta} + 2\dot{r}\dot{\theta}) \sin \theta \qquad ...(iii)$$

Differentiating equation (*ii*) with respect to *t*, we have

$$\ddot{y} = \ddot{r} \sin\theta + \dot{r} \cos \theta \dot{\theta} + \dot{r} \cos \theta \dot{\theta} - r\sin \theta \dot{\theta}^2 + r\cos \theta \ddot{\theta}$$

$$= (\ddot{r} - r\dot{\theta}^2) \sin \theta + (r\ddot{\theta} + 2\dot{r}\dot{\theta}) \cos \theta \qquad ...(iv)$$

Multiplying (*iii*) by $\cos \theta$, (*iv*) by $\sin \theta$ and adding, we get

$$\ddot{x} \cos \theta + \ddot{y} \sin \theta = (\ddot{r} - r\dot{\theta}^2)(\cos^2 \theta + \sin^2 \theta)$$

∴ $\ddot{r} - r\dot{\theta}^2 = \ddot{x} \cos \theta + \ddot{y} \sin \theta = \dfrac{\ddot{x}x + \ddot{y}y}{(x^2 + y^2)^{\frac{1}{2}}}$ $\left[\because \cos\theta = \dfrac{x}{r} = \dfrac{x}{(x^2 + y^2)^{\frac{1}{2}}} \text{ and} \right.$

$\left. \sin \theta = \dfrac{y}{r} = \dfrac{y}{(x^2 + y^2)^{\frac{1}{2}}} \right]$

or $|\vec{a_r}| = (\ddot{r} - r\dot{\theta}^2) = \dfrac{\ddot{x}x + \ddot{y}y}{(x^2 + y^2)^{\frac{1}{2}}}$

Multiplying (*iii*) by $\sin \theta$, (*iv*) by $\cos \theta$ and subtracting (*iii*) from (*iv*), we get

$$\ddot{y} \cos\theta - \ddot{x} \sin \theta = (r\ddot{\theta} + 2\dot{r}\dot{\theta})(\cos^2 \theta + \sin^2 \theta)$$

∴ $r\ddot{\theta} + 2\dot{r}\dot{\theta} = \ddot{y} \cos \theta - \ddot{x} \sin \theta = \dfrac{\ddot{y}x - \ddot{x}y}{(x^2 + y^2)^{\frac{1}{2}}}$

or $|\vec{a_\theta}| = (r\ddot{\theta} + 2\dot{r}\dot{\theta}) = \dfrac{\ddot{y}x - \ddot{x}y}{(x^2 + y^2)^{\frac{1}{2}}}$

Q. 2.13. What is spherical polar co-ordinate system r, θ, ϕ? What are the limits of r, θ and ϕ? Derive the relation between spherical polar co-ordinates and three dimensional cartesian co-ordinates. *(Pbi. U.* 2007, 2006, 2003, 2001, 1999; *G.N.D.U.* 2009, 2007, 2004; *P.U.* 2009, 2008, 2001, 2000; 1991; *H.P. U.* 2000, 1994; *Gauhati U.* 2000)

Ans. Spherical polar co-ordinate system. The spherical polar co-ordinate system provides a convenient method of representing the co-ordinates of a point on the surface of a sphere. The **three** co-ordinates for a point P in this system are

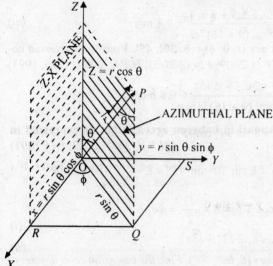

Fig. 2.11

(*i*) The *radial distance* of the point from the origin $\overrightarrow{OP} = \vec{r}$

Limits of $\vec{r}$. r is *always positive and can take any value from* 0 *to infinity.*

(*ii*) The angle that the radius vector $\vec{r}$ makes with the vertical (*positive*) Z-axis is called the *co-latitude angle* or *zenith angle* = θ.

Limits of θ. *The zenith angle θ always lies between* 0 *and* π.

(*iii*) The angle which the vertical plane containing $\vec{r}$ known as the *azimuthal plane* makes with the ZX plane, called the *azimuthal angle* = ϕ. As shown in Fig. 2.11, it is the angle that the line OQ makes with the positive direction of X-axis OX; measured *counter-clockwise*.

Limits of ϕ. *The azimuthal angle ϕ can take any value between* 0 *and* 2π.

Thus r, θ and ϕ are the spherical polar co-ordinates of the point P.

Relation between three dimensional cartesian co-ordinates and polar co-ordinates. If x, y, z are the cartesian co-ordinates of the point P, then as shown in Fig. 2.11,

The projection of OP in the X-Y plane $= OQ = r \sin \theta$

$\therefore$ $\quad\quad\quad\quad x = OR = OQ \cos \phi = r \sin \theta \cos \phi$

and $\quad\quad\quad\quad y = OS = OQ \sin \phi = r \sin \theta \sin \phi$

also $\quad\quad\quad\quad z = PQ = r \cos \theta$

$\therefore$ The relation between cartesian and polar co-ordinates is as under

$$x = r \sin \theta \cos \phi \quad\quad\quad\quad\quad ...(i)$$

$$y = r \sin \theta \sin \phi \quad\quad\quad\quad\quad ...(ii)$$

$$z = r \cos \theta \quad\quad\quad\quad\quad\quad\quad ...(iii)$$

Relation between spherical polar co-ordinates and cartesian co-ordinates. From relations (*i*), (*ii*) and (*iii*), we have

$$x^2 + y^2 + z^2 = r^2 \sin^2\theta \cos^2\phi + r^2 \sin^2\theta \sin^2\phi + r^2 \cos^2\theta$$

$$= r^2 (\sin^2\theta + \cos^2\theta) = r^2$$

or $\quad\quad\quad\quad r = (x^2 + y^2 + z^2)^{1/2} \quad\quad\quad\quad ...(iv)$

Again $\quad\quad\quad x^2 + y^2 = r^2 \sin^2\theta \cos^2\phi + r^2 \sin^2\theta \sin^2\phi = r^2 \sin^2\theta$

$$r \sin \theta = (x^2 + y^2)^{1/2}$$

Hence $\qquad \tan \theta = \dfrac{r \sin \theta}{r \cos \theta} = \dfrac{(x^2 + y^2)^{1/2}}{z}$ ...(v)

$\therefore \qquad \theta = \tan^{-1} \dfrac{(x^2 + y^2)^{1/2}}{z}$

Also $\qquad \tan \phi = \dfrac{r \sin \theta \sin \phi}{r \sin \theta \cos \phi} = \dfrac{y}{x} \quad \therefore \phi = \tan^{-1} \dfrac{y}{x}$ ...(vi)

Q. 2.14. **The polar co-ordinates of a point are $(r, \theta, \phi) = 8, 30°, 45°$. Find the cartesian co-ordinates of the same point.** (*P.U.* 2009; *Pbi.U.* 2003; *H.P.U.* 2000, 1995, 1993)

Ans. Polar co-ordinates of the point $r = 8$; $\theta = 30°$; $\phi = 45°$

Let the cartesian co-ordinates of the same point be x, y, z, then

$$x = r \sin \theta \cos \phi = 8 \sin 30° \cos 45° = 8 \times \frac{1}{2} \times \frac{1}{\sqrt{2}} = 2\sqrt{2}$$

$$y = r \sin \theta \sin \phi = 8 \sin 30° \sin 45° = 8 \times \frac{1}{2} \times \frac{1}{\sqrt{2}} = 2\sqrt{2}$$

$$z = r \cos \theta = r \cos 30° = 8 \times \frac{\sqrt{3}}{2} = 4\sqrt{3}$$

$\therefore$ Cartesian co-ordinates of the point are $(2\sqrt{2}, 2\sqrt{2}, 4\sqrt{3})$.

Exercise. *The polar co-ordinates of a point are* $(16, 60°, 30°)$. *Find the cartesian co-ordinates of this point.* (*Pbi. U.* 2006; *P.U.* 2001, 2000, 1995; *H.P.U.* 1999, 1994)

Ans. $(12, 4\sqrt{3}, 8)$

Q. 2.15. **The cartesian co-ordinates of a point are $(1, 0, 0)$. Find the spherical polar co-ordinates of this point.** (*Pbi.U.* 2002; *G.N.D.U.*, 1994)

Ans. Cartesion co-ordinates of the point are $x = 1 \quad y = 0 \quad z = 0$.

Let the spherical polar co-ordinates of the same point be (r, θ, ϕ), then

$$r = (x^2 + y^2 + z^2)^{1/2} = 1$$

$$\tan \theta = \frac{(x^2 + y^2)^{1/2}}{z} = \infty \qquad \therefore \theta = \frac{\pi}{2}$$

$$\tan \phi = \frac{y}{x} = 0 \qquad \therefore \phi = 0$$

Thus spherical polar co-ordinates are $\left(1, \dfrac{\pi}{2}, 0\right)$.

Exercise 1. *The Cartesian co-ordinates of a point are* $(1, 0, 1)$. *Find the spherical polar co-ordinates of the point.* (*G.N.D.U.* 1993)

Ans. $\left(\sqrt{2}, \dfrac{\pi}{4}, 0\right)$

Exercise 2. *Calculate spherical polar co-ordinates of a point whose cartesian co-ordinates are* $(1, 0, \sqrt{3})$. (*H.P.U.* 2003)

Hint. $x = 1, y = 0, z = \sqrt{3}; \quad r = \sqrt{1^2 + 0 + 3} = 2; \quad \tan \theta = \dfrac{(x^2 + y^2)^{1/2}}{z} = \dfrac{1}{\sqrt{3}}$

$\therefore \qquad \theta = 30°; \quad \tan \phi = \dfrac{y}{x} = 0, \quad \therefore \phi = 0$ **Ans.** $(2, 30°, 0)$

Q. 2.16. What are the three unit vectors in spherical polar co-ordinate system? Express the unit vectors $(\hat{r}, \hat{\theta}, \hat{\phi})$ or $(\hat{e}_r, \hat{e}_\theta, \hat{e}_\phi)$ in terms of unit vectors $\hat{i}, \hat{j}, \hat{k}$ making a labelled diagram.

(*G.N.D.U.* 2007, 2006; *H.P.U.* 1992)

Ans. Unit vectors in spherical polar co-ordinates. In a three dimensional case of cartesian co-ordinate system the three unit vectors are

$\hat{i}$ along x-axis $\hat{j}$ along y-axis   and $\hat{k}$ along z-axis.

In a similar way the three unit vectors in the three dimensional spherical polar co-ordinate system are

$(\hat{e}_r)$ or $\hat{r}$ along the direction of increasing radius vector r;

$(\hat{e}_\theta)$ or $\hat{\theta}$ along the direction of increasing θ; and

$(\hat{e}_\phi)$ or $\hat{\phi}$ along the direction of increasing ϕ.

Note. *In our treatment we shall use $\hat{r}, \hat{\theta}$ and $\hat{\phi}$ as unit vectors.*

The unit vector $\hat{\theta}$ is perpendicular to $\hat{r}$ and unit vector $\hat{\phi}$ is perpendicular to both $\hat{r}$ and $\hat{\theta}$.

In other words, unit vectors $\hat{r}, \hat{\theta}$ and $\hat{\phi}$ are mutually perpendicular and constitute a right handed system of orthogonal unit vectors.

Unit vector $\hat{r}$ in terms of $\hat{i}, \hat{j}, \hat{k}$. If P is a point having cartesian co-ordinates (x, y, z) and polar co-ordinates (r, θ, ϕ), then $\overrightarrow{OP} = \vec{r}$. The unit vector $\hat{r}$ will be along $\overrightarrow{OP}$ and the unit vector $\hat{\theta}$ will be perpendicular to OP as shown, in the direction of increasing θ.

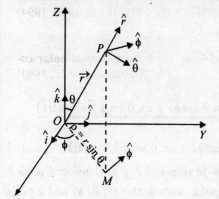

Fig. 2.12

Now $\vec{r} = x\hat{i} + y\hat{j} + z\hat{k}$

But $x = r \sin\theta \cos\phi$

$y = r \sin\theta \sin\phi$

and $z = r \cos\theta$

$\therefore$ $\vec{r} = r \sin\theta \cos\phi\,\hat{i} + r \sin\theta \sin\phi\,\hat{j} + r \cos\theta\,\hat{k}$

or $\hat{r} = \dfrac{\vec{r}}{r} = \sin\theta \cos\phi\,\hat{i} + \sin\theta \sin\phi\,\hat{j} + \cos\theta\,\hat{k}$ ...(i)

Unit vector $\hat{\theta}$ in terms of $\hat{i}, \hat{j}, \hat{k}$. As unit vector $\hat{\theta}$ is perpendicular to unit vector $\hat{r}$ and leads $\hat{r}$ by $\pi/2$.

$\hat{\theta} = \sin(\theta + \pi/2) \cos\phi\,\hat{i} + \sin(\theta + \pi/2) \sin\phi\,\hat{j} + \cos(\theta + \pi/2)\hat{k}$

or $\hat{\theta} = \cos\theta \cos\phi\,\hat{i} + \cos\theta \sin\phi\,\hat{j} - \sin\theta\,\hat{k}$ ...(ii)

Unit vector $\hat{\phi}$ in terms of $\hat{i}, \hat{j}, \hat{k}$. To find the value of unit vector $\hat{\phi}$ draw perpendicular PM on X-Y plane and let

$OM = \vec{r} \sin\theta = \vec{\rho}$

The unit vector $\hat{\phi}$ will be perpendicular to unit vector $\vec{\rho}$ and lead it by $\pi/2$.

Vectorially $\vec{\rho} = \rho \cos\phi\,\hat{i} + \rho \sin\phi\,\hat{j}$

$\therefore$ $\hat{\rho} = \dfrac{\vec{\rho}}{\rho} = \cos\phi\,\hat{i} + \sin\phi\,\hat{j}$

Hence
$$\hat{\phi} = \left(\cos\phi + \frac{\pi}{2}\right)\hat{i} + \sin\left(\phi + \frac{\pi}{2}\right)\hat{j}$$

or
$$\hat{\phi} = -\sin\phi\,\hat{i} + \cos\phi\,\hat{j} \qquad\qquad ...(iii)$$

Alternative treatment

Unit vector $\hat{r}$ in terms of $\hat{i},\,\hat{j},\,\hat{k}$. Consider a point $P\,(r,\,\theta,\,\phi)$ and a point $Q\,(r + dr,\,\theta,\,\phi)$ as shown in Fig. 2.13.

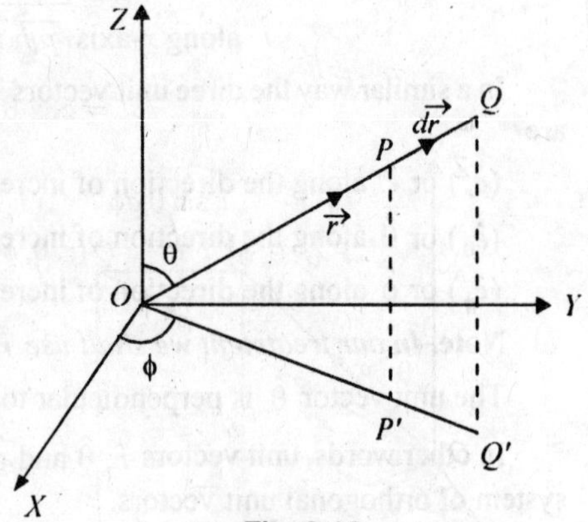

Then, in terms of unit vector $\hat{i},\,\hat{j},\,\hat{k}$.

$$\overrightarrow{OP} = r\sin\theta\cos\phi\,\hat{i} + r\sin\theta\sin\phi\,\hat{j} + r\cos\theta\,\hat{k}$$

$$\overrightarrow{OQ} = (r + dr)\sin\theta\cos\phi\,\hat{i} + (r + dr)\sin\theta\sin\phi\,\hat{j}$$
$$+ (r + dr)\cos\theta\,\hat{k}$$

$$\therefore\ \overrightarrow{PQ} = \overrightarrow{OQ} - \overrightarrow{OP}$$

$$= dr\,[\sin\theta\cos\phi\,\hat{i} + \sin\theta\sin\phi\,\hat{j} + \cos\theta\,\hat{k}]$$

The magnitude of $|\overrightarrow{PQ}|$

$$= dr\,[\sin^2\theta\cos^2\phi + \sin^2\theta\sin^2\phi + \cos^2\theta]^{1/2}$$

$$= dr\,[\sin^2\theta + \cos^2\theta]^{1/2} = dr$$

Fig. 2.13

Since $\hat{r}$ is a unit vector in the direction of increasing r

$$\hat{r} = \frac{\overrightarrow{PQ}}{|\overrightarrow{PQ}|}$$

$$= \frac{dr\,[\sin\theta\cos\phi\,\hat{i} + \sin\theta\sin\phi\,\hat{j} + \cos\theta\,\hat{k}]}{dr}$$

$$= \sin\theta\cos\phi\,\hat{i} + \sin\theta\sin\phi\,\hat{j} + \cos\theta\,\hat{k} \qquad ...(iv)$$

Unit vector $\hat{\theta}$ in terms of $\hat{i},\,\hat{j},\,\hat{k}$. Consider a point P having spherical polar co-ordinates $(r,\,\theta,\,\phi)$ and a point $Q\,(r,\,\theta + d\theta,\,\phi)$. Then in terms of unit vectors $\hat{i},\,\hat{j}$ and $\hat{k}$,

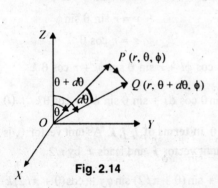

Fig. 2.14

$$\overrightarrow{OP} = r\sin\theta\cos\phi\,\hat{i} + r\sin\theta\sin\phi\,\hat{j} + r\cos\theta\,\hat{k}$$

and
$$\overrightarrow{OQ} = r\sin(\theta + d\theta)\cos\phi\,\hat{i} + r\sin(\theta + d\theta)\sin\phi\,\hat{j} + r\cos(\theta + d\theta)\,\hat{k}$$

The vector $\overrightarrow{PQ} = \overrightarrow{OQ} - \overrightarrow{OP} = r\,[\sin(\theta + d\theta) - \sin\theta]\cos\phi\,\hat{i}$

$$+ r\,[\sin(\theta + d\theta) - \sin\theta]\sin\phi\,\hat{j} + r\,[\cos(\theta + d\theta) - \cos\theta]\,\hat{k}$$

Now $\sin(\theta + d\theta) - \sin\theta = \sin\theta\cos d\theta + \cos\theta\sin d\theta - \sin\theta = \cos\theta\,d\theta$

because $\cos d\theta = \cos 0 = 1$ and $\sin d\theta = d\theta$

and $(\cos\theta + d\theta) - \cos\theta = \cos\theta\cos d\theta - \sin\theta\sin d\theta - \cos\theta = -\sin\theta\,d\theta$

$$\therefore\qquad \overrightarrow{PQ} = r\,d\theta\,[\cos\theta\cos\phi\,\hat{i} + \cos\theta\sin\phi\,\hat{j} - \sin\theta\,\hat{k}]$$

The magnitude of $\quad |\overrightarrow{PQ}| = r\,d\theta\,[\cos^2\theta\,\cos^2\phi + \cos^2\theta\,\sin^2\phi + \sin^2\theta]^{\frac{1}{2}}$

$$= r\,d\theta\,[\cos^2\theta + \sin^2\theta]^{\frac{1}{2}} = r\,d\theta$$

Since $\hat\theta$ is a unit vector in the direction of increasing θ

$$\hat\theta = \frac{\overrightarrow{PQ}}{|\overrightarrow{PQ}|} = \frac{r\,d\theta[\cos\theta\,\cos\phi\,\hat i + \cos\theta\,\sin\phi\,\hat j - \sin\theta\,\hat k]}{r\,d\theta}$$

$$= \cos\theta\,\cos\phi\,\hat i + \cos\theta\,\sin\phi\,\hat j - \sin\theta\,\hat k \qquad\qquad ...(v)$$

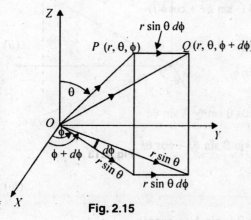

Fig. 2.15

Unit vector $\hat\phi$ in terms of $\hat i, \hat j, \hat k$. Consider a point P having spherical polar co-ordinates (r, θ, ϕ) and a point $Q\,(r, \theta, \phi + d\phi)$. Then in terms of unit vectors $\hat i, \hat j$ and $\hat k$

$$\overrightarrow{OP} = r\,\sin\theta\,\cos\phi\,\hat i + r\,\sin\theta\,\sin\phi\,\hat j + r\,\cos\theta\,\hat k$$

and $\quad \overrightarrow{OQ} = r\,\sin\theta\,\cos(\phi + d\phi)\,\hat i + r\,\sin\theta\,\sin$

$$(\phi + d\phi)\,\hat j + r\,\cos\theta\,\hat k$$

The vector

$$\overrightarrow{PQ} = \overrightarrow{OQ} - \overrightarrow{OP} = r\,\sin\theta\,[\cos(\phi + d\phi) - \cos\phi]\,\hat i$$
$$+ r\,\sin\theta\,[\sin(\phi + d\phi) - \sin\phi]\,\hat j$$

But $\quad \cos(\phi + d\phi) - \cos\phi = \cos\phi\,\cos d\phi - \sin\phi\,\sin d\phi - \cos\phi = -\sin\phi\,d\phi$

because $\quad \cos d\phi = \cos 0 = 1$ and $\sin d\phi = d\phi$

and $\quad \sin(\phi + d\phi) - \sin\phi = \sin\phi\,\cos d\phi + \cos\phi\,\sin d\phi - \sin\phi = \cos\phi\,d\phi$

$\therefore \qquad\qquad \overrightarrow{PQ} = -r\,\sin\theta\,\sin\phi\,d\phi\,\hat i + r\,\sin\theta\,\cos\phi\,d\phi\,\hat j$

The magnitude of $\quad |\overrightarrow{PQ}| = r\,\sin\theta\,d\phi\,[\sin^2\phi + \cos^2\phi]^{\frac{1}{2}} = r\,\sin\theta\,d\phi$

Since $\hat\phi$ is a unit vector in the direction of increasing ϕ

$$\hat\phi = \frac{\overrightarrow{PQ}}{|\overrightarrow{PQ}|} = \frac{-r\,\sin\theta\,\sin\phi\,d\phi\,\hat i + r\,\sin\theta\,\cos\phi\,d\phi\,\hat j}{r\,\sin\theta\,d\phi}$$

$$= -\sin\phi\,\hat i + \cos\phi\,\hat j \qquad\qquad ...(vi)$$

Hence the spherical polar unit vectors $\hat r, \hat\theta, \hat\phi$ in terms of cartesian co-ordinate unit vectors $\hat i, \hat j, \hat k$ are as under

$$\hat r = \sin\theta\,\cos\phi\,\hat i + \sin\theta\,\sin\phi\,\hat j + \cos\theta\,\hat k$$

$$\hat\theta = \cos\theta\,\cos\phi\,\hat i + \cos\theta\,\sin\phi\,\hat j - \sin\theta\,\hat k$$

and $\qquad\qquad \hat\phi = -\sin\phi\,\hat i + \cos\phi\,\hat j$

Q. 2.17. If $\hat r, \hat\theta$ and $\hat\phi$ are the unit vectors in spherical polar co-ordinate system, find the value of $\left(\dfrac{\partial \hat r}{\partial \theta}, \dfrac{\partial \hat r}{\partial \phi}\right), \left(\dfrac{\partial \hat\theta}{\partial \theta}, \dfrac{\partial \hat\theta}{\partial \phi}\right)$ and $\left(\dfrac{\partial \hat\phi}{\partial \theta}, \dfrac{\partial \hat\phi}{\partial \phi}\right).$ $\qquad\qquad$ (*G.N.D.U.*, 2001)

Ans. Value of $\dfrac{\partial \hat{r}}{\partial \theta}$ and $\dfrac{\partial \hat{r}}{\partial \phi}$

Unit vector $\qquad\qquad\qquad \hat{r} = \sin\theta\cos\phi\,\hat{i} + \sin\theta\sin\phi\,\hat{j} + \cos\theta\,\hat{k}$

$\therefore \qquad\qquad\qquad\qquad \dfrac{\partial \hat{r}}{\partial \theta} = \cos\theta\cos\phi\,\hat{i} + \cos\theta\sin\phi\,\hat{j} - \sin\theta\,\hat{k}$

or $\qquad\qquad\qquad\qquad\quad \dfrac{\partial \hat{r}}{\partial \theta} = \hat{\theta}$ ...(i)

and $\qquad \dfrac{\partial \hat{r}}{\partial \phi} = -\sin\theta\sin\phi\,\hat{i} + \sin\theta\cos\phi\,\hat{j} = \sin\theta\,(-\sin\phi\,\hat{i} + \cos\phi\,\hat{j})$

or $\qquad\qquad\qquad\qquad\quad \dfrac{\partial \hat{r}}{\partial \phi} = \sin\theta\,\hat{\phi}$ ...(ii)

Value of $\dfrac{\partial \hat{\theta}}{\partial \theta}$ **and** $\dfrac{\partial \hat{\theta}}{\partial \phi}$

Unit vector $\qquad\qquad\qquad \hat{\theta} = \cos\theta\cos\phi\,\hat{i} + \cos\theta\sin\phi\,\hat{j} - \sin\theta\,\hat{k}$

$\therefore \qquad\qquad\qquad\qquad \dfrac{\partial \hat{\theta}}{\partial \theta} = -\sin\theta\cos\phi\,\hat{i} - \sin\theta\sin\phi\,\hat{j} - \cos\theta\,\hat{k}$

or $\qquad\qquad\qquad\qquad\quad \dfrac{\partial \hat{\theta}}{\partial \theta} = -\hat{r}$ ...(iii)

And $\qquad \dfrac{\partial \hat{\theta}}{\partial \phi} = -\cos\theta\sin\phi\,\hat{i} + \cos\theta\cos\phi\,\hat{j} = \cos\theta\,(-\sin\phi\,\hat{i} + \cos\phi\,\hat{j})$

or $\qquad\qquad\qquad\qquad\quad \dfrac{\partial \hat{\theta}}{\partial \phi} = \cos\theta\,\hat{\phi}$ ...(iv)

Value of $\dfrac{\partial \hat{\phi}}{\partial \theta}$ **and** $\dfrac{\partial \hat{\phi}}{\partial \phi}$

Unit vector $\qquad\qquad\qquad \hat{\phi} = -\sin\phi\,\hat{i} + \cos\phi\,\hat{j}$

$\therefore \qquad\qquad\qquad\qquad \dfrac{\partial \hat{\phi}}{\partial \theta} = 0$ ...(v)

And $\qquad\qquad\qquad\qquad \dfrac{\partial \hat{\phi}}{\partial \phi} = -\cos\phi\,\hat{i} - \sin\phi\,\hat{j} = -\hat{\rho}$ ...(vi)

Since $\hat{r}$, $\hat{\theta}$ and $\hat{\phi}$ are orthogonal vectors

$$\hat{r} \times \hat{\theta} = \hat{\phi};\quad \hat{\theta} \times \hat{\phi} = \hat{r} \text{ and } \hat{\phi} \times \hat{r} = \hat{\theta}$$

Q. 2.18. (*a*) **Show that the spherical polar unit vectors $\hat{r}$, $\hat{\theta}$ and $\hat{\phi}$ (or $\hat{e}_r$, $\hat{e}_\theta$ and $\hat{e}_\phi$) are mutually perpendicular to each other.** (*Pbi. U.* 2007; *P.U.*, 2003)

(*b*) **In case of spherical polar co-ordinates prove that $\hat{\theta} \times \hat{\phi} = \hat{r}$, $\hat{\phi} \times \hat{r} = \hat{\theta}$, and $\hat{r} \times \hat{\theta} = \hat{\phi}$.**
(*P.U.* 2006, 2005; *G.N.D.U.*, 2003)

Ans. (*a*) **Orthogonality of polar unit vectors.** When two unit vectors are perpendicular to one another, they are said to be *orthogonal*. The spherical polar unit vectors $\hat{r}$, $\hat{\theta}$ and $\hat{\phi}$ are mutually *orthogonal* or *perpendicular to each other*. To prove this we shall find the angle between $\hat{r}$ and $\hat{\theta}$, $\hat{r}$ and $\hat{\phi}$, and $\hat{\theta}$ and $\hat{\phi}$.

(*i*) **Angle between** $\hat{r}$ **and** $\hat{\theta}$. The unit vector

$$\hat{r} = \sin\theta\,\cos\phi\,\hat{i} + \sin\theta\,\sin\phi\,\hat{j} + \cos\theta\,\hat{k}$$

and the unit vector $\quad\hat{\theta} = \cos\theta\,\cos\phi\,\hat{i} + \cos\theta\,\sin\phi\,\hat{j} - \sin\theta\,\hat{k}$

The scalar product of $\hat{r}$ and $\hat{\theta}$, *i.e.*

$$\hat{r}\,.\,\hat{\theta} = (\sin\theta\,\cos\,\phi\,\hat{i} + \sin\theta\,\sin\phi\,\hat{j} + \cos\theta\,\hat{k}).(\cos\theta\cos\,\phi\,\hat{i} + \cos\theta\,\sin\,\phi\,\hat{j} - \sin\theta\,\hat{k})$$

$$= \sin\theta\,\cos\theta\,\cos^2\,\phi + \sin\theta\,\cos\theta\,\sin^2\,\phi - \cos\theta\,\sin\theta$$

$$= \sin\theta\,\cos\theta\,[\cos^2\,\phi + \sin^2\,\phi] - \cos\theta\,\sin\theta = 0$$

because $\quad\hat{i}.\hat{i} = \hat{j}.\hat{j} = \hat{k}.\hat{k} = 1$ and $\hat{i}.\hat{j} = \hat{j}.\hat{k} = \hat{k}.\hat{i} = 0$

Hence the angle between $\hat{r}$ and $\hat{\theta} = \pi/2$. Therefore $\hat{r}$ and $\hat{\theta}$ are perpendicular to each other.

(*ii*) **Angle between** $\hat{r}$ **and** $\hat{\phi}$. The unit vector

$$\hat{\phi} = -\sin\phi\,\hat{i} + \cos\phi\,\hat{j}$$

$$\therefore \qquad \hat{r}\,.\,\hat{\phi} = (\sin\theta\,\cos\phi\,\hat{i} + \sin\theta\,\sin\phi\,\hat{j} + \cos\phi\,\hat{k})\,.\,(-\sin\phi\,\hat{i} + \cos\phi\,\hat{j})$$

$$= -\sin\theta\,\sin\,\phi\,\cos\phi + \sin\theta\,\sin\,\phi\,\cos\phi = 0$$

Hence the angle between $\hat{r}$ and $\hat{\phi} = \pi/2$. Therefore $\hat{r}$ and $\hat{\phi}$ are perpendicular to each other.

(*iii*) **Angle between** $\hat{\theta}$ **and** $\hat{\phi}$. The dot product of $\hat{\theta}$ and $\hat{\phi}$

$$\hat{\theta}\,.\,\hat{\phi} = (\cos\theta\,\cos\phi\,\hat{i} + \cos\theta\,\sin\,\phi\,\hat{j} - \sin\theta\,\hat{k})\,.\,(-\sin\,\phi\,\hat{i} + \cos\,\phi\,\hat{j})$$

$$= -\cos\theta\,\sin\,\phi\,\cos\,\phi + \cos\theta\,\sin\,\phi\,\cos\,\phi = 0$$

Hence the angle between $\hat{\theta}$ and $\hat{\phi} = \pi/2$. Therefore $\hat{\theta}$ and $\hat{\phi}$ are perpendicular to each other.

Thus the polar unit vectors $\hat{r}$, $\hat{\theta}$ *and* $\hat{\phi}$ *are mutually perpendicular to each other i.e., these constitute a system of orthogonal unit vectors.*

(*b*) In spherical polar co-ordinates

$$\hat{r} = \sin\theta\,\cos\,\phi\,\hat{i} + \sin\theta\,\sin\,\phi\,\hat{j} + \cos\theta\,\hat{k}$$

$$\hat{\theta} = \cos\theta\,\cos\,\phi\,\hat{i} + \cos\theta\,\sin\phi\,\hat{j} - \sin\theta\,\hat{k}$$

$$\hat{\phi} = -\sin\phi\,\hat{i} + \cos\,\phi\,\hat{j}$$

(*i*) $\qquad \hat{\theta}\times\hat{\phi} = (\cos\theta\,\cos\,\phi)\hat{i} + (\cos\theta\,\sin\,\phi)\,\hat{j} - (\sin\theta)\hat{k}]$

$$\times\,[(-\sin\,\phi)\hat{i} + (\cos\,\phi)\,\hat{j}]$$

$$= \begin{vmatrix} \hat{i} & \hat{j} & \hat{k} \\ \cos\theta\,\cos\phi & \cos\theta\,\sin\phi & -\sin\theta \\ -\sin\phi & \cos\phi & 0 \end{vmatrix}$$

$$= (\sin\theta\,\cos\,\phi)\hat{i} + (\sin\theta\,\sin\,\phi)\,\hat{j} + (\cos\theta\,\cos^2\,\phi + \cos\theta\,\sin^2\,\phi)\hat{k}$$

$$= (\sin\theta\,\cos\,\phi)\hat{i} + (\sin\theta\,\sin\phi)\,\hat{j} + (\cos\theta)\hat{k}$$

$$= \hat{r}$$

(ii) $\hat{\phi} \times \hat{r} = [-\sin \phi \hat{i} + \cos \phi \hat{j}] \times [(\sin \theta \cos \phi) \hat{i} + (\sin \theta \sin \phi) \hat{j} + \cos \theta \hat{k}]$

$$= \begin{vmatrix} \hat{i} & \hat{j} & \hat{k} \\ -\sin \phi & \cos \phi & 0 \\ \sin \theta \cos \phi & \sin \theta \sin \phi & \cos \theta \end{vmatrix}$$

$$= (\cos \phi \cos \theta) \hat{i} + (\sin \phi \cos \theta) \hat{j} + (-\sin \theta \sin^2 \phi - \sin \theta \cos^2 \phi) \hat{k}$$

$$= (\cos \theta \cos \phi) \hat{i} + (\cos \theta \sin \phi) \hat{j} - \sin \theta \hat{k}$$

$$= \hat{\theta}$$

(iii) $\hat{r} \times \hat{\theta} = [(\sin \theta \cos \phi) \hat{i} + (\sin \theta \sin \phi) \hat{j} + \cos \theta \hat{k}]$

$$\times [(\cos \theta \cos \phi) \hat{i} + (\cos \theta \sin \phi) \hat{j} - \sin \theta \hat{k}]$$

$$= \begin{vmatrix} \hat{i} & \hat{j} & \hat{k} \\ \sin \theta \cos \phi & \sin \theta \sin \phi & \cos \theta \\ \cos \theta \cos \phi & \cos \theta \sin \phi & -\sin \theta \end{vmatrix}$$

$$= [-\sin^2 \theta \sin \phi - \cos^2 \theta \sin \phi] \hat{i} + [\cos^2 \theta \cos \phi + \sin^2 \theta \cos \phi] \hat{j}$$

$$+ (\sin \theta \cos \theta \sin \phi \cos \phi - \sin \theta \cos \theta \sin \phi \cos \phi) \hat{k}$$

$$= -\sin \phi \hat{i} + \cos \phi \hat{j}$$

$$= \hat{\phi}$$

Exercise. *Prove* $\hat{r} \times \hat{\theta} = \hat{\phi}$ *and also* $\hat{r}$ *and* $\hat{\theta}$ *are perpendicular to each other.*   (*P.U.* 2006)

Hint. $\hat{r} \times \hat{\theta} = \hat{\phi}$. See question given above and (*b*) (*iii*)

$\hat{r}$ *and* $\hat{\theta}$ *are perpendicular to each other.* See question given above under (*a*)(*i*)

Q. 2.19. (*a*) **Obtain relation for displacement in spherical polar co-ordinates.**

(*G.N.D.U.*, 2002)

(*b*) **Drawing a neat diagram prove that for motion of a particle in space** $\vec{v} = \dot{r} \hat{r} + r \dot{\theta} \hat{\theta} + r \sin \theta \dot{\phi} \hat{\phi}$ **where the symbols have their usual meanings. Give the physical significance of each term.** (*Pbi. U.* 2007; *G.N.D.U.* 2007; *H.P.U.* 2001, 1995, 1994; *P.U.* 2006, 2003, 2000)

Ans. (*a*) **Displacement.** The position of a point P in a co-ordinate system can be specified by a single vector *i.e.*, the *displacement* of the particle relative to the origin O of the co-ordinate system. This vector is called the *position vector* of the point and denoted by $\overrightarrow{OP} = \vec{r}$. It gives the *magnitude* as well as the *direction of displacement*. If $\hat{r}$, is a unit vector along $\overrightarrow{OP}$ *i.e.*, along the direction or $\vec{r}$, then

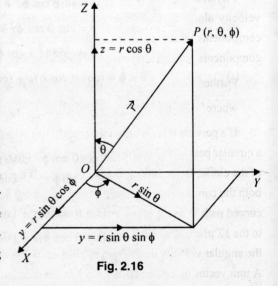

Fig. 2.16

$$\vec{r} = r\hat{r}$$

If (r, θ, ϕ) are the polar co-ordinates of the particle P at any instant and (x, y, z) the corresponding cartesian co-ordinates, then

$x = r \sin \theta \cos \phi$; $y = r \sin \theta \sin \phi$; $z = r \cos \theta$

As shown in Fig. 2.16 $\vec{r} = x\hat{i} + y\hat{j} + z\hat{k}$

∴ Displacement $\qquad \vec{r} = r\sin \theta \cos \phi \hat{i} + r\sin \theta \sin \phi \hat{j} + r\cos \theta \hat{k}$

Hence $\qquad \hat{r} = \sin\theta \cos \phi \hat{i} + \sin \theta \sin \phi \hat{j} + \cos \theta \hat{k}$

Since the unit vector $\hat{\theta}$ in the direction of increasing θ is at right angles to $\hat{r}$,

∴ $\qquad \hat{\theta} = \cos \theta \cos \phi \hat{i} + \cos \theta \sin \phi \hat{j} - \sin \theta \hat{k}$

As unit vector $\hat{\phi}$ is at right angles to the component $r \sin \theta$ and lies in the x-y plane,

∴ $\qquad \hat{\phi} = -\sin \phi \hat{i} + \cos \phi \hat{j} \qquad\qquad$ (Also see Q. 2.16)

(b) Velocity *is the time rate of change of displacement.*

∵ Displacement $\qquad \vec{r} = r\hat{r}$

Velocity $\quad \vec{v} = \dfrac{d\vec{r}}{dt} = \dfrac{d}{dt}(r\hat{r}) = \dfrac{dr}{dt}\hat{r} + r\dfrac{d\hat{r}}{dt}$

Now $\qquad \dfrac{d\hat{r}}{dt} = \dfrac{d}{dt}[\sin \theta \cos \phi \hat{i} + \sin \theta \sin \phi \hat{j} + \cos \theta \hat{k}]$

$\qquad = (\cos\theta \cos \phi \dot{\theta} - \sin \theta \sin \phi \dot{\phi})\hat{i} + (\cos \theta \sin \phi \dot{\theta} + \sin \theta \cos \phi \dot{\phi})\hat{j} - (\sin \theta \dot{\theta})\hat{k}$

$\qquad = \dot{\theta}(\cos \theta \cos \phi \hat{i} + \cos \theta \sin \phi \hat{j} - \sin \theta \hat{k}) + \sin \theta \dot{\phi}(-\sin \phi \hat{i} + \cos \phi \hat{j})$

∴ $\qquad \dfrac{d\hat{r}}{dt} = \dot{\theta}\hat{\theta} + \sin \theta \dot{\phi}\hat{\phi} \qquad\qquad\qquad$ ...(i)

∴ $\qquad \vec{v} = \dot{r}\hat{r} + r\dot{\theta}\hat{\theta} + r\sin\theta\dot{\phi}\hat{\phi} \qquad\qquad$ ..(ii)

The above relation can be put in the form $\vec{v} = \vec{v_r} + \vec{v_\theta} + \vec{v_\phi}$.

Physical significance. Now $\vec{v_r}$ is the velocity along $\vec{r}$, $\vec{v_\theta}$ the velocity along θ and $\vec{v_\phi}$ the velocity along ϕ. The three velocity vectors $\vec{v_r}$, $\vec{v_\theta}$ and $\vec{v_\phi}$, therefore, act as three orthogonal components in the polar co-ordinate system in the same way as $\vec{v_x}$, $\vec{v_y}$ and $\vec{v_z}$ are rectangular components in the cartesian co-ordinate system.

Further $\qquad |\vec{v}^2| = \vec{v}.\vec{v} = \dot{r}^2 + r^2\dot{\theta}^2 + r^2 \sin^2 \theta\dot{\phi}^2 = v_r^2 + v_\theta^2 + v_\phi^2$

where $\qquad v_r = |\vec{v_r}| = \dot{r} \quad v_\theta = |\vec{v_\theta}| = r\dot{\theta} \quad v_\phi = |\vec{v_\phi}| = r \sin \theta\dot{\phi}$

If a particle travels only in a straight line it has only the linear velocity $\vec{v} = \dot{r}\hat{r}$, if it moves along a circular path with a uniform velocity, it has only an angular velocity $v_\theta = r\dot{\theta}\hat{\theta}$ where r is the radius of the circle, $\dot{\theta}$ the rate of change of angle. If the particle moves along a curved path in a plane it has both the components $\vec{v_r}$ along $\hat{r}$ and $\vec{v_\theta}$ along $\hat{\theta}$ at right angles to $\hat{r}$. When the particle moves in a curved path in space it has in addition the third components $r \sin \theta\dot{\phi}$ in the XY plane perpendicular to the YZ plane in which $\hat{r}$ and $\hat{\theta}$ lie. $r \sin \theta$ is the component of $\vec{r}$ in the XY plane and $r \sin \theta\dot{\phi}$ gives the angular velocity due to rate of change of ϕ in the direction $\hat{\phi}$ perpendicular to the vector $r \sin \theta$. A unit vector in the direction $r \sin \theta$ is denoted by $\hat{\rho}$.

Q. 2.20. Starting from the relationship between spherical polar co-ordinates and cartesian co-ordinates, find the value of v_r, v_θ and v_ϕ in terms of x, y, z and $\dot{x}, \dot{y}, \dot{z}$.

(*G.N.D.U.* 2007; *P.U.* 2001, 1999)

Ans. The cartesian co-ordinates x, y, z of a point are related to its spherical polar co-oprdinates r, θ, ϕ as under

$$x = r \sin\theta \cos\phi, \ y = r \sin\theta \sin\phi, \ z = r \cos\theta$$

$$\therefore \quad \dot{x} = \dot{r} \sin\theta \cos\phi + r \cos\theta\dot{\theta} \cos\phi - r \sin\theta \sin\phi\dot{\phi} \qquad \ldots(i)$$

$$\dot{y} = \dot{r} \sin\theta \sin\phi + r \cos\theta\dot{\theta} \sin\phi + r \sin\theta \cos\phi\dot{\phi} \qquad \ldots(ii)$$

$$\dot{z} = \dot{r} \cos\theta - r \sin\theta\dot{\theta} \qquad \ldots(iii)$$

Multiplying (*i*) by $x = r \sin\theta \cos\phi$, (*ii*) by $y = r \sin\theta \sin\phi$ and (*iii*) by $z = r \cos\theta$, we have

$$x\dot{x} = r\dot{r} \sin^2\theta \cos^2\phi + r^2 \sin\theta \cos\theta\dot{\theta} \cos^2\phi - r^2 \sin^2\theta \sin\phi \cos\phi\dot{\phi}$$

$$y\dot{y} = r\dot{r} \sin^2\theta \sin^2\phi + r^2 \sin\theta \cos\theta\dot{\theta} \sin^2\phi + r^2 \sin^2\theta \sin\phi \cos\phi\dot{\phi}$$

$$z\dot{z} = r\dot{r} \cos^2\theta - r^2 \sin\theta \cos\theta\dot{\theta}$$

Adding, we get $x\dot{x} + y\dot{y} + z\dot{z} = r\dot{r}$

$$\therefore \quad |\vec{v_r}| = \dot{r} = \frac{x\dot{x} + y\dot{y} + z\dot{z}}{r} = \frac{x\dot{x} + y\dot{y} + z\dot{z}}{(x^2 + y^2 + z^2)^{\frac{1}{2}}} \qquad \ldots(iv)$$

Again $x\dot{x} + y\dot{y} = r\dot{r} \sin^2\theta + r^2 \sin\theta \cos\theta\dot{\theta} = r\sin\theta(\dot{r}\sin\theta + r\cos\theta\dot{\theta})$

Now $r \sin\theta = (r^2 \sin^2\theta\cos^2\phi + r^2 \sin^2\theta \sin^2\phi)^{\frac{1}{2}} = \sqrt{x^2 + y^2} = \rho$ $\qquad \ldots(iv)\ (a)$

$$\therefore \quad \frac{x\dot{x} + y\dot{y}}{\rho} = \dot{r} \sin\theta + r \cos\theta\dot{\theta}$$

Multiplying both sides by $z = r \cos\theta$, we get

$$(x\dot{x} + y\dot{y})\frac{z}{\rho} = r\dot{r} \sin\theta \cos\theta + r^2 \cos^2\theta\dot{\theta}$$

Now multiplying (*iii*) and (*iv*) (*a*) $\dot{z}\rho = r\dot{r} \sin\theta \cos\theta - r^2 \sin^2\theta\dot{\theta}$

$$\therefore \quad (x\dot{x} + y\dot{y})\frac{z}{\rho} - \dot{z}\rho = r^2\dot{\theta}$$

or $$\dot{\theta} = \frac{(x\dot{x} + y\dot{y})\dfrac{z}{\rho} - \dot{z}\rho}{x^2 + y^2 + z^2}$$

or $$r\dot{\theta} = |\vec{v_\theta}| = \frac{(x\dot{x} + y\dot{y})\dfrac{z}{\rho} - \dot{z}\rho}{(x^2 + y^2 + z^2)^{\frac{1}{2}}} \qquad \ldots(v)$$

Multiplying (*ii*) by $x = r \sin\theta \cos\phi$ and (*i*) by $y = r \sin\theta \sin\phi$ and subtracting, we have

$$x\dot{y} - y\dot{x} = r\dot{r} \sin^2\theta \sin\phi \cos\phi + r^2 \sin\theta \cos\theta\dot{\theta} \sin\phi \cos\phi$$

$$+ r^2 \sin^2\theta \cos^2\phi\dot{\phi} - r\dot{r} \sin^2\theta \sin\phi \cos\phi$$

$$- r^2 \sin\theta \cos\theta\dot{\theta} \sin\phi \cos\phi + r^2 \sin^2\theta \sin^2\phi\dot{\phi}$$

$$= r^2 \sin^2\theta\dot{\phi}$$

$$\therefore \quad \dot{\phi} = \frac{x\dot{y} - y\dot{x}}{x^2 + y^2} \quad \text{or} \quad |\vec{v_\phi}| = r \sin\theta\dot{\phi} = \frac{x\dot{y} - y\dot{x}}{(x^2 + y^2)^{\frac{1}{2}}} \qquad \ldots(vi)$$

Q. 2.21. Starting from the expression for velocity $v = \dot{r}\hat{r} + r\dot{\theta}\hat{\theta} + r\sin\theta\dot{\phi}\hat{\phi}$ **obtain an expression for acceleration in spherical polar co-ordinates.**

(*Pbi. U.* 2005; *H.P.U.* 2000, 1999; *P.U.* 2009, 2008, 2007, 2005, 2004, 2003)

Ans. Acceleration. The velocity of a particle in spherical polar co-ordinates is given by

Velocity $\qquad\qquad \vec{v} = \dot{r}\hat{r} + r\dot{\theta}\hat{\theta} + r\sin\theta\,\dot{\phi}\hat{\phi}$

Acceleration is the derivative of $\vec{v}$ *with respect to time t.*

$\therefore$ Acceleration $\qquad \vec{a} = \dfrac{d\vec{v}}{dt} = \ddot{r}\hat{r} + \dot{r}\dfrac{d\hat{r}}{dt} + \dot{r}\dot{\theta}\hat{\theta} + r\ddot{\theta}\hat{\theta} + r\dot{\theta}\dfrac{d\hat{\theta}}{dt} + \dot{r}\sin\theta\dot{\phi}\hat{\phi}$

$$+ r\cos\theta\dot{\theta}\dot{\phi}\hat{\phi} + r\sin\theta\ddot{\phi}\hat{\phi} + r\sin\theta\dot{\phi}\dfrac{d\hat{\phi}}{dt} \qquad ...(i)$$

Now unit vectors $\hat{r}$, $\hat{\theta}$, $\hat{\phi}$ in spherical polar co-ordinates in terms of unit vectors $\hat{i}$, $\hat{j}$, $\hat{k}$ in cartesian co-ordinates are given by

$$\hat{r} = \sin\theta\cos\phi\,\hat{i} + \sin\theta\sin\phi\,\hat{j} + \cos\theta\hat{k}$$

$$\hat{\theta} = \cos\theta\cos\phi\,\hat{i} + \cos\theta\sin\phi\,\hat{j} - \sin\theta\hat{k}$$

and $\qquad\qquad \hat{\phi} = -\sin\phi\,\hat{i} + \cos\phi\,\hat{j}$

$\therefore \qquad\qquad \dfrac{d\hat{r}}{dt} = \dfrac{d}{dt}[\sin\theta\cos\phi\,\hat{i} + \sin\theta\sin\phi\,\hat{j} + \cos\theta\hat{k}]$

$$= (\cos\theta\cos\phi\dot{\theta} - \sin\theta\sin\phi\dot{\phi})\hat{i}$$

$$+ (\cos\theta\sin\phi\dot{\theta} + \sin\theta\cos\phi\dot{\phi})\hat{j} - (\sin\theta\dot{\theta})\hat{k}$$

$$= \dot{\theta}(\cos\theta\cos\phi\,\hat{i} + \cos\theta\sin\phi\,\hat{j} - \sin\theta\hat{k})$$

$$+ \sin\theta\dot{\phi}(-\sin\phi\,\hat{i} + \cos\phi\,\hat{j})$$

$$= \dot{\theta}\hat{\theta} + \sin\theta\dot{\phi}\hat{\phi}$$

$\dfrac{d\hat{\theta}}{dt} = \dfrac{d}{dt}[\cos\theta\cos\phi\,\hat{i} + \cos\theta\sin\phi\,\hat{j} - \sin\theta\hat{k}]$

$$= (-\sin\theta\dot{\theta}\cos\phi - \cos\theta\sin\phi\dot{\phi})\,\hat{i}$$

$$+ (-\sin\theta\dot{\theta}\sin\phi + \cos\theta\cos\phi\dot{\phi})\,\hat{j} - (\cos\theta\dot{\theta})\hat{k}$$

$$= -\dot{\theta}(\sin\theta\cos\phi\,\hat{i} + \sin\theta\sin\phi\,\hat{j} + \cos\theta\hat{k})$$

$$+ \cos\theta\dot{\phi}(-\sin\phi\,\hat{i} + \cos\phi\,\hat{j})$$

$$= -\dot{\theta}\hat{r} + \cos\theta\dot{\phi}\hat{\phi}$$

and $\qquad\qquad \dfrac{d\hat{\phi}}{dt} = \dfrac{d}{dt}[-\sin\phi\,\hat{i} + \cos\phi\,\hat{j}]$

$$= (-\cos\phi\dot{\phi}\,\hat{i} - \sin\phi\dot{\phi}\,\hat{j})$$

$$= -\dot{\phi}(\cos\phi\,\hat{i} + \sin\phi\,\hat{j})$$

Now $\cos\phi\,\hat{i} + \sin\phi\,\hat{j} = \sin\theta\hat{r} + \cos\theta\hat{\theta}$

$\therefore \qquad\qquad \dfrac{d\hat{\phi}}{dt} = -\sin\theta\dot{\phi}\,\hat{r} - \cos\theta\dot{\phi}\,\hat{\theta}$

Substituting the values of $\dfrac{d\hat{r}}{dt}$, $\dfrac{d\hat{\theta}}{dt}$ and $\dfrac{d\hat{\phi}}{dt}$ in (i), we have

$$\vec{a} = \ddot{r}\hat{r} + \dot{r}\dot{\theta}\hat{\theta} + \dot{r}\sin\theta\dot{\phi}\hat{\phi} + \dot{r}\dot{\theta}\hat{\theta} + r\ddot{\theta}\hat{\theta}$$

$$- r\dot{\theta}^2\hat{r} + r\cos\theta\dot{\theta}\dot{\phi}\hat{\phi} + \dot{r}\sin\theta\dot{\phi}\hat{\phi} + r\cos\theta\dot{\theta}\dot{\phi}\hat{\phi}$$

$$+ r\sin\theta\ddot{\phi}\hat{\phi} - r\sin^2\theta\dot{\phi}^2\,\hat{r} - r\sin\theta\cos\theta\dot{\phi}^2\hat{\theta}$$

$$= (\ddot{r} - r\dot{\theta}^2 - r\dot{\phi}^2\sin^2\theta)\,\hat{r} + (2\dot{r}\dot{\theta} + r\ddot{\theta} - r\sin\theta\cos\theta\dot{\phi}^2)\hat{\theta}$$

$$+ (2\dot{r}\dot{\phi}\sin\theta + 2r\cos\theta\dot{\theta}\dot{\phi} + r\sin\theta\ddot{\phi})\,\hat{\phi}$$

$$= \vec{a}_r + \vec{a}_\theta + \vec{a}_\phi$$

where
$$\vec{a}_r = (\ddot{r} - r\dot{\theta}^2 - r\sin^2\theta\dot{\phi}^2)\,\hat{r}$$

$$\vec{a}_\theta = (r\ddot{\theta} + 2\dot{r}\dot{\theta} - r\sin\theta\cos\theta\dot{\phi}^2)\,\hat{\theta}$$

$$\vec{a}_\phi = (r\sin\theta\ddot{\phi} + 2\dot{r}\dot{\phi}\sin\theta + 2r\cos\theta\dot{\theta}\dot{\phi})\,\hat{\phi}$$

As $\hat{r}$, $\hat{\theta}$ and $\hat{\phi}$ are orthogonal to one another, the magnitude of acceleration

$$|\vec{a}| = [|\vec{a}_r|^2 + |\vec{a}_\theta|^2 + |\vec{a}_\phi|^2]^{\frac{1}{2}}$$

Q. 2.22. A rectangular parallelopiped has the position vector at its extreme ends as $\vec{r}$ and $\vec{r} + \vec{dr}$. Calculate the value of line element joining the extreme ends and show that the line element of the body diagonals are equal in magnitude but different in direction.

Ans. Line element. Consider a ractangular parallelopiped $ABCDEFGH$, the position vector of $A = \vec{r}$ and position vector of $H = \vec{r} + d\vec{r}$ as shown in Fig. 2.17, then

$$\overrightarrow{AH} = (\vec{r} + d\vec{r}) - \vec{r} = d\vec{r}$$

This incremental vector is known as line element. If the cartesian co-ordinates of the point A are x, y and z and those of H are $x + dx$, $y + dy$ and $z + dz$ and $\hat{i}$, $\hat{j}$, $\hat{k}$ are the unit vectors along X, Y and Z axes respectively, then

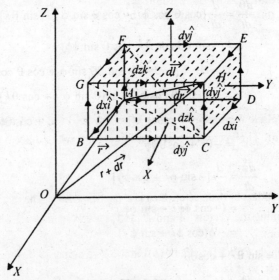

Fig. 2.17

$$\vec{r} = x\hat{i} + y\hat{j} + z\hat{k} \text{ and}$$
$$\vec{r} + d\vec{r} = (x + dx)\hat{i} + (y + dy)\hat{j} + (z + dz)\hat{k}$$

∴ Line element $\quad d\vec{r} = (\vec{r} + d\vec{r}) - \vec{r}$

or $\qquad\qquad d\vec{r} = dx\hat{i} + dy\hat{j} + dz\hat{k}$ ...(i)

Thus $\qquad\qquad dx\hat{i} = d\vec{x} = \overrightarrow{AB}$

$$dy\hat{j} = d\vec{y} = \overrightarrow{AD}$$

and $\qquad\qquad dz\hat{k} = d\vec{z} = \overrightarrow{AF}$

are the rectangular components of the line element $d\vec{r}$.

The magnitude of $d\vec{r} = |d\vec{r}| = \sqrt{dx^2 + dy^2 + dz^2}$

Consider two body diagonals $\overrightarrow{AH}$ and $\overrightarrow{CF}$ of the rectangular parallelopiped, then

$$\overrightarrow{AH} = d\vec{r} = dx\hat{i} + dy\hat{j} + dz\hat{k}$$

The body diagonal $\quad \overrightarrow{CF} = \overrightarrow{CG} + \overrightarrow{GF} = \overrightarrow{CB} + \overrightarrow{BG} + \overrightarrow{GF}$

or $\qquad\qquad \overrightarrow{CF} = d\vec{l} = -dy\hat{j} + dz\hat{k} - dx\hat{i}$

The magnitude of $\quad |d\vec{l}| = \sqrt{dx^2 + dy^2 + dz^2}$

Thus the line elements of the body diagonals are equal in magnitude. But $d\vec{r} \neq d\vec{l}$. Hence the two vectors representing the two body diagonals of the parallelopiped are unequal. Therefore they have different directions.

Q. 2.23. (*a*) **Find an expression for the area element in rectangular Cartesian co-ordinate system.** (*Pbi. U.* 2003, 2001, 1999)

(*b*) **A rectangular parallelopiped has the position vectors at its extreme ends as $\vec{r}$ and $\vec{r} + d\vec{r}$. Calculate the area of each face and volume of the parallelopiped in terms of rectangular components of $d\vec{r}$.** (*G.N.D.U.* 1996, 1995)

(*c*) **Find the expression for volume in rectangular cartesian co-ordinates. Justify the choice of area as a vector and volume as a scalar quantity.** (*P.U.* 2000; *G.N.D.U.* 2007, 1996, 1995)

(*d*) **Three edges of a parallelopiped are given by vectors**

$$\vec{a} = 2\hat{i} + 3\hat{j} - 2\hat{k}$$

$$\vec{b} = \hat{i} - 2\hat{j} - 3\hat{k}$$

and $\qquad\qquad \vec{c} = 3\hat{i} - 2\hat{j} - \hat{k}$

Find the area of the plane formed by vectors $\vec{a}$ and $\vec{b}$ and the total volume. (*Pbi. U.* 2008)

Ans. (*a*) **Area element.** The vector area of a parallelogram with adjacent sides represented by the vectors $\vec{A}$ and $\vec{B}$ is given by

$$\text{area} = \vec{A} \times \vec{B}$$

This being the vector product of two vectors area is a vector quantity. The direction of area vector is normal to the plane containing the vectors $\vec{A}$ and $\vec{B}$ and is given by the rule for the direction of the cross-product of two vectors.

Now, consider a rectangle $PQRS$ [Fig. 2.18 (*b*)] in the $X-Y$ plane. The x-co-ordinate of the point $P(x, y)$ is x and of $Q(x + dx, y)$ is $(x + dx)$.

∴ $\qquad\qquad \overrightarrow{PQ} = (\vec{x} + d\vec{x}) - \vec{x} = d\vec{x} = dx\hat{i}$

Similarly the y-co-ordinate of the point $P(x, y)$ is y and of $S(x, y + dy)$

$$\therefore \qquad \overrightarrow{PS} = (\vec{y} + \vec{dy}) - \vec{y} = \vec{dy} = dy\,\hat{j}$$

The area $PQRS$ is called an *area element* $\vec{dA}$.

$$\therefore \qquad \vec{dA} = \vec{dx} \times \vec{dy} = dx\,\hat{i} \times dy\,\hat{j} = dx\,dy\,\hat{k}$$

i.e. the direction of the area is along $\hat{k}$ i.e. $+Z$ direction

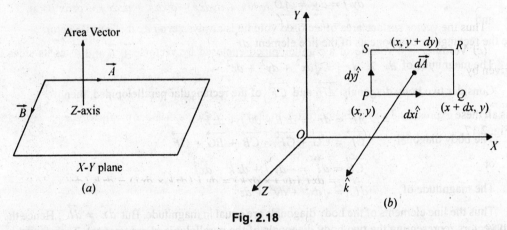

Fig. 2.18

(b) Area of each face of a parallelopiped. The rectangular parallelopiped shown in Fig. 2.17 has three pairs of elements of area.

As proved in **Q. 2.22**, the sides of rectangular parallelopiped are $\vec{dx}$, $\vec{dy}$ and $\vec{dz}$ where $\vec{dx} = dx\,\hat{i}$, $\vec{dy} = dy\,\hat{j}$ and $\vec{dz} = dz\,\hat{k}$.

(i) Upper face of area $HEFG = (\vec{dA})_{xy} = \overrightarrow{FG} \times \overrightarrow{FE} = \vec{dx} \times \vec{dy} = dx\,\hat{i} \times dy\,\hat{j} = dx\,dy\,\hat{k}$

Hence the magnitude of the area vector $= dx\,dy$ and its direction is along the outward drawn normal to the upper x-y plane *i.e.*, along the **positive** direction of Z-axis or along $\hat{k}$.

(ii) Lower face of area $ADCB = (\vec{dA})_{yx} = \overrightarrow{AD} \times \overrightarrow{AB} = \vec{dy} \times \vec{dx} = dy\,\hat{j} \times dx\,\hat{i} = -dx\,dy\,\hat{k}$.

Hence the magnitude of the area vector $= dx\,dy$ and its direction is along the outward drawn normal to the lower x-y plane *i.e.*, along the **negative** direction of Z-axis or along $-\hat{k}$.

(iii) Front face of area $GHCB = (dA)_{yz} = \overrightarrow{BC} \times \overrightarrow{CH} = \vec{dy} \times \vec{dz} = dy\,\hat{j} \times dz\,\hat{k} = dy\,dz\,\hat{i}$

Hence the magnitude of the area vector $= dy\,dz$ and its direction is along the outward drawn normal to the front y, z plane *i.e.*, along the **positive** direction of X-axis or along $\hat{i}$.

(iv) Back face of area $AFED = (\vec{dA})_{zy} = \overrightarrow{AF} \times \overrightarrow{AD} = \vec{dz} \times \vec{dy} = dz\,\hat{k} \times dy\,\hat{j} = -dy\,\hat{j} = -dy\,dz\,\hat{i}$.

Hence the magnitude of the area vector $= dy\,dz$ and its direction is along the outward drawn normal to the back y, z plane *i.e.*, along the **negative** direction of X-axis or along $-\hat{i}$.

(v) Right face of area $DEHC = (\vec{dA})_{zx} = \overrightarrow{DE} \times \overrightarrow{EH} = \vec{dz} \times \vec{dx} = dz\,\hat{k} \times dx\,\hat{i} = dz\,dx\,\hat{j}$

Hence the magnitude of the area vector $= dz\,dx$ and its direction is along the outward drawn normal to the right z, x plane *i.e.*, along the **positive** direction of Y-axis or along $\hat{j}$.

(*vi*) Left face of area $ABGF = (d\vec{A})_{xz} = \overrightarrow{AB} \times \overrightarrow{BG} = \vec{dx} \times \vec{dz} = dx\,\hat{i} \times dz\,\hat{k} = -dz\,dx\,\hat{j}$

Hence the magnitude of the area vector $= dz\,dx$ and its direction is along the outward drawn normal to the left *z-x* plane *i.e.*, along the **negative** direction of *Y*-axis or along $-\hat{j}$.

If $d\vec{A}$ is the total vector area of the *closed* surface of the rectangular parallelopiped, then

$$d\vec{A} = (d\vec{A})_{xy} + (d\vec{A})_{yx} + (d\vec{A})_{yz} + (d\vec{A})_{zy} + (d\vec{A})_{zx} + (d\vec{A})_{xz}$$

$$= dxdy\,\hat{k} - dxdy\,\hat{k} + dydz\,\hat{i} - dydz\,\hat{i} + dzdx\,\hat{j} - dzdx\,\hat{j} = 0.$$

Thus the vector surface area of a closed volume is always **zero** *i.e.*, it is a **null vector.**

(*c*) **Volume.** The volume of a parallelopiped enclosed by vectors $\vec{A}$, $\vec{B}$ and $\vec{C}$ as its sides is given by

$$V = \vec{A}\,.\,(\vec{B} \times \vec{C}) = \vec{B}.(\vec{A} \times \vec{C}) = \vec{C}.(\vec{A} \times \vec{B})$$

as all these expressions give the same result. In the case of the rectangular parallelopiped as shown in Fig. 2.17,

$$\vec{V} = \vec{dx}\,.(\vec{dy} \times \vec{dz}) = \vec{dy}\,.(\vec{dz} \times \vec{dx}) = \vec{dz}\,.(\vec{dx} \times \vec{dy})$$

$$= dx\,\hat{i}\,.(dy\,\hat{j} \times dz\,\hat{k}) = dy\,\hat{j}.(dz\,\hat{k} \times dx\,\hat{i}) = dz\,\hat{k}.(dx\,\hat{i} \times dy\,\hat{j})$$

$$= dx\,\hat{i}\,.(dydz)\hat{i} = dy\,\hat{j}.(dzdx)\,\hat{j} = dz\,\hat{k}.(dxdy)\hat{k} = dx\,dy\,dz$$

since $\hat{i}.\hat{i} = \hat{j}.\hat{j} = \hat{k}.\hat{k} = 1$

Though $(\vec{B} \times \vec{C})$ is a vector quantity $\vec{A}.(\vec{B} \times \vec{C})$ being the scalar product of two vectors is a scalar quantity.

Choice of area as a vector. Area is taken as a vector quantity because the area of a parallelogram is given by the **vector product** of two vectors $\vec{A}$ and $\vec{B}$ representing the adjacent sides of the parallelogram. The magnitude of $\vec{A} \times \vec{B} = |AB\sin\theta|$ where A and B are the magnitudes of $\vec{A}$ and $\vec{B}$ and θ the angle between them. Thus the expression automatically gives the area. The vector product of two vectors also being a vector, the area is a vector quantity.

Volume a scalar quantity. The volume is a scalar quantity as the volume of a parallelopiped $= \vec{A}.(\vec{B} \times \vec{C})$. This being a **scalar** product of the vector $\vec{A}$ and the resultant vector of $(\vec{B} \times \vec{C})$, the volume is a scalar quantity. Moreover the result is the same if we choose any order for the three vectors $\vec{A}$, $\vec{B}$ and $\vec{C}$.

(*d*) The vector area is given by

$$\overrightarrow{area} = \vec{a} \times \vec{b}$$

$$= (2\hat{i} + 3\hat{j} - 2\hat{k}) \times (\hat{i} - 2\hat{j} + 3\hat{k})$$

$$= \begin{vmatrix} \hat{i} & \hat{j} & \hat{k} \\ 2 & 3 & -2 \\ 1 & -2 & +3 \end{vmatrix} = \hat{i}\,(9-4) + \hat{j}\,(-2-6) + \hat{k}\,(-4-3)$$

$$= 5\hat{i} - 8\hat{j} - 7\hat{k}$$

The magnitude of the area $A = \sqrt{5^2 + (-8)^2 + (-7)^2}$

$$= \sqrt{25 + 64 + 49} = \sqrt{138} = 11.75 \text{ units}$$

Volume $V = (\vec{a} \times \vec{b}) \cdot \vec{c} = (5\hat{i} - 8\hat{j} - 7\hat{k}) \cdot (3\hat{i} + 2\hat{j} - \hat{k})$

$$= 15 - 16 + 7 = 6 \text{ units}$$

Q. 2.24. Find the value of line element and area element in plane polar co-ordinates.

(Pbi. U., 2002)

Ans. Line element in plane polar co-ordinates. Consider two points A and B having co-ordinates (r, θ) and $(r + dr, \theta + d\theta)$ respectively;

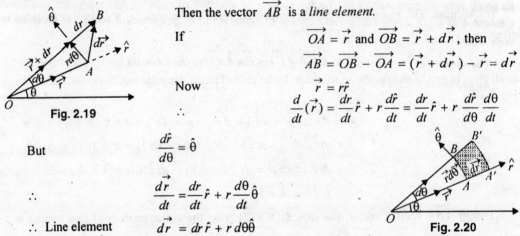

Then the vector $\overrightarrow{AB}$ is a *line element*.

If $\qquad \overrightarrow{OA} = \vec{r}$ and $\overrightarrow{OB} = \vec{r} + \vec{dr}$, then

$$\overrightarrow{AB} = \overrightarrow{OB} - \overrightarrow{OA} = (\vec{r} + \vec{dr}) - \vec{r} = \vec{dr}$$

Now $\qquad \vec{r} = r\hat{r}$

$\therefore \qquad \dfrac{d}{dt}(\vec{r}) = \dfrac{dr}{dt}\hat{r} + r\dfrac{d\hat{r}}{dt} = \dfrac{dr}{dt}\hat{r} + r\dfrac{d\hat{r}}{d\theta}\dfrac{d\theta}{dt}$

Fig. 2.19

But $\qquad \dfrac{d\hat{r}}{d\theta} = \hat{\theta}$

$\therefore \qquad \dfrac{d\vec{r}}{dt} = \dfrac{dr}{dt}\hat{r} + r\dfrac{d\theta}{dt}\hat{\theta}$

$\therefore$ Line element $\qquad \vec{dr} = dr\,\hat{r} + r\,d\theta\,\hat{\theta}$

Fig. 2.20

Area element. If a small increment $dr = AA'$ is given to $\vec{r} = \overrightarrow{OA}$ in the direction of $\hat{r}$ and a small increment $d\theta = \angle AOB$ is given to θ in the direction of $\hat{\theta}$, then AA' traces out an area element $AA'B'B$ given by

$$\vec{dA} = \overrightarrow{AA'} \times \overrightarrow{AB} = dr\,\hat{r} \times r\,d\theta\,\hat{\theta} = r\,dr\,d\theta\,(\hat{r} \times \hat{\theta})$$

or $\qquad \vec{dA} = r\,dr\,d\theta\,\hat{n}$

where $\hat{n}$ is a unit vector normal to r, θ plane containing the area.

The *magnitude* of the area $dA = r\,dr\,d\theta$

Q. 2.25. Determine the area of a circle of radius a by using plane polar co-ordinates.

(P.U., 1994)

Ans. Area of a circle. Consider a circle of radius a with its centre at the origin O of the co-ordinate system. Let dA be a small portion of the area of the circle around the point P having plane polar co-ordinates (r, θ). The magnitude of the area of this small element is $dA = r\,dr\,d\theta$.

To get the area of the circle we integrate the above expression with respect to r in the limits 0 to a and with respect to θ in the limits 0 to 2π.

$\therefore$ Area of the circle

$$A = \int_{r=0}^{a} \int_{\theta=0}^{2\pi} r\,dr\,d\theta = \int_{r=0}^{a} r\,dr \int_{\theta=0}^{2\pi} d\theta$$

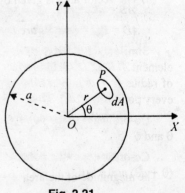

Fig. 2.21

$\therefore$ $A = \left[\dfrac{r^2}{2}\right]_0^a [\theta]_0^{2\pi} = \dfrac{a^2}{2} \cdot 2\pi = \pi a^2$

Q. 2.26. (*a*) **Derive an expression for the line element, area element and volume element, in spherical polar co-ordinate system.**

(*G.N.D.U.* 2007, 2006; *Gauhati U.* 2000; *H.P.U.* 2003;
P.U. 2006, 2004, 2000, 1991; *Pbi. U.* 2006, 2001 1995)

(*b*) **Is area a vector or a scalar? What about volume?**   (*H.P.U.* 2003)

Ans. (*a*) **Line element.** Consider a small rectangular element of volume $ABCD\,D'A'B'C'$ so that its small area element $ABCD$ lies on the surface of a sphere of radius r and a parallel small area element $A'B'C'D'$ on the surface of a sphere of radius $r + dr$, then the radius vectors of the extreme ends A and C' are $\vec{r}$ and $\vec{r} + d\vec{r}$.

The vector $\overrightarrow{AC'} = (\vec{r} + d\vec{r}) - \vec{r} = d\vec{r}$ is known as the *line element* (or *length element*).

As proved in **Q. 2.19** relation (*i*)

$$\dfrac{d\hat{r}}{dt} = \dot{\theta}\hat{\theta} + \sin\theta\,\dot{\phi}\hat{\phi} = \dfrac{d\theta}{dt}\hat{\theta} + \sin\theta\dfrac{d\phi}{dt}\hat{\phi}$$

or $d\hat{r} = d\theta\hat{\theta} + \sin\theta\,d\phi\hat{\phi}$ ...(*i*)

Now $\vec{r} = r\hat{r}$ where r and $\hat{r}$ are both variables. Differentiating, we have

$$d\vec{r} = r\,d\hat{r} + dr\hat{r}$$

Substituting the value of $d\hat{r}$ from (*i*), we have

$$d\vec{r} = dr\hat{r} + r\,d\theta\,\hat{\theta} + r\sin\theta\,d\phi\,\hat{\phi}$$ ...(*ii*)

The magnitude of $d\vec{r} = |d\vec{r}| = \sqrt{dr^2 + r^2\,d\theta^2 + r^2\sin^2\theta\,d\phi^2}$

Area element. For the small element of area $ABCD$ on the surface of a sphere of a radius r, the radial co-ordinates of every point is r. (Fig. 2.22)

The co-ordinates of the point A are r, θ and ϕ.

Co-ordinates of the point B are r, $(\theta + d\theta)$ and ϕ.

Co-ordinates of the point D are r, θ and $(\phi + d\phi)$.

$\therefore\ AB = DC = r\,d\theta$

$AD = BC = r\sin\theta\,d\phi$

Similarly for the parallel small area element $A'B'C'D'$ on the surface of a sphere of radius $(r + dr)$, the radial co-ordinate of every point is $(r + dr)$. Thus

Co-ordinates of the point A' are $(r + dr)$, θ and ϕ

Co-ordinates of the point B' are $(r + dr)$, $(\theta + d\theta)$ and ϕ

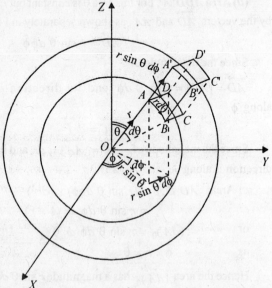

Fig. 2.22

Co-ordinates of the point D' are $(r + dr)$, θ and $(\phi + d\phi)$

Co-ordinates of the point C' are $(r + dr)$, $(\theta + d\theta)$ and $(\phi + d\phi)$

The points $ABCD\ D'\ C'\ B'\ A'$ enclose a rectangular parallelopiped which has three pairs of area elements.

(*i*)   Area $A'\ B'\ C'\ D'$ = Area $ABCD$

(*ii*) Area $ADD'\ A'$ = Area $BCC'\ B'$

(*iii*) Area $ABB'\ A'$ = Area $DCC'\ D'$

(*i*) **Area ABCD.** For this area r is *constant* but θ and ϕ are variable. The two sides are represented by the vectors $\overrightarrow{AB}$ and $\overrightarrow{AD}$ as shown separately in Fig. 2.23 where $\overrightarrow{AB} = r\,d\theta\hat{\theta}$.

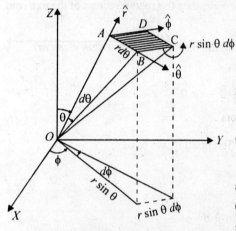

Fig. 2.23

Since the magnitude of $\overrightarrow{AB} = |\overrightarrow{AB}| = r\,d\theta$ and its direction is along $\hat{\theta}$.

$$\overrightarrow{AD} = r\sin\theta\,d\phi\,\hat{\phi}$$

Since the magnitude of $\overrightarrow{AD} = |\overrightarrow{AD}| = r\sin\theta\,d\phi$ and its direction is along $\hat{\phi}$

$\therefore$ Area $ABCD = (r\,d\theta\hat{\theta}) \times (r\sin\theta\,d\phi\hat{\phi})$

or $(d\overrightarrow{A})_r = r^2 \sin\theta\,d\theta\,d\phi(\hat{\theta} \times \hat{\phi})$

$$= r^2 \sin\theta\,d\theta\,d\phi\,\hat{r} \qquad ...(iii)$$

as $\hat{\theta} \times \hat{\phi} = \hat{r}$ since $\hat{r}$, $\hat{\theta}$ and $\hat{\phi}$ constitute a right handed (orthogonal) system of co-ordinates.

Hence the area $(d\overrightarrow{A})_r$ has a magnitude $r^2 \sin\theta\,d\theta\,d\phi$ and the area vector has its direction along $\hat{r}$ *i.e.*, the surface is perpendicular to $\hat{r}$ and is in the plane contained by vectors $\hat{\theta}$ and $\hat{\phi}$.

(*ii*) **Area ADD'A'.** For this area θ is constant but r and ϕ are *variable*. The two sides are represented by the vectors $\overrightarrow{AD}$ and $\overrightarrow{AA'}$ as shown separately in Fig. 2.24.

$$\overrightarrow{AD} = r\sin\theta\,d\phi\hat{\phi}$$

Since the magnitude of

$\overrightarrow{AD} = |\overrightarrow{AD}| = r\sin\theta\,d\phi$ and its direction is along $\hat{\phi}$

$$\overrightarrow{AA'} = dr\,\hat{r}$$

Since the magnitude of $\overrightarrow{AA'} = |\overrightarrow{AA'}| = dr$ and its direction is along $\hat{r}$.

$\therefore$ Area $AD\ D'A' = (r\sin\theta\,d\phi\hat{\phi}) \times (dr\hat{r})$

$$= r\sin\theta\,d\phi\,dr\,(\hat{\phi} \times \hat{r})$$

or $(d\overrightarrow{A})_\theta = r\sin\theta\,d\phi\,dr\,\hat{\theta} \qquad ...(iv)$

as $\hat{\phi} \times \hat{r} = \hat{\theta}$

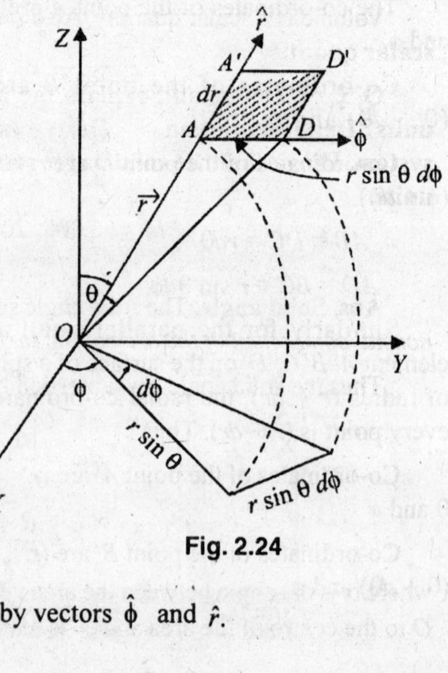

Hence the area $(d\overrightarrow{A})_\theta$ has a magnitude $r\sin\theta\,d\phi$ dr and the area vector has its direction along $\hat{\theta}$ *i.e.*, the surface is perpendicular to $\hat{\theta}$ and is in the plane contained by vectors $\hat{\phi}$ and $\hat{r}$.

Fig. 2.24

(iii) **Area** *ABB'A'*. For this area ϕ is *constant* but r and θ are *variable*. The two sides are represented by the vectors $\overrightarrow{AA'}$ and $\overrightarrow{AB}$ as shown separately in Fig. 2.25 where $\overrightarrow{AA'} = dr\,\hat{r}$.

Since the magnitude of $\overrightarrow{AA'} = |\overrightarrow{AA'}| = dr$ and its direction is along $\hat{r}$

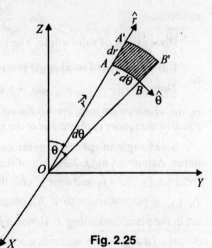

$$\overrightarrow{AB} = r\,d\theta\hat{\theta}$$

Since the magnitude of $\overrightarrow{AB} = |\overrightarrow{AB}| = rd\theta$ and its direction is along $\hat{\theta}$.

$$\therefore \text{ Area } \quad ABB'\,A' = (dr\hat{r}) \times (rd\theta\hat{\theta})$$

$$= r\,dr\,d\theta(\hat{r} \times \hat{\theta})$$

or $\qquad (d\vec{A})_\phi = r\,dr\,d\theta\hat{\phi} \qquad \qquad \text{...}(v)$

as $\qquad \hat{r} \times \hat{\theta} = \hat{\phi}$

Fig. 2.25

Hence the area $(d\vec{A})_\phi$ has a magnitude $r\,dr\,d\theta$ and the area vector has its direction along $\hat{\phi}$ *i.e.* the surface is perpendicular to $\hat{\phi}$ and is in the plane contained by vectors $\hat{r}$ and $\hat{\theta}$.

Volume of the element. The volume of the elementary parallelopiped (Fig. 2.22) $ABCD\,D'\,C'B'A'$ enclosed by the vector lengths $\overrightarrow{AB} = rd\theta\hat{\theta}$, $\overrightarrow{AD} = r\sin\theta\,d\phi\hat{\phi}$ and $\overrightarrow{AA'} = dr\,\hat{r}$ is given by

$$V = \overrightarrow{AA'} . (\overrightarrow{AB} \times \overrightarrow{AD})$$

$$= dr\hat{r}\,.\,(r\,d\theta\hat{\theta} \times r\sin\theta\,d\phi\hat{\phi}) = r^2\sin\theta\,dr\,d\theta\,d\phi[\hat{r}.(\hat{\theta} \times \hat{\phi})]$$

$$= r^2\sin\theta\,dr\,d\theta\,d\phi\,[\hat{r}\,.\,\hat{r}] = r^2\sin\theta\,dr\,d\theta\,d\phi \qquad \text{...}(vi)$$

$$\because \qquad (\hat{\theta} \times \hat{\phi}) = \hat{r} \text{ and } \hat{r}\,.\,\hat{r} = 1$$

Volume is a scalar quantity.

(b) Area is a vector. The direction of the area vector being along the outward drawn normal.

Volume is a scalar quantity. Also see **Q 2.23** under **'Choice of area as a vector'** and **'Volume a scalar quantity'**.

Q. 2.27. Define and explain the term solid angle. What are its dimensions ? What are its units? Define steradian.   Derive an expression for solid angle in spherical polar co-ordinate system. Prove that the solid angle subtended at the centre of sphere by surface of sphere is 4π units.

(Pbi. U. 2008, 2007, 2006; *H.P.U.* 2003; *P.U.* 2006, 2005, 2001, 1999, 1991;
G.N.D.U. 2009, 2007, 2006, 2004, 2002, 1999)

Ans. Solid angle. The solid angle subtended by a surface at a point is measured by the *ratio of* the *normal component of the area of the surface to the square of the distance of the surface from the point.*

Thus the solid angle $d\omega$ subtended by the area $d\vec{A}$ at a point O at a distance r from it is given by

$$d\omega = \frac{|d\vec{A}|\cos\alpha}{r^2}$$

$$= \frac{d\vec{A}\,.\,\hat{r}}{r^2}$$

where α is the angle between the area vector $d\vec{A}$ and the direction of vector $\vec{r}$ which joins the point O to the centre of the area and $\hat{r}$ is a unit vector in the direction of increasing r. (Fig. 2.26)

If the area $d\vec{A}$ is a normal to the line joining any point on the boundary of the area to the point O, or if the normal component of the area is in the direction of increasing r, i.e., $\hat{r}$, then

$$d\omega = \frac{dA}{r^2}$$

Dimensions of solid angle. The solid angle has no dimensions.

Unit. The unit of solid angle is a *steradian*. If in the relation $d\omega = \frac{dA}{r^2}$; $dA = r^2$

Then $d\omega = 1$ steradian

$\therefore$ *A steradian is defined as the solid angle subtended at the centre of a sphere by a surface area equal to the square of the radius of the sphere.*

Solid angle in spherical polar co-ordinates. As proved in Q. 2.26, out of the three areas $(d\vec{A})_r$, $(d\vec{A})_\theta$ and $(d\vec{A})_\phi$ only the area $(d\vec{A})_r$ is perpendicular to $\hat{r}$. All other areas are in the plane containing $\hat{r}$. Hence it is only the area $(d\vec{A})_r$ which subtends a solid angle at O. The magnitude of the area $(d\vec{A})_r = r^2 \sin\theta \, d\theta \, d\phi$

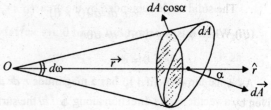

Fig. 2.26

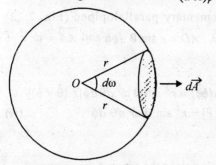

Fig. 2.27

$\therefore$ The solid angle subtended by the area $(dA)_r$ at O

$$d\omega = \frac{(dA)_r}{r^2} = \frac{r^2 \sin\theta \, d\theta \, d\phi}{r^2} = \sin\theta \, d\theta \, d\phi \quad ...(i)$$

Solid angle subtended at the centre of the sphere. Consider an elementary area dA on the surface of the sphere as shown in Fig. 2.27. The solid angle subtended by the area at the centre O of the sphere in spherical polar co-ordinates is given by relation (i)

$$d\omega = \sin\theta \, d\theta \, d\phi$$

The solid angle subtended at the centre of the sphere by the whole of its surface is obtained by integrating the expression for $d\omega = \sin\theta \, d\theta \, d\phi$ with respect to θ from 0 to π and with respect to ϕ from 0 to 2π.

$$\therefore \quad \omega = \int_{\theta=0}^{\pi} \int_{\phi=0}^{2\pi} \sin\theta \, d\theta \, d\phi = \int_0^{\pi} \sin\theta \, d\theta \int_0^{2\pi} d\phi$$

$$= [-\cos\theta]_0^{\pi} \, [\phi]_0^{2\pi} = (1+1) \, 2\pi = 4\pi \text{ steradian}$$

Q. 2.28. (a) Show that only one type of area element in spherical polar co-ordinates subtends a solid angle at the origin. *(P.U., 1992)*

(b) Determine the surface area of a sphere of radius r by using spherical polar co-ordinates. *(P.U. 2009)*

Ans. (*a*) (*i*) **When r is a constant but θ and ϕ are variable.** The area $(d\vec{A})_r$ is given by

$$(d\vec{A})_r = r^2 \sin\theta \, d\theta \, d\phi \, \hat{r}$$

$\therefore$ $|d\vec{A}_r| = r^2 \sin\theta \, d\theta \, d\phi$

Solid angle subtended at the centre $= \dfrac{|d\vec{A}_r|}{r^2}$

$$\therefore \qquad d\omega = \frac{r^2 \sin\theta \, d\theta \, d\phi}{r^2}$$

or $\qquad\qquad d\omega = \sin\theta \, d\theta \, d\phi$

(ii) **When θ is constant but r and ϕ are variable.** The area $(\vec{dA})_\theta$ is given by

$$(\vec{dA})_\theta = r \sin\theta \, d\phi \, dr \, \hat{\theta}$$

As $\hat{\theta}$ is perpendicular to $\hat{r}$, the component of the area $(\vec{dA})_\theta$ in the direction of increasing r is given by $|d\vec{A_\theta}| \cos 90° = 0$ i.e., the area is co-planar with r.

$\therefore$ The solid angle subtended by the area $(\vec{dA})_\theta$ at the centre $= 0$

(iii) **When ϕ is constant but r and θ are variable.** The area $(\vec{dA})_\phi$ is given by

$$(\vec{dA})_\phi = r \, dr \, d\theta \hat{\phi}$$

As $\hat{\phi}$ is perpendicular to $\hat{r}$, the component of area $(\vec{dA})_\phi$ in the direction of increasing r is given by

$$|d\vec{A_\phi}| \cos 90° = 0$$

i.e., the area is co-planar with r.

$\therefore$ The solid angle subtended by the area $(\vec{dA})_\phi$ at the centre $= 0$.

Hence only one type of area element $(\vec{dA})_r$ for which the area vector is along $\hat{r}$, i.e., the area is perpendicular to the direction of $\hat{r}$ subtends a solid angle at the centre.

(b) **Surface area of a sphere.** Consider a sphere of radius r with centre O. Let $\vec{dA}$ be a small area on the surface of this sphere. For this area, r is constant and only other spherical co-ordinates θ and ϕ are variable. The area is, therefore, given by

$$(\vec{dA})_r = r^2 \sin\theta \, d\theta d \, \phi \hat{r}$$

[For proof See Q. 2.2.6(i) *Area ABCD*]

$$\therefore \qquad dA = r^2 \sin\theta \, d\theta d \, \phi$$

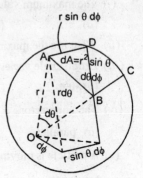

Fig. 2.28.

The total area of the surface of the sphere is obtained by integrating the expression for $dA = r^2 \sin\theta \, d\theta d \, \phi$ with respect to θ from 0 to π, and with respect to ϕ from 0 to 2π.

$$\therefore \qquad A = r^2 \int_0^\pi \sin\theta \, d\theta \int_0^{2\pi} d\phi = r^2 \left[-\cos\theta\right]_0^\pi \left[\phi\right]_0^{2\pi}$$

$$= r^2 [1+1][2\pi] = 4\pi r^2$$

Q. 2.29. Show that the solid angle subtended by a ring element cut from a sphere of radius R is given by $d\omega = 4\pi \sin\theta/2 \cos\theta/2 \, d\theta$ where θ is the angle between the normal through the centre of the ring and the line joining centre of the sphere with a point on the internal circumference and $d\theta$ is the angular width of the element. (*G.N.D.U.* 2008; *P.U.*, 1996; *H.P.U.*, 1992)

Ans. Solid angle subtended by a ring element. Consider a ring element $ABCD$ of radius r and thickness AB cut from a sphere of radius R as shown in Fig. 2.29.

Let B be a point on the internal circumference of the ring and OP the normal through the centre of the ring, then

$$\angle BOP = \theta$$

Angular width of the ring element $= \angle AOB = d\theta$

$\therefore$ Width of the ring $= AB = Rd\theta$

Radius of the ring $= BE = r = R \sin \theta$

$\therefore$ Area of the surface of the ring element

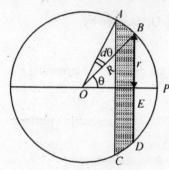

Fig. 2.29

$= $ Circumference of the ring $\times$ width $= 2\pi r \times Rd\theta$

$= 2\pi R \sin \theta \times Rd\theta = 2\pi R^2 \sin \theta \, d\theta$

Solid angle subtended by the ring at O

$$d\omega = \frac{\text{Area of the surface of the ring}}{R^2} = \frac{2\pi R^2 \sin \theta \, d\theta}{R^2}$$

$$= 2\pi \sin \theta \, d\theta$$

$$= 2\pi \times 2 \sin \frac{\theta}{2} \cos \frac{\theta}{2} d\theta$$

$$= 4\pi \sin \frac{\theta}{2} \cos \frac{\theta}{2} d\theta$$

2.30. Mark the correct answer

(i) The maximum value of θ in spherical polar co-ordinates can be

    (a) $\pi/2$ (b) π (c) 2π (d) none of these   (H.P.U., 1993)

(ii) What are the maximum values of θ and ϕ in polar co-ordinates?   (G.N.D.U., 1994)

(iii) Zenith angle varies from

    (a) 0 to 2π (b) 0 to π (c) 0 to $\pi/2$ (d) $-\pi$ to $+\pi$ (P.U., 1993)

(iv) The unit vectors $\hat{r}, \hat{\theta}$ and $\hat{\phi}$ are

    (a) parallel   (b) perpendicular   (c) none of these   (H.P.U., 1991)

(v) A particle is moving in a plane; its velocity $\vec{v}$ is given by

    (a) $r\dot{\theta}\hat{r}$ (b) $\dot{r}\hat{r} + r\dot{\theta}\hat{\theta}$ (c) $\dot{r}\hat{r}$ (d) $r\dot{\theta}\hat{\theta}$

(vi) Total vector surface area of a closed volume is

    (a) $\vec{A}_x \cdot \vec{A}_y \cdot \vec{A}_z$ (b) $\vec{A}_x \times \vec{A}_y \times \vec{A}_z$ (c) Null vector.   (H.P.U., 1995)

(vii) The area of an elementary surface $(d\vec{A})_r$ in spherical polar co-ordinates when radial vector is constant is given by

    (a) $r \sin \theta \, dr \, d\phi \, \hat{\theta}$ (b) $r dr \, d\theta \hat{\phi}$ (c) $r^2 \sin \theta \, d\theta \, d\phi \hat{r}$

    (d) $r \sin \theta \, dr \, d\phi \hat{r}$

(viii) The volume element in spherical polar co-ordinates is

    (a) $r \, dr \sin \theta \, d\theta \, d\phi$ (b) $r^2 \, dr \sin \theta \, d\phi$ (c) $r^2 \, dr \sin \theta \, d\theta \, d\phi$ (H.P.U., 1993)

(ix) Solid angle $d\omega$ subtended by a small surface element $(d\vec{A})_\theta$ when θ is kept constant at the origin is

    (a) $\sin \theta \, d\theta \, d\phi$ (b) zero   (c) $\sin \theta \, dr \, d\theta$ (d) $dr \, d\theta \, d\phi$

(x) A spherical surface subtends at its centre an angle of

    (a) π (b) 2π (c) 4π steradian   (H.P.U., 1991)

(xi) Solid angle subtended by a closed surface of any shape at any point lying well within it is

    (a) 0   (b) 2π (c) $2\pi/3$ (d) 4π (H.P.U., 2001)

(xii) Is area a vector or scalar? What do you know about volume?   (P.U., 1996)

Ans.   (i) b   (ii) $\theta = \pi, \ \phi = 2\pi$ (iii) b   (iv) b

        (v) b   (vi) c   (vii) c   (viii) c

        (ix) b   (x) c   (xi) d

(xii) Area is a vector. Volume is scalar.

EXERCISES

1. The motion of a particle can be expressed in terms of the following parametric equations:

$$x = 5t^2 - 7; \ y = 7 \cos t \text{ and } z = 3 \sin t.$$

Find the magnitude of instantaneous velocity and acceleration of the particle.

$$\left[\textbf{Ans.} \ |v| = \sqrt{9 + 40 \sin^2 t + 100 \, t^2} \right.$$

$$\left. |a| = \sqrt{109 + 40 \cos^2 t} \right]$$

2. A particle moving in the X-Y plane has co-ordinates $(4t, 4t^2)$ m at any instant. Find the velocity of the particle.   (P.U., 2000)

                                          [**Ans.** $(4\hat{i} + 8\hat{j})$]

3. The motion of a particle is observed for 10 sec. and is found to be in accord with the following equation

$$r = R \text{ (a constant)}, \ \theta = \frac{\pi}{12}t \text{ and } \phi = \pi t$$

Find the velocity and acceleration of the particle at an arbitrary time $t < 10$ sec.

                                          (G.N.D.U., 1990)

Hint. $v = \dot{r}\hat{r} + r\dot{\theta}\hat{\theta} + r \sin \theta \dot{\phi}\hat{\phi}$

and $a = (\ddot{r} - r\dot{\theta}^2 - r\dot{\phi}^2 \sin^2 \theta)\hat{r} + (2\dot{r}\dot{\theta} + r\ddot{\theta} - r \sin \theta \cos \theta \dot{\phi}^2)\hat{\theta}$

                                    $+ (2\dot{r}\dot{\phi}\sin \theta + 2r \cos \theta \dot{\theta}\dot{\phi} + r \sin \theta \ddot{\phi})\hat{\phi}$

$$\left[\textbf{Ans.} \ |\vec{v}| = \left(\frac{\pi R}{12}\right)\left[1 + 144 \sin^2 \frac{\pi t}{12}\right]^{1/2}\right.$$

$$\left. |\vec{a}| = \frac{\pi^2 R}{144}\left(577 + 204485 \sin^2 \frac{\pi t}{12}\right)^{1/2}\right]$$

3

Conservation of Momentum and Energy

Q. 3.1. What was Newton's notion of space? What are the classical properties of space? What is Eucledian flatness of space? What is the meaning of isotropy of space? Distinguish between homogeneity and isotropy of space.

(P.U. 2000; *G.N.D.U.,* 1995; *Pbi. U.,* 1991; *H.P.U.,* 1992, 1991)

Ans. Newton's notion of space. According to Newton, *'Absolute space in its own nature without relation to anything external remains always similar and immovable.'* According to Newton, *main classical properties* of space are :

1. Space is three dimensional. The concept of space and time is fundamental to the study of mechanics. All objects occupy space and have a length, a breadth and a height. Space is, therefore, *three dimensional.* This is why the position of a point can be specified completely by the three co-ordinates (x, y, z) or (r, θ, ϕ).

2. Space is flat. Space is flat *i.e.,* it possesses *Eucledian flatness.* This means that the shortest distance between any *two* points in space is a straight line. If we take *three* points in space to form a triangle, the sum of angles is equal to π. If it is a right angled triangle, then the three sides are related by Pythagoras Theorem *i.e.,* Hypotenuse^2 = Base^2 + Altitude^2.

However, according to latest theory, space is *not exactly flat* but somewhat curved. The departure from flatness is very small and can be ignored in the study of classical mechanics.

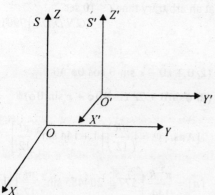

Fig. 3.1

3. Space is homogeneous. In other words, *space is everywhere alike. Homogeneity of free space* (a space in which fields and forces are absent) means *translational invariance* of its properties *i.e.,* the result of an experiment is not altered due to linear displacement of the co-ordinate systems.

For further details see **Q. 3.5** (*a*).

4. Space is isotropic. It means that if we consider a point *O* in space and we move from this point in any direction, the properties are the same *i.e.,* there is nothing to distinguish one direction from the other. In other words, there is no preferred direction in space or one direction is as good as any other direction.

Distinction between homogeneity and isotropy. The *homogeneity* of space means *translational invariance* of the properties of space.

If we consider two co-ordinate systems S and S' displaced with respect to one another as shown in Fig. 3.1, then an experiment performed in system S will give exactly the same results in the system S'.

On the other hand, *isotropy* means *rotational invariance* of free space.

Thus, if we have two co-ordinate systems S and S' rotating with respect to one another as shown in Fig. 3.2, then again an experiment performed in system S will give exactly the same result in system S'.

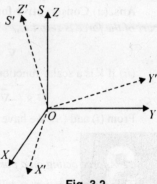

Fig. 3.2

Q. 3.2. What is linear momentum? State and explain the principle of conservation of linear momentum with examples. (*A.U.*, 1994; *V.S.U.*, 1992)

Ans. Linear momentum. *The linear momentum of a body is defined as the product of its mass and linear velocity.* If m is the mass of the body and $\vec{v}$ its velocity, then

Linear momentum $\qquad \vec{p} = m\vec{v}$

It is a *vector* quantity. Its units are kg ms^{-1}.

Principle of conservation of linear momentum. It states, "*The total linear momentum of a system of particles free from the action of external forces and subjected only to their mutual interaction remains constant, no matter how complicated the forces are.*"

Mathematically, according to Newton's second law of motion $\vec{F} = \dfrac{d\vec{p}}{dt}$ where $\vec{F}$ is the applied external force acting on the system. If for an isolated system the external force is absent, $\vec{F} = 0$

$\therefore \qquad\qquad \dfrac{d\vec{p}}{dt} = 0 \text{ or } \vec{p} = \text{a constant}$

i.e., the total momentum of the system remains constant.

Example. When a bullet is fired from a gun, the bullet of mass m moves forward with a velocity $\vec{v}$ and the gun of mass M kicks backward with a velocity $\vec{V}$.

Momentum of the bullet in the forward direction $= m\vec{v}$

Momentum of the gun in the backward direction $= -M\vec{V}$.

Now $\qquad\qquad m\vec{v} = -M\vec{V} \quad \text{or} \quad m\vec{v} + M\vec{V} = 0$

This shows that the total momentum of the bullet and the gun which was zero before the bullet was fired remains the same even after firing the bullet *i.e.*, the linear momentum is conserved.

Q. 3.3. (*a*) What are conservative and non-conservative forces? Give examples of each.

(*H.P.U.* 1999; *G.N.D.U.* 2000)

(*b*) **The potential energy of a particle under the action of force is**

$$V = 2x^4 + 3x^2$$

Find the force acting on the particle. (*Pbi. U.* 2007)

Ans. (a) Conservative forces. (*i*) *A force* $\vec{F}$ *acting on a particle is a conservative force if the curl of the force is zero i.e.,*

$$\vec{\nabla} \times \vec{F} = 0 \qquad \qquad ...(i)$$

(*ii*) If V is a scalar function of co-ordinates of the particle, then

$$\vec{\nabla} \times (-\vec{\nabla} V) = 0 \qquad \qquad ...(ii)$$

From (*i*) and (*ii*), we have

$$\vec{F} = -\vec{\nabla} V \qquad \qquad ...(iii)$$

∴ *A force acting on a particle is conservative if it is given by the gradient of a scalar function V.*

This scalar function is called the *potential energy* of the particle.

When the force is acting along the X-axis

$$\vec{F} = F\hat{i} \qquad \qquad ...(iv)$$

Accoring to relation (*iii*)

$$\vec{F} = -\vec{\nabla} V$$

$$= -\frac{\partial V}{\partial x}\hat{i} - \frac{\partial V}{\partial y}\hat{j} - \frac{\partial V}{\partial z}\hat{k} \qquad \qquad ...(v)$$

Comparing the co-efficients of $\hat{i}$ in (*iv*) and (*v*)

$$F = -\frac{\partial V}{\partial x}$$

(*iii*) If the force $\vec{F}$ acting on the particle displaces it from the position A to B, then work done by the force

$$W = \int_A^B \vec{F} \cdot \vec{dr}$$

If $\vec{F}$ is a conservative force $\vec{F} = -\vec{\nabla} V$ and $W = \int_A^B -\vec{\nabla} V \cdot d\vec{r}$

Now $\qquad \vec{\nabla} V = \frac{\partial V}{\partial x}\hat{i} + \frac{\partial V}{\partial y}\hat{j} + \frac{\partial V}{\partial z}\hat{k}$ and $d\vec{r} = dx\hat{i} + dy\hat{j} + dz\hat{k}$

∴ $\qquad \vec{\nabla} V \cdot d\vec{r} = \frac{\partial V}{\partial x}dx + \frac{\partial V}{\partial y}dy + \frac{\partial V}{\partial z}dz = dV$

∴ $\qquad W = \int_A^B -\vec{\nabla} V \cdot d\vec{r} = -\int_A^B dV = V_A - V_B$

i.e., the work done depends only on the value of potential function V at the initial and final positions but is independent of the path joining A and B.

Hence, '*A force $\vec{F}$ acting on a particle is conservative if the work done in taking the particle from one point to the other depends only on the initial and final positions but is independent of the actual path.*'

Non-conservative force. A force $\vec{F}$ acting on a particle is non-conservative if

(*i*) The curl of the force does not vanish *i.e.* $\vec{\nabla} \times \vec{F} \neq 0$.

or *(ii)* It cannot be expressed as the gradient of a scalar function, and

(iii) The work done in moving the particle from one point to another depends upon the actual path of displacement.

Examples. Conservative forces *(i)* The gravitational force between two masses

(ii) The coulomb force between two stationary charges.

Non - conservative forces. *(i)* Exchange forces in nuclear Physics

(ii) Forces between moving charges.

(b) Given $V = 2x^4 + 3x^2$

Now force $F = -\dfrac{dV}{dx} = -\dfrac{d}{dx}(2x^4 + 3x^2) = -8x^3 - 6x$

or $F = -(8x^3 + 6x)$ is the required force.

Q. 3.4. Derive the law of conservation of linear momentum from Newton's laws of motion.

Ans. Law of conservation of linear momentum. According to Newton's first law of motion, *"A body remains at rest or continues to move with a uniform velocity if no external force is acting on it."* According to Newton's second law of motion, *"The rate of change of momentum of a body is proportional to the force acting on it."* Mathematically, if a particle of mass m is moving with a velocity $\vec{v}$, its linear momentum $\vec{p} = m\vec{v}$

When a force $\vec{F}$ is applied to it, the momentum changes at the rate $\dfrac{d\vec{p}}{dt}$

$\therefore$ $\vec{F} = \dfrac{d\vec{p}}{dt} = \dfrac{d(m\vec{v})}{dt}$

Clearly when $\vec{F} = 0$, $\dfrac{d\vec{p}}{dt} = 0$ or $\vec{p} = m\vec{v}$ = a constant

i.e., a particle continues to move with a constant velocity. *Thus Newton's first law of motion is only a special case of second law.*

Now consider a system of two particles which are acted only by forces of interaction like Coulomb's forces or gravitational forces and *no external forces act on the system.* Let $\vec{F}_{12}$ be the force exerted by the first particle on the second, known as **action** and $\vec{F}_{21}$ the force exerted by the second on the first, known as **reaction**, then according to Newton's third law of motion, *action and reaction being equal and opposite.* $\vec{F}_{12} = -\vec{F}_{21}$

According to Newton's second law of motion,

$$\vec{F}_{12} = \dfrac{d\vec{p}_2}{dt} = \dfrac{d(m_2\vec{v}_2)}{dt} = m_2 \dfrac{d\vec{v}_2}{dt}$$

where m_2, $\vec{v}_2$ and $\vec{p}_2$ are the mass, velocity and momentum of the second particle.

Similarly $\vec{F}_{21} = \dfrac{d\vec{p}_1}{dt} = \dfrac{d}{dt}(m_1\vec{v}_1) = m_1 \dfrac{d\vec{v}_1}{dt}$

where m_1, $\vec{v}_1$ and $\vec{p}_1$ are the mass, velocity and momentum of the first particle.

$\because$ $\vec{F}_{12} = -\vec{F}_{21}$ $\vec{F}_{12} + \vec{F}_{21} = 0$

or $\dfrac{d\vec{p}_1}{dt} + \dfrac{d\vec{p}_2}{dt} = 0$ or $\dfrac{d}{dt}(\vec{p}_1 + \vec{p}_2) = 0$

Integrating, we have $\vec{p_1} + \vec{p_2} =$ a constant   or $m_1 \vec{v_1} + m_2 \vec{v_2} =$ a constant

The quantity $\vec{p_1} + \vec{p_2} = m_1 \vec{v_1} + m_2 \vec{v_2}$ represents the total linear momentum of the system. Hence we conclude that

'If Newton's second and third law of motion hold good, the total linear momentum of the system of two particles remains constant'. The above law can be extended to a system of three or more interacting particles. The law of conservation of linear momentum is, therefore, a basic law and is stated as under :

"The total linear momentum of a system of particles free from the action of external forces and subjected only to their mutual interaction remains constant, no matter how complicated the forces are."

Q. 3.5. (a) What does the term translational invariance of space imply? Explain.

(Pbi. U. 2002, 2001; G.N.D.U., 1994)

(b) Show that the linear uniformity of space leads to Newton's third law of motion and hence to the law of conservation of linear momentum.   *(P.U. 2008; M.D.U. 2003; Pbi. U., 1995, 1991)*

OR

Prove that law of conservation of linear momentum is a consequence of homogeneity of space.   *(Pbi. U. 2007, 2008; G.N.D.U., 2007, 2004)*

Ans. (a) Translational invariance. Translational invariance of the properties of free space is due to the homogeneity of free space.

To understand it, consider two inertial frames of reference S and S' with their X-axes along the same line and Y and Z axes parallel to each other. The origin O' of S' is displaced by a distance b along the positive direction of X-axis. If x and x' are the co-ordinates of a point in the two systems respectively, then x' = x – b.

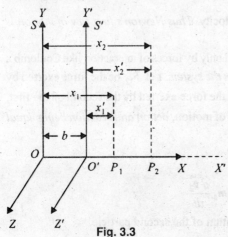

Fig. 3.3

Let there be two particles P_1 and P_2 lying on the X-axis of inertial systems, the x-co-ordinates of P_1 being x_1 and x_1' and those of P_2 being x_2 and x_2' in the systems S and S' respectively. Suppose the two particles have masses m_1 and m_2 respectively and exert gravitational forces on each other, then the force between two particles being only due to their mutual interaction is a conservative force and is given by $F_x = -\dfrac{\partial U}{\partial x}$ where U is the potential energy of the particle and x its co-ordinate on the X-axis.

The form of the function U should be such that it is a *scalar function and force derived from it is independent of the inertial system*, i.e.,

$$F_x = -\frac{\partial U}{dx} = -\frac{\partial U'}{\partial x'}$$

where U and U' are the potential energies and x and x' the co-ordinates of the particle in the S and S' systems respectively. Since U is a function of x_1 and x_2 the co-ordinates of the two particles, the various simple forms which satisfy the above two conditions are

$$U = a|(x_1 - x_2)|, \quad U = \frac{a}{|(x_1 - x_2)|}, \quad U = (x_1 - x_2)^2$$

We shall select the last form because even if $x_1 - x_2$ is a vector, $(x_1 - x_2)^2$ is a scalar quantity.

$\therefore \qquad\qquad U(x_1, x_2) = (x_1 - x_2)^2,$

and $\qquad\qquad U(x_1', x_2') = (x_1' - x_2')^2$

$\qquad\qquad\qquad\qquad = [(x_1 - b) - (x_2 - b)]^2 = (x_1 - x_2)^2 = U(x_1, x_2)$

This shows that the above form of potential energy function U is independent of the co-ordinate system or the frame of reference.

The physical meaning of the above relation is that U is independent of the absolute value of x_1 and x_2 as long as $(x_1 - x_2)^2$ is the same. In other words, so long as the magnitude of $|x_1 - x_2|$ remains constant, it is immaterial where two particles are situated along the x-axis. This means that the properties of space are independent of the positions of x_1 and x_2 or the *free space possesses linear uniformity or has translational invariance.*

(b) **Law of conservation of linear momentum from linear uniformity or homogeneity of space.** We shall make use of the property of linear uniformity of space and the results obtained in part (a) to prove the law of conservation of linear momentum with the help of Newton's third law of motion. The linear uniformity of space demands that the force between the two particles P_1 and P_2 be independent of displacement between two frames of reference, *i.e.*,

$$F_x = -\frac{\partial U}{\partial x} = -\frac{\partial U'}{\partial x'}$$

The magnitude of the force on the particle P_1 acting along the X-axis

$$= F_{21} = -\frac{\partial U}{\partial x_1} = -\frac{\partial U'}{\partial x_1'}$$

The magnitude of the force on the particle P_2 acting along the X-axis

$$= F_{12} = -\frac{\partial U}{\partial x_2} = \frac{-\partial U'}{\partial x_2'}$$

If $\qquad\qquad U(x_1, x_2) = (x_1 - x_2)^2$ and $U(x_1', x_2') = (x_1' - x_2')^2$

the forces are independent of the frames of reference.

Put $x_1 - x_2 = s \qquad \therefore \frac{\partial s}{\partial x_1} = 1$ and $\frac{\partial s}{\partial x_2} = -1$

Hence $\qquad\qquad F_{21} = -\frac{\partial U}{\partial x_1} = -\left(\frac{\partial U}{\partial s}\right)\left(\frac{\partial s}{\partial x_1}\right) = \frac{-\partial U}{\partial s}$

and $\qquad\qquad F_{12} = -\frac{\partial U}{\partial x_2} = -\left(\frac{\partial U}{\partial s}\right)\left(\frac{\partial s}{\partial x_2}\right) = \frac{\partial U}{\partial s}$

$\therefore \qquad\qquad F_{12} = -F_{21}$

which is Newton's third law of motion.

Therefore, if free space possesses the property of linear uniformity, the forces and potentials are independent of the linear displacement of the frame of reference which as proved above leads to the third law of motion. We have already proved the law of conservation of momentum with the help of Newton's third law of motion. Hence the linear uniformity (or homogeneity) of space proves the law of conservation of momentum with the help of Newton's third law of motion.

Q. 3.6. Radioactive $_8O^{15}$ decays into $_7N^{15}$ by emitting a positron and a neutrino. The positron and the neutrino are observed to move at right angles to each other and carry momenta 2×10^{-22} and 5×10^{-23} kg m sec^{-1} respectively. Find the momentum of the recoiling nucleus.

Ans. Let the positron move along the $+X$ direction and the neutrino along $+Y$ direction with momenta $\vec{p_1} = 2 \times 10^{-22} = 20 \times 10^{-23}$ kg m sec^{-1} and $\vec{p_2} = 5 \times 10^{-23}$ kg m sec^{-1} respectively. If $\vec{P}$ is the momentum of the recoiling nucleus, then according to the principle of conservation of linear momentum

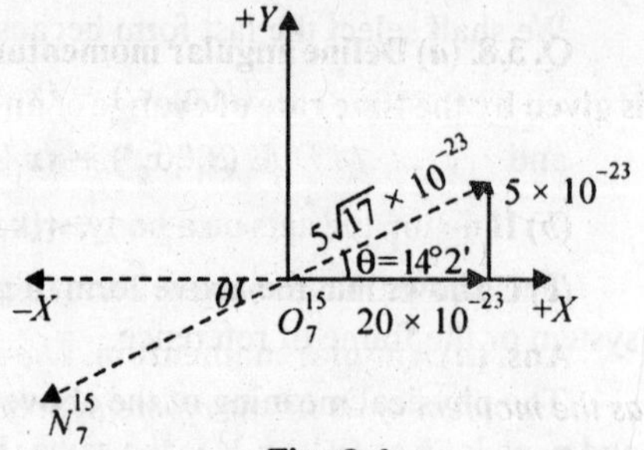

$$\vec{p_1} + \vec{p_2} + \vec{P} = 0 \quad \text{or} \quad \vec{P} = -(\vec{p_1} + \vec{p_2})$$

Now $\quad \left|\vec{p_1} + \vec{p_2}\right| = \sqrt{(20 \times 10^{-23})^2 + (5 \times 10^{-23})^2}$

$$= 5\sqrt{17} \times 10^{-23} \text{ kg m sec}^{-1}$$

Fig. 3.4

and its direction is given by

$$\tan \theta = \frac{5 \times 10^{-23}}{20 \times 10^{-23}} = \frac{1}{4} = 0.25$$

or $\qquad\qquad\qquad \theta = 14°2'$

$\therefore \vec{P} = 5\sqrt{17} \times 10^{-23}$ kg m sec^{-1} and it makes an angle $14°2'$ with $-X$ direction or $(180° + 14°2')$ = $194°2'$ with $+X$ direction.

Q. 3.7. A body at rest explodes and breaks up into three pieces. Two pieces of equal mass fly off perpendicular to one another with the same speed of 30 m/sec. The third piece has three times the mass of each of the other pieces. Find the magnitude and direction of the velocity immediately after explosion.

Ans. As the body is at rest, initial linear momentum = 0. Let $\vec{p_1}$ and $\vec{p_2}$ be the linear momentum of the two pieces of equal mass and $\vec{P}$ the linear momentum of the heavy mass, then according to the principle of conservation of linear momentum

$$\vec{p_1} + \vec{p_2} + \vec{P} = 0 \quad \text{or} \quad \vec{P} = -(\vec{p_1} + \vec{p_2})$$

As the two pieces of equal mass fly off perpendicular to one another, let one of them go towards $+X$ direction and the other in $+Y$ direction and m be their mass, then

$$\vec{p_1} = 30 \; m\hat{i} \quad \text{and} \quad \vec{p_2} = 30 \; m\hat{j}$$

$$\therefore \qquad \vec{P} = -[30\,m\hat{i} + 30\,m\hat{j}]$$

Let $\vec{v}$ be the velocity of the heavy mass $3m$.

$$\therefore \qquad \vec{P} = 3m\vec{v} = -[30\,m\hat{i} + 30\,m\hat{j}]$$

or $\qquad\qquad v = -10\hat{i} - 10\hat{j}$

$\therefore$ Magnitude of

$$\vec{v} = \sqrt{(-10)^2 + (-10)^2} = 10\sqrt{2} \; m/\text{sec}.$$

Direction of $\vec{v}$ is given by $\tan \theta = \dfrac{-10}{-10} = +1$

or $\theta = 45°$ with $-X$ direction or $180 + 45° = 225°$ with $+X$ direction.

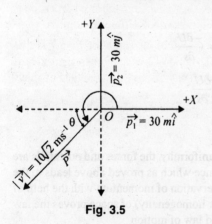

Fig. 3.5

Q. 3.8. (*a*) **Define angular momentum** $\vec{J}$ **and torque** $\vec{\tau}$ **. What are their units? Show that torque is given by the time rate of change of angular momentum.** (*Meerut U.* 2006, 2002; *M.D.U.* 2000; *Kerala U.* 2001; *A.U.,* 1995, 1993; *K.U.,* 1993, 1991; *Luck. U.* 1993)

(*b*) **If no torque acts on a body, will its angular velocity remain conserved?** (*P.U.,* 1996)

(*c*) **Can a particle rotate without experiencing any torque ? Explain.** (*P.U.* 2007)

Ans. (*a*) **Angular momentum.** *The angular momentum of a particle about a fixed point is defined as the moment of its linear momentum about that point.* It is measured by the vector product of linear momentum $\vec{p} = m\vec{v}$ of the particle and its vector distance $\vec{r}$ from the fixed point in the inertial frame.

∴ Angular momentum $\quad \vec{J} = \vec{r} \times \vec{p} = \vec{r} \times m\vec{v}$

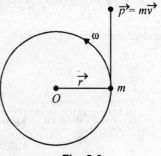

Angular momentum being the vector product of two vectors is obviously a *vector* quantity. Its direction is perpendicular both to $\vec{r}$ and $\vec{P}$ or $\vec{v}$ as given by the right hand screw rule.

Angular momentum of a particle. In the case of a particle of mass *m* describing a circle of radius *r* with a uniform angular velocity of magnitude ω and linear velocity $v = r\omega$, the magnitude of the angular momentum $= mvr = mr^2\omega$ and its direction is perpendicular to the plane of the circle.

Fig. 3.6

In a general case also, the magnitude of the angular momentum of a particle is given by

$$|\vec{J}| = r\,(mv) = r\,(mr\omega) = mr^2\omega$$

$$= mr^2 \frac{d\theta}{dt} = mr^2\,\dot\theta \qquad\qquad\qquad ...(i)$$

Angular momentum of a rigid body. *The sum of the moments of the linear momentum of all the particles of a rotating rigid body about the axis of rotation is called its angular momentum.*

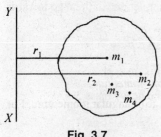

Fig. 3.7

When a body is free to rotate about an axis the angular velocity of all the particles, at whatever distance they may be, is the same. Since the distance of the various particles from the axis of rotation is not the same, their linear velocities will be different.

Consider the particles $m_1, m_2...$ of the rigid body lying at distances $r_1, r_2...$ from the axis of rotation *XY* and having magnitudes of linear velocities $v_1, v_2 ...$ respectively. If ω is the magnitude of angular velocity, then

Linear velocity of the particle $m_1 = v_1 = r_1\omega$

∴ Magnitude of linear momentum of the particle $m_1 = m_1 v_1 = m_1 r_1 \omega$.

Hence the magnitude of moment of linear momentum or angular momentum of the particle m_1 about the axis of rotation $= m_1\,v_1\,r_1 = m_1\,r_1^2\,\omega$.

Similarly the moment of linear momentum or angular momentum of the particle m_2 about the axis of rotation $= m_2\,v_2\,r_2 = m_2\,r_2^2\omega$

∴ Sum of the magnitudes of moments of linear momentum or angular momentum of all the particles $= m_1\,r_1^2\,\omega + m_2\,r_2^2\,\omega +...$ or $J = \Sigma\,m\,r^2\omega = I\omega$

where $I = \Sigma mr^2$ = moment of inertia of the rigid body about the axis of rotation and *J* is the magnitude of the angular momentum.

Vectorially $\vec{J} = I\vec{\omega}$

Hence the angular momentum of a rigid body is the product of its moment of inertia and angular velocity.

Units. The unit of angular momentum is Kg m^2 s^{-1} or Joule sec.

Torque. *If a force $\vec{F}$ acts on a particle at a point P whose position with respect to the origin O of the inertial frame is given by the displacement vector $\vec{r}$, the torque $\vec{\tau}$ on the particle with respect to the origin O is defined as $\vec{\tau} = \vec{r} \times \vec{F}$.*

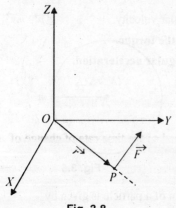

Fig. 3.8

Torque is a vector quantity. Its direction is normal to the plane formed by $\vec{r}$ and $\vec{F}$ and the sense is given by the right hand rule for the cross product of two vectors.

Units. The unit of torque is Newton metre (*Nm*).

Torque as the time rate of change of angular momentum. The angular momentum

$$\vec{J} = \vec{r} \times \vec{p}$$

Differentiating this expression with respect to time, we get

$$\frac{d\vec{J}}{dt} = \frac{d}{dt}(\vec{r} \times \vec{p}) = \frac{d\vec{r}}{dt} \times \vec{p} + \vec{r} \times \frac{d\vec{p}}{dt}$$

But $\dfrac{d\vec{r}}{dt} \times \vec{p} = \vec{v} \times m\vec{v} = m(\vec{v} \times \vec{v}) = 0$

and $\dfrac{dp}{dt}$ = rate of change of linear momentum

                                            = $\vec{F}$ the force acting on the particle

$\therefore$ $\dfrac{d\vec{J}}{dt} = \vec{r} \times \vec{F}$

But $\vec{r} \times \vec{F}$ is the torque $\vec{\tau}$ acting on the particle

$\therefore$ Torque $= \dfrac{d\vec{J}}{dt} = \vec{\tau} = \vec{r} \times \vec{F}$

Hence torque is also defined as the time rate of change of angular momentum.

Torque on a rigid body. Torque is defined as the time rate of change of angular momentum. For a rigid body, Angular momentum $\vec{J} = I\vec{\omega}$

$\therefore$ Torque $\tau = \dfrac{d\vec{J}}{dt} = I\dfrac{d\vec{\omega}}{dt} = I\vec{\alpha}$

where $\vec{\alpha}$ is the angular acceleration.

$\therefore$ Torque on a rigid body is the product of moment of inertia and angular acceleration.

(*b*) Torque $\vec{\tau} = I\vec{\alpha} = I\dfrac{d\vec{\omega}}{dt}$

If no torque acts on a body $\vec{\tau} = 0$

$\therefore$ $I\dfrac{d\vec{\omega}}{dt} = 0$. As I cannot be zero, $\dfrac{d\omega}{dt} = 0$ or $\vec{\omega}$ = is a constant.

$\therefore$ Angular velocity remains conserved.

(c) Yes, a particle can rotate without experiencing any torque. In order that a particle may rotate, it is necessary that it should possess an angular momentum. Torque may or may not be acting on the particle.

Angular momentum $\vec{J} = I\omega$

Therefore, when a particle rotates with uniform angular velocity $\vec{\omega}$, it only requires an angular momentum.

$$\text{Torque } \tau = I\alpha = I\frac{d\omega}{dt}$$

Therefore, a torque is required only if there is a change in angular velocity.

3.9. (a) Establish the vector relation between the force and the torque.

(b) (i) Establish the relation between torque applied and angular acceleration.

(Kan. U. 1995, 1993)

(ii) A torque of 1 Nm is applied to a wheel of mass 10 Kg and radius of gyration 50 cm. What is the resulting acceleration? *(K.U. 2002)*

Ans. (a) Relation between force and torque. Torque is defined as the time rate of change of angular momentum.

$\therefore$ Torque $\qquad \vec{\tau} = \dfrac{d\vec{J}}{dt}$

but $\qquad\qquad \vec{J} = \vec{r} \times \vec{p}$

Now $\qquad \dfrac{d\vec{J}}{dt} = \dfrac{d}{dt}(r \times p) = \dfrac{d\vec{r}}{dt} \times \vec{p} + \vec{r} \times \dfrac{d\vec{p}}{dt}$

But $\qquad \dfrac{d\vec{r}}{dt} \times \vec{p} = \vec{v} \times m\vec{v} = m(\vec{v} \times \vec{v}) = 0$

$\therefore \qquad\qquad \vec{\tau} = \vec{r} \times \dfrac{d\vec{p}}{dt} = \vec{r} \times \vec{F} \qquad\qquad \left[\because \vec{F} = \dfrac{d\vec{p}}{dt} \right]$

$\therefore$ Torque is the vector product of position vector $\vec{r}$ and force $\vec{F}$

(b) (i) Relation between torque and angular acceleration

$\qquad\qquad$ Torque $\vec{\tau} = I\vec{\alpha}$

For proof See **Q. 3.8.** *'Torque on a rigid body'*.

(ii) Here mass of the wheel $M = 10$ Kg

$\qquad$ Radius of gyration $K = 50$ cm $= 0.5$ m

Moment of inertia of the wheel $I = MK^2$

$\qquad\qquad\qquad\qquad = 10 \times 0.5 \times 0.5 = 2.5$ kg m^2

$\qquad$ Torque $\tau = 1$ Nm

Now $\tau = I\alpha$ where α is the angular acceleration

$\therefore \qquad\qquad\qquad \alpha = \dfrac{\tau}{I} = \dfrac{1}{2.5} = 0.4$ rad s^{-2}

Q. 3.10. (a) State and explain the law of conservation of angular momentum. Illustrate with examples. What are the consequences of the law of conservation of angular momentum?

(G. N.D.U. 2001; Luck. U. 2001; Meerut U. 2001; Gauhati U. 2000; Bang. U. 2000; P.U. 1994; Kan. U. 1991; Gharwal U. 1999)

(b) **Explain why an ice skater always utilises the principle of conservation of angular momentum.**

(*M.D.U.* 2000)

Ans. (*a*) **Law of conservation of angular momentum.** It states that *"When the total external torque acting on a system of particles is zero, the total angular momentum of the system remains constant."*

When there is no external torque acting on a system of particles $\vec{\tau} = 0$

Now torque $\tau = \dfrac{d\vec{J}}{dt}$ where $\vec{J}$ is the total angular momentum of the system.

$$\therefore \quad \dfrac{d\vec{J}}{dt} = 0 \quad \text{or} \quad \vec{J} = \text{a constant.}$$

i.e. when there is no external torque acting on a system of particles, the total angular momentum of the system remains constant.

Examples and Consequences. (*i*) Suppose a person carrying heavy weights in his hands stretched out is standing on a rotating platform. When the person suddenly folds his arms, his moment of Inertia *I* decreases. As angular momentum $\vec{L} = I\vec{\omega}$ is constant, the angular velocity $\vec{\omega}$ of his body which is the same as the angular velocity of the rotating platform increases.

(*ii*) The angular speed of the inner layers of whirlwind (or tornado) is always very high. In a whirlwind, air from nearby regions gets concentrated in a small space thereby decreasing the moment of inertia *I*. As angular momentum $\vec{L} = I\vec{\omega} = $ constant, $\vec{\omega}$ increases and attains very high values as *I* decreases.

(*iii*) The angular velocity of revolution of a planet around the Sun in an elliptic orbit increases when the planet comes closer to the Sun and vice-versa.

(*iv*) As the motion of the earth around the Sun is under gravitational force which is a central force, the angular momentum of the earth moving round the sun is conserved. When the earth is at the *perihilion i.e.* closest to the sun, the angular velocity is *maximum* and when the earth is at the *apehilion, i.e.* farthest away from the sun, its angular velocity is *minimum*.

(*b*) **Ice-Skater.** During the course of the performance an ice-skater (or a ballet dancer) takes advantage of the principle of conservation of angular momentum by stretching out its arms and legs or vice-versa. On doing so the moment of inertia increases / decreases and hence angular velocity decreases/increases.

Q. 3.11. (*a*) **State the principle of conservation of angular momentum. Show that the angular momentum of a particle under the influence of a central force always remains constant.**

(*G.N.D.U.* 2001)

(*b*) **What is the difference between linear momentum and angular momentum ?**

(*G.N.D.U.* 2006)

Ans. (*a*) **Principle of conservation of angular momentum.** See Q. 3.10.

Angular momentum remains constant under a central force. From the relation $\vec{\tau} = \dfrac{d\vec{J}}{dt} = \vec{r} \times \vec{F}$ we find that the torque acting on the particle is zero and hence the angular momentum remains conserved if (*i*) its position vector $\vec{r} = 0$, (*ii*) the force $\vec{F}$ applied to it is zero but if $\vec{r} \neq 0$ and $\vec{F} \neq 0$ the third condition that must be satisfied for $\vec{J} = $ constant is, (*iii*) the direction of both $\vec{r}$ and $\vec{F}$ should be the same *i.e.*, the line of action of the force passes through the fixed or the reference point. The third condition is satisfied in the case of a *central force, i.e.,* a force which is always directed towards or away from a fixed point.

Consider a particle subjected to a central force depending upon the distance from the fixed point. Such a force can be represented as $\vec{F} = f(r)\hat{r}$

where $f(r)$ is some scalar function of the distance and $\hat{r}$ is a unit vector along $\vec{r}$ given by $\dfrac{\vec{r}}{|\vec{r}|}$.

$$\therefore \quad \vec{\tau} = \frac{d\vec{J}}{dt} = \vec{r} \times \vec{F} = r \times f(r)\hat{r} = f(r)(\vec{r} \times \hat{r}) = f(r)\left(\vec{r} \times \frac{\vec{r}}{|\vec{r}|}\right) = 0 \quad [\because \vec{r} \times \vec{r} = 0]$$

$\therefore$ Torque acting on a particle under the influence of a central force = 0

$$\because \qquad \vec{\tau} = \frac{d\vec{J}}{dt} = 0 \quad \therefore \quad \vec{J} = \text{a constant}$$

Hence the angular momentum of a particle under the influence of a central force always remains constant.

(b) Difference between linear momentum and angular momentum. The linear momentum of a body $\vec{p}$ is the product of its mass (m) and linear velocity ($\vec{v}$)

or $$\vec{p} = m\vec{v}$$

The angular momentum $\vec{J}$ of the body is the product of its moment of inertia (I) and angular velocity $\vec{\omega}$

or $$\vec{J} = I\vec{\omega}$$

The angular momentum of a particle about a fixed point is also the moment of its linear momentum about that point and is measured by the vector product of linear momentum $\vec{p} = m\vec{v}$ of the particle and its vector distance $\vec{r}$ from the fixed point.

$$\therefore \qquad \vec{J} = \vec{r} \times \vec{p} = \vec{r} \times m\vec{v}$$

(For details see Q. 3.2 and Q. 3.8)

Q. 3.12. (a) What does the term rotational invariance (isotropy) of free space imply?

(b) Show that the property of rotational invariance of space (isotropy) leads to the law of conservation of angular momentum.

(*M.D.U.* 2003; *G.N.D.U.* 2008, 2007, 2004, 2002, 2001, 2000, 1996, 1994; *Pbi, U.* 2005, 2001, 2000, 1995, 1991; *P.U.* 2009, 2006, 2000, 1999; *H.P.U.* 2003, 1999, 1995, 1993)

Ans. (a) Isotropy and Rotational invariance of space. Space is *isotropic i.e.*, if we move in any direction from a point, there is nothing to distinguish one direction from another. For example, if we keep a particle P_1 fixed and move another particle P_2 on the surface of a sphere with P_1 as centre, the interaction energy between the two will be the same for all positions of P_2 on the surface of the sphere. *Isotropy* thus means *rotational* invariance of the properties of free space.

The term rotational invariance of space further implies that the potential energy of interaction between two particles is an *invariant, i.e.*, does not change if position co-ordinates of both the particles are rotated through the same angle about an arbitrary axis.

(b) Conservation of angular momentum and rotational invariance (isotropy of space). The space simultaneously possesses the property of

(i) Linear uniformity and   (ii) Rotational invariance

Therefore the form of potential energy function $U(r_1, r_2) = U(r)$ where

$$r = |\vec{r}| = |\vec{r_1} - \vec{r_2}|, \vec{r_1} \text{ and } \vec{r_2}$$ being the space co-ordinates of the two interacting particles P_1 and P_2 respectively, satisfies both the conditions stated above. The potential U depends upon the magnitude of the separation of the two points $|\vec{r_1} - \vec{r_2}|$ but is independent of the actual value of the space co-ordinates and their direction.

The force on the particle $P_1 = \vec{F}_{21} = -\left(\dfrac{\partial U}{\partial r_1}\right)\hat{r} = -\left(\dfrac{\partial U}{\partial r}\right)\left(\dfrac{\partial r}{\partial r_1}\right)\hat{r}$

The force on the particle $P_2 = \vec{F}_{12} = -\left(\dfrac{\partial U}{\partial r_2}\right)\hat{r} = -\left(\dfrac{\partial U}{\partial r}\right)\left(\dfrac{\partial r}{\partial r_2}\right)\hat{r}$

where $\hat{r}$ is a unit vector along $\vec{r}$, i.e., the direction along which either force of interaction acts.

Two cases arise :

(i) $r_1 > r_2$

In such a case $r = r_1 - r_2$ $\therefore$ $\dfrac{\partial r}{\partial r_1} = 1$ and $\dfrac{\partial r}{\partial r_2} = -1$

$\therefore \qquad \vec{F}_{21} = -\left(\dfrac{\partial U}{\partial r}\right)\hat{r}$ and $\vec{F}_{12} = +\left(\dfrac{\partial U}{\partial r}\right)\hat{r}$

Hence $\vec{F}_{12} = -\vec{F}_{21}$

(ii) $r_2 > r_1$

In such a case $r = r_2 - r_1$ $\therefore$ $\dfrac{\partial r}{\partial r_1} = -1$ and $\dfrac{\partial r}{\partial r_2} = +1$

$\therefore \qquad \vec{F}_{21} = +\left(\dfrac{\partial U}{\partial r}\right)\hat{r}$ and $\vec{F}_{12} = -\left(\dfrac{\partial U}{\partial r}\right)\hat{r}$

Hence again $\vec{F}_{12} = -\vec{F}_{21}$

Thus the potential function $U(r)$ leads to Newton's third law of the motion whether

$$r_1 > r_2 \text{ or } r_2 > r_1.$$

As proved above

$$\vec{F}_{21} = \pm\left(-\dfrac{\partial U}{\partial r}\right)\hat{r} \quad \text{and} \quad \vec{F}_{12} = \pm\left(-\dfrac{\partial U}{\partial r}\right)\hat{r}$$

If $-\dfrac{\partial U}{\partial r} = F(r)$, $\vec{F}_{12}$ as well as $\vec{F}_{21}$ can be expressed as $\pm F(r)\hat{r}$. In other words, the force will depend only on r the distance between the centres of the two particles. It is, therefore, a **central** force. Thus we find that rotational invariance of space requires motion under a central force.

Now the torque $\vec{\tau}$ for a force about the centre of the force is given by

$$\vec{\tau} = \vec{r} \times \vec{F} = \vec{r} \times F(r)\hat{r} = F(r)\vec{r} \times \hat{r} = F(r)\,r[\hat{r} \times \hat{r}] = 0$$

$\therefore$ For such a force, torque $\tau = 0$

But torque is the rate of change of angular momentum $\vec{J}$ $\quad \therefore \quad \vec{\tau} = \dfrac{d\vec{J}}{dt} = 0$

Integrating, we get $\vec{J}$ = a constant. This proves the law of conservation of angular momentum. Thus the rotational invariance or isotropy of space shows that

(i) There is a central force between the two particles interacting with each other.

(ii) $\vec{F}_{21} = -\vec{F}_{12}$, i.e., Newton's third law of motion holds good.

These two properties, on combination, show that the angular momentum is a constant. *Hence the rotational invariance of space leads to the principle of conservation of angular momentum.*

Q. 3.13. The potential energy of interaction between two particles is written as $U = C(x_1 - x_2)^2 \exp\{-(x_1 - x_2)^2\}$. Show that this satisfies the condition for rotational invariance of space. (*P.U.* 2008, 2001)

Ans. Given $\qquad U = C(x_1 - x_2)^2 \exp\{-(x_1 - x_2)^2\}$

The force on particle 1 due to particle 2 is given by

$$F_{12} = -\frac{\partial U}{\partial x_1} = \frac{-\partial}{\partial x_1}\left[C(x_1 - x_2)^2 \exp\{-(x_1 - x_2)^2\}\right]$$

$$= -2C(x_1 - x_2)\exp\{-(x_1-x_2)^2\} - C(x_1-x_2)^2 \exp\{-(x_1-x_2)^2\}(-2)(x_1-x_2)$$

$$= -2C(x_1 - x_2)\exp\{-(x_1-x_2)^2\}[1 - (x_1-x_2)^2] \qquad \qquad ...(i)$$

The force on particle 2 due to particle 1 is given by

$$F_{21} = -\frac{\partial U}{\partial x_2} = -\frac{\partial}{\partial x_2}\left[C(x_1 - x_2)^2 \exp\{-(x_1 - x_2)^2\}\right]$$

$$= 2C(x_1 - x_2)\exp\{-(x_1-x_2)^2\} - C(x_1-x_2)^2 \exp\{-(x_1-x_2)^2(2)(x_1-x_2)\}$$

$$= 2C(x_1 - x_2)\exp\{-(x_1-x_2)^2\}[1 - (x_1-x_2)^2] \qquad \qquad ...(ii)$$

From (i) and (ii), we have $F_{12} = -F_{21}$. This shows that the forces acting on the two particles (1 and 2) are equal and opposite.

Thus the given potential energy function leads to Newton's third law of motion.

It has been proved in **Q. 3.12** that the rotational invariance of space leads to Newton's third law of motion. Conversely, therefore, if the potential energy function $U = C(x_1 - x_2)^2 \exp\{-(x_1 - x_2)^2\}$ also leads to Newton's third law of motion, it satisfies the condition for rotational invariance of space.

Exercise. *The mutual potential energy of interaction between two particles is given by*

$$U = -\frac{C}{(x_1 - x_2)^2} + D(x_1 - x_2)^2$$

where C and D are constants. Show that the force between the two particles satisfies Newton's third law. (*P.U.* 2009)

Hint. $\qquad F_{12} = -\dfrac{\partial U}{\partial x_1} = -\dfrac{\partial}{\partial x_1}\left[C(x_1 - x_2)^{-2} + D(x_1 - x_2)^2\right]$

$$= 2C(x_1 - x_2)^{-3} - 2D(x_1 - x_2) \qquad \qquad ...(i)$$

and $\qquad F_{12} = -\dfrac{\partial U}{\partial x_2} = -\dfrac{\partial}{\partial x_2}\left[C(x_1 - x_2)^{-2} + 2D(x_1 - x_2)^2\right]$

$$= -2C(x_1 - x_2)^{-3} + 2D(x_1 - x_2) \qquad \qquad ...(ii)$$

From (i) and (ii), we have $F_{12} = -F_{21}$

Thus the force between the two particles due to given potential energy function satisfies Newton's third law of motion.

Q. 3.14. (a) A particle of mass m moves on a path given by equation

$$\vec{r} = a \cos\omega t\, \hat{i} + b \sin\omega t\, \hat{j}.$$

Calculate the torque and angular momentum about the origin.   (*Kan. U.*, 1996, 1994)

(b) **Calculate the angular momentum of the earth rotating about its own axis of rotation.**

Mass of the earth = 6×10^{24} kg

Mean radius = 6.4×10^6 metre.   (*Meerut U.* 2007)

Ans. (a) $\vec{r} = a \cos\omega t\, \hat{i} + b \sin\omega t\, \hat{j}$

∴ Velocity of the particle $\vec{v} = \dfrac{d\vec{r}}{dt} = \omega(-a \sin\omega t\, \hat{i} + b \cos\omega t\, \hat{j})$

and acceleration of the particle $\vec{a} = \dfrac{d^2\vec{r}}{dt^2} = -\omega^2 (a \cos\omega t\, \hat{i} + b \sin\omega t\, \hat{j}) = -\omega^2\,\vec{r}$

Hence force on the particle $F = ma = -m\omega^2\,\vec{r}$

Thus the force $\vec{F}$ is a linear *restoring force* and is a *central force*.

Torque. As the force is in the direction of $\vec{r}$

$$\text{Torque } \vec{\tau} = \vec{r} \times \vec{F} = -m\omega^2\,\vec{r} \times \vec{r} = 0$$

Angular momentum. $\vec{J} = \vec{r} \times m\vec{v}$

$$= (a \cos\omega t\, \hat{i} + b \sin\omega t\, \hat{j}) \times m\omega(-a\sin\omega t\, \hat{i} + b\cos\omega t\, \hat{j})$$
$$= m\omega(ab\cos^2 \omega t\, \hat{k} + ab\sin^2 \omega t\, \hat{k})$$
$$= m\omega\, ab\,\hat{k} = mab\,\vec{\omega}$$

where $\vec{\omega}$ acts in the positive Z-direction.

(b) Angular momentum $J = I\omega$

Taking the earth to be a solid sphere, moment of inertia of the earth about its own axis (a diameter) $I = \dfrac{2}{5} Mr^2$.

As the earth rotates once in 24 hrs. about its own axis, the

$$\text{Angular velocity } \omega = \frac{2\pi}{24 \times 60 \times 60} = 7.27 \times 10^{-5} \text{ rad/sec.}$$

$$\text{Moment of inertia } I = \frac{2}{5} \times 6 \times 10^{24} \times 6.4 \times 10^6 \times 6.4 \times 10^6 = 9.83 \times 10^{36} \text{ kg m}^2$$

∴   Angular momentum $J = I\omega$

$$= 98.3 \times 10^{36} \times 7.27 \times 10^{-5} = 714 \times 10^{31}$$
$$= 7.14 \times 10^{33} \text{ kg m}^2/\text{sec}$$

Q. 3.15. Two equal masses M each are connected by a rigid rod of negligible mass and length 'a'. The centre of mass of this dumb-bell system is stationary in gravity free space and the system rotates about the centre of mass with angular velocity ω. One of the rotating masses strikes a third stationary mass M which sticks to it. What is the angular momentum of the three mass system about the centre of mass at the instant prior to the collision and at the instant following the collision?   (*G.N.D.U.*, 1991)

Ans. Suppose at the time of collision, the rod is along the X-axis. Let us take O the centre of mass of the two masses M each, as origin of the co-ordinate system. Then the position of the centre of mass of the three mass system is given by

$$\overrightarrow{R}_{cm} = \frac{-M\left(\dfrac{a}{2}\right)\hat{i} + 2M\left(\dfrac{a}{2}\right)\hat{i}}{3M} = \frac{a}{6}\,\hat{i}$$

∴ Distance of the left mass M from the *c.m.* of the three mass system

$$= \frac{a}{2}\hat{i} + \frac{a}{6}\hat{i} = \frac{2}{3}\,a\hat{i}$$

Distance of the right mass $2M = (M + M)$ from the *c.m.* of the three mass system

$$= \frac{a}{2}\hat{i} - \frac{a}{6}\hat{i} = \frac{1}{3}\,a\hat{i}$$

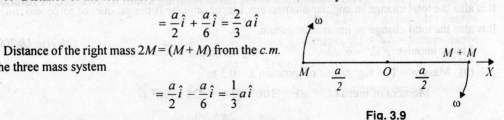

Fig. 3.9

Linear velocity of right mass M before collision

$= \dfrac{a}{2}\omega\,\hat{j}$ and linear velocity of left mass M before collision $= -\dfrac{a}{2}\omega\,\hat{j}$

Angular momentum $\qquad \overrightarrow{J} = \overrightarrow{r} \times m\overrightarrow{v}$

∴ Angular momentum of the three particles about *their* centre of mass *just* before collision

$$\overrightarrow{J} = \left(-\frac{2}{3}\,a\hat{i}\right) \times M\left(-\frac{a}{2}\,\omega\,\hat{j}\right) + \left(\frac{a}{3}\,\hat{i}\right) \times M\left(\frac{a}{2}\,\omega\,\hat{j}\right)$$

$$= \frac{1}{2}\,M\,a^2\,\omega\,\hat{k} \qquad \text{...[∵ linear momentum of the third mass = 0]}$$

Thus the angular momentum vector acts along the positive Z-direction and has a magnitude $\dfrac{1}{2}\,Ma^2\omega$.

As no external torque acts on the three particle system about the centre of mass during the collision, the angular momentum is conserved.

∴ Angular momentum just after collision $\overrightarrow{J} = \dfrac{1}{2}\,M\,a^2\omega\,\hat{k}$

Q. 3.16. (*a*) **Define angular impulse. Distinguish between momentum, angular impulse and linear impulse.**

(*b*) **A flywheel of mass 100 kg and radius of gyration 0.5 m is rotating with a speed of 90 revolutions per minute. Calculate the torque required to bring it to rest in 4 minutes.**

(*Bangalore U.*, 1991)

Ans. Angular impulse. If an unbalanced external torque $\overrightarrow{\tau}$ is applied to a body rotating with an angular velocity $\overrightarrow{\omega}_1$ for a time t so that the angular velocity changes to $\overrightarrow{\omega}_2$, then

Angular acceleration $\qquad \overrightarrow{\alpha} = \dfrac{\text{Change in angular velocity}}{\text{time}}$

$$= \frac{\overrightarrow{\omega}_2 - \overrightarrow{\omega}_1}{t} \qquad\qquad \text{...(}i\text{)}$$

But torque $\qquad \overrightarrow{\tau} = I\overrightarrow{\alpha} = \dfrac{I\overrightarrow{\omega}_2 - I\overrightarrow{\omega}_1}{t}$

or $\qquad \overrightarrow{\tau}\,t = I\overrightarrow{\omega}_2 - I\overrightarrow{\omega}_1$

The product of the torque and the time for which it acts is called **angular impulse.** *It is measured by the total change in angular momentum that the rotating body undergoes.*

If the torque acts for a small time dt and brings about a small change in angular velocity $d\omega$, then,

Angular impulse $\vec{\tau}\, dt = I\, d\vec{\omega}$

Angular momentum and linear momentum. Linear momentum is the product of mass and linear velocity, whereas angular momentum is the product of moment of inertia and angular velocity,

Linear momentum $\vec{p} = m\,\vec{v}$ Angular momentum $\vec{J} = I\,\vec{\omega}$

Angular impulse and linear impulse. Angular impulse is the product of the torque and the time. It is also the total change in angular momentum. Linear impulse is the product of force and time. It is also the total change in linear momentum.

Linear impulse $\vec{F}\, dt = m\, d\vec{v}$ Angular impulse $\vec{\tau}\, dt = I\, d\vec{\omega}$

(*b*) Mass $m = 100$ Kg; radius of gyration $k = 0.5$ m

∴   Moment of inertia $I = mk^2 = 100 \times (0.5)^2 = 25$ kg m^2

Angular velocity $\omega = 90$ rev/min $= \dfrac{2\pi \times 90}{60} = 3\pi$ rad s^{-1}

Final angular velocity $= 0$ Time $t = 4$ min $= 240$ s

Angular acceleration $\alpha = \dfrac{0 - 3\pi}{240} = -\dfrac{\pi}{80}$ rad s^{-2}

Hence Torque $\tau = I\alpha = -25 \times \dfrac{\pi}{80} = \dfrac{5\pi}{16} = 0.98$ Nm

Q. 3.17 (*a*) Give Newton's classical definition of time and its properties.

(*G.N.D.U.*, 1996, 1995)

(*b*) What is homogeneity of time? Show that homogeneity of time and Newton's second law of motion result in law of conservation of energy.   (*G.N.D.U.* 2007, 2004, 1999, 1995, 1994; *P.U.* 2005, 2003, 2001, 2000, 1999; Pbi. U. 2006; *H.P.U.* 1994)

Ans. (*a*) Time. According to Newton, '*Absolute true and mathematical time of itself and from its own nature, flows equally without relation to anything external and is otherwise called duration.*'

Properties. (*i*) One dimensionality. Time is one dimensional. It flows only in one direction. It is, therefore, specified by a single variable t. It is independent of space.

(*ii*) **Homogeneity.** Time is homogeneous, *i.e.*, it flows uniformly. The results of an experiment do not change when we change the time of an experiment. In other words, '*The result of an experiment is independent of the change in the origin of time.*' This property is known as homogeneity of time.

(*iii*) **Isotropy.** Theoretically time is isotropic, *i.e.*, the laws of Physics remain unaltered by changing $+t$ to $-t$.

(*b*) Law of conservation of energy from homogeneity of time. Time is homogeneous, *i.e.*, it flows uniformly.

The total energy E of a system is given by $E = U + K$

where U is the potential energy and K the kinetic energy.

The Coulomb force between two charges q_1 and q_2, a distance r apart, is given by

$$\vec{F}_c = \frac{1}{4\pi\varepsilon_0}\left(\frac{q_1 \cdot q_2}{r^2}\right)\hat{r} = k\,\frac{q_1 \cdot q_2}{r^2}\,\hat{r}$$

where k is a constant $= 1/4\pi\varepsilon_0$.

Similarly, the gravitational force between two masses m_1 and m_2, a distance r apart, is also given by

$$\vec{F_g} = G\left(\frac{m_1 . m_2}{r^2}\right)\hat{r}$$

where G is the gravitational constant.

We find that in the above expressions for force, time does not appear *explicitly*. By *explicit* dependence on time we mean that time should occur as such directly in the expression for force.

Now, for a conservative system $\vec{F} = -\left(\dfrac{\partial U}{\partial r}\right)\hat{r}$

In other words, U is a function of $\vec{F}$ and $\vec{r}$. If time flows uniformly, the forces acting at a point do not depend explicitly on time *i.e.*, force $\vec{F}$ is a function of $\vec{r}$ only. Since U is a function of $\vec{F}$ and $\vec{r}$, it is also function of $\vec{r}$ only. The principle of homogeneity of time, therefore, states $\dfrac{\partial U}{\partial t} = 0$.

The expression for kinetic energy $K = \dfrac{1}{2}mv^2$ also does not depend explicitly on time.

$\therefore \qquad \dfrac{\partial K}{\partial t} = 0$

If total energy E is a function of $\vec{r}$ and t, then $E = E(\vec{r}, t)$

and

$$dE = \frac{\partial E}{\partial r}dr + \frac{\partial E}{\partial t}dt = \frac{\partial}{\partial t}(U+K)dr + \frac{\partial}{\partial r}(U+K)dt$$

$$= \left(\frac{\partial U}{\partial r} + \frac{\partial K}{\partial r}\right)dr + \left(\frac{\partial U}{\partial t} + \frac{\partial K}{\partial t}\right)dt = \left[\left(\frac{\partial U}{\partial r}\right) + \left(\frac{\partial K}{\partial r}\right)\right]dr \qquad ...(i)$$

as
$$\frac{\partial U}{\partial t} = 0 \quad \text{and} \quad \frac{\partial K}{\partial t} = 0$$

From (i), we have
$$\frac{dE}{dt} = \left(\frac{\partial U}{\partial r} + \frac{\partial K}{\partial r}\right)\frac{dr}{dt}$$

Now
$$\frac{\partial U}{\partial r} = -F \quad \text{and} \quad \frac{\partial K}{\partial r} = \frac{\partial}{\partial r}\left(\frac{1}{2}mv^2\right) = mv\frac{\partial v}{\partial r}$$

Since v does not depend explicitly on time. $\dfrac{\partial v}{\partial r} = \dfrac{dv}{dr}$

$\therefore \qquad \dfrac{\partial K}{\partial r} = mv\dfrac{dv}{dr} = m\dfrac{dr}{dt}\cdot\dfrac{dv}{dr} = m\dfrac{dv}{dt} = ma$

Hence
$$\frac{dE}{dt} = (-F + ma)\frac{dr}{dt}$$

The expression within brackets is zero as $F = ma$, according to Newton's second law of motion.

$\therefore \qquad \dfrac{dE}{dt} = 0$ or $E =$ a constant.

Thus we find that the homogeneity of time (or time symmetry) (*i.e.*, if time flows uniformly) and Newton's second law of motion lead to the principle of conservation of energy.

3.18. (*a*) **A particle of mass m moving in a circular orbit of radius r has angular momentum J about its centre. Calculate the kinetic energy of the particle in terms of J, m and r.**   (A.U., 1995)

(*b*) **What physical quantity does dimensional formula $\dfrac{J^2}{mr^2}$ represent?**   (Pbi. U. 2006)

Ans. (a) The angular momentum of a particle of mass m moving in a circular orbit of radius r is given by

$$J = mvr \qquad \qquad ...(i)$$

If E is the kinetic energy of the particle, then $E = \dfrac{1}{2}mv^2$.

From equation (i), we get $\quad v = \dfrac{J}{mr} \quad$ or $\quad v^2 = \dfrac{J^2}{m^2 r^2}$

$$\therefore \qquad K.E. = \frac{1}{2}mv^2 = \frac{1}{2}m\,\frac{J^2}{m^2 r^2} = \frac{J^2}{2mr^2}$$

(b) The relation $\dfrac{J^2}{2mr^2}$ represents the kinetic energy of a particle of mass m moving in a circular orbit of radius r and having angular momentum $\vec{J}$. [For proof see part (a)]

Hence the dimensional formula $\dfrac{J^2}{mr^2}$ has dimensions of energy.

Q. 3.19. Two bodies of different masses are moving with the same kinetic energy of translation. Which has greater momentum? (A.U., 1994)

Ans. Let m_a and v_a be the mass and velocity of mass A and m_b, v_b that of mass B with $m_a > m_b$, then

$$\text{K.E. of mass } A = \frac{1}{2}m_a v_a^2 \text{ and K.E. of mass } B = \frac{1}{2}m_b v_b^2$$

Now $\quad \dfrac{1}{2}m_a v_a^2 = \dfrac{1}{2}m_b v_b^2 \quad \therefore \dfrac{m_a}{m_b} = \dfrac{v_b^2}{v_a^2}$ or $\sqrt{\dfrac{m_a}{m_b}} = \dfrac{v_b}{v_a}$

Linear momentum of $A, p_a = m_a v_a$

Linear momentum of $B, P_b = m_b v_b$

$$\therefore \qquad \frac{p_a}{p_b} = \frac{m_a v_a}{m_b v_b} = \frac{m_a}{m_b}\sqrt{\frac{m_b}{m_a}} = \sqrt{\frac{m_a}{m_b}} \text{ but } m_a > m_b$$

$$\therefore \qquad p_a > p_b$$

i.e., the body A with greater mass has greater momentum.

Q. 3.20. Using conservation of energy principle, show that angular speed of a simple pendulum is

$$\dot{\theta} = \left[\frac{2}{ml^2}\{E - mgl(1 - \cos\theta)\}\right]^{1/2}$$

where the symbols have their usual meanings. (A.U., 1993)

Ans. Let OA be the mean position of a simple pendulum of length l having a bob of mass m and OB the position when it is displaced through a small angle θ, then

$$AB = l\theta = x \text{ (say)}$$

Now $\qquad \qquad OA = OC + CA = OB\cos\theta + CA$

or $\qquad \qquad l = l\cos\theta + h$

$\therefore \qquad \qquad h = l - l\cos\theta = l(1 - \cos\theta)$

Potential energy of the pendulum bob at B

$$= mgh = mgl(1 - \cos\theta)$$

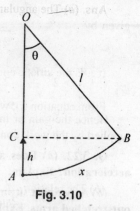

Kinetic energy of the bob at $B = \dfrac{1}{2} mv^2 = \dfrac{1}{2} m \left(\dfrac{l \, d\theta}{dt} \right)^2$

Since $\qquad\qquad\qquad v = \dfrac{dx}{dt} = \dfrac{l \, d\theta}{dt}$

$\therefore$ Total energy $\qquad E = mgl \, (1 - \cos\theta) + \dfrac{1}{2} ml^2 \left(\dfrac{d\theta}{dt} \right)^2$

or $\qquad\qquad \left(\dfrac{d\theta}{dt} \right)^2 = \dfrac{2}{ml^2} [E - mgl \, (1 - \cos\theta)]$

$\therefore \qquad\qquad \dfrac{d\theta}{dt} = \dot{\theta} = \left[\dfrac{2}{ml^2} \{ E - mgl \, (1 - \cos\theta) \} \right]^{1/2}$

Fig. 3.10

Q. 3.21. A particle of mass m is attached to a string and constrained to move in a horizontal plane. The particle rotates with a velocity V when the length of the string is R. How much work is done in shortening the string to R_0 ? Show that the work done is equal to the increase in kinetic energy.

OR

Show that the gain in kinetic energy of a particle on shortening its circular orbit is supplied by the work done against the centrifugal force acting on the particle. *(Kan. U., 1990)*

Ans. Mass of the particle $= m$; Velocity of rotation $= V$; Radius of the circular path $= R$

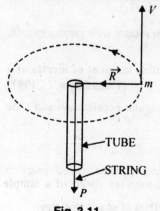

Fig. 3.11

Let the particle be connected to a string whose other end passes through a tube. By this arrangement the radius of the circle and hence the length of the string can be shortened by pulling the string at the end P.

The force acting on the particle due to the string is directed along the radius R, *i.e.*, it is radial.

$\therefore \qquad$ Torque $= \vec{R} \times \vec{F} = RF \sin\theta = 0 \; [\because \sin\theta = 0]$

When there is no external torque acting on a particle, the total angular momentum is conserved. Let the velocity of the particle be V_0 when the radius is decreased to R_0.

$\therefore$ According to the principle of conservation of angular momentum,

$$mVR = mV_0 \cdot R_0 = k \,(\text{say})$$

The centrifugal force on the particle when it is moving in a circle of radius $r = \dfrac{mv^2}{r}$

$\therefore$ Work done against the centrifugal force in shortening the string from R to R_0 is

$$W = \int_R^{R_0} -\frac{mv^2}{r} \, dr = -\int_R^{R_0} \frac{m}{r} \left(\frac{k}{mr} \right)^2 dr = -\int_R^{R_0} \frac{k^2}{mr^3} \, dr = -\frac{k^2}{2m} \left[-\frac{1}{r^2} \right]_R^{R_0}$$

$$= \frac{k^2}{2m} \left[\frac{1}{R_0^2} - \frac{1}{R^2} \right] = \frac{k^2}{2mR_0^{\,2}} - \frac{k^2}{2mR^2}$$

Now $\qquad \dfrac{k^2}{2 m R_0^2} = \dfrac{m^2 V_0^2 R_0^2}{2 m R_0^{\,2}} = \dfrac{1}{2} m V_0^2 \quad$ and

$$\frac{k^2}{2\,m\,R^2} = \frac{m^2\,V^2\,R^2}{2\,m\,R^2} = \frac{1}{2}m V^2$$

$$\therefore \quad W = \frac{1}{2}m V_0^2 - \frac{1}{2}\,m V^2 = \text{Final kinetic energy} - \text{Initial kinetic energy}$$

$$= \text{Increase in kinetic energy}$$

Hence the gain or increase in kinetic energy of the particle on shortening its circular orbit is supplied by the work done against the centrifugal force acting on the particle.

Q. 3.22. (a) Does a particle moving along a circular path with uniform speed possess acceleration? Explain. (*Bangalore U.*, 1994)

(b) A gymnast sitting on a rotating platform with his arms outstretched suddenly folds his outstretched arms. Explain what happens. (*Bangalore U.*, 1994)

Ans. (a) When a particle moves along a circular path with uniform speed, the magnitude of its velocity remains constant but the direction goes on continuously changing. As velocity is a vector having a magnitude (speed) and direction, any change in direction means a change in velocity or acceleration. Thus a particle moving along a circular path with uniform speed has an acceleration.

As there is only a change in direction, the acceleration acts at right angles to the direction of motion, *i.e.*, along the radius towards the centre. Hence it is called centripetal acceleration.

(b) When a gymnast sitting on a rotating platform with his arms outstretched suddenly folds his outstretched arms, the radius of gyration of his body decreases. As there is no external torque acting on the body, the angular momentum $J = I\omega$ where ω is the angular velocity, remains constant. In other words, if J remains constant, as I decreases ω increases.

Hence angular velocity of the gymnast increases, *i.e.*, the platform rotates with greater angular velocity.

Q. 3.23. How torque is related with angular acceleration? Define moment of inertia of a body from it. (*Vidya Sagar. U.* 1991)

Ans. Torque is given by the relation $\vec{\tau} = I\vec{\alpha}$ where $\vec{\alpha}$ is the angular acceleration and I the moment of inertia of the body.

If $\qquad\qquad\qquad \vec{\alpha} = 1; \; I = \vec{\tau}$ (numerically).

Hence moment of inertia of a body is numerically equal to the torque required to produce a unit angular acceleration in it.

Q. 3.24. Discuss various conservation laws in terms of symmetries of space and time. (*G.N.D.U.* 2006)

Ans. Various conservation laws are :

(*i*) *Law of conservation of linear momentum*

This law can be derived from the property of *homogeneity* or *translational invariance of space*.

For details see **Q. 3.5.**

(*ii*) *Law of conservation of angular momentum*

This law can be derived from the property of *isotropy* or *rotational invariance of space*.

For details see **Q. 3.12.**

(*iii*) *Law of conservation of energy*

This law can be derived from the property of *homogeneity of time* or *time symmetry*.

For details see **Q. 3.17**

Q.3.25. Show that the angular momentum of two particles interacting mutually is conserved if the force between them acts along the line joining the particles. (*GN.D.U.* 2009)

Ans. Consider two particles P_1 and P_2 which are interacting mutually. Let m_1 be the mass, $\vec{r_1}$ the position vector, and $\vec{v_1}$ the velocity of particle P_1 and m_2, $\vec{r_2}$ and $\vec{v_2}$ the corresponding values for particle P_2 as shown in Fig. 3.12.

Let $\vec{F_{12}}$ be the force acting on particle P_1 due to the particle P_2 and $\vec{a_1}$ the acceleration produced in it, then

$$m_1 \vec{a_1} = \vec{F_{12}}$$

Similarly, if $\vec{F_{21}}$ is the force acting on the particle P_2 due to the particle P_1 and $\vec{a_2}$ the acceleration produced in it, then

$$m_2 \vec{a_2} = \vec{F_{21}}$$

According to Newton's third law of motion

$$\vec{F_{12}} = -\vec{F_{21}}$$

The angular momentum (vector) of particle P_1

$$\vec{j_1} = \vec{r_1} \times m_1 \vec{v_1}$$

and angular momentum (vector) of particle P_2

$$\vec{j_2} = \vec{r_2} \times m_2 \vec{v_2}$$

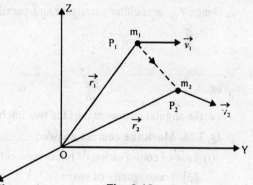

Fig. 3.12.

Therefore, the total angular momentum of the system consisting of particles P_1 and P_2

$$\vec{J} = \vec{j_1} + \vec{j_2} = m_1 \vec{r_1} \times \vec{v_1} + m_2 \vec{r_2} \times \vec{v_2}$$

The rate of change of total angular momentum with time is given by

$$\frac{d\vec{J}}{dt} = \frac{d}{dt}\left(m_1 \vec{r_1} \times \vec{v_1}\right) + \frac{d}{dt}\left(m_2 \vec{r_2} \times \vec{v_2}\right)$$

$$= m_1\left(\frac{d\vec{r_1}}{dt} \times \vec{v_1} + \vec{r_1} \times \frac{d\vec{v_1}}{dt}\right) + m_2\left(\frac{d\vec{r_2}}{dt} \times \vec{v_2} + \vec{r_2} \times \frac{d\vec{v_2}}{dt}\right)$$

$$= m_1\left(\vec{v_1} \times \vec{v_1} + \vec{r_1} \times \vec{a_1}\right) + m_2\left(\vec{v_2} \times \vec{v_2} + \vec{r_2} \times \vec{a_2}\right)$$

But $\vec{v_1} \times \vec{v_1} = 0$ and $\vec{v_2} \times \vec{v_2} = 0$,

$$\therefore \qquad \frac{d\vec{J}}{dt} = m_1 \vec{r_1} \times \vec{a_1} + m_2 \vec{r_2} \times \vec{a_2}$$

$$= \vec{r_1} \times m_1\, \vec{a_1} + \vec{r_2} \times m_2\, \vec{a_2}$$

$$= \vec{r_1} \times \vec{F_{12}} + \vec{r_2} \times \vec{F_{21}}$$

$$= \vec{r_1} \times \vec{F_{12}} - \vec{r_2} \times \vec{F_{12}}$$

$$= \left(\vec{r_1} - \vec{r_2} \right) \times \vec{F_{12}}$$

But $\vec{r_1} - \vec{r_2} = \overrightarrow{OP_1} - \overrightarrow{OP_2} = \overrightarrow{P_1P_2}$

$$\therefore \qquad \frac{d\vec{J}}{dt} = \overrightarrow{P_1P_2} \times \vec{F_{12}}$$

The force between the two interacting particles acts along the line joining them.

Hence $\vec{F_{12}}$ acts either parallel or anti-parallel to P_1P_2

$$\therefore \qquad \overrightarrow{P_1P_2} \times \vec{F_{12}} = 0$$

or $\qquad\qquad \dfrac{d\vec{J}}{dt} = 0 \qquad$ or $\qquad \vec{J}$ = a constant (vector)

i.e. the angular momentum of the two interacting particles is conserved.

Q. 3.26. Mark the correct answer.

(*i*) Law of conservation of linear momentum is consequence of   (*H.P.U.* 2001, 1994)

    (*a*) homogeneity of space   (*b*) isotropy of space

    (*c*) homogeneity of space and time   (*d*) homogeneity of time

(*ii*) Law of conservation of angular momentum is consequence of   (*H.P.U.* 1992)

    (*a*) homogeneity of space   (*b*) isotropy of space

    (*c*) homogeneity of space and time   (*d*) homogeneity of time

(*iii*) Homogeneity of time leads to conservation of   (*P.U.*, 1993)

    (*a*) linear momentum   (*b*) angular momentum

    (*c*) total energy   (*d*) kinetic energy

(*iv*) Which is not explicit function of time?   (*P.U.*, 1993)

    (*a*) velocity   (*b*) acceleration   (*c*) potential energy   (*d*) momentum

(*v*) A bicycle in motion does not fall because one of the following is conserved

    (*a*) linear momentum   (*b*) angular momentum

    (*c*) kinetic energy   (*P.U.*, 1994)

(*vi*) Number of dimensions space has is

    (*a*) one   (*b*) two   (*c*) three   (*d*) four

(*vii*) Newton's laws of motion are based on the assumption that space is

    (*a*) homogeneous   (*b*) isotropic   (*c*) homogeneous and isotropic

    (*d*) invariant under rotation

(*viii*) Two masses M and m, ($M > m$) have the same momentum. If their speeds are small, mass M will have

    (*a*) less kinetic energy than that of m (*b*) more kinetic energy than that of m

    (*c*) same kinetic energy as that of m (*P.U.*, 1994)

Ans.   (*i*) *a*   (*ii*) *b*   (*iii*) *c*   (*iv*) *c*

         (*v*) *b*   (*vi*) *c*   (*vii*) *c*   (*viii*) *a*

3.25. Fill in the blanks. The unit of angular momentum is .....   (*Meerut U.* 2001)

Ans. Kg $m^2 s^{-1}$ or Joule second.

EXERCISES

1.   The earth is moving around the sun under gravitational force and its orbit has semi-major axis of 1.495×10^8 km. When the earth passes closest to the sun (*i.e.*, at its perhilion) its distance is 1.47×10^8 km and its orbital velocity is 0.303 km s^{-1}. Find earth's velocity at the apehilion and also its angular velocities at the two positions.

    Hint. Angular momentum $\vec{J} = r \times \overrightarrow{mv}$ is conserved.

$$\text{[Ans. } v_a = 293 \text{ km s}^{-1}; \; \omega_p = 0.206 \times 10^{-8} \text{ rad s}^{-1}; \; \omega_a = 0.193 \times 10^{-9} \text{ rad s}^{-1}]$$

2.   A sandbag of mass 10 kgm is suspended with a three-metre-long weightless string. A bullet of mass 200 gm is fired with a speed of 20 m/sec into the bag and stays in the bag. Calculate the speed acquired by the bag and maximum displacement of the bag.

$$\text{[Ans. } v = 39.2 \text{ cm/sec.; Max. displacement} = 29°54']$$

3.   A bomb weighing 50 kg explodes into three pieces in flight when its velocity is $20\hat{i} + 22\hat{j} + 10\hat{k}$ ms^{-1}. Two fragments of the bomb weighing 10 and 20 kg are found to have velocities $100\hat{i} + 50\hat{j} + 20\hat{k}$ and $30\hat{i} + 20\hat{j} + 10\hat{k}$ ms^{-1}. Find the velocity of the third piece.   (*Pbi. U.*, 1991)

    Hint. The mass of third piece = 20 kg. Let its velocity be $(x\hat{i} + y\hat{j} + z\hat{k})ms^{-1}$,

    then $50(20\hat{i} + 22\hat{j} + 10\hat{k}) = 10(100\hat{i} + 50\hat{j} + 20\hat{k})$

$$+ \; 20(30\hat{i} - 20\hat{j} - 10\hat{k}) + 20(x\hat{i} + y\hat{j} + z\hat{k})$$

$$\text{[Ans. } (-30\hat{i} + 50\hat{j} - 25\hat{k})ms^{-1}]$$

4.   A grindstone weighing 40 kg has a radius of 1.2 m. Starting from rest it acquires a speed of 150 r.p.m. in 12 sec. Calculate the torque acting on it.   (*Bangalore U.*, 1996)

    Hint. $I = \dfrac{1}{2}MR^2 = \dfrac{1}{2} \times 40 \times 1.2 \times 1.2 = 28.8 \text{ Kg m}^2$

$$\alpha = \frac{2\pi \times 150}{60 \times 12} = \frac{5\pi}{12} \text{ rad s}^{-2} \qquad \tau = I\alpha = \frac{28.8 \times 5\pi}{12} = 37.7 \text{ Nm}$$

4

Moment of Inertia and Rigid Body Dynamics

Q. 4.1. (*a*) **What is a Rigid Body ?** (*P.U.* 2008)

(*b*) **What is inertia? Obtain an expression for the kinetic energy of a rotating body.**
(*Kerala U.*, 2001; *M.D.U.*, 2003)

(*c*) **Explain Moment of Inertia and Radius of Gyration. Give the dimensions and units of moment of inertia. Is it a vector or scalar quantity?** (*Kerala U.*, 2001;

M.D.U., 2008, 2006, 2003, 2001; *Gharwal U.*, 1999; *Nagpur U.*, 2003;

Bang. U., 1996, 1994; *Luck. U.*, 1996, 1995, 1994; *K.U.*, 1991; *Meerut U.*, 2007, 1990)

(*d*) **Prove that $L^2 = 2EI$ where L, E and I are the angular momentum, kinetic energy of rotation and moment of inertia respectively.** (*M.D.U.*, 2000)

Ans. (a) **Rigid Body.** A rigid body is an assembly of a large number of particles in which the inter-particle distance remains the same when it is acted upon by an external force or torque.

The shape of the body, therefore, remains unaltered during its motion which may be translational or rotational or combination of the two.

(*b*) **Inertia.** According to Newton's first law of motion a body at rest will remain at rest and a body moving with uniform velocity in a straight line will continue to do so unless an external force is applied to it. This property of a body by virtue of which it is unable to change its state of rest or of uniform motion in a straight line by itself is known as "inertia". For translatory motion the value of inertia depends only on the mass of the body. The greater is the mass greater is the inertia.

Kinetic energy of rotation. For translatory motion kinetic energy depends upon mass m and velocity v and is given by $\dfrac{1}{2} mv^2$.

When a body rotates about an axis, the kinetic energy of its rotation is determined not only by its mass m and angular velocity ω, but also depends upon the position of the axis about which it rotates and the distribution of mass about this axis.

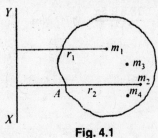

Fig. 4.1

If a body A rotates about an axis XY (Fig. 4.1) with an angular velocity ω, all its particles have the same angular velocity, but as they are at different distances from the axis of rotation, their linear velocities are different. Let the linear velocities of the particles of mass m_1, m_2...; distant r_1, r_2... from the axis of rotation be v_1, v_2... respectively. The kinetic energy of the body is, therefore, equal to the sum of the kinetic energies of the various particles and is given by

$$\text{Total K.E.} = \frac{1}{2} m_1 v_1^2 + \frac{1}{2} m_2 v_2^2 + ...$$

Since $v = r\omega$

$$\therefore \text{Total K.E.} = \frac{1}{2} m_1 r_1^2 \omega^2 + \frac{1}{2} m_2 r_2^2 \omega^2 + \frac{1}{2} m_3 r_3^2 \omega^2 + ...$$

$$= \frac{1}{2}(\Sigma mr^2)\omega^2 = \frac{1}{2}\omega^2 \Sigma mr^2 = \frac{1}{2} I\omega^2$$

where I is the moment of inertia of the body about the axis XY and is equal to Σmr^2.

(c) **Moment of inertia.** We have expressed the moment of inertia as Σmr^2.

Hence *the moment of inertia of a body about an axis is defined as the sum of the products of the mass and the square of the distance of the different particles of the body from the axis of rotation.*

In the above case we have seen that K.E. of rotation $= \frac{1}{2} I\omega^2$

If $\omega = 1$, then $I = 2 \times$ kinetic energy.

Hence moment of inertia may also be defined as twice the kinetic energy of rotation of a body when its angular velocity is unity.

Radius of gyration. If the entire mass of the body is supposed to be concentrated at a point such that the kinetic energy of rotation is the same as that of the body itself, then the distance of that point from the axis of rotation is called the *radius of gyration* of the body about that axis. If k denotes the radius of gyration and M the mass of the body supposed to be concentrated at the point, then we have

$$K.E. = \frac{1}{2} I\omega^2 = \frac{1}{2} \Sigma mr^2 \omega^2 = \frac{1}{2} Mk^2 \omega^2$$

$$\therefore \qquad Mk^2 = \Sigma mr^2 = mn\left(\frac{r_1^2 + r_2^2 + ...}{n}\right)$$

where n is the number of particles each of mass m into which the given mass M is divided.

Now $M = mn$ $\therefore k = \left(\frac{r_1^2 + r_2^2 + ...}{n}\right)^{1/2}$

Hence *the radius of gyration is the square root of the mean square distance of the particles of the body from the axis of rotation.*

Dimensions of radius of gyration and moment of inertia. According to the definition of radius of gyration given above the dimensions of k are those of length $[L^1]$ alone.

Now moment of inertia $I = Mk^2$ $\therefore$ Dimensions of $I = [M^1 L^2]$

Units of moment of inertia. In S.I. units the moment of inertia is expressed as kg-m^2.

Moment of inertia - a scalar. Moment of inertia is a *scalar* quantity because the value of I about a given axis remains unchanged by reversing its direction of rotation about that axis. In other words it has no direction. The total moment of inertia of a number of bodies about a given axis is equal to the sum of their individual moments of inertia about that axis.

(d) $L^2 = 2\ EI$. The angular momentum of a rotating body $L = I\omega$ where I is the moment of inertia of the body about the axis of rotation and ω the angular velocity.

Kinetic energy of rotation $E = \frac{1}{2} I\omega^2$

$$\therefore \qquad L^2 = I^2 \omega^2 = 2 \times \frac{1}{2} I\omega^2 \times I = 2\ EI$$

Q. 4.2. What is the physical significance of Moment of inertia?

(*Nagpur U.*, 2003; *M.D.U.*, 2008, 2002; *Gharwal U.*, 2000;
Indore U., 2001; *Gowhati U.*, 2000; *K.U.*, 1996; *Meerut U.*, 2007, 1992)

OR

Moment of inertia plays the same role in rotation as mass does in translation. Justify.

(*Cal. U.*, 1992)

Ans. Physical significance. Moment of inertia plays the same role in rotatory motion as mass does in linear motion, *i.e.*, moment of inertia is an analogue of mass in linear motion.

According to Newton's first law of motion, a body continues in its state of rest or of uniform motion in a straight line unless some external force acts upon it. This propety of matter is known as **inertia.** A body always resists an external force tending to change its state of rest or of linear motion. *Greater the mass of the body greater is the force required to produce a given linear acceleration.*

Similarly bodies possess rotational inertia, *i.e.*, a body free to rotate about an axis opposes any change in its state of rest or of rotation. *Greater the moment of inertia of a body greater is the couple required to produce a given angular acceleration.*

The moment of inertia depends not only on the mass of a body but also on the distribution of mass about the axis of rotation.

If a solid disc and a wheel have the same mass, wheel will have a greater moment of inertia as the mass in it is distributed at larger distances from the axis of rotation passing through the centre. The analogy between the moment of inertia in rotational motion and mass in linear motion will be clear from the similarity in the relation for momentum, force, impulse, energy and work as illustrated below:

Translatory motion	*Rotatory motion*
Linear momentum $= mv$	Angular momentum $= I\omega$
Force $= ma$	Torque or moment of the couple $= I \times$ angular acceleration $= I\alpha$
Impulse $= m\,(v_2 - v_1)$	Angular impulse $= I\,(\omega_2 - \omega_1)$
Kinetic energy $= \dfrac{1}{2}\,mv^2$	Rotational $K.E. = \dfrac{1}{2}\,I\omega^2$
Work $=$ Force $\times$ distance	Work $=$ Couple $\times$ angular displacement

Q.4.3. State and prove the theorem of perpendicular axis for moment of inertia.

(*M.D.U.* 2007, 2006; *Meerut U.*, 2001; *Os.U.*, 1997; *Kan. U.*, 1995, 1992;
Bang.U., 1996, 1993; *K.U.*, 1993; *A.U.*, 1995, *Burd.U.*, 1992, 1990;
Cal.U., 2003, 1992, 1990; *Vid. S.U.*, 1991)

Ans. Theorem of perpendicular axis. *It states that the moment of inertia of a plane lamina about an axis perpendicular to the plane of the lamina is equal to the sum of the moments of inertia of the lamina about the two axes at right angles to each other, in its own plane intersecting each other at the point where the perpendicular axis passes through it.*

To put the above in mathematical form let I_x and I_y be the moments of inertia about the two axes perpendicular to each other in the plane of the lamina then the moment of inertia I about a line passing through the point of intersection and perpendicular to its plane is given by $I = I_x + I_y$.

Let OX and OY be the two perpendicular axes in the plane of the lamina. Let m_1 be the mass of a particle distant r_1 from an axis through O perpendicular to the plane XOY. The distance of this particle from the Y-axis is x_1 and that from the X-axis is y_1.

Moment of inertia of this particle about the X-axis $= m_1 y_1^2$ and moment of inertia of this particle about the Y-axis $= m_1 x_1^2$.

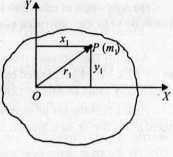

If we divide the whole lamina into a number of particles of masses $m_1, m_2, m_3...$ etc. at distances r_1, r_2, r_3 ... etc. so that the corresponding distances are y_1, y_2, y_3 ...from the X-axis and x_1, x_2, x_3 ... from the Y-axis, then

Moment of inertia of the lamina about X-axis

$$I_x = m_1 y_1^2 + m_2 y_2^2 + ... = \Sigma m y^2$$

and the moment of inertia of the lamina about the Y-axis

Fig. 4.2

$$I_y = m_1 x_1^2 + m_2 x_2^2 + ... = \Sigma m x^2$$

$\therefore$ Moment of inertia of the lamina about a perpendicular axis through O

$$I = m_1 r_1^2 + m_2 r_2^2 ... = \Sigma m r^2$$
$$= m_1 (x_1^2 + y_1^2) + m_2 (x_2^2 + y_2^2) + ...$$
$$= m_1 x_1^2 + m_2 x_2^2 + ... + m_1 y_1^2 + m_2 y_2^2 + ...$$
$$= \Sigma m x^2 + \Sigma m y^2 = I_x + I_y$$

Q. 4.4. State and prove theorem of parallel axes for moment of inertia.

(*M.D.U.*, 2008, 2003; *Meerut U.*, 2007, 2002, 2001; *Gharwal U.*, 2000; *Os.U.*, 1997; *Cal.U.*, 2003, 1990; *Kan.U.*, 1996, 1991; *Burd.U.*, 1992, 1990; *Vid. S.U.*, 1991; *Bang.U.*,1990; *K.U.*, 1994)

Ans. Theorem of parallel axes. *It states that the moment of inertia of a body about any axis is equal to the sum of its moment of inertia about a parallel axis through its centre of gravity and the product of its mass and the square of the distance between the two axes.*

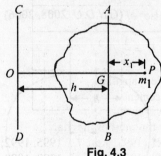

Let CD be an axis in the plane of the paper and AB a parallel axis through G the centre of mass of the body. The perpendicular distance between the two axes is h. Let M be the mass of the body and m_1 the mass of the element at P distant x_1 from AB.

Moment of inertia of m_1 about $CD = m_1 (x_1 + h)^2$

$$= m_1 (x_1^2 + h^2 + 2x_1 h)$$
$$= m_1 x_1^2 + m_1 h^2 + 2m_1 x_1 h$$

$\therefore$ Moment of inertia of the body about CD

Fig. 4.3

$$I = \Sigma m_1 x_1^2 + \Sigma m_1 h^2 + 2\Sigma m_1 x_1 h$$

If I_g is the moment of inertia of the body about AB, an axis through G, then $\Sigma m_1 x_1^2 = I_g$

$\therefore$

$$I = I_g + Mh^2 + 2h\Sigma m_1 x_1$$

Now $\Sigma m_1 x_1$ is the sum of the moments of all the particles about AB passing through G the centre of gravity. Since the body is balanced about the centre of mass G, therefore the algebraic sum of all the moments about G is zero.

$\therefore$

$$\Sigma m_1 x_1 = 0$$

Hence

$$I = I_g + Mh^2$$

Q. 4.5. (*a*) **The inter-molecular distance between two atoms of hydrogen molecule is 0.77 Å and mass of the proton is 1.67×10^{-27} Kg. Calculate the moment of inertia of the molecule.**

(*Gharwal U.*, 1999)

(*b*) **A flywheel of mass 500 kg, radius 1 metre makes 500 revolutions per minute. Assuming the mass to be concentrated along the rim, calculate the energy of the flywheel.**

(*Bangalore U.*, 1999)

Ans. (*a*) The hydrogen molecule consists of two atoms of hydrogen which are point masses each $m = 1.67 \times 10^{-27}$ kg separated by a distance $0.77\ Å = 0.77 \times 10^{-10}$ m. The molecule has a moment of inertia only about an axis perpendicular to the line joining the two atoms.

Hence the moment of inertia of the hydrogen molecule about an axis passing through the mid-point of the line joining the two atoms and perpendicular to it

$$I = 2m\left(\frac{l}{2}\right)^2 = \frac{ml^2}{2} = \frac{1.67 \times 10^{-27} (0.77 \times 10^{-10})^2}{2}$$

$$= 0.495 \times 10^{-47}\ \text{kg m}^2$$

(*b*) Mass of the flywheel $M = 500$ kg

As the mass is concentrated along the rim, distance of the mass from the axis or radius of gyration

$$k = 1\text{m}$$

Angular velocity $\qquad \omega = 500$ rev/min. $= \dfrac{500 \times 2\pi}{60}$ rad/sec

Moment of inertia $I = Mk^2 = 500 \times 1 = 500$ kg-m^2

$\therefore$ K.E. of flywheel $\qquad = \dfrac{1}{2} I\omega^2 = \dfrac{1}{2} Mk^2\omega^2 = \dfrac{1}{2} \times 500 \times \left(\dfrac{500 \times 2\pi}{60}\right)^2$

$$= 6.871 \times 10^5\ \text{J}.$$

Q. 4.6. (*a*) **Prove from first principles that out of an infinite number of straight lines which may be drawn parallel to a given direction the moment of inertia of a body is least about the one passing through its centre of gravity.**

(*b*) **Determine the moment of inertia of a diatomic molecule.** (*G.N.D.U.* 2008, 2006)

Ans. (*a*) According to the principle of parallel axes the moment of inertia I of a body about an axis is equal to the sum of its moment of inertia about a parallel axis through its centre of gravity I_g and the product of its mass M and the square of the distance h between the two axes *i.e.*, $I = I_g + Mh^2$

Fig. 4.4(*a*)

Hence for a number of axes which are all parallel to each other at distances h_1, h_2, h_3 etc. from the axis AB passing through the centre of gravity the moment of inertia is respectively given by

$$(I_g + Mh_1^2),\ (I_g + Mh_2^2)$$

and so on. The value of h^2 is always positive whether h is towards the left or right of AB. Hence Mh^2 is a positive quantity.

The least value of I is obtained when $h = 0$ *i.e.*, when the axis passes through the centre of gravity.

(*b*) **Moment of inertia of a diatomic molecule (about its Centre of mass).** A diatomic molecule consists of two atoms (similar or dissimilar) separated by a distance greater than the atomic dimensions. The familiar examples of diatomic molecules are H_2, O_2, HCl etc.

To find the moment of inertia of a diatomic molecule like HCl about an axis passing through its centre of mass, let m_1 and m_2 be the masses of the atoms separated by a distance r (the inter-nuclear distance).

If the centre of mass of the molecule lies at O at a distance r_1 from m_1 and r_2 from m_2, then

$$m_1 r_1 = m_2 r_2$$

or

$$m_1(r - r_2) = m_2 r_2$$

$$\therefore \quad r_2 = \frac{m_1 r}{m_1 + m_2}$$

Similarly

$$r_1 = \frac{m_2 r}{m_1 + m_2}$$

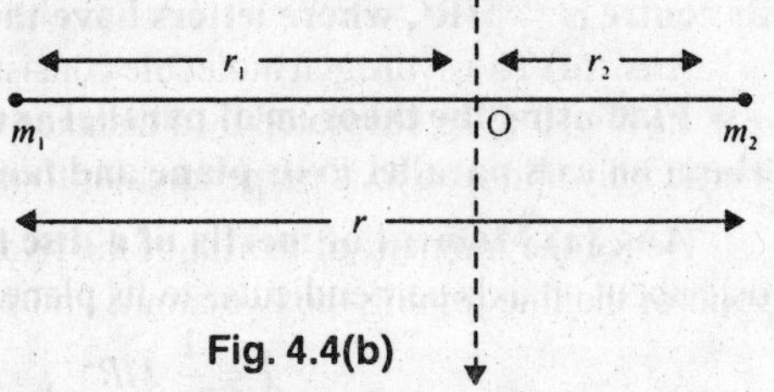

Fig. 4.4(b)

The moment of inertia of the molecule about an axis, passing through O, the centre of mass and perpendicular to the line joining the two nuclei is given by

$$I = m_1 r_1^2 + m_2 r_2^2$$

$$= m_1 \left(\frac{m_2 r}{m_1 + m_2} \right)^2 + m_2 \left(\frac{m_1 r}{m_1 + m_2} \right)^2$$

$$= \frac{m_1 m_2}{m_1 + m_2} r^2 \left[\frac{m_2}{m_1 + m_2} + \frac{m_1}{m_1 + m_2} \right]$$

$$= \frac{m_1 m_2}{m_1 + m_2} r^2 = \mu r^2$$

where $\mu = \dfrac{m_1 m_2}{m_1 + m_2}$ is known as the reduced mass of the molecule.

Q. 4.7. Determine the M.I. of a plane circular disc about an axis through its centre perpendicular to its plane. (*P.U.* 2009; *Madurai U.*, 2003; *Cal.U.*, 1992; *Meerut U.*, 1995)

Ans. Moment of inertia of a circular disc about an axis through its centre perpendicular to its plane. Let M be the mass of the disc and R its radius. Consider an elementary ring of radius x and width dx as shown in Fig. 4.5. Its area is equal to the product of the circumference and width *i.e.*, $2\pi x\, dx$.

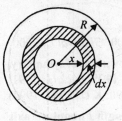

Fig. 4.5

$$\text{Mass per unit area} = \frac{M}{\pi R^2}$$

$$\therefore \quad \text{Mass of the element} = \frac{M}{\pi R^2} 2\pi x dx = \frac{2M}{R^2} x dx$$

Moment of inertia of the element about an axis through its centre perpendicular to its plane

$$= \frac{2M}{R^2} x dx \; x^2 = \frac{2M}{R^2} x^3 dx$$

Hence moment of inertia of the whole disc about this axis

$$I = \frac{2M}{R^2} \int_0^R x^3 dx = \frac{2M}{R^2} \left[\frac{x^4}{4} \right]_0^R = \frac{1}{2} MR^2$$

Q. 4.8. Determine the moment of inertia of a circular disc. (*a*) about a diameter (*b*) about a tangent. (*Burd. U.*, 1992; *Cal. U.*, 1992; *Vid. S.U.*, 1991)

OR

The moment of inertia of a disc about an axis perpendicular to its plane and passing through its centre is $\frac{1}{2} MR^2$, where letters have their usual meaning.

Find using the theorem of parallel and perpendicular axis the moment of inertia of the disc about an axis parallel to its plane and tangential to it. (*G.N.D.U.* 2007)

Ans. (*a*) Moment of inertia of a disc about its diameter. The moment of inertia of a circular disc about an axis perpendicular to its plane and passing through its centre is given by

$$I = \frac{1}{2} MR^2$$

where M is the mass and R its radius.

Now consider two perpendicular diameters AB and CD of the circular disc as in Fig. 4.6. Since all the diameters are symmetrical the moment of inertia of the disc about one diameter is the same as that about any other diameter.

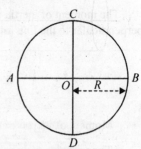

Fig. 4.6

If I_1 and I_2 are the moment of inertia of the disc about two axes perpendicular to each other, then applying the *principle of perpendicular axis*, the moment of inertia I of the disc about an axis perpendicular to the plane of the disc through O.

$$I = I_1 + I_2$$

Since the two diameters are symmetrical with respect to the disc $I_1 = I_2$

$$\therefore \quad I = 2I_1 \quad \text{or} \quad I_1 = \frac{I}{2} = \frac{MR^2}{2} \times \frac{1}{2} = \frac{MR^2}{4}$$

(*b*)   Moment of inertia about a tangent.

Moment of inertia of a disc about a diameter CD, $I_1 = \frac{MR^2}{4}$

Applying the principle of parallel axis, the moment of inertia I about the tangent XY at A. (Fig. 4.7)

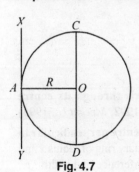

Fig. 4.7

$$I = I_1 + M \times OA^2 = \frac{MR^2}{4} + MR^2 = \frac{5}{4} MR^2$$

Q. 4.9 (*a*) Calculate the moment of inertia of a solid cylinder about

(*i*) **axis of cylindrical symmetry.** (*Gauhati U.* 2000; *Gharwal U.* 2000)

(*ii*) **about the axis passing through its centre and perpendicular to its own axis of symmetry.**
(*M.D.U.*, 2002, 1999; *A.U.*, 1994; *Bang.U.*, 1995; *Luck.U.*, 1991; *Cal.U.*, 1990; *K.U.*, 1992, 1994)

(*b*) Calculate the moment of inertia of a thin rod of mass M and length l about an axis passing through its centre and perpendicular to its length. If this rod rotates about the above axis with a constant angular speed ω, determine its angular momentum and kinetic energy.
(*Luck.U.* 2001, 1991)

(*c*) Find the moment of inertia of a thin uniform rod about an axis passing through one end and perpendicular to its length. (*Kerala* 2001)

Ans. (*a*) (*i*) Moment of inertia of the solid cylinder about its axis of symmetry. A cylinder is a thick circular disc or it may be considered to be a combination of a number of thin discs each of mass m and radius R placed one above the other. The moment of inertia of the cylinder will be equal to the sum of the moments of inertia of each of the discs about an axis through the centre and perpendicular to the plane.

Moment of inertia of one disc $= \frac{1}{2} mR^2$

$\therefore$ Moment of inertia of the cylinder $= \Sigma \frac{1}{2} mR^2 = \frac{1}{2} R^2 \Sigma m = \frac{1}{2} MR^2$

where M is the mass of the cylinder.

(ii) Moment of inertia of the solid cylinder about an axis passing through its centre and perpendicular to its own axis of symmetry. Let M be the mass of the cylinder, R its radius and l its length then its mass per unit length $= \frac{M}{l}$.

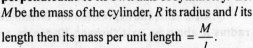
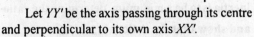

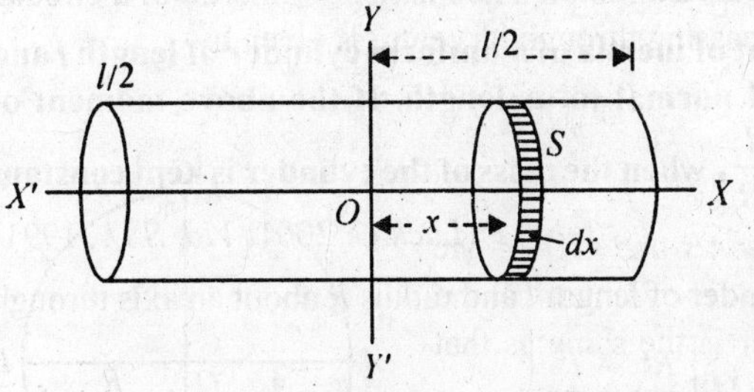

Fig. 4.8

Let YY' be the axis passing through its centre and perpendicular to its own axis XX'.

Consider a thin slice S of thickness dx at a distance x from O.

Mass of the disc $S = \frac{M}{l} dx$

Moment of inertia of this disc about any diameter $= \frac{M}{l} dx \times \frac{R^2}{4}$

The moment of inertia of this disc about a parallel axis YY'; by the principle of parallel axis

$$= \frac{M}{l} dx \frac{R^2}{4} + \frac{M}{l} dx\, x^2$$

The moment of inertia of the cylinder about the axis YY' is obtained by integrating the above expression within the limits $x = +\frac{l}{2}$ and $x = -\frac{l}{2}$.

$$\therefore \ I = \frac{M}{l} \int_{-l/2}^{+l/2} \left[\frac{R^2}{4} + x^2 \right] dx = \frac{M}{l} \left[\frac{R^2}{4} x + \frac{x^3}{3} \right]_{-l/2}^{+l/2} = \frac{M}{l} \left[\frac{R^2}{4} \left(\frac{l}{2} + \frac{l}{2} \right) + \left(\frac{l^3}{24} + \frac{l^3}{24} \right) \right]$$

$$= \frac{M}{l} \left[\frac{R^2 l}{4} + \frac{l^3}{12} \right] = M \left[\frac{R^2}{4} + \frac{l^2}{12} \right]$$

(b) Moment of inertia I of a thin rod. The moment of inertia of a solid cylinder of mass M, length l and radius R about an axis passing through its centre and perpendicular to its own axis of symmetry is given by

$$I = M \left(\frac{R^2}{4} + \frac{l^2}{12} \right)$$

In the case of a thin rod $R = 0$

$$\therefore \qquad I = M \frac{l^2}{12}$$

and radius of gyration $\qquad k = \left(\frac{l^2}{12} \right)^{1/2}$

If this rod rotates about the above axis with constant angular speed ω, then its

Kinetic energy $= \frac{1}{2} I\omega^2 = \frac{1}{2} \frac{Ml^2}{12} \omega^2 = \frac{1}{24} Ml^2\omega^2$

and   Angular momentum $= I\omega = \dfrac{Ml^2}{12}\omega = \dfrac{1}{12}Ml^2\omega$

(c) Moment of inertia of a thin uniform rod of mass M and length l about an axis passing through

its centre and perpendicular to its length $= M\dfrac{l^2}{12}$

∴ Moment of inertia about an axis passing through one end and perpendicular to its length by the

principle of parallel axis $= M\left[\dfrac{l^2}{12} + \left(\dfrac{l}{2}\right)^2\right] = M\left[\dfrac{l^2}{12} + \dfrac{l^2}{4}\right] = M\dfrac{l^2}{3}$

Q. 4.10. State the expression for the moment of inertia of a uniform cylinder of length l and radius R about an axis through its centre and normal to its length. If the above moment of inertia is to be a minimum, determine the ratio $\dfrac{l}{R}$, when the mass of the cylinder is kept constant and show that the ratio is $\sqrt{3} : \sqrt{2}$.

                                                                 (*Luck. U.* 2001; *Vid. S.U.*, 1991)

Ans. The moment of inertia of a uniform cylinder of length l and radius R about an axis through

its centre and normal to its length is given by $I = M\left[\dfrac{R^2}{4} + \dfrac{l^2}{12}\right]$

The mass of the cylinder $M = \pi R^2 l\rho$

where ρ is the density of the material of the cylinder

or $R^2 = \dfrac{M}{\pi l\rho}$ ∴ $I = M\left[\dfrac{M}{4\pi l\rho} + \dfrac{l^2}{12}\right]$

In order that the moment of inertia be a minimum $\dfrac{dI}{dl} = M\left[\dfrac{2l}{12} - \dfrac{M}{4\pi l^2\rho}\right] = 0$

or $\dfrac{2l}{12} = \dfrac{M}{4\pi l^2\rho} = \dfrac{\pi R^2 l\rho}{4\pi l^2\rho} = \dfrac{R^2}{4l}$

or $4l^2 = 6R^2$

or $\dfrac{l}{R} = \sqrt{\dfrac{3}{2}}$

Hence the ratio of $l : R$ is $\sqrt{3} : \sqrt{2}$.

Q. 4.11. What must be the relation between l and R if the moment of inertia of the cylinder about its axis is to be the same as the moment of inertia about the equatorial axis?

                                                                 (*Gharwal U.*, 1999; *A.U.*, 1994)

Ans. M.I. of a cylinder about its own axis $I = \dfrac{1}{2}MR^2$

M.I. about equatorial axis is given by $I' = M\left(\dfrac{l^2}{12} + \dfrac{R^2}{4}\right)$

When both are equal *i.e.* $I = I'$ we get $\dfrac{1}{2}MR^2 = M\left(\dfrac{l^2}{12} + \dfrac{R^2}{4}\right)$

or $l^2 = 3R^2$ ∴ $l = \sqrt{3}\,R$

Q. 4.12. Obtain an expression for the moment of inertia of an annular ring about an axis (a) passing through the centre and perpendicular to its plane. (b) about its diameter.

Ans. (*a*) **About an axis passing through its centre and perpendicular to its plane.** An annular ring or an annular disc is an ordinary disc having a concentric circular hole in it.

Let R_1 and R_2 be the radii of the inner and the outer discs and let M be its mass.

$\therefore$ Area of the face of the disc $= \pi\,(R_2^2 - R_1^2)$

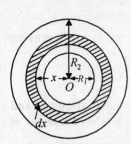

Fig. 4.9

$\therefore$ Mass per unit area $= \dfrac{M}{\pi\,(R_2^2 - R_1^2)}$

Consider a coaxial disc or a ring of inner radius x and outer radius $(x + dx)$, then

Face area of the ring $= 2\pi x . dx$

$\therefore$ Mass of the ring $= \dfrac{M}{\pi\,(R_2^2 - R_1^2)} . 2\pi x\, dx = \dfrac{2Mx\,dx}{(R_2^2 - R_1^2)}$

$\therefore$ Moment of inertia of this ring about an axis passing through O and perpendicular to its plane

$$= \frac{2Mx\,dx}{R_2^2 - R_1^2}\, x^2 = \frac{2Mx^3}{R_2^2 - R_1^2}\, dx$$

The moment of inertia of the whole annular disc is obtained by integrating the above expression between the limits $x = R_1$ and $x = R_2$.

$\therefore$ M.I. of the annular disc about an axis through O and perpendicular to the plane

$$= \frac{2M}{(R_2^2 - R_1^2)} \int_{R_1}^{R_2} x^3\, dx = \frac{2M}{(R_2^2 - R_1^2)} \left[\frac{x^4}{4} \right]_{R_1}^{R_2}$$

$$= \frac{2M}{(R_2^2 - R_1^2)} \left[\frac{R_2^4 - R_1^4}{4} \right] = \frac{M\,(R_2^2 + R_1^2)}{2}$$

(*b*) **About its diameter.** Since the annular ring is symmetrical, the moment of inertia of the annular disc about one diameter is equal to the moment of inertia about another diameter. If I is the moment of inertia about any diameter, then the sum of the moments of inertia about two perpendicular diameters, by the principle of perpendicular axes, will be equal to the moment of inertia about an axis through O and perpendicular to its plane, *i.e.*, $\dfrac{M\,(R_2^2 + R_1^2)}{2}$

$\therefore \quad I + I = \dfrac{M\,(R_2^2 + R_1^2)}{2} \quad$ or $\quad I = \dfrac{M\,(R_2^2 + R_1^2)}{4}$

Q. 4.13. Two thin discs each of mass 0.1 kg and radius 0.05 m are placed at either end of a rod 0.2 m long and 0.01 m in diameter. What is the moment of inertia of the system about an axis passing through the centre of the rod and perpendicular to its length? Density of the material of the rod is 7.8×10^3 kg m^{-3}.

Ans. Let D_1 and D_2 be the two discs of mass M at the ends of the rod AB and YY' the axis passing through the centre O of the rod and perpendicular to its length.

Mass of disc $M = 0.1$ kg

Radius of disc $R = 0.05$ m

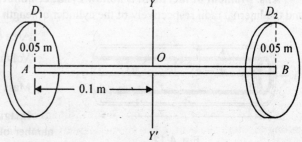

Fig. 4.10

M.I. of each disc about one of its diameter $I_g = \dfrac{1}{4} MR^2$

$$= \dfrac{1}{4} \times 0.1 \times (0.05)^2$$

$$= .0625 \times 10^{-3} \, \text{kg m}^2$$

Distance of YY' from A, $h = 0.1$ m

$\therefore$ M.I. of each disc about the parallel axis YY'

$$= I_g + Mh^2 = .0625 \times 10^{-3} + 0.1 \times 0.1 \times 0.1 = 1.0625 \times 10^{-3} \, \text{kg m}^2$$

Length of rod $l = 0.2$ m and radius $r = 0.005$ m

Mass of rod $m = \pi \times (0.005)^2 \times 0.2 \times 7.8 \times 10^3 = 0.1225$ kg

M.I. of rod about $YY' = m\left[\dfrac{r^2}{4} + \dfrac{l^2}{12}\right] = 0.1225 \left[\dfrac{(0.005)^2}{4} + \dfrac{(0.2)^2}{12}\right]$

$$= 409.2 \times 10^{-6} = 0.4092 \times 10^{-3} \, \text{kg m}^2$$

M.I. of whole system about the axis $YY' = 2 \times 1.0625 \times 10^{-3} + 0.4092 \times 10^{-3}$

$$= 2.5342 \times 10^{-3} \, \text{kg m}^2$$

Q. 4.14. A flat thin uniform disc of radius a has a hole of radius b in it at a distance c from the centre of the disc $\{c < (a - b)\}$. If the disc were free to rotate about a smooth circular rod of radius b passing through the hole, calculate the moment of inertia about the axis of rotation.

Ans. Let M be the mass of the disc of radius a and having a hole of radius b at a distance c from the centre of the disc.

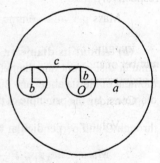

If the hole were supposed to be at the centre, then the moment of inertia of the disc about an axis through O and perpendicular to the plane of the disc

$$I_0 = \dfrac{M(a^2 + b^2)}{2}$$

Applying the principle of parallel axis, moment of inertia about an axis, passing through the centre of a circle of radius b at a distance c from the centre of the disc

$$I = I_0 + Mc^2$$

$$= \dfrac{M(a^2 + b^2)}{2} + Mc^2$$

Fig. 4.11

Q. 4.15. Obtain an expression for the moment of inertia of a hollow cylinder about its own axis of symmetry.

Ans. Moment of inertia of a hollow cylinder about its own axis. Let R and r be the external and the internal radii respectively of the cylinder of length l, and mass M, then

Area of the face of the cylinder $= \pi (R^2 - r^2)$

Volume of the cylinder $= \pi (R^2 - r^2)l$

Mass per unit volume $= \dfrac{M}{\pi(R^2 - r^2)\, l}$

Fig. 4.12

Imagine that the cylinder is made up of a large number of thin coaxial cylinders. Let one of such cylinders be of radius x and thickness dx, then

Face area of such a cylinder $= 2\pi x dx$

and Volume of such a cylinder $= 2\pi x dx l$

$\therefore$ Mass of such a cylinder $= \dfrac{M}{\pi(R^2 - r^2)l} \times 2\pi x.dx.l = \dfrac{2Mx dx}{(R^2 - r^2)}$

The moment of inertia of such a cylinder about its axis $XX' = \dfrac{2Mx dx}{(R^2 - r^2)}\, x^2 = \dfrac{2M}{(R^2 - r^2)}\, x^3 dx$

Hence moment of inertia of the cylinder about its axis can be obtained by integrating the above expression between the limits $x = r$ and $x = R$.

$\therefore$ Moment of inertia $I = \displaystyle\int_r^R \dfrac{2M}{(R^2 - r^2)}\, x^3.\,dx = \dfrac{2M}{(R^2 - r^2)}\left[\dfrac{x^4}{4}\right]_r^R = \dfrac{2M}{R^2 - r^2}\left[\dfrac{R^4 - r^4}{4}\right]$

$\qquad = \dfrac{M(R^2 + r^2)}{2}$

Note. *Alternative method.* If we suppose the hollow cylinder to be made up of a number of annular rings of mass m each placed one above the other, then

$$\text{M.I.} = \Sigma m\, \dfrac{R^2 + r^2}{2} = M\, \dfrac{R^2 + r^2}{2}$$

Q. 4.16. Derive an expression for the moment of inertia of a hollow cylinder about an axis through the centre and perpendicular to its own axis.   (*K.U.* 2000)

Ans. Let M, R, r and l be the mass, external radius, internal radius and length of the cylinder respectively, then

Mass per unit volume $= \dfrac{M}{\pi(R^2 - r^2)l}$

Imagine the cylinder to be made of a large number of annular discs of external and internal radii R and r respectively, placed one above the other.

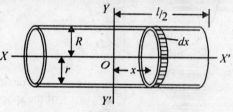

Fig. 4.13

Consider one such disc of thickness dx at a distance x from the axis YY', then

Volume of the disc $= \pi(R^2 - r^2)\, dx$

$\therefore$ Mass of the disc $= \dfrac{M}{\pi(R^2 - r^2)l} \times \pi(R^2 - r^2)\, dx = \dfrac{M}{l}\, dx$

Moment of inertia of the annular disc of external and internal radii R and r respectively about its own diameter $=$ Mass $\times \dfrac{(R^2 + r^2)}{4}$

or M.I. about its diameter $= \dfrac{M}{l}\, dx\, \dfrac{(R^2 + r^2)}{4}$

Hence by the principle of parallel axes the moment of inertia of the disc about the axis YY' is given by

$$\dfrac{M(R^2 + r^2)}{4l}\, dx + \dfrac{M}{l}\, dx\, x^2$$

Then moment of inertia I of the hollow cylinder can be obtained by integrating the above expression between the limits

$x = +\dfrac{l}{2}$ and $x = -\dfrac{l}{2}$.

$$\therefore \quad I = \int_{-l/2}^{+l/2} \frac{M(R^2 + r^2)}{4l} \, dx + \int_{-l/2}^{+l/2} \frac{M}{l} x^2 \, dx$$

$$= \frac{M(R^2 + r^2)}{4l} [x]_{-l/2}^{+l/2} + \frac{M}{l} \left[\frac{x^3}{3}\right]_{-l/2}^{+l/2} = \frac{M(R^2 + r^2)}{4l} \left[\frac{l}{2} + \frac{l}{2}\right] + \frac{M}{l} \left[\frac{l^3}{24} + \frac{l^3}{24}\right]$$

$$= M \left[\frac{(R^2 + r^2)}{4} + \frac{l^2}{12}\right]$$

Q. 4.17. Derive the formula for the moment of inertia of a uniform solid sphere (*i*) about its diameter and (*ii*) about its tangent.   (*P.U.* 2008; *M.D.U.* 2001; *K.U.* 2000, 1996; *A.U.*, 1993; *Meerut U.*, 1990; *Luck.U.*, 1995, 1991; *Bang.U.*, 1990; *Burd.U.*, 1990)

Ans. (*i*) Moment of inertia of the sphere about a diameter. A section of a sphere of radius *r* through the centre *O* is shown in Fig. 4.14. Let *AB* be the diameter about which the moment of inertia is to be found. Consider a thin circular slice of thickness *dx* at a distance *x* from the centre, then

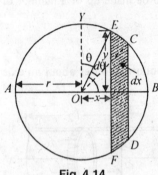

Fig. 4.14

Radius of the slice, $y = \sqrt{r^2 - x^2}$

$\therefore$ Volume of slice $= \pi (r^2 - x^2) \, dx$

Let *m* be the mass per unit volume of the sphere, then

Mass of slice, $M_1 = m\pi (r^2 - x^2) \, dx$

Moment of inertia of the slice (disc) about *AB*

$$= \frac{1}{2} M_1 y^2 = \frac{1}{2} m\pi (r^2 - x^2) \, dx \, (r^2 - x^2)$$

$$= \frac{1}{2} m\pi (r^2 - x^2)^2 \, dx$$

Considering all such elementary discs, the moment of inertia of the sphere about the diameter *AB* is given by

$$I = 2 \int_0^r \frac{1}{2} m\pi (r^2 - x^2)^2 \, dx = m\pi \int_0^r (r^4 + x^4 - 2r^2x^2) \, dx$$

$$= m\pi \left[r^4 x + \frac{x^5}{5} - \frac{2r^2x^3}{3}\right]_0^r = m\pi \left[r^5 + \frac{r^5}{5} - \frac{2r^5}{3}\right] = \frac{8m\pi r^5}{15}$$

Now mass of the sphere $M = \frac{4}{3} \pi r^3 m$

$$\therefore \quad I = \frac{8m\pi r^5}{15} = \frac{4}{3} \pi r^3 m \times \frac{2}{5} r^2 = \frac{2}{5} Mr^2$$

or   Moment of inertia of the sphere about a diameter $I = \frac{2}{5} Mr^2$

(*ii*) Moment of inertia of the sphere about a tangent. The tangent to the sphere at any point is parallel to one, of its diameters and is at a distance equal to *r* from the centre. Therefore, by the principle of parallel axis, the moment of inertia of the sphere about a tangent

$$= \frac{2}{5} Mr^2 + Mr^2 = \frac{7}{5} Mr^2$$

Q. 4.18. (*a*) Assuming earth to be a sphere of uniform density 5520 kg. m^{-3} and radius 6400 km, calculate the M.I. about its axis of rotation.   (*Bang. U.*, 1991)

(*b*) Moment of inertia of a bigger solid sphere about its diameter is *I*. 64 smaller, equal spheres are made out of bigger sphere. What will be the moment of inertia of such smaller sphere about its diameter?   (*Luck. U.*, 1995)

(c) A sphere has a radius of 0.60 m calculate its moment of inertia about its tangent. Density of material is 7.8×10^3 kg/m³. (M.D.U. 2008)

Ans. (a) Density of earth $\rho = 5520$ kgm⁻³

Radius of earth $R = 6400$ km $= 6400 \times 10^3$ m

$\therefore$ Mass of earth $M = \dfrac{4}{3} \pi R^3 \rho = \dfrac{4}{3} \pi [6400 \times 10^3]^3 \times 5520 = 6.06 \times 10^{24}$ kg

Moment of inertia of the earth about its axis $= \dfrac{2}{5} MR^2$

$= \dfrac{2}{5} \times 6.06 \times 10^{24} \times [6400 \times 10^3]^2 = 9.93 \times 10^{37}$ kg m²

(b) Moment of inertia of the bigger sphere $I = \dfrac{2}{5} MR^2$

where M is its mass and R its radius. Let ρ be the density of the material of the sphere, then

$$M = \dfrac{4}{3} \pi R^3 \rho$$

Let m be the mass of the smaller sphere, then $m = \dfrac{M}{64}$

If r is the radius of the smaller sphere, then

$$m = \dfrac{4}{3} \pi r^3 \rho = \dfrac{1}{64} \times \dfrac{4}{3} \pi R^3 \rho$$

or $\qquad\qquad r^3 = \dfrac{R^3}{64}$ or $r = \dfrac{R}{4}$

$\therefore$ Moment of inertia of the smaller sphere $= I_s = \dfrac{2}{5} mr^2$

$$= \dfrac{2}{5} \dfrac{M}{64} \dfrac{R^2}{16} = \dfrac{1}{1024} \times \dfrac{2}{5} MR^2 \qquad \text{or} \qquad I_s = \dfrac{I}{1024}$$

(c) $\qquad\qquad$ Volume of the sphere $= \dfrac{4}{3} \pi r^3$

Mass of the sphere $M = \dfrac{4}{3} \pi r^3 \rho = \dfrac{4}{3} \times \dfrac{22}{7} \times (0.60)^3 \times 7.8 \times 10^3$

$$= 7.06 \times 10^3 \text{ kg}$$

Moment of inertia of a solid sphere about a tangent

$$I = \dfrac{7}{5} Mr^2 = \dfrac{7}{5} \times 7.06 \times 10^3 \times (0.60)^2$$

$$= 3.56 \times 10^3 \text{ kg m}^2$$

Exercise. Obtain moment of inertia of a solid sphere of radius 40 cm about a tangent. The density of the sphere is 7 gm/cm³. (M.D.U. 2007)

Ans. 42×10^8 gm cm².

Q 4.19. (a) **Calculate the moment of inertia of a thin spherical shell (hollow sphere) about (i) a diameter and a tangent.** (M.D.U. 2008, 2007, 2006; P.U. 2006)

(b) **Hence derive the moment of inertia of (i) a solid sphere about a diameter and a tangent and (ii) a thick shell about an axis through the centre.** (Meerut U. 2003; K.U. 2001; Kerala U. 2001; M.D.U. 2003, 2001; Gauhati U. 2000)

Ans. (a) **Moment of inertia of a spherical shell.** Consider a section of a spherical shell through its centre O. Let r be its radius and M its mass, then

Surface area of the shell $= 4\pi r^2$ $\qquad \therefore$ Mass per unit area $= \dfrac{M}{4\pi r^2}$

Now consider a thin element of the shell bounded by two parallel planes EF and CD at a distance x and $x + dx$ respectively from O. The slice has a radius equal to y and width EC (not dx).

Area of the thin element of the shell = circumference × width = $2\pi y \times EC$

$$= 2\pi y \, rd\theta = 2\pi \, ryd\theta \qquad \qquad ...(i)$$

It is clear from the figure that,

$$y = r \cos \theta \text{ and } x = r \sin \theta$$

Differentiating, we have $dx = r \cos \theta d\theta = y \, d\theta$

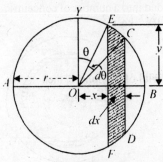

Fig. 4.15

Substituting $dx = y \, d\theta$ in (i), we have

Area of the element = $2\pi r \, dx$

∴ Mass of the element $= \dfrac{M}{4\pi r^2} \, 2\pi r \, dx = \dfrac{M}{2r} \, dx$

Now $y^2 = r^2 - x^2$

Moment of inertia of the slice about a diameter AB

$$= \frac{M}{2r} \, dx \, (r^2 - x^2)$$

∴ Moment of inertia of the shell about a diameter

$$= \int_{-r}^{+r} \frac{M}{2r} (r^2 - x^2) \, dx = \frac{M}{2r} \left[\int_{-r}^{+r} r^2 dx - \int_{-r}^{+r} x^2 dx \right]$$

$$= \frac{M}{2r} \left[r^2 x \right]_{-r}^{+r} - \frac{M}{2r} \left[\frac{x^3}{3} \right]_{-r}^{+r} = \frac{M}{2r} \left[(r^3 + r^3) - \left(\frac{r^3}{3} + \frac{r^3}{3} \right) \right] = \frac{M}{2r} \left[2r^3 - \frac{2}{3} r^3 \right]$$

$$= \frac{M}{2r} \frac{4}{3} r^3 = \frac{2}{3} Mr^2$$

(ii) Moment of inertia of a hollow sphere about a tangent. The tangent to a hollow sphere at any point is parallel to one of its diameters and is at a distance equal to r from its centre.

Therefore, by principle of parallel axes, the moment of inertia of a hollow sphere about a tangent

$$= \frac{2}{3} Mr^2 + Mr^2 = \frac{5}{3} Mr^2$$

(b) (i) Moment of inertia of the solid sphere (*about a diameter*). To calculate the moment of inertia of a solid sphere from a knowledge of the moment of inertia of the shell, suppose the sphere is divided into a number of concentric shells of thickness dx each. Now consider a shell at a distance x from the centre.

Volume of the shell = $4\pi x^2 \, dx$

Volume of the sphere $= \dfrac{4}{3} \pi r^3$

Mass of the sphere = M

∴ Mass per unit volume $= \dfrac{3M}{4\pi r^3}$

Hence mass of the shell $= \dfrac{3}{4} \dfrac{M}{\pi r^3} 4\pi x^2 dx = \dfrac{3M}{r^3} x^2 dx$

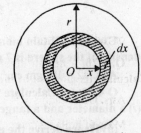

Fig. 4.16

Moment of inertia of the shell about a diameter

$$= \frac{2}{3} \text{ mass} \times \text{(radius)}^2 = \frac{2}{3} \frac{3M}{r^3} x^2 dx . x^2 = \frac{2M}{r^3} x^4 dx$$

Moment of inertia of the sphere about a diameter $= \dfrac{2M}{r^3} \displaystyle\int_0^r x^4 dx = \dfrac{2M}{r^3} \left[\dfrac{x^5}{5} \right]_0^r = \dfrac{2}{5} Mr^2$

Moment of inertia about a tangent. The distance between a tangent and a diameter of the sphere = r

Applying principle of parallel axes, we have

Moment of inertia of the sphere about a tangent

$$= \frac{2}{5} Mr^2 + Mr^2 = \frac{7}{5} Mr^2.$$

(*ii*) **Moment of inertia of a thick shell.** Consider a thick shell or a hollow sphere of external radius R and internal radius r. To find the moment of inertia suppose it is divided into a number of concentric thin shells of thickness dx each. Consider a shell at a distance x from the centre, then

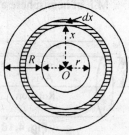

Fig. 4.17

Volume of the shell = $4\pi x^2 dx$

Total volume of the hollow sphere of external radius R and internal

radius $r = \frac{4}{3} \pi (R^3 - r^3)$

If M is the mass of the hollow sphere, then

Mass per unit volume $= \dfrac{3M}{4\pi(R^3 - r^3)}$

$\therefore$ Mass of the shell $= \dfrac{3M}{4\pi(R^3 - r^3)} 4\pi x^2 \, dx = \dfrac{3Mx^2 \, dx}{(R^3 - r^3)}$

Moment of inertia of the thin shell about a diameter $= \dfrac{2}{3} \dfrac{3M}{(R^3 - r^3)} x^2 \, dx \, x^2 = \dfrac{2M}{(R^3 - r^3)} x^4 dx$

$$\left.\begin{array}{l}\text{Moment of inertia of the hollow} \\ \text{sphere of external radius } R \text{ and} \\ \text{internal radius } r\end{array}\right] = \dfrac{2M}{(R^3 - r^3)} \int_r^R x^4 dx = \dfrac{2M}{(R^3 - r^3)}\left[\dfrac{R^5 - r^5}{5}\right]$$

$$= \dfrac{2}{5} M \left(\dfrac{R^5 - r^5}{R^3 - r^3}\right)$$

Exercise. *Calculate the radius of gyration of a solid sphere rotating about its diameter if its radius is 5.0 cm.*   (M.D.U., 2003)

Hint. M.I of solid sphere $= \dfrac{2}{5} Mr^2 = Mk^2$

$\therefore$ $k^2 = \dfrac{2}{5} r^2 = \dfrac{2}{5} \times 5^2 = \dfrac{2}{5} \times 25 = 10$ cm^2

or radius of gyration $k = \sqrt{10}$ cm

Q. 4.20. A hollow steel sphere has its inner and outer radii 5 cm and 12 cm respectively. Calculate its moment of inertia about a diameter. Density of steel is 7.8×10^3 kg m^{-3}.

Ans. Outer radius $R = 12$ cm $= 0.12$ m, Inner radius $r = 5$ cm $= 0.05$ m

Mass of hollow sphere $M = \dfrac{4}{3} \pi (R^3 - r^3) \rho$

M.I. of hollow sphere $I = \dfrac{2}{5} M \left(\dfrac{R^5 - r^5}{R^3 - r^3}\right) = \dfrac{2}{5} \times \dfrac{4}{3} \pi (R^3 - r^3). \rho \left(\dfrac{R^5 - r^5}{R^3 - r^3}\right)$

$$= \dfrac{8}{15} \times 3.142 \times 7.8 \times 10^3 \, (R^5 - r^5)$$

$$= 13.07 \times 10^3 \, (0.12^5 - 0.05^5) = 0.3211 \text{ kg m}^2$$

Q. 4.21. The flat surface of a hemisphere of radius *r* is cemented to one flat surface of a cylinder of radius *r* and length *L*. If the total mass is *M*, show that the M.I. of combination about the axis of the cylinder will be

$$Mr^2 \, \frac{(L/2 + 4r/15)}{(L + 2r/3)}.$$

(*Kan. U.*, 1996; *A.U.*, 1995)

Ans. Suppose *m* is the mass of cylinder and *m'* that of the hemisphere and ρ the density of the material, then

M.I. of cylinder about its axis $= \dfrac{mr^2}{2} = \pi r^2 L\rho \times \dfrac{r^2}{2} = \dfrac{\pi r^4 L\rho}{2}$

M.I. of hemisphere about the axis of cylinder $= \dfrac{2}{5} m'r^2 = \dfrac{2}{5} \times \dfrac{2}{3} \pi r^3 \rho r^2 = \dfrac{4}{15} \pi r^5 \rho$

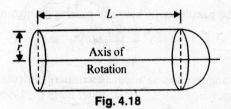

Fig. 4.18

M.I. of the combination about the axis of the cylinder,

$$I = \pi r^4 \, \rho \, (L/2 + 4r/15)$$

Now $\qquad M = m + m' = \pi r^2 L\rho + \dfrac{2}{3} \pi r^3 \rho$

$$= \pi r^2 \rho \, (L + 2/3 \, r)$$

Hence $\qquad I = Mr^2 \, \dfrac{(L/2 + 4r/15)}{(L + 2/3r)}$

Q. 4.22. Obtain an expression for the moment of inertia of a solid cone (*i*) about its vertical axis and (*ii*) about an axis through its vertex and parallel to its base.   (*Cal. U. Hons.*, 1991)

Ans. Moment of inertia of a cone. (*i*) *About its vertical axis.*

Let *M* be the mass of the cone, *h* its vertical height and *R* the radius of its base.

Volume of the cone $= \dfrac{1}{3} \pi R^2 h$ $\therefore$ Mass per unit volume $= \dfrac{3M}{\pi R^2 h}$

Imagine that the cone is made up of a number of discs parallel to the base placed one above the other. Consider one such disc of radius *r* and thickness *dx* at a distance *x* from the vertex *A*.

If α is half the vertical angle of the cone, then $r = x \tan \alpha$

Also $\tan \alpha = \dfrac{R}{h}$ or $r = \dfrac{xR}{h}$

Now the volume of the disc $= \pi r^2 \, dx$

$\therefore$ Mass of the disc $= \dfrac{\pi r^2 \, dx}{\pi R^2 h} \dfrac{3M}{} = \dfrac{3Mr^2}{R^2 h} \, dx$

The moment of inertia of the disc about the axis *AO* passing through the centre and perpendicular to its plane

$= \dfrac{\text{Mass of the disc} \times (\text{radius})^2}{2} = \dfrac{3Mr^2}{R^2 h} \, dx \, \dfrac{r^2}{2} = \dfrac{3M}{2R^2 h} r^4 \, dx$

But $\qquad\qquad r = \dfrac{xR}{h}$

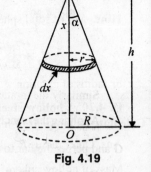

Fig. 4.19

$\therefore$ M.I. of the disc $= \dfrac{3M}{2R^2 h} \dfrac{R^4 x^4}{h^4} \, dx = \dfrac{3MR^2}{2h^5} x^4 \, dx$

Hence the moment of inertia of the whole cone about the vertical axis *AO* will be the integral of the above expression between the limits $x = 0$ and $x = h$.

$\therefore$ M.I. of the cone about its vertical axis $I = \dfrac{3MR^2}{2h^5} \displaystyle\int_0^h x^4 \, dx = \dfrac{3MR^2}{2h^5} \left[\dfrac{x^5}{5} \right]_0^h = \dfrac{3MR^2}{10}$

(ii) About an axis through its vertex and parallel to its base: Now, again if we consider a disc at a distance x from the vertex of the cone, then its moment of inertia about its diameter

$$= \frac{\text{Mass of the disc} \times (\text{radius})^2}{4} = \frac{3Mr^2}{R^2h} dx \frac{r^2}{4}$$

Applying principle of parallel axis, the moment of inertia of this disc about a parallel axis XX' through the vertex of the cone, is given by $I = \frac{3Mr^4}{4R^2h} dx + \frac{3Mr^2}{R^2h} dx \, x^2$

Substituting the value of $r = \frac{xR}{h}$, we get

Moment of inertia of disc $= \frac{3Mx^4R^4}{4R^2h^5} dx + \frac{3MR^2}{R^2h^3} x^4 dx$

$\therefore$ Moment of inertia of the cone about an axis XX' parallel to its base and passing through its

vertex $= \int_0^h \frac{3MR^2}{4h^5} x^4 \, dx + \int_0^h \frac{3M}{h^3} x^4 \, dx = \frac{3MR^2}{4h^5} \left[\frac{x^5}{5} \right]_0^h + \frac{3M}{h^3} \left[\frac{x^{5}}{5} \right]_0^h = \frac{3MR^2}{20} + \frac{3Mh^2}{5}$

Q. 4.23. Calculate the moment of inertia of a rectangular lamina about an axis perpendicular to its plane and passing through its centre of gravity. *(P.U. 2007; Bang.U., 1990)*

Ans. Let M be the mass of the rectangular lamina of sides a and b as shown. Consider an axis AB parallel to the side a and passing through G, the centre of mass. Consider a small strip of breadth dx parallel to the side a at a distance x from the axis AB.

Area of the strip $= adx$

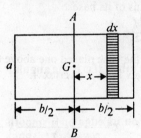

Fig. 4.20

Mass per unit area of the lamina $= \dfrac{M}{ab}$

$\therefore$ Mass of the strip $= \dfrac{M}{ab} \times adx = \dfrac{M}{b} dx$

Moment of inertia of the strip about the axis $AB = \dfrac{M}{b} x^2 \, dx$

Moment of inertia of the lamina about the axis AB is obtained by integrating the above expression between the limits $x = \dfrac{b}{2}$ and $x = -\dfrac{b}{2}$.

$\therefore \quad I_y = \int_{-b/2}^{b/2} \frac{M}{b} x^2 \, dx = \frac{M}{b} \left[\frac{x^3}{3} \right]_{-b/2}^{b/2} = \frac{M}{b} \left[\frac{b^3}{24} + \frac{b^3}{24} \right] = \frac{M}{b} \frac{b^3}{12} = M \frac{b^2}{12}$

Similarly the moment of inertia of the lamina about an axis parallel to the side b, $I_x = M \dfrac{a^2}{12}$

Applying the principle of perpendicular axis, the moment of inertia about an axis passing through G and perpendicular to the plane is given by $I = I_x + I_y = \dfrac{Ma^2}{12} + \dfrac{Mb^2}{12} = M \dfrac{a^2 + b^2}{12}$

Q. 4.24. (a) Find an expression for the moment of inertia of a rectangular solid bar of length l about an axis perpendicular to its length and passing through its centre of gravity. *(Pbi. U. 2007, 2005; Kan.U., 1990; K.U., 2002, 2000, 1994, 1992)*

(b) Deduce an expression for the moment of inertia of a rectangular bar about an axis perpendicular to the length of the bar and passing through one of its sides. Hence find the moment of inertia of a square bar about the same axis. *(M.D.U. 2007, 2000; Kerala U. 2001)*

Ans. (a) Moment of inertia of a rectangular bar. (i) *About an axis through its C.G. and perpendicular to its length.* Consider a rectangular bar of length l, breadth b and thickness a having a mass M.

Suppose it is divided into a number of thin laminas of mass m each placed one above the other as shown. The M.I. of a lamina about the axis YY' perpendicular to its plane and passing through its centre

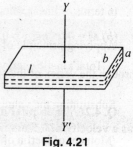

$$= m\,\frac{l^2 + b^2}{12}$$

$\therefore$ M.I. of the rectangular bar about the axis YY'

$$I_y = \Sigma m\,\frac{l^2 + b^2}{12} = M\,\frac{l^2 + b^2}{12}$$

Fig. 4.21

(b) *About an axis perpendicular to its length and passing through one of its sides.* The M.I. of the bar about a parallel axis through the corner AB as shown in Fig. 4.22

$$= I_y + M \times AC^2$$

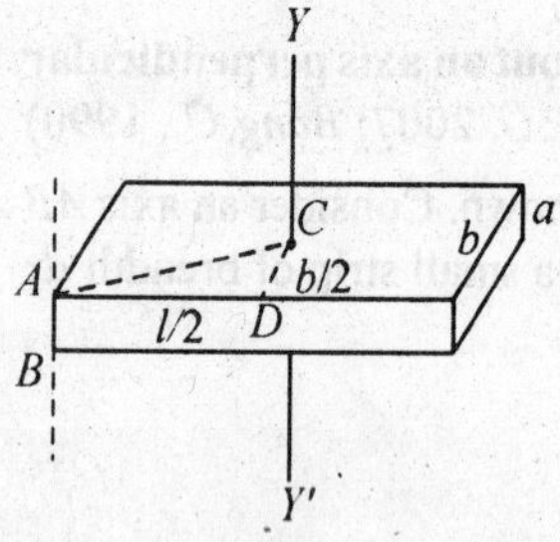

But $\quad AC^2 = AD^2 + CD^2 = \left(\dfrac{l}{2}\right)^2 + \left(\dfrac{b}{2}\right)^2$

M.I. about the axis $AB = M\left[\dfrac{l^2 + b^2}{12}\right] + M\left[\dfrac{l^2}{4} + \dfrac{b^2}{4}\right]$

$$= M\,\frac{l^2 + b^2}{3}$$

For a bar of **square cross-section** $l = b$

$\therefore \qquad$ M.I. $= \dfrac{2}{3}Mb^2$

Fig. 4.22

Q. 4.25. (a) A circular disc of mass M and radius r is set rolling on a table. If ω is the angular velocity show that its total energy E is given by $\dfrac{3}{4}Mr^2\,\omega^2$.

(b) A flat circular disc of mass 0.05 kg and diameter 0.02 m rolls on its edge on a smooth horizontal surface with a velocity 0.05 ms^{-1}. Calculate its total energy.   (*Bang. U.*, 1995)

Ans. (a) When a circular disc rolls on a table a point on its circumference rotates about an axis passing through its centre and perpendicular to its plane. In addition, the point moves forward. In other words it possess an angular velocity and a linear velocity. Therefore, it possesses two kinds of energies:

(i) Energy due to linear motion, and (ii) Energy due to rotation about an axis through its centre.

If v is the linear velocity, the energy due to linear motion $= \dfrac{1}{2}Mv^2$

If ω is the angular velocity, then the kinetic energy due to rotational motion $= \dfrac{1}{2}I\omega^2$

where I is the moment of inertia of the disc about an axis perpendicular to its plane and passing through its C.G.

Now $I = \dfrac{1}{2}Mr^2$ $\therefore$ K.E. due to rotation $= \dfrac{1}{2}\times\dfrac{1}{2}Mr^2\omega^2 = \dfrac{1}{4}Mr^2\,\omega^2$

$\therefore$ Total K.E. $= \dfrac{1}{2}Mv^2 + \dfrac{1}{4}Mr^2\omega^2$

Now $v = r\omega$ $\quad \therefore$ K.E. $= \dfrac{1}{2} Mr^2 \omega^2 + \dfrac{1}{4} Mr^2 \omega^2 = \dfrac{3}{4} Mr^2 \omega^2$

In terms of linear velocity, K.E. $= \dfrac{3}{4} Mv^2$

(b) $M = 0.05$ kg, $v = 0.05$ ms^{-1}

$\therefore$ Total kinetic energy $= \dfrac{3}{4} Mv^2 = \dfrac{3}{4} \times 0.05 \times (0.05)^2$

$\qquad\qquad = 93.75 \times 10^{-6}$ kg m^2 s^{-2} or Joule

Q. 4.26. An annular disc of mass 0.2 kg and radii 0.2 m and 0.25 m rolls such that the centre has a velocity of 0.5 ms^{-1}. Calculate its kinetic energy.

Ans. Here $M = 0.2$ kg, $v = 0.5$ ms^{-1}

$\therefore$ K.E. due to linear motion $= \dfrac{1}{2} mv^2 = \dfrac{1}{2} \times 0.2 \times (0.5)^2 = 0.025$ J

M.I. of annular disc about the axis of rotation $I = \dfrac{1}{2} M (R_2^{~2} + R_1^{~2})$

Now $R_2 = 0.25$ m and $R_1 = 0.20$ m

$\therefore \qquad I = \dfrac{1}{2} \times 0.2 (0.25^2 + 0.2^2) = 1.025 \times 10^{-2}$ kg m^2

Angular velocity $\omega = \dfrac{v}{R_2} = \dfrac{0.5}{0.25} = 2$ rad s^{-1}

$\therefore$ K.E. of rotation $= \dfrac{1}{2} I\omega^2 = \dfrac{1}{2} \times 1.025 \times 10^{-2} \times 4 = 2.05 \times 10^{-2}$ J

Total K.E. $= 0.025 + 0.0205 = 0.0455$ J

Q. 4.27. A solid spherical ball rolls on a table. Find the ratio of its translational and rotational kinetic energies and the total energy of the spherical ball. What fraction of the total energy is rotational?   (*Kerala U.* 2001; *Gowhati U.* 2000)

Ans. When a solid spherical ball rolls on a table a point on its surface rotates about an axis passing through its centre and perpendicular to its plane of rotation. The ball also moves forward. It, therefore, possesses both angular velocity and linear velocity due to which it has a rotational kinetic energy and a translational kinetic energy.

Energy due to linear motion $= \dfrac{1}{2} Mv^2$ ...(i)

where M is the mass of the spherical ball and v its linear velocity.

Energy due to rotation $= \dfrac{1}{2} I\omega^2$

where I is the moment of inertia of the spherical ball and ω is angular velocity.

For a spherical ball of radius r, $I = \dfrac{2}{5} Mr^2$

$\therefore$ Energy due to rotation $= \dfrac{1}{2} \dfrac{2}{5} Mr^2 \omega^2 = \dfrac{1}{5} Mv^2$

Total energy $= \dfrac{1}{2} Mv^2 + \dfrac{1}{5} Mv^2 = \dfrac{7}{10} Mv^2$

Hence $\quad \dfrac{\text{Translational K.E.}}{\text{Rotational K.E.}} = \dfrac{\dfrac{1}{2} Mv^2}{\dfrac{1}{5} Mv^2} = \dfrac{5}{2}$; $\quad \dfrac{\text{Rotational K.E.}}{\text{Total K.E.}} = \dfrac{\dfrac{1}{5} Mv^2}{\dfrac{7}{10} Mv^2} = \dfrac{2}{7}$

$$\frac{\text{Translational K.E.}}{\text{Total K.E.}} = \frac{\frac{1}{2} Mv^2}{\frac{7}{10} Mv^2} = \frac{5}{7}$$

Q. 4.28. A solid sphere of mass 0.1 kg and radius 2.5 cm rolls without slipping with a uniform velocity of 0.1 ms^{-1} along a straight line on a horizontal table. Calculate its total energy.

Ans. As the sphere rolls without slipping it has both energy of translation and rotation.

Here $M = 0.1$ kg, $r = 2.5$ cm $= 0.025$ m, $v = 0.1$ ms^{-1}

$$\therefore \quad \omega = \frac{v}{r} = \frac{0.1}{0.025} = 4 \text{ rad s}^{-1}$$

K.E. of translation $= \dfrac{1}{2} Mv^2 = \dfrac{1}{2} \times 0.1 \times 0.1 \times 0.1 = 0.0005$ J

K.E. of rotation $= \dfrac{1}{2} I\omega^2 = \dfrac{1}{2} \times \dfrac{2}{5} Mr^2 \omega^2 = \dfrac{1}{5} \times 0.1 \times (.025)^2 \times 16 = 0.0002$ J

Total energy $= 0.0005 + 0.0002 = 0.0007$ J $= 7 \times 10^{-4}$ J.

Q. 4.29. A fly wheel in the form of a solid disc of 5000 kg and 1 m radius is rotating making 120 r.p.m. Compute (i) K.E. and (ii) angular impulse if the wheel is brought to rest in 2 seconds.
(K.U., 1994)

Ans. Here $M = 5000$ kg, $R = 1$ m, $n = \dfrac{120}{60} = 2$ r.p.s.

Moment of inertia $I = \dfrac{1}{2} MR^2 = \dfrac{1}{2} \times 5000 \times 1 = 2500$ kg m^2

Angular velocity $\omega = 2\pi n = 2\pi \times 2 = 4\pi$ rad s^{-1}

(i) K.E. $= \dfrac{1}{2} I\omega^2 = \dfrac{1}{2} \times 2500 \times 16\pi^2 = 1.974 \times 10^5$ J

(ii) Initial angular momentum $L_1 = I\omega = 2500 \times 4\pi = 3.142 \times 10^4$ N-m

Final angular moment $L_2 = 0$

$\therefore$ Angular impulse $= \dfrac{L_1 - L_2}{2} = \dfrac{3.142 \times 10^4}{2} = 1.571 \times 10^4$ N-ms^{-1}

Q. 4.30. Derive an expression for the acceleration of a body rolling down a smooth inclined plane without slipping. What are the values of acceleration for a cylinder, solid sphere and hollow sphere of the same radius? *(K.U., 2002, 2001; M.D.U. 2003, 2001, 1999; Meerut U. 2006; Gharwal U., 2001; Bang.U., 2000, 1994)*

Ans. Let a body of radius r and mass M roll without slipping down a smooth inclined plane having an angle of inclination θ. Suppose v is the velocity acquired by the body after traversing a distance S along the plane. Let ω be the angular velocity about an axis through the centre of the body.

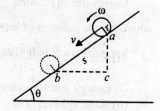

Now, in one revolution the body moves a distance $2\pi r$ whereas a point on the rim truns through 2π radians in the same time.

$\therefore$ Linear velocity $v = r\omega$ or $\omega = \dfrac{v}{r}$

Fig. 4.23

If I is the moment of inertia and k the radius of gryation of the body about the axis of rotation, then the total kinetic energy of the body consists of

(i) Energy of translation $= \dfrac{1}{2} Mv^2$ and (ii) Energy of rotation $= \dfrac{1}{2} I\omega^2 = \dfrac{1}{2} Mk^2\omega^2$

$\therefore$ Total energy $= \dfrac{1}{2} Mv^2 + \dfrac{1}{2} Mk^2\omega^2$

In moving a distance s from a to b the body comes down vertically a distance

$$ac = s \sin \theta$$

Hence the change in potential energy $= Mgs \sin \theta$

Since there is no slipping, no energy is dissipated and the total gain in kinetic energy is equal to the change in potential energy.

$\therefore \qquad Mgs \sin \theta = \dfrac{1}{2} Mv^2 + \dfrac{1}{2} Mk^2\,\omega^2 = \dfrac{1}{2} Mv^2 + \dfrac{1}{2} Mk^2 \dfrac{v^2}{r^2} = \dfrac{1}{2} Mv^2 \left(1 + \dfrac{k^2}{r^2}\right)$

or $\qquad sg \sin \theta = \dfrac{v^2}{2}\left(1 + \dfrac{k^2}{r^2}\right)$

Differentiating with respect to time t, we get

$$\dfrac{ds}{dt} g \sin \theta = \dfrac{2v}{2}\dfrac{dv}{dt}\left(1 + \dfrac{k^2}{r^2}\right) = v\dfrac{dv}{dt}\left(1 + \dfrac{k^2}{r^2}\right)$$

Now $\dfrac{ds}{dt} =$ linear velocity v and $\dfrac{dv}{dt} =$ acceleration a

$\therefore \qquad \dfrac{dv}{dt} v\left(1 + \dfrac{k^2}{r^2}\right) = vg \sin \theta$ or $\dfrac{dv}{dt} = a = \dfrac{g \sin \theta}{\left(1 + \dfrac{k^2}{r^2}\right)}$

This shows that for a given angle of inclination of the plane θ the acceleration is inversely proportional to $\left(1 + \dfrac{k^2}{r^2}\right)$. Thus

(i) Greater the value of k as compared to r the smaller is the acceleration of the body moving down an inclined plane and hence greater is the time taken in rolling down the plane.

(ii) The acceleration is independent of the mass of the body.

Special cases (i) Cylinder. The moment of inertia of a cylinder about its axis of symmetry about which it rolls $= \dfrac{1}{2} Mr^2$

$\therefore \qquad I = \dfrac{1}{2} Mr^2 = Mk^2$ or $k^2 = \dfrac{r^2}{2}$ and $\dfrac{k^2}{r^2} = \dfrac{1}{2}$

Hence $\qquad a = \dfrac{g \sin \theta}{1 + \dfrac{k^2}{r^2}} = \dfrac{g \sin \theta}{1 + \dfrac{1}{2}} = \dfrac{2}{3} g \sin \theta$

(ii) Solid sphere. The moment of inertia of a solid sphere about a diameter about which it rolls $= \dfrac{2}{5} Mr^2$

$\therefore \qquad I = \dfrac{2}{5} Mr^2 = Mk^2$ or $k^2 = \dfrac{2}{5} r^2$ and $\dfrac{k^2}{r^2} = \dfrac{2}{5}$

Hence $a = \dfrac{g\sin\theta}{1 + \dfrac{k^2}{r^2}} = \dfrac{g\sin\theta}{1 + \dfrac{2}{5}} = \dfrac{5}{7} g\sin\theta$

(ii) **Hollow sphere.** The moment of inertia of a hollow sphere about a diameter about which it rolls

$= \dfrac{2}{3} Mr^2$

$\therefore$ $I = \dfrac{2}{3} Mr^2 = Mk^2$ or $k^2 = \dfrac{2}{3} r^2$ and $\dfrac{k^2}{r^2} = \dfrac{2}{3}$

Hence $a = \dfrac{g\sin\theta}{1 + \dfrac{k^2}{r^2}} = \dfrac{g\sin\theta}{1 + \dfrac{2}{3}} = \dfrac{3}{5} g\sin\theta$

As an example for $g = 9.8$ ms^{-2} and $\theta = 30°$; $\sin\theta = \dfrac{1}{2}$, we have

For cylinder $a = \dfrac{2}{3} \times \dfrac{1}{2} \times 9.8 = 3.27$ ms^{-2}

For solid sphere $a = \dfrac{5}{7} \times \dfrac{1}{2} \times 9.8 = 3.5$ ms^{-2}

For hollow sphere $a = \dfrac{3}{5} \times \dfrac{1}{2} \times 9.8 = 2.94$ ms^{-2}

Q. 4.31. How can a solid sphere be distinguished from a hollow sphere, the two being identical in all respects?   (*Meerut U., 1994; K.U., 1996; A.U., 1994*)

OR

A solid sphere and a hollow sphere of the same mass and same radius are allowed to roll down an inclined plane from the same position. Which one will come down with greater acceleration? Justify your answer.   (*Burd. U., 1991*)

Ans. Let the external radius of the solid sphere as well as that of the hollow sphere be R, then

Moment of inertia of the solid sphere $I = Mk_1^2 = \dfrac{2}{5} MR^2$ $\therefore$ $k_1^2 = \dfrac{2}{5} R^2$

If r is the internal radius of the hollow sphere of the same mass, then

Moment of inertia of the hollow sphere $= Mk_2^2 = \dfrac{2}{5} M \dfrac{(R^5 - r^5)}{(R^3 - r^3)}$

$\therefore$ $k_2^2 = \dfrac{2}{5} \dfrac{(R^5 - r^5)}{(R^3 - r^3)} = \dfrac{2}{5} R^2 \left[\dfrac{1 - r^5 / R^5}{1 - r^3 / R^3} \right]$

As r is less than R, $\dfrac{r}{R}$ is a fraction less than 1 $\therefore$ $\left(\dfrac{r}{R}\right)^5 < \left(\dfrac{r}{R}\right)^3$

Hence $1 - \left(\dfrac{r}{R}\right)^5 > 1 - \left(\dfrac{r}{R}\right)^3$ or $k_2^2 > k_1^2$

Thus we see that the value of k^2 for a hollow sphere is greater than that for a solid sphere of the same mass and external radius. Therefore a hollow sphere, when allowed to move along an inclined plane, will have a smaller acceleration and will move slower than the solid sphere because acceleration

is inversely proportional to $\left(1 + \dfrac{k^2}{r^2}\right)$. Hence the time taken to move down a certain distance by the hollow sphere will be greater than that for the solid sphere. This is how these can be distinguished from each other.

Q. 4.32. A solid cylinder (a) rolls, (b) slides from rest down an inclined plane. Neglect friction and compare the velocities in both cases when the cylinder reaches the bottom of the inclined plane.   (K.U., 1996)

Ans. (a) When the cylinder rolls down an inclined plane without slipping, its acceleration

$$a_1 = \frac{g \sin \theta}{1 + \frac{k^2}{r^2}} \qquad \qquad ...(i)$$

where θ is the angle of inclination of the inclined plane, k the radius of gyration and r the radius of cylinder.

Now the moment of inertia of the cylinder about its axis of symmetry about which it rolls

$$= \frac{1}{2} Mr^2 \quad \therefore Mk^2 = \frac{1}{2} Mr^2 \text{ or } k^2 = \frac{1}{2} r^2$$

Substituting in (i), we have $a_1 = \dfrac{g \sin \theta}{1 + \dfrac{\frac{1}{2} r^2}{r^2}} = \dfrac{2g \sin \theta}{3}$

(b) When the cylinder slides from rest, the acceleration $a_2 = g \sin \theta$ ...(ii)

Let S be the total distance from the top to the bottom of the inclined plane. As the cylinder starts from rest, the final velocity in the first case $v_1^2 = 2a_1 S = 2.\dfrac{2}{3} g \sin \theta . S$ ...(iii)

and in the second case $v_2^2 = 2g \sin \theta . S$.   ...(iv)

Dividing (iii) by (iv), we have $\dfrac{v_1^2}{v_2^2} = \dfrac{2}{3}$ or $\dfrac{v_1}{v_2} = \sqrt{\dfrac{2}{3}} = 0.8166$

Q. 4.33. A body of radius R and mass m is rolling horizontally without slipping with speed v. It rolls up a hill to a maximum height $h = 3v^2/4g$. Neglecting friction, find the moment of inertia of the body. What can be the shape of the body?   (Kan. U., 1994)

Ans. Kinetic energy due to linear motion $= \dfrac{1}{2} mv^2$

Kinetic energy due to rotation $= \dfrac{1}{2} I\omega^2 = \dfrac{1}{2} I \dfrac{v^2}{R^2}$

$\therefore$ Total kinetic energy $= \dfrac{1}{2} mv^2 + \dfrac{1}{2} I v^2 / R^2$

As the body rolls up the hill to a height h, the whole of the K.E. is converted into potential energy given by $mgh = mg \dfrac{3v^2}{4g} = \dfrac{3}{4} mv^2$

$\therefore \dfrac{1}{2} mv^2 + \dfrac{1}{2} I v^2 / R^2 = \dfrac{3}{4} mv^2$ or $\dfrac{1}{2} I v^2 / R^2 = \dfrac{1}{4} mv^2$ or $I = \dfrac{1}{2} mR^2$

The shape of the body is, therefore, a circular disc of radius R.

4.34. (a) A body of mass m, radius r and radius of gyration k rolls down an inclined plane having inclination θ and vertical height h. Obtain an expression for acceleration, velocity when it reaches the ground and the time taken by it to reach the ground.   (Meerut U. 2002)

(b) (i) Find the ratio of translational kinetic energy to rotational kinetic energy for a solid cylinder rolling down a plane without slipping.   (G.N.D.U. 2008) *(ii)* A solid cylinder of diameter 8 cm and mass 0.25 kg rolls down an inclined plane rising 3 in 20 without slipping. Find the acceleration and total energy of the cylinder after 5 sec.

(K.U. 1994, 1991)

Ans. *(a)* **Acceleration.** Acceleration of the body rolling down the inclined plane

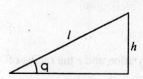

Fig. 4.24 (a)

$$a = \frac{g \sin \theta}{1 + \dfrac{k^2}{r^2}}$$

For proof see Q. 4.30

Velocity. Let l be the length of the inclined plane,

$$\text{then} \quad \frac{h}{l} = \sin \theta \quad \text{or} \quad l = \frac{h}{\sin \theta}$$

Now $v^2 - u^2 = 2\,a\,s$. Here $u = 0$ as the body starts from rest and $s = l$

$$\therefore \quad v^2 = 2\,al = 2a\,\frac{h}{\sin \theta} = \frac{2g \sin \theta}{1 + \dfrac{k^2}{r^2}} \cdot \frac{h}{\sin \theta} = \frac{2gh}{1 + \dfrac{k^2}{r^2}}$$

$$\text{or} \quad v = \sqrt{\frac{2gh}{1 + \dfrac{k^2}{r^2}}}$$

Time to reach the ground. If t is the time to reach the ground,

$$\text{then} \quad v = u + at = at \qquad\qquad [\because u = 0]$$

$$\therefore \quad t = \frac{v}{a} = \sqrt{\frac{2gh}{1 + \dfrac{k^2}{r^2}}} \times \frac{1 + \dfrac{k^2}{r^2}}{g \sin \theta} = \frac{\sqrt{2\,\dfrac{h}{g}\left(1 + \dfrac{k^2}{r^2}\right)}}{\sin \theta}$$

(b) *(i)* Let M be the mass of the solid cylinder and R its radius,

Then its moment of inertia about its axis of symmetry

$$I = \frac{1}{2}\,MR^2$$

If ω is the angular velocity of the solid cylinder rolling down the inclined plane, then its

$$\text{Rotational K.E.} = \frac{1}{2}\,I\omega^2 = \frac{1}{2} \times \frac{1}{2}\,MR^2\omega^2 = \frac{1}{4}\,MR^2\omega^2$$

The linear velocity of the cylinder rolling down the plane

$$v = R\omega$$

$$\therefore \quad \text{Translational K.E.} = \frac{1}{2}\,Mv^2 = \frac{1}{2}\,MR^2\omega^2$$

$$\therefore \quad \frac{\text{Translational K.E.}}{\text{Rotational K.E.}} = \frac{\dfrac{1}{2}\,MR^2\omega^2}{\dfrac{1}{4}\,MR^2\omega^2}$$

$$= 2$$

(ii) M.I. of the cylinder about an axis of symmetry $= \dfrac{1}{2} Mr^2 = Mk^2 \therefore k^2 = \dfrac{1}{2} r^2$

Also $\sin \theta = \dfrac{3}{20}$

When the cylinder rolls down an inclined plane without slipping, the acceleration

$$a = \frac{g \sin \theta}{1 + \dfrac{k^2}{r^2}} = \frac{g \sin \theta}{1 + \dfrac{1}{2}} = \frac{2g \sin \theta}{3} = \frac{2 \times 9.8 \times 3}{3 \times 20} = 0.98 \ ms^{-2}$$

Linear velocity of cylinder after 5 sec, $v = u + at = 0.98 \times 5 = 4.9 \ ms^{-1}$

Angular velocity after 5 sec, $\omega = \dfrac{v}{r} \ rad \ s^{-1}$

K.E. of translation $= \dfrac{1}{2} Mv^2 = \dfrac{1}{2} \times 0.25 \times 4.9 \times 4.9 = 3.0 \ J.$

K.E. of rotation $= \dfrac{1}{2} I\omega^2 = \dfrac{1}{2} \cdot \dfrac{1}{2} Mr^2 \times \dfrac{v^2}{r^2} = \dfrac{1}{4} Mv^2 = 1.5 \ J$

Total energy $= 3.0 + 1.5 = 4.5 \ J$

Q. 4.35. A uniform thin bar of mass 3 kg and length 0.9 m is bent to make an equilateral triangle. Calculate the moment of inertia about an axis passing through the centre of mass and perpendicular to the plane of the triangle. (A.U., 1995)

Ans. Let ABC be an equilateral triangle made from the bar of mass 3 kg and length 0.9 m. Thus

$AB + BC + CA = 0.9$ m and $AB = BC = CA = 0.3$ m

Mass of each arm $m = \dfrac{3}{3} = 1$ kg

This mass acts from the centre of each arm.

Let O be the centre of mass of this system through which the axis of rotation passes perpendicular to the lamina. It is at equal distance from the centre of each side. Thus

$Om_1 = Om_2 = Om_3 = Bm_1 \tan 30°$

Now $Bm_1 = \dfrac{0.3}{2} = 0.15$ m

$\therefore \quad Om_1 = \dfrac{0.15}{\sqrt{3}} = 0.05 \times \sqrt{3} = 0.0866$ m

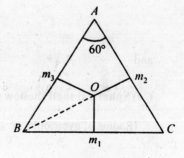

Fig. 4.24 (b)

Required M.I. $= m \ [(Om_1)^2 + (Om_2)^2 + (Om_3)^2]$

$= 1 \times 3 \times (0.0866)^2 = 0.6225 \ kg\text{-}m^2$

Q. 4.36. A solid sphere, a solid cylinder (circular disc), a spherical shell (hollow sphere) and a ring of the same mass and radius are allowed to roll down from rest simultaneously on an inclined plane form the same height without slipping. Prove that the sphere reaches down first, then the cylinder, thereafter the shell and the last the ring.

(Kerala U. 2001; Gowhati U. 2000; Kan. U., 1995, 1993)

Ans. Let all the four bodies have a radius R. If k is the radius of gyration, then the acceleration of the body rolling down an inclined plane at angle θ to the horizontal is given by

$$a = \frac{g \sin \theta}{1 + \dfrac{k^2}{R^2}}$$

If S is the length of the inclined plane and t is the time taken by a body to reach the bottom of the inclined plane from rest at the top, then

$$S = \frac{1}{2} at^2$$

or

$$t = \frac{\sqrt{2S}}{a}$$

(i) **Solid Sphere.** Moment of inertia of a solid sphere $= \frac{2}{5} MR^2$

$\therefore$ (Radius of gyration)^2 or $k^2 = \frac{2}{5} R^2$

and

$$1 + \frac{k^2}{R^2} = 1 + \frac{2}{5} = \frac{7}{5}$$

$\therefore$

$$a = \frac{g \sin \theta}{7/5} = \frac{5}{7} g \sin \theta$$

and

$$t = \sqrt{\frac{2S}{a}} = \sqrt{\frac{2 \times 7 \times S}{5g \sin \theta}} = \sqrt{\frac{14}{5}} \sqrt{\frac{S}{g \sin \theta}} = \sqrt{2.8} \sqrt{\frac{S}{g \sin \theta}} \qquad \ldots(i)$$

(ii) **Cylinder (Circular disc).** Moment of inertia of a cylinder (circular disc) $= \frac{1}{2} MR^2$

$\therefore$ (Radius of gyration)^2 or $k^2 = \frac{1}{2} R^2$

and

$$1 + \frac{k^2}{R^2} = 1 + \frac{1}{2} = \frac{3}{2}$$

$\therefore$

$$a = \frac{g \sin \theta}{3/2} = \frac{2g \sin \theta}{3}$$

and

$$t = \sqrt{\frac{2S}{a}} = \sqrt{\frac{2 \times 3 \times S}{2g \sin \theta}} = \sqrt{3} \sqrt{\frac{S}{g \sin \theta}}$$

(iii) **Spherical shell (hollow sphere).** Moment of inertia of a spherical shell $= \frac{2}{3} MR^2$

$\therefore$ (Radius of gyration)^2 or $k^2 = \frac{2}{3} R^2$

and

$$1 + \frac{k^2}{R^2} = 1 + \frac{2}{3} = \frac{5}{3}$$

$\therefore$

$$a = \frac{g \sin \theta}{5/3} = \frac{3g \sin \theta}{5}$$

and

$$t = \sqrt{\frac{2S}{a}} = \sqrt{\frac{2 \times 5S}{3g \sin \theta}} = \sqrt{\frac{10}{3}} \sqrt{\frac{S}{g \sin \theta}} = \sqrt{3.33} \sqrt{\frac{S}{g \sin \theta}}$$

(iv) **Ring.** Moment of inertia of a ring $= MR^2$

$\therefore$ (Radius of gyration)^2 or $k^2 = R^2$

and

$$1 + \frac{k^2}{R^2} = 2$$

$\therefore$

$$a = \frac{g \sin \theta}{2}$$

and
$$t = \sqrt{\frac{2S}{a}} = \sqrt{\frac{2 \times 2S}{g \sin \theta}} = \sqrt{4}\sqrt{\frac{S}{g \sin \theta}}$$

Putting $\sqrt{\frac{S}{g \sin \theta}} = T$, we find that time taken by the solid sphere, cylinder (circular disc), spherical shell (hollow sphere) and ring are $\sqrt{2.8}\ T$, $\sqrt{3}\ T$, $\sqrt{3.33}\ T$ and $\sqrt{4}\ T$ i.e., the sphere reaches down the inclined plane first, then the cylinder (circular disc), thereafter the shell (hollow sphere) and last the ring.

Exercise. *Find the time taken by a solid sphere to roll down an inclined plane 8m long and having slope 1 in 2* $\left(\sin \theta = \frac{1}{2} \right)$ *(M.D.U. 2008)*

Hint. According to relation (*i*), time taken by a solid sphere to roll down an inclined plane
$$t = \sqrt{\frac{14S}{5g \sin \theta}}$$

∴
$$t = \sqrt{\frac{14 \times 8}{5 \times 9.8 \times 0.5}} = \sqrt{\frac{112}{24.5}} = 2.13 \text{ sec}$$

Q. 4.37. Centres of four solid spheres of diameter $2a$ and mass m make a square of side b. Calculate the moment of inertia of the system about one side of the square.   *(Kan. U., 1997)*

Ans. Four spheres A, B, C, D each of diameter $2a$ and mass m are placed at the corners of the square of side b as shown, then

Moment of inertia of sphere A about diameter $AC = \frac{2}{5} ma^2$

Moment of inertia of sphere C about diameter $AC = \frac{2}{5} ma^2$

Moment of inertia of sphere B about diameter $BD = \frac{2}{5} ma^2$

Moment of inertia of sphere D about diameter $BD = \frac{2}{5} ma^2$

By the principle of parallel axes, moment of inertia of the sphere B about

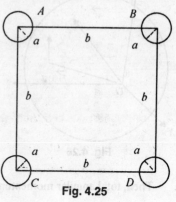

Fig. 4.25

$$AC = \frac{2}{5} ma^2 + mb^2$$

Similarly the moment of inertia of the sphere D about $AC = \frac{2}{5} ma^2 + mb^2$

Hence moment of inertia of the system about the side AC of the square
$$= \frac{2}{5} ma^2 + \frac{2}{5} ma^2 + \frac{2}{5} ma^2 + mb^2 + \frac{2}{5} ma^2 + mb^2$$
$$= \frac{2}{5} m[4a^2] + 2mb^2$$
$$= \frac{2}{5} m[4a^2 + 5b^2]$$

Q. 4.38. What are the dimensions of the quantity $\dfrac{L^2}{\mu R^2}$?   *(P.U. 2004)*

Ans. The dimensions of $\mu R^2 = I$ moment of inertia

It has been proved in **Q. 4.1** that $L^2 = 2EI$ or $\dfrac{L^2}{I} = 2E$

$\therefore$ Dimensions of $\dfrac{L^2}{\mu R^2} = \dfrac{L^2}{I}$ are that of energy or work $= M^1L^2T^{-2}$

Q. 4.39. (a) Define a rigid body.   *(G.N.D.U.* 2006)

(b) Derive an expression for the angular momentum of a rigid body and hence define inertia tensor.   *(G.N.D.U.* 2007, 2006; *Pbi. U.* 2007)

Ans. (a) Rigid body. *A rigid body is defined as a system of particles in which the relative distance between its constituent particles remains constant and unchanged during its translational or rotational motion.*

Suppose a rigid body is made up of a large number of particles. Let (x_i, y_i, z_i) and (x_j, y_j, z_j) be the co-ordinates of the *i*th and *j*th particle of the body and r_{ij} the distance between them. Then

$$r_{ij} = \left[(x_i - x_j)^2 + (y_i - y_j)^2 + (z_i - z_j)^2\right]^{1/2}$$

For a rigid body r_{ij} = a constant during any translational or rotational motion of the body. The translational motion may be, one, two or three dimensional. The rotational motion can only be either two or three dimensional.

(b) Angular momentum of a rigid body. Consider a rigid body rotating about a fixed point with

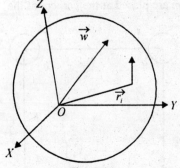

Fig. 4.26

angular velocity $\vec{\omega}$. Take the origin O at this fixed point and the three co-ordinate axes *X, Y* and *Z* as shown in Fig. 4.26.

The linear velocity of a particle *i*, having position vector $\vec{r_i}$

$$\vec{v_i} = \vec{\omega} \times \vec{r_i}$$

If m_i is the mass of this particle, then the angular momentum of the particle *i* about the fixed point O.

$$\vec{l_i} = \vec{r_i} \times m_i \vec{v_i}$$

$$= \vec{r_i} \times m_i \left(\vec{\omega} \times \vec{r_i}\right) = m_i \vec{r_i} \times \left(\vec{\omega} \times \vec{r_i}\right)$$

Then, total angular momentum of the rigid body

$$\vec{L} = \sum_i \vec{l_i} = \sum_i m_i \vec{r_i} \times \left(\vec{\omega} \times \vec{r_i}\right) \qquad \qquad ...(i)$$

where $\displaystyle\sum_i$ represents summation over all the particles of the rigid body

Using the vector identity

$$\vec{A} \times \left(\vec{B} \times \vec{C}\right) = \vec{B}\left(\vec{A}.\vec{C}\right) - \vec{C}\left(\vec{A}.\vec{B}\right), \text{ we get}$$

$$\vec{L} = \sum_i m_i \left[\vec{\omega}\left(\vec{r_i}.\vec{r_i}\right) - \vec{r_i}\left(\vec{r_i}.\vec{\omega_i}\right)\right]$$

$$= \sum_i m_i \left[\vec{\omega}\, r_i^2 - \vec{r_i}\left(\vec{r_i}.\vec{\omega}\right)\right] \qquad \qquad ...(ii)$$

If (x_i, y_i, z_i) are the Cartesian co-ordinates of the particle i and $(\omega_x, \omega_y, \omega_z)$. The components of angular velocity $\vec{\omega}$ along the three co-odinate axes, then

$$\vec{r_i} = x_i\hat{i} + y_i\hat{j} + z_i\hat{k} \text{ and therefore } r_1{}^2 = x_i{}^2 + y_i{}^2 + z_i{}^2$$

and

$$\vec{\omega} = \omega_x\hat{i} + \omega_y\hat{j} + \omega_z\hat{k}$$

$$\therefore \quad \vec{r_i}\cdot\vec{\omega} = (x_i\hat{i} + y_i\hat{j} + z_i\hat{k})\cdot(\omega_x\hat{i} + \omega_y\hat{j} + \omega_z\hat{k})$$

$$= x_i\omega_x + y_i\omega_y + z_i\omega_z$$

Substituting the values of ω, $r_i{}^2$ and $\vec{r_i}\cdot\vec{\omega}$ in component form in Eq. (*ii*) we get

$$\vec{L} = \sum_i m_i\left[(\omega_x\hat{i} + \omega_y\hat{j} + \omega_z\hat{k})(x_i^2 + y_i^2 + z_i^2) - (x_i\hat{i} + y_i\hat{j} + z_i\hat{k})(x_i\omega_x + y_i\omega_y + z_i\omega_z)\right]$$

$$= \sum_i m_i\left[\hat{i}(\omega_x x_i^2 + \omega_x y_i^2 + \omega_x z_i^2 - \omega_x x_i^2 - \omega_y x_i y_i - \omega_z x_i z_i)\right.$$

$$+ \hat{j}(\omega_y x_i^2 + \omega_y y_i^2 + \omega_y z_i^2 - \omega_x x_i y_i - \omega_y y_i^2 - \omega_z y_i z_i)$$

$$\left.+ \hat{k}(\omega_z x_i^2 + \omega_z y_i^2 + \omega_z z_i^2 - \omega_x x_i z_i - \omega_y y_i z_i - \omega_z z_i^2)\right]$$

If L_x, L_y and L_z are components of $\vec{L}$ along the three co-ordinate axes, then

$$L_x = \sum_i m_i(y_i^2 + z_i^2)\omega_x - \sum_i m_i x_i y_i \omega_y - \sum_i m_i x_i z_i \omega_z \qquad\qquad ...(iii)$$

$$L_y = -\sum_i m_i y_i x_i \omega_x + \sum_i m_i(z_i^2 + x_i^2)\omega_y - \sum_i m_i y_i z_i \omega_z \qquad ...(iv)$$

and $\quad L_z = -\sum_i m_i z_i x_i \omega_x - \sum_i m_i z_i y_i \omega_y + \sum_i m_i(x_i^2 + y_i^2)\omega_z \quad ...(v)$

We now substitute

$$\sum_i m_i(y_i^2 z_i^2) = I_{xx} \;; -\sum_i m_i x_i y_i = I_{xy} \;; -\sum_i m_i x_i z_i = I_{xz}$$

$$-\sum_i m_i y_i x_i = I_{yx} \;; -\sum_i m_i(z_i^2 + x_i^2) = I_{yy} \;; -\sum_i m_i y_i z_i = I_{yz}$$

and

$$-\sum_i m_i z_i x_i = I_{zx} \;; -\sum_i m_i z_i y_i = I_{zy} \;; \sum_i m_i(x_i^2 + y_i^2) = I_{zz}$$

Equations (*iii*), (*iv*) and (*v*) now become

$$L_x = I_{xx}\omega_x + I_{xy}\omega_y + I_{xz}\omega_z \qquad\qquad\qquad ...(vi)$$

$$L_y = I_{yx}\omega_x + I_{yy}\omega_y + I_{yz}\omega_z \qquad\qquad\qquad ...(vii)$$

and

$$L_z = I_{zx}\omega_x + I_{zy}\omega_y + I_{zz}\omega_z \qquad\qquad\qquad ...(viii)$$

$$\therefore \quad \vec{L} = \hat{i}(I_{xx}\omega_x + I_{xy}\omega_y + I_{xz}\omega_z) + \hat{j}(I_{yx}\omega_x + I_{yy}\omega_y + I_{yz}\omega_z) + \hat{k}(I_{zx}\omega_x + I_{zy}\omega_y + I_{zz}\omega_z)$$

This equation shows that the angular momentum vector $\vec{L}$ is, in general, not in the same direction as the angular velocity vector $\vec{\omega}$ nor it is in the direction of axis of rotation.

In the matrix form equations (*vi*), (*vii*) and (*viii*) may be expressed as under

$$\begin{bmatrix} L_x \\ L_y \\ L_z \end{bmatrix} = \begin{bmatrix} I_{xx} & I_{xy} & I_{xz} \\ I_{yx} & I_{yy} & L_{yz} \\ I_{zx} & I_{zy} & I_{zz} \end{bmatrix} \begin{bmatrix} \omega_x \\ \omega_y \\ \omega_z \end{bmatrix}$$

Moment of inertia Tensor. In vector notation the result stated above in matrix form may be expressed as

$$\vec{L} = \overset{\leftrightarrow}{I}\,\overset{\rightarrow}{\omega} \text{ where } \overset{\leftrightarrow}{I} = \begin{bmatrix} I_{xx} & I_{xy} & I_{xz} \\ I_{yx} & I_{yy} & L_{yz} \\ I_{zx} & I_{zy} & I_{zz} \end{bmatrix}$$

is called the *moment of inertia tensor* or simply *inertia tensor*. It is a tensor of second rank, which has nine components.

Q.4.40. Define principal moments of inertia, products of inertia and principal axes of a rigid body. Why are they important ?   (*G.N.D.U.* 2007, 2006; *Pbi. U.* 2007)

Ans. Principal moments of inertia. In vector notation the angular momentum $\vec{L}$ of a rigid body may be expressed as

$$\vec{L} = \overset{\leftrightarrow}{I}\,\overset{\rightarrow}{\omega} \text{ where } \overset{\leftrightarrow}{I} = \begin{bmatrix} I_{xx} & I_{xy} & I_{xz} \\ I_{yx} & I_{yy} & L_{yz} \\ I_{zx} & I_{zy} & I_{zz} \end{bmatrix}$$

is called the *moment of inertia tensor*.

The nine quantities $I_{xx}, I_{xy}, I_{xz}; I_{yx}, I_{yy}, I_{yz};$ and I_{zx}, I_{zy}, I_{zz} are the components of the moment of inertia of the body about the fixed *X, Y* and *Z* axes.

The diagonal elements I_{xx}, I_{yy} and I_{zz} are the moments of inertia of the rigid body about X-axis, Y-axis and Z-axis respectively and are called *principal moments of inertia* (or *principal moments*).

Products of inertia. The off diagonal elements $I_{xy}, I_{xz}, I_{yx}, I_{yz};$ and I_{zx}, I_{zy} are called products of inertia. These occur in symmetric pairs *i.e.,*

$$I_{xy} = I_{yx}; I_{yz} = I_{zy}; \text{ and } I_{xz} = I_{zx}$$

Importance. The rotational behaviour of a rigid body about a given point is determined by a set of six quantities, the *three principal moments of inertia* and the *three products of inertia*.

Principal axes of inertia. A set of three mutually perpendicular axes drawn through a point in the rigid body taken as origin, such that the products of inertia ($I_{xy}, I_{yx}; I_{yz}, I_{zy}; I_{xz}, I_{zx}$) about then vanish *i.e.* each is equal to zero whereas (I_{xx}, I_{yy}, I_{zz}) the principal moments of inertia are non zero are called principal axes of inertia or simply principal axes.

Importance. In terms of principal axes, the angular momentum of a rigid body is given by

$$\vec{L} = I_{xx}\omega_x\hat{i} + I_{yy}\omega_y\hat{j} + I_{zz}\omega_z\hat{k}$$

Q.4.41 (*a*) Explain the statement 'Inertia tensor is symmetric'.   (*G.N.D.U.* 2006)

(*b*) **State the properties of moment of inertia tensor.**

Ans. (*a*) Inertia tensor is symmetric. The moment of inertia tensor is given by

$$\overset{\leftrightarrow}{I} = \begin{bmatrix} I_{xx} & I_{xy} & I_{xz} \\ I_{yx} & I_{yy} & I_{yz} \\ I_{zx} & I_{zy} & I_{zz} \end{bmatrix}$$

It is called symmetric because its off diagonal elements known as *products of inertia* are equal *i.e.*

$$I_{xy} = I_{yx}; I_{xz} = I_{zx}; I_{yz} = I_{zy}$$

(*b*) **Properties of moment of inertia tensor.** 1. The moment of inertia tensor is a symmetric tensor *i.e.* its off diagonal elements are equal

∴ $$I_{xy} = I_{yx}; I_{xz} = I_{zx}; I_{yz} = I_{zy}$$

As a result of this, there are only six independent components

$$I_{xx}, I_{yy}, I_{zz} \text{ and } I_{xy}, I_{yz}, I_{zx}$$

As the products of inertia about the three principal axes are zero, *i.e.*

$$I_{xy} = I_{yx} = I_{xz} = I_{zx} = I_{yz} = I_{zy} = 0$$

Only three components are left, I_{xx}, I_{yy} and I_{zz} which are sometimes written as I_x, I_y, I_z.

2. Spherical top. A rigid body for which $I_{xx} = I_{yy} = I_{zz}$ is called a *spherical top*. In a spherical top all the axes are symmetric. A sphere is an example of a spherical top.

3. Symmetric top. A rigid body for which

$$I_{xx} = I_{yy} \neq I_{zz}$$

is called a *symmetric top*. A cylinder satisfies this condition. If the axis of the cylinder is taken as principal Z-axis, then X and Y-axes are symmetric axes. But *a cylinder is not called a symmetric top*. On the other hand all rigid bodies which do not have cylindrical shape but satisfy the condition given above are considered as a *symmetric top*. The earth flattened at the poles and bulging at the equator satisfies the above condition and is taken to be a symmetrical top.

4. Asymmetric top. A rigid body for which

$$I_{xx} \neq I_{yy} \neq I_{zz}$$

is called an *asymmetric top*. A rigid body, in general is an asymmetric top.

5. Rotor. A rigid body for which

$$I_{xx} = I_{yy} \quad \text{and} \quad I_{zz} = 0$$

is called a **rotor**. Example, a diatomic molecule.

Q.4.42. Show that the moment of inertia of a rigid body about an axis making angles α, β and γ with the principal axes is

$$I = I_1 \cos^2\alpha + I_2\cos^2\beta + I_3 \cos^2\gamma \qquad \text{(P.U. 2007, 2005)}$$

Ans. Moment of inertia of a rigid body about an arbitrary axis. Consider three mutually perpendicular axes *OX, OY* and *OZ*. Suppose OA is the axis making angles α, β and γ respectively with these axes and $\hat{n}$ a unit vector along OA. Then

$$\hat{n} = \cos\alpha\,\hat{i} + \cos\beta\,\hat{j} + \cos\gamma\,\hat{k}$$

Now, consider the *i*th particle of the rigid body, situated at *P*, having mass m_i and position co-ordinates x_i, y_i, z_i so that its position vector

$$\overrightarrow{OP} = \vec{r_i} = x_i\hat{i} + y_i\hat{j} + z_i\hat{k}$$

If $d_i = PN$ is the perpendicular distance of *P* from the axis *OA*, then.

Moment of inertia of the particle *P* about the axis $OA = m_i d_i^2$

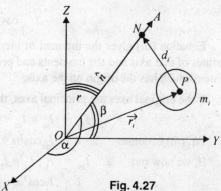

Fig. 4.27

$\therefore$ Moment of inertia of the whole rigid body about the axis $OA = \sum_i m_i d_i^2$

Where the summation extends over the whole of the rigid body.

Now $\qquad\qquad d_i = \left| \hat{n} \times \vec{r_i} \right|$

$\therefore$ $\qquad\qquad I = \sum_i m_i \left| \hat{n} \times \vec{r_i} \right|^2$ ...(i)

Again $\qquad \hat{n} \times \vec{r_i} = \begin{vmatrix} \hat{i} & \hat{j} & \hat{k} \\ \cos\alpha & \cos\beta & \cos\gamma \\ x_i & y_i & z_i \end{vmatrix}$

$\qquad\qquad = \hat{i}(z_i\cos\beta - y_i\cos\gamma) + \hat{j}(x_i\cos\gamma - z_i\cos\alpha) + \hat{k}(y_i\cos\alpha - x_i\cos\beta)$

$\therefore \quad \left| \hat{n} \times \vec{r_i} \right|^2 = (z_i\cos\beta - y_i\cos\gamma)^2 + (x_i\cos\gamma - z_i\cos\alpha)^2 + (y_i\cos\alpha - x_i\cos\beta)^2$

$\qquad\qquad = z_i^2\cos^2\beta + y_i^2\cos^2\gamma - 2z_iy_i\cos\beta\cos\gamma + x_i^2\cos^2\gamma + z_i^2\cos^2\alpha$

$\qquad\qquad - 2xz_i\cos\gamma\cos\alpha + y_i^2\cos^2\alpha + x_i^2\cos^2\beta - 2y_ix_i\cos\alpha\cos\beta$

$\qquad\qquad = \cos^2\alpha\,(y_i^2 + z_i^2) + \cos^2\beta\,(z_i^2 + x_i^2) + \cos^2\gamma\,(x_i^2 + y_i^2)$

$\qquad\qquad - 2x_iy_i\cos\alpha\cos\beta - 2y_iz_i\cos\beta\cos\gamma - 2z_ix_i\cos\gamma\cos\alpha$ ...(ii)

Substituting the value of $\left| \hat{n} \times \vec{r_i} \right|^2$ from Eq. (ii) in Eq. (i), we get

$I = \cos^2\alpha \sum_i m_i(y_i^2 + z_i^2) + \cos^2\beta \sum_i m_i(z_i^2 + x_i^2) + \cos^2\gamma \sum_i m_i(x_i^2 + y_i^2)$

$\qquad - 2\cos\alpha\cos\beta \sum_i m_ix_iy_i - 2\cos\beta\cos\gamma \sum_i m_iy_iz_i - 2\cos\gamma\cos\alpha \sum_i m_iz_ix_i$

Now $\quad \sum_i m_i(y_i^2 + z_i^2) = I_{xx} ; \sum_i m_i(z_i^2 + x_i^2) = I_{yy} ; \sum_i m_i(x_i^2 + y_i^2) = I_{zz}$

$\qquad \sum_i m_ix_iy_i = I_{xy} ; \sum_i m_iy_iz_i = I_{yz} ;$ and $\sum_i m_iz_ix_i = I_{zx}$

$\therefore \qquad I = I_{xx}\cos^2\alpha + I_{yy}\cos^2\beta + I_{zx}\cos^2\gamma - 2I_{xy}\cos\alpha\cos\beta$

$\qquad\qquad - 2I_{yz}\cos\beta\cos\gamma - 2I_{zx}\cos\alpha\cos\gamma$ ...(iii)

Equation (iii) gives the moment of inertia of a rigid body about any axis in terms of direction cosines of that axis and the moments and products of inertia of the body in an arbitrary co-ordinate system which has the origin on the axis.

If the original axes are principal axes, then

$\qquad\qquad I_{xy} = I_{yz} = I_{zx} = 0$

Eq. (iii) becomes $\quad I = I_{xx}\cos^2\alpha + I_{yy}\cos^2\beta + I_{zz}\cos^2\gamma$

If, we now put $\quad I_{xx} = I_1 ; I_{yy} = I_2 ;$ and $I_{zz} = I_3$, then

$\qquad\qquad I = I_1\cos^2\alpha + I_2\cos^2\beta + I_3\cos^2\gamma$

Q.4.43. Find the moment of inertia of a uniform rectangular lamina about diagonal as principal axis. (*P.U.* 2007)

Ans. A uniform rectangular lamina *ABCD* of mass m and sides a and b lying in the *X–Y* plane is shown in Fig. 4.28. The origin *O* lies at the centre of the lamina and the axes *OX* and *OY* are as shown. The Z-axis is perpendicular to the lamina and passes through *O*. It is clear from symmetry that these are *principal axes*. The axis of rotation lies along *AC* the diagonal of the rectangular lamina which makes angles α, β and γ with *X, Y* and *Z*-axes respectively. The moment of inertia of the body in terms of principal axes is given by

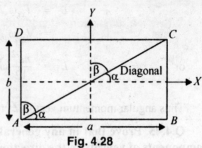

Fig. 4.28

$$I = I_{xx}\cos^2\alpha + I_{yy}\cos^2\beta + I_{zz}\cos^2\gamma \qquad ...(i)$$

where cos α, cos β and cos γ are the direction cosines of the axis of rotation. Now, principal moments of inertia of the lamina are

$$I_{xx} = \frac{mb^2}{12}; \quad I_{yy} = \frac{ma^2}{12} \qquad \therefore \quad I_{zz} = \frac{m(a^2+b^2)}{12}$$

The direction cosines of the diagonal are

$$\cos\alpha = \frac{a}{\sqrt{a^2+b^2}}; \quad \cos\beta = \frac{b}{\sqrt{a^2+b^2}}; \quad \cos\gamma = \cos\frac{\pi}{2} = 0$$

Substituting all these values in Eq. (*i*), we get

$$I = \frac{mb^2}{12}\cdot\frac{a^2}{(a^2+b^2)} + \frac{ma^2}{12}\cdot\frac{b^2}{(a^2+b^2)} = \frac{m}{12}\frac{2a^2b^2}{(a^2+b^2)} = \frac{ma^2b^2}{6(a^2+b^2)}$$

Q.4.44. A thin uniform rod of mass m and length l is made to rotate with angular velocity $\vec{\omega}$ about an axis passing through the centre making an angle θ with the rod. Find the angular momentum of the rod. (*P.U.* 2008)

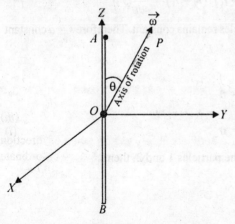

Fig. 4.29

Ans. Consider a rod *AB* of length l and mass m placed along the Z-axis in the *YZ* plane so that the X-axis is normal to the plane pointing in the upward direction.

Suppose the rod is rotating about an axis *OP* making an angle θ with the rod, with angular velocity $\vec{\omega}$ then the direction of $\vec{\omega}$ is along $\vec{OP}$. The moment of inertia of the rod about *X, Y* and *Z* axes is given by

$$I_{xx} = I_{yy} = \frac{ml^2}{12}$$

and $I_{zz} = 0$

All other moments and products of inertia are zero.

As the axis of rotation or the direction of $\vec{\omega}$ lies in the *YZ* plane, the components of $\vec{\omega}$ are

$$\omega_x = 0; \quad \omega_y = \omega\sin\theta \quad \text{and} \quad \omega_z = \omega\cos\theta$$

The angular momentum of the rigid body in terms of principal axes is given by

$$\vec{L} = I_{xx}\omega_x\hat{i} + I_{yy}\omega_y\hat{j} + I_{zz}\omega_z\hat{k}$$

$$= I_{yy}\omega_y\hat{j} \qquad\qquad [\because \omega_x = 0 \text{ and } I_{zz} = 0]$$

or $\qquad\qquad \vec{L} = \dfrac{ml^2}{12}\omega\sin\theta\hat{j}$

Thus angular momentum vector $\vec{L}$ remains in the Y-direction and rotates with the rod around $\vec{\omega}$.

Q.4.45. Prove that in any general motion of the rigid body any two particles have equal components of velocity in the direction of line joining the particles. *(Pbi. U. 2005)*

Ans. Consider two particles marked 1 and 2 of a rigid body having position vectors $\vec{r_1}$ and $\vec{r_2}$ respectively. Suppose particle 1 is moving with velocity $\vec{v_1}$ and particle 2 with velocity $\vec{v_2}$, then

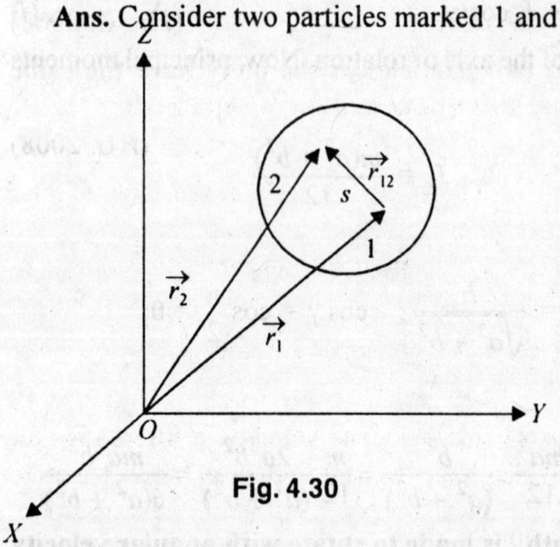

$$\vec{v_1} = \dfrac{d\vec{r_1}}{dt} \text{ and } \vec{v_2} = \dfrac{d\vec{r_2}}{dt}$$

If s is the distance between the two particles, then

$$s = \left|\vec{r_2} - \vec{r_1}\right|$$

or $\qquad\qquad s^2 = \left|\left(\vec{r_2} - \vec{r_1}\right)\right|^2$

$$= \left(\vec{r_2} - \vec{r_1}\right)\cdot\left(\vec{r_2} - \vec{r_1}\right)$$

Fig. 4.30

Differentiating both sides, with respect to t, we have

$$\left(\vec{r_2} - \vec{r_1}\right)\cdot\dfrac{d}{dt}\left(\vec{r_2} - \vec{r_1}\right) + \dfrac{d}{dt}\left(\vec{r_2} - \vec{r_1}\right)\cdot\left(\vec{r_2} - \vec{r_1}\right) = \dfrac{d}{dt}(s^2)$$

For a rigid body the distance between any two particles remains constant. Therefore $s = a$ constant and $\dfrac{d}{dt}(s^2) = 0$

$$\therefore \quad \left(\vec{r_2} - \vec{r_1}\right)\cdot\left(\vec{v_2} - \vec{v_1}\right) + \left(\vec{v_2} - \vec{v_1}\right)\cdot\left(\vec{r_2} - \vec{r_1}\right) = 0$$

or $\qquad\qquad \left(\vec{r_2} - \vec{r_1}\right)\cdot\left(\vec{v_2} - \vec{v_1}\right) = 0 \qquad\qquad ...(i)$

Suppose $\hat{n}$ is a unit vector along the line joining the particles 1 and 2, then

$$\hat{n} = \dfrac{\vec{r_{12}}}{r_{12}} = \dfrac{\vec{r_2} - \vec{r_1}}{\left|\vec{r_2} - \vec{r_1}\right|}$$

$$\therefore \quad \vec{r_2} - \vec{r_1} = \hat{n}\left|\vec{r_2} - \vec{r_1}\right| = \hat{n}s$$

Substituting this value of $\vec{r_2} - \vec{r_1}$ in Eq. (*i*), we get

$$\left(\vec{v_2} - \vec{v_1}\right).\hat{n}s = 0 \quad \text{or} \quad \left(\vec{v_2} - \vec{v_1}\right).\hat{n} = 0$$

or $\quad v_2.\hat{n} - v_1.\hat{n} = 0 \quad$ or $\quad v_2.\hat{n} = v_1.\hat{n}$

Thus the two particles have equal components of velocity in the direction of line joining the particles.

Q.4.46. (*a*) **If two points in a rigid body are fixed in space, then how many co-ordinates are required to specify the configuration of the rigid body ?** (*G.N.D.U.* 2009)

(*b*) **A rigid body is moving in such a way that all particles in the body have the same instantaneous velocity at all times. What do you conclude about the motion of the body ?** (*Pbi. U.* 2008)

(*c*) **A rigid body is moving in such a way that two particles in the body have the same instantaneous velocity at all times. What do you conclude about motion of rigid body ?** (*P.U.* 2008)

Ans. (*a*) If two points in a rigid body are fixed in space, then it means that the fixed axis of rotation about which the body rotates lies along the line joining these two points. In such a case, the body can undergo only pure rotation about this fixed axis. As such only one co-ordinate is required to specify the orientation of the rigid body.

(*b*) As all the particles of the rigid body have the same instantaneous velocity at all times, the motion of the rigid body is that of pure translation.

(*c*) As two particles in the rigid body have the same instantaneous velocity, it means that all particles lying on the line joining the two particles will also have the same velocity. In other words, the line is itself moving with a constant velocity. This line, therefore, defines the line of translation. The particles which do not lie on this line can have rotational motion about this line. We, therefore, conclude that the motion of the rigid body is that of translation plus rotation about an axis.

Q.4.47. Find the general expression for kinetic energy of a rigid body rotating about a point. What will be the kinetic energy of a rotating sphere ? (*G.N.D.U.* 2009, *Pbi. U.* 2008)

OR

Show that for a symmetrical rigid body, the rotational kinetic energy T is given by

$$T = \sum_{j=1}^{3} I_j \omega_j^2 \text{ where the letters have their usual meanings.}$$ (*P.U.* 2009)

Ans. Kinetic energy of rotation of a rigid body about principal axes. Consider a rigid body rotating about a *fixed point* O with angular velocity $\vec{\omega}$. Let the fixed point O be the origin of the co-ordinate axes X, Y and Z.

Suppose $m_1, m_2 .... m_i ....m_n$ are the masses of the particles constituting the body and $\vec{r_1}, \vec{r_2} .... \vec{r_i} .... \vec{r_n}$ are their respective position vectors. The instantaneous linear velocity of the *i*th particle $\vec{v_i}$ is given by $\vec{v_i} = \vec{\omega} \times \vec{r_i}$. The kinetic energy of the particle will, therefore, be given by

$$T_i = \frac{1}{2}m_i v_i^2 = \frac{1}{2}m_i \vec{v_i}.\vec{v_i} = \frac{1}{2}m_i \left(\vec{\omega} \times \vec{r_i}\right).\left(\vec{\omega} \times \vec{r_i}\right)$$

The total Kinetic energy of the rigid body about an instantaneous axis

$$T = \sum_i \frac{1}{2} m_i \left(\vec{\omega} \times \vec{r_i} \right) . \left(\vec{\omega} \times \vec{r_i} \right)$$

Using the vector identity

$$\left(\vec{A} \times \vec{B} \right) . \left(\vec{C} \times \vec{D} \right) = \vec{A} . \left[\vec{B} \times \left(\vec{C} \times \vec{D} \right) \right]$$

The above equation becomes

$$T = \frac{1}{2} \sum_i m_i \vec{\omega} . \left[\vec{r_i} \times \left(\vec{\omega} \times \vec{r_i} \right) \right]$$

$$= \frac{1}{2} \sum_i \vec{\omega} . m_i \left(\vec{r_i} \times \vec{v_i} \right)$$

$$= \frac{1}{2} \sum_i \vec{\omega} . \vec{L} \qquad\qquad ...(i) \qquad \left[\because \sum_i m_i \left(\vec{r_i} \times \vec{v_i} \right) = \vec{L} \right]$$

If ω_x, ω_y and ω_z are the components of angular velocity $\vec{\omega}$ and L_x, L_y and L_z are components of angular momentum $\vec{L}$. Then

$$\vec{\omega} = \omega_x \hat{i} + \omega_y \hat{j} + \omega_z \hat{k}$$

and

$$\vec{L} = L_x \hat{i} + L_y \hat{j} + L_z \hat{k}$$

Substituting the values of $\vec{\omega}$ and $\vec{L}$ in Eq. (i), we have

$$T = \frac{1}{2} (\omega_x \hat{i} + \omega_y \hat{j} + \omega_z \hat{k}) . (L_x \hat{i} + L_y \hat{j} + L_z \hat{k})$$

or

$$T = \frac{1}{2} (\omega_x L_x + \omega_y L_y + \omega_z L_z) \qquad\qquad ...(ii)$$

Now,

$$L_x = I_{xx} \omega_x + I_{xy} \omega_y + I_{xz} \omega_z$$
$$L_y = I_{yx} \omega_x + I_{yy} \omega_y + I_{yz} \omega_z$$

and

$$L_z = I_{zx} \omega_x + I_{zy} \omega_y + I_{zz} \omega_z$$

Substituting these values of L_x, L_y and L_z in Eq. (ii), we get

$$T = \frac{1}{2} [\omega_x (I_{xx} \omega_x + I_{xy} \omega_y + I_{xz} \omega_z) + \omega_y (I_{yx} \omega_x + I_{yy} \omega_y + I_{yz} \omega_z)$$
$$+ \omega_z (I_{zz} \omega_x + I_{zy} \omega_y + I_{zz} \omega_z)]$$

or

$$T = \frac{1}{2} [(I_{xx} \omega_x^2 + I_{yy} \omega_y^2 + I_{zz} \omega_z^2) + (I_{xy} \omega_x \omega_y + I_{yx} \omega_x \omega_y)$$
$$+ (I_{yz} \omega_y \omega_z + I_{zy} \omega_y \omega_z) + (I_{zx} \omega_z \omega_x + I_{zx} \omega_z \omega_x) \qquad ...(iii)$$

Now, we identify the three co-ordinate axes as the *principal axes*, then

$$I_{xy} = I_{yx} = I_{yz} = I_{zy} = I_{zx} = I_{xz} = 0$$

∴ Eq. (*iii*), now becomes

$$T = \frac{1}{2}I_{xx}\omega_x^2 + \frac{1}{2}I_{yy}\omega_y^2 + \frac{1}{2}I_{zz}\omega_z^2 \qquad \qquad ...(iv)$$

The above equation gives the kinetic energy of rotation of a rigid body about the principal axes.

Special Case. If the rigid body is a sphere

$$I_{xx} = I_{yy} = I_{zz} = I$$

and

$$T = \frac{1}{2}I(\omega_x^2 + \omega_y^2 + \omega_z^2) = \frac{1}{2}I\omega^2$$

where

$$\omega^2 = \omega_x^2 + \omega_y^2 + \omega_z^2$$

OR

To prove $T = \dfrac{1}{2}\sum\limits_{j=1}^{3} I_j\omega_j^2$. If we put $I_{xx} = I_1, I_{yy} = I_2$ and $I_{zz} = I_3$; $\omega_x = \omega_1, \omega_y = \omega_2, \omega_z = \omega_3$, equation

(*iv*) can be written as

$$T = \frac{1}{2}[I_1\omega_1^2 + I_2\omega_2^2 + I_3\omega^3] = \frac{1}{2}\sum_{j=1}^{3} I_j\omega_j^2$$

where $\sum\limits_{j=1}^{3}$ represents summation for $j = 1, j = 2$ and $j = 3$

I_j has values I_1 for $j = 1, I_2$ for $j = 2$ and I_3 for $j = 3$

and ω_j has values ω_1 for $j = 1, \omega_2$ for $j = 2$ and ω_3 for $j = 3$.

Q.4.48. Derive Euler's equations of rotation of a rigid body about a fixed point.

(*G.N.D.U.* 2009, 2007; *P.U.* 2006; *Pbi. U.* 2007)

Ans. Euler's equations. The time rate of change of angular momentum of a rigid body about a fixed point is equal to the resultant external torque acting on the body about that fixed point.

If $\vec{\tau}$ is the torque and $\vec{L}$ the angular momentum, then

$$\vec{\tau} = \frac{d\vec{L}}{dt} \qquad \qquad ...(i)$$

This equation holds good if the system of axes has a fixed orientation in space *i.e.* the inertial frame is fixed in space.

In order to study the rotation of a rigid body, the system of axes should be fixed in the body itself and the origin should be coincident with the fixed point about which the body is rotating so that as the body rotates the co-ordinate axes also rotate with the body.

The time rate of change of any vector in a fixed frame can be transferred to the time rate of change of the same vector in a rotating frame using operator equation

$$\left(\frac{d}{dt}\right)_s (-) = \left(\frac{d}{dt}\right)_R (-) + \vec{\omega} \times (-)_R$$

where $\left(\dfrac{d}{dt}\right)_s$ represents the time rate of change in stationary frame,

$\left(\dfrac{d}{dt}\right)_R$ the time rate of change in the rotating frame and   (–) the rotating vector.

Applying this operator equation to equation (i), we get

$$\vec{\tau}_R = \left(\frac{d\vec{L}}{dt}\right)_s = \left(\frac{d\vec{L}}{dt}\right)_R + \left(\vec{\omega} \times \vec{L}\right)_R$$

or $$\vec{\tau} = \frac{d\vec{L}}{dt} + \vec{\omega} \times \vec{L}$$ ...(ii) (ignoring the subscripts R in each case)

Now, the angular momentum of a rigid body rotating with angular velocity $\vec{\omega}$ about a fixed point is given by

$$\vec{L} = L_x\hat{i} + L_y\hat{j} + L_z\hat{k}$$

$$= (I_{xx}\,\omega_x + I_{xy}\omega_y + I_{xz}\omega_z)\hat{i} + (I_{yx}\,\omega_x + I_{yy}\omega_y + I_{yz}\,\omega_z)\hat{j}$$

$$+ (I_{zx}\,\omega_x + I_{zy}\,\omega_y + I_{zz}\,\omega_z)\hat{k}$$

If $\hat{i}, \hat{j}$ and $\hat{k}$ are the unit vectors along the principal axes of inertia at the fixed point in the rigid body about which it is rotating, Then

$$I_{xy} = I_{yx} = I_{zx} = I_{xz} = I_{yz}\,I_{zy} = 0$$

and we get $$\vec{L} = I_{xx}\,\omega_x\,\hat{i} + I_{yy}\,\omega_y\hat{j} + I_{zz}\,\omega_z\hat{k}$$

$\therefore$ $$\frac{d\vec{L}}{dt} = I_{xx}\frac{d\omega_x}{dt}\hat{i} + I_{yy}\frac{d\omega_y}{dt}\hat{j} + I_{zz}\frac{d\omega_z}{dt}\hat{k}$$ ...(iii)

This gives the first term on the right hand side of eq. (ii).

To find the value of second term, we have

$$\vec{\omega} \times \vec{L} = \begin{vmatrix} \hat{i} & \hat{j} & \hat{k} \\ \omega_x & \omega_y & \omega_z \\ I_{xx}\omega_x & I_{yy}\omega_y & I_{zz}\omega_z \end{vmatrix}$$

$$= \hat{i}(I_{zz}\,\omega_y\,\omega_z - I_{yy}\,\omega_y\,\omega_z) + \hat{j}\,(I_{xx}\,\omega_x\,\omega_z - I_{zz}\,\omega_x\,\omega_z)$$

$$+ \hat{k}\,(I_{yy}\,\omega_x\,\omega_y - I_{xx}\,\omega_x\,\omega_y)$$

$$= \hat{i}\,\omega_y\omega_z\,(I_{zz} - I_{yy}) + \hat{j}\,\omega_x\omega_z\,(I_{xx} - I_{zz}) + \hat{k}\,\omega_x\omega_y\,(I_{yy} - I_{xx})$$ ...(iv)

Substituting the value of $\dfrac{d\vec{L}}{dt}$ from Eq. (iii) and $\vec{\omega} \times \vec{L}$ from Eq. (iv) in Eq. (ii), we get

$$\vec{\tau} = I_{xx}\frac{d\omega_x}{dt}\hat{i} + I_{yy}\frac{d\omega_y}{dt}\hat{j} + I_{zz}\frac{d\omega_z}{dt}\hat{k}$$

$$+ \hat{i}\,\omega_y\,\omega_z\,(I_{zz} - I_{yy}) + \hat{j}\,\omega_x\,\omega_z\,(I_{xx} - I_{zz}) + \hat{k}\,\omega_x\,\omega_y\,(I_{yy} - I_{xx})$$ ...(v)

Now $$\vec{\tau} = \tau_x\hat{i} + \tau_y\hat{j} + \tau_z\hat{k}$$ ...(vi)

Comparing (v) and (vi), we get

$$\tau_x = I_{xx}\frac{d\omega_x}{dt} + \omega_y\,\omega_z\,(I_{zz} - I_{yy}) \qquad\qquad ...(vii)$$

$$\tau_y = I_{yy}\frac{d\omega_y}{dt} + \omega_x\,\omega_z\,(I_{xx} - I_{zz}) \qquad\qquad ...(viii)$$

$$\tau_z = I_{zz}\frac{d\omega_z}{dt} + \omega_x\,\omega_y\,(I_{yy} - I_{xx}) \qquad\qquad ...(ix)$$

Eq. numbers (vii), ($viii$) and (ix) for τ_x, τ_y and τ_z are known as Euler's equations for the motion of

the rigid body. These equations give the values of components of torque $\vec{\tau} = \dfrac{d\vec{L}}{dt}$ relative to the

rotating principal axes, in terms of angular velocity of the principle axes and principal moments of inertia.

Q.4.49. (a) Define an elementary gyroscope. *(G.N.D.U. 2006)*

(b) **What is precession? Why does it occur when torque is applied on the axis of rotation of fast rotating disc?**

(c) **Define the terms (i) Precessional torque and (ii) precessional angular velocity.**

(d) **Obtain an expression for precessional angular velocity and periodic time of precessional motion of a rotating body or gyroscope.** *(P.U. 2007, 2006, 2005; Pbi. U. 2007, 2006;*
G.N.D.U. 2009, 2007)

Ans. (a) Elementary gyroscope. Any symmetrical body rotating on an axis such that the axis can freely change its direction is called a gyroscope.

In practice, an elementary gyroscope is a circular disc mounted on three gimbals or rings so that it can turn about three mutually perpendicular axes one gimble is mounted in the next gimble with the help of bearings. Also see Q. 4.53.

(b) **Precession. Why does it occur?** Consider a circular disc spinning (or rotating) about its axis. Let O the centre of mass of the disc be the origin of the co-ordinate system. The axle of the disc lies

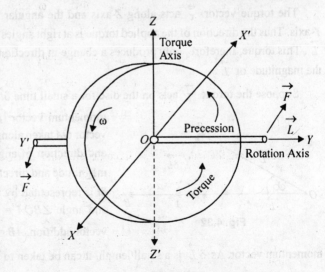

along the $Y'OY$ axis perpendicular to the disc and the other two axes XOX' and ZOZ' lie in the plane of the disc. YOY' is, therefore, the *rotation axis*. The angular velocity of rotation of the

disc is $\vec{\omega}$ in a direction Z to X axis (anticlock wise). If I is the moment of inertia of the disc about the axis of rotation, then angular momentum of the disc (about the axis of rotation)

$\vec{L} = I\vec{\omega}$. The angular momentum vector $\vec{L}$ acts along the direction OY.

In now two equal and opposite forces $\vec{F}$ and $\vec{F}$ are applied to the axle of the disc along the direction OX and OX', as shown, then these forces

Fig. 4.31

will produce a torque $\vec{\tau}$ acting along OZ in the direction of Z-axis as shown. The Z-axis is, therefore, known as the *torque axis*.

If the disc were stationary, this torque will bring about rotation of the disc about the axis ZOZ'. But if the disc is rotating in the direction as shown, the disc as a whole rotates about the axis XOX' in the anticlockwise direction *i.e.*, Y end of the axle turns towards Z and Y' end towards Z'.

This motion of the axis of rotation of the disc is called **precession**. Precession is, therefore, defined as under :

When a torque is applied to a rotating body in a direction perpendicular to its axis of rotation, the rotation produced in the direction of its axis of rotation, is called precession.

Precessional torque. *The torque which brings about the rotation of the axis of rotation (precession) of the rotating body is called precessional torque.*

Precessional angular velocity. *The time rate of rotation of the axis of rotation of the rotating body due to precession is called rate of precession or precessional angular velocity.*

Units. *The units of precessional angular velocity denoted as Ω are radian per second (rad s^{-1}).*

(*c*) **Precessional angular velocity.** Again consider a disc rotating in the XOZ plane with constant angular velocity $\vec{\omega}$ in the anticlockwise direction from Z to X about the axis YOY' perpendicular to the plane of the disc and passing through its centre of mass O (Fig. 4.31).

If I is the moment of inertia of the disc about the axis of rotation, then angular momentum of the disc (about the axis of rotation) $\vec{L} = I\vec{\omega}$. The angular momentum vector $\vec{L}$ acts along the direction OY.

If now, two equal and opposite forces $\vec{F}$ and $\vec{F}$ are applied to the axle of the disc along the directions OX and OX' as shown in Fig. 4.31, then these forces will produce a torque $\vec{\tau}$ acting along OZ in the direction of Z-axis. As a result of this the axis of rotation of the disc will turn about OZ in the XOY plane.

The torque vector $\vec{\tau}$ acts along Z-axis and the angular momentum vector $\vec{L}$ acts along the Y-axis. Thus the direction of the applied torque is at right angles to the direction of angular momentum $\vec{L}$. This torque, therefore, only produces a change in direction of $\vec{L}$ without making any change in the magnitude of $\vec{L}$.

Suppose the torque $\vec{\tau}$ acts on the disc for a small time δt and changes the direction of angular

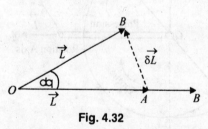

Fig. 4.32

momentum vector $\vec{L}$ through a small angle $\delta\theta$. Let the vector OA taken along Y-axis represent the initial magnitude and direction of angular momentum vector $\vec{L}$, then the magnitude and direction of the vector $\vec{L}$ after a small time δt is represented by the vector OB, where $OB = OA = \vec{L}$ and angle $\angle BOA = \delta\theta$. According to the triangle law of vector addition, $AB = \delta\vec{L}$ represents the change in angular momentum vector. As $\delta\vec{L}$ is a small length, it can be taken to be the arc of a circle so that

$$\frac{|\vec{\delta L}|}{|\vec{L}|} = \delta\theta \qquad\qquad ...(i)$$

Also torque $\overrightarrow{\tau}$ is the time rate of change of angular momentum

$$\therefore \quad \overrightarrow{\tau} = \frac{dL}{dt} = \frac{\delta L}{\delta t} \qquad\qquad\qquad ...(ii)$$

Comparing relations (*i*) and (*ii*), we have

$$\overrightarrow{L}\,\delta\theta = \overrightarrow{\tau}\,\delta t$$

or
$$\frac{\delta\theta}{\delta t} = \frac{\overrightarrow{\tau}}{\overrightarrow{L}} = \frac{\tau}{L} = \frac{\tau}{I\omega} \qquad\qquad \left[\because \overrightarrow{L} = I\omega\right]$$

But $\dfrac{\delta\theta}{\delta t}$ represents the angular velocity of precession (or rate of precession) Ω.

$\therefore$ Angular velocity of precession $\Omega = \dfrac{\tau}{I\omega}$.

Thus we find that, the rate of precession is

(*i*) directly proportional to the torque applied

(*ii*) inversely proportional to the moment of inertia of the disc and

(*iii*) inversely proportional to the angular velocity ω with which the disc rotates.

Time period of precession. The time period of precession is given by

$$T = \frac{2\pi}{\Omega} = \frac{2\pi\, I\omega}{\tau}$$

Q.4.50. (*a*) **Discuss the precession of a symmetric top spinning in the presence of gravity. What is mutation?**

(*b*) **A solid sphere of diameter 2 cm and mass 50 gm has a pivot pin 5 mm long fixed normally to its surface. When it spins like a top, it makes 20 revolutions per second. Find its precessional angular velocity** *(Pbi. U. 2008)*

Ans. (*a*) **Precession of symmetric spinning top.** *A symmetric top is a rigid body having an axis of symmetry which ends at a sharp point called the tip of the top.* When the top is made to spin about its tip its axis of symmetry can undergo precession due to the effect of gravity.

Consider a top of mass *m* spinning rapidly about its axis of symmetry with an angular velocity $\overrightarrow{\omega}$, then angular momentum of the top $\overrightarrow{L} = I\overrightarrow{\omega}$, where *I* is the moment of inertia of the top about its axis of symmetry. Suppose the vector $\overrightarrow{OA}$ taken along the axis of symmetry of the top represents the angular momentum of the top at any instant and it makes an angle α with the vertical *OP*. The weight *mg* of the top acts at its centre of mass *C* in the downward direction and the reaction of the pivot *R* acts upward. These constitute a couple which produces a torque $\overrightarrow{\tau}$. If the distance of the centre of mass *C* of the top from the pivot or tip point *O* is *r*, then

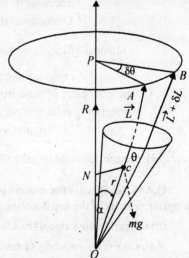

Fig. 4.33

$$\vec{\tau} \; = \; mg \times CN = mg\, r \sin \alpha$$

where CN is perpendicular from C on OP.

Suppose that in a small time interval δt the torque rotates the angular momentum vector through a small angle APB = angle AOB = $\delta\theta$. As the top is in steady motion, the magnitude of the angular momentum of the top remains constant and only its direction changes, thereby giving

Change in angular momentum $\delta \vec{L} = AB$.

The change in direction of angular momentum is, therefore, given by

$$\delta\theta \; = \; \frac{AB}{PA}$$

Now $\qquad\qquad \overrightarrow{OA} \; = \; \vec{L} \qquad \therefore \quad PA = L \sin \alpha$

and $\qquad\qquad \delta\theta \; = \; \dfrac{AB}{PA} = \dfrac{\delta L}{L \sin \alpha}$

Again $\qquad\qquad \tau \; = \; \dfrac{dL}{dt} = \dfrac{\delta L}{\delta t} \quad$ or $\quad \delta L = \tau\, \delta t$

$$\therefore \qquad\qquad \delta\theta \; = \; \frac{\tau\, \delta t}{L \sin \alpha} = \frac{\tau\, \delta t}{I\omega \sin \alpha} = \frac{mgr \sin \alpha\, \delta t}{I\omega \sin \alpha} = \frac{mgr}{I\omega}\, \delta t$$

or The rate of precession $\Omega = \dfrac{d\theta}{dt} = \displaystyle\lim_{\delta t \to 0} \dfrac{\delta\theta}{\delta t} = \dfrac{mgr}{I\omega}$

Here Ω is the precessional angular velocity of the top in the presence of acceleration due to gravity.

Mutation. The variation in the value of angle θ due to precession of the spinning top is called *mutation.* Due to variation in the value of angle θ, the axis of rotation moves up or down.

Hence mutation is defined as the up or down motion of the axis of rotation of the spinning top.

(b) Precessional angular velocity $\Omega = \dfrac{mgr}{I\omega}$

Here mass of the sphere $= 50$ gm;

Diameter of the sphere $= 2$ cm. $\quad \therefore$ Radius of the sphere $R = 1$ cm.

Moment of Inertia of the sphere $I \; = \; \dfrac{2}{5} m R^2 = \dfrac{2}{5} \times 50 \times 1^2 = 20$ gm cm^2

Length of the pivot pin $= 5$ mm $= 0.5$ cm

$\therefore$ Distance of centre of mass from the tip of the pivot $r = 1 + 0.5 = 1.5$ cm

Number of revolutions per second $n = 20$

$\therefore \qquad\qquad$ Angular velocity $\omega = 2\pi n = 2\pi \times 20 = 40 \pi$ rad s^{-1}

Hence precessional angular velocity $\Omega \; = \; \dfrac{mgr}{I\omega} = \dfrac{50 \times 980 \times 1.5}{20 \times 40\pi} = 29.2$ rad s^{-1}

Q.4.51. (*a*) **Discuss the motion of a freely rotating symmetric top. Show that the projection of angular velocity of the top describes a circle.**

(b) **Calculate the value of its kinetic energy and angular momentum.**

Ans. (a) Freely rotating symmetric top (*Force free rotation of a symmetrical body*). A body is said to rotate freely if no torque is acting on it. To start with, a torque may be applied to set the body into rotation. When the torque is removed, the body continues to rotate freely.

In case of a freely rotating body, since the external torque is zero ; $\tau_x = \tau_y = \tau_z = 0$ and Euler's equations of motion reduce to

$$I_{xx} \frac{d\omega_x}{dt} + \omega_y \, \omega_z \, (I_{zz} - I_{yy}) = 0$$

or $\qquad\qquad I_x \, \dot\omega_x \,=\, (I_y - I_z) \, \omega_y \, \omega_z \qquad\qquad$ [putting $I_{xx} = I_x$ and $\dfrac{d\omega_x}{dt} = \dot\omega_x$]

Similarly. $\qquad\qquad I_y \, \dot\omega_y \,=\, (I_z - I_x) \, \omega_z \, \omega_x$

and $\qquad\qquad I_z \, \dot\omega_z \,=\, (I_x - I_y) \omega_x \, \omega_y$

The rotating top has cylindrical symmetry and let Z-axis be the principal axis of rotation, then

$$I_x \,=\, I_y \neq I_z$$

Substituting $I_x = I_y$ and re-arranging the above three equations, we get

$$\dot\omega_x \,=\, -\left[\frac{I_z - I_x}{I_x}\omega_z\right]\omega_y \qquad\qquad\qquad …(i)$$

$$\dot\omega_y \,=\, +\left[\frac{I_z - I_x}{I_x}\omega_z\right]\omega_x \qquad\qquad\qquad …(ii)$$

and $\qquad\qquad I_z \, \dot\omega_z \,=\, 0 \quad$ or $\quad \dot\omega_z = 0 \quad$ or $\quad \omega_z = $ constant $\qquad …(iii)$

Put $\qquad\qquad \dfrac{I_z - I_x}{I_x}\omega_z \,=\, \Omega \qquad\qquad$ [Here Ω has dimensions of angular velocity]

Then Eqs. (i) and (ii) become

$$\dot\omega_x \,=\, -\Omega \, \omega_y \qquad\qquad\qquad …(iv)$$

and $\qquad\qquad \dot\omega_y \,=\, +\Omega \, \omega_x \qquad\qquad\qquad …(v)$

Differentiating Eq. (iv), we get

$$\ddot\omega_x \,=\, -\Omega \, \dot\omega_y = -\Omega^2 \, \omega_x \qquad\qquad [\because \, \dot\omega_y = +\Omega\omega_x]$$

or $\qquad\qquad \ddot\omega_x + \Omega^2 \omega_x = 0$

This is the equation of simple harmonic motion and the solution of this equation is

$$\omega_x \,=\, \omega_0 \cos(\Omega t + \alpha) \qquad\qquad\qquad …(vi)$$

where $\omega_0 = $ a constant is the amplitude of ω_x and α is the phase constant.

Differentiating Eq. (vi), we get

$$\dot\omega_x \,=\, -\omega_0 \, \Omega \sin(\Omega t + \alpha) \qquad\qquad\qquad …(vii)$$

Comparing Eqs. (iv) and (vii), we get

$$-\Omega \, \omega_y \,=\, -\omega_0 \, \Omega \sin(\Omega t + \alpha)$$

or $\qquad\qquad \omega_y \,=\, \omega_0 \sin(\Omega t + \alpha) \qquad\qquad\qquad …(viii)$

If we choose $\alpha = 0$, the Eqs. (vi) and (viii) take the form

$$\omega_x \,=\, \omega_0 \cos \Omega t \qquad\qquad\qquad …(ix)$$

and $\qquad\qquad \omega_y \,=\, \omega_0 \sin \omega t \qquad\qquad\qquad …(x)$

Squaring and adding Eq. (ix) and (x), we get

$$\omega_x^2 + \omega_y^2 \,=\, \omega_0^2$$

Since ω_0 is a constant, this is the equation of a circle.

Thus, we conclude that the projection of angular velocity $\vec{\omega}$ *on the* $x - y$ *plane describes a circle of radius* ω_0 *with angular frequency* Ω.

Time period. The time period of precession

$$t = \frac{2\pi}{\Omega} = \frac{2\pi I_x}{\omega_x (I_z - I_x)} \qquad \qquad ...(xi)$$

Magnitude of angular velocity. The components ω_x and ω_y of the angular velocity $\vec{\omega}$ of the rigid body always lie in the X-Y plane. If $\vec{\omega}_p$ is the angular velocity of the rigid body in the X-Y plane, then

$$\vec{\omega}_p = \omega_x \hat{i} + \omega_y \hat{j} = \omega_0 \cos \Omega t \, \hat{i} + \omega_0 \sin \Omega t \, \hat{j}$$

The magnitude of $\vec{\omega}_p$ is given by

$$\omega_p = \left[\omega_x^2 + \omega_y^2 \right]^{1/2} = (\omega_0 \cos \Omega t)^2 + (\omega_0 \sin \Omega t)^2 = \omega_0 \text{ (a constant)}$$

Now

$$\vec{\omega} = \omega_x \hat{i} + \omega_y \hat{j} + \omega_z \hat{k} = \vec{\omega}_p - \omega_z \hat{k}$$

$$\omega^2 = \omega_p^2 + \omega_z^2 = \text{a constant}$$

$$[\because \omega_p = \omega_o \text{ a constant and } \omega_z = \text{a constant}]$$

Direction. The direction of rotation of $\vec{\omega}$ depends upon the relaive values of ω_p and ω_z. The values ω_x and ω_y are changing with time but ω_z and $\vec{\omega}$ have constant magnitude which shows that the direction of $\vec{\omega}$ is continously changing. This direction changes in such a way that the projection of $\vec{\omega}$ on space axes always remains constant. This shows that $\vec{\omega}$ makes a constant angle θ with the Z-axis and precesses about the Z-axis. The cone described by the precessing angular velocity is called *body cone* and the angle of precession is given by

$$\tan \theta = \frac{|\vec{\omega}_p|}{\omega_z} = \frac{\omega_0}{\omega_z}$$

(b) Kinetic energy. The kinetic energy of the rotating body is given by

$$T = \frac{1}{2} I_x \omega_x^2 + \frac{1}{2} I_y \omega_y^2 + \frac{1}{2} I_z \omega_z^2$$

Putting $I_y = I_x$ and substituting the values of ω_x and ω_y (with $\alpha = 0$), we get

$$T = \frac{1}{2} I_x (\omega_0 \cos \Omega t)^2 + \frac{1}{2} I_x (\omega_0 \sin \Omega t)^2 + \frac{1}{2} I_z \omega_z^2$$

or

$$T = \frac{1}{2} I_x \omega_0^2 + \frac{1}{2} I_z \omega_z^2$$

Angular momentum. The angular momentum of the rotating body is given by

$$\vec{L} = I_x \omega_x \hat{i} + I_y \omega_y \hat{j} + I_z \omega_z \hat{k}$$

or

$$L = \left[I_x^2 \omega_x^2 + I_y^2 \omega_y^2 + I_z^2 \omega_z^2 \right]^{1/2}$$

Putting $I_y = I_x$ and again substituting the values of ω_x and ω_y as above, we get

$$L = \left[I_x^2 \, (\omega_0 \cos \Omega t)^2 + I_x^2 \, (\omega_0 \sin \Omega t)^2 + I_z^2 \, \omega_z^2 \right]^{1/2}$$

$$= \left[I_x^2 \, \omega_0^2 + I_z^2 \, \omega_z^2 \right]^{1/2}$$

Q.4.52. Prove through observed and calculated values of the period of precession that earth is not perfectly rigid body.   (*P.U.* 2004)

Ans. Earth not perfectly rigid body. The earth resembles in shape to a spheroid which is slightly flattened at the poles. It is symmetrical about the polar axis and its axis of rotation is slightly inclined to the polar axis at an angle of about 0.2 sec. of arc.

The external torques acting on the earth due to sun, other planets and the moon are very weak. Therefore, the rotational motion of the earth may be considered as that of a *force free body*. As a force free body the earth should precess about the Z-principal axis with an angular velocity

$$\Omega = \frac{I_z - I_x}{I_x} \omega_z .$$

The polar and equatorial radii of the earth are nearly 6357 km and 6378 km respectively. This gives the calculated value of $\dfrac{I_z - I_x}{I_x} = \dfrac{1}{306} = 0.00327$. Also ω_z is very nearly to ω, the angular velocity of rotation of the earth about its axis of rotation which is 2π radians per day.

$$\therefore \qquad \Omega = \frac{2\pi}{306} \text{ rad day}^{-1}$$

Hence the period of precession of the earth about its Z-principal axis should be

$$T = \frac{2\pi}{\Omega} = \frac{2\pi}{2\pi / 306} = 306 \text{ days}.$$

But in actual practice, it has been found that the period of precession is about 420 days.

The difference in the observed and calculated periods of precession is due to the reason that earth is not a perfectly rigid body but is elastic to some extent. Because of this reason some part of the equatorial bulge follows along with the shift in the axis of rotation. This results in reducing the difference between I_z and I_x, thereby increasing the period of precession.

However, in case the earth were completely fluid there would be no difference between I_z and I_x i.e., $I_z - I_x$ will be zero. As a result no precession could be possible.

Q.4.53. What is a gyroscope? Give its uses and applications.

(*G.N.D.U.* 2009, 2007, 2006; *Pbi. U.* 2007, 2006; *P.U.* 2006)

Ans. Gyroscope. A gyroscope is a heavy symmetrical body (top) in the form of a heavy circular disc or fly wheel rotating at a very high speed about its axle. The gyroscope is mounted in gimbals so that the disc and axle are both free to turn as a whole about any one of the three perpendicular axes XX', YY' and ZZ', which intersect at a common point O. Each gimbal is mounted in the next gimbal with jewelled bearings which are made up of a very hard material like agate or saphire to reduce frictional torque.

The spinning disc D is fixed in a ring PP which is free to rotate about its axle coinciding with the axis of symmetry XX'. The ring PP in turn is fixed in another ring QQ which is free to rotate along YY'

axis perpendicular to XX'. Further the ring QQ is fixed in a rigid frame work FF along the axis ZZ'. In this rigid frame work the gyroscope possesses three degrees of freedom and can rotate about any of the three axes. The motion of the gyroscope consists of *rotation, precession* and *nutation*.

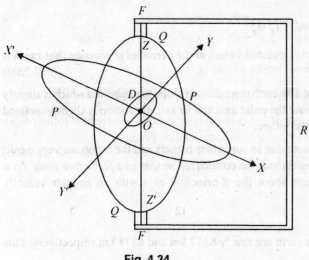

Fig. 4.34

When a torque is applied to the axis of rotation of the disc it give rise to the precession of the axis of rotation.

The rate of precession $\Omega = \dfrac{\tau}{I\omega}$.

As Ω is inversely proportional to I and ω, larger the value of I—the moment of inertia of the disc and greater the angular velocity ω smaller will be the rate of precession. But a gyroscope, to be useful and effective, must have a large value of angular momentum, which is possible only with a *heavy disc rotating at a very high speed.*

Uses and applications. (*i*) **Gyrocompass.** The gyroscopes are used in ships and aeroplanes to give a continuous indication of the north-south direction. For this purpose the gyroscope is set along the magnetic meridian. Such a gyroscope is known as a *gyrocompass.*

(*ii*) **Gyrostabiliser.** Gyroscopes are used to stabilise a ship against its up and down movement due to rough weather and stormy sea conditions.

For this purpose, a large and heavy gyroscope is used. The gyroscope is mounted in such a way that it can spin at a very high speed about a vertical axle, which can tilt forward or backward. The shaft of the gyroscope disc is supported in bearings fixed to the ship. When the ship rolls up and down the gyroscope is automatically tilted forward or backward so that its precession gives rise to a torque which acts in a direction opposite to that of the rolling ship. This torque brings the ship back to its stable position. Such a gyroscope is called a *gyrostabiliser.*

Q.4.54. A cyclist is riding a bicycle without holding the handle. He wishes to turn to one side. Explain how.   (*P.U. 2009*)

Ans. When a cyclist is riding a bicycle without holding the handle and he wishes to turn the bicycle to one side, he will himself tilt to that side. When he does this, he exerts a torque on the axis of rotation of the front wheel. Because of gyroscopic action, the axle of the front wheel and hence its plane of rotation gets turned about the vertical. This results in turning the bicycle in the desired direction.

Q. 4.55. Choose the correct answer.

(*a*) Moment of inertia is

(*i*) 2K.E. × ω^2 (*ii*) $\dfrac{2\text{K.E.}}{\omega^2}$ (*iii*) $\dfrac{2\text{P.E.}}{\omega^2}$ (*iv*) 3K.E.ω^2

(*b*) Units of M.I. are

(*i*) kg-m   (*ii*) kg-m^2 (*iii*) kg^2-m   (*iv*) kg^2-m^2

(c) M.I. of a thin rod is

(i) $\dfrac{Ml^2}{12}$ (ii) $\dfrac{Ml^4}{12}$ (iii) $\dfrac{M^2l^4}{12}$ (iv) $\dfrac{Ml^3}{12}$

(d) M.I. of a solid sphere is

(i) $\dfrac{2}{3} M^2 r^2$ (ii) $\dfrac{3}{2} Mr^2$ (iii) $\dfrac{2}{5} Mr^2$ (iv) $\dfrac{3}{5} Mr^2$

(e) Total energy of a circular disc rolling on a table is

(i) $\dfrac{3}{4} Mr^2\omega^2$ (ii) $\dfrac{1}{2} Mr^2\omega^2$ (iii) $\dfrac{3}{4} M^2 r^2\omega^2$ (iv) $\dfrac{1}{2} Mr^2\omega^2$

(f) An inclined plane makes an angle of 30° with the horizontal. A solid sphere rolling down the inclined plane from rest without slipping has a linear acceleration given by

(Meerut U., 2000)

(i) g/3   (ii) 2g/3   (iii) 5g/14

Ans. (a) $\dfrac{2KE}{\omega^2}$ (b) kg-m^2 (c) $\dfrac{Ml^2}{12}$ (d) $\dfrac{2}{5} Mr^2$

(e) $\dfrac{3}{4} Mr^2\omega^2$ (f) 5g / 14

EXERCISES

1. Determine the moment of inertia of the earth, assuming it to be a uniform sphere of radius 6400 km and mass 6×10^{24} kg.   **[Ans. 98.3×10^{35} kg m^2]**

2. A flywheel of mass 500 kg and 2 metres diameter makes 500 revolutions per minute. Assuming the mass to be concentrated at the rim calculate the angular velocity, the energy and the moment of inertia of the flywheel.   **[Ans. 50 π/3 rad/sec; 68.57×10^4 Joule; 500 kg m]**

3. A thin hollow cylinder open at both ends and weighing 96 kg (a) slides with a speed of 10 m/sec without rotating, (b) rolls with the same speed without slipping. Compare the kinetic energies of the cylinder in the two cases.   (Burd.U., 1992)

Hint. As the cylinder is thin $\therefore$ $R = r = a$ and $I = \dfrac{M(R^2 + r^2)}{2} = Ma^2$

(a) K.E. $= \dfrac{1}{2} Mv^2$

(b) K.E. $= \dfrac{1}{2} Mv^2 + \dfrac{1}{2} I\omega^2$

$= \dfrac{1}{2} Mv^2 + \dfrac{1}{2} Ma^2 \left(\dfrac{v}{a}\right)^2 = \dfrac{1}{2} Mv^2 + \dfrac{1}{2} Mv^2 = Mv^2$

[Ans. (a) 4800 Joule (b) 9600 Joule]

5

Frames of Reference

Q. 5.1. Distinguish between inertial and non-inertial frames of reference. Give one example of each. Is earth an inertial frame ? Give reasons.

(*H.P.U.*, 2003, 2001, 2000; *Bhopal U.*, 2004; *Bang. U.*, 2004; *Osm. U.*, 2004; *M.D.U.*, 2008, 2003; *P.U.*, 2006, 2004, 2001, 1999; *Guwahati U.*, 2000; *Pbi.U.*, 1999, 1995; *G.N.D.U.*, 2007, 2006, 1999; *K.U.*, 1996; *A.U.*, 1995; *Cal. U.* (*Hons*), 1992)

Ans. Inertial frame. Newton's first law of motion is also known as the *law of inertia*. A reference frame *e.g.*, a co-ordinate system in which Newton's first law of motion holds good, is known as an *inertial frame of reference*. In an inertial frame a body continues in its state of rest or of uniform motion in a straight line as long as no external force acts on it. All the Newton's law of motion hold good in an inertial frame. All frames of reference moving with a *constant velocity* with respect to an inertial frame are also inertial frames of reference. So inertial frame of reference can be called an unaccelerated frame of reference.

Example. The best approximation to an inertial frame is the frame of reference in the intergalactic space.

Non-inertial frame. The basic laws of Physics are not changed in form in inertial frames of reference. But when a frame of reference is accelerated relative to an inertial frame the form of basic physical laws such as Newton's second law of motion becomes completely different. Such frames of reference having an accelerated motion relative to an inertial frame are called *non-inertial frames of reference*. Since a uniformly rotating frame has a centripetal acceleration it is also a non-inertial frame.

Example. A non-inertial frame is either a frame having *uniform linear acceleration* or a frame which is *uniformly rotating*.

Earth a non-inertial frame. Earth is not an inertial frame. It is a non-inertial frame. The earth is a rotating sphere as it is rotating about its own axis. It has a centripetal acceleration due to rotation.

In addition, earth also revolves round the sun in a period of one year in an orbit of radius 1.49×10^8 km.

$\therefore$ Its orbital velocity $\quad v = \dfrac{2\pi r}{T} = \dfrac{2\pi \times 1.49 \times 10^8 \times 10^3}{365 \times 24 \times 60 \times 60} = 3 \times 10^4 \text{ ms}^{-1}$

and centripetal acceleration of the earth due to revolution

$$= \frac{v^2}{r} = \frac{3 \times 10^4 \times 3 \times 10^4}{1.49 \times 10^8 \times 10^3} = 6 \times 10^{-3} \text{ ms}^{-2}$$

Thus the reference frame attached to the earth is an *accelerated* frame and is, therefore, *non-inertial*.

Q. 5.2. What is Newtonian principle of relativity? Discuss with examples. Why should laws of nature be the same in all inertial frames of reference?

(M.D.U. 2008; H.P.U., 2000; G.N.D.U., 1996; Pbi.U., 1993)

Ans. Newtonian principle of relativity. It states '*By performing physical experiments entirely is one inertial frame, we cannot determine its motion with respect to some other inertial frame and the phenomenon occurring in a closed system are independent of any unaccelerated motion of the system as a whole.*'

In other words, the laws of physics are the same in all inertial frames of reference.

As an example, consider an observer A in a train at rest and another observer B standing outside on the platform. The observer A throws a ball vertically upward and finds that the ball returns vertically downward to him. The same thing is observed by the observer B standing on the platform.

Now, suppose the train starts moving with a uniform velocity along a straight track. If the observer A repeats his experiment *i.e.*, throws the ball vertically upward he again finds that the ball falls vertically downward to him. But the observer B standing on the platform finds that the ball thrown upward by the observer A in the moving train follows a parabolic path. Thus we find that :

(*i*) The observer in the train cannot distinguish whether the train is moving or not because he observes exactly the same thing whether the train is at rest or in uniform motion in a straight line. Therefore, we conclude that

'*It is not possible to detect the state of rest or of uniform rectilinear motion of a system by performing mechanical experiments within the system itself.*'

(*ii*) The vertically upward and vertically downward motion of the ball for observer A and the motion of the ball along the parabolic path for the observer B can be explained by the same laws of Mechanics *i.e.*, the laws of Mechanics remains unchanged due to uniform rectilinear motion of the frames of reference. Thus

'*All inertial frames are equivalent and the laws of Physics (nature) are the same in all inertial frames of reference.*'

Q. 5.3. What are Galelian transformations ? Derive Galelian transformation equations for two inertial frames. State and prove Galelian invariance.

(Pbi.U., 2007, 2001, 1993; K.U., 2001; M.D.U., 2007, P.U., 2000; G.N.D.U., 2006, 2000, 1999; Guwahati U., 2000; Calicut U., 2003)

Ans. Galelian transformations. When a physical phenomenon is observed in two inertial frames moving with uniform velocity relative to each other and the time interval registered in both the frames is the same, then the datas of results in one frame of reference can be transformed to those in the second frame. This process is known as Galelian transformation.

The equations which connect the position vectors of a particle (or event) it two-inertial frames are known as Galelian transformations.

Galelian transformation equations. We can derive Galelian transformation equation as under. We shall discuss two cases.

(*i*) **When one inertial frame is moving relative to the other along positive direction of x-axis.** Let S and S' be the two inertial frames, whose origins O and O' coincide at $t = t' = 0$. Their X-axes OX and $O'X'$ are along the same line and Y and Z-axes are parallel to each other as shown in Fig. 5.1. The frame S' is moving with a uniform velocity v with respect to the frame S along the positive direction of X-axis. Now consider an event P in the frame S specified by space co-ordinate x, y, z and

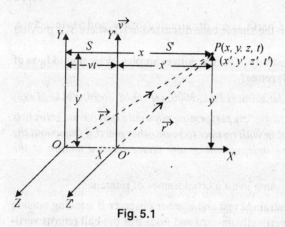

Fig. 5.1

time co-ordinate t. An event is completely known from the space co-ordinates of the point of its occurrence and from the time co-ordinate of its happening. An event can be a collision between two particles.

Let the corresponding space and time co-ordinates of the same event in the inertial frame S' be x', y', z' and t'.

Then after a time t, $O'O = vt$ and $x' = x - vt$

$$y' = y \quad z' = z \quad t' = t$$

The last equation is based upon the universal nature of time as assumed in classical physics. It means that a clock in S measures the same time as a clock in S' provided these were synchronised at time $t = t' = 0$. These equations are known as Galelian transformation equations.

The inverse Galelian transformation equations can be written by changing v to $-v$, x to x', t to t' and so on. These are $x = x' + vt \quad y = y' \quad z = z' \quad t = t'$

If $\vec{r} = \overrightarrow{OP}$ is the position vector of the point P in the inertial frames S and $\vec{r'} = \overrightarrow{O'P}$ the position vector of P in the frame S', then $\vec{r} = x\hat{i} + y\hat{j} + z\hat{k}$ and $\vec{r'} = x'\hat{i} + y'\hat{j} + z'\hat{k}$

$\therefore \quad \vec{r'} = (x - vt)\,\hat{i} + y\hat{j} + z\hat{k} = (x\hat{i} + y\hat{j} + z\hat{k}) - vt\,\hat{i} = \vec{r} - \vec{v}t$ where $\vec{v} = v\hat{i}$

Thus Galelian transformations can also be put as $\vec{r'} = \vec{r} - \vec{v}t \qquad t' = t$

The corresponding inverse Galelian transformations are $\vec{r} = \vec{r'} + \vec{v}t' \qquad t = t'$

(ii) **When one inertial frame is moving relative to the other in any direction.** Now let the frame S' move with respect to the frame S with uniform velocity $\vec{v}$ given by $\vec{v} = v_x\,\hat{i} + v_y\,\hat{j} + v_z\,\hat{k}$ in any direction where v_x, v_y and v_z are the components of $\vec{v}$ along x, y and z directions respectively. The origins and the axes of the two frame are so chosen that these coincide at $t = t' = 0$. After a time t the frame S' is separated from the frame S by a distance $v_x t$, $v_y t$ and $v_z t$ along the x, y and z axes respectively. If x, y, z, t are the co-ordinates of an event P in the frame S and x', y', z', t' of the same event in the frame S', then

$$x' = x - v_x t \quad y' = y - v_y t \quad z' = z - v_z t \quad t' = t$$

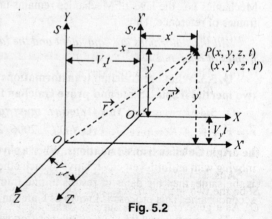

Fig. 5.2

In this case $\quad \vec{r_1'} = (x - v_x t)\,\hat{i} + (y - v_y t)\,\hat{j} + (z - v_z t)\,\hat{k}$

$$= (x\hat{i} + y\hat{j} + z\hat{k}) - (v_x\,\hat{i} + v_y\,\hat{j} + v_z\,\hat{k})\,t = \vec{r} - \vec{v}t$$

$$(\text{where } \vec{v} = v_x\,\hat{i} + v_y\,\hat{j} + v_z\,\hat{k})$$

Thus Galelian transformations can also be put as $\vec{r'} = \vec{r} - \vec{v}t \qquad t' = t$

We shall, however, restrict our discussion to the simple case discussed in (i) where S' is moving along the x-axis relative to the frame S.

Galelian invariance. It states that '*The basic laws of mechanics do not change under Galelian transformations*'. The basic laws of Newtonian mechanics are the Newton's laws of motion, laws of conservation of momentum and energy etc. We shall prove below that a space interval is invariant under Galelian transformation.

Consider a rod at rest in the inertial frame S having its two ends at the points x_2 and x_1, then for the observer S

The length of the rod $= x_2 - x_1$

The observer S' will consider the rod to be moving with velocity $- v$ from O' to O and will observe the two ends to be at the points x_2' and x_1' at the **same time.**

For the observer S' the length of the rod $= x_2' - x_1'$

$$= (x_2 - vt_2) - (x_1 - vt_1) = (x_2 - x_1) - v(t_2 - t_1)$$

but the ends of the rod have been observed at one and the same time

$$\therefore \qquad t_1 = t_2 \text{ or } t_2 - t_1 = 0 \qquad \therefore x_2' - x_1' = x_2 - x_1 \qquad ..(i)$$

Relation (i) shows that the *space interval or the distance between two points (or length) is invariant under Galelian transformations.*

Thus we find that the space-interval measurement and time-interval measurement are independent of the relative motion of the inertial frames. Classical physics already assumes that mass of a body is constant and independent of its motion with respect to an inertial frame. *Thus all the three fundamental quantities length, mass and time are invariant of the relative motion of the observer.*

This property is known as **Galelian invariance.** Hence,

(i)   The mass of a body is the same for all observers and it is independent of the motion of the observer *i.e.*, mass is an absolute quantity.

(ii)   The motion has no effect on time. If the clocks in two inertial frames which are in uniform motion agree at one instance, they will agree at all later times *i.e.*, $t = t'$. Time is an absolute quantity.

(iii)   The length of a rod does not change due to relative motion of an inertial frame with respect to another. Hence space interval is an invariant quantity.

Q. 5.4. Prove that the Galelian transformation of position vector is expressed as $\vec{r} = \vec{r'} + \vec{vt'} + \vec{R}$ where $\vec{v}$ is the linear velocity of the frame S' and $\vec{R}$ is the position vector of the origin O' as measured by the frame S' at time $t' = 0$. (*A.U., 1994*)

Ans. Transformation of position vector. Let S and S' be the two inertial frames whose origins are O and O'. As a general case it is supposed that the X', Y', Z' axes of the frame S' are not parallel to the corresponding X, Y, Z axes of the frame S. Let $\vec{R}$ be the position vector of the origin O' with respect to O at $t = t' = 0$.

Now consider an event P in the frame S specified by space co-ordinate $\vec{r}$ and time co-ordinate t. An event is completely known from the space co-ordinates of the point of occurrence and from the time co-ordinate of the time of happening.

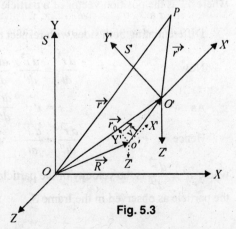

Fig. 5.3

Let the corresponding space and time co-ordinates of the same event in the inertial frame S' be $\vec{r'}$ and t'.

Let the inertial frame S' move with a linear velocity $\vec{v}$ with respect to the frame S. As the position vector of O' with respect to O at $t = 0$ is $\vec{R}$, the position vector of O' with respect to O at time t' in S'

$$OO' = \vec{r_0} = \vec{R} + \vec{vt'}$$

∴ At time $t = t'$

$$\vec{r} = \vec{r_0} + \vec{r'} = \vec{R} + \vec{vt'} + \vec{r'} = \vec{r'} + \vec{vt'} + \vec{R} \qquad ...(i)$$

Special cases. (a) *When the origins of both the frames coincide initially.* $\vec{R} = 0$

∴ $\vec{r} = \vec{r'} + \vec{vt'}$ or $\vec{r'} = \vec{r} - \vec{vt}$ ...(ii) [∵ $t = t'$]

(b) *When the origins of both the frames coincide initially and their co-ordinate axes are parallel, then* $\vec{r'} = x'\hat{i} + y'\hat{j} + z'\hat{k}$; $\vec{r} = x\hat{i} + y\hat{j} + z\hat{k}$ and $\vec{v} = v_x\hat{i} + v_y\hat{j} + v_z\hat{k}$; $\vec{R} = 0$

Substituting the values in relation (ii), we have

$$x'\hat{i} + y'\hat{j} + z'\hat{k} = x\hat{i} + y\hat{j} + z\hat{k} - (v_x\hat{i} + v_y\hat{j} + v_z\hat{k})\,t \qquad ...(iii)$$

Equating x, y, z components, we have $x' = x - v_x t; y' = y - v_y t; z' = z - v_z t$

(c) *When the origins of both the frames coincide initially, their co-ordinate axes are parallel and the origin of the frames S' is moving along the $+ x$ axis with velocity $\vec{v}$ relative to O.* Then relation (iii) becomes $x'\hat{i} + y'\hat{j} + z'\hat{k} = x\hat{i} + y\hat{j} + z\hat{k} - vt\,\hat{i}$

Equating x, y, z-components on both sides, we have $x' = x - vt$ $y' = y$ $z' = z$

Hence the restricted Galelian transformations are $x' = x - vt$; $y' = y$; $z' = z$ and $t' = t$.

Q. 5.5. (a) **Show that the distance between two points (or length) is invariant under Galelian transformation.**   (*P.U., 2001; G.N.D.U., 2008, 2000, 1999*)

(b) **Show that under Galelian transformations velocity is variant and acceleration is in-variant.**   (*Pbi. U. 2007, 2006; P.U., 2001; K.U., 2001; M.D.U., 2008, 2003, 2001; G.N.D.U., 2006, 2000*)

Ans. (a) **Length is invariant.** See Q. 5.3

(b) **Velocity.** When an inertial frame S' is moving with a uniform velocity $\vec{v}$ with respect to an inertial frame S and their origins coincide at time $t = t' = 0$, Galelian transformation equation for position vector is $\vec{r'} = \vec{r} - \vec{vt}$

where $\vec{r'}$ is the position vector of a particle in the frame S' and $\vec{r}$ in the frame S.

Differentiating both sides with respect to time, we get $\dfrac{d\vec{r'}}{dt} = \dfrac{d\vec{r}}{dt} - \vec{v}$

Now $\dfrac{d\vec{r'}}{dt} = \dfrac{d\vec{r'}}{dt'} \cdot \dfrac{dt'}{dt}$

As $t = t'$ $\dfrac{dt'}{dt} = 1$ ∴ $\dfrac{d\vec{r'}}{dt} = \dfrac{d\vec{r'}}{dt'}$

Hence $\dfrac{d\vec{r'}}{dt'} = \dfrac{d\vec{r}}{dt} - \vec{v}$ or $\vec{u'} = \vec{u} - \vec{v}$ ...(i)

where $\vec{u'} = \dfrac{d\vec{r'}}{dt'}$ is the velocity of the particle as observed in frame S' and $\vec{u} = \dfrac{d\vec{r}}{dt}$ is the velocity of the particle as observed in the frame S.

The relation $\vec{u'} = \vec{u} - \vec{v}$ is known as Galelian transformation equation for velocity. This equation clearly shows that velocity in the frame S' is not the same as in the frame S i.e., velocity is a variant under Galelian transformations.

Acceleration. Differentiating equation (i), with respect to time, we get

$$\frac{d\vec{u'}}{dt} = \frac{d\vec{u}}{dt} \text{ as } \vec{v} = \text{a constant}$$

But

$$\frac{d\vec{u'}}{dt} = \frac{d\vec{u'}}{dt'} \cdot \frac{dt'}{dt} = \frac{d\vec{u'}}{dt'} \qquad\qquad \left[\because \frac{dt'}{dt} = 1 \right]$$

$$\therefore \qquad \frac{d\vec{u'}}{dt'} = \frac{d\vec{u}}{dt} \text{ or } \vec{a'} = \vec{a} \qquad\qquad ...(ii)$$

where $\vec{a'} = \dfrac{d\vec{u'}}{dt'}$ is the acceleration of the particle in the frame S' and $\vec{a} = \dfrac{d\vec{u}}{dt}$ is the acceleration in the frame S. This shows that the acceleration of a particle is independent of the uniform velocity of one inertial frame of reference relative to another. In other words *acceleration is invariant to Galelian transformations*.

Q. 5.6. (*a*) **A moving particle has co-ordinates $(6t + 3)$, $8t$, 5 m in frame S at any time t. The frame S' is moving relative to S with a velocity $3\hat{i} + 4\hat{j}$ m/s. Find the co-ordinates and velocity of the particle in frame S'.** (*P.U., 1994*)

(*b*) **The position vector of a point in the frame S' moving with constant velocity of 10 cm/sec along X-axis is given by (11, 9, 8) cm. Calculate the position with respect to the frame S if the two frames were coincident only $\dfrac{1}{2}$ sec. earlier.** (*P.U., 2001, 2000*)

Ans (*a*) Galelian transformation equations for space co-ordinates are

$$x' = x - v_x t \quad y' = y - v_y t \quad z' = z - v_z t$$

Now

$$x = 6t + 3 \quad y = 8t \quad z = 5; \quad v_x = 3 \quad v_y = 4 \quad v_z = 0$$

$$\therefore \qquad x' = x - v_x t = 6t + 3 - 3t = 3t + 3$$

$$y' = y - v_y t = 8t - 4t = 4t \; ; z' = z - v_z t = 5 - 0 = 5$$

∴ Co-ordinates of the particle in S' are $3t + 3$, $4t$, 5.

Velocity. $x' = 3t + 3$ $\qquad \therefore \quad \dfrac{dx'}{dt'} = \dfrac{dx'}{dt} \cdot \dfrac{dt}{dt'} = \dfrac{dx'}{dt}$ $\qquad\qquad \left[\begin{array}{l} \because t' = t \\ dt' = dt \end{array} \right]$

Hence $\qquad \dfrac{dx'}{dt} = 3 \text{ or } \vec{u'_x} = 3\hat{i}$

Similarly $\qquad \dfrac{dy'}{dt'} = \dfrac{dy'}{dt} = 4 \quad \text{or} \quad \vec{u'_y} = 4\hat{j} \qquad \dfrac{dz'}{dt'} = \dfrac{dz'}{dt} = 0$

∴ Velocity in frame S', $\vec{u'} = \vec{u'_x} + \vec{u'_y} + \vec{u'_z} = 3\hat{i} + 4\hat{j}$

(*b*) As the position co-ordinates are given in the frame S' which is moving with constant velocity of $v = 10$ cm s^{-1} along $+ X$-axis, the position co-ordinates in the frame S are given by inverse Galelian transformations

$$x = x' + vt; \quad y = y'; \quad z = z'; \quad t = t'$$

Here $\qquad x' = 11$ cm $\quad y' = 9$ cm $\quad z' = 8$ cm $\quad t' = \dfrac{1}{2}$ sec.

$$\therefore \qquad x = x' + vt = 11 + 10 \times \frac{1}{2} = 16 \text{ cm}; \; y' = 9 \text{ cm}; \; z' = 8 \text{ cm}$$

$\therefore$ The position co-ordinates of the point in the frame S are $(16, 9, 8)$ cm.

Q. 5.7. A frame S' is moving with velocity $5\hat{i} + 7\hat{j}$ m/s relative to an inertial frame S. A particle is moving with velocity $(t + 5)\hat{i} + 9\hat{j}$ m/s with respect to S. Find the acceleration of the particle in the frame S'.

(G.N.D.U., 1993)

Ans. Velocity of the particle in frame S, $\vec{u} = (t + 5)\hat{i} + 9\hat{j}$ ms^{-1}

Velocity of frame S' relative to S, $\qquad \vec{v} = 5\hat{i} + 7\hat{j}$

According to Galelian transformation equations for velocity,

Velocity of the particle with respect to frame S',

$$\vec{u'} = \vec{u} - \vec{v} = (t + 5)\hat{i} + 9\hat{j} - (5\hat{i} + 7\hat{j}) = t\hat{i} + 2\hat{j} \text{ ms}^{-1}$$

$\therefore$ Acceleration of the particle in the frame S', $\vec{a'} = \dfrac{d\vec{u'}}{dt'} = \dfrac{d\vec{u'}}{dt}$ ...$[\because \; dt' = dt]$

$$= \frac{d}{dt}[t\hat{i} + 2\hat{j}] = \hat{i} \quad \therefore \; \vec{a'} = \hat{i} \text{ ms}^{-2}$$

Q. 5.8. (a) What are Galelian transformations ? Prove that Newton's laws of motion are invariant under Galelian transformations ? (P.U., 2006, 2000; M.D.U., 2003)

(b) What are the quantities which are invariant under Galelian transformations ?

(P.U., 2006, 2003; Pbi.U., 2002, 1999)

Ans. (a) Galelian transformations. See Q. 5.3.

Newton's laws of motion are invariant to Galelian transformations. To prove that Newton's laws of motion are invariant to Galelian transformations we shall first prove that acceleration is invariant to these transformations. We shall consider the case when the co-ordinates axes of the two frames are parallel, their origins coincide at $t' = t = 0$ and the frame S' moves with a uniform velocity $\vec{v}$ with respect to the frame S in the $+ X$ direction. In such a case Galelian transformation equations are

$x' = x - vt \qquad\qquad y' = y \qquad\qquad z' = z \qquad\qquad t' = t$

Differentiating we get, $\quad dx' = dx - vdt, \qquad dy' = dy$

$$dz' = dz \qquad\qquad dt' = dt$$

Dividing left hand side of each equation by dt' and right hand side by dt we have

$$\frac{dx'}{dt'} = \frac{dx}{dt} - v, \; \frac{dy'}{dt'} = \frac{dy}{dt}, \quad \frac{dz'}{dt} = \frac{dz}{dt}$$

Now $\dfrac{dx'}{dt'} = u'_x = x$ – component of the velocity $\vec{u'}$ as measured in the frame S'

and $\dfrac{dx}{dt} = u_x = x$ – component of the velocity $\vec{u}$ as measured in the frame S

$\therefore \qquad\qquad\qquad u'_x = u_x - v$

Similarly $\qquad\qquad\qquad u'_y = u_y, \qquad u'_z = u_z$

Combining the equations for x, y and z components we have

$$u'_x \hat{i} + u'_y \hat{j} + u'_z \hat{k} = (u_x - v)\hat{i} + u_y \hat{j} + u_z \hat{k} = u_x \hat{i} + u_y \hat{j} + u_z \hat{k} - v\hat{i}$$

or $\qquad\qquad\qquad\qquad \vec{u'} = \vec{u} - \vec{v}$ ...(i)

Differentiating equation (i) again we have $du'_x = d(u_x - v) = du_x$

Since $v = a$ constant

Similarly $du'_y = du_y$ and $du'_z = du_z$

Dividing left hand side of each equation by dt' and right hand side by dt, we have

$$\frac{du'_x}{dt'} = \frac{du_x}{dt} \; ; \; \frac{du'_y}{dt'} = \frac{du_y}{dt} \; ; \; \frac{du'_z}{dt'} = \frac{du_z}{dt}$$

or
$$a'_x = a_x, a'_y = a_y, a'_z = a_z$$

where a'_x, a'_y, a'_z are the x, y and z components of acceleration in the frame S' and a_x, a_y and a_z in the frame S.

Combining the equations for x, y and z components we have

$$a'_x \hat{i} + a'_y \hat{j} + a'_z \hat{k} = a_x \hat{i} + a_y \hat{j} + a_z \hat{k} \quad \text{or} \quad \vec{a'} = \vec{a} \qquad \qquad ...(ii)$$

Hence the components of acceleration of a particle are independent of the uniform velocity of one inertial frame of reference relative to another. In other words **acceleration is an invariant** for a transformation from one inertial frame to another which is having a uniform relative motion of translation.

Newton's laws of motion. Newton's second law of motion is the real law of motion and includes the first and the third law. In mathematical form the second law is stated as $\vec{F} = m\vec{a}$ where $\vec{F}$ is the force acting on a mass m in the frame S. If $\vec{F'}$ is the force acting on the same mass in the frame S' and $\vec{a'}$ is the acceleration produced in the mass as observed in the frame S', then

$$\vec{F'} = m\vec{a'}$$

As proved above in equation (ii) $\vec{a'} = \vec{a}$

$$\therefore \quad \vec{F'} = \vec{F}$$

showing thereby the law is invariant to Galelian transformations. Hence **Newton's laws of motion are invariant to Galelian transformations,** and *the relation F = ma holds true under Galelian transformations.*

(*b*) The quantities invariant under Galelian transformations are (*i*) mass (*ii*) length (*iii*) time (*iv*) acceleration (*v*) force.

Exercise. Show that the relation $F = ma$ holds true under Galelian transformations.

(*G.N.D.U.,* 2009, 2007)

Hint. See Q. 5.8(a)

Q. 5.9. (*a*) **Show that a frame of reference having a uniform translatory motion (or moving with constant velocity) relative to an inertial frame is also inertial.**

(*P.U.,* 2001; *Cal.U.Hons.,* 1992, 1991)

(*b*) **Show that the force on the particle is the same in two frames connected by Galelian transformations. Hence justify that if the relation $\vec{F} = m\vec{a}$ is used to define force observers in all frames of reference would agree on the magnitude and direction of the force $\vec{F}$ independent of relative velocity of reference frames.** (*Guwahati.U.,* 2000; *G.N.D.U.,* 1994)

Ans. (*a*) **Inertial frame in uniform translatory motion.** If an inertial frame S' is moving relative to another inertial frame S with a uniform velocity $\vec{v}$, along a straight line, then $\vec{a'} = \vec{a}$ i.e., the acceleration of a particle is the same in the two inertial frames. In other words, if a particle is unaccelerated in frame S, it is unaccelerated in S' i.e., a particle at rest or in uniform motion in a straight line (zero acceleration) in S will also be at rest or in uniform motion in a straight line in S'. **Hence if S is an inertial frame then S' having a uniform translatory motion relative to it is also an inertial frame.**

(b) **Force same in two inertial frames.** As stated above for two inertial frames connected by Galelian transformations the acceleration of a particle is invariant i.e., $\vec{a'} = \vec{a}$ ...(i)

In Newtonian mechanics the mass of a particle is also invariant. Hence multiplying both sides of relation (i) by m we have $m\vec{a'} = m\vec{a}$ or $\vec{F'} = \vec{F}$ where $\vec{F}$ is the force on the particle in frame S and $\vec{F'}$ the force on the same particle in frame S'.

Thus force acting on a particle is the same in two frames of reference connected by Galelian transformations. In other words, "*If the relation $\vec{F} = m\vec{a}$ is used to define force observers in all frames of reference would agree on the magnitude and direction of force $\vec{F}$ independent of relative velocity of reference frames.*"

Q. 5.10. Show that the laws of conservation of Momentum and Energy are invariant to Galelian transformations.

(*Pbi.U., 2008, 2001, 1999; P.U., 2007, 2000; G.N.D.U., 2004, 2003, 1990*)

Ans. The two important laws of physics which are invariant to Galelian transformations are

(i) Law of conservation of linear momentum and (ii) Law of conservation of energy.

(i) **Law of Conservation of Linear Momentum.** The principle of conservation of momentum states,

"When a number of particles interact and there is no external force acting on them, the total momentum of the system is conserved."

The law of conservation of momentum is an invariant i.e., remains unchanged in the two frames of reference connected by Galelian transformations. To prove the same consider two particles of mass m_1 and m_2 moving with velocities $\vec{u_1}$ and $\vec{u_2}$ respectively in the inertial frame S. Let their velocities after collision be $\vec{v_1}$ and $\vec{v_2}$ respectively. If we assume that the velocities of the particles are **small** as compared to the velocity of light, then

(i) Newton's second law $\vec{F} = m\vec{a} = m\dfrac{d\vec{v}}{dt}$ and

(ii) Law of conservation of mass

$m_1 + m_2$ (before collision) $= m_1 + m_2$ (after collision) hold good.

Hence according to the law of conservation of momentum

$$m_1\vec{v_1} + m_2\vec{v_2} = m_1\vec{u_1} + m_2\vec{u_2}$$ ...(i)

Let $\vec{u_1'}$, and $\vec{u_2'}$ be the velocities of m_1 and m_2 before collision and $\vec{v_1'}$ and $\vec{v_2'}$ after collision as seen by an observer in the frame S' moving relative to frame S with a constant velocity $\vec{V}$. According to inverse Galelian transformation equations as applied to velocities

$$\vec{u_1} = \vec{u_1'} + \vec{V} \qquad \vec{u_2} = \vec{u_2'} + \vec{V} \qquad \vec{v_1} = \vec{v_1'} + \vec{V} \qquad \vec{v_2} = \vec{v_2'} + \vec{V}$$

Substituting these values in equation (i), we have

$$m_1(\vec{v_1'} + \vec{V}) + m_2(\vec{v_2'} + \vec{V}) = m_1(\vec{u_1'} + \vec{V}) + m_2(\vec{u_2'} + \vec{V})$$

or $$m_1 \vec{v_1} + m_2 \vec{v_2} = m_1 \vec{u_1} + m_2 \vec{u_2}$$

i.e., the law of conservation of momentum holds good in the moving system also.

(*ii*) **Law of Conservation of Energy.** According to the principle of conservation of energy, in the above case of collision between two particles, we have

$$\frac{1}{2} m_1 v_1^2 + \frac{1}{2} m_2 v_2^2 = \frac{1}{2} m_1 u_1^2 + \frac{1}{2} m_2 u_2^2 - E$$

where E is the part of the energy which appears as heat, light etc. or as potential energy. Applying the Galelian transformation equation for velocities we have, for the frame S'

$$\frac{1}{2} m_1 (\vec{v_1} + \vec{V})^2 + \frac{1}{2} m_2 (\vec{v_2} + \vec{V})^2 = \frac{1}{2} m_1 (\vec{u_1} + \vec{V})^2 + \frac{1}{2} m_2 (\vec{u_2} + \vec{V})^2 - E$$

or $$\frac{1}{2} m_1 (\vec{v_1} + \vec{V}) \cdot (\vec{v_1} + \vec{V}) + \frac{1}{2} m_2 (\vec{v_2} + \vec{V}) \cdot (\vec{v_2} + \vec{V})$$

$$= \frac{1}{2} m_1 (\vec{u_1} + \vec{V}) \cdot (\vec{u_1} + \vec{V}) + \frac{1}{2} m_2 (\vec{u_2} + \vec{V}) \cdot (\vec{u_2} + \vec{V}) - E$$

or $$\frac{1}{2} m_1 (v_1'^2 + 2\vec{v_1'} \cdot \vec{V} + V^2) + \frac{1}{2} m_2 (v_2'^2 + 2\vec{v_2'} \cdot \vec{V} + V^2)$$

$$= \frac{1}{2} m_1 (u_1'^2 + 2\vec{u_1'} \cdot \vec{V} + V^2) + \frac{1}{2} m_2 (u_2'^2 + 2\vec{u_2'} \cdot \vec{V} + V^2) - E$$

or $$\frac{1}{2} m_1 v_1'^2 + \frac{1}{2} m_2 v_2'^2 + (m_1 \vec{v_1'} + m_2 \vec{v_2'}) \cdot \vec{V}$$

$$= \frac{1}{2} m_1 u_1'^2 + \frac{1}{2} m_2 u_2'^2 + (m_1 \vec{u_1'} + m_2 \vec{u_2'}) \cdot \vec{V} - E$$

but $$m_1 \vec{v_1'} + m_2 \vec{v_2'} = m_1 \vec{u_1'} + m_2 \vec{u_2'}$$ according to the principle of conservation of momentum

$$\therefore \quad \frac{1}{2} m_1 v_1'^2 + \frac{1}{2} m_2 v_2'^2 = \frac{1}{2} m_1 u_1'^2 + \frac{1}{2} m_2 u_2'^2 - E$$

which is the law of conservation of energy as observed in the moving frame S'. Hence the law of conservation of energy is invariant under Galelian transformations.

Q. 5.11. (*a*) **Show that the electromagnetic wave equation**

$$\frac{\partial^2 \phi}{dx^2} + \frac{\partial^2 \phi}{\partial y^2} + \frac{\partial^2 \phi}{\partial z^2} - \frac{1}{c} \frac{\partial^2 \phi}{\partial t^2}$$

is non invariant in Galelian transformation equations where ϕ is scalar potential.

(*PU.* 2006)

(*b*) **Show that the path of a projectile as seen from another projectile will always be a straight line.**

(*A.U.* 1994)

Ans. (*a*) Let an inertial frame S' move along x-direction with respect to the frame S with a speed v. If x, y, z, t are the co-ordinates of a point in frame S and x', y', z', t' the co-ordinates of the same point in frame S', then

$$\frac{\partial \phi}{\partial x} = \frac{\partial \phi}{\partial x'} \frac{\partial x'}{\partial x} + \frac{\partial \phi}{\partial y'} \frac{\partial y'}{\partial x} + \frac{\partial \phi}{\partial z'} \frac{\partial z'}{\partial x} + \frac{\partial \phi}{\partial t'} \frac{\partial t'}{\partial x} \qquad ...(i)$$

$$\frac{\partial \phi}{\partial y} = \frac{\partial \phi}{\partial x'} \frac{\partial x'}{\partial y} + \frac{\partial \phi}{\partial y'} \frac{\partial y'}{\partial y} + \frac{\partial \phi}{\partial z'} \frac{\partial z'}{\partial y} + \frac{\partial \phi}{\partial t'} \frac{\partial t'}{\partial y} \qquad ...(ii)$$

$$\frac{\partial \phi}{\partial z} = \frac{\partial \phi}{\partial x'}\frac{\partial x'}{\partial z} + \frac{\partial \phi}{\partial y'}\frac{\partial y'}{\partial z} + \frac{\partial \phi}{\partial z'}\frac{\partial z'}{\partial z} + \frac{\partial \phi}{\partial t'}\frac{\partial t'}{\partial z} \qquad \text{...(iii)}$$

$$\frac{\partial \phi}{\partial t} = \frac{\partial \phi}{\partial x'}\frac{\partial x'}{\partial t} + \frac{\partial \phi}{\partial y'}\frac{\partial y'}{\partial t} + \frac{\partial \phi}{\partial z'}\frac{\partial z'}{\partial t} + \frac{\partial \phi}{\partial t'}\frac{\partial t'}{\partial t} \qquad \text{...(iv)}$$

For the motion of S' along the x-direction of S, the Galelian transformation equations are

$$x' = x - vt, \quad y' = y, \quad z' = z \quad \text{and} \quad t' = t \qquad \text{...(v)}$$

From Eq. (v), we get

$$\frac{\partial x'}{\partial x} = 1, \quad \frac{\partial y'}{\partial x} = 0, \quad \frac{\partial z'}{\partial x} = 0, \quad \frac{\partial t'}{\partial x} = 0 \qquad \text{...(vi)}$$

Thus Eq. (i) becomes,

$$\frac{\partial \phi}{\partial x} = \frac{\partial \phi}{\partial x'} \quad \text{or} \quad \frac{\partial}{\partial x} = \frac{\partial}{\partial x'}$$

$$\therefore \qquad \frac{\partial^2 \phi}{\partial x^2} = \frac{\partial}{\partial x}\left(\frac{\partial \phi}{\partial x}\right) = \frac{\partial}{\partial x'}\left(\frac{\partial \phi}{\partial x'}\right) = \frac{\partial^2 \phi}{\partial x'^2} \qquad \text{...(vii)}$$

Similarly, we can prove that

$$\frac{\partial^2 \phi}{\partial y^2} = \frac{\partial^2 \phi}{\partial y'^2} \qquad \text{...(viii)}$$

$$\frac{\partial^2 \phi}{\partial z^2} = \frac{\partial^2 \phi}{\partial z'^2} \qquad \text{...(ix)}$$

Again from Eq. (v), we get

$$\frac{\partial x'}{\partial t} = -v, \quad \frac{\partial y'}{\partial t} = 0, \quad \frac{\partial z'}{\partial t} = 0, \quad \frac{\partial t'}{\partial t} = 1$$

$\therefore$ Eq. (iv), becomes
$$\frac{\partial \phi}{\partial t} = -v\frac{\partial \phi}{\partial x'} + \frac{\partial \phi}{\partial t'}$$

or
$$\frac{\partial}{\partial t} = -v\frac{\partial}{\partial x'} + \frac{\partial}{\partial t'}$$

$\therefore$
$$\frac{\partial^2 \phi}{\partial t^2} = \frac{\partial}{\partial t}\left(\frac{\partial \phi}{\partial t}\right) = \left(-v\frac{\partial}{\partial x'} + \frac{\partial}{\partial t'}\right)\left(-v\frac{\partial \phi}{\partial x'} + \frac{\partial \phi}{\partial t'}\right)$$

or
$$\frac{\partial^2 \phi}{\partial t^2} = v^2\frac{\partial^2 \phi}{\partial x'^2} - v\frac{\partial^2 \phi}{\partial x' \partial t'} - v\frac{\partial^2 \phi}{\partial t' \partial x'} + \frac{\partial^2 \phi}{\partial t'^2}$$

or
$$\frac{\partial^2 \phi}{\partial t^2} = v^2\frac{\partial^2 \phi}{\partial x'^2} - 2v\frac{\partial^2 \phi}{\partial x' \partial t'} + \frac{\partial^2 \phi}{\partial t'^2} \qquad \text{...(x)}$$

Using Eqs. (vii), $(viii)$, (ix) and (x) and substituting these values in electromagnetic wave equation, we get

$$\frac{\partial^2 \phi}{\partial x^2} + \frac{\partial^2 \phi}{\partial y^2} + \frac{\partial^2 \phi}{\partial z^2} - \frac{1}{c^2}\frac{\partial^2 \phi}{\partial t^2} = \frac{\partial^2 \phi}{\partial x'^2} + \frac{\partial^2 \phi}{\partial y'^2} + \frac{\partial^2 z}{\partial z'^2} - \frac{v^2}{c^2}\frac{\partial^2 \phi}{\partial x'^2} + \frac{2v}{c^2}\frac{\partial^2 \phi}{\partial x' \partial t'} - \frac{1}{c^2}\frac{\partial^2 \phi}{\partial t'^2}$$

$$= \left(1 - \frac{v^2}{c^2}\right)\frac{\partial^2 \phi}{\partial x'^2} + \frac{\partial^2 \phi}{\partial y'^2} + \frac{\partial^2 \phi}{\partial z'^2} - \frac{1}{c^2}\frac{\partial^2 \phi}{\partial t'^2} + \frac{2v}{c^2}\frac{\partial^2 \phi}{\partial x' \partial t'}$$

The right hand side is the equation of $e.m.$ wave in the inertial frame S'. It does not have the same form as it has in the frame S. This proves that electromagnetic wave equation is not invariant under Galelian transformation.

(b) Let v_1 be the magnitude of velocity of one projectile moving in a direction making an angle θ_1 with the horizontal. The magnitude of its horizontal and vertical components are given by $v_1 \cos \theta_1$ and $v_1 \sin \theta_1$ respectively.

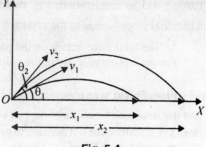

Let v_2 be the velocity of the second projectile making an angle θ_2 with the horizontal. Its horizontal and vertical components are given by $v_2 \cos \theta_2$ and $v_2 \sin \theta_2$ respectively.

Let the motion be in the X-Y plane. The horizontal distance travelled by the projectiles in time t is given by

$$x_1 = v_1 \cos \theta_1 t$$

and

$$x_2 = v_2 \cos \theta_2 t$$

Fig. 5.4

The vertical distance travelled by the projectiles in the same time is given by

$$y_1 = v_1 \sin \theta_1 t_1 - \frac{1}{2} gt^2$$

and

$$y_2 = v_2 \sin \theta_2 t - \frac{1}{2} gt^2$$

Hence the x and y co-ordinates of one projectile relative to other are

$$x = (x_1 - x_2) = (v_1 \cos \theta_1 - v_2 \cos \theta_2) t$$
$$y = (y_1 - y_2) = (v_1 \sin \theta_1 - v_2 \sin \theta_2) t$$

$$\therefore \quad \frac{y}{x} = \frac{v_1 \sin \theta_1 - v_2 \sin \theta_2}{v_1 \cos \theta_1 - v_2 \cos \theta_2} = \text{a constant } (m)$$

Hence

$$y = mx$$

which is the equation of a straight line.

Hence the motion of one projectile as seen from another projectile will always be a straight line.

Q. 5.12. Explain the terms non-inertial frame of reference and fictitious force. Calculate the total force and fictitious force acting on a body in a non-inertial frame. Give two examples.

(Pbi.U., 2001, 2000, 1999; *Guwahati U.,* 2000; *A.U.,* 1995, 1993; *G.N.D.U.,* 1992;
Calicut U., 2003)

Ans. Non-inertial frame. See Q. 5.1.

Fictitious force. Consider a reference frame S' moving with an acceleration $\vec{a_0}$ relative to a frame S. If the frame S is an inertial frame, then the frame S' will be non-inertial frame and vice-versa.

Now consider a particle of mass m on which *no external force is acting* in the reference frame S. Then the acceleration of the particle in the frame S is **zero** but the particle will appear to have an acceleration $-\vec{a_0}$ relative to the frame S'. In other words, to an observer in the frame S' a force $\vec{F_0} = -m\vec{a_0}$ will appear to be acting on the particle whereas for an observer in the frame S there is no force acting on the particle. *Such a force which appears only due to the acceleration of the frame of reference is called* **fictitious force, apparent or pesudo force.**

Total force. Suppose the particle has an acceleration $\vec{a_i}$ as observed in the inertial frame S, then according to Newton's second law of motion the force acting on the particle is given by $\vec{F_i} = m\vec{a_i}$

When this force is observed from the reference frame S', then the frame S may be assumed to be moving with an acceleration $-\vec{a_0}$ relative to S'. Hence the particle will appear to be acted upon by an additional force $-m\vec{a_0}$ in the system S' due to its acceleration.

∴ The total force acting on the particle as observed by an observer in the reference frame S'

$$= \vec{F'} = m\vec{a_i} - m\vec{a_0} = m(\vec{a_i} - \vec{a_0}) \text{ or } \vec{F'} = \vec{F_i} - \vec{F_0}$$

which means that to an observer in the frame S' the total force acting on the particle appears to be $\vec{F'}$ and the net acceleration $(\vec{a_i} - \vec{a_0})$. The force $\vec{F_0} = -m\vec{a_0}$ is clearly the fictitious force. This force does not actually exist but appears to come into being only as a result of the acceleration of the frame S' with respect to the frame S. Hence

Fictitious force $\vec{F_0}$ = (mass) (Acceleration of non-inertial frame with sign reversed)

$$= m(-\vec{a_0}) = -m\vec{a_0}$$

Newton's second law of motion will also hold good in a non-inertial frame S' i.e., S' will behave as an inertial frame if we add to the **true force** $\vec{F_i}$ a fictitious force $\vec{F_0} = -m\vec{a_0}$ and take the total force $\vec{F'} = \vec{F_i} - \vec{F_0}$ and total acceleration as $\vec{a'} = \vec{a_i} - \vec{a_0}$.

Example 1: Centrifugal force. An interesting example of fictitious force is that of "*centrifugal force*". Consider a point mass m at rest in a non-inertial frame *i.e.*, $\vec{a_i} = 0$. Suppose the non-inertial frame rotates uniformly about an axis fixed with respect to the inertial frame. The acceleration of the point mass with respect to the inertial frame can be written as $\vec{a_0} = -\omega^2 \vec{r}$

where $\vec{r}$ is the position vector of the particle and is directed outward to the particle from the axis.

Now $\vec{F'} = \vec{F_i} - \vec{F_0}$

But $\vec{F_i} = 0$ ∴ $\vec{F'} = -\vec{F_0} = -m\vec{a_0} = -m\omega^2\vec{r}$

Example 2. Coriolis force See Q. 5.18.

Q. 5.13. (a) Can a particle be in equilibrium in a non-inertial frame?

(Pbi.U., 2003; H.P.U., 1993)

(b) A particle happens to be accelerated without any external force acting on it. What conclusions do you draw?   *(P.U. 2008)*

Ans. (a) A particle can be in equilibrium in a non-inertial frame. A particle is said to be in equilibrium when no net force is acting on it. This condition is satisfied when the external force acting on the particle is equal and opposite to the fictitious force due to the non-inertial frame.

The total force $\vec{F'}$ acting on a particle in a non-inertial frame is given by

$$\vec{F'} = \vec{F_i} - \vec{F_0}$$

where $\vec{F_i}$ is the external force acting on the particle as observed in an inertial frame and $\vec{F_0}$ is the fictitious force due to the non-inertial frame. Clearly $\vec{F'} = 0$ when $\vec{F_i} = \vec{F_0}$ and the particle is in equilibrium.

(b) As the particle is being accelerated without any external force acting on it, there must be some force due to co-ordinate system *i.e.*, the particle is in a *non-inertial frame of reference*. The total force $\vec{F'}$ acting in a non-inertial frame is given by

$$\vec{F'} = \vec{F_i} - \vec{F_0}$$

where $\vec{F_i}$ is the external force acting on the particle and $\vec{F_0}$ the fictitious force due to the non-inertial frame. As $\vec{F_i} = 0$, the only force acting on the particle is fictitious force $\vec{F_0}$ due to the non-inertial frame.

Q. 5.14. Prove that a frame of reference moving with uniform translational acceleration with respect to an inertial frame is a non-inertial frame. *(P.U., 2000, 1999; H.P.U., 1994)*

Ans. A frame with uniform translational acceleration is non-inertial. Consider an inertial frame S with its origin O. Let S' be another frame with origin O' moving relative to O with uniform translational acceleration $\vec{a_0}$. When the origins O' and O coincide let $t' = t = 0$.

Suppose the frame S' starts from rest, then displacement $\overrightarrow{OO'}$ of the origin O' in time $t = \frac{1}{2} \vec{a_0} t^2$. If P is a particle moving in space and $\vec{r}$ and $\vec{r'}$ are its position vectors at time t in the frames S and S' respectively, then

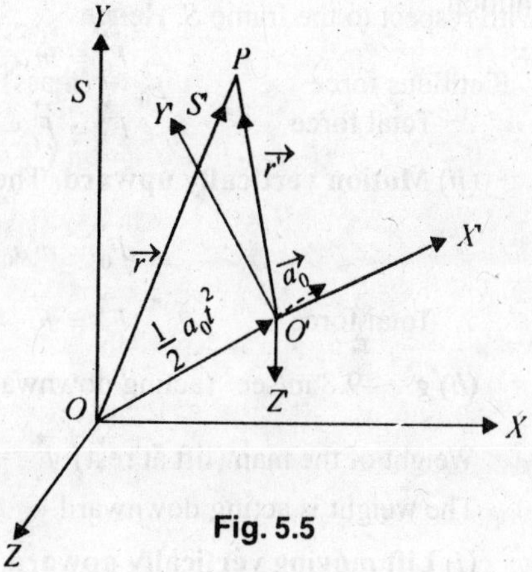

Fig. 5.5

$$\overrightarrow{OP} = \vec{r} \text{ and } \overrightarrow{O'P} = \vec{r'}$$

Now $\overrightarrow{OP} = \overrightarrow{OO'} + \overrightarrow{O'P}$ or $\vec{r} = \vec{r'} + \frac{1}{2} \vec{a_0} t^2$ ...(i)

Differentiating equation (i), twice we have

$$\frac{d\vec{r}}{dt} = \frac{d\vec{r'}}{dt} + \vec{a_0} t$$

and

$$\frac{d^2 \vec{r}}{dt^2} = \frac{d^2 \vec{r'}}{dt^2} + \vec{a_0} \quad \text{or} \quad \vec{a_i} = \vec{a'} + \vec{a_0} \qquad \qquad ...(ii)$$

where $\vec{a_i}$ and $\vec{a'}$ are the accelerations of the particle P in the frame S (inertial) and S' respectively.

If m is the mass of the particle, then multiplying both sides of relation (ii) by m, we have

$$m \vec{a_i} = m \vec{a'} + m \vec{a_0} \quad \text{or} \quad \vec{F_i} = \vec{F'} + \vec{F_0} \quad \text{or} \quad \vec{F'} = \vec{F_i} - \vec{F_0}$$

When no real force acts on the particle P in the inertial frame S, $\vec{F_i} = 0$. In such a case $\vec{F'} = -\vec{F_0}$.

Thus we find that in the frame S' the particle P appears to experience a force $-\vec{F_0}$ even when no force is acting on it in the inertial frame S. This force arises due to the uniform translational acceleration of the frame S' and is, therefore, a fictitious force. This fictitious force has not been applied from outside but arises because of the frame of reference selected by us. It is, therefore, a non-inertial force and the *frame of reference which is moving with a uniform translational acceleration with respect to an inertial frame is a non-inertial frame.*

Q. 5.15. (a) Calculate the fictitious force and total force acting on a mass of 5 kgm in a frame of reference moving (i) vertically downward and (ii) vertically upward with an acceleration of 5 metres/sec². Acceleration due to gravity = 9.8 metres/sec².

(H.P.U., 2001; Pbi.U., 2000; G.N.D.U., 1991, 1990)

(b) A man weighing 80 kg is standing in a lift calculate the effective weight of the man when the lift is moving with an acceleration of 3m/sec².

(*i*) vertically upward, (*ii*) vertically downward.   (*Pbi. U.* 2006)

Ans. (*a*) The acceleration due to gravity = 9.8 metres/sec^2

Take the earth to be an inertial frame of reference and upward direction as positive, (downward direction negative)

$$m = 5 \text{ kg} \quad \vec{a_0} = 5 \text{ metres/sec}^2$$

$\therefore$ Weight of the body $\vec{F_i} = mg = 5 \times (-9.8) = -49$ Newton

(The negative sign indicates that the weight is acting downward.)

(*i*) **Motion vertically downward.** The fictitious force acting on the mass during downward motion

$$\vec{F_0} = m\vec{a_0} = 5(-5) = -25 \text{ Newton (upward)}$$

$\therefore$ Total force $\vec{F'} = \vec{F_i} - \vec{F_0} = -49 + 25 = -24$ Newton (downward)

(*ii*) **Motion vertically upward.** The fictitious force acting on the mass during upward motion

$$\vec{F_0} = m\vec{a_0} = 5(5) = 25 \text{ Newton (downward)}$$

$\therefore$ Total force $\vec{F'} = \vec{F_i} - \vec{F_0} = -49 - 25 = -74$ Newton (downward)

(*b*) $g = -9.8$ m/sec^2 (acting downward)

Weight of the man (lift at rest) $\vec{F_i} = (80 \times (-9.8)) = -784$ Newton
The weight is acting downward.

(*i*) **Lift moving vertically upward.** Acceleration $\vec{a_0} = +3$ m/sec^2

Fictitious force acting on the man $\vec{F_0} = m\vec{a_0} = 80 \times 3 = 240$ Newton

$\therefore$ Total force $\vec{F'} = \vec{F_i} - \vec{F_0} = -784 - 240 = -1024$ Newton

The effective weight of the man is acting downward and has *increased.*

(*ii*) **Lift moving vertically downward.** Acceleration $\vec{a_0} = -3$ m/sec^2

Fictitious force acting on the man $\vec{F_0} = m\vec{a_0} = 80 \times -3 = -240$ Newton

$\therefore$ Total force $\vec{F'} = \vec{F_i} - \vec{F_0} = -784 + 240 = -544$ Newton

The effective weight of the man is acting downward and has *decreased.*

Q. 5.16. Calculate the total force acting on a freely falling body of mass 5 kg with reference to a frame moving with a downward acceleration of 2 metres per second^2.

(*P.U.* 2006; *G.N.D.U.,* 1990, 1991)

Ans. The force $\vec{F'}$ acting on a body in a non-inertial frame is given by $\vec{F'} = \vec{F_i} - \vec{F_0}$ where $\vec{F_i}$ is the force on the same body in an inertial frame and $\vec{F_0}$ is the fictitious force due to the accelerated motion of the non-inertial frame. As the body is falling freely, downward force on it in the inertial frame of the earth $\vec{F_i} = 0$

$\therefore$ $\vec{F'} = -\vec{F_0}$ or $\vec{F'} = -m\vec{a_0}$

where $\vec{a_0}$ is the acceleration of the non-inertial frame and m the mass of the body.

As the reference frame is moving downward with an acceleration of 2 m/s² $\vec{a_0} = -2 \text{ ms}^{-2}$

$$\therefore \qquad \vec{F'} = -m\vec{a_0} = -(-2 \times 5) = +10 \text{ N}$$

The positive sign indicates that the fictitious force is acting upward.

Exercise. *A frame of reference is moving with an acceleration of 5 m/sec² downward. Find the fictitious or apparent force and total force acting on a body of mass 10 kg falling freely relative to the frame.*   *(Gharwal U., 1999)*

Ans.   Apparent force = Total force = $-(-5 \times 10) = 50$ N (upward)

Q. 5.17. Calculate the effective weight of an astronaut ordinarily weighing 60 kg when his rocket moves vertically upward with 5 g acceleration.   *(G.N.D.U., 1992)*

Ans. As the rocket moves vertically upward with an acceleration 5 g, it is a non-inertial frame and therefore the total force on the astronaut is given by $\vec{F'} = \vec{F_i} - \vec{F_0}$

where $\vec{F_i}$ is the force on the astronaut in an inertial frame and $\vec{F_0}$ is the fictitious force on the astronaut due to the acceleration of the rocket.

$$\text{Now } \vec{F_i} = 60 \text{ kg. wt} = 60 \text{ g N}$$

and

$$\vec{F_0} = -m\vec{a_0} = -60 \times 5 \text{ g N} = -300 \text{ g N}$$

$\therefore$ Effective weight of the astronaut $\vec{F'} = \vec{F_i} - \vec{F_0} = 60 \text{ g} - (-300 \text{ g})$

$$= 360 \text{ g N} = 360 \text{ kg}$$

Q. 5.18. A reference frame 'a' rotates with respect to another reference frame 'b' with an angular velocity $\vec{\omega}$. If the position, velocity and acceleration of a particle in frame 'a' are represented by $\vec{r}, \vec{v_a}$ and $\vec{a_a}$ show that acceleration of the particle in frame 'b' is given by $\vec{a_b}$ where

$$\vec{a_b} = \vec{a_a} + 2\,\vec{\omega} \times \vec{v_a} + \vec{\omega} \times (\vec{\omega} \times \vec{r}) + \frac{d\vec{\omega}}{dt} \times \vec{r}$$

Explain the physical significance of various terms in the above expression and show that Coriolis and centrifugal forces are consequences of rotation of frame of reference.

(P.U., 2004, 2001, 1996, 1992; G.N.D.U., 2004, 1995, 1991; H.P.U., 2001, 1995, 1993, Pbi.U., 2005, 1999, 1991; Guwahati U., 2000; Bhopal U., 2004)

Ans. Rotating frame. Let XYZ represent the cartesian co-ordinate axes of the frame 'b' and $X'Y'Z'$ those of the frame 'a' rotating with angular velocity $\vec{\omega}$ with respect to the frame 'b' considered as inertial frame, about an axis passing through the common origin O. The rotating frame of reference 'a' is a **non-inertial frame.**

Let the position vector $\overrightarrow{OP}$ of a point P in the inertial frame 'b' be represented by

$$\overrightarrow{OP} = \vec{r} = x\hat{i} + y\hat{j} + z\hat{k}$$

where x, y, z are the co-ordinates of the point P and $\hat{i}, \hat{j}, \hat{k}$ the unit vectors along the X, Y, and Z directions respectively in the non-rotating frame 'b'.

The components of the position vector $\vec{r}$ in the rotating non-inertial frame 'a' are represented by

$$\vec{r} = x'\hat{i}' + y'\hat{j}' + z'\hat{k}' \qquad \qquad ...(i)$$

where x', y', z' are the co-ordinates of the point P and $\hat{i}'$, $\hat{j}'$, $\hat{k}'$, the unit vectors along X' Y' Z' directions respectively in the rotating frame 'a'.

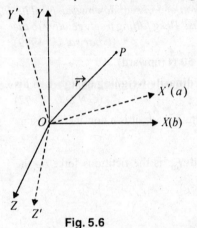

Fig. 5.6

As the frame 'a' is rotating the directions of X', Y' and Z' axes are continuously changing. The directions of unit vectors $\hat{i}'$, $\hat{j}'$ and $\hat{k}'$ therefore, are also continuously changing.

Hence $\hat{i}'$, $\hat{j}'$, $\hat{k}'$ although constant in magnitude keep on changing direction.

$\therefore \quad \dfrac{d\hat{i}'}{dt}, \dfrac{d\hat{j}'}{dt}$ and $\dfrac{d\hat{k}'}{dt}$ are not zero.

But unit vectors $\hat{i}$, $\hat{j}$ and $\hat{k}$ in the inertial frame 'b' are constant in magnitude as well as in direction.

$\therefore \quad \dfrac{d\hat{i}}{dt}, \dfrac{d\hat{j}}{dt}$ and $\dfrac{d\hat{k}}{dt}$ are zero.

Differentiating equation (i) with respect to t, we get

$$\left(\frac{d\vec{r}}{dt}\right)_b = \frac{dx'}{dt}\hat{i}' + \frac{dy'}{dt}\hat{j}' + \frac{dz'}{dt}\hat{k}' + x'\frac{d\hat{i}'}{dt} + y'\frac{d\hat{j}'}{dt} + z'\frac{d\hat{k}'}{dt} \qquad ...(ii)$$

Now $\left(\dfrac{d\vec{r}}{dt}\right)_b = \vec{v}_b$ the velocity of the particle P with respect to the inertial frame b (X, Y, Z).

Further $\dfrac{dx'}{dt}\hat{i}' + \dfrac{dy'}{dt}\hat{j}' + \dfrac{dz'}{dt}\hat{k}' = \vec{v}_a$ is the velocity of the particle P with respect to the rotating frame 'a' (X', Y', Z'). Let us denote it by $\left(\dfrac{d\vec{r}}{dt}\right)_a$ the time rate of change of position vector $\vec{r}$ in the rotating frame 'a'.

As the linear velocity of a particle is given by

$$\frac{d\vec{r}}{dt} = \vec{\omega} \times \vec{r} \text{ where } \vec{\omega} \text{ is the angular velocity, we have}$$

$$\frac{d\hat{i}'}{dt} = \vec{\omega} \times \hat{i}'; \frac{d\hat{j}'}{dt} = \vec{\omega} \times \hat{j}'; \frac{d\hat{k}'}{dt} = \vec{\omega} \times \hat{k}'$$

Hence equation (ii) can be written as $\left(\dfrac{d\vec{r}}{dt}\right)_b = \left(\dfrac{d\vec{r}}{dt}\right)_a + \vec{\omega} \times (x'\hat{i}' + y'\hat{j}' + z'\hat{k}')$

$$= \left(\frac{d\vec{r}}{dt}\right)_a + \vec{\omega} \times \vec{r} \text{ or } \vec{v}_b = \vec{v}_a + \vec{\omega} \times \vec{r} = \vec{v}_a + \vec{v}_0 \qquad ...(iii)$$

In other words, *the velocity of the particle in the inertial frame $\vec{v_b}$ is equal to the vector sum of its velocity in the rotating frame $\vec{v_a}$ and the linear velocity due to rotation $\vec{v_0}$ the value of which at any instant depends upon the value of $\vec{r}$ at that instant.*

The relation $\left(\dfrac{d\vec{r}}{dt}\right)_b = \left(\dfrac{d\vec{r}}{dt}\right)_a + \vec{\omega} \times \vec{r}$ holds good for other similar vectors and may be expressed as an operator equation $\left(\dfrac{d}{dt}\right)_b (\ ) = \left(\dfrac{d}{dt}\right)_a (\ ) + \vec{\omega} \times (\ )$

Applying the operator equation to the velocity vector $\vec{v_b}$ instead of displacement vector $\vec{r}$, we have

$$\left(\frac{d\vec{v_b}}{dt}\right)_b = \left(\frac{d\vec{v_b}}{dt}\right)_a + \vec{\omega} \times \vec{v_b}$$

Substituting the value of $\vec{v_b}$ from (*iii*) on the right hand side of the above equation, we have

$$\left(\frac{d\vec{v_b}}{dt}\right)_b = \frac{d}{dt}(\vec{v_a} + \vec{\omega} \times \vec{r})_a + \vec{\omega} \times (\vec{v_a} + \vec{\omega} \times \vec{r})$$

$$= \left(\frac{d\vec{v_a}}{dt}\right)_a + \left(\frac{d\vec{\omega}}{dt} \times \vec{r}\right)_a + \vec{\omega}\left(\frac{d\vec{r}}{dt}\right)_a + \vec{\omega} \times \vec{v_a} + \vec{\omega} \times (\vec{\omega} \times \vec{r})$$

$$= \left(\frac{d\vec{v_a}}{dt}\right)_a + \left(\frac{d\vec{\omega}}{dt} \times \vec{r}\right)_a + \vec{\omega} \times \vec{v_a} + \vec{\omega} \times \vec{v_a} + \vec{\omega} \times (\vec{\omega} \times \vec{r})$$

$$= \left(\frac{d\vec{v_a}}{dt}\right)_a + 2\vec{\omega} \times \vec{v_a} + \vec{\omega} \times (\vec{\omega} \times \vec{r}) + \left(\frac{d\vec{\omega}}{dt} \times \vec{r}\right)_a$$

or $$\vec{a_b} = \vec{a_a} + 2\vec{\omega} \times \vec{v_a} + \vec{\omega} \times (\vec{\omega} \times \vec{r}) + \left(\frac{d\vec{\omega}}{dt} \times \vec{r}\right)_a \qquad ...(iv)$$

where $\vec{a_a}$ is the acceleration in the rotating frame 'a' and $\vec{a_b}$ the acceleration in the stationary inertial frame 'b'.

The term $2\vec{\omega} \times \vec{v_a}$ is known as **Coriolis acceleration** after the name of its discoverer. The term appears only when the particle moves in the rotating frame *i.e.*, v_a is not equal to zero.

The term $\vec{\omega} \times (\vec{\omega} \times \vec{r})$ is the **centripetal acceleration**. The last term $\dfrac{d\vec{\omega}}{dt} \times \vec{r}$ is the **acceleration due to change in $\vec{\omega}$**. This is **zero** when the angular velocity $\vec{\omega}$ of the rotating frame is **a constant**. This is the acceleration experienced by a rider when a merry go round is just started.

Hence for a uniform angular velocity ω, $\dfrac{d\omega}{dt} = 0$ and we have

$$\vec{a_b} = \vec{a_a} + 2\vec{\omega} \times \vec{v_a} + \vec{\omega} \times (\vec{\omega} \times \vec{r})$$

or $\qquad \vec{a}_a = \vec{a}_b - 2\vec{\omega} \times \vec{v}_a - \vec{\omega} \times (\vec{\omega} \times \vec{r})$ ...(v)

Physical significance. According to Newton's second law of motion, the effective force on the particle of mass m in the rotating frame 'a' is given by $m\vec{a}_a = \vec{F'}$

and the **true force** in the inertial frame 'b' is given by $m\vec{a}_b = \vec{F}$

Multiplying relation (iv) by m on both sides, we have

$$m\vec{a}_b = m\vec{a}_a + 2m\vec{\omega} \times \vec{v}_a + m\vec{\omega} \times (\vec{\omega} \times \vec{r}) + m\frac{d\vec{\omega}}{dt} \times \vec{r}$$

Hence the force acting on the particle in the rotating frame may be expressed as

$$\vec{F'} = \vec{F} - 2m(\vec{\omega} \times \vec{v}_a) - m\vec{\omega} \times (\vec{\omega} \times \vec{r}) - m\frac{d\vec{\omega}}{dt} \times \vec{r}$$

or $\qquad \vec{F'} = \vec{F} + \vec{F}_0$

where $\vec{F}_0$ is the **fictitious force** acting in the non-inertial frame and is given by

$$\vec{F}_0 = -2m(\vec{\omega} \times \vec{v}_a) - m\vec{\omega} \times (\vec{\omega} \times \vec{r}) - m\frac{d\vec{\omega}}{dt} \times \vec{r}$$

As ω = a constant $\dfrac{d\vec{\omega}}{dt} = 0$. Hence $m\dfrac{d\vec{\omega}}{dt} \times \vec{r} = 0$

$\therefore \qquad \vec{F}_0 = -2m(\vec{\omega} \times \vec{v}_a) - m\vec{\omega} \times (\vec{\omega} \times \vec{r})$

or $\qquad$ Fictitious force = Coriolis force + Centrifugal force

(a) Coriolis force. The Coriolis force is given by $-2m(\vec{\omega} \times \vec{v}_a)$. *It is defined as the fictitious force which acts on a particle when it is in motion relative to a rotating frame of reference.*

It is proportional to the angular velocity $\vec{\omega}$ of the rotating frame and to the velocity $\vec{v}_a$ of the particle relative to it. It will obviously be zero if either $\vec{v}_a$ or $\vec{\omega}$ is zero *i.e.*, if the particle is at rest relative to the rotating frame or if the reference frame is non-rotating one.

The direction of Coriolis force is always perpendicular to $\vec{\omega}$ and $\vec{v}_a$ *i.e.*, angular velocity of the rotating frame and the velocity of the particle relative to the rotating frame. The *negative sign* indicates that Coriolis force is in the direction *opposite* to that given by right hand screw rule. Coriolis force can be written as

$$\text{Coriolis force} = -2m\omega v_a \sin\theta\, \hat{n}$$

where ω and v_a are the magnitude of $\vec{\omega}$ and $\vec{v}_a$, θ is the angle between the direction of $\vec{\omega}$ and $\vec{v}_a$ and $\hat{n}$ is a unit vector perpendicular to both $\vec{\omega}$ and $\vec{v}_a$.

If $\theta = 0$, Coriolis force = 0. This is so when the angular velocity vector of the rotating frame and the linear velocity of the particle relative to the rotating frame are *parallel*.

If $\theta = \dfrac{\pi}{2}$, $\sin\theta = 1$. Coriolis force $= -2m\omega v_a$ which is the maximum value *i.e.*, when $\vec{\omega}$ and $\vec{v}_0$ are perpendicular to each other, Coriolis force is a maximum.

(b) Centrifugal force. The centrifugal force is given by $-m\vec{\omega} \times (\vec{\omega} \times \vec{r})$. *It is defined as the fictitious force which acts on a particle at rest relative to a rotating frame of reference.* It is numerically equal to the centripetal force but is oppositely directed *i.e.*, *outward away from the axis of rotation.* Its value $= m\omega^2 \vec{r}_n$ where $\vec{r}_n$ is the distance of the particle from the centre of rotation or the component of $\vec{r}$ perpendicular to the axis of rotation.

It is clear from the above discussion that Coriolis and centrifugal forces are consequences of rotation of frame of reference. Whereas centrifugal force acts on a particle at rest relative to a rotating frame of reference, Coriolis force acts on a particle having a velocity with respect to the rotating frame of reference.

Q. 5.19. (*a*) **Taking earth to be a rotating frame of reference discuss the effect of centrifugal force due to rotation on the value of g and discuss variation of g with latitude. Show that the effect is maximum at the equator and minimum at the poles.**

(*G.N.D.U.* 2009, 2007, 2006; *P.U.* 2008, 2007, 2005, 1999)

OR

Derive the equation of effect of rotation of earth about its own axis on acceleration due to gravity.   (*P.U.* 2006)

(*b*) **Hence find the angle through which a plumb line will be deflected at a place in latitude λ. Calculate the deflection for $\lambda = 45°$.**

Ans. (*a*) **Effect of centrifugal force on g. Variation of g with latitude** the acceleration of a particle in a rotating frame is given by

$$\vec{a_i} = \vec{a_r} + 2\vec{\omega} \times \vec{v_r} + \vec{\omega} \times (\vec{\omega} \times \vec{r}) + \frac{d\vec{\omega}}{dt} \times \vec{r}$$

where $\vec{a_i}$ = acceleration of the particle with respect to the inertial frame

$\vec{a_r}$ = acceleration of the particle with respect to the rotating frame

$\vec{v_r}$ = the velocity of the particle in the rotating frame

$\vec{\omega}$ = the angular velocity of the rotating frame

$\vec{r}$ = the position vector of the particle.

When the particle is at **rest** in the rotating frame the Coriolis acceleration $2\vec{\omega} \times \vec{v_r} = 0$

If $\vec{\omega}$ = a constant, then the last term $\dfrac{d\vec{\omega}}{dt} \times \vec{r} = 0$

In such a case the only force acting due to rotation is the centrifugal force given by $(\vec{\omega}) \times (\vec{\omega} \times \vec{r})$.

$\therefore$ $\vec{a_i} = \vec{a_r} + \vec{\omega} \times (\vec{\omega} \times \vec{r})$ or $\vec{a_r} = \vec{a_i} - \vec{\omega} \times (\vec{\omega} \times \vec{r})$

The earth is rotating form west to east and a reference frame fixed in it is rotating frame of reference. To consider the effect of centrifugal force on the acceleration due to gravity we take angular velocity vector $\vec{\omega}$ along the y-axis and x-axis is taken perpendicular to it as shown in Fig. 5.7, then the actual value of $\vec{g}$ at a point P in the latitude λ will act along the direction PO where O is the centre of the earth. The components of $\vec{g}$ are

– $g \cos \lambda \, \hat{i}$ along x-axis and – $g \sin \lambda \, \hat{j}$ along y-axis

$\therefore$ $\vec{g} = - g \, (\cos \lambda \, \hat{i} + \sin \lambda \, \hat{j})$

Also $\vec{\omega} = \omega \, \hat{j}$

From P draw PC perpendicular to OY, then $CP = \vec{r}$

where $\vec{r}$ is the radius of the circle in which a particle at P rotates.

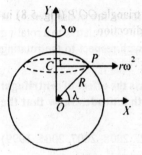

Fig. 5.7

Hence $CP = \vec{r} = R \cos \lambda = R \cos \lambda \, \hat{i}$

where R = magnitude of the radius of the earth.

The observed value of acceleration due to gravity at P taking into consideration the effect of centrifugal acceleration and neglecting the effect of Coriolis acceleration due to the rotation of the earth is given by

$$\vec{g'} = \vec{g} - \vec{\omega} \times (\vec{\omega} \times \vec{r})$$

$$= - g\,(\cos \lambda \, \hat{i} + \sin \lambda \, \hat{j}) - \omega \hat{j} \times (\omega \hat{j} \times R \cos \lambda \, \hat{i})$$

$$= - [(g \cos \lambda - \omega^2 R \cos \lambda)\, \hat{i} + g \sin \lambda \, \hat{j}]$$

$\therefore$ Magnitude of $g' = [(g \cos \lambda - \omega^2 R \cos \lambda)^2 + g^2 \sin^2 \lambda]^{1/2}$

$$= \left[g^2 \cos^2 \lambda \left(1 - \frac{\omega^2 R}{g} \right)^2 + g^2 \sin^2 \lambda \right]^{1/2}$$

$$= \left[g^2 \cos^2 \lambda \left(1 - \frac{2\omega^2 R}{g} \right) + g^2 \sin^2 \lambda \right]^{1/2}$$

since $\dfrac{\omega^2 R}{g} \ll 1$, its square is a negligible quantity.

$\therefore$ $$g' = g \left[\cos^2 \lambda - \frac{2\omega^2 R \cos^2 \lambda}{g} + \sin^2 \lambda \right]^{1/2}$$

$$= g \left[1 - \frac{2\omega^2 R}{g} \cos^2 \lambda \right]^{1/2} = g \left[1 - \frac{\omega^2 R}{g} \cos^2 \lambda \right] = g - \omega^2 R \cos^2 \lambda$$

Taking $R = 6.38 \times 10^6$ m, the value of

$$R\omega^2 = 6.38 \times 10^6 \times \left(\frac{2\pi}{24 \times 60 \times 60} \right)^2 = 0.03372 \text{ ms}^{-2} = 3.372 \text{ cm/sec}^2$$

At the equator. At the equator $\lambda = 0$, $\cos \lambda = 1$

$\therefore$ $$g' = g - \omega^2 R \cos^2 \lambda = g - \omega^2 R = g - 3.372 \text{ cm/sec}^2$$

$\therefore$ Due to rotation of the earth the value of g at the equator decreases by 3.372 cm/sec^2.

At the poles. At the poles $\lambda = 90°$, $\cos \lambda = 0$. Therefore decrease in the value of g due to rotation is zero. The observed difference between the value of g at the poles and at the equator is about 5.2 cm/sec^2. This is due to the fact that earth is flattened at the poles and even if it were not rotating the value of g at the poles would have been greater than that at the equator.

At latitude 45°. At latitude 45°, the decrease in the value of $g = R\omega^2 \cos^2 \lambda = 3.372 \times \dfrac{1}{2} = 1.686$ cm/sec^2.

Hence if the earth were to stop rotating, the value of g at the equator will increase by 3.372 cm/sec^2 and at a point in latitude 45° by 1.686 cm/sec^2.

In other words, the effect of centrifugal force due to rotation of the earth on the acceleration due to gravity is *maximum* at the *equator* and *minimum* at the *poles*.

(b) Direction of g'. Deflection of plumb line. The direction of g' will not be exactly along the vertical OP but will be deviated from the vertical by a small angle say α.

The value of α can be found out by applying the law of sines to the triangle $OO'P$ (Fig. 5.8) in which various sides represent the acceleration vectors in magnitude and direction

$$\frac{g'}{\sin \lambda} = \frac{R\omega^2 \cos \lambda}{\sin \alpha} \quad \text{or} \quad \sin \alpha = \frac{R\omega^2 \cos \lambda \sin \lambda}{g'}$$

As α is small $\sin \alpha = \alpha$

$$\therefore \quad \alpha = \frac{R\omega^2 \cos \lambda \sin \lambda}{g'} = \frac{R\omega^2}{2g'} \sin 2\lambda$$

Now $R\omega^2 = 3.372$ cm/sec^2 and taking $g' = 981$ cm/sec^2

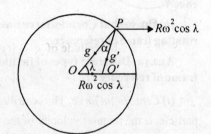

Fig. 5.8

$$\therefore \quad \frac{R\omega^2}{g'} = \frac{3.372}{981} = \frac{1}{291}$$

Deflection at latitude 45°. At a place $\lambda = 45°$, $2\lambda = 90°$, $\sin 2\lambda = 1$

Angle of deviation

$$\alpha = \frac{1}{2} \cdot \frac{1}{291} = 1.7 \times 10^{-3} \text{ radian} = \frac{1}{10} \text{ degree} = 6'$$

Hence a plumb line at P will not point in the true vertical direction PO but along PO' which is displaced from the vertical by a small angle equal to $6'$ (at a place $\lambda = 45°$).

Q. 5.20. (*a*) **How much faster than its present speed should the earth rotate so that bodies lying on the equator may fly off into space?** (*H.P.U., 1994*)

OR

How fast than its present speed of rotation, earth should start rotating so that acceleration due to gravity be zero at the equator.

(*b*) **If the earth were to cease rotating about its axis what will be the change in the value of g at a place of latitude 45° assuming the earth to be a sphere of radius 6.38×10^8 cm ?**

Ans. (*a*) The centrifugal force acting on a body of mass m at the equator is equal to $m R\omega^2$ where R is the radius of the earth and ω its angular velocity. If g is the acceleration due to gravity when the earth is at rest, then g' the acceleration when the earth has an angular velocity ω is given by

$$g' = g - R\omega^2 \cos^2 \lambda = g - R\omega^2 \quad [\because \lambda = 0, \cos \lambda = 1 \text{ and } \cos^2 \lambda = 1]$$

For the body to fly off into space the new angular speed ω' should be such that

$$g - R\omega'^2 = 0 \quad \text{or} \quad \frac{R\omega'^2}{g} = 1 \qquad \qquad ...(i)$$

but $$\frac{R\omega^2}{g} = \frac{1}{291} \qquad \qquad ...(ii)$$

Dividing (*i*) by (*ii*), we have $\dfrac{\omega'^2}{\omega^2} = 291 \quad$ or $\quad \dfrac{\omega'}{\omega} = \sqrt{291} = 17.06$

Hence the earth should have about seventeen times the present angular velocity so that bodies lying on the equator may fly into space.

OR

Hence if the earth rotates at an angular velocity 17.06 times its present angular velocity the value of g at the equator will be zero.

(b) We know that $\qquad\qquad g' = g - R\omega^2 \cos^2 \lambda \quad$ or $\quad g - g' = R\omega^2 \cos^2 \lambda$

Now $\qquad\qquad\qquad\qquad \lambda = 45°; R = 6.38 \times 10^8$ cm, $\omega = 2\pi/60 \times 60 \times 24$

Substituting, we have $g - g' = \dfrac{6.38 \times 10^8 \times 4\pi^2}{60 \times 60 \times 60 \times 60 \times 24 \times 24} \cos^2 45°$

$$= 3.372 \times \frac{1}{2} = 1.686 \text{ cm/sec}^2.$$

Q. 5.21. (a) What are different types of fictitious forces in a uniformly rotating frame of reference ? *(G.N.D.U., 2004)*

(b) Prove that Coriolis force owes its existence to the motion of the particle with respect to a rotating frame of reference. *(P.U., 2001, 2000; Pbi.U., 2000; H.P.U., 1993, 1991)*

Ans. (a) Different types of fictitious forces acting on a particle (body) in a uniformly rotating frame of reference are :–

(i) Centrifugal force. The centrifugal force is given by $- m \vec{\omega} \, (\vec{\omega} \times \vec{r})$ where m is the mass of the particle, ω the angular velocity of the rotating frame and $\vec{r}$ the position vector of the particle. This force acts on the particle even when it is at rest relative to the rotating frame.

(ii) Coriolis force. See part *(b)*

(b) Coriolis force. Coriolis force is given by $- 2m \, (\vec{\omega} \times \vec{v_a})$ where $\vec{v_a}$ is the velocity of the particle with respect to the rotating frame of reference. It will obviously be zero if the particle is at rest relative to the rotating frame. Thus Coriolis force owes its existence to the motion of the particle with respect to a rotating frame of reference.

Q. 5.22. (a) Define Coriolis force. Discuss the effect of Coriolis force on a particle moving on the surface of the earth. Calculate the horizontal and vertical components of Coriolis force. *(Pbi.U., 2003, P.U. 2007; G.N.D.U. 2007)*

(b) Calculate the Cariolis force on a mass of 50 gm placed at a distance of 10 cm from the axis of a rotating system if the angular speed of the frame is 10 rad/sec. *(Pbi. U. 2008)*

Ans. (a) Coriolis force. *It is defined as the fictitious force which acts on a particle when it is in motion relative to a rotating frame of reference.*

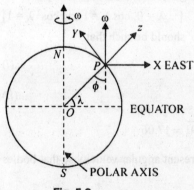

Fig. 5.9

Coriolis force acting on a particle moving with velocity $\vec{v}$ in a reference frame rotating with an angular velocity $\vec{\omega}$ is given by $\vec{F}_{cor} = - 2m \, (\vec{\omega} \times \vec{v})$ where m is the mass of the particle.

Coriolis force due to earth's rotation. Let P be a point on the surface of the earth at latitude λ or $\left[\text{co-latitude } \phi \, ; \text{ co-latitude is } \left(\dfrac{\pi}{2} - \lambda \right) \right]$. Consider a rectangular cartesian co-ordinate system with its origin rigidly fixed to the earth at P. The Z-axis of the system is taken '*vertically upward*' at P *i.e.*, radially outwards from the centre of the earth.

The X-Y plane is the horizontal plane containing the point P, the X-axis pointing towards the East and Y-axis pointing towards the North. The earth rotates from West to East and the positive direction of X-axis is taken towards the East. The *angular velocity vector* lies in the Y-Z plane in a direction parallel to the polar axis about which the earth rotates. The vector $\vec{\omega}$, therefore, has no component in the East-West direction *i.e.*, along the X-axis. If $\hat{i}$, $\hat{j}$ and $\hat{k}$ are the unit vectors along X, Y and Z axes respectively, then

$$\vec{\omega} = \omega_x \hat{i} + \omega_y \hat{j} + \omega_z \hat{k}$$

where
$$\omega_x = 0 ; \quad \omega_y = \omega \cos \lambda \text{ and } \omega_z = \omega \sin \lambda$$

Let a particle be projected from P with a velocity $\vec{v}$, then $\vec{v} = v_x \hat{i} + v_y \hat{j} + v_z \hat{k}$

$$= \dot{x} \hat{i} + \dot{y} \hat{j} + \dot{z} \hat{k}$$

Coriolis force acting on a particle moving with a velocity $\vec{v}$ in a reference frame rotating with an angular velocity $\vec{\omega}$ is given by $\vec{F}_{cor} = - 2m (\vec{\omega} \times \vec{v})$.

As the particle has been projected horizontally, the vertical component of its velocity $\vec{v}_z = \dot{z} \hat{k} = 0$ and its horizontal components are $\dot{x} \hat{i} + \dot{y} \hat{j}$.

To find the value of Coriolis force evaluate $(\vec{\omega} \times \vec{v})$ which is given by

$$\vec{\omega} \times \vec{v} = \begin{vmatrix} \hat{i} & \hat{j} & \hat{k} \\ 0 & \omega_y & \omega_z \\ \dot{x} & \dot{y} & 0 \end{vmatrix} = (- \omega_z \dot{y}) \hat{i} + (\omega_z \dot{x}) \hat{j} - (\omega_y \dot{x}) \hat{k}$$

$$\therefore \qquad \vec{F}_{cor} = - 2m [- \dot{y}\omega \sin \lambda \, \hat{i} + \dot{x}\omega \sin \lambda \, \hat{j} - \dot{x}\omega \cos \lambda \, \hat{k}]$$

$$= - 2m\omega [- \dot{y}\sin \lambda \, \hat{i} + \dot{x}\sin \lambda \, \hat{j} - \dot{x}\cos \lambda \, \hat{k}] \qquad ...(i)$$

The magnitude of Coriolis force is given by

$$|\vec{F}_{cor}| = 2m\omega [\dot{y}^2 \sin^2 \lambda + \dot{x}^2 \sin^2 \lambda + \dot{x}^2 \cos^2 \lambda]^{1/2}$$

$$= 2m\omega [\dot{y}^2 \sin^2 \lambda + \dot{x}^2]^{1/2} = 2m\omega [v_y^2 \sin^2 \lambda + v_x^2]^{1/2}$$

In terms of the co-latitude ϕ, $|\vec{F}_{cor}| = 2m\omega [v_y^2 \cos^2 \phi + v_x^2]^{1/2}$

The **horizontial component** of Coriolis force is given by

$$(\vec{F}_{cor})_{horizontal} = - 2m\omega [- \dot{y}\sin \lambda \, \hat{i} + \dot{x}\sin \lambda \, \hat{j}] = - 2m\omega \sin \lambda [- \dot{y}\hat{i} + \dot{x}\hat{j}]$$

The **magnitude of horizontal component** is given by

$$|(\vec{F}_{cor})_H| = 2m\omega \sin \lambda [\dot{y}^2 + \dot{x}^2]^{1/2}$$

$$= 2m\omega \sin \lambda [v_x^2 + v_y^2]^{1/2} = 2m\omega \, v \sin \lambda$$

In terms of co-latitude ϕ, the magnitude of horizontal component is

$$= 2m\omega \cos \phi [v_x^2 + v_y^2]^{1/2} = 2m \, v \cos \phi$$

The horizontal component of Coriolis force has maximum value at the poles ($\lambda = 90°$) and zero at the equator ($\lambda = 0$).

The **vertical component of Coriolis force** is given by

$$(\vec{F}_{cor})_{vertical} = - 2m\omega [- \dot{x} \cos \lambda \hat{k}] = + 2m\omega \, \dot{x} \cos \lambda \hat{k}$$

The **magnitude of the vertical component** is given by

$$|\vec{F}_{cor}|_v = 2m\omega \, \dot{x} \cos \lambda = 2m\omega \, v_x \cos \lambda$$

and in terms of co-latitude $\qquad = 2m\omega \, v_x \sin \phi$

The vertical component $(\vec{F}_{cor})_{vertical} = + 2\, m\omega\, \dot{x} \cos \lambda \hat{k}$ *i.e.*, it acts in the direction of $+ Z$-axis which means vertically upward. At the equator if the body has an initial velocity x it will appear to be lifted upwards.

(**b**)   Coriolis force $\vec{F} = -2\,m\,(\vec{\omega} \times \vec{v})$

∴   Magnitude of $\vec{F} = |F| = 2\,m\,\omega v \sin \theta$

where θ is the angle between the direction of $\vec{\omega}$ and $\vec{v}$.

∴ $F = 2\,m\,\omega\,v\ [\because \theta = \dfrac{n}{2}\,;\ \vec{\omega}$ and $\vec{v}$ being at right angles to each other]

$= 2\,mr\,\omega^2$ $[\because v = r\omega]$

or $F = 2 \times 50 \times 10 \times 10^2 = 10^5$ dynes.

Q. 5.23. Find the magnitude and direction of Coriolis force that acts on a 800 kg van running due north at 144 km hr^{-1} at a place where latitude is 30° N.

(*G.N.D.U., 2004; H.P.U., 1993*)

Ans. Mass of the van $m = 800$ kg

Velocity $\vec{v} = 144$ km hr$^{-1} = \dfrac{144 \times 1000}{60 \times 60} = 40$ ms^{-1} due North

Latitude of the place $\lambda = 30°$ N ∴ $\sin \lambda = \sin 30 = \dfrac{1}{2}$

ω for the earth $= \dfrac{2\pi}{24 \times 60 \times 60}$ rad/sec.

The X-axis is taken towards the East, Y-axis towards the North and Z-axis in the vertically upward direction.

Coriolis force is given by $\vec{F}_{cor} = -2m\,(\vec{\omega} \times \vec{v}_a)$

Horizontal component of Coriolis force

$(\vec{F}_{cor})_{Horizontal} = + 2m\omega \sin \lambda\,(v_y\,\hat{i} - v_x\,\hat{j})$

and vertical component

$(\vec{F}_{cor})_{Vertical} = 2\,m\omega\,v_x \cos \lambda \hat{k}$

As the van is running due North (along $+ Y$-axis) the component of its velocity due East (along $+ X$-axis) *i.e.*, $v_x = 0$ and $v_y = \vec{v}_a = \vec{v}$

∴ Vertical component of Coriolis force $= 0$

Horizontal component of Coriolis force,

$(\vec{F}_{cor})_H = + 2m\omega \sin \lambda v_y\,\hat{i}$

$= 2 \times 800 \times \dfrac{2\pi}{24 \times 60 \times 60} \times \dfrac{1}{2} \times 40 = 7$ Newton

This force will act along $+ \hat{i}$, *i.e.*, towards East.

Note. If the latitude of the place is 30° S, the force will act along $- \hat{i}$, *i.e.*, towards the West.

Q. 5.24. A bullet is fired horizontally with a velocity 500 ms^{-1} at 60° N colatitude, (*a*) Eastwards (*b*) Northwards. Calculate the magnitude of the Coriolis acceleration due to rotation of earth. Also calculate the magnitude of Coriolis force if the mass of the bullet is 5.0 gm.

(*P.U., 2001; Pbi.U., 2005, 1991*)

Ans. Velocity of the bullet $\vec{v} = 500$ ms^{-1}

Co-latitude $\qquad\qquad\qquad \phi = 60°$ ∴ Latitude $\lambda = (90 - \phi) = 30°$ and $\sin \lambda = \sin 30 = \dfrac{1}{2}$

The X-axis is taken towards the East, Y-axis towards the North and Z-axis in the vertically   upward direction

Coriolis acceleration is given by $\vec{a_a} = -2\vec{\omega} \times \vec{v_a}$

Horizontal component of Coriolis acceleration $(\vec{a_a})_H = 2\omega \sin \lambda \, (v_y \, \hat{i} - v_x \, \hat{j})$

and Vertical component of Coriolis acceleration $(\vec{a_a})_V = 2\omega \, v_x \, \cos \lambda \, \hat{k}$

(a) **Bullet fired Eastward.** Then $v_x = \vec{v} = 500$ ms^{-1}; $v_y = 0$

∴ Horizontal component of Coriolis acceleration

$$(\vec{a_a})_H = -2 \, \omega \sin \lambda v \hat{j}$$

$$= 2 \times \dfrac{2\pi}{24 \times 60 \times 60} \times \dfrac{1}{2} \times 500 = 0.036 \text{ ms}^{-1}$$

along $-\hat{j}$ i.e., $-Y$ direction or towards South.

Vertical component of Coriolis acceleration

$$(\vec{a_a})_V = 2\omega v_x \cos \lambda \, \hat{k}$$

$$= 2 \times \dfrac{2\pi}{24 \times 60 \times 60} \times \dfrac{\sqrt{3}}{2} \times 500 = 0.036 \sqrt{3}$$

along $+\hat{k}$ i.e., $+Z$ direction or vertically upwards.

∴ Magnitude of the resultant acceleration

$$|\vec{a_a}| = |(\vec{a_a})_H|^2 + |(\vec{a_a})_V|^2 = \sqrt{(0.036)^2 + (0.036 \times \sqrt{3})^2} = 0.072 \text{ ms}^{-1}$$

Force $F = ma = \dfrac{50}{1000} \times 0.072 = 3.6 \times 10^{-3}$ Newton

(b) **Bullet fired northwards.** Then $v_y = \vec{v} = 500$ ms^{-1}; $v_x = 0$

∴ Horizontal component of coriolis acceleration $(\vec{a_a})_H = 2\omega \sin \lambda v \hat{i} = 0.036$ ms^{-1} along $\hat{i}$ i.e., $+X$ direction

Vertical component of coriolis acceleration $(\vec{a_a})_V = 2\omega v_x \cos \lambda \hat{k} = 0$

∴ Resultant acceleration $= 0.036$ ms^{-1} along $+X$ direction.

Force $F = ma = \dfrac{50}{1000} \times 0.036 = 1.8 \times 10^{-3}$ Newton

Q. 5.25. What will be the direction of Coriolis force in Northern and Southern hemispheres?
(P.U., 2007, 2001, 2000; Pbi.U., 2005, 2000; G.N.D.U., 1996; H.P.U., 1995)

Ans. Direction of Coriolis force. The Coriolis force is given by $\vec{F}_{cor} = -2m \, (\vec{\omega} \times \vec{v})$ i.e., by the negative of the cross product of $\vec{\omega}$ the angular velocity of rotation of the earth and $\vec{v}$ the linear velocity of the body. The direction of $\vec{\omega}$ the angular velocity vector is always along the axis of the earth from S to N.

In the northern hemisphere if a body is moving towards North (*i.e.*, along + *Y*-axis) an application of the rule for the direction of vector product of two vectors indicates that this force will act towards the East (*i.e.*, along + *X*-axis). On the other hand if the body is moving towards South (*i.e.*, along – *Y*-axis) the Coriolis force will act towards the West (*i.e.*, along – *X*-axis). In other words, in the northern hemisphere a moving body turns towards the **right.**

Similarly in the Southern hemisphere a moving body will turn towards the **left** due to the effect of Coriolis force.

Q. 5.26 (*a*) Discuss the effect of Coriolis force in the case of freely falling body on the surface of the earth and calculate the deviation from the vertical suffered by a body dropped from rest from a height *h*.

(*P.U.* 2009; *Pbi.U.*, 2002; *H.P.U.*, 1999; *G.N.D.U.*, 2009, 2008, 1993; *Cal.U. Hons.*, 1991)

(*b*) Find the value of the deviation when *h* = 100 metres at (*a*) north pole (*b*) equator (*c*) latitude 60° N and (*d*) latitude 45° N.

Ans. (*a*) Deviation from the vertical. Let *P* be a point at height *h* from the surface of the earth at latitude λ. Consider a rectangular cartesian co-ordinate system rigidly fixed to the earth at *P*. The *Z*-axis of the system is taken '*vertically upward*' at *P i.e.*, radially outward from the centre of the earth. The *X-Y* plane is the horizontal plane containing the point *P*, the *X*-axis pointing towards the east and *Y*-axis pointing towards the north as shown in Fig. 5.9. The earth rotates from west to east and the positive direction of *X*-axis is taken towards the east. The angular velocity vector lies in the *Y-Z* plane in a direction parallel to the polar axis about which the earth rotates. The vector $\vec{\omega}$, therefore, has no component in the East-West direction *i.e.*, along the *X*-axis. If $\hat{i}, \hat{j}$ and $\hat{k}$ are the unit vectors along *X*, *Y* and *Z* axes respectively, then $\vec{\omega} = \omega_x \hat{i} + \omega_y \hat{j} + \omega_z \hat{k}$ where $\omega_x = 0$, $\omega_y = \omega \cos \lambda$ and $\omega_z = \omega \sin \lambda$.

Let the body be dropped from *P* and attain a velocity $\vec{v}$ after a time *t*. The velocity will be in the vertical direction *i.e.*, along *Z*-axis

∴ $$\vec{v} = v_x \hat{i} + v_y \hat{j} + v_z \hat{k} = v_z \hat{k} = \dot{z} \hat{k}$$

since the components along *X* and *Y* axis are zero *i.e.*, $v_x = \dot{x} = 0$ and $v_y = \dot{y} = 0$

The Coriolis force acting on the body at the instant when its velocity is $\vec{v}$ is given by

$$\vec{F}_{cor} = -2m (\vec{\omega} \times \vec{v})$$

The value of $\vec{\omega} \times \vec{v}$ is given by $\vec{\omega} \times \vec{v} = \begin{vmatrix} \hat{i} & \hat{j} & \hat{k} \\ 0 & \omega_y & \omega_z \\ 0 & 0 & \dot{z} \end{vmatrix} = \omega_y \dot{z} \hat{i}$

∴ $$\vec{F}_{cor} = -2m\omega_y \dot{z} \hat{i} = +2m\omega v \cos \lambda \hat{i}$$

because for a body moving vertically downward *v* is negative. The Coriolis force, therefore, acts towards the **positive** direction of *x*-axis *i.e.*, towards the **East** in the northern hemisphere.

According to Newton's second law of motion if $\dfrac{d^2 \vec{x}}{dt^2}$ is the acceleration produced by this force in the positive direction of *x*-axis, then $m \dfrac{d^2 \vec{x}}{dt^2} \hat{i} = 2m\omega v \cos \lambda \hat{i}$ or $\dfrac{d^2 x}{dt} = 2\omega v \cos \lambda$

If g is the acceleration due to gravity, then after a time t from the instant the body is dropped, the

velocity $v = gt$ $\begin{bmatrix} v = u + at \\ u = 0, \ a = g \end{bmatrix}$

$$\therefore \qquad \frac{d^2 x}{dt^2} = 2\omega gt \cos \lambda$$

Integrating w.r.t. to t we get $\dfrac{dx}{dt} = 2\omega g \cos \lambda \dfrac{t^2}{2} + A$ ...(i)

where A is the constant of integration . At $t = 0$, $\dfrac{dx}{dt} = 0$

Substituting these values in (i) we have $A = 0$ $\therefore$ $\dfrac{dx}{dt} = \omega g \cos \cos \lambda \ t^2$

This equation gives the velocity along the x-axis at a time t from start due to Coriolis force. The effect of centrifugal force has been ignored.

Integrating again, we have $x = \omega g \cos \lambda \dfrac{t^3}{3} + B$ ...(ii)

where B is another constant of integration. As the body is *dropped* vertically downward

at $t = 0 \quad x = 0$

Substituting these values in (ii), we have $B = 0$

$$\therefore \qquad x = \frac{1}{3} \omega g \cos \lambda t^3$$ ...(iii)

The above equation represents the deviation along the x-axis at any instant t. If the body is dropped from a height h, then the time t in which it touches the ground is given by

$$h = \frac{1}{2} gt^2 \text{ or } t = \sqrt{\frac{2h}{g}}$$

Substituting this value of t in relation (iii), we have $x = \dfrac{1}{3} \omega g \cos \lambda \left(\dfrac{2h}{g}\right)^{3/2}$

$$= \frac{1}{3} \omega g \cos \lambda \frac{2h}{g} \left(\frac{2h}{g}\right)^{1/2} = \frac{2}{3} \omega h \cos \lambda \left(\frac{2h}{g}\right)^{1/2}$$

This relation gives the deviation in terms of the height of fall h. The deviation is towards the right in the northern hemisphere.

(b) The value of ω for the earth is given by $\omega = \dfrac{2\pi}{24 \times 60 \times 60} = 7.29 \times 10^{-5}$ radian/sec.

$h = 100$ metres $\therefore$ Deviation $x = \dfrac{2}{3} \omega h \cos \lambda \left(\dfrac{2h}{g}\right)^{1/2}$

$$= \frac{2}{3} \times 7.29 \times 10^{-5} \times 100 \times \left(\frac{2 \times 100}{9.8}\right)^{1/2} \cos \lambda = 0.022 \cos \lambda.$$

(i) At the equator $\lambda = 0$ $\therefore \cos \lambda = 1$ and $x = 0.022$ metre

(ii) At the poles $\lambda = \dfrac{\pi}{2}$ $\therefore \cos \lambda = 0$ and $x = 0$

(iii) At 60° N latitude $\lambda = 60°$ $\therefore \cos \lambda = \dfrac{1}{2}$ and $x = 0.011$ metre

(iv) At 45° N latitude $\lambda = 45°$ $\therefore$ $\cos \lambda = \dfrac{1}{\sqrt{2}}$ and $x = 0.022 \times \dfrac{1}{\sqrt{2}} = 0.0156$ metre

Q. 5.27. Calculate the magnitude and direction of Coriolis acceleration of a rocket moving with a velocity of 2 km S^{-1} at 60° South latitude.

Ans. For a body moving in a vertical direction, Coriolis force is given by

$$\vec{F}_{cor} = -2m\omega_y \ \dot{z} \ \hat{i} \qquad\qquad\qquad \text{[For proof See Q. 5.26]}$$

For a rocket moving vertically *upwards* at 60° *South* latitude (λ)

$$\dot{z} = +v \quad \text{and} \quad \omega_y = -\omega \cos \lambda \quad \therefore \quad \vec{F}_{cor} = +2m\omega v \cos \lambda \ \hat{i}$$

The Coriolis force, therefore acts towards the **positive** direction of x-axis *i.e.*, towards the **East**. The magnitude of Coriolis acceleration = $2\omega v \cos \lambda$

$$= 2 \times \dfrac{2\pi}{24 \times 60 \times 60} \times 2 \times 10^3 \times \cos 60 = 14.58 \times 10^{-2} \ \text{met/sec}^2.$$

Q. 5.28. Discuss the effect of Coriolis force due to rotation of the earth on the setting up of cyclones, trade winds and describe other geographical effects of this force. Cyclones do not occur at equator. Explain.

(*H.P.U.*, 2003, 1995, 1991; *P.U.*, 2008, 2006, 2004, 2003, 2001, 2000; *Bhopal U.*, 2004)

OR

Name some phenomenon due to Coriolis force.   (*P.U.* 2006)

Ans. The Coriolis force called into play due to the rotation of the earth causes a deflection in the direction of trade winds, gives a rotatory effect to cyclones, brings about erosion of the right bank of rivers etc.

(*i*) **Direction of trade winds.** Due to heating of earth's surface near the equator, the air in contact with it also gets heated and rises up. The cooler air from the north or the south rushes towards the equator. In the northern hemisphere the air does not follow the north-south direction but is deflected towards the west due to Coriolis force. The Coriolis force is given by $- 2m(\vec{\omega} \times \vec{v})$. The direction of ω the angular velocity vector is along the axis of the earth upward from the north pole. The wind which is flowing from north to south tangential to earth's surface has a velocity component perpendicular to the axis and directed away from it. An application of the rules for vector product of two vectors indicates that this force will deflect the moving particles to their **right** *i.e.*, towards the west in the northern hemisphere giving rise to a north-west trade wind. For the same reason the deflection of the air rushing to the equator from the south in the southern hemisphere will be towards its **right** *i.e.*, towards the east thus giving rise to a south-east trade wind.

(*ii*) **Cyclones.** Whenever a region of low pressure arises in the northern hemisphere the air from the surrounding areas rushes towards it. The Coriolis force deflects this rushing air towards its right giving rise to a clock wise rotation round the low pressure zone. The process continues till the thrust due to pressure gradient is balanced by the thrust due to Coriolis force.

Cyclones do not occur at equator. At the equator the horizontal component of Coriolis force $2m\omega v \sin \lambda$ which is effective in deflecting the wind = 0 as $\lambda = 0$. There are, therefore, *no cyclones produced on the equator*.

(*iii*) **Greater erosion of the right bank of rivers.** The water of the rivers flowing north to south or south to north experiences a Coriolis force towards its right with the result that the *right bank of the river is eaten away more rapidly and is steeper than the left bank*. It should be noted that in the northern hemisphere for a river-flowing from north to south the right bank is to the west and for a river flowing from south to north the right bank is to the east.

(*iv*) **Gulf stream.** The warm Gulf stream flows from south to north and deflects towards the east thereby producing a temperate effect on the climate of some countries of Europe.

(*v*) **Firing of a missile.** The speed of a missile is very large. Therefore, while firing a missile the deviation due to Coriolis force is taken into account in calculating the direction of the target.

Exercise 1. What is Coriolis force? How it effects flow of rivers?   (*Pbi. U.* 2006)

Hint. Coriolis force. See Q. 5.18.

Effect on flow or rivers. See Question given above under (*iii*) *Greater erosion of right bank of rivers.*

Exercise 2. No cyclones are formed at the equator. Explain.   (*Pbi. U.* 2005)

Hint. See under the head '*Cyclones do not occur at the equator*'.

Q. 5.29. (*a*) Describe the construction of a Foucault's pendulum. Show that the bob of the pendulum describes an ellipse which rotates with an angular velocity $\omega \sin \lambda$ where λ is the latitude of the place.   (*H.P.U.,* 2000; *G.N.D.U.,* 2009, 2007, 2006, 1999;
P.U., 2006, 2000, 1999, 1995; *Calicut U.,* 2003)

(*b*) **Show that the rotation of the plane of oscillation of the Foucault's pendulum is a direct proof of the rotation of the earth about its own axis.**
(*H.P.U.,* 2000, 1992, 1991; *G.N.D.U.,*1999; *P.U.,* 1991)

OR

For what purpose Foucault's pendulum is used ?   (*G.N.D.U.* 2007)

(*c*) **State the assumptions made in the treatment of Foucault's pendulum.**   (*Pbi.U.,* 2000)

Ans. (*a*) Foucault's pendulum. It is a simple device for conveniently detecting even slow rotation of the earth and provides a direct experimental evidence that the earth rotates about its axis from *West to East* once in 24 hours.

Construction. It consists of a very heavy mass (28 kg in the original experiment performed by Foucault in Paris in 1851) suspended by a very long wire (70 metres) so that the time period of the pendulum was large (about 17 seconds). The attachment of the upper end of the wire allows the pendulum to swing with equal freedom in any direction so that its period of oscillation in any plane is exactly the same. Such a pendulum once set oscillating continues to oscillate for a fairly long time.

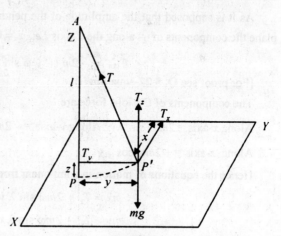

Fig. 5.10

Working. When the pendulum is started it swings in a definite vertical plane. The plane of oscillation is observed to precess around the vertical axis during a period of several hours. If the pendulum were to be set up at the north pole of the earth, it may oscillate as a simple pendulum in a vertical plane which remains fixed in an inertial or Galelian frame of reference. Since the earth under it rotates from *West to East* with an angular velocity ω the plane of oscillation of the pendulum will appear to an observer on the surface of the earth to be turning with angular velocity ω in the opposite direction (from *East to West*) to that of earth. It is not necessary that the pendulum should be situated right at the north or the south pole. An apparent rotation of the earth will be observed in any latitude except at the equator.

Normally the pendulum describes an ellipse and by making it vibrate carefully the ellipse can be made to approximate to a straight line so that the pendulum swings in a vertical plane very approximately. That the motion of the bob of the pendulum will be along an *ellipse* under the various forces acting on it can be proved as under.

Proof. Foucault's pendulum with its suspension along the vertical Z-axis is shown in Fig. 5.10. The bob of the pendulum vibrates with a *small amplitude* in the horizontal x-y plane. When the bob is displaced through a small angle from its mean position P to P' the various external forces acting on the bob are mg acting downward, the tension $\vec{T}$ in the string acting along $P'A$ and the *fictitious forces* acting on it due to the rotation of the earth. If the net acceleration of the bob is $\ddot{r}$, then

$$m\ddot{r} = (m\vec{g} + \vec{T}) - 2m\,(\vec{\omega} \times \vec{v_a}) - m\omega \times (\vec{\omega} \times \vec{r}) - m\frac{d\omega}{dt} \times \vec{r}$$

where $\vec{v_a} = \dot{r} =$ the time rate of change of the position vector $\vec{r}$ of the bob P

$\vec{\omega} =$ angular velocity of rotation of the earth taken as a rotating frame of reference.

$-2m\,(\vec{\omega} \times \vec{v_a}) = -2m\,(\vec{\omega} \times \dot{r}) =$ Coriolis force

$-m\vec{\omega} \times (\vec{\omega} \times \vec{r}) =$ centrifugal force due to earth's rotation.

The last factor $-m\dfrac{d\vec{\omega}}{dt} \times \vec{r} = 0$ as $\dfrac{d\vec{\omega}}{dt} = 0$, $\vec{\omega}$ being a constant.

In our treatment we shall neglect the centrifugal force because its magnitude $= mr\omega^2$ and ω being a small quantity. ω^2 can be neglected.

The general equation of motion for a Focault's pendulum is

$$m\ddot{r} = m\vec{g} + \vec{T} - 2m\,(\vec{\omega} \times \dot{r})$$

The components of $m\ddot{r}$ are $m\ddot{x}$, $m\ddot{y}$ and $m\ddot{z}$, $m\vec{g}$ has only one component in the vertical Z-direction $= mg$ and the components of $\vec{T}$ are T_x, T_y and T_z.

As it is supposed that the amplitude of the pendulum is small and it vibrates almost in the xy plane the components of $\dot{r}$ along the Z-axis i.e., $\dot{z} = 0$. The Coriolis force is, therefore, given by

$$\vec{F}_{cor} = -2m\,(-\dot{y}\,\omega \sin \lambda \hat{i} + \dot{x}\,\omega \sin \lambda \hat{j} - \dot{x}\,\omega \cos \lambda \hat{k})$$

[For proof see **Q. 5.22** equation (*i*)]

The components of Coriolis force are

Along x-axis $= 2m\,\omega \sin \lambda\dot{y}$; Along y-axis $= -2m\omega \sin \lambda\dot{x}$

Along z-axis $= +2m\omega \cos \lambda\dot{x}$

Hence the equations of motion in component from are

$$m\ddot{x} = T_x + 2m\omega \sin \lambda\,\dot{y} \qquad\qquad …(i)$$

$$m\ddot{y} = T_y - 2m\omega \sin \lambda\,\dot{x} \qquad\qquad …(ii)$$

$$m\ddot{z} = T_z - mg + 2m\omega \cos \lambda\,\dot{x} \qquad\qquad …(iii)$$

Let x, y, z be the co-ordinates of the point P' and l the length of Foucault's pendulum then

$$\frac{T_x}{T} = \frac{-x}{l} \text{ or } T_x = -T\frac{x}{l}$$

$$\frac{T_y}{T} = \frac{-y}{l} \text{ or } T_y = -T\frac{y}{l}$$

$$\frac{T_z}{T} = \frac{l-z}{l} \quad \text{or} \quad T_z = T\frac{l-z}{l}$$

As the amplitude of the pendulum is small $z = 0$

$$\therefore \qquad\qquad\qquad\qquad T_z = T \qquad\qquad\qquad\qquad\qquad\qquad \text{(approximately)}$$

Again as $\qquad\qquad\qquad z = 0,\ \dot{z} = 0 \text{ and } \ddot{z} = 0$

Substituting $\qquad\qquad T_z = T$ and $\ddot{z} = 0$ in equation (iii), we have

$$0 = T - mg + 2m\omega \cos \lambda \dot{x}$$

The quantity $2m\omega \cos \lambda \dot{x}$ is the vertical component of Coriolis force. It is a very small quantity and can be neglected as compared to mg. $\quad \therefore \quad T = mg$

Substituting $\qquad\qquad T = mg$ in equation (i) and (ii), we have

$$m\ddot{x} = -mg\frac{x}{l} + 2m\omega \sin \lambda\, \dot{y} \qquad\qquad\qquad\qquad\qquad ...(iv)$$

and $\qquad\qquad\qquad m\ddot{y} = -mg\frac{y}{l} - 2m\,\omega \sin \lambda\, \dot{x} \qquad\qquad\qquad\qquad ...(v)$

The time-period of the pendulum is given by $t = 2\pi\sqrt{\dfrac{l}{g}}$ or $\dfrac{2\pi}{t} = \sqrt{\dfrac{g}{l}}$

Let $\qquad\qquad\qquad \dfrac{2\pi}{t} = \omega_0 \quad$ then $\dfrac{g}{l} = \omega_0^2$

Substituting $\dfrac{g}{l} = \omega_0^2$ in (iv) and (v), we get

$$\ddot{x} = -\omega_0^2\, x + 2\omega \sin \lambda\, \dot{y} \qquad\qquad\qquad\qquad\qquad\qquad ...(vi)$$

$$\ddot{y} = -\omega_0^2\, y - 2\omega \sin \lambda\, \dot{x} \qquad\qquad\qquad\qquad\qquad\qquad ...(vii)$$

Multiplying (vii) by $i = \sqrt{-1}$ and adding to (vi), we get

$$\ddot{x} + i\ddot{y} = -\omega_0^2\,[x + iy] - 2i\omega \sin \lambda\,[\dot{x} + i\dot{y}]$$

or $\qquad\qquad (\ddot{x} + i\ddot{y}) + 2i\omega \sin \lambda\,(\dot{x} + i\dot{y}) + \omega_0^2\,(x + iy) = 0$

Put $\qquad\qquad x + iy = u \quad$ then $\dot{u} = \dot{x} + i\dot{y}$ and $\ddot{u} = \ddot{x} + i\ddot{y}$

Hence $\qquad\qquad \ddot{u} + 2i\,\omega \sin \lambda\dot{u} + \omega_0^2\,u = 0$

Substituting $\qquad \omega \sin \lambda = \omega_z$, we get $\ddot{u} + 2i\,\omega_z\,\dot{u} + \omega_0^2\,u = 0 \qquad\qquad ...(viii)$

The above equation in the operator form is put as $(D^2 + 2i\,\omega_z\,D + \omega_0^2)\,u = 0$

where $\qquad\qquad\qquad D = \dfrac{d}{dt}$ and $D^2 = \dfrac{d^2}{dt^2}$

or $\qquad D^2 + 2i\omega_z D + \omega_0^2 = 0$

The two roots of the above equation are $D = \dfrac{-2i\omega_z \pm \sqrt{4\,(-1)\,\omega_z^2 - 4\,\omega_0^2}}{2}$

$$= -i\omega_z \pm i\omega_1$$

where $\qquad\qquad\qquad \omega_1^2 = \omega_z^2 + \omega_0^2$

or $\qquad\qquad D_1 = -i\,(\omega_z - \omega_1) \quad$ and $\quad D_2 = -i\,(\omega_z + \omega_1)$

The general solution of equation (viii) is

$$u = Ae^{-i\,(\omega_z - \omega_1)\,t} + Be^{-i\,(\omega_z + \omega_1)\,t} = \left(Ae^{+i\omega_1 t} + Be^{-i\omega_1 t}\right)e^{-i\omega_z t} \qquad ...(ix)$$

where A and B are arbitrary constants.

We have stated above that $\omega_1^2 = \omega_0^2 + \omega_z^2$

where $\omega_0 = \dfrac{2\pi}{t} = \sqrt{\dfrac{l}{g}} =$ angular velocity of oscillation of the pendulum and ω_z the Z-component $\omega \sin \lambda$ of the angular velocity of rotation of the earth which is very small as compared to ω_0.

$\therefore$ ω_z^2 can be neglected as compared to ω_0^2.

Hence $\omega_1^2 = \omega_0^2 + \omega_z^2 = \omega_0^2$ (approximately)   or $\omega_1 = \omega_0$

Substituting $\omega_1 = \omega_0$ in equation (ix) we get $u = \left(Ae^{+i\omega_0 t} + Be^{-i\omega_0 t} \right) e^{-i\omega_z t}$ ...(x)

Considering $\omega_z = 0$ we get $u = Ae^{+i\omega_0 t} + Be^{-i\omega_0 t}$

The above equation gives the trajectory of the path traced out by the bob.

Now $Ae^{+i\omega_0 t} = A \cos \omega_0 t + iA \sin \omega_0 t$

and $Be^{-i\omega_0 t} = B \cos \omega_0 t - iB \sin \omega_0 t$

$\therefore$ $Ae^{+i\omega_0 t} + Be^{-i\omega_0 t} = (A + B) \cos \omega_0 t + i (A - B) \sin \omega_0 t$

But $u = x + iy$

$\therefore$ $(A + B) \cos \omega_0 t = x$ and $(A - B) \sin \omega_0 t = y$

Squaring and adding we get $\dfrac{x^2}{(A + B)^2} + \dfrac{y^2}{(A - B)^2} = \cos^2 \omega_0 t + \sin^2 \omega_0 t = 1$

which is the equation of an ellipse with its centre at the origin. Thus we find the trajectory of the bob of a Foucault's pendulum is elliptical.

(b) **Direct proof of earth's rotation (Use of Foucault's pendulum).** The complex factor $e^{-i\omega_z t}$ in relation (x) super imposes a rotation on this ellipse about the vertical z-axis with an angular velocity $\omega_z = \omega \sin \lambda$. The period of rotation about the vertical axis is, then $T = \dfrac{2\pi}{\omega \sin \lambda}$.

The rotation of the plane of swing of a pendulum about a vertical axis as given by the above relation and its verification provides a conclusive proof of the rotation of the earth about its axis.

At the poles $\lambda = 90°$ $\therefore$ $\omega_z = \omega$

The plane of oscillation of the pendulum makes a complete revolution at the poles in $\dfrac{2\pi}{\omega} = 24$ hours.

At any other latitude the period is more than 24 hours.

At the equator $\lambda = 0$

$\therefore$ $\omega_z = \omega \sin \lambda = 0$, the period will be infinite.

In the northern hemisphere when the bob of Foucault's pendulum swings from south to north the Coriolis force acts from West to East (to the right) and when it swings back from north to south the force acts from East to West. This causes the rotation of the plane of oscillation of the pendulum in the clockwise direction in the northern hemisphere. In the southern hemisphere the plane of oscillation of the pendulum rotates in the anti-clockwise direction.

This clearly shows that there is a relative motion between the plane of oscillation of the pendulum bob and the earth in either hemisphere. The relative angular shift of the plane of oscillation of the pendulum over a long period not only provides a direct proof of the rotation of the earth about its own axis but also enables us to measure the value of ω.

(c) **Assumptions.** The following assumptions have been made in the treatment of Foucault's pendulum to show that the trajectory of the bob of the pendulum is elliptical.

(i) The amplitude of the pendulum is small.

(ii) As ω the angular velocity of earth's rotation is small the effect of centrifugal force $(mr\omega^2)$ being proportional to ω^2 is neglected.

(iii) The pendulum oscillates very approximately in the X-Y plane and hence the component of $\vec{r}$ along Z-axis i.e., $\vec{z} = 0$

(iv) The vertical component of Coriolis force $2m\omega \cos \lambda \; \dot{x}$ is a very small quantity and is neglected as compared to mg.

Q. 5.30. Find latitude of a place where the plane of vibration of Foucault's pendulum rotates once a day. (G.N.D.U., 2009, 1994)

Ans. The period of rotation of a Foucault's pendulum at a latitude λ is given by

$$T = \frac{2\pi}{\omega \sin \lambda} \quad \text{Now} \quad \frac{2\pi}{\omega} = 24 \text{ hours}$$

For a place where plane of vibration of a Foucault's pendulum rotates once a day $T = 24$ hours.

$\therefore \; \sin \lambda = 1$ or $\lambda = \dfrac{\pi}{2}$ i.e., at a latitude $\lambda = \dfrac{\pi}{2}$ or at the poles.

Q. 5.31 (a) Calculate the rate of rotation of the plane of oscillation of a pendulum at latitude 30° and hence obtain the time it will take to turn through (i) a full right angle and (ii) 60°. (P.U., 2006, 2001; H.P.U., 1999, 1995)

(b) Find the latitude at which the plane of vibtation of Foucault's pendulum does not rotate at all. (Pbi.U., 2003; P.U., 2003)

Ans. (a) At a latitude $\qquad \lambda = 30°; \sin \lambda = \dfrac{1}{2}$

$\therefore$ The period of rotation $T = \dfrac{2\pi}{\omega \sin \lambda} = \dfrac{2\pi}{\omega \dfrac{1}{2}} = 24 \times 2 = 48$ hours

Hence rate of rotation $= \dfrac{2\pi}{48}$ radian/hour

and time taken to turn through (i) a full right angle or $\pi/2$ radian $= \dfrac{\pi/2}{2\pi/48} = \dfrac{48}{4} = 12$ hours

and (ii) through $\qquad 60° = \dfrac{\pi/3}{2\pi/48} = \dfrac{48}{6} = 8$ hours.

(b) When the plane of vibration of Foucault's pendulum does not rotate at all its time period is infinite.

$\therefore \qquad$ The period of rotation $T = \infty$

and $\qquad \dfrac{2\pi}{\omega \sin \lambda} = \infty$ or $\lambda = 0$

Thus the plane of vibration of a Foucault's pendulum does not rotate at all at the Equator.

Exercise 1. Calculate the period of oscillation of a Foucault's pendulum to make one complete revolution, if the pendulum is located at (i) North pole, (ii) South pole, (iii) Equator and (iv) Latitude 45°N. (G.N.D.U. 2007)

Hint. (i) *North pole* $\qquad \lambda = \dfrac{\pi}{2}; \sin \dfrac{\pi}{2} = 1$

$$\therefore \quad T = \frac{2\pi}{\omega \sin \lambda} = \frac{24}{1} = 24 \text{ hrs.}$$

(*ii*) *South pole* $\qquad \lambda = \frac{\pi}{2}. \quad \therefore \quad T = 24 \text{ hrs}$

(*iii*) *Equator* $\qquad \lambda = 0; \quad \sin \lambda = 0$

$$\therefore \quad T = \frac{2\pi}{\omega \sin \lambda} = \infty \ i.e., \text{ the pendulum does not rotate at all.}$$

(*iv*) $\qquad \lambda = 45°\text{N} \quad \sin 45° = 0.707$

$$\therefore \quad T = \frac{2\pi}{\omega \sin \lambda} = \frac{24}{0.707} = 33.95 \text{ hrs}$$

Exercise 2. Find the time taken by plane of oscillation of a pendulum to turn through an angle of 30° at a point where latitude is 60°.   (*P.U.* 2009)

Hint. $\lambda = 60°$; $\sin 60° = 0.866$

$$\therefore \qquad \text{Period of oscillation } T = \frac{2\pi}{\omega \sin \lambda} = \frac{24}{0.866} = 27.7 \text{ hrs.}$$

$$\text{Time taken to turn through } 30° = \frac{30}{360} \times 27.7 = 2.31 \text{ hrs.}$$

Q. 5.32. A Foucault's pendulum is oscillating along NS direction at a place where latitude is 30°. What time must elapse before the pendulum starts oscillating along NE-SW direction ?

(*H.P.U., 1992*)

Ans. At a latitude $\qquad \lambda = 30°, \sin \lambda = \sin 30 = \frac{1}{2}$

Fig. 5.11

$\therefore$ Period of rotation

$$T = \frac{2\pi}{\omega \sin \lambda} = \frac{2\pi}{\omega \cdot \frac{1}{2}}$$

$$= 24 \times 2 = 48 \text{ hours.}$$

Hence rate of rotation $= \frac{2\pi}{48}$ radians per hour

In turning from NS to NE-SW direction the pendulum turns through $45° = \frac{\pi}{4}$ radian as shown.

$$\therefore \text{ Time taken} = \frac{\frac{\pi}{4}}{2\pi/48} = \frac{48}{8} = 6 \text{ hours}$$

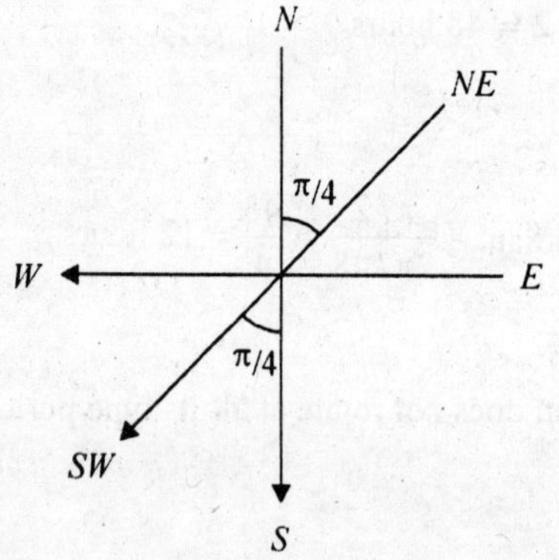

Q. 5.33. Show that at latitude θ, the plane of oscillation of Foucault's pendulum rotates through $2\pi \sin \theta$ every day. Explain this physically on a pole of the earth.   (*P.U., 1994*)

Ans. The period of rotation of a Foucault's pendulum at a latitude θ is given by

$$T = \frac{2\pi}{\omega \sin \theta}$$

where $\dfrac{2\pi}{\omega} = 24$ hours. $\therefore$ $T = \dfrac{24}{\sin\theta}$ hours

In T hours the plane rotates through 2π radians.

$\therefore$ In 24 hours the plane will rotate through an angle

$$\phi = \dfrac{2\pi}{T} \times 24 = \dfrac{2\pi}{24} \sin\theta \times 24 = 2\pi \sin\theta \text{ radian}$$

At the poles $\qquad\qquad \theta = 90°, \sin\theta = \sin 90° = 1$

$\therefore$ $\qquad\qquad\qquad \phi = 2\pi$ radians

Thus the plane of oscillation of a Foucault's pendulum rotates through 2π radians in 24 hours at the poles which means that the period of rotation of the earth about its own axis is 24 hours.

Q. 5.34. Descrribe how a Foucault's pendulum is used as a device to illustrate that the earth is not an inertial frame. *(G.N.D.U., 1997)*

Ans. See Q. 5.29 (*b*) where it is proved that the Foucault's pendulum provides a direct proof of the rotation of the earth about its own axis showing thereby that the earth being a rotating body is not an inertial frame since it has an (centripetal) acceleration.

Q.5.35. Why is earth flattened at the poles? *(P.U. 2007)*

Ans. The earth is flattened at the poles because fluids in the earth tend to come to rest with their surface perpendicular to the direction of effective acceleration due to gravity.

Q. 5.36. Mark the correct answer.

(*i*) Which one is invariant under Galelian transformation ?

    (*a*) velocity   (*b*) length   (*c*) momentum

    (*d*) potential energy   *(P.U., 1994)*

(*ii*) The expression for Coriolis force is

    (*a*) $-2m\,\omega v\sin\theta$ (*b*) $-2m\omega v\cos\theta$ (*c*) $-2m\times(\vec{\omega}\,.\,\vec{v})$ *(H.P.U., 1995)*

(*iii*) In a non-inertial frame of reference a body experiences Coriolis force only when

    (*a*) The frame has rotational motion and body also rotates

    (*b*) The frame has rotational motion and the body is at rest

    (*c*) The frame has rotational motion and the body has linear motion

    (*d*) none of above   *(H.P.U., 1994)*

(*iv*) The trajectory of the bob of Foucault's pendulum is

    (*a*) circular   (*b*) ellipse   (*c*) parabola   (*d*) hyperbola

                                                                   (H.P.U., 1994)

(*v*) Foucault's pendulum is used for

    (*a*) finding g at a place   (*b*) detecting revolution of the earth

    (*c*) detecting rotation of the earth   (*d*) measuring earthquake.

                                                      (P.U., 1993; H.P.U., 2001)

(*vi*) Time period of Foucault's pendulum on equator is

    (*a*) zero   (*b*) 24 hours   (*c*) ∞ (*d*) 48 hours

                                                                 (P.U., 1993)

(*vii*) The Foucault's pendulum experiment cannot be performed purposefully at place whose latitude is

(*a*) $\pi/2$ (*b*) $\pi/4$ (*c*) 0   (*d*) $\pi/3$

(*H.P.U., 1993*)

Ans.   (*i*) *b*   (*ii*) *a*   (*iii*) *c*   (*iv*) *b*

(*v*) *c*   (*vi*) *c*   (*vii*) *c*

EXERCISES

1. Calculate the time required for the plane of vibration of a Foucault's pendulum to rotate once at a latitude 45°. How much time will it take to rotate through 60° at that place and at a place of latitude 60°?   (*P.U., 1991; Pbi.U., 1993*)

[**Ans.** $24\sqrt{2}$ hrs.; $4\sqrt{2}$ hrs.; $\dfrac{8}{\sqrt{3}}$ hrs.]

2. A man weights 70 kg. What would be his weight in lift moving (*i*) upward (*ii*) downward, with acceleration 25% of *g* ?   (*P.U., 1991*)

[**Ans.** (*i*) 87.5 kg (*ii*) 52.5 kg]

3. Calculate the fictitious force and total force acting on a freely falling body of mass 18 kg with respect to a frame moving with a downward acceleration of 6 m/sec^2.   (*A.U., 1993*)

[**Ans.** 108 N]

4. A particle is thrown vertically upwards with a velocity 70 m/sec at a place with latitude 60°. Find how far from the original position will it land.   (*Cal.U.Hons., 1991*)

[**Ans.** 0.00643 m]

6

Gravitation

Q. 6.1. State Newton's law of gravitation. What is meant by gravitational constant? What are its dimensions? *(Bang. U., 1995, 1994, 1990; Cal. U., 1991)*

Ans. Newton's law of gravitation. *Every body in this universe attracts every other body with a force which varies directly as the product of the masses of the two bodies and inversely as the square of the distance between them.* Mathematically, $F = -\,G\,\dfrac{m_1\,m_2}{r^2}$ ...(i)

where m_1 is the mass of one body, m_2 that of the other, r the distance between their centres, G *the* constant of gravitation and F the force with which the bodies attract each other. The negative sign indicates that it is an attractive force.

Gravitational constant. If in the above equation $m_1 = m_2 = 1$ and $r = 1$

then $\qquad\qquad F = G$ (numerically)

Therefore, the *gravitational constant is equal to the force of attraction between two bodies each of unit mass lying at a unit distance apart.* The value of G is 6.66×10^{-11} newton m^2/kg^2 in S.I. units.

Dimensions of G. From relation (i)

$$G = \frac{Fr^2}{m_1\,m_2}\ (\text{numerically})$$

∴ Dimensions of G are $\dfrac{M^1\,L^1 T^{-2} L^2}{M^2} = [\,M^{-1}\,L^3\,T^{-2}\,]$

Q. 6.2. A sphere of mass 19 kg. is attracted by another sphere of mass 150 kg. when their centres are separated by a distance 0.28 m with a force equal to the weight of 0.25 mg. Calculate the gravitational constant. If the distance is halved what would be the new force in Newton? Assume $g = 9.8$ ms⁻². *(Bang. U. 1993)*

Ans. Here $\qquad\qquad m_1 = 19$ kg; $m_2 = 150$ kg; $r = 0.28$ m

Force $\qquad\qquad F = 0.25$ mg. wt $= 0.25 \times 10^{-6} \times 9.8$ N

Now $\qquad\qquad F = \dfrac{G\,m_1\,m_2}{r^2}\ \text{or}\ G = \dfrac{Fr^2}{m_1\,m_2}$

$$= \frac{0.25 \times 10^{-6} \times 9.8 \times (0.28)^2}{19 \times 150} = 6.74 \times 10^{-11}\ \mathrm{Nm^2\ kg^{-2}}$$

When the distance is halved, the force F' between the two masses becomes 4 times as the force is inversely proportional to the square of the distance between the centres of the two masses.

$$\therefore \qquad F' = 4F = 4 \times 0.25 \times 10^{-6} \times 9.8 = 9.8 \times 10^{-6} \text{ Newton.}$$

Q. 6.3. (*a*) **Suppose the earth is revolving round the Sun in a circular orbit of radius one astronomical unit (1.5×10^8 km). Find the mass of the Sun. $G = 6.67 \times 10^{-11} \text{Nm}^2 \text{ kg}^{-2}$.**

(Gharwal U. 2000)

(*b*) **If the mass of Sun is 2×10^{30} kg, distance of earth from the Sun is 1.5×10^{11}m and period of revolution of the former around the latter is 365. 3 days, find the value of G.**

Ans. (*a*) The earth revolves round the sun in more or less circular orbit of radius r. The gravitational force of attraction between the sun of mass M and earth of mass m is balanced by the centripetal force $mr\omega^2$, where ω is the angular velocity of earth.

$$\therefore \qquad \omega = \frac{2\pi}{365 \times 24 \times 3600} = 1.99 \times 10^{-7} \text{ rad } s^{-1}$$

$$r = 1.5 \times 10^8 \text{ km} = 1.5 \times 10^{11} \text{ m}$$

Now
$$\frac{GMm}{r^2} = mr\omega^2$$

$$\therefore \qquad M = \frac{r^3 \omega^2}{G} = \frac{(1.5 \times 10^{11})^3 \times (1.99 \times 10^{-7})^2}{6.67 \times 10^{-11}} = 2.004 \times 10^{30} \text{ kg}$$

(*b*) The force of attraction F between the sun of mass M and earth of mass m separated by a distance r is given by $F = \dfrac{GMm}{r^2}$

This force is balanced by the centripetal force $mr\omega^2$ where ω is the angular velocity of earth.

$$\therefore \qquad \frac{GMm}{r^2} = mr\omega^2 \text{ or } G = \frac{r^3\omega^2}{M}$$

Now
$$M = 2 \times 10^{30} \text{ kg, } r = 1.5 \times 10^{11} \text{ m, } G = ?$$

$$\omega = \frac{2\pi}{365.3 \times 24 \times 3600} = 1.991 \times 10^{-7} \text{ rad } s^{-1}$$

$$\therefore \qquad G = \frac{(1.5 \times 10^{11})^3 \times (1.991 \times 10^{-7})^2}{2 \times 10^{30}} = 6.688 \times 10^{-11} \text{ Nm}^2 - \text{kg}^{-2}.$$

Q. 6.4. A satellite revolves in a circular orbit at a height of 200 km from the surface of earth. If the period of revolution of satellite is 90 mts, $G = 6.66 \times 10^{-11} \text{ Nm}^2 \text{ kg}^{-2}$ and mean radius of earth is 6×10^6 m, calculate the average density of earth.

Ans. Distance of satellite from the centre of earth

$$R_1 = 6 \times 10^6 + 0.2 \times 10^6 = 6.2 \times 10^6 \text{ m}$$

If M is the mass of earth and m that of satellite, then $\dfrac{GMm}{R_1^2} = mR_1\omega^2$

or $\qquad M = \dfrac{R_1^3 \omega^2}{G} = \dfrac{4}{3} \pi R^3 \rho$

or $\qquad \rho = \dfrac{3R_1^3 \omega^2}{4\pi R^3 G} = \dfrac{3 \times (6.2 \times 10^6)^3}{4\pi \times (6 \times 10^6)^3 \times 6.66 \times 10^{-11}} \times \left(\dfrac{2\pi}{90 \times 60}\right)^2 = 5.355 \times 10^3 \text{ kg m}^{-3}$

Q. 6.5. Mention the various forces existing in nature giving their relative strengths.

(G.N.D.U. 2006, 2001, 2000; Pbil. U. 2002)

Ans. Various forces existing in nature are:-

(*i*)   Gravitational force

(*ii*)   Electromagnetic force

(*iii*)   Weak force

(*iv*)   Strong (nuclear) force

(*i*) **Gravitational force.** It is the weakest of the four types of forces. It has infinite range. Although gravitation has measurable influence on objects of macroscopic size, its value for particles of atomic or sub-atomic size is almost negligible. This force is governed by Newton's law of univer-

sal gravitation $F = -\dfrac{G m_1 m_2}{r^2}$.

The gravitational force is always *attractive*. It is a *central* force and *varies inversely as the square of the distance between the particles.*

(*ii*) **Electromagnetic force.** All charged particles are acted upon by electromagnetic force. The electromagnetic force also has an infinite range. The force between two stationary charged particles having charges q_1 and q_2 a distance r apart in vacuum or free space is governed by Coulomb's law and is given by

$$F = \frac{1}{4\pi\varepsilon_0} \frac{q_1\, q_2}{r^2}$$

where ε_0 is the permittivity of free space and has a value $8.85 \times 10^{-12}\ C^2/Nm^2$.

A fundamental difference between the gravitational and electromagnetic force is that gravitational force is always attractive whereas electromagnetic forces can be attractive or repulsive depending upon the sign of charges. This force is about 10^{38} times stronger than the gravitational force.

(*iii*) **Weak force.** It is an extremely short range force having a range of the order of $10^{-17}\ m$. This force is responsible for the β-decay of the nucleus. It is about 10^{27} times stronger than the gravitational force.

(*iv*) **Strong (nuclear) force.** This force was introduced in order to explain the existence of stable nuclei. The force is of nuclear origin and is very strong so that it can overcome the repulsive force between densely packed protons within the nucleus. This is dominant force which is responsible for most of the nuclear phenomenon, nuclear energy levels etc. The strong (nuclear) force is independent of charge *i.e.*, it is the same for p - p, p - n and n - n interaction. This strong force may be conceived as due to exchange of *pions* (π^+, π^-, π^0) or π- mesons. Its range is about 10^{-15} m and it is about 10^{40} times stronger than gravitational force.

Relative strength of forces. The relative strength and range of these four types of forces is as under :

Force	Relative strength	Range
Gravitation	1	∞
Weak	10^{27}	10^{-17}m
Electromagnetic	10^{38}	∞
Strong	10^{40}	10^{-15} m

Q. 6.6. Explain the terms gravitational field and gravitational potential. Find the relation between them. *(Nagpur U. 2003, 2001; Meerut U. 2006, 2003, 2002, 2000, 1991; Bang U. 1993; Vid. S. U. 1992, 1990; K. U. 1992, 1991)*

Ans. Gravitational field. *The space around a body within which its gravitational force of attraction can be experienced is called the gravitational field.*

The intensity of the gravitational field or gravitational attraction at a point is the force experienced by a unit mass placed at the point.

The intensity of the gravitational field at a point distant r from a point mass $m = -\dfrac{Gm}{r^2}$ since a unit mass lying there is attracted by this force. The negative sign indicates that the force is directed towards the mass m.

Gravitational potential. *The work done in moving a unit mass from infinity to any point in the gravitational field of a body is called the gravitational potential at the point due to the body.*

Gravitational potential at a point in a gravitational field may also be defined as the potential energy of unit mass placed at that point.

The difference of gravitational potential between two points in a gravitational field is the work done in moving a unit mass from one point to the other along the gravitational force of attraction.

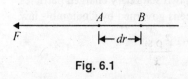

Fig. 6.1

Relation between gravitational field and potential. If there are two points A and B lying very near each other at a distance dr in a gravitational field F acting in the direction indicated, then the work done in moving a unit mass from B to A along the direction of the force $= F\,dr$. If dV is the difference of gravitational potential between the point A and B, then

$$V_A - V_B = dV = -F\,dr; \qquad \therefore \ F = -\frac{dV}{dr}$$

Hence the intensity of gravitational field at any point is equal to the potential gradient or the negative of the space rate of change of gravitational potential.

Gravitational potential due to a point mass. Consider a point A at a distance r from a particle of mass m, then

Force experienced by a unit mass at A

$$F = -\frac{GM}{r^2} \text{ along } Am$$

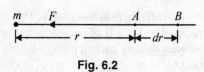

Fig. 6.2

$\therefore$ Difference of gravitational potential between two points A and B at a distance dr apart

$$V_A - V_B = dV = -F\,dr - = -\left(\frac{-Gm}{r^2}\right)dr = \frac{Gm}{r^2}\,dr$$

Hence potential at $\qquad A = \int_{\infty}^{r} dV = \int_{\infty}^{r} \frac{Gm}{r^2}\,dr$ or $V = GM\left[-\frac{1}{r}\right]_{\infty}^{r} = -\frac{Gm}{r}$

Q. 6.7. (*a*) **Obtain an expression for the gravitational potential due to a thin uniform spherical shell at a point (*i*) outside (*ii*) at the surface and (*iii*) inside the shell.**

(Meerut U. 2001; Gharwal U. 2000; Bang. U. 1996, 1992; Kanpur U. 1995, 1993; A. U. 1994; K. U. 1992, 1991; Burd. U. 1991; Vid. S. U. 1990)

(*b*) **Graphically represent the variation of potential with distance due to a thin spherical shell.**
                                                                                    (Kerala U. 2001)

Ans. (*a*) **Potential due to a shell.** (*i*) *Point outside the shell.* Consider a point P outside the spherical shell at a distance r from its centre O.

Let the radius of the spherical shell be a and ρ its mass per unit area of the surface.

Join OP. Draw two planes very close to each other perpendicular to OP and cutting the shell in CD and EF respectively.

Then these planes cut a ring or slice from the shell of radius CK and thickness CE as shown separately in Fig. 6.4.

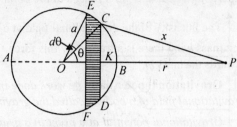

Join OC and OE and let the angle BOC be θ and the small angle COE be $d\theta$.

$\therefore$ Thickness of the shell $CE = a\, d\theta$

Radius of the shell $CK = a \sin \theta$

Circumference of the shell $= 2\pi . CK = 2\pi a \sin \theta$

Fig. 6.3

Hence surface area of the slice $= 2\pi a \sin \theta\, a\, d\theta = 2\pi a^2 \sin \theta\, d\theta$

Mass of the slice $= 2\pi a^2 \sin \theta\, d\theta\, \rho$

Every point on the rim of this slice or ring is at a distance CP, i.e., x from P

$\therefore$ Potential at P due to the ring

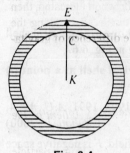

$$dV = -\frac{G 2\pi a^2 \rho \sin \theta\, d\theta}{x} \qquad \qquad ...(i)$$

To find the value of x.

In triangle OCP, $x^2 = a^2 + r^2 - 2ar \cos \theta$

Differentiating, we get $2x\, dx = 2ar \sin \theta\, d\theta$

[$\because$ a and r are constant]

Fig. 6.4

$$\therefore \qquad x = \frac{ar \sin \theta\, d\theta}{dx}$$

Substituting the value of x in (i), we get

$$dV = -\frac{G\, 2\pi a^2 \rho \sin \theta\, d\theta}{ar \sin \theta\, d\theta}\, dx = -\frac{2\pi a \rho G}{r}\, dx \qquad ...(ii)$$

Integrating equation (ii) for the whole shell between the limits

$PB = (r - a)$ and $PA = (r + a)$, we get

$$V = -\int_{r-a}^{r+a} \frac{2\pi a\rho G}{r}\, dx$$

$$= -\frac{2\pi a\rho G}{r}\big[x\big]_{r-a}^{r+a} = \frac{4\pi a^2 \rho G}{r}$$

But $4\pi a^2$ is the surface area of the whole shell.

Therefore m the mass of the whole shell $= 4\pi a^2 \rho$

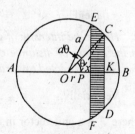

Fig. 6.5

or   Potential $V = -\dfrac{Gm}{r}$

Hence the mass of the whole shell behaves as if it were concentrated at the centre.

(ii) Potential on the surface of the shell. For a point on the surface of the shell $r = a$

$$\therefore \qquad \text{Potential } V = -\frac{Gm}{a}$$

(*iii*) *Point inside the shell.* Proceeding exactly in the same way to find the potential at *P* due to the ring *CDEF*, we get $dV = -\dfrac{2\pi a\rho G}{r}\, dx$ ...(*iii*)

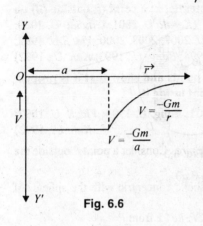

Fig. 6.6

Now $OP = r$ as shown in Fig 6.5.

∴ Integrating equation (*iii*) between the limit $PB = (a - r)$ and $PA = (a + r)$, we get

$$V = -\int_{a-r}^{a+r} \frac{2\pi a\rho G}{r}\, dx$$

$$= -\frac{2\pi a\rho G}{r} [x]_{a-r}^{a+r} = -\frac{2\pi a\rho G}{r} 2r = -4\pi a\rho G$$

Multiplying and dividing by *a*, we get $V = -\dfrac{4\pi a^2 \rho G}{a}$

Substituting $4\pi a^2 \rho = m$, we have $V = -\dfrac{Gm}{a}$

This value is the same as at a point on the surface of the shell.

Hence the potential at every point within a spherical shell is the same as on the surface of the shell itself.

(*b*) **Graphical representation..** The variation of gravitational potential due to a spherical shell for points outside the shell, on the surface of the shell and inside it is shown in Fig. 6.6.

Q. 6.8. Find the intensity of gravitational field due to a thin spherical shell at a point (*i*) external to the shell (*ii*) at the surface of the shell and (*iii*) inside the shell.

(*Nagpur U.*, 2001; *Gharwal U.*, 2000; *Bang. U.*, 1996; *Kan. U.*, 1995, 1991; *A.U.*, 1994; *Gauhati. U.* 2000)

Ans. Gravitational field. (*i*) *Point outside the shell.* The gravitational field, *F* is negative space rate of the change of gravitational potential *V* or $F = -\dfrac{dV}{dr}$

Since the gravitational potential at a point outside the shell is given by $V = -\dfrac{Gm}{r}$

∴ Field $F = -\dfrac{dV}{dr} = -\dfrac{Gm}{r^2}$

Hence the intensity of gravitational field varies inversely as the square of distance of the point from the centre of the shell and is directed towards the centre.

Vectorially $\vec{F} = -\dfrac{Gm}{r^2}\hat{r}$

where $\hat{r}$ is a unit vector in the direction of increasing *r*.

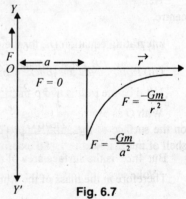

Fig. 6.7

(*ii*) *Point on the surface of shell.* On the surface $r = a$

∴ $F = -\dfrac{Gm}{a^2}$

(*iii*) *Point inside the shell.* In this case $V = -\dfrac{Gm}{a}$

∴ $F = -\dfrac{dV}{dr} = 0$ $\left[\because \dfrac{Gm}{a} = \text{constant} \right]$

Hence the intensity of gravitational field inside the shell is zero.

Graphical representation. The variation of gravitational field due to a spherical shell for a point outside the shell, on the surface of the shell and inside it is given in Fig. 6.7.

Q. 6.9 (a) Derive an expression for the gravitational potential at a point (i) outside (ii) on the surface and (iii) inside a solid sphere.   (Kerala U. 2001; Gauhati U. 2000; Indore U. 2001; Meerut U. 2007, 2003, 2000; Vid. S.U. 1992; K.U. 1995; A.U. 1995, 1994; Bang. U., 1993; Kan. U., 1992)

(b) Hence find gravitational field (attraction) at these points and show that it is proportional to the distance from the centre of the sphere for a point inside it.

(Indore U. 2001; Meerut U. 2000, 1990; Kerala. U. 2001; Bang. U. 1993; Vid. S. U. 1992; Kan. U., 1992)

Ans. Potential due to solid sphere. (i) *Point outside the sphere.* Consider a point P outside the sphere at a distance r from its centre O.

Divide the sphere into a large number of thin spherical shells concentric with the sphere, of masses m_1, m_2, m_3 ......, etc. respectively.

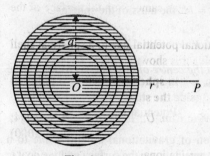

Now potential at a point outside the shell is given by

$$V = -\frac{Gm}{r}$$

where r is the distance of the point form the centre of the shell.

∴ Potential at P due to all the shells is

$$V = -\left[\frac{Gm_1}{r} + \frac{Gm_2}{r} + \frac{Gm_3}{r} + ...\right]$$

$$= -\frac{G}{r}(m_1 + m_2 + m_3 + ...) = -\frac{GM}{r}$$

Fig. 6.8

where M is the mass of the solid sphere.

Hence in the case of a solid sphere also the whole mass can be supposed to be concentrated at its centre.

(ii) *Point on the surface.* For a point on the surface of the sphere of radius $a, r = a$ and $V = -\dfrac{GM}{a}$

(iii) *Point inside the sphere.* Consider a point P inside the sphere at a distance r from its centre O.

Let a be the radius and ρ the density of the sphere.

With O as centre and radius OP draw a sphere. Then the point P lies on the surface of the solid sphere of radius r and inside the spherical shell of internal radius r and external radius a.

Volume of the inner solid sphere = $\dfrac{4}{3}\pi r^3$

∴ Mass of the inner solid sphere = $\dfrac{4}{3}\pi r^3 \rho$

Hence potential at P due to the inner solid sphere

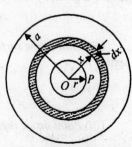

Fig. 6.9

$$V_1 = -\frac{4}{3}\frac{\pi r^3 \rho G}{r} = -\frac{4}{3}\pi r^2 \rho G$$

To find the potential due to the outer spherical shell, draw two concentric spheres with radii x and x + dx respectively forming a thin spherical shell of thickness dx.

Now surface area of the spherical shell $= 4\pi x^2$

Volume of the shell $= 4\pi\, x^2\, dx$ $\therefore$ Mass of the shell $= 4\pi x^2 dx\rho$

Remembering that the potential at any point within a spherical shell is the same as on the surface, we have

Potential at P due to the shell $= -\dfrac{4\pi x^2\, dx\, \rho G}{x} = -4\pi x\, dx\, \rho G$ ...(ii)

$\therefore$ Potential V_2 at P due to the shell of internal radius r and external radius a is obtained by integrating equation (ii) between the limits $x = r$ and $x = a$.

$$\therefore \qquad V_2 \int_r^a - 4\pi\rho G x\, dx = -4\pi\rho G\left[\frac{x^2}{2}\right]_r^a = -4\pi\rho G\left(\frac{a^2}{2} - \frac{r^2}{2}\right) = -2\pi\rho G(a^2 - r^2)$$

$$\therefore \qquad \text{Total potential at } P = V_1 + V_2 = -\left[\frac{4}{3}\pi r^2 \rho G + 2\pi\rho G(a^2 - r^2)\right]$$

$$= -2\pi\rho G\left(\frac{2}{3}r^2 + a^2 - r^2\right) = -\frac{2}{3}\pi\rho G(3a^2 - r^2) = -\frac{4}{3}\pi a^3\, \rho G\,\frac{(3a^2 - r^2)}{2a^3}$$

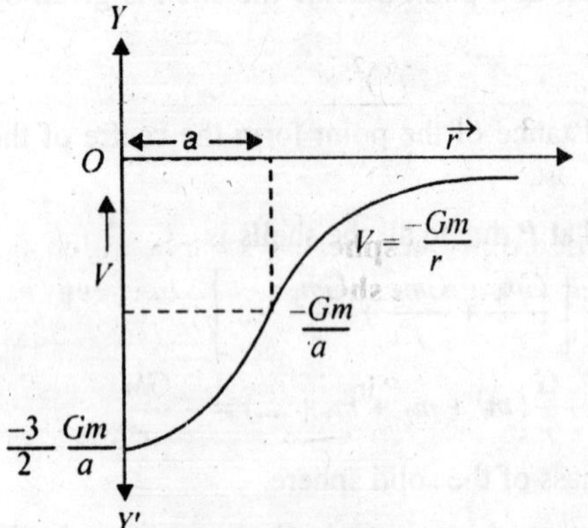

But $\dfrac{4}{3}\pi a^3 \rho = M$ the mass of the sphere

$$\therefore \qquad \text{Potential } V = -GM\,\frac{3a^2 - r^2}{2a^3}$$

(iv) *Point at the centre of the sphere.* At the centre of the sphere $r = 0$

$$\therefore \qquad \text{Potential } V = -\frac{3}{2}\frac{GM}{a}$$

The variation of gravitational potential due to a sphere at a point outside it, on the surface and inside it is shown in Fig. 6.10.

(b) **Gravitational field (attraction).** (i) *Point outside the sphere.*

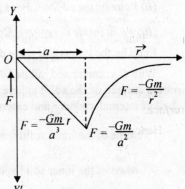

Fig. 6.10

The gravitational field $F = -\dfrac{dV}{dx}$

Since the gravitational potential at a point outside the sphere is given by $V = -\dfrac{GM}{r}$

$$\therefore \qquad F = -\frac{dV}{dr} = -\frac{GM}{r^2}$$

(ii) *Point on the surface.* For a point on the surface of the sphere $r = a$

$$\therefore \qquad F = -\frac{GM}{a^2}$$

(iii) *Point inside the sphere.* For a point inside the sphere

$$V = -GM\,\frac{3a^2 - r^2}{2a^3}$$

$$\therefore \qquad F = -\frac{dV}{dr} = -\frac{GM}{2a^3}\,2r = -\frac{GM}{a^3}r$$

Fig. 6.11

Hence the gravitational field at a point inside the solid sphere is proportional to its distance from the centre.

The variation of gravitational field due to a sphere for a point outside the sphere, on the surface and inside it is shown in Fig.6.11.

6.10. (a) The gravitational potential at a point at a distance r from the centre of a solid sphere is given by $V = -\dfrac{GM(3a^2 - r^2)}{2a^3}$ **where M is the mass and a the radius of the sphere. Find the field intensity at this point.** *(Meerut U., 2003)*

(b) The radius of earth is 6.637×10^6 m , its mean density 5.57×10^3 kg m^{-3} and gravitational constant 6.66×10^{-11} N m^2 kg^{-2}. Calculate the earth's surface potential.

(Meerut U., 1993; K.U., 1991)

Ans. (*a*) For field intensity see Q. 6.9 (*b*) (*iii*) **point inside the sphere**

(*b*) Considering the earth to be a homogeneous sphere, the magnitude of gravitational potential on its surface

$$= \frac{GM}{r} = \frac{G \cdot \frac{4}{3}\pi r^3 \rho}{r} = \frac{4G\pi r^2 \rho}{3}$$

$$= \frac{4 \times 6.66 \times 10^{-11} \times \pi \times (6.637 \times 10^6)^2 \times 5.57 \times 10^3}{3}$$

$$= 6.845 \times 10^7 \text{ J/kg}$$

Q. 6.11. Find the gravitational potential and attraction due to a spherical shell bounded by spheres of radii a and b at a point (*i*) inside the shell, (*ii*) outside the shell and (*iii*) between the two surfaces. *(Cal. U., 2003)*

Ans. Gravitational potential. (*i*) *Inside the shell.* Consider a point P inside the shell bounded by two concentric spheres of radii a and b respectively, at a distance r from the centre O.

With O as centre and radius x and $x + dx$ draw two concentric spheres enclosing a thin spherical shell of thickness dx

The volume of the thin shell $= 4\pi x^2 dx$

∴   Mass of the thin shell $= 4\pi x^2 dx \rho$

∴ Potential at P due to the thin shell

$$= -\frac{G4\pi x^2 dx \rho}{x} = -4\pi \rho G x\, dx$$

since the potential inside a shell is the same as on its surface.

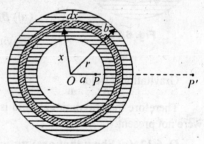

Fig. 6.12

Hence potential V at P due to the shell formed by two spheres of radii a and b is given by

$$V = \int_a^b - 4\pi\rho Gx\,dx = -4\pi\rho G\left[\frac{x^2}{2}\right]_a^b = -2\pi\rho G(b^2 - a^2) \quad \ldots(i)$$

(*ii*) *Outside the shell.* When the point P lies outside the shell at a distance r from the centre, the potential at P due to the thin shell $= \dfrac{G4\pi x^2\, dx \rho}{r}$

since the mass behaves as if it were concentrated at the centre.

Hence potential V at P' due to the shell bounded by two spheres of radii a and b is given by

$$V = \int_a^b -\frac{4\pi\rho G}{r} x^2\, dx = -\frac{4\pi\rho G}{r}\left[\frac{x^3}{3}\right]_a^b = -\frac{4\pi\rho G}{3r}(b^3 - a^3) \qquad ...(ii)$$

But $\frac{4}{3}\pi(b^3 - a^3)\rho = M$ the mass of the whole shell Hence $V = -\dfrac{GM}{r}$ $\qquad ...(ii)\,(a)$

(iii) *Between the two surfaces.* Let the point P lie between the two surfaces at a distance r from the centre O. With O as centre draw a sphere of radius r, as shown in Fig. 6. 13.

As the point P lies just *inside* the spherical shell of internal radius r and external radius b, the potential at $P = -2\pi\rho G(b^2 - r^2)$ [Compare with equation (i)]

As the point P lie, just *outside* the spherical shell of internal radius a and external radius r the

potential at $P = -\dfrac{4\pi\rho G}{3r}(r^3 - a^3)$ [Compare with equation (ii)]

Total Potential at $P = -\left[2\pi\rho G(b^2 - r^2) + \dfrac{4\pi\rho G}{3r}(r^3 - a^3)\right]$

$$= -\left[2\pi\rho G\left(b^2 - r^2 + \frac{2}{3}r^2 - \frac{2}{3}\frac{a^3}{r}\right)\right] = -\left[2\pi\rho G\left(b^2 - \frac{r^2}{3} - \frac{2a^3}{3r}\right)\right] \qquad ...(iii)$$

Gravitational field (*attraction*). (i) *Inside the shell:*

Gravitational potential $\qquad V = -2\pi\rho G(b^2 - a^2)$

$\therefore$ Gravitational field $\qquad F = -\dfrac{dV}{dr} = 0$

as $2\pi\rho G(b^2 - a^2)$ is constant quantity.

(ii) *Outside the shell :*

Gravitational potential $\qquad V = -\dfrac{4\pi\rho G}{3r}(b^3 - a^3)$

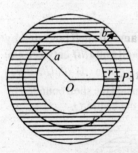

Fig. 6.13

$\therefore$ Gravitational field $\qquad F = -\dfrac{dv}{dr} = -\dfrac{4\pi\rho G}{3r^2}(b^3 - a^3) = -\dfrac{GM}{r^2}$

(iii) *Between the two surfaces:*

Gravitational potential $\qquad V = -2\pi\rho G\left(b^2 - \dfrac{r^2}{3} - \dfrac{2a^3}{3r}\right)$

Gravitational field $\qquad F = -\dfrac{dV}{dr} = 2\pi\rho G\left(-\dfrac{2r}{3} + \dfrac{2a^3}{3r^2}\right) = -\dfrac{4\pi\rho G}{3r^2}(r^3 - a^3)$

Therefore the gravitational field is the same as if the part of the shell lying outside the point P were not present.

Q. 6.12. (a) **Show that gravitational intensity and potential at any point on the surface of the earth are 'g' and 'gR' respectively assuming the earth to be a uniform sphere of radius 'R'.**

(Vid. S. U., 1990)

(b) **Radius of the earth is equal to 6.4×10^6m, acceleration due to gravity $g = 9.8$ m/sec^2, Gravitational constant $G = 6.7 \times 10^{-11}$ S.I. units. Estimate the mass of the earth.**

(Gauhati U. 2000)

Ans. (a) The intensity of gravitational field on the surface of a sphere $= -\dfrac{GM}{R^2}$

The negative sign indicates that the field is directed towards the centre of the earth.

Now a body of mass m lying on the earth's surface is attracted by the earth with a force

$$mg = \frac{GMm}{R^2} \text{ or } g = \frac{Gm}{R^2}$$

Hence the intensity of gravitational field on the surface of the earth $= g$ (numerically).

The gravitational potential on the surface of a sphere $= -\dfrac{GM}{R} = -R\dfrac{GM}{R^2} = gR$ (numerically).

(b) As proved above $\qquad g = \dfrac{GM}{R^2}$ or $M = \dfrac{gR^2}{G}$

Substituting the given values

$$M = \dfrac{gR^2}{G} = \dfrac{9.8 \times 6.4 \times 6.4 \times 10^{12}}{6.7 \times 10^{-11}} = 59.9 \times 10^{23} \text{ Kg.}$$

Q. 6.13. Show that gravitational potential at the centre of a solid sphere is 3/2 times that on its surface. (*Kan. U., 1994; A.U., 1993; Gharwal U., 1999*)

Ans. Gravitational potential on the surface of a solid sphere of radius $a = -\dfrac{GM}{a}$ . ..(i)

Gravitational potential at a point inside the sphere distant r form the centre of the sphere

$$= -GM\dfrac{3a^2 - r^2}{2a^3}$$

∴ Gravitational potential at the centre of the sphere $= -GM\left(\dfrac{3a^2 - 0}{2a^3}\right) = -\dfrac{3}{2}\dfrac{GM}{a}$ ...(ii)

Dividing (ii) by (i), we get $\dfrac{\text{Potential at centre}}{\text{Potential at surface}} = \dfrac{3}{2}$

Hence potential at the centre is $\dfrac{3}{2}$ times that on the surface.

Q. 6.14. (a) Discuss the effect of altitude on the value of g.

(b) Acceleration due to gravity near the polar region is greater than that at the equatorial region. Why? (*Bang. U. 2000, 1994*)

Ans. (a) Effect of altitude. Let g be the acceleration due to gravity at a place and m the mass of the body, then the gravitational force exerted by the earth on this mass

$$mg = \dfrac{GMm}{R^2} \qquad\qquad\qquad ...(i)$$

If now the mass m is moved to a height h from the surface of the earth, then considering the earth to be a homogeneous sphere the value of acceleration due to gravity at this point is given by

$$mg' = \dfrac{GM.m}{(R + h)^2} \qquad\qquad\qquad ...(ii)$$

Dividing (ii) by (i), we have $\dfrac{g'}{g} = \dfrac{R}{(R + h)^2} = \dfrac{1}{\left(1 + \dfrac{h}{R}\right)^2} = \left(1 + \dfrac{h}{R}\right)^{-2}$

$$= 1 - \dfrac{2h}{R} + \text{higher powers of } \left(\dfrac{h}{R}\right) \text{ which are negligible.}$$

∴ $\qquad \dfrac{g'}{g} = 1 - \dfrac{2h}{R}$ or $g' = g\left(1 - \dfrac{2h}{R}\right)$

(b) The shape of the earth is not a perfect sphere. Earth is flattened at the poles. Thus the polar radius is less than the equatorial radius. As the acceleration due to gravity

$$g = \dfrac{Gm}{R^2}, g \propto \dfrac{1}{R^2}$$

At a point where R is less, g is greater.

Hence the value of g is greater at the poles than at the equator.

Q. 6.15. Discuss the effect of depth on the value of g. Justify the statement that value of g is zero at the centre of the earth. *(Bang. U. 1996.)*

Ans. Effect of depth. Considering the earth to be a homogeneous sphere the gravitational attraction on a mass m at its surface is given by

$$mg = \frac{GmM}{R^2} = \frac{G\frac{4}{3}\pi R^3 . \rho \times m}{R^2} = \frac{4\pi GR\rho.m}{3} \qquad ...(i)$$

where ρ is the uniform density of earth and g the acceleration due to gravity. The gravitational pull on the mass m at a depth d is due to the inner spherical part of radius $(R-d)$. If g' is the acceleration due to gravity at that point, then

$$mg' = \frac{G\frac{4}{3}\pi (R-d)^3 . \rho \ m}{(R-d)^2} = \frac{4\pi G (R-d)\rho.m}{3} \qquad ...(ii)$$

Dividing (ii) by (i), we have

$$\frac{g'}{g} = \frac{4\pi G(R-d)\rho.m}{3} \times \frac{3}{4\pi GR\rho m} = \frac{R-d}{R}$$

or $\quad g' = g\left(1 - \frac{d}{R}\right) = \frac{g}{R}(R-d) = \frac{g}{R} \times$ distance from the centre of earth $\qquad ...(iii)$

Hence the acceleration due to gravity decreases with depth and at a point below the earth's surface it is proportional to its distance from its centre. As a result *the acceleration due to gravity at the centre will be zero.*

Actually, the density of earth is not uniform, its inner layers being much denser than the outer layers, therefore, for some distance g increases as we descend downward from the surface.

Q. 6.16. No work is done in moving an object from one point to another on the surface of spherical shell. Explain. *(Bang. U., 1992)*

Ans. The gravitational potential at a point on the surface of a spherical shell is given by

$$V = -\frac{Gm}{a}$$

where m is the mass of the shell and a the radius.

The surface of a spherical shell is, therefore an equipotential surface. Hence there is no difference of potential between any two points on the surface of a spherical shell. Thus no work is done in moving an object from one point to another on the surface of a spherical shell.

Q. 6.17. The earth's mass is 80 times that of the moon and their diameters are 12800 km and 3200 km respectively. What is the value of g on the moon? g on earth is 9.8 ms⁻².

(Bang. U., 1993)

Ans. The acceleration due to gravity on the surface of a sphere is given by $g = \dfrac{GM}{R^2}$ where M is the mass and R the radius of the sphere. Taking the earth and moon to be spheres, acceleration due to gravity on the surface of the earth

$$g = G\frac{80\,m}{(64\times 10^5)^2}\ \text{ms}^{-2}$$

where m is the mass of the moon and 64×10^5 m the radius of the earth.

Acceleration due to gravity on the surface of the moon

$$g' = \frac{Gm}{(16\times 10^5)^2} \qquad \text{where } 16\times 10^5 \text{ m is the radius of the moon.}$$

$$\therefore \quad \frac{g'}{g} = \frac{(64 \times 10^5)^2}{80 \times (16 \times 10^5)^2} = \frac{1}{5} \quad \therefore \ g' = 9.8 \times \frac{1}{5} = 1.96 \ \text{ms}^{-2}$$

Q. 6.18. Two bodies of mass M_1 and M_2 are kept separated by a distance d. Prove that at the point where the value of gravitational intensity produced by them is zero, the potential is

$$V = -\frac{G}{d}(M_1 + M_2 + 2\sqrt{M_1 M_2}).$$ (Kan.U., 1995)

Ans. Let the point where the gravitational intensity produced by the two bodies is zero, be at a distance x from mass M_1, then

$$-\frac{GM_1}{x^2} + \frac{GM_2}{(d-x)^2} = 0 \quad \text{or} \quad \frac{GM_1}{x^2} = \frac{GM_2}{(d-x)^2}$$

$$\therefore \quad \frac{M_2}{M_1} = \frac{(d-x)^2}{x^2} \quad \text{or} \quad \frac{\sqrt{M_2}}{\sqrt{M_1}} = \frac{(d-x)}{x} = \frac{d}{x} - 1$$

or $\quad \dfrac{d}{x} = \dfrac{\sqrt{M_2}}{\sqrt{M_1}} + 1 \quad$ or $\quad x = \dfrac{d\sqrt{M_1}}{\sqrt{M_2} + \sqrt{M_1}}$

Gravitational potential at the same point

$$= -\frac{GM_1}{x} - \frac{GM_2}{d-x} = -\left[\frac{GM_1(\sqrt{M_2} + \sqrt{M_1})}{d\sqrt{M_1}} + \frac{GM_2}{d - \dfrac{d\sqrt{M_1}}{\sqrt{M_2} + \sqrt{M_1}}}\right]$$

$$= -\frac{G}{d}\left[\sqrt{M_1}(\sqrt{M_2} + \sqrt{M_1}) + \frac{M_2(\sqrt{M_2} + \sqrt{M_1})}{\sqrt{M_2}}\right]$$

$$= -\frac{G}{d} \cdot [\sqrt{M_1 M_2} + M_1 + M_2 + \sqrt{M_1 M_2}]$$

or $\qquad V = -\dfrac{G}{d}[M_1 + M_2 + 2\sqrt{M_1 M_2}]$

Q. 6.19. Two particles having masses M and m respectively are initially at rest an infinite distance apart and attract each other according to the law of gravitation. Show that their velocity of approach $v = \sqrt{\dfrac{2G(M+m)}{a}}$ where a is their separation.   (Gharwal U. 1999)

Ans. Initial distance between the particles $= \infty$

Final distance between the particles $= a$

Force between the two particles at a distance r apart $F = -\dfrac{GMm}{r^2}$

$\therefore$ Work done in bringing the particle of mass m from infinity to a distance a from the other particle of mass M

$$= \int_{\infty}^{a} \frac{-GMm}{r^2} dr = \left[\frac{GMm}{r}\right]_{\infty}^{a} = \frac{GMm}{a}$$

This work is stored in the mass m as its self energy. If v_m is the velocity gained by the mass m, then its kinetic energy $= \dfrac{1}{2}m\, v_m^2$

Hence $\qquad \dfrac{1}{2}m\, v_m^2 = \dfrac{GMm}{a} \quad$ or $v_m^2 = \dfrac{2GM}{a}$

$$\therefore \qquad v_m = \sqrt{\frac{2GM}{a}}$$

The velocity v_m of the mass m is directed towards the mass M.

Similarly work done in bringing the particle of mass M form infinity to a distance a from the other mass $m = \dfrac{GMm}{a}$ and the kinetic energy gained by it is $\dfrac{1}{2}Mv_M^2$ where v_M is the velocity gained by the mass M.

$$\therefore \quad \frac{1}{2}Mv_M^2 = \frac{GMm}{a} \quad \text{or} \quad v_M^2 = \frac{2Gm}{a}$$

$$\therefore \quad v_M = \sqrt{\frac{2Gm}{a}}.$$

The velocity v_M of the mass M is directed towards the mass m.

The velocity of approach between the two masses

$$v = v_m + v_M = \sqrt{\frac{2GM}{a}} + \sqrt{\frac{2Gm}{a}}$$

$$= \sqrt{\frac{2G(M+m)}{a}}$$

6.20. Distinguish between inertial and gravitational mass.(*Gauhati U.* 2000; *Gharwal U.* 2000)

Ans. Mass. *The mass of a body is the quantity of matter possessed by the body.*

There are two different concepts about the mass of a body.

(*i*) **Inertial mass:** Inertial mass of a body is related to its inertia in linear motion. It is defined by Newton's second law of motion.

Consider a body of mass m_i moving with an acceleration a under the action of an external force F, then according to Newton's second law of motion

$$F = m_i a$$

If $a = 1, m_i = F$

Hence the inertial mass of a body is equal to the external force required to produce unit acceleration in the body.

According to the special theory of relativity, the inertial mass of a body increases with its velocity. When the body moves with a velocity v, its inertial mass is given by

$$m = \frac{m_0}{\sqrt{1 - \dfrac{v^2}{c^2}}}$$

where m_0 is the rest (inertial) mass of the body and c the velocity of light in vacuum.

(*ii*) **Gravitational mass.** The gravitational mass of a body is related to the gravitational pull on the body. It is defined by Newton's law of gravitation.

Consider a body of mass m_G placed on the surface of the earth of radius R and mass M, then earth's gravitational pull on the body

$$F = \frac{-GMm_G}{R^2}$$

or $m_G = \dfrac{F}{(-GM/R^2)} = \dfrac{F}{E}$

where $E = -\dfrac{GM}{R^2}$ is the intensity of gravitational field on the surface of the earth. If $E = 1$. Then $m_G = F$

Hence gravitational mass of a body is equal to the gravitational pull experienced by the body in a gravitational field of unit intensity.

The properties of gravitational mass are the same as those of inertial mass. Thus inertial mass and gravitational mass of a body are identical.

6.21. Mark the correct answer.

(*i*) Units of gravitational constant G are

   (*a*) N-m-kg^{-2} (*b*) N-m^2-kg^{-2} (*c*) N^2-m^2-kg^{-2} (*d*) N-m^2-kg

(*ii*) Mass of sun is

   (*a*) 2×10^{30} kg   (*b*) 2×10^{25} kg   (*c*) 3×10^{30} kg   (*d*) 4×10^{30} kg

(*iii*) Gravitational potential due to a point mass is:

   (*a*) $+\dfrac{Gm}{r^2}$ (*b*) $-\dfrac{Gm}{r^2}$ (*c*) $-\dfrac{Gm}{r}$ (*d*) $+\dfrac{Gm}{r}$

(*iv*) Gravitational potential due to a shell at a point outside it is

   (*a*) $-\dfrac{Gm}{r^2}$ (*ii*) $+\dfrac{Gm}{r^2}$ (*iii*) $+\dfrac{Gm}{r}$ (*iv*) $-\dfrac{Gm}{r}$

(*v*) Gravitational potential inside a spherical shell is :

   (*a*) Equal to that on the surface   (*b*) Greater than that on the surface

   (*c*) Less than that on the surface   (*d*) Zero

(*vi*) In a gravitational field the work done in transporting a mass from one point to the other

   (*a*) depends upon end positions   (*b*) depends upon distance between them

   (*c*) depends upon actual path of motion.   (*Meerut U.* 2000)

Ans. (*i*) (*b*) N-m^2-kg^{-2} (*ii*) (*a*) 2×10^{30} kg   (*iii*) (*c*) $-\dfrac{Gm}{r}$ (*iv*) (*d*) $-\dfrac{Gm}{r}$

     (*v*) (*a*) Equal to that on the surface.   (*vi*) (*a*) depends upon end positions.

EXERCISES

1. A spherical mass of 20 kgm situated at the surface of the earth is attracted by another mass of 150 kgm. with a force equal to the weight of 0.25 mgm when the centres of masses are 30 cm apart. Calculate the mass and mean density of the earth assuming the radius of the earth to be 6×10^5 cm.

   Hint: $0.25 \times 10^{-3} g = \dfrac{Gm_1 m_2}{r^2}$ and $M = \dfrac{g}{G} R^2$. Calculate $\dfrac{g}{G}$ from the first relation and substitute in the second.   **[Ans.** $M = 4.8 \times 10^{27}$ gm and mean density = 5.31 gm/cc]

2. The moon describes a circular orbit of radius 3.8×10^5 kilometres about the earth in 27 days and the earth describes a circular orbit of radius 1.5×10^8 kms round the sun in 365 days. determine the mass of the sun in terms of the earth.

   Hint: $\dfrac{GM}{d^2} = d \left(\dfrac{2\pi}{T_1} \right)^2$ or

   $T_1^2 = \dfrac{4\pi^2}{GM} d^3$ Similarly $T_2^2 = \dfrac{4\pi^2}{GE} . x^3$ Hence $\dfrac{M}{E} = \dfrac{d^3}{x^3} . \dfrac{T_2^2}{T_1^2}$ [$3.3666 \times 10^5 E$]

3. A sphere of mass 40 kg is attracted by another sphere of mass 80 kg when the centres are 0.3 m apart with a force equal to the weight of 0.25 mg. Calculate the gravitational constant G.   (*Bang. U.*, 1991) [**Ans.** 6.89×10^{-11} Nm^2 kg^{-2}]

7 Motion Under a Central Force

Q.7.1. (*a*) **What are central and non-central forces? Give three characteristics of each. Give two examples of central and non-central forces.**

(*Pbi. U. 2008, 2001, 1999; P.U. 2000, 1999; G.N.D.U. 2009, 2008, 2007, 2006, 2000; H.P.U. 1999; Luck. U. 2001; Kerala U. 2001; Gharwal U. 2000; Osm. U. 2004*)

(*b*) (*i*) **Why gravitational and Coulomb forces are called inverse square law forces?**

(*H.P.U., 2000*)

(*ii*) **Why nuclear force is called non-central force ?** (*H.P.U., 2001*)

Ans. (*a*) **Central force.** *A central force is that force which is always directed away or towards a fixed centre and the magnitude of which is a function only of the distance from the centre taken as origin.*

In spherical polar co-ordinates we express the central force as $\vec{F}(r) = F(r)\,\hat{r}$ where $\hat{r}$ is a unit vector along $\vec{r}$ and $\vec{F}(r)$ is a function of r.

Characteristics. The characteristics of central force between two bodies are :

(*i*) Central forces are *long range* forces *i.e.* they are effective even when the distance between the interacting bodies is very large. The magnitude of the force depends only on the distance between the centres of the two bodies.

(*ii*) It acts along the line joining the centres of the two bodies. If $\vec{r}$ is a vector joining the centres of the two bodies and $\hat{r}$ a unit vector along $\vec{r}$, then a central force can always be represented as $F(r)\,\hat{r}$.

(*iii*) A central force is a **conservative force** because the work done under this force is independent of the path. The curl of a central force is zero. Mathematically $\vec{\nabla} \times \vec{F} = 0$. A central force is the gradient of some scalar function U *i.e* $\vec{F} = -\,\text{grad}\,U = -\,\vec{\nabla}\,U$.

Examples. Familiar examples of central force are :

(*i*) Gravitational force of attraction between two masses.

If m_1 and m_2 are two isolated masses at a distance r apart, then the gravitational force of attraction on the mass m_1 due to the mass m_2 is given by $\vec{F}_{12} = -\dfrac{Gm_1 m_2}{r^2}\,\hat{r} = F(r)\,\hat{r}$

where $F(r) = -\dfrac{Gm_1 m_2}{r^2} = -\dfrac{c}{r^2}$ and $c = Gm_1 m_2$

(*ii*) Electrostatic force (or coulomb force) of attraction or repulsion between two charges. This is also known as *electromagnetic force*.

If $+ q_1$ and $+ q_2$ are two isolated point charges at a distance r apart, then the electrostatic force of repulsion on the charge $+ q_1$ due to the charge $+q_2$ in vacuum is given by $\vec{F}_{12} = K \dfrac{q_1 q_2}{r^2} \hat{r} = F(r) \hat{r}$

where $F(r) = \dfrac{K q_1 q_2}{r^2} = + \dfrac{c}{r^2}$ and $c = K q_1 q_2$

In S.I. units $K = \dfrac{1}{4 \pi \varepsilon_0}$, where ε_0 is the permittivity of free space.

Non-central force. A non-central force is that force which does not simply depend upon the distance between the centres of the two interacting bodies but also on other parameters such as their *spin* and *relative orientation*.

Characteristics. The characteristics of non-central forces are :

(*i*) They are short range forces *i.e,* the force acts only when the interacting particles are very close to each other.

(*ii*) Non-central forces do not necessarily act along the line joining the centres of the two bodies.

(*iii*) A non-central force is non-conservative and cannot be derived from some scalar potential *i.e.* they are not the gradient of some scalar function.

Examples. Familiar examples of non-central forces are :

(*i*) **Weak forces** called into play in β-decay and decay processes where the decay products are *leptons* (electrons, positrons, neutrinos, μ-mesons etc.) are non-central. Weak forces are non-zero only when the interacting particles just overlap.

(*ii*) **Strong nuclear forces** between proton-proton (*p-p* interaction), proton-neutron (*p-n* interaction) and neutron-neutron (*n-n* interaction) are non-central as these are due to the exchange of π^+, π^- and π^0 mesons respectively. Also see **Q. 6.5** for other forces and details.

(*b*) **Why gravitational and Coulomb forces are called central forces?** See part (*a*) Central force-Examples.

(*ii*) **Why nuclear forces are called non-central forces?** See part (*a*) Non-central force Examples.

Q.7.2. (*a*) **Prove that a central force is a conservative force and a conservative force can be expressed as negative gradient of potential or as-grad** V **where** V **is potential energy.**

(*M.D.U.* 2003; *G.N.D.U.* 2007, 2004, 2003; *Meerut U.* 2007, 2006, 2002; *P.U.* 1999)

(*b*) **Give two examples of conservative and non-conservative forces.**

(*H.P.U.* 2001; *G.N.D.U.* 2000; *Guwahati U.* 2000)

(*c*) **Prove that the work done by a conservative force round a closed path is zero.**

(*Meerut 2007*)

Ans. (*a*) A central force is conservative force and *a conservative force is the negative gradient of scalar potential*. Therefore a central force is negative gradient of scalar potential. It is proved as under.

(*i*) **Central force a conservative force.** A central force is represented as $\vec{F} = F(r) \hat{r}$ where $F(r)$ is a function of r only and $\hat{r}$ a unit vector along $\vec{r}$. Suppose the force acts on a particle and displaces it through a small distance $d \vec{r}$, then work done by the force

$$dW = \vec{F}.\vec{dr}$$

∴ Work done in moving the particle from the position $A = r_1$ to $B = r_2$ is given by

$$W = \int_A^B \vec{F}.\vec{dr} = \int_A^B F(r)\,\hat{r}.\vec{dr} = \int_A^B F(r)\,\hat{r}.dr\,\hat{r}$$

$$= \int_A^B F(r)\,dr = [V]_A^B$$

As $F(r)$ is a function of r only, its integral (V) is also a function of r i.e.

$$W = [V]_A^B = V_B - V_A$$

Thus the work done depends only on the values of the integral V at $r = r_1$ at A, (V_A) and at $r = r_2$ at B, (V_B) i.e. at the two end points and not on the actual path followed.

Hence a central force is conservative force.

Note. *The Coulomb force is a central force and hence Coulomb force is conservative.*

(*ii*) **Conservative force as negative gradient of scalar potential.** If $\vec{F}$ is a conservative force, then according to the definition of potential energy

$$\int_A^B \vec{F}.\vec{dr} = V_A - V_B = [-V]_A^B = -\int_A^B dV$$

∴ $$-dV = \vec{F}.\vec{dr} \quad \text{and} \quad -V = \int \vec{F}.\vec{dr} \qquad ...(i)$$

The negative sign simply indicates that the work done by the conservative force is equal to the corresponding decrease in potential energy.

In Cartesian co-ordinates

$$\vec{dr} = dx\,\hat{i} + dy\,\hat{j} + dz\,\hat{k}$$

and $$\vec{F} = F_x\,\hat{i} + F_y\,\hat{j} + F_z\,\hat{k}$$

According to relation (*i*)

$$-V = \int \vec{F}.\vec{dr}$$
$$= \int (F_x\,\hat{i} + F_y\,\hat{j} + F_z\,\hat{k}).(dx\,\hat{i} + dy\,\hat{j} + dz\,\hat{k})$$
$$= \int F_x\,dx + \int F_y\,dy + \int F_z\,dz \qquad ...(ii)$$

Partially differentiating V with respect to x, y and z, we get

$$-V = -\left[\frac{\partial V}{\partial x}dx + \frac{\partial V}{\partial y}dy + \frac{\partial V}{\partial z}dz\right] \qquad ...(iii)$$

Comparing (*ii*) and (*iii*), we have

$$F_x = \frac{-\partial V}{\partial x}; \quad F_y = \frac{-\partial V}{\partial y}; \quad F_z = \frac{-\partial V}{\partial z}$$

∴ $$\vec{F} = -\left[\frac{\partial V}{\partial x}\hat{i} + \frac{\partial V}{\partial y}\hat{j} + \frac{\partial V}{\partial z}\hat{k}\right]$$

$$= -\left(\hat{i}\,\frac{\partial}{\partial x} + \hat{j}\,\frac{\partial}{\partial y} + \hat{k}\,\frac{\partial}{\partial z}\right)V$$

$$= -\vec{\nabla}\,V = -\operatorname{grad} V$$

Thus a conservative force can be expressed as the negative gradient of scalar potential function V.

As the central force is a conservative force, a central force is also the negative gradient of scalar potential function.

(*b*) **Conservative forces.** (*i*) Gravitational force between two masses (ii) Coulomb force between two stationary charges.

Non-conservative forces. (*i*) Nuclear (strong) force between nucleons *i.e. p-p* (proton-proton), *p-n* (proton-neutron) and *n-n* (neutron-neutron) interaction.

(*ii*) Force between moving charges.

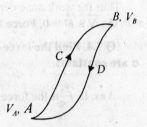

(*c*) **Work done by a conservative force round a closed path.**
Consider a closed path *ACBDA*. Let V_A be the value of potential energy at *A* and V_B that at *B*, then as proved in part (*a*) of this question.

Work done in going from *A* to *B* via the path *ACB*,

$$W = V_B - V_A$$

Similarly, work done in going from *A* to *B* via the path *ADB*,

$$W = V_B - V_A$$

Fig. 7.1

because for a conservative force work done depends only on the value of potential energy at the end points and not on the path.

If we go along the closed path *ACDBA* under the action of a central force (conservative force), the total work done

$$= (V_B - V_A) + (V_A - V_B)$$

$$= (V_B - V_A) - (V_B - V_A) = 0$$

Hence the work done by a conservative force round a closed path is zero.

Q. 7.3. (*a*) **What is a conservative force ? Show that the force** $\vec{F} = yz\,\hat{i} + zx\,\hat{j} + xy\,\hat{k}$ **is a conservative force.** (*Pbi. U.*, 2007, 2006, 2003)

(*b*) **Show that the force** $\vec{F} = y^3 i + 3xy^2\hat{j}$ **is conservative.** (*G.N.D.U.* 2009; *P.U.* 2003)

Ans. (*a*) **Conservative force.** *A force is said to be conservative if the curl of the force is zero.*

or $$\vec{\nabla} \times \vec{F} = 0$$

Given $$\vec{F} = yz\,\hat{i} + zx\,\hat{j} + xy\,\hat{k}$$

$$\therefore \quad \vec{\nabla} \times \vec{F} = \begin{vmatrix} \hat{i} & \hat{j} & \hat{k} \\ \dfrac{\partial}{\partial x} & \dfrac{\partial}{\partial y} & \dfrac{\partial}{\partial z} \\ yz & zx & xy \end{vmatrix}$$

$$= \hat{i}\left[\frac{\partial}{\partial y}(xy) - \frac{\partial}{\partial z}(zx)\right] + \hat{j}\left[\frac{\partial}{\partial z}(yz) - \frac{\partial}{\partial x}(xy)\right] + \hat{k}\left[\frac{\partial}{\partial x}(zx) - \frac{\partial}{\partial y}(yz)\right]$$

$$= \hat{i}\,(x - x) + \hat{j}\,(y - y) + \hat{k}\,(z - z) = 0$$

As $\vec{\nabla} \times \vec{F} = 0$, force $\vec{F}$ is conservative.

(b) A force is said to be conservative if, $\vec{\nabla} \times \vec{F} = 0$

Now $\vec{F} = y^3 \hat{i} + 3xy^2 \hat{j}$

$\therefore \qquad \vec{\nabla} \times \vec{F} = \begin{vmatrix} \hat{i} & \hat{j} & \hat{k} \\ \dfrac{\partial}{\partial x} & \dfrac{\partial}{\partial y} & \dfrac{\partial}{\partial z} \\ y^3 & 3xy^2 & 0 \end{vmatrix}$

$$= \hat{i}\,(0-0) + \hat{j}\,(0-0) + \hat{k}\,(3y^2 - 3y^2)$$

$$= 0$$

As $\vec{\nabla} \times \vec{F} = 0$, Force F is conservative.

Q.7.4. Find the force field associated with the potential energy $V = Ae^{\alpha(x+y+z)}$ where A and α are constants.
(*H.P.U.*, 2003)

Ans. If $\vec{F}$ is the force field associated with the potential energy V, then

$$\vec{F} = -\vec{\nabla} V = -\left(\hat{i}\,\frac{\partial}{\partial x} + \hat{j}\,\frac{\partial}{\partial y} + \hat{k}\,\frac{\partial}{\partial z} \right) V$$

$$= -\hat{i}\,\frac{\partial V}{\partial x} - \hat{j}\,\frac{\partial V}{\partial y} - \hat{k}\,\frac{\partial V}{\partial z}$$

Now $V = Ae^{\alpha(x+y+z)}$

$\therefore \qquad \dfrac{\partial V}{\partial x} = A\,\alpha\,e^{\alpha(x+y+z)}$

$\qquad \qquad \dfrac{\partial V}{\partial y} = A\,\alpha\,e^{\alpha(x+y+z)}$

$\qquad \qquad \dfrac{\partial V}{\partial z} = A\,\alpha\,e^{\alpha(x+y+z)}$

$\therefore \qquad \vec{F} = -A\,\alpha\,e^{\alpha(x+y+z)}\,(\hat{i} + \hat{j} + \hat{k})$

Q.7.5. Show that in a central force field the angular momentum of a particle is conserved.
(*Calicut U.*, 2003; *Meerut U.*, 2003; *Luck.U.*, 1995, 1991; *P. U.*, 2004, 1996, 1992, 1991)

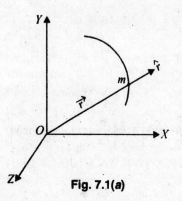

Ans. Angular momentum conserved in central force field.
Consider a particle of reduced mass m moving about the origin O. The force acting on the particle is a central force. It is, therefore, given by

$$\vec{F} = \vec{F}\,(r)\,\hat{r}$$

where $\hat{r}$ is a unit vector along the direction of $\vec{r}$ and $\vec{r}$ is the position vector of the mass m.

The torque acting on a particle subjected to a central force is zero. This is proved as under.

Fig. 7.1(a)

Torque is defined as the vector product $\vec{r} \times \vec{F}$ where $\vec{F}$ is the force acting on the particle and $\vec{r}$ its vector distance from the origin.

$\therefore$ Torque $\vec{\tau} = \vec{r} \times \vec{F} = |\vec{r}| \hat{r} \times F(r) \hat{r}$

$$= |\vec{r}| F(r) (\hat{r} \times \hat{r}) = 0 \qquad\qquad [\because \hat{r} \times \hat{r} = 0]$$

Now torque $\vec{\tau}$ is the time rate of change of angular momentum $\vec{J}$.

or $\qquad\qquad\qquad\qquad \vec{\tau} = \dfrac{d\vec{J}}{dt}$

If $\qquad\qquad\qquad\qquad \vec{\tau} = 0, \quad \dfrac{d\vec{J}}{dt} = 0$ or $J =$ a constant

Hence *the angular momentum of a particle under a central force always remains constant and is, therefore, a constant of motion.* In other words, '*in a central force field the angular momentum of a particle is conserved.*'

Q. 7.6. **The earth is moving round the sun under gravitational force and its orbit has semi-major axis 1.495×10^8 km. When the earth passes closest to the sun at its perihilion, its distance is 1.47×10^8 km and its orbital velocity is 0.303 kms^{-1}. Find the velocity of the earth at the apehilion and its angular velocities at the two points.**

Ans. As the motion of the earth round the sun is under gravitational force which is a central force, the angular momentum of the earth at the two positions, the perihilion and the apehilion, is conserved.

or   Angular momentum at apehilion = angular momentum at perihilion

or $\qquad\qquad\qquad\qquad mv_{ap}\, r_{ap} = mv_{peri}\, r_{peri}$

Now $\qquad\qquad\qquad\qquad r_{peri} = 1.47 \times 10^8$ km $\qquad\qquad\qquad ...(i)$

Semi major axis $a = 1.495 \times 10^8$ km $\qquad \therefore$ Major axis $= 2a = 2.990 \times 10^8$ km

Now $\qquad\qquad\qquad\qquad r_{ap} + r_{peri} = 2a$

$\therefore \qquad\qquad\qquad\qquad r_{ap} = 2a - r_{peri} = 2.990 \times 10^8 - 1.47 \times 10^8 = 1.520 \times 10^8$ km

Substituting in (i), we have $v_{ap} \times 1.52 \times 10^8 = 0.303 \times 1.47 \times 10^8$

$\therefore$ Velocity of the earth at apehilion $\qquad v_{ap} = \dfrac{0.303 \times 1.47 \times 10^8}{1.52 \times 10^8} = 0.293$ kms^{-1}

The angular velocity at the perihilion $\omega_{peri} = \dfrac{v_{peri}}{r_{peri}} = \dfrac{0.303}{1.47 \times 10^8} = 0.206 \times 10^{-8}$ rad s^{-1}

The angular velocity at the apehilion $\omega_{ap} = \dfrac{v_{ap}}{r_{ap}} = \dfrac{0.293}{1.520 \times 10^8} = 0.193 \times 10^{-8}$ rad s^{-1}

Exercise. *The minimum and maximum distance of a comet from the Sun are 7×10^{10} and 1.4×10^{12} m respectively. If the speed of the comet at the nearest point is 6×10^4 m/s calculate the speed at the farthest point.*   (*Gharwal. U.*, 1999)

Hint : $7 \times 10^{10} \times 6 \times 10^4 = 1.4 \times 10^{12} \times V$ [**Ans.** $V = 3 \times 10^3$ m/s]

Q.7.7. A particle moves under a central force. Show that (*i*) its orbit lies in a plane and (*ii*) the radius vector from the centre of the force to the particle sweeps area at a constant rate.
(*Meerut U.* 2002; *P. U.* 2001; *Guwahati U.* 1999; *Luck. U.* 1995, 1991; *G.N.D.U.* 2003, 1991)

OR

If $\vec{r}$ is the radius vector joining a particle of mass m with centre of force and $\vec{A}$ the area swept by the radius vector, show that $d\vec{A} = \dfrac{1}{2}\vec{r} \times d\vec{r}$ and $\dfrac{d\vec{A}}{dt} = \dfrac{J}{2m}$ where J is the angular momentum of the particle about the centre of force.   (*P. U.* 2004; *Kan. U.*, 1992)

Ans. (*i*) **Motion under central force-orbit lies in a plane.** The angular momentum of a particle of mass m moving with a velocity $\vec{v}$ (having a linear momentum $\vec{p} = m\vec{v}$) is given by

$$\vec{J} = \text{moment of linear momentum} = \vec{r} \times \vec{p} = \vec{r} \times m\vec{v}$$

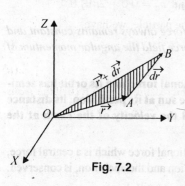

Fig. 7.2

where $\vec{r}$ is the position vector of the particle with respect to the centre of the force lying at O, the origin of the co-ordinate system. For a central force the angular momentum $\vec{J}$ remains constant.

When $\vec{J}$ remains constant its magnitude as well as direction remains the same. The direction of $\vec{J}$ is perpendicular to the plane containing the vectors $\vec{r}$ and $\vec{v}$. Hence *the path of the particle under a central force must always lie in one plane i.e.,* the plane containing the vectors $\vec{r}$ and $\vec{v}$. If we take the direction of angular momentum $\vec{J}$ along the Z–axis,, the motion of the particle will take place in X-Y plane as $\vec{r}$ and $\vec{v}$ will both lie in this plane.

Hence we conclude that motion under a central force is the motion in a plane.

The angular momentum of the earth as it moves in its orbit round the sun under a central gravitational force remains constant in direction as well as in magnitude. Hence the orbit lies in a plane containing the vector $\vec{v}$ the velocity of the earth and the vector $\vec{r}$ representing its vector distance from the sun.

(*ii*) **Areal velocity.** Let m be the reduced mass of the particle and $\vec{r}$ its instantaneous position vector at the point A with respect to the centre of force lying at O, the origin of the co-ordinate system. If the position vector changes to $\vec{r} + d\vec{r}$ at B in time dt, then $\vec{AB} = (\vec{r} + d\vec{r}) - \vec{r} = d\vec{r}$

The area $OAB = d\vec{A}$ swept by the radius vector $\vec{r}$ in time dt is given by $d\vec{A} = \dfrac{1}{2}\vec{r} \times d\vec{r}$

The rate at which the radius vector $\vec{r}$ sweeps the area is known as areal velocity.

$\therefore$ Areal velocity, $\dfrac{d\vec{A}}{dt} = \dfrac{1}{2}\vec{r} \times \dfrac{d\vec{r}}{dt} = \dfrac{1}{2m}\vec{r} \times \dfrac{m\,d\vec{r}}{dt}$

$$= \dfrac{1}{2m}\vec{r} \times m\vec{v} = \dfrac{1}{2m}\vec{r} \times \vec{p} = \dfrac{\vec{J}}{2m} = \text{a constant}$$

as the angular momentum $\vec{J}$ is a constant of motion and m is also a constant.

Thus the areal velocity of the radius vector for a particle under a central force is constant or the radius vector sweeps area at a constant rate.

Q. 7.8. (*a*) State the expression for acceleration of a particle moving in a plane in polar co-ordinates and derive (*i*) the radial equation of motion, (*ii*) equation of motion of θ-coordinates.

(b) **Derive the relation for total energy and effective potential energy of a reduced mass moving under the action of central force. Prove that total energy is conserved.**

OR

Prove the law of conservation of energy in central motion.

(P.U. 2009, 2006; H.P.U. 1999; Guwahati. U. 1999)

Ans. Acceleration of a particle. The acceleration of a particle in plane polar co-ordinates (r, θ) is given by

$$\vec{a} = (\ddot{r} - r\dot{\theta}^2)\,\hat{r} + (r\ddot{\theta} + 2\dot{r}\dot{\theta})\,\hat{\theta} = \vec{a_r} + \vec{a_\theta}$$

where $\vec{a_r}$ is the *radial acceleration* and $\vec{a_\theta}$ the *transverse acceleration*.

Writing the two independently we have $\vec{a_r} = (\ddot{r} - r\dot{\theta}^2)\,\hat{r}$ and $\vec{a_\theta} = (r\ddot{\theta} + 2\dot{r}\dot{\theta})\,\hat{\theta}$

Multiplying the above relations by m the *reduced mass* of the particle, we have

$$m\vec{a_r} = m\,(\ddot{r} - r\dot{\theta}^2)\,\hat{r} = F\,(r)\,\hat{r} \qquad \qquad ...(i)$$

and $$m\vec{a_\theta} = m\,(r\ddot{\theta} + 2\dot{r}\dot{\theta})\,\hat{\theta} = F\,(\theta)\,\hat{\theta} \qquad \qquad ...(ii)$$

where $F(r)\hat{r}$ gives the *radial force* along the direction of increasing $\vec{r}$ and $F(\theta)\hat{\theta}$ the *transverse force* along the direction of increasing θ.

(i) **Radial equation of motion.** From equation (i), we have $m\ddot{r} - mr\dot{\theta}^2 = F(r)$

This equation is known as *radial equation of motion*.

(ii) **Equation of motion of θ-coordinate.** In the case of a central force $F(\theta)\hat{\theta}$ which represents the component of force depending upon angle is zero as the force only acts along the direction of r and is denoted as $F(r)\hat{r}$. To prove that $F(\theta)\hat{\theta} = 0$ for a central force we have,

The magnitude of angular momentum $J = |\vec{J}| = mr^2\,\dot{\theta}$ $\qquad \qquad ...(iii)$

$$\therefore \qquad \frac{d|\vec{J}|}{dt} = 2mr\,\dot{r}\dot{\theta} + mr^2\,\ddot{\theta} = mr\,(r\ddot{\theta} + 2\dot{r}\dot{\theta}) = 0$$

as in the case of a central force $\vec{J} = $ a constant and therefore $\dfrac{d|\vec{J}|}{dt} = 0$

Hence equation (ii) can be stated as $F(\theta)\hat{\theta} = m\,(r\ddot{\theta} + 2\dot{r}\dot{\theta})\hat{\theta} = 0$

or $\qquad \qquad mr\ddot{\theta} + 2m\,\dot{r}\dot{\theta} = 0$

This equation is known as *equation of motion of θ co-ordinate*.

(b) **Total energy of a particle.** For a particle of *reduced mass* m moving under a central force

Total energy = Kinetic energy + Potential energy

Now kinetic energy is $\dfrac{1}{2}mv^2$ and in plane polar co-ordinates

$$\vec{v} = \dot{r}\,\hat{r} + r\,\dot{\theta}\,\hat{\theta}$$

and the magnitude of $\vec{v}$

$$|\vec{v}| = \sqrt{\dot{r}^2 + r^2\dot{\theta}^2} \qquad \text{or} \qquad v^2 = \dot{r}^2 + r^2\dot{\theta}^2$$

$$\therefore \qquad \qquad \text{K.E.} = \frac{1}{2}m\left(\dot{r}^2 + r^2\dot{\theta}^2\right)$$

and total energy $= \dfrac{1}{2}m\dot{r}^2 + \dfrac{1}{2}mr^2\dot{\theta}^2 + U$

where U is the effective potential energy (or potential)

Law of conservation of energy. According to the radial equation of motion

$$F(r) = m\ddot{r} - mr\dot{\theta}^2 \qquad \qquad ...(iv)$$

Also magnitude of angular momentum $J = mr^2\dot{\theta}$ or $\dot{\theta} = \dfrac{J}{mr^2}$

Substituting this value of $\dot{\theta}$ in Eq. (iv), we get $m\ddot{r} - \dfrac{J^2}{mr^3} = F(r)$

A central force is also a conservative force, and conservative force is represented as negative gradient of potential   or $F(r) = -\dfrac{dU}{dr}$ $\therefore \ m\ddot{r} - \dfrac{J^2}{mr^3} = -\dfrac{dU}{dr}$

or

$$m\ddot{r} = -\dfrac{d}{dr}\left[U + \dfrac{J^2}{2mr^2}\right]$$

Multiplying both sides of the equation by $\dot{r}$ we get $m\dot{r}\ddot{r} = -\dfrac{d}{dr}\left[U + \dfrac{J^2}{2mr^2}\right]\dot{r}$

or

$$\dfrac{d}{dt}\left[\dfrac{1}{2}m\dot{r}^2\right] = -\dfrac{d}{dr}\left[U + \dfrac{J^2}{2mr^2}\right]\dfrac{dr}{dt} = -\dfrac{d}{dt}\left[U + \dfrac{J^2}{2mr^2}\right]$$

$$\therefore \ \dfrac{d}{dt}\left[\dfrac{1}{2}m\dot{r}^2 + \dfrac{J^2}{2mr^2} + U\right] = 0 \ \text{ or } \ \dfrac{1}{2}m\dot{r}^2 + \dfrac{1}{2}mr^2\dot{\theta}^2 + U = \text{a constant} \qquad ...(v)$$

as

$$\dfrac{J^2}{2mr^2} = \dfrac{(mr^2\dot{\theta})^2}{2mr^2} = \dfrac{1}{2}mr^2\dot{\theta}^2$$

Now in Eq. (v) $\dfrac{1}{2}m\dot{r}^2$ represents the kinetic energy of translation, $\dfrac{1}{2}mr^2\dot{\theta}^2$ the energy due to centripetal force and U the potential energy. In other words, the left hand side of the equation gives the total energy of the system. Since it is equal to a constant it means the *total energy is conserved* and proves the law of conservation of energy directly from the equations of motion using the expression for acceleration of a particle moving in a plane in polar coordinates.

$$\therefore \ \dfrac{1}{2}m\dot{r}^2 + \dfrac{J^2}{2mr^2} + U = E = \text{a constant}$$

where E is the total energy.

Exercise. Prove that in a central force field

$$2\dot{r}\dot{\theta} = -r\ddot{\theta} \qquad\qquad\qquad (Pbi. \ U. \ 2007; \ P.U. \ 2005)$$

Hint. It has been proved in part (a) (ii) of this question that equation of motion of θ-co-ordinate is

$$mr\ddot{\theta} + 2m\dot{r}\dot{\theta} = 0$$

Hence $2\dot{r}\dot{\theta} = -r\ddot{\theta}$

Q.7.9. State the relation showing total energy for a particle moving under a central force. Hence derive a relation between (i) r and t (ii) θ and t and (iii) θ and r.

Ans. Total energy of a particle. The total energy of a particle moving under a central force is given by

$$E = \dfrac{1}{2}m\dot{r}^2 + \dfrac{J^2}{2mr^2} + U$$

where $\dfrac{1}{2}m\dot{r}^2$ represents the kinetic energy, $\dfrac{J^2}{2mr^2} = \dfrac{1}{2}mr^2\dot{\theta}^2$ the energy due to centripetal force and $U = -\int F(r)\,dr$ the potential energy due to central force.

(i) Relation between r and t. From the above equation, we have

$$\dot{r} = \frac{dr}{dt} = \left[\frac{2}{m}\left(E - U - \frac{J^2}{2mr^2}\right)\right]^{1/2} \quad \text{or} \quad dt = \frac{dr}{\left[\frac{2}{m}\left(E - U - \frac{J^2}{2mr^2}\right)\right]^{1/2}} \qquad ...(i)$$

Hence $t = \displaystyle\int \frac{dr}{\left[\frac{2}{m}\left(E - U - \frac{J^2}{2mr^2}\right)\right]^{1/2}}$

where $r = r_0$ at $t = 0$. This equation gives the relation between r and t.

(ii) Relation between θ and t. To find the relation between θ and t, we have

$$mr^2\dot{\theta} = mr^2\frac{d\theta}{dt} = J \qquad \therefore \ d\theta = \frac{J}{mr^2}\,dt \qquad ...(ii)$$

or $\qquad \theta = \displaystyle\int \frac{J}{mr^2}\,dt + \theta_0$ where θ_0 is the value of θ at $t = 0$

This equation gives the relation between θ and t.

(iii) Relation between θ and r. From relation (ii), we have $d\theta = \dfrac{J}{mr^2}\,dt$

Substituting the value of dt from equation (i), we get

$$d\theta = \frac{\dfrac{J}{mr^2}\,dr}{\left[\dfrac{2}{m}\left(E - U - \dfrac{J^2}{2mr^2}\right)\right]^{1/2}} = \frac{\dfrac{J}{r^2}\,dr}{\left[2m\left(E - U - \dfrac{J^2}{2mr^2}\right)\right]^{1/2}}$$

or $\qquad \theta = \displaystyle\int \frac{\dfrac{J}{r^2}\,dr}{\left[2m\left(E - U - \dfrac{J^2}{mr^2}\right)\right]^{1/2}} \qquad ...(iii)$

This equation gives the relation between θ and r.

Q.7.10. (a) Discuss the nature of orbital motion under a central force field when the force obeys inverse square law and is (i) repulsive, (ii) zero and (iii) attractive.

(b) What is potential energy curve? Making use of potential energy curve explain the nature of motion when total energy is (i) positive, (ii) zero, (iii) negative but greater than minimum value and (iv) minimum.
(Utkal U. 2003; P.U. 2004, 2003, 2000; G.N.D.U. 2008, 2000, 1996; Gharwal U. 1999)

Ans. (a) Motion of a particle under central force. A central force obeying inverse square law is, in general, represented as $F(r) = \pm \dfrac{c}{r^2}$.

The positive sign being taken for a repulsive force and negative sign for an attractive force. The corresponding potential energy is given by

$$U = -\int F(r)\,dr = -\int +\frac{c}{r^2}\,dr = +\frac{c}{r}$$

for a repulsive force and

$$U = - \int F(r)\, dr = - \int - \frac{c}{r^2}\, dr = - \frac{c}{r}$$

for an attractive force.

The total energy of a particle moving under a central force is given by

$$E = \frac{1}{2} m\dot{r}^2 + \frac{J^2}{2mr^2} + U \qquad \text{...(i)}$$

$$= \frac{1}{2} m\dot{r}^2 + \frac{J^2}{2mr^2} \pm \frac{c}{r} \qquad \text{...(ii)}$$

where $\dfrac{c}{r}$ is the potential energy due to inverse square law force, $\dfrac{J^2}{2mr^2} = \dfrac{1}{2} mr^2 \dot{\theta}^2$ the potential energy associated with centrifugal force and $\dfrac{1}{2} m\dot{r}^2$ the radial kinetic energy.

$\therefore$ Effective potential energy $U' = U + \dfrac{J^2}{2mr^2}$

Hence equation (i) can be written as $E = \dfrac{1}{2} m\dot{r}^2 + U' \qquad \text{...(iii)}$

1. Repulsive force. $U = + \dfrac{c}{r}$. As $\dfrac{J^2}{2mr^2}$ is always positive, U' is a positive quantity and hence E is positive.

2. Zero force. For no force $U = 0$, $U' = \dfrac{J^2}{2mr^2}$ is positive and E is positive.

3. Attractive force. For an attractive force $U = -\dfrac{c}{r}$ and $U' = \dfrac{J^2}{2mr^2} - \dfrac{c}{r}$.

For further discussion see part (b)

(b) Potential energy curve. *Potential energy curve is a graph showing the variation of potential energy of a particle moving under a central force with distance r.*

The variation of $\dfrac{J^2}{2mr^2}$, the potential energy associated with centrifugal force, with r is shown in Fig. 7.3 [Curve (i)].

The variation of $U = -\dfrac{c}{r}$, the potential energy due to attractive central force obeying inverse square law, with r is shown in [curve (ii)].

As U is a negative quantity, U' can have a positive, zero or negative value. For $\dfrac{c}{r} < \dfrac{J^2}{2mr^2}$, U' is positive; for $\dfrac{c}{r} = \dfrac{J^2}{2mr^2}$, U' is zero; and for $\dfrac{c}{r} > \dfrac{J^2}{2mr^2}$; U' is negative. The variation of U', the effective potential energy with r is shown in Fig. 7.3 [curve (iii)].

Nature of motion : For *negative* values of U' the total energy E is positive for $U' < \dfrac{1}{2} m\dot{r}^2$, E is zero for $U' = \dfrac{1}{2} m\dot{r}^2$ and E is negative for $U' > \dfrac{1}{2} m\dot{r}^2$. Hence three cases arise corresponding to total energy E positive, zero or negative.

Total energy E positive (Greater than zero). Suppose the particle has a total positive energy

$E = E_1$. The particle comes from infinity, where $r = \infty$ and $U' = \dfrac{J^2}{2mr^2} - \dfrac{c}{r} = 0$ and $E = E_1 = \dfrac{1}{2} m\dot{r}^2$

As the particle travels from infinity towards the other mass U' first becomes negative, reaches a minimum (negative) value and then goes on increasing till $U' = E$, for $r = r_1$ at A as shown in Fig. 7.3 [curve (iii)]. The particle can-

not come closer than r_1, because then U' will be greater than E_1 and $E_1 - U'$ will have a nega-

tive value but $E_1 - U' = \dfrac{1}{2} m\dot{r}^2$, the radial kinetic en-

ergy which must always be positive. Thus the region to the right of A is entirely accessible to the particle and the region to the left of A is strictly forbid-den. The point A at which the radial kinetic energy vanishes is called a *turning point*. Hence such a motion will be un-bounded *i.e.*, the particle will come from infinity go, up to r_1 and return back to infinity. The path is a *hyperbola*.

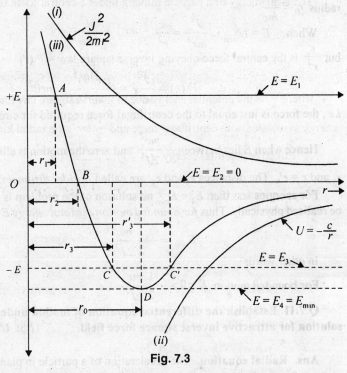

Fig. 7.3

Total energy E zero (Less than zero). Suppose the par-ticle has total energy $E = E_2 = 0$. In this case its energy line coincides with r axis and there is only one turning point at B where $OB = r_2$, the value of r_2 being greater than r_1. The motion of the particle is still unbounded. The path is a *parabola*.

Total energy E negative. In this case we shall deal with two different situations.

(i) Suppose the particle has a total negative energy $E = E_3$. The total energy line for E_3 cuts the curve for U' at two points C and C' corresponding to radial distance r_3 and r'_3. Thus there are two turning points. At these points $U' = \dfrac{1}{2} m\dot{r}^2$, the radial kinetic energy. The regions $r < r_3$ and $r > r_3'$ are forbidden and the motion of the particle is bounded in the region $r_3 < r < r_3'$ the path is an *ellipse*.

(ii) Suppose the particle has a total negative energy $E = E_4$ so that total energy line for E_4 meets the curve for U' at the minima D corresponding to radial distance r_0. The value of r at which U' has a minimum value can be calculated by equating $\dfrac{dU'}{dr} = 0$ or $\dfrac{d}{dr}\left\{\dfrac{J^2}{2mr^2} - \dfrac{c}{r}\right\} = 0$

or $\dfrac{-J^2}{mr^3} + \dfrac{c}{r^2} = 0$ or $r = \dfrac{J^2}{mc}$ ...(iv)

$\therefore$ Minimum value of $r = r_0 = \dfrac{J^2}{mc}$

The minimum total energy corresponding to r_0 is given by

$$E_{min} = U'_{min} = \frac{J^2}{2mr_0^2} - \frac{c}{r_0} = \frac{mc^2}{2J^2} - \frac{mc^2}{J^2} = -\frac{1}{2}\frac{mc^2}{J^2}$$

Hence when $E = E_4 = U'_{min}$ the motion is possible only at one radius r_0. The orbit is a *circle* of radius $r_0 = \dfrac{J^2}{mc}$

When $E = U'_{min}$, $\dfrac{J^2}{mr^3} = \dfrac{c}{r^2}$ [from relation (*iv*)]

but $\dfrac{c}{r^2}$ is the central force obeying inverse square law $= F(r)$

$$\therefore \quad F(r) = \frac{J^2}{mr^3} = \frac{(mr^2\dot{\theta})^2}{mr^3} = mr\dot{\theta}^2$$

i.e., the force is just equal to the centrifugal force required for circular motion.

Hence when E lies between $-\dfrac{mc^2}{2J^2}$ and zero the motion is elliptic with *two turning points* at $r = r_3$ and $r = r'_3$. The distances r_3 and r_3' are called *apsidal distances*.

For energies less than $E_4 = E_{min}$ no solution of the problem is possible and the condition cannot be realised physically. Thus *for bounded motion the total energy E must be negative* but not less than

$$E_{min} = -\frac{1}{2}\frac{mc^2}{J^2}$$

In other words

For bounded motion $E <0> -\dfrac{1}{2}\dfrac{mc^2}{J^2}$.

Q.7.11. Establish the differential equation of motion under a central force and deduce its solution for attractive inverse square force field.   (*Pbi. U.* 2008; *H.P.U.* 2003, 2001, 1995; *G.N.D.U.*, 2007, 2006, 1993)

Ans. Radial equation. The acceleration of a particle in plane polar co-ordinates is given by

$$\vec{a} = (\ddot{r} - r\dot{\theta}^2)\hat{r} + (r\ddot{\theta} + 2\dot{r}\dot{\theta})\hat{\theta} = \vec{a_r} + \vec{a_\theta}$$

The inverse square law force is a central force and may be represented by $F(r)\hat{r}$ where $F(r)$ is a function depending upon r. For such a force the component of acceleration along the direction of increasing θ *i.e.,* $\vec{a_\theta} = 0$

If m is the reduced mass, then

$$F(r)\hat{r} = m\vec{a_r} = (m\ddot{r} - mr\dot{\theta}^2)\hat{r}$$

or $F(r) = m\ddot{r} - mr\dot{\theta}^2$

The *magnitude* of angular momentum $J = mr^2\dot{\theta}$ or $\dot{\theta} = J/mr^2$

$$\therefore \quad mr\dot{\theta}^2 = \frac{J^2 mr}{m^2 r^4} = \frac{J^2}{mr^3}$$

Hence $F(r) = m\ddot{r} - \dfrac{J^2}{mr^3}$

or $m\ddot{r} = F(r) + \dfrac{J^2}{mr^3}$ ...(*i*)

or $\ddot{r} - \dfrac{J^2}{m^2 r^3} = \dfrac{F(r)}{m}$

The relation (*i*) gives the radial equation of motion of a particle of reduced mass m under a central force $F(r)$.

Differential equation of motion. To get the differential equation of the orbit and hence the shape of the trajectory of the particle moving under inverse square law force it is convenient to put $r = \dfrac{1}{u}$

So that $\quad\quad\quad\quad\quad \dot{r} = -\dfrac{1}{u^2}\dfrac{du}{dt} = -\dfrac{1}{u^2}\dfrac{du}{d\theta}\dfrac{d\theta}{dt} = -\dfrac{1}{u^2}\dot{\theta}\dfrac{du}{d\theta}$ ...(ii)

As stated above $\quad\quad J = mr^2\,\dot{\theta} \quad \therefore\; r^2\dot{\theta} = \dfrac{1}{u^2}\dot{\theta} = \dfrac{J}{m}$

Substituting this value of $\dfrac{1}{u^2}\dot{\theta}$ in (ii), we have $\dot{r} = -\dfrac{J}{m}\dfrac{du}{d\theta}$

Differentiating again we get $\ddot{r} = \dfrac{d}{dt}\,(\dot{r}) = -\dfrac{J}{m}\dfrac{d}{dt}\left(\dfrac{du}{d\theta}\right) = -\dfrac{J}{m}\dfrac{d\theta}{dt}\cdot\dfrac{d}{d\theta}\left(\dfrac{du}{d\theta}\right)$

$$= -\dfrac{J}{m}\dot{\theta}\dfrac{d^2u}{d\theta^2}$$ ...(iii)

Substituting $\dot{\theta} = \dfrac{J}{mr^2}$ in (iii) we have

$$\ddot{r} = -\dfrac{J^2}{m^2r^2}\dfrac{d^2u}{d\theta^2} = -\dfrac{J^2u^2}{m^2}\dfrac{d^2u}{d\theta^2}$$

Substituting the value of $\ddot{r}$ and $\dot{r}$ in the equation of motion given in (i), we get

$$m\left[-\dfrac{J^2u^2}{m^2}\dfrac{d^2u}{d\theta^2}\right] = F\left(\dfrac{1}{u}\right) + \dfrac{J^2}{m}u^3$$

or $\quad\quad\quad\quad\quad \dfrac{d^2u}{d\theta^2} = -u - \dfrac{m}{J^2u^2}F\left(\dfrac{1}{u}\right)$ ...(iv)

which is the *differential equation of motion*.

[**Note.** For $J = 0$, the above equation is absurd but since $J = mr^2\dot{\theta}$; $J = 0$ means $\dot{\theta} = 0$ or θ = constant which gives the equation of the straight line passing through the origin.]

Attractive inverse square force. For an inverse square law *attractive* force, say the force of gravitation

$$F(r) = F(r)\,\hat{r} = -\left(\dfrac{Gm_1m_2}{r^2}\right)\hat{r} = -\dfrac{c}{r^2}\hat{r}$$

or $\quad\quad\quad\quad\quad F(r) = -\dfrac{c}{r^2} \quad$ or $\quad F\left(\dfrac{1}{u}\right) = -cu^2$

Taking the case of gravitational attractive force and substituting $F\left(\dfrac{1}{u}\right) = -cu^2$ in (iv), we have

$$\dfrac{d^2u}{d\theta^2} + u = \dfrac{mc}{J^2}$$

This equation can be put in the form $\dfrac{d^2}{d\theta^2}\left(u - \dfrac{mc}{J^2}\right) + \left(u - \dfrac{mc}{J^2}\right) = 0$ ...(v)

as $\dfrac{mc}{J^2}$ = a constant. To find a solution of the above equation put $y = u - \dfrac{mc}{J^2}$

$$\therefore \quad\quad \dfrac{dy}{d\theta} = \dfrac{du}{d\theta} \quad \text{and} \quad \dfrac{d^2y}{d\theta^2} = \dfrac{d^2u}{d\theta^2}$$

Substituting in (v) we get $\dfrac{d^2y}{d\theta^2} + y = 0$

This is the differential equation of simple harmonic motion. Its solution is

$$y = A \cos (\theta - \theta_0)$$

where A and θ_0 are constants to be determined from boundary conditions.

Hence
$$u - \frac{mc}{J^2} = A \cos (\theta - \theta_0) \quad \text{or} \quad u = \frac{mc}{J^2} + A \cos (\theta - \theta_0) \quad \text{...} (vi)$$

In terms of r, we can put the above equation as

$$\frac{1}{r} = \frac{mc}{J^2} + A \cos (\theta - \theta_0) \quad \text{...}(vii)$$

If we orient our co-ordinate system such that θ_0 in the above equation is zero, then

$$\frac{1}{r} = \frac{mc}{J^2} + A \cos \theta = \frac{mc}{J^2} \left\{ 1 + \frac{J^2 A}{mc} \cos \theta \right\} \quad \text{...}(viii)$$

This gives the polar (r, θ) equation of the orbit of a particle moving under an inverse square law attractive force.

Comparing equation (viii) with the general equation of a conic in polar co-ordinates

$$\frac{1}{r} = \frac{1}{l} (1 + \varepsilon \cos \theta)$$

where l = a constant, we find that it represents a conic section with $l = \dfrac{J^2}{mc}$ and $\varepsilon = \dfrac{AJ^2}{mc}$.

The quantity ε is called the eccentricity. Thus the trajectory of the particle is given by

$$\frac{1}{r} = \frac{mc}{J^2} (1 + \varepsilon \cos \theta) \quad \text{...}(ix)$$

The shape of the trajectory of the particle, therefore, depends upon the value of ε and hence on J and A.

(a) For $\varepsilon > 1$ the path is a *hyperbola*.

(b) For $\varepsilon = 1$ the path is a *parabola*.

(c) For ε having a value between 0 and 1. $(0 < \varepsilon < 1)$ the path is an *ellipse*.

(d) For $\varepsilon = 0$ the path is a *circle*.

Q.7.12. (a) **A particle of mass m traces a circle of radius r under attractive inverse square force $-\dfrac{c}{r^2}$. Show that the energy of the particle at any point on the circle is $-\dfrac{c}{2r}$.** (P.U. 2007)

(b) **Show that the differential equation of motion of a particle of mass m under the influence of a central isotropic force can be written as**

$$\frac{d^2 u}{d\theta^2} + u = - \frac{m}{J^2 u^2} F \left(\frac{1}{u} \right)$$

where $u = \dfrac{1}{r}$, (r, θ) are the plane polar co-ordinates of the particle and J the angular momentum. (Cal. U. Hons., 1991)

Ans. (a) The total energy of a particle moving under a central force is given by

$$E = \frac{1}{2} m\dot{r}^2 + \frac{J^2}{2mr^2} + U$$

For motion in a circle r = a constant

$$\therefore \qquad \dot{r} = 0$$

Hence
$$E = \frac{J^2}{2mr^2} + U$$

For attractive inverse square force $U = -\dfrac{c}{r}$ $\therefore E = \dfrac{J^2}{2mr^2} - \dfrac{c}{r}$

The radius of the circular orbit is given by $r = \dfrac{J^2}{mc}$ [See Eq. (ix) Q. 7.11 when $\varepsilon = 0$]

Thus
$$E = r \cdot \frac{c}{2r^2} - \frac{c}{r} = \frac{c}{2r} - \frac{c}{r} = -\frac{c}{2r}$$

(b) According to Eq. (iv) proved in Q. 7.11

$$\frac{d^2u}{d\theta^2} = -u - \frac{m}{J^2 u^2} F\left(\frac{1}{u}\right)$$ (Prove as in Q. 7.11)

$$\therefore \quad \frac{d^2u}{d\theta^2} + u = -\frac{m}{J^2 u^2} F\left(\frac{1}{u}\right)$$

Q.7.13. Derive the polar equation of the orbit of a particle of mass m moving under the action of a force field $F = \dfrac{c}{r^2}$ about a fixed centre.   (*Pbi. U.*, 1995; *P. U.* 2008, 2001, 1996)

Ans. Polar equation. As the particle moves under the action of a force $F = \dfrac{c}{r^2}$ about the fixed centre, the motion is under a *central force* obeying *inverse square law*. The force is $F = \dfrac{c}{r^2}$. It can be

$F = +\dfrac{c}{r^2}$ (repulsive force) or $F = -\dfrac{c}{r^2}$ (attractive force).

The polar equation of a particle under the attractive (gravitational) force has been derived in **Q. 7.11** Eq. (*viii*) and is

$$\frac{1}{r} = \frac{mc}{J^2}\left\{1 + \frac{J^2 A}{mc}\cos\theta\right\}$$

where J is the angular momentum of the particle and A a constant.

For repulsive force $F = +\dfrac{c}{r^2}$. Substituting in Eq. (*iv*) Q. 7.11 the value of $F(r) = +\dfrac{c}{r^2}$

or $F\left(\dfrac{1}{u}\right) = + cu^2$ we have

$$\frac{d^2u}{d\theta^2} = -u - \frac{mc}{J^2} = -\left[u + \frac{mc}{J^2}\right] \quad \text{or} \quad \frac{d^2u}{d\theta^2} + \left[u + \frac{mc}{J^2}\right] = 0$$

or $$\frac{d^2}{d\theta^2}\left(u + \frac{mc}{J^2}\right) + \left(u + \frac{mc}{J^2}\right) = 0 \qquad \left[\because \frac{mc}{J^2} = \text{a constant}\right]$$

Proceeding as in **Q. 7.11** Eq. (*v*) we get the solution of the above equation as

$$u + \frac{mc}{J^2} = A\cos(\theta - \theta_0) \quad \text{or} \quad u = A\cos(\theta - \theta_0) - \frac{mc}{J^2}$$

$$= \frac{mc}{J^2}\left[\frac{AJ^2}{mc}\cos(\theta - \theta_0) - 1\right] = \frac{mc}{J^2}\left[\varepsilon\cos(\theta - \theta_0) - 1\right]$$

where $$\varepsilon = \frac{AJ^2}{mc}.$$

If we orient our co-ordinate system such that θ_0 in the above equation is zero, then

$$u = \frac{mc}{J^2}(\varepsilon \cos \theta - 1) \qquad \text{or} \qquad \frac{1}{r} = \frac{mc}{J^2}(\varepsilon \cos \theta - 1)$$

This is the *polar* (r, θ) equation of the orbit under a central force given by $F = +\dfrac{c}{r^2}$.

Q.7.14. (*a*) **Prove that the shape of the orbit traced by a particle moving under attractive inverse square force depends on the angular momentum and total energy of the particle. What are turning points ? What is the number of turning points in an elliptic orbit?**

(*P. U. 2008, 2007, 2006, 2005, 2001, 1999; G.N.D.U. 2008, 2007, 2006, 2000;*

Pbi. U. 2006, 2005, 2003)

(*b*) **What will be the shape of the orbit of a particle moving under repulsive inverse square force ? Explain.**   (*Pbi. U., 1995; G.N.D.U., 2009, 1994*)

Ans. (*a*) **Polar equation of the orbit.** The polar equation of the orbit traced by a particle moving under central *attractive* inverse square force is given by

$$\frac{1}{r} = \frac{mc}{J^2} + A \cos(\theta - \theta_0) \qquad\qquad \text{[See Q. 7.11 Eq. (}vii\text{)]}$$

where *m is the reduced mass of the particle, c* the force constant, *J* the angular momentum, *A* and θ_0 constants of motion. To find the value of *A* we shall find the turning points of the trajectory of the particle.

Maximum and minimum value of *r*. In the above equation if $(\theta - \theta_0) = 0$, $\cos(\theta - \theta_0) = 1$, then $\dfrac{1}{r}$ has the maximum value [*i.e., r* has the minimum value].

$$\therefore \qquad \left(\frac{1}{r}\right)_{max} = \frac{mc}{J^2} + A \qquad\qquad\qquad\qquad ...(i)$$

If $(\theta - \theta_0) = \pi$, $\cos(\theta - \theta_0) = -1$, then $\dfrac{1}{r}$ has the minimum value [*i.e., r* has the maximum value].

$$\therefore \qquad \left(\frac{1}{r}\right)_{min} = \frac{mc}{J^2} - A \qquad\qquad\qquad\qquad ...(ii)$$

Turning points. The total energy *E* of the particle under a central force is given by

$$E = \frac{1}{2}m\dot{r}^2 + \frac{J^2}{2mr^2} + U$$

where $\dfrac{1}{2}m\dot{r}^2$ is the kinetic energy, $\dfrac{J^2}{2mr^2} = \dfrac{1}{2}mr^2\dot{\theta}^2$ is the energy due to centripetal force and *U* the potential energy. For a gravitational force of attraction *obeying* inverse square law

$$U = -\frac{c}{r} \text{ where } c = G\,m_1\,m_2 \qquad \therefore \ E = \frac{1}{2}m\dot{r}^2 + \frac{J}{2mr^2} - \frac{c}{r}$$

The quantity $\dfrac{J}{2mr^2} - \dfrac{c}{r}$ is known as *effective potential energy* for *attractive force.*

For an electrostatic force of repulsion between two like charges in S.I. units

$$U = +\frac{c}{r} \text{ where } c = \frac{1}{4\pi\varepsilon_0}\,q_1 q_2 \qquad \therefore \ E = \frac{1}{2}m\dot{r}^2 + \frac{J^2}{2mr^2} + \frac{c}{r}$$

The quantity $\dfrac{J}{2mr^2} + \dfrac{c}{r}$ is known as *effective potential energy for repulsive force.*

Now, because *E*, the total energy, is a constant, we can evaluate it at any convenient point on orbit. We take the *turning points* where *r* is a maximum or a minimum. At these points

$$\frac{dr}{dt} = \dot{r} = 0$$

Thus the turning point is defined as a point at which the radial velocity $\dot{r}$ of the particle is zero.

In such a case the kinetic energy of the particle given by $\frac{1}{2} m\dot{r}^2 = 0$ and total energy $E = \frac{J^2}{2mr^2} - \frac{c}{r}$ is the *effective potential energy* because $\frac{J^2}{2mr^2} = \frac{1}{2} mr^2\dot{\theta}^2$ is the energy due to centripetal force and $-\frac{c}{r}$ the energy due to gravitational *attractive* force.

Thus a turning point may also be defined as that point at which the total energy E of the particle is equal to its effective potential energy.

Location of turning points. Considering the case of an *attractive* inverse square force, at the turning points

$$E = \frac{J^2}{2mr^2} - \frac{c}{r} \qquad \text{or} \qquad \frac{J^2}{2m}\frac{1}{r^2} - c\frac{1}{r} - E = 0$$

This is an equation in $\frac{1}{r}$ and its two roots give the value of $\left(\frac{1}{r}\right)_{max}$ and $\left(\frac{1}{r}\right)_{min}$. The two roots are

$$\frac{1}{r} = c \pm \frac{\sqrt{c^2 + 4\dfrac{J^2}{2m} E}}{\dfrac{J^2}{m}}$$

These values of r give the position of turning points. Thus turning points occur at

$$\left(\frac{1}{r}\right)_{max} = \frac{mc}{J^2} + \left[\left(\frac{mc}{J^2}\right)^2 + \left(\frac{2mE}{J^2}\right)\right]^{1/2} \qquad \text{...(iii)}$$

and

$$\left(\frac{1}{r}\right)_{min} = \frac{mc}{J^2} - \left[\left(\frac{mc}{J^2}\right)^2 + \left(\frac{2mE}{J^2}\right)\right]^{1/2} \qquad \text{...(iv)}$$

Value of A for attractive inverse square force.

Comparing the values of $\left(\frac{1}{r}\right)_{max}$ with that in Eq. (*i*), we have

$$\frac{mc}{J^2} + A = \frac{mc}{J^2} + \left[\left(\frac{mc}{J^2}\right)^2 + \left(\frac{2mE}{J^2}\right)\right]^{1/2}$$

$$\therefore \qquad A^2 = \left(\frac{mc}{J^2}\right)^2 + \frac{2mE}{J^2} = \frac{m^2c^2}{J^4} + \frac{2mE}{J^2} \qquad \text{...(v)}$$

If we orient our co-ordinate system such that θ_0 in Eq. $\frac{1}{r} = \frac{mc}{J^2} + A \cos(\theta - \theta_0)$ is zero, then

$$\frac{1}{r} = \frac{mc}{J^2}\left(1 + \frac{AJ^2}{mc}\cos\theta\right) \qquad \text{...(vi)}$$

Relation between eccentricity and energy. Comparing equation (*vi*) with the general equation of conic in polar co-ordinates

$$\frac{1}{r} = \frac{1}{l}(1 + \varepsilon \cos \theta)$$

where l = a constant, we find that it represents a conic section with $l = \dfrac{J^2}{mc}$ and $\varepsilon = \dfrac{AJ^2}{mc}$.

The quantity ε is called the *eccentricity* and its value is given by

$$\varepsilon^2 = \frac{A^2 J^4}{m^2 c^2} = 1 + \frac{2J^2 E}{mc^2} \qquad \therefore \varepsilon = \left[1 + \frac{2J^2 E}{mc^2}\right]^{1/2} \qquad \ldots(vii)$$

and the trajectory of the particle is given by

$$\frac{1}{r} = \frac{mc}{J^2}(1 + \varepsilon \cos \theta) \qquad \ldots(viii)$$

Shape of the orbit. From relation (*viii*) we find that the shape of the trajectory of the particle depends upon the value of ε and hence on the relationship between the total energy E and its angular momentum J.

(*i*)   If $E > 0$ (+ ve); $\varepsilon > 1$ the path is a *hyperbola*.

(*ii*) If $E = 0$; $\varepsilon = 1$ the path is a *parabola*.

(*iii*) If $E < 0$ (– ve); $\varepsilon < 1$ the path is an *ellipse*.

(*iv*) If $E = -\dfrac{mc^2}{2J^2}$; $\varepsilon = 0$ the path is a *circle*, as shown in Fig. 7.4.

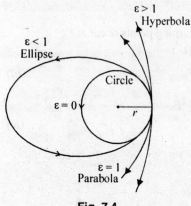

Fig. 7.4

Number of turning points. When the shape of the orbit is a hyperbola or parabola, there is only one turning point. When the shape of the orbit is elliptic or circular, there are two turning points.

(*b*) Repulsive inverse square force. For a *repulsive* force

$$E = \frac{1}{2} m\dot{r}^2 + \frac{J^2}{mr^2} + \frac{c}{r}$$

all the quantities on the right hand side are positive.

Therefore $E > 0$ and the trajectory of the body under the influence of a repulsive force is always a hyperbola. The most familiar example is the path of a positively charged α-particle moving under the influence of a positively charged nucleus.

Conclusion. Hence we conclude that

For an **attractive** force $E = \dfrac{1}{2} m\dot{r}^2 + \dfrac{J^2}{mr^2} - \dfrac{c}{r}$

The first two quantities on the right hand side are positive and the last quantity is negative.

$\therefore E > = < 0$ according as $\dfrac{1}{2} m\dot{r}^2 + \dfrac{J^2}{2mr^2} > = < \dfrac{c}{r}$ and hence accordingly the trajectory will be a hyperbola, a parabola or an ellipse.

For $E = -\dfrac{mc^2}{2J^2}$ the trajectory is a circle.

For repulsive force the trajectory is always a hyperbola.

Q. 7.15. The equation of the orbit of a particle of mass m moving under the action of a central force field about a fixed centre is $r = \dfrac{1}{2\theta}$. Find the force law.   *(P. U. 2000)*

Ans. The equation of the orbit of the particle is given by

$$r = \frac{1}{2\theta}$$

$\therefore \qquad u = \dfrac{1}{r} = 2\theta \quad$ and $\quad \dfrac{du}{d\theta} = 2; \qquad \dfrac{d^2u}{d\theta^2} = 0$

The differential equation of motion of the orbit of a particle under a central force is given by

$$\frac{d^2u}{d\theta^2} = -u - \frac{m}{J^2 u^2} F\left(\frac{1}{u}\right)$$

$\therefore \qquad \dfrac{m}{J^2 u^2} F\left(\dfrac{1}{u}\right) = -u - \dfrac{d^2u}{d\theta^2} = -u$

or $\qquad F\left(\dfrac{1}{u}\right) = \dfrac{-J^2 u^3}{m}$

$\therefore \qquad F(r) = -\dfrac{J^2}{mr^3} = -\dfrac{J^2}{m}\left(\dfrac{1}{r^3}\right)$

This is the required force law.

Q. 7.16. A particle follows a spiral orbit given by $r = c\theta^2$ under an unknown force law. Prove that such an orbit is possible in a central field. Also find the form of the force law.

(P. U. 2000; Cal. U. Hons., 1991; H. P. U., 1996)

Ans. The motion of the particle is given by $r = c\theta^2$. $\therefore \ u = \dfrac{1}{r} = \dfrac{1}{c\theta^2}$

Hence $\qquad \dfrac{du}{d\theta} = \dfrac{-2}{c\theta^3} \quad$ and $\quad \dfrac{d^2u}{d\theta^2} = \dfrac{6}{c\theta^4}$

The differential equation of motion is $\dfrac{d^2u}{d\theta^2} = -u - \dfrac{m}{J^2 u^2} F\left(\dfrac{1}{u}\right)$

or $-\dfrac{m}{J^2 u^2} F\left(\dfrac{1}{u}\right) = u + \dfrac{d^2u}{d\theta^2} = \dfrac{1}{c\theta^2} + \dfrac{6}{c\theta^4} \quad$ or $\quad -F\left(\dfrac{1}{u}\right) = \dfrac{J^2 u^2}{m}\left[\dfrac{1}{c\theta^2} + \dfrac{6}{c\theta^4}\right]$

or $-F(r) = \dfrac{J^2}{m}\dfrac{1}{r^2}\left[\dfrac{1}{c\theta^2} + \dfrac{6}{c\theta^4}\right] = \dfrac{J^2}{m}\left[\dfrac{1}{c^3\theta^6} + \dfrac{6}{c^3\theta^8}\right] = \dfrac{J^2}{m}\left[\dfrac{1}{(c\theta^2)^3} + \dfrac{6}{(c\theta^2)^4}\right] = \dfrac{J^2}{m}\left[\dfrac{1}{r^3} + \dfrac{6c}{r^4}\right]$

Hence $\qquad F(r) = -\dfrac{J^2}{m}\left[\dfrac{1}{r^3} + \dfrac{6c}{r^4}\right]$

As $F(r)$ depends upon $\left[\dfrac{1}{r^3} + \dfrac{6c}{r^4}\right]$ it is a central force.

Q. 7.17. A particle moving under a central force describes spiral orbit given by $r = a \exp(b\theta)$ where a and b are some constants. Obtain the force law.

(Pb. U. 2000; G.N.D.U. 2002, 1996; H.P.U., 1992)

Ans. The motion of the particle is given by $r = ae^{b\theta}$.

$\therefore \ u = \dfrac{1}{r} = \dfrac{1}{a} e^{-b\theta} \qquad$ Hence $\quad \dfrac{du}{d\theta} = -\dfrac{b}{a} e^{-b\theta} \qquad$ and $\quad \dfrac{d^2u}{d\theta^2} = +\dfrac{b^2}{a} e^{-b\theta}$

The differential equation of motion of the orbit of a particle moving under a central force is given

by
$$\frac{d^2u}{d\theta^2} = -u - \frac{m}{J^2u^2} F\left(\frac{1}{u}\right)$$

$$\therefore \quad \frac{m}{J^2u^2} F\left(\frac{1}{u}\right) = -u - \frac{d^2u}{d\theta^2} = -\frac{1}{a}e^{-b\theta} - \frac{b^2}{a}e^{-b\theta}$$

$$= -\frac{1}{a}e^{-b\theta}[1+b^2] = -u[1+b^2]$$

$$\therefore \quad F\left(\frac{1}{u}\right) = -\frac{J^2u^3}{m}[1+b^2] \quad \text{or} \quad F(r) = -\frac{J^2}{m}(1+b^2)\left(\frac{1}{r^3}\right)$$

This is the required force law.

Q. 7.18. The motion of a particle under the influence of a central force is described by $r = a \sin \theta$. **Find an expression for the force.** *(G.N.D.U., 1990)*

Ans. The motion of the particle is given by

$$r = a \sin \theta$$

$$\therefore \quad u = \frac{1}{r} = \frac{1}{a \sin \theta} = \frac{\operatorname{cosec} \theta}{a}$$

Hence
$$\frac{du}{d\theta} = -\frac{\operatorname{cosec} \theta \cot \theta}{a}$$

and
$$\frac{d^2u}{d\theta^2} = -\frac{1}{a}(-\operatorname{cosec} \theta \operatorname{cosec}^2 \theta - \operatorname{cosec} \theta \cot \theta \cot \theta)$$

$$= \frac{1}{a}\operatorname{cosec} \theta (\operatorname{cosec}^2 \theta + \cot^2 \theta)$$

The differential equation of motion of the orbit of a particle moving under a central force is given

by
$$\frac{d^2u}{d\theta^2} = -u - \frac{m}{J^2u^2} F\left(\frac{1}{u}\right)$$

$$\therefore \quad \frac{m}{J^2u^2} F\left(\frac{1}{u}\right) = -u - \frac{d^2u}{d\theta^2}$$

$$= -\frac{1}{a}[\operatorname{cosec} \theta + \operatorname{cosec} \theta (\operatorname{cosec}^2 \theta + \cot^2 \theta)]$$

$$= -\frac{1}{a}\operatorname{cosec} \theta (1 + \operatorname{cosec}^2 \theta + \cot^2 \theta)$$

$$= -\frac{2}{a}\operatorname{cosec}^3 \theta = -2a^2u^3$$

$$\therefore \quad F\left(\frac{1}{u}\right) = \frac{-(2J^2 u^5 a^2)}{m} = \frac{-2J^2 a^2 u^5}{m} \quad \therefore \quad F(r) = \frac{-2J^2a^2}{m}\left(\frac{1}{r^5}\right) \quad \text{or} \quad F(r) \propto \frac{1}{r^5}$$

This is the required force law, *i.e.*, the face varies inversely as the fifth power of distance.

Exercise. The path of a particle moving under the action of force is given by $r = 2a \cos \theta$. **Find the law of force.** *(Pbi. U. 2005)*

Hint. Proceed as above. The required law of force is

$$F(r) = \frac{-8J^2a^2}{m}\left[\frac{1}{r^5}\right] \quad \text{or} \quad F(r) \propto \frac{1}{r^5}$$

i.e. the force varies inversely as the fifth power of the distance

Q. 7.19. A particle is in bound state with respect to another particle exerting inverse square law force on it. Discuss the trajectory of the particle and turning points. (*Pbi. U.* 2002)

Ans. Trajectory of a particle. It has been proved in **Q. 7.10** Eq. (*ii*) that total energy of a particle moving under a central (inverse square law) force is given by

$$E = \frac{1}{2} m\dot{r}^2 + \frac{J^2}{2mr^2} \pm \frac{c}{r}$$

where $\frac{c}{r}$ is the potential energy due to inverse square law force, $\frac{J^2}{2mr^2} = \frac{1}{2} mr^2\dot{\theta}^2$ the potential

energy associated with centrifugal force and $\frac{1}{2} m\dot{r}^2$ the radial kinetic energy.

When the total energy E is *positive* the motion is *unbounded* with only *one turning point* and the path of the particle (trajectory) is a *hyperbola* (**Q. 7.10** under **total energy positive**).

When the total energy E is *zero*, the motion is still *unbounded* with again only *one turning point* and the path of the particle (trajectory) is a *parabola* (**Q. 7.10** under **total energy zero**).

When the total energy E is *negative*, there are *two turning points* and the motion is *bounded*, the path of the particle (trajectory) is an *ellipse* (or *circle*) (**Q. 7.10** under **total energy negative**).

When a particle is in a bound state with respect to another particle exerting inverse square law force, the force is *attractive* and the total energy E is *negative*.

In such a case the differential equation of motion in plane polar co-ordinates (r, θ) is given by

$$\frac{1}{r} = \frac{mc}{J^2} (1 + \varepsilon \cos \theta)$$

where ε is the eccentricity given by

$$\varepsilon = \left[1 + \frac{2J^2 E}{mc^2}\right]^{1/2}$$

[For proof see Eq. (*viii*) and Eq. (*vii*) **Q. 7.14**]

The shape of the trajectory of the particle, therefore, depends upon the value of ε and hence on the relationship between the total energy E and angular momentum J. For E negative i.e. $E < 0$, ε lies between zero and 1 (ε is not negative).

For $\varepsilon < 1$ the path of the particle (trajectory) is an *ellipse*.

For $\varepsilon = 0$ the path of the particle (trajectory) is a *circle*.

Q.7.20. A planet moving round the sun is suddenly stopped. Find the time taken by the planet to fall into the sun in terms of the period of revolution of the planet around the sun.
(*G.N.D.U.* 1992)

Ans. Period of revolution of a planet around the sun is given by $T^2 = \frac{4\pi^2 ma^3}{c}$

[For proof **See Q. 7.23** Eq. (*ii*)]

where m is the mass of the planet, a the semi-major axis of the orbit and $c = GMm$ where G is the gravitational constant and M the mass of the sun.

$$\therefore \quad T^2 = \frac{4\pi^2 ma^3}{GMm} = \frac{4\pi^2 a^3}{GM} \qquad ...(i)$$

Considering the orbit to be approximately circular a gives the radius of the orbit or the average distance of the planet from the sun.

As soon as the planet stops, it is attracted towards the sun with a force $F = \dfrac{GMm}{a^2}$ and has an acceleration $\dfrac{F}{m} = \dfrac{GM}{a^2}$

If we take the distance of the planet from the sun small as compared to the radius of the sun, the acceleration can be taken to be almost constant. If t is the time taken to fall into the sun i.e., to cover the distance a, then $a = \dfrac{1}{2}$ acceleration $\times t^2 = \dfrac{1}{2} \dfrac{GM}{a^2} \times t^2$ or $\dfrac{t^2}{2} = \dfrac{a^3}{GM}$

Substituting the value of $\dfrac{a^3}{GM} = \dfrac{t^2}{2}$ in (i), we have $T^2 = 2\pi^2 t^2$ or $\dfrac{t^2}{T^2} = \dfrac{1}{2\pi^2}$

or $\qquad\qquad \dfrac{t}{T} = \dfrac{1}{\sqrt{2\pi}} = 0.225 \qquad \therefore \ t = 0.225 \ T.$

Q. 7.21. What parameters determine the shape and size of an elliptic orbit of a planet? Explain. (G.N.D.U., 1993)

Ans. Shape and size of the elliptic orbit. A planet revolves round the sun in an elliptic orbit under the gravitational attractive inverse square law force.

The polar equation of the orbit is given by $\dfrac{1}{r} = \dfrac{mc}{J^2}(1 + \varepsilon \cos \theta)$

or $\qquad\qquad r = \dfrac{J^2/mc}{(1 + \varepsilon \cos \theta)}$ ...(i)

where J is the angular momentum and m the mass of the planet, c a constant $= GMm$, G being the gravitational constant and M the mass of the sun. ε is the eccentricity of the orbit given by

$\varepsilon = \left(1 + \dfrac{2J^2E}{mc^2}\right)^{1/2}$. As the orbit of the planet is elliptic, the eccentricity $\varepsilon < 1$ and E the total energy is **negative.**

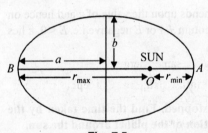

Fig. 7.5

The value of r is a minimum when $\cos \theta = + 1$

$\therefore \qquad r_{min} = \dfrac{J^2}{mc\,(1 + \varepsilon)}$

At this point the planet is closest to the sun and this point is called *perihilion* as shown at A in Fig. 7.5.

The value of r is a maximum when $\cos \theta = - 1$

$\therefore \qquad r_{max} = \dfrac{J^2}{mc\,(1 - \varepsilon)}$

At this point the planet is farthest from the sun and the point is called *apehilion* as shown at B in Fig. 7.5.

The semi-major axis of the ellipse is given by $a = \dfrac{AB}{2} = \dfrac{AO + OB}{2} = \dfrac{r_{min} + r_{max}}{2}$

$\therefore \qquad a = \dfrac{J^2}{2mc}\left(\dfrac{1}{1 + \varepsilon} + \dfrac{1}{1 - \varepsilon}\right) = \dfrac{J^2}{mc}\dfrac{1}{(1 - \varepsilon^2)}$

Now $\qquad\qquad \varepsilon = \left[1 + \dfrac{2J^2E}{mc^2}\right]^{1/2}$

or $\qquad\qquad \varepsilon^2 - 1 = \dfrac{2J^2E}{mc^2} \qquad$ Hence $a = -\dfrac{J^2}{mc}\cdot\dfrac{mc^2}{2J^2E} = -\dfrac{c}{2E}$

As E is negative, we put $a = \dfrac{c}{2|E|}$ where $|E|$ is the magnitude of E.

The relation $a = \dfrac{c}{2|E|}$ shows that the length of *the major axis of the elliptic orbit of the planet depends only on the total energy E but is independent of the angular momentum J.*

The semi-minor axis of the ellipse is given by $b = a\sqrt{1-\varepsilon^2} = a\sqrt{\dfrac{2J^2|E|}{mc^2}}$

$$= \dfrac{aJ}{c}\sqrt{\dfrac{2|E|}{m}} = \dfrac{c}{2|E|}\dfrac{J}{c}\sqrt{\dfrac{2|E|}{m}} = \dfrac{J}{\sqrt{2m|E|}} \qquad \ldots(ii)$$

Equation (ii) shows that the length of the minor axis of the elliptic orbit of the planet depends upon both, the total energy E and angular momentum J.

Thus E determines the length of the major axis and E and J both determine the length of the minor axis of the elliptic orbit.

Hence the parameters which determine the shape and size of the elliptic orbit of the planet are

1. Total energy E and

2. Angular momentum J.

Q. 7.22. Prove that all ellipses with the same major axes have the same energy.

Ans. The semi-major axis of an ellipse is given by $a = \dfrac{J^2}{mc\,(1-\varepsilon^2)}$ or $(1-\varepsilon^2) = \dfrac{J^2}{amc}$

Now $\qquad\qquad \varepsilon^2 = 1 + \dfrac{2EJ^2}{mc^2}$ or $\varepsilon^2 - 1 = \dfrac{2EJ^2}{mc^2}$

$\therefore \qquad\qquad \dfrac{-J^2}{amc} = \dfrac{2EJ^2}{mc^2} \qquad$ Hence $a = \dfrac{-c}{2E}$

or $E = -\dfrac{c}{2a}$ = a constant for the same value of a

This shows that all ellipses with the same major axis have the same energy.

Q.7.23. (a) State and prove Kepler's laws of planetary motion using the concept of reduced mass. (G.N.D.U. 2009, 2007, 2006; Calicut U., 2003)

(b) Show that the areal velocity of a planet round the sun is constant.

OR

Show that the radius vector joining the sun to a planet sweeps out equal areas in equal intervals of time.

(c) Show that the square of the time period of revolution of a planet is proportional to the cube of semi-major axis of the orbit. [Bhopal U. 2004; Osm. U. 2004; P. U. 2006, 2001, 2000, 1999, 1992; Gharwal U. 2000; G.N.D.U. 2002, 2001, 2000, 1999, 1996; Pbi. U. 2006, 2003, 2000; H.P.U. 1999; Indore U. 2001; Kerala U. 2001; Meerut U. 2002; Luck. U. 1994, 1992; Cal. U. (Hons.), 1990]

Ans. (a) Kepler's laws of planetary motion. Kepler's three laws of planetary motion are :

(1) *Each planet moves in an ellipse with sun at its focus.*

(2) *The radius vector i.e., the line joining the sun to a given planet sweeps out equal areas in equal intervals of time.*

(3) *The square of the period of revolution of the planet about the sun divided by the cube of the major axis of the orbit is a constant.*

First law. The eccentricity of the orbit of a particle moving under attractive inverse square law force is given by $\varepsilon^2 = 1 + \dfrac{2EJ^2}{mc^2}$ [Eq. (*vii*) **Q. 7.14.**]

where J is the angular momentum of the particle of reduced mass m, E the total energy, c a constant which in the case of gravitational force $= GMm$, M being the mass of the body about which the particle moves and G, the gravitational constant.

$$\therefore \qquad E = -\frac{mc^2}{2J^2}(1 - \varepsilon^2)$$

In the case of a planet revolving round the sun, if $\varepsilon < 1$ the total energy of the system (planet and the sun) is **negative** *i.e.,* the planet remains bound to the attracting centre, the sun. As the planet is bound to the sun and cannot escape from it, it moves around the sun in a closed elliptic orbit. This establishes Kepler's first law of planetary motion.

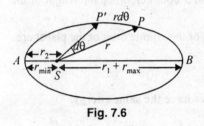

Fig. 7.6

In the case of the motion of a planet round the sun, the sun is at one focus which is taken as the centre of the co-ordinate system of the ellipse. Thus each planet moves in an ellipse with sun at its focus as shown in Fig. 7.6. The point A where the planet is closest to the sun is called *perihelion* and the point B where it is farthest from the sun is called *apehelion*.

(*b*) **Second law.** Supose a planet P is moving in an elliptic orbit as shown in Fig. 7.6. If it moves from P to P' in a small time dt the area swept out by the radius vector is the area of the figure SPP'. If dt is infinitesimally small. PP' is a straight line $= rd\theta$ and SPP' is a triangle.

The area of the triangle $SPP' = dA = \dfrac{1}{2}r.rd\theta = \dfrac{1}{2}r^2\,d\theta$

This is the area swept out in a time dt.

$\therefore$ Rate at which area is swept $= \dfrac{dA}{dt} = \dfrac{1}{2}r^2.\dfrac{d\theta}{dt} = \dfrac{1}{2}r^2\,\dot{\theta}$

The angular momentum $J = mr^2\,\dot{\theta}$ and is a constant under a **central force.**

$\therefore \quad r^2\dot{\theta} = \dfrac{J}{m} = $ a constant under gravitational force or $\dfrac{1}{2}r^2\dot{\theta} = \dfrac{J}{2m} = $ a constant.

Hence $\dfrac{dA}{dt} = \dfrac{1}{2m}J = $ a constant which verifies the second law that *the radius vector joining the sun to the planet sweeps out equal areas in equal intervals of time.* In other words, *the areal velocity of a planet around the sun is constant.*

(*c*) **Third law.** As proved above $\dfrac{dA}{dt} = \dfrac{J}{2m}$ or $dA = \dfrac{J}{2m}dt$ or $\displaystyle\int_0^T dA = \int_0^T \dfrac{J}{2m}dt$

where T is the time period of one full revolution.

Integrating we get $A = \dfrac{JT}{2m}$ where $A = $ area of the ellipse

Now the area of the ellipse $= \pi ab$

where $a = $ semi-major axis and $b = $ semi-minor axis.

$$\therefore \qquad \frac{JT}{2m} = \pi ab \quad \text{or} \quad T = \frac{2\pi mab}{J}$$

Now

$$b = a\sqrt{1 - \varepsilon^2}$$

$$\therefore \qquad T = \frac{2\pi ma^2 \sqrt{1 - \varepsilon^2}}{J} \quad \text{or} \quad T^2 = \frac{4\pi^2 m^2 a^4 (1 - \varepsilon^2)}{J^2} \qquad \ldots(i)$$

As the origin is taken as the focus S, $2a = r_{max} + r_{min}$

Now

$$\frac{1}{r} = \frac{mc}{J^2}\left(1 + \frac{AJ^2}{mc}\cos\theta\right) = \frac{mc}{J^2}(1 + \varepsilon \cos\theta) \quad \ldots \text{[Eq. } (vi) \text{ Q. 7.14]}$$

$$\therefore \qquad \left(\frac{1}{r}\right)_{max} = \frac{mc}{J^2}(1 + \varepsilon)$$

or

$$(r)_{min} = \frac{J^2}{mc}\frac{1}{1 + \varepsilon}$$

Similarly

$$r_{max} = \frac{J^2}{mc}\frac{1}{1 - \varepsilon}$$

Hence

$$2a = \frac{J^2}{mc}\left[\frac{1}{1 + \varepsilon} + \frac{1}{1 - \varepsilon}\right]$$

or

$$a = \frac{J^2}{2mc}\left[\frac{2}{1 - \varepsilon^2}\right] = \frac{J^2}{mc(1 - \varepsilon^2)}$$

Now from (i) we have $T^2 = \dfrac{4\pi^2 m^2 a^4 (1 - \varepsilon^2)}{J^2} = \dfrac{4\pi^2 m^2 a^3}{J^2} \cdot \dfrac{J^2 (1 - \varepsilon^2)}{mc(1 - \varepsilon^2)} = \dfrac{4\pi^2 m a^3}{c}$

Hence

$$\frac{T^2}{a^3} = \frac{4\pi^2 m}{c} = \text{a constant} \qquad \ldots(ii)$$

Thus the square of the period of revolution of the planet about the sun divided by the cube of major axis of the orbit is a constant which is Kepler's third law.

or *The square of time period of revolution of a planet is proportional to the cube of semi-major axis of the orbit.*

$$T^2 \propto a^3$$

Q.7.24. Calculate the period of revolution of Neptune round the sun given that the diameter of the orbit is 30 times the diameter of the earth's orbit round the sun, both orbits being assumed to be circular.

Ans. Let a_1 and a_2 be the mean radii of the orbit of the earth and Neptune respectively.

$$\therefore \qquad \frac{a_2}{a_1} = 30$$

Period of revolution of earth T_1 = one year.

Let T_2 be the period of revolution of Neptune. Then according to Kepler's third law

$$\frac{T_2^2}{T_1^2} = \left(\frac{a_2}{a_1}\right)^3 \qquad \therefore T_2^2 = T_1^2\left(\frac{a_2}{a_1}\right)^3 = 30 \times 30 \times 30$$

or

$$T_2 = 30\sqrt{30} \text{ years} = 164.3 \text{ years}$$

Q.7.25. Using Kepler's laws show that the force between the sun and the planet obeys inverse square law.   (*P.U.* 2005; *Pbi. U.* 2004)

Ans. Suppose a planet of mass m is moving around the sun in a circular orbit of radius r due to the attractive force of the sun on the planet. This attractive force provides the necessary centripetal force which makes the planet move in a circular path.

If F is the force that the sun exerts on the planet, then

$$F = \frac{mv^2}{r} \qquad \qquad \qquad ...(i)$$

where v is the orbital velocity of the planet round the sun given by

$$v = \frac{2\pi r}{T} \qquad \qquad \qquad ...(ii)$$

where T is the period of revolution of the planet.

Substituting the value of v from Eq. (*ii*) in Eq. (*i*), we get

$$F = \frac{m}{r} \times \left(\frac{2\pi r}{T}\right)^2 = \frac{4\pi^2 mr}{T^2} \qquad \qquad ...(iii)$$

According to Kepler's third law

$$T^2 \propto r^3 \qquad \text{or} \qquad T^2 = kr^3$$

where k is a constant. Substituting the value of $T^2 = kr^3$ in Eq. (*iii*), we get

$$F = \frac{4\pi^2 mr}{kr^3} = \frac{4\pi^2 m}{m} \cdot \frac{1}{r^2}$$

But

$$\frac{4\pi^2 mr}{k} = \text{a constant}$$

$$\therefore \qquad F \propto \frac{1}{r^2}$$

Hence the force between the sun and the planet obeys inverse square law.

Q.7.26. Mark the correct answer.

(*i*) Gravitational forces are

    (*a*) strong   (*b*) weak   (*c*) short range   (*d*) non-central

                                                                                    (*P.U.*, 1993)

(*ii*) The velocity of the earth around the sun is   (*H.P.U.*, 1994, 1993)

    (*a*) 3 km/s   (*b*) 30 km/s   (*c*) 0.3 km/s   (*d*) 300 km/s

(*iii*) The force required to keep the satellite in the orbit is provided by   (*H.P.U.*, 1996, 1994)

    (*a*) gravitation   (*b*) electrostatic attraction

    (*c*) terminal velocity   (*d*) electromagnetic force

(*iv*) The condition for conservative force is   (*H.P.U.* 1995)

    (*a*) $\vec{F} = \vec{\nabla}.U$ (*b*) $\vec{F} = \vec{\nabla} \times U$ (*c*) $\vec{F} = -\vec{\nabla}U$ (*d*) $\vec{F} = -\nabla^2 U$

(*v*) What remains constant in a field of central force?   (*Meerut U.*, 2001, 2000)

    (*a*) potental energy   (*b*) kinetic energy   (*c*) angular momentum.

(*vi*) If the total energy of a particle is negative but not minimum, the path is   (*P.U.*, 1994)

    (*a*) hyperbolic   (*b*) circular   (*c*) elliptical   (*d*) parabolic (*vii*) If the eccentricity of a trajectory is zero, the trajectory is   (*P. U.*, 1994)

    (*a*) parabola   (*b*) circle   (*c*) hyperbola   (*d*) ellipse

(*viii*) A body under the action of inverse square force will follow an elliptic path if eccentricity is

                                                                          (*H.P.U.*, 1992)

    (*a*) $e = 0$ (*b*) $e = 1$ (*c*) $e > 1$ (*d*) $e < 1$

(*ix*) A body under the inverse square force will move along a circular path if total energy is

                                                                          (*H.P.U.*, 1994)

    (*a*) zero

    (*b*) positive

    (*c*) negative but equal to minimum potential energy

    (*d*) negative but greater than minimum potential energy.

(*x*) A body moving under attractive central force will describe a circle if its total energy is

    (*a*) zero   (*b*) positive   (*c*) negative   (*d*) $- mc^2 / 2J^2$

(*xi*) A satellite revolves round a planet of radius R in time T. What will be the period of revolution around another planet of radius $3R$?

    (*a*) $3T$ (*b*) $3\sqrt{3}\,T$ (*c*) $\sqrt{T}$ (*d*) $9T$

Ans.   (*i*) *b*   (*ii*) *c*   (*iii*) *a*   (*iv*) *c*

         (*v*) *c*   (*vi*) *c*   (*vii*) *b*   (*viii*) *d*

        (*ix*) *c*   (*x*) *d*   (*xi*) *b*

EXERCISE

1. A satellite revolves round a planet in an elliptical orbit. Its maximum and minimum distances from the planet are 1.5×10^7 m and 0.5×10^7 m respectively. If the speed of the satellite at the farthest point is 5×10^3 ms^{-1}, calculate the speed at the nearest point.

                                                                        [Ans. 15×10^{-3} ms^{-1}**]**

8

Rockets and Satellites

Q. 8.1. What is a rocket? Describe the principle of a rocket. Establish the following relation for a rocket

$$V = V_0 + V_e \log_e \frac{M_0}{M}$$

Calculate the burnt-out velocity when rocket starts from rest.

(Nagpur U. 2003; Cal. U. 2003; Meerut U. 2006, 2001; A.U., 1995)

Ans. Rocket. It is a device which is used to place a satellite into an orbit.

Principle of a rocket. Rocket propulsion is based on the *principle of conservation of momentum.* A rocket carries both the *fuel* and the *oxidiser* which burn in a combustion chamber within the rocket. When the rocket is *fired* the exhaust gases rush *downward* at a high speed and push the rocket *upward.* Thus the *thrust* on the rocket is supplied by the reaction forces of the high speed gases ejected at the rear.

To derive the relation for the propulsion, let us suppose that rocket along with its fuel has a mass M and is moving with a velocity $\vec{V}$ at any instant. Let this velocity be considered with respect to some *inertial frame of reference* which is assumed to be the earth in this discussion. After a time Δt, let the mass of fuel ejected be ΔM with an exhaust velocity $\vec{V_e}$ with respect to the *moving rocket.* The velocity $\vec{V_e}$ is constant and being *downward* relative to the rocket is an intrinsic *negative quantity.* The velocity of the ejected gases with respct to the earth is given by $\vec{V_0} = \vec{V} + \vec{V_e}$.

As mass ΔM has been fired out of the rocket, the mass of rocket decreases to $(M - \Delta M)$ after the exhaust and the velocity increases to $(\vec{V} + \Delta\vec{V})$ where $\Delta\vec{V}$ is a small increase in velocity.

In the inertial frame of earth

Initial momentum of rocket with fuel $\vec{p_1} = M\vec{V}$

Final momentum of rocket and exhaust gases

$$\vec{p_2} = (M - \Delta M)(\vec{V} + \Delta\vec{V}) + \Delta M \ (\vec{V} + \vec{V_e})$$

$$\therefore \quad \Delta\vec{p} = \vec{p_2} - \vec{p_1} = (M - \Delta M) \ (\vec{V} + \Delta\vec{V}) + \Delta M \ (\vec{V} + \vec{V_e}) - M\vec{V}$$

$$= M\Delta\vec{V} - \Delta M \Delta\vec{V} + \Delta M \vec{V_e}$$

or $\quad \Delta\vec{p} = M\Delta\vec{V} + \Delta M \vec{V_e}$ ...(i) neglecting $\Delta M \, \Delta \vec{V}$ being the product of two very small quantities as $\Delta M \to 0$ and $\Delta V \to 0$

Dividing (i) by Δt and taking limits when $\Delta t \to 0$, we have $\dfrac{d\vec{p}}{dt} = M \dfrac{d\vec{V}}{dt} + \vec{V_e} \dfrac{dM}{dt}$

We have considered ΔM the mass of the ejected gases as a positive quantity but as the mass of the rocket decreases with time, the expression $\dfrac{dM}{dt}$ is also an *intrinsic negative quantity* for the rocket system. Taking magnitudes, we get

$$\frac{dp}{dt} = M \frac{dV}{dt} + V_e \left(-\frac{dM}{dt} \right)$$

According to Newton's second law of motion as applied to the total system consisting of the rocket and ejected gases

$$\frac{d\vec{p}}{dt} = \vec{F_e}$$

where $\vec{F_e}$ is the external force acting on the system.

$\therefore$
$$\vec{F_e} = M \frac{d\vec{V}}{dt} - \vec{V_e} \frac{dM}{dt}$$

or
$$M \frac{d\vec{V}}{dt} = \vec{F_e} + \vec{V_e} \frac{dM}{dt} \qquad \qquad ...(ii)$$

$M \dfrac{d\vec{V}}{dt}$ gives the net force acting on the rocket.

Thrust on the rocket. If the rocket is moving in a region *outside the influence of the gravitational pull of the earth* and there is no air resistance or any other external force acting on the rocket, then $F_e = 0$.

Hence force acting on the rocket is given by $M \dfrac{d\vec{V}}{dt} = \vec{V_e} \dfrac{dM}{dt}$ $\qquad \qquad ...(iii)$

The quantity $V_e \dfrac{dM}{dt}$ is the *reaction force* exerted on the rocket by the exhaust of gases and gives the **thrust**.

$\therefore$ Rocket thrust $= \vec{V_e} \dfrac{dM}{dt}$

As both $\vec{V_e}$ and $\dfrac{dM}{dt}$ are intrinsic negative quantities $\vec{V_e} \dfrac{dM}{dt}$ is positive *i.e. the thrust on the rocket is in upward direction.*

Near the earth the upward thrust on the rocket is opposed by the external force of gravitation $\vec{Mg}$ = the weight of the rocket (neglecting friction etc.)

$\therefore$
$$\vec{F_e} = \vec{Mg}$$

Hence
$$M \frac{d\vec{V}}{dt} = \vec{V_e} \frac{dM}{dt} + \vec{Mg} \qquad \qquad ...(iv)$$

$\vec{Mg}$ is a negative quantity as g acts in the downward direction and has a magnitude $-g$.

In order to have a large thrust

(a) The velocity of exhaust $\vec{V_e}$, should be large and

(b) $\dfrac{dM}{dt}$, the rate at which the fuel is burnt and ejected should be large.

Equation of motion. To get the equation of motion of a rocket which is *far away* from the earth,

we have, rewriting equation (*iii*) $d\vec{V} = \vec{V_e} \dfrac{dM}{M}$ ...(*v*)

If M_0 is the initial mass of the rocket and fuel, $\vec{V_0}$ the initial velocity of the rocket and $\vec{V}$ and M
the instantaneous values of velocity and mass of the rocket respectively, then integrating equation (*v*)

We have $$\int_{v_0}^{v} d\vec{v} = \vec{V_e} \int_{M_0}^{M} \dfrac{dM}{M}$$

or $$\left[\vec{V}\right]_{v_0}^{v} = \vec{V_e} \left[\log_e M\right]_{M_0}^{M} \quad \text{or} \quad \vec{V} - \vec{V_0} = \vec{V_e} \log_e \dfrac{M}{M_0}$$

or $$\vec{V} = \vec{V_0} + \vec{V_e} \log_e \dfrac{M}{M_0}$$

Taking magnitudes, we get $V = V_0 - V_e \log_e \dfrac{M}{M_0}$ or $V = V_0 + V_e \log_e \dfrac{M_0}{M}$ ...(*vi*)

as direction of V_e is opposite to that of V.

Maximum (burnt out) velocity. If M_f is the mass of the (empty) rocket at *burnt out i.e.*, when

the entire fuel has been exhausted and $\vec{V_f}$ is the maximum or final velocity called *burnt out velocity*,
then from equation (*vi*), we have

$$\vec{V_f} - \vec{V_0} = -\vec{V_e} \log_e \dfrac{M_0}{M_f}$$ ...(*vii*)

The negative sign indicates that the velocity imparted to the rocket $\vec{V_f}$ is in a direction opposite
to the velocity of the ejected gases. If the rocket starts from rest $\vec{V_0} = 0$

$\therefore$ $$\vec{V_f} = -\vec{V_e} \log_e \dfrac{M_0}{M_f}$$ ...(*viii*)

Q. 8.2. Show that the rocket speed is twice the exhaust speed when $\dfrac{M_0}{M} = e^2$.

(*A.U., 1995*)

Ans. If V_0 is the speed of the rocket and V_e the exhaust speed, then $\dfrac{V_0}{V_e} = \log_e \dfrac{M_0}{M}$.

Now $\dfrac{M_0}{M} = e^2$ $\quad \therefore \dfrac{V_0}{V_e} = \log_e e^2 = 2$

i.e., the rocket speed is twice the exhaust speed.

**Q. 8.3. A 6000 kg rocket is set for vertical firing. If the gas exhaust speed is 1000 ms^{-1}, how
much gas must be ejected each second to supply the thrust needed (*i*) to overcome the weight of
the rocket and (*ii*) to give the rocket an initial upward acceleration of 20 ms^{-2}?**

Ans. (*i*) Here mass of the rocket and fuel $M = 6000$ kg

Exhaust velocity $V_e = -1000$ ms^{-1} Acceleration due to gravity $g = -9.8$ ms^{-2}

Net force on the rocket $M \dfrac{dV}{dt} = V_e \dfrac{dM}{dt} + Mg$

To overcome the weight of the rocket, the resultant force acting on it $M \dfrac{dV}{dt} = 0$

$\therefore \quad 0 = -1000 \dfrac{dM}{dt} - 6000 \times 9.8 \quad$ or $\dfrac{dM}{dt} = -6 \times 9.8 = -58.8$ kg s^{-1}

(ii) To give the rocket an initial upward acceleration of 20 ms^{-2}, the resultant force

$$M \dfrac{dV}{dt} = Ma = 20 \times M \quad \therefore \ 20 \times 6000 = -1000 \times \dfrac{dM}{dt} - 6000 \times 9.8$$

or $\quad \dfrac{dM}{dt} = -\dfrac{6000(20 + 9.8)}{1000} = -178.8$ kg s^{-1}

Q. 8.4. A rocket of mass 20 kg has 180 kg of fuel. The exhaust velocity of fuel is 1.60 km s^{-1}. Calculate the ultimate vertical speed gained by the rocket when the rate of consumption of fuel is 2 kg s^{-1}.

Ans. If V_f is the final velocity of the rocket when the entire fuel has been exhausted, V_e the

exhaust velocity, and rocket starts from rest, then $V_f = -V_e \log_e \dfrac{M_0}{M_f}$

where M_0 is the initial mass of rocket and fuel and M_f the mass of the empty rocket.

Now $\ M_0 = 20 + 180 = 200$ kg

Consumption of fuel $= 2$ kg s^{-1}

Time to consume whole of fuel $= \dfrac{180}{2} = 90$ s

Exhaust velocity $V_e = -1.6$ kms$^{-1} = -1.6 \times 10^3$ ms^{-1}

$\therefore V_f = 1.6 \times 10^3 \times 2.3026 \log_{10} \dfrac{200}{20} = 3.684 \times 10^3$ ms$^{-1} = 3.684$ km s^{-1}

Q. 8.5. A rocket starts vertically upward with a speed of v_0. Show that its speed at a height h is given by $v_0^2 - v^2 = \dfrac{2gh}{1 + h/R}$ where R is the radius of earth and g is acceleration due to gravity at earth's surface.

Ans. Let m be the mass of the rocket and M that of the earth, then

Kinetic energy of the rocket at earth's surface $= \dfrac{1}{2} m v_0^2$

and Potential energy of the rocket at earth's surface $= -\dfrac{GmM}{R}$

Negative sign indicates that it is a force of attraction.

When the rocket reaches a height h above the surface of earth, its

Kinetic energy $= \dfrac{1}{2} m v^2$ and potential energy $= \dfrac{-GmM}{R + h}$

According to the law of conservation of energy, we have

$$\dfrac{1}{2} m v_0^2 - \dfrac{GmM}{R} = \dfrac{1}{2} m v^2 - \dfrac{GmM}{R + h}$$

or $\quad v_0^2 - v^2 = \dfrac{2GM}{R} - \dfrac{2GM}{R + h} = 2GM \left[\dfrac{1}{R} - \dfrac{1}{R + h} \right]$

If g is the acceleration due to gravity on earth's surface, then $g = \dfrac{GM}{R^2}$

or $GM = gR^2$ $\therefore$ $v_0{}^2 - v^2 = 2R^2 g \left[\dfrac{1}{R} - \dfrac{1}{R+h} \right] = \dfrac{2gh}{1 + h/R}$

Q. 8.6. A rocket is going from earth to sun. Find the point at which it becomes weightless. The mass of the earth is 6×10^{24} kg, that of sun 2×10^{30} kg and distance between them 1.5×10^{11} m.   *(Kerala U., 2001)*

Ans. The rocket will become weightless when the gravitational force on the rocket due to the sun is equal and opposite to the gravitational force on the rocket due to the earth. Let x be the distance of such a point from the earth and $(r - x)$ from the sun where $r = 1.5 \times 10^{11}$ m, the distance of the sun from the earth.

Now   Mass of Sun $= M_S = 2 \times 10^{30}$ Kg

               Mass of earth $= M_E = 6 \times 10^{24}$ Kg

Let m be the mass of the rocket, then

$$\dfrac{G M_E \, m}{x^2} = \dfrac{G M_S \, m}{(r - x)^2}$$

or $\dfrac{(r - x)^2}{x^2} = \dfrac{M_S}{M_E}$ or $\dfrac{r - x}{x} = \sqrt{\dfrac{M_S}{M_E}} = \sqrt{\dfrac{2 \times 10^{30}}{6 \times 10^{24}}} = \dfrac{10^3}{\sqrt{3}}$

or $\dfrac{r}{x} - 1 = \dfrac{10^3}{\sqrt{3}}$ or $\dfrac{r}{x} = \dfrac{10^3}{\sqrt{3}} + 1 = \dfrac{\sqrt{3} + 10^3}{\sqrt{3}}$

$\therefore$ $x = \dfrac{r\sqrt{3}}{\sqrt{3} + 10^3} = \dfrac{1.5 \times 10^{11} \sqrt{3}}{\sqrt{3} + 10^3} = \dfrac{1.5 \times 1.732 \times 10^{11}}{1.732 + 1000}$

or $x = 2.59 \times 10^8$ m.

Q. 8.7. A rocket has a velocity of 50 km s^{-1} when at a distance of 10,000 km from the centre of earth. What will be its velocity when it is 50,000 km away? Radius of earth is 6.38×10^6 m.

Ans. If v_1 is the velocity of the rocket when at a distance of 10,000 km from the centre of earth, then $R_1 = 10,000$ km $= 10^7$ m; $v_1 = 50$ kms$^{-1} = 50 \times 10^3$ ms^{-1}

If v_2 is the velocity of the rocket when at a distance of 50,000 km from the centre of earth, then $R_2 = 50,000$ km $= 5 \times 10^7$ m.

$\therefore$ $v_1{}^2 - v_2{}^2 = 2R^2 g \left[\dfrac{1}{R_1} - \dfrac{1}{R_2} \right]$ [For proof see **Q. 8.5**]

or $(50 \times 10^3)^2 - v_2{}^2 = 2 \times (6.38 \times 10^6)^2 \times 9.8 \left[\dfrac{1}{10^7} - \dfrac{1}{5 \times 10^7} \right] = 63.825 \times 10^6$

or $v_2{}^2 = 2500 \times 10^6 - 63.825 \times 10^6 = 2436.2 \times 10^6$

$\therefore$ $v_2 = 49.36 \times 10^3$ ms^{-1} $= 49.36$ kms^{-1}

Q. 8.8. (a) What is an artificial satellite. Calculate the minimum velocity and period of revolution of an artificial satellite at a height h from the surface of the earth.

(b) A small artificial satellite is revolving round the earth very close to it. If the radius of the earth is 6400 km and acceleration due to gravity 9.8 m sec^{-2}, find the period of revolution of the satellite.   *(Cal. U., 1991)*

Ans. Artificial satellite. The earth revolves round the sun and the moon revolves round the earth. The earth is, therefore, said to be a satellite of the sun and the moon a satellite of the earth. These are *natural* satellites. If a body is hurled into space with the help of powerful rockets so that it begins circling round the earth, it is known as an *artificial satellite* of the earth.

Minimum Velocity. The satellite while circling round the globe or earth at a height h is in dynamic equilibrium under the action of two forces

(*i*) Gravitational forces $= \dfrac{GmM}{(R+h)^2}$ acting inward towards the centre of the earth, where R is the radius and M the mass of the earth and m the mass of the satellite.

(*ii*) The fictitious centrifugal force $F = m\,(R+h)\,\omega^2 = \dfrac{mv^2}{R+h}$

acting outwards away from the centre of the earth, where ω is the angular velocity and v the linear (orbital) velocity of the satellite.

$$\therefore \qquad m\,(R+h)\,\omega^2 = \frac{GMm}{(R+h)^2} \text{ or } \omega^2 = \frac{GM}{(R+h)^3} \text{ or } \omega = \left[\frac{GM}{(R+h)^3}\right]^{1/2} \qquad \qquad ...(i)$$

Hence orbital velocity $v = (R+h)\,\omega = \left[\dfrac{GM}{R+h}\right]^{1/2}$ $\qquad\qquad ...(ii)$

When the satellite is on the earth it is attracted by a force $mg = \dfrac{GmM}{R^2} \quad \therefore\; GM = gR^2$

Substituting in (*i*) we get $\omega = \left[\dfrac{gR^2}{(R+h)^3}\right]^{1/2}$ $\qquad\qquad ...(iii)$

and orbital velocity $\qquad v = \left[\dfrac{gR^2}{(R+h)}\right]^{1/2}$ $\qquad\qquad ...(iv)$

This is the minimum velocity of the artificial satellite at a height h from the surface of the earth.

The time of revolution $\quad T = \dfrac{2\pi}{\omega} = \dfrac{2\pi(R+h)}{v} = 2\pi\,(R+h)\sqrt{\dfrac{R+h}{GM}}$ $\qquad\qquad ...(v)$

$$= \frac{2\pi}{R}\sqrt{\frac{(R+h)^3}{g}} \qquad\qquad ...(vi)$$

(*b*) **Satellite very close to the earth.** When the satellite is very close to the surface of the earth, h is very nearly equal to zero and $R+h$ is approximately equal to R.

Substituting $R+h = R$ in (*iii*), (*iv*), (*v*) we have $\omega = \sqrt{\dfrac{g}{R}}$; $v = \sqrt{gR}$ $\qquad\qquad ...(vii)$

and $T = \dfrac{2\pi}{\omega} = 2\pi\sqrt{\dfrac{R}{g}}$

$v = \sqrt{gR}$ is the minimum velocity of the satellite when it is very close to the surface of the earth.

Now radius of the earth $R = 6400$ km $= 6.4 \times 10^6$ m

$$g = 9.8 \text{ ms}^{-2}$$

$\therefore$ Time period of revolution $T = \dfrac{2\pi}{\omega} = 2\pi\sqrt{\dfrac{R}{g}}$

$$= 2 \times \frac{22}{7} \times \sqrt{\frac{6.4 \times 10^6}{9.8}} = 5080 \text{ sec} = 1.41 \text{ hour.}$$

Q. 8.9. An artificial satellite moves in a circular orbit around the earth at a height $\frac{1}{2} R_e$ from the surface of the earth where R_e is the radius of the earth. Calculate the period of revolution. $R_e = 6.38 \times 10^6$ m; $g = 9.8$ ms^{-2}. *(Osm. U. 1997)*

Ans. Here height of the satellite from the surface of the earth

$$h = \frac{1}{2} R_e$$

Radius of the earth $R_e = 6.38 \times 10^6$ m, $g = 9.8$ ms^{-2}

Period of revolution $T = \dfrac{2\pi (R_e + h)}{v}$

Now $\qquad v = \left[\dfrac{g R_e^2}{R_e + h} \right]^{1/2} = \left[\dfrac{g R_e^2}{R_e + \dfrac{R_e}{2}} \right] = \left[\dfrac{2}{3} g R_e \right]^{1/2}$

$$= \left[\frac{2}{3} \times 9.8 \times 6.38 \times 10^6 \right]^{1/2} = 6.46 \times 10^3 \text{ ms}^{-1}$$

$$\therefore \qquad T = \frac{2\pi (6.38 \times 10^6 + 3.19 \times 10^6)}{6.46 \times 10^3} = 9312 \text{ s}$$

$$= 2.587 \text{ hour.}$$

Q. 8.10. A satellite is orbiting very close to a planet of density $8 \times 10^{+3}$ kg m^{-3}. If gravitational constant $G = 6.67 \times 10^{-11}$ Nm^2 kg^{-2}, find the time period of the satellite. *(Luck. U., 1992)*

Ans. If R is the radius of the planet and ρ its density, then

Mass of planet $M = \dfrac{4}{3} \pi R^3 \rho$

Orbital velocity $v_0 = \sqrt{\dfrac{GM}{R}} = 2R \sqrt{\dfrac{\pi \rho G}{3}}$

Also $\qquad v_0 = \dfrac{2\pi R}{T} \qquad \therefore \qquad \dfrac{2\pi R}{T} = 2R \sqrt{\dfrac{\pi \rho G}{3}}$

or $\qquad T = \sqrt{\dfrac{3\pi}{\rho G}} = \sqrt{\dfrac{3 \times 3.142}{8 \times 10^3 \times 6.67 \times 10^{-11}}}$

$$= 4202 \text{ s} = 1.167 \text{ hour.}$$

Q. 8.11. (*a*) **Calculate the height of an artificial satellite if its time period of revolutions is known.**

(*b*) **What is geo-stationary satellite? Calculate the altitude of an artificial satellite if it is always above a certain place on the earth's surface assuming that its orbit is circular. Mean radius of the earth = 6400 km and g = 9.8 m/sec.** *(Gharwal U. 1999)*

Ans. (*a*) **Altitude of a satellite.** If T is the time period of revolution of a satellite at a height h above the surface of the earth, then from relation (*iii*) Q. 8.8 we have $\omega = \dfrac{2\pi}{T} = \left[\dfrac{gR^2}{(R + h)^3} \right]^{1/2}$

or $\qquad \dfrac{gR^2}{(R+h)^3} = \dfrac{4\pi^2}{T^2} \qquad$ or $(R+h)^3 = \dfrac{gR^2 T^2}{4\pi^2} \qquad$ or $R+h = \left\{ \dfrac{gR^2 T^2}{4\pi^2} \right\}^{1/3}$

$$\therefore \qquad h = \left\{ \dfrac{gR^2 T^2}{4\pi^2} \right\}^{1/3} - R \qquad\qquad\qquad ...(i)$$

(b) Geo-stationary satellite. *It is a satellite which revolves round the earth at a suitable height with the same velocity and in the same direction as earth does about its own axis.* The relative velocity of such a satellite with respect to the earth is zero. The apparent position of such a satellite, therefore, appears stationary to an observer on the surface of earth. The time period of such a satellite is the same as that of earth about its own axis and is equal to the length of the day *i.e.*, 24 hrs.

The height of such a satellite from the surface of the earth is given by $h = \left\{ \dfrac{gR^2 T^2}{4\pi^2} \right\}^{1/3} - R$.

where $T = 24 \times 60 \times 60 = 86400$ sec. As calculated below, the value of $h = 35950$ km.

This satellite at a distance of 35950 km is said to be in a synchronous orbit at the equator. Such a satellite if placed over Atlantic could be seen by the American continent. Europe and Africa and thus can be used for communication purpose for all the 24 hours. Three such satellites placed at 120 degree interval about the equator can effectively cover the whole globe except some regions at the north and south poles. Such systems can carry a number of television programmes and thus can relay to the whole world. The height of a geostationary satellite is a constant.

Height of a geostationary satellite. Substituting the values of g, R and $T = 86400$ sec, in (i), we have

$$h = \left[\dfrac{9.80 \times (6400 \times 10^3)^2 \times 86400^2}{4\pi^2} \right]^{1/3} - 6400 \times 10^3$$

$$= 42350 \times 10^3 - 6400 \times 10^3 = 35950 \times 10^3 \text{ m} = 35950 \text{ km}.$$

Q. 8.12. Calculate the eccentricity of the orbit of a satellite projected horizontally with a velocity v from a height h above the surface of the earth. Hence find the velocity of launch for the orbit to be circular and close to the earth.

Ans. Eccentricity. The magnitude of the angular momentum of a satellite of mass m launched *horizontally* from a height h above the surface of the earth of radius R and mass M with a velocity v is given by $\qquad\qquad\qquad J = mv\,(R+h) \qquad\qquad\qquad ...(i)$

The total energy E of the satellite is then given by

$$E = \dfrac{1}{2} mv^2 + U = \dfrac{1}{2} mv^2 - \dfrac{GMm}{R+h} = \dfrac{1}{2} mv^2 - \dfrac{mgR^2}{R+h} \qquad\qquad ...(ii)$$

If the value of E is negative $(E < 0)$ the satellite will go into an elliptic orbit of eccentricity ε given

by $\varepsilon = \left[1 + \dfrac{2J^2 E}{mc^2} \right]^{1/2}$ $\qquad\qquad$ [For proof see relation (vii), Q. 7.14]

Substituting the value of J from (i), E from (ii) and $c = GMm = mg\,R^2$, we get

$$\varepsilon = \left(1 + \dfrac{2 \left(\dfrac{1}{2} mv^2 - \dfrac{mgR^2}{R+h} \right) m^2 v^2 (R+h)^2}{m^3 g^2 R^4} \right)$$

$$= \left\{ 1 + \left[\frac{v^2 (R + h)}{gR^2} \right]^2 - 2 \left[\frac{v^2 (R + h)}{gR^2} \right] \right\}^{1/2} \qquad \therefore \ \varepsilon = 1 - \frac{v^2 (R + h)}{gR^2} \qquad \qquad ...(iii)$$

Circular orbit. If the satellite launched horizontally is to move in a circular orbit, then $\varepsilon = 0$.

$$\therefore \quad \varepsilon = 1 - \frac{v^2 (R + h)}{gR^2} = 0 \quad \text{or} \quad \frac{v^2 (R + h)}{gR^2} = 1 \quad \text{or} \quad v = \sqrt{\frac{gR^2}{R + h}} \qquad \qquad ...(iv)$$

This gives the value of the velocity v with which the satellite must be launched at a height h above the surface of the earth so that its orbit is circular.

Orbit close to the earth. If the satellite is launched in a circular orbit close to the earth, $h = 0$ and $v = \sqrt{gR}$.

This also gives the *minimum* value of the velocity with which a body must be projected so that it becomes a satellite of the earth.

If $R = 6.4 \times 10^6$ m and $g = 9.8$ m/sec^2; $v = \sqrt{gR} = \sqrt{9.8 \times 6.4 \times 10^6}$

$$= 7.92 \times 10^3 \text{ m/sec} = 7.92 \text{ km/sec}.$$

Thus for a body to be a satellite of the earth it should be projected with a velocity greater than $v = 7.92$ km/sec but less than 11.2 km/sec (escape velocity).

Q. 8.13. (a) What do you understand by the terms perigee and apogee as applied to an earth satellite?

(b) Show that the ratio of the velocity of the satellite at perigee to its velocity at apogee is inversely proportional to the ratio of its distances from the earth at these points.

Ans. (a) Suppose a satellite is moving round the earth in an elliptic orbit as shown in Fig. 8.1 with earth as one of its foci.

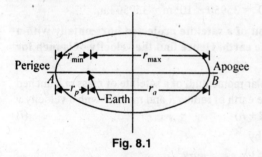

The point A closest to the earth on the trajectory of the satellite is called *perigee* whereas the point B farthest from the earth is called *apogee*. Every particle whose perigee distance is greater than the radius of the earth is its satellite whereas a particle whose perigee distance is less than R is called a projectile.

Fig. 8.1

(b) For a particle moving under a central force as in the case of earth satellite, the angular momentum

$$J = mr^2 \dot{\theta} = mrv = \text{a constant} \qquad \qquad ...(i)$$

where m is the mass of the particle, r its radial distance and v the corresponding velocity at a point on its trajectory.

At the perigee the distance of the satellite from the earth has a minimum value and therefore the velocity is maximum. At the apogee the distance of the satellite has the maximum value and therefore, the velocity is a minimum.

If we denote the distance from the earth and velocity at perigee as r_p and v_p and the corresponding values for apogee as r_a and v_a, then (i) $mr_p v_p = mr_a v_a$ or $\dfrac{v_p}{v_a} = \dfrac{r_a}{r_p}$

In other words, the ratio of the velocity of the satellite at the perigee to its velocity at the apogee is inversely proportional to the distances of these points from the earth which is the focus of the elliptic orbit.

Q. 8.14 (*a*) **Calculate the maximum velocity with which a body may be projected so that it may become a satellite of the earth. Show that it is $\sqrt{2}$ times the minimum velocity with which it may be projected to move in a circular orbit close to the earth.**

(*b*) **Show that the binding energy of a satellite is** $\dfrac{GMm}{2(R+h)}$.   (*Meerut. U.* 2001)

Ans. (*a*) Consider a body of mass m lying at a distance x from the centre of the earth of radius R and mass M. The force with which it is attracted by the earth $= -\dfrac{GMm}{x^2}$

If this mass is moved through a distance dx away from the earth, then

Work done $= -\dfrac{GMm}{x^2}\,dx$

The total work done in taking the mass from a point at the height h above the surface of the earth to infinity is given by $\displaystyle\int_{R+h}^{\infty} -\dfrac{GMm}{x^2}\,dx = \left[\dfrac{GMm}{x}\right]_{R+h}^{\infty}$

$$= -\dfrac{GMm}{R+h}$$

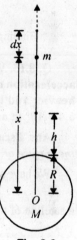

Fig. 8.2

This gives the potential energy of the mass m at a height h above the surface of the earth

$$\therefore \qquad U = -\dfrac{GMm}{R+h} \qquad\qquad\qquad ...(i)$$

If the point of launching is at a height h above the surface of the earth and the mass is imparted a velocity v at the point of launching so that its kinetic energy $E_k = \dfrac{1}{2}mv^2$, then

Total energy $E = E_k + U = \dfrac{1}{2}mv^2 - \dfrac{GMm}{R+h}$ \qquad ...(ii)

For the mass to become a satellite of the earth it should move in a closed orbit the condition for which is that its total energy E should be negative $E < 0$.

$$\therefore \qquad \dfrac{1}{2}mv^2 < \dfrac{GMm}{R+h} \quad \text{or } v < \sqrt{\dfrac{2GM}{R+h}}$$

The acceleration due to gravity on the surface of the earth $g = \dfrac{GM}{R^2}$ or $GM = gR^2$

$$\therefore \qquad v < \sqrt{\dfrac{2gR^2}{R+h}}$$

Thus the maximum velocity with which a body may be projected so that it becomes a satellite of the earth should be less than $\sqrt{\dfrac{2gR^2}{R+h}}$.

For the launching from a point on the surface of the earth $h = 0$ and maximum velocity

$$v_{max} = \sqrt{2gR}$$

The minimum velocity with which a body may be projected to move in a circular orbit close to earth is given by $v_{min} = \sqrt{gR}$ \qquad $\therefore \dfrac{v_{max}}{v_{min}} = \sqrt{2}$

(b) **Binding energy of a satellite.** *The energy required to remove a satellite from its orbit around the earth to infinity is called the binding energy of the satellite.*

Binding energy is equal to negative value of total energy of a satellite in its orbit.

The potential energy of a satellite of mass m revolving round the earth at a height h,

$$U = \frac{-GMm}{R + h}$$

The orbital velocity $v = \sqrt{\dfrac{GM}{R + h}}$ [Eq (ii) Q. 8.8]

$\therefore$ Kinetic energy $k = \dfrac{1}{2} mv^2 = \dfrac{1}{2} m \dfrac{GM}{R + h} = \dfrac{GMm}{2 (R + h)}$

and total energy $E = U + k = -\dfrac{GMm}{R + h} + \dfrac{GMm}{2(R + h)}$

$$= -\frac{GMm}{2(R + h)}$$

$\therefore$ Binding energy $= -E = \dfrac{GMm}{2(R + h)}$

Q. 8.15. What is escape velocity? Derive an expression for escape velocity in terms of acceleration due to gravity and radius of the earth. Will the escape velocity be the same for heavier and lighter bodies? Calculate the value of escape velocity if the radius of earth is 6.4×10^6 m and $g = 9.81$ ms^{-2}.   (*Burd. U.* 1991; *Cal. U.* 1991; *Meerut U.* 2003, 1992)

Ans. Escape velocity. *The minimum velocity with which a body is projected so that it escapes the surface of a planet without further propulsion is known as escape velocity.*

We have seen that the maximum velocity with which a body may be projected so that it becomes a satellite of the earth should be less than $\sqrt{\dfrac{2gR^2}{R + h}}$. When the velocity of projection is equal to or greater than $\sqrt{\dfrac{2gR^2}{R + h}}$ the body will escape from the gravitaional field of the earth (or a planet).

Therefore $\sqrt{\dfrac{2gR^2}{R + h}}$ is called the escape velocity of the body from a height h above the surface of the earth and is denoted by $(v_e)_h$.

If the launch point is on the surface of the earth $h = 0$ and the escape velocity

$$(v_e)_0 = \sqrt{2gR} \qquad \therefore (v_e)_h = (v_e)_0 \sqrt{\frac{R}{R + h}}$$

The escape velocity is different for different planets. It is about 11 km/sec for the surface of the earth, 60 km/sec for Jupiter and 2.5 km/sec for the moon. In the above calculations the loss of energy due to friction etc. has been neglected.

As the escape velocity $(v_e)_0 = \sqrt{2gR}$, it is independent of the mass of the body to be projected. Hence the escape velocity is the same for heavier as well as lighter bodies.

Escape velocity $(v_e)_0 = \sqrt{2gR} = \sqrt{2 \times 9.81 \times 6.4 \times 10^6}$

$$= 11.2 \times 10^3 \text{ m/sec} = 11.2 \text{ km/sec}.$$

Q. 8.16. A satellite is moving in a nearly circular orbit around the earth. Show that the air friction will increase the velocity of the satellite. *(G.N.D.U. 2004)*

Ans. When a satellite revolves around the earth of mass M, the centripetal force required is provided by the gravitational force of the earth

i.e.
$$\frac{mv_0^2}{r} = \frac{GMm}{r^2}$$

or $mv_0^2 r = GMm$ or $(mv_0 r) v_0 = GMm$.

But $mv_0\, r = L$, the angular momentum of the satellite of mass m moving with a linear velocity v_0 in a circular orbit of radius r

$\therefore$
$$Lv_0 = GMm = \text{a constant} \qquad \qquad ...(i)$$

As no external torque is acting on the satellite

i.e. $\qquad \tau = 0, \qquad L = \text{constant}$

But air friction reduces L. Therefore according to Eq. (*i*) v_0 increases *i.e.* air friction will increase the velocity of the satellite.

Q. 8.17. Calculate the velocity with which a body must be thrown vertically upward from the surface of earth so that it may reach a height of $10\,R$ where R the radius of earth is equal to 6.4×10^6 m, mass of earth $= 6 \times 10^{24}$ kg and $G = 6.7 \times 10^{-11}$ N m^2 kg^{-2}. *(Luck. U., 1993)*

Ans. Distance of point from centre of earth $= R + 10\,R = 11\,R$

Work done in taking a mass m from the surface to $10\,R$ is given by

$$\int_R^{11R} -\frac{GMm}{x^2}\, dx = \left[\frac{GMm}{x}\right]_R^{11R} = GMm\left[\frac{1}{11R} - \frac{1}{R}\right] = -\frac{10}{11}\frac{GMm}{R}$$

If v is the velocity of projection to reach a height $10\,R$, then

$$\frac{1}{2}mv^2 = -\frac{10}{11}\frac{GMm}{R}$$

or
$$v = \left[\frac{20}{11} \times \frac{6.67 \times 10^{-11} \times 6 \times 10^{24}}{6.4 \times 10^6}\right]^{1/2}$$

$$= 10.687 \times 10^3 \text{ ms}^{-1} = 10.687 \text{ kms}^{-1}$$

Q. 8.18. A rocket is moving upward with acceleration $3\,g$. Calculate the effective weight of an astronaut sitting in the rocket when his actual weight is 75 kg. *(A.U., 1995)*

Ans. If M is the mass of astronaut sitting in the rocket, the forces acting on it are:

(*i*) Weight Mg acting in the downward direction

(*ii*) Reaction R of the floor in the upward direction

If the rocket is moving up with an acceleration a, then $R - Mg = Ma$

or $\qquad$ Apparent weight $\quad R = M(a + g)$

Now $\quad a = 3g$ and $M = 75$ kg $\qquad \therefore R = 75\ (3g + g) = 300\ g \quad$ N $= 300$ kg.

Q. 8.19. With what initial velocity a body should be projected from the earth so that it may (*i*) just escape the gravitational field of the earth and (*ii*) revolve in a circular orbit very close to the earth? Radius of earth $= 6400$ km and $g = 9.8$ ms^{-2}. *(Delhi, 1990)*

Ans. Here $R = 6400$ km $= 6.4 \times 10^6$ m, $g = 9.8$ ms^{-2}

(i) The maximum velocity with which a body may be projected so that it just escapes the gravitational field is given by $v = \sqrt{2gR} = \sqrt{2 \times 9.8 \times 6.4 \times 10^6}$

$$= 11.2 \times 10^3 \text{ ms}^{-1} = 11.2 \text{ kms}^{-1}$$

(ii) The minimum velocity with which the body may be projected so that it moves in a circular orbit close to earth is given by $v = \sqrt{gR} = \sqrt{9.8 \times 6.4 \times 10^6}$

$$= 7.92 \times 10^3 \text{ ms}^{-1} = 7.92 \text{ kms}^{-1}$$

Q. 8.20. Moon has no atmosphere. Why?   (*Kerala U.* 2001)

Ans. Moon has no atmosphere. At N.T.P. the root mean square velocity for hydrogen molecules is nearly 1.92 km /sec, for oxygen 0.48 km/sec and for nitrogen slightly higher than this. This is much less than the escape velocity of 11.2 km/sec from the surface of the earth so that earth's atmosphere is retained. Some leakage of hydrogen does take place due to its higher R.M.S veloctiy. Thus there is excess of oxygen and Nitrogen in earth's atmosphere.

The escape velocity on the surface of moon is 2.38 km/sec. Therefore nearly all molecules of hydrogen have escaped out from moon's atmosphere and only rare molecules of oxygen, nitrogen and other gases have been left.

This is why moon has no atmosphere.

Q. 8.21. Mark the correct answer.

(i) The minimum velocity with which a body may be projected to become a satellite of the earth is

   (a) 11.2 km/sec   (b) 7.92 km/sec   (c) 10.5 km/sec   (d) 5.8 km/sec

(ii) The value of escape velocity is

   (a) 11.2 km/sec   (b) 7.92 km/sec   (c) 22.4 km/sec   (d) 15.94 km/sec

(iii) The time period of a geostationary satellite is

   (a) 12 hours   (b) 6 hours   (c) 24 hours   (d) 18 hours.

(iv) The orbit of an artificial satellite is

   (a) hyperbolic   (b) parabolic   (c) elliptic   (d) none of these.

(v) If a satellite is launched into a circular orbit close to the earth, its velocity is

   (a) $\sqrt{2gR}$ (b) $\sqrt{gR}$ (c) gR (d) $2gR$

(vi) A satellite is revolving round the earth with kinetic energy E. How much kinetic energy should be given to it so that it escapes from the earth?

   (a) $\dfrac{E}{\sqrt{2}}$ (b) $\dfrac{E}{2}$ (c) E (d) $2E$

Ans.   (i) b   (ii) a   (iii) c   (iv) c   (v) b   (vi) c

EXERCISE

1.   The world's first artificial satellite was reported to be circling the globe at a distance of 900 km. Calculate its minimum velocity and period of revolution. Radius of the earth = 6.4×10^6 metres and $g = 9.8$ m/sec².   (*Bang.U.* 2000)

[**Ans.** (i) 7.416 m/sec; (ii) 1 hr 43 min 4 sec]

9

Elastic and Inelastic Collisions

Q. 9.1. Define centre of mass. Show that when no external force acts on a body the acceleration of the centre of mass is zero and its velocity is a constant.

(*M.D.U.* 2006; *G.N.D.U.* 2002; *Indore U.* 2001; *P.U.* 1995; *H.P.U.* 1994)

Ans. Centre of mass. Suppose we have a system of total mass M consisting of n particles or mass points of masses $m_1, m_2 \ldots\ldots m_i \ldots\ldots\ldots m_n$ whose position vectors are represented by $\vec{r_1}, \vec{r_2} \ldots\ldots\ldots \vec{r_i} \ldots\ldots \vec{r_n}$ respectively, then the centre of mass of the system is defined as the point whose position vector $\vec{R}$ is given by

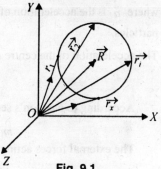

$$\vec{R} = \frac{m_1 \vec{r_1} + m_2 \vec{r_2} + \ldots\ldots + m_i \vec{r_i} + \ldots\ldots + m_n \vec{r_n}}{m_1 + m_2 + \ldots\ldots\ldots + m_i + \ldots\ldots + m_n}$$

$$= \frac{\sum m_i \vec{r_i}}{\sum m_i} = \frac{\sum m_i \vec{r_i}}{M}$$

as $\sum m_i = M$ the total mass of the system. If the centre of mass coincides with the origin of the system, then

$$\vec{R} = 0 \text{ vector}, \quad \sum m_i \vec{r_i} = 0 \text{ vector}$$

Fig. 9.1

The centre of mass is thus defined as a point in space such that the vector sum of the moments of the mass points around it is zero.

Velocity of centre of mass. Let us consider the motion of the system consisting of n particles and total mass M assuming that the mass of the system remains constant *i.e.*, no mass enters or leaves the system.

$$\therefore \qquad M\vec{R} = \sum m_i \vec{r_i} = m_1 \vec{r_1} + m_2 \vec{r_2} + \ldots\ldots + \ldots + m_i \vec{r_i} + \ldots\ldots + m_n \vec{r_n}$$

Differentiating with respect to time, we get

$$M\frac{d\vec{R}}{dt} = m_1 \frac{d\vec{r_1}}{dt} + m_2 \frac{d\vec{r_2}}{dt} + \ldots\ldots + m_i \frac{d\vec{r_i}}{dt} + \ldots\ldots + m_n \frac{d\vec{r_n}}{dt}$$

But $\frac{d\vec{R}}{dt} = \vec{V}$ the velocity of centre of mass

and $\frac{d\vec{r_1}}{dt} = \vec{v_1}, \frac{d\vec{r_2}}{dt} = \vec{v_2} \ldots\ldots \frac{d\vec{r_i}}{dt} = \vec{v_i}$ and $\frac{d\vec{r_n}}{dt} = v_n$

which represent the velocities of individual particles.

$$\therefore \quad M\vec{V} = m_1\vec{v_1} + m_2\vec{v_2} + ... + m_i\vec{v_i} + ... + m_n\vec{v_n} = \Sigma m_i\vec{v_i} \qquad ...(i)$$

The velocity of centre of mass is given by

$$\vec{V} = \frac{m_1\vec{v_1} + m_2\vec{v_2} + ... + m_i\vec{v_i} + ... + m_n\vec{v_n}}{M} = \frac{\Sigma m_i\vec{v_i}}{M} \qquad ...(ii)$$

From relation (i) we also find the *vector sum of the linear momenta of the individual particles i.e., the total linear momentum of the system is equal to the product of the total mass of the system and the velocity of centre of mass.*

In the absence of any external force, the total linear momentum of the system $\vec{P}$ is conserved

$$\therefore \quad M\vec{V} = \Sigma m_i\vec{v_i} = \vec{P} = \text{a constant}$$

or $\qquad \vec{V} = \text{a constant vector}$

Hence the velocity of the centre of mass of a system remains constant if no external force is applied to it.

Acceleration. Differentiating equation (i) with respect to time t, we have

$$M\frac{d\vec{V}}{dt} = m_1\frac{d\vec{v_1}}{dt} + m_2\frac{d\vec{v_2}}{dt} + ... + m_i\frac{d\vec{v_i}}{dt} + ... + m_n\frac{d\vec{v_n}}{dt}$$

or $\qquad M\vec{a} = m_1\vec{a_1} + m_2\vec{a_2} + ... + m_i\vec{a_i} + ... + m_n\vec{a_n}$

where $\vec{a}$ is the acceleration of the centre of mass and $\vec{a_1}, \vec{a_2}$ etc. are the accelerations of individual particles.

The acceleration of the centre of mass is given by

$$\vec{a} = \frac{m_1\vec{a_1} + m_2\vec{a_2} + ... + m_i\vec{a_i} + ... + m_n\vec{a_n}}{M} = \frac{\Sigma m_i\vec{a_i}}{M} \qquad ...(iii)$$

According to Newton's second law of motion

$$m_1\vec{a_1} = \vec{F_1}, m_2\vec{a_2} = \vec{F_2}.......m_i\vec{a_i} = \vec{F_i}.........m_n\vec{a_n} = \vec{F_n}$$

The external forces acting on different particles

$$\therefore \quad M\vec{a} = \vec{F_1} + \vec{F_2} + ... + \vec{F_i} + ... + \vec{F_n}$$

Thus the product of the total mass of a system and the vector acceleration of the centre of mass is equal to the vector sum of all the external forces acting on the individual particles of the system.

When no external force is acting

$$\therefore \quad \vec{F_1} + \vec{F_2} + ... + \vec{F_i} + ... + \vec{F_n} = \Sigma\vec{F_i} = 0 \quad \therefore \quad M\vec{a} = 0 \text{ or } \vec{a} = 0 \text{ vector}$$

Hence in the absence of an external force, the acceleration of the centre of mass is zero and therefore the velocity is a constant vector.

Q. 9.2. What is centre of mass ? Find the total linear momentum of a system of particles about the centre of mass and show that it is zero. (P.U. 2006; Gharwal.U. 2000; A.U. 1993)

Ans. Centre of mass, See Q. 9.1.

Total linear momentum about the centre of mass. Let C be the centre of mass of a number of particles of mass $m_1, m_2 ..... m_i......m_n$ and $\vec{r_1}, \vec{r_2} ......\vec{r_i} .....\vec{r_n}$ their position vectors with respect to the origin O, then

Position vector of centre of mass

$$\vec{R} = \frac{m_1\vec{r_1} + m_2\vec{r_2} + ... + m_i\vec{r_i} + ... + m_n r_n}{m_1 + m_2 + ... + m_i + ... + m_n} = \frac{\Sigma m_i\vec{r_i}}{\Sigma m_i} = \frac{\Sigma m_i\vec{r_i}}{M} \qquad ...(i)$$

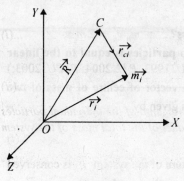

Fig. 9.2

where
$$M = m_1 + m_2 + ... + m_i + ... + m_n = \Sigma m_i$$

Consider one of the particles of mass m_i having position vector $\vec{r}_i$ then its position with respect to the centre of mass C, $\vec{r}_{ci}$ is given by $\vec{R} + \vec{r}_{ci} = \vec{r}_i$

The position of all other particles with respect to the centre of mass C is also given by similar relations.

Substituting $\vec{r}_i = \vec{R} + \vec{r}_{ci}$ in Equation (i), we get

$$M\vec{R} = \Sigma m_i (\vec{R} + \vec{r}_{ci}) = \Sigma m_i \vec{R} + \Sigma m_i \vec{r}_{ci} = M\vec{R} + \Sigma m_i \vec{r}_{ci}$$

or $\qquad \Sigma m_i \vec{r}_{ci} = 0 \qquad ...(ii)$

i.e., the sum of the products of mass and position vector of all the particles about the centre of mass is zero.

Differentiating relation (ii) with respect to t we get $\Sigma m_i \dfrac{d\vec{r}_{ci}}{dt} = \Sigma m_i \vec{v}_{ci} = 0$

because $\dfrac{d\vec{r}_{ci}}{dt} = \vec{v}_{ci}$ = velocity of the particle of mass m_i relative to centre of mass. $\Sigma m_i \vec{v}_{ci}$,

therefore gives the total linear momentum of all the particles about the centre of mass.

Thus the total linear momentum of the system of particles about the centre of mass is zero.

Note. The centre of mass frame is, therefore, sometimes called zero momentum frame.

Q. 9.3. Show that centre of mass of two particle system divides the line joining the two particles in the inverse ratio of their masses. (G.N.D.U. 2007; P.U. 2008, 2003; Pbi.U. 2003)

Ans. Position of centre of mass. The position of centre of mass for a number of particles is mathematically given by

$$\vec{R} = \frac{\Sigma m_i \vec{r}_i}{\Sigma m_i}$$

For two mass points m_1 and m_2, $\vec{R} = \dfrac{m_1 \vec{r}_1 + m_2 \vec{r}_2}{m_1 + m_2}$ ...(i)

where $\vec{r}_1$ and $\vec{r}_2$ are the vector distances of the particles of mass m_1 and m_2 respectively from the origin O.

If, however, the centre of mass lies at the origin of the co-ordinate system as in Fig. 9.4

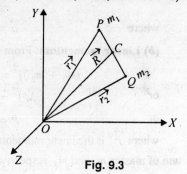

Fig. 9.3

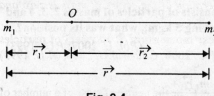

Fig. 9.4

$$\vec{R} = 0$$

$$\therefore \quad m_1 \vec{r}_1 + m_2 \vec{r}_2 = 0 \quad \text{or} \quad \frac{m_1}{m_2} = \frac{-\vec{r}_2}{\vec{r}_1}$$

Thus the centre of mass divides the line joining the two masses in the inverse ratio of the masses i.e., the heavier mass lies nearer the centre of mass of the two particle system. It should be noted that if O is the origin and $\vec{r}_2$ is positive, $\vec{r}_1$ must be negative.

Q. 9.4. (a) Two particles of masses m_1 and m_2 and position vectors $\vec{r}_1$ and $\vec{r}_2$ are moving with velocities $\vec{v}_1$ and $\vec{v}_2$ respectively.

(*i*) **What is the position vector of centre of mass?**

(*ii*) **What is the velocity and acceleration of centre of mass?**

(*b*) **Show that the linear momentum of the system of two particles is equal to the linear momentum of the centre of mass.** (*Gharwal U.* 2000; *G.N. D.U.* 1993, *P.U.* 2004; *Pbi.U.* 2003;)

Ans. (*a*) **Position vector of centre of mass.** The position vector of centre of mass of two particles of masses m_1 and m_2 and position vectors $\vec{r_1}$ and $\vec{r_2}$ is given by

$$\vec{R} = \frac{m_1 \vec{r_1} + m_2 \vec{r_2}}{m_1 + m_2} \qquad \qquad ...(i)$$

See Q. 9.3. Eq. (*i*)

Velocity of centre of mass. Rewriting equation (*i*) we have $m_1 \vec{r_1} + m_2 \vec{r_2} = (m_1 + m_2) \vec{R}$

Differentiating with respect to time we have $m_1 \vec{\dot{r_1}} + m_2 \vec{\dot{r_2}} = (m_1 + m_2) \vec{\dot{R}}$

or   Velocity of centre of mass $\vec{\dot{R}} = \dfrac{m_1 \vec{\dot{r_1}} + m_2 \vec{\dot{r_2}}}{m_1 + m_2}$ $\qquad \qquad ...(ii)$

or $\vec{V} = \dfrac{m_1 \vec{v_1} + m_2 \vec{v_2}}{m_1 + m_2}$ $\qquad \qquad ...(iii)$

where $V = \vec{\dot{R}}, \vec{v_1} = \vec{\dot{r_1}}$ and $\vec{v_2} = \vec{\dot{r_2}}$.

Acceleration of centre of mass. Differentiating equation (*ii*) again with respect to time, we have the acceleration of the centre of mass

$$\vec{\ddot{R}} = \frac{m_1 \vec{\ddot{r_1}} + m_2 \vec{\ddot{r_2}}}{m_1 + m_2} \text{ or } \vec{a} = \frac{m_1 \vec{a_1} + m_2 \vec{a_2}}{M} \qquad ...(iv)$$

where $\vec{a} = \vec{\ddot{R}}, a_1 = \vec{\ddot{r_1}}, a_2 = \vec{\ddot{r_2}}$ and $M = m_1 + m_2$

(*b*) **Linear momentum.** From equation (*iii*) we have

$$(m_1 + m_2) \vec{V} = m_1 \vec{v_1} + m_2 \vec{v_2}$$

or $M \vec{V} = m_1 \vec{v_1} + m_2 \vec{v_2}$ $\qquad \qquad$ [where $M = m_1 + m_2$]

or $\vec{P} = p_1 + p_2$

where $\vec{P}$ is the linear momentum of the centre of mass and $m_1 \vec{v_1}$ and $m_2 \vec{v_2}$ the linear momentum of masses m_1 and m_2 respectively.

Hence the linear momentum of a system of two particles is equal to linear momentum of the centre of mass.

Q. 9.5. Centre of mass is at $P(1, 1, 1)$ when system consists of particles of masses 2, 3, 4 and 5 kgm. If the centre of mass shifts to $Q(2, 2, 2)$ on removing 5 kgm,, what was its position?

(*Pbi. U.* 2007; *P.U.,* 1993)

Ans. The position vector of centre of mass is given by

$$\vec{R} = \frac{m_1 \vec{r_1} + m_2 \vec{r_2} + m_3 \vec{r_3} + m_4 \vec{r_4} + ...}{m_1 + m_2 + m_3 + m_4 + ...}$$

1st case $\vec{R_1} = (\hat{i} + \hat{j} + \hat{k}) = \dfrac{2\vec{r_1} + 3\vec{r_2} + 4\vec{r_3} + 5\vec{r_4}}{2 + 3 + 4 + 5}$ $\qquad ...(i)$

2nd case $\vec{R_2} = (2\hat{i} + 2\hat{j} + 2\hat{k}) = \dfrac{2\vec{r_1} + 3\vec{r_2} + 4\vec{r_3}}{2 + 3 + 4}$ $\qquad ...(ii)$

From (*i*) we have $\qquad 14\hat{i} + 14\hat{j} + 14\hat{k} = 2\vec{r_1} + 3\vec{r_2} + 4\vec{r_3} + 5\vec{r_4}$ ...(*iii*)

From (*ii*) we have $\qquad 18\hat{i} + 18\hat{j} + 18\hat{k} = 2r_1 + 3\vec{r_2} + 4\vec{r_3}$ ...(*iv*)

Subtracting (*iv*) form (*iii*), we get $-4\hat{i} - 4\hat{j} - 4\hat{k} = 5\vec{r_4}$

$$\therefore \qquad \vec{r_4} = -\frac{4}{5}\hat{i} - \frac{4}{5}\hat{j} - \frac{4}{5}\hat{k}$$

$\therefore$ Co-ordinates of the mass of 5 kg are $\left(-\frac{4}{5}, -\frac{4}{5}, -\frac{4}{5}\right)$.

Q. 9.6. Two bodies of masses 2 g and 10 g have position vectors $(3\hat{i} + 2\hat{j} - \hat{k})$ and $(\hat{i} - \hat{j} + 3\hat{k})$ respectively. Find the position vectors and the distance of centre of mass from the origin. *(G.N.D.U. 1995, 1997)*

Ans. The position of centre of mass of two particles is given by $\vec{R} = \dfrac{m_1 \vec{r_1} + m_2 \vec{r_2}}{m_1 + m_2}$

$$\therefore \qquad \vec{R} = \frac{2(3\hat{i} + 2\hat{j} - \hat{k}) + 10(\hat{i} - \hat{j} + 3\hat{k})}{2 + 10}$$

$$= \frac{16\hat{i} - 6\hat{j} + 28\hat{k}}{12} = \frac{4}{3}\hat{i} - \frac{1}{2}\hat{j} + \frac{7}{3}\hat{k}$$

Distance of centre of mass from the origin

$$|\vec{R}| = \sqrt{\left(\frac{4}{3}\right)^2 + \left(\frac{1}{2}\right)^2 + \left(\frac{7}{3}\right)^2} = \sqrt{\frac{16}{9} + \frac{1}{4} + \frac{49}{9}} = 2.73 \text{ units.}$$

Exercise. *The masses and positions of two particles are* $6\,kg\,(6\hat{i} + 7\hat{j})$ *and* $2kg\,(2\hat{i} + 11\hat{j} - 8\hat{k})$, *find the position of centre of mass.* *(Indore.U. 2001)*

Hint. $\vec{R} = \dfrac{m_1 \vec{r_1} + m_2 \vec{r_2}}{m_1 + m_2} = \dfrac{6(6\hat{i} + 7\hat{j}) + 2(2\hat{i} + 11\hat{j} - 8\hat{k})}{6 + 2} = 5\hat{i} - 8\hat{j} - 2\hat{k}$

Q. 9.7. The distance between Carbon and Oxygen atom in '*CO*' molecule is 1.12 $\mathring{A}$. Find the centre of mass of '*CO*' molecule with respect to '*C*' atom. *(H.P.U. 1995)*

Ans. Let us take the centre of mass as the origin of the co-ordinate system and axis of '*CO*' molecule along *X*-axis, then

Position of Carbon atom of mass 12

$$= \vec{r_1} = -r_1\hat{i}$$

Position of Oxygen atom of mass 16

$$= \vec{r_2} = (1.12 \times 10^{-10} - r_1)\hat{i}$$

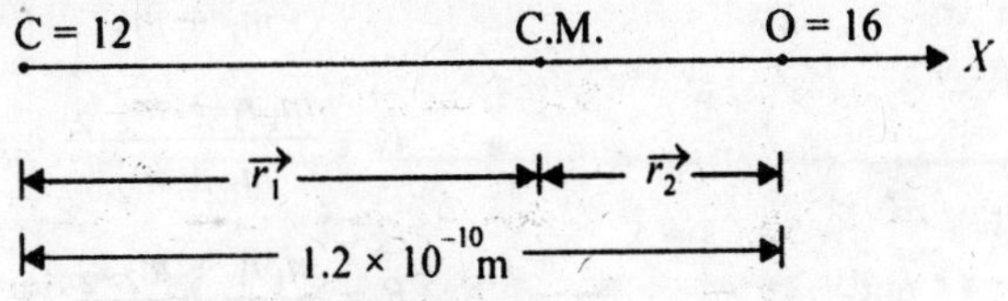

As centre of mass is taken as the origin of the co-ordinate system

$$\vec{R} = \frac{m_1 \vec{r_1} + m_2 \vec{r_2}}{m_1 + m_2} = 0$$

or $\qquad m_1 \vec{r_1} + m_2 \vec{r_2} = 0$

$\therefore \qquad -12 r_1 \hat{i} + 16(1.12 \times 10^{-10} - r_1)\hat{i} = 0$

or $\qquad 28 r_1 \hat{i} = 16 \times 1.12 \times 10^{-10}\,\hat{i}$

$$\therefore \qquad r_1 = \frac{16 \times 1.12 \times 10^{-10}}{28} = 0.64 \times 10^{-10} \text{ m} = 0.64\,\mathring{A}$$

Fig. 9.5 (*a*)

As the position of Carbon atom with respect to centre of mass = $-r_1\hat{i}$, the position of centre of mass with respect to 'C' atom $= +r_1 i = +0.64 \times 10^{-10}$ m.

Q. 9.8. Two particles of masses m_1 and m_2 separated by a distance r exert gravitational force on each other. If no other force acts on the system, show that the acceleration of centre of mass is zero and the velocity is constant. Prove that this is true for any central force.

(G.N.D.U. 2004, 2003, 2000, 1994; H. P. U. 1991)

Ans. Velocity and acceleration under gravitational force. Consider two isolated masses m_1 and m_2 at a distance r apart, then the gravitational force (of attraction) on the mass m_1 due to the mass m_2 is given by

$$\vec{F}_{12} = -G\frac{m_1 m_2}{r^2}\hat{r}$$

where G is the gravitational constant. Let O be the position of the centre of mass of the two masses m_1 and m_2. Let the position of m_1 be represented by the vector $\vec{r_1}$ and that of m_2 by the vector $\vec{r_2}$, then, if $\vec{r_2}$ is positive, $\vec{r_1}$ is negative as shown in Fig.9.5 (b).

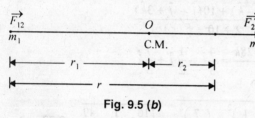

Fig. 9.5 (b)

If the force $\vec{F}_{12}$ produces an acceleration $\ddot{\vec{r_1}}$ in mass m_1, then

$$\vec{F}_{12} = m_1\ddot{\vec{r_1}} = -\frac{Gm_1 m_2}{r^2}\hat{r}$$

where $\hat{r}$ is unit vector along Om_2.

Similarly the gravitational force on the mass m_2 due to the mass m_1 is given by

$$\vec{F}_{21} = +\frac{Gm_1 m_2}{r^2}\hat{r} \text{ or } \vec{F}_{21} = m_2\ddot{\vec{r_2}} = +\frac{Gm_1 m_2}{r^2}\hat{r}$$

The force $\vec{F}_{21}$ acts on m_2 towards O i.e., in a direction opposite to $\hat{r}$ (along $m_2 O$)

$$\therefore \qquad m_1\ddot{\vec{r_1}} + m_2\ddot{\vec{r_2}} = 0 \qquad\qquad ...(i)$$

The position vector $\vec{R}$, the velocity $\dot{\vec{R}}$ and acceleration $\ddot{\vec{R}}$ of the centre of mass of two point masses m_1 and m_2 at position vectors $\vec{r_1}$ and $\vec{r_2}$ is given by

$$\vec{R} = \frac{m_1\vec{r_1} + m_2\vec{r_2}}{m_1 + m_2} \qquad\qquad ...(ii)$$

$$\dot{\vec{R}} = \frac{m_1\dot{\vec{r_1}} + m_2\dot{\vec{r_2}}}{m_1 + m_2} \qquad\qquad ...(iii)$$

and
$$\ddot{\vec{R}} = \frac{m_1\ddot{\vec{r_1}} + m_2\ddot{\vec{r_2}}}{m_1 + m_2} \qquad\qquad ...(iv)$$

Comparing equations (i) and (iv), we have $\ddot{\vec{R}} = 0$

Hence in the case of gravitational force acting between two masses the acceleration of the centre of mass is zero.

Integrating (i), we have $m_1\dot{\vec{r_1}} + m_2\dot{\vec{r_2}}$ = a constant

It implies that the total linear momentum of the system is constant.

Comparing with equation (iii), we have $\dot{\vec{R}} = \dfrac{m_1\dot{\vec{r_1}} + m_2\dot{\vec{r_2}}}{m_1 + m_2}$ = a constant

Hence in the case of gravitational force acting between two masses, the velocity of centre of mass is constant.

Central force. A central force is that force which is always directed away or towards a fixed centre and the magnitude of which is a function only of the distance from the fixed centre taken as the origin. In spherical polar co-ordinates we can express the central force as $\vec{F}(r) = F(r)\hat{r}$ where $F(r)$ is a function of the distance r from the origin and $\hat{r}$ is a unit vector along $\vec{r}$. In the above example the gravitational force between two particles is a central force.

$$F(r) = -\frac{G m_1 m_2}{r^2}$$

Similarly the force of attraction or repulsion between two charges is a central force.

The centre of mass always lies on the line joining the two particles m_1 and m_2. Therefore, the force on m_1 due to m_2 as well as the force on m_2 due to m_1 are both directed towards the centre of mass. If we denote the force on m_1 as $F(r)\hat{r}$, the force on m_2 being equal but opposite will be denoted by $-F(r)\hat{r}$.

$$\therefore \qquad m_1\vec{\ddot{r}}_1 = F(r)\hat{r} \text{ and } m_2\vec{\ddot{r}}_2 = -F(r)\hat{r}$$

Hence $\qquad m_1\vec{\ddot{r}}_1 + m_2\vec{\ddot{r}}_2 = 0$

from which it follows that $\vec{\ddot{R}} = 0$ and $\vec{\dot{R}} = $ a constant.

Hence in the case of a central force acting between two particles, the velocity of the centre of mass is a constant and the acceleration is zero.

Q. 9.9. (a) (i) What is reduced mass? Reduce two body problem to one body problem and obtain equation of motion for equivalent one body problem for two masses.

(*H.P.U.* 2001, 2000, 1999; *Luck.U.* 2001; *P.U.* 2006, 2000, 1992; *Gharwal U.* 2000; *Pbi.U.* 2007, 1999; *G.N.D.U.* 2006, 1996)

(ii) What are the consequences of the motion of reduced mass when a large body attracts a very small body ? (*P.U.* 2009)

(b) Discuss the motion of reduced mass under the influence of inverse square force. (*H.P.U.* 2000)

(c) Distinguish between centre of mass and reduced mass. What is their importance in Physics? (*H.P.U.* 1999)

(d) Find the reduced mass of atomic hydrogen. (*P.U.* 2006)

Ans. *(a) (i)* **Reduced mass.** Consider two mass points m_1 and m_2 as shown in Fig. 9.6. If c.m. is the centre of mass for these two mass points and $\vec{R}$ the radius vector for the centre of mass, then

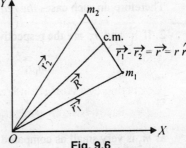

$$\vec{R} = \frac{m_1\vec{r}_1 + m_2\vec{r}_2}{m_1 + m_2}$$

where $\vec{r}_1$ is the radius vector for mass point m_1 and $\vec{r}_2$ that for mass point m_2.

Fig. 9.6

Equivalent one body problem. Suppose there is no *external* force acting on the system and the only forces are those of mutual interaction, then the velocity of the centre of mass is a *constant*. As the centre of mass must be on the line joining m_1 and m_2, the force on m_1 due to m_2 as well as the force on m_2 due to m_1 are both directed towards the centre of mass. Hence these forces are *central forces*.

If we denote the force on m_1 as $\vec{F}_{12} = F(r)\hat{r}$ the force on m_2 being equal and opposite will be denoted by $\vec{F}_{21} = -F(r)\hat{r}$.

$$\therefore \qquad m_1 \frac{d^2 \vec{r}_1}{dt^2} = \vec{F}_{12} = F(r)\hat{r} \text{ or } \frac{d^2 \vec{r}_1}{dt^2} = \frac{1}{m_1}F(r)\hat{r} \qquad \qquad ...(i)$$

$$\text{and} \qquad m_2 \frac{d^2 \vec{r}_2}{dt^2} = \vec{F}_{21} = -F(r)\hat{r} \text{ or } \frac{d^2 \vec{r}_2}{dt^2} = -\frac{1}{m_2}F(r)\hat{r} \qquad \qquad ...(ii)$$

Subtracting (ii) from (i) we have $\dfrac{d^2 \vec{r}_1}{dt^2} - \dfrac{d^2 \vec{r}_2}{dt^2} = \left(\dfrac{1}{m_1} + \dfrac{1}{m_2}\right)F(r)\hat{r}$

Now $\qquad \dfrac{d^2 \vec{r}_1}{dt^2} - \dfrac{d^2 \vec{r}_2}{dt^2} = \dfrac{d^2}{dt^2}(\vec{r}_1 - \vec{r}_2) = \dfrac{d^2 \vec{r}}{dt^2} \qquad\qquad [\because \vec{r} = \vec{r}_1 - \vec{r}_2]$

If we put $\qquad \dfrac{1}{\mu} = \dfrac{1}{m_1} + \dfrac{1}{m_2} = \dfrac{m_1 + m_2}{m_1 m_2}$ or $\mu = \dfrac{m_1 m_2}{m_1 + m_2}$

then $\qquad \dfrac{d^2 \vec{r}}{dt^2} = \left(\dfrac{1}{m_1} + \dfrac{1}{m_2}\right)F(r)\hat{r} = \dfrac{1}{\mu}F(r)\hat{r}$ or $\mu\vec{r} = F(r)\hat{r} \qquad ...(iii)$

i.e., the system behaves as a single particle of mass $\mu = \dfrac{m_1 m_2}{m_1 + m_2}$

Here μ is known as the **reduced mass** of the system and acts at a point known as *centre of mass* which divides the line joining the two masses in the inverse ratio of the masses.

The relation $\mu\vec{r} = F(r)\hat{r}$ gives the equation of motion of a particle having mass equal to reduced mass μ at a vector distance $\vec{r}$ from one of the particles to the other and shows that two separate equations of motion (i) and (ii) have been reduced to a single equation involving reduced mass.

We have thus reduced the two body problem to a one body problem.

(ii) Consequences of motion of reduced mass when a large body attracts a very small body. When a large body of mass m_1 attracts a very small body of mass m_2, the motion of the reduced mass has the consequences given below.

1. Reduced mass $\mu = \dfrac{m_1 m_2}{m_1 + m_2} = \dfrac{m_1 m_2}{m_1}$ [$\because m_2$ is very small and can be ignored as compared to m_1]

$$\therefore \qquad \qquad \mu = m_2$$

Therefore, in such cases *the reduced mass is practically equal to the mass of the small body.*

2. If $\vec{r}_1$ and $\vec{r}_2$ are the respective distances of the bodies of mass m_1 and m_2, then

$$m_1 \vec{r}_1 = m_2 \vec{r}_2$$

or $\qquad \qquad r_1 = \dfrac{m_2}{m_1}r_2 \approx 0$

as m_2 is very small as compared to m_1, $\dfrac{m_2}{m_1} \approx 0$.

Hence in such cases the *centre of mass practically coincides with the centre of the larger body.*

In the absence of an external force, the centre of mass of the system moves either with constant velocity or remains at rest. Therefore, under the effect of only the gravitational force between the two masses, only the motion of the lighter mass with respect to the heavier mass should be considered.

(b) **Motion of reduced mass under inverse square force.** The most familiar example of inverse square force is the gravitational force. For forces of gravitational attraction between the two mass points m_1 and m_2

$$\vec{F}(r) = -\frac{G m_1 m_2}{r^2}\hat{r} \ \text{ or } \ \mu\frac{d^2\vec{r}}{dt^2} = \mu\ddot{\vec{r}} = -\frac{G m_1 m_2}{r^2}\hat{r}$$

or

$$\frac{m_1 m_2}{m_1 + m_2}\ddot{\vec{r}} = -\frac{G m_1 m_2}{r^2}\hat{r}$$

∴

$$\ddot{\vec{r}} = -\frac{GM}{r^2}\hat{r} \ \text{ where } \ M = m_1 + m_2$$

This is clearly the equation of motion of a particle of **unit** mass at a vector distance r (equal to the distance between the two particles) from a fixed mass $M = m_1 + m_2$ exerting a force of attraction on it. Further the acceleration of one mass with respect to the other mass will appear to be the same but in opposite direction whether the observer is at mass m_1 or m_2.

Motion in centre of mass frame. In the absence of any external forces acting on the system, its total linear momentum is conserved. Hence the velocity of centre of mass remains constant in an inertial frame. However, in the centre of mass frame the velocity of centre of mass is *zero*. The two particles or bodies move around the centre of mass in such a way that the vector distance $\vec{r}$ between them remains constant. Hence to an observer at the centre of mass the heavier mass seems to describe a circle with smaller radius and the lighter mass seems to describe a circle with larger radius because $\dfrac{r_2}{r_1} = -\dfrac{m_1}{m_2}$.

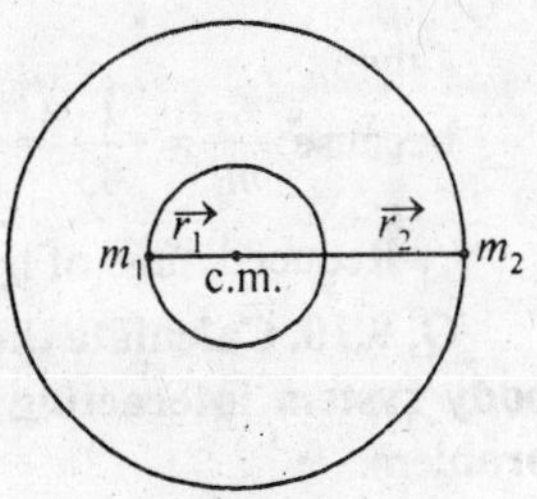

Fig. 9.7

(c) **Distinction between centre of mass and reduced mass.**

Centre of mass of two particles For definition See. Q. 9.1

Centre of mass of two particles. For two particles or mass points m_1 and m_2 lying at vector distances $\vec{r_1}$ and $\vec{r_2}$ from the origin, the position $\vec{R}$ of centre of mass is given by

$$\vec{R} = \frac{m_1 \vec{r_1} + m_2 \vec{r_2}}{m_1 + m_2} \qquad\qquad \text{[See Q. 9.3. Eq. } (i)]$$

The centre of mass of two particles lies on the line joining the two particles.

When the centre of mass lies at the origin $\vec{R} = 0$ and

$$m_1 \vec{r_1} + m_2 \vec{r_2} = 0 \ \text{ or } \ \frac{m_1}{m_2} = -\frac{\vec{r_2}}{\vec{r_1}}$$

Thus the centre of mass is a point which divides the line joining the two particles in the inverse ratio of masses.

Reduced mass. When there is no external force acting on the system of two particles and the only forces are those of mutual interaction, then the system behaves as a single particle of mass

$$\mu = \frac{m_1 m_2}{m_1 + m_2}.$$

In such a case μ is known as **reduced mass** of the system. *It acts at a point known as centre of mass which divides the line joining the two particles in the inverse ratio of masses.*

Importance in Physics. (i) The importance of centre of mass and reduced mass lies in the fact that instead of having two separate equations of motion

$$m_1 \ddot{\vec{r_1}} = \vec{F}_{12} = \vec{F}(r)\hat{r} \ \text{ and } \ m_2 \ddot{\vec{r_2}} = \vec{F}_{21} = -\vec{F}(r)\hat{r}$$

we have a single equation of motion involving reduced mass μ given by $\mu\ddot{\vec{r}} = F(r)\hat{r}$ where $\vec{r} = (\vec{r_1} - \vec{r_2})$ thereby reducing the two body problem to a one body problem.

(*ii*) When the centre of mass is taken as the origin of the co-ordinate system $\vec{R} = 0$, the velocity of centre of mass $V = \dot{\vec{R}} = \dfrac{d\vec{R}}{dt} = 0$ and linear momentum $\vec{P} = \mu\vec{V}$ of the system is also $= 0$; μ being the reduced mass. This fact is made use of in having a *centre of mass frame of reference* for the study of collision phenomenon between particles.

For advantages of centre of mass reference frame See Q. 9.12.

(*d*) **Reduced mass of atomic hydrogen.** The hydrogen atom consists of a proton and an electron. If m_1 is the mass of proton and m_2 that of electron, the reduced mass

$$\mu = \frac{m_1 m_2}{m_1 + m_2} + \frac{m_2}{1 + \dfrac{m_2}{m_1}} = m_2\left(1 + \frac{m_2}{m_1}\right)^{-1}$$

$$= m_2\left(1 - \frac{m_2}{m_1}\right) \text{ (by benomial theorem)}$$

$$\approx m_2$$

because $\dfrac{m_2}{m_1} = \dfrac{1}{183}$ = a very small quantity which may be neglected as compared to unity.

$\therefore$ Reduced mass of hydrogen $\approx m_2$ the mass of the electron.

Q. 9.10. Calculate the changes in the values of energy and angular momentum when a two body system interacting through gravitational force is reduced to an equivalent one body problem.

(*H.P.U.* 1999)

Ans. Change in total energy. Consider two bodies of masses m_1 and m_2 at positions having radius vectors $\vec{r_1}$ and $\vec{r_2}$ respectively, then

Position vector of $\qquad m_1 = \vec{r_1} \qquad \therefore$ Velocity of $m_1 = \dot{\vec{r_1}}$

Position vector of $\qquad m_2 = \vec{r_2} \qquad \therefore$ Velocity of $m_2 = \dot{\vec{r_2}}$

Distance between m_1 and $m_2 = \vec{r_1} - \vec{r_2} = \vec{r} = r\hat{r}$

The gravitational force of attraction $\vec{F}(r)\hat{r}$ between the two masses m_1 and m_2 is given by

$$F(r)\hat{r} = -\frac{G m_1 m_2}{r^2}\hat{r}$$

Taking magnitudes only, we have $F(r) = -\dfrac{G m_1 m_2}{r^2}$

The gravitational potential energy U is, therefore, given by

$$U = -\int F(r)\,dr = -\int -\frac{Gm_1m_2}{r^2}\,dr = \frac{-Gm_1m_2}{r} + K$$

where K is the constant of integration.

For $\qquad\qquad r = \infty, U = 0 \qquad \therefore K = 0$

Hence $\qquad\qquad U = \dfrac{-Gm_1m_2}{r} = \dfrac{-Gm_1m_2}{\left|\vec{r_1} - \vec{r_2}\right|}$

i.e, the gravitational potential energy between two mass points varies inversely as the distance between them.

Hence total energy of the two body system E_2 = Kinetic energy of m_1 + Kinetic energy of m_2 + Potential energy of interaction due to gravitational force between them.

$$\therefore \qquad E_2 = \frac{1}{2} m_1 \left| \vec{r}_1 \right|^2 + \frac{1}{2} m_2 \left| \vec{r}_2 \right|^2 - \frac{G m_1 m_2}{\left| \vec{r}_1 - \vec{r}_2 \right|} \qquad \qquad ...(i)$$

If we reduce the two body system to an *equivalent one body system*, then

Effective reduced mass $\qquad \mu = \dfrac{m_1 m_2}{m_1 + m_2}$

$\therefore$ Total energy of the equivalent one body system E_1 = Kinetic energy of effective (reduced) mass + Potential energy of interaction due to gravitational force

$$\therefore \qquad E_1 = \frac{1}{2} \mu \left| \vec{r} \right|^2 - \frac{G m_1 m_2}{\left| \vec{r}_1 - \vec{r}_2 \right|} = \frac{1}{2} \frac{m_1 m_2}{m_1 + m_2} \left| \vec{r}_1 - \vec{r}_2 \right|^2 - \frac{G m_1 m_2}{\left| \vec{r}_1 - \vec{r}_2 \right|}$$

$$= \frac{1}{2} \frac{m_1 m_2}{m_1 + m_2} \left[\left| \vec{r}_1 \right|^2 + \left| \vec{r}_2 \right|^2 - 2 \vec{r}_1 \cdot \vec{r}_2 \right] - G \frac{m_1 m_2}{\left| \vec{r}_1 - \vec{r}_2 \right|} \qquad ...(ii)$$

$\therefore$ Change in total energy

$$E_1 - E_2 = \frac{1}{2} \frac{m_1 m_2}{m_1 + m_2} \left[\left| \vec{r}_1 \right|^2 + \left| \vec{r}_2 \right|^2 - 2 \vec{r}_1 \cdot \vec{r}_2 \right] - \frac{G m_1 m_2}{\left| \vec{r}_1 - \vec{r}_2 \right|}$$

$$- \frac{1}{2} m_1 \left| \vec{r}_1 \right|^2 - \frac{1}{2} m_2 \left| \vec{r}_2 \right|^2 + \frac{G m_1 m_2}{\left| \vec{r}_1 - \vec{r}_2 \right|}$$

$$= \frac{1}{2} \frac{1}{m_1 + m_2} \left[m_1 m_2 \left| \vec{r}_1 \right|^2 + m_1 m_2 \left| \vec{r}_2 \right|^2 - 2 m_1 m_2 (\vec{r}_1 \cdot \vec{r}_2) \right]$$

$$- \frac{1}{2} \frac{1}{m_1 + m_2} \left[m_1^2 \left| \vec{r}_1 \right|^2 + m_1 m_2 \left| \vec{r}_1 \right|^2 + m_2^2 \left| \vec{r}_2 \right|^2 + m_1 m_2 \left| \vec{r}_2 \right|^2 \right]$$

$$= - \frac{1}{2} \frac{1}{m_1 + m_2} \left[m_1^2 \left| \vec{r}_1 \right|^2 + m_2^2 \left| \vec{r}_2 \right|^2 + 2 m_1 m_2 (\vec{r}_1 \cdot \vec{r}_2) \right]$$

$$= - \frac{1}{2} \frac{1}{m_1 + m_2} (m_1 \vec{r}_1 + m_2 \vec{r}_2)^2 \qquad \qquad ...(iii)$$

The position of centre of mass of the two particle system is given by $\vec{R} = \dfrac{m_1 \vec{r}_1 + m_2 \vec{r}_2}{m_1 + m_2}$.

$\therefore$ Velocity of centre of mass $\vec{V} = \dfrac{d\vec{R}}{dt} = \dot{\vec{R}} = \dfrac{m_1 \dot{\vec{r}}_1 + m_2 \dot{\vec{r}}_2}{m_1 + m_2}$

Substituting $\left| m_1 \dot{\vec{r}}_1 + m_2 \dot{\vec{r}}_2 \right|^2 = (m_1 + m_2)^2 \left| \dot{\vec{R}} \right|^2$ in (iii), we have

$$E_1 - E_2 = - \frac{1}{2} (m_1 + m_2) \left| \dot{\vec{R}} \right|^2$$

But $\dfrac{1}{2} (m_1 + m_2) \left| \dot{\vec{R}} \right|^2$ is the kinetic energy of the centre of mass.

As $E_1 - E_2$ is negative, *the total energy of the system decreases by an amount equal to the kinetic energy of the centre of mass.*

Change in angular momentum. The angular momentum of the system = sum of the angular momenta of the two masses

$$\therefore \qquad \vec{J}_2 = \vec{r}_1 \times (m_1 \dot{\vec{r}}_1) + \vec{r}_2 \times (m_2 \dot{\vec{r}}_2) \qquad \qquad ...(iv)$$

The angular momentum of the equivalent one body system

$$\vec{J_1} = \vec{r} \times \mu \, \dot{\vec{r}} = (\vec{r_1} - \vec{r_2}) \times \frac{m_1 m_2}{m_1 + m_2} \, (\dot{\vec{r_1}} - \dot{\vec{r_2}})$$

$$= \frac{m_1 m_2}{m_1 + m_2} \, (\vec{r_1} - \vec{r_2})(\dot{\vec{r_1}} - \dot{\vec{r_2}}) \qquad \ldots (v)$$

$\therefore$ Change in angular momentum

$$\vec{J_1} - \vec{J_2} = \frac{m_1 m_2}{m_1 + m_2} \, (\vec{r_1} \times \dot{\vec{r_1}} - \vec{r_1} \times \dot{\vec{r_2}} - \vec{r_2} \times \dot{\vec{r_1}} + \vec{r_2} \times \dot{\vec{r_2}}) - (m_1 \vec{r_1} \times \dot{\vec{r_1}} + m_2 \vec{r_2} \times \dot{\vec{r_2}})$$

$$= \frac{1}{m_1 + m_2} \left[-m_1 m_2 \, \vec{r_1} \times \dot{\vec{r_2}} - m_1 m_2 \, \vec{r_2} \times \dot{\vec{r_1}} \right] + \left(\frac{m_1 m_2}{m_1 + m_2} - m_1 \right) \vec{r_1} \times \dot{\vec{r_1}}$$

$$+ \left(\frac{m_1 m_2}{m_1 + m_2} - m_2 \right) \vec{r_2} \times \dot{\vec{r_2}}$$

$$= \frac{1}{m_1 + m_2} \left[-m_1 m_2 \, \vec{r_1} \times \dot{\vec{r_2}} - m_1 m_2 \, \vec{r_2} \times \dot{\vec{r_1}} + (m_1 m_2 - m_1^2 - m_1 m_2) \, \vec{r_1} \times \dot{\vec{r_1}} \right.$$

$$\left. + (m_1 m_2 - m_1 m_2 - m_2^2) \, \vec{r_2} \times \dot{\vec{r_2}} \right]$$

$$= \frac{1}{m_1 + m_2} \left[-m_1 m_2 \, \vec{r_1} \times \dot{\vec{r_2}} - m_1 m_2 \, \vec{r_2} \times \dot{\vec{r_1}} - m_1^2 \, \vec{r_1} \times \dot{\vec{r_1}} - m_2^2 \, \vec{r_2} \times \dot{\vec{r_2}} \right]$$

$$= -\frac{1}{m_1 + m_2} \left[m_1 \vec{r_1} \times m_2 \dot{\vec{r_2}} + m_2 \vec{r_2} \times m_1 \dot{\vec{r_1}} + m_1 \vec{r_1} \times m_1 \dot{\vec{r_1}} + m_2 \vec{r_2} \times m_2 \dot{\vec{r_2}} \right]$$

$$= -\frac{1}{m_1 + m_2} \left[(m_1 \vec{r_1} + m_2 \vec{r_2}) \times (m_1 \dot{\vec{r_1}} + m_2 \dot{\vec{r_2}}) \right] \qquad \ldots (vi)$$

The angular momentum of the centre of mass is given by $\vec{R} \times (m_1 + m_2) \dot{\vec{R}}$. But

$$\vec{R} = \frac{m_1 \vec{r_1} + m_2 \vec{r_2}}{m_1 + m_2} \quad \text{and} \quad \dot{\vec{R}} = \frac{m_1 \dot{\vec{r_1}} + m_2 \dot{\vec{r_2}}}{m_1 + m_2}$$

$\therefore$ Angular momentum of centre of mass $= \dfrac{m_1 \vec{r_1} + m_2 \vec{r_2}}{m_1 + m_2} \times (m_1 + m_2) \dfrac{m_1 \dot{\vec{r_1}} + m_2 \dot{\vec{r_2}}}{m_1 + m_2}$

$$\frac{1}{m_1 + m_2} \left[(m_1 \vec{r_1} + m_2 \vec{r_2}) \times (m_1 \dot{\vec{r_1}} + m_2 \dot{\vec{r_2}}) \right] \qquad \ldots (vii)$$

Comparing (vii) and (vi) we find that *the angular momentum of the system decreases by an amount equal to the angular momentum of the centre of mass.*

Q. 9.11. (*a*) **What is a collision? Explain briefly elastic and inelastic (collision) scattering. Discuss two types of inelastic scattering. What is the difference between scattering and reaction?**

(*b*) **What is the advantage of studying a collision process?** (*G.N.D.U.* 2008, 2006, 2004, 2001, 1992; *Osm.U.* 2004; *Nagpur U.* 2003; *P.U.* 1999, 1993; *H.P.U.* 1992; *Pbi.U.* 1991)

Ans. Collision. *When two bodies are approaching each other, a force comes into play between them for a finite time and brings about a measurable change in their velocities, momenta and energy according to the respective laws of conservation, a collision is said to have taken place.*

It should, however, be clearly understood that in Physics, collision does not necessarily mean physical contact between the two bodies.

During collision, the force of some interaction comes into play between the two colliding particles or systems for a finite small time which brings about a change in their relative motions. If the collision acts for a time t_0 to $t_0 + \Delta t$, then a time t less than t_0 is known as *time before collision* and a time t greater than $t_0 + \Delta t$ is called *time after collision.*

The collision is termed **scattering** if the nature of particles does not change after collision. Familiar examples of collision or scattering are the deflection of a comet as it passes near the solar system and the deflection of an α-particle by an atomic nucleus. The study of collision is of particular importance in atomic and nuclear physics. The bodies involved may be atoms, nuclei or various elementary particles such as electrons, protons etc.

Elastic scattering (or elastic collision). A collision (scattering) is said to be an elastic collision if (*i*) the final particles after collision are the same as the initial particles before collision,

(*ii*) the sum of the kinetic energies of the particles after collision is the same as the sum of the kinetic energies of the particle before collision.

Inelastic scattering (or inelastic collision). A collision is said to be an inelastic collision if

(*i*) the final particles after collision are the same as the initial particles before collision.

(*ii*) the sum of the kinetic energies of the particles after collision is either more or less than the sum of the kinetic energies of the particles before collision.

A collision is said to be perfectly inelastic if the particles stick permanently together on impact and the loss of kinetic energy is *maximum*, consistent with the law of conservation of momentum.

Conservation of linear momentum. Consider two particles of masses m_1 and m_2 moving with velocities $\vec{u_1}$ and $\vec{u_2}$ respectively before collision in an inertial frame of reference. After collision, their velocities become $\vec{v_1}$ and $\vec{v_2}$ respectively. When no external force acts on the particles their *total linear momentum is conserved.* $\therefore\ m_1\vec{u_1} + m_2\vec{u_2} = m_1\vec{v_1} + m_2\vec{v_2}$

This relation holds good both for elastic as well as inelastic collisions.

Conservation of kinetic energy. In the case of an elastic collision the kinetic energy is also conserved. $\qquad \therefore\ \dfrac{1}{2}m_1u_1^2 + \dfrac{1}{2}m_2u_2^2 = \dfrac{1}{2}m_1v_1^2 + \dfrac{1}{2}m_2v_2^2$

Examples of elastic collision are :

(*i*) Collision between molecules of gases according to kinetic theory,

(*ii*) Collisions between atoms and nuclei, and

(*iii*) Collisions between particles like electrons, protons, α-particles etc.

Two types of inelastic collisions. In the case of *inelastic* collisions there may be an increase or decrease of kinetic energy giving rise to two types of inelastic collisions *i.e.,* (*i*) **endoergic** and (*ii*) **exoergic.**

Endoergic collision. For bodies of *macroscopic* size the loss of kinetic energy occurs as heat, sound etc. but in the case of atoms, molecules etc., the atoms may absorb a part of the kinetic energy and move into an excited state. The kinetic energy of the particles is then reduced and we have

$$\frac{1}{2}m_1u_1^2 + \frac{1}{2}m_2u_2^2 = \frac{1}{2}m_1v_1^2 + \frac{1}{2}m_2v_2^2 + E$$

where E is the excitation energy. Such a collision in which the kinetic energy of the final particles is less than the kinetic energy of the initial particles is known as **endoergic** collision.

Exoergic collision. If, however, the atoms are already in the excited state and after collision come down to the normal state, the excitation energy adds up to the final kinetic energy and we have

$$\frac{1}{2}m_1u_1^2 + \frac{1}{2}m_2u_2^2 + E = \frac{1}{2}m_1v_1^2 + \frac{1}{2}m_2v_2^2$$

Such a collision in which the kinetic energy of the final particles is more than the kinetic energy of the initial particles is known as **exoergic** collision.

Reaction. A collision (or scattering) is said to be a reaction if

(*i*) the final particles after collision (known as *products*) are entirely different from the initial particles (known as *reactants*) before collision.

(*ii*) the sum of the kinetic energies of the particles after collision is different from the sum of the kinetic energies of the particles before collision.

In all the above cases the law of conservation of linear momentum and the law of conservation of angular momentum hold good. It is because in each case the interacting particles being isolated, no external torque acts on the system.

Another point to be carefully noted is that in the case of inelastic collision and reaction, only the sum of the kinetic energies after collision is different from the sum of the kinetic energies before collision but the total energy of the system, including kinetic energy, potential energy and any other form of energy remains conserved.

(b) Advantages of studying collision process. Various types of interactions and forces are operating in nature at microscopic as well as macroscopic levels. A study of collision process *i.e.* relative motion between the two interacting particles helps us to understand the basic nature and characteristics of these interactions and forces. This is done by measuring the initial and final energy and linear as well as angular momentum of the participating particles in accordance with the laws of conservation of energy and momentum.

The deflection of the path of a comet passing near the solar system and the elliptic path of planets within the solar system helps us to understand the nature of gravitational forces.

Collision between molecules of gases according to Kinetic theory leads to understanding of inter-atomic and intermolecular forces.

Scattering of α-particles in Rutherford scattering, scattering of high energy photons in Compton scattering, nuclear reactions involving high energy electrons, protons, neutrons, deutrons and α- particles, scattering of slow neutrons by nuclei and emission of α and β particles from radioactive nuclei help us to understand the nature of nuclear forces, properties of the nucleus and atomic structure.

Q. 9.12. Explain laboratory and centre of mass systems (or frames of reference). What is the advantage of studying a collision process in centre of mass system? (*G.N.D.U.* 2004, 2001, 2000; *Meerut U.* 2003; *P.U.* 2005, 2004, 2001, 2000, 1991; *Pbi.U.* 2008. 2005, 2001. 2000, 1999; *Gauhati U.* 2000; *H.P.U.* 1999, 1997, 1994; *Osm.U.* 1997)

Ans. Laboratory system (Frame of reference). In the study of collisions between two particles we shall come across the laboratory system or laboratory frame of reference and the centre of mass system or centre of mass frame of reference.

A reference frame is the space determined by a rigid body regarded as the base. The rigid body is supposed to extend in all directions as far as necessary. A point in space is located by the three   co-ordinates taken with respect to the origin of the reference system.

If the origin of the reference system is a point rigidly fixed to the laboratory, it is known as the **laboratory frame.**

The laboratory frame is inertial so long as earth is taken to be an inertial frame.

Centre of mass system (Frame of reference). *If the origin of the reference system is a point rigidly fixed to the centre of mass of a system of particles on which no external force is acting, it is known as the* **centre of mass frame of reference.**

In the centre of mass reference frame the position vector of the centre of mass $\vec{R} = 0$ as the centre of mass is itself the origin of the reference system.

∴ The velocity of centre mass $\vec{V} = \dfrac{d\vec{R}}{dt} = 0$

and the linear momentum $\vec{P} = M\vec{V}$ of the system is also = 0. Hence it is known as a *zero momentum frame.*

Advantages of studying collision process in centre of mass system. (*i*) In the absence of any external force the velocity of the centre of mass is a *constant.* In other words, the centre of mass reference frame moves with a constant velocity with respect to the laboratory frame. *Hence the centre of mass frame is also an inertial frame.*

Various physical quantities measured in the two systems are related to each other by Galelian transformations provided the velocity of centre of mass is small as compared to the velocity of light.

(*ii*) A system of two particles requires six co-ordinates to describe the motion in the laboratory system. Three co-ordinates are required to describe the motion of centre of mass and three more co-ordinates are required to describe the relative motion. But in the centre of mass frame we require only three co-ordinates as the centre of mass is itself at rest in this frame.

The discussion of a collision process, therefore, becomes much simpler in the centre of mass frame of reference than in the laboratory frame.

Q. 9.13. A particle of mass m_1 moving with a velocity u collides head on with a particle of mass m_2 at rest such that after the collision they travel with velocity v_1 and v_2 respectively. If the collision is perfectly elastic one, show that $v_2 = \dfrac{2m_1 u_1}{m_1 + m_2}$. **(*G.N.D.U.* 2003)**

Ans. Perfectly elastic collision. Let m_1 be the mass of the particle moving with a velocity u_1 and m_2 the mass of the particle at rest with which it has a head-on collision, so that after collision the mass m_1 moves with a velocity v_1 and mass m_2 with a velocity v_2 along the line joining their centres, then as the collision is perfectly elastic, according to the principle of conservation of linear momentum

$$m_1 u_1 = m_1 v_1 + m_2 v_2$$

or $\qquad m_1 (u_1 - v_1) = m_2 v_2$ ...(*i*)

and according to the law of conservation of energy

$$\frac{1}{2} m_1 u_1^2 = \frac{1}{2} m_1 v_1^2 + \frac{1}{2} m_2 v_2^2$$

or $\qquad m_1 (u_1^2 - v_1^2) = m_2 v_2^2$ ...(*ii*)

Dividing (*ii*) by (*i*), we have

$$u_1 + v_1 = v_2 \quad \text{or} \quad v_1 = v_2 - u_1$$

Substituting in (*i*), we have

$$m_1 (u_1 - v_2 + u_1) = m_2 v_2$$

or $\qquad 2 m_1 u_1 = v_2 (m_1 + m_2)$

or $\qquad v_2 = \dfrac{2m_1 u_1}{m_1 + m_2}$.

Q. 9.14. Discuss the phenomenon of collision in one dimension between two particles when the collision is (*i*) elastic and (*ii*) inelastic in the laboratory frame as well as in the centre of mass frame. *(H.P.U.* 1999; *Madurai U.* 2003; *Calicut U.* 2003)*

Ans. Perfectly elastic collision in one dimension -Laboratory frame. Let m_1 and m_2 be the masses of the two particles $\vec{u_1}$ and $\vec{u_2}$ and $\vec{v_1}, \vec{v_2}$ their respective velocities before and after an elastic one dimensional collision *i.e., a head-on collision along the line joining their centres,* then according to the principle of conservation of linear momentum

$$m_1 \vec{u_1} + m_2 \vec{u_2} = m_1 \vec{v_1} + m_2 \vec{v_2}$$ ...(*i*)

and according to the law of conservation of energy

$$m_1 u_1^2 + m_2 u_2^2 = m_1 v_1^2 + m_2 v_2^2$$ ...(*ii*)

Rewriting equations (*i*) and (*ii*) and taking magnitudes only we have

$$m_1 (u_1 - v_1) = m_2 (v_2 - u_2)$$ ...(*iii*)

and $\qquad\qquad m_1 (u_1^2 - v_1^2) = m_2 (v_2^2 - u_2^2)$ ...(iv)

Dividing (iv) by (iii) we have $u_1 + v_1 = v_2 + u_2$ or $u_1 - u_2 = - (v_1 - v_2)$ ...(v)

This shows that *in an elastic one dimensional collision the relative velocity with which the two particles approach each other before collision is equal to the relative velocity with which they recede away from each other after collision.*

Velocity after collision. From equation (v) we have $v_1 = v_2 + u_2 - u_1$

and $\qquad\qquad\qquad\qquad\qquad v_2 = v_1 + u_1 - u_2$

Substituting the value of v_2 in (iii), we have

$$m_1 (u_1 - v_1) = m_2 (v_1 + u_1 - u_2 - u_2)$$

or $\qquad\qquad v_1 (m_1 + m_2) = (m_1 - m_2) u_1 + 2m_2 u_2$

or $\qquad\qquad\qquad v_1 = \dfrac{m_1 - m_2}{m_1 + m_2} u_1 + \dfrac{2m_2}{m_1 + m_2} u_2$ ... (vi)

Similarly $\qquad\qquad v_2 = \dfrac{m_2 - m_1}{m_1 + m_2} u_2 + \dfrac{2m_1}{m_1 + m_2} u_1$ ... (vii)

Exercise. Show that the relative velocity of two particles in a head-on collision remains unchanged in magnitude but reverses in direction. (*G.N.D.U.* 2007)

Hint. It has been proved above that in an elastic one dimensional collision the relative velocity with which the two particles approach each other before collision is equal to the relative velocity with which they recede away from each other after collision. In other words, it means that '*the relative velocity of two particles in a head-on collision remains unchanged in magnitude but only reverses in direction*'.

Special cases. (*i*) **One of the colliding particles is initially at rest.** Let m_2 be initially at rest, then $u_2 = 0$.

Hence $\qquad\qquad v_1 = \dfrac{m_1 - m_2}{m_1 + m_2} u_1$ and $v_2 = \dfrac{2m_1}{m_1 + m_2} u_1$ ...(viii)

(*ii*) **The particles have the same mass.** In such a case $m_1 = m_2$.

Substituting in (vi), we have $v_1 = u_2$ and substituting in (vii), we have $v_2 = u_1$

Hence in one dimensional elastic collision of two particles of equal mass, the particles simply interchange their velocities after collision.

If m_2 is also initially at rest, then $u_2 = 0 \therefore v_1 = 0$ and as before $v_2 = u_1$

Hence *the first particle of mass m_1 comes to rest after collision and the second particle of mass m_2 acquires the initial velocity of the first.*

(*iii*) **Particle at rest is very massive.** If m_2 is very heavy as compared to m_1 and $u_2 = 0$, then

$m_1 = 0$, $m_1 - m_2 = - m_2$ and $m_1 + m_2 = m_2$ $\therefore v_1 = - u_1$ and $v_2 = 0$

This shows that *when a very light particle collides against a very massive particle at rest, the heavy particle continues to remain at rest and the velocity of the light particle is reversed.*

A familiar example of this is the dropping of a steel ball on an equally hard horizontal surface on the ground. This is in fact a collision between the light ball and the massive ground at rest. The velocity of the ball is reversed on impact. This is judged from the fact that the ball rises to the same height from which it was dropped.

(*iv*) **Particle at rest is very light.** If the particle at rest is very light

$$m_2 = 0; \quad m_1 - m_2 = m_1 \text{ and } m_1 + m_2 = m_1$$

Substituting in relation (viii) we have $v_1 = u_1$ and $v_2 = 2u_1$

This shows *that the velocity of the heavy particle remains almost the same after collision and the light particle acquires nearly twice the velocity of the heavy particle.*

Exercise. *A massive ball comes moving and collides elastically with a comparatively very light stationary ball. Immediately after the collision, what is the approximate ratio of speeds of lighter and massive ball?*   (*Luck. U.* 2001)

Hint. As proved in (*iv*) above, in such a case the velocity of heavy particle remains almost the same after collision and the light particle acquires nearly twice the velocity of heavy particle.

$$\therefore \qquad \frac{\text{Speed of lighter particle}}{\text{Speed of heavy (massive) particle}} = 2$$

Centre of mass frame. When no external force is acting, the velocity of centre of mass is given by

$$\vec{V}_{cm} = \frac{m_1 \vec{u_1} + m_2 \vec{u_2}}{m_1 + m_2}$$

As the collision is one dimensional, therefore taking magnitudes only $V_{cm} = \dfrac{m_1 u_1 + m_2 u_2}{m_1 + m_2}$

Velocity of the particle of mass m_1 before collision relative to centre of mass frame according to Galelian transformations is given by

$$\vec{u_1'} = \vec{u_1} - \vec{V}_{cm} = \vec{u_1} - \frac{m_1 \vec{u_1} + m_2 \vec{u_2}}{m_1 + m_2}$$

$$= \frac{m_1 \vec{u_1} + m_2 \vec{u_1} - m_1 \vec{u_1} - m_2 \vec{u_2}}{m_1 + m_2} = \frac{m_2 (\vec{u_1} - \vec{u_2})}{m_1 + m_2}$$

Taking magnitudes only $u_1' = \dfrac{m_2 (u_1 - u_2)}{m_1 + m_2}$ ... (*ix*)

Velocity of the particle of mass m_2 before collision relative to centre of mass frame according to Galelian transformations is given by

$$\vec{u_2'} = \vec{u_2} - \vec{V}_{cm} = \vec{u_2} - \frac{m_1 \vec{u_1} + m_2 \vec{u_2}}{m_1 + m_2}$$

$$= \frac{m_1 \vec{u_2} + m_2 \vec{u_2} - m_1 \vec{u_1} - m_2 \vec{u_2}}{m_1 + m_2} = \frac{m_1 (\vec{u_2} - \vec{u_1})}{m_1 + m_2}$$

Taking magnitudes only $u_2' = \dfrac{m_1 (u_2 - u_1)}{m_1 + m_2}$ ... (*ix*) (*a*)

Velocity after collision. The velocity of the particle of mass m_1 after collision relative to centre of mass frame according to Galelian transformations is given by $\vec{v_1'} = \vec{v_1} - \vec{V}_{cm}$

Taking magnitudes only

$$v_1' = v_1 - V_{cm} = \frac{(m_1 - m_2) u_1 + 2 m_2 u_2}{m_1 + m_2} - \frac{m_1 u_1 + m_2 u_2}{m_1 + m_2}$$

$$= \frac{m_1 u_1 - m_2 u_1 + 2 m_2 u_2 - m_1 u_1 - m_2 u_2}{m_1 + m_2} = \frac{- m_2 (u_1 - u_2)}{m_1 + m_2} \qquad ...(x)$$

The velocity of the particle of mass m_2 after collision in the centre of mass frame according to Galelian transformations is given by

$$\vec{v_2'} = \vec{v_2} - \vec{V}_{cm}$$

Taking magnitudes only

$$v_2' = v_2 - V_{cm} = \frac{(m_2 - m_1) u_2 + 2 m_1 u_1}{m_1 + m_2} - \frac{m_1 u_1 + m_2 u_2}{m_1 + m_2}$$

$$= \frac{m_2 u_2 - m_1 u_2 + 2m_1 u_1 - m_1 u_1 - m_2 u_2}{m_1 + m_2} = \frac{-m_1(u_2 - u_1)}{m_1 + m_2} \quad \ldots (xi)$$

The centre of mass is at rest before and after collision relative to the centre of mass reference frame.

When the collision is perfectly inelastic. A collision is said to be perfectly inelastic if the two particles stick together after collision. We shall discuss the problem in the laboratory frame as well as in the centre of mass frame.

Laboratory frame. Let m_1 and m_2 be the masses and $\vec{u_1}$ and $\vec{u_2}$ the velocities of two particles before collision. Since the two particles stick together on impact, let their velocity after collision be $\vec{v}$. According to the law of conservation of momentum $m_1 \vec{u_1} + m_1 \vec{u_2} = (m_1 + m_2) \vec{v}$

$$\therefore \qquad \vec{v} = \frac{m_1 \vec{u_1} + m_2 \vec{u_2}}{m_1 + m_2}$$

Special case. When the second particle of mass m_2 is at rest $\vec{u_2} = 0$

$$\therefore \qquad m_1 \vec{u_1} = (m_1 + m_2) \vec{v} \quad \text{or} \quad \vec{v} = \frac{m_1 \vec{u_1}}{m_1 + m_2}$$

Loss of kinetic energy. For the special case when m_2 is at rest.

$$\text{K.E. of the particle before collision} = \frac{1}{2} m_1 u_1^2$$

$$\text{and K. E. of the particles after collision} = \frac{1}{2}(m_1 + m_2) v^2 = \frac{1}{2}(m_1 + m_2) \left(\frac{m_1}{m_1 + m_2} \right)^2 u_1^2$$

$$= \frac{1}{2} \frac{m_1^2 u_1^2}{m_1 + m_2}$$

$$\text{Loss of K. E.} = \frac{1}{2} m_1 u_1^2 \left[1 - \frac{m_1}{m_1 + m_2} \right] = \frac{1}{2} m_1 u_1^2 \left[\frac{m_2}{m_1 + m_2} \right]$$

which is always a positive quantity, showing that there is always a loss of energy.

$$\text{Also} \quad \frac{\text{K.E. after collision}}{\text{K.E. before collision}} = \frac{\frac{1}{2} m_1^2 u_1^2}{(m_1 + m_2)(\frac{1}{2} m_1 u_1^2)} = \frac{m_1}{m_1 + m_2}$$

which is a quantity less than unity, showing that kinetic energy after collision is always less than K.E. before collision. This energy is used up in excitation of atoms and molecules or given out in the form of radiation.

Centre of mass frame. When no external force is applied the velocity of the centre of mass for two particle system is given by $\vec{V}_{cm} = \dfrac{m_1 \vec{u_1} + m_1 \vec{u_2}}{m_1 + m_2}$.

Again consider the special case when m_2 is at rest $\vec{u_2} = 0$. The velocity of the centre of mass in the laboratory frame is then given by $\vec{V}_{cm} = \dfrac{m_1 \vec{u_1}}{m_1 + m_2}$.

In other words, the centre of mass reference frame moves with respect to the laboratory frame with a velocity $\vec{V}_{cm}$.

Let $\vec{u_1'}$ and $\vec{u_2'}$ be the initial velocities of masses m_1 and m_2 respectively in the centre of mass frame, then according to Galelian transformations

$$\vec{u'_1} = \vec{u_1} - \vec{V}_{cm} = \vec{u_1}\left[1 - \frac{m_1}{m_1 + m_2}\right] = \frac{m_2}{m_1 + m_2}\vec{u_1}$$

$$\vec{u'_2} = \vec{u_2} - \vec{V}_{cm}$$

But $\qquad\qquad \vec{u_2} = 0 \quad \therefore \quad \vec{u'_2} = -\vec{V}_{cm} = -\dfrac{m_1\vec{u_1}}{m_1 + m_2}$

After collision the two particles stick together and have a combined mass $(m_1 + m_2)$. Hence *the final velocity in the centre of mass frame is zero i.e.,* the stuck particles are at rest in the centre of mass frame but have a velocity $\vec{v} = \dfrac{m_1\vec{u_1}}{m_1 + m_2} = \vec{V}_{cm}$ in the laboratory frame.

9.15. Two masses constrained to move in a horizontal plane collide. Given initially $m_1 =$ 85 gms, $m_2 = 200$ gms; $u_1 = 6.48$ cms/sec and $u_2 = -6.78$ cms/sec, find the velocity of centre of mass.

Ans. The velocity of centre of mass is given by $\vec{V}_{cm} = \dfrac{m_1\vec{u_1} + m_2\vec{u_2}}{m_1 + m_2}$

$\therefore \qquad \vec{V}_{cm} = \dfrac{85 \times 6.48 + 200 \times (-6.78)}{85 + 200} = 2.82$ cm / sec in the direction of motion of m_2.

Q. 9.16. A particle of mass m moving with velocity u collides with a target particle of unknown mass initially at rest. If, after the collision, the target particle travels forward with a velocity $\dfrac{u}{3}$ while the incident particle moves backward with a velocity $\dfrac{2u}{3}$, find the mass of the target particle. *(G.N.D.U. 2004)*

Ans. Mass of the incident particle $= m$

Velocity of incident particle before collision $= u$

Mass of the target particle (at rest) $= M$

Velocity of the target particle after collision $v_2 = \dfrac{u}{3}$

Velocity of the incident particle after collision $v_1 = \dfrac{-2u}{3}$

as the particle moves backward.

When one of the colliding particles is initially at rest

$$v_1 = \frac{m - M}{m + M}u \quad \text{and} \quad v_2 = \frac{2m}{m + M}u$$

$\therefore \qquad v_1 = -\dfrac{2u}{3} = \dfrac{m - M}{m + M}u \qquad\qquad\qquad ...(i)$

and $\qquad v_2 = \dfrac{u}{3} = \dfrac{2m}{m + M}u \qquad\qquad\qquad\qquad ...(ii)$

Dividing (i) by (ii), we have

$$-2 = \frac{m - M}{2m} \quad \text{or} - 4m = m - M$$

or $\qquad\qquad M = 5m.$

Q. 9.17. What happens to the velocities of individual particles after an elastic collision in centre of mass system? *(P.U. 2003)*

Ans. Velocities after elastic collision in centre of mass system. Let m_1 and m_2 be the masses of the two particles u_1 and u_2, and v_1 and v_2 their respective velocities in the *laboratory frame* before and after an elastic collision *i.e.* a head-on collision along the line joining their centres.

If $u_1{}'$ is the velocity of the particle of mass m_1 and $u_2{}'$ that of mass m_2 in the *centre of mass frame* before collision, then

$$u_1' = \frac{m_2(u_1 - u_2)}{m_1 + m_2} \qquad\qquad\qquad\qquad \text{[Eq (ix) Q. 9.14.]}$$

and

$$u_2' = \frac{m_1(u_2 - u_1)}{m_1 + m_2} \qquad\qquad\qquad\qquad \text{[Eq. (ix a) Q. 9.14]}$$

Again if $v_1{}'$ is the velocity of mass m_1 and $v_2{}'$ that of mass m_2 after collision, then

$$v_1' = \frac{-m_2(u_1 - u_2)}{m_1 + m_2} \qquad\qquad\qquad\qquad \text{[Eq. (x) Q. 9.14]}$$

and

$$v_2' = \frac{-m_1(u_2 - u_1)}{m_1 + m_2} \qquad\qquad\qquad\qquad \text{[Eq. (xi) Q. 9.14]}$$

Thus in the centre of mass frame the incident and target particles approach the centre of mass, collide and then go away from the centre of mass in the opposite direction with the same velocities.

Q. 9.18. Two particles each of mass 2 kg are moving with velocities $2\hat{i} + 4\hat{j}$ m/s and $5\hat{i} + 6\hat{j}$ m/s respectively. Find the kinetic energy of the system relative to centre of mass.

(G.N.D.U., 1993)

Ans. Given $\qquad m_1 = m_2 = 2$ kg.; $u_1 = 3\hat{i} + 4\hat{j}$; $u_2 = 5\hat{i} + 6\hat{j}$

Velocity of centre of mass $\vec{V}_{cm} = \dfrac{m_1 \vec{u_1} + m_2 \vec{u_2}}{m_1 + m_2} = \dfrac{2(3\hat{i} + 4\hat{j}) + 2(5\hat{i} + 6\hat{j})}{2 + 2} = 4\hat{i} + 5\hat{j}$

Velocity of m_1 in centre of mass frame $\vec{u_1'} = \vec{u_1} - \vec{V}_{cm}$

or $\qquad\qquad\qquad \vec{u_1'} = 3\hat{i} + 4\hat{j} - 4\hat{i} - 5\hat{j} = -\hat{i} - \hat{j}$

Velocity of m_2 in centre of mass $\vec{u_2'} = \vec{u_2} - \vec{V}_{cm}$

or $\qquad\qquad\qquad \vec{u_2'} = 5\hat{i} + 6\hat{j} - 4\hat{i} - 5\hat{j} = -\hat{i} - \hat{j}$

Kinetic energy relative to centre of mass before collision $= \dfrac{1}{2} m_1 u_1'^2 + \dfrac{1}{2} m_2 u_2'^2$

$$= \frac{1}{2} m_1 \left| \sqrt{(-1)^2 + (-1)^2} \right|^2 + \frac{1}{2} m_2 \left| \sqrt{(+1)^2 + (+1)^2} \right|^2$$

$$= 2 + 2 = 4 \text{ Joule.}$$

Q. 9.19. A particle of mass m_1 moving with a velocity $\vec{u_1}$ is elastically scattered from another particle of mass m_2. After collision the two particles move in opposite directions with the same speed. Find the relation between the two masses. (G.N.D.U. 1992)

Ans. Let $\vec{v_1}$ and $\vec{v_2}$ be the velocities of the two particles after collision, then $\vec{v_1} = -\vec{v_2}$

The particle of mass m_2 is at rest.

$\therefore$ Linear momentum before collision $= m_1 \vec{u_1}$

Linear momentum after collision $= m_1 \vec{v_1} + m_2 \vec{v_2} = m_1 \vec{v_1} - m_2 \vec{v_1} = (m_1 - m_2)\vec{v_1}$

According to the law of conservation of linear momentum

$$m_1 \vec{u_1} = (m_1 - m_2)\vec{v_1}$$

or $\qquad\qquad\qquad \vec{v_1} = \dfrac{m_1}{m_1 - m_2} \vec{u_1}$

Considering magnitudes only $|\vec{v_1}| = \dfrac{m_1}{m_1 - m_2}\,|\vec{u_1}|$

According to the law of conservation of energy

$$\frac{1}{2}m_1\left|\vec{u_1}\right|^2 = \frac{1}{2}m_1\left|\vec{v_1}\right|^2 + \frac{1}{2}m_2\left|\vec{v_1}\right|^2 \qquad\qquad [\,\because |\vec{v_2}| = |\vec{v_1}|\,]$$

$$= \frac{1}{2}(m_1 + m_2)\left|\vec{v_1}\right|^2 = \frac{1}{2}\frac{m_1 + m_2}{(m_1 - m_2)^2}\,m_1^2\left|\vec{u_1}\right|^2$$

$$\therefore \qquad (m_1 - m_2)^2 = (m_1 + m_2)\,m_1$$

or $\qquad m_1^2 + m_2^2 - 2m_1 m_2 = m_1^2 + m_1 m_2$

$$\therefore \qquad\qquad m_2^2 = 3m_1 m_2 \text{ or } m_2 = 3m_1$$

Q. 9.20. (*a*) **A particle of mass m_1 suffers perfectly elastic collision with another particle of mass m_2 at rest in the laboratory frame of reference. After scattering m_1 and m_2 move at angles θ_1 and θ_2 with respect to the original direction of m_1. Discuss the elastic collision between the two particles in the lab system.** (*P.U.* 2000; *H.P.U.* 1994)

(*b*) **Show that in the lab system the particles of the same mass will move at right angles to each other after collision if one of them were at rest before collision.** (*P.U.* 2000)

Ans. (*a*) **Laboratory frame.** Consider a particle of mass m_1 moving with a velocity $\vec{u_1}$ in the laboratory frame (*incident particle*) and let it have an *elastic* collision with a particle of mass m_2 at rest (*target particle*). After collision, the incident particle (now called the *scattered particle*) moves with a velocity $\vec{v_1}$ making an angle θ_1 with the initial direction and the target particle of mass m_2 moves with a velocity $\vec{v_2}$ making an angle θ_2 with the initial direction of motion of m_1.

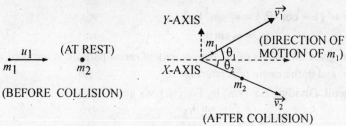

Fig. 9.8

. **Angle of scattering.** The angle θ_1 is known as *angle of scattering. It is defined as the angle between the initial direction and final direction of the incident particle* (or scattered particle) *after it has gone far away.*

Recoil angle. The angle θ_2 is known as *recoil angle. It is defined as the angle between the direction of target* (or recoil) *particle after collision and initial direction of the incident particle.*

Suppose the initial path of the particle m_1 is along the X-axis and also the plane containing $\vec{u_1}$ and $\vec{v_1}$ is the XY plane. Then according to the principle of conservation of momentum

$$m_1 v_1 \cos\theta_1 + m_2 v_2 \cos\theta_2 = m_1 u_1 \qquad\qquad ...(i)$$

and $\qquad m_1 v_1 \sin\theta_1 - m_2 v_2 \sin\theta_2 = 0 \qquad\qquad ...(ii)$

because before collision, the y-component of momentum is zero.

As the collision is perfectly elastic, the total kinetic energy is also conserved.

$$\therefore \qquad \frac{1}{2}m_1 v_1^2 + \frac{1}{2}m_2 v_2^2 = \frac{1}{2}m_1 u_1^2 \qquad\qquad ...(iii)$$

The three equations (i), (ii) and (iii) contain four unknown quantities v_1, v_2, θ_1 and θ_2. To find a solution of these equations at least one of these must be known. Let us suppose θ_1 is known. For simplicity, we further assume that $m_1 = m_2 = m$. Hence equations (i), (ii) and (iii) become

$$v_1 \cos \theta_1 + v_2 \cos \theta_2 = u_1 \qquad\qquad \text{...}(iv)$$
$$v_1 \sin \theta_1 - v_2 \sin \theta_2 = 0 \qquad\qquad \text{...}(v)$$
$$v_1^2 + v_2^2 = u_1^2 \qquad\qquad \text{...}(vi)$$

Rearranging we get

$$u_1 - v_1 \cos \theta_1 = v_2 \cos \theta_2 \qquad\qquad \text{...}(vii)$$
$$v_1 \sin \theta_1 = v_2 \sin \theta_2 \qquad\qquad \text{...}(viii)$$
$$u_1^2 - v_1^2 = v_2^2 \qquad\qquad \text{...}(ix)$$

Squaring and adding equations (vii) and ($viii$), we get

$$u_1^2 + v_1^2 \cos^2 \theta_1 - 2u_1 v_1 \cos\theta_1 + v_1^2 \sin^2 \theta_1 = v_2^2 \cos^2 \theta_2 + v_2^2 \sin^2 \theta_2$$

or $\qquad u_1^2 + v_1^2 - 2u_1 v_1 \cos\theta_1 = v_2^2$

But $\qquad\qquad v_2^2 = u_1^2 - v_1^2 \quad \therefore \quad u_1^2 + v_1^2 - 2u_1 v_1 \cos\theta_1 = u_1^2 - v_1^2$

or $\qquad\qquad 2v_1^2 = 2u_1 v_1 \cos\theta_1 \quad \therefore \quad v_1 = u_1 \cos\theta_1 \qquad\qquad \text{...}(x)$

Velocity of scattered particle. Equation (x) gives the value of v_1 the *velocity of scattered particle* in terms of known quantities u_1, the *velocity of incident particle* and θ_1 the *angle of scattering*.

$$\therefore \qquad\qquad v_1 = u_1 \cos\theta_1 \qquad\qquad \text{...}(x)\,(a)$$

Velocity of recoil particle. Substituting $v_1 = u_1 \cos\theta_1$ in equation (ix), we get

$$u_1^2 - u_1^2 \cos^2 \theta_1 = v_2^2$$

or $\qquad v_2^2 = u_1^2 (1 - \cos^2 \theta_1) = u_1^2 \sin^2 \theta_1$

$$\therefore \qquad\qquad v_2 = u_1 \sin\theta_1 \qquad\qquad \text{...}(xi)$$

This relation gives the values of v_2 the *velocity of recoil* particle in terms of u_1, the *velocity of incident particle* and θ_1 the *angle of scattering*.

Angle of recoil. Dividing Eq. ($viii$) by Eq. (vii), we get

$$\tan \theta_2 = \frac{v_1 \sin \theta_1}{u_1 - v_1 \cos \theta_1}$$

Substituting $v_1 = u_1 \cos\theta_1$, we have

$$\tan \theta_2 = \frac{u_1 \cos \theta_1 \sin \theta_1}{u_1 - u_1 \cos^2 \theta_1} = \frac{u_1 \cos \theta_1 \sin \theta_1}{u_1 (1 - \cos^2 \theta_1)} = \cot \theta_1 = \tan (\pi/2 - \theta_1)$$

or $\qquad\qquad \tan\theta_2 = \tan (\pi/2 - \theta_1) \quad \therefore \quad \theta_2 = \pi/2 - \theta_1 \qquad\qquad \text{...}(xii)$

This relation gives the value of θ_2 the *angle of recoil* in terms of θ_1, the *angle of scattering*.

(*b*) **Angle between scattered particle and recoil particle.** Relation (xii) can be put in the form $\theta_1 + \theta_2 = \pi/2$.

This relation shows that if the incident particle collides with a target particle of equal mass at rest in the laboratory frame, both the particles move in directions perpendicular to each other after an elastic collision.

Q. 9.21. (*a*) **Prove that in centre of mass system the magnitude of the velocities (or speeds) of the particles remains unaltered in elastic collision.**

(*Pbi.U.* 2001; *G.N.D.U.* 1999, 1997; *P.U.* 2000, 1994)

(*b*) **State the relation between velocities in centre of mass system and laboratory system.**

(*Pbi.U.* 2001, 1995)

Ans. (*a*) **Centre of mass frame.** Consider a particle of mass m_1 moving with a velocity $\vec{u_1}$ in the laboratory frame and let it suffer a perfectly elastic collision with a particle of mass m_2 at rest.

The velocity of centre of mass of a system of two particles relative to the laboratory frame is given by

$$\vec{V}_{cm} = \frac{m_1 \vec{u_1} + m_2 \vec{u_2}}{m_1 + m_2}$$

Since we have assumed the mass m_2 to be initially at rest in the laboratory frame,

$$\vec{u_2} = 0 \quad \text{and} \quad \vec{V}_{cm} = \frac{m_1}{m_1 + m_2} \vec{u_1}$$

This shows that $\vec{V}_{cm}$ and $\vec{u_1}$ have the same direction.

Relation between initial velocities (before collision) in centre of mass frame and laboratory frame. Let $\vec{u_1'}$ and $\vec{u_2'}$ be the initial velocities of the particles of mass m_1 and m_2 before collision *in the centre of mass frame,* then according to Galelian transformation equations

$$\vec{u_1'} = \vec{u_1} - \vec{V}_{cm} = \vec{u_1}\left(1 - \frac{m_1}{m_1 + m_2}\right) = \frac{m_2}{m_1 + m_2} \vec{u_1}$$

and

$$\vec{u_2'} = \vec{u_2} - \vec{V}_{cm} = -\vec{V}_{cm} = -\frac{m_1}{m_1 + m_2} \vec{u_1} \qquad [\because \vec{u_2} = 0]$$

We also have $\vec{u_1'} - \vec{u_2'} = \vec{u_1} - \vec{u_2}$ *i.e.,* the relative velocity between the two particles in the laboratory frame and centre of mass frame is the same.

Taking magnitude only $\qquad u_1' = \dfrac{m_2}{m_1 + m_2} u_1 \qquad\qquad\qquad ...(i)$

$$u_2' = -\frac{m_1}{m_1 + m_2} u_1 \qquad\qquad\qquad ...(ii)$$

Relation between final velocities and initial velocities in centre of mass frame.

Let $\vec{v_1'}$ and $\vec{v_2'}$ be the final velocities of the particles of mass m_1 and m_2 after collision in the centre of mass frame, then $\vec{v_1'} = \vec{v_1} - \vec{V}_{cm}$ and $\vec{v_2'} = \vec{v_2} - \vec{V}_{cm}$ where $\vec{v_1}$ and $\vec{v_2}$ are the final velocities of m_1 and m_2 in the laboratory frame.

In the centre of mass frame, the centre of mass is always at rest, therefore, the total linear momentum before and after collision is not only conserved but is also equal to zero.

$$\therefore \qquad m_1 \vec{u_1'} + m_2 \vec{u_2'} = 0 \quad \text{and} \quad m_1 \vec{v_1'} + m_2 \vec{v_2'} = 0$$

From the above relation we get $\vec{u_1'} = -\dfrac{m_2}{m_1} \vec{u_2'}$ and $\vec{v_1'} = -\dfrac{m_2}{m_1} \vec{v_2'}$

Taking magnitudes only $\qquad u_1' = -\dfrac{m_2}{m_1} u_2' \qquad\qquad\qquad ...(iii)$

and $\qquad v_1' = -\dfrac{m_2}{m_1} v_2' \qquad\qquad\qquad ...(iv)$

The negative signs indicate that $\vec{u_1'}$ and $\vec{u_2'}$ act along the same straight line in opposite directions. Similarly $\vec{v_1'}$ and $\vec{v_2'}$ also act along the same straight line in opposite direction as shown in Fig. 9.9 (*a*) and (*b*).

In other words, in the C.M. system the two particles move towards each other before collision and away from each other after collision.

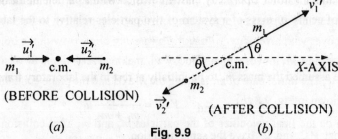

(BEFORE COLLISION)

(a)   Fig. 9.9   (b)

(AFTER COLLISION)

As collision is elastic, the kinetic energy is also conserved.

$$\therefore \quad \frac{1}{2}m_1 u_1'^2 + \frac{1}{2}m_2 u_2'^2 = \frac{1}{2}m_1 v_1'^2 + \frac{1}{2}m_2 v_2'^2 \qquad \ldots(v)$$

Substituting the values of u_1' and v_1' from (iii) and (iv) in equation (v), we have

$$\frac{1}{2}m_1 \frac{m_2^2}{m_1^2} u_2'^2 + \frac{1}{2}m_2 u_2'^2 = \frac{1}{2}m_1 \frac{m_2^2}{m_1^2} v_2'^2 + \frac{1}{2}m_2 v_2'^2$$

or $\quad u_2'^2 \left[\dfrac{m_2^2}{2m_1} + \dfrac{1}{2}m_2 \right] = v_2'^2 \left[\dfrac{m_2^2}{2m_1} + \dfrac{1}{2}m_2 \right]$

$$\therefore \qquad\qquad u_2' = v_2' \qquad\qquad\qquad \ldots(vi)$$

Similarly $\qquad\qquad u_1' = v_1' \qquad\qquad\qquad \ldots(vii)$

In other words, in an elastic collision in the centre of mass frame, the magnitudes of the velocities of the particles (speeds) do not change *i.e.*, **there is only a change in direction.**

(b) Relation between final velocities of the particles after collision in the centre of mass frame with the initial velocities before collision in the laboratory frame. A particle of mass m_1 moving with a velocity $\vec{u_1}$ in the laboratory frame suffers a perfectly elastic collision with a particle of mass m_2 at rest,

$\therefore$ *In the laboratory frame* $\vec{u_2} = 0$ *or* $|\vec{u_2}| = u_2 = 0$

If $\vec{u_1'}$ and $\vec{u_2'}$ are the initial velocities and $\vec{v_1'}$ and $\vec{v_2'}$ the final velocities after collision of the particles of mass m_1 and m_2 respectively in the *centre of mass frame*, then

$$v_1' = u_1' = \frac{m_2}{m_1 + m_2} u_1 \qquad \text{[According to Eq. (vii) and (i)] } \ldots(viii)$$

and $\qquad\qquad v_2' = u_2' = \dfrac{m_1}{m_1 + m_2} u_1 \qquad \text{[According to Eq. (vi) and (ii)] } \ldots(ix)$

Q. 9.22. (a) Deduce the relation between scattering angles in the laboratory and centre of mass frames for particles undergoing elastic collision. Discuss the case when (i) $m_1 < m_2$, (ii) $m_1 = m_2$ and (iii) $m_1 > m_2$. Show that when colliding particles are of equal masses, the scattering angle in laboratory system is one half of the scattering angle in centre of mass system.

(*Pbi.U.* 2003, 2001, 1993; *P.U.* 2007, 2004, 2001, 1999; *G.N.D.U.* 2006, 2002, 2000, 1994, 1993; *Osm. U.* 1997)

(b) Derive the relation between angle of recoil in laboratory system and angle of scattering in centre of mass system. Prove that in laboratory system two particles of equal masses move at right angles to each other after collision if one of them were at rest before collision.

(*Pbi.U.* 2005, 2001; *G.N.D.U.* 2000; *P.U.* 2004, 1999)

Ans. (*a*) **Relation between scattering angle** θ_1 **in the laboratory frame and** θ **in the centre of mass frame.** Consider a particle of mass m_1 moving with a velocity $\vec{u_1}$ in the laboratory frame and let it collide with a particle of mass m_2 at rest, the collision being perfectly elastic. After collision the incident particle moves with a velocity $\vec{v_1}$ making *scattering angle* θ_1 with the initial direction and the target particle of mass m_2 moves with a velocity $\vec{v_2}$ making *recoil angle* θ_2 with the initial direction of motion of m_1. The initial path of m_1 is along the X-axis and the plane containing $\vec{u_1}$ and $\vec{v_1}$ is the X-Y plane as shown in Fig. 9.8 (*b*).

Let $\vec{v_1'}$ and $\vec{v_2'}$ be the final velocities of the particles m_1 and m_2 after collision in the centre of mass frame making an angle θ with the X-axis as shown in Fig. 9.9 (*b*), then

$$\vec{v_1'} = \vec{v_1} - \vec{V_{cm}} \text{ and } \vec{v_2'} = \vec{v_2} - \vec{V_{cm}} \text{ As } \vec{u_2} = 0, \; V_{cm} = \frac{m_1 \vec{u_1}}{m_1 + m_2}$$

i.e., $\vec{V_{cm}}$ and $\vec{u_1}$ have the same direction along X-axis. Therefore $\vec{V_{cm}}$ has no component along the Y-axis. The y-component of the final velocity of the first particle of mass m_1 is the same in both the frames.

$$\therefore \qquad\qquad v_1 \sin \theta_1 = v_1' \sin \theta \qquad\qquad\qquad\qquad ...(i)$$

As the centre of mass has a velocity $\vec{V_{cm}}$ along X-axis with respect to the laboratory frame.

$$\therefore \qquad\qquad v_1 \cos\theta_1 = v_1' \cos\theta + V_{cm} \qquad\qquad\qquad\qquad ...(ii)$$

Dividing (*i*) by (*ii*), we have

$$\tan \theta_1 = \frac{v_1' \sin \theta}{v_1' \cos \theta + V_{cm}} = \frac{\sin \theta}{\cos \theta + \dfrac{V_{cm}}{v_1'}}$$

but

$$\vec{V_{cm}} = \frac{m_1}{m_1 + m_2} u_1$$

and

$$v_1' = \frac{m_2}{m_1 + m_2} u_1 \qquad\qquad \text{[For proof See 9.21 Eq. (\textit{viii})]}$$

Dividing, we get

$$\frac{V_{cm}}{v_1'} = \frac{m_1}{m_2}$$

$$\therefore \qquad\qquad \tan \theta_1 = \frac{\sin \theta}{\cos \theta + \dfrac{m_1}{m_2}} \qquad\qquad\qquad\qquad ...(iii)$$

This gives the relation between scattering angle θ_1 in the laboratory frame and scattering angle θ in the centre of mass frame.

Exercise. *If θ and ϕ are angles of scattering in Lab system and C.M. system respectively, prove that*

$$\tan \theta = \frac{\sin \phi}{\cos \phi + \dfrac{m_1}{m_2}} \qquad\qquad\qquad (P.U.\ 2009)$$

Hint. It has been proved in Eq. (*iii*) that

$$\tan \theta_1 = \frac{\sin \theta}{\cos \phi + \dfrac{m_1}{m_2}}$$

Here $\theta_1 = \theta$ and $\theta = \phi$ $\therefore$ $\tan \theta = \dfrac{\sin \phi}{\cos \phi + \dfrac{m_1}{m_2}}$

Special cases. (*i*) When $m_1 \ll m_2$. In this case m_1/m_2 can be neglected in relation (*iii*), and we get

$$\tan \theta_1 = \frac{\sin \theta}{\cos \theta} = \tan \theta$$

Thus if the incident particle is very light as compared to the target particle, the angles of scattering for the incident particle in the laboratory and C.M. system are very nearly equal.

(*i*) **When $m_1 = m_2$.** In this case $m_1/m_2 = 1$

Hence $\qquad \tan \theta_1 = \dfrac{\sin \theta}{1 + \cos \theta} = \dfrac{2 \sin \theta/2 \, \cos \theta/2}{1 + 2 \cos^2 \theta/2 - 1} = \tan \theta/2 \text{ or } \theta_1 = \theta/2 \qquad ...(iv)$

Thus if the incident and target particles are of equal masses, the angle of scattering in the laboratory system is half the angle of scattering in the C.M. system.

In other words, when θ takes the values from 0 to π, θ_1 varies from 0 to $\pi/2$. Hence all the particles in the laboratory frame are scattered in the *forward hemisphere* only.

(*iii*) **When $m_1 > m_2$.** The maximum value of $\tan\theta_1$ i.e.

$$\tan \theta_{1(max)} = \left[\frac{m_1^2 - m_2^2}{m_2^2} \right]^{-1/2}$$

from which we get $\qquad \sin \theta_{1(max)} = \dfrac{m_2}{m_1},$ $\qquad\qquad$ [For proof see Eq. (*iv*) and (*v*) Q. 9.23]

When $m_1 > m_2$ i.e. $\dfrac{m_1}{m_2} > 1$ or $\dfrac{m_2}{m_1} < 1$, θ_1 has a finite positive value. Therefore, all particles in the laboratory frame are scattered in a *forward cone.*

(*b*) **Relation between recoil angle θ_2 in the laboratory frame and scattering angle θ in the centre of mass frame.** The y-component of the final velocity of the particle of mass m_2 is the same in both the frames.

$\therefore \qquad\qquad v_2 \sin \theta_2 = v_2' \sin \theta$

As the centre of mass has a velocity $\vec{V}_{cm}$ along X- axis with respect to laboratory frame,

$$v_2 \cos \theta_2 = \vec{V}_{cm} - v_2' \cos \theta$$

$\therefore \qquad\qquad \tan \theta_2 = \dfrac{v_2' \sin \theta}{\vec{V}_{cm} - v_2' \cos \theta} = \dfrac{\sin \theta}{\dfrac{\vec{V}_{cm}}{v_2'} - \cos \theta}$

Now $\qquad\qquad v_2' = u_2'$ and $\vec{u}_2' = -\vec{V}_{cm}$

or $\qquad\qquad \dfrac{|\vec{V}_{cm}|}{|\vec{u}_2'|} = \dfrac{\vec{V}_{cm}}{u_2'} = \dfrac{\vec{V}_{cm}}{v_2'} = 1$

Hence $\qquad\qquad \tan \theta_2 = \dfrac{\sin \theta}{1 - \cos \theta}$

$$= \frac{2 \sin \theta/2 \, \cos \theta/2}{1 - 1 + 2 \sin^2 \theta/2} = \cot \frac{\theta}{2} = \tan \left(\frac{\pi}{2} - \frac{\theta}{2} \right)$$

$\therefore \qquad\qquad \theta_2 = \dfrac{\pi - \theta}{2} \text{ or } 2\theta_2 = \pi - \theta \qquad\qquad\qquad ...(v)$

The relation $2\theta_2 = \pi - \theta$ is independent of m_1 and m_2 and hence independent of their velocities and energies.

Special case. When $m_1 = m_2$. The relation between scattering angle θ_1 in the laboratory frame and the angle θ in the centre of mass frame is given by

$$\tan \theta_1 = \frac{\sin \theta}{\cos \theta + \dfrac{m_1}{m_2}}$$

If the two particles are of the same mass $m_1 = m_2$, then according to relation (*iv*)

$$\theta_1 = \theta/2 \text{ or } \theta = 2\theta_1$$

Substituting in (*v*) we get

$$2\theta_2 = \pi - 2\theta_1 \text{ or } \theta_2 = \pi/2 - \theta_1 \text{ or } \theta_1 + \theta_2 = \pi/2 \qquad \qquad ...(vi)$$

In other words, in the laboratory frame the two particles of the same mass will move at right angles to each other after collision, if one of these were at rest before collision.

Exercise. *If the angle of scattering for incident particle in C.M. system is* θ, *then show that the stationary target particle is scattered in the lab. system by an angle*

$$\theta_2 = 90 - \frac{\theta}{2} \qquad \qquad (P.U.\ 2006)$$

Hint. See proof given above to obtain Eq. (*v*).

Q. 9.23. (*a*) **Prove that the angle of scattering in the laboratory frame** θ_1 **will be maximum when the angle of scattering in the centre of mass frame is equal to** $\cos^{-1}\left[-\dfrac{m_2}{m_1}\right]$ **and the maximum value of** θ_1 **is given by** $\tan^{-1}\left[\dfrac{m_1^2}{m_2^2} - 1\right]^{-\frac{1}{2}}$.

(*b*) **What is the range of scattering angle in centre of mass frame? Does it depend upon the masses of colliding particles?** (*Pbi. U.* 2002)

Ans. (*a*) **Maximum value of angle of scattering in laboratory frame.** The angle of scattering in the laboratory frame θ_1 is related to the angle of scattering in the centre of mass frame by the equation

$$\tan \theta_1 = \frac{\sin \theta}{\cos \theta + \dfrac{m_1}{m_2}} = \sin \theta \left(\cos \theta + \frac{m_1}{m_2} \right)^{-1} \qquad \qquad ...(i)$$

[For proof See Eq. (*iii*) Q. 9.22.]

For $\tan \theta_1$ to be maximum $\dfrac{d}{d\theta}(\tan \theta_1) = 0$

$$\therefore \qquad \frac{d}{d\theta}(\tan \theta_1) = \cos \theta \left(\cos \theta + \frac{m_1}{m_2} \right)^{-1} + \sin \theta \left(\cos \theta + \frac{m_1}{m_2} \right)^{-2} \sin \theta$$

$$= \frac{\cos^2 \theta + \sin^2 \theta + \dfrac{m_1}{m_2} \cos \theta}{\left(\cos \theta + \dfrac{m_1}{m_2} \right)^2} = \frac{1 + \dfrac{m_1}{m_2} \cos \theta}{\left(\cos \theta + \dfrac{m_1}{m_2} \right)^2} = 0$$

Hence $\qquad 1 + \dfrac{m_1}{m_2} \cos \theta = 0$ or $\cos \theta = -\dfrac{m_2}{m_1}$ or $\theta = \cos^{-1}\left[-\dfrac{m_2}{m_1}\right]$ $\qquad ...(ii)$

and $\qquad \sin \theta = \sqrt{1 - \cos^2 \theta} = \sqrt{1 - \dfrac{m_2^2}{m_1^2}}$ $\qquad \qquad ...(iii)$

Substituting the value of $\sin\theta$ from (iii) and $\cos\theta$ from (ii) in (i), we have

$$\tan\theta_{1(max)} = \frac{\sqrt{1-\dfrac{m_2^2}{m_1^2}}}{-\dfrac{m_2}{m_1}+\dfrac{m_1}{m_2}} = \frac{\sqrt{m_1^2-m_2^2}}{\dfrac{m_1}{m_1 m_2}(m_1^2-m_2^2)} = \frac{m_2}{(m_1^2-m_2^2)^{1/2}} = \left(\frac{m_1^2}{m_2^2}-1\right)^{-\frac{1}{2}}$$

or $\quad \tan\theta_{1(max)} = \left(\dfrac{m_1^2-m_2^2}{m_2^2}\right)^{-\frac{1}{2}}$ or $\theta_{1(max)} = \tan^{-1}\left[\dfrac{m_1^2}{m_2^2}-1\right]^{-\frac{1}{2}}$ ...(iv)

We can also find from the above relation the value of $\sin\theta_{1(max)}$. From relation (iv)

$$\cot^2\theta_1 = \frac{m_1^2}{m_2^2}-1 \text{ or } 1+\cot^2\theta_1 = \frac{m_1^2}{m_2^2}$$

or $\qquad \csc^2\theta_1 = \dfrac{m_1^2}{m_2^2} \therefore \csc\theta_1 = \dfrac{m_1}{m_2}$ or $\sin\theta_{1(max)} = \dfrac{m_2}{m_1}$ ...(v)

From equation (ii) we find that angle θ has a finite value if $m_1 > m_2 \left[i.e., \dfrac{m_2}{m_1} < 1 \right]$ i.e., the striking particle is heavier than the target particle.

Again from equation (v) we find that angle θ_1 has a finite value if $m_1 > m_2 \left[i.e., \dfrac{m_2}{m_1} < 1 \right]$

(b) The mximum value of θ_1 the angle of scattering in the laboratory frame is given by $\sin\theta_1\,(max) = \dfrac{m_2}{m_1}$ [Eq. (v)] and is obtained when $m_2 = m_1$ or $m_2/m_1 = 1$. The maximum value of $\theta_1 = \pi/2$

$\therefore$ The value of θ_1 ranges from $0-\pi/2$.

When $m_1 = m_2$, θ the angle of scattering in the centre of mass frame is given by $\theta_1 = \theta/2$.

$\therefore$ The value of θ ranges from $0\to\pi$.

The range of θ the angle of scattering in the centre of mass frame is independent of masses.

Q. 9.24. (a) **A particle of mass m_1 suffers an elastic collision with a particle of mass m_2 initially at rest. If T_1 and T_2 are the kinetic energies of the two particles respectively and T_0 the total energy in the laboratory frame, T_1', T_2' and T_0' the corresponding values in centre of mass frame, show that $T_0 = T_0' + T_{c.m.}$ where $T_{c.m.}$ is the kinetic energy of C.M., and find the value of $\dfrac{T_0}{T_0'}$ and $\dfrac{T_1'}{T_0'}$.**

(Pbi. U. 2001; P.U. 2000)

OR

Find the relation between kinetic energies in Lab and C.M. system in a two body elastic collision.

(P.U. 2006)

(b) **Prove that the kinetic energy of the two colliding particles in the centre of mass system are inversely proportional to their masses.**

(P.U. 2003, 2000; H.P.U. 1997, 1996, 1994)

Ans. (a) **Elastic collision–Laboratory frame.** Let $\vec{u_1}$ be the initial velocity of mass m_1 in the Lab. system and $\vec{u_2} = 0$ the velocity of mass m_2. Let T_1 be the kinetic energy of mass m_1, T_2 the kinetic energy of mass m_2 and T_0 total kinetic energy of the system of two particles before scattering (or elastic collision), then

$$T_0 = T_1 + T_2 = \frac{1}{2} m_1 u_1^2 + \frac{1}{2} m_2 u_2^2 \text{ but } \vec{u_2} = 0 \quad \therefore \quad T_0 = \frac{1}{2} m_1 u_1^2 \quad ...(i)$$

Centre of mass frame. Let $\vec{u_1'}$ and $\vec{u_2'}$ be the velocities of masses m_1 and m_2 respectively in the centre of mass frame T_1' and T_2' their kinetic energies and T_0' the total initial kinetic energy of the system, then

$$T_0' = T_1' + T_2' = \frac{1}{2} m_1 u_1'^2 + \frac{1}{2} m_2 u_2'^2$$

Also the centre of mass system is moving with respect to the Lab. system with a velocity $\vec{V}_{cm}$ where

$$\vec{V}_{cm} = \frac{m_1 \vec{u_1} + m_2 \vec{u_2}}{m_1 + m_2} = \frac{m_1 \vec{u_1}}{m_1 + m_2} \qquad [\because \vec{u_2} = 0]$$

Now

$$\vec{u_1'} = \vec{u_1} - \vec{V}_{cm} = \vec{u_1} - \frac{m_1 \vec{u_1}}{m_1 + m_2} = \frac{m_2}{m_1 + m_2} \vec{u_1}$$

and

$$\vec{u_2'} = \vec{u_2} - \vec{V}_{cm} = -\vec{V}_{cm} = - \frac{m_1 \vec{u_1}}{m_1 + m_2}$$

$$\therefore \quad T_0' = \frac{1}{2} m_1 \frac{m_2^2}{(m_1 + m_2)^2} u_1^2 + \frac{1}{2} m_2 \frac{m_1^2}{(m_1 + m_2)^2} u_1^2 = \frac{1}{2} \frac{m_1 m_2}{m_1 + m_2} u_1^2 \quad ...(ii)$$

Hence

$$T_0 - T_0' = \frac{1}{2} m_1 u_1^2 - \frac{1}{2} \frac{m_1 m_2}{m_1 + m_2} u_1^2$$

$$= \frac{1}{2} \left[\frac{m_1^2 u_1^2 + m_1 m_2 u_1^2 - m_1 m_2 u_1^2}{(m_1 + m_2)} \right] = \frac{1}{2} \frac{m_1^2 u_1^2}{m_1 + m_2} \quad ...(iii)$$

Kinetic energy of centre of mass $= \frac{1}{2}(m_1 + m_2) V_{c.m.}^2$

or

$$T_{c.m.} = \frac{1}{2}(m_1 + m_2) \frac{m_1^2 u_1^2}{(m_1 + m_2)^2} = \frac{1}{2} \frac{m_1^2 u_1^2}{m_1 + m_2} \quad ...(iv)$$

From (iii) and (iv), we get $T_0 - T_0' = T_{c.m.}$ or $T_0 = T_0' + T_{c.m.}$ ...(iv)(a)

Thus the initial kinetic energy in laboratory system is the sum of the initial kinetic energy in the centre of mass system and kinetic energy of centre of mass itself. It shows that the initial kinetic energy in the centre of mass system is always less than the kinetic energy in the laboratory system. The difference is equal to the kinetic energy of centre of mass.

Exercise. *Prove that the K.E. of the system in Lab System is always greater than the K.E. of the system in C.M. system provided the collision is elastic.*   (G.N.D.U. 2007)

Hint. It has been proved in Eq. (iv)(a) that in an elastic collision

$$T_0 - T_0' = T_{c.m.}$$

where T_0 is the total initial Kinetic energy of the system in Lab. system and T_0' the total kinetic energy of the system in centre of mass (C.M.) system.

As $T_0 - T_0' = T_{c.m.}$ where $T_{c.m.}$ is a positive quantity, $T_1 > T_0'$ i.e. initial kinetic energy of the system in Lab. system is always greater than the Kinetic energy of the system in C.M. system.

Value of $\dfrac{T_0}{T_0'}$ Dividing (i) by (ii), we have

$$\frac{T_0}{T_0'} = \frac{\frac{1}{2} m_1 u_1^2}{\frac{1}{2} \frac{m_1 m_2}{m_1 + m_2} u_1^2} = \frac{m_1 + m_2}{m_2} = 1 + \frac{m_1}{m_2} \quad ...(v)$$

According to the above relation T_0' is less than T_0. The rest of the energy appears as $T_{c.m.}$.

If $$m_1 = m_2$$

$$T_0 = 2T_0' \text{ or } T_0' = \frac{T_0}{2} \qquad \therefore \ T_{c.m.} = T_0' - T_0 = \frac{T_0}{2}$$

(b) Value of $\dfrac{T_1'}{T_2'}$

$$T_1' = \frac{1}{2} m_1 u_1'^2 = \frac{1}{2} m_1 \frac{m_2^2}{(m_1 + m_2)^2} u_1^2 = \frac{m_2^2}{(m_1 + m_2)^2} T_0$$

Similarly

$$T_2' = \frac{1}{2} m_2 u_2'^2 = \frac{1}{2} m_2 \frac{m_1^2}{(m_1 + m_2)^2} u_1^2 = \frac{m_1 m_2}{(m_1 + m_2)^2} T_0$$

$$\therefore \qquad \frac{T_1'}{T_2'} = \frac{m_2}{m_1}$$

This shows that the kinetic energies of the two colliding particles in the centre of mass systems are inversely proportional to their masses.

Q. 9.25. (a) A particle of mass m_1 suffers an elastic collision with a particle of mass m_2 initially at rest. If t_1 and t_2 are their kinetic energies respectively after scattering in the Lab. system and T_0 the total energy, show that

$$\frac{t_1}{T_0} = 1 - \frac{2m_1 m_2}{(m_1 + m_2)^2} (1 - \cos\theta)$$

$$\frac{t_2}{T_0} = \frac{2m_1 m_2}{(m_1 + m_2)^2} (1 - \cos\theta)$$

where θ is the angle through which m_1 and m_2 are scattered in the centre of mass system.

(G.N.D.U. 2004, 1996)

(b) If $m_1 = m_2$, show that $\dfrac{t_1}{T_0} = \cos^2\theta_1$ and $\dfrac{t_2}{T_0} = \sin^2\theta_1$ where θ_1 is the angle through which m_1 is scattered in the Lab. system.

Ans. (a) Let $\vec{u_1}$ be the initial velocity of mass m_1 in the Lab. system and $\vec{u_2} = 0$ the velocity of mass m_2 before scattering (or collision). Let $\vec{v_1}$ and $\vec{v_2}$ be their respective velocities after collision in the Lab. system and $\vec{v_1'}$ and $\vec{v_2'}$ in the centre of mass system. If t_1 and t_2 are the kinetic energies of m_1 and m_2 after collision, then

$$t_1 = \frac{1}{2} m_1 v_1^2 \text{ and } t_2 = \frac{1}{2} m_2 v_2^2$$

The total kinetic energy before collision in the Lab. system $T_0 = \dfrac{1}{2} m_1 u_1^2 \ [\because u_2 = 0]$

$$\therefore \qquad \frac{t_1}{T_0} = \frac{v_1^2}{u_1^2}$$

Now according to parallelogram law of velocities $v_1'^2 = v_1^2 + V_{c.m.}^2 - 2v_1 V_{c.m.} \cos\theta_1$ (Fig.9.10)

or

$$v_1^2 = v_1'^2 - V_{c.m.}^2 + 2v_1 V_{c.m.} \cos\theta_1$$

$$\therefore \qquad \frac{t_1}{T_0} = \frac{v_1'^2 - V_{c.m.}^2 + 2v_1 V_{c.m} \cos\theta_1}{u_1^2}$$

$$= \frac{v_1'^2}{u_1^2} - \frac{V_{c.m.}^2}{u_1^2} + 2v_1 \frac{V_{c.m.}}{u_1^2} \cos\theta_1 \qquad \qquad ... (i)$$

Now $$v_1' = u_1' = \frac{m_2}{m_1 + m_2} u_1 \quad \therefore \quad \frac{v_1'}{u_1} = \frac{m_2}{m_1 + m_2}$$

Also $$V_{c.m.} = \frac{m_1}{m_1 + m_2} u_1 \qquad [\because u_2 = 0\,]$$

$$\therefore \quad \frac{V_{c.m.}}{u_1} = \frac{m_1}{m_1 + m_2}$$

and $$v_1 \sin\theta_1 = v_1' \sin\theta \quad \therefore \quad v_1 = v_1' \frac{\sin\theta}{\sin\theta_1}$$

Hence $$2v_1 \frac{V_{c.m.}}{u_1^2} \cos\theta_1 = 2v_1' \frac{\sin\theta}{\sin\theta_1} \frac{V_{c.m.}}{u_1^2} \cos\theta_1 = \frac{2\sin\theta\cos\theta_1}{\sin\theta_1} \cdot \frac{v_1'}{u_1} \cdot \frac{V_{c.m.}}{u_1}$$

$$= \frac{2\sin\theta\cos\theta_1}{\sin\theta_1} \cdot \frac{m_2}{m_1 + m_2} \cdot \frac{m_1}{m_1 + m_2}$$

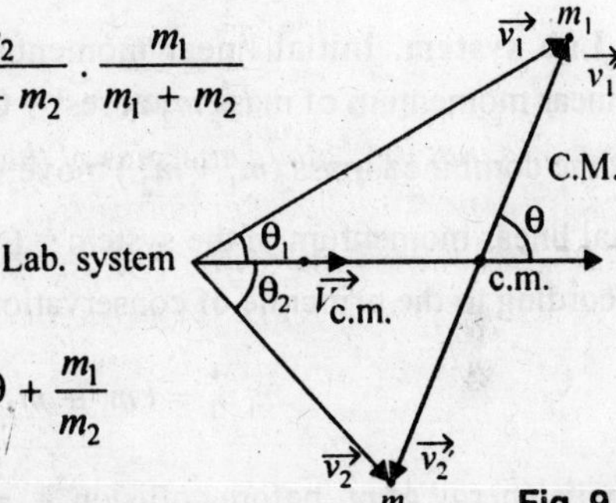

$\vec{v_1}$
m_1
$\vec{v_1'}$
C.M. system
θ
θ_1
Lab. system
θ_2
c.m.
$\vec{V}_{c.m.}$
$\vec{v_2}$
$\vec{v_2'}$
m_2

Fig. 9.10

Further $$\frac{\sin\theta\cos\theta_1}{\sin\theta_1} = \frac{\sin\theta}{\tan\theta_1}$$

$$= \frac{\sin\theta\left(\cos\theta + \frac{m_1}{m_2}\right)}{\sin\theta} = \cos\theta + \frac{m_1}{m_2}$$

because $$\left(\tan\theta_1 = \frac{\sin\theta}{\cos\theta + \frac{m_1}{m_2}}\right)$$ [For proof See Eq. (*iii*) Q. 9.22]

$$\therefore \quad \frac{2v_1 V_{c.m.}}{u_1^2} \cos\theta_1 = \frac{2m_1 m_2}{(m_1 + m_2)^2}\left(\cos\theta + \frac{m_1}{m_2}\right)$$

Hence $$\frac{t_1}{T_0} = \frac{m_2^2}{(m_1 + m_2)^2} - \frac{m_1^2}{(m_1 + m_2)^2} + \frac{2m_1 m_2}{(m_1 + m_2)^2}\left(\cos\theta + \frac{m_1}{m_2}\right)$$

$$= \frac{m_2^2 - m_1^2 + 2m_1 m_2 \cos\theta + 2m_1^2}{(m_1 + m_2)^2}$$

$$= \frac{m_2^2 + m_1^2 + 2m_1 m_2 - 2m_1 m_2 + 2m_1 m_2 \cos\theta}{(m_1 + m_2)^2}$$

$$= \frac{(m_1 + m_2)^2}{(m_1 + m_2)^2} - \frac{2m_1 m_2}{(m_1 + m_2)^2}(1 - \cos\theta)$$

or $$\frac{t_1}{T_0} = 1 - \frac{2m_1 m_2}{(m_1 + m_2)^2}(1 - \cos\theta) \qquad ...(i)$$

Again $$T_0 = t_1 + t_2 \quad \therefore \quad \frac{t_2}{T_0} = 1 - \frac{t_1}{T_0} = \frac{2m_1 m_2}{(m_1 + m_2)^2}(1 - \cos\theta) \qquad ...(ii)$$

(*b*) If $m_1 = m_2 = m$ (say), then

$$\frac{t_1}{T_0} = 1 - \frac{2m^2}{4m^2}(1 - \cos\theta) = 1 - \frac{(1 - \cos\theta)}{2} = \cos^2\theta/2$$

When $m_1 = m_2 \quad \theta_1 = \theta/2$ [For proof Eq. (iv) Q. 9.22]

$$\therefore \quad \frac{t_1}{T_0} = \cos^2\theta_1$$

Similarly $\dfrac{t_2}{T_0} = \sin^2 \dfrac{\theta}{2} = \sin^2 \theta_1$

Q. 9.26. A particle of mass m_1 moving with velocity $\vec{u_1}$ suffers a perfectly inelastic collision with a particle of mass m_2 at rest. Calculate the kinetic energy of the system before and after collision into the laboratory system and centre of mass system. Show that the decrease in kinetic energy is the same in two cases.

OR

Show that in perfectly inelastic collision in Laboratory system there is always loss of kinetic energy.   (*G.N.D.U.* 2004)

Ans. Perfectly inelastic collision. A *collision is said to be perfectly inelastic when the two particles stick together after collision and move with a common velocity.*

(*i*) **Lab system.** Initial linear momentum of mass m_1 moving with a velocity $\vec{u_1} = m_1 \vec{u_1}$. Initial linear momentum of mass m_2 at rest = 0

Let the combined mass $(m_1 + m_2)$ move with a velocity $\vec{v}$ in the initial direction, then

Final linear momentum of the system $= (m_1 + m_2) \vec{v}$

According to the principle of conservation of linear momentum

$$m_1 \vec{u_1} = (m_1 + m_2) \vec{v} \quad \therefore \quad \vec{v} = \dfrac{m_1}{m_1 + m_2} \vec{u_1}$$

Kinetic energy of m_1 before collision $= \dfrac{1}{2} m_1 u_1^2$

Kinetic energy of m_2 before collision = 0   [$\because m_2$ is at rest]

$\therefore$ Total kinetic energy before collision $T_1 = \dfrac{1}{2} m_1 u_1^2$

Kinetic energy of combined mass $(m_1 + m_2)$ after collision $T_2 = \dfrac{1}{2} (m_1 + m_2) v^2$

$$= \dfrac{1}{2} (m_1 + m_2) \dfrac{m_1^2 u_1^2}{(m_1 + m_2)^2} = \dfrac{1}{2} \dfrac{m_1^2}{m_1 + m_2} u_1^2$$

$$\therefore \qquad \dfrac{T_2}{T_1} = \dfrac{1}{2} \dfrac{m_1^2 u_1^2}{m_1 + m_2} \times \dfrac{1}{\dfrac{1}{2} m_1 u_1^2} = \dfrac{m_1}{m_1 + m_2}$$

As $m_1 < m_1 + m_2$, $T_2 < T_1$ *i.e., the final kinetic energy after collision is less than the kinetic energy before collision in the lab system.*

Decrease in energy. The decrease in energy $E = T_1 - T_2 = \dfrac{1}{2} m_1 u_1^2 - \dfrac{1}{2} \dfrac{m_1^2 u_1^2}{m_1 + m_2}$

$$= \dfrac{1}{2} \left[\dfrac{m_1^2 u_1^2 + m_1 m_2 u_1^2 - m_1^2 u_1^2}{m_1 + m_2} \right] = \dfrac{1}{2} \dfrac{m_1 m_2}{m_1 + m_2} u_1^2 = \dfrac{1}{2} \mu u_1^2 \quad \cdots (i)$$

where $\mu = \dfrac{m_1 m_2}{m_1 + m_2}$ is the reduced mass.

(*ii*) **Centre of mass system.** Velocity of centre of mass $\vec{V}_{c.m.} = \dfrac{m \vec{u_1}}{m_1 + m_2}$ [$\because \vec{u_2} = 0$]

Velocity of m_1 before collision in C. M. System $= \vec{u_1'} = \vec{u_1} - \vec{V}_{c.m.}$

$$= u_1 - \dfrac{m_1}{m_1 + m_2} \vec{u_1} = \dfrac{m_2}{m_1 + m_2} \vec{u_1}$$

Velocity of m_2 before collision in C. M. System $\vec{u_2'} = \vec{u_2} - \vec{V}_{c.m.} = -\vec{V}_{c.m.} = -\dfrac{m_1}{m_1 + m_2}\vec{u_1}$

After collision the two particles stick together and the combined mass ($m_1 + m_2$) moves with a velocity equal to the velocity of centre of mass with respect to the lab. system and is at rest with respect to the centre of mass system itself. Hence according to the principle of conservation of linear momentum $m_1\vec{u_1'} + m_2\vec{u_2'} = 0$ [∵ The final linear momentum = 0]

or $m_1\vec{u_1'} = -m_2\vec{u_2'}$

Initial kinetic energy of m_1 in C.M. system $= \dfrac{1}{2}m_1 u_1'^2$

Initial kinetic energy of m_2 in C.M. system $= \dfrac{1}{2}m_2 u_2'^2$

∴ Total initial kinetic energy in C.M. system $T_1' = \dfrac{1}{2}m_1 u_1'^2 + \dfrac{1}{2}m_2 u_2'^2$

Final kinetic energy of the combined mass ($m_1 + m_2$) $= T_2' = 0$

                     [∵ ($m_1 + m_2$) is at rest w.r.t. C.M. system]

Decrease in kinetic energy. The decrease in kinetic energy

$$E = T_1' - T_2' \qquad\qquad\qquad [\because\ T_2' = 0]$$

$$= \dfrac{1}{2}m_1 u_1'^2 + \dfrac{1}{2}m_2 u_2'^2$$

$$= \dfrac{1}{2}m_1\left(\dfrac{m_2 u_1}{m_1 + m_2}\right)^2 + \dfrac{1}{2}m_2\left(\dfrac{m_1 u_1}{m_1 + m_2}\right)^2$$

$$= \dfrac{1}{2}\dfrac{m_1 m_2 u_1^2}{(m_1 + m_2)^2}[m_1 + m_2] = \dfrac{1}{2}\dfrac{m_1 m_2}{m_1 + m_2}u_1^2$$

$$= \dfrac{1}{2}\mu u_1^2 \qquad\qquad\qquad\qquad ...(ii)$$

where $\mu = \dfrac{m_1 m_2}{m_1 + m_2}$ is the reduced mass.

Comparing relations (i) and (ii), we find that the decrease in kinetic energy after collision is the same in the lab. system as well as in the C. M. systems.

This decrease in K.E. may appear as excitation energy of the scattered particle.

It may also be noted that decrease in energy of the combined mass in C.M. system is equal to the initial kinetic energy of the particles in the same system.

Q. 9.27. Define scattering cross-section and express it in terms of number of scattered particles per second and incident flux density. What is differential and total scattering cross-section? Show that scattering cross-section has dimensions of area.

(G.N.D.U. 2007, 2006, 2003, 2001, 2000, 1999, 1997, 1995; Pbi.U. 2007, 2006 2001, 1999, 1993; P.U. 2006, 2004, 2001, 1992; H.P.U. 2003, 1996; Calicut U. 2003)

Ans. Scattering cross-section. Suppose a number of particles are incident on a target. Some of them are elastically scattered and others either go unscattered or are inelastically scattered.

*The ratio of the number of particles elastically scattered to the total number of particles incident on the target is called the **probability of scattering**.*

Consider a target consisting of n particles and having an area A on which other particles are incident. Let the number of particles incident per unit area per unit time be I then I is known as **incident flux density**. If $N_{(sc)}$ is the number of particles elastically scattered per scatterer per unit time, then the number of particles scattered per unit time $= nN_{(sc)}$

$$\therefore \text{ Probability of scattering } = \frac{\text{Number of particles elastically scattered per unit time}}{\text{Total number of incident particles per unit time}} = \frac{nN_{(sc)}}{IA}$$

Now suppose each target particle offers an effective area of **cross-section** $\sigma_{(sc)}$ to the incoming beam of particles, then the total effective area of cross-section which n target particles will offer is given by $n\sigma_{(sc)}$

As the total area of the target particles is A, then probability of scattering may also be defined as

$$\frac{\text{Total effective area of cross-section of target particles}}{\text{Total area of the target}} = \frac{n\sigma_{(sc)}}{A}$$

$$\therefore \qquad \frac{nN_{(sc)}}{IA} = \frac{n\sigma_{(sc)}}{A}$$

or $$\sigma_{(sc)} = \frac{N_{(sc)}}{I} = \frac{\text{Number of particles scattered per scatterer per unit time}}{\text{Number of particles incident per unit area per unit time}}$$

$$= \frac{\text{Number of particles scattered per scatterer per second}}{\text{Incident flux density}}$$

*Hence the **scattering cross-section** (also called geometrical cross-section) is defined as the ratio of the number of particles scattered per scatterer per unit time to the number of particles incident per unit area per unit time (or incident flux density).*

*The **differential scattering cross-section** $\sigma(\phi)$ is defined as the ratio of the number of particles scattered per scatterer at an angle ϕ per unit solid angle per unit time [$N(\phi)$] to the total number of particles incident per unit time per unit area of the target [I].*

$$\therefore \qquad \sigma(\phi) = \frac{N(\phi)}{I}$$

If the particles are scattered into an infinitesimally small solid angle $d\Omega$, then

$$\sigma(\phi)\,d\Omega = \frac{N(\phi)}{I}\,d\Omega \text{ or } N(\phi)\,d\Omega = I\sigma(\phi)d\Omega = I\sigma(\phi)\,2\pi \sin\phi\,d\phi$$

This gives the number of particles scattered per second into the solid angle $d\Omega$ or annular ring between the angles ϕ and $\phi + d\phi$.

Total scattering cross-section. *It is defined as the total number of particles scattered in all directions per unit time per scatterer per unit flux density.*

$$\therefore \qquad \sigma_{total} = \iiint \sigma(\phi)\,d\Omega = 2\pi \int \sigma(\phi)\sin\phi\,d\phi$$

Dimensions of $\sigma(\phi)$. As $N(\phi)$ is the number of particles scattered per scatterer per unit solid angle per unit time, its dimensions are T^{-1}. The dimensions of I are $L^{-2}\,T^{-1}$ as it is the number of particles incident per unit area per unit time.

$$\therefore \text{ Dimensions of } \sigma(\phi) \qquad = \text{Dimensions of } \frac{N(\phi)}{I}$$

$$= \frac{T^{-1}}{L^{-2}T^{-1}} = L^2$$

i.e., the dimensions of $\sigma(\phi)$ are that of area. This is why it is called scattering **cross-section**. The unit of σ is **barn**. 1 barn $= 10^{-28}$ m^2

Q. 9.28. What is Rutherford scattering? Show that the differential scattering cross-section for scattering of α-particles by an atomic nucleus is given by

$$\sigma(\phi) = \frac{1}{4}\left[\frac{Ze^2}{4\pi\varepsilon_0 E}\right]^2 \frac{1}{\sin^4\frac{\phi}{2}}$$

where the letters have their usual meaning.

(H.P.U. 2003, 2000, 1999, 1995, 1993; G.N.D.U. 2008, 2006, 2002, 2001, 2000, 1999, 1997, 1994; Pbi.U. 2003, 2002, 2000, 1999, 1993; P.U. 2006, 2005, 2003, 1999)

Ans. Rutherford Scattering. Rutherford studied the problem of scattering of α-particles by various materials and thereby laid the foundation of the 'nuclear model' of the atom. He observed the differential cross-section of elastic scattering in the above process assuming that

(*i*) The target and incident atoms were only point masses.

(*ii*) The scattering of positively charged α-particles takes place from the positively charged nucleus due to the electrostatic force of repulsion which obeys inverse square law and the effect of the charge on the electrons is neglected.

(*iii*) The scattering (target) nucleus has an infinite mass and remains at rest during the scattering process.

Let the incident particle come from infinity along the direction *XO*. This particle will follow an unbounded orbit because being initially at an infinite distance from the centre of the force (the atomic nucleus) will start journey along the straight line path *XO*. As it approaches the centre of force it begins to deflect from this straight line trajectory and after some time approaches the point *A*, the **point of closest approach** to the force centre. Thereafter, the particle begins to move away from the centre of force and finally picks up a straight line path *OY*. As the final direction of motion

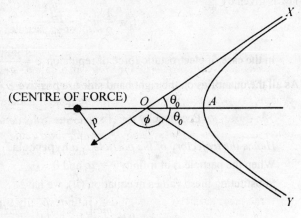

Fig. 9.11

is not the same as the incident direction of the particle, the particle is said to be scattered through an angle φ between the two directions of motion *i.e. XO* produced and *OY*. This angle is known as the **angle of scattering.**

The particle incident along *XO* makes an angle θ_0 with the axis of symmetry of the trajectory of the particle. The direction *OY* along which the particle finally moves when at infinity after being scattered will also make an angle θ_0 with the axis of symmetry as the trajectory being symmetrical about this axis a particle incident along *YO* will be scattered along *OX*.

∴ $\angle XOA = \angle YOA = \theta_0$

where θ_0 is the angle which the initial or the final radius vectors from the centre of force make with the axis of symmetry.

Hence $\phi = \pi - 2\theta_0$ or $\theta_0 = \dfrac{\pi}{2} - \dfrac{\phi}{2}$ ... (*i*)

Impact parameter. Let the particle have an initial velocity v_0 and let it be travelling in such a direction that, if undeflected it would pass at a perpendicular distance *p* from the centre of force. This distance is known as **impact parameter** *and is defined as the perpendicular distance between the* *centre of force or the line of head-on collision and the direction of incident velocity vector when the particle is at infinity.*

Note. The line of head-on collision is the line parallel to the direction of incident velocity vector OX and passing through the centre of force.

When the incident particle is at infinity all its energy is kinetic.

$\therefore$ Total energy $\qquad\qquad E = \dfrac{1}{2} m v_0^2$

and Angular momentum = moment of momentum

$$J = m v_0 p$$

Hence $\qquad\qquad\qquad J = p \sqrt{2mE} \qquad\qquad\qquad\qquad\qquad\qquad ...(i)\,(a)$

The trajectory of a particle moving under a central force is given by

$$\frac{1}{r} = \frac{mc}{J^2} [1 + \varepsilon \cos \theta] \qquad\qquad\qquad\text{[Eq. }(viii)\text{ Q. 7.14]}$$

where $\qquad\qquad \varepsilon^2 = 1 + \dfrac{2EJ^2}{mc^2} \qquad \therefore \dfrac{1}{r} = \dfrac{mc}{J^2}\left[1 + \left(\sqrt{1 + \dfrac{2EJ^2}{mc^2}}\right)\cos\theta\right] \qquad ...(ii)$

The value of total energy E for a particle moving under a repulsive force obeying inverse square law is given by

$$E = \frac{1}{2} m \dot{r}^2 + \frac{J^2}{2mr^2} + \frac{c}{r} \qquad\qquad\text{[Eq. }(ii)\text{ Q. 7.10]}$$

In the case of electrostatic force of repulsion $c = \dfrac{+q_1 q_2}{4\pi\varepsilon_0}$ in S. I. units and is a positive quantity.

As all the quantities on the right hand side are positive E is always a positive quantity.

$$\therefore \qquad\qquad \text{Eccentricity } \varepsilon = \sqrt{1 + \frac{2EJ^2}{mc^2}} > 1$$

Hence the trajectory of the particle is a **hyperbola.**

When the particle is at infinity $r = \infty$ and $\theta = \theta_0$

Substituting these values in equation (ii), we have

$$0 = \frac{mc}{J^2}\left[1 + \left(\sqrt{1 + \frac{2EJ^2}{mc^2}}\right)\cos\theta_0\right]$$

$$\therefore \qquad \left[\sqrt{1 + \frac{2EJ^2}{mc^2}}\right]\cos\theta_0 = -1$$

or $\qquad \left(1 + \dfrac{2EJ^2}{mc^2}\right)\cos^2\theta_0 = 1$

or $\qquad\qquad 1 + \dfrac{2EJ^2}{mc^2} = \dfrac{1}{\cos^2\theta_0} = \sec^2\theta_0$

$$\therefore \qquad \frac{2EJ^2}{mc^2} = \sec^2\theta_0 - 1 = \tan^2\theta_0 \qquad\qquad\qquad ...(iii)$$

Substituting $J = p\sqrt{2mE}$ in (iii), we have

$$\frac{2Ep^2 \cdot 2mE}{mc^2} = \tan^2\theta_0 \qquad \therefore \ \tan\theta_0 = \frac{2pE}{c}$$

But $\qquad\qquad \theta_0 = \dfrac{\pi}{2} - \dfrac{\phi}{2} \qquad\qquad \therefore \ \tan\theta_0 = \tan\left(\dfrac{\pi}{2} - \dfrac{\phi}{2}\right) = \cot\dfrac{\phi}{2}$

$$\therefore \qquad \cot\frac{\phi}{2} = \frac{2pE}{c} \quad \text{or} \quad p = \frac{c}{2E}\cot\frac{\phi}{2} \qquad\qquad ...(iv)$$

Let the particles be incident on the target in the form of a beam. If I is the incident flux density, then the number of particles flowing in the beam per unit area per unit time $= I$.

The number of particles having an impact parameter between p and $p + dp = IdA$ where dA is the area of the annular ring of internal radius p and external radius $p + dp$.

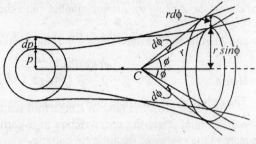

The area of the annular ring $dA = 2\pi p.dp$.

The total number of particles falling within the annular ring $= IdA = I\,2\pi pdp$.

These particle will be scattered between the angles ϕ and $\phi + d\phi$. The particles having larger values of p will be scattered through smaller

Fig. 9.12

angles and vice-versa. For very large values of p the particles will almost go straight along their path. This is because larger the value of p, the smaller the force between the particles and lesser the inter-action.

Let the scattered particles lie within the angles ϕ and $\phi + d\phi$ and make an annular ring which forms a cone having its apex at the centre of mass C. If r is the distance of a point on the ring from the centre of mass, then

The internal radius of the annular ring $= r\sin\phi$ and thickness of the annular ring $= rd\phi$

The solid angle angle subtended by the annular ring at the centre of mass

$$d\Omega = \frac{2\pi r\sin\phi\,rd\phi}{r^2} = 2\pi\sin\phi\,d\phi$$

If $N(\phi)$ is the number of particles scattered per scatterer per unit solid angle per unit time and $\sigma(\phi)$ the differential cross-section of scattering, then

$$\sigma(\phi) = \frac{N(\phi)}{I} \quad \text{or} \quad N(\phi) = I\,\sigma(\phi)$$

$\therefore$ The number of particles scattered per scatterer per unit time within the solid angle

$$d\Omega = N(\phi)\,d\Omega = I\,\sigma(\phi)\,2\pi\sin\phi d\phi$$

All the particles incident within the annular ring having radii lying between p and $p + dp$ will be scattered through angles lying between ϕ and $\phi + d\phi$.

$$\therefore \qquad I.\,2\pi p\,dp = I\,\sigma(\phi)\,2\pi\sin\phi d\phi \quad \therefore \sigma(\phi) = \frac{p}{\sin\phi}\cdot\frac{dp}{d\phi}$$

According to relation (iv) $\quad p = \frac{c}{2E}\cot\frac{\phi}{2} \qquad \therefore \frac{dp}{d\phi} = \frac{c}{2E}\frac{1}{2}\text{cosec}^2\frac{\phi}{2}$

$$\therefore \qquad \sigma(\phi) = \frac{c}{2E}\cot\frac{\phi}{2}\cdot\frac{1}{\sin\phi}\cdot\frac{c}{2E}\frac{1}{2}\text{cosec}^2\frac{\phi}{2} = \frac{c^2}{(4E)^2}\cdot\frac{1}{\sin^4\frac{\phi}{2}} \qquad ...(v)$$

In the above discussion the scattering centre has been taken to be of infinite mass so that it remains at rest during the scattering process. In such a case $E = T_0 = T_0'$ where T_0 is the kinetic energy of the particle in the Lab. system and T_0' in the centre of mass system. If the mass of the scattering centre is not infinite, then $T_0' = T_0 - T_{c.m.}$ where $T_{c.m.}$ is the kinetic energy of the centre of mass, and $T_0 = E$ the kinetic energy of the incident particle when it is at infinite distance *i.e.*, outside the influence of the nucleus. Hence in the centre of mass system

$$\sigma(\phi) = \frac{c^2}{(4T_0')^2} \cdot \frac{1}{\sin^4 \frac{\phi}{2}} = \frac{c^2}{(4T_0')^2} \operatorname{cosec}^4 \frac{\phi}{2}$$

Scattering of α-Particles. In the case of scattering of α-particle of charge $+ 2e$ from a nucleus of charge Ze, Z being the atomic number and e the electronic charge $c = + \dfrac{q_1 q_2}{4\pi\varepsilon_0} = \dfrac{2Ze^2}{4\pi\varepsilon_0}$

Substituting the value of c in Eq. (v), we have

$$\sigma(\phi) = \frac{(2Ze^2)^2}{(4\pi\varepsilon_0)^2 (4E)^2} \frac{1}{\sin^4 \frac{\phi}{2}} = \left[\frac{Ze^2}{4\pi\varepsilon_0 E} \right]^2 \frac{1}{\sin^4 \frac{\phi}{2}} \qquad \qquad ...(vi)$$

This result gives the famous Rutherford scattering cross-section for α-particles and shows that the differential scattering cross-section of α-particles by a nucleus is inversely proportional to the square of the energy of the incident particle.

Q. 9.29. (*a*) **What is impact parameter? How is it connected with angular momentum?**

(*G.N.D.U.* 2007, 2002, 1993; *P.U.* 1993; *H.P.U.* 1993)

(*b*) **What is the value of total scattering cross-section for Rutherford scattering?**

(*G.N.D.U.* 1993)

(*c*) **What is the angle of scattering for an α-particle approaching the nucleus with zero impact parameter?**   (*G.N.D.U.* 1994)

(*d*) **What is the value of impact parameter for 180° scattering angle?**   (*H.P.U.* 2003)

(*e*) **Is the orbital angular momentum of α-particle in Rutherford scattring conserved ?**

(*Pbi. U.* 2008)

Ans. (*a*) **Impact parameter.** For **Ans.** see Q. 9.28.

For an incident particle of mass m having an initial velocity $\vec{v_0}$, and an impact parameter p

Angular momentum $\vec{J} = m\vec{v_0}\, p$

(*b*) **Total scattering cross-section.** The value of total scattering cross-section for Rutherford scattering is *infinity* as the total cross-section represents the number of particles scattered in all directions.

(*c*) The angle of scattering ϕ is given by the relation

$$p = \frac{c}{2E} \cot \frac{\phi}{2}$$

where p is the impact parameter, E the kinetic energy of the incident α-particle and $c = \dfrac{2Ze^2}{4\pi\varepsilon_0}$

where Ze is the charge on the atomic nucleus and $2e$ the positive charge on the α-particle.

$$\therefore \qquad \cot \frac{\phi}{2} = \frac{2pE}{c} = \frac{2pE}{2Ze^2 / 4\pi\varepsilon_0}$$

or $\qquad \qquad \tan \dfrac{\phi}{2} = \dfrac{2Ze^2 / 4\pi\varepsilon_0}{2pE}$

When $\qquad \qquad p = 0 \qquad \tan \dfrac{\phi}{2} = \infty$ and $\dfrac{\phi}{2} = \dfrac{\pi}{2}$

or $\qquad \qquad \phi = \pi = 180°$

Thus the angle of scattering for the α-particle is 180°. *It means that an α-particle approaching the nucleus along the line of head-on collision will be scattered back.*

(d) For $180° = \pi$ scattering angle the impact parameter $p = 0$ because $\tan\phi/2 = \tan\pi/2 = \infty$.

(e) The motion of the α-particle in Rutherford scattering is under an inverse square *Central force*. The orbital angular momentum is, therefore, conserved. For proof see Q. 7.5.

Q. 9.30. Find the scattering cross-section $\sigma(\phi)$ of lead Pb (Z = 82, A = 207) for 7 MeV α-particles corresponding to $\phi = 30°$ a.m.u. $= 1.67 \times 10^{-27}$ kg.   *(Pbi.U. 1991)*

Ans. Kinetic energy of the α-particle in Lab. system $T_0 = 7 \ MeV$

$$= 7 \times 1.6 \times 10^{-13} \ J = 11.2 \times 10^{-13} \ J$$

Mass of the α-particle $m_1 = 4 \times 1.67 \times 10^{-27}$ kg $= 6.68 \times 10^{-27}$ kg

Mass of the target atom lead $m_2 = 207 \times 1.67 \times 10^{-27}$ kg $= 3.46 \times 10^{-25}$ kg

Let v_0 be the velocity of the α-particle, then $\dfrac{1}{2} m_1 v_0^2 = 11.2 \times 10^{-13} \ J$

$$\therefore \qquad v_0 = \left\{ \frac{2 \times 11.2 \times 10^{-13}}{6.68 \times 10^{-27}} \right\}^{1/2} = 1.8 \times 10^7 \ \text{m/s}$$

Velocity of the centre of mass $V = \dfrac{m_1}{m_1 + m_2} v_0$ [As the target particle lead is at rest.]

$$= \frac{4}{4 + 207} \times 1.8 \times 10^7 = 3.47 \times 10^5 \ \text{m/s}$$

Kinetic energy of the centre of mass

$$T_{c.m.} = \frac{1}{2}(m_1 + m_2)V^2 = \frac{1}{2} \times 211 \times 1.67 \times 10^{-27} \times (3.47 \times 10^5)^2$$

$$= 2 \times 10^{-14} \ J = 0.2 \times 10^{-13} \ J$$

$\therefore$ Kinetic energy of the α-particle in c.m. frame

$$E = T_0' = T_0 - T_{c.m.} = 11.2 \times 10^{-13} - 0.2 \times 10^{-13} = 11 \times 10^{-13} \ J$$

Charge on the electron $= 1.6 \times 10^{-19}$ C

$\therefore$ Charge on the α-particle $q_1 = 2e = 2 \times 1.6 \times 10^{-19}$ C

and charge on the Pb nucleus $q_2 = 82e = 82 \times 1.6 \times 10^{-19}$ C

$$\therefore \qquad c = \frac{q_1 q_2}{4\pi\varepsilon_0} = 2 \times 1.6 \times 10^{-19} \times 82 \times 1.6 \times 10^{-19} \times 9 \times 10^9 = 3.8 \times 10^{-26}$$

The angle of scattering θ in the C.M. frame and θ_1 in the Lab. frame are connected by the relation

$$\tan\theta_1 = \frac{\sin\theta}{\cos\theta + \dfrac{m_1}{m_2}}.$$

In this case $m_1 = 4$ and $m_2 = 207$. Therefore $m_1 \ll m_2$ and $\dfrac{m_1}{m_2}$ can be neglected.

$$\therefore \qquad \tan\theta_1 = \tan\theta$$

i.e., the angle of scattering in C.M. frame = Angle of scattering in Lab. frame

Hence angle of scattering in C. M. frame $\phi = 30°$ $\therefore$ $\dfrac{\phi}{2} = 15°$ $\sin\dfrac{\phi}{2} = 0.2588$

$$\therefore \qquad \sigma(\phi_0) = \frac{c^2}{(4T_0')^2} \frac{1}{\sin^4 \dfrac{\phi}{2}} = \frac{3.8 \times 3.8 \times 10^{-52}}{(4 \times 11 \times 10^{-13})^2} \frac{1}{(.2588)^4}$$

$$= 0.74 \times 10^{-26} \times \frac{1}{(.2588)^4} = 1.8 \times 10^{-26} \ \text{m}^2$$

Q. 9.31. α-particle of energy 5 *MeV* are scattered through an angle of 60° in passing through the gold foil. Find the differential scattering cross-section. Given that Z and A for gold are 79 and 197 respectively and 1 *a. m. u.* = 1.67 × 10⁻²⁴ g.   (*P.U.* 1999)

Ans. Kinetic energy of the α-particle in Lab. system $T_0 = 5$ *MeV*

$$= 5 \times 1.6 \times 10^{-13} \text{ J} = 8 \times 10^{-13} \text{ J}$$

Mass of the α-particle $m_1 = 4 \times 1.67 \times 10^{-24}$ g $= 4 \times 1.67 \times 10^{-27}$ kg $= 6.68 \times 10^{-27}$ kg

Mass of target atom (Gold) $m_2 = 197 \times 1.67 \times 10^{-27}$ kg $= 3.29 \times 10^{-25}$ J

Let V_0 be the velocity of the α-particle, then $\frac{1}{2} m_1 v_0^2 = 8 \times 10^{-13}$ J

$$\therefore \qquad v_0 = \left[\frac{2 \times 8 \times 10^{-13}}{6.68 \times 10^{-27}} \right] = 1.55 \times 10^7 \; m\,s^{-1}$$

Velocity of centre of mass $V = \dfrac{m_1}{m_1 + m_2} v_0$ \qquad [As the target particle (Gold) is at rest.]

$$= \frac{4}{4 + 197} \times 1.55 \times 10^7 = 3.08 \times 10^5 \text{ m/s}$$

Kinetic energy of centre of mass

$$T_{c.m} = \frac{1}{2}(m_1 + m_2)V^2 = \frac{1}{2}(4 + 197) \times 1.67 \times 10^{-27} \times (3.08 \times 10^5)^2$$

$$= 1592 \times 10^{-17} \text{ J} = 0.1592 \times 10^{-13} \text{ J}$$

Kinetic energy of the α-particle in centre of mass frame

$$E = T_0' = T_0 - T_{c.m.} = 8 \times 10^{-13} - 0.1592 \times 10^{-13} = 7.84 \times 10^{-13} \text{ J}$$

Charge on the α-particle \qquad $q_1 = 2e = 2 \times 1.6 \times 10^{-19}$ C.

and \; Charge on the gold nucleus $q_2 = 79 \; e = 79 \times 1.6 \times 10^{-19}$ C

$$\therefore \quad c = \frac{q_1 q_2}{4\pi\varepsilon_0} = 2 \times 1.6 \times 10^{-19} \times 79 \times 1.6 \times 10^{-19} \times 9 \times 10^9 = 3.64 \times 10^{-26}$$

The angle of scattering θ in the C.M. frame and θ_1 in the Lab. frame are connected by the

relation $\tan \theta_1 = \dfrac{\sin \theta}{\cos \theta + \dfrac{m_1}{m_2}}$

In this case $m_1 = 4$ and $m_2 = 197$. Therefore $m_1 \ll m_2$ and $\dfrac{m_1}{m_2}$ can be neglected.

$$\therefore \qquad\qquad \tan \theta_1 = \tan \theta$$

i.e., the angle of scattering in C.M. frame = Angle of scattering in Lab. Frame.

Hence angle of scattering in centre of mass frame

$$\phi = 60° \qquad \therefore \frac{\phi}{2} = 30° \qquad \sin \frac{\phi}{2} = \frac{1}{2}$$

$$\therefore \qquad \sigma(\phi) = \frac{c^2}{(4T_0')^2} \frac{1}{\sin^4 \dfrac{\phi}{2}} = \frac{(3.64 \times 10^{-26})^2 \times 16}{(4 \times 7.84 \times 10^{-13})^2} = 0.216 \times 10^{-26}$$

$$= 2.16 \times 10^{-27} \text{ m}^2.$$

Q. 9.32. (*a*) Derive a relation between impact parameter and distance of closest approach of a charged particle to a nucleus of atomic number Z.

(*b*) **Calculate the impact parameter of a 2.5 Mev α-particle where distance of closest approach to lead nucleus (Z = 82) = 1.9 × 10⁻¹¹ cm.**   (*H.P.U,* 1997)

Ans. (*a*) **Relation between impact parameter and distance of closest approach.** Consider a charged particle carrying charge *q* approaching a heavy nucleus of charge *Ze* (Atomic number *Z*).

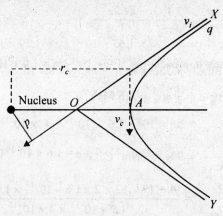

Fig. 9.13

Suppose the charged particle is at a very large distance from the nucleus and has a velocity v_i. Due to the presence of the positively charged nucleus it suffers a force of repulsion and is deviated from its original straight line path. As the the charged particle comes closer and closer to the nucleus, the Coulomb force of repulsion goes on increasing. When the particle reaches *A*, the distance of nearest approach, it is deflected and follows a hyperbolic path with the nucleus as one of its foci. The distance r_c between the nucleus and the point of closest approach *A* is called the *distance of closest approach.* The perpendicular distance *p* of the nucleus from the initial direction *XO* of the charged particle is called *impact parameter*.

Let *m* be the mass v_i the initial velocity of the charged particle at infinite distance from the nucleus, then

Initial kinetic energy of the particle $E_i = \dfrac{1}{2} mv_i^2$

Initial potential energy of the particle $U_i = 0$

Initial angular momentum of the particle about the nucleus $= J_i = mv_i p$

If v_c be the velocity of the particle at *A*, the distance of closest approach r_c, then

Kinetic energy of the particle at *A*, $E_c = \dfrac{1}{2} mv_c^2$

Potential energy of the particle at $A = U_c = \dfrac{1}{4\pi\varepsilon_0} \dfrac{Zeq}{r_c}$

Angular momentum of the particle at *A* about the nucleus $= J_c = mv_c r_c$

Since the force is central, angular momentum is conserved.

∴ $mv_c r_c = mv_i p$

∴ $v_c = \dfrac{v_i p}{r_c}$

According to the law of conservation of energy

$$\frac{1}{2}mv_i^2 = \frac{1}{2}\frac{mv_i^2 \, p^2}{r_c^2} + \frac{1}{4\pi\varepsilon_0}\frac{Zeq}{r_c}$$

or $\qquad \frac{1}{2} m v_i^2 \left(1 - \frac{p^2}{r_c^2} \right) = \frac{1}{4\pi\varepsilon_0} \frac{Zeq}{r_c}$

For an α- particle $\qquad q = 2e$

$\therefore \qquad 1 - \frac{p^2}{r_c^2} = \frac{1}{4\pi\varepsilon_0} \frac{Ze.2e}{r_c \times \frac{1}{2} m v_i^2}$ ...(i)

(b) Now distance of closest approach $r_c = 1.9 \times 10^{11}$ cm $= 1.9 \times 10^{-13}$ m; $Z = 82$

Energy of the α-particle $= \frac{1}{2} m v_i^2 = 2.5$ MeV

$= 2.5 \times 10^6 \times 1.6 \times 10^{-19} = 4 \times 10^{-13}$ J

$\frac{1}{4\pi\varepsilon_0} = 9 \times 10^9$ Nm^{2}C^{-2}; $e = 1.6 \times 10^{-19}$ C

$\therefore \quad \frac{1}{4\pi\varepsilon_0} \frac{Ze2e}{r_c \times \frac{1}{2} m v_i^2} = \frac{9 \times 10^9 \times 82 \times 2 \times 1.6 \times 10^{-19} \times 1.6 \times 10^{-19}}{1.9 \times 10^{-13} \times 4 \times 10^{-13}} = 0.497$

$\therefore \quad 1 - \frac{p^2}{r_c^2} = 0.497$ or $\frac{p^2}{r_c^2} = 1 - 0.497 = 0.503$

or $\qquad p = (0.503 \times r_c^2)^{1/2} = (0.503)^{1/2} \times 1.9 \times 10^{-13}$

$= 1.35 \times 10^{-13}$ m

Exercise. *Calculate the impact parameter for 2MeV α- particles where distance of closest approach to a gold nucleus (Z = 70) is 2 × 10⁻¹¹cm.* (H. P. U. 2003)

Hint. Impact parameter p and distance of closest approach r_c are connected by the relation

$1 - \frac{p^2}{r_c^2} = \frac{1}{4\pi\varepsilon_0} \frac{Ze.2e}{r_c \times \frac{1}{2} m v_i^2}$

Here $\frac{1}{4\pi\varepsilon_0} \frac{Ze.2e}{r_c \times \frac{1}{2} m v_i^2} = \frac{9 \times 10^9 \times 70 \times 1.6 \times 10^{-19} \times 2 \times 1.6 \times 10^{-19}}{2 \times 10^{-15} \times 3.2 \times 10^{-13}} = 0.504$

$\frac{p^2}{r_c^2} = 1 - 0.504 = 0.496$

$\therefore \qquad p = (0.496)^{1/2} \times 2 \times 10^{-13} = 0.704 \times 2 \times 10^{-13} = 1.408 \times 10^{-13}$ m

Q. 9.33. (a) **How does the distance of closest approach of α-particle differ from minimum distance of closest approach in Rutherford scattering ?** (P.U. 2007)

(b) **How is collision between two balls different from a collision between α-particle and nucleus?** (P.U. 2008)

Ans. (a) The distance of closest approach r_c of an α-particle in Rutherford scattering is given by the relation

$1 - \frac{p^2}{r_c^2} = \frac{1}{4\pi\epsilon_0} \frac{Ze.2e}{r_c \times \frac{1}{2} m v_i^2}$ ...(i)

where $p = impact\ parameter\ i.e.$ perpendicular distance of the line of approach of the α-particle from the nucleus, Ze the total charge on the nucleus, $2e$ the charge on the α-particle and $\dfrac{1}{2}mv_i^2 = E$ the initial kinetic energy of the α-particle when it is at an infinite distance from the nucleus.

The **minimum** distance of closest approach is obtained when the line of approach of the α-particle passes directly through the nucleus $i.e.$ the impact parameter $p = 0$.

Substituting $p = 0$ and $\dfrac{1}{2}mv_i^2 = E$ in relation (i), we have

$$1 = \frac{2Ze^2}{4\pi\,\epsilon_0}\cdot\frac{1}{r_c E}$$

or minimum distance of closest approach

$$r_c\,(\text{minimum}) = \frac{2Ze^2}{4\pi\,\epsilon_0}\cdot\frac{1}{E}$$

Thus, the minimum distance of closest approach has only **one** value for a given kinetic energy E of the α-particle. On the other hand, the distance of closest approach for a given energy of the α-particle has infinite number of values depending upon the value of impact parameter p.

(b) When a collision occurs between two balls, the balls exert a force on each other for a *very short duration,* whereas when a collision takes place between an α-particle and a nucleus, the force theoretically acts for an infinite duration of time because the electrostatic force between the charge on the α-particle and charge on the nucleus has an infinite range.

Q. 9.34. Mark the correct answer.

(i) The number of co-ordinates required to describe a collision in laboratory frame is

    (a) 2   (b) 4   (c) 6   (d) 8

(ii) The number of co-ordinates required to describe a collision in centre of mass frame is

    (a) 3   (b) 6   (c) 8   (d) 12

(iii) Initial kinetic energy of a system in C.M. frame compared to lab. frame is

    (a) greater   (b) lesser   (c) equal   (d) unrelated

                                                                        (P.U. 1993)

(iv) In inelastic collision there is a conservation of

    (a) linear momentum   (b) kinetic energy   (c) total energy   (d) mass

                                                                      (P.U. 1993)

(v) Centre of mass lies

    (a) closer to smaller body   (b) closer to heavier body

    (c) At mid-point of the line joining the two masses

    (d) On the other side of the heavier body   (P.U., 1994)

(vi) Some paste is thrown on a wall which sticks to it. The collision is

    (a) perfectly elastic   (b) nearly elastic   (c) inelastic   (P.U., 1994)

(*vii*) The scattering cross-section has the dimensions of

(*a*) area   (*b*) volume

(*c*) length   (*d*) momentum   (*P.U.*, 1994)

(*viii*) If ϕ is the angle of scattering in Lab and θ in C.M. system, then for $m_1 = m_2$ we have

(*a*) $\phi = 2\theta$ (*b*) $\phi = \theta$ (*c*) $2\phi = \theta$.

(*d*) $\phi = \dfrac{\theta}{2}$ (*P.U.*, 1994)

(*ix*) When the velocities get intercharged after collision of two bodies, the collision is

(*a*) perfectly elastic   (*b*) nearly elastic   (*c*) inelastic

(*x*) The path of an α-particle in Rutherford scattering is always

(*a*) hyperbola   (*b*) parabola   (*c*) ellipse

(*xi*) Two particles A and B initially at rest move towards each other under a mutual force of attraction. Also the instant when the speed of A is v and the speed of B is $2v$, the speed of the centre of mass of the system is

(*a*) zero   (*b*) v (*c*) $1.5\,v$ (*Meerut. U.* 2000)

Ans.   (*i*) *c*   (*ii*) *a*   (*iii*) *b*   (*iv*) *a*

(*v*) *b*   (*vi*) *c*   (*vii*) *a*   (*viii*) *d*

(*ix*) *a*   (*x*) *a*   (*xi*) *a*

EXERCISES

1. A body of mass 100 gms moving with a velocity $(8\hat{i} - 6\hat{j} - 10\hat{k})$ cm s^{-1} collides with a body of mass 200 gm moving with velocity $(-10\hat{i} + 6\hat{j} - 8\hat{k})$ cm s^{-1} and attain velocities $(3\hat{i} - 4\hat{j} - 5\hat{k})$ and $(-4\hat{i} + 5\hat{j} - 6\hat{k})$ cms^{-1} respectively. Find kinetic energy before and after collision in the Lab. system. Is the collision elastic ?

Hint. Energy before collision $= \dfrac{1}{2}100(8\hat{i} - 6\hat{j} - 10\hat{k})^2 + \dfrac{1}{2}200(-10\hat{i} + 6\hat{j} - 8\hat{k})^2$

$$= 50 \times 200 + 100 \times 200 = 30{,}000 \text{ ergs}$$

Energy after collision $= \dfrac{1}{2}100(3\hat{i} - 4\hat{j} - 5\hat{k})^2 + \dfrac{1}{2}200(-4\hat{i} + 5\hat{j} - 6\hat{k})^2$

$$= 50 \times 50 + 100 \times 77 = 10{,}200 \text{ ergs.}$$

The collision is *inelastic* as the kinetic energy is not conserved.

2. Calculate the impact parameter of 2.4 MeV α-particle scattered by Thorium ($Z = 90$) for 2×10^{-11} cm distance of closest approach.   (*G.N.D.U.*, 1997)

[**Ans.** 1.36×10^{-13} m]

10

Relativity

Q. 10.1. (a) What was the aim of Michelson-Morley experiment? Describe Michelson-Morley experiment and obtain the expected fringe shift under classical assumptions. Explain how the negative results obtained therefrom are interpreted. Give Lorentz Fitzgerald explanation.

(Pbi.U. 2008, 2007, 2006, 2001, 2000, 1999; P.U. 2009, 2008, 2007, 2006, 2005, 2004, 2001, 2000; K.U. 2002, 2001, 2000, 1999; M.D.U. 2007, 2006, 2000, 1999; H.P.U. 2001; Mithila U. 1999; G.N.D.U. 2009, 2008, 2007, 2006, 1996, 1995; Calicut U. 2003; Meerut U. 2007,)

(b) What do you conclude from Michelson-Morley experiment? If ether does not exist, in what medium does light travel? What vibrates in light waves? *(H.P.U. 2003; Pbi.U. 2001)*

Ans. (a) Aim. The aim of Michelson-Morley experiment was to prove the existence of '*ether*' by finding the velocity of drift between the *ether* and the earth.

Ether hypothesis. Sound waves are longitudinal and require a material medium to travel. These waves, therefore, can travel through a gas, a liquid or a solid but not through vacuum. On the other hand, light is a form of transverse wave motion. It can pass through material media like glass, water etc. as also through vacuum. But a wave motion always requires a material medium to travel. In order to put the '*wave theory of light*' on a sound footing it was supposed that a hypothetical medium which was given the name '*ether*' exists everywhere, even in vacuum. Light waves thus were a result of the vibrations of ether particles. The velocity of wave motion is given

by $v = \sqrt{\dfrac{E}{\rho}}$ where E is the *elasticity of* the medium and ρ the *density*. The velocity of light has a large value of 3×10^8 m/sec. Hence '*ether*' must have a very large elasticity and very low density. These two properties are self-contradictory *i.e.*, opposed to each other, and, therefore, there were grave doubts regarding the actual existence of '*ether*'.

Electromagnetic theory. Electromagnetic theory of light was predicted by Maxwell. According to this theory the velocity of light or that of electromagnetic waves in free space is given by

$$c = \frac{1}{\sqrt{\mu_0 \, \varepsilon_0}} = 3 \times 10^8 \text{ ms}^{-1}$$

where μ_0 and ε_0 are the permeability and permittivity of free space. *Since μ_0 and ε_0 are absolute quantities related only to empty space, the velocity of light appears to be an absolute constant.* But Galilean transformation equations predict different velocities for observers in different inertial frames.

Galilean transformations not valid for velocity of light. Consider two inertial frames S and S' such that S' is moving with respect to S in the $+X$ direction with a velocity $\vec{v}$ so that $\vec{v} = v\hat{i} = v\hat{i}'$.

If a beam of light travels in the frame S with a velocity $\vec{c}$ along the $+X$ direction, then $\vec{c} = c\hat{i}$.

According to Galelian transformations in Newtonian mechanics the velocity of light as observed by an observer in S' will be $\vec{c'} = \vec{c} - \vec{v} = (c - v)\hat{i}$.

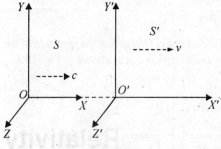

Fig. 10.1

Thus the speed of light in frame S' will be $(c - v)$.

This result is absolutely different from that predicted by Maxwell's equations of electromagnetic field. Thus Galelian transformation equations are not valid for electromagnetic radiations or light waves.

Michelson Morley Experiment. To prove the existence of '*ether*' attempt was made to find the velocity of drift between the ether and the earth. If ether is assumed to be at rest, the velocity of the earth relative to ether will be its orbital velocity which is about 30 km per second and the velocity of the *ether drift* relative to the earth will be equal in magnitude but opposite in direction.

To detect the presumed motion of the earth through ether Michelson devised an ingeneous experiment with the help of Morley using his interferometer. The experiment is classically known as **Michelson Morley experiment.** In Michelson's interferometer a beam of monochromatic light is split into two parts by a half silvered glass plate G. A part known as *longitudinal part* is transmitted through it along the X-direction and reflected at the front silvered mirror M_2. It retraces its path and after reflection from the back surface of G enters the telescope T.

The other part known as *transverse part,* after reflection from the silvered back surface of G, falls on the mirror M_1 along the Y-direction, retraces its path and after refraction through G enters the telescope T. The two beams, therefore, produce interference if the optical path $AB = AC = d$.

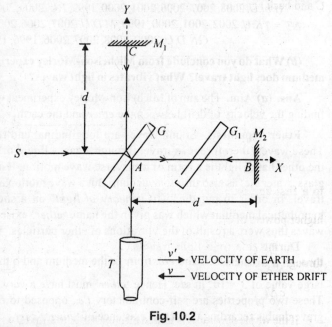

Fig. 10.2

Time for light to go from A to B and back to A. If the velocity of the apparatus (or earth) relative to *ether* is v from left to right in the direction AB, then the velocity of *ether* drift is also v but from right to left. If c is the velocity of light, then time taken by light to go from A to $B = \dfrac{d}{c - v}$

and time taken by light to go from B to A $= \dfrac{d}{c + v}$

∴ Time taken by light to go from A to B and back to A

$$T_x = \frac{d}{c - v} + \frac{d}{c + v} = \frac{2cd}{c^2 - v^2} = \frac{2cd}{c^2\left(1 - \dfrac{v^2}{c^2}\right)} = \frac{2d}{c\left(1 - \dfrac{v^2}{c^2}\right)}$$

Time taken by light to go from A to C and back to A. The beam of light reflected from A must leave the half silvered plate G along the path AD, so that the resultant of velocity of light and the velocity of ether drift may act in the direction AC as shown in Fig. 10.3.

∴ The resultant velocity of light along $AC = \sqrt{c^2 - v^2}$

After reflection at C from the mirror M_1, the light is reflected along CE, so that the resultant of the velocity of light and the velocity of *ether* drift again acts in the direction CA as shown in Fig. 10.3.

∴ The resultant velocity of light $= \sqrt{c^2 - v^2}$ along CA

Hence time taken by light to go from A to C and back from C to A

$$T_y = \frac{d}{\sqrt{c^2 - v^2}} + \frac{d}{\sqrt{c^2 - v^2}} = \frac{2d}{\sqrt{c^2 - v^2}} = \frac{2d}{c\sqrt{1 - \frac{v^2}{c^2}}}$$

Expected classical fringe shift. Thus due to *ether drift*, time taken by light to go from A to B and back again to A will be greater than the time taken by light to go from A to C and back again to A by an amount

$$\Delta T = T_x - T_y$$

$$= \frac{2d}{c\left[1 - \frac{v^2}{c^2}\right]} - \frac{2d}{c\sqrt{1 - \frac{v^2}{c^2}}}$$

$$= \frac{2d}{c}\left\{1 + \frac{v^2}{c^2} - 1 - \frac{1}{2}\frac{v^2}{c^2}\right\}$$

$$= \frac{2d}{c}\left\{\frac{v^2}{2c^2}\right\} = \frac{d}{c}\frac{v^2}{c^2}$$

to a first approximation neglecting higher powers of $\frac{v^2}{c^2}$.

During this time light travels through a distance

$$c\,\Delta T = c \cdot \frac{d}{c}\frac{v^2}{c^2} = \frac{dv^2}{c^2}$$

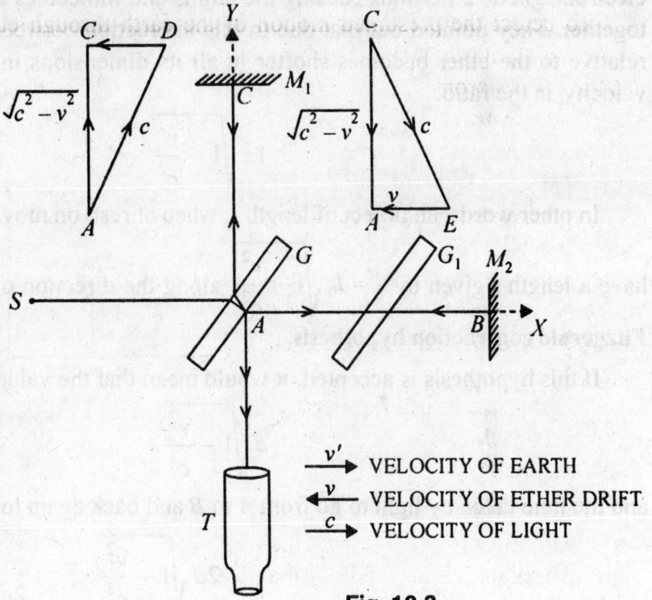

VELOCITY OF EARTH
VELOCITY OF ETHER DRIFT
VELOCITY OF LIGHT

Fig. 10.3

If the whole apparatus is turned through 90°, the arm AC will become optically longer than the arm AB by an amount $\frac{dv^2}{c^2}$. Hence the effect of rotation of the apparatus is to produce a path difference $\frac{2dv^2}{c^2}$. The fringe pattern observed in the telescope will, therefore, shift through a number of fringes n given by $\frac{2dv^2}{c^2} = n\lambda$ or $n = \frac{2dv^2}{c^2} \cdot \frac{1}{\lambda}$ where λ is the wavelength of light used.

The effective optical path d used by Michelson and Morley in their experiment in 1881 was 11 metres. As the value of orbital velocity of earth is 3×10^4 m/sec the number of fringes shifted by rotating the apparatus through 90° for sodium light $\lambda = 6 \times 10^{-7}$ m is given by

$$n = \frac{2 \times 11 \times 9 \times 10^8}{9 \times 10^{16} \times 6 \times 10^{-7}} = 0.37$$

This displacement of fringes could be very easily measured with Michelson-Morley apparatus which was highly sensitive and capable of measuring a shift of $\frac{1}{100}$th of a fringe.

Michelson and Morley floated the whole apparatus in a large trough of mercury and kept it in slow rotation at the rate of about 10 complete rotations per hour. The results indicated that no significant shift occurred. This indicates that the relative velocity between the earth and *ether* is zero.

Explanation of null results. (*i*) Michelson tried to explain this null result on the hypothesis that the earth dragged the ether along with it, so that there was no relative motion between the earth and the ether. Lodge in 1892 measured the speed of light near rapidly rotating bodies and found that not more than 0.5% of the velocity of the body was communicated to the ether. Michelson's explanation was, therefore, not tenable.

(*ii*) **Lorentz-Fitzgerald Hypothesis.** An alternative explanation of the null result was given by Lorentz and Fitzgerald in 1892. According to Lorentz all matter is made up of atoms and atoms are made up of charged particles that produce electric and magnetic fields. These fields must exert forces on the electromagnetic ether thus causing the atoms and molecules in moving matter to be pushed closer together. They pointed out that due to this interaction between *ether* and *matter*, an object moving relative to the ether becomes shorter in all its dimensions in the direction parallel to the relative velocity, in the ratio

$$1 : \sqrt{1 - \frac{v^2}{c^2}}$$

In other words, an object of length l_0 when at rest, on moving with a velocity v will contract and have a length l given by $l = l_0 \sqrt{1 - \frac{v^2}{c^2}}$ along the direction of motion. This is known as **Lorentz-Fitzgerald contraction hypothesis.**

If this hypothesis is accepted, it would mean that the value of d along AB will become

$$d \sqrt{1 - \frac{v^2}{c^2}}$$

and the time taken by light to go from A to B and back again to A

$$T_x = \frac{2d \sqrt{1 - \frac{v^2}{c^2}}}{c \left(1 - \frac{v^2}{c^2}\right)} = \frac{2d}{c \sqrt{1 - \frac{v^2}{c^2}}}$$

which is the same as T_y. Hence $\Delta T = 0$ so that there is no path difference and hence no fringe-shift. The contraction could not, however, be logically derived from theory.

(*iii*) **Einstein's explanation.** In 1905 Einstein proposed an explanation of the null results of Michelson-Morley experiment in a very simple manner. He argued that the reason why it is not possible to detect relative motion through ether is that the *velocity of light is an invariant*. In other words, the velocity of light is constant and does not depend upon the motion of the source, observer or the medium. This is one of the postulates of the special theory of relativity which mathematically explains why the length of an *object* should contract in the ratio $1 : \sqrt{1 - \frac{v^2}{c^2}}$ when it is in motion with a velocity v.

(b) Michelson-Morley experiment conclusively proved that relative velocity between the earth and ether is zero. Therefore, it is concluded that a medium like ether does not exist.

Light waves are electromagnetic waves and require no material medium for their propagation. Light travels through vacuum (or free space) with a velocity $c = \dfrac{1}{\sqrt{\mu_0\,\varepsilon_0}}$ where μ_0 is the permeability and ε_0 the permittivity of free space.

As $\mu_0 = 4\pi \times 10^{-7}$ kg m/coul^2 and $\varepsilon_0 = \dfrac{1}{36\pi \times 10^9}$ coul^2 sec^2/kg m^3, the value of

$$c = \sqrt{\dfrac{1}{4\pi \times 10^{-7}}} \times 36\pi \times 10^9 = 3 \times 10^8\,\text{ms}^{-1}$$

Light is propagated as transverse wave in which electric field vector $\vec{E}$ and magnetic field vector $\vec{H}$ oscillate or vibrate at right angles to the direction of propagation of the wave. The vectors $\vec{E}$ and $\vec{H}$ are also at right angles to each other. If the wave propagates along $\vec{Z}$ axis and $\vec{E}$ is directed along $\vec{X}$-axis, then $\vec{H}$ is directed along $\vec{Y}$-axis and vice-versa.

Exercise. *Ether was assigned contradictory properties. Explain.* (*G.N.D.U.*, 2008)

Hint: See part (*a*) under '*Ether hypothesis*'.

Q. 10.2. (*a*) **What efforts were made to explain the null results of Michelson-Morley experiment on the basis of ether hypothesis?** (*Pbi. U.*, 1993)

(*b*) **Explain what makes the transverse path of rays oblique when viewed from ether frame.** (*G.N.D.U.*, 1997, 1996)

(*c*) **Draw a ray diagram in ether frame after 90° rotation of the apparatus.** (*G.N.D.U.*, 1995)

Ans. (*a*) **Explanation of null results.** (See Q. 10.1.)

(*b*) **Reason for oblique transverse path.** Consider Michelson Morely interferometer as moving along with the earth relative to ether frame with a velocity $\vec{v}$ from left to right in the direction *AB* or AM_2 along the $+X$ direction of its longitudinal arm. A parallel beam of monochromatic light coming from the source *S* is split into two parts by a half silvered glass plate *G*. A part is transmitted through it along longitudinal $+X$ direction and reflected at *B* from the front silvered mirror M_2. It retraces its path and after reflection from the back surface of *G* at *A* enters the telescope *T*. In the mean time the mirror M_2 occupies the position M_2' and the glass plate *G*, the position G'.

The transverse part of the beam after reflection from the silvered back surface of *G* falls on the mirror M_1. In order that the resultant of the velocity of light and velocity of ether drift may act in the transverse direction *AC*, the beam of light must leave the plate *G* along the oblique path AC'. After reflection at C' from the mirror M_1 in the position M_1' (when the plate *G* is in the position G'), the light is reflected along the oblique path $C'\,A''$ so that the re-

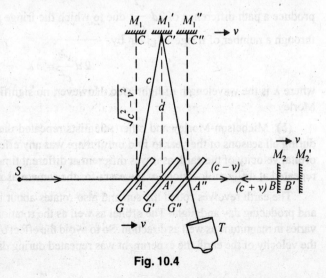

Fig. 10.4

sultant of the velocity of light and the velocity of ether drift again acts in the transverse direction $C'A'$ and enters the plate G at A'' because in the mean time the mirror M_1 occupies the position M_1'' and the plate G the position G''.

Thus when viewed from ether frame the ray of light travelling along the longitudinal direction (AB) falls on the mirror M_2 at B and is reflected back to A whereas the transverse ray of light travelling along the oblique direction AC' falls on the mirror M_1 at C' in the position M_1' and after reflection travels along the oblique path $C'A''$ to meet the glass plate G at A'' (in the position G'') when the mirror M_1 is in the position M_1''.

(c) **After 90° rotation.** After 90° rotation of Michelson-Morley apparatus as shown in Fig.

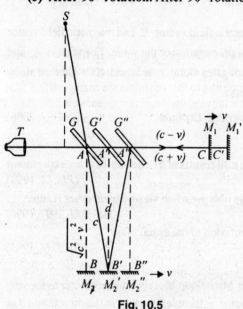

Fig. 10.5

10.5, the arms interchange their positions and roles. The transverse arm becomes the longitudinal arm and the longitudinal arm becomes the transverse arm. The half silvered glass plate G also turns through 90°. In the transverse arm in this orientation light is rendered oblique by the motion of the source S (or the collimating lens) which also has been rotated through 90° as also the telescope T.

Q. 10.3. (a) **Why the apparatus of Michelson-Morley experiment was rotated through 90°?**
(G.N.D.U. 2003)

(b) **Why did Michelson and Morley repeat the experiment during day and night and during all seasons of the year?** (K.U. 1996)

Ans. (a) The apparatus in Michelson-Morley experiment was rotated through 90° to make the arm AC as shown in Fig. 10.2 become optically longer than the arm AB by an amount $d\dfrac{v^2}{c^2}$ where d is the distance between half silvered glass plate and the mirror M_1 or M_2. The effect of rotation is to produce a path difference of $2d\dfrac{v^2}{c^2}$ due to which the fringe pattern observed in the telescope shifts through a number of fringes n given by

$$2d\frac{v^2}{c^2} = n\lambda$$

where λ is the wavelength of light used. However, no significant shift was observed by Michelson-Morley.

(b) Michelson-Morley and other scientists repeated the experiment during day and night and during all seasons of the year to find out if there was any effect due to the change in the direction of orbital velocity of the earth as it was different at different times of the year. The experiment was also repeated at different locations of the earth for the same reason.

The earth revolves round the sun and also rotates about its own axis causing change in seasons and producing day and night. The orbital as well as the rotational velocity of earth is non-uniform and varies in magnitude as well as direction. So to avoid the effect of variation in direction and magnitude of the velocity of the earth the experiment was repeated during day and night and all seasons of the year.

Q. 10.4. (*a*) **State and explain the (basic) fundamental postulates of the special theory of relativity.** (*M.D.U. 2008, Pbi. U. 2009, 2007, 2006; G.N.D.U. 2007; H.P.U. 2003; P.U. 2006*)

(*b*) **A reference frame S′ moves with respect to another frame S with uniform velocity $\vec{v}$. Derive Lorentz space and time transformation equations giving x', y', z', t' in terms of x, y, z, t, the moving frame coincides with stationary one at $t' = t = 0$. Prove that when $\vec{v}$ is much smaller than velocity of light Lorentz transformations reduce to Galelian transformations.**

(*P.U. 2003, 2001, 2000, 1999; G.N.D.U. 2009, 2008, 2001, 2000, 1999; K.U. 2002, 2001, 2000; Pbi. U. 2002, 2001, 2000; Bang. U. 2001, 2000; Kerala U. 2001; Meerut U. 2000; M.D.U. 2002*)

Ans. (*a*) **Special theory of relativity.** The special theory of relativity was enunciated in 1905 by Albert Einstein. It has two fundamental postulates :

(*i*) *The laws of Physics are invariant in all inertial systems.*

An inertial system is defined as a co-ordinate frame of reference within which the law of inertia *i.e.*, Newton's first law of motion holds. A body on which no net external force acts will move with a uniform velocity if it is in an inertial system. Hence according to this postulate the mathematical form of a physical law remains the same for any two observers moving with constant linear velocity relative to each other. It is, therefore, not possible to distinguish one inertial system from another by an experiment in Physics, as the laws of Physics are the same for an inertial system. In other words, there is no preferred inertial system.

(*ii*) *The speed of light in vacuum is a constant independent of the inertial system, the source and the observer.*

In other words, the velocity of light is an **invariant.**

(*b*) **Lorentz transformations.** The equations in relativity Physics which relate the space and time co-ordinates of two co-ordinate systems moving with a uniform velocity relative to one another are called **Lorentz transformations.**

Consider two observers O and O' located in two separate inertial co-ordinate system S and S' respectively. The system S' moves with a uniform velocity v to the *right* along the X-axis relative to S. This is equivalent to the motion of S to the left with a velocity v relative to S'. Suppose each observer carries a *metre rod* (*i.e.*, an arrangement for measuring length) and a *clock* (*i.e.*, an arrangement for measuring time) to measure the position and time of a particle relative to an inertial system. By specifying the *position* and *time* of a physical phenomenon, the observer describes what is called an **event.**

The space and time co-ordinates of an *event* at P described by the observer O are (x, y, z, t) and the co-ordinates of the *same event* as described by the observer O' are $(x'\ y'\ z'\ t')$. The space co-ordinates x, y, z give the distances from the origin O along the X, Y and Z directions as measured by the metre stick of the observer O and t gives the time that he reads on his clock. Suppose both the observers are temporarily at rest with respect to each other when they compare their metre sticks and synchronise their clocks. The system S' is then set in motion with respect to system S. When the origin of S' passes the origin of S both the clocks read zero *i.e.*, $t = 0$ and $t' = 0$ and at this instant $x = x'$.

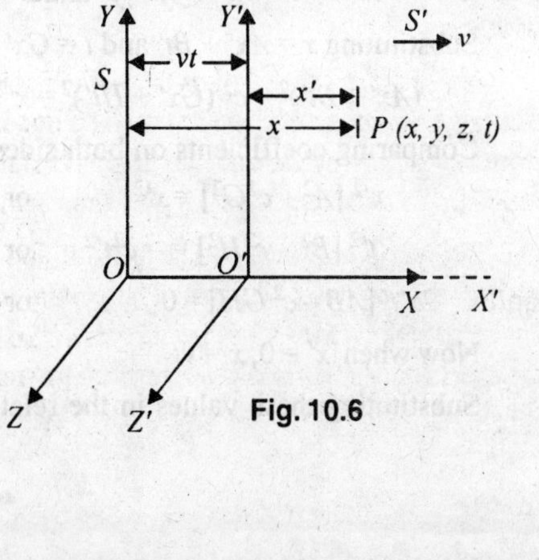

It is evident from Fig. 10.6 that after a time t as measured by O the origin of the system S' is at a distance vt from the origin of the system S,

$$\therefore \qquad x' = x - vt$$

Fig. 10.6

As the relative motion between S' and S is at right angles to Y and Z axes, the position co-ordinates

$$y' = y \quad z' = z$$

Further, according to classical Physics the two observers O and O' will compute the same time for any signal originating from P after giving allowance for the velocity of S'

$$\therefore \qquad\qquad t' = t$$

Hence non-relativistic Galelian transformation equations are

$$x' = x - vt, \quad y' = y, \quad z' = z, \quad t' = t$$

Lorentz transformation equations which satisfy the relativity requirements according to the two postulates must also be *linear* and not quadratic or of a higher order. A quadratic equation has two roots and a higher order equation even more. In order that an event (x, y, z, t) in the inertial system S may correspond to a *single* event (x', y', z', t') in the inertial system S' and *vice-versa* there must be a *one to one correspondence* and the transformation equations must be linear in space co-ordinates as well as in time co-ordinates.

As the inertial system S' is moving with respect to the inertial system S along the X-direction, a ray of light parallel to the X-axis remains always parallel to X'-axis.

$$\therefore \qquad\qquad y = y' \quad \text{and} \qquad z = z'$$

Hence x and t will both depend upon x' and t'.

We shall, therefore, assume the simplest *linear* equations for Lorentz transformations *i.e.*,

$$x = Ax' + Bt', \qquad y = y', z = z', \qquad t = Gx' + Ht'$$

It has been assumed in the above equations that it is possible that the time interval for the two observers O and O' in the inertial systems S and S' may not be identical.

Imagine that at the time $t = t' = 0$ when the origin O' coincides with the origin O a spherical pulse of light leaves the common origin of S and S'. As the velocity of light is *invariant* each observer sees a spherical wave expanding outwards with the speed c in his own system as measured by his own metre stick and clock.

$$\therefore \text{ For the observer } O \text{ in the system } S, \ c = \frac{\sqrt{x^2 + y^2 + z^2}}{t}$$

or $\qquad\qquad x^2 + y^2 + z^2 = c^2 t^2 \quad$ or $\quad x^2 + y^2 + z^2 - c^2 t^2 = 0 \qquad\qquad$ ...(i)

Similarly for the observer O' in the system S', $c = \dfrac{\sqrt{x'^2 + y'^2 + z'^2}}{t}$

or $\qquad\qquad x'^2 + y'^2 + z'^2 = c^2 t'^2 \quad$ or $\quad x'^2 + y'^2 + z'^2 - c^2 t'^2 = 0 \qquad\qquad$ ...(ii)

From (i) and (ii) we have $x^2 + y^2 + z^2 - c^2 t^2 = x'^2 + y'^2 + z'^2 - c^2 t'^2$

$$\because \qquad\qquad y = y' \text{ and } z = z' \therefore x^2 - c^2 t^2 = x'^2 - c^2 t'^2$$

Substituting $x = Ax' + Bt'$ and $t = Gx' + Ht'$ we have

$$(Ax' + Bt')^2 - c^2 (Gx' + Ht')^2 = x'^2 - c^2 t'^2$$

Comparing coefficients on both sides we have

$$x'^2 [A^2 - c^2 G^2] = x'^2 \qquad\qquad \text{or} \qquad A^2 - c^2 G^2 = 1 \qquad\qquad\qquad\qquad \text{...(iii)}$$

$$t'^2 [B^2 - c^2 H^2] = - c^2 t'^2 \qquad \text{or} \qquad B^2 - c^2 H^2 = - c^2 \qquad\qquad\qquad \text{...(iv)}$$

and $\quad 2x't' [AB - c^2 GH] = 0 \qquad\qquad \text{or} \qquad AB - c^2 GH = 0 \qquad\qquad\qquad\quad \text{...(v)}$

Now when $x' = 0, x = vt$

Substituting these values in the relations

$$x = Ax' + Bt' \quad \text{and} \quad t = Gx' + Ht' \text{ we get } vt = Bt' \text{ and } t = Ht'$$

$$\therefore \quad vHt' = Bt' \quad \text{or} \quad B = vH$$

Substituting $B = vH$ in (iv) we have $v^2H^2 - c^2H^2 = -c^2$

or $\quad H^2 = \dfrac{c^2}{c^2 - v^2}$

$$\therefore H = \dfrac{1}{\sqrt{1 - \dfrac{v^2}{c^2}}}$$

Substituting this value of H in $B = vH$, we have

$$B = \dfrac{v}{\sqrt{1 - \dfrac{v^2}{c^2}}}$$

Substituting $B = vH$ in (v), we have

$$AvH - c^2GH = 0 \quad \text{or} \quad Av - c^2G = 0$$

$$\therefore \quad G = \dfrac{Av}{c^2}$$

Substituting the value of $G = \dfrac{Av}{c^2}$ in (iii), we have

$$A^2 - A^2\dfrac{v^2}{c^2} = 1$$

or

$$A = \dfrac{1}{\sqrt{1 - \dfrac{v^2}{c^2}}}$$

Hence

$$G = \dfrac{\dfrac{v}{c^2}}{\sqrt{1 - \dfrac{v^2}{c^2}}}$$

Substituting these values of A B G and H, the Lorentz transformation equation, are

$$x = \dfrac{x' + vt'}{\sqrt{1 - \dfrac{v^2}{c^2}}}$$

$$t = \dfrac{t' + \dfrac{v}{c^2}x'}{\sqrt{1 - \dfrac{v^2}{c^2}}}$$

$$\boxed{y = y'} \quad \text{and} \quad \boxed{z = z'}$$

Inverse Lorentz transformations. To get the inverse transformation equations we note that O is moving with a velocity $- v$ relative to O'. So interchanging x, y, z, t with x', y', z', t' and putting $-v$ in place of v we get

$$x' = \dfrac{x - vt}{\sqrt{1 - \dfrac{v^2}{c^2}}}$$

$$t' = \frac{t - \dfrac{v}{c^2}x}{\sqrt{1 - \dfrac{v^2}{c^2}}}$$

$$y' = y; z' = z.$$

Galelian transformations special case of Lorentz transformations. When the velocity of moving frame S' i.e., v is much smaller than the velocity of light c, then $v/c \ll 1$ so that $\dfrac{v}{c^2}$ and $\dfrac{v^2}{c^2}$ tend to zero and in the limit

$$x' = x - vt$$
$$y' = y ; z' = z \text{ and } t' = t$$

i.e., the *Lorentz transformation equations reduce to Galelian transformations.*

Q. 10.5. (a) Show by means of Lorentz transformation equations that

$$x'^2 - c^2 t'^2 = x^2 - c^2 t^2.$$ *(Kerala U. 2001; Pbi. U., 1995)*

(b) What do you understand by the statement that velocity of light is absolute?   *(P.U. 2005)*

OR

What is the principle of constancy of light ?

(G.N.D.U., 2008)

Ans. (a) Suppose x', y', z', t' and x, y, z, t are the space-time co-ordinates of an event in the inertial frames S' and S respectively and S' is moving with a velocity $\vec{v}$ along the X-direction relative to S, then Lorentz transformation equations are

$$x' = \frac{x - vt}{\sqrt{1 - \dfrac{v^2}{c^2}}}; \; y' = y; z' = z \text{ and } t' = \frac{t - \dfrac{v}{c^2}x}{\sqrt{1 - \dfrac{v^2}{c^2}}}$$

$$\therefore \qquad x'^2 = \frac{x^2 + v^2 t^2 - 2xvt}{1 - \dfrac{v^2}{c^2}}$$

and

$$t'^2 = \frac{t^2 + \dfrac{v^2}{c^4}x^2 - \dfrac{2xvt}{c^2}}{1 - \dfrac{v^2}{c^2}}$$

or

$$c^2 t'^2 = \frac{c^2 t^2 + \dfrac{v^2}{c^2}x^2 - 2xvt}{1 - \dfrac{v^2}{c^2}}$$

$$\therefore \qquad x'^2 - c^2 t'^2 = \frac{x^2 + v^2 t^2 - 2xvt - c^2 t^2 - \dfrac{v^2}{c^2}x^2 + 2xvt}{1 - \dfrac{v^2}{c^2}}$$

$$= \frac{x^2\left(1 - \frac{v^2}{c^2}\right) - c^2 t^2\left(1 - \frac{v^2}{c^2}\right)}{1 - \frac{v^2}{c^2}} = x^2 - c^2 t^2$$

(b) The statement 'velocity of light is absolute' means that the speed of light in vacuum is a constant, independent of the inertial system, the speed of source and the observer. In other words, the velocity of light is an invariant. It has the same value in all inertial frames regardless of the motion of the source of light relative to the observer i.e., it is an absolute quantity.

Q. 10.6. (a) Show that electromagnetic wave equation $\nabla^2 \phi - \frac{1}{c^2} \frac{\partial^2 \phi}{\partial t^2} = 0$ is invariant under Lorentz transformations where ϕ is a scalar potential.

(b) Name the transformations under which Maxwell's equations are invariant.

(G.N.D.U. 1993)

Ans. (a) Electromagnetic wave equation is invariant. Consider an inertial frame S' moving with a uniform velocity $\vec{v}$ along the X-direction with respect to frame S. The scalar potential ϕ is a function of space time co-ordinates (x', y', z', t') in the frame S' and (x, y, z, t) in the frame S.

The wave equation

$$\nabla^2 \phi - \frac{1}{c^2} \frac{\partial^2 \phi}{\partial t^2} = \frac{\partial^2 \phi}{\partial x^2} + \frac{\partial^2 \phi}{\partial y^2} + \frac{\partial^2 \phi}{\partial z^2} - \frac{1}{c^2} \frac{\partial^2 \phi}{\partial t^2} = 0 \qquad \qquad ...(i)$$

In the frame S', $\phi = \phi(x', y', z', t')$. Now

$$\frac{\partial \phi}{\partial x} = \frac{\partial \phi}{\partial x'} \frac{\partial x'}{\partial x} + \frac{\partial \phi}{\partial y'} \frac{\partial y'}{\partial x} + \frac{\partial \phi}{\partial z'} \frac{\partial z'}{\partial x} + \frac{\partial \phi}{\partial t'} \frac{\partial t'}{\partial x} \qquad \qquad ...(ii)$$

$$\frac{\partial \phi}{\partial y} = \frac{\partial \phi}{\partial x'} \frac{\partial x'}{\partial y} + \frac{\partial \phi}{\partial y'} \frac{\partial y'}{\partial y} + \frac{\partial \phi}{\partial z'} \frac{\partial z'}{\partial y} + \frac{\partial \phi}{\partial t'} \frac{\partial t'}{\partial y} \qquad \qquad ...(iii)$$

$$\frac{\partial \phi}{\partial z} = \frac{\partial \phi}{\partial x'} \frac{\partial x'}{\partial z} + \frac{\partial \phi}{\partial y'} \frac{\partial y'}{\partial z} + \frac{\partial \phi}{\partial z'} \frac{\partial z'}{\partial z} + \frac{\partial \phi}{\partial t'} \frac{\partial t'}{\partial z} \qquad \qquad ..(iv)$$

and

$$\frac{\partial \phi}{\partial t} = \frac{\partial \phi}{\partial x'} \frac{\partial x'}{\partial t} + \frac{\partial \phi}{\partial y'} \frac{\partial y'}{\partial t} + \frac{\partial \phi}{\partial z'} \frac{\partial z'}{\partial t} + \frac{\partial \phi}{\partial t'} \frac{\partial t'}{\partial t} \qquad \qquad ...(v)$$

According to Lorentz transformation equations

$$x' = \frac{x - vt}{\sqrt{1 - \frac{v^2}{c^2}}} = \beta(x - vt), y' = y, z' = z, \text{ and } t' = \frac{t - vx/c^2}{\sqrt{1 - \frac{v^2}{c^2}}} = \beta\left(t - \frac{vx}{c^2}\right) \qquad ...(vi)$$

where

$$\beta = \frac{1}{\sqrt{1 - \frac{v^2}{c^2}}}$$

Differentiating Eq. (vi) w.r.t x, we get

$$\frac{\partial x'}{\partial x} = \beta, \quad \frac{\partial y'}{\partial x} = 0, \quad \frac{\partial z'}{\partial x} = 0, \quad \frac{\partial t'}{\partial x} = -\beta \frac{v}{c^2}$$

Substituting in Eq. (ii), we have

$$\frac{\partial \phi}{\partial x} = \beta \frac{\partial \phi}{\partial x'} - \beta \frac{v}{c^2} \frac{\partial \phi}{\partial t'} = \beta \left(\frac{\partial \phi}{\partial x'} - \frac{v}{c^2} \frac{\partial \phi}{\partial t'} \right)$$

or

$$\frac{\partial}{\partial x} = \beta \left(\frac{\partial}{\partial x'} - \frac{v}{c^2} \frac{\partial}{\partial t'} \right)$$

so that

$$\frac{\partial^2 \phi}{\partial x^2} = \frac{\partial}{\partial x} \left(\frac{\partial \phi}{\partial x} \right) = \beta^2 \left(\frac{\partial}{\partial x'} - \frac{v}{c^2} \frac{\partial}{\partial t'} \right) \left(\frac{\partial \phi}{\partial x'} - \frac{v}{c^2} \frac{\partial \phi}{\partial t'} \right)$$

$$= \beta^2 \left(\frac{\partial^2 \phi}{\partial x'^2} + \frac{v^2}{c^4} \frac{\partial^2 \phi}{\partial t'^2} - \frac{2v}{c^2} \frac{\partial^2 \phi}{\partial x' \partial t'} \right) \qquad \ldots(vii)$$

Again differentiating Eq. (vi) w.r.t y, we get

$$\frac{\partial x'}{\partial y} = 0, \quad \frac{\partial y'}{\partial y} = 1, \quad \frac{\partial z'}{\partial y} = 0, \quad \frac{\partial t'}{\partial y} = 0$$

Substituting in Eq. (iii), we have

$$\frac{\partial \phi}{\partial y} = \frac{\partial \phi}{\partial y'} \quad \text{or} \quad \frac{\partial}{\partial y} = \frac{\partial}{\partial y'}$$

so that

$$\frac{\partial^2 \phi}{\partial y^2} = \frac{\partial}{\partial y} \left(\frac{\partial \phi}{\partial y} \right) = \frac{\partial}{\partial y'} \left(\frac{\partial \phi}{\partial y'} \right) = \frac{\partial^2 \phi}{\partial y'^2} \qquad \ldots(viii)$$

Similarly from Eq. (iv), we get

$$\frac{\partial^2 \phi}{\partial z^2} = \frac{\partial^2 \phi}{\partial' z^2} \qquad \ldots(ix)$$

Now differentiating Eq. (vi) w.r.t. t we get

$$\frac{\partial x'}{\partial t} = -\beta v, \quad \frac{\partial y'}{\partial t} = 0, \quad \frac{\partial z'}{\partial t} = 0 \quad \text{and} \quad \frac{\partial t'}{\partial t} = \beta . \qquad \ldots(x)$$

Substituting in Eq. (v), we have

$$\frac{\partial \phi}{\partial t} = -\beta v \frac{\partial \phi}{\partial x'} + \beta \frac{\partial \phi}{\partial t'} = \beta \left(\frac{\partial \phi}{\partial t'} - v \frac{\partial \phi}{\partial x'} \right)$$

or

$$\frac{\partial}{\partial t} = \beta \left(\frac{\partial}{\partial t'} - v \frac{\partial}{\partial x'} \right)$$

so that

$$\frac{\partial^2 \phi}{\partial t^2} = \frac{\partial}{\partial t} \left(\frac{\partial \phi}{\partial t} \right) = \beta^2 \left(\frac{\partial}{\partial t'} - v \frac{\partial}{\partial x'} \right) \left(\frac{\partial \phi}{\partial t'} - v \frac{\partial \phi}{\partial x'} \right)$$

$$= \beta^2 \left(\frac{\partial^2 \phi}{\partial t'^2} + v^2 \frac{\partial^2 \phi}{\partial x'^2} - 2v \frac{\partial^2 \phi}{\partial t' \partial x'} \right) \qquad \ldots(xi)$$

Substituting the values of $\frac{\partial^2 \phi}{\partial x^2}$ from (vii), $\frac{\partial^2 \phi}{\partial y^2}$ from (viii), $\frac{\partial^2 \phi}{\partial z^2}$ from (ix) and $\frac{\partial^2 \phi}{\partial t^2}$ from (xi) in wave equation (i), we get

$$\frac{\partial^2 \phi}{\partial x^2} + \frac{\partial^2 \phi}{\partial y^2} + \frac{\partial^2 \phi}{\partial z^2} - \frac{1}{c^2} \left(\frac{\partial^2 \phi}{\partial t^2} \right) = \beta^2 \left[\frac{\partial^2 \phi}{\partial x'^2} + \frac{v^2}{c^4} \frac{\partial^2 \phi}{\partial t'^2} - \frac{2v}{c^2} \frac{\partial^2 \phi}{\partial x' \partial t'} \right]$$

$$+ \frac{\partial^2 \phi}{\partial y'^2} + \frac{\partial^2 \phi}{\partial z'^2} - \frac{\beta^2}{c^2} \left[\frac{\partial^2 \phi}{\partial t'^2} + \frac{v^2}{c^2} \frac{\partial^2 \phi}{\partial x'^2} - 2v \frac{\partial^2 \phi}{\partial t' \partial x'} \right]$$

$$= \beta^2 \left(1 - \frac{v^2}{c^2}\right) \frac{\partial^2 \phi}{\partial x'^2} + \frac{\partial^2 \phi}{\partial y'^2} + \frac{\partial^2 \phi}{\partial z'^2} - \frac{\beta^2}{c^2} \left[1 - \frac{v^2}{c^2}\right] \frac{\partial^2 \phi}{\partial t'^2}$$

$$= \frac{\partial^2 \phi}{\partial x'^2} + \frac{\partial^2 \phi}{\partial y'^2} + \frac{\partial^2 \phi}{\partial z'^2} - \frac{1}{c^2} \frac{\partial^2 \phi}{\partial t'^2} \qquad \qquad \left[\because 1 - \frac{v^2}{c^2} = \frac{1}{\beta^2}\right]$$

Hence $\qquad \frac{\partial^2 \phi}{\partial x^2} + \frac{\partial^2 \phi}{\partial y^2} + \frac{\partial^2 \phi}{\partial z^2} - \frac{1}{c^2} \frac{\partial^2 \phi}{\partial t^2} = \frac{\partial^2 \phi}{\partial x'^2} + \frac{\partial^2 \phi}{\partial y'^2} + \frac{\partial^2 \phi}{\partial z'^2} - \frac{1}{c^2} \frac{\partial^2 \phi}{\partial t'^2}$

i.e., the wave equation $\nabla^2 \phi - \frac{1}{c^2} \frac{\partial^2 \phi}{\partial t^2} = 0$ is invariant to Lorentz transformations.

(*b*) Maxwell's equations are also invariant under Lorentz transformations.

Q. 10.7. Explain the terms 'frame of reference', 'event' and 'observer' in relativity.

(*M.D.U.* 2001; *P.U.* 2000; *H.P.U.* 1999, 1995)

Ans. Frame of reference. In order to describe the motion of a particle a 'co-ordinate system' or a 'reference frame' is required. A frame of reference is a co-ordinate system (designed to measure three 'space' co-ordinates) plus a clock (designed to register 'time' co-ordinate). Thus an inertial co-ordinate system plus a clock is called '*inertial frame of reference*'.

Event. An event is a physical concept. An event may be collision between two particles or the striking of a building by a thunderbolt. An event happens at a point in space at a particular time and is thus assigned four co-ordinates —the three position co-ordinates x, y, z that measure the distance from the origin of the co-ordinate system where the observer is located and the time co-ordinate 't' that the observer records with his clock.

Observer. An observer is normally considered as a person or an instrument which can make measurements. Such an observer occupies a particular position in a reference frame and records an event only when a light signal from the event reaches it.

But in the theory of relativity it is supposed that the event is recorded instantaneously at the place and time of its occurrence in any given reference frame. For this purpose the observer must be present *at all places, at all times*.

Hence, in relativity *an observer is an infinite set of recording clocks and measuring scales synchronised with respect to one another distributed throughout the space of the inertial frame.*

Q. 10.8. (*a*) **On the basis of Lorentz transformations derive an expression for length contraction.**

OR

Prove that the length of an object measured in a frame moving with respect to an observer is smaller than the length of the same object as observed in stationary frame.

(*b*) **Define proper length.** (*G.N.D.U.,* 2006)

(*c*) **A circle and a square are moving along X-axis. How will they appear to a stationary observer?** (*P.U.* 2007, 2006, 2001, 2000, 1999; *K.U.* 2001, 1994; *Bang.U.* 2001; *G.N.D.U.* 2004, 2002,2000;

M.D.U. 2003; *Luck.U.* 1996; *Pbi U.* 1995; *Osm.U.* 2004)

(*d*) **Why length contraction is not observed in daily life?** (*Pbi.U.,* 2005)

Ans. (*a*) **Lorentz transformations.** If two inertial systems S and S' are in relative motion so that S' moves with a uniform velocity v to the right along the X-axis relative to S and (x, y, z, t) and (x', y', z', t') are the space and time co-ordinates of an event P in the inertial systems S and S' respectively, then according to Lorentz transformation equations

$$x' = \frac{x - vt}{\sqrt{1 - \dfrac{v^2}{c^2}}}$$

$$y' = y, z' = z$$

$$t' = \frac{t - \dfrac{v}{c^2}x}{\sqrt{1 - \dfrac{v^2}{c^2}}}$$

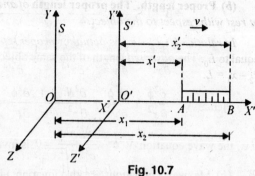

Fig. 10.7

Length contraction. In classical Physics the length of an object is the same for all observers irrespective of their velocities relative to the object.

According to the theory of relativity, the length of an object depends upon the velocity of the observer with respect to the object.

Suppose the observers O and O' in the inertial systems S and S' are at rest with respect to each other with their origins coinciding at some time. They compare their measuring rods and find that both give the same values for the length of an object AB and let it be $= L_0$. Now S' moves to the right along the X-axis with a uniform velocity v with respect to S with the object AB lying along its X-axis. The observer in the system S' places his measuring rod along the X-axis with its left end at $A = x_1'$ and the right end at $B = x_2'$.

$\therefore$ For S', $AB = x_2' - x_1' = L_0$

Let us now find the length of the object AB moving with the frame S' as measured by the observer O in the frame S. Suppose the position of the object AB in the reference frame S is x_1 for the end A and x_2 for the end B, then the length of the object lying in the moving frame as measured by S

$$= x_2 - x_1 = L \text{ (say)}$$

As S' is moving to the right along the X-axis with a velocity v with respect to S, therefore according to Lorentz transformations

$$x_1' = \frac{x_1 - vt_1}{\sqrt{1 - \dfrac{v^2}{c^2}}}$$

and

$$x_2' = \frac{x_2 - vt_2}{\sqrt{1 - \dfrac{v^2}{c^2}}}$$

$\therefore$

$$x_2' - x_1' = \frac{(x_2 - x_1) - v(t_2 - t_1)}{\sqrt{1 - \dfrac{v^2}{c^2}}}$$

Now in order that S may be able to measure the length of the object AB of S' he should mark the two ends A and B of the object simultaneously *i.e. at one and the same time,*

$$t_2 = t_1$$

$\therefore$

$$x_2' - x_1' = \frac{x_2 - x_1}{\sqrt{1 - \dfrac{v^2}{c^2}}} \qquad \qquad ...(i)$$

(b) **Proper length.** **The proper length** *of an object is defined as the length measured by a scale at rest with respect to the object.*

In relation (i) $x_2' - x_1'$ *is actual or proper length of the object as measured by* S' *himself and is equal to* L_0. *The observed length of the same object as measured by* S *when* S' *is in motion is equal to* $x_2 - x_1 = L$.

$$\therefore \quad L_0 = \frac{L}{\sqrt{1 - \dfrac{v^2}{c^2}}}$$

or

$$L = L_0 \sqrt{1 - \frac{v^2}{c^2}}$$

Hence when measuring the length of an object in the system S' moving with a velocity v with respect to an observer in the system S the observer finds the length to be contracted by the factor

$\sqrt{1 - \dfrac{v^2}{c^2}}$. The contraction is *reciprocal i.e.*, the observer in the system S' also finds the length of an object lying in the system S whose *proper* length is L_0 to be equal to

$$L = L_0 \sqrt{1 - \frac{v^2}{c^2}} \qquad \qquad ...(ii)$$

This phenomenon is known as **length contraction** or space contraction. As it was suggested by Lorentz and Fitzgerald, it is also called Lorentz-Fitzgerald contraction.

Thus, according to the theory of relativity, the length of an object is not absolute, but depends upon the relative motion of the object with respect to the observer. It is maximum when the object is at rest in the observer's inertial system. In other words, *the length of an object measured in a frame moving with respect to an observer is smaller than the length of the same object as observed in stationary frame.*

(c) **Square and circle in motion.** When an inertial frame S' is moving with a velocity $\vec{v}$ along the X-axis with respect to an inertial frame S, then according to relation (i)

$$x_2 - x_1 = (x_2' - x_1') \sqrt{1 - \frac{v^2}{c^2}}$$

or

$$L = L_0 \sqrt{1 - \frac{v^2}{c^2}}$$

i.e. there is a contraction in length of the object in a direction parallel to X-axis. Further according to Lorentz transformations $y_1' = y_1, y_2' = y_2$ and $z_1' = z_1, z_2' = z_2$ *i.e.*, $y_2' - y_1' = y_2 - y_1$ and $z_2' - z_1' = z_2 - z_1$, *i.e.* there is no length contraction in a direction perpendicular to the direction of motion. Thus a moving square appears as a rectangle with the shorter side along its direction of motion (X-axis) and a circle appears as an ellipse with its minor axis along its direction of motion as shown in Fig. 10.8.

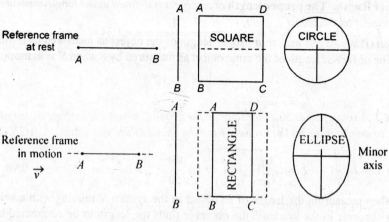

Fig. 10.8

When v is very small as compared to c, $\dfrac{v^2}{c^2}$ is negligible and therefore Eq. (i) reduces to $L = L_0$ i.e., for ordinary velocities length of an object can be taken to be a constant.

(*d*) The length contraction is not observed in daily life because in our daily life speed of objects is very small as compared to the velocity of light.

Q. 10.9. (*a*) The length of a rod as measured in different frames is 10.0 cm., 10.1 cm., 9.8 cm., 9.9 cm. The rod is at rest in one of the frames. Which one? Explain your answer.

(*P.U.* 2003)

(*b*) **A rod 1 m long is moving along its length with a velocity 0.6 c. Calculate its length as it appears to (*i*) an observer on the earth (*ii*) moving with the rod itself.** (*Pbi. U.* 1995)

Ans. (*a*) The rod is at rest in the frame in which its length is measured as 10.1 cm.

It is because, in a moving frame length contraction takes place and its apparent length decreases. It is not possible for the length to increase in a moving frame. So the frame at rest is that in which length has the highest value.

(*b*) The proper length of the rod in the moving (*S'*) frame

$$L_0 = 1 \text{ m}$$

∴ To an observer moving with the rod itself, the length appears to be 1 metre.

Let L be the length of the rod as it appears to an observer on earth, then

$$L = L_0 \sqrt{1 - \frac{v^2}{c^2}} = 1\sqrt{1 - (0.6)^2} = \sqrt{1 - 0.36}$$

$$= \sqrt{0.64} = 0.8 \text{ m}$$

Exercise 1. *A rod has a length of 2m. Find its length when carried in a rocket with a speed of 2.7×10^8 ms^{-1}.* (*K.U.* 2002, 2000) [**Ans.** 0.872 m]

Hint:
$$L = L_0 \sqrt{1 - \frac{v^2}{c^2}} = 2\sqrt{1 - \left(\frac{2.7 \times 10^8}{3 \times 10^8}\right)^2} = 2 \times \sqrt{1 - 0.81}$$

$$= 2 \times \sqrt{0.19} = 2 \times 0.436 = 0.872 \text{ m}$$

Exercise 2. *The apparent length of a rod in the direction of motion moving with a velocity of 2 $\times 10^8$ m/sec. is 1 metre. What is the length of rod at rest?* (*P.U.*, 2006)

Hint: $L = L_0 \sqrt{1 - \dfrac{v^2}{c^2}}; \therefore L_0 = \dfrac{L}{\sqrt{1 - \dfrac{v^2}{c^2}}} = \dfrac{1}{\sqrt{1 - \dfrac{\left(2 \times 10^8\right)^2}{\left(3 \times 10^8\right)^2}}} = 1.34 \, m$

Exercise 3. *A spaceship is 50 metre long on the ground. When it is in flight its length appears to be 49 metres to an observer on the ground. Find the speed of the spaceship.* (G.N.D.U. 2004)

Hint. $L = L_0 \sqrt{1 - \dfrac{v^2}{c^2}}$ or $\dfrac{L}{L_0} = \sqrt{1 - \dfrac{v^2}{c^2}}$ or $\dfrac{49}{50} = \sqrt{1 - \dfrac{v^2}{c^2}}$ or $\sqrt{1 - \dfrac{v^2}{c^2}} = 0.98$

or $\quad 1 - \dfrac{v^2}{c^2} = (0.98)^2 = 0.9604 \quad \therefore \quad \dfrac{v^2}{c^2} = 1 - 0.9604 = 0.0396$

or $\quad \dfrac{v}{c} = 0.199$ or $v = 3 \times 0.199 \times 10^8 = 0.597 \times 10^8 \, ms^{-1}$

Exercise 4. *The length of a spaceship when at rest on the ground measures 100m. Its length in flight as measured by an observer on the ground is 81 m. Calculate the velocity with which the space-ship is moving.* (G.N.D.U., 2008)

Hint: $L = L_0 \sqrt{1 - \dfrac{v^2}{c^2}}$ or $\dfrac{81}{100} = \sqrt{1 - \dfrac{v^2}{c^2}} = 0.81$

$1 - \dfrac{v^2}{c^2} = (0.81)^2 = 0.6561 \therefore \dfrac{v^2}{c^2} = 1 - 0.6561 = 03439$

$\therefore \quad \dfrac{v}{c} = 0.5864$ or $v = 1.759 \times 10^8$ m/sec

Q. 10.10. Calculate the percentage contraction of a rod moving with a velocity 0.8 times the velocity of light in a direction inclined at (a) 60° (b) 45° to its own length.

(K.U., 1996; M.D.U. 1999)

Ans. *(a)* The vector length L of the rod can be resolved into two components :

(i) Along the direction of motion $L_x = L \cos 60° = \dfrac{1}{2} L$

(ii) Perpendicular to the direction of motion $L_y = L \sin 60° = \dfrac{\sqrt{3}}{2} L$

The relativistic contraction occurs only along the direction of motion. There will be a *decrease* in the component L_x. Let its value be L_x'.

$\therefore \qquad L_x' = L_x \sqrt{1 - \dfrac{v^2}{c^2}} = \dfrac{1}{2} L \sqrt{1 - (0.8)^2} = 0.3 \, L$

The component L_y remains unchanged $\quad \therefore L'_y = L_y$

$\therefore \quad$ Length of the rod in the moving frame $L' = \sqrt{\left(L_x'\right)^2 + \left(L_y'\right)^2}$

$= \sqrt{(0.3L)^2 + \left(\dfrac{\sqrt{3}}{2} L\right)^2} = 0.916 \, L$

Percentage contraction $\dfrac{L - 0.916\,L}{L} \times 100 = 0.084 \times 100 = 8.4\%$

(b) Here $L_x = L\cos 45° = \dfrac{L}{\sqrt{2}}$; $L_x' = L_x\sqrt{1 - \dfrac{v^2}{c^2}} = \dfrac{L}{\sqrt{2}}\sqrt{1 - (0.8)^2} = 0.3\sqrt{2}\,L$

$L_y = L\sin 45° = \dfrac{L}{\sqrt{2}}$; $L_y' = L_y$

$L' = \sqrt{\left(L_x'\right)^2 + \left(L_y'\right)^2} = \sqrt{(0.3\sqrt{2}\,L)^2 + \left(\dfrac{L}{\sqrt{2}}\right)^2} = \sqrt{0.68\,L} = 0.825\,L$

Percentage contraction $= \dfrac{L - 0.825\,L}{L} \times 100 = 0.175 \times 100 = 17.5\%$

Exercise. *Calculate the percentage contraction of a rod moving with velocity 0.6c in a direction at 60° to its own length.*   *(Pbi.U., 2005)*

Hint: Here $L_x = L\cos 60° = \dfrac{1}{2}L$; $L_y = L\sin 60° = \dfrac{\sqrt{3}}{2}L$

$L'_x = L_x\sqrt{1 - \dfrac{v^2}{c^2}} = \dfrac{1}{2}L\sqrt{1 - (0.6)^2} = 0.4L$

$L'_y = L_y\dfrac{\sqrt{3}}{2}L$ $\therefore$ $L'\sqrt{(0.4L)^2 + \left(\dfrac{\sqrt{3}}{2}L\right)^2} = 0.95L$

$\therefore$ **Percentage contraction** $= \dfrac{L - 0.95L}{L} \times 100 = 5\%$

Q. 10.11. (*a*) **Calculate the length and orientation of a rod of length 5 metres in a frame of reference which is moving with a velocity 0.6 c in a direction making an angle of 30° with the rod.**
                                                                                                      (P.U. 2001)

(*b*) **The length of a rod is found to be half of its length when at rest. What is the speed of the rod relative to the observer?**   *(H.P.U. 2003; K.U., 1997)*

Ans. (*a*) The vector length L of the rod can be resolved into two components :

(*i*) Along the direction of motion $L_x = L\cos 30°$

(*ii*) Perpendicular to the direction of motion $L_y = L\sin 30°$

The relativistic contraction occurs only along the direction of motion. There will thus be a *decrease* in the component L_x. Let its value be L_x'.

$\therefore$ $L_x' = L_x\sqrt{1 - \dfrac{v^2}{c^2}} = L\cos 30°\sqrt{1 - (0.6)^2}$

$= 5 \times \dfrac{\sqrt{3}}{2} \times 0.8 = 2\sqrt{3} = 3.464$ metres

The component L_y remains unchanged.

$\therefore$ $L_y' = L_y = L\sin 30° = 5 \times \dfrac{1}{2} = 2.5$ metres

$\therefore$ Length of the rod in the moving frame $L' = \sqrt{(L_x')^2 + (L_y')^2}$.

$$= \sqrt{(2\sqrt{3})^2 + (2.5)^2} = 4.27 \text{ metres}$$

Orientation of the rod is given by the angle θ that the rod makes with the direction of velocity v.

$$\therefore \quad \tan \theta = \frac{L_y'}{L_x'} = \frac{2.5}{3.464} = 0.72$$

or $\quad \theta = \tan^{-1}(0.72) = 35° 45'$

(b) Let L_0 be the length of the rod at rest and L its length when moving with a velocity v, then

$$L = L_0 \sqrt{1 - \frac{v^2}{c^2}}$$

But $\quad L = \frac{1}{2} L_0$

$$\therefore \quad \frac{1}{2} L_0 = L_0 \sqrt{1 - \frac{v^2}{c^2}} \quad \text{or} \quad \frac{1}{2} = \sqrt{1 - \frac{v^2}{c^2}}$$

$$\therefore \quad \frac{1}{4} = 1 - \frac{v^2}{c^2} \quad \text{or} \quad \frac{v^2}{c^2} = 1 - \frac{1}{4} = \frac{3}{4}$$

$$\therefore \quad \frac{v}{c} = \frac{\sqrt{3}}{2} \quad \text{or} \quad v = \frac{\sqrt{3}}{2} c = 0.866 c$$

Exercise. *The length of a rod is 100 metres. If length of this rod is measured by the observer moving parallel to its length is 51 metres, find the speed of the observer.* (P.U. 2004)

Hint: $\quad L = L_0 \sqrt{1 - \frac{v^2}{c^2}} \quad \text{or} \quad 51 = 100 \sqrt{1 - \frac{v^2}{c^2}} \quad \text{or} \quad (0.51)^2 = 1 - \frac{v^2}{c^2}$

or $\quad \frac{v^2}{c^2} = 1 - 0.2601 = 0.7399 \quad \therefore \quad \frac{v}{c} = 0.86 \quad \text{or} \quad v = 0.86\, c.$

Q. 10.12. (a) The area of a square as measured from the frame attached to it is A_0. What will be its area with respect to an observer who is moving with velocity $\vec{v}$ along one side of the square?
(P.U., 2000)

(b) With what speed should a circular disc move parallel to its diameter for its area to become half the area at rest? (Kerala U., 2001)

Ans. (a) Consider a square of side l_0 lying in the X-Y plane of the co-ordinate system S attached to it with one side parallel to X-axis and the other side parallel to Y-axis. Suppose another co-ordinate system S′ is moving with a velocity $\vec{v}$ along X-axis. To an observer in S′ the side of the square along X-axis will appear to be contracted to l given by

$$l = l_0 \sqrt{1 - \frac{v^2}{c^2}}$$

The side of the square along Y-axis as measured by the observer in the frame S′ will remain unaffected and $= l_0$

$\therefore$ The area of the square with respect to an observer in the frame S′ moving with velocity $\vec{v}$ along one side of the square (X-axis)

$$= A = l l_0 = l_0^2 \sqrt{1 - \frac{v^2}{c^2}} = A_0 \sqrt{1 - \frac{v^2}{c^2}}$$

(b) Let a be the radius of the circular disc. Suppose the disc moves along X-axis with a velocity v parallel to the X-Y plane of the co-ordinate system at rest, then its diameter $2a$ along X-axis appears to contract to the value $2b$ such that $b = a\sqrt{1 - \dfrac{v^2}{c^2}}$ and the diameter along Y-axis appears to be the same. Thus the circular disc of radius a at rest appears as an ellipse of semi-major axis a along Y-axis (perpendicular to the direction of motion) and semi-minor axis b along X-axis (parallel to the direction of motion).

$\therefore$ The observed area (of the ellipse) $= \pi a b$

Now, the area of the disc moving with velocity v parallel to its diameter = half its area at rest

$\therefore \qquad \pi a b = \dfrac{1}{2}\pi a^2$

But $\qquad b = a\sqrt{1 - \dfrac{v^2}{c^2}} \qquad\qquad \therefore \quad \pi a^2 \sqrt{1 - \dfrac{v^2}{c^2}} = \dfrac{1}{2}\pi a^2$

or $\qquad \sqrt{1 - \dfrac{v^2}{c^2}} = \dfrac{1}{2} \qquad$ or $\qquad 1 - \dfrac{v^2}{c^2} = \dfrac{1}{4}$

or $\qquad \dfrac{v^2}{c^2} = 1 - \dfrac{1}{4} = \dfrac{3}{4} \qquad \therefore \quad \dfrac{v}{c} = \dfrac{\sqrt{3}}{2}$ or $v = \dfrac{\sqrt{3}}{2} c = 0.866\, c$

Q. 10.13. Transform the displacement vector $(4\hat{i} + 3\hat{j})$ cm in a system S to system S' when S' has a velocity $0.8\, c\,\hat{i}$ relative to S'. *(P.U. 2001)*

Ans. In the frame S'

Displacement along X-axis $L_x = 4$ cm

Displacement along Y-axis $L_y = 3$ cm.

S' is moving with a velocity $0.8\, c\,\hat{i}$ relative to S. This velocity is along X-axis.

$\therefore$ Observed displacement along X-axis, $L_x' = L_x \sqrt{1 - \dfrac{v^2}{c^2}}$

$= 4\sqrt{1 - (0.8)^2} = 4 \times 0.6 = 2.4$ cm

There is no effect on the displacement in a perpendicular direction *i.e.* along Y-axis.

$\therefore L_y' = L_y = 3$ cm

$\therefore$ Displacement vector with respect to system S'

$= (2.4\hat{i} + 3\hat{j})$ cm.

Q. 10.14. What do you understand by time dilation? On the basis of Lorentz transformations discuss the variation of time with velocity according to special theory of relativity. Explain why does a moving clock appear to run slow. Explain the terms proper time and non-proper time. Show that when $v \ll c$ Lorentz transformations for time reduce to Galelian transformations.

(Kerala U. 2001; Bang. U. 2001; G.N.D.U. 2006, 2003, 2000, 1999; K.U. 2002, 2001, 1997; Luck.U. 1996, 1994; P. U.2007, 2006, 2004; 1996; H.P.U. 1994; A.U. 1993; Osm.U. 2004; M.D.U. 2007, 2006)

(b) Describe an experiment to verify time dilation. *(Kerala U. 2001; H. P. U. 1994; P. U. 1990)*

Ans. (a) Time dilation. Suppose two observers O and O' in the inertial systems S and S' respectively are at rest with respect to each other. They synchronise their respective clocks and they agree that the time interval between any *two events* as measured by their own clocks is the same. Let the clock in the system S give signals at regular intervals and suppose the system S' moves to the right along the X-axis with a uniform velocity v with respect to S. The observer O in the frame S keeps his clock at a fixed point x_1 in his system and measures the time interval T_0 that elapses between two events (say two signals) that occur at times t_1 and t_2 in his frame.

$$\therefore \qquad T_0 = t_2 - t_1 \qquad \qquad ...(i)$$

Let the times registered by the observer O' in the inertial system S' between the *same* two events be t_1' and t_2'. As S is moving to the right with a uniform velocity v with respect to S', therefore, according to Lorentz transformations,

$$t_1' = \frac{t_1 - \frac{v}{c^2} x_1}{\sqrt{1 - \frac{v^2}{c^2}}}$$

and

$$t_2' = \frac{t_2 - \frac{v}{c^2} x_1}{\sqrt{1 - \frac{v^2}{c^2}}}$$

$$\therefore \qquad t_2' - t_1' = \frac{(t_2 - t_1) - \frac{v}{c^2}(x_2 - x_1)}{\sqrt{1 - \frac{v^2}{c^2}}}$$

The clock in the system S remains fixed at the point x_1.

$$\therefore \qquad x_2 = x_1$$

Hence

$$t_2' - t_1' = \frac{t_2 - t_1}{\sqrt{1 - \frac{v^2}{c^2}}}$$

Thus the moving observer O' in the inertial system S' measures the time interval $t_2' - t_1' = T$ between the same two events for which the observer O in the system S measures the time interval

$$t_2 - t_1 = T_0$$

$$\therefore \qquad T = \frac{T_0}{\sqrt{1 - \frac{v^2}{c^2}}}$$

Exercise. *Prove the equation of transformation of time in relativity.* (P.U., 2006)

Hint: The equation of transformation of time in relativity is

$$T = \frac{T_0}{\sqrt{1 - \frac{v^2}{c^2}}}$$

For proof see under the head **'Time dilation'**.

Why moving clock appears to run slow? As discussed above, the moving observer O' in the inertial system S' measures the time interval T between the same two events for which the observer O in the system S measures time interval T_0 and

$$T = \frac{T_0}{\sqrt{1 - \frac{v^2}{c^2}}}$$

As v is less than c, $T > T_0$. Hence the observer S' measures a longer interval of time between the two events with his clock at rest with respect to him. In other words, a clock in the frame S appears to **go slow** to an observer in the frame S' who is in motion with respect to the frame S. **This phenomenon is known as time dilation**. If there are two observers in relative motion with respect to each other, each observer would find the other moving observer's clock to run slow. Thus the consequence of time dilation is reciprocal. As an example of the phenomenon of time dilation, suppose that the velocity of the observer

$$v = 0.98\,c, \text{ then}$$

$$\sqrt{1 - \frac{v^2}{c^2}} = \sqrt{1 - \frac{0.98^2\,c^2}{c^2}} = 0.2$$

$$\therefore \qquad T = \frac{T_0}{0.2} = 5T_0$$

In other words, if the moving observer in the inertial frame S' measures a time interval of 5 seconds between two events by his own clock, the interval between the same two events, as measured by him on the clock of the stationary observer in the inertial frame S, will be 1 second and *vice-versa*.

Proper and non-proper time. We have seen that an observer O in the inertial frame S measures a time interval $T_0 = t_2 - t_1$ between two events by a clock fixed in his frame at a position, say x_1, whereas

the time interval between the same two events is measured as $T = t_2' - t_1' = \dfrac{t_2 - t_1}{\sqrt{1 - \dfrac{v^2}{c^2}}}$ by the

observer O' in the inertial frame S' moving with a velocity v in the $+X$ direction with respect to the clock in the frame S'.

The time interval between two events which occur at the same position measured by a clock in the inertial frame in which the events occur is called proper time.

The time interval between the same two events measured by an observer from an inertial frame which is moving with respect to the clock is known as non-proper or relativistic time.

When $v \ll c$. When $v \ll c$ Lorentz transformations for time reduce to Galelian transformations. For proof See Q. 10.4.

(b) Experimental verification of time dilation. The high energy particles produced by a synchro-cyclotron give rise to π^+ mesons moving with a velocity $0.99\,c$ when they strike a target. To verify experimentally time dilation, as given by the theory of relativity, the flux of these π^+ mesons was measured at two places 30 metres apart. The π^+ mesons decay with a half-life of $t = 1.8 \times 10^{-8}$ sec. The time taken by π^+ mesons to travel a distance of 30 metres, as measured by an observer at rest in the laboratory, is given by

$$T = \frac{30}{0.99 \times 3 \times 10^8} = 10 \times 10^{-8} \text{ sec. (Approx.)}$$

If N_0 is the number of π^+ mesons in the beginning and N after travelling a distance of 30 metres *i.e.*, after a time, T, then fractional flux $\qquad \dfrac{N}{N_0} = \left(\dfrac{1}{2}\right)^{T/t}$

Now $\qquad \dfrac{T}{t} = \dfrac{10 \times 10^{-8}}{1.8 \times 10^{-8}} = 5.6$

$\therefore \qquad \dfrac{N}{N_0} = \dfrac{1}{2^{5.6}} = \dfrac{1}{48.5} = 2\% \text{ (Approx.)}$

i.e., the flux should fall to 2% of the original value. On actual observation, the flux was found to be nearly 60% of the actual value. This discrepancy has been explained by calculating the *proper time* T_0 in the moving frame of π^+ meson, according to the theory of relativity, which gives

$$T = \dfrac{T_0}{\sqrt{1 - \dfrac{v^2}{c^2}}}$$

or $\qquad T_0 = T \sqrt{1 - \dfrac{v^2}{c^2}} = 10 \times 10^{-8} [1 - (0.99)^2]^{1/2} = 1.4 \times 10^{-8} \text{ sec.}$

During this time T_0, $\dfrac{T_0}{t} = \dfrac{1.4 \times 10^{-8}}{1.8 \times 10^{-8}} = 0.78$

and the fractional flux is given by

$$\dfrac{N}{N_0} = \dfrac{1}{2^{0.78}} = \dfrac{1}{1.714} = 60\% \quad \text{(Approx.)}$$

It is clear from the above experiment that in the laboratory measurement, time taken by π^+ mesons to travel a distance of 30m is 10×10^{-8} sec, whereas π^+ mesons themselves measure the time as 1.4×10^{-8} secs. This verifies experimentally the time dilation.

Q. 10.15. (*a*) **Explain simultaneity of two events in relativity. Show from Lorentz transformation equations that two events simultaneous at different positions in reference frame S are not generally simultaneous in reference frame S' moving with a velocity $v\,\hat{i}$ relative to S.**

(*Pbi. U.* 2005; *H.P.U.* 1999; *G.N.D.U.,* 1992)

(*b*) **Two events occur at different points on X-axis separated by a distance Δx in an inertial frame at the same instant. Show that in another inertial frame moving with uniform velocity v along X-direction with respect to it, these events are not simultaneous but separated by a time interval**

$$\Delta t' = \dfrac{v \Delta x}{\sqrt{1 - v^2/c^2}}.$$

(*Luck. U.,* 1992)

Ans. (*a*) **Simultaneity of two events.** Consider two events characterised by the space and time co-ordinates (x_1, y_1, z_1, t_1) and (x_2, y_2, z_2, t_2) in the frame S and by (x_1', y_1', z_1', t_1') and (x_2', y_2', z_2', t_2') in the frame S'. The frame S' is moving with a velocity $v\hat{i}$ relative to S *i.e.*, along $+X$ axis.

The time co-ordinates of the two events are connected by Lorentz transformations

$$t_1' = \dfrac{t_1 - \dfrac{v}{c^2} x_1}{\sqrt{1 - \dfrac{v^2}{c^2}}} \quad \text{and} \quad t_2' = \dfrac{t_2 - \dfrac{v}{c^2} x_2}{\sqrt{1 - \dfrac{v^2}{c^2}}} \qquad \qquad ...(i)$$

If the two events are *simultaneous* in the frame S, $t_1 = t_2$ and therefore from (*i*) we have $t_1' \neq t_2'$ because $x_1 \neq x_2$. Hence the two events are not simultaneous in S'. Similarly events which are simultaneous in S' will not be so in S.

Thus two events which are simultaneous at *different positions* in reference frame S are not simultaneous in reference frame S' moving with velocity $v\hat{i}$ relative to S.

Order of events. Let us now consider the *order of events* as observed in the two frames. Let event t_1 occurs first and t_2 later in the frame S. The time difference between the same two events in S' will be given by

$$t_2' - t_1' = \frac{t_2 - \dfrac{v}{c^2}x_2}{\sqrt{1 - \dfrac{v^2}{c^2}}} - \frac{t_1 - \dfrac{v}{c^2}x_1}{\sqrt{1 - \dfrac{v^2}{c^2}}}$$

$$= \frac{1}{\sqrt{1 - \dfrac{v^2}{c^2}}}\left[(t_2 - t_1) - \frac{v}{c^2}(x_2 - x_1)\right]$$

If the term within brackets is **zero**, the two events will be *simultaneous* in S'.

If the term within brackets is **positive** *i.e.*, greater than zero, the *order of events is the same* in both the frames.

However, if the term within brackets is **negative** *i.e.*, less than zero, then the events in S' will be observed to be in the reverse order, but this is an *impossible case*.

The last case will happen if

$$\frac{v}{c^2}(x_2 - x_1) > (t_2 - t_1)$$

As v is always less than c

$$\frac{1}{c}(x_2 - x_1) > (t_2 - t_1)$$

or

$$(x_2 - x_1) > c(t_2 - t_1)$$

But this is not possible, as no signal can travel with a velocity greater than that of light. *Hence the order of events shall remain the same in both the inertial frames.*

(b) When two events occur in an inertial frame S at time t_1 and position x_1 and at time t_2 and position x_2, then to an observer in the inertial frame S' moving with velocity v along the X-axis with respect to the inertial frame S, these two events will appear to occur at times t_1' and t_2' given by the relation

$$t_2' - t_1' = \frac{(t_2 - t_1) - \dfrac{v}{c^2}(x_2 - x_1)}{\sqrt{1 - \dfrac{v^2}{c^2}}}$$

When the events are simultaneous in the frame S, $(t_2 - t_1) = 0$ and if the two points are **separated** by a distance Δx, then

$$\Delta x = (x_2 - x_1)$$

The two events will, therefore, appear separated by a time interval

$$t_2' - t_1' = \Delta t' = \frac{-\dfrac{v}{c^2}\Delta x}{\sqrt{1 - \dfrac{v^2}{c^2}}}$$

Q. 10.16. Prove that the four dimensional volume element dx, dy, dz, dt is invariant under Lorentz transformations. *(P.U., 1995)*

Ans. Four dimensional volume element. Lorentz transformation equations lead to the formulae of length contraction and time dilation. These are

(i) $L = L_0 \sqrt{1 - \dfrac{v^2}{c^2}}$ where L is the observed length in the moving frame S' and L_0 the proper length in the stationary frame S.

(ii) $T = \dfrac{T_0}{\sqrt{1 - \dfrac{v^2}{c^2}}}$ where T is observed time in the moving frame S' and T_0 the proper time in the stationary frame S.

Denoting the observed length in the frame S' as dx' and proper length in the frame S as dx, we have

$$dx' = dx \sqrt{1 - \dfrac{v^2}{c^2}}$$

The moving frame S' is taken to move with velocity $\vec{v}$ along the X-axis. Therefore $dy' = dy$; $dz' = dz$.

Similarly denoting the observed time in the frame S' as dt', and proper time in the frame S as dt, we have

$$dt' = \dfrac{dt}{\sqrt{1 - \dfrac{v^2}{c^2}}}$$

∴ The four dimensional volume element in the moving frame is

$$dx'\, dy'\, dz'\, dt' = dx \sqrt{1 - \dfrac{v^2}{c^2}}\; dy\, dz\; \dfrac{dt}{\sqrt{1 - \dfrac{v^2}{c^2}}}$$

$$= dx\, dy\, dz\, dt$$

Hence the four dimensional volume element $dx\, dy\, dz\, dt$ is invariant under Lorentz transformations.

Q. 10.17. Half-life of a particle at rest is 17.8 nanosecond. What will be the half-life when its speed is 0.8 c? *(Pbi. U. 2001; P.U., 1993)*

Ans. Half-life of the particle in the rest frame $T_0 = 17.8 \times 10^{-9}\, s$

Let T be the half-life of the particle when its speed v is $0.8\, c$, then

$$T = \dfrac{T_0}{\sqrt{1 - \dfrac{v^2}{c^2}}} = \dfrac{17.8 \times 10^{-9}}{\sqrt{1 - \dfrac{(0.8c)^2}{c^2}}} = \dfrac{17.8 \times 10^{-9}}{\sqrt{1 - 0.64}}$$

$$= \dfrac{17.8 \times 10^{-9}}{0.6} = 2.97 \times 10^{-8}\, s$$

Q. 10.18. With what velocity should a rocket move so that every year spent on it corresponds to 4 years on earth ?   *(Pbi.U. 2007, 2003; H.P.U., 1995)*

Ans. The rocket is the moving frame and earth is the rest frame. The time of 1 year on the rocket is the proper time T_0 and the corresponding time on earth is the relativistic time $T = 4$ years.

Now
$$T = \frac{T_0}{\sqrt{1 - \dfrac{v^2}{c^2}}}$$

where v is the velocity with which the rocket should move.

Hence
$$4 = \frac{1}{\sqrt{1 - \dfrac{v^2}{c^2}}} \quad \text{or} \quad \sqrt{1 - \frac{v^2}{c^2}} = \frac{1}{4}$$

$\therefore$
$$1 - \frac{v^2}{c^2} = \frac{1}{16} \quad \text{or} \quad \frac{v^2}{c^2} = 1 - \frac{1}{16} = \frac{15}{16}$$

$\therefore$
$$v = \sqrt{\frac{15}{16}} \, c = 0.968 \, c$$

Q. 10.19. (a) Determine the time (as measured by a clock at rest on the rocket) taken by a rocket to reach a distant star and return to earth with a constant velocity v equal to $\sqrt{0.9999} \, c$, if the distance to the star is 4 light years.

(b) A clock keeps correct time. With what speed should it travel relative to an observer so that it appears to lose 1 minute in 24 hours?   *(P.U. 2000; G.N.D.U., 1997)*

Ans. *(a)* Distance of the star = 4 light years

Time taken by light to reach the star = 4 years

Velocity of the rocket, $v = \sqrt{0.9999} \, c$

Time taken by the rocket to go to the star and back, as measured by an observer on the rocket on a stationary clock on the earth

$$T = \frac{2 \times 4c}{\sqrt{0.9999} \, c} = \frac{8}{\sqrt{0.9999}} \text{ years}$$

Let T_0 be the time measured by the observer on the rocket on the clock in the rocket, then

$$T = \frac{T_0}{\sqrt{1 - \dfrac{v^2}{c^2}}} = \frac{T_0}{\sqrt{1 - 0.9999}} = \frac{T_0}{0.01}$$

$\therefore$
$$T_0 = T \times 0.01 = \frac{8 \times 0.01}{\sqrt{0.9999}} = 0.08 \text{ year.}$$

(b) Time as measured by the clock $T = 24 \times 60$ minutes

Time as measured by the observer when the clock is in motion $T_0 = (24 \times 60 - 1)$ minute.

Let v be the velocity of the clock, then

$$T = \frac{T_0}{\sqrt{1 - \dfrac{v^2}{c^2}}}$$

or $\qquad 1 - \dfrac{v^2}{c^2} = \left(\dfrac{T_0}{T}\right)^2 = \left(\dfrac{24 \times 60 - 1}{24 \times 60}\right)^2 = \left(\dfrac{1439}{1440}\right)^2 = (0.9993)^2$

$\qquad\qquad\qquad\qquad\qquad\qquad\qquad\qquad\qquad\qquad\qquad = 0.9986$

or $\qquad\qquad \dfrac{v^2}{c^2} = 1 - 0.9986 = 0.0014$

or $\qquad\qquad \dfrac{v}{c} = 0.0374$

$\therefore \qquad\qquad v = c \times 0.0374 = 3 \times 10^8 \times 0.0374 = 0.1122 \times 10^8 \, ms^{-1}$

Exercise 1. *A clock keeps correct time on earth. It is put on a spaceship moving uniformly with a speed of* $1 \times 10^8 \, ms^{-1}$*. How many hours does it appear to lose per day?* (*P.U.* 2003)

Hint. Time measured by an observer moving with the clock $T = 24$ hrs

Time measured by an observer on earth $= T_0$

Now $\qquad T = \dfrac{T_0}{\sqrt{1 - \dfrac{v^2}{c^2}}} = \dfrac{T_0}{\sqrt{1 - \left(\dfrac{1 \times 10^8}{3 \times 10^8}\right)^2}} = \dfrac{3 T_0}{\sqrt{8}}$

or $\qquad T_0 = \dfrac{24 \times \sqrt{8}}{3} = 8\sqrt{8} = 22.627$ hrs

Time lost per day $= 24 - 22.627 = 1.373$ hrs $= 1$ hr 22 min 23 sec.

Exercise 2. *If a clock moving along with S′ frame with a velocity $0.95c$ shows an interval of 1 hour, how much time might have elapsed in frame S at rest on earth?*

Hint. $\qquad T = \dfrac{T_0}{\sqrt{1 - \dfrac{v^2}{c^2}}} = \dfrac{60}{\sqrt{(1 - 0.95)^2}} = 192 \, m = 3 \, hrs \, 12 \, min$

Exercise 3. *Calculate the velocity of a watch when it seems to be slowed down by 1 minute in one hour.* (*Meerut. U.,* 2007)

Hint: $\left(\dfrac{T_0}{T}\right)^2 = 1 - \dfrac{v^2}{c^2} = \left(\dfrac{60 - 1}{60}\right) = \left(\dfrac{59}{60}\right)^2 = 0.9669$

$\therefore \qquad\qquad \dfrac{v^2}{c^2} = 1 - 0.9669 = 0.0331 \qquad$ or $\qquad \dfrac{v}{c} = 0.1819$

$\therefore \qquad\qquad v = 0.1819c.$

Q. 10.20. (*a*) **In the laboratory, the lifetime of particle moving with speed 2.8×10^8 m/sec is found to be 2×10^{-7} sec. Calculate the proper lifetime of the particle.** (*P.U.* 2001; *Luck. U.* 1995)

(*b*) **The proper lifetime of an unstable particle is 2.5×10^{-8} sec. At what velocity will it appear to have mean lifetime 2.5×10^{-7} sec ?** (*G.N.D.U.* 2007)

Ans. (*a*) The proper lifetime of a particle is the lifetime in a frame of reference in which the particle is at rest *i.e.*, the frame of reference is moving relative to the laboratory with a velocity equal to the speed of the particle.

Let the proper lifetime $= T_0$

Observed lifetime in Lab. frame $T = 2 \times 10^{-7}$ sec.

Velocity of particle $v = 2.8 \times 10^8$ m/sec

Now
$$T = \frac{T_0}{\sqrt{1 - \frac{v^2}{c^2}}}$$

$$\therefore \quad T_0 = T\sqrt{1 - \frac{v^2}{c^2}} = 2 \times 10^{-7}\left[1 - \left(\frac{2.8}{3}\right)^2\right]^{1/2}$$

$$= 2 \times 10^{-7} \times 0.3588 = 7.176 \times 10^{-3} \text{ sec.}$$

(b) Proper lifetime $T_0 = 2.5 \times 10^{-8}$ sec.

Observed lifetime $T = 2.5 \times 10^{-7}$ sec.

Velocity of the particle $v = ?$

Now $T = \dfrac{T_0}{\sqrt{1 - \frac{v^2}{c^2}}}$ or $2.5 \times 10^{-7} = \dfrac{2.5 \times 10^{-8}}{\sqrt{1 - \frac{v^2}{c^2}}}$ or $\sqrt{1 - \frac{v^2}{c^2}} = \dfrac{2.5 \times 10^{-8}}{2.5 \times 10^{-7}} = 10^{-1} = \dfrac{1}{10}$

$$\therefore \quad 1 - \frac{v^2}{c^2} = \frac{1}{100} \quad \text{or} \quad \frac{v^2}{c^2} = 1 - \frac{1}{100} = \frac{99}{100} \quad \text{or} \quad \frac{v^2}{c} = \frac{\sqrt{99}}{10} = \frac{9.9499}{10} = 0.99499$$

$$\therefore \quad v = 0\,0.99499c = 0.995c.$$

Q. 10.21. What is the mean life of a burst of π^+ mesons travelling with $\beta = 0.73$ (Proper mean life time $T_0 = 2.5 \times 10^{-8}$ sec)? What is the distance travelled at this velocity during one mean life?

Ans. The mean life of a moving meson is given by

$$T = \frac{T_0}{\sqrt{1 - \frac{v^2}{c^2}}}$$

where T_0 is the proper mean life and v the velocity of the meson.

$$\therefore \quad T = \frac{2.5}{[1 - (0.73)^2]^{1/2}} = 3.658 \times 10^{-8} \text{ sec.}$$

The distance travelled by this meson in time T

$$= vT = 0.73 \times 3 \times 10^8 \times 3.658 \times 10^{-8} = 8 \text{ metres}$$

Q. 10.22. A beam of μ-mesons, produced at a height of 20 kms in the earth's atmosphere, travels downwards with a velocity of 0.99c. If 99% of the original mesons decay before reaching the earth's surface, find the mean lifetime of the μ-mesons.

Ans. Let T be the time noted by an observer in the earth's frame for a μ-meson to travel a distance of 20 km with a velocity 0.99 c with respect to the earth, then

$$T = \frac{20 \times 10^3}{0.99 \times 3 \times 10^8} = 67.34 \times 10^{-6} \text{ sec.}$$

If T_0 is the corresponding time noted by an observer moving with the μ-meson i.e., in an inertial frame in which the μ-meson is at rest, then

$$T = \frac{T_0}{\left[1 - \frac{v^2}{c^2}\right]^{1/2}} \quad \text{or} \quad T_0 = T\left(1 - \frac{v^2}{c^2}\right)^{1/2}$$

$$= 67.34 \times 10^{-6} [1-(0.99)^2]^{1/2} = 67.34 \times 10^{-6} \times 0.141$$
$$= 9.495 \times 10^{-6} \text{ sec.}$$

During this time T_0 measured in the rest frame of the μ-meson 99% of the mesons decay. If λ is the decay constant, N_0 the number of μ-mesons in the beginning and N at the end of this time, then

$$N = N_0 e^{-\lambda T_0} \quad \text{or} \quad \frac{N_0}{N} = e^{+\lambda T_0}$$

or
$$\lambda T_0 = \log_e \frac{N_0}{N} = 2.3026 \times \log_{10} \frac{N_0}{N}.$$

But N the number of μ-mesons at the end of time T_0 is only 1% as 99% of the original mesons decay before reaching the earth's surface.

∴
$$\frac{N_0}{N} = \frac{100}{1} = 100$$

Hence
$$\lambda T_0 = 2.3026 \log_{10} 100 = 2 \times 2.3026 = 4.6052$$

or
$$\lambda = \frac{4.6052}{T_0} = \frac{4.6052}{9.495 \times 10^{-6}}$$

But mean lifetime
$$= \frac{1}{\lambda} = \frac{9.495 \times 10^{-6}}{4.6052} = 2.06 \times 10^{-6} \text{ sec}$$

Q. 10.23. A burst of 10^4 π⁺ mesons travels in a circular path of radius 20 m at a speed $v = 0.99\ c$. The proper mean life of π⁺ meson is 2.5×10^{-8} sec.

(i) How many mesons survive when the burst returns to the point of origin ?

(ii) How many mesons would be left in a burst that had remained at rest at the origin for the same period of time?   (GN.D.U., 1991)

Ans. Length of the circular path $= 2\pi r = 2\pi \times 20 = 40\ \pi$ metres

Let T be the time noted by an observer in the laboratory frame for a π⁺ meson to travel the circular path of 40 π metres with a velocity $v = 0.99\ c$, then

$$T = \frac{40\pi}{0.99 \times 3 \times 10^8} = 4.232 \times 10^{-7} \text{ s}$$

If T_0 is the corresponding time noted by an observer moving with the π⁺ meson, i.e., in the inertial frame in which π⁺ meson is at rest, then

$$T = \frac{T_0}{\sqrt{1 - \frac{v^2}{c^2}}}$$

or
$$T_0 = T\left(1 - \frac{v^2}{c^2}\right)^{1/2} = 4.232 \times 10^{-7} \times [1 - (0.99)^2]^{1/2}$$
$$= 4.232 \times 0.141 \times 10^{-7}\text{s} = 0.5967 \times 10^{-7}\text{s}$$

The proper mean life of π⁺ meson $= 2.5 \times 10^{-8}$ s

∴ Decay constant $\lambda = \dfrac{1}{\text{mean life}} = \dfrac{1}{2.5 \times 10^{-8}} = 4 \times 10^7.$

(i) Let N be the number of π⁺ mesons out of $N_0 = 10^4$ which survive after the burst returns to the point of origin, then

∴
$$N = N_0 e^{-\lambda T_0}$$

or $$\frac{N_0}{N} = e^{+\lambda T_0} = e^{4 \times 10^7 \times 0.5967 \times 10^{-7}} = 10.88$$

$$\therefore \quad N = \frac{N_0}{10.88} = \frac{10^4}{10.88} = 920$$

(ii) If the burst had remained at rest at the origin, then

$$T_0 = T = 4.232 \times 10^{-7} \text{ s}$$

and $$\frac{N_0}{N} = e^{+\lambda T} = e^{4 \times 10^7 \times 4.232 \times 10^{-7}}$$

$$= e^{16.928} = 2.248 \times 10^7$$

$$\therefore \quad N = \frac{N_0}{2.248 \times 10^7} = \frac{10^4}{2.248 \times 10^7} \ll 1$$

i.e., NO π^+ meson would survive.

Q. 10.24. The proper life of π^+ meson is 2.5×10^{-8} sec. If a beam of these mesons of velocity 0.8 c is produced, calculate the distance the beam can travel before the flux of the meson beam is reduced to (i) $\frac{1}{e}$ and (ii) $\frac{1}{e^2}$ times the initial flux.   (G.N.D.U., 1992)

Ans. Proper mean lifetime of π^+ meson $T_0 = 2.5 \times 10^{-8}$ s

Observed mean lifetime when the π^+ meson beam has a velocity 0.8 c.

$$T = \frac{T_0}{\sqrt{1 - \frac{v^2}{c^2}}} = \frac{2.5 \times 10^{-8}}{\sqrt{1 - (0.8)^2}} = \frac{2.5 \times 10^{-8}}{0.6} = 4.166 \times 10^{-8} \text{ s}$$

If λ is the decay constant, N_0 the flux of the meson beam in the beginning and N at the end of time t, then

$$N = N_0 e^{-\lambda t}$$

Now $$\lambda = \frac{1}{\text{mean lifetime}} = \frac{1}{T} = \frac{1}{4.166 \times 10^{-8}} \text{ s}^{-1}$$

Hence $$N = N_0 e^{-t/T}$$

(i) If t is the time during which the flux reduces to 1/e, then

$$\frac{N}{N_0} = \frac{1}{e} \text{ or } \frac{1}{e} = e^{-t/T} \text{ or } e^{-1} = e^{-t/T}$$

$$\therefore \quad \frac{t}{T} = 1 \text{ or } t = T = 4.166 \times 10^{-8} \text{ s}$$

Hence the distance travelled by the beam in this time $= vT = 0.8 \times 3 \times 10^8 \times 4.166 \times 10^{-8} = 10$m

(ii) If t is the time during which the flux reduces to $1/e^2$, then

$$\frac{N}{N_0} = \frac{1}{e^2} \text{ or } \frac{1}{e^2} = e^{-t/T}$$

or $$e^{-2} = e^{-\frac{t}{T}}$$

$$\therefore \quad \frac{t}{T} = 2 \text{ or } t = 2T = 2 \times 4.166 \times 10^{-8} \text{ s}$$

Hence the distance travelled by the beam in this time $= 2vt$

$$= 0.8 \times 3 \times 10^8 \times 2 \times 4.166 \times 10^{-8} = 20 \text{ m}$$

Q. 10.25. What do you understand by the term twin paradox? Explain.

(*Pbi. U.* 2002; *H.P.U.*, 1993, 1992, 1991)

Ans. Twin paradox. The time dilation effect is reciprocal in nature. If an inertial frame S' is moving with a velocity $\vec{v}$ with respect to a frame S, then the S-frame observer feels that S' - clock is running slow whereas S'-frame observer feels that S-clock is running slow. Does any of the two clocks actually run slow?

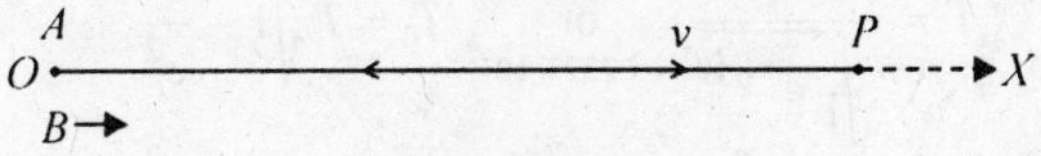

Fig. 10.9

Suppose A and B are twin brothers born at the origin O of the co-ordinate system at a time $t = 0$.

The brother B is immediately set in motion along the X-axis with a high speed $v = \dfrac{\sqrt{3}}{2}c$. Suppose he travels for 15 years as measured by his own clock up to the point P and then returns back to O with the same speed and therefore in the same time. In the opinion of the brother B who is in the moving frame S', he has been travelling for 30 years since his birth and therefore his age is 30 years. This is the *proper time* T_0 as it has been measured by a clock in the inertial frame in which the event takes place, the event being the ageing of B.

The age of B or the corresponding *observed time* T as measured by his twin brother A who is staying at O in the stationary frame S with respect to which brother B is moving is given by

$$T = \frac{T_0}{\sqrt{1 - \dfrac{v^2}{c^2}}} = \frac{30}{\sqrt{1 - \dfrac{3}{4}}} = 60 \text{ years}$$

Therefore the age of B is 60 years from the point of view of the twin brother A who has stayed at O. But when B returns back to O he is only 30 years old.

If we examine the situation from the point of view of the twin brother B who is in the moving frame S', the brother A who has stayed at O is moving with a velocity $\dfrac{\sqrt{3}}{2}c$ in the opposite direction. Therefore we might expect A to be 30 years old upon the return of twin B (who is in the moving frame S') who himself will be 60 years old at this time—the precise *opposite* of the result obtained in the preceding paragraph.

This problem is known as *twin paradox*.

To resolve this paradox we must note that the twin B who is in the moving frame S' is in an *accelerated* reference frame, because he undergoes an acceleration at various times in his journey; when he takes off; when he turns round; and when he finally comes to a stop. The results of special theory of relativity which hold only for frames of reference in relative motion at *constant velocity* cannot be applied at all to the above situation. We must apply the formulas of *general* theory of relativity which holds for accelerated frames of reference. According to the principle of equivalence, in this theory a large acceleration produces effects similar to those produced by strong gravitaitonal fields due to which the clocks tick more slowly.

Hence the brother B in the moving frame S' is *indeed younger* on his return back to the point O, than his twin brother A in the stationary frame S. It should, however, be clearly noted that B's life span has not been *extended to him* since however long his 30 years in the moving frame may have seemed to his brother A, it has been 30 years as far as B is concerned.

Q. 10.26. How much younger an astronaut will appear to earth observer if he returns after one year having moved with a velocity 0.5 c ? (P.U., 1994)

Ans. Let T_0 be the proper time in the spaceship of the astronaut corresponding to observed (or ordinary) time T of 1 year on earth.

The ordinary time T on earth is more than the proper time T_0 in the spaceship of the astronaut and

$$T = \frac{T_0}{\sqrt{1 - \dfrac{v^2}{c^2}}} \quad \text{or} \quad T_0 = T\sqrt{1 - \frac{v^2}{c^2}}$$

or
$$T_0 = 1 \times \sqrt{1 - (0.5)^2} = \sqrt{0.75} = 0.866 \text{ year} = 10 \text{ months } 12 \text{ days}$$

∴   The astronaut is younger by

$$T - T_0 = 12 - (10 \text{ m} + 12 \text{ d}) = 1 \text{ month } 18 \text{ days}.$$

∴   The astronaut is younger by 1 month and 18 days.

Q. 10.27. (*a*) **Starting from Lorentz transformation equations for space and time co-ordinates derive equations for relativistic addition of velocities. Hence prove that no material particle can move with a velocity greater than that of light .**

(*b*) **Show that the law agrees with velocity addition formula for non-relativistic velocities.**

(P.U. 2008, 2007, 2001, 1999, 1995; G.N.D.U. 2009, 2007, 2000, 1993; Meerut U. 2000; M.D.U. 2007; K.U. 2000; Luck. U. 1995; Pbi.U. 2007, H.P.U. 1991; Cal.U. 1992)

Ans. (*a*) **Relativistic addition of velocities.** The Lorentz transformation equations enable us to transform the velocity from one frame of reference to another, in relative motion with respect to it and lead to a relativistic formula for the addition of velocities, known as **Einstein's velocity addition Theorem.**

Let S and S' be the two inertial frames in relative motion, so that S' moves with a uniform velocity v to the right along the X-axis relative to S.

Let $\vec{u}$ and $\vec{u'}$ be the velocities of a particle respectively measured in the inertial frames S and S'. The components of these velocities are (u_x, u_y, u_z) and (u_x', u_y', u_z') given by

$$u_x = \frac{dx}{dt}, \quad u_y = \frac{dy}{dt}, \quad u_z = \frac{dz}{dt}$$

and
$$u_x' = \frac{dx'}{dt'}, \quad u_y' = \frac{dy'}{dt'}, \quad u_z' = \frac{dz'}{dt'}$$

According to Lorentz transformation equations

$$x' = \frac{x - vt}{\sqrt{1 - \dfrac{v^2}{c^2}}}; \quad y' = y; \quad z' = z \quad \text{and} \quad t' = \frac{t - \dfrac{v}{c^2}x}{\sqrt{1 - \dfrac{v^2}{c^2}}}$$

Taking the differentials of above transformation equations, we have

$$dx' = \frac{dx - v.dt}{\sqrt{1 - \dfrac{v^2}{c^2}}}; \quad dy' = dy; \quad dz' = dz; \quad dt' = \frac{dt - \dfrac{v}{c^2}dx}{\sqrt{1 - \dfrac{v^2}{c^2}}}$$

$$\therefore \quad \frac{dx'}{dt'} = \frac{dx - v.dt}{dt - \dfrac{v}{c^2}dx} = \frac{\dfrac{dx}{dt} - v}{1 - \dfrac{v}{c^2}\dfrac{dx}{dt}}$$

or

$$\boxed{u_x' = \frac{u_x - v}{1 - \dfrac{v}{c^2}u_x}} \qquad\qquad ...(i)$$

and

$$\frac{dy'}{dt'} = \frac{dy\sqrt{1 - \dfrac{v^2}{c^2}}}{dt - \dfrac{v}{c^2}dx} = \frac{\dfrac{dy}{dt}\sqrt{1 - \dfrac{v^2}{c^2}}}{1 - \dfrac{v}{c^2}\dfrac{dx}{dt}}$$

or

$$\boxed{u_y' = \frac{u_y\sqrt{1 - \dfrac{v^2}{c^2}}}{1 - \dfrac{v}{c^2}u_x}} \qquad\qquad ...(ii)$$

Similarly

$$\frac{dz'}{dt'} = \frac{dz\sqrt{1 - \dfrac{v^2}{c^2}}}{dt - \dfrac{v}{c^2}dx} = \frac{\dfrac{dz}{dt}\sqrt{1 - \dfrac{v^2}{c^2}}}{1 - \dfrac{v}{c^2}\dfrac{dx}{dt}}$$

or

$$\boxed{u_z' = \frac{u_z\sqrt{1 - \dfrac{v^2}{c^2}}}{1 - \dfrac{v}{c^2}u_x}} \qquad\qquad ...(iii)$$

Inverse transformation equations. The inverse transformation equations are obtained by putting $v = -v$ and $u_x' = u_x$, $u_y' = u_y$, $u_z' = u_z$. Hence

$$\boxed{u_x = \frac{u_x' + v}{1 + \dfrac{v}{c^2}u_x'}} \qquad\qquad ...(iv)$$

$$\boxed{u_y = \frac{u_y'\sqrt{1 - \dfrac{v^2}{c^2}}}{1 + \dfrac{v}{c^2}u_x'}} \qquad\qquad ...(v)$$

$$\boxed{u_z = \frac{u_z'\sqrt{1 - \dfrac{v^2}{c^2}}}{1 + \dfrac{v}{c^2}u_x'}} \qquad\qquad ...(vi)$$

If the velocity of the particle is along the X-axis

$$u_x = u \quad u_y = 0 \quad u_z = 0 \quad \text{then}$$

$$u_x' = \frac{u - v}{1 - \dfrac{v}{c^2}u}; \; u_y' = 0; \; u_z' = 0$$

$$\therefore \quad u' = \frac{u - v}{1 - \dfrac{v}{c^2}u} \qquad\qquad\qquad …(vii)$$

Conversely $$u = \frac{u' + v}{1 + \dfrac{v}{c^2}u'} \qquad\qquad\qquad …(viii)$$

No particle can have velocity greater than light. Now suppose a particle is moving with the velocity of light (It is possible for a particle of zero rest mass like the photon) as observed by the observer O, then $u = c$. The velocity of the same particle, as observed by the observer O', is given by

$$u' = \frac{c - v}{1 - \dfrac{v}{c}} = c$$

i.e., the observer in the inertial frame S' also finds the particle moving with the velocity c. In other words, it is not possible for a particle to move faster than light. *This also shows that Lorentz transformation equations are in accordance with the constancy of velocity of light.*

(*b*) **Formula for non-relativistic velocities.** When v and u are very small as compared to c, $\dfrac{vu}{c^2}$ and $\dfrac{v^2}{c^2}$ are nearly equal to zero and in such a case $\sqrt{1 - \dfrac{v^2}{c^2}}$ and $\left(1 - \dfrac{vu}{c^2}\right)$ are very nearly equal to one.

$$\therefore \quad u_x' = u_x - v, \; u_y' = u_y, \; u_z' = u_z$$

which are similar to Galelian velocity transformation equations in non-relativistic or classical Newtonian mechanics.

Q. 10.28. Starting with Einstein's velocity addition formula show that it is in conformity with principle of constancy of speed of light. (*K.U.* 2000; *H.P.U.*, 1991; *G.N.D.U.*, 1994)

Ans. Einstien's formula. Consider a light photon moving parallel to the X-axis in the inertial frame S with velocity c. If S' is an inertial frame moving with uniform velocity v in the positive X-direction, then relativistic transformation equations for velocity (Einstein's velocity addition theorem) are

$$u_x' = \frac{u_x - v}{1 - \dfrac{v}{c^2}u_x}$$

$$u_y' = \frac{u_y\sqrt{1 - \dfrac{v^2}{c^2}}}{1 - \dfrac{v}{c^2}u_x}$$

$$u_z' = \frac{u_z\sqrt{1 - \dfrac{v^2}{c^2}}}{1 - \dfrac{v}{c^2}u_x}$$

Constancy of speed of light. As the light photon is moving parallel to X-axis with a velocity c

$$u_x = c \quad u_y = 0 \quad u_x = 0$$

$$\therefore \qquad u_x' = \frac{c - v}{1 - \dfrac{v}{c}} = c; \quad u_y' = 0; \quad u_z' = 0$$

$\therefore$ The velocity of the photon in the inertial frame $S' = c$.

Similarly if we assume the velocity of light photon in the inertial frame S' to be c along the $+X$ direction and apply inverse velocity transformation equations by substituting $u_x' = c$, we get

$$u_x = \frac{c + v}{1 + \dfrac{v}{c}} = c; \quad u_y = 0; u_z = 0$$

If the light photon is moving in the $+Y$ direction with a velocity c, in the inertial frame S, then

$$u_x = 0 \; ; u_y = c \; ; u_z = 0$$

The corresponding velocity components, as observed in the inertial frame S', are

$$u_x' = \frac{u_x - v}{1 - \dfrac{v}{c^2} u_x} = -v$$

$$u_y' = \frac{u_y \sqrt{1 - \dfrac{v^2}{c^2}}}{1 - \dfrac{v}{c^2} u_x}$$

$$= u_y \sqrt{1 - \frac{v^2}{c^2}} = c \sqrt{1 - \frac{v^2}{c^2}}$$

$$u_z' = 0$$

$\therefore$ The speed of light, as measured in S'

$$u' = \sqrt{u_x'^2 + u_y'^2 + u_z'^2} = \sqrt{v^2 + c^2 - v^2} = c$$

Similarly if the light photon is moving in the $+Z$ direction with a velocity c, then $u_x = 0$, $u_y = 0$, $u_z = c$ and we get, as in the above case, $u' = c$.

In other words, the observers in both the frames measure the same value of the speed of light. *Thus the velocity of light is independent of the frame of reference and is, therefore an absolute constant.* We can also say that the velocity addition theorem is in conformity with principle of constancy of speed of light.

Q. 10.29. (*a*) **Two particles are moving along a straight line towards each other with uniform velocities 0.8c and 0.5 c respectively. Calculate the relative velocity of approach between them.**

(*Luck.U.*, 1994)

(*b*) **In the laboratory two particles are observed to travel in opposite directions each with a velocity of 2.8 × 10⁸ m/s. Find their relative velocity.** (*GN.D.U.*, 2000)

(*c*) **Two spacecrafts A and B are moving away from the earth in the same direction with speed 0,8c and 0.6c respectively. Find the velocity of B with respect to A.** (*GN.D.U.* 2009)

Ans (*a*). As the particles are moving along a straight line towards each other, they are moving in opposite directions. If, therefore, the velocity of one of these (*u*) is taken as *positive*, the velocity of the other (*v*) is taken as *negative*.

The relative velocity of approach between the two particles is the velocity of one of the particles which an observer stationed on the other particle will measure. Let this velocity be u', then according to Lorentz velocity transformation equation

$$u' = \frac{u - v}{1 - \dfrac{uv}{c^2}} = \frac{0.8c - (-0.5c)}{1 - \dfrac{.8c(-0.5c)}{c^2}} = \frac{1.3}{1.4} c = 0.93\, c$$

(b) As the particles travel in opposite directions, the velocity of one of them (u) is taken as *positive* and the velocity of the other (v) is taken as *negative*. According to Lorentz velocity transformation equations.

$$\text{Relative velocity} \quad u' = \frac{u - v}{1 - \dfrac{uv}{c^2}} = \frac{2.8 \times 10^8 - (-2.8 \times 10^8)}{1 + \dfrac{2.8 \times 10^8 \times 2.8 \times 10^8}{3 \times 10^8 \times 3 \times 10^8}}$$

$$= \frac{5.6}{1.87} \times 10^8 = 2.995 \times 10^8 \text{ ms}^{-1}$$

(c) Velocity of B, $u = 0.6c$; Velocity of A, $v = 0.8c$

$$\therefore \quad \text{Velocity of B with respect to} \quad A = \frac{u - v}{1 - \dfrac{uv}{c^2}} = \frac{(0.6 - 0.8)C}{1 - \dfrac{(0.6 \times 0.8)c^2}{c^2}}$$

$$= \frac{-0.2c}{1 - 0.48} = -\frac{0.2}{0.52} = -0.38c$$

Exercise. *A rocket moving with speed $10^8 ms^{-1}$ ejects a projectile in its direction of motion with speed relative to rocket 2×10^8 ms^{-1}. Find the speed as measured by an observer on earth.*

(P.U. 2008)

Hint: Velocity of projectile relative to earth $u = \dfrac{u' + v}{1 + \dfrac{vu'}{c^2}}$

$$= \frac{2 \times 10^8 + 10^8}{1 + \dfrac{2 \times 1 \times 10^{16}}{9 \times 10^{16}}} = \frac{3 \times 10^8 \times 9 \times 10^{16}}{9 \times 10^{16} + 2 \times 10^{16}} = \frac{27}{11} \times 10^8$$

$$= 2.45 \times 10^8 \text{ ms}^{-1}$$

Q. 10.30 (a). A spaceship moving away from the earth with velocity 0.6 c fires a rocket (whose velocity relative to the spaceship is 0.7 c)

(i) away from the earth (ii) towards the earth.

What will be the velocity of the rocket, as observed from the earth in the two cases? (P.U. 2001)

(b) A rocket is sent with a velocity 0.9c. A light pulse is also sent along the same path. What is the velocity of the light pulse relative to the rocket? (GN.D.U. 2008)

(c) A spacecraft moving away from the earth with velocity 0.5c fires a rocket towards the earth. The velocity of the rocket relative to the spacecraft is 0.8c. Find the velocity of the rocket as observed from the earth. (GN.D.U. 2009, P.U. 2009)

Ans (a). Velocity of the rocket relative to the earth is given by

$$u = \frac{u' + v}{1 + \frac{v}{c^2} u'}$$

where u' = velocity of the rocket relative to spaceship
         v = velocity of the spaceship relative to the earth

The velocity away from the earth is taken as +ve and that towards the earth as –ve.

Here $u' = 0.7c$ and $v = 0.6\,c$

(i) *Rocket fired away from the earth* : $u' = +0.7\,c$

$$\therefore \quad u = \frac{+0.7c + 0.6c}{1 + 0.6 \times 0.7} = 0.91c$$

(ii) *Rocket fired towards the earth* : $u' = -0.7\,c$

$$\therefore \quad u = \frac{-0.7c + 0.6c}{1 - 0.6 \times 0.7} = 0.17c$$

(b) Velocity of the light pulse $u = c$

Velocity of the rocket $v = 0.9c$

Velocity of the light pulse relative to the rocket

$$u' = \frac{u-v}{1-\frac{uv}{c^2}} = \frac{c-v}{1-\frac{cv}{c^2}} = \frac{c-v}{1-\frac{v}{c}} = c$$

$\therefore$ Velocity of light pulse relative to the rocket is also c as the *velocity of light is an invariant.*

(c) Velocity of the rocket relative to the earth is given by

$$u = \frac{u'+v}{1+\frac{v}{c^2}u'}$$

where u' = velocity of the rocket relative to the spacecraft = $0.8c$

v = velocity of spacecraft relative to the earth = $0.5c$

As the rocket is fired towards the earth $u' = -0.8c$

$$\therefore \quad u = \frac{-0.8c + 0.5c}{1 - \frac{(0.5 \times 0.8)c^2}{c^2}} = \frac{-0.3c}{1-0.4} = \frac{-0.3c}{+0.6} = -0.5c$$

Q. 10.31. A radioactive atom moves with a velocity $v = 0.1\,c$ along the X-axis of a system S. It emits a β-particle of velocity $0.95c$ relative to the system S' in which the radioactive atom is at rest. If the β particle is emitted along the X'-axis of S', find its speed relative to S. Compare the values as obtained by Galelian transformations and comment on the results.   (Pbi.U. 1991)

Ans. Let the velocity of the β-particle with respect to the system $S = u_x$ and its velocity with respect to the system $S' = u_x' = 0.95\,c$

As the radioactive atom is at rest in the system S'.

$\therefore$ Velocity of the system $S' = v = 0.1\,c$

(*i*) According to Lorentz velocity transformation equations

$$u_x = \frac{u_x' + v}{1 + \dfrac{v}{c^2} u_x'} = \frac{0.95c + 0.1c}{1 + 0.1 \times 0.95}$$

$$= \frac{1.05}{1.095} c = 0.903 c$$

(*ii*) According to Galelian transformation equations

$$u_x = u_x' + v$$

$$= 0.95c + 0.1\, c = 1.05\, c$$

Comments. According to Galelian transformation equations the velocity of the β-particle in the system *S* comes out to be greater than the velocity of light, which is against the postulate of special theory of relativity that velocity of light is an invariant. This means that Galelian transformation equations no longer hold valid when the velocities concerned are of the order of the velocity of light. For smaller values of *v*, the difference is very small and negligible. This is why Lorentz transformation equations reduce to Galelian transformation equations for values of $v \ll c$.

Q. 10.32. Two electron beams travel along the same straight line but in opposite directions with velocities $V = 0.9\, c$ relative to the laboratory frame. Find the relative velocity of the electrons according to Newtonian mechanics. What will be the velocity measured by an observer moving with one of the electron beams?

(*M.D.U.* 2001; *A.U.*, 1993; *P.U.* 1992; *G.N.D.U.*, 1990)

Ans. As the two electron beams travel along the same straight line in opposite directions with a velocity 0.9*c*, with respect to the laboratory frame, the velocity of one of these (*u*) is taken as *positive* and that of the other (*v*) is taken as *negative*.

According to Newtonian mechanics, relative velocity of the electrons

$$u' = u - v = 0.9\, c - (-0.9\, c) = 1.8\, c$$

Velocity measured by an observer moving with one of the electron beams

$$u' = \frac{u - v}{1 - \dfrac{vu}{c^2}} = \frac{0.9c - (-0.9c)}{1 - \dfrac{(-0.9c)\,0.9c}{c^2}} = \frac{1.8}{1 + 0.81} = 0.994\ c$$

NOTE: The readers will observe that calculation of relative velocity according to Newtonian Mechanics, gives erroneous results as velocity cannot be greater than the velocity of light.

Q. 10.33. A particle moves in *XY* plane with a velocity 6×10^9 cm s^{-1} at an angle of 60° with *X*-axis in system *S'*. Find the magnitude and direction of its velocity as observed by an observer in system *S'* when *S'* has a velocity 3×10^9 cm s^{-1} along positive direction of *X*-axis.

(*P.U.* 1999)

Ans. Velocity of the frame *S'* relative to the frame *S along the X-axis* $v = 3 \times 10^9$ cm s^{-1}

Velocity of the particle in frame *S'*, $u = 6 \times 10^9$ cm s^{-1}

The velocity of the particle *u* can be resolved into two components

Components along the *X*-axis, $u_x = u \cos 60° = 6 \times 10^9 \times \dfrac{1}{2} = 3 \times 10^9$ cm s^{-1}

Component along the *Y*-axis, $u_y = u \sin 60° = 6 \times 10^9 \times \dfrac{\sqrt{3}}{2} = 3\sqrt{3} \times 10^9$ cm s^{-1}

Let u_x' and u_y' be the value of the components as observed by a person in the frame *S'*, then according to Lorentz velocity transformation equations

$$u_x' = \frac{u_x - v}{1 - \frac{u_x v}{c^2}} = \frac{3 \times 10^9 - 3 \times 10^9}{1 - \frac{3 \times 10^9 \times 3 \times 10^9}{3 \times 10^{10} \times 3 \times 10^{10}}} = 0$$

$$u_y' = \frac{u_y \sqrt{1 - \frac{v^2}{c^2}}}{1 - \frac{u_x v}{c^2}} = \frac{3\sqrt{3} \times 10^9 \sqrt{1 - \frac{3 \times 10^9 \times 3 \times 10^9}{3 \times 10^{10} \times 3 \times 10^{10}}}}{1 - \frac{3 \times 10^9 \times 3 \times 10^9}{3 \times 10^{10} \times 3 \times 10^{10}}} = \frac{3\sqrt{3} \times 10^9}{\sqrt{1 - 0.01}}$$

$$= \frac{3\sqrt{3} \times 10^9}{\sqrt{0.99}} = \frac{3 \times 1.732 \times 10^9}{0.995} = 5.22 \times 10^9 \text{ cm s}^{-1}$$

The resultant velocity u', as observed by a person in the frame S', is given by

$$u' = \sqrt{u_x'^2 + u_y'^2} = 5.22 \times 10^9 \text{ cm s}^{-1} \text{ along } Y\text{-axis.}$$

Q. 10.34. Two photons approach each other, what is their relative velocity?

(G.N.D.U., 2000, 1999, 1993)

Ans. Velocity of each photon $= c$

Suppose the photons move along the direction of X-axis.

As they are approaching each other, applying inverse velocity transformation equation

$$u = \frac{u' + v}{1 + \frac{v}{c^2} u'}$$

we have

$$u = \frac{c + c}{1 + \frac{c^2}{c^2}} = c$$

Hence the relative velocity of two photons approaching each other is equal to the velocity of light.

Exercise. *Two photons are moving with velocity c in opposite directions to each other. What will be the relative velocity of one with respect to the other?* (P.U. 2008)

Hint: Solve as above   **Ans.** c

Q. 10.35. If u and u' are the velocities of a particle in the frames S and S' which are moving with velocity v relative to each other, prove that

$$\sqrt{1 - \frac{u'^2}{c^2}} = \frac{\sqrt{\left(1 - \frac{v^2}{c^2}\right)\left(1 - \frac{u^2}{c^2}\right)}}{\left(1 - \frac{v}{c^2} u_x\right)}.$$

Also give the corresponding inverse transformations. (H.P.U., 1991)

Ans. Velocity of the particle in the frame $S' = u'$

Let its components be u_x', u_y' and u_z'.

$\therefore \quad u'^2 = u_x'^2 + u_y'^2 + u_z'^2$

Similarly, let the components of u be u_x, u_y and u_z.

Now according to Lorentz velocity transformation equations

$$u'_x = \frac{u_x - v}{1 - \frac{v}{c^2}u_x}, \quad u'_y = \frac{u_y\sqrt{1 - \frac{v^2}{c^2}}}{1 - \frac{v}{c^2}u_x}, \quad u'_z = \frac{u_z\sqrt{1 - \frac{v^2}{c^2}}}{1 - \frac{v}{c^2}u_x}$$

$$\therefore \quad u'^2 = \frac{(u_x - v)^2 + u_y^2\left(1 - \frac{v^2}{c^2}\right) + u_z^2\left(1 - \frac{v^2}{c^2}\right)}{\left(1 - \frac{v}{c^2}u_x\right)^2}$$

$$= \frac{(u_x - v)^2 + (u_y^2 + u_z^2)\left(1 - \frac{v^2}{c^2}\right)}{\left(1 - \frac{v}{c^2}u_x\right)^2}$$

$$= \frac{(u_x - v)^2 + (u^2 - u_x^2)\left(1 - \frac{v^2}{c^2}\right)}{\left(1 - \frac{v}{c^2}u_x\right)^2}$$

or

$$\frac{u'^2}{c^2} = \frac{\left(\frac{u_x}{c} - \frac{v}{c}\right)^2 + \left(\frac{u^2}{c^2} - \frac{u_x^2}{c^2}\right)\left(1 - \frac{v^2}{c^2}\right)}{\left(1 - \frac{v}{c^2}u_x\right)^2}$$

$$\therefore \quad 1 - \frac{u'^2}{c^2} = \frac{\left(1 - \frac{v}{c^2}u_x\right)^2 - \left(\frac{u_x}{c} - \frac{v}{c}\right)^2 - \left(\frac{u^2}{c^2} - \frac{u_x^2}{c^2}\right)\left(1 - \frac{v^2}{c^2}\right)}{\left[1 - \frac{v}{c^2}u_x\right]^2}$$

$$= \frac{1 + \frac{v^2}{c^4}u_x^2 - 2\frac{vu_x}{c^2} - \frac{u_x^2}{c^2} - \frac{v^2}{c^2} + \frac{2u_x v}{c^2} - \frac{u^2}{c^2} + \frac{u_x^2}{c^2} + \frac{u^2 v^2}{c^4} - \frac{u_x^2 v^2}{c^4}}{\left[1 - \frac{v}{c^2}u_x\right]^2}$$

$$= \frac{1 - \frac{v^2}{c^2} - \frac{u^2}{c^2} + \frac{u^2 v^2}{c^4}}{\left(1 - \frac{v}{c^2}u_x\right)^2}$$

$$= \frac{\left(1 - \frac{v^2}{c^2}\right)\left(1 - \frac{u^2}{c^2}\right)}{\left(1 - \frac{v}{c^2}u_x\right)^2}$$

Hence
$$\sqrt{1 - \frac{u'^2}{c^2}} = \frac{\sqrt{\left(1 - \frac{v^2}{c^2}\right)\left(1 - \frac{u^2}{c^2}\right)}}{\left(1 - \frac{v}{c^2}u_x\right)}$$

Inverse transformation equations. To get the corresponding inverse transformation equation, put

$$u' = u, \quad u = u' \text{ and } \quad u_x = u_x'$$

$$\therefore \qquad \sqrt{1 - \frac{u^2}{c^2}} = \frac{\sqrt{\left(1 - \frac{v^2}{c^2}\right)\left(1 - \frac{u'^2}{c^2}\right)}}{\left(1 - \frac{v}{c^2}u_x'\right)}$$

**Q. 10.36 (a). Discuss relativistic Doppler effect and derive relations for longitudinal and trans-
verse Doppler effect. What is meant by the terms red shift and blue shift?**
*(Meerut U. 2003, 2001, 2000; P.U. 2006, 2003, 2000; G.N.D.U. 2007; H.P.U. 2001, 1995, 1992;
Pbi. U. 2007, 2006)*

**(b) The light of wavelength 434 nm is emitted by a star. This light is observed to have wavelength
532 nm on earth. Find the speed with which the star is receding from the earth.**
(P.U. 2006; Pbi. U. 2006)

Ans (a). Relativistic Doppler effect. *The apparent change in the frequency of light due to the
motion of the observer relative to the source of the light is known as Doppler effect.*

Longitudinal Doppler effect. Consider
two inertial frames S and S' such that S' is moving with respect to S with a constant speed v
in the $+x$-direction. Suppose a plane wave of
light of frequency v is travelling in the
x-direction in the frame S. We represent this
wave by the relation

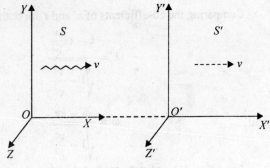

Fig. 10.10

$$a = a_0 \cos\frac{2\pi}{\lambda}(x - ct)$$

$$= a_0 \cos(kx - \omega t)$$

where $k = \dfrac{2\pi}{\lambda}$, the *propagation constant,* λ being the wavelength of light, $\omega = \dfrac{2\pi c}{\lambda} = 2\pi v, c$
being the velocity of light wave.

The wave as seen by an observer in the frame S' is given by

$$a = a_0 \cos(k'x' - \omega' t')$$

where $k' = \dfrac{2\pi}{\lambda'}$ is the propagation constant, λ' being the wavelength as seen in the frame S' and

$\omega' = 2\pi v'$, v' being the frequency as seen in the frame S'.

The quantity $kx - \omega t = \phi_s$ is known as the *phase* of the wave in frame S and $k'x' - \omega' t' = \phi_s'$ is the
phase of the wave as seen in the frame S'.

In the S' frame the wave will still be a plane wave because Lorentz transformation equations are linear and transform a plane wave into a plane. The phase of the wave is, therefore, invariant under Lorentz transformation *i.e.*, $\phi_s = \phi_{s'}$

or
$$kx - \omega t = k' x' - \omega' t' \qquad \qquad \qquad ...(i)$$

The Lorentz transformation equations are

$$x = \frac{x' + vt'}{\sqrt{1 - \dfrac{v^2}{c^2}}}$$

$$t = \frac{t' + \dfrac{v}{c^2} x'}{\sqrt{1 - \dfrac{v^2}{c^2}}}$$

Substituting the values of x and t in terms of x' and t' in Eq. (i), we have

$$k \frac{(x' + vt')}{\sqrt{1 - \dfrac{v^2}{c^2}}} - \frac{\omega \left(t' + \dfrac{v}{c^2} x'\right)}{\sqrt{1 - \dfrac{v^2}{c^2}}} = k' x' - \omega' t'$$

or
$$\frac{k - \omega \dfrac{v}{c^2}}{\sqrt{1 - \dfrac{v^2}{c^2}}} x' - \frac{\omega - kv}{\sqrt{1 - \dfrac{v^2}{c^2}}} t' = k' x' - \omega' t'$$

Comparing the co-efficients of x' and t' on both sides, we get

$$k' = \frac{k - \omega \dfrac{v}{c^2}}{\sqrt{1 - \dfrac{v^2}{c^2}}} \qquad \qquad \qquad ...(ii)$$

and
$$\omega' = \frac{\omega - kv}{\sqrt{1 - \dfrac{v^2}{c^2}}} \qquad \qquad \qquad ...(iii)$$

From Eqs. (ii) and (iii), we find that the propagation constant k' and angular frequency ω' of the wave observed in the frame S' are different from the corresponding values in the frame S.

Now $\omega' = 2\pi\nu'$ and $\omega = 2\pi\nu$

Substituting these values in Eq. (iii), we have

$$2\pi\nu' = \frac{2\pi\nu - kv}{\sqrt{1 - \dfrac{v^2}{c^2}}} = \frac{2\pi\nu - \dfrac{2\pi}{\lambda} v}{\sqrt{1 - \dfrac{v^2}{c^2}}}$$

$\therefore$
$$\nu' = \frac{\nu - \dfrac{v}{\lambda}}{\sqrt{1 - \dfrac{v^2}{c^2}}}$$

For a wave propagating in vacuum $c = v\lambda$ or $\dfrac{1}{\lambda} = \dfrac{v}{c}$

$$\therefore \quad v' = \frac{v - \dfrac{vv}{c}}{\sqrt{1 - \dfrac{v^2}{c^2}}} = \frac{v\left(1 - \dfrac{v}{c}\right)}{\sqrt{1 - \dfrac{v^2}{c^2}}} = v\sqrt{\frac{1 - \dfrac{v}{c}}{1 + \dfrac{v}{c}}}$$

or $\qquad\qquad v' = v\sqrt{\dfrac{c - v}{c + v}}$ \hfill ...(iv)

In terms of wavelength $\lambda' = \lambda\sqrt{\dfrac{c + v}{c - v}}$ \hfill ...(v)

Eqs. (iv) and (v) are known as *Longitudinal Doppler effect formulae* as the light travels parallel to the direction of motion of S' frame.

Eq. (iv) gives the apparant frequency of light as observed from a frame moving with respect to the source of light. Eq (v) gives the corresponding values of the wavelength of light.

Red shift. From Eqs. (iv) and (v) we find that when the source of light and the observer are *moving away* from each other

$$v' = v\sqrt{\frac{c - v}{c + v}} \quad \text{and} \quad \lambda' = \lambda\sqrt{\frac{c + v}{c - v}}$$

where v and λ are the frequency and wavelength respectively emitted by the source in the frame S and v' and λ' the corresponding values as observed by the observer in the frame S'. It is clear from relation (iv) that v' is *less* than v. Hence when the source is receding away from the observer the frequency of the emitted light appears to have decreased i.e., the *wavelength appears to increase* as is also evident from relation (v).

This is known as *red shift* since the red colour is on the longer wavelength side of the visible spectrum and explains the red shift of the spectral lines of light received from distant stars. The red shift implies the stars (or nebulae) showing red shift are moving away from us.

Blue shift. Eqs. (iv) and (v) hold good when the source and the observer are moving away from each other. When the source and observer are moving *towards* each other v is taken as *negative*.

In such a case the observed frequency appears to increase i.e., the wavelength appears to decrease. This effect is sometimes called *blue shift*.

Transverse Doppler effect. Consider a plane wave of light of angular frequency ω propagating in the Y direction. Such a wave is represented by the equation

$$a = a_0 \cos(ky - \omega t)$$

where $k = \dfrac{2\pi}{\lambda}$ and $\omega = 2\pi v$ are the propagation constant and angular frequency in the frame S. The phase of the wave in the frame $S = \phi_s = ky - \omega t$

Let the phase of the wave in the frame

$S' = \phi_{s'} = k'y' - \omega't'$ where $k' = \dfrac{2\pi}{\lambda'}$ and $\omega' = 2\pi v'$ are the propagation constant and the angular frequency as observed in the frame S'.

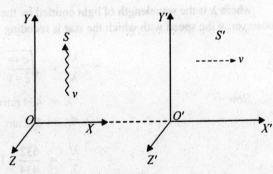

Fig. 10.11

As the phase is invariant under Lorentz transformations, we have $ky - \omega t = k' y' - \omega' t'$

Using Lorentz transformation equations $y = y'$ and

$$t = \frac{t' + \dfrac{v}{c^2} x'}{\sqrt{1 - \dfrac{v^2}{c^2}}}, \quad \text{we get}$$

$$k y' - \frac{\omega \left(t' + \dfrac{v}{c^2} x' \right)}{\sqrt{1 - \dfrac{v^2}{c^2}}} = k' y' - \omega' t'$$

or

$$k y' - \frac{\omega t'}{\sqrt{1 - \dfrac{v^2}{c^2}}} - \frac{\dfrac{\omega v}{c^2} x'}{\sqrt{1 - \dfrac{v^2}{c^2}}} = k' y' - \omega' t'$$

Comparing co-efficients of y', t' and x' on both sides, we get

$$k = k' \; ; \quad \frac{\omega}{\sqrt{1 - \dfrac{v^2}{c^2}}} = \omega' ; \quad \frac{\dfrac{\omega v}{c^2} x'}{\sqrt{1 - \dfrac{v^2}{c^2}}} = 0$$

As $\omega = 2\pi\nu$ and $\omega' = 2\pi\nu'$, we have

$$\frac{2\pi\nu}{\sqrt{1 - \dfrac{v^2}{c^2}}} = 2\pi\nu'$$

or

$$\nu' = \frac{\nu}{\sqrt{1 - \dfrac{v^2}{c^2}}} \qquad \qquad \qquad ...(vi)$$

This is known as *transverse Doppler effect* formula. This is a purely relativistic relation and has no classical analogue.

(b) According to longitudinal Doppler effect given in relation (v) we have,

$$\lambda' = \lambda \sqrt{\frac{c+v}{c-v}}$$

where λ is the wavelength of light emitted by the source and λ' the wavelength measured by the observer, v the speed with which the star is receding with respect to the earth

$$\therefore \qquad \frac{\lambda'}{\lambda} = \sqrt{\frac{c+v}{c-v}}$$

Now

$$\lambda = 434 \text{ nm and}$$
$$\lambda' = 532 \text{ nm}$$

$$\therefore \qquad \frac{\lambda'}{\lambda} = \frac{532}{434} = 1.226$$

$$\therefore \qquad \sqrt{\frac{c+v}{c-v}} = 1.226 \quad \text{or} \quad \frac{c+v}{c-v} = (1.226)^2 = 1.503$$

or $\quad 1.503(c-v) = c+v$

or $\quad 0.503c = 2.503v$

$$\therefore \qquad v = \frac{0.503}{2.503}c = 0.201c = 6.03 \times 10^7 \text{ m/sec}$$

Q. 10.37. (a) Derive the formula for relativistic variation of mass with velocity, $m = \dfrac{m_0}{\sqrt{1-\dfrac{v^2}{c^2}}}$.

(*P.U.* 2006, 2005, 2004, 2001, 2000, 1992; *M.D.U.* 2002, 2001, 2000; *Indore U.* 2001, *Pbi. U.* 2003; *K.U.* 2002, 2000; *H.P.U.* 2003, 1999, 1997, 1995; *G.N.D.U.* 2008, 1996; *Luck. U.* 1996; *A.U.* 1994)

(b) Hence prove that it is not possible for a material particle to have a velocity equal to or greater than the velocity of light. (*P.U.* 2001, 2000; *G.N.D.U.* 2004)

Ans. (a) Variation of mass with velocity. Consider two observers O and O' in the inertial frames S and S' at rest with respect to each other with their X-axis lying at a distance apart. The observer O in the system S has a small *hard* sphere A and observer O' in the system S' has an *exactly similar* small hard sphere B. The masses of A and B are the *same* when compared at rest in the same inertial frame. The frame S' now moves to the right along the X-axis with a uniform velocity v. The observer O throws the sphere A in his $+Y$ direction with a speed u as measured by his own measuring scale and his own clock.

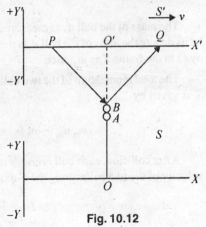

At the same time, the observer O' throws the sphere B in his $-Y$ direction with the same speed u, as measured by his own measuring scale and his own clock.

It is supposed that the motion of the particles is confined in the X-Y plane.

Fig. 10.12

The two spheres have an elastic collision midway between the two X-axes. For this to happen the observer O' must project his sphere from a point P. This sphere will appear to the observer O to travel along PB with the resultant velocity of u along $-Y$ direction and v along $+X$-direction. As the velocity along the Y-direction is independent of the velocity along the X-direction, the sphere B will have an *elastic* collision with the sphere A at a point exactly midway between the two X-axes, when the observers O and O' are exactly opposite to each other. As the X-component of the velocity of B is not affected by collision, it will appear to the observer O to move back along BQ.

Now let us denote the velocity of the sphere A as measured by the observer O in the frame S as u_a and let its two components in the X-Y plane be u_{ax} and u_{ay}. As the velocity of the sphere A is along $+Y$-direction. $\qquad u_{ax} = 0$ and $u_{ay} = u_a = +u$

Similarly let us denote the velocity of the sphere B as measured by the observer O' in the frame S' as $u_b' = -u$ (being along the direction of $-Y$-direction) and let its two components in the X-Y plane be u_{bx}' and u_{by}'.

$$\therefore \qquad u_{bx}' = 0 \text{ and } u_{by}' = u_b' = -u$$

Let us now denote the velocity of the sphere B as measured by the observer O in the frame S as

u_b and let its two components in the X-Y plane be u_{bx} and u_{by}. To find the value of u_{bx} and u_{by} in terms of u_{bx}' and u_{by}' we make use of *Lorentz velocity transformation equations*, which are

$$u_x = \frac{u_x' + v}{1 + \frac{v}{c^2} u_x'}$$

$$u_y = \frac{u_y' \sqrt{1 - \frac{v^2}{c^2}}}{1 + \frac{v}{c^2} u_x'}$$

$$\therefore \quad u_{bx} = \frac{u_{bx}' + v}{1 + \frac{v}{c^2} u_{bx}'} = +v \qquad\qquad [\because u_{bx}' = 0]$$

and

$$u_{by} = u_{by}' \frac{\sqrt{1 - \frac{v^2}{c^2}}}{1 + \frac{v}{c^2} u_{bx}'} = -u \sqrt{1 - \frac{v^2}{c^2}}$$

The mass of the ball A, as measured by O and that of the ball B as measured by O' is the same but let us denote the mass of the ball A as measured by $O = m_a$ and the mass of the ball B as measured again by O in the frame S as m_b, then

The total momentum of the two balls along Y-axis **before collision** as observed by O in the system S, is given by

$$m_a u_{ay} + m_b u_{by} = m_a u - m_b u \sqrt{1 - \frac{v^2}{c^2}}$$

After collision, each ball *reverses* its Y-component of velocity. Therefore the Y-component of the velocity of the two balls along the Y-axis **after collision** as observed by O in the system S is given by

$$u_{ay} = -u \text{ and } u_{by} = +u \sqrt{1 - \frac{v^2}{c^2}}$$

Therefore, total momentum of the two balls along Y-axis **after collision**, as observed by O in the system S, is given by

$$m_a u_{ay} + m_b u_{by} = -m_a u + m_b u \sqrt{1 - \frac{v^2}{c^2}}$$

According to the principle of conservation of momentum:

Total momentum before collision = Total momentum after collision

$$\therefore \quad m_a u - m_b u \sqrt{1 - \frac{v^2}{c^2}} = -m_a u + m_b u \sqrt{1 - \frac{v^2}{c^2}}$$

or

$$2 m_a u = 2 m_b u \sqrt{1 - \frac{v^2}{c^2}}$$

or

$$\frac{m_b}{m_a} = \frac{1}{\sqrt{1 - \frac{v^2}{c^2}}}$$

where m_a and m_b respectively are the masses of the spheres A and B as measured by the observer O. It is evident that this equation cannot be satisfied unless m_a and m_b are different. But these masses were equal when both of these were measured at rest with respect to stationary observers. Hence the mass also depends upon velocity. As m_a is the mass of the sphere A, in the inertial system S at rest we denote $m_a = m_0$ and as m_b is the mass of the sphere B in the inertial system S' moving with respect to S with a velocity v, we denote

$$m_b = m$$

$$\therefore \quad \frac{m}{m_0} = \frac{1}{\sqrt{1 - \dfrac{v^2}{c^2}}} \quad \text{or} \quad m = \frac{m_0}{\sqrt{1 - \dfrac{v^2}{c^2}}}$$

Hence the mass of a particle, when it is moving with a velocity v, is greater than its mass when it is at rest. In other words, the mass of a body increases with its velocity of motion.

(b) Material particle cannot have velocity equal to or greater than velocity of light.

When the velocity of a moving body is equal to the velocity of light, its mass is *infinite*. On the other hand, if its velocity is greater than the velocity of light its mass is *negative*. Both these things are, however, impossible. It, therefore, means that material particle cannot have a velocity equal to or greater than the velocity of light.

Q. 10.38. An electron having rest mass 9×10^{-31} kg moves with velocity equal to 80% of that of light. Find its mass. What will be the mass of electron to an observer who is moving with it?

(P.U. 2007, Pbi.U. 2007)

Ans. Velocity of the electron $v = \dfrac{80}{100} c = 0.8c$ or $\dfrac{v}{c} = 0.8$

Rest mass of the electron $m_0 = 9 \times 10^{-31}$ kg

$\therefore$ Relativistic mass of electron when it is moving with a velocity v,

$$m = \frac{m_0}{\sqrt{1 - \dfrac{v^2}{c^2}}} = \frac{9 \times 10^{-31}}{\sqrt{1 - 0.64}} = \frac{9 \times 10^{-31}}{0.6} = 1.5 \times 10^{-30} \text{ kg}$$

To an observer, who is moving with the electron, the electron appears to be at rest. So the mass measured by the observer, who is moving with the electron, is the rest mass of the electron $= 9 \times 10^{-31}$ kg.

Exercise. *An electron moves with a velocity of 0.6×10^8 m/s. Calculate its mass. $m_0 = 9 \times 10^{-31}$ kg*

Hint: $$m = \frac{m_0}{\sqrt{1 - \dfrac{v^2}{c^2}}} = \frac{9 \times 10^{-31}}{\sqrt{1 - \dfrac{0.6 \times 10^8 \times 0.6 \times 10^8}{3 \times 10^8 \times 3 \times 10^8}}} = 9.183 \times 10^{-31} \text{ kg.}$$

Q. 10.39. Calculate the velocity at which electron mass is $\sqrt{3}$ times the rest mass.

(P.U., 1991)

Ans. $m = \sqrt{3}\, m_0$ or $\dfrac{m_0}{m} = \dfrac{1}{\sqrt{3}}$

Now $\quad m = \dfrac{m_0}{\sqrt{1 - \dfrac{v^2}{c^2}}}$

$\therefore \quad \dfrac{m_0}{m} = \sqrt{1 - \dfrac{v^2}{c^2}} = \dfrac{1}{\sqrt{3}} \quad$ or $\quad 1 - \dfrac{v^2}{c^2} = \dfrac{1}{3}$

$\therefore \quad \dfrac{v^2}{c^2} = 1 - \dfrac{1}{3} = \dfrac{2}{3} \quad$ or $\quad \dfrac{v}{c} = \sqrt{\dfrac{2}{3}} \qquad \therefore \; v = \sqrt{\dfrac{2}{3}}\, c$

or $\qquad\qquad v = 0.816\, c = 0.816 \times 3 \times 10^8 = 2.448 \times 10^8 \, \mathrm{ms^{-1}}$

Exercise. *What should be the speed of electron so that its relativistic mass is twice its rest mass?*

(P.U., 2004)

Hint. Relativistic mass $m = \dfrac{m_0}{\sqrt{1 - \dfrac{v^2}{c^2}}}$ where m_0 is the rest mass or $\dfrac{m}{m_0} = 2$

$\therefore \quad 1 - \dfrac{v^2}{c^2} = \left(\dfrac{m_0}{m}\right)^2 = \dfrac{1}{4}$ or $\dfrac{v^2}{c^2} = 1 - \dfrac{1}{4} = \dfrac{3}{4}$ or $\dfrac{v}{c} = \dfrac{\sqrt{3}}{2} = 0.866$ or $v = 0.866\, c.$

Q. 10.40. At what speed must a particle move for its mass to be four times its rest mass?

(H.P.U., 1997)

Ans. Let v be the velocity at which the mass m has a value four *times* the rest mass m_0.

$\therefore \qquad\qquad m = 4 m_0$

Now $\qquad\qquad m = \dfrac{m_0}{\sqrt{1 - \dfrac{v^2}{c^2}}}\quad$ or $\quad 4 m_0 = \dfrac{m_0}{\sqrt{1 - \dfrac{v^2}{c^2}}}$

Squaring we get $\qquad 16\left(1 - \dfrac{v^2}{c^2}\right) = 1\;$ or $\;\dfrac{v^2}{c^2} = 1 - \dfrac{1}{16} = \dfrac{15}{16}$

$\therefore \qquad\qquad v^2 = \dfrac{15}{16}\, c^2 \quad$ or $\quad v = \sqrt{\dfrac{15}{16}}\; c = 0.968\, c$

$= 0.968 \times 3 \times 10^8 = 2.904 \times 10^8 \, \mathrm{ms^{-1}}$

Q. 10.41. With what velocity a particle should move so that its mass appears to increase by 20% of its rest mass?

(Pbi. U. 2006; P.U., 2001)

Ans. Let m_0 be the rest mass of the particle. If v is the velocity of the particle at which the mass m of the particle appears to increase by 20%, then

$$\dfrac{m}{m_0} = \dfrac{100 + 20}{100} = \dfrac{6}{5}$$

Now $\qquad\qquad m = \dfrac{m_0}{\sqrt{1 - \dfrac{v^2}{c^2}}}\;$ or $\;\dfrac{m_0}{m} = \sqrt{1 - \dfrac{v^2}{c^2}}\;$ or $\;\dfrac{5}{6} = \sqrt{1 - \dfrac{v^2}{c^2}}$

$\therefore \quad \dfrac{25}{36} = 1 - \dfrac{v^2}{c^2}\;$ or $\;\dfrac{v^2}{c^2} = 1 - \dfrac{25}{36} = \dfrac{11}{36}\;$ or $\;\dfrac{v}{c} = \dfrac{\sqrt{11}}{6} = 0.553$

$\therefore \qquad\qquad v = 0.553\, c$

Q. 10.42 (a). Establish mathematically Einstein's mass energy relationship. Explain physical significance of this relation. Mention two nuclear phenomena supporting this relation.

(GN.D.U. 2004, 2001, 2000; P.U. 2001; Bang. U. 2004, 2001; Osm. U. 2004;
Pbi. U. 2003, 2001; M.D.U. 2002, 2000, 1999; J.P.U. 1999; Meerut U. 2003, 2002;
K.U. 1997; A.U. 1995; Luck U. 1994)

(b) Show that if variation of mass with velocity is taken into account the kinetic energy particle of rest mass m_0 moving with velocity v is given by

$$E = m_0 c^2 \left[\left(1 - \frac{v^2}{c^2} \right)^{-\frac{1}{2}} - 1 \right]$$

(P.U. 2008)

Ans. (a) Mass of a moving body. According to the classical theory, the mass of a moving body is constant and independent of its velocity. According to the theory of relativity, however, it can be proved that the mass of a moving body varies with velocity. According to this theory the *effective mass* of a body when it is moving with a velocity v relative to an observer, is given by

$$m = \frac{m_0}{\sqrt{1 - \frac{v^2}{c^2}}}$$

where m_0 is the *rest mass i.e.*, the mass of body when it is at rest relative to the observer and c the velocity of light.

Mass energy relation. According to Newton's second law of motion, the force acting on a body is equal to the rate of change of momentum it produces. If a body of mass m moving with a velocity v has a force F applied to it, then

$$F = \frac{d}{dt}(mv) = m \frac{dv}{dt} + v \frac{dm}{dt}$$

as m and v are both variables.

If the force F acts for a small distance dx, the work done F dx is stored in the body as its kinetic energy given by

$$dE_k = Fdx = m \frac{dv}{dt} dx + v \frac{dm}{dt} dx = m \, dv \frac{dx}{dt} + v \, dm \frac{dx}{dt}$$

$$= mv \, dv + v^2 dm \qquad \qquad ...(i)$$

Since

$$\frac{dx}{dt} = v$$

Now

$$m = \frac{m_0}{\sqrt{1 - \frac{v^2}{c^2}}} \quad \text{or } m^2 = \frac{m_0^2 c^2}{c^2 - v^2}$$

or

$$m^2 c^2 - m^2 v^2 = m_0^2 c^2$$

Differentiating both sides, we get

$$2m \, dm \, c^2 - 2m \, dm \, v^2 - 2v \, dv \, m^2 = 0$$

or

$$dm \, c^2 = (mv \, dv + v^2 \, dm)$$

or

$$dm \, c^2 = dE_k$$

Integrating both sides, we get

$$c^2 \int_{m_0}^{m} dm = \int dE_k$$

or $\qquad\qquad\qquad c^2(m - m_0) = E_k$ $\qquad\qquad\qquad\qquad\qquad\qquad$ ...(ii)

or $\qquad\qquad\qquad\qquad E_k = \Delta mc^2$

where $\Delta m = (m - m_0)$ and is the mass converted into kinetic energy. The equation $E_k = \Delta mc^2$ shows that the kinetic energy of a moving mass is c^2 times the gain in mass. It thus points out that the increase in mass is an indication and measure of the kinetic energy. The mass m_0 is often termed as the rest-mass of the body and the term $m_0 c^2$ as the rest-energy of the body. The rest-energy is regarded as a form of internal energy inherent in the nature of particles constituting matter. Rewriting the equation $c^2(m - m_0) = E_k$ we get

$$mc^2 = E_k + m_0 c^2 \qquad\qquad\qquad\qquad\qquad\qquad \text{...(iii)}$$

or $\qquad\qquad$ Total energy = Rest mass energy + kinetic energy

If we denote the total energy by E, we get the famous mass energy relation

$$E = mc^2 \qquad\qquad\qquad\qquad\qquad\qquad \text{...(iv)}$$

This is known as Einstein's mass energy relationship.

Physical significance The relation $E = mc^2$ expressing mass energy equivalence is the most important result of the special theory of relativity. This relation shows that under suitable conditions mass can be converted into energy and *vice-versa*. In classical Newtonian mechanics there are two separate conservation laws namely (*i*) The law of conservation of mass and (*ii*) The law of conservation of energy. Einstein's mass energy relationship in special theory of relativity combines these two laws into one *i.e.*, Law of conservation of mass and energy. In nuclear phenomenon in which energy is released there is a corresponding decrease in total mass and in such phenomenon in which energy is absorbed there is an equivalent increase in mass. But as the velocity of light in free space is very large 3×10^8 ms^{-1}, a very small decrease in mass results in the release of a very large amount of energy. For example, the conversion of rest mass of 1 a.m.u. $(1.65 \times 10^{-27}$ kg) releases 931 MeV of energy.

Supporting nuclear phenomenon. (*i*) Nuclear phenomena like *fission* and *fusion* are very important examples of conversion of mass into energy and are most popular present-day methods of producing energy.

(*ii*) The mass energy relationship helps us to determine the binding energy of various nuclei on the basis of mass defect.

(*iii*) Energy released in the annihilation of matter, *e.g.*, annihilation of electron-positron pair also supports the mass-energy relationship.

(*b*) According to Eq.(*ii*)

Kinetic energy $E_k = c^2(m - m_0)$

Putting $E_k = T$, we have $T = c^2(m - m_0)$

Now $\qquad\qquad\qquad\qquad m = \dfrac{m_0}{\sqrt{1 - \dfrac{v^2}{c^2}}} = m_0 \left(1 - \dfrac{v^2}{c^2}\right)^{-1/2}$

$\therefore \qquad\qquad T = c^2(m - m_0) = mc^2 - m_0 c^2 = m_0 \left(1 - \dfrac{v^2}{c^2}\right)^{-1/2} c^2 - m_0 c^2$

$$= m_0 c^2 \left[\left(1 - \frac{v^2}{c^2} \right)^{-1/2} - 1 \right]$$

Q. 10.43. (a) Comment on the statement that special theory of relativity ascribes energies to all masses and masses to all energies.   (G.N.D.U. 2004)

(b) Calculate the ratio of mass of the electron to its rest mass when it is moving with a kinetic energy of 9.5 MeV. Rest mass of electron 0.5 MeV.   (K.U. 2001; Luck. U. 1996)

Ans. (a) See Q. 10.42 under 'Physical significance.

(b) Let m_0 be the rest mass of the electron and m the mass when moving with a kinetic energy of 9.5 MeV.

$$\text{Kinetic energy} = (m - m_0) c^2 = 9.5 \text{ MeV}$$

Also rest-mass (energy) of the electron (Given) $= m_0 c^2 = 0.5$ MeV

$$\therefore \qquad mc^2 = m_0 c^2 + 9.5 \text{ MeV} = 0.5 + 9.5 = 10 \text{ MeV}$$

Hence $\qquad \dfrac{m}{m_0} = \dfrac{mc^2}{m_0 c^2} = \dfrac{10}{0.5} = 20$

Exercise. *Calculate the ratio of the mass of the electron to its rest mass when it is moving with a kinetic energy of* 1000MeV. *Rest mass of the electron* = 0.51 MeV.   (Luck. U. 1996, 1991)

Hint. $(m - m_0)c^2 = 1000$ MeV; $m_0 c^2 = 0.51$ MeV; $mc^2 = m_0 c^2 + 1000$ MeV

$$= 1000.51 \text{ MeV} \therefore \frac{m}{m_0} = \frac{1000.51}{0.51} = 1961.78$$

Q. 10.44 (a). Calculate the velocity of 1 MeV electron.   (Pbi.U. 2008, K.U., 1996; P.U., 1992)

(b) Calculate the rest mass of an electron in MeV. Also calculate the speed at which the total relativistic energy is 1.25 times the rest mass energy.

$$m_0 = 9.1 \times 10^{-31} \text{ kg.}$$ (G.N.D.U. 2007)

Ans (a). 1 MeV electron means the kinetic energy of the electron = 1 MeV = 1.6×10^{-13} Joule

Let m_0 be the rest mass of the electron, m its mass when moving with a velocity v and E_k its kinetic energy, then

$$E_k = (m - m_0) c^2$$

$$= \left[\frac{m_0}{\sqrt{1 - \dfrac{v^2}{c^2}}} - m_0 \right] c^2 = m_0 c^2 \left[\frac{1}{\sqrt{1 - \dfrac{v^2}{c^2}}} - 1 \right]$$

or $\qquad \dfrac{1}{\sqrt{1 - \dfrac{v^2}{c^2}}} = \dfrac{E_k}{m_0 c^2} + 1 = \dfrac{1.6 \times 10^{-13}}{9 \times 10^{-31} \times 9 \times 10^{16}} + 1 = \dfrac{160}{81} + 1 = \dfrac{241}{81}$

$$\therefore \qquad \sqrt{1 - \frac{v^2}{c^2}} = \frac{81}{241} = 0.336$$

or $\qquad 1 - \dfrac{v^2}{c^2} = (0.336)^2 = 0.113$

$$\therefore \qquad \frac{v^2}{c^2} = 1 - 0.113 = 0.887$$

or
$$\frac{v}{c} = 0.94 \quad \text{Hence } v = 0.94\, c$$

or
$$v = 2.82 \times 10^8 \text{ ms}^{-1}$$

(b) Rest mass energy in MeV $= m_0 c^2 = 9.1 \times 10^{-31} \times 3 \times 10^8 \times 3 \times 10^8$ Joule

$$= \frac{9.1 \times 10^{-31} \times 9 \times 10^{16}}{1.6 \times 10^{-19}} eV = 51.2 \times 10^4 \, eV$$

$$= 0.512 \, \text{MeV}$$

Total relativistic energy $= K.E +$ Rest mass energy

or
$$mc^2 = \frac{m_0 c^2}{\sqrt{1 - \frac{v^2}{c^2}}} = 1.25 m_0 c^2$$

$$\therefore \qquad \frac{1}{\sqrt{1 - \frac{v^2}{c^2}}} = 1.25 \quad \text{or} \quad \sqrt{1 - \frac{v^2}{c^2}} = \frac{1}{1.25}$$

or
$$1 - \frac{v^2}{c^2} = \left(\frac{1}{1.25}\right)^2 \quad \text{or} \quad \frac{v^2}{c^2} = 1 - \left(\frac{1}{1.25}\right)^2 = 1 - 0.64 = 0.36$$

$$\therefore \qquad \frac{v}{c} = 0.6 \quad \text{or} \quad v = 0.6c$$

Exercise. *What will be the velocity of a 2 MeV electron?*

Given $m_0 c^2 = 0.51$ *MeV*

(*Meerut. U.* 2006)

Hint: As proved in part (*a*) of this question,

$$\frac{1}{\sqrt{1 - \frac{v^2}{c^2}}} = \frac{E_k}{m_0 c^2} + 1$$

or
$$\frac{1}{\sqrt{1 - \frac{v^2}{c^2}}} = \frac{2\,MeV}{0.51 MeV} + 1 = 4.92$$

$$\therefore \qquad \frac{v}{c} = 0.9791 \quad \text{or} \quad v = 0.9791c = 2.937 \times 10^8 \text{ m/sec.}$$

Q. 10.45. Kinetic energy of a particle is (*i*) 3 times, (*ii*) twice and (*iii*) equal to its rest mass energy. What is its velocity?

(*G.N.D.U.* 2009, 2007, *Pbi.U.* 2003; *H.P.U.*, 1996; *P.U.* 2007, 2003, 2001, 1993)

Ans. (*i*) Kinetic energy $E_k = (m - m_0) c^2$

Rest mass energy $= m_0 c^2$

Now Kinetic energy $= 3 \times$ Rest mass energy

or $$(m - m_0) c^2 = 3 m_0 c^2$$

or $$m = 4 m_0$$

But $m = \dfrac{m_0}{\sqrt{1 - \dfrac{v^2}{c^2}}}$ $\therefore$ $4 m_0 = \dfrac{m_0}{\sqrt{1 - \dfrac{v^2}{c^2}}}$

or $$\dfrac{1}{\sqrt{1 - \dfrac{v^2}{c^2}}} = 4$$

$\therefore$ $$1 - \dfrac{v^2}{c^2} = \dfrac{1}{16}$$

or $$\dfrac{v^2}{c^2} = 1 - \dfrac{1}{16} = \dfrac{15}{16}$$

$\therefore$ $$\dfrac{v}{c} = \sqrt{\dfrac{15}{16}} = 0.968$$

Hence $v = 0.968\, c = 0.968 \times 3 \times 10^8 = 2.904 \times 10^8\ \text{ms}^{-1}$

(*ii*) Kinetic energy $= 2 \times$ Rest mass energy

or $$(m - m_0) c^2 = 2 m_0 c^2 \text{ or } m = 3 m_0$$

But $m = \dfrac{m_0}{\sqrt{1 - \dfrac{v^2}{c^2}}}$ $\therefore$ $3 m_0 = \dfrac{m_0}{\sqrt{1 - \dfrac{v^2}{c^2}}}$ or $\dfrac{1}{\sqrt{1 - \dfrac{v^2}{c^2}}} = 3$

$\therefore$ $$1 - \dfrac{v^2}{c^2} = \dfrac{1}{9} \text{ or } \dfrac{v^2}{c^2} = 1 - \dfrac{1}{9} = \dfrac{8}{9}$$

or $$\dfrac{v}{c} = \sqrt{\dfrac{8}{9}} = 0.943$$

Hence $v = 0.943\, c = 0.943 \times 3 \times 10^8 = 2.829 \times 10^8\ \text{ms}^{-1}$

(*iii*) Kinetic energy = Rest mass energy

or $$(m - m_0) c^2 = m_0 c^2 \text{ or } m = 2 m_0$$

But $m = \dfrac{m_0}{\sqrt{1 - \dfrac{v^2}{c^2}}}$ $\therefore$ $2 m_0 = \dfrac{m_0}{\sqrt{1 - \dfrac{v^2}{c^2}}}$ or $\dfrac{1}{\sqrt{1 - \dfrac{v^2}{c^2}}} = 2$

$\therefore$ $$1 - \dfrac{v^2}{c^2} = \dfrac{1}{4} \text{ or } \dfrac{v^2}{c^2} = 1 - \dfrac{1}{4} = \dfrac{3}{4}$$

or $$\dfrac{v}{c} = \sqrt{\dfrac{3}{4}} = 0.866$$

Hence $v = 0.866\, c = 0.866 \times 3 \times 10^8 = 2.598 \times 10^8\ \text{ms}^{-1}$

Exercise 1. *The total energy of a particle is excatly equal to twice its rest mass energy. What is the velocity of the particle?* (*Pbi.U. 2007*)

Hint: $mc^2 = 2m_0 c^2$, $\therefore$ $m = 2\, m_0$ Hence $v = \dfrac{\sqrt{3}}{2} c$

(as proved in (iii) above)

Exercise 2. *What is the speed of a particle whose kinetic energy is equal to half of its rest mass energy?*   (P.U. 2006)

Hint: $(m - m_0)c^2 = \dfrac{1}{2}\, m_0 c^2$ $\quad \therefore\ m = \dfrac{3}{2} m_0$ or $\dfrac{m_0}{\sqrt{1 - \dfrac{v^2}{c^2}}} = \dfrac{3}{2} m_0$

$\therefore$ $\sqrt{1 - \dfrac{v^2}{c^2}} = \dfrac{2}{3};\ 1 - \dfrac{v^2}{c^2} = \dfrac{4}{9};\ \dfrac{v^2}{c^2} = \dfrac{5}{9};\ \dfrac{v}{c} = \dfrac{\sqrt{5}}{3} = 0.745$

Hence $v = 0.745c$

Q. 10.46. Find the increase in mass of 2 kg metal piece of specific heat 0.2 when heated through 800°C.   (H.P.U., 2001)

Ans. Heat supplied to the metal $E = 2000 \times 0.2 \times 800 = 3.2 \times 10^5$ cal

$$= 3.2 \times 10^5 \times 4.2 = 13.44 \times 10^5 \text{ J}$$

Increase in mass of metal $= \dfrac{E}{c^2} = \dfrac{13.44 \times 10^5}{9 \times 10^{16}} = 1.493 \times 10^{-11}$ kg.

Exercise. *Calculate the increase in mass of 500 gm of metal of specific heat 0.15 cal g^{-1} K^{-1} when heated through 900°C.*   (P.U. 1993)

Hint. $E = 500 \times 0.15 \times 900 = 6.75 \times 10^4$ cal $= 28.35 \times 10^4$ J

Increase in mass $= \dfrac{28.35 \times 10^4}{9 \times 10^{16}} = 3.15 \times 10^{-12}$ kg.

Q. 10.47. (a) The rest mass of electron is 9.028×10^{-31} kg. Calculate the energy equivalent in electron volts.

(b) The atomic mass unit (a.m.u.) is 1.6558×10^{-27} kg. Find the corresponding energy in electron volts.   (G.N.D.U. 2006)

Ans. (a) Rest mass of the electron $m_0 = 9.028 \times 10^{-31}$ kg

Energy equivalent $m_0 c^2 = 9.028 \times 10^{-31} \times (3 \times 10^8)^2$ Joule $= 81.252 \times 10^{-15}$ J

Now one electron volt $= 1.6 \times 10^{-19}$ J

$\therefore$ Energy in electron volts $= \dfrac{81.252 \times 10^{-15}}{1.6 \times 10^{-19}} = 0.5078 \times 10^6$ eV $= 0.5078$ MeV

(b) Atomic mass unit $= 1.6558 \times 10^{-27}$ kg

$\therefore$ Energy equivalent $= \dfrac{1.6558 \times 10^{-27} \times (3 \times 10^8)^2}{1.6 \times 10^{-19}} = 931 \times 10^6$ eV $= 931$ MeV

10.48. If one gram of a substance is fully converted into energy in one second, how many calories of heat will be produced and how much power will be generated?   (G.N.D.U. 2001; P.U. 1995)

Ans. Mass of the substance $= m_0 = 1$ gm $= 10^{-3}$ kg

$\therefore$ Energy produced $= m_0 c^2 = 10^{-3} \times (3 \times 10^8)^2 = 9 \times 10^{13}$ J

$$= \frac{9 \times 10^{+13}}{4.2} = 2.14 \times 10^{13} \text{ calories}$$

As 9×10^{13} J of energy are produced in one second,

Power generated $= 9 \times 10^{13}$ Watts $= 9 \times 10^7$ Mega Watts

Q. 10.49 (a). A proton has a total relativistic energy 900 MeV. If the rest mass of the proton is 1.6×10^{-27} kg, find its speed and kinetic energy. (*Pbi. U.* 2002; *P. U.* 1999; *G.N.D.U.*, 1993)

(b) Work out the energy of a proton moving at 0.9c. The rest mass of the proton is 940 MeV.

(*G.N.D.U.* 2006)

Ans. (a) Total relativistic energy of the proton = 900 MeV

$$= 900 \times 10^6 \times 1.6 \times 10^{-19} \text{ J} = 14.4 \times 10^{-11} \text{ J}$$

Now relativistic energy $E = mc^2$

$\therefore$ Relativistic mass of the proton

$$m = \frac{E}{c^2} = \frac{14.4 \times 10^{-11}}{(3 \times 10^8)^2} = \frac{14.4 \times 10^{-11}}{9 \times 10^{16}} = 1.6 \times 10^{-27} \text{ kg}$$

Rest mass of the proton $= 1.6 \times 10^{-27}$ kg

As the rest mass of the proton = Relativistic mass

$\therefore$ The proton is at rest and hence its speed as well as kinetic energy is zero.

(b) Total relativistic energy of the proton $E = mc^2 = \dfrac{m_0 c^2}{\sqrt{1 - \dfrac{v^2}{c^2}}}$

Now $$\sqrt{1 - \frac{v^2}{c^2}} = \sqrt{1 - (0.9)^2} = \sqrt{1 - 0.81} = 0.4359$$

$\therefore$ $$\frac{1}{\sqrt{1 - \dfrac{v^2}{c^2}}} = \frac{1}{0.4359} = 2.294$$

$\therefore$ $$E = 2.294 \, (m_0 c^2) = 2.294 \times 940 = 2156 \text{ MeV}$$

Exercise. *A proton has a total relativistic energy 9×10^4 MeV. Find its speed. Rest mass of proton is 1.6×10^{-27} kg.* (*P.U.* 2009)

Hint: Here, Total relativistic energy $E = 9 \times 10^4$ MeV

$$= 9 \times 10^4 \times 1.6 \times 10^{-13} = 14.4 \times 10^{-9} \text{ J} \quad [\therefore 1 \text{ MeV} = 1.6 \times 10^{-13} \text{ J}]$$

Relativistic mass of the proton $m = \dfrac{E}{c^2} = \dfrac{14.4 \times 10^{-9}}{9 \times 10^{16}} = 1.6 \times 10^{-25}$ kg

If m_0 is the rest mass of the proton, then $m = \dfrac{m_0}{\sqrt{1 - \dfrac{v^2}{c^2}}}$

$$\therefore \qquad \sqrt{1 - \frac{v^2}{c^2}} = \frac{m_0}{m} = \frac{1.6 \times 10^{-27}}{1.6 \times 10^{-25}} = 10^{-2}$$

or $\qquad 1 - \dfrac{v^2}{c^2} = 10^{-4}$ or $\dfrac{v^2}{c^2} = 1 - 10^{-4} = 0.9999$

$$\therefore \qquad v = \sqrt{0.9999}\, c = 0.99995\, c$$

Q. 10.50. Dynamite liberates 5.4×10^6 J/kg when it explodes. What fraction of total energy content is this?   (*H.P.U.*, 1993, 1991)

Ans. Total energy content of 1 kg. mass $= m_0\, c^2 = 1 \times (3 \times 10^8)^2 = 9 \times 10^{16}$ Joule

Energy liberated per kg in explosion $= 5.4 \times 10^6$ Joule

Fraction of total energy $= \dfrac{5.4 \times 10^6}{9 \times 10^{16}} = 0.6 \times 10^{-10}$

Q. 10.51. (a) Give relation for relativistic kinetic energy of a particle. Show that for $v \ll c$ the kinetic energy of the particle is given by classical relation $\dfrac{1}{2} m_0 v^2$.

(*P.U.* 2004, 2001; *G.N.D.U.* 1996; *A.U.* 1995; *Luck U.* 1994, 1993)

(b) An electron of rest mass 9×10^{-31} kg moves with a speed of 80% of that of light. Find its kinetic energy.   (*Kerala U.* 2001)

Ans. (a) Relativistic kinetic energy. The kinetic energy of a particle of rest mass m_0 is given by

$$E_k = (m - m_0)\, c^2 \qquad\qquad \text{...(i)}$$

where m is the mass of the particle when it is moving with a velocity v and is given by

$$m = \frac{m_0}{\sqrt{1 - \dfrac{v^2}{c^2}}}$$

$$\therefore \qquad E_k = \left\{ \frac{m_0}{\sqrt{1 - \dfrac{v^2}{c^2}}} - m_0 \right\} c^2 = m_0\, c^2 \left[\frac{1}{\sqrt{1 - \dfrac{v^2}{c^2}}} - 1 \right] \qquad\qquad \text{...(ii)}$$

This expression gives the kinetic energy of a particle of rest mass m_0 moving with a velocity v.

When $v \ll c$. Relation (*ii*) is the expression for *relativistic kinetic energy* of a particle of rest-mass m_0 moving with a velocity v. When the *speed v* is very small as compared to c,

$$\left(1 - \frac{v^2}{c^2}\right)^{-1/2} = 1 + \frac{1}{2} \frac{v^2}{c^2}$$

Neglecting higher powers of $\dfrac{v^2}{c^2}$. In such a case

$$E_k = m_0\, c^2 \left(\frac{1}{2} \frac{v^2}{c^2} \right) = \frac{1}{2} m_0 v^2$$

This is the usual *non-relativistic* expression for the kinetic energy of a moving particle.

Hence we find that the relativistic expression for kinetic energy of a moving particle reduces to the classical expression for *very small* velocities.

(b) Velocity of the electron $v = \dfrac{80}{100} c = \dfrac{4}{5} c$

Kinetic energy of the electron $E_k = (m - m_0)c^2 = m_0 c^2 \left[\dfrac{1}{\sqrt{1 - \dfrac{v^2}{c^2}}} - 1 \right]$

$$= m_0 c^2 \left[\dfrac{1}{\sqrt{1 - \dfrac{16}{25}}} - 1 \right] = m_0 c^2 \times \dfrac{2}{3}$$

$$\therefore \quad E_k = 9 \times 10^{-31} \times 9 \times 10^{16} \times \dfrac{2}{3} = 54 \times 10^{-15} \text{ J} = 5.4 \times 10^{-14} \text{ J}$$

Q. 10.52. (a) **Calculate the speed of the electron which has kinetic energy 1.02 MeV. Given rest-mass of the electron = 0.51 MeV.** *(GN.D.U. 1995)*

(b) **Given that the total energy of a particle is exactly equal to two times its rest energy, what is the velocity of the particle?** *(Pbi.U. 2007; P.U. 1999)*

Ans. (a) Total energy of the electron is given by

$$E = E_k + m_0 c^2$$

where E_k is the kinetic energy and $m_0 c^2$ the rest mass energy.

Now $E_k = 1.02$ MeV $= 2 \times 0.51 = 2 \times$ rest mass energy $= 2 m_0 c^2$

Total energy $E = mc^2 = \dfrac{m_0 c^2}{\sqrt{1 - \dfrac{v^2}{c^2}}}$ where v is the velocity (speed) of the electron.

$$\therefore \quad \dfrac{m_0 c^2}{\sqrt{1 - \dfrac{v^2}{c^2}}} = 2 m_0 c^2 + m_0 c^2$$

or $\quad \dfrac{1}{\sqrt{1 - \dfrac{v^2}{c^2}}} = 3$

$$\therefore \quad 1 - \dfrac{v^2}{c^2} = \dfrac{1}{9}$$

or $\quad v = \dfrac{c}{3}\sqrt{8} = 0.943\, c = 2.829 \times 10^8$ m/sec.

(b) Total energy $E = mc^2 = \dfrac{m_0 c^2}{\sqrt{1 - \dfrac{v^2}{c^2}}} = 2 m_0 c^2$

where m_0 is the rest mass and v the velocity of the particle when its energy is twice the rest energy.

$$\therefore \quad \dfrac{1}{\sqrt{1 - \dfrac{v^2}{c^2}}} = 2 \quad \text{or} \quad 1 - \dfrac{v^2}{c^2} = \dfrac{1}{4} \quad \text{or} \quad \dfrac{v^2}{c^2} = 1 - \dfrac{1}{4} = \dfrac{3}{4}$$

$$\therefore \qquad \frac{v}{c} = \frac{\sqrt{3}}{2} \quad \text{or} \quad v = \frac{\sqrt{3}}{2}\, c = 0.866\, c = 2.598 \times 10^8 \text{ met/sec.}$$

Exercise. *A particle of rest mass m_0 moves with a speed $\dfrac{c}{\sqrt{2}}$. Calculate the mass, momentum, total energy and kinetic energy.*

(G.N.D.U. 2006)

Hint:

$$\text{Mass } m = \frac{m_0}{\sqrt{1 - \dfrac{v^2}{c^2}}} = \frac{m_0}{\sqrt{1 - \dfrac{c^2}{2c^2}}} = \frac{m_0}{\sqrt{1 - \dfrac{1}{2}}} = \sqrt{2}\, m_0$$

$$\text{Momentum} = mv = m\frac{c}{\sqrt{2}} = \sqrt{2} m_0 \frac{c}{\sqrt{2}} = m_0 c$$

Total energy $\qquad\qquad = mc^2 = \sqrt{2}\, m_0\, c^2$

Kinetic energy $\qquad\qquad = $ Total energy $-$ Rest mass energy

$$= mc^2 - m_0 c^2 = \sqrt{2}\, m_0 c^2 - m_0 c^2$$

$$= \left(\sqrt{2} - 1\right) m_0 c^2 = 0.414\, m_0 c^2$$

Q. 10.53. The earth receives 1400 W/m² of solar energy. Distance between the earth and the sun is 1.5×10^{11} m. Estimate the rate of decrease of the mass of the sun.

(*Kerala U.* 2001)

Ans. Solar energy received by the earth = 1400 W/m² = 1400 Joules / m² s

Distance of the earth from the sun $R_0 = 1.5 \times 10^{11}$ m

$\therefore$ Total energy radiated by the sun per second

$$E = 4\pi R_0^2 \times 1400 = 4\pi \times 1.5 \times 1.5 \times 10^{22} \times 1400 \text{ Joules s}^{-1}$$

If m is the rate of decrease of mass of the sun, then

$$mc^2 = 4\pi \times 1.5 \times 1.5 \times 10^{22} \times 1400 \text{ J/s}$$

or $\qquad m = \dfrac{4 \times 22 \times 1.5 \times 1.5 \times 10^{22} \times 1400}{7 \times 3 \times 3 \times 10^{16}} = 4.4 \times 10^9$ kg/s.

Q. 10.54. What is the error involved in calculating the kinetic energy of a particle according to (*i*) Classical Physics (*ii*) Relativistic Physics when it is moving at $v = 0.5c$?

(*H.P.U.*, 1993, 1991)

Ans. Let the rest mass of the particle be = m_0

Velocity of the particle $v = 0.5\, c = 1.5 \times 10^8$ ms^{-1}

(*i*) Kinetic energy of the particle according to Classical Physics

$$= \frac{1}{2} m_0 v^2 = \frac{1}{2} m_0 \times 1.5 \times 1.5 \times 10^8 \times 10^8 = m_0 \times 1.125 \times 10^{16} \text{ J}$$

(*ii*) Kinetic energy according to Relativistic Physics

$$E_k = (m - m_0)\, c^2$$

$$= \left(\frac{m_0}{\sqrt{1-\dfrac{v^2}{c^2}}} - m_0\right)c^2 = \left(\frac{1}{\sqrt{1-\dfrac{v^2}{c^2}}} - 1\right)m_0 c^2$$

$$= m_0\left(\frac{1}{\sqrt{1-\dfrac{1}{4}}} - 1\right)3 \times 3 \times 10^{16}$$

$$= m_0\left(\frac{2-\sqrt{3}}{\sqrt{3}}\right) \times 9 \times 10^{16} = m_0 \times 1.395 \times 10^{16}\text{ J}$$

∴ Percentage error

$$= m_0 \times 10^{16} \times \frac{[1.395 - 1.125]}{m_0 \times 1.395 \times 10^{16}} \times 100 = \frac{1.395 - 1.125}{1.395} \times 100 = 19.4\%$$

Q. 10.55. Derive transformation formulae for relativistic momentum and energy and hence prove that the quantity $\left(p^2 - \dfrac{E^2}{c^2}\right)$ **is an invariant.**

(*P.U.* 2009; 2006; 2001; *G.N.D.U.* 1999; *H.P.U.* 2000, 1996)

Ans. Transformation formula for relativistic momentum. Let m be the mass of a particle moving with a velocity $\vec{u}$, then its momentum

$$\vec{p} = m\vec{u}$$

Let the components of $\vec{p}$ be $p_x, p_y,$ and p_z. If u_x, u_y and u_z are the components of $\vec{u}$, then

$$p_x = mu_x = \frac{m_0 u_x}{\sqrt{1-\dfrac{u^2}{c^2}}}$$

where m_0 is the rest mass of the particle whose mass is m when moving with the velocity u. Similarly

$$p_y = mu_y = \frac{m_0 u_y}{\sqrt{1-\dfrac{u^2}{c^2}}}$$

and

$$p_z = mu_z = \frac{m_0 u_z}{\sqrt{1-\dfrac{u^2}{c^2}}}$$

The total energy E is given by

$$E = mc^2 = \frac{m_0 c^2}{\sqrt{1-\dfrac{u^2}{c^2}}}$$

If $\vec{p}$ is the momentum of the same particle in the inertial frame S', m' its mass, $\vec{u'}$ its velocity in this frame, p_x', p_y', p_z' the components of $\vec{p'}$ and u_x', u_y', u_z' the components of $\vec{u'}$, then

$$p_x' = m'u_x' = \frac{m_0}{\sqrt{1-\dfrac{u'^2}{c^2}}} u_x'$$

$$p_y' = m'u_y' = \frac{m_0}{\sqrt{1 - \dfrac{u'^2}{c^2}}}\, u_y' \qquad p_z' = m'u_z' = \frac{m_0}{\sqrt{1 - \dfrac{u'^2}{c^2}}}\, u_z'$$

and

$$E' = m'c^2 = \frac{m_0 c^2}{\sqrt{1 - \dfrac{u'^2}{c^2}}}$$

Consider the relation $\quad p_x' = \dfrac{m_0 u_x'}{\sqrt{1 - \dfrac{u'^2}{c^2}}}$ ...(i)

To get its value in terms of u_x and u we have the Lorentz velocity transformation equations

$$u_x' = \frac{u_x - v}{1 - \dfrac{v}{c^2} u_x}$$

and

$$\sqrt{1 - \frac{u'^2}{c^2}} = \frac{\sqrt{\left(1 - \dfrac{v^2}{c^2}\right)\left(1 - \dfrac{u^2}{c^2}\right)}}{1 - \dfrac{v}{c^2} u_x}$$

(For proof see Q. 10.35)

Substituting these values of u_x' and $\sqrt{1 - \dfrac{u'^2}{c^2}}$ in (i) we have

$$p_x' = m_0 \frac{(u_x - v)\left(1 - \dfrac{v}{c^2} u_x\right)}{\left(1 - \dfrac{v}{c^2} u_x\right)\sqrt{\left(1 - \dfrac{v^2}{c^2}\right)\left(1 - \dfrac{u^2}{c^2}\right)}}$$

$$= \frac{m_0 (u_x - v)}{\sqrt{1 - \dfrac{u^2}{c^2}}\,\sqrt{1 - \dfrac{v^2}{c^2}}}$$

$$= \frac{m_0 u_x - m_0 v}{\sqrt{1 - \dfrac{u^2}{c^2}}\,\sqrt{1 - \dfrac{v^2}{c^2}}}$$

$$= \frac{p_x}{\sqrt{1 - \dfrac{v^2}{c^2}}} - \frac{E \dfrac{v}{c^2}}{\sqrt{1 - \dfrac{v^2}{c^2}}}$$

$$\therefore \qquad \boxed{p_x' = \frac{p_x - \dfrac{v}{c^2} E}{\sqrt{1 - \dfrac{v^2}{c^2}}}} \qquad\qquad ...(ii)$$

Now consider the relation

$$p_y' = \frac{m_0 u_y'}{\sqrt{1 - \frac{u'^2}{c^2}}} \qquad \qquad ...(iii)$$

Here

$$u_y' = \frac{u_y \sqrt{1 - \frac{v^2}{c^2}}}{1 - \frac{v}{c^2} u_x}$$

Substituting the value of u_y' and the value of $\sqrt{1 - \frac{u'^2}{c^2}}$ in (iii), we have

$$p_y' = \frac{m_0 u_y \sqrt{1 - \frac{v^2}{c^2}} \left(1 - \frac{v}{c^2} u_x\right)}{\left[1 - \frac{v}{c^2} u_x\right] \sqrt{\left(1 - \frac{v^2}{c^2}\right)\left(1 - \frac{u^2}{c^2}\right)}}$$

$$= \frac{m_0 u_y}{\sqrt{1 - \frac{u^2}{c^2}}}$$

or

$$p_y' = p_y \qquad \qquad ...(iv)$$

Similarly

$$p_z' = p_z \qquad \qquad ...(v)$$

Equations (ii), (iv) and (v) give Lorentz transformations for momentum components of the particle.

Inverse momentum transformation equations. The inverse momentum transformation equations are

$$p_x = \frac{p_x' + \frac{v}{c^2} E}{\sqrt{1 - \frac{v^2}{c^2}}} \qquad \qquad ...(vi)$$

$$p_y = p_y' \qquad \qquad ...(vii)$$
$$p_z = p_z' \qquad \qquad ...(viii)$$

Transformation equations for energy. To establish the relation between energy in the inertial frames S and S', let E' be the energy of the particle in the inertial frame S', then

$$E' = m' c^2 = \frac{m_0 c^2}{\sqrt{1 - \frac{u'^2}{c^2}}}$$

$$= \frac{m_0 c^2 \left(1 - \frac{v}{c^2} u_x\right)}{\sqrt{1 - \frac{v^2}{c^2}} \sqrt{1 - \frac{u^2}{c^2}}}$$

$$\frac{\dfrac{m_0 c^2}{\sqrt{1 - \dfrac{u^2}{c^2}}} - \dfrac{m_0 u_x}{\sqrt{1 - \dfrac{u^2}{c^2}}} \cdot v}{\sqrt{1 - \dfrac{v^2}{c^2}}}$$

or

$$E' = \frac{E - v p_x}{\sqrt{1 - \dfrac{v^2}{c^2}}} \qquad \qquad ...(ix)$$

The inverse energy transformation equation is

$$E = \frac{E' + v p_x'}{\sqrt{1 - \dfrac{v^2}{c^2}}} \qquad \qquad ...(x)$$

To show that $\left(p^2 - \dfrac{E^2}{c^2} \right)$ is an invariant. The quantity $\left(p^2 - \dfrac{E^2}{c^2} \right)$ will be an invariant if

$\left(p'^2 - \dfrac{E'^2}{c^2} \right) = \left(p^2 - \dfrac{E^2}{c^2} \right)$ under a Lorentz transformation.

Now $\quad p'^2 = p_x'^2 + p_y'^2 + p_z'^2 = \dfrac{\left(p_x - \dfrac{v}{c^2} E \right)^2}{1 - \dfrac{v^2}{c^2}} + p_y^2 + p_z^2$

and

$$\frac{E'^2}{c^2} = \frac{(E - v p_x)^2}{c^2 \left(1 - \dfrac{v^2}{c^2} \right)}$$

$\therefore \qquad p'^2 - \dfrac{E'^2}{c^2} = \dfrac{\left(p_x - \dfrac{v}{c^2} E \right)^2}{1 - \dfrac{v^2}{c^2}} + p_y^2 + p_z^2 - \dfrac{(E - v p_x)^2}{c^2 \left(1 - \dfrac{v^2}{c^2} \right)}$

$$= p_x^2 \frac{\left(1 - \dfrac{v^2}{c^2} \right)}{\left(1 - \dfrac{v^2}{c^2} \right)} + p_y^2 + p_z^2 - \frac{\dfrac{E^2}{c^2} \left(1 - \dfrac{v^2}{c^2} \right)}{\left(1 - \dfrac{v^2}{c^2} \right)}$$

$$= p_x^2 + p_y^2 + p_z^2 - \frac{E^2}{c^2}$$

$$= p^2 - \frac{E^2}{c^2}$$

Thus $p^2 - \dfrac{E^2}{c^2}$ is invariant under Lorentz transformations.

Q. 10.56 (a). Show that the velocity u of a relativistic particle is given by

$$u = \frac{pc}{\sqrt{p^2 + m_0^2 c^2}} \quad \text{and} \quad E = \sqrt{p^2 c^2 + m_0^2 c^4}$$

where p is the relativistic momentum. Hence write down formulae for energy and momentum of a photon.   (*P.U.* 2006; 2001; *H.P.U.* 2000, 1999, 1994; *G.N.D.U.* 1999, 1996; *A.U.* 1995; *Luck U.* 1995)

(*b*) What should be the speed of a particle of rest mass m_0 in order that its relativistic momentum is $m_0 c$? Find its total relativistic energy.   (*P.U.* 2009, 2005)

Ans. (*a*) Velocity of a relativistic particle. The momentum of a particle of mass m (rest mass m_0) moving with a velocity u is given by

$$\vec{p} = m\vec{u} = \frac{m_0 \vec{u}}{\sqrt{1 - \dfrac{u^2}{c^2}}}$$

$$\therefore \qquad p^2 = \vec{p} \cdot \vec{p} = \left(\frac{m_0 \vec{u}}{\sqrt{1 - \dfrac{u^2}{c^2}}} \right) \left(\frac{m_0 \vec{u}}{\sqrt{1 - \dfrac{u^2}{c^2}}} \right)$$

$$= \frac{m_0^2 u^2}{1 - \dfrac{u^2}{c^2}}$$

or $$p^2 = \frac{m_0^2 u^2 c^2}{c^2 - u^2} \qquad \qquad ...(i)$$

or $$p^2 c^2 = u^2 \left(p^2 + m_0^2 c^2 \right)$$

$$\therefore \qquad u = \frac{pc}{\sqrt{p^2 + m_0^2 c^2}} \qquad \qquad ...(ii)$$

Energy momentum relation. Multiplying Equation (*i*) by c^2, we have

$$p^2 c^2 = \frac{m_0^2 u^2 c^4}{c^2 - u^2} \qquad \qquad ...(iii)$$

The total energy E of the particle is given by

$$E = mc^2 = \frac{m_0 c^2}{\sqrt{1 - \dfrac{u^2}{c^2}}}$$

$$\therefore \qquad E^2 = \frac{m_0^2 c^4}{1 - \dfrac{u^2}{c^2}} = \frac{m_0^2 c^6}{c^2 - u^2} \qquad \qquad ...(iv)$$

Subtracting (*iii*) from (*iv*) we have

$$E^2 - p^2 c^2 = \frac{m_0^2 c^4 (c^2 - u^2)}{c^2 - u^2} = m_0^2 c^4$$

$$\therefore \qquad E^2 = p^2 c^2 + m_0^2 c^4 \qquad \qquad ...(v)$$

or $$E = \sqrt{p^2 c^2 + m_0^2 c^4} = c\sqrt{p^2 + m_0^2 c^2} \qquad \qquad ...(vi)$$

Energy and momentum of a photon. For a photon the rest mass $m_0 = 0$

$\therefore$ Energy of the photon $E = pc$

The energy of a photon of frequency $\nu = h\nu$

$\therefore$ Momentum of the photon $p = \dfrac{E}{c} = \dfrac{h\nu}{c} = \dfrac{h}{\lambda}$

(b) The relativistic momentum of a particle of rest mass m_0 moving with a velocity u is given by

$$\vec{p} = m\vec{u} = \dfrac{m_0 \vec{u}}{\sqrt{1 - \dfrac{u^2}{c^2}}}$$

Here $p = m_0 c$ $\qquad \therefore \quad m_0 c = \dfrac{m_0 \vec{u}}{\sqrt{1 - \dfrac{u^2}{c^2}}}$ or $c = \dfrac{u}{\sqrt{1 - \dfrac{u^2}{c^2}}}$

or $\qquad\qquad\qquad c^2 = \dfrac{u^2}{1 - \dfrac{u^2}{c^2}}$ or $c^2 - u^2 = u^2$ or $c^2 = 2u^2$

$\therefore \qquad\qquad\qquad 2u^2 = c^2$ or $u^2 = \dfrac{c^2}{2}$ or $u = \dfrac{c}{\sqrt{2}}$

Total relativistic energy $\quad E = c\sqrt{p^2 + m_0^2 c^2}$

Substituting $p = m_0 c$, we get, $E = c\sqrt{m_0^2 c^2 + m_0^2 c^2} = \sqrt{2}\, m_0 c^2$

Q. 10.57. (a) Derive relation between relativistic momentum and energy of a free particle.

(P.U. 2003)

(b) Prove that the momentum p of a body of rest mass m_0 and kinetic energy T is given by

$p = \sqrt{\dfrac{T^2}{c^2} + 2m_0 T}$.

(P.U. 1996)

Ans. (a) The relation between relativistic momentum p and energy E of a free particle is

$$E^2 = p^2 c^2 + m_0^2 c^4$$

For proof see [Q. 10.56 (b) Eq (v)]

(b) Relation between momentum and kinetic energy. The kinetic energy of a particle of relativistic mass m is given by

$$T = (m - m_0) c^2 \quad \therefore \quad T = mc^2 - m_0 c^2$$

$mc^2 = E$ is known as total energy or relativistic energy of the particle.

$\therefore \qquad\qquad\qquad mc^2 = E = T + m_0 c^2$

Also $\qquad\qquad\qquad E = \sqrt{p^2 c^2 + m_0^2 c^4}$

$\therefore \qquad\qquad \sqrt{p^2 c^2 + m_0^2 c^4} = T + m_0 c^2$

Squaring both sides, we get

$$p^2 c^2 + m_0^2 c^4 = T^2 + m_0^2 c^4 + 2 m_0 c^2 T$$

or $$p^2 c^2 = T^2 + 2 m_0 c^2 T$$

∴ $$p^2 = \frac{T^2}{c^2} + 2m_0 T$$

or $$p = \sqrt{\frac{T^2}{c^2} + 2 m_0 T}$$

Q. 10.58 (a). Calculate the effective mass of a photon of wavelength 1Å.

(GN.D.U. 2008; P.U., 1991)

(b) Prove that the rest mass of the photon is zero. (P.U. 2006)

(c) Comment on the statement that the rest mass of a particle can be zero. Give examples.

(P.U. 2006; 2005)

Ans. (a) If m is the effective mass of the photon, then

$$h\nu = mc^2$$

where h is Planck's constant and ν the frequency of the photon.

∴ $$m = \frac{h\nu}{c^2} = \frac{h}{\lambda c} = \frac{6.63 \times 10^{-34} \text{ J.s}}{10^{-10} \times 3 \times 10^8} = 2.21 \times 10^{-22} \text{ kg}$$

(b) According to mass variation formula $m = \dfrac{m_0}{\sqrt{1 - \dfrac{v^2}{c^2}}}$

or $$m_0 = m\sqrt{1 - \frac{v^2}{c^2}}$$ where m_0 is the rest mass and v is the velocity with

which the mass is moving. A photon moves with the velocity of light. Therefore, for a photon $v = c$.

Hence the rest mass of the photon $m_0 = m\sqrt{1 - \dfrac{c^2}{c^2}} = m \times 0 = 0$. However, we cannot speak about

the rest mass of a photon because there exists no frame of reference in which the photons are at rest.

(c) The mass of a particle in a frame of reference in which the particle is at rest is called its *rest mass*. The rest mass of a particle can be zero. For example, the rest mass of particles like a photon and a neutrino is zero.

Q. 10.59. (a) What is the momentum of a proton having kinetic energy 1 BeV ? Rest mass of proton = 938.3 MeV. (GN.D.U. 1991)

(b) Calculate the linear momentum of a 25 GeV proton assuming that rest mass energy of the proton is approximately 1 GeV. (GN.D.U. 2003)

Ans. (a) According to the theory of relativity the total energy E of a particle of rest mass m_0 is related to its momentum p by the relation

$$E^2 = p^2 c^2 + m_0^2 c^4$$

The total energy E = Rest mass energy + K.E. = $m_0 c^2$ + K.E.

The rest mass energy of a proton $m_0 c^2 = 938.3$ MeV

K.E. of the proton = 1 BeV = 10^9 eV = 10^3 MeV

∴ $$(10^3 + 938.3)^2 \text{ (MeV)}^2 = p^2 c^2 + (938.3)^2 \text{ (MeV)}^2$$

$$\therefore \qquad pc = \sqrt{10^6\,(1+1.877)}\ \text{MeV} = 1.696 \times 10^3\ \text{MeV}$$

or
$$p = 1.696 \times 10^3\ \text{MeV}/c$$

$$= \frac{1.696 \times 10^3 \times 1.6 \times 10^{-13}\ \text{J}}{3 \times 10^8\ \text{ms}^{-1}}$$

$$= 9.045 \times 10^{-19}\ \text{Newton sec (kg ms}^{-1})$$

(b) This problem is a little different from the problem given in (a). In this problem total energy of the proton including its rest mass energy is given whereas in the problem given in (a) above only kinetic energy of the proton is given.

$$E = 25\ \text{GeV} = 25 \times 10^9\ \text{eV};\ m_0\,c^2 = 1\ \text{GeV} = 10^9\ \text{eV}$$

Now total energy E of a particle of rest mass m_0 is related to its momentum p by the relation

$$E^2 = p^2 c^2 + m_0^2\,c^4$$

$$\therefore \qquad (25 \times 10^9)^2 = p^2 c^2 + (1 \times 10^9)^2$$

or
$$625 \times 10^{18} = p^2 c^2 + 10^{18}$$

or
$$p^2 c^2 = 624 \times 10^{18}$$

or
$$pc = \sqrt{624} \times 10^9\ \text{eV}$$

$$= \sqrt{624} \times 10^9 \times 1.6 \times 10^{-19}\ \text{J}$$

$$\therefore \qquad p = \frac{\sqrt{624} \times 1.6 \times 10^{-10}}{3 \times 10^8}\ \text{Newton Sec.}$$

$$= 13.3 \times 10^{-18}\ \text{Newton Sec.}$$

Q. 10.60 (a). Calculate the wavelength of the radiation emitted by the annihilation of an electron with a positron each of rest mass 9.1×10^{-31} kg.

(b) Find the momentum and relativistic mass of photon of wavelength $\lambda = 4000$ Å. Given $h = 6.6 \times 10^{-27}$ kg sec. *(P.U. 2008)*

Ans. When an electron-positron pair is annihilated, the total rest mass of both the particles is converted into energy and a *pair* of photons of high frequency radiations is given out. The energy will not appear in the form of a single photon, because to conserve the total linear momentum two photons travelling in opposite directions and each sharing half the energy are required. If m is the mass of the electron as well as that of the positron and a pair of photons of frequency ν are emitted, then

$$mc^2 + mc^2 = 2\,h\nu = \frac{2hc}{\lambda}$$

$$\therefore \qquad \lambda = \frac{hc}{mc^2} = \frac{h}{mc}$$

where h is Planck's constant 6.62×10^{-34} Joule sec. and λ the wavelength of the radiation emitted corresponding to the frequency ν of the photon. Hence

$$\lambda = \frac{6.62 \times 10^{-34}}{9.1 \times 10^{-31} \times 3 \times 10^8} = 0.024 \times 10^{-10}\ \text{m}$$

(b) Energy of the photon $E = h\nu = \dfrac{hc}{\lambda}$

Momentum of the photon $p = \dfrac{E}{c} = \dfrac{1}{c} \cdot \dfrac{hc}{\lambda} = \dfrac{h}{\lambda}$

$$= \frac{6.6 \times 10^{-27}}{4000 \times 10^{-8}} = 1.65 \times 10^{-22} \, \text{gm cm/sec}$$

$E = mc^2 = pc, \quad \therefore \qquad m = \dfrac{p}{c} = \dfrac{1.65 \times 10^{-22}}{3 \times 10^{10}} = 0.55 \times 10^{-32} \, \text{gm}$

$$= 5.5 \times 10^{-33} \, \text{gm}.$$

Q. 10.61. Consider a γ-ray of energy E_γ which strikes a proton at rest in the laboratory. Find out the velocity of centre of mass in the laboratory frame. (G.N.D.U., 1990)

Ans. For two particles of mass m_1 and m_2 moving with velocities $\vec{v_1}$ and $\vec{v_2}$ the velocity of centre of mass

$$\vec{V} = \frac{m_1 \vec{v_1} + m_2 \vec{v_2}}{m_1 + m_2} = \frac{\vec{p_1} + \vec{p_2}}{m_1 + m_2}$$

where $\vec{p_1} = m_1 \vec{v_1}$ and $\vec{p_2} = m_2 \vec{v_2}$ are linear momenta of the particles of mass m_1 and m_2 respectively.

Now momentum of γ-ray of energy $E_\gamma = p_1 = \dfrac{E_\gamma}{c}$

Momentum of proton at rest $p_2 = 0$

Effective mass of γ-ray (photon) $m_1 = \dfrac{E_\gamma}{c^2}$

Mass of proton $m_2 = m_p$

$$\therefore \qquad V = \frac{\dfrac{E_\gamma}{c}}{\dfrac{E_\gamma}{c^2} + m_p} = \frac{E_\gamma \, c}{E_\gamma + m_p c^2}$$

Q. 10.62. Derive Lorentz transformation equations for force.

Ans. Lorentz transformation equations for force. Consider a particle on which a force, $\vec{F}$ is acting in an inertial frame S. If $\vec{p}$ is the momentum of the particle, then

$$\vec{F} = \frac{d\vec{p}}{dt}$$

If F_x, F_y, F_z are the components of the force $\vec{F}$ and p_x, p_y, p_z the components of momentum $\vec{p}$, then

$$F_x = \frac{dp_x}{dt}, \quad F_y = \frac{dp_y}{dt}, \quad F_z = \frac{dp_z}{dt}$$

Let the inertial frame S' having co-ordinate axes parallel to the respective axes of the system S move with a velocity $\vec{v}$ along the positive direction of X-axis. In the system S' let an observer measure the force acting on the particle as $\vec{F'}$ and momentum $\vec{p'}$, then

$$F_x' = \frac{dp_x'}{dt'}, \quad F_y' = \frac{dp_y'}{dt'}, \quad F_z' = \frac{dp_z'}{dt'}$$

According to Lorentz transformation equations for momentum,

$$p_x' = \frac{p_x - \frac{v}{c^2}E}{\sqrt{1 - \frac{v^2}{c^2}}}; \quad p_y' = p_y; \quad p_z' = p_z$$

Also

$$t' = \frac{t - \frac{v}{c^2}x}{\sqrt{1 - \frac{v^2}{c^2}}} \quad \therefore \quad dt' = \frac{dt - \frac{v}{c^2}dx}{\sqrt{1 - \frac{v^2}{c^2}}} \quad \text{or} \quad \frac{dt'}{dt} = \frac{1 - \frac{v}{c^2}\frac{dx}{dt}}{\sqrt{1 - \frac{v^2}{c^2}}}$$

Hence

$$F_x' = \frac{dp_x'}{dt'} = \frac{dp_x'}{dt} \cdot \frac{dt}{dt'}$$

$$= \frac{\frac{dp_x}{dt} - \frac{v}{c^2}\frac{dE}{dt}}{\sqrt{1 - \frac{v^2}{c^2}}} \cdot \frac{\sqrt{1 - \frac{v^2}{c^2}}}{1 - \frac{v}{c^2}\frac{dx}{dt}}$$

$$= \frac{F_x - \frac{v}{c^2}\frac{dE}{dt}}{1 - \frac{v}{c^2}u_x} \qquad \qquad ...(i)$$

Since $\frac{dx}{dt} = u_x$ - The x-component of the velocity of the particle (u) in the frame S.

According to momentum energy relationship for a free particle,

$$E^2 = p^2 c^2 + m_0^2 c^4 = \vec{p} \cdot \vec{p} c^2 + m_0^2 c^4$$

$$\therefore \quad 2E\frac{dE}{dt} = \left(\vec{p} \cdot \frac{d\vec{p}}{dt} + \frac{d\vec{p}}{dt} \cdot \vec{p}\right)c^2 = 2c^2 \vec{p} \cdot \frac{d\vec{p}}{dt} = 2mc^2 \vec{u} \cdot \vec{F} \qquad ...(ii)$$

where $\vec{p} = m\vec{u}$, m being the relativistic mass of the particle. As $E = mc^2$, we have from relation (ii)

$$\frac{dE}{dt} = \vec{u} \cdot \vec{F} = (u_x\hat{i} + u_y\hat{j} + u_z\hat{k}) \cdot (F_x\hat{i} + F_y\hat{j} + F_z\hat{k})$$

$$= u_x F_x + u_y F_y + u_z F_z$$

Substituting the value of $\frac{dE}{dt}$ in (i), we have

$$F_x' = \frac{F_x - \frac{v}{c^2}(u_x F_x + u_y F_y + u_z F_z)}{1 - \frac{v}{c^2}u_x}$$

$$= \frac{F_x\left(1 - \frac{v}{c^2}u_x\right) - \frac{v}{c^2}(u_y F_y + u_z F_z)}{1 - \frac{v}{c^2}u_x}$$

$$= F_x - \frac{\frac{v}{c^2}}{1 - \frac{v}{c^2}u_x}(u_y F_y + u_z F_z) \qquad \text{...(iii)}$$

This is the transformation relation for the x component of the force.

Again
$$F_y' = \frac{dp_y'}{dt'} = \frac{dp_y'}{dt}\frac{dt}{dt'}$$

$$= \frac{dp_y}{dt}\frac{\sqrt{1 - \frac{v^2}{c^2}}}{1 - \frac{v}{c^2}\frac{dx}{dt}} = \frac{F_y\sqrt{1 - \frac{v^2}{c^2}}}{1 - \frac{v}{c^2}u_x} \quad (\because p_y' = p_y) \qquad \text{...(iv)}$$

Similarly
$$F_z' = \frac{F_z\sqrt{1 - \frac{v^2}{c^2}}}{1 - \frac{v}{c^2}u_x} \qquad \text{...(v)}$$

These are the transformation relations for y and z components.

If the velocity of the particle $u = u_x = v$; $u_y = 0$; $u_z = 0$, the transformation equations for force become

$$F_x' = F_x ; \quad F_y' = \frac{F_y}{\sqrt{1 - \frac{v^2}{c^2}}} = \gamma F_y ; \quad F_z' = \gamma F_z$$

Q. 10.63. (*a*) **What do you mean by Minkowski space? Explain. What are space like and time like intervals? What is their significance?**

(*Pbi. U.*, 1995; *H.P.U.*, 1995 *G.N.D.U.* 2009, 2007, 2006, *P.U.* 2007, 2005)

(*b*) **Show that** $x^2 + y^2 + z^2 - c^2t^2$ **is invariant under Lorentz transformations.**

(*G.N.D.U.* 2007; *Meerut U.* 2003)

Ans. (*a*) **Minkowski space.** According to Newtonian classical mechanics *space* and *time* are independent of each other. But from the study of special theory of relativity, we learn that *space* and *time* are interdependent and can be treated on equal basis. In three dimensional space we talk of *position* of a point and denote it by three space co-ordinates x, y, z but in *four dimensional space time continuum* we speak of an *event* and the place and time of its occurrence is denoted by three space co-ordinates x, y, z and fourth time co-ordinate t. To give the time co-ordiante the *same dimension* of length as of x, y, z co-ordinates, the time co-ordinate is multiplied by the velocity of light c and is chosen as an *imaginary* quantity ict where $i = \sqrt{-1}$. A vector in this four dimensional space will be represented by components along four mutually perpendicular axes.

The four dimensional space time continuum is known as *Minkowski's space* and the four co-ordinates in Minkowski's space are x, y, z, ict.

The position vector $\vec{r}$ or the vector distance between the origin and a point in three dimensional space having co-ordinates x, y, z is given by

$$r^2 = x^2 + y^2 + z^2$$

It is not invariant to Lorentz transformations *i.e.*,

$$x^2 + y^2 + z^2 \neq x'^2 + y'^2 + z'^2$$

Similarly the vector interval $\vec{s}$ between an event at the origin and an event in four dimensional space having co-ordinates x, y, z, ict is given by

$$s^2 = x^2 + y^2 + z^2 + (ict)^2$$
$$= x^2 + y^2 + z^2 - c^2 t^2$$

It can be shown that this value of s^2 is *invariant* to Lorentz transformations.

(b) Lorentz transformation equations are

$$x' = \frac{x - vt}{\sqrt{1 - \dfrac{v^2}{c^2}}} \;;\; y' = y\,;\, z' = z \text{ and } t' = \frac{t - \dfrac{v}{c^2}x}{\sqrt{1 - \dfrac{v^2}{c^2}}}$$

In the frame S, $\quad s^2 = x^2 + y^2 + z^2 - c^2 t^2$

In the frame S', $s'^2 = x'^2 + y'^2 + z'^2 - c^2 t'^2$

Substituting the values of x', y', z' and t' in terms of x, y, z and t, we get

$$x'^2 + y'^2 + z'^2 - c^2 t'^2 = \frac{(x - vt)^2}{1 - \dfrac{v^2}{c^2}} + y^2 + z^2 - c^2 \frac{\left(t - \dfrac{v}{c^2}x\right)^2}{1 - \dfrac{v^2}{c^2}}$$

$$= \frac{x^2 + v^2 t^2 - 2xvt - c^2 t^2 - \dfrac{v^2}{c^2}x^2 + 2xvt}{1 - \dfrac{v^2}{c^2}} + y^2 + z^2$$

$$= \frac{x^2\left(1 - \dfrac{v^2}{c^2}\right) - c^2 t^2\left(1 - \dfrac{v^2}{c^2}\right)}{1 - \dfrac{v^2}{c^2}} + y^2 + z^2$$

$$= x^2 + y^2 + z^2 - c^2 t^2$$

Thus the quantity $\qquad s^2 = x^2 + y^2 + z^2 - c^2 t^2 = x'^2 + y'^2 + z'^2 - c^2 t'^2$

and is *invariant* under Lorentz transformations. In other words, the four dimensional element is invariant under Lorentz transformations.

Time like and space like interval and their significance. The interval s in Minkowski space is given by

$$s^2 = x^2 + y^2 + z^2 - c^2 t^2 = x^2 + y^2 + z^2 + (ict)^2$$

If $x^2 + y^2 + z^2 < c^2 t^2$ or $r < ct$, r being given by

$$r = \sqrt{x^2 + y^2 + z^2}$$

The interval is called *time like interval*. In this case two events can be connected by a light signal.

If $r > ct$, the interval is known as *space like interval*. In this case two events cannot be connected by a light signal. In order to relate the two events having a space like interval, we require signals moving faster than light which is not possible in accordance with the special theory of relativity.

Q. 10.64. Write short note on Four vectors. Give two examples of four vectors.

(H.P.U., 1995, 1991)

Ans. Four vectors. A four vector is a mathematical entity having four components which transform in a way similar to x, y, z and ict. Lorentz transformation equations for x, y, z and t are

$$x' = \frac{x - vt}{\sqrt{1 - \frac{v^2}{c^2}}}; \quad y' = y, z' = z \text{ and } t' = \frac{t - \frac{v}{c^2}x}{\sqrt{1 - \frac{v^2}{c^2}}}$$

Now put $x = x_1, y = x_2, z = x_3$ and $ict = x_4$, then $t = \frac{1}{i}\frac{x_4}{c} = -\frac{i}{c}x_4$

Applying Lorentz transformation equations, we get

$$x_1' = \frac{x_1 + \frac{iv}{c}x_4}{\sqrt{1 - \frac{v^2}{c^2}}}; \quad x_2' = x_2; x_3' = x_3$$

and

$$\frac{x_4'}{ic} = \frac{\frac{x_4}{ic} - \frac{v}{c^2}x_1}{\sqrt{1 - \frac{v^2}{c^2}}} \text{ or } x_4' = \frac{x_4 - \frac{iv}{c}x_1}{\sqrt{1 - \frac{v^2}{c^2}}}$$

Also $s = \sqrt{x^2 + y^2 + z^2 + (ict)^2} = \sqrt{x_1^2 + x_2^2 + x_3^2 + x_4^2}$

Suppose $\vec{A}$ is a four vector and its components are A_1, A_2, A_3, A_4. These components in the frame S will transform to A_1', A_2', A_3', A_4' in the frame S' as x_1, x_2, x_3, x_4 transform to x_1', x_2', x_3' and x_4'.

$$\therefore \quad A_1' = \frac{A_1 + \frac{iv}{c}A_4}{\sqrt{1 - \frac{v^2}{c^2}}}; \quad A'_2 = A_2; A'_3 = A_3$$

and

$$A_4' = \frac{A_4 - \frac{iv}{c}A_1}{\sqrt{1 - \frac{v^2}{c^2}}}$$

The length of a four vector is given by $s^2 = A_1^2 + A_2^2 + A_3^2 + A_4^2$ and is invariant to Lorentz transformation *i.e.*,

$$A_1'^2 + A_2'^2 + A_3'^2 + A_4'^2 = A_1^2 + A_2^2 + A_3^2 + A_4^2$$

The four vector is *space like* if $A_1^2 + A_2^2 + A_3^2 + A_4^2$ is a positive quantity.
A four vector is *time like* if $A_1^2 + A_2^2 + A_3^2 + A_4^2$ is a negative quantity.
Examples. (*i*) Position four vector (x, y, z, ct)

(*ii*) Momentum four vector $\left(p_x, p_y, p_z, \frac{E}{c}\right)$

Q. 10.65. (*a*) Show that in a perfectly inelastic collision between two particles there is an increase in rest mass after the collision. What is this increase due to? (P.U. 2005)

OR

Show that in a perfectly inelastic collision of two identical particles of rest mass m_0 mass of the system increases by a faction $2m_0\,(\gamma-1)$ where $\gamma = \left(1-\dfrac{v^2}{c^2}\right)^{-1/2}$ *(P.U. 2009)*

(b) **Two particles each of mass 1 gm moving with $\dfrac{4}{5}c$ velocity in opposite directions collide and come to rest. If no heat is lost by annihilation, what is the total increase in rest mass?**   *(P.U. 2000)*

Ans. *(a)* **Increase in mass in an inelastic collision.** An inelastic collision is that in which linear momentum is conserved but kinetic energy is not conserved.

Consider two frames of reference S and S' such that S' is moving with respect to S with velocity v in $+X$ direction. At time $t = t'$ the two origins O and O' are coincident with each other.

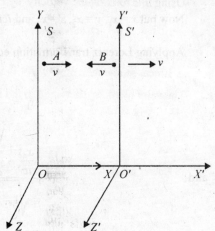

Take two identical particles A and B each of rest mass m_0 in frame S. The particle A moving with velocity v along $+X$ direction undergoes an inelastic collision with particle B moving along $-X$ direction with the same velocity v. The two particles after collision stick together and form a bigger particle.

Fig. 10.13

Frame S—Before collision.

Linear momentum of particle $A = p_A = \dfrac{m_0 v}{\sqrt{1-\dfrac{v^2}{c^2}}}$ ...(i)

Linear momentum of particle $B = p_B = \dfrac{-m_0 v}{\sqrt{1-\dfrac{v^2}{c^2}}}$ ...(ii)

$\therefore$ Total linear momentum of the system

$$p = p_A + p_B = \dfrac{m_0 v}{\sqrt{1-\dfrac{v^2}{c^2}}} - \dfrac{m_0 v}{\sqrt{1-\dfrac{v^2}{c^2}}} = 0 \qquad\qquad ...(iii)$$

After collision. After collision the two particles A and B stick together to form a bigger particle C of mass M. Suppose this particle moves with a velocity v_c, then

Total linear momentum of the system

$$p_c = M v_c$$

But the total linear momentum of the system is conserved in an inelastic collision.

$\therefore$ $p_c = p = 0$

or $M v_c = 0$ or $v_c = 0$ ...(iv)

Therefore, after collision the particle C will be at rest in the frame S'.

Frame S'—Before collision. Let us see how this collision will appear to an observer in the frame S'.

According to relativistic velocity addition formula,

$$u'_x = \frac{u_x - v}{1 - \dfrac{v}{c^2} u_x}$$

where u'_x is the velocity of the particle (along X-axis) as measured in the frame S', which is moving with a velocity v along $+X$ direction relative to frame S in which the velocity of the particle is u_x (along X-axis).

Using this relation the velocity v'_A of the particle A in the frame S' (before collision) is given by

$$v'_A = \frac{v - v}{1 - \dfrac{v}{c^2} v} = 0 \qquad \qquad \text{...(v)}$$

$\therefore$ Linear momentum of A, $p'_A = 0$ ...(vi)

The velocity of the particle B in the frame S' (before collision)

$$v'_B = \frac{-v - v}{1 + \dfrac{v}{c^2} v} = -\frac{2v}{1 + \dfrac{v^2}{c^2}} \qquad \qquad \text{...(vii)}$$

$\therefore$ Linear momentum of B, $p'_B = m_B v'_B$

$$= \frac{m_0}{\sqrt{1 - \dfrac{(v'_B)^2}{c^2}}} \frac{(-2v)}{\left(1 + \dfrac{v^2}{c^2}\right)} \qquad \qquad \text{...(viii)}$$

$\therefore$ Total linear momentum of the system

$$p' = p'_A + p'_B = \frac{-2m_0 v}{\sqrt{1 - \dfrac{(v'_B)^2}{c^2}} \left(1 + \dfrac{v^2}{c^2}\right)} \qquad \qquad \text{...(ix)}$$

After collision The two particles combine together after collision to form a particle C of rest mass M. The velocity of particle C in frame S' (according to velocity addition formula)

$$v'_c = \frac{v_c - v}{1 - \dfrac{v}{c^2} v_c} = -v \qquad \qquad [\because v_c = 0 \text{ according to Eq. } (iv)]$$

$\therefore$ Total linear momentum of the system (after collision)

$$p'_c = \frac{M}{\sqrt{1 - \dfrac{v^2}{c^2}}} \times (-v) = -\frac{Mv}{\sqrt{1 - \dfrac{v^2}{c^2}}}$$

As the total linear momentum of the system is conserved

$$p'_c = p'$$

or

$$\frac{-Mv}{\sqrt{1 - \dfrac{v^2}{c^2}}} = \frac{-2m_0 v}{\sqrt{1 - \dfrac{(v'_B)^2}{c^2}} \left(1 + \dfrac{v^2}{c^2}\right)}$$

$\therefore$

$$M = \frac{2m_0 \sqrt{1 - \dfrac{v^2}{c^2}}}{\sqrt{1 - \dfrac{(v'_B)^2}{c^2}} \left(1 + \dfrac{v^2}{c^2}\right)} \qquad \qquad \text{...(x)}$$

Value of $\sqrt{1 - \dfrac{(v'_B)^2}{c^2}}$. To find the value of $\sqrt{1 - \dfrac{(v'_B)^2}{c^2}}$ substitute $v'_B = \dfrac{-2v}{1 + \dfrac{v^2}{c^2}}$ (from *vii*), then

$$\sqrt{1 - \frac{(v'_B)^2}{c^2}} = \sqrt{1 - \frac{\dfrac{4v^2}{c^2}}{\left(1 + \dfrac{v^2}{c^2}\right)^2}} = \sqrt{\frac{1 + \dfrac{v^4}{c^4} + \dfrac{2v^2}{c^2} - \dfrac{4v^2}{c^2}}{\left(1 + \dfrac{v^2}{c^2}\right)^2}}$$

$$= \frac{1 - \dfrac{v^2}{c^2}}{1 + \dfrac{v^2}{c^2}} \qquad \qquad \qquad ...(xi)$$

Substituting in Eq. (*x*) we get

$$M = \frac{2m_0 \sqrt{1 - \dfrac{v^2}{c^2}} \left(1 + \dfrac{v^2}{c^2}\right)}{\left(1 - \dfrac{v^2}{c^2}\right)\left(1 + \dfrac{v^2}{c^2}\right)} = \frac{2m_0}{\sqrt{1 - \dfrac{v^2}{c^2}}}$$

$\therefore$ Increase in rest mass $\Delta m = M - 2m_0 = \dfrac{2m_0}{\sqrt{1 - \dfrac{v^2}{c^2}}} - 2m_0$

$$= 2m_0 \left[\frac{1}{\sqrt{1 - \dfrac{v^2}{c^2}}} - 1\right] = 2m_0(\gamma - 1) \text{ where } \gamma = \frac{1}{\sqrt{1 - \dfrac{v^2}{c^2}}} = \left[1 - \frac{v^2}{c^2}\right]^{-1/2}$$

The quantity within brackets is always *positive* i.e. Δm is a positive quantity. *Hence in an inelastic collision there is an increase in mass of the system.*

Reason. The increase in rest mass of the combined particle is due to the fact that some kinetic energy has been lost during the inelastic collision.

(*b*) Increase in mass in an inelastic collision is given by

$$\Delta m = 2m_0 \left[\frac{1}{\sqrt{1 - \dfrac{v^2}{c^2}}} - 1\right]$$

$$= 2 \times 1 \left[\frac{1}{\sqrt{1 - \left(\dfrac{4}{5}\right)^2}} - 1\right] = 2\left[\frac{1}{\sqrt{1 - \dfrac{16}{25}}} - 1\right]$$

$$= 2\left[\frac{1}{0.6} - 1\right] = 2\left[\frac{5}{3} - 1\right] = 2 \times \frac{2}{3}$$

$$= 1.33 \text{ gm.}$$

Q. 10.66. What are Tachyons ?   (*Pbi U.*, 2005, 2003)

Ans. Tachyons. Tachyons are, as yet, hypothetical particles that would move faster than light, if they exist. According to special theory of relativity, the mass of a particle moving with a velocity

v is given by $m = \dfrac{m_0}{\sqrt{1 - \dfrac{v^2}{c^2}}}$. As such, no material particle can move with a velocity greater than the

velocity of light because the mass of the particle would become infinite even at $v = c$. For v greater than c, the mass of the particle would become imaginary.

However, physicists like Fienberg have suggested that it is possible that a particle may be produced moving with a velocity greater than the velocity of light from its very birth. These particles have been named by Fienberg as Tachyons, meaning '*swiftly moving*'.

It has been postulated that Tachyons cannot move with a velocity less than the velocity of light. They have an infinite mass when moving with the velocity of light and as the velocity increases the mass decreases and becomes zero at infinity.

The energy equation governing the motion of Tachyons may be written as

$$E = \frac{\mu c^2}{\sqrt{\dfrac{v^2}{c^2} - 1}}$$

The energy of such a particle will be real if its mass is imaginary and may be related to mass in real universe by the equation

$$\mu = \frac{m}{\sqrt{-1}}$$

So far, it has not been possible to experimentally prove the existence of such a particle.

Q. 10.67. Is the second law of motion $\vec{F} = m\,\vec{a}$ always valid in special theory of relativity ?
                                                                                              (*P.U.* 2005)

Ans. No. the second law of motion $\vec{F} = m\,\vec{a}$ holds in special theory of relativity only if the velocity $\vec{v}$ is perpendicular to acceleration $\vec{a}$.

Q. 10.68. What are absolute quantities? Name three absolute quantities in (a) Newtonian mechanics (b) relativity mechanics.   (*P.U.* 2005)

Ans. The quantities which have the same value in all frames of reference are known as absolute quantities.

Examples. In Newtonion mechanics, length, mass and time are absolute quantities.

In relativity mechanics, velocity of light, phase of a wave, and interval between two events are invariant.

Q. 10.69. The concept of length, mass and time which were absolute before Einstein became interdependent after Einstein. Explain it.   (*GN.D.U.* 2008)

Ans. The postulates of special theory of relativity put forward by Einstein led to the revision of the concept of length, mass and time. The length, mass and time, which were considered *absolute quantities* according to Newtonian mechanics, actually depend upon the frame of reference of the observer in accordance with Einstein's theory.

For example, when a frame of reference is moving with a uniform velocity v with respect to an observer, there is an apparent *length contraction, time dilation and increase in mass.*

It L_0 is the length of a rod when it is at rest, the apparent length L when it is moving with a uniform velocity v is given by

$$L = L_0 \sqrt{1 - v^2/c^2}$$

Similarly, if T_0 is the time interval noted by an observer with respect to which the clock is at rest, the time interval indicated by a clock to an observer with respect to whom it is moving with a uniform velocity v, is given by

$$T = \frac{T_0}{\sqrt{1 - \dfrac{v^2}{c^2}}}$$

There is also an apparent increase in mass given by

$$m = \frac{m_0}{\sqrt{1 - \dfrac{v^2}{c^2}}}$$

where m_0 is the rest mass and m the apparent mass of the same body moving with a uniform velocity v.

As a consequence of this, there is an equivalence between mass and energy given by $E = mc^2$ *i.e.*, mass and energy are now considered interconvertible whereas before Einstein, the mass and energy were considered two separate independent entities.

Q. 10.70. Why electrons cannot be accelerated by a cyclotron while protons can be accelerated?
                                                                                                                (*G.N.D.U.* 2008)

Ans. When electrons are accelerated by a cyclotron, the mass of the electron increases with increase in velocity. In order that the electron may be accelerated in a cyclotron, the frequency of the alternating current applied across the two Dees or the strength of the applied magnetic field has to be constantly adjusted so that the electrons reach the cyclotron between the two Dees after a fixed time interval. Since the mass of the electron is very small, it varies so rapidly with increase in its speed that it is not possible to keep its motion in phase with the applied alternating electric or magnetic field.

This howevers, is not the case with the proton, because the mass of the proton is very large as compared to that of the electron. The proton being about 1836 times heavier than the electron, the increase in its mass with velocity is rather slow so that it becomes possible to keep the motion of the proton in phase with the applied alternating electric or magnetic field.

Q. 10.71. Mark the correct answer.

(*i*) Velocity of light in free space is

    (*a*) $\sqrt{\mu_0 \varepsilon_0}$ (*b*) $(\mu_0 \varepsilon_0)^{-1/2}$ (*c*) $\sqrt{\dfrac{\mu_0}{\varepsilon_0}}$ (*d*) $\sqrt{\dfrac{\varepsilon_0}{\mu_0}}$

                                                                                                                (*P.U.*, 1993)

(*ii*) Michelson-Morley experiment was performed to

    (*a*) measure speed of light   (*b*) prove existence of ether

    (*c*) measure speed of earth relative to ether

    (*d*) test the isotropy of space.

                                                                                                                (*P.U.*, 1994)

   (iii) The postulates of special theory of relativity are applicable to
      (a) stationary frame   (b) accelerated frames
      (c) inertial frames   (d) none of these.   (P.U., 1994)

   (iv) Frame S' moves along the positive X-direction of S frame. A rod placed along Y'-axis if observed from S frame appears
      (a) contracted   (b) elongated   (c) unchanged   (P.U., 1994)

   (v) Rest volume L_0^3 is connected to relativistic volume as
      (a) $L_0^3 (1 - \beta^2)^{3/2}$ (b) $L_0^3 (1 - \beta^2)$

      (c) $L_0^3 \sqrt{1 - \beta^2}$ (d) $\dfrac{L_0^3}{\sqrt{1 - \beta^2}}$ (P.U., 1993)

   (vi) Relativistic time is given by
      (a) $\dfrac{t + vx'}{\sqrt{1 - \beta^2}}$ (b) $\dfrac{t - \dfrac{vx}{c^2}}{\sqrt{1 - \beta^2}}$

      (c) $\left(t - \dfrac{v}{c^2}\right)(1 - \beta^2)^{-1/2}$ (d) $\left(t + \dfrac{vc^2}{x}\right)(1 - \beta^2)^{-1/2}$ (P.U., 1993)

   (vii) Decay of μ-meson supports
      (a) length contraction   (b) time dilation
      (c) relativity of mass   (d) relativity of energy

  (viii) Of the two twin brothers, one goes on a relativistic tour and comes back. The brother on tour will
      (a) become younger   (b) become older
      (c) be of the same age.   (P.U., 1994)

   (ix) A rocket has a velocity $0.6c$. Velocity of light with respect to rocket is   (P.U., 1993)
      (a) $0.5\,c$ (b) $1.6\,c$ (c) $0.4\,c$ (d) c

   (x) Two photons approach each other. Their relative velocity will be
      (a) 0   (b) less than c (c) more than c (d) c
                                                          (H.P.U. 1993)

   (xi) Two photons recede from each other. Their relative velocity will be
      (a) zero   (b) $\dfrac{c}{2}$ (c) $2c$ (d) c
                                                         (H.P.U., 1994)

  (xii) When one kgm of mass is fully converted into energy, it produces
      (a) 9×10^{16} J   (b) 3×10^{10} J   (c) 10^{20} J   (d) 10^{16} J
                                                         (P.U., 1994)

  (xiii) If one gm of a substance is converted into energy, the heat produced is
      (a) 2.15×10^{13} cal   (b) 21.5×10^{13} cal   (c) 215×10^{13} cal.

  (xiv) A stone is raised to the top of Mount Everest. Its rest mass has
      (a) increased   (b) decreased   (c) remained same   (P.U., 1994)

  (xv) A body of mass m falls through h metres. The decrease in its mass is equivalent to
      (a) mgh (b) $mghc^2$ (c) mgh/c (d) mgh/c^2
                                                          (P.U., 1994)

(xvi) At what velocity the kinetic energy of a body is equal to its rest mass energy?

    (a) $\sqrt{2}c$ *(b)* $c/3$ *(c)* $c/2$ *(d)* $\sqrt{3}/2\,c$

                                                            (P.U., 1994)

(xvii) A body moves with $0.2c$ velocity. The ratio of the moving mass to rest mass is

    (a) 1.2   *(b)* 1.02   *(c)* 0.2   *(d)* 1.0

                                                            (P.U., 1994)

(xviii) Two bodies of same momentum have different masses. The total mass energy will be greater for   *(P.U., 1994)*

    (a) lighter body   *(b)* heavier body   *(c)* none

(xix) The rest mass of a photon is

    (a) 0   *(b)* p/c *(c)* $\dfrac{E}{c^2}$ *(H.P.U., 1992, 1991)*

(xx) The velocity of earth around the sun is

    (a) 300 km/sec   *(b)* 3 km/sec   *(c)* 30 km/sec   *(d)* 3000 km/sec

(xxi) Relativistic transformations were suggested by

    (a) Newton   *(b)* Einstein

    (c) Huygen   *(d)* H.A. Lorentz   *(H.P.U. 2001)*

(xxii) The apparent length of a metre rod moving parallel to its length with velocity. $0.8c$ will be

    (a) 0.5 m   *(b)* 0.6 m   *(c)* 1 m   *(Meerut U. 2000)*

Ans. *(i)* b   *(ii)* c   *(iii)* c   *(iv)* c   *(v)* c   *(vi)* b   *(vii)* b   *(viii)* a

    (ix) d   *(x)* d   *(xi)* d   *(xii)* a   *(xiii)* a   *(xiv)* a   *(xv)* d   *(xvi)* d

    (xvii) b   *(xviii)* b   *(xix)* a   *(xx)* c   *(xxi)* d   *(xxii)* b

EXERCISES

1. A rod has a length of 1.2 metre. It is placed in a space ship moving with a velocity $0.6\,c$ relative to earth. Calculate its length as measured by an observer on *(i)* spaceship and *(ii)* earth.

                                                               (A.U., 1993)

                                          [Ans. *(i)* 1.2 m *(ii)* 0.96 m**]**

2. Calculate the percentage contraction of a rod moving with a velocity 60% that of light in a direction 60° to its own length.   *(H.P.U., 1992)*

                                                    [Ans. 5%]

3. Atomic particles in the form of a beam have a velocity 98% of the velocity of light. What is the relativistic mass of an atomic particle as compared with its rest mass?   **[Ans.** $5\,m_0$**]**

4. A radioactive atom moving along X-axis with a velocity $0.5\,c$ in the laboratory frame of reference emits an electron with a speed $0.95\,c$ along the X-axis of a system in the radioactive atom. Calculate the speed of the electron in the laboratory system.   **[Ans. 0.983]**

5. Taking velocity of light as 3×10^8 m/s, calculate energy corresponding to a mass of 1.2 gm.

                                                  [Ans. 10.8×10^{13} Joule**]**

6. Find the velocity at which the mass of a particles is *(i)* double and *(ii)* $\sqrt{3}$ times its rest-mass.

                                                          (P.U., 1991)

    [Ans. *(i)* 2.59×10^8 ms^{-1} *(ii)* 2.8284×10^8 ms^{-1}**]**

7. How much mass does an electron gain when it is accelerated to a potential energy of 500 MeV?   **[Ans. 1.77×10^{-28} kg]**

8. At what speed should a particle move so that its kinetic energy becomes 1.3 times its rest energy?   *(P.U. 1994)*
   [Ans. $0.9\,c$]

9. Calculate the velocity which 1 a.m.u. will have if it has a kinetic energy three times the rest mass energy.   *(H.P.U., 1996)*
   [Ans. $0.968\,c$]

10. If 1000 kg of water is heated from 0 to 100°C, calculate the increase in mass of water.
    (K.U., 1997)
    [Ans. 4.67×10^{-8} kg]

11

Elasticity

Q. 11.1. (*a*) **Explain the terms stress and strain. Define Young's modulus** *Y*, **the bulk modulus** *k*, **rigidity modulus** η **and poisson's ratio** σ. **Write dimensions of** σ.

(*M.D.U.* 2006, 2003; *Meerut U.* 2003; *Nagpur U.* 2001; *K.U.* 2000, 1992; *Bang.* 1995, 1994; *Madurai U.* 2003)

(*b*) **State Hooke's law and define related terms.** (*M.D.U.* 2007)

(*c*) **Define Elastic limit and breaking stress.** (*M.D.U.* 2008)

(*d*) **Poisson's ratio is the ratio between_____.** (*Meerut U.* 2001)

Ans. (*a*) **Stress and strain.** When an external force acts upon a body relative displacement of its various parts takes place. The displaced particles tend to come to their original position to restore the original length, volume or shape of the body and thus exert a restoring force.

The restoring force per unit area called into play inside the body is called the **stress.**

The reaction set up in the body is equal and opposite to the applied force, so long as there is no permanent change produced in the body. The restoring force, is, therefore, equal to the applied force.

Hence if the force *F* is applied normally to the area of cross-section *a* of a wire, then

$$\text{Stress} = \frac{F}{a}$$

The external force acting on the body causes a relative displacement of its various parts. A change in the length, volume or shape takes place. The body is then said to be under a strain.

Strain *is defined as the ratio of the change in length, volume or shape to the original length, volume or shape.* Strain is thus a pure ratio and has no units.

Young's modulus. *It is defined as the ratio of stress to longitudinal strain within elastic limits.*

When a change of length takes place the strain is known as **longitudinal strain.** *It is measured by the change in length per unit length.* If *L* is the length of a wire and an increase *l* in length is caused by a force, then

$$\text{Strain} = \frac{l}{L}$$

Hence Young's modulus of elasticity $= \dfrac{\text{Stress}}{\text{Strain}}$

or

$$Y = \frac{F}{a} \div \frac{l}{L} = \frac{FL}{al}$$

Bulk modulus. *It is defined as the ratio of stress to volumetric strain.* When a force is applied normally to the surface of a body and a change in volume takes place, the strain is known as **volumetric strain.** *It is measured by the change in volume per unit volume and is equal to v/V* where v is the change in volume produced by the force F in the original volume V. Hence bulk modulus k is given by

$$k = \frac{F}{a} \div \frac{v}{V} = \frac{FV}{av} = \frac{PV}{v} = \frac{P}{v/V}$$

where $\dfrac{F}{a} = P$ (applied pressure).

When a very small pressure dP is applied, the change in volume being very small is represented by dV, then

$$k = -\frac{dP}{dV/V}$$

The negative sign indicates that an increase in applied pressure causes a decrease in volume.

Modulus of rigidity. *It is defined as the ratio of the tangential stress to shearing strain.*

To find the value of the shearing strain, consider a solid cube *ABCDefgh*. The lower face *CDgh* is fixed and a *tangential force F* is applied over the face *ABef* so that it is displaced to the position of *A′ B′ e′ f′*. Each horizontal layer of the cube is then displaced, the displacement being proportional to its distance form the fixed plane. Then

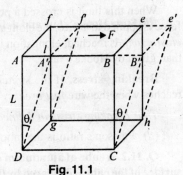

Fig. 11.1

Shearing strain $= \dfrac{\text{Displacement of a plane}}{\text{Distance from the fixed plane}}$

$$= \frac{AA'}{AD} = \frac{l}{L} = \tan\theta$$

When θ is small $\tan\theta = \theta$

$\therefore$ Shearing strain $= \theta$

Hence the angle through which a line originally perpendicular to the fixed plane is turned is a measure of the shearing strain.

Now modulus of rigidity $= \dfrac{\text{Tangential stress}}{\text{Shearing strain}}$

$\therefore$

$$\eta = \frac{F}{a} \div \theta = \frac{F}{a\theta} = \frac{T}{\theta}$$

where a is the area of the face *ABef* and T is the tangential force applied per unit area.

Poisson's ratio. When a wire is stretched, its length increases but its diameter decreases. In general, when an elongation is produced by a *longitudinal stress* in a certain direction a contraction results in the *lateral dimensions* of the body under strain. The lateral strain is proportional to the longitudinal strain so long as it is small.

The ratio $\dfrac{\text{Lateral strain}}{\text{Longitudinal strain}}$ is called *Poisson's ratio* and is denoted by the letter σ.

Let the length of the wire $= L$,   Diameter of the wire $= D$

Increase in length $= l$,   Corresponding decrease in diameter $= d$

The poisson's ratio $\sigma = \dfrac{d/D}{l/L} = \dfrac{\beta}{\alpha}$

where β is the lateral strain and α the longitudinal strain.

(b) **Hooke's law** *It states that within elastic limits, stress is directly proportional to strain. i.e.,*

$Stress \propto \dfrac{Stress}{Strain} = E$ (a constant)

The constant E is known as *modulus of elasticity*

Corresponding to longitudinal, volumetric and shearing strain there are three types of modulus of elasticity *i.e.,* Young's modulus, Bulk modulus and modulus of rigidity. For details see part (a) of this question.

(c) **Elastic limit.** There is a certain limit upto which the behaviour of a body remains elastic *i.e.,* it regains its original (initial) shape or size after the removal of deforming forces. This limit is called *elastic limit*.

When this limit is crossed a permanent change occurs in the body. For example, if a stretching force is applied to a wire, the elongation produced is proportional to the stretching force. But when the *elastic limit* is reached, elongation is not proportional to the force applied but increases more rapidly than given by Hooke's law.

Breaking stress. If the stretching force is further increased beyond the elastic limit a stage reaches when the wire *just breaks*. This force per unit area or stress is called *breaking stress*.

Thus breaking stress in defined as the limiting value of stress necessary to just break the wire.

(d) Poisson's ratio is the ratio between *'Lateral strain and longitudinal strain'*.

Q. 11.2. A cube of aluminium of side 10 cm is subjected to a shearing force of 100 N. The top surface of the cube is displaced by 0.01 cm with respect to the bottom. Calculate the shearing stress, shearing strain and modulus of rigidity. *(Bang. U., 1995)*

Ans. Each side of aluminium cube $L = 10$ cm $= 0.1$ m

Area of face $a = 0.1 \times 0.1 = 0.01$ m^2

Tangential force $F = 100$ N

Shearing stress $T = \dfrac{F}{a} = \dfrac{100}{0.01} = 10^4$ Nm^{-2}

Displacement $l = 0.01$ cm $= 0.0001$ m

Thickness $L = 10$ cm $= 0.1$ m

Shearing strain $\theta = \dfrac{l}{L} = \dfrac{0.0001}{0.1} = 10^{-3}$

Modulus of rigidity $\eta = \dfrac{T}{\theta} = \dfrac{10^4}{10^{-3}} = 10^7$ Nm^{-2}

Q. 11.3. (a) **What force is required to stretch a steel wire $\dfrac{1}{2}$ sq.cm. in cross-section to double its length?** $Y = 2 \times 10^{11}$ Nm^{-2}. *(Bang. U., 1992)*

(b) **A steel wire 1.5 mm in diameter is just stretched between two fixed points at a temperature 40°C. Determine the tension in the wire if the temperature falls to 30°C. Given that for steel $\alpha = 0.000012/°C$ and Y for steel $= 20 \times 10^{10}$ Nm^{-2}.** *(Bang. U., 1991)*

Ans. (a) Given $Y = 2 \times 10^{11}$ Nm^{-2}

Area of cross-section $a = \dfrac{1}{2}$ sq. cm $= 0.5 \times 10^{-4}$ m^2

When the length is doubled; increase in length l = original length L

Now Young's modulus $Y = \dfrac{FL}{al}$ $\therefore F = \dfrac{Yal}{L} = Ya$

or Force required, $F = 2 \times 10^{11} \times 0.5 \times 10^{-4} = 10^7$ Newton

(b) Here $Y = 20 \times 10^{10}$ Nm^{-2} $\alpha = 0.00012/°C$

If L is the length of the wire at 40°C, then decrease in length at 30°C $= L \times \alpha \times (40 - 30)$

$$= L \times 0.000012 \times 10 = 0.00012\, L$$

$\therefore$ Longitudinal strain $= \dfrac{0.00012\, L}{L} = 0.00012$

Now stress $= Y \times$ strain $= 20 \times 10^{10} \times 0.00012 = 2.4 \times 10^7$ Nm^{-2}

Area of cross-section $a = \pi r^2 = \pi \times \left(\dfrac{1.5 \times 10^{-3}}{2}\right)^2 = 1.766 \times 10^{-6}$ m^2

$$\text{Stress} = \dfrac{F}{a}$$

$\therefore$ Tension in the wire $F = a \times$ stress $= 1.766 \times 10^{-6} \times 2.4 \times 10^7 = 42.4$ Newton

Q. 11.4. (a) **Calculate the length of the wire that will break under its own weight when suspended vertically. Given breaking stress $= 9.8 \times 10^8$ Nm^{-2}, density of wire $= 10^4$ kg m^{-3} and $g = 9.8$ ms^{-2}.**

(*Bang. U.*, 1993; *K.U.*, 1992, 1994)

(b) **A steel wire of length 2.00 m and cross-section 1×10^{-6} m^2 is held between rigid supports with a tension of 200 N. If the middle of the wire is pulled 5 mm sideways, calculate change in tension. Also calculate change in tension if temperature changes by 5°C. For steel $Y = 2.2 \times 10^{11}$ Nm^{-2} and $\alpha = 8 \times 10^{-6}$ deg^{-1}.**

(*Kan. U.*, 1995)

Ans. (a) When the wire hangs vertically its weight mg acts as a longitudinal force. Let L be the maximum length of the wire that can hang without breaking and a its area of cross-section, then

Weight of wire $mg = L \times a \times \rho \times g$ N

$$= L \times a \times 10^4 \times g\, \text{N}$$

Breaking load = Breaking stress $\times a = 9.8 \times 10^8 \times a$ N

$\therefore$ $L \times a \times g \times 10^4 = 9.8 \times 10^8 \times a$

or $L = \dfrac{9.8 \times 10^8}{9.8 \times 10^4} = 10^4$ m = 10 km

The wire of length 10 km *will break* under its own weight if the applied stress is greater than the breaking stress. It will not break if the applied stress $\leq$ the breaking stress.

(b) (i) Initial length of wire $L = 2$ m

Final length of wire when it is pulled sideways at the centre by 5 mm $= 5 \times 10^{-3}$ m

$$L' = 2[l^2 + (5 \times 10^{-3})^2]^{1/2} = 2\,[1 + 25 \times 10^{-6}]^{1/2}$$

$$= 2\left[1 + \dfrac{1}{2} \times 25 \times 10^{-6}\right] \text{ by applying Binomial theorem and neglecting}$$

higher powers of 25×10^{-6} as it is a very small quantity.

$\therefore L' = 2 + 25 \times 10^{-6}$ m

Increase in length $l = L' - L = 25 \times 10^{-6}$ m

Area of cross-section of the wire $a = 1 \times 10^{-6}$ m^2

Let F be the additional tension in the wire due to increase in length, then

Young's modulus $Y = \dfrac{\text{stress}}{\text{strain}} = \dfrac{F/a}{l/L} = \dfrac{FL}{al}$

or $F = \dfrac{Yal}{L} = \dfrac{2.2 \times 10^{11} \times 10^{-6} \times 25 \times 10^{-6}}{2} = 2.75$ N

(ii) When the temperature changes by $\theta = 5°C$, the change in length

$$l = L \times \alpha \times \theta = 2 \times 8 \times 10^{-6} \times 5 = 8 \times 10^{-5} \text{ m}$$

$\therefore$ Change in tension $F = \dfrac{Yal}{L} = \dfrac{2.2 \times 10^{11} \times 1 \times 10^{-6} \times 8 \times 10^{-5}}{2} = 8.8$ N

Q. 11.5. (a) **Find the work done in stretching a wire.**   (*Kerala U.* 2001; *Burd. U.*, 1991)

(b) **A wire 0.5 m long and 1 sq. mm in cross-section has Young's modulus 1.24×10^{11} N-m^{-2}. How much work is done in stretching it through 1 mm ?**   (*K.U.* 2002, 1994)

Ans. (a) The Young's modulus of elasticity

$$Y = \frac{FL}{al} \quad \text{or} \quad F = \frac{Yal}{L}$$

$\therefore$ Work done in producing a stretching $dl = F.dl = \dfrac{Yal}{L} \times dl$

Hence work done to produce a stretching of the wire from 0 to l

$$W = \int_0^l \frac{Yal}{L} dl = \frac{Ya}{L} \left[\frac{l^2}{2} \right]_0^l$$

$$= \frac{1}{2} \frac{Yal^2}{L} = \frac{1}{2} \frac{Yal}{L} \times l = \frac{1}{2} F \times l$$

$$= \frac{1}{2} \times \text{stretching force} \times \text{elongation produced}$$

(b) $a = 1$ sq. mm $= 10^{-6}$ m^2, $l = 1$ mm $= 10^{-3}$ m, $L = 0.5$ m

     $Y = 1.24 \times 10^{11}$ N-m^2

Work done $W = \dfrac{1}{2} \dfrac{Yal}{L} l = \dfrac{1.24 \times 10^{11} \times 10^{-6} \times 10^{-3} \times 10^{-3}}{2 \times 0.5} = 0.124$ J

Q. 11.6. **A steel wire of length 2.0 m is stretched through 2.0 mm. The cross sectional area of wire is 40 mm^2. Calculate the elastic potential energy stored in the wire in the stretched condition. Young's modulus of steel $= 2.0 \times 10^{11}$ N/m^2.**   (*Meerut U.*, 1995)

Ans. $L = 2.0$ m, $l = 2.0$ mm $= 2 \times 10^{-3}$ m, $a = 40$ mm$^2 = 40 \times 10^{-6}$ m^2

     $Y = 2 \times 10^{11}$ N/m^2

Elastic potential energy stored = Work done in stretching the wire

$$= \frac{1}{2} Y \frac{al^2}{L} = \frac{1}{2} \times \frac{2 \times 10^{11} \times 40 \times 10^{-6} \times 2 \times 10^{-3} \times 2 \times 10^{-3}}{2} = 8 \text{ J}$$

Exercise. *Find the work done in stretching a wire of 1sq mm cross-section, Young's modulus 2×10^{11} N/m² and 2 m long through 0.1 mm.*   (*Gharwal U.* 1999) **[Ans.** 5×10^{-4} J**]**

Q. 11.7. (*a*) **Show that shear is equivalent to an elongation strain and compression strain at right angles to each other and each is half of shearing angle.**

(*Cal. U.* 2003; *Kan. U.*, 1996; *Ranchi U.*, 1991; *Burd. U.*, 1990)

(*b*) **Prove that a shearing stress is equivalent to a linear tensile stress and an equal compression stress mutually at right angles.**   (*Vid. S. U.*, 1990; *Kan. U.*, 1993)

Ans. (*a*) **Shear is equivalent to elongation strain and compression strain at right angles.** Consider a cube *ABCD* having each side equal to *L* with its face *DC* fixed. Let a tangential force *F* be applied so that the face *ABCD* is sheared to the position *A'B'CD* through an angle θ.

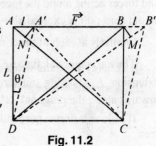

Fig. 11.2

Now $AA' = BB' = l$

The diagonal *DB* is elongated to *DB'* and the diagonal *AC* is shortened to *A'C*.

Draw perpendiculars *A'N* on *AC* and *BM* on *DB'*, then

$$DB = DM = L\sqrt{2}$$

Since the angle of shear θ is very small, therefore triangles *ANA'* and *BMB'* are isosceles right angles triangles

and $\angle BB'M = \angle A'AN = 45°$

∴ $B'M = BB' \cos 45° = \dfrac{BB'}{\sqrt{2}} = \dfrac{l}{\sqrt{2}}$

The extension strain along the diagonal *DB*

$$= \frac{B'M}{DB} = \frac{l}{\sqrt{2}} \times \frac{1}{L\sqrt{2}} = \frac{l}{2L} = \frac{\theta}{2} \quad \text{as} \quad \frac{l}{L} = \theta$$

Similarly the compression strain along the diagonal *AC*

$$= \frac{AN}{AC} = \frac{AA' \cos 45°}{L\sqrt{2}} = \frac{l}{\sqrt{2}} \cdot \frac{1}{L\sqrt{2}} = \frac{l}{2L} = \frac{\theta}{2}$$

Thus we see that a shear θ is equivalent to an extension and a compression strain at right angle to each other, each of value $\dfrac{\theta}{2}$ *i.e., half the shearing angle.*

(*b*) Consider a cube *ABCD* with its face *DC* fixed. Let *L* be the length of each side and *a* the area of each face. Suppose a tangential force *F* is applied to the face *AB* as shown in Fig. 11.3 to produce a shear θ, then

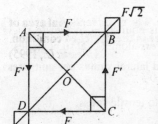

Fig. 11.3

Shearing stress = *F/a*

It is to be proved that this *shearing stress* is equivalent to a *linear tensile stress* along the diagonal *DB* and an equivalent *compression stress* along diagonal *AC* mutually at right angles.

If there is only one force *F* acting on the face *AB*, then the cube should move as a whole in the direction of the force. But as the cube is fixed at the face *DC*, an equal and opposite force acts on the lower face *DC*. These two forces, therefore, constitute a couple and tend to rotate it in the clockwise direction.

The cube, however, does not rotate, hence the face DC which is fixed exerts an equal and opposite couple by exerting force (say F') on the faces AD and CB as shown.

Now moment of clockwise couple $= F \times AD$

and moment of the anti-clockwise couple $= F' \times AB$

But as the cube is in equilibrium.

$$\therefore \qquad F \times AD = F' \times AB$$

or $\qquad F = F'$

Hence a tangential force F applied to the face AB gives rise to equal tangential forces acting along all the faces in suitable directions, as shown in Fig. 11.3.

Now, the forces acting along the faces AB and CB give rise to a resultant force $F\sqrt{2}$ along OB and forces acting along the faces AD and CD also give rise to a resultant force $F\sqrt{2}$ along OD. Hence an outward pull is exerted along the diagonal BD at the corners B and D.

Similarly at each of the corners A and C resultant force $F\sqrt{2}$ acts inwards along the diagonal AC.

Thus a tangential force F acting on one of the faces of the cube is equivalent to a force of extension $F\sqrt{2}$ acting outwards along the diagonal BD and a force of compression $F\sqrt{2}$ acting inwards along the diagonal AC.

If a plane is drawn perpendicular to the plane of the paper through the diagonal AC it will have an area

$$= L \times L\sqrt{2} = L^2 \sqrt{2} = a\sqrt{2}$$

The force $F\sqrt{2}$ acting along BD will act normally to the area.

$$\therefore \text{ Tensile stress along } BD = \frac{F\sqrt{2}}{a\sqrt{2}} = \frac{F}{a}$$

Similarly compression stress along $AC = \dfrac{F\sqrt{2}}{a\sqrt{2}} = \dfrac{F}{a}$

Hence a shearing stress along AB is equivalent to a tensile stress along BD and an equal compression stress along AC at right angles.

Q. 11.8. (*a*) **Show that for a homogeneous isotropic medium $Y = 2\eta (1 + \sigma)$ where letters have their usual meaning.**   (*Meerut U.* 2003; *Cal. U.* 2003; *K. U.* 2002; *M.D. U.* 2007, 2006, 2003)

(*b*) **If $\eta = 8 \times 10^{11}$ N/m^2 and $Y = 20 \times 10^{11}$ N/m^2 for iron, calculate Poisson's ratio.**

Ans. Relation between Y, η and σ. When a tangential force F is applied to the upper face $ABef$ of a cube $ABCD$ ... then the face $ABCD$ is displaced to the position $A'B'CD$. The diagonal DB increases in length to DB' whereas the diagonal CA decreases CA'.

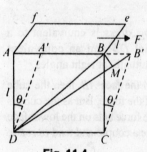

Fig. 11.4

Shearing stress $= \dfrac{F}{\text{area } ABef} = T$

Now a shearing stress along AB is equivalent to *tensile stress* along DB and an equal *compression stress* along CA at right angles.

If α and β are the longitudinal and lateral strains per unit stress respectively, then

Extension along diagonal DB due to tensile stress

$$= DB. T. \alpha$$

and extension along diagonal DB due to compression stress along AC

$$= DB. T. \beta$$

$\therefore$ Total extension along $DB = DB.T. (\alpha + \beta) = \sqrt{2}.L.T.(\alpha + \beta)$

Draw a perpendicular BM on DB'. Then increase in the length of diagonal DB is practically equal to $B'M$.

Since θ is very small, therefore, angle $AB'C$ is nearly $90°$ and hence $\angle BB'M = 45°$.

$\therefore B'M = BB' \cos 45° = \dfrac{BB'}{\sqrt{2}} = \dfrac{l}{\sqrt{2}}$

Hence
$$T(\alpha + \beta) L \sqrt{2} = \dfrac{l}{\sqrt{2}}$$

$$T.\dfrac{L}{l} = \dfrac{1}{2(\alpha + \beta)} \qquad \qquad ...(i)$$

But
$$T.\dfrac{L}{l} = \dfrac{T}{l/L} = \dfrac{T}{\theta} = \eta \qquad \qquad ...(ii)$$

Hence from (i) and (ii), we have, the coefficient of rigidity

$$\eta = \dfrac{1}{2(\alpha + \beta)} = \dfrac{1}{2\alpha(1 + \beta/\alpha)} \qquad \qquad ...(iii)$$

But Poisson's ratio
$$\sigma = \dfrac{\text{Lateral strain}}{\text{Longitudinal strain}} = \dfrac{\beta}{\alpha}$$

and Young's modulus
$$Y = \dfrac{\text{Stress}}{\text{Longitudinal strain}}$$

$$= \dfrac{1}{\text{Longitudinal strain per unit stress}} = \dfrac{1}{\alpha}$$

Substituting in (iii), we get

$$\eta = \dfrac{Y}{2(1 + \sigma)} \qquad \qquad ...(iv)$$

or
$$Y = 2\eta (1 + \sigma)$$

(b) From the relation $Y = 2\eta (1 + \sigma)$, we have

$$\sigma = \dfrac{Y}{2\eta} - 1 = \dfrac{20 \times 10^{11}}{2 \times 8 \times 10^{11}} - 1 = 0.25.$$

Exercise. *Calculate the value of Young's modulus given* $\eta = 2 \times 10^{10}$ N/m^2 *and* $\sigma = 0.25$.

(Nagpur U., 2001) **[Ans. 5×10^{10} Nm^{-2}]**

Q. 11.9. If Y, k and σ represent Young's modulus, Bulk modulus and Poisson's ratio respectively, then prove that $k = \dfrac{Y}{3(1 - 2\sigma)}$. *(M.D.U. 2001; J.P.U. 1999; Cal. U., 1991; Meerut U., 1994)*

Ans. Consider a **unit cube** $ABCDefgh$ and let forces T_x, T_y and T_z act perpendicular to the faces $BehC$ and $AfgD$, $efgh$ and $ABCD$, $ABef$ and $CDgh$ respectively as shown in Fig. 11.5.

*If α is the increase in length per unit length per unit tension along the direction of the force,*then the elongation produced in the edges AB, Be and BC will be $T_x\,\alpha$, $T_y\,\alpha$ and $T_z\,\alpha$ respectively.

If β is the contraction produced per unit length per unit tension in a direction perpendicular to the force, then the contraction produced perpendicular to the edges AB, Be and BC will be $T_x\,\beta$, $T_y\,\beta$ and $T_z\,\beta$ respectively.

Thus the lengths of the edges are as follows:

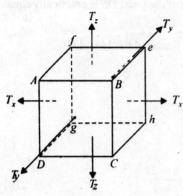

Fig. 11.5

$$AB = 1 + T_x\alpha - T_y\beta - T_z\beta$$
$$Be = 1 + T_y\alpha - T_x\beta - T_z\beta$$
$$BC = 1 + T_z\alpha - T_x\beta - T_y\beta$$

Hence the new volume of the cube now becomes

$$AB \times Be \times BC = (1 + T_x\alpha - T_y\beta - T_z\beta)$$
$$\times (1 + T_y\alpha - T_x\beta - T_z\beta)$$
$$\times (1 + T_z\alpha - T_x\beta - T_y\beta)$$

Since α and β are very small quantities, terms containing their squares and higher powers can be neglected.

$$\therefore \text{Volume} \quad = 1 + \alpha\,(T_x + T_y + T_z) - 2\beta\,(T_x + T_y + T_z)$$
$$= 1 + (\alpha - 2\beta)\,(T_x + T_y + T_z)$$

If the deforming forces acting on the three faces are equal, then

$$T_x = T_y = T_z = T$$

$$\therefore \text{Volume} = 1 + 3T(\alpha - 2\beta)$$

If instead of applying a stretching force T outwardly, a pressure P is applied on all the faces to compress the cube, the contraction in volume

$$= 3P\,(\alpha - 2\beta)$$

$$\therefore \text{Volumetric strain} \quad = 3P\,(\alpha - 2\beta)/1 \qquad\qquad [\because \text{It is a unit cube.}]$$

Hence Bulk modulus $k = \dfrac{\text{Stress}}{\text{Volumetric strain}} = \dfrac{P}{3P\,(\alpha - 2\beta)}$

$$= \dfrac{1}{3\,(\alpha - 2\beta)} \qquad\qquad\qquad ...(i)$$

Divide the numerator and the denominator by α, then

$$k = \dfrac{\dfrac{1}{\alpha}}{3\,(1 - 2\beta/\alpha)} = \dfrac{Y}{3\,(1 - 2\sigma)} \qquad\qquad ...(ii)$$

$$\left[\because \dfrac{1}{\alpha} = Y \text{ and } \dfrac{\beta}{\alpha} = \sigma \text{ (the Poisson's ratio)}\right]$$

Q. 11.10. If Y, k, η and σ represent the Young's modulus, bulk modulus, coefficient of rigidity and Poisson's ratio, then derive various relations connecting each other and prove that σ is less than 0.5 and cannot be less than -1. What are the practical limits for Poisson's ratio (σ)?

(*Madurai U.* 2003; *Kerala U.* 2001; *Nagpur U.* 2001; *Indore U.* 2001; *M.D.U.* 2008; 2001, 1999; *K.U.* 2001, 2000; *Meerut; U.* 2006; *Bang. U.* 2000, 1996, 1995; *Guwahati U.* 2000; *Gharwal U.* 2000; *Kanpur U.* 1996; *Meerut U.* 1994, 1993)

Ans. (*i*) Relation between Y, η and σ [See Q 11.8 relation (*iv*)]

$$\eta = \dfrac{Y}{2\,(1 + \sigma)} \qquad\qquad\qquad ...(i)$$

or $Y = 2\eta\,(1 + \sigma)$ \qquad\qquad\qquad ...(*i*)(*a*)

(*ii*) Relation between Y, k and σ (See Q. 11.9 relation (*ii*))

$$k = \frac{Y}{3(1-2\sigma)} \qquad \qquad ...(ii)$$

or
$$Y = 3k(1-2\sigma) \qquad \qquad ...(ii)(a)$$

(iii) Relation between Y, η and k

$$Y = \frac{9\eta k}{\eta + 3k} \qquad \qquad ...(iii)$$

From relation (i), we have $2 + 2\sigma = \dfrac{Y}{\eta}$

From relation (ii), we have $1 - 2\sigma = \dfrac{Y}{3k}$

Adding, we have

$$3 = \frac{Y}{3k} + \frac{Y}{\eta} = Y\left(\frac{1}{3k} + \frac{1}{\eta}\right) = Y\left(\frac{\eta + 3k}{3\eta k}\right)$$

Hence
$$Y = \frac{9\eta k}{\eta + 3k}$$

or
$$\frac{9}{Y} = \frac{1}{k} + \frac{3}{\eta}$$

(iv) Relation between k, η and σ

From relation (i), we have

$$Y = 2\eta(1+\sigma) \qquad \qquad ...(iv)$$

and from relation (ii), we have

$$Y = 3k(1-2\sigma) \qquad \qquad ...(v)$$

$$\therefore \qquad 2\eta(1+\sigma) = 3k(1-2\sigma)$$

or
$$2\eta + 2\eta\sigma = 3k - 6k\sigma$$

or
$$\sigma(2\eta + 6k) = 3k - 2\eta$$

$$\therefore \qquad \sigma = \frac{3k - 2\eta}{6k + 2\eta} = \frac{3k - 2\eta}{2(3k + \eta)} \qquad \qquad ...(v)(a)$$

Limiting value of σ. From relations (iv) and (v), we have

$$3k(1-2\sigma) = 2\eta(1+\sigma) \qquad \qquad ...(vi)$$

The bulk modulus k and coefficient of rigidity η are both positive quantities. If therefore, equation (vi) is true and (i) *Poisson's ratio is to be positive*, the right hand expression and also the left hand expression must be positive. This is possible only if

$$2\sigma < 1 \text{ or } \sigma < 0.5$$

(ii) If σ *is a negative* quantity the left-hand expression is positive. The right hand expression also must then be positive. This is possible only if $1 + \sigma$ is positive or σ is not less than -1.

Thus for a homogeneous isotropic material the value of σ must lie between + 0.5 and −1.

Theoretically it cannot be greater than $+ 0.5 \left(+\dfrac{1}{2}\right)$ and less than -1.

Practical limits of σ. In actual practice σ cannot be negative.

A negative value of σ would mean that on being extended a body would also expand laterally. Since no substance behaves in this way *in actual practice σ lies between 0 and + 0.5.*

Q. 11.11 (a) Calculate the Poisson's ratio for silver. Given Young's modulus for silver is 7.25 × 10^{10} N/m² and bulk modulus is 11 × 10^{10} N/m².
(Meerut U., 2001)

(b) The volume of a solid does not vary with pressure. Find Poisson's ratio for the solid.
(Gharwal U., 1999; Meerut U., 2003)

Ans. (a) $Y = 7.25 \times 10^{10}$ N/m² $k = 11 \times 10^{10}$ N/m²

Now $Y = 3k(1 - 2\sigma)$ ∴ $1 - 2\sigma = \dfrac{Y}{3k}$ or $2\sigma = 1 - \dfrac{Y}{3k}$

∴ $\sigma = \dfrac{1}{2}\left[1 - \dfrac{Y}{3k}\right] = \dfrac{1}{2}\left[1 - \dfrac{7.25 \times 10^{10}}{3 \times 11 \times 10^{10}}\right] = \dfrac{1}{2}(1 - 0.22) = 0.39$

(b) Young's modulus Y, bulk modulus k, and Poisson's ratio σ are connected by the relation

$$Y = 3k(1 - 2\sigma) \text{ or } 1 - 2\sigma = \dfrac{Y}{3k}$$

Now bulk modulus $k = \dfrac{\text{Applied pressure}}{\text{Volumetric strain}} = \dfrac{P}{v/V}$

As the volume of the solid does not vary with pressure, the volumetric strain is zero or $v/V = 0$.

Therefore $k = \infty$ (infinity) and $\dfrac{Y}{3k} = 0$.

Hence $1 - 2\sigma = 0$ or $2\sigma = 1$ ∴ $\sigma = \dfrac{1}{2} = 0.5$

Q. 11.12. (a) What is the difference between angle of twist and angle of shear? Deduce an expression for the couple required to twist a uniform solid cylinder by an angle.
(Kerala U. 2001; Meerut U. 2007; 2002, 2000, 1995; M.D.U. 2008; 2002; Gharwal U. 1999; K.U. 1997, 1996; A.U. 1995, 1993; Nagpur U. 2003)

(b) What is the value of the couple for a hollow cylinder of inner radius r_1 and outer radius r_2?
(Kan. U. 1995, 1993, 1992)

Ans. (a) **Angle of twist.** Consider a short cylinder of length l and radius a clamped at the upper end AB. Suppose a twisting couple is applied to the face $A'B'$ as shown by the arrow head, in a direction perpendicular to the length of the cylinder. The radius $O'P$ is twisted through an angle θ to the position $O'P'$.

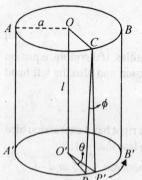

Fig. 11.6

θ *is known as the* **angle of twist.**

This is an example of pure shear because the twist neither produces a change in length nor a change in the radius of the cylinder.

Due to elasticity of the material a *restoring couple* is set up inside the cylinder which is equal and opposite to the *twisting couple.*

Angle of shear. Due to the application of the twisting couple a line such as CP on the rim of the cylinder parallel to OO' is displaced to the position CP' through an angle ϕ, due to the twisting couple. Here ϕ is the *angle of shear.* The displacement PP' is maximum for the points lying on the rim and goes on decreasing as we move towards O', the centre of the cylinder.

Couple required to twist a uniform solid cylinder. To find the value of the *twisting couple* imagine the solid cylinder to consist of a large number of *co-axial* cylindrical shells. Consider one such cylindrical shell of radius x and thickness dx. (Fig. 11.7)

Each radius of the lower end of the cylinder is turned through the same angle θ *but the displacement is maximum at the rim and decreases as we move towards the centre* O' *were it is reduced to zero.*

The angle of shear φ will have the maximum value when $x = a$ and least at O' where $x = 0$. This shows that the shearing strain is not constant throughout the cylinder. It is maximum on the rim and least for the innermost layer.

Thus angle of shear is the same for any one of the *hollow cylinders,* being greatest for the outermost and least for the innermost cylinder.

If the points P and P' are supposed to lie on the rim of the hollow cylinder of radius x and φ is the angle of shear, then from Fig. 11.6, we have $PP' = l\phi$ (as φ is small)

And also from Fig. 11.7

$$PP' = x\theta$$

∴ $$l\phi = x\theta$$

or $$\phi = \frac{x\theta}{l} \qquad \qquad ...(i)$$

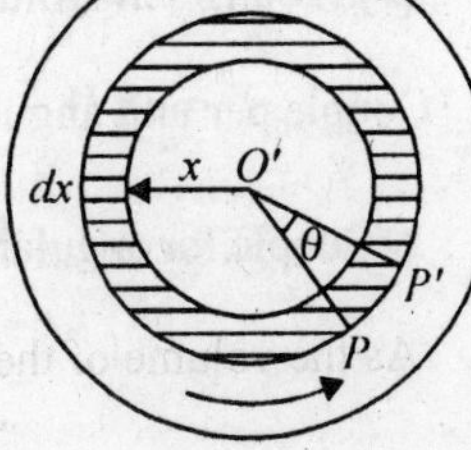

If η is the coefficient of rigidity, then

$$\eta = \frac{\text{Shearing stress}}{\text{Angle of shear}} = \frac{T}{\phi}$$

Fig. 11.7

∴ $$T = \eta\phi = \frac{\eta x\theta}{l} \qquad \qquad ...(ii)$$

Now the face area of the hollow cylinder $= 2\pi x.dx$

∴ Total shearing force on this area $= 2\pi x dx . \dfrac{\eta x\theta}{l} = \dfrac{2\pi\eta\theta}{l} . x^2 dx$

Moment of the force about $OO' = \dfrac{2\pi\eta\theta}{l} . x^2 dx.x$

The twisting couple applied to the whole cylinder can be obtained by integrating this quantity for limits $x = 0$ and $x = a$.

Hence twisting couple $= \dfrac{2\pi\eta\theta}{l} \displaystyle\int_0^a x^3 \, dx = \dfrac{2\pi\eta\theta}{l} \left[\dfrac{x^4}{4} \right]_0^a$

$$= \frac{2\pi\eta\theta}{l} \frac{a^4}{4} = \frac{\pi\eta\theta a^4}{2l}$$

This relation is used to find the value of rigidity by the statical method.

If in the above relation $\theta = 1$ radian, then

Twisting couple per unit angular twist $c = \dfrac{\pi\eta a^4}{2l} \qquad \qquad ...(iii)$

This twisting couple per unit angular twist of the wire or cylinder is called its **modulus of torsion** *or torsional rigidity.*

It is evident from relation (*iii*) that the couple required is proportional to the *fourth* power of the radius.

(b) Couple for a hollow cylinder. For a hollow cylinder with inner radius r_1 and outer radius r_2, the twisting couple is obtained by integrating $\dfrac{2\pi\eta\theta}{l} x^3 \, dx$ between the limits $x = r_1$ and $x = r_2$.

Hence twisting couple $= \dfrac{2\pi\eta\theta}{l} \int_{r_1}^{r_2} x^3\, dx = \dfrac{2\pi\eta\theta}{l}\left[\dfrac{x^4}{4}\right]_{r_1}^{r_2} = \dfrac{\pi\eta\theta}{2l}[r_2^4 - r_1^4]$

$\therefore$ Twisting couple per unit angular twist $c' = \dfrac{\pi\eta}{2l}[r_2^4 - r_1^4]$ ...(iv)

Q. 11.13. What couple must be applied to a wire one metre long, 1 mm in diameter in order to twist one end of it, through 90°, the other end remaining fixed. Rigidity of material of the wire is 2.8 × 10¹⁰ N-m⁻².

(Burd. U., 1990)

Ans. Here $l = 1$ m; radius $a = 0.5$ mm $= 0.5 \times 10^{-3}$ m

$\eta = 2.8 \times 10^{10}$ N-m⁻², $\theta = 90° = \pi/2$ radian

Couple per unit angular twist $c = \dfrac{\eta\pi a^4}{2l}$

$\therefore$ Couple for angular twist $\theta = c\theta = \eta\dfrac{\pi a^4}{2l} \times \dfrac{\pi}{2} = \dfrac{\eta\pi^2 a^4}{4l}$

$= \dfrac{2.8 \times 10^{10} \times \pi^2 \times (0.5 \times 10^{-3})^4}{4 \times 1}$

$= 43.19 \times 10^{-4}$ N-m

Q. 11.14. A circular bar one metre long and 8 mm diameter is rigidly clamped at one end in a vertical position. A couple of magnitude 2.5 Nm is applied at the other end. As a result a mirror fixed at this end deflects a spot of light by 0.15 m on the scale one metre away. Calculate the modulus of rigidity of the bar.

Ans. Here $l = 1$m, radius $a = 4$ mm $= 4 \times 10^{-3}$ m

Couple $c = 2.5$ N-m, $\eta = ?$

The spot of light is deflected through 0.15 m on a scale one metre away, the angle 2θ through which the reflected ray turns is given by

$\tan 2\theta = 0.15$ or $2\theta = 8°32'$

$\therefore \theta = 4°16' = 0.0745$ rad

Twisting couple $c = \dfrac{\pi\eta a^4}{2l}.\theta$

or $\eta = \dfrac{2cl}{\pi a^4 \theta} = \dfrac{2 \times 2.5 \times 1}{\pi (4 \times 10^{-3})^4 \times 0.0745}$

$= 8.344 \times 10^{10}$ Nm⁻²

Exercise. *A cylindrical bar of length 1m and diameter 8 mm is fixed at one end and the other end is twisted through an angle of 5° by the application of a couple of 2.5 Nm. Calculate the modulus of rigidity of the material of the bar.*

(Kerala U. 2001)

Hint. $5° = \dfrac{5\pi}{180} = 0.0873$ rad. $\eta = \dfrac{2cl}{\pi a^4 \theta} = \dfrac{2 \times 2.5 \times 1}{\pi (4 \times 10^{-3})^4 \times 0.0873}$

[**Ans.** = 7.12 × 10¹⁰ Nm⁻²]

Q. 11.15. (a) Calculate the work done in twisting a wire.

(b) A power of 6 kilowatts is transmitted by a shaft of length 4 metres and radius 2.5 cm at a speed of 200 revolutions per minute. If the modulus of rigidity of the material is 9 × 10¹⁰ Nm⁻², calculate the relative twist between the ends of the shaft.

Ans. *(a)* **Work done in twisting a wire.** Let a wire of length l and radius r be fixed at the upper end. A couple is applied at the lower end of the wire so as to produce a twist of an angle θ at this end.

If c is the couple per unit angular twist of the wire, then the couple required to produce a twist θ in the wire $= c\theta$. Now, the work done in twisting the wire through a small angle $d\theta$ is given by

$$dW = c\theta \, d\theta$$

Hence the total work done in twisting the wire through an angle θ is given by

$$W = \int_0^\theta c\theta \, d\theta = \frac{1}{2} c\theta^2$$

Now $c = \eta \dfrac{\pi r^4}{2l}$ where η is the coefficient of rigidity, r the radius and l the length of the wire

$\therefore$
$$W = \frac{\eta \pi r^4}{4l} \theta^2$$

The energy spent in doing the work is stored in the wire and is known as the **strain energy.**

(b) Here $l = 4$ m; $a = 2.5$ cm $= 2.5 \times 10^{-2}$ m

$\eta = 9 \times 10^{10}$ N–m^{-2}; Power $= 6$ K.watt $= 6000$ Js^{-1}

Time of one revolution $= \dfrac{60}{200} = \dfrac{3}{10}$ sec

Work done/rev $W = \dfrac{6000 \times 3}{10} = 1800$ J

If θ is the relative shift between the ends of the shaft and c the couple per unit angular twist, then

$$\frac{1}{2} c\theta^2 = W$$

or
$$\frac{1}{2} \frac{\pi \eta a^4}{2l} \theta^2 = 1800$$

$\therefore$
$$\theta = \sqrt{\frac{1800 \times 4 \times 4}{\pi \times 9 \times 10^{10} \times (2.5 \times 10^{-2})^4}} = 0.51 \text{ radian}$$

Exercise. *One end of a steel wire of length 0.2 m and radius 2×10^{-3} m is fixed. If the work done in twisting the free end of the wire is 3.85×10^{-2} J, calculate the angle through which the wire is twisted. Given rigidity modulus of steel $= 8.075 \times 10^{11}$ Nm^{-2}.* (Bang. U., 2000)

Hint.
$$c = \frac{\eta \pi r^4}{2l} = \frac{8.075 \times 10^{11} \times 22 \times 2^4 \times 10^{-12}}{2 \times 0.2 \times 7} = 101.5$$

$$\frac{1}{2} c\theta^2 = W \quad \therefore \theta^2 = \frac{2W}{c} = \frac{2 \times 3.85 \times 10^{-2}}{101.5} = 0.07586 \times 10^{-2}$$

or
$$\theta = 0.02754 \text{ rad} = 1.58° \qquad\qquad \text{[Ans. } 1.58°]$$

Q. 11.16. A sphere of mass 0.8 kg and radius 3 cm is suspended by a wire 1 m long of radius 0.5 m. If the time for one torsional vibration is 1.23 sec, determine the modulus of rigidity of the wire.

Ans. Here $l = 1$ m, $M = 0.8$ kg, $R = 3$ cm $= 3 \times 10^{-2}$ m

$a = 0.5$ mm $= 0.5 \times 10^{-3}$ m, $t = 1.23$ sec

M.I. of sphere $I = \dfrac{2}{5} MR^2 = \dfrac{2}{5} \times 0.8 \times (3 \times 10^{-2})^2$

$$= 2.88 \times 10^{-4} \text{ kg-m}^2$$

Now
$$t = 2\pi \sqrt{\frac{I}{c}} = 2\pi \sqrt{\frac{2lI}{\eta \pi a^4}}$$

$$\therefore \quad \eta = \frac{8\pi l l}{t^2 a^4} = \frac{8 \times \pi \times 2.88 \times 10^{-4} \times 1}{(1.23)^2 \times (0.5 \times 10^{-3})^4}$$

$$= 7.654 \times 10^{10} \text{ N-m}^{-2}$$

Q. 11.17. A cylindrical metal bar of length 0.24 m and diameter 4 cm is suspended by a wire 0.5 m long such that the axis of the bar is horizontal. The arrangement makes 100 torsional vibrations in 235.9 sec. Determine the co-efficient of rigidity of the material of wire. Given density of material of bar = 9×10^3 kgm^{-3} and radius of wire = 0.1 cm.

Ans. For cylindrical bar $L = 0.24$ m, $R = 2$ cm = 2×10^{-2} m

Density $\rho = 9 \times 10^3$ kg m^{-3}

Volume $V = \pi R^2 L = \pi \times 4 \times 10^{-4} \times 0.24 = 3.016 \times 10^{-4}$ m^3

$\therefore$ Mass $M = 3.016 \times 10^{-4} \times 9 \times 10^3 = 2.715$ kg.

M.I. of cylindrical bar about an axis passing through its centre and perpendicular to the length

$$I = M\left[\frac{R^2}{4} + \frac{l^2}{12}\right] = 2.715\left[\frac{4 \times 10^{-4}}{4} + \frac{.24 \times .24}{12}\right] = 133.04 \times 10^{-4} \text{ kg-m}^2$$

Time period $T = \dfrac{235.9}{100} = 2.359$ sec

Now $\quad T = 2\pi\sqrt{\dfrac{I}{c}}$ or $c = \dfrac{4\pi^2 I}{T^2}$ and $c = \dfrac{\pi\eta a^4}{2l}$

$$\therefore \quad \frac{\pi\eta a^4}{2l} = \frac{4\pi^2 I}{T^2}$$

or $\quad \eta = \dfrac{8\pi l l}{T^2 a^4} = \dfrac{8\pi \times 133.04 \times 10^{-4} \times 0.5}{(2.359)^2 (1 \times 10^{-3})^4} = 3 \times 10^{10} \text{ N-m}^{-2}$

Q. 11.18. A gold wire 0.32 mm in diameter elongates by 1 mm, when stretched by a force of 0.33 kg wt. and twists through one radian when equal and opposite torques of 145 dyne-cm are applied at its ends. Find the Poisson's ratio for gold given $g = 9.8$ ms^{-2}.

Ans. Here $d = 0.32$ mm = 0.32×10^{-3} m

$\therefore$ Radius $r = 0.16 \times 10^{-3}$ m, $l = 1.0$ mm = 10^{-3} m

Couple $c = 145$ dyne-cm = 145×10^{-7} N-m

Area of cross-section $a = \pi (0.16 \times 10^{-3})^2$ m^2

Force $F = 0.33 \times 9.8$ N

If L is the length of wire, then

Young's modulus $\quad Y = \dfrac{FL}{al} = \dfrac{0.33 \times 9.8 \times L}{\pi(0.16 \times 10^{-3})^2 \times 10^{-3}}$ Nm^{-2}

Now couple $\quad c = \dfrac{\pi\eta r^4}{2L}$

$$\therefore \quad \eta = \frac{c \times 2L}{\pi r^4} = \frac{145 \times 10^{-7} \times 2L}{\pi(0.16 \times 10^{-3})^4}$$

Now $\quad 2(1 + \sigma) = \dfrac{Y}{\eta} = \dfrac{0.33 \times 9.8 \times L}{\pi(0.16 \times 10^{-3})^2 \times 10^{-3}} \times \dfrac{\pi(0.16 \times 10^{-3})^4}{145 \times 10^{-7} \times 2L}$

$$= \frac{0.33 \times 9.8 \, (0.16 \times 10^{-3})^2}{10^{-3} \times 145 \times 10^{-7} \times 2} = 2.854$$

$$\therefore \qquad \sigma = \frac{2.854}{2} - 1 = 0.427$$

Q. 11.19. Explain why a hollow cylinder is stronger than a solid cylinder of the same length, mass and material.   (*Gharwal U.* 2001, 2000; *A.U.*, 1994; *K.U.* 2001, 1991; *M.D.U.* 2008; *Kan. U.*, 1995; *Bang. U.* 2000)

Ans. Hollow cylinder is sronger than solid cylinder of same length, mass and material. Consider two cylinders of same length, mass and material. One is solid of radius r and the other is hollow of inner radius r_1 and outer radius r_2.

Torsional couple for solid cylinder per unit angular twist $c = \dfrac{\eta \pi r^4}{2l}$

Torsional couple for hollow cylinder per unit angular twist $c' = \dfrac{\pi \eta (r_2^4 - r_1^4)}{2l}$

$$\therefore \qquad \frac{c'}{c} = \frac{r_2^4 - r_1^4}{r^4} = \frac{(r_2^2 - r_1^2)(r_2^2 + r_1^2)}{r^4}$$

As the cylinders are of the same length and mass

$$\pi (r_2^2 - r_1^2) \, l\rho = \pi r^2 l \rho$$

$$\therefore \qquad r_2^2 - r_1^2 = r^2$$

Hence $\qquad \dfrac{c'}{c} = \dfrac{(r_2^2 - r_1^2)(r_2^2 + r_1^2)}{r^2 \times r^2} = \dfrac{r_2^2 + r_1^2}{r^2}$

Thus $c' > c$ *i.e.*, torsional rigidity for hollow cylinder is greater than that for the solid cylinder of the same mass, length and material. Hence the hollow cylinder is stronger than solid cylinder.

This shows also that hollow shaft is stronger than the solid one.

Q. 11.20. (*a*) **A solid cylinder of radius 5 cm is converted into a hollow cylinder of same mass and length and external radius 7 cm. If the restoring couple per unit radian twist in original cylinder is c, deduce the same for the new hollow cylinder.**

(*Kan. U.*, 1994, 1992; *A.U.,1993*)

(*b*) **Two cylinders have the same length and mass and are made of same material; one is solid while the other which is hollow has an external radius twice the internal radius. Compare the torsional rigidities of the two cylinders. Show that second cylinder is stronger.**

(*Kan. U.*, 1996; *Cal U.*, 1992)

Ans. (*a*) If r is the radius of solid cylinder and r_2 and r_1 the outer and inner radii of the hollow cylinder of the same mass and length as that of solid cylinder, then

$$\pi r^2 l \rho = \pi (r_2^2 - r_1^2) \, l\rho$$

or $\qquad\qquad r^2 = r_2^2 - r_1^2$

Now $\qquad\qquad r = 5 \text{ cm and } r_2 = 7 \text{ cm}$

$$\therefore \qquad r_1^2 = r_2^2 - r^2 = 49 - 25 = 24 \text{ cm}^2$$

If c' is the restoring couple for the hollow cylinder, then

$$\frac{c'}{c} = \frac{r_2^2 + r_1^2}{r^2} = \frac{49 + 25}{24} = 2.92$$

$$\left[\text{For proof of } \frac{c'}{c} = \frac{r_2^2 + r_1^2}{r^2} \text{ see Q. 11.19}\right]$$

$$\therefore \qquad c' = 2.92\ c$$

(b) Length of each cylinder $= l$; Density of material of each cylinder $= \rho$

Radius of solid cylinder $= a$

Outer radius of hollow cylinder $= r_2$; Inner radius of hollow cylinder $= r_1$

Given $r_2 = 2r_1$

Mass of the solid cylinder $= \pi a^2 l \rho$

Mass of the hollow cylinder $= \pi (r_2^2 - r_1^2)\ l\ \rho = \pi [(2r_1)^2 - r_1^2]\ l\rho = \pi\ 3r_1^2 l\rho$

As the two cylinders have the same mass

$$\pi a^2 l\rho = \pi 3 r_1^2 l\rho$$

$$\therefore \qquad a^2 = 3r_1^2$$

Couple per unit angular twist (or torsional rigidity) of solid cylinder $c = \dfrac{\pi \eta a^4}{2l} = \dfrac{\pi \eta}{2l}\ 9r_1^4$

Couple per unit angular twist (or torsional rigidity) of hollow cylinder

$$c' = \frac{\pi \eta}{2l}\ [r_2^4 - r_1^4] = \frac{\pi \eta}{2l}\ [(2r_1)^4 - r_1^4] = \frac{\pi \eta}{2l}\ 15\ r_1^4\ .$$

$$\therefore \qquad \frac{c'}{c} = \frac{\dfrac{\pi \eta}{2l}\ 15\ r_1^4}{\dfrac{\pi \eta}{2l}\ 9\ r_1^4} = \frac{15}{9} = \frac{5}{3}$$

As the hollow cylinder has a greater torsional rigidity it is stronger than the solid cylinder of the same mass, length and material.

Q. 11.21. (a) Define the term neutral surface, plane of bending, neutral axis and bending moment. Derive an expression for the couple required to bend a uniform straight metallic strip into an arc of a circle of small curvature. What is meant by flexural rigidity?

(Kerala U. 2001; Luck. U. 2001; Nag. U. 2001; Gharwal U. 2000, 1999; Bang. U. 1994, 1991; M.D.U. 2006)

(b) A rod of rectangular cross-section having breadth and thickness each 0.5 cm is bent in the form of an arc of radius of curvature 1000 cm. If Young's modulus of the material of the rod is 10^{12} dynes/cm² calculate (i) stress, strain at the curved sufrace and (ii) bending moment.

(Kan. U., 1993)

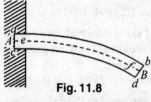

Fig. 11.8

Ans. (a) Neutral sufrace. When a metallic strip is fixed at one end and loaded at the other a bending is produced due to the moment of the load. The deformation produced by the load brings about restoring forces due to elasticity tending to bring the strip back to its original position. In equilibrium position

Restoring couple = Bending couple

These two couples act in the opposite directions.

Suppose a metallic strip consists of a large number of filaments of small thickness lying one above the other. When a load is applied at the end B, the end A being fixed, inner filament like cd are shortened or compressed while the outer filaments like ab are elongated as shown in Fig. 11.8 and 11.9. Along the section lying in between these two portions a filament like ef is neither stretched nor compressed. Such a surface is called the *neutral surface*.

Plane of bending. *The plane in which bending takes place is known as plane of bending.* When the beam is placed horizontally the plane of bending is a vertical plane perpendicular to the beam.

Neutral axis. *The section of the neutral surface (ef) by the plane of bending which is perpendicular to it is called the neutral axis.*

The change in length of any filament is proportional to the distance of the filament from the neutral axis.

Bending moment. Consider a small part XY of the neutral axis of the strip bent into an arc of radius R subtending an angle θ at the centre of curvature O, as shown in Fig. 11.9.

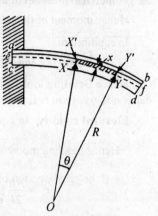

Let $X'Y'$ be another filament at a distance x from the neutral surface, then

$$XY = R\theta$$

and $$X'Y' = (R + x)\theta$$

∴ Increase in length of the filament

$$= X'Y' - XY$$

$$= (R + x)\theta - R\theta = x\theta$$

∴ Strain $= \dfrac{\text{change in length}}{\text{original length}} = \dfrac{x\theta}{R\theta} = \dfrac{x}{R}$

Now Young's modulus $Y = \dfrac{\text{Stress}}{\text{Strain}}$

Fig. 11.9

∴ Stress $= Y \times$ Strain $= \dfrac{Yx}{R}$

Consider a section $ABCD$ (drawn rectangular for convenience) of the strip at right angles to its length and the plane of bending (Fig. 11.10). Then the forces acting on the strip are perpendicular to this section and the line EF lies on the neutral surface. *The forces producing elongations act in the upper half $ABEF$ and those producing contraction act in the lower half $CDEF$ in opposite directions perpendicular to the section $ABCD$ and hence constitute a couple.*

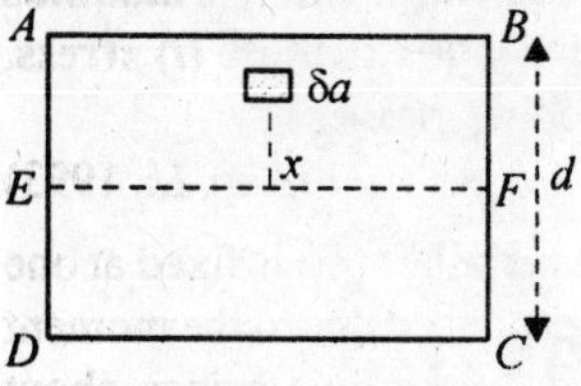

To find the moment of this couple consider a small area δa lying at a distance x from the neutral axis EF, then

Force on area δa = stress × area $= \dfrac{Yx.\delta a}{R}$

Moment of the force about the axis EF

$$= \dfrac{Yx\delta a.x}{R} = \dfrac{Y.x^2\delta a}{R}$$

Hence moment of all the forces acting at various points of the whole face $ABCD$ are

$$= \dfrac{Y}{R} \Sigma x^2\, \delta a$$

Fig. 11.10

To find the value of $\Sigma x^2 \delta a$ let us suppose that we can divide the whole area into a number of such parts each of area δa and let the number of such parts be n, then

$$\Sigma x^2\delta a = x_1^2\delta a + x_2^2\delta a + \text{.......}n \text{ times}$$

$$= n\delta a\,\dfrac{x_1^2 + x_2^2 + \text{.....} + x_n^2}{n} = ak^2$$

where $a = n\delta a$ is the area of the face $ABCD$ and k^2 is the square of radius of gyration k of $ABCD$ about the axis EF.

$$\therefore \qquad \frac{Y}{R} \Sigma x^2 \delta a = \frac{Yak^2}{R} \qquad\qquad ...(i)$$

The quantity $ak^2 =$ Moment of inertia of the beam if it has a unit mass per unit area and is called the **geometrical moment of inertia** I.

$$\text{Hence moment of the restoring couple} = \frac{Yak^2}{R} = \frac{YI}{R} \qquad\qquad ...(ii)$$

In equilibrium

Restoring couple = bending couple (or bending moment).

Hence **Bending moment** *may be defined as the total moment of all the couples arising in a bent beam and trying to resist its deformation caused by an external couple.*

Flexural rigidity. In equation (ii) the quantity $YI = Yak^2$ *is called flexural rigidity.*

$$\text{Hence bending moment} = \frac{YI}{R} = \frac{\text{Flexural rigidity}}{\text{Radius of curvature of neutral surface}}$$

(i) If the cross-section of the beam is rectangular, then

$$a = b \times d$$

where b is the breadth of the face $ABCD$ and d the thickness. The moment of inertia of the rectangle $ABCD$ about the axis EF parallel to the side AB

$$Mk^2 = M \frac{d^2}{12} \ \text{or} \ k^2 = \frac{d^2}{12}$$

$$\therefore \text{Geometrical moment of Inertia} \ I = ak^2 = bd \frac{d^2}{12} = \frac{bd^3}{12}$$

Substituting the value of I in (ii), we have

$$\text{The moment of the restoring couple} = \frac{Y}{R} \frac{bd^3}{12} = \frac{Ybd^3}{12R}$$

and in equilibrium this is equal to the **bending couple (or bending moment)**.

(ii) If the cross-section is circular and has a radius r, then

$$a = \pi r^2$$

and moment of inertia

$$= \frac{Mr^2}{4} \ \text{or} \ k^2 = r^2 / 4$$

$$\therefore \text{Geometrical moment of inertia} \ I = ak^2 = \pi r^2 \frac{r^2}{4} = \frac{\pi r^4}{4}$$

Substituting this value of I in (ii), we have

$$\text{The moment of the restoring couple} = \frac{Y}{R} \cdot \frac{\pi r^4}{4} = \frac{\pi Y r^4}{4R}$$

and in equilibrium this is equal to the **bending couple (or bending moment)**.

$(b)(i)$ When a bar is bent, the tensile strain on any filament at a distance x from the neutral surface is given by

$$\text{strain} = \frac{\text{change in length}}{\text{original length}} = \frac{x}{R}$$

where R is the radius of curvature of the neutral surface.

The neutral surface lies along the middle of the bar.

Thickness of the bar = 0.5 cm = 0.005 m

∴ For the convex surface of the bent bar $x = \dfrac{0.005}{2} = 0.0025$ m

Radius of curvature of the curved surface $R = 1000$ cm $= 10$ m

Hence tensile strain $= \dfrac{x}{R} = \dfrac{0.0025}{10} = 0.00025 = 25 \times 10^{-5}$

Young's modulus $Y = 10^{12}$ dynes/cm^2 = 10^{11} Nm^{-2}

∴ Tensile stress = $Y \times$ tensile strain $= 10^{11} \times 25 \times 10^{-5} = 25 \times 10^{6}$ Nm^{-2}

(*ii*) Geometrical moment of inertia of the rectangular bar

$$I = \frac{bd^3}{12}$$

Now $b = d = 0.005$ m

$$I = \frac{(0.005)^4}{12} = \frac{625 \times 10^{-12}}{12} = 52 \times 10^{-12}$$

∴ Bending moment $= \dfrac{YI}{R} = \dfrac{10^{11} \times 52 \times 10^{-12}}{10} = 52 \times 10^{-2}$ Nm

Exercise. *A steel rod of length 50 cm, width 2 cm and thickness 1 cm is bent into the form of an arc of radius of curvature 2.0 m. Calculate the bending moment. Young's modulus of the material of the rod* $= 2 \times 10^{11}$ *N/m*^{2}.   (*Kerala U.*, 2001)

Hint. $b = 2$cm $= 2 \times 10^{-2}$ m; $d = 1$ cm $= 10^{-2}$ m

∴ $$I = \frac{bd^3}{12} = \frac{2 \times 10^{-2} \times 10^{-6}}{12} = \frac{1}{6} \times 10^{-8}$$

∴ Bending moment $= \dfrac{YI}{R} = \dfrac{2 \times 10^{11}}{2} \times \dfrac{1}{6} \times 10^{-8} = \dfrac{10^3}{6} = 166.67$ Nm

Q. 11.22. (*a*) **What is a cantilever? Derive an expression for the depression of the loaded end of a cantilever of (*i*) circular cross-section and (*ii*) rectangular cross-section of negligible weight.**

(*Meerut U.* 2002; *K.U.* 2002, 2001, 1994; *Kan.U.* 1996; *Bang. U.* 1994;
M.D.U. 2007, 2006; *Ranchi U.* 1991; *M.D.U.* 2003)

(*b*) **Hence derive an expression for the bending of a bar supported at the two ends and loaded in the middle. Describe an experiment to determine *Y* by bending.**

(*Luck.U.* 2001; *K.U.* 2000, 1997, 1996; *M.D.U.* 1999; *Mithila U.* 1999)

Ans. (*a*) **Cantilever.** *It is a beam fixed horizontally at one end and loaded at the other.*

Depression at loaded end. Suppose *EF* represents the *neutral axis* of the cantilever of length *l* fixed at the end *E* and loaded with a load *W* at *F* as shown in Fig. 11.11. Let the end *F* be deflected to the position *F'* under the action of the load.

Consider a section of the beam as at *P* at a distance *x* from the fixed end *E*, then the moment of the couple due to the load *W*

$$= W \times PF' = W(l - x)$$

As the point *F'* is very close to *F*, *PF'* is almost perpendicular to *FW*.

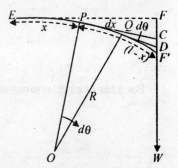

Fig. 11.11

Since the beam is in equilibrium the bending couple is equal to the restoring couple $\dfrac{YI}{R}$ where R is the radius of curvature of the neutral axis at P, Y the Young's modulus and I the geometrical moment of inertia. Hence

$$W(l-x) = \frac{YI}{R}$$

or

$$\frac{1}{R} = \frac{W(l-x)}{YI}$$

As we move towards the fixed end E the moment of the load increases. Hence the radius of curvature will be different at different points and decreases as we move towards E. Consider another point Q lying very close to P at distance dx. The radius of curvature at Q is practically the same as dx is very small.

$$\therefore \qquad PQ = R \cdot d\theta = dx$$

or

$$d\theta = \frac{dx}{R} = \frac{W(l-x)\,dx}{YI}$$

Draw tangents at P and Q meeting the vertical line at C and D respectively. Then the depression of Q below P is evidently

$$CD = dy = (l-x)\,d\theta$$

where $d\theta$ is the angle between the two tangents.

$$\therefore \qquad dy = \frac{(l-x)\,W \cdot (l-x)\,dx}{YI}$$

$$= \frac{W}{YI}(l-x)^2\,dx$$

$$\therefore \qquad \text{Total depression} \quad FF' = y = \int_0^l \frac{W}{YI}(l-x)^2\,dx$$

$$= \frac{W}{YI}\int_0^l (l^2 + x^2 - 2lx)\,dx$$

$$= \frac{W}{YI}\left[l^2 x + \frac{x^3}{3} - \frac{2lx^2}{2}\right]_0^l$$

$$= \frac{W}{YI}\left[l^3 + \frac{l^3}{3} - l^3\right]$$

$$= \frac{Wl^3}{3YI}$$

For a bar of circular cross-section of radius r

$$I = \frac{\pi r^4}{4}$$

$$\therefore \qquad y = \frac{4Wl^3}{3Y\pi r^4}$$

If for a rectangular rod b is the breadth and d the depth, then

$$I = ak^2 = b.d \times \frac{d^2}{12} = \frac{bd^3}{12}$$

$$\therefore \quad y = \frac{Wl^3}{3Y} \times \frac{12}{bd^3} = \frac{4Wl^3}{Ybd^3}$$

(b) Bar supported at two ends and loaded in the middle. Suppose we take a rod of a certain material and support it at two knife edges A and B. If the rod is loaded at the centre C with a load W, then the reaction at each knife edge will be $W/2$ in the upward direction.

Since the middle part of the rod is practically horizontal, it may be considered as equal to two inverted cantilevers fixed at C and being loaded at A and B with a load $W/2$ acting in the upward direction. If l is the length of the beam, then the depression y at C is given by

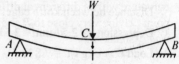

Fig. 11.12

$$y = \frac{W/2 . \left(\frac{l}{2}\right)^3}{3YI} = \frac{Wl^3}{48YI}$$

(i) If the rod is circular in cross-section and has a radius r, then geometrical moment of inertia

$$I = ak^2 = \pi r^2 . \frac{r^2}{4} = \frac{\pi r^4}{4}$$

$$\therefore \quad y = \frac{Wl^3}{48Y} . \frac{4}{\pi r^4} = \frac{Wl^3}{12Y\pi r^4} \qquad \qquad ...(i)$$

or
$$Y = \frac{Wl^3}{12\, y\, \pi\, r^4} \qquad \qquad ...(ii)$$

(ii) If the rod is rectangular and has a breadth b and depth d, then geometrical moment of inertia

$$I = ak^2$$

$$= b.d\, \frac{d^2}{12} = \frac{bd^3}{12}$$

$$\therefore \quad y = \frac{Wl^3}{48Y} \times \frac{12}{bd^3} = \frac{Wl^3}{4Ybd^3} \qquad \qquad ...(iii)$$

or
$$Y = \frac{Wl^3}{4bd^3\, y} \qquad \qquad ...(iv)$$

Experimental determination. The depression y at the centre of the rod can be found out accurately with the help of a spherometer or a travelling microscope. By loading the rod at the centre with a load increasing in equal steps and then decreasing the load in the same equal steps, the mean depression y for a certain load can be found out. The breadth b and the depth d are also measured and Young's modulus of elasticity is calculated from the relation given above.

Q. 11.23. (a) In case of bending of a rod, Young's modulus only comes into play and not modulus of rigidity even though there is a change in shape. Explain. *(Bang. U., 1995)*

(b) A brass bar 1 cm square in cross-section is supported on two knife edges one metre apart. A load of 1 kg at the centre of the bar depresses that point 2.51 mm. What is Young's modulus of brass?

Ans. (*a*) When a rod undergoes bending certain filaments of the rod are extended, some are contracted, while others remain unaltered. As a result of elastic reaction against extension and contraction of filaments longitudinal stresses are developed. Due to the presence of longitudinal stress and longitudinal strain, Young's modulus comes into play.

When the thickness of the rod is small in comparison to its length, then for small bending the shearing stress over any section of the rod is negligible and hence modulus of rigidity is not involved and does not occur in the expression for depression.

(*b*) As the bar is 1 cm square

$\therefore \qquad b = d = 1 \text{ cm} = 10^{-2} \text{ m}$

Distance between knife edges $l = 1$ m

Depression $y = 2.51 \text{ mm} = 2.51 \times 10^{-3} \text{ m}$

Load $W = 1$ kg wt. $= 9.8$ N

Now $\qquad\qquad\qquad Y = \dfrac{Wl^3}{4bd^3 y}$

$\qquad\qquad\qquad\quad = \dfrac{9.8 \times 1}{4 \times 10^{-2} \times 10^{-6} \times 2.51 \times 10^{-3}}$

$\qquad\qquad\qquad\quad = 9.761 \times 10^{10} \text{ N-m}^{-2}$

Q. 11.24. In an experiment the diameter of the rod was 1.26 cm and distance between the knife edges 0.7 m. On putting a load of 0.9 kg at the mid-point, the depression was 0.025 cm. Find Young's modulus of elasticity of the material of rod.

Ans. Here $\quad l = 0.7 \text{ m}$,

$\qquad\qquad\qquad W = 0.9 \text{ kg-wt} = 0.9 \times 9.8 \text{ N}$

$\qquad\qquad\qquad r = 0.63 \text{ cm} = 0.63 \times 10^{-2} \text{ m}$

$\qquad\qquad\qquad y = 0.025 \text{ cm} = 2.5 \times 10^{-4} \text{ m}$

Now $\qquad\qquad\qquad Y = \dfrac{Wl^3}{12\pi r^4 y}$

$\qquad\qquad\qquad\quad = \dfrac{0.9 \times 9.8 \times 0.7 \times 0.7 \times 0.7}{12\pi \times (0.63 \times 10^{-2})^4 \times 2.5 \times 10^{-4}}$

$\qquad\qquad\qquad\quad = 20.374 \times 10^{10} \text{ Nm}^2$

Q. 11.25. Compare the loads required to produce equal depressions for two beams made of the same material and having the same length and weight with only difference that one has circular cross-section while the cross-section of the other is square.   (*A.U.*, 1995)

Ans. If *l* is the length of each bar, ρ its density, *r* the radius of circular bar and *a* each side of the face of square bar, then

Mass of square bar $= a^2 l\rho$

Mass of circular bar $= \pi r^2 l\rho$

As the mass of the bars are equal

$\therefore \qquad\qquad\qquad \pi r^2 l\rho = a^2 l\rho$

or $\qquad\qquad\qquad\quad \pi r^2 = a^2$ ...(*i*)

If I_1 is the geometrical *M.I.* of the square bar and I_2 that of the circular bar, then

Depression for square bar $y = \dfrac{W_1}{YI_1} \cdot \dfrac{l^3}{3}$ ...(ii)

and Depression for circular bar $y = \dfrac{W_2}{YI_2} \cdot \dfrac{l^3}{3}$ ...(iii)

From (ii) and (iii), we get

$$\frac{W_1}{I_1} = \frac{W_2}{I_2}$$

or

$$\frac{W_1}{W_2} = \frac{I_1}{I_2}$$

Now

$$I_1 = \frac{a^4}{12} \text{ and}$$

$$I_2 = \frac{\pi r^4}{4}$$

$\therefore$

$$\frac{W_1}{W_2} = \frac{a^4}{12} \times \frac{4}{\pi r^4}$$

$$= \frac{a^4}{3\pi r^4}$$

$$= \frac{\pi^2 r^4}{3\pi r^4} = \frac{\pi}{3} = 1.05$$

Q. 11.26. A uniform rod of length 1m is clamped horizontally at one end. A weight of 0.1 kg is attached at the free end. Calculate the depression of the free end of the rod. The diameter of the rod is 0.02 m; Young's modulus of the material of the rod = 1×10^{10} Nm^{-2}.

(*Bang. U.*, 1996)

Ans. Depression at the free end of a cantilever

$$y = \frac{Wl^3}{3YI}$$

where W = Load at the free end

l = length of the cantilever

Y = Young's modulus of the material of the cantilever

I = Geometrical moment of inertia

For a bar of circular cross-section of radius r geometrical moement of inertia

$$I = ak^2$$

$$= \pi r^2 \cdot \frac{r^2}{4}$$

$$= \frac{\pi r^4}{4}$$

Now $W = 0.1$ kg. $= 0.1 \times 9.8$ N

$l = 1$ m

$Y = 1 \times 10^{10}$ Nm^{-2}

$r = 0.01$ m $= 10^{-2}$ m

$\therefore$ Depression of the free end $y = \dfrac{0.1 \times 9.8 \times 1^3 \times 4}{3 \times 10^{10} \times \pi \times (10^{-2})^4}$

$= 0.41 \times 10^{-2}\,\text{m}$

$= 4.1 \times 10^{-3}\,\text{m} = 4.1\,\text{mm}.$

Exercise. *A steel rod of circular cross-section of radius 1 cm is rigidly fixed at one end. The other end which is at a distance of 1m from the fixed end is loaded with 8 kg. Calculate the depression of the free end. $Y = 2 \times 10^{11}\,Nm^2$.*   (M.D.U. 2006)

Hint: $W = 8\,\text{kg} = 8 \times 9.8\,N;\, l = 1m$

$Y = 2 \times 10^{11}\,Nm^{-2};\, r = 1\,\text{cm} = 0.01\,m = 10^{-2}m$

$$I = \frac{\pi r^4}{4}$$

$$y = \frac{W l^3}{3YI} = \frac{8 \times 9.8 \times 1^3 \times 4}{3 \times 2 \times 10^{11} \times \pi \times (10^{-2})^4}$$

$$= 16.6 \times 10^{-3}\,m = 16.6\,\text{mm}.$$

Q. 11.27. (a) Explain why steel girders have I section?

(*Madurai U.* 2003; *M.D.U.* 2002; *Bang. U.* 2000)

(b) A square bar of length 1m and cross-section 1cm^2 is clamped horizontally at one end and a weight of 1 kgm is applied at the other end. Neglecting weight of the bar calculate the depression of the loaded end. Given $Y = 9.78 \times 10^{10}$ N/m^2 and $g = 9.78$ m/sec^2.   (*Nag. U.* 2001; *M.D.U.* 2002)

Ans. (a) Why steel girders have I-section? A steel girder undergoes bending under the action of a load. As such the filaments of the girder above the neutral surface are compressed and those below the neutral surface are extended. This compression or extension of a filament is proportional to its distance from the neutral surface and, therefore, the compression or extension increases as the distance of the filament from the neutral surface increases. Its value is zero at the neutral surface and maximum at the lower or upper faces. Therefore, outer layers undergo much greater strain than inner layers. Hence to make the outer layers stronger than inner layers the girders are manufactured in I-shape. This considerably saves the material and reduces weight and cost without in any way sacrificing the strength of the girder.

(*b*) Here $l = 1$m. As it is a square bar $d = b = 1$ cm $= 10^{-2}$ m.

$W = 1\,\text{kgm} = 1 \times 9.78 = 9.78\,N;\, Y = 9.78 \times 10^{10}\,Nm^{-2}$

$\therefore$ Depression of the loaded end $y = \dfrac{4Wl^3}{Ybd^3}$ for a rectangular bar

$= \dfrac{4Wl^3}{Yb^4}$ for a square bar

$= \dfrac{4 \times 9.78 \times 1}{9.78 \times 10^{10} \times 10^{-8}} = 4 \times 10^{-2}\,\text{m} = 4\,\text{cm}.$

Q. 11.28. Mark the correct answer.

(i) Dimensions of Young's modulus are that of

    (a) F (b) $\dfrac{F}{l}$ (c) $\dfrac{F}{l^2}$ (d) $\dfrac{F}{l^3}$

(ii) The dimensions of σ are

    (a) L (b) L^2 (c) L^3 (d) dimensionless

(iii) Relation between Y, η and σ is

    (a) $Y = 2\eta(1+\sigma)$ (b) $Y = \eta(1+\sigma)$

    (c) $Y = \eta(1+2\sigma)$ (d) $2Y = \eta(1+\sigma)$

(iv) Twisting couple per unit angular twist is

    (a) $\dfrac{\pi\eta a^4}{l}$ (b) $\dfrac{\pi\eta a^4}{2l}$ (c) $\dfrac{2\pi\eta a^4}{l}$ (d) $\dfrac{\pi\eta a^2}{2l}$

(v) A rod is supported on two knife edges and loaded in the middle. The depression at the centre is noted. The kinfe edges are shifted slightly outwards. The depression will

    (a) increase   (b) decrease   (c) remain the same.

(vi) Poisson's ratio cannot have a value

    (a) 0.7   (b) 0.2   (c) 0.5   (Meerut U., 2000)

(vii) What is the relation between Y, k and η for an isotropic material?

    (a) $Y = \dfrac{9k\eta}{3k+\eta}$ (b) $\eta = \dfrac{9kY}{4k+Y}$ (c) $\eta = \dfrac{3kY}{9k+Y}$ (Meerut U., 2000)

(viii) The upper end of a wire of radius 4 mm and length 100 cm is clamped and its other end is twisted through an angle of 30°. The angle of shear is

    (a) 12°   (b) 0.12°   (c) 30°   (Meerut U., 2000)

Ans. (i) c   (ii) d   (iii) a   (iv) b   (v) a

    (vi) a   (vii) a   (viii) c

EXERCISES

1. Poisson's ratio for a material is 0.379 and rigidity is 2.87×10^{-2} Nm^{-2}, find Young's modulus.
    [Ans. 7.196×10^{-2} Nm^{-2}]

2. A cylinder of diameter 4 cm and length 5 cm is suspended horizontally by a steel wire of length 100 cm and radius 0.02 cm. Calculate the time of one vibration. The coefficient of rigidity of steel is 8×10^{11} dynes/cm^2 and the density of lead is 11.4 gms/c.c.
    [Ans. 6.586 seconds]

    Hint. $M = \pi R^2 l\rho$ and $I = M\left[\dfrac{R^2}{4} + \dfrac{L^2}{12}\right]$

       $t = 2\pi\sqrt{\dfrac{I}{c}} = 2\pi\sqrt{\dfrac{1.2 l}{\eta\pi r^4}}$

3. A metallic strip of width 2 cm and thickness 3 mm supported horizontally on knife edges 80 cm apart is loaded with 50 gm at its middle. Find by how much the centre of the metallic strip is depressed. Young's modulus for the material is 2×10^{11} Nm^{-2}.   **[Ans. 0.581×10^{-2} m]**

4. A steel rod of circular cross-section of radius 1 cm is rigidly fixed at one end, the other end which is at a distance of 1 metre from the fixed end, is loaded with 8 kg. Calculate the deflection of the rod. Given Young's modulus of elasticity $= 2 \times 10^{11}$ Nm^{-2}.

[**Ans.** 1.663×10^{-2} m]

5. A steel wire of 1.00 mm radius is bent in the form of a circular arc of radius 50 cm. Calculate (*i*) The bending moment (*ii*) maximum stress. Given $Y = 2 \times 10^{11}$ Nm^{-2}.

[**Ans.** (*i*) 0.314 Newton metre (*ii*) 4×10^{8} Nm^{-2}]

12

Surface Tension

Q. 12.1. (*a*) **Explain what do you understand by surface tension of a liquid.**

(*Bhopal U.*, 2004; *Nag.U.*, 2003; *Gharwal U.*, 1999; *Meerut U.*, 1990; *Cal.U.*, 1992, 1990)

(*b*) **Give an account of molecular theory of surface tension.**

(*Cal.U.*, 2003, 1992, 1990; *Bhopal U.*, 2004; *Bang. U.*, 1995; *Burd.U.*, 1991;)

Ans. (*a*) **Surface tension.** A stretched body is in a state of tension and has a natural tendency to contract. For example, when we stretch a rubber tube it has a tendency to shorten its length and if a rubber sheet is stretched it has a tendency to reduce its area. On account of the *cohesive forces* between the molecules of a liquid, the free surface of a liquid always behaves like *stretched membrane or sheet and tends to contract to the smallest possible area.* Since for a given volume a sphere has the least surface area, the liquid assumes a spherical shape. This is why the rain drops and mercury globules are spherical. Ordinarily the effect is not so marked as the liquids tend to spread due to the force of gravity. If the force of gravity is eliminated the liquid will asssume a perfectly spherical shape.

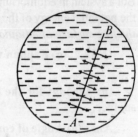

Fig. 12.1

Suppose a line *AB* is drawn in the free surface of a liquid. The molecules lying just on its one side try to pull away from the molecules lying just on the other side in order to decrease the surface area.

Hence surface tension is defined as the force per unit length acting on either side of a line drawn in the liquid surface in equilibrium the direction of the force being tangential to the surface and perpendicular to the line.

It is measured in Newton per meter in S.I. units.

(*b*) **Molecular theory of surface tension.** The molecules of a liquid attract each other. This force of attraction between them is called the force of *cohesion*. The force of cohesion varies inversely as some high power of the distance. It, therefore, becomes negligible at an appreciable distance from a molecule.

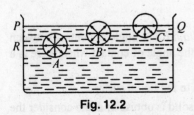

Fig. 12.2

The maximum distance up to which the force of cohesion between two molecules can act is called their molecular range. It is of the order of 10^{-9} m. being different for different substances.

The sphere drawn with the molecule as centre having a radius equal to the molecular range, is called the sphere of influence.

A molecule attracts and is in turn attracted by the molecules lying within its *sphere of influence*. Let us consider three molecules of a liquid; *A* well inside it, *B* just below the surface and *C* on the surface, with their sphere of influence drawn around them.

The sphere of influence of *A* lies wholly in the liquid. The molecule is attracted equally in all directions as shown. *Hence there is no resultant cohesive force acting on it.*

The sphere of influence of *B* lies partly outside the liquid. The number of molecules in the upper half, attracting it upwards is less than the number of molecules in the lower half attracting it downwards. *Hence there is a resultant downward force acting on it.*

The sphere of influence of *C* is exactly half outside the liquid and half inside it. *Hence it is attracted downwards with the maximum force, perpendicular to the surface.*

If a plane *RS* is drawn parallel to the free surface *PQ* of the liquid at a distance equal to the molecular range, then the layer of the liquid between the planes *PQ* and *RS* is called the *surface film. Hence all the molecules in the surface film are pulled downward due to the cohesive force between molecules.* The downward pull, however, increases as we go up from the plane *RS* towards the free surface of the liquid.

If a molecule is brought from within the liquid to the surface film, work has to be done against the downward cohesive force and its potential energy increases. *Hence the potential energy of the molecules lying within the surface film is greater than the potential energy of the molecules lying below.* But a system in equilibrium always tries to have the *lowest potential* energy. Thus in order to decrease the potential energy of the molecules in the surface film the area of the film must be least. *This is why the free surface of a liquid always tends to have the minimum surface area.*

Q. 12.2. (*a*) Explain what do you understand by the angle of contact in the case of a liquid.
(*Bang. U.*, 1993; *Cal. U.*, 1992; *Meerut U.*, 1990)

(*b*) **Account for the curvature of the surface of a liquid in the neighbourhood of a solid surface.**

Ans. (*a*) **Angle of contact.** If a plate of glass is dipped in water with its sides vertical, it will be observed that water is drawn up along the plate and assumes a curved shape as shown in Fig. 12.3 (*i*).

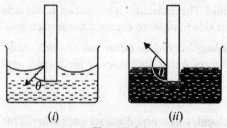

(*i*)   (*ii*)

Fig. 12.3

If on the other hand, the plate is dipped in mercury the surface is again curved but is depressed below as shown in Fig. 12.3 (*ii*).

The angle θ between the tangent to the liquid surface at the point of contact and the solid surface inside the liquid is known as **angle of contact** *between the solid and the liquid.*

The angle of contact for *pure water* and *clean* glass is zero, for ordinary water and glass it is 8° and for silver and water is 90°. For mercury and clean glass the angle of contact is *obtuse* being about 140°.

The angle of contact depends upon

(*i*) *the nature of the liquid and the solid.*

(*ii*) *the material which exists above the free surface of the liquid.* The angle of contact between mercury and glass when air is above mercury, is different from the angle of contact when there is a layer of water above mercury.

(*iii*) It is independent of the angle of inclination of the solid to the liquid surface.

To find whether the angle of contact between a liquid and a solid is obtuse or acute consider the case of a solid, liquid and air in contact. Let θ be the angle of contact of the liquid with the solid and

T_1 the surface tension for air liquid, T_2 for air solid and T_3 for liquid-solid surface respectively as shown in Fig. 12.4 (a).

For equilibrium

$$T_3 + T_1 \cos \theta = T_2$$

or
$$\cos \theta = \frac{T_2 - T_3}{T_1}$$

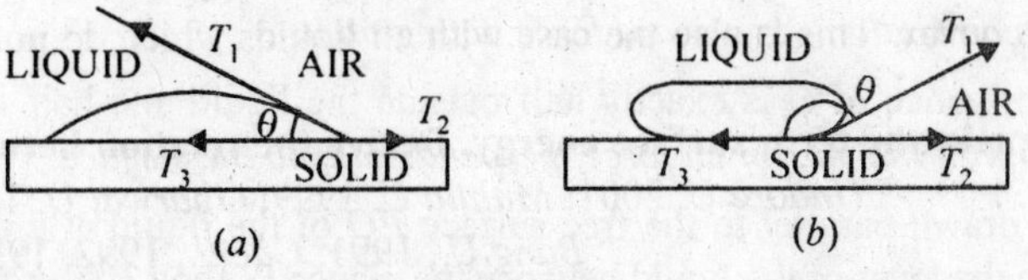

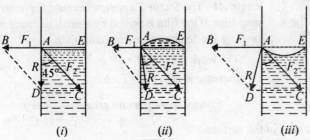

Fig. 12.4

Thus if T_2 is greater than T_3, $\cos \theta$ is positive and θ is less than 90° (acute), but if T_2 is less than T_3, $\cos \theta$ is negative and θ is obtuse as shown in Fig. 12.4 (b). If, however, T_2 is greater than $(T_1 + T_3)$, there will be no equilibrium and the liquid will spread over the solid.

(b) **Curvature of liquid surface.** Dip a glass capillary tube vertically in a liquid. Consider a molecule A on the surface touching the wall of the tube. In addition to its weight which may be neglected it is acted upon by the following forces:

(i) The outward pull due to the molecules of the solid wall called the *force of adhesion*. This force acts along AB at right angles to the wall of the tube as shown in Fig. 12.5 (i). Let it be denoted by F_1.

Fig. 12.5

(ii) The pull due to other molecules of the liquid, called the *force of cohesion*. The molecule A is pulled along AE by this force by the molecules in the surface, along AD [Fig. 12.5 (i)] by the molecules vertically below it with the same force and along directions lying between AD and AE by other molecules. The resultant of all these forces acts along AC and is inclined to the vertical at an angle of 45°. Let this be denoted by F_2. The two forces F_1 and F_2 are thus inclined at an angle of 135°.

The direction of resultant R of the forces F_1 and F_2 depends upon the magnitude of F_1 and F_2.

(1) If $F_1 = F_2 \sin 45° = \dfrac{F_2}{\sqrt{2}}$. The resultant acts vertically downwards as in Fig. 11.5 (i) and the liquid surface is plane.

(2) If F_1 is less than $\dfrac{F_2}{\sqrt{2}}$ as shown in Fig. 12.5 (ii), the resultant R *lies inwards* and the liquid surface will become *convex*.

(3) If F_1 is greater than $\dfrac{F_2}{\sqrt{2}}$, as shown in Fig. 12.5 (iii), the resultant R *lies outwards* and the liquid surface will become *concave*.

This is because a liquid cannot withstand any shearing stress, its surface at every point sets itself at right angle to the resultant force.

In the case of water the force of *adhesion* F_1 is greater than $\dfrac{1}{\sqrt{2}}$ times the force of *cohesion* F_2 and the meniscus is *concave*. This is also the case with all liquids which wet the walls of the tube.

In the case of mercury the force of adhesion F_1 is less than $\dfrac{1}{\sqrt{2}}$ times the force of cohesion F_2 and the meniscus is *convex*. This is also the case with all liquids which do not wet the walls of the tube.

Q. 12.3. (a) Explain the term surface energy. Derive the relation between surface tension and surface energy.   *(Indore U. 2001; Mithila U. 1999; Gharwal U. 1999; Vid. S.U., 1991; Bang.U., 1991; Cal.U., 1992, 1990; Meerut U., 1990)*

(b) Calculate the work done in spraying a drop of mercury of 1 mm radius into one million identical drops all of the same size. Surface tension of mercury is 550×10^{-3} Nm^{-1}.
(Cal. U. 2003; Bhopal U. 2004; Bang. U., 1995, 1993)

Ans. **(a) Surface energy.** The surface of a liquid is in a state of tension. The force of surface tension tends to decrease the surface area. Hence when the area of a liquid surface is increased work is done against surface tension. This work is stored in the surface as surface energy.

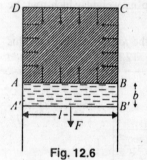

Fig. 12.6

Consider a wire frame $ABCD$ in which the wire AB is movable. Form a soap film over it. The wire AB is pulled inwards due to surface tension by a force $2T \times l$, where T is the surface tension and l is the length AB. The factor 2 appears because there are two surfaces of the soap film. If the film is pulled by a small distance b to the position $A'B'$ keeping the temperature constant, then

The work done $= 2T \times l \times b$

Increase in area $= 2 \times l \times b$

$\therefore$ Energy spent per unit area $= \dfrac{2Tlb}{2lb} = T$

This energy is stored in the surface.

Hence the surface energy per unit area of a surface is numerically equal to the surface tension.

(b) Radius of big drop $= 1$ mm $= 10^{-3}$ m   Surface tension $T = 550 \times 10^{-3}$ Nm^{-1}

Number of droplets formed $= 10^6$

Let r be the radius of each small droplets, then   Volume of big drop = Volume of all small drops

$\therefore$ $\dfrac{4}{3}\pi R^3 = 10^6 \times \dfrac{4}{3}\pi r^3$

or $R = 100\, r$

$\therefore$ $r = \dfrac{10^{-3}}{100} = 10^{-5}$ m

Surface area of big drop $= 4\pi \times (10^{-3})^2 = 4\pi \times 10^{-6}$ m^2

Surface area of all small drops $= 4\pi \times (10^{-5})^2 \times 10^6 = 4\pi \times 10^{-4}$ m^2

Increase in surface area $= 4\pi\,(10^{-4} - 10^{-6}) = 4\pi \times 10^{-6}\,(100 - 1) = 4\pi \times 10^{-6} \times 99$ m^2

Energy expended $= 4\pi \times 10^{-6} \times 99 \times 550 \times 10^{-3}$

$= 6843.3 \times 10^{-7}$ J $= 6.843 \times 10^{-4}$ J

Q. 12.4. What amount of energy will be liberated if 1000 droplets of water each of 10^{-8} m in diameter coalesce to form a one large spherical drop? Surface tension of water $= 75 \times 10^{-3}$ Nm^{-1}. (*Meerut U.*, 1990)

Ans. Radius of each droplet $= 0.5 \times 10^{-8}$ m

Volume of 1000 droplets $= \dfrac{4}{3} \pi \ (0.5 \times 10^{-8})^3 \times 1000$

If R is the radius of bigger drop formed, then

$$\frac{4}{3} \pi R^3 = \frac{4}{3} \pi \ (0.5 \times 10^{-8})^3 \times 1000$$

$\therefore \quad R = 10 \times 0.5 \times 10^{-8} = 5 \times 10^{-8}$ m

Surface area of big drop $= 4 \pi \ (5 \times 10^{-8})^2$ m^2

Surface area of 1000 droplets $= 1000 \times 4\pi \ (0.5 \times 10^{-8})^2$ m$^2 = 10 \times 4\pi \ (5 \times 10^{-8})^2$ m^2

Decrease in area $= 10 \times 4\pi \ (5 \times 10^{-8})^2 - 4\pi \ (5 \times 10^{-8})^2$

$$= 4\pi \ (5 \times 10^{-8})^2 \ (10 - 1) = 4\pi \times 9 \times (5 \times 10^{-8})^2 \ \text{m}^2$$

$\therefore$ Energy liberated $= 4\pi \times 9 \times (5 \times 10^{-8})^2 \times 75 \times 10^{-3} = 2.12 \times 10^{-14}$ J.

Q. 12.5. (*a*) **Deduce an expression for the difference of pressure on the two sides of a spherical drop.**

(*b*) **How will the problem be altered in dealing with a spherical soap bubble? Hence show that the pressure inside a spherical bubble of radius r exceeds that outside it by $\dfrac{4T}{R}$, T being the surface tension.**

(*Nag. U.* 2001; *Gauhati U.* 2000; *Cal. U.* 2003; *Gharwal U.* 1999; *Burd.U.* 1991;)

Ans. (*a*) All the molecules lying within the surface film of a liquid are pulled downwards due to the cohesive force between the molecules. *This downward force exerted per unit area of a liquid surface is called cohesion pressure.*

If the free surface of a liquid is *plane*, the resultant force on a molecule due to surface tension is *zero* as shown in Fig. 12.7 (*i*) and the cohesion pressure is negligible.

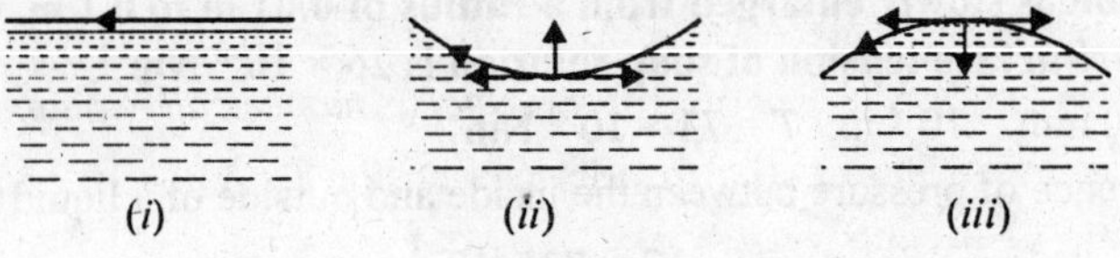

(*i*)   (*ii*)   (*iii*)

Fig. 12.7

If the free surface of a liquid is *concave*, the resultant force on it acts *outwards* (away from the liquid) as shown in Fig. 12.7 (*ii*) and the cohesion pressure is *decreased.*

If the free surface of a liquid is *convex*, the resultant force on it acts *inwards* (into the liquid) as shown in Fig. 12.7 (*iii*) and the cohesion pressure is *increased.*

Spherical drop. A spherical liquid drop has a convex surface as in Fig. 12.8 (*i*). The molecules on the surface, therefore, experience a resultant force acting inwards due to surface tension. Hence the pressure within the drop is greater than the pressure outside it by a certain amount, say p. Now consider the equilibrium of the upper half of the drop as shown in Fig. 12.8 (*ii*). There are two forces acting on it.

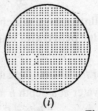 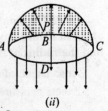

(*i*)   (*ii*)

Fig. 12.8

(*i*) *The upward force* on the plane face ABCD due to the excess pressure in the other half. If *r* is the radius of the drop, then this upward force

$$= p \times \pi r^2$$

(*ii*) The *downward force* due to surface tension acting round the edge of the circle ABCD. If *T* is the surface tension, then this force

$$= T \times 2\pi r$$

If we neglect the weight of the drop, the hemisphere is in equilibrium under the action of these two forces.

$$\therefore \qquad p \times \pi r^2 = T \times 2\pi r$$

or

$$p = \frac{2T}{r}$$

The treatment would be similar if we consider an air bubble surrrounded on all sides by a liquid.

In other words, the pressure inside a spherical *drop* exceeds that outside it by $\dfrac{2T}{R}$.

(*b*) **Soap bubble.** The case of a soap bubble is different from a spherical drop. It has air inside as well as outside it and, therefore, has *two surfaces* like a spherical shell.

The total force due to surface tension will be $2 \times T \times 2\pi r$.

Hence for equilibrium

$$p \times \pi r^2 = 2 \times T \times 2\pi r$$

or

$$p = \frac{4T}{r}$$

In other words, the pressure inside a spherical *bubble* exceeds that outside it by $\dfrac{4T}{R}$.

Thus the excess pressure inside a spherical drop or a bubble is inversely proportional to its radius *i.e.*,

$$p \propto \frac{1}{r}$$

Q. 12.6. (*a*) **What is the difference of pressure between the inside and outside of a spherical drop of water of radius 1 mm? Surface tension of water = 73×10^{-3} Nm^{-1}.**

(*b*) **A soap bubble is slowly enlarged from a radius of 0.01 m to 0.1 m. Calculate the work done in the process. Surface tension of soap solution is 26×10^{-3} Nm^{-1}.**   (*Bang. U.*, 1996)

Ans. (*a*) $r = 1.0$ mm $= 10^{-3}$ m; $T = 73 \times 10^{-3}$ Nm^{-1}

If *p* is the difference of pressure between the inside and outside of a liquid drop, then

$$p = \frac{2T}{r} = \frac{2 \times 73 \times 10^{-3}}{10^{-3}} = 146 \text{ Nm}^{-2}$$

(*b*) As the radius of soap bubble is increased its surface area increases. Hence work done in the process = Surface tension × increase in surface area

$$= 26 \times 10^{-3} \times 4\pi [(0.1)^2 - (0.01)^2]$$
$$= 26 \times 10^{-3} \times 4\pi \times 99 \times 10^{-4} = 3.235 \times 10^{-3} \text{ J}$$

Q. 12.7. **A small hollow sphere which has a small hole in it is immersed in water to a depth of 0.4 m before any water penetrates into it. If the surface tension of water is 73×10^{-3} Nm^{-1}, find the radius of hole.**   (*Burdwan U.*, 1990)

Ans. Depth of water $h = 0.4$ m, Density of water $= 10^3$ kg m^{-3}

Excess pressure of water at a depth *h* metre

$$= hdg = 0.4 \times 10^3 \times 9.8 = 3.92 \times 10^3 \text{ Nm}^{-2}$$

If r is the radius of the hole, then before water enters into the hollow sphere, an air bubble of radius r will escape. Thus excess pressure inside the bubble

$$p = \frac{2T}{r} = \frac{2 \times 73 \times 10^{-3}}{r} \text{ Nm}^{-2}$$

Hence in equilibrium

$$hdg = \frac{2T}{r}$$

or

$$r = \frac{2T}{hdg} = \frac{2 \times 73 \times 10^{-3}}{3.92 \times 10^3} = 37.25 \times 10^{-6} \text{ m}$$

Q. 12.8. Calculate the excess pressure inside a soap bubble of radius 3×10^{-3} m. Surface tension of soap solution is 20×10^{-3} Nm^{-1}. Also calculate surface energy.

(Bang. U., 1995; Cal. U., 1992)

Ans. Radius of soap bubble = 3×10^{-3} m; Surface Tension $T = 20 \times 10^{-3}$ Nm^{-1}

Excess pressure $p = \dfrac{4T}{r} = \dfrac{4 \times 20 \times 10^{-3}}{3 \times 10^{-3}} = 26.67$ Nm^{-2}

Surface energy = Surface tension × area of surface

$$= 4\pi r^2 T = 4\pi \times 9 \times 10^{-6} \times 20 \times 10^{-3}$$

$$= 22.62 \times 10^{-7} \text{ Joule.}$$

Exercise. *Calculate the work done in blowing a soap bubble of radius 10 cm and surface tension 30 dynes per cm.*   *(Gharwal U. 1999)*

Hint. Work done = Surface tension × area of surface.

A soap bubble has two surfaces.

∴ Work done = 2 × surface tension × area of surface

$$= 2 \times T \times 4\pi r^2 = 2 \times 30 \times 4 \times \frac{22}{7} \times 10 \times 10$$

$$= 7.54 \times 10^4 \text{erg} = 7.54 \times 10^{-3} \text{ J}$$

Q. 12.9. A spherical bubble is rising slowly through a column of mercury in a long vertical tube. If the radius of bubble at a depth of 1.24 m is 0.1 mm, calculate the depth at which the radius will be 0.12 mm. Surface tension of mercury is 560×10^{-3} Nm^{-1}, atmospheric pressure = 1 Standard atmosphere and density of mercury = 13.6×10^3 Kg m^{-3}.

Ans. Total pressure of mercury at a depth of 1.24 m

$$= (1.24 + 0.76)\ 13.6 \times 10^3 \times 9.8 = 266.56 \times 10^3 \text{ N-m}^{-2}$$

Radius of air bubble r_1 = 0.1 mm = 0.1×10^{-3} m

Surface tension of mercury $T = 560 \times 10^{-3}$ Nm^{-1}

Excess pressure inside the bubble $= \dfrac{2T}{r_1} = \dfrac{2 \times 560 \times 10^{-3}}{0.1 \times 10^{-3}} = 11.2 \times 10^3$ Nm^{-2}

Total pressure of air in the bubble,

$$P_1 = 266.56 \times 10^3 + 11.2 \times 10^3 = 277.76 \times 10^3 \text{ Nm}^{-2}$$

Volume of air bubble $V_1 = \dfrac{4}{3} \pi\ (0.1 \times 10^{-3})^3$ m^3

Let h be the depth at which radius $r_2 = 0.12 \times 10^{-3}$ m^3

Pressure at depth $h = (0.76 + h)\ 13.6 \times 10^3 \times 9.8$ Nm^{-2}

Excess pressure inside the bubble $= \dfrac{2T}{r_2} = \dfrac{2 \times 560 \times 10^{-3}}{0.12 \times 10^{-3}} = 9333.3$ Nm^{-2} = 9.333×10^3 Nm^{-2}

Volume of bubble $V_2 = \frac{4}{3}\pi (0.12 \times 10^{-3})^3$ m^3

Total pressure $P_2 = (0.76 + h)\, 13.6 \times 10^3 \times 9.8 + 9.333 \times 10^3$

According to Boyles law $P_2 V_2 = P_1 V_1$

$\therefore\quad 10^3 [(0.76 + h)\,133.28 + 9.333] \times \frac{4}{3}\pi (0.12 \times 10^{-3})^3$

$\qquad = 277.76 \times 10^3 \times \frac{4}{3}\pi (0.1 \times 10^{-3})^3$

or $\qquad 133.28\,h + 101.293 + 9.333 = \dfrac{277.76(0.1)^3}{(0.12)^3}$

$\therefore\qquad 133.28\,h = 277.76 \times 0.57847 - 110.626$

or $\qquad h = \dfrac{50.05}{133.28} = 0.3755$ m

Q. 12.10. A wire ring 0.03 m radius is rested flat on the surface of a liquid and is then raised. The pull required is 3.03 gm wt more before the film breaks than it is after. Calculate the surface tension of the liquid.

Ans. When a ring is gradually raised out of the liquid, in addition to the weight an extra downward pull due to surface tension also acts. As the liquid touches the ring on the outside as well inside.

$\therefore$ Extra downward pull $= 2 \times 2\pi r T$

where r is the radius of the ring. This is on the supposition that the wire forming the ring is very thin so that the inside and outside radii are the same. Now

$$r = 0.03$$

$\therefore$ Extra downward pull $= 3.03$ gm wt $= 3.03 \times 10^{-3} \times 9.8$ N

$$\therefore\quad T = \frac{3.03 \times 10^{-3} \times 9.8}{4\pi \times 0.03} = 78.76 \times 10^{-3}\ \text{Nm}^{-1}$$

Q. 12.11. Show that the excess pressure acting on the curved surface of a curved membrane is given by $p = 2T\left(\dfrac{1}{r_1} + \dfrac{1}{r_2}\right)$, where r_1 and r_2 are the radii of curvature and T the surface tension of the membrane. (*Bang. U.,* 1993, 1990; *Cal. U.,* 1991)

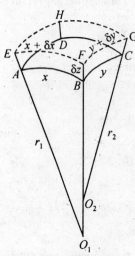

Fig. 12.9

Ans. Excess pressure on curved surface. If there is a curved liquid surface at rest, the inward pressure on it due to surface tension is balanced by an equal pressure acting outwards. To find the value of excess pressure consider a *small* curvilinear rectangular element $ABCD$ of a liquid surface. Its side AB is of length x and radius of curvature r_1 with centre at O_1 and the side BC is of length y and radius of curvature r_2 with centre at O_2 as shown in Fig. 12.9.

$\therefore$ Area of the element $ABCD = xy$

If the excess pressure on the concave side is p when the liquid surface is at rest, then the outward thrust on the element $ABCD = pxy$.

If the liquid surface is moved outward parallel to itself through a very small distance δz, such that the curvature in the two planes remains the same, then

$$\text{Work done} = pxy.\delta z$$

The side AB increases in length from x to $x + \delta x$ and the side BC from y to $y + \delta y$.

∴ New area of the element $EFGH$

$$= (x + \delta x)(y + \delta y)$$
$$= xy + x\delta y + y\delta x + \delta x \, \delta y$$

But $\delta x \delta y$ being the product of two very small quantities, can be neglected.

∴ Increase in area of the surface $= x\delta y + y\delta x$

Hence increase in surface energy $= T(x\delta y + y\delta x)$

Now the work done in moving the surface outward is equal to the increase in surface energy.

∴ $$pxy.\delta z = T(x\delta y + y\delta x)$$

or $$p = T\left(\frac{1}{y} \cdot \frac{\delta y}{\delta z} + \frac{1}{x} \cdot \frac{\delta x}{\delta z}\right) \qquad ...(i)$$

As the side EF is parallel to AB and AB is very small, the figures ABO_1 and EFO_1 can be taken as *similar triangles*.

∴ $$\frac{EF}{AB} = \frac{FO_1}{BO_1}$$

or $$\frac{x + \delta x}{x} = \frac{r_1 + \delta z}{r_1}$$

Subtracting 1 from both sides, we have

$$\frac{\delta x}{x} = \frac{\delta z}{r_1}$$

or $$\frac{1}{x} \frac{\delta x}{\delta z} = \frac{1}{r_1}$$

Similarly $$\frac{1}{y} \frac{\delta y}{\delta z} = \frac{1}{r_2}$$

Substituting these values in eqution (i), we have

$$p = T\left(\frac{1}{r_1} + \frac{1}{r_2}\right)$$

Now in the case of an air or a soap bubble there are two surfaces, an inner and an outer one, and the increase in area is twice as much as given above. Hence

$$p = 2T\left(\frac{1}{r_1} + \frac{1}{r_2}\right)$$

When the centres of curvature of AB and AC lie on opposite sides, one of the surfaces is convex and the other is a concave. The radii r_1 and r_2 of the two surfaces in such a case will have opposite signs and hence

$$p = 2T\left(\frac{1}{r_1} - \frac{1}{r_2}\right)$$

if r_2 is greater then r_1.

Q. 12.12. (a) Derive an expression for the height h through which a liquid of surface tension T will rise in a capillary tube of radius r. Explain clearly from where the energy comes when the liquid rises against gravity in the capillary tube.

(J.P.U. 1999; Cal.U. 1992, 1990; Vid. S.U., 1990; Burd.U., 1990; Bang.U., 1991)

(b) What will happen if the length of the capillary tube is smaller than h?

Ans. (a) Rise of liquid in a capillary. When a capillary tube, open at both ends, is dipped vertically in a liquid, the surface of the liquid inside the tube is generally curved. If the liquid wets the tube as in the case of water the surface is *concave upwards*, and the pressure in the liquid just below the meniscus is less than atmospheric pressure above it by an amount $\dfrac{2T}{r}$, where T is the surface tension of the liquid and r the radius of curvature of the meniscus. Hence the liquid rises in the capillary tube and the weight of the liquid in it balances this difference of pressure.

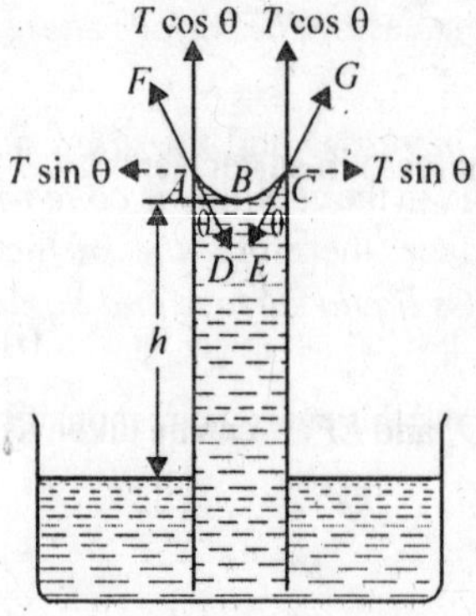

Fig. 12.10

Let h be the height of the liquid in the tube from the horizontal surface in the vessel to the tangent plane at the bottom B of meniscus, r the radius of the tube and ρ the density of the liquid.

The volume of the liquid between the liquid surface in the vessel and the tangent plane at $B = \pi r^2 h$.

If the capillary is *fine*, the meniscus is hemispherical and its radius of curvature is equal to the radius of the tube.

∴ Volume of the liquid in the meniscus = Volume of the cylinder of height r–volume of the hemisphere.

$$= \pi r^2 \times r - \frac{2}{3}\pi r^3 = \frac{1}{3}\pi r^3$$

∴ Total volume of the liquid $= \pi r^2 h + \dfrac{1}{3}\pi r^3 = \pi r^2\left(h + \dfrac{r}{3}\right)$

Hence weight of the liquid $= \pi r^2\left(h + \dfrac{r}{3}\right)\rho g$

The weight of the liquid is supported by forces due to surface tension. To explain this :

Draw a tangent plane AD to the liquid surface at any point A and let it make an angle θ with the vertical wall of the tube. Then θ is the *angle of contact* and the surface tension T at A acts *inwards* along AD. It, therefore, exerts a pull on the glass. According to Newtons's third law of motion, '*action and reaction are equal and opposite*'. Hence the glass pulls the liquid at A *outwards along AF* with the same force. The outward reaction due to surface tension can be resolved into two components.

(i) $T\cos\theta$ acting vertically upwards

and (ii) $T\sin\theta$ acting in the horizontal direction.

Considering the meniscus which touches the inner surface of the tube all round the circumference $2\pi r$, the horizontal components acting in one half of the circumference are equal and opposite to those acting in the other half and hence cancel each other.

∴ Total force acting vertically upward $= 2\pi r.T\cos\theta$

This vertically upward force supports the weight of the liquid acting in the downward direction.

∴ $2\pi r\, T\cos\theta = \pi r^2\,(h + r/3)\,\rho g$

or $T = \dfrac{r(h + r/3)\,\rho g}{2\cos\theta}$

If the capillary is very fine r is very-very small and $r/3$ can be neglected as compared to h. In such a case

$$T = \frac{r\,h\,\rho g}{2\cos\theta}$$

∴ Liquid rises through a height $h = \dfrac{2T\cos\theta}{r\rho g}$

For a liquid for which $\theta = 0$; $\cos\theta = 1$; $h = \dfrac{2T}{r\rho g}$

From where the energy comes. When a liquid rises against gravity in a capillary tube, its potential energy increases. Question arises, "From where does this energy come?"

Now, there are three media; glass, liquid and air and they have three surfaces of separation, *i.e.*, (*i*) glass-air surface, (*ii*) liquid-air surface and (*iii*) glass-liquid surface.

Each surface has its own surface tension which is different in different cases. *The surface energy per unit area of surface is always equal to its surface tension.*

As the liquid rises in the capillary tube the *glass liquid* surface *increases* and the *glass air* surface *decreases* by the same amount. Moreover the surface of the liquid in the capillary is *concave* instead of plane and hence there is an *increase* in the liquid air surface, therefore, *the surface energy of glass air surface decreases wheras the surface energy of glass liquid surface and liquid air surface increases.*

But, on the whole, there is a decrease in the total energy of the system and this energy is responsible for raising the liquid against gravity.

(*b*) Length of the tube smaller than *h*. The liquid in a capillary rises to a *maximum* height *h*, given by

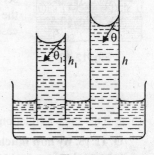

$$T = \frac{r(h + r/3)\,\rho g}{2 \cos \theta}$$

Neglecting the factor $r/3$, we get

$$T = \frac{rh\,\rho g}{2 \cos \theta}$$

or

$$\frac{2T}{r\rho g} = \frac{h}{\cos \theta} = \text{a constant}$$

as T, r, ρ and g are constants at a place for a given liquid and the capillary tube.

Fig. 12.11

When the length of the capillary tube is less than the maximum height to which the liquid can rise, the liquid will rise to the top of the capillary as shown in Fig. 12.11 (smaller tube) and in its attempt to rise further the radius of curvature of the liquid surface will increase. This will also cause an increase in the value of the angle of contact θ and the liquid will have no tendency to further increase its curvature when the new angle of contact θ_1 is such that

$$\frac{h}{\cos \theta} = \frac{h_1}{\cos \theta_1}$$

Q. 12.13. Calculate the height to which a liquid will rise in a capillary tube of radius 0.2 mm when surface tension of liquid is 26×10^{-3} Nm^{-1} and density 800 kg m^{-3}. Take angle of contact 0.

Ans. Here $r = 0.2$ mm $= 2 \times 10^{-4}$ m, $T = 26 \times 10^{-3}$ Nm^{-1}

$$\theta = 0, \quad \rho = 800 \text{ kgm}^{-3}, \quad g = 9.8 \text{ ms}^{-2}$$

Now

$$T = \frac{r(h + r/3)\,\rho g}{2 \cos \theta} = \frac{\rho g h r}{2}$$

$$\therefore \quad h = \frac{2T}{\rho g r} = \frac{2 \times 26 \times 10^{-3}}{800 \times 9.8 \times 2 \times 10^{-4}} = 0.033 \text{ m}$$

Q. 12.14. Explain why a liquid is either raised or depressed in a capillary tube.

Ans. The elevation or depression of a liquid in a capillary tube is given by

$$T = \frac{r(h + r/3)\,\rho g}{2 \cos \theta}$$

The factor $r/3$ is negligibly small. Hence neglecting $r/3$, we have

$$T = \frac{rh\rho g}{2 \cos \theta} \qquad \qquad \qquad ...(i)$$

where T is the surface tension of the liquid, h the elevation or depression of the liquid column in the capillary tube with respect to the liquid level in the vessel outside, ρ the density of the liquid, θ the angle of contact between the liquid and the solid material of the capillary and r the radius of the capillary tube.

When the liquid wets the sides of the capillary, it rises in the capillary tube as shown in Fig. 12.10. The weight of the liquid column is supported by the upward component $T \cos \theta$ of the reaction due to surface tension.

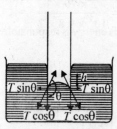

Fig. 12.12

When the liquid does not wet the sides of the capillary, it is depressed below the outside level, because the vertical component of the reaction of the force of surface tension acts in the downward direction as shown in Fig. 12.12. It is because the angle of contact θ is obtuse ($> \pi/2$). The liquid column moves downwards till the hydrostatic pressure over the area of cross-section of the capillary tube due to the level of the liquid outside balances the downward components of the reaction of the surface tension. In such a case again

$$2\pi r T \cos \theta = \pi r^2 \ (h + r/3) \ \rho g.$$

Neglecting $\dfrac{r}{3}$ we get the relation

$$T = \frac{rh\rho g}{2 \cos \theta}$$

which is the same as relation (i).

Q. 12.15. By how much will the surface of liquid be depressed in a glass tube of radius 0.02 cm if the angle of contact of the liquid is 135° and surface tension 547×10^{-3} Nm^{-1}? Assume the density to be 13.5×10^3 kg^{-3} and $g = 9.8$ m^{-2}.

Ans. $T = 547 \times 10^{-3}$ Nm^{-1}, $r = 0.02$ cm $= 2 \times 10^{-4}$ m

$\rho = 13.5 \times 10^3$ kgm^{-3}, $g = 9.8$ ms^{-2}

$\theta = 135°$ $\therefore$ cos 135 = $-$ cos 45 = $-$ 0.7071

Now $h = \dfrac{2T \cos \theta}{\rho g r} = \dfrac{-2 \times 547 \times 10^{-3} \times 0.7071}{13.5 \times 10^3 \times 9.8 \times 2 \times 10^{-4}}$

$= -2.924 \times 10^{-2}$ m

Negative sign indicates that liquid is depressed.

Q. 12.16. The two arms of a U-tube have diameters 2 mm and 1 mm. The tube is partly filled with water and is held with its arms vertical. Find the difference in the levels of water in the two limbs if the surface tension of water is 70×10^{-3} Nm^{-1}.   *(Cal. U., 1990)*

Ans. The rise of liquid in a capillary tube is given by the relation

$$\frac{2T \cos \theta}{r} = h\rho g$$

where T is the surface tension of the liquid, θ the angle of contact, r the radius of the tube, h the height of the liquid column, ρ the density of the liquid and g the acceleration due to gravity.

If we have a U-tube, the two limbs of which have different radii say r_1 and r_2, then

Rise of liquid in the limb of radius $r_1 = \dfrac{2T \cos \theta}{r_1 \rho g}$

Rise of liquid in the limb of radius $r_2 = \dfrac{2T \cos \theta}{r_2 \rho g}$

∴ Difference in the height of liquid column in the two limbs of the U-tube

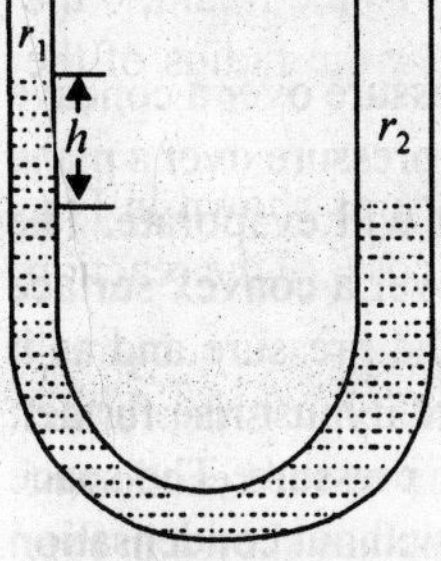

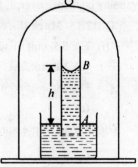

$$h = \frac{2T \cos \theta}{\rho g}\left[\frac{1}{r_1} - \frac{1}{r_2}\right]$$

Now $r_1 = 1$ mm $= 1 \times 10^{-3}$ m; $\quad r_2 = 2$ mm $= 2 \times 10^{-3}$ m

$$T = 70 \times 10^{-3} \text{ Nm}^{-1}; \theta = 0; \rho = 10^3 \text{ Kgm}^{-3}; g = 9.8 \text{ ms}^{-2}$$

∴ $\quad h = \dfrac{2 \times 70 \times 10^{-3}}{10^3 \times 9.8}\left[\dfrac{1}{1 \times 10^{-3}} - \dfrac{1}{2 \times 10^{-3}}\right] = \dfrac{2 \times 70 \times 1}{10^3 \times 9.8 \times 2}$

Fig. 12.13

$$= 7.1 \times 10^{-3} \text{ m} = 7.1 \text{ mm.}$$

Q. 12.17. (*a*) **Obtain the relation between the vapour pressure over a curved surface and that over a flat surface.**

(*b*) **What is the function of dust nuclei in the formation of clouds?**

Ans. (*a*) **Vapour pressure over a curved surface.** Dip a capillary tube vertically in a liquid which wets the tube. The liquid rises to a height h in it. Enclose the whole arrangement in a bell-jar and exhaust it of the air it contains. The liquid evaporates and equilibrium is reached when the space within the bell-jar is saturated with vapour.

Let P be the vapour pressure over the horizontal surface A and σ the density of the vapour, then

Vapour pressure *just above* the concave surface $B = P - h\sigma g$

If ρ is the density of the liquid, then

Pressure *just below* the concave surface $B = P - h\rho g$

∴ Pressure *just above* the concave surface B is greater then the pressure *just below* it and excess of pressure

Fig. 12.14

$$= (P - h\sigma g) - (P - h\rho g) = hg\,(\rho - \sigma)$$

As the tube is narrow the meniscus is *nearly hemispherical* and has a radius r equal to that of the tube.

∴ Excess of pressure just above the meniscus over that *just below it* $= \dfrac{2T}{r}$

Hence $\qquad \dfrac{2T}{r} = hg\,(\rho - \sigma)$

or $\qquad h = \dfrac{2T}{rg\,(\rho - \sigma)}$

Now vapour pressure *just above* the concave surface B

$$= P - h\sigma g$$

$$= P - \frac{2T}{r}\,\frac{\sigma}{(\rho - \sigma)}$$

Hence vapour pressure over the concave surface is less than the vapour pressure over the plane surface by an amount p given by

$$p = \frac{2T}{r}\frac{\sigma}{(\rho - \sigma)}$$

It can be proved in a similar way that the vapour pressure over a convex surface is greater than the vapour pressure over the plane surface by the same amount.

(b) **Function of dust nuclei.** It has been proved above that the vapour pressure over a concave liquid surface is less and over a convex liquid surface is greater than the vapour pressure over a plane surface. If we have a space *saturated* with vapour, a liquid drop placed in it will evaporate. The reason is that surface of a drop is convex and the maximum vapour pressure over a convex surface must be more than that on a plane surface. The drop evaporates to increase the pressure and as it evaporates its radius decreases and the value of saturation vapour pressure over it must rise further. The drop, therefore, evaporates more and more rapidly to increase the vapour pressure. The space then contains more vapour than that required for saturation at that temperature without condensation taking place and the vapour is said to be *supersaturated.*

If the atmosphere is absolutely free from dust or charged particles, a saturated vapour or even super-saturated vapour does not condense into drops, because as soon as a tiny drop is formed, the saturation vapour pressure required over it must be greater than the existing pressure. The drop again evaporates and no condensation takes place. When dust particles or ions are present the vapour condenses on them and the size of the drop formed even in the beginning is sufficiently large. The surface of a large drop is almost flat and it has no tendency to evaporate. As more and more of the vapours condense over it, its size increases and its tendency to evaporate is further reduced.

Q. 12.18. Mark the correct answer.

(*i*) The S.I. unit of surface tension is

    (*a*) Newton/m^3 (*b*) Newton/m^2 (*c*) Newton/m   (*d*) Newton

(*ii*) The angle of contact of mercury with glass is

    (*a*) 0   (*b*) less than 90°   (*c*) 90°   (*d*) more than 90°

(*iii*) Excess of pressure insider a bubble of radius *r* formed from a liquid of surface tension *T* is

    (*a*) $\dfrac{T}{r}$ (*b*) $\dfrac{2T}{r}$ (*c*) $\dfrac{3T}{r}$ (*d*) $\dfrac{4T}{r}$

(*iv*) The height to which liquid for which angle of contact $\theta = 0$ rises in a capillary tube is

    (*a*) $\dfrac{T}{r\rho g}$ (*b*) $\dfrac{2T}{r\rho g}$ (*c*) $\dfrac{T}{2r\rho g}$ (*d*) Zero

Ans. (*i*) *c*   (*ii*) *d*   (*iii*) *d*   (*iv*) *b*

EXERCISES

1. A sphere of water of radius 1 mm is sprayed into a million drops all of the same size. Find the energy expended in doing so. Surface tension of water = 72×10^{-3} N/m.

                                                                        [Ans. 8.96 × 10^{-5} J]

2. A U-tube made up of two capillary tubes of diameter 0.5 mm and 1.0 mm respectively contains water (S.T. 72×10^{-3} N/m). What would be the difference of levels between the two arms?   **[Ans. 1.47 × 10^{-2} m]**

13

Viscosity

Q. 13.1. State and prove Bernoulli's theorem for a liquid along a stream line.

(*Osm.U.*, 2004; *Nag.U.*, 2003, 2001; *Indore U.*, 2001; *Burd.U.*, 1992; *Cal.U.*, 1990)

Ans. Bernoulli's theorem. The energy of a liquid in motion at any point consists of the following three forms:

(*i*) Potential energy (*ii*) Kinetic energy (*iii*) Pressure energy.

(*i*) **Potential energy.** The potential energy of a liquid of mass m at a height h above the ground level $= mgh$

$\therefore$ P.E. per unit mass $= gh$

and   P.E. per unit volume $= \rho gh$

where ρ is the density or mass per unit volume.

(*ii*) **Kinetic energy.** The kinetic energy of a liquid of mass m moving witn a velocity v is given by

$$\text{K.E.} = \frac{1}{2}mv^2$$

$\therefore$ K.E. per unit mass $= \frac{1}{2}v^2$

and   K.E. per unit volume $= \frac{1}{2}\rho v^2$

(*iii*) **Pressure energy.** When a liquid flows through a pipe AB as shown, the volume V of the liquid entering A in a time t is equal to the volume of the liquid leaving B in the same time.

Let a_1 be the area of cross-section of the tube, v_1 the velocity of the liquid and P_1 the pressure exerted by the liquid at A and a_2, v_2 and P_2 the corresponding values at B, then

Force exerted by the liquid at $A = P_1 a_1$

Distance travelled by the liquid in time $t = v_1 t$

$\therefore$ Work done $= P_1 a_1 v_1 t$

But $a_1 v_1 t = V$

where V is the volume of the liquid entering A.

$\therefore$ Work done $= P_1 V$

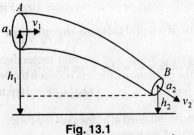

Fig. 13.1

This work is stored in the liquid and is known as its pressure energy.

Hence pressure energy at A $\qquad = P_1 V$

$\therefore$ Pressure energy per unit volume at $A = P_1$

and pressure energy per unit mass at $A = \dfrac{P_1}{\rho}$

If m is the mass of the liquid entering A in a given time, then

Pressure energy of the liquid at $A = m \dfrac{P_1}{\rho}$

Potential energy of the liquid at $A = mgh_1$

where h_1 is the height of the centre of the tube at A from the ground level.

Kinetic energy of the liquid at $A = \dfrac{1}{2} m v_1^2$

$\therefore$ Total energy at $A = m \dfrac{P_1}{\rho} + mgh_1 + \dfrac{1}{2} m v_1^2$

Similarly total energy at $B = m \dfrac{P_2}{\rho} + mgh_2 + \dfrac{1}{2} m v_2^2$

By the principle of conservation of energy

$$m \frac{P_1}{\rho} + mgh_1 + \frac{1}{2} m v_1^2 = m \frac{P_2}{\rho} + mgh_2 + \frac{1}{2} m v_2^2$$

or $\qquad \dfrac{P_1}{\rho} + gh_1 + \dfrac{1}{2} v_1^2 = \dfrac{P_2}{\rho} + gh_2 + \dfrac{1}{2} v_2^2 = \text{constant.}$ $\qquad$ ...(i)

or $\qquad \qquad \dfrac{P}{\rho} + gh + \dfrac{1}{2} v^2 = \text{constant}$

This is **Bernoulli's theorem.** *It states that the total energy of a small amount of an incompressible liquid flowing from one point to another remains constant throughout the displacement.*

Dividing (i) by g, we get

$$\frac{P_1}{\rho g} + h_1 + \frac{v_1^2}{2g} = \frac{P_2}{\rho g} + h_2 + \frac{v_2^2}{2g} = \text{constant}$$ $\qquad$ ...(ii)

or $\qquad \qquad \dfrac{P}{\rho g} + h + \dfrac{v^2}{2g} = \text{constant.}$

$\dfrac{P}{\rho g}$ is called the *pressure head, h the elevation head* and $\dfrac{v^2}{2g}$ the *velocity head* and the theorem may be put in the following form:

In streamline motion of a liquid the sum of the pressure head, the elevation head and the velocity head is constant at all points.

Q. 13.2. (*a*) **Calculate the velocity of efflux and range of flow of a liquid through an orifice in a reservoir.**

(*b*) **A tank contains water to a height H. Calculate the range of flow of water from an orifice at depth $\dfrac{H}{4}$, $\dfrac{H}{2}$ and $\dfrac{3H}{4}$ from the surface of water.** (*Indore U.,* 2001)

Ans. (*a*) **Velocity of efflux.** Consider an ideal liquid of density ρ contained in a tank provided with a narrow orifice O. Let H be the total depth of the tank, h the height of the surface of the liquid above O and h' the height of the orifice above the bottom of the tank.

Suppose v is the velocity of discharge. As the liquid flows out of the orifice it falls through a height h (from the top of the liquid surface upto the orifice) and its potential energy is converted into kinetic energy. If m is the mass of water flowing out

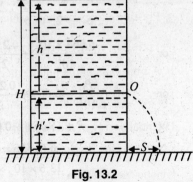

$$P.E = mgh \qquad \text{and} \qquad K.E = \frac{1}{2} mv^2$$

$$\therefore \qquad mgh = \frac{1}{2} mv^2 \qquad \text{or} \qquad v = \sqrt{2gh}$$

This is known as *velocity of efflux*.

Range of flow. As the liquid escapes through the orifice O, it has zero initial velocity in the vertical direction. If flows out in the form of a parabolic jet and strikes the ground at a distance S from the tank after a time t. The vertical distance covered by the jet in time $t = h'$

Fig. 13.2

$$\therefore \qquad h' = \frac{1}{2} gt^2 \qquad \text{or} \qquad t = \sqrt{\frac{2h'}{g}}$$

Hence the horizontal distance covered by the jet or range of liquid flow

$$S = vt = \sqrt{2gh} \sqrt{\frac{2h'}{g}} = 2\sqrt{hh'}$$

(b) (i) *When the orifice is at a depth* $\dfrac{H}{4}$

$$h = \frac{H}{4}, \ h' = H - \frac{H}{4} = \frac{3H}{4}$$

$$\text{Range} \quad S = 2\sqrt{hh'} = 2\sqrt{\frac{H}{4} \times \frac{3H}{4}} = \frac{\sqrt{3}}{2} H$$

(ii) *When the orifice is at a depth* $\dfrac{H}{2}$

$$h = \frac{H}{2}, \ h' = H - \frac{H}{2} = \frac{H}{2}$$

$$\text{Range} \quad S = 2\sqrt{hh'} = 2\sqrt{\frac{H}{2} \times \frac{H}{2}} = H$$

(iii) *When the orifice is at a depth* $\dfrac{3H}{4}$

$$h = \frac{3H}{4}, \ h' = H - \frac{3H}{4} = \frac{H}{4}$$

$$\text{Range} \quad S = 2\sqrt{hh'} = 2\sqrt{\frac{3H}{4} \times \frac{H}{4}} = \frac{\sqrt{3}}{2} H.$$

Q. 13.3. Water flows through a horizontal pipe line of varying cross-section. At a point where the pressure of water is 0.05m of mercury the velocity of flow is 0.25m/s. Calculate the pressure at another point where velocity of flow is 0.4 m/s. Density of water $= 10^3$ kg/m^3.

(Nag. U., 2001)

Ans. Here $P_1 = 0.05$ m of Hg $= 0.05 \times 13.6 \times 10^3 \times 9.8$
$$= 6.664 \times 10^3 \ Nm^{-2}$$
$$v_1 = 0.25 \ ms^{-1}, \quad v = 0.4 \ ms^{-1} \quad P_2 = ?$$

As the pipe is horizontal, according to Bernoulli's theorem

$$\frac{P_1}{\rho} + \frac{v_1^2}{2} = \frac{P_2}{\rho} + \frac{v_2^2}{2}$$

or $\quad \dfrac{6.664 \times 10^3}{10^3} + \dfrac{0.25^2}{2} = \dfrac{P_2}{10^3} + \dfrac{0.4^2}{2}$

or $\quad \dfrac{P_2}{10^3} = 6.664 + \dfrac{0.25^2}{2} - \dfrac{0.4^2}{2}$

or $\quad P = (6.664 + 0.03125 - 0.08)\, 10^3 = 6.61525 \times 10^3 \ \text{Nm}^{-2}$

$$= \frac{6.61525 \times 10^3}{13.6 \times 10^3 \times 9.8} = 0.0496 \ \text{m of mercury}$$

Q. 13.4. Show how Bernoulli's theorem is applied to measure the rate of discharge through city water mains. Explain the principle and application of venturi meter. (*Osm. U.* 2004)

Ans. Measurement of rate of discharge. When a liquid flows through a horizontal pipe, with a constriction, as shown in Fig. 13.3 the speed of the liquid increases as it enters the constriction whereas the pressure decreases.

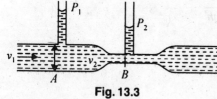

Fig. 13.3

Suppose water flows from a wide tube of area of cross-section a_1 at A into a narrow tube of area of cross-section a_2 at B, then the pressure of water at A, i.e., P_1 is greater than the pressure of water at B, i.e., P_2 whereas the velocity of water at B, i.e., v_2 is greater than the velocity of water at A i.e., v_1.

According to Bernoulli's theorem

$$\frac{P_1}{\rho g} + h_1 + \frac{v_1^2}{2g} = \frac{P_2}{\rho g} + h_2 + \frac{v_2^2}{2g} \qquad \qquad ...(i)$$

When the tube is horizontal $h_1 = h_2$

$\therefore \qquad \dfrac{P_1}{\rho} + \dfrac{v_1^2}{2} = \dfrac{P_2}{\rho} + \dfrac{v_2^2}{2} \qquad \qquad ...(ii)$

or $\quad P_1 - P_2 = \dfrac{\rho}{2}(v_2^2 - v_1^2) = \dfrac{\rho v_1^2}{2}\left(\dfrac{v_2^2}{v_1^2} - 1\right) \qquad \qquad ...(iii)$

Now the volume of water entering per second into the pipe at A = volume of water leaving the pipe at B per second.

$\therefore \qquad a_1 v_1 = a_2 v_2$

or $\quad \dfrac{v_2}{v_1} = \dfrac{a_1}{a_2}$

Substituting in (*iii*), we have

$$P_1 - P_2 = \frac{\rho v_1^2}{2}\left(\frac{a_1^2}{a_2^2} - 1\right) = \frac{\rho v_1^2}{2}\left(\frac{a_1^2 - a_2^2}{a_2^2}\right)$$

or $\quad v_1^2 = \dfrac{2(P_1 - P_2)\, a_2^2}{\rho(a_1^2 - a_2^2)}$

$$\therefore \qquad v_1 = a_2 \sqrt{\frac{2(P_1 - P_2)}{\rho(a_1^2 - a_2^2)}} = a_2 \sqrt{\frac{2(P_1 - P_2)}{(a_1^2 - a_2^2)}}$$

since the density of water is 1 gm. per c.c. in C.G.S. system.

$\therefore$ Volume of water entering at A per second or the rate of flow of water through the pipe

$$= a_1 v_1 = a_1 a_2 \sqrt{\frac{2(P_1 - P_2)}{(a_1^2 - a_2^2)}} \qquad\qquad ...(iv)$$

Venturi meter. This equation given above is used to determine the rate of flow of water through a pipe or the rate of discharge through city water mains. For this purpose a tube similar to that shown in Fig. 13.3 is used having a constriction between the inlet and the outlet sections of large diameters. Such a tube is called a **venturi tube.** A meter used to measure the rate of flow of water, which utilises a venturi tube and is calibrated with the help of the above equation is called a **venturi flow meter.**

Q. 13.5. A pipe is running full of water. At a certain point A it tapers from 0.6 m diameter to 0.2 m diameter at B. The pressure difference between A and B is 1 m of water column. Find the rate of flow of water through the pipe.

Ans. Let p_1, v_1 be the pressure and velocity at A and p_2 and v_2 the corresponding values at B, then

$$p_1 - p_2 = 1 \times 10^3 \times 9.8 \text{ Nm}^{-2}$$

Rate of flow at $A = v_1 \times$ area $= \pi \times 0.3^2 \times v_1 = 0.09 \pi v_1$

Rate of flow at $B = v_2 \times$ area $= \pi \times 0.1^2 \times v_2 = 0.01 \pi v_2$

For a steady flow $\qquad 0.01 \pi v_2 = 0.09 \pi v_1$

or $$\qquad\qquad v_2 = 9v_1$$

As the height remains the same, according to Bernoulli's theorem, we have

$$\frac{p_1}{\rho} + \frac{v_1^2}{2} = \frac{p_2}{\rho} + \frac{v_2^2}{2}$$

or $$\frac{p_1 - p_2}{\rho} = \frac{1}{2}(v_2^2 - v_1^2)$$

or $$\frac{10^3 \times 9.8}{10^3} = \frac{1}{2}(81 v_1^2 - v_1^2)$$

$$\therefore \qquad\qquad v_1 = \sqrt{\frac{9.8}{40}} = 0.495 \text{ ms}^{-1}$$

$\therefore$ Rate of flow $= \pi \times 0.09 \times 0.495 = 0.14 \text{ m}^3 \text{s}^{-1}$

Q. 13.6. Water issues into the air from a horizontal nozzle whose area of cross-section is 0.125 $\times 10^{-4}$ m^2. Its speed is such that 1.875 kg emerge in one minute. The water strikes a fixed wall which is at right angles to the nozzle and 0.5 m from it and then falls in a vertical plane. Calculate the vertical distance below the nozzle of the point where the jet strikes the wall and the force which the water exerts on the wall.

Ans. Volume of water flowing out per second $V = \dfrac{1.875}{60 \times 10^3} = 31.25 \times 10^{-6} \text{ m}^3$

Area of nozzle $a = 0.125 \times 10^{-4} \text{ m}^2$

If v is the velocity with which water issues, then $V = av$

or $$v = \frac{V}{a} = \frac{31.25 \times 10^{-6}}{0.125 \times 10^{-4}} = 250 \times 10^{-2} \text{ ms}^{-1}$$

Distance of wall from the nozzle = 0.5 m

∴ Time taken by water to reach the wall $= \dfrac{0.5}{250 \times 10^{-2}} = 0.2$ sec

Vertical distance through which water falls in 0.2 sec

$$= \frac{1}{2} gt^2 = \frac{1}{2} \times 9.8 \times (.2)^2 = 0.196 \text{ m}$$

Hence the water jet will strike the wall at a point 0.196 m below the nozzle.

Force exerted on wall = Momentum imparted by water in one second

$$= \frac{1.875}{60} \times 250 \times 10^{-2} = 7.813 \times 10^{-2} \text{ N}$$

Q. 13.7 (a) Describe the working of a Pitot's tube.

(b) A Pitot's tube is fixed to a water pipe of diameter 10 cms and the difference of pressure indicated by the gauge is 4 cm. of water column. Find the volume of water flowing per second through the pipe.   (Os. U., 1997)

Ans. (a) Pitot's tube. It is a device used for the measurement of the velocity of liquids or gases through pipes. The working of Pitot's tube is based upon Bernoulli's principle. It consists of a U-tube having small aperture at the ends X and Y. The plane of the aperture at X is parallel to the direction of flow of the liquid and that of the aperture at Y is perpendicular to the direction of flow. If the pipe is horizontal, then the plane of the aperture at X is horizontal and that at Y is vertical.

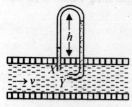

Fig. 13.4 (a)

Suppose the velocity of flow of the liquid in the pipe is v and pressure head (or static pressure) is P_x. The velocity of the liquid falls rapidly to zero as it enters the aperture at Y and hence the velocity head falls to zero so that the pressure head is very much increased, say to P_y.

Applying Bernoulli's theorem for horizontal flow to points X and Y, we have

$$\frac{P_x}{\rho g} + h + \frac{v^2}{2g} = \frac{P_y}{\rho g} + h + 0$$

or

$$P_x + \frac{1}{2} \rho v^2 = P_y$$

∴

$$v = \sqrt{\frac{2(P_y - P_x)}{\rho}}$$

Now $P_y - P_x = h\rho g$ where h is the difference in heights of the liquid column in the two limbs of Pitot's tube.

Hence

$$v = \sqrt{2gh}$$

The device is sometimes calibrated to read the value of velocity v directly and is then known as *speed indicator.*

The arrangement for finding the velocity of flow of gases is shown in Fig. 13.4 (b). Here again

$$v = \sqrt{\frac{2(P_y - P_x)}{\rho}}$$

where ρ is the density of the gas. If d is the density of the liquid (usually mercury) in Pitot's tube, then

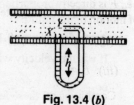

Fig. 13.4 (b)

$$P_y - P_x = hdg$$

and
$$v = \sqrt{\frac{2\,hdg}{\rho}}$$

(b) Diameter of the pipe $D = 10$ cm $= 0.1$ m

Difference of pressure $P_y - P_x = h = 4$ cm of water column $= 0.04$ m of water column

∴   Velocity of flow $v = \sqrt{2gh} = \sqrt{2 \times 9.8 \times 0.04} = 28 \times 10^{-3/2}$ ms^{-1}

Volume of water flowing per second through the pipe

$$Q = v \times a \times t$$

where a is the area of cross-section and t is the time.

Now
$$a = \frac{\pi D^2}{4} = \frac{\pi}{4} \times (0.1)^2 = \frac{\pi}{4} \times 10^{-2} \text{ m}^{-2}$$

$$t = 1 \text{sec.}$$

∴
$$Q = 28 \times 10^{-3/2} \times \frac{\pi}{4} \times 10^{-2} \times 1 = 21.994 \times 10^{-7/2} \text{m}^3$$

$$= 69.56 \times 10^{-3} \text{m}^3$$

Q. 13.8. Explain the term viscosity and coefficient of viscosity. Give the dimensions of coefficient of viscosity.   (*Bhopal U.*, 2004; *Nag. U.*, 2003, 2001; *Gharwal U., 2000;*
Meerut. U. 2006; *Bang. U.*, 1996, 1990; *A.U.*, 1994)

Ans. Viscosity. When the motion of a liquid over a horizontal solid surface is slow and steady, its layer in contact with the solid surface is stationary. In other words, its velocity along the sufrace is zero. The velocity of any other layer is proportional to its distance from the stationary layer and is maximum for the topmost layer.

If we consider any particular layer of the liquid, we find that the layer *immediately above it is moving faster* than the layer *immediately below it.*

Hence the upper layer tends to increase the velocity of the lower layer whereas the lower layer tends to decrease the velocity of the upper layer. The two layers together tend to destroy their relative motion as if there is some backward dragging force acting tangentially on the layers. Consequently, if a relative velocity is to be maintained between the two layers of a liquid, an external force is required to ovecome this backward drag.

This property by virtue of which a liquid opposes relative motion between its different layers is called viscosity.

Coefficient of viscosity. Let a layer *RS* of a liquid move with velocity v relative to a parallel layer *PQ* which is at a distance r from it. Let the force on an area A required to produce this motion be F. This force must act on *RS* in the direction of motion. An equal force will, therefore, act on it in the oppostie direction due to viscosity. This backward dragging force F depends upon the following factors:

  (*i*) $F \propto - v$

i.e., F is directly proportional to the relative velocity v and acts in a direction opposite to the direction of motion of the liquid.

  (*ii*) $F \propto A$ and

  (*iii*) $F \propto \dfrac{1}{r}$

Combining all these factors, we have

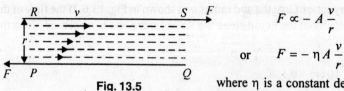

Fig. 13.5

$$F \propto - A \frac{v}{r}$$

or $\quad F = - \eta A \frac{v}{r}$

where η is a constant depending upon the nature of the liquid and is called the **coefficient of viscosity**. If the two layers are very close together, then denoting the distance between them by dr and relative velocity by dv, we get

$$F = - \eta A \frac{dv}{dr}$$

$\frac{dv}{dr}$ is called the **velocity gradient** or the rate of change of velocity with distance.

If $\qquad A = 1$ and $\frac{dv}{dr} = 1$, then

$$F = \eta \text{ (numerically)}.$$

The coefficient of viscosity is thus defined as the tangential force per unit area required to maintain a unit velocity gradient, i.e., a unit relative velocity between two layers a unit distance apart.

Unit. A fluid has a viscosity of one **poise** if a tangential force of 1 dyne per square cm is required to maintain a relative velocity of 1 cm per second between two layers 1 cm apart. The S.I. unit of viscosity is a **Decapoise.** A fluid has a viscosity of one **decapoise** if a tangential force of 1 Newton per square metre is required to maintain a relative velocity of 1 metre per second between two layers one metre apart.

Now $\qquad\qquad \eta = \dfrac{Fr}{Av}$

$\therefore \qquad$ Poise $= \dfrac{\text{dyne} \times \text{cm}}{\text{cm}^2 \times \text{cm per second}}$

$\qquad$ Deca poise $= \dfrac{\text{Newton} \times \text{metre}}{\text{metre}^2 \times \text{metre per second}} = \dfrac{10^5 \text{ dyne} \times 100 \text{ cm}}{10^4 \text{ cm}^2 \times 100 \text{ cm per second}}$

$\qquad\qquad = \dfrac{10 \text{ dyne} \times \text{cm}}{\text{cm}^2 \times \text{cm per second}} = 10 \text{ poise}$

$\therefore$ 1 Deca poise = 10 poise

Dimensions. The dimensions of viscosity are $[M^1 L^{-1} T^{-1}]$ as proved below.

$$\text{Viscosity} = \frac{Fr}{Av} = \frac{M^1 L^1 T^{-2} L^1}{L^2 L^1 T^{-1}} = M^1 L^{-1} T^{-1}$$

Q. 13.9. (*a*) **Give with necessary theory Poiseuille's method of determining the coefficient of viscosity of a liquid. State clearly the assumptions made.**

(*b*) **Why is correction of Poiseuille's equation necessary? Obtain the corrected version.**

(*Bhopal U.* 2004; *Utkal U.* 2003; *Nag. U.* 2003, 2001; *Meerut U.* 2003, 2002, 2001, 2000, 1993; *Indore U.* 2001; *Guwahati U.* 2000; *Gharwal U.* 2000; *J.P.U.* 1999; *Bang. U.* 1996, 1995; *Kan. U.* 1994, 1993; *A. U.* 1993; *Cal. U.* 1992; *V.S. U.* 1992; *Ranchi U.* 1991)

Ans. (*a*) **Poiseuille method.** Poiseuille determined the viscosity of a liquid by measuring the volume of the liquid flowing through a capillary tube.

Theory. Let AB be a capillary tube of length l and radius a as shown in Fig. 13.6. If the flow of the liquid through it is steady, the velocity of the liquid along the walls is zero and is maximum along the axis of the tube.

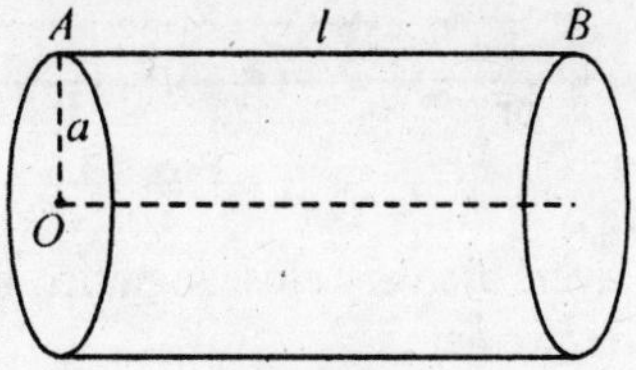

In Fig. 13.7 is shown a cross-section of the tube. Consider a cylindrical layer of the liquid co-axial with the tube of inner radius r and outer radius $r + dr$, shown separately in Fig. 13.7. The velocity of the liquid at a distance r from the axis of the tube is v and at a distance $r + dr$ is $v - dv$, so that $\dfrac{dv}{dr}$ is the *velocity gradient.*

Fig. 13.6

The surface area of the cylinder $= 2\pi rl$.

The liquid on the inner side of this cylindrical layer is moving faster while that on the outer side is moving slower.

∴ The tangential force exerted by the outer layer on the inner layer *opposite* to the direction of motion.

$$F = - \eta\, 2\pi rl\, \frac{dv}{dr}$$

The forward push due to the difference of pressure P on the two sides of the cylinder of radius r

$$= P \times \pi r^2$$

When the motion is steady, there is no acceleration of the liquid and thus, we have

$$- \eta\, 2\pi rl\, \frac{dv}{dt} = P\pi r^2$$

$$dv = \frac{-P}{2\eta l}\, r\, dr$$

Integrating both sides, we have

$$v = -\frac{P}{2\eta l} \times \frac{r^2}{2} + C$$

where C is the constant of integration.

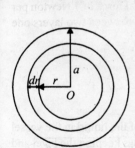

Fig. 13.7

But as the velocity of the liquid along the sides of the tube is zero, therefore if $r = a$.

$$v = 0$$

Substituting these values, we get

$$0 = -\frac{P}{2\eta l} \times \frac{a^2}{2} + C$$

or

$$C = \frac{P}{2\eta l} \times \frac{a^2}{2}$$

Hence

$$v = \frac{P}{4\eta l}\,[a^2 - r^2] \qquad \qquad ...(i)$$

This gives the velocity of flow at a distance r from the axis of the tube through the cylindrical layer.

The area of cross-section of the cylindrical layer of radius r and thickness $dr = 2\pi r\, dr$

∴ Volume of liquid passing per second through this area $dV = v.2\pi r\, dr$

Hence the volume of the liquid passing through the whole tube per second is given by

$$\int dV = \int_0^a 2\pi v r\, dr$$

or

$$V = \int_0^a \frac{P}{4\eta l}(a^2 - r^2)\, 2\pi r\, dr$$

$$= \frac{\pi P}{2\eta l}\int_0^a (a^2 r - r^3)\, dr = \frac{\pi P}{2\eta l}\left[\frac{a^2 r^2}{2} - \frac{r^4}{4}\right]_0^a$$

$$= \frac{\pi P}{2\eta l}\left[\frac{a^4}{2} - \frac{a^4}{4}\right] = \frac{\pi P a^4}{8\eta l}$$

$$\therefore \qquad\qquad \eta = \frac{\pi P a^4}{8 l V}$$

Thus if we know P, a, l and V the coefficient of viscosity can be determined.

Experimental details. A capillary tube AB of a uniform circular bore is fixed horizontally in the side of a *constant level vessel* as shown in Fig. 13.8.

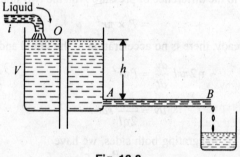

Fig. 13.8

The liquid enters the vessel through the inlet tube i and when the level of the liquid in the vessel rises above the open end of the outlet tube O, the excess of the liquid overflows keeping the level and hence the difference of pressure at the ends of the tube constant. A weighed beaker is placed below the free end B of the capillary and the weight w of the liquid collected in it in time t is found out. The volume V of the liquid flowing per second $= \dfrac{w}{\rho t}$ where ρ is the density of the liquid. If h is the height of the liquid in the vessel above the axis of the tube, the difference of pressure $p = h\rho g$. The length of the capillary tube is measured by a metre rod and the radius with a high power microscope, accurately.

Assumptions. (*i*) The flow is steady and stream line. The stream lines are everywhere parallel to the axis of the tube.

(*ii*) The pressure over any section normal to the axis of the tube is constant so that there is no radial flow.

(*iii*) The liquid layer in contact with the walls of the tube is at rest and the velocity of any layer of the liquid is only a function of distance of the layer from the axis of the tube.

(*b*) **Corrections.** In deducing Poiseuille's equation the following two factors have not been considered and therefore some corrections are necessary.

(*i*) **Length.** When the liquid enters the tube its motion is accelerated at the inlet end and as a result of this the velocity distribution becomes uniform and stream line only when the liquid has travelled a short length of the tube. This necessitates a correction for the effective length of the tube from l to $(l + 1.64\,a)$.

(*ii*) **Pressure.** When the liquid leaves the tube it has some velocity. Hence the entire pressure difference $P = h\rho g$ is not used up in overcoming the viscous resistance. But a part of it is spent in imparting kinetic energy to the liquid. The effective pressure is less than the actual pressure by an amount $\dfrac{V^2 \rho}{\pi^2 a^4}$.

Hence effective pressure $P_1 = h\rho g - \dfrac{V^2 \rho}{\pi^2 a^4}$

Substituting the value of P_1 instead of P in Poiseuille's equation

we get

$$\eta = \frac{\pi a^4\, h\rho g}{8V\,(l + 1.64\,a)} - \frac{V\rho}{8\pi\,(l + 1.64\,a)}$$

which is the corrected version.

Exercise. *Find the volume of the liquid flowing per second through a capillary tube.*

(Meerut. U. 2006)

Hint: Derive the relation.

$$V = \frac{\pi \rho a^4}{8\eta l}$$

as in the above question.

Q. 13.10. Deduce an expression for the distribution of velocity of a liquid flowing through a uniform capillary tube of circular cross-section. What is the nature of velocity profile?

(A.U., 1995; Meerut U., 2006, 1994)

Ans. For deduction of velocity of a liquid flowing through a uniform capillary tube see **Q. 13.9.**

The equation (*i*) for velocity

$$v = \frac{P}{4\eta l}\,(a^2 - r^2) \qquad ...(i)$$

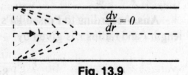

shows that velocity of flow at a distance r from the axis of the tube through the layer is a parabola as shown in Fig. 13.9. Hence the velocity profile is parabolic in nature.

Fig. 13.9

Q. 13.11. Calculate the mass of water flowing in 10 minute through a tube 0.1 cm in diameter, 40 cm long if there is a constant pressure head of 20 cm of water. The co-efficient of viscosity of water is 0.0089 C.G.S. units.

(Kan. U., 1997; A.U., 1995, 1993)

Ans. Here $l = 40$ cm $= 0.4$ m, $\eta = 0.0089$ C.G.S. units $= 0.00089$ deca-poise

$P = 20$ cm of water column $= 0.2 \times 9.8 \times 10^3 = 1.96 \times 10^3$ Nm^{-2}

Diameter $= 0.1$ cm or Radius $a = 0.05 \times 10^{-2}$ m

Rate of flow $V = \dfrac{P\pi a^4}{8\eta l} = \dfrac{1.96 \times 10^3 \times \pi \times (0.05 \times 10^{-2})^4}{8 \times 0.00089 \times 0.4} = 135.13 \times 10^{-9}$ m^3

Mass flowing/sec $= 135.13 \times 10^{-9} \times 10^3 = 135.13 \times 10^{-6}$ kg

Mass flowing in 10 min $= 135.13 \times 10^{-6} \times 600 = 81.078 \times 10^{-3}$ kg

Q. 13.12. In the Poiseuille experiment the following observations were made. Volume of water collected in 5 minutes = 40 c.c.; Head of water = 0.4 m; length of capillary tube = 0.602 m and radius of capillary tube = 0.52 × 10⁻³ m. Calculate the co-efficient of viscosity of water.

(Bang. U., 1994)

Ans. Volume of water collected per second

$$V = \frac{40}{5 \times 60} \text{ cm}^3 = \frac{40}{50 \times 60} \times 10^{-6} \text{ m}^3 = \frac{2}{15} \times 10^{-6} \text{ m}^3$$

Head of water $h = 0.4$ m

∴ Difference of pressure $P = h\rho g = 0.4 \times 10^3 \times 9.8 \text{ Nm}^{-2} = 3.92 \times 10^3 \text{ Nm}^{-2}$

Length of capillary tube $l = 0.602$ m

Radius of the capillary tube $a = 0.52 \times 10^{-3}$ m

Now co-efficient of viscosity $\eta = \dfrac{\pi P a^4}{8 l V}$

$$= \frac{3.142 \times 3.92 \times 10^3 \times (0.52)^4 \times 10^{-12} \times 15}{8 \times 0.602 \times 2 \times 10^{-6}} = 1.4 \times 10^{-3} \text{ Nm}^{-2} \text{ (or decapoise)}$$

Q. 13.13. A plate of metal 100 sq. cm. in area rests on a layer of castor oil 2 mm thick whose co-efficient of viscosity is 15.5 poise. Calculate the horizontal force required to move the plate with a speed of 0.03 ms⁻¹. *(Bang. U., 1992)*

Ans. Area $A = 100$ sq. cm. $= 10^{-2}$ m², $v = 0.03$ ms⁻¹, $r = 2$ mm $= 0.2 \times 10^{-2}$ m, $\eta = 15.5$ poise $= 1.55$ decapoise

Horizontal viscous force $F = -\eta A \dfrac{v}{r} = \dfrac{-1.55 \times 10^{-2} \times 0.03}{0.2 \times 10^{-2}} = -0.2325$ N

∴ External force required = 0.2325 N

Q. 13.14. If two capillaries of radii r_1 and r_2 and length l_1 and l_2 are joined in series, derive an expression for the rate of flow of the liquid through the arrangement using Poiseuille's formula.

(Kan. U., 1994; A.U., 1994; Meerut U., 1991)

Ans. According to Poiseuille's formula, the rate of flow V of a liquid through a capillary tube of length l and radius r is given by

$$V = \frac{\pi p r^4}{8 \eta l}$$

where p is the pressure difference across the ends of the tube and η the co-efficient of viscosity.

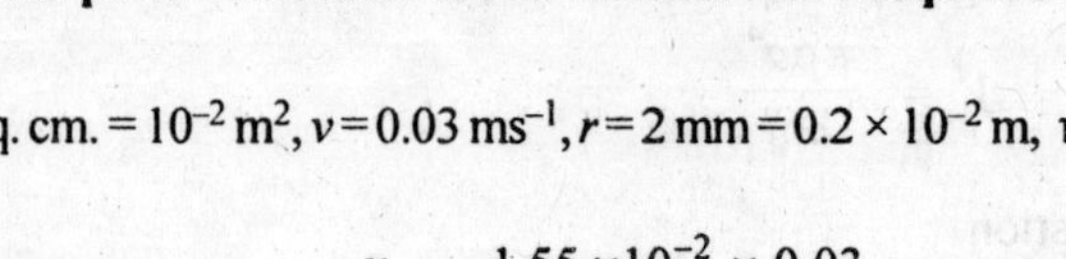

Fig. 13.10

Consider two capillaries of lengths l_1 and l_2 having radii r_1 and r_2 respectively connected in series. If p_1 is the pressure difference between the ends of capillary AB and p_2 that between the ends of the capillary BC, then as the same volume of liquid is flowing through each of the capillaries

$$V = \frac{\pi p_1 r_1^4}{8 \eta l_1} = \frac{\pi p_2 r_2^4}{8 \eta l_2}$$

So that $\qquad P_1 = \dfrac{8\eta l_1}{\pi r_1^4} V$ and $P_2 = \dfrac{8\eta l_2}{\pi r_2^4} V$

If p is the effective pressure across the ends A and C, then

$$p = p_1 + p_2 = \left(\dfrac{8\eta l_1}{\pi r_1^4} + \dfrac{8\eta l_2}{\pi r_2^4} \right) V$$

$\therefore$ Rate of flow $\qquad V = \dfrac{\pi p}{8\eta \left(\dfrac{l_1}{r_1^4} + \dfrac{l_2}{r_2^4} \right)}$

Q. 13.15. A horizontal tube of 1 mm bore is joined to another horizontal tube of 0.5 mm bore. Water enters at the free end of the first tube at a pressure equal to 0.5 m of water above the atmospheric pressure and leaves at the free end of the second tube at the atmospheric pressure. Calculate the pressure at the junction of the tubes if the lengths of the tubes are equal.

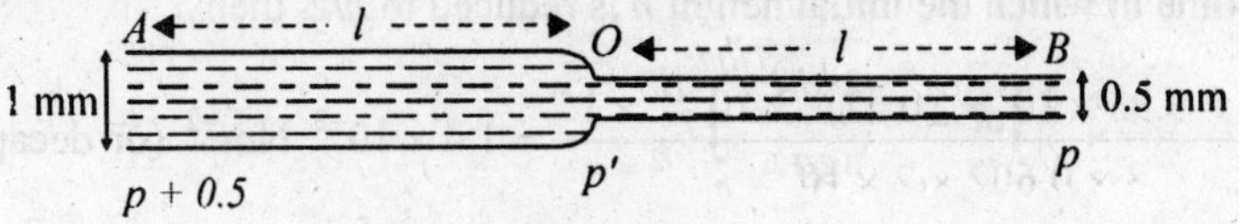

Fig. 13.11

Ans. According to Poiseuille's equation $V = \dfrac{\pi P a^4}{8\eta l}$

If p' is the pressure at the junction O of the two tubes each of length l, then difference of pressure between A and $O = p + 0.5 - p'$

$\therefore$ Volume of water flowing through AO per second

$$= \dfrac{\pi (p + 0.5 - p') (0.5 \times 10^{-3})^4}{8\eta l}$$

Difference of pressure between O and $B = p' - p$

$\therefore$ Volume of water flowing per second through $OB = \dfrac{\pi (p' - p) (0.25 \times 10^{-3})^4}{8\eta l}$

As the two tubes are joined end to end, the volume of water flowing per second through them is the same.

$$\therefore \qquad \dfrac{\pi (p + 0.5 - p') (0.5 \times 10^{-3})^4}{8\eta l} = \dfrac{\pi (p' - p) (0.25 \times 10^{-3})^4}{8\eta l}$$

or $\qquad p + 0.5 - p' = \dfrac{(p' - p)}{16}$

$\qquad 17 (p' - p) = 8$

$\therefore \qquad p' - p = \dfrac{8}{17} = 0.47$ m of water column

Hence pressure at O is 0.47 m of water column.

Q. 13.16. A capillary tube of radius a and length l is fitted horizontally at the bottom of a cylindrical flask of cross-section area A. Initially there is water in the flask up to a height h. What time would be required for half the liquid to flow out, if the coefficient of viscosity of the liquid is η?

Ans. According to Poiseuille's equation the volume V of the water flowing through a tube of length l and radius a is given by

$$V = \frac{\pi P a^4}{8\eta l} \qquad \qquad ...(i)$$

As A is the area of cross-section of the vessel and h the height of water above the capillary tube.

$\therefore$ Pressure head $P = hg$ [$\because \rho = 1$ for water in C.G.S. system]

Suppose in a small time dt the level of water in the vessel falls through a height dh, then

Volume of water flowing in time $dt = A.dh$

$\therefore$ Rate of flow $V = -A\dfrac{dh}{dt}$

The negative sign shows that the height decreases with time.

Substituting the value of P and V in (i), we have

$$-A\frac{dh}{dt} = \frac{\pi h g a^4}{8\eta l} \quad \text{or} \quad dt = -\frac{8\eta l A}{\pi g a^4} \cdot \frac{dh}{h} \qquad ...(ii)$$

Let t be the time in which the initial height h is reduced to $h/2$, then

$$\int_0^t dt = -\frac{8\eta l A}{\pi g a^4}\int_h^{h/2} \frac{dh}{h}$$

$$\therefore \qquad t = -\frac{8\eta l A}{\pi g a^4}\left[\log_e h\right]_h^{h/2} = \frac{8\eta l A}{\pi g a^4}\left[\log_e h - \log_e \frac{h}{2}\right]$$

$$= \frac{8\eta l A}{\pi g a^4}\log_e 2 = 2.3026 \times A\,\frac{8\eta l}{\pi g a^4}\log_{10} 2$$

Q. 13.17. Distinguish between streamline and turbulent flow of a liquid. Discuss briefly the idea of critical velocity and explain the significance of the Reynold's number.

(*Meerut U.* 2003, 1992; *Osm. U.*, 2004; *Nag. U.* 2003, 2001; *Bang. U.* 2000; *J.P.U.* 1999; *Cal. U.*, 1991; *V.S.U.*, 1990; *Burd. U.*, 1992; *P.U.*,1994)

Ans. Consider a liquid flowing in a pipe and let the velocity of flow be v_1 at A, v_2 at B and so on as shown in Fig. 13.12. *If with time the velocity at every point in the liquid remains constant in magnitude as well as direction, then the flow is said to be* **steady**. In other words, in a steady flow each particle follows exactly the same path and has the same velocity as its predecessor. In such a case the liquid is said to have an orderly or a **streamline flow**. *The line along which the liquid moves when the flow is steady is known as* **streamline.** The tangent at any point on this line gives the direction of the velocity of flow at that point. A streamline, therefore, represents a fixed path curved or straight followed by an orderly procession of particles. In tubes of constant area of cross-section all the streamlines are parallel to the axis of the tube. The flow is streamline only as long as the velocity of the liquid does not exceed a particular value called the **critical velocity**. When the velocity is greater than the critical value the flow of the liquid does not remain steady but becomes **turbulent**. When the flow is unsteady or turbulent there are eddies and whirlpools in the motion and the paths as well as the velocities of the particles are continuously changing.

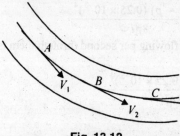

Fig. 13.12

Critical velocity. To show the existence of critical velocity experimentally, consider a tube AB about 2 centimetres in diameter in which the liquid (water) enters at C and leaves at D. At the end A of the tube AB there is a rubber cork through which passes an inlet tube I, drawn out into a capillary

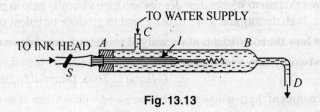

Fig. 13.13

about 10 cm. long and 0.5 mm. in diameter. The tube I is connected to a reservoir containing ink, the flow of ink through it is controlled by a screw type pinch-cock S. At C is conneted a constant level tank, the position of which is so adjusted that water flows very slowly through the tube AB. In this position it is seen that long column of ink escapes from the jet along the central axis of the stream. Under these conditions the liquid is having a streamline motion and all filaments move parallel to the axis of the tube. The head of water is slowly increased so that the velocity of flow also increases. It is seen that beyond a certain velocity the coloured band of ink is broken up by eddies and mixes with water. This state shows the turbulent flow.

Hence the **critical velocity** *of a liquid is that velocity of flow above which the flow ceases to be streamline.*

The expression for critical velocity v_c can easily be deduced by the method of dimensions. The value of v_c is found to depend upon

(i) η the coefficient of viscosity
(ii) ρ the density of the liquid, and
(iii) r the radius of the tube.

Hence the $v_c = K \eta^\alpha \rho^b r^c$ where K is a constant.

Substituting the dimensions of the various quantities, we have

$$[LT^{-1}] = [ML^{-1}T^{-1}]^a \ [ML^{-3}]^b \ [L]^c$$

$$[LT^{-1}] = [M^{a+b} L^{-a-3b+c} T^{-a}]$$

According to the principle of homogeneity of dimensions

$$a + b = 0; \ -a - 3b + c = +1 \ \text{and} - a = -1$$

$$\therefore \quad a = 1 \qquad b = -1 \quad \text{and} \quad c = -1$$

Hence $v_c = K \dfrac{\eta}{\rho r}$ \qquad or \qquad $\dfrac{v_c \rho r}{\eta} = K$

This constant K is known as Reynold's number. It is a pure numerical and is independent of the system of units used. Its value is about 2000.

Significance of Reynold's number. The significance of the equation

$$v_c = K \frac{\eta}{\rho r}$$

lies in the fact that a non-dimensional quantity of the form $\dfrac{v_c \rho r}{\eta}$ determines the process that takes place during the motion of a liquid through a tube and when this quantity attains a certain value the flow changes from a steady streamline flow to a turbulent one in which eddies are formed. Thus the critical velocity of a liquid is

(i) directly proportional to its viscosity,
(ii) inversely proportional to its density and
(iii) inversely proportional to the radius of the tube.

It, therefore, follows that narrow tubes, low density and high viscosity help in producing orderly motion and wide tubes, high density and low viscosity tend to produce turbulent motion.

Q. 13.18. (*a*) **Show how the co-efficients of viscosity of two liquids may be compared.**

(*b*) **How does the viscosity vary with temperature and pressure?**

(*Meerut U.* 2003; *Gharwal U.* 2000; *Cal U.*, 1992)

Ans. (*a*) The viscosities of the two liquids can be compared with the help of an apparatus known as **Ostwald's viscometer.**

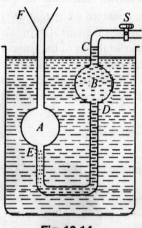

Fig. 13.14

Construction. The apparatus consists of two glass bulbs *A* and *B* joined by a capillary tube bent into a U-form. The other end of the bulb *A* is connected to a funnel *F* and that of *B* to an exhaust pump through a stop-cock *S*. The whole apparatus is placed inside a constant temperature bath.

Working. The liquid is filled into the apparatus through the funnel, so that it occupies the volume *CDE* of the apparatus where *C*, *D* and *E* are fixed marks as shown in Fig. 13.14. The stop-cock is now opened and the pump slightly worked so that the liquid rises a little above the level *C* when the stop-cock is closed. The pump is removed and the stop-cock is again opened. The pressure on both sides of the tube is now the same so that the liquid flows into the bulb *A* to equalise the level. A stop-watch is started when the liquid meniscus passes the mark *C* and stopped when it passes the mark *D*. The time t_1 is noted. Similarly the time t_2 taken by the second liquid to pass between the same two marks is noted. Then

$$\frac{\eta_2}{\eta_1} = \frac{t_2}{t_1} \frac{\rho_2}{\rho_1}$$

where η_1 and η_2 are the coefficients of viscosity and ρ_1 and ρ_2 the densities of the two liquids respectively.

Theory. The rate of flow of the liquid from the bulb *B* to the bulb *A* is regulated by the capillary tube *DE* and the volume *V* passing per second through it is given by the formula

$$V = \frac{\pi P a^4}{8\eta l}$$

where *P* is the difference of pressure at the two ends, *a* the radius and *l* the length of the capillary.

For the first liquid

$$V_1 = \frac{\pi P_1 a^4}{8\eta_1 l}$$

and for the second liquid

$$V_2 = \frac{\pi P_2 a^4}{8\eta_2 l}$$

$$\therefore \qquad \frac{V_1}{V_2} = \frac{P_1}{P_2} \times \frac{\eta_2}{\eta_1} \qquad \qquad ...(i)$$

But the pressure of the liquid in each case is proportional to the density of the liquid since all other factors remain the same *i.e.*,

$$P_1 \propto \rho_1 \text{ and } P_2 \propto \rho_2$$

$$\therefore \qquad \frac{P_1}{P_2} = \frac{\rho_1}{\rho_2} \qquad \qquad ...(ii)$$

If *Q* is the volume of the liquid flowing through the capillary in the first case in time t_1 and in the second case in time t_2, then

The rate of flow $V_1 = \dfrac{Q}{t_1}$ and $V_2 = \dfrac{Q}{t_2}$

$$\therefore \quad \frac{V_1}{V_2} = \frac{t_2}{t_1} \qquad\qquad ...(iii)$$

Substituting the value $\dfrac{P_1}{P_2}$ from (ii) and $\dfrac{V_1}{V_2}$ from (iii) in equation (i), we have

$$\frac{t_2}{t_1} = \frac{\rho_1}{\rho_2} \times \frac{\eta_2}{\eta_1} \quad \text{or} \quad \frac{\eta_2}{\eta_1} = \frac{t_2}{t_1} \times \frac{\rho_2}{\rho_1}$$

(b) **Variation of viscosity of liquids/gases with temperature.** The viscosity of liquids decreases with temperatue e.g., the viscosity of water decreases from 0.0101 poise at 20°C to 0.0047 at 60°C and that of castor oil from 24.18 poise at 10°C to 9.86 at 20°C. No definite relation has been found to exist between viscosity and temperature, but various empirical formulae have been suggested from time to time which are all approximate. One of these relations has the form

$$\log \eta = a + \frac{b}{T}$$

where a and b are constants and T is the absolute temperature.

In the case of gases, the viscosity increases with temperature. According to the kinetic theory of gases, the variation of viscosity with temperature is given by

$$\eta = a\eta_0 \, T^{1/2}$$

where a is a constant, η_0 the viscosity at 0°C and T the absolute temperature at which the viscosity is η. Sutherland taking into consideration the small force of attraction between the neighbouring molecules modified the formula to

$$\eta = \eta_0 \, \frac{aT^{1/2}}{1 + \dfrac{S}{T}}$$

where S is known as Sutherland's constant. For small ranges of temperatures this formula holds true for many gases.

Variation of viscosity with pressure. The viscosity of liquids, in general, increases with increase of pressure. For example, the vicosity of ether at 20°C is raised by about 60% when pressure is increased to 500 atmospheres.

In case of water at normal temperature, there is decrease in viscosity for the first few hundred atmospheres. For more viscous liquids the increase in viscosity with pressure is much more than in case of fairly mobile liquids.

For moderate pressures, the viscosity of a gas is found to be independent of pressure. But at very high pressures, the viscosity increases with increasing pressure.

Q. 13.19. A large bottle is fitted with a siphon made of a capillary glass tubing. Compare the time taken to empty the bottle when it is filled with (i) water of density 1×10^3 kg/m³. (ii) Petroleum of density 0.8×10^3 kg/m³ given the co-efficient of viscosity of water is half the co-efficient of viscosity of petroleum. (Meerut U., 1994)

Ans. Density of water $\rho_\omega = 1 \times 10^3$ kg/m³

Density of petroleum $\rho_p = 0.8 \times 10^3$ kg/m³

$$\frac{\text{Viscosity of water}}{\text{Viscosity of petroleum}} = \frac{\eta_\omega}{\eta_\pi} = \frac{1}{2}$$

Now
$$\frac{\eta_2}{\eta_1} = \frac{t_2}{t_1} \times \frac{\rho_2}{\rho_1}$$

or
$$\frac{\eta_\omega}{\eta_p} = \frac{t_\omega}{t_p} \times \frac{\rho_\omega}{\rho_p}$$

or
$$\frac{1}{2} = \frac{t_\omega}{t_p} \times \frac{1}{0.8}$$

∴
$$\frac{t_\omega}{t_p} = \frac{0.8}{2} = \frac{2}{5}$$

∴ $$\frac{\text{Time taken by water to empty the bottle}}{\text{Time taken by petroleum to empty the bottle}} = \frac{2}{5} = 2:5$$

Q. 13.20. (*a*) **Why does a body attain terminal velocity in falling through a viscous liquid?**

(*Cal. U.*, 1990)

(*b*) **Derive Stoke's formula for the velocity of a small sphere falling through a viscous liquid using the method of dimensions. Explain how this is utilised to determine the viscosity of a liquid like castor oil. Mention one more application of Stoke's law.**

(*Guwahati U.* 2000; *V.S.U.*, 1991; *Meerut U.*, 1995, 1990)

Ans. (*a*) **Terminal velocity.** When a body falls through a liquid (or gas) it carries along with it the layer of the fluid in contact and thus tends to produce a realtive motion between the layers of the fluid. The relative motion is opposed by forces due to viscosity. The *opposing force* increases with the velocity of the body and if the body is small it soon becomes equal to the *driving force* producing motion. The body then moves with a constant veocity, known as **terminal velocity.**

(*b*) **Stoke's formula.** For a small sphere falling through a viscous medium the opposing force is directly *proportional* to the velocity v and also depends upon:

(*i*)   radius r of the sphere

(*ii*) coefficient of viscosity η of the medium and

(*iii*) density of the medium d.

Combining all these factors, we have $F = Kvr^a\eta^b d^c$

where K is a constant and a, b and c are the dimensional coefficients. Now putting the dimensions of various quantities on both sides of the equation, we get

$$M^1L^1T^{-2} = (L^1T^{-1})(L^a)(M^bL^{-b}T^{-b})(M^cL^{-3c})$$

$$= M^{b+c}L^{1+a-b-3c}T^{-1-b}$$

Comparing the coefficients of similar terms, we get

$$b + c = 1 \qquad \qquad \qquad \qquad ...(i)$$

$$1 + a - b - 3c = 1 \text{ or } a - b - 3c = 0 \qquad ...(ii)$$

$$-1 - b = -2 \text{ or } b = 1 \qquad \qquad ...(iii)$$

Substituting $b = 1$ in (*i*), we have $c = 0$

and substituting $b = 1$ and $c = 0$ in (*ii*), we have $a = 1$

∴ $F = kvr\eta$

Stokes calculated the value of K to be 6π.

Hence $F = 6\pi\eta rv$

If the density of the material of the body is ρ, then downward force due to gravity on the small sphere $= \dfrac{4}{3}\,\pi r^3 \rho g$ and upward thrust due to buoyancy = weight of the fluid displaced.

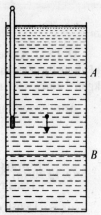

$$= \dfrac{4}{3}\,\pi r^3 dg$$

$\therefore$ Resultant downward force $F = \dfrac{4}{3}\,\pi r^3 (\rho - d) g$

Hence $\dfrac{4}{3}\,\pi r^3 (\rho - d) g = 6\,\pi \eta r v$ or $v = \dfrac{2r^2 (\rho - d)\,g}{9\eta}$

Determination of viscosity of a liquid. The viscosity of a viscous liquid like castor oil is determined by finding the teminal velocity of a small sphere of a suitable size falling through the liquid.

A small sphere of about one mm. radius is placed on the surface of the liquid almost at the centre. It begins to fall down and acquires a constant velocity after falling through a distance of about 10 to 15 cm. The time t taken by the sphere to fall through the distance AB is noted.

Fig. 13.15

$\therefore$ Terminal velocity $v = \dfrac{AB}{t}$

The radius of ~~the sphere is measured by~~ a travelling microscope. The coefficient of viscosity is then determined by the formula given above.

Application. Stoke's formula is used to find the rate of fall of an ion in an electric field and thus the charge on the ion is calculated as in Millikan's method.

Q. 13.21. Two drops of water of the same size are falling through air with terminal velocity 1 ms⁻¹. If the two drops combine to form a single drop, calculate the terminal velocity.

(*Vid. S.U.*, 1992)

Ans. Let r be the radius of each drop and r_1 that of the combined drop, then

$$4/3\,\pi\,r_1^3 = 2 \times 4/3\,\pi\,r^3$$

$\therefore$

$$r_1 = 2^{1/3}\,r$$

If v is the terminal velocity of each drop and v_1 that of the combined drop then according to Stoke's law

$$v = \dfrac{2r^2\,(\rho - d)\,g}{9\eta}$$

and

$$v_1 = \dfrac{2r_1^2\,(\rho - d)\,g}{9\eta}$$

$\therefore$

$$\dfrac{v_1}{v} = \dfrac{r_1^2}{r^2}$$

$$= \dfrac{2^{2/3}\,r^2}{r^2} = 2^{2/3}$$

$$= 1.588\ \text{ms}^{-1} \qquad\qquad [\because\ v = 1\ \text{ms}^{-1}]$$

Exercise. *Eight drops of water of the same size are falling through air with terminal velocity of 10 m/sec. If the eight drops combine to form a single drop what will be the new terminal velocity?*

(*Gharwal U.*, 1999)

Hint. $\dfrac{4}{3}\pi r_1^3 = 8 \times \dfrac{4}{3}\pi r^3$ or $r_1 = 2r$

$$\dfrac{v_1}{v} = \dfrac{r_1^2}{r^2} = \dfrac{2^2\,r^2}{r^2} = 4 \quad \text{or} \quad v_1 = 4 \times 10 = 40 \text{ m/s}$$

Q. 13.22. A steel ball of radius 2×10^{-3} m falls in a vertical column of castor oil. The co-efficient of viscosity of castor oil is 0.7 Nm^{-2} and its density 0.98×10^3 kg m^{-3}. The density of steel is 7.8×10^3 kg m^{-3} and $g = 9.8$ ms^{-2}. Find its terminal velocity.   *(Bang. U., 1994)*

Ans. According to Stoke's formula, the terminal velocity is given by

$$v = \dfrac{2r^2\,(\rho - d)\,g}{9\eta}$$

Now radius of the ball $r = 2 \times 10^{-3}$ m

Density of steel ball $\rho = 7.8 \times 10^3$ kg m^{-3}

Density of castor oil $d = 0.98 \times 10^3$ kg m^{-3} ; $g = 9.8$ ms^{-2}

Viscosity of castor oil $\eta = 0.7\,Nm^{-2}$

$$\therefore \quad v = \dfrac{2 \times (2 \times 10^{-3})^2\,(7.8 \times 10^3 - 0.98 \times 10^3)\,9.8}{9 \times 0.7}$$

$$= \dfrac{2 \times 4 \times 10^{-3} \times 6.82 \times 9.8}{9 \times 0.7}$$

$$= 84.87 \times 10^{-3}\,ms^{-1}$$

Q. 13.23. Mark the correct answer.

(i) The dimensions of viscosity are
    (a) $M^1L^1T^1$ (b) $M^1L^1T^{-1}$ (c) $M^1L^{-1}\,T^{-1}$ (d) $M^{-1}L^{-1}\,T^{-1}$

(ii) The velocity profile of a liquid flowing through a capillary is
    (a) straight lines   (b) circular arcs   (c) hyperbolic   (d) parabolic

(iii) Deca-poise is S.I. unit of
    (a) Surface tension   (b) viscosity
    (c) rigidity   (d) Young's Modulus

(iv) Two small balls of the same metal one having a radius twice the other are dropped in a tall jar filled with a liquid. The terminal velocity of the larger ball as compared to that of the smaller ball will be
    (a) same   (b) twice   (c) four times   (d) eight times

(v) Two capillary tubes A and B are of equal radius and equal length. The rate of flow through either tube under a pressure p is 8 cm^3/sec. If the two tubes are connected in series and the same pressure is maintained across the combination, the flow will be
    (a) 8 cm^3/sec   (b) 2 cm^3/sec   (c) 4 cm^3/sec

                                                              (Meerut U., 2000)

(vi) The viscous force on a small sphere of radius R moving in a fluid is proportional to
    (a) R^2 (b) R (c) $1/R$ *(Meerut U., 2000)*

(vii) To calculate the rate of flow of a liquid through a capillary tube which of the following is used?
    (a) Stoke's law   (b) Bernoulli's theorem
    (c) Poiseuille's law   *(Meerut U., 2000)*

Ans. (i) c   (ii) d   (iii) b   (iv) c   (v) c   (vi) b   (vii) c

EXERCISES

1. In an experiment with Poiseuillue's apparatus the following figures were obtained: Volume of water issuing out/mt. = 7.08 c.c.; Head of water = 34.1 cm.; Length of the tube = 56.45 cm.; Radius of the tube = 0.0514 cm. Find the coefficient of viscosity.

(*Burdwan U.,* 1990)

[**Ans.** 0.01377 poise]

2. A capillary tube of bore 1 mm. and length 20 cm. is fitted horizontally to a sufficiently big vessel kept full of alcohol of denity 0.8 gm./c.c. The depth of the centre of the capillary tube below the surface of alcohol is 30 cms. If the viscosity of alcohol is 0.012 poise find the amount that will flow in 5 minutes. [**Ans.** 72.19 c.c.]

3. A water drop is observed to fall through a gas of density 0.001 gm/c.c. with a constant velocity of 980 cm/sec. What is the radius of the drop? The co-efficient of viscosity of the gas is 2×10^{-4} poise. [**Ans.** 3×10^{-2} cm]

14 Classical Mechanics
(Lagrangian and Hamiltonian Formulation)

Q. 14.1. (*a*) **Explain the terms 'Degrees of freedom of a particle' and 'degrees of freedom of a system of particles'.**

(*b*) **What are constraints? Explain various types of constraints. What do you mean by** (*i*) **holonomic and non-holonomic constraints** (*ii*) **Scleronomic and rheonomic constraints? Explain with examples.** (*M.D.U.* 2003; *P.U.* 2001; *G.N.D.U.* 2004.)

Ans. (*a*) **Degrees of freedom.** *The number of independent co-ordinates required to completely specify the position of a particle gives the degrees of freedom of the particle.*

The position of a particle in space can be specified by three co-ordinates *i.e.* x, y, z in Cartesian co-ordinate system and r, θ, ϕ in spherical polar co-ordinate system. Such a particle has *three* degrees of freedom.

If the particle is restricted to move in a plane, its position can be specified by only two co-ordinates. The particle has *two* degrees of freedom.

If the particle is restricted to move only along a line, its position can be specified by only one co-ordinate. The particle has only *one* degree of freedom.

System of particles. If we have a system of N particles which are free to move in space, then each particle requires three co-ordinates to specify its position and therefore the number of co-ordinates required to specify completely the simultaneous position of all the N-particles will be $3N$. In other words, the number of degrees of freedom of a system of N particles in space is $3N$.

(*b*) **Constraints.** The motion of a particle or an object is, in general restricted in one form or another.

The geometrical restrictions imposed on the freedom of motion of a particle or a system of particles are known as constraints.

Examples (*i*) A constraint is said to have been imposed if

(*a*) a particle is restricted to move in a plane or

(*b*) a cylinder is restricted to move down an inclined plane

(*ii*) The motion of gas molecules in a vessel is restricted by the walls of the container as the gas molecules are constrained to move only within the container.

Classification of constraints. Various kinds of constraints can be classified into the following categories

(*i*) *Holonomic constraint* (*ii*) *Non-holonomic constraint* (*iii*) *Scleronomic constraint* (*iv*) *Rheonomic constraint*

(*i*) **Holonomic constraint.** *A constraint is said to be holonomic if the conditions of the constraint can be expressed in the form of an equation connecting the co-ordinates of the system and time.*

The general form of such an equation for a system of N particles subject to K constraints is given by

$$f_i\ (r_1,\ r_2\ \text{........}\ r_n,\ t\ ) = 0$$

or $\quad f_i\ (x_1, y_1,\ z_1;\ x_2, y_2,\ z_2;\ \text{.......};\text{.........} x_n,\ y_n,\ z_n \text{......}\ t\ ) = 0$ ... (*i*)

Here i denotes the i th constraint. It can take K values *i.e.,* 1, 2 .... K.

Examples (*i*) Consider a bead free to move in the X-Y plane. As it moves only two co-ordinates x and y vary whereas the third co-ordinate z will be zero for all times. The equation of this constraint will be

$$z = 0$$

(*ii*) Suppose now that the bead can only slide along a straight wire lying in the X–Y plane. This will impose another constraint on the bead. Let the equation of the straight line represented by the wire be

$$y = mx + c$$

where m is the slope of the straight line with X-axis and c the intercept on the Y- axis. Then the two constraints the co-ordinates x, y, z of the beam should satisfy are

(*i*) $z = 0$

(*ii*) $y = mx + c$ or $y - mx - c = 0$

Both these constraints satisfy Eq. (*i*). Hence both these constraints are holonomic.

(*ii*) **Non-holonomic constraints.** *A constraint is said to be non-holonomic if the conditions of the constraint cannot be expressed in the form of an equation connecting the co-ordinates of the system.*

Examples (*i*) The constraints involved in the motion of the gas molecules in a container are non-holonomic.

(*ii*) If a particle can move on or away from the surface of a sphere of radius a, then this constraint can be represented by

$$r^2 - a^2 \geq 0.$$

Clearly the constraint is non-holonomic.

(*iii*) **Scleronomic constraint.** *A constraint which is independent of time is known as scleronomic constraint.*

Examples (*i*) A rigid body is a system of particles in which the distance between any pair of particles remains constant with time. If we consider two particles i and j of the rigid body having position vector $\vec{r}_i$ and $\vec{r}_j$. then

$$\left| \vec{r}_i - \vec{r}_j \right| = \text{a constant} .$$

This condition represents a scleronomic constraint (This constraint is also holonomic).

(*ii*) Consider a simple pendulum of length l oscillating about the fixed point O in the X - Y plane and let the co-ordinates of the bob at point P at any time be $(x,\ y\ )$, then

$$x^2 + y^2 = l^2$$

The equations of constraint, therefore, are

$$z = 0$$

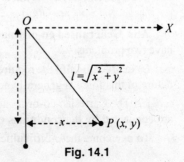

Fig. 14.1

$$x^2 + y^2 = l^2$$

As both these constraints are independent of time, the constraints are scleronomic (These two constraints are also holonomic).

(*iv*) **Rheonomic constraints.** *A constraint which is dependent on time explicitly is known as rheonomic constraint.*

Example (*i*) A simple pendulum suspended from a moving support so that the length of the pendulum changes with time is an example of rheonomic constraint.

Q. 14.2. What are constraints? How do they do effect the motion of a mechanical system? Take specific example to explain the forces of constraints. (*P.U.* 2000)

Ans. Constraints See Q. 14.1

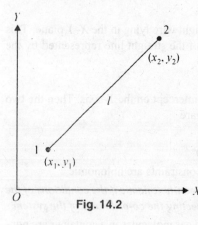

Fig. 14.2

Forces of constraint. Suppose we have a system which is subjected to some constraints. In order to enforce a constraint some force must act on the system. Such forces are known as *'forces of constraint'*.

Constraints reduce the degrees of freedom. Consider two particles marked 1 and 2 lying in the *X-Y* plane. The motion of this system of two particles can be described by four Cartesian co-ordinates (x_1, y_1) of particle 1 and (x_2, y_2) of particle 2. This system, therefore, has *four* degrees of freedom.

The particles are now connected by a wire of length *l*. The particles have thus been subjected to a constraint which requires that the distance between the two should remain constant = *l*, the length of the wire. This constraint can be put in the form

$$\left[(x_2 - x_1)^2 + (y_2 - y_1)^2 \right]^{1/2} = l \qquad ...(i)$$

Knowing x_1, x_2 and y_1, we can find the value of y_2 from Eq. (*i*). It means now only three co-ordinates are required to describe the motion of the system. The number of degrees of freedom have now been reduced by 1 *i.e.* from 4 to 3. We, therefore, conclude that

'*The degrees of freedom of a system subject to constraints is equal to the number of co-ordinates required to specify the configuration of the system minus the number of independent equations of constraints.*

If the system has *N* particles and is subjected to *K* constraints, then

Number of degrees of freedom of the system = $3 N - K$.

Q. 14.3. Define generalised co-ordinates and obtain expression for generalised displacement and generalised velocity. What is real and virtual displacement?

(*M.D.U.* 2008, 2003; *P.U.* 2001, 2000)

Ans. Generalised co-ordinates. To find the solution of the constrained motion of a particle, we have two problems:-

(*i*) In order to fulfil the requirements of the constraint a constraint force *f* must be introduced. The nature of this force is generally not known.

(*ii*) The Cartesian co-ordinates of the particles of the system are not independent because they are connected by the conditions of the equations of constraint.

To overcome these difficulties we make use of generalised co-ordinates.

The generalised co-ordinates are a set of independent co-ordinates so that if we change one co-ordinate other co-ordinates remain unchanged.

The number of generalised co-ordinates is equal to the number of degrees of freedom of the system. If a system has n degrees of freedom, then the number of generalised co-ordinates is also equal to n. These are q_1, q_2 ...... q_n each of which may depend upon time. If the system contains N particles, then the Cartesian co-ordinates of these N particles $(x_1, y_1, z_1), (x_2, y_2, z_2) .... (x_N, y_N, z_N)$ can be expressed in terms of $q_1, q_2 ... q_n$ which may also depend on time. The transformation equations are

$$x_1 = x_1(q_1, q_2, ... q_n, t)$$
$$y_1 = y_1(q_1, q_2, ... q_n, t)$$

....
....

$$z_N = z_N(q_1, q_2, ... q_n, t)$$

These can be combined into a single equation

$$\vec{r_i} = \vec{r_i}(q_1, q_2, ...q_n, t) \qquad\qquad ... (i)$$
$$\text{where} \quad i = 1, 2, 3 .... N$$

It has been proved in **Q. 14.2** that when K constraints are imposed on a system of N particles, then the number of degrees of freedom of the system is equal to $3N - K$. Hence there are $3N - K$ independent variables $q_1, q_2 ..... q_{3N-K}$. The position co-ordinates in such a case is given by

$$\vec{r_i} = \vec{r_i}(q_1, q_2, ...q_{3N-K}, t) \qquad\qquad ... (ii)$$

Generalised displacement. The generalised position vector of the i th particle according to Eq. (i) is given by

$$\vec{r_i} = \vec{r_i}(q_1, q_2, ...q_n, t)$$

where $i = 1, 2 ...... N$, N being the number of particles in the system. Suppose the q's change from initial values $q_1, q_2 ..... q_n$ to very close neighbouring values $q_1 + dq_1, q_2 + dq_2....., q_n + dq_n$, then the corresponding change in position vectors is given by

$$d\vec{r_i} = \frac{\partial \vec{r_i}}{\partial q_1} dq_1 + \frac{\partial \vec{r_i}}{\partial q_2} dq_2 + ... + \frac{\partial \vec{r_i}}{\partial q_n} \partial q_n + \frac{\partial \vec{r_i}}{\partial t} dt .$$

or $\qquad\qquad d\vec{r_i} = \sum_{j=1}^{n} \frac{\partial \vec{r_i}}{\partial q_j} dq_j + \frac{\partial \vec{r_i}}{\partial t} dt \qquad\qquad ... (iii)$

The subscript i refers to the particle and has values $i = 1, 2 ....N$ and subscript j refers to generalised co-ordinates and has values 1, 2, ...n. dq_j's are called the *generalised displacement* or *virtual arbitrary displacement*. If q_j is a cartesian co-ordinate, then dq_j represents, a *linear displacement* and if q_j is an angle, then dq_j represents an *angular displacement*.

Real and virtual displacement. Consider a particle falling freely under the action of gravity. Its displacement is directed vertically downward and takes place in a finite interval of time. Such displacements are known as *real displacement*. It is denoted by $d\vec{r}$ and given by

$$d\vec{r_i} = \sum_{j=1}^{n} \frac{\partial \vec{r_i}}{\partial q_j} dq_j + \frac{\partial \vec{r_i}}{\partial t} dt \qquad\qquad ... (iv)$$

A real displacement is, therefore defined as the small displacement which takes place along the trajectory of the particle and occurs in a finite interval of time.

The displacement of the particle is *virtual* if

(*i*) *it is not along the trajectory of the particle* and

(*ii*) *takes place in zero time.*

It is denoted by $\delta \vec{r}$ and given by

$$\delta \vec{r_i} = \sum_{j=1}^{n} \frac{\partial \vec{r_i}}{\partial q_j} \, \delta q_j \qquad\qquad \ldots (v)$$

Generalised velocity. *Generalised velocity is defined as the time derivative $\dot{q}_j$ of the generalised co-ordinates q_j.*

As proved in Eq. (*iii*), the generalised displacement

$$d \vec{r_i} = \sum_{j=1}^{n} \frac{\partial \vec{r_i}}{\partial q_j} \, dq_j + \frac{\partial \vec{r_i}}{\partial t} \, dt \qquad\qquad \ldots (vi)$$

Dividing both sides of Eq. (*vi*) by dt we get

$$\frac{d \vec{r_i}}{dt} = \sum_{j=1}^{n} \frac{\partial \vec{r_i}}{\partial q_j} \frac{dq_j}{dt} + \frac{\partial \vec{r_i}}{\partial t}$$

Now $\dfrac{dq_j}{dt} = \dot{q}_j$ is the time derivative of the generalised co-ordinate q_j and represents the *generalised velocity.*

Putting $\dfrac{d \vec{r_i}}{dt} = \dot{\vec{r_i}}$, we have

$$\dot{\vec{r_i}} = \sum_{j=1}^{n} \frac{\partial \vec{r_i}}{\partial q_j} \, \dot{q}_j + \frac{\partial \vec{r_i}}{\partial t} \qquad\qquad \ldots (vii)$$

If the generalised co-ordinate q_j involves both Cartesian and angle co-ordinates, the generalised velocity associated with Cartesian co-ordinates x is the corresponding linear velocity $\dot{x}$ and the generalised velocity associated with θ is the corresponding angular velocity $\dot{\theta}$.

Q. 14.4. Explain the principle of virtual work.   (*P.U.* 2000)

Ans. To explain the principle of virtual work we shall first define '*configuration space*' and '*virtual work.*'

Configuration space. Consider a system of N particles having n degrees of freedom. The instantaneous configuration of the system is specified by the values of n generalised co-ordiantes $q_1, q_2 \ldots q_n$. The n co-ordinates refer to a point in an n-dimensional space where each q forms a co-ordinate axis. *This n-dimensional space is known as configuration space.*

Virtual work. Suppose the configuration of N particles (1, 2, ... N) is specified by position vectors $\vec{r_1}, \vec{r_2}, \ldots \vec{r_N}$ and forces $\vec{F_1}, \vec{F_2} \ldots \vec{F_N}$ act on corresponding particles giving them virtual displacements $\delta \vec{r_1}, \delta \vec{r_2}, \delta \vec{r_N}$ respectively.

The work done by the forces acting on the system causing virtual displacement is called virtual work.

$\therefore$ Virtual work $\delta W = \sum_{i=1}^{N} \vec{F_i} \cdot \delta \vec{r_i}$ ...(*i*)

Principle of virtual work. Suppose a system is in equilibrium. Then the sum of all the forces acting on a particle say *i*th particle is zero *i.e.* $\vec{F_i} = 0$. As such the work done *i.e.* the virtual work is given by $\vec{F_i} \cdot \delta \vec{r_i} = 0$ ...(*ii*)

For the whole system Eq. (ii) becomes

Virtual work			$\delta W = \sum\limits_{i=1}^{N} \vec{F_i} \cdot \delta\vec{r_i} = 0$				... (iii)

Now, suppose that the system of N-particles is also subject to some constraints. The constraints on the system are due to forces exerted on the system by the agency enforcing the constraints. Therefore, the total force acting on a particle say ith will be the sum of the applied external force $(\vec{F_i})_e$ and the force of constraint $\vec{f_i}$ i.e.

$$\vec{F_i} = (\vec{F_i})_e + \vec{f_i}$$

Substituting this value of $\vec{F_i}$ in Eq. (i), we get

Virtual work			$\delta W = \sum\limits_{i=1}^{N} \left[(\vec{F_i})_e + \vec{f_i} \right] \cdot \delta\vec{r_i}$

or				$\delta W = \sum\limits_{i=1}^{N} (\vec{F_i})_e \cdot \delta\vec{r_i} + \sum\limits_{i=1}^{N} \vec{f_i}\, \delta\vec{r_i}$				... (iv)

If the force of constraint is perpendicular to the direction of motion of the particle, then

$$\vec{f_i} \cdot \delta\vec{r_i} = 0$$

Such constraints are known as *workless constraints*.

In such a case Eq. (iv) can be written as

$$\delta W = \sum\limits_{i=1}^{N} \left(\vec{F_i} \right)_e \cdot \delta\vec{r_i}$$				... (v)

The system of N particles is said to be in a state of equilibrium if the vector sum of all forces acting on each particle is zero.

In such a case		$\left(\vec{F_i} \right)_e = 0$.

Eq. (v), now becomes

$$\delta W = \sum\limits_{i=1}^{N} \left(\vec{F_i} \right)_e \cdot \delta\vec{r_i} = 0$$				... (vi)

This is known as *principle of virtual work.* This principle states that:

'If a system of particles with workless constraints is in a state of equilibrium, then the virtual work of the applied external forces becomes zero.

Q. 14.5. Explain the principle of virtual work and D'Alembert's principle.	(P.U. 2000)

Ans. Principle of virtual work. See Q. 14.4

D'Alembert's principle. Consider a system of N particles subject to constraints. Suppose a number of forces (say n) act on the i th particle, then the total force acting on the particle is given by

$$\vec{F_i} = \vec{F_1} + \vec{F_2} \ldots\ldots + \vec{F_n}$$

If $\vec{a_i}$ is the acceleration produced in the ith particle of mass m_i.

then				$\vec{F_i} = m_i \vec{a_i}$

or				$\vec{F_i} - m_i \vec{a_i} = 0$				... (i)

$m_i \vec{a_i}$ is the *effective inertial force* acting on the particle and $- m_i \vec{a_i}$ is known as 'reverse effective force'.

If $(\vec{F_i})_e$ is the external applied force and $\vec{f_i}$, the constraint force acting on the ith particle, then

$$\vec{F_i} = (\vec{F_i})_e + \vec{f_i}$$

Substituting this value of $\vec{F_i}$ is Eq. (i), we get

$$(\vec{F_i})_e + \vec{f_i} - m_i\,\vec{a_i} = 0 \qquad\qquad ...(ii)$$

According to Eq. (ii) '*The vector sum of all the forces (applied + constraint + inertial) acting on a particle of the system is zero*'.

Therefore, according to the principle of virtual work, we have

$$\sum_{i=1}^{N}\left[\,(\vec{F_i})_e + \vec{f_i} - m_i\,\vec{a_i}\,\right].\delta\vec{r_i} = 0$$

or

$$\sum_{i=1}^{N}(\vec{F_i})_e.\delta\vec{r_i} + \sum_{i=1}^{N}\vec{f_i}.\delta\vec{r_i} - \sum_{i=1}^{N}m_i\,\vec{a_i}.\delta\vec{r_i} = 0 \qquad\qquad ...(iii)$$

If the forces of constraint are *workless* or are at right angles to the direction of motion of the body, then

$$\sum_{i=1}^{N}\vec{f_i}.\delta\vec{r_i} = 0$$

In such a case, Eq. (iii) becomes

$$\sum_{i=1}^{N}(\vec{F_i})_e.\delta\vec{r_i} - \sum_{i=1}^{N}m_i\,\vec{a_i}.\delta\vec{r_i} = 0$$

or

$$\sum_{i=1}^{N}\left[(\vec{F_i})_e - m_i\,\vec{a_i}\right]\delta\vec{r_i} = 0 \qquad\qquad ...(iv)$$

This equation is known as D'Alembert's principle.

According to Newton's second law of motion

$$m_i\,\vec{a_i} = \vec{p_i}$$

D'Alembert's principle may, therefore, be also put in the form

$$\sum_{i=1}^{N}\left[(\vec{F_i})_e - \vec{p_i}\right].\delta r_i = 0$$

The equation representing D'Alembert's principle has the following advantages:

(i) The forces due to constraints disappear and are not involved in any way.

(ii) By including the '*inertial force*' the problem of 'dynamics' has been reduced to one of 'statics'.

Q. 14.6. Define generalised co-ordinates and obtain the expression for generalised force.

(*P.U. 2000; GauhatiU. 2000*)

Ans. For generalised co-ordinates **see Q. 14.3**

Generalised force. Consider a system of N particles under some constraints. Let the particles be denoted as 1, 2 .... N, their position vectors as $\vec{r_1}, \vec{r_2} ....\vec{r_N}$ at any time t and forces applied to corresponding particles as $\vec{F_1}, \vec{F_2} ......F_N$. If the system undergoes virtual displacement, then the virtual work done by the forces

$$\delta W = \sum_{i=1}^{N}\vec{F_i}.\delta\vec{r_i} \qquad\qquad ...(i)[\text{ See Eq. } (i)\text{ Q. 14.4 }]$$

Let n generalised co-ordinates $q_1, q_2 ..... q_n$ describe the system at any time t. Then the position vector $\vec{r_i}$ in terms of generalised co-ordinates is given by

$$\vec{r_i} = \vec{r_i}\,(q_1, q_2, ...q_n, t)$$

Suppose that q's change from initial values $q_1, q_2 ....q_n$ to very close neighbouring values $q_1 + \delta q_1, q_2 + \delta q_2, ..., q_n + \delta q_n$, then virtual displacement

$$\delta \vec{r_i} = \frac{\partial \vec{r_i}}{\partial q_1}\delta q_1 + \frac{\partial \vec{r_i}}{\partial q_2}\delta q_2 + \dots + \frac{\partial \vec{r_i}}{\partial q_n}\delta q_n + \frac{\partial \vec{r_i}}{\partial t}\delta t$$

Since we are considering virtual displacement which occurs in zero time, we have $\delta t = 0$

$$\therefore \qquad \delta \vec{r_i} = \frac{\partial \vec{r_i}}{\partial q_1}\delta q_1 + \frac{\partial \vec{r_i}}{\partial q_2}\delta q_2 + \dots + \frac{\partial \vec{r_i}}{\partial q_n}\delta q_n$$

$$\text{or} \quad \delta \vec{r_i} = \sum_{j=1}^{n} \frac{\partial \vec{r_i}}{\partial q_j}\delta q_j \qquad \dots (ii)$$

Substituting the value of $\delta \vec{r_i}$ from Eq. (ii) in Eq. (i), we have

$$\delta W = \sum_{i=1}^{N}\vec{F_i}\sum_{j=1}^{n}\frac{\partial \vec{r_i}}{\partial q_j}\delta q_j$$

$$= \sum_{j=1}^{n}\left[\sum_{i=1}^{N}\vec{F_i}\frac{\partial \vec{r_i}}{\partial q_j}\right]\delta q_j$$

$$\text{or} \quad \delta W = \sum_{j=1}^{n} Q_j\,\delta q_j$$

Where $Q_j = \sum_{i=1}^{N}\vec{F_i}\frac{\partial \vec{r_i}}{\partial q_j}$ is called the *generalised force* associated with generalised co-ordinate q_j.

The dimensions of Q_j depend upon the dimensions of corresponding co-ordinates q_j. If q_j has the dimensions of length, then Q_j has the dimensions of force. If q_j has the dimensions of an angle, then Q_j has the dimensions of torque. It means that in all cases the dimensions of the product $Q_j\,\delta q_j$ will be that of work.

Q. 14.7 (a). Using D'Alembert's principle derive Lagrange's equation of motion of a particle moving under the action of a conservative force. (*P.U.* 2003, 2001, 2000)

(b) Write the rules for framing Lagrange's equations. (*M.D.U.* 2006)

Ans (a). Lagrange's equation. Consider a system of N particles (or a rigid body). If the system has n degrees of freedom then it will have n generalised co-ordinates $q_1, q_2 \dots q_n$. Let m_i be the mass of the i th particle and $\vec{r_i}$ its position vector, then

$$\vec{r_i} = \vec{r_i}\,(q_1, q_2 \dots q_n) \qquad \dots (i)$$

The arbitrary virtual displacement $\delta \vec{r_i}$ is given by

$$\delta \vec{r_i} = \frac{\partial \vec{r_i}}{\partial q_1}\delta q_1 + \frac{\partial \vec{r_i}}{\partial q_2}\delta q_2 + \dots + \frac{\partial \vec{r_i}}{\partial q_n}\delta q_n$$

$$\text{or} \quad \delta \vec{r_i} = \sum_{j=1}^{n}\frac{\partial \vec{r_i}}{\partial q_j}\delta q_j \qquad \dots (ii)$$

Differentiating Eq. (i), with respect to t, we have the velocity of the i th particle

$$\vec{v_i} = \frac{d\vec{r_i}}{dt} = \dot{\vec{r_i}} = \frac{\partial \vec{r_i}}{\partial q_1}\frac{\partial q_1}{\partial t} + \frac{\partial \vec{r_i}}{\partial q_2}\frac{\partial q_2}{\partial t} + \dots + \frac{\partial \vec{r_i}}{\partial q_n}\frac{\partial q_n}{\partial t}$$

$$= \frac{\partial \vec{r_i}}{\partial q_1}\dot{q_1} + \frac{\partial \vec{r_i}}{\partial q_2}\dot{q_2} + \dots + \frac{\partial \vec{r_i}}{\partial q_n}\dot{q_n}$$

$$\text{or} \quad \vec{v_i} = \dot{\vec{r_i}} = \sum_{j=1}^{n}\frac{\partial \vec{r_i}}{\partial q_j}\dot{q_j} \qquad \dots (iii)$$

where $\dot{q_j}$ are called generalised velocities.

If $\vec{F_i}$ is the external force acting on the ith particle and the constraints on the system are workless, then according to *D'Alembert's principle*

$$\sum_{i=1}^{N}(\vec{F_i} - m_i\,\vec{a_i})\,\delta\vec{r_i} = 0 \qquad\qquad ...(iv)\;[\text{Eq. iv Q. 14. 5}]$$

Substituting the value of $\delta\vec{r_i}$ from Eq. (ii) in Eq. (iv), we get

$$\sum_{i=1}^{N}(\vec{F_i} - m_i\,\vec{a_i})\sum_{j=1}^{n}\frac{\partial\vec{r_i}}{\partial q_j}\,\delta q_j = 0$$

or
$$\sum_{j=1}^{n}\sum_{i=1}^{N}(\vec{F_i} - m_i\,\vec{a_i})\frac{\partial\vec{r_i}}{\partial q_j}\,\delta q_j = 0$$

or
$$\sum_{j=1}^{n}\left[\sum_{i=1}^{N}\vec{F_i}\frac{\partial\vec{r_i}}{\partial q_j}\right]\delta q_j - \sum_{j=1}^{n}\left[\sum_{i=1}^{N}m_i\,\vec{a_i}\frac{\partial\vec{r_i}}{\partial q_j}\right]\delta q_j = 0$$

or
$$\sum_{j=1}^{n}Q_j\,\delta q_j - \sum_{j=1}^{n}\left[\sum_{i=1}^{N}m_i\,\vec{a_i}\frac{\partial\vec{r_i}}{\partial q_j}\right]\delta q_j = 0 \qquad\qquad ...(v)$$

where Q_j is the generalised force given by $\sum_{i=1}^{N}\vec{F_i}\frac{\partial\vec{r_i}}{\partial q_j}$.

Now
$$\frac{d}{dt}\left[m_i v_i\,\frac{\partial\vec{r_i}}{\partial q_j}\right] = m_i\,\vec{v_i}\frac{d}{dt}\left[\frac{\partial\vec{r_i}}{\partial q_j}\right] + \frac{d}{dt}\left(m_i\,\vec{v_i}\right)\frac{\partial\vec{r_i}}{\partial q_j}$$

$$= m_i\,\vec{v_i}\frac{d}{dt}\left[\frac{\partial\vec{r_i}}{\partial q_j}\right] + m_i\,\vec{a_i}\frac{\partial\vec{r_i}}{\partial q_j} \qquad\left[\because \frac{d}{dt}\vec{v_i} = \vec{a_i}\right]$$

$\therefore$
$$m_i\,\vec{a_i}\frac{\partial\vec{r_i}}{\partial q_j} = \frac{d}{dt}\left[m_i\,\vec{v_i}\frac{\partial\vec{r_i}}{\partial q_j}\right] - m_i\,\vec{v_i}\frac{d}{dt}\left(\frac{\partial\vec{r_i}}{\partial q_j}\right) \qquad ...(vi)$$

Substituting the value of $m_i\,\vec{a_i}\frac{\partial\vec{r_i}}{\partial q_j}$ from Eq. (vi) in Eq. (v), we get

$$\sum_{j=1}^{n}Q_j\,\delta q_j - \sum_{j=1}^{n}\sum_{i=1}^{N}\frac{d}{dt}\left[m_i\,\vec{v_i}\frac{\partial\vec{r_i}}{\partial q_j}\right]\delta q_j$$

$$+ \sum_{j=1}^{n}\sum_{i=1}^{N}m_i\,\vec{v_i}\frac{d}{dt}\left[\frac{\partial\vec{r_i}}{\partial q_j}\right]\delta q_j = 0 \qquad\qquad ...(vii)$$

Again
$$\frac{\partial\vec{r_i}}{\partial q_j} = \frac{\partial\vec{r_i}}{\partial\dot{q_j}} = \frac{\partial\vec{v_i}}{\partial\dot{q_j}} \quad\text{and}\quad \frac{d}{dt}\left[\frac{\partial\vec{r_i}}{\partial q_j}\right] = \frac{\partial\vec{v_i}}{\partial q_j}$$

Substituting these values in Eq. (vii), we get

$$\sum_{j=1}^{n}Q_j\,\delta q_j - \sum_{j=1}^{n}\sum_{i=1}^{N}\frac{d}{dt}\left[m_i\,\vec{v_i}\frac{\partial\vec{v_i}}{\partial\dot{q_j}}\right]\delta q_j$$

$$+ \sum_{j=1}^{n}\sum_{i=1}^{N}m_i\,\vec{v_i}\frac{\partial\vec{v_i}}{\partial q_j}\,\delta q_j = 0 \qquad\qquad ...(viii)$$

Further
$$\frac{d}{dt}\left[\vec{A}.\vec{A}\right] = 2\vec{A}.\frac{d\vec{A}}{dt} \quad\text{or}\quad \vec{A}.\frac{d\vec{A}}{dt} = \frac{1}{2}\frac{d}{dt}\left[\vec{A}.\vec{A}\right]$$

Hence
$$\vec{v}_i \cdot \frac{d\,\vec{v}_i}{\partial \dot{q}_j} = \frac{1}{2} \frac{\partial}{\partial \dot{q}_j}\left[\vec{v}_i \cdot \vec{v}_i\right] = \frac{1}{2}\frac{\partial}{\partial \dot{q}_j} v_i^2 \qquad \ldots (ix)$$

and
$$\vec{v}_i \cdot \frac{d\,\vec{v}_i}{\partial q_j} = \frac{1}{2}\frac{\partial}{\partial q_j}\left[\vec{v}_i \cdot \vec{v}_i\right] = \frac{1}{2}\frac{\partial}{\partial q_j}v_i^2 \qquad \ldots (x)$$

Substituting the values of Eq. (ix) and (x) in Eq. $(viii)$, we have

$$\sum_{j=1}^{n} Q_j\,\delta q_j - \sum_{j=1}^{n}\sum_{i=1}^{N}\frac{d}{dt}\left[\frac{\partial}{\partial \dot{q}_j}\left(\frac{1}{2}m_i \cdot v_i^2\right)\right]\delta q_j$$

$$+ \sum_{j=1}^{n}\sum_{i=1}^{N}\frac{\partial}{\partial q_j}\left(\frac{1}{2}m_i \cdot v_i^2\right)\delta q_j = 0$$

or
$$\sum_{j=1}^{n}Q_j\,\delta q_j - \sum_{j=1}^{n}\frac{d}{dt}\left[\frac{\partial}{\partial \dot{q}_j}\left(\sum_{i=1}^{N}\frac{1}{2}m_i \cdot v_i^2\right)\delta q_j\right]$$

$$+ \sum_{j=1}^{n}\frac{\partial}{\partial q_j}\left[\sum_{i=1}^{N}\frac{1}{2}m_i\,v_i^2\right]\delta q_j = 0 \qquad \ldots (xi)$$

But $\dfrac{1}{2}m_i\,v_i^2$ is the kinetic energy of the ith particle.

$$\therefore \qquad \sum_{i=1}^{N}\frac{1}{2}m_i\,v_i^2 = T = \text{Kinetic energy of the system of } N \text{ particles}$$

Eq. (xi) now becomes

$$\sum_{j=1}^{n}Q_j\,\delta q_j - \sum_{j=1}^{n}\frac{d}{dt}\left(\frac{\partial T}{\partial \dot{q}_j}\right)\delta q_j + \sum_{j=1}^{n}\frac{\partial T}{\partial q_j}\delta q_j = 0$$

or
$$\sum_{j=1}^{n}\left[Q_j - \frac{d}{dt}\left(\frac{\partial T}{\partial \dot{q}_j}\right) + \frac{\partial T}{\partial q_j}\right]\delta q_j = 0 \qquad \ldots (xii)$$

Eq. (xii) is a restatement of D'Alembert's principle in terms of generalised co-ordinates and generalised force.

Since q_j's are independent variables Eq. (xii) holds good only if the co-efficients of each δq_j in this equation is zero. This means

$$Q_j - \frac{d}{dt}\left(\frac{\partial T}{\partial \dot{q}_j}\right) + \frac{\partial T}{\partial q_j} = 0$$

or
$$\frac{d}{dt}\left(\frac{\partial T}{\partial \dot{q}_j}\right) - \frac{\partial T}{\partial q_j} = Q_j \qquad \ldots (xiii)\,[\,j = 1, 2 \ldots n\,]$$

i.e. there are n such equations. These n equations are known as Lagrange's equations of motion and are valid for conservative as well as non-conservative systems.

For conservative system. For a conservative system the forces acting on the system are derivable from a scalar potential energy function V.

$\therefore$ The force acting on the i th particle of the system is given by

$$\vec{F}_i = -\vec{\Delta} V$$

But the potential energy V is a function of co-ordinates $\vec{r}_i$ and q_j only

$$\therefore \qquad \vec{F}_i = -\frac{\partial V_i}{\partial \vec{r}_i}$$

The components of generalised force are therefore given by

$$Q_j = \sum_{i=1}^{N} \vec{F_i} \frac{\partial \vec{r_i}}{\partial q_j} = - \sum_{i=1}^{N} \frac{\partial V_i}{\partial \vec{r_i}} \cdot \frac{\partial \vec{r_i}}{\partial q_j}$$

$$= - \sum_{i=1}^{N} \frac{\partial V_i}{\partial q_j} = - \frac{\partial}{\partial q_j} \sum_{i=1}^{N} V_i$$

$\because \quad \sum_{i=1}^{N} V_i = V$ the total potential of the system, we get

$$Q_j = - \frac{\partial V}{\partial q_j} \qquad \qquad ...(xiv)$$

According to the general form of Lagrange's equation [Eq. (xiii)]

$$\frac{d}{dt}\left(\frac{\partial T}{\partial \dot{q_j}} \right) - \frac{\partial T}{\partial q_j} = Q_j$$

Using the value of Q_j from Eq. (xiv), we get

$$\frac{d}{dt}\left(\frac{\partial T}{\partial \dot{q_j}} \right) - \frac{\partial T}{\partial q_j} = - \frac{\partial V}{\partial q_j}$$

or $\qquad \frac{d}{dt}\left(\frac{\partial T}{\partial \dot{q_j}} \right) - \frac{\partial}{\partial q_j}(T - V) = 0 \qquad ...(xv)$

Since V depends only on the generalised co-ordinates q_j and not on generalised velocities $\dot{q_j}$,

$\frac{\partial V}{\partial \dot{q_j}} = 0$. Hence we can write

$$\frac{d}{dt}\left(\frac{\partial T}{\partial \dot{q_j}} \right) = \frac{d}{dt}\left[\frac{\partial}{\partial \dot{q_j}}(T - V) \right]$$

Substituting in Eq. (xv) , we have

$$\frac{d}{dt}\left[\frac{\partial}{\partial \dot{q_j}}(T - V) \right] - \frac{\partial}{\partial q_j}(T - V) = 0 \qquad ...(xvi)$$

Now put $T - V = L$, which is known as Lagrangian function or simply Lagrangian or (Kinetic potential) of the system, the Eq. (xvi) becomes.

$$\frac{d}{dt}\left[\frac{\partial L}{\partial \dot{q_j}} \right] - \frac{\partial}{\partial q_j} L = 0 \qquad ...(xvii)$$

This is Lagrangian equation for a conservative system.

(b) **Rules for framing Lagrange's equation: Lagrange's equation of motion can be framed by applying the following rules.**

(i) Choose a suitable (generalised) co-ordinate system to specify the configuration of the system.

(ii) Obtain the value of kinetic energy $\left(T = \sum_{i=1}^{N} \frac{1}{2} m_1 v_i^2 \right)$ in terms of the co-ordinates and their derivatives with respect to time.

(iii) If the system is conservative, find the total potential energy V of the system as a function of these co-ordinates.

Q. 14.8. (*a*) **Using Lagrange's equation derive Newton's equations of motion for a particle in cartesian co-ordinates.**

(*b*) **Two bodies of masses m_1 and m_2 are connected by an inextensible string and the string is passed over a smooth and small pulley. Set up the Lagrangian of the system and hence find the acceleration of the system.** (*P. U.* 2001)

OR

Set up Lagrangian equation for an Atwood machine and find an expression for its acceleration. (*M. D.U.* 2008; 2003)

Ans. (*a*) Consider a particle of mass m having cartesian co-ordinates (x, y, z). Let F_x, F_y and F_z be the components of generalised force and v_x, v_y and v_z the components of the velocity of the particle along X, Y and Z axes respectively.

$\therefore$ Kinetic energy $T = \dfrac{1}{2} m (v_x^2 + v_y^2 + v_z^2) = \dfrac{1}{2} m (\dot{x}^2 + \dot{y}^2 + \dot{z}^2)$

As T is a function of $\dot{x}$, $\dot{y}$ and $\dot{z}$ but is not a function of x, y, z

$$\frac{\partial T}{\partial \dot{x}} = m\dot{x} \; ; \; \frac{\partial T}{\partial \dot{y}} = m\dot{y} \; ; \; \frac{\partial T}{\partial \dot{z}} = m\dot{z} \qquad \qquad ...(i)$$

$$\frac{\partial T}{\partial x} = 0 \; ; \; \frac{\partial T}{\partial y} = 0 \; ; \; \frac{\partial T}{\partial z} = 0 \qquad \qquad ...(ii)$$

According to general form of Lagrange's equation

$$\frac{d}{dt}\left(\frac{\partial T}{\partial \dot{q}_j} \right) - \frac{\partial T}{\partial q_j} = Q_j$$

In terms of cartesian co-ordinates it can be written as

$$\left. \begin{array}{l} \dfrac{d}{dt}\left(\dfrac{\partial T}{\partial \dot{x}} \right) - \dfrac{\partial T}{\partial x} = F_x \\[2mm] \dfrac{d}{dt}\left(\dfrac{\partial T}{\partial \dot{y}} \right) - \dfrac{\partial T}{\partial y} = F_y \\[2mm] \dfrac{d}{dt}\left(\dfrac{\partial T}{\partial \dot{z}} \right) - \dfrac{\partial T}{\partial z} = F_z \end{array} \right\} \qquad \qquad ...(iii)$$

Substituting the corresponding values from Eqs. (*i*) and (*ii*) in Eq. (*iii*), we get

$$\frac{d}{dt}(m\dot{x}) = F_x \qquad \text{or} \quad F_x = m\ddot{x} \qquad \qquad ...(iv)(a)$$

$$\frac{d}{dt}(m\dot{y}) = F_y \qquad \text{or} \quad F_y = m\ddot{y} \qquad \qquad ...(iv)(b)$$

$$\frac{d}{dt}(m\dot{z}) = F_z \qquad \text{or} \quad Fz = m\ddot{z} \qquad \qquad ...(iv)(c)$$

Eqs. (*iv*) (*a*), (*b*) and (*c*) are Newton's equations of motion for the particle.

(*b*) An Atwood machine consists of two masses m_1 and m_2 connected by a light inextensible string of length l which passes over a small, smooth pulley. The two masses move only vertically and, therefore the system has only one degree of freedom. It is an example of a conservative system having holonomic and scleronomic constraints. Let $Pm_1 = x$, then $Pm_2 = l - x$ because the length of the string connecting the two masses $= l$.

Here x is the only independent co-ordinate.

$\therefore$ $q_1 = x$

Assuming that the pulley is frictionless (smooth) and mass less (small), potential energy of the system with respect to the axis of the pulley taken as the line of reference

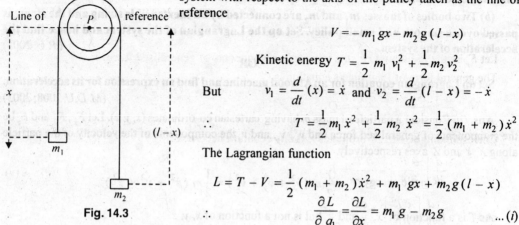

Line of reference

$(l-x)$

m_1

m_2

Fig. 14.3

$$V = -m_1\,gx - m_2\,g\,(l-x)$$

Kinetic energy $T = \dfrac{1}{2}\,m_1\,v_1^2 + \dfrac{1}{2}m_2\,v_2^2$

But $\qquad v_1 = \dfrac{d}{dt}(x) = \dot{x}$ and $v_2 = \dfrac{d}{dt}(l-x) = -\dot{x}$

$$\therefore\quad T = \dfrac{1}{2}m_1\,\dot{x}^2 + \dfrac{1}{2}m_2\,\dot{x}^2 = \dfrac{1}{2}(m_1+m_2)\dot{x}^2$$

The Lagrangian function

$$L = T - V = \dfrac{1}{2}(m_1+m_2)\dot{x}^2 + m_1\,gx + m_2 g(l-x)$$

$$\therefore\quad \dfrac{\partial L}{\partial q_1} = \dfrac{\partial L}{\partial x} = m_1\,g - m_2 g \qquad\qquad ...(i)$$

and $\qquad \dfrac{\partial L}{\partial \dot{q}_1} = \dfrac{\partial L}{\partial \dot{x}} = (m_1+m_2)\dot{x} = m_1\dot{x} + m_2\dot{x} \qquad ...(ii)$

The Lagrangian equation is

$$\dfrac{d}{dt}\left[\dfrac{\partial L}{\partial \dot{q}_1}\right] - \dfrac{\partial L}{\partial q_1} = 0 \qquad\qquad (iii)$$

Substituting the values of $\dfrac{\partial L}{\partial q_1}$ and $\dfrac{\partial L}{\partial \dot{q}_1}$ from Eqs. (i) and (ii) in Eq. (iii) we get

$$\dfrac{d}{dt}\left[m_1\dot{x} + m_2\dot{x}\right] - m_1 g + m_2\,g = 0$$

or $\qquad m_1\ddot{x} + m_2\ddot{x} - (m_1 - m_2)g = 0$

or $\qquad (m_1+m_2)\ddot{x} = (m_1-m_2)g$

$\therefore$ Acceleration of the system $\vec{a} = \ddot{x} = \dfrac{m_1-m_2}{m_1+m_2}\,g$

It should be noted that force of constraint i.e. tension in the string does not appear in the expression for acceleration.

Q. 14.9. (a) **Using Lagrange's equation derive the equation of motion of a particle in plane polar co-ordinates.**

(b) **Obtain Lagrangian equation for a simple pendulum.**

(Gauhati. U. 2000)

Ans. (a) Let (r, θ) be the plane polar co-ordinates of a particle whose cartesian co-ordinates in the XY plane are (x, y) then

$$x = r\cos\theta\,;\ y = r\sin\theta \qquad ...(i)$$

The x and y components of the velocity of the particle are

$$\dot{x} = \dot{r}\cos\theta - r\dot{\theta}\sin\theta \qquad ...(ii)$$

$$\dot{y} = \dot{r}\sin\theta + r\dot{\theta}\cos\theta \qquad ...(iii)$$

$\therefore$ K. E. of the particle $T = \dfrac{1}{2}m\dot{x}^2 + \dfrac{1}{2}m\dot{y}^2$

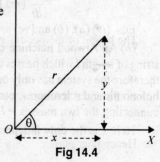

Fig 14.4

$$= \frac{1}{2} m \left[(\dot{r} \cos\theta - r\dot{\theta}\sin\theta)^2 + (\dot{r}\sin\theta + r\dot{\theta}\cos\theta)^2 \right]$$

or
$$T = \frac{1}{2} m \left[\dot{r}^2 + (r\dot{\theta})^2 \right] \qquad \qquad ...(iv)$$

Let F_r be the radial and rF_θ the transverse components of generalised force

The general form of Lagrange's equation is

$$\frac{d}{dt} \left[\frac{\partial T}{\partial \dot{q}_j} \right] - \frac{\partial T}{\partial q_j} = Q_j$$

Corresponding to the co-ordinates r, θ this equation becomes

$$\frac{d}{dt} \left[\frac{\partial T}{\partial \dot{r}} \right] - \frac{\partial T}{\partial r} = F_r \qquad \qquad ...(v)$$

and
$$\frac{d}{dt} \left[\frac{\partial T}{\partial \dot{\theta}} \right] - \frac{\partial T}{\partial \theta} = rF_\theta \qquad \qquad ...(vi)$$

From Eq. (iv)
$$\frac{\partial T}{\partial r} = m r \dot{\theta}^2 \text{ and } \frac{\partial T}{\partial \dot{r}} = m\dot{r} \qquad \qquad ...(vii)$$

and
$$\frac{\partial T}{\partial \theta} = 0 \text{ and } \frac{\partial T}{\partial \dot{\theta}} = mr^2 \dot{\theta} \qquad \qquad ...(viii)$$

Using Eq. (vii), Eq. (v) becomes

$$\frac{d}{dt} \left[m\dot{r} \right] - mr\dot{\theta}^2 = F_r \text{, or } m\ddot{r} - m r\dot{\theta}^2 = F_r \qquad \qquad ...(ix)$$

Using Eq. $(viii)$ Eq. (vi) becomes

$$\frac{d}{dt} \left[mr^2 \dot{\theta} \right] = r F_\theta \text{ or } mr^2 \ddot{\theta} + 2mr\dot{r}\dot{\theta} = r F_\theta$$

or
$$m (r\ddot{\theta} + 2\dot{r}\dot{\theta}) = F_\theta \qquad \qquad .....(x)$$

Equations (ix) and (x) give the equations of motion of a particle in plane polar co-ordinates.

(b) Simple pendulum. Consider a simple pendulum of length l having a bob of mass m suspended from a fixed support O capable of oscillating in the X-Y plane. Let θ be the angle made by the pendulum string with the vertical when the pendulum is displaced to Q from its equilibrium position P.

The system has one degree of freedom. We, therefore, choose the variable $q = \theta$ as the generalised co-ordinate.

At the position Q, the velocity of the bob

$$v = l\omega = l \frac{d\theta}{dt} = l\dot{\theta}$$

∴ Kinetic energy of the bob of simple pendulum

$$T = \frac{1}{2} mv^2 = \frac{1}{2} ml^2\dot{\theta}^2 \qquad \qquad ...(i)$$

The height of the pendulum bob at Q with respect to the equilibrium position P,

$$RP = OP - OR = l(1 - \cos\theta)$$

or
$$h = l(1 - \cos\theta)$$

∴ Potential energy of the bob of simple pendulum

$$V = mgh = mgl(1 - \cos\theta)$$

Hence Lagrangian

$$L = T - V = \frac{1}{2} m l^2 \dot{\theta}^2 - mgl (1 - \cos \theta) \qquad \qquad ...\, (i)\,(a)$$

The general form of Lagrangian equation is

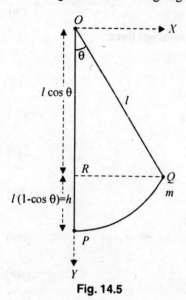

Fig. 14.5

$$\frac{d}{dt} \left(\frac{\partial L}{\partial \dot{q}} \right) - \frac{dL}{\partial q} = 0 \qquad \qquad ...\, (ii)$$

Now $\qquad \dfrac{dL}{\partial q} = \dfrac{dL}{\partial \theta} = -mgl\, \sin \theta$

and $\qquad \dfrac{dL}{\partial \dot{q}} = \dfrac{dL}{\partial \dot{\theta}} = ml^2 \dot{\theta} \qquad \qquad ...\, (iii)$

Substituting the values in Eq. (ii), we get

$$\frac{d}{dt} \left(ml^2\, \dot{\theta} \right) + mgl\, \sin \theta = 0$$

or $\qquad ml^2\, \ddot{\theta} + mgl\, \sin \theta = 0$

or $\qquad \ddot{\theta} + \dfrac{g}{l} \sin \theta = 0$

This is the required equation of motion for the simple pendulum.

If θ is small, $\sin \theta = \theta$ and we get

$$\ddot{\theta} + \frac{g}{l}\, \theta = 0$$

This is the equation of a simple harmonic motion of time period $t = 2\pi \sqrt{\dfrac{l}{g}}$.

Q. 14.10. (a) **Using Lagrange's equation derive the equation of motion of a one dimensional harmonic oscillator.**   (M.D.U. 2007, 2006)

(b) **Set up the Lagrangian for a compound pendulum oscillating in a vertical plane about a fixed horizontal axis.**   (P.U. 2003)

Ans. (a) **Harmonic oscillator.** Consider a particle of mass m oscillating about a fixed point along the X-axis. We, therefore, choose the variable $q = x$ to represent the configuration of the oscillator so that x gives the displacement of the oscillator from the mean position.

Kinetic energy of the oscillator $T = \dfrac{1}{2} m v^2 = \dfrac{1}{2} m \dot{x}^2 \qquad \qquad ...\, (i)$

To find the potential energy of the oscillator, we know that the restoring force acting on the particle is proportional to displacement and acts in the opposite direction.

i.e. $\qquad F = -kx$

where k is the constant of proportionality.

But $\qquad F = -\dfrac{dV}{dx}$ where V is the potential energy.

or $\qquad dV = -F\, dx = kx\, dx$

$\therefore \qquad V = \int dV = \int kx\, dx = \dfrac{1}{2} kx^2 + C$

where C is the constant of integration

At $\qquad x = 0$ (mean position), $V = 0 \therefore C = 0$

Hence $\qquad V = \dfrac{1}{2} kx^2 \qquad \qquad ...\, (ii)$

The Lagrangian function is $L = T - V$

$$L = \frac{1}{2}m\dot{x}^2 - \frac{1}{2}kx^2 \qquad\qquad ...(iii)$$

The Lagrangian equation is

$$\frac{d}{dt}\left[\frac{\partial L}{\partial \dot{q}}\right] - \frac{\partial L}{\partial q} = 0$$

As we have chosen $q = x$, the above equation becomes

$$\frac{d}{dt}\left[\frac{\partial L}{\partial \dot{x}}\right] - \frac{\partial L}{\partial x} = 0 \qquad\qquad ...(iv)$$

From Eq. (iii), we have

$$\frac{\partial L}{\partial \dot{x}} = m\dot{x} \text{ and } \frac{\partial L}{\partial x} = -kx$$

Substituting in Eq. (iv), we get

$$\frac{d}{dt}(m\dot{x}) - (-kx) = 0$$

or $\qquad m\ddot{x} + kx = 0$

This is the equation of motion of a one dimensional harmonic oscillator.

(b) Compound pendulum. A rigid body capable of oscillating in a vertical plane about a fixed horizontal axis is known as a compound pendulum. Let the vertical plane of oscillation be XY; O, the point through which the axis of rotation passes and C the centre of mass of the pendulum.

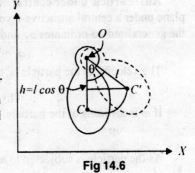

Suppose the mass of the pendulum is m, and I its moment of inertia about the axis of rotation O. If θ is the angle through which the pendulum is deflected, then θ represents the generalised co-ordinate q and the angular velocity $\omega = \dot{\theta}$.

Fig 14.6

$\therefore$ Kinetic energy of the pendulum $T = \frac{1}{2}I\omega^2 = \frac{1}{2}I\dot{\theta}^2$

and Potential energy relative to a horizontal plane through O

$$V = -mgh = -mgl\cos\theta$$

where l is the distance of the centre of mass C from the centre of suspension O.

Hence Lagrangian $\qquad L = T - V = \frac{1}{2}I\dot{\theta}^2 + mgl\cos\theta$

$$\therefore \qquad \frac{\partial L}{\partial\dot{\theta}} = I\dot{\theta} \text{ and } \frac{\partial L}{\partial\theta} = -mgl\sin\theta$$

According to Lagrangian equation

$$\frac{d}{dt}\left(\frac{\partial L}{\partial\dot{q}}\right) - \frac{\partial L}{\partial q} = 0 \text{ , we have}$$

$$\frac{d}{dt}\left(\frac{\partial L}{\partial\dot{\theta}}\right) - \frac{\partial L}{\partial\theta} = 0 \qquad\qquad [\text{Here } q = \theta]$$

$$\therefore \qquad \frac{d}{dt}(I\dot{\theta}) + mgl\sin\theta = 0$$

or $\qquad I\ddot{\theta} + mgl\sin\theta = 0$

or $\qquad \ddot{\theta} + \frac{mgl}{I}\sin\theta = 0$

This is the equation of motion of the compound pendulum.

If θ is small, $\sin \theta = \theta$, then

$$\ddot{\theta} + \frac{mgl}{I} \theta = 0 .$$

This is the equation of simple harmonic motion of time period

$$t = 2\pi \sqrt{\frac{I}{mgl}}$$

If k is the radius of gyration of the pendulum about the centre of mass, then

$$I = m(k^2 + l^2)$$

Hence $$t = 2\pi \sqrt{\frac{m(k^2 + l^2)}{mgl}} = 2\pi \sqrt{\frac{k^2 + l^2}{lg}}$$

Q. 14.11. (a) Using Lagrangian equation derive the equation of motion of a particle moving in a plane under a central attractive inverse square force.

(b) A particle of mass m is projected with an initial velocity u at an angle α with the horizontal. Use Lagrange's equation to describe the motion of the particle. The resistance of air may be neglected.

(P.U. 2000)

Ans. Particle under central attractive inverse square force. Consider a particle moving in a plane under a central attractive inverse square force. Such a system has two degrees of freedom and the generalised co-ordinates q_1 and q_2 in terms of plane polar co-ordinates are

$$q_1 = r ; q_2 = \theta$$

The velocity of the particle is, therefore given by

$$v = \sqrt{\dot{r}^2 + r^2 \dot{\theta}^2}$$

If m is the mass of the particle, then kinetic energy

$$T = \frac{1}{2} mv^2 = \frac{1}{2} m (\dot{r}^2 + r^2 \dot{\theta}^2) = \frac{1}{2} m\dot{r}^2 + \frac{1}{2} mr^2 \dot{\theta}^2$$

As the particle is subjected to attractive inverse square force

$$F = -\frac{k}{r^2}$$

The potential energy $$V = \int -Fdr = \int \frac{k}{r^2} dr = -\frac{k}{r}$$

∴ Lagrangian function $L = T - V$

$$= \frac{1}{2} m\dot{r}^2 + \frac{1}{2} m r^2 \dot{\theta}^2 + \frac{k}{r}$$

As there are two independent co-ordinates r and θ, the two Lagrange's equations are

$$\frac{d}{dt}\left[\frac{\partial L}{\partial \dot{q}_1} \right] - \frac{\partial L}{\partial q_1} = 0 \quad \text{or} \quad \frac{d}{dt}\left[\frac{\partial L}{\partial \dot{r}} \right] - \frac{\partial L}{\partial r} = 0$$

and $$\frac{d}{dt}\left[\frac{\partial L}{\partial \dot{q}_2} \right] - \frac{\partial L}{\partial q_2} = 0 \quad \text{or} \quad \frac{d}{dt}\left[\frac{\partial L}{\partial \dot{\theta}} \right] - \frac{\partial L}{\partial \theta} = 0$$

Now $$\frac{\partial L}{\partial \dot{r}} = m\dot{r}, \quad \frac{\partial L}{\partial r} = mr\dot{\theta}^2 - \frac{k}{r^2}$$

$$\frac{\partial L}{\partial \dot{\theta}} = mr^2 \dot{\theta}, \quad \frac{\partial L}{\partial \theta} = 0$$

∴ Lagrange's equations are

$$\frac{d}{dt}(m\dot{r}) - mr\dot{\theta}^2 + \frac{k}{r^2} = 0$$

or $\qquad m\,\ddot{r} - mr\,\dot{\theta}^2 + \dfrac{k}{r^2} = 0$ ...(i)

and $\qquad \dfrac{d}{dt}\left(mr^2\,\dot{\theta}\right) - 0 = 0$

or $\qquad \dfrac{d}{dt}\left(mr^2\,\dot{\theta}\right) = 0$

or $\qquad 2mr\dot{r}\dot{\theta} + mr^2\,\ddot{\theta} = 0$

or $\qquad 2m\dot{r}\dot{\theta} + mr\,\ddot{\theta} = 0$ ... (ii)

(b) Let the horizontal direction be the X-axis and vertical direction the Y-axis with O as the origin from where the particle of mass m is projected with a velocity u making an angle α with the X- axis.

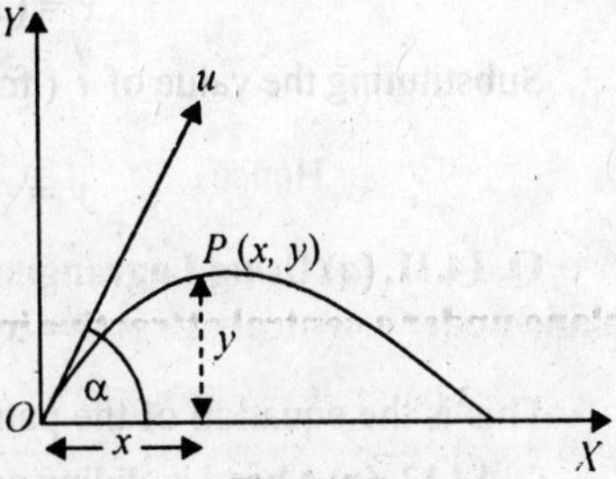

The position of the particle at any instant t at P is x, y. Such a system has two degrees of freedom and therefore two generalised co-ordinates

$\qquad\qquad q_1 = x\,;\, q_2 = y$

∴ The velocity of the particle at $P = \sqrt{\dot{x}^2 + \dot{y}^2}$

Fig. 14.7

and $\qquad$ Kinetic energy $T = \dfrac{1}{2}m(\dot{x}^2 + \dot{y}^2)$

Taking the X - axis as the reference level, potential energy of the particle at P

$$V = mgy$$

∴ Lagrangian $\qquad L = T - V = \dfrac{1}{2}m\,(\dot{x}^2 + \dot{y}^2) - mgy$ ...(i)

and Lagrange's equations are

$$\dfrac{d}{dt}\left(\dfrac{\partial L}{\partial \dot{q}_1}\right) - \dfrac{\partial L}{\partial q_1} = 0 \text{ or } \dfrac{d}{dt}\left(\dfrac{\partial L}{\partial \dot{x}}\right) - \dfrac{\partial L}{\partial x} = 0 \qquad \text{... (ii)}$$

$$\dfrac{d}{dt}\left(\dfrac{\partial L}{\partial \dot{q}_2}\right) - \dfrac{\partial L}{\partial q_2} = 0 \text{ or } \dfrac{d}{dt}\left(\dfrac{\partial L}{\partial \dot{y}}\right) - \dfrac{\partial L}{\partial y} = 0 \qquad \text{... (iii)}$$

From Eq. (i) $\qquad \dfrac{\partial L}{\partial x} = m\dot{x}\,;\, \dfrac{\partial L}{\partial x} = 0$ ... (iv)

$$\dfrac{\partial L}{\partial \dot{y}} = m\dot{y}\,;\, \dfrac{\partial L}{\partial y} = -mg \qquad\qquad \text{... (v)}$$

Substituting the values from Eq. (iv) in Eq. (ii), we have

$\qquad \dfrac{d}{dt}(m\dot{x}) + 0 = 0 \text{ or } m\ddot{x} = 0 \text{ or } \ddot{x} = 0$ ... (vi)

Substituting the values from Eq. (v) in Eq. (iii), we have

$\qquad \dfrac{d}{dt}(m\dot{y}) + mg = 0 \text{ or } m\ddot{y} + mg = 0 \text{ or } \ddot{y} + g = 0 \text{ or } \ddot{y} = -g$ ... (vii)

Integrating Eq. (vi) we get $\dot{x} = A$ ...(viii)

and again integrating we get $\quad x = At + B$ ... (ix)

Integrating Eq. (vii), we get $\dot{y} = -gt + C$ ... (x)

and again integrating we get $\quad y = -\dfrac{1}{2}gt^2 + Ct + D$ ... (xi)

Now, applying boundary conditions to Eqs. (viii) and (ix), we get

At $t = 0$, $x = 0$ and $\dot{x} = v_x = u \cos \alpha$ (Along X-axis)

$\therefore$ $A = u \cos\alpha$ and $B = 0$ ... (xii)

Applying boundary conditions to Eqs. (x) and (xi), we get

At $t = 0$, $\dot{y} = u \sin \alpha$ (along Y- axis) or $C = u \sin \alpha$ ... (xiii)

At $t = 0$, $y = 0$ or $D = 0$ ... (xiv)

Substituting $B = 0$ and $A = u \cos \alpha$ from Eq. (xii) in Eq. (ix), we get

$$x = (u \cos \alpha) t \text{ or } t = \frac{x}{u \cos \alpha}$$ ... (xv)

Substituting the value of t (for Eq. xv), C from Eq. (xiii) and D from Eq. (xiv) in Eq. (xi), we get

$$y = -\frac{1}{2} g \left(\frac{x}{u \cos \alpha} \right)^2 + u \sin \alpha \left(\frac{x}{u \cos \alpha} \right)$$

$$= x \tan \alpha - \frac{1}{2} g \frac{x^2}{u^2} \sec^2 \alpha$$

This is the equation of the path of the projectile.

Q. 14.12. (a) A bead is sliding on a uniformly rotating wire in a force free space. Using Lagrange's equation derive the equation of motion of the particle and calculate its centripetal acceleration.

(Cal. U. 2003)

(b) A bead slides on a wire in the shape of a cycloid described by the equation

$$x = a (\theta - \sin\theta)$$
$$y = a (1 + \cos \theta)$$

where $0 \leq \theta \leq 2\pi$.

Find the Lagrangian function and the equation of motion. Neglect the friction between the bead and the wire.

(P.U. 2000)

Ans. (a) Consider the bead as a particle. Suppose the wire is straight and is rotating uniformly about a fixed axis with angular speed ω perpendicular to the length of the wire. In this case, therefore the constraint is time dependent given by the relation $\omega = \dot{\theta}$ or $\theta = \omega t$.

The transformation equations relating the cartesian co-ordinates (x, y) and polar co-ordinates (r, θ) contain time explicitly and are given by

$$x = r \cos\theta = r \cos \omega t$$

and $$y = r \sin\theta = r \sin \omega t$$

$\therefore$ $$\dot{x} = \dot{r} \cos \omega t - r \omega \sin \omega t$$ ... (i)

$$\dot{y} = \dot{r} \sin \omega t + r \omega \cos \omega t$$ ... (ii)

Hence Kinetic energy of the particle $T = \frac{1}{2} m (\dot{x}^2 + \dot{y}^2)$

or $$T = \frac{1}{2} m \left[(\dot{r} \cos \omega t - r \omega \sin \omega t)^2 + (\dot{r} \sin \omega t + r \omega \cos \omega t)^2 \right]$$

$$= \frac{1}{2} m \left[\dot{r}^2 + r^2 \omega^2 \right]$$ ... (iii)

The general form of Lagrange's equation (for non-conservative system) is

$$\frac{d}{dt} \left[\frac{\partial T}{\partial \dot{q}_j} \right] - \frac{\partial T}{\partial q_j} = Q_j$$ ... (iv)

or $$\frac{d}{dt} \left[\frac{\partial T}{\partial \dot{r}} \right] - \frac{\partial T}{\partial r} = Q_j$$ (Substituting $q_j = r$)

Since the bead is sliding in a force free space $Q_j = 0$

$$\therefore \qquad \frac{d}{dt}\left[\frac{\partial T}{\partial \dot r}\right] - \frac{\partial T}{\partial r} = 0 \qquad \qquad \qquad \text{...(v)}$$

$\therefore$ From Eq. (iii) $\dfrac{\partial T}{\partial r} = mr\omega^2$ and $\dfrac{\partial T}{\partial \dot r} = m\dot r$

Substituting in Eq. (v) we get

$$\frac{d}{dt}(m\dot r) - mr\omega^2 = 0$$

or $\qquad\qquad m\ddot r - mr\omega^2 = 0 \qquad\qquad\qquad\qquad \text{... (vi)}$

This is the equation of motion of the bead.

Centripetal acceleration $\quad \ddot r = r\omega^2 \qquad\qquad\qquad\qquad\qquad\qquad \text{...(vii)}$

This is the centripetal acceleration of the bead.

(b) Let $P(x, y)$ be the position of the bead of mass m at any instant of time t. The path of the bead is a cycloid represented by

$$\begin{aligned} x &= a(\theta - \sin\theta) & \text{... (i)} \\ y &= a(1 + \cos\theta) & \text{... (ii)} \\ \dot x &= a(\dot\theta - \cos\theta\dot\theta) & \text{... (iii)} \\ \dot y &= -a\sin\theta\dot\theta & \text{... (iv)} \end{aligned}$$

The kinetic energy of the bead at P is given by

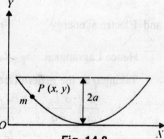

Fig. 14.8

$$T = \frac{1}{2}m(\dot x^2 + \dot y^2)$$

$$= \frac{1}{2}m\left[a^2(\dot\theta - \cos\theta\,\dot\theta)^2 + a^2\sin^2\theta\,\dot\theta^2\right]$$

$$= \frac{1}{2}m\left[a^2\dot\theta^2 + a^2\cos^2\theta\,\dot\theta^2 + a^2\sin^2\theta\dot\theta^2 - 2\dot\theta^2\cos\theta\right]$$

$$= ma^2\dot\theta^2(1 - \cos\theta) \qquad\qquad \text{... (v)}$$

The potential energy of the bead, taking X-axis as the reference level is given by

$$V = mgy = mga(1 + \cos\theta) \qquad\qquad\qquad \text{... (vi)}$$

$\therefore$ Lagrangian $\qquad L = T - V = ma^2\dot\theta^2(1 - \cos\theta) - mga(1 + \cos\theta) \qquad \text{... (vii)}$

From Eq. (vii) $\qquad \dfrac{\partial L}{\partial\dot\theta} = 2ma^2\dot\theta(1 - \cos\theta) \qquad\qquad\qquad\qquad \text{... (viii)}$

and $\qquad\qquad \dfrac{\partial L}{\partial\theta} = ma^2\dot\theta^2\sin\theta + mga\sin\theta \qquad\qquad\qquad \text{... (ix)}$

The Lagrangian equation of motion is

$$\frac{d}{dt}\left(\frac{\partial L}{\partial\dot\theta}\right) - \frac{\partial L}{\partial\theta} = 0 \qquad\qquad\qquad\qquad\qquad \text{... (x)}$$

Substituting the values from Eq. (viii) and (ix) in Eq. (x), we get

$$\frac{d}{dt}\left[2ma^2\dot\theta(1 - \cos\theta)\right] - \left[ma^2\dot\theta^2\sin\theta + mga\sin\theta\right] = 0$$

or $\qquad\qquad 2ma^2\ddot\theta(1 - \cos\theta) + 2ma^2\dot\theta\sin\theta\,\dot\theta - ma^2\dot\theta^2\sin\theta - mga\sin\theta = 0$

or $$\ddot{\theta}(1-\cos\theta)+\frac{1}{2}\sin\theta\,\dot{\theta}^2-\frac{g}{2a}\sin\theta=0$$

This is the required equation of motion.

Q. 14.13. An electrical circuit contains an inductance L and a capacitance C. Find the Lagrangian equation of motion when the charge of the condenser is q. (G.N.D.U. 2004)

Ans. The Lagrangian for an electrical circuit consisting of a finite number of inductances, capacitances and resistances is expressed as

$$L_E = T_M - V_E$$

where L_E is the Lagrangian of the electrical circuit, T_M the magnetic energy of the electrical circuit analogous to the kinetic energy of the mechanical system and V_E the electrical energy of the electrical circuit analogous to the potential energy of the mechanical system.

The Lagrangian equation of motion for such a circuit can be written as

$$\frac{d}{dt}\left(\frac{\partial L_E}{\partial \dot{q}_j}\right)-\frac{\partial L_E}{\partial q_j}=Q_j$$

where Q_j is the generalised force due to friction while the conservative forces are included in L_E. If the system is free from any frictional or dissipative forces $Q_j = 0$ so that the equation of motion becomes

$$\frac{d}{dt}\left(\frac{\partial L_E}{\partial \dot{q}_j}\right)-\frac{\partial L_E}{\partial q_j}=0$$

When the circuit contains an inductance L and a capacitance C charged to q coulombs, we have

Magnetic energy $\qquad T_M = \frac{1}{2}L\,i^2 = \frac{1}{2}L\dot{q}^2$ ... (i)

and Electrical energy $\qquad V_E = \frac{1}{2}\frac{q^2}{C}$ ... (ii)

Hence Lagrangian $\qquad L_E = \frac{1}{2}L\dot{q}^2 - \frac{1}{2}\frac{q^2}{C}$ ... (iii)

Taking q as the generalised co-ordinate, we have

$$\frac{d}{dt}\left(\frac{\partial L_E}{\partial \dot{q}}\right)-\frac{\partial L_E}{\partial q}=0$$ .. (iv)

From Eq. (iii) $\qquad \dfrac{\partial L_E}{\partial \dot{q}} = L\dot{q}$ and $\dfrac{\partial L_E}{\partial q} = -\dfrac{q}{C}$

Hence Eq. (iv) becomes

$$\frac{d}{dt}(L\dot{q})+\frac{q}{C}=0$$

or $\qquad L\ddot{q}+\dfrac{q}{C}=0$ ... (v)

Eq. (v) is the required equation of motion.

Q. 14.14. Derive the Lagrangian of a charged particle in an electromagnetic field.

(Gharwal U. 2000)

Ans. Lagrangian of charged particle in electro-magnetic field. When a charged particle moves in an electro-magnetic field it experiences Lorentz force given by

$$\vec{F} = q\,(\vec{E} + \vec{v}\times\vec{B})$$ ... (i)

To incorporate Eq. (i) in Lagrangian formulation we express $\vec{B}$ and $\vec{E}$ is terms of vector potential $\vec{A}$ and scalar potential ϕ. Then in S. I. units

$$\vec{B} = \vec{\nabla} \times \vec{A} \text{ and } \vec{E} = - \vec{\nabla}\phi - \frac{\partial \vec{A}}{\partial t}$$

Substituting in Eq. (*i*) , we get

$$\vec{F} = q\left[- \vec{\nabla}\phi - \frac{\partial \vec{A}}{\partial t} + \vec{v} \times (\vec{\nabla} \times \vec{A}) \right] \qquad ...(ii)$$

Using the expression for vector triple product

$$\vec{A} \times \vec{B} \times \vec{C} = \vec{B}\,(\vec{A}.\vec{C}) - \vec{C}\,(\vec{A}.\vec{B}), \text{ we get}$$

$$\vec{v} \times \vec{\nabla} \times \vec{A} = \vec{\nabla}\,(\vec{v}.\vec{A}) - \vec{A}\,(\vec{v}.\vec{\nabla}) = \vec{\nabla}\,(\vec{v}.\vec{A}) - (\vec{v}.\vec{\nabla})\,\vec{A} \qquad ...(iii)$$

As $\qquad\qquad \vec{F} = \dfrac{d}{dt}\,(m\vec{v})$, Eq. (*ii*) can be written as

$$\frac{d}{dt}\,(m\vec{v}) = q\left[- \vec{\nabla}\phi - \left\{ \frac{\partial \vec{A}}{\partial t} + (\vec{v}.\vec{\nabla})\,\vec{A} - \vec{\nabla}(\vec{v}.\vec{A}) \right\} \right]$$

$$= q\left[- \vec{\nabla}\,(\phi - \vec{v}.\vec{A}) - \frac{\partial \vec{A}}{\partial t} \right] \left[\because (\vec{v}.\vec{\nabla})\,\vec{A} = 0 \right] \qquad ...(iv)$$

or $\qquad \dfrac{d}{dt}(m\vec{v} + q\vec{A}) = -q\,\vec{\nabla}\,(\phi - \vec{v}.\vec{A})$

or $\qquad \dfrac{d}{dt}(m\vec{v} + q\vec{A}) + \vec{\nabla}\,[q(\phi - \vec{v}.\vec{A})] = 0 \qquad\qquad ...(v)$

Comparing Eq. (*v*) with general form of Lagrange's equation

i.e. $\qquad \dfrac{d}{dt}\left(\dfrac{\partial L}{\partial \dot{q}_j} \right) - \dfrac{\partial L}{\partial q_j} = 0$

we have

$$\frac{\partial L}{\partial \dot{q}_j} = \frac{\partial L}{\partial \dot{x}_j} = \frac{\partial L}{\partial v} = m\vec{v} + q\vec{A} \qquad (\because \dot{x}_j = \dot{x} = v \text{ the generalised velocity}) ... (vi)$$

and $\qquad \dfrac{\partial L}{\partial q_j} = \dfrac{\partial L}{\partial x_j} = -\vec{\nabla}\left[q\,(\phi - \vec{v}.\vec{A}) \right]$

$$= \frac{\partial}{\partial x}\left[-q\,(\phi - \vec{v}.\vec{A}) \right]$$

or $\qquad \dfrac{\partial L}{\partial x} = \dfrac{\partial}{\partial x}\left[-q\,(\phi - vA) \right] \qquad\qquad ...(vii)$

$$[\because \vec{v} \text{ and } \vec{A} \text{ are acting in the same direction } \vec{v}.\vec{A} = vA]$$

For a single particle of charge q Eq. (*vi*) and (*vii*) are valid only if $L = T - V$

where $\qquad\qquad T = \dfrac{1}{2}\,mv^2 \text{ and } V = q(\phi - vA)$

$\therefore \qquad\qquad L = \dfrac{1}{2}\,mv^2 - q\phi + qvA \qquad\qquad ....(viii)$

On differentiating Eq. (*viii*) with respect to $\dot{x}$ (or v) we get

$$\frac{\partial L}{\partial \dot{x}} = mv + q\,A \text{ which is given by Eq. } (vi)$$

Hence the Lagrangian of a charged particle in an electro-magnetic field is represented by

$$L = \frac{1}{2}\,mv^2 - q\phi + qv\,A$$

where A is the vector potential.

Q. 14.15. Define Hamiltonian function from Lagrangian of a system. Hence derive Hamilton's (cannonical) equations. *(P.U. 2000; Gauhati U. 2000; Gharwal U. 2000)*

Ans. Hamilton's function. Lagrangian is in general a function of generalised co-ordinates q_j, $\dot{q}_j$ and t i.e.

$$L = L\,(q_j, q_j, t)$$

$$\therefore \qquad \frac{dL}{dt} = \Sigma\frac{\partial L}{\partial q_j}\,\dot{q}_j + \Sigma\frac{\partial L}{\partial \dot{q}_j}\,\ddot{q}_j + \frac{\partial L}{\partial t} \qquad\qquad\qquad ...(i)$$

The Lagrangian equation for a conservative system is

$$\frac{d}{dt}\left[\frac{\partial L}{\partial \dot{q}_j}\right] - \frac{\partial L}{\partial q_j} = 0$$

or $\qquad\qquad \dfrac{d}{dt}\left[\dfrac{\partial L}{\partial \dot{q}_j}\right] = \dfrac{\partial L}{\partial q_j}$

Substituting in Eq. (i), we get

$$\frac{dL}{dt} = \Sigma\frac{d}{dt}\left[\frac{\partial L}{\partial \dot{q}_j}\right]\dot{q}_j + \Sigma\frac{\partial L}{\partial \dot{q}_j}\,\ddot{q}_j + \frac{\partial L}{\partial t}$$

$$= \Sigma\frac{d}{dt}\left[\frac{\partial L}{\partial \dot{q}_j}\,\dot{q}_j\right] + \frac{\partial L}{\partial t}$$

or $\qquad\qquad \dfrac{\partial L}{\partial t} = \dfrac{d}{dt}\left[L - \Sigma\dfrac{\partial L}{\partial \dot{q}_j}\,\dot{q}_j\right] \qquad\qquad\qquad ...(ii)$

Now $\qquad\qquad \dfrac{\partial L}{\partial \dot{q}_j} = p_j \qquad\qquad\qquad$ (generalised momentum)

$\therefore$ Eq. (ii) becomes

$$\frac{\partial L}{\partial t} = \frac{d}{dt}\left[L - \Sigma\,p_j\,\dot{q}_j\right]$$

or $\qquad \dfrac{d}{dt}\left[\Sigma\,p_j\,\dot{q}_j - L\right] = -\dfrac{\partial L}{\partial t} \qquad\qquad\qquad ...(iii)$

The function $\Sigma\,p_j\,\dot{q}_j - L = H$ is known as Hamiltonian function.

Hamilton's equations of motion. Hamiltonian function

$$H = \Sigma\,p_j\,\dot{q}_j - L$$

H is, therefore, an explicit function of p, $\dot{q}$ and t given by

$$H = \overset{n}{\underset{j=1}{\Sigma}}\,\dot{q}_j\,p_j - L(q_j, \dot{q}_j, t) \qquad\qquad\qquad ...(iii)\,(a)$$

Taking differentials on both sides

$$dH = d \sum_{j=1}^{n} q_j \, p_j - dL \, (q_j, \dot{q}_j, t)$$

$$= \sum_{j=1}^{n} \dot{q}_j \, dp_j + \sum_{j=1}^{n} p_j \, d\dot{q}_j - \sum_{j=1}^{n} \frac{\partial L}{\partial q_j} \, dq_j$$

$$- \sum_{j=1}^{n} \frac{\partial L}{\partial \dot{q}_j} d\dot{q}_j - \frac{\partial L}{\partial t} dt \qquad \qquad ... (iv)$$

But $\dfrac{\partial L}{\partial \dot{q}_j} = p_j$ (generalised momentum)

∴ Eq. (iv) becomes

$$dH = \sum_{j=1}^{n} \dot{q}_j \, dp_j - \sum_{j=1}^{n} \frac{\partial L}{\partial q_j} dq_j - \frac{\partial L}{\partial t} dt \qquad ... (v)$$

The Lagrange equations of motion are

$$\frac{d}{dt}\left[\frac{\partial L}{\partial \dot{q}_j} \right] - \frac{\partial L}{\partial q_j} = 0$$

As $\dfrac{\partial L}{\partial \dot{q}_j} = p_j \, , \, \dfrac{d}{dt}\left(p_j \right) - \dfrac{\partial L}{\partial q_j} = 0$

or $\dot{p}_j = \dfrac{\partial L}{\partial q_j}$ ... (vi)

Substituting the value of $\dfrac{\partial L}{\partial q_j} = \dot{p}_j$ in Eq. (v), we have

$$dH = \sum_{j=1}^{n} \dot{q}_j \, dp_j - \sum_{j=1}^{n} \dot{p}_j \, dq_j - \frac{\partial L}{\partial t} dt \qquad ... (vii)$$

As already stated H is a function of p_j, q_j and t.

∴ $dH = \sum_{j=1}^{n} \dfrac{\partial H}{\partial q_j} \, dq_j + \sum_{j=1}^{n} \dfrac{\partial H}{\partial p_j} \, dp_j + \dfrac{\partial H}{\partial t} dt \qquad ... (viii)$

Comparing Eqs. (vii) and (viii), we have

$$\frac{\partial H}{\partial q_j} = - \dot{p}_j \qquad \qquad ... (ix)$$

$$\frac{\partial H}{\partial p_j} = \dot{q}_j \qquad \qquad ... (x)$$

$$\frac{\partial H}{\partial t} = - \frac{\partial L}{\partial t} \qquad \qquad ... (xi)$$

Eqs. (ix), (x) and (xi) are known as *Hamiltonian equations* or *Hamiltonian cannonical equations*.

Q. 14.16. What is Hamiltonian? Explain its physical significance.   (*Gharwal U.* 2000)

Ans. Hamiltonian or Hamilton's function. See Q. 14.15.

Physical significance of Hamiltonian function. (*i*) The Hamiltonian H is an explicit function of p, q and t

or $H = H\,(p, q, t)$

∴ $\dfrac{dH}{dt} = \Sigma \dfrac{\partial H}{\partial p_j} \, \dot{p}_j + \Sigma \dfrac{\partial H}{\partial q_j} \, \dot{q}_j + \dfrac{\partial H}{\partial t}$

According to Hamilton's equations

$$\frac{\partial H}{\partial p_j} = \dot{q}_j, \frac{\partial H}{\partial q_j} = -\dot{p}_j \, ; \, \frac{\partial H}{\partial t} = -\frac{\partial L}{\partial t}$$

Using these equations

$$\frac{d H}{d t} = \Sigma \dot{q}_j \, \dot{p}_j - \Sigma \dot{p}_j \, \dot{q}_j - \frac{\partial L}{\partial t} = -\frac{\partial L}{\partial t}$$

If L is not an explicit function of time, then $\frac{\partial L}{\partial t} = 0$.

$\therefore$ $\qquad\qquad \dfrac{d H}{d t} = 0$ or $H = $ a constant

Hence *Hamiltonian H is a constant if L is not an explicit function of time.*

(*ii*) For a conservative system, the Hamiltonian

$$H = \Sigma p_j \dot{q}_j - L$$

and $\qquad\qquad p_j = \dfrac{\partial L}{\partial \dot{q}_j}$

$\therefore \qquad\qquad H = \Sigma \dfrac{\partial L}{\partial \dot{q}_j} \dot{q}_j - L = \Sigma \dot{q}_j \, \dfrac{\partial L}{\partial \dot{q}_j} - L$

But $\qquad L = T - V; \, \therefore \, H = \Sigma \dot{q}_j \cdot \dfrac{\partial (T - V)}{\partial \dot{q}_j} - (T - V)$

or $\qquad\qquad H = \Sigma \dot{q}_j \cdot \left[\dfrac{\partial T}{\partial \dot{q}_j} - \dfrac{\partial V}{\partial \dot{q}_j} \right] - (T - V)$

$$= \Sigma \dot{q}_j \frac{\partial T}{\partial \dot{q}_j} - (T - V) \qquad\qquad \left[\because \frac{\partial V}{\partial \dot{q}_j} = 0 \right]$$

Now $\qquad\qquad T = \dfrac{1}{2} mv^2 = \dfrac{1}{2} m \dot{q}_j^2 \quad \therefore \dfrac{\partial T}{\partial \dot{q}_j} = m \dot{q}_j$

Hence $\qquad\qquad H = \Sigma \dot{q}_j \, m \dot{q}_j - (T - V) = \Sigma m \dot{q}_j^2 - (T - V)$

But $\qquad\qquad \Sigma \, m \dot{q}_j^2 = 2 \Sigma \dfrac{1}{2} m \dot{q}_j^2 = 2T$

$\therefore \qquad\qquad H = 2T - T + V = T + V = E \,(\text{Total energy})$

Thus *Hamiltonian function is equal to the total energy of the conservative system.*

Q. 14. 17. State and explain Hamilton's principle.   (*M.D.U.* 2007; *Gauhati U.* 2000)

Ans. Hamilton's principle. This principal states that

'*Out of all possible paths along which a dynamical system can move from one configuration to another within a given interval of time, the actual path taken is that which minimises the time integral of the Lagrangian function.*'

Mathematically it means that the motion of the system from time t_1 to t_2 takes place in such a way

that the integral $\; I = \displaystyle\int_{t_1}^{t_2} L \; dt \;$ has a maximum or a minimum (*i.e.* extremum) value for the path of motion.

In Hamilton's principle the end points of the path are fixed both in space and time but there is no restriction on the nature of dynamical system.

For the integral $I = \int\limits_{t_1}^{t_2} L \, dt$ to have a stationary (maximum or minimum) value

$$\delta I = \delta \int\limits_{t_1}^{t_2} L \, dt = \delta \int\limits_{t_1}^{t_2} (T - V) \, dt = 0 \qquad \qquad ...(i)$$

Now, Hamiltonian is defined as

$$H = \Sigma \, p_j \, \dot{q}_j - L$$

or $\quad L = \Sigma \, p_j \, \dot{q}_j - H \, (p, q, t) \qquad \qquad [\because H$ is a function of $p, q, t.]$

$\therefore \qquad\qquad \delta I = \delta \int\limits_{t_1}^{t_2} \Big[\, \Sigma \, p_j \, \dot{q}_j - H(p, q, t) \, \Big] \, dt = 0$

$$= \delta \int\limits_{t_1}^{t_2} \Big[\, \Sigma \, p_j \, \frac{d}{dt} q_j - H(p, q, t) \, \Big] \, dt = 0 \qquad \Big[\because \dot{q}_j = \frac{d}{dt} q_j \Big]$$

or $\qquad\qquad \delta I = \delta \sum\limits_{J=1}^{n} \int p_j \cdot d \, q_j - \delta \int\limits_{t_1}^{t_2} H \, dt = 0 \qquad \qquad ...(ii)$

Eq. (*ii*) is a modified form of Hamilton's principle.

Q. 14.18. State Hamilton's principle and derive Lagrange's equation of motion from it.

(M.D.U. 2007; *P.U.* 2000)

Ans. Hamilton's principle. See Q. 14.17.

Lagrange's equation from Hamilton's principle. Lagrangian function L is a function of q, $\dot{q}$ and t or

$$L = (q, \, \dot{q} , \, t)$$

If the Lagrangian function does not depend upon time explicitly

$$L = L(q, \, \dot{q})$$

$\therefore \qquad\qquad \delta L = \Sigma \dfrac{\partial L}{\partial q_j} \, \delta q_j + \Sigma \dfrac{\partial L}{\partial \dot{q}_j} \, \delta \dot{q}_j \qquad \qquad ...(i)$

Integrating *w.r.t.* time within the limits t_1 and t_2, we get

$$\int\limits_{t_1}^{t_2} \delta L \, dt = \int\limits_{t_1}^{t_2} \Sigma \frac{\partial L}{\partial q_j} \, \delta q_j \, dt + \int\limits_{t_1}^{t_2} \Sigma \frac{\partial L}{\partial \dot{q}_j} \delta \dot{q}_j \, dt \qquad \qquad ...(i)(a)$$

But according to Hamilton's principle

$$\delta \int\limits_{t_1}^{t_2} L \, dt = 0 \quad \text{or} \quad \int\limits_{t_1}^{t_2} \delta L \, dt = 0 \qquad \qquad [\text{Eq. } (i) \text{ Q. 14. 17}]$$

$\therefore$ Eq. (*i*) (*a*) becomes $\int\limits_{t_1}^{t_2} \Sigma \dfrac{\partial L}{\partial q_j} \, \delta q_j \, dt + \int\limits_{t_1}^{t_2} \Sigma \dfrac{\partial L}{\partial \dot{q}_j} \, \delta \dot{q}_j \, dt = 0 \qquad \qquad ...(ii)$

Now $\qquad\qquad \delta \dot{q}_j = \dfrac{d}{dt} \delta q_j$ or $\delta \dot{q}_j \cdot dt = d(\delta q_j)$

Substituting in Eq. (*ii*), we get

$$\int\limits_{t_1}^{t_2} \Sigma \frac{\partial L}{\partial q_j} \delta q_j \, dt + \int\limits_{t_1}^{t_2} \Sigma \frac{\partial L}{\partial q_j} \, d(\delta q_j) = 0$$

Integrating by parts, we get

$$\int_{t_1}^{t_2} \Sigma \frac{\partial L}{\partial q_j} \delta q_j \, dt + \left\{ \Sigma \left[\frac{\partial L}{\partial \dot{q}_j} \delta q_j \right]_{t_1}^{t_2} - \Sigma \int_{t_1}^{t_2} \frac{d}{dt} \left(\frac{\partial L}{\partial \dot{q}_j} \right) \delta q_j \, dt \right\} = 0$$

Now $\delta q_j = 0$ at t_1 and t_2

$\therefore$ $\frac{\partial L}{\partial \dot{q}_j} \delta q_j = 0$ at t_1 and t_2 or $\left[\frac{\partial L}{\partial \dot{q}_j} \delta q_j \right]_{t_1}^{t_2} = 0$

$\therefore$ $\int_{t_1}^{t_2} \Sigma \frac{\partial L}{\partial q_j} \delta q_j \, dt - \Sigma \int_{t_1}^{t_2} \frac{d}{dt} \left(\frac{\partial L}{\partial \dot{q}_j} \right) \delta q_j \, dt = 0$

or $\int_{t_1}^{t_2} \Sigma \left[\frac{\partial L}{\partial q_j} - \frac{d}{dt} \left(\frac{\partial L}{\partial \dot{q}_j} \right) \right] \delta q_j \, dt = 0$

or $\left[\frac{\partial L}{\partial q_j} - \frac{d}{dt} \left(\frac{\partial L}{\partial \dot{q}_j} \right) \right] \delta q_j \, dt = 0$

or $\frac{\partial L}{\partial q_j} - \frac{d}{dt} \left(\frac{\partial L}{\partial \dot{q}_j} \right) = 0$ $[\because \delta q_j \, dt \neq 0] \ldots (iii)$

$\therefore$ $\frac{d}{dt} \left(\frac{\partial L}{\partial \dot{q}_j} \right) - \frac{\partial L}{\partial q_j} = 0$ $\ldots (iv)$

Eq. (iv) is the required Lagrange's equation.

Q. 14.19. Use Hamilton's canonical equations to obtain equations of motion of a simple pendulum.   (P.U. 2000)

Ans. Equation of motion of simple pendulum from Hamilton's equation.

In **Q. 14.9.** (b) we have shown in Eq. (i) that kinetic energy of the bob of a simple pendulum is $T = \frac{1}{2} ml^2 \dot{\theta}^2$ and the potential energy

$$V = mgl \, (1 - \cos\theta) \text{ so that the Lagrangian}$$

$$L = T - V = \frac{1}{2} ml^2 \dot{\theta}^2 - mgl(1 - \cos\theta) \quad \ldots (i) \, [\text{Eq. } (i) \, (a) \, \mathbf{Q} \, \mathbf{14.9}]$$

Now $p_\theta = \frac{\partial L}{\partial \dot{\theta}} = ml^2 \dot{\theta}$ $\ldots (ii)$

and Hamiltonian $H = \Sigma p_j \dot{q}_j - L$ $[\text{See } \mathbf{Q. \, 14.15} \text{ Eq. } (iii) \, (a)]$

In terms of p_θ and $\dot{\theta}$, $H = p_\theta \dot{\theta} - L$

$$= ml^2 \dot{\theta}^2 - \frac{1}{2} ml^2 \dot{\theta}^2 + mgl(1 - \cos\theta)$$

$$= \frac{1}{2} ml^2 \dot{\theta}^2 + mgl(1 - \cos\theta) \quad \ldots (iii)$$

$$= T + V$$

Thus H is the total energy of the system.

Substituting $\dot{\theta} = \frac{p_\theta}{ml^2}$ from Eq. (ii) in Eq. (iii), we get

$$H = \frac{1}{2} ml^2 \left(\frac{p_\theta}{ml^2} \right)^2 + mgl \, (1 - \cos\theta) \quad \ldots (iv)$$

From Eq. (*iv*)

$$\frac{\partial H}{\partial p_\theta} = \frac{p_\theta}{ml^2} \text{ and } \frac{\partial H}{\partial \theta} = mgl \sin\theta$$

The Hamiltonian equations of motion for this system now become

$$\dot{\theta} = \frac{\partial H}{\partial p_\theta} = \frac{p_\theta}{ml^2} \qquad \qquad ...(v)$$

and

$$\dot{p}_\theta = -\frac{\partial H}{\partial \theta} = -mgl \sin\theta \qquad \qquad ...(vi)$$

From Eq. (*v*) $p_\theta = ml^2\dot{\theta}$ or $\dot{p}_\theta = ml^2\ddot{\theta}$

Substituting in Eq. (*vi*) we get

$$ml^2\ddot{\theta} = -mgl \sin\theta$$

or

$$\ddot{\theta} = -\frac{g}{l}\sin\theta$$

or

$$\ddot{\theta} + \frac{g}{l}\sin\theta = 0$$

which represents the equation of motion of a simple pendulum.

Q. 14.20. Show that when a charged particle moves inside an electromagnetic field it experiences a force which is derivable from a velocity dependent potential. Hence obtain expression for Lagrangian and Hamiltonian of the charged particles. (*P.U.* 2001)

Ans. It has been proved in **Q. 14. 14** Eq. (*iv*) that when a charged particle moves in an electro magnetic field, the force acting on it

$$\vec{F} = \frac{d}{dt}(m\vec{v}) = q\left[-\vec{\nabla}(\phi - \vec{v}.\vec{A}) - \frac{\partial\vec{A}}{\partial t} \right]$$

The quantity $\qquad \phi - \vec{v}.\vec{A} \qquad \qquad ...(i)$

is the *velocity dependent potential*.

(*i*) **Lagrangian for charged particle.** According to Eq. (*viii*) **Q. 14.14** Lagrangian for the charged particle

$$L = T - V = \frac{1}{2}mv^2 - q\phi + q(\vec{v}.\vec{A}) \qquad \qquad ...(ii)$$

$$= \frac{1}{2}mv^2 - q\phi + qvA \quad [\because \vec{v} \text{ and } \vec{A} \text{ act in the same direction.}] ...(iii)$$

(*ii*) **Hamiltonian for charged particle.** From Eq. (*iii*) we have, by differentiating with respect to v

$$p = \frac{\partial L}{\partial v} = mv + qA$$

or

$$v = \frac{1}{m}(p - qA)$$

$\therefore$ Kinetic energy $\qquad T = \frac{1}{2}mv^2 = \frac{1}{2m}(p - qA)^2 \qquad \qquad ...(iv)$

As given in Eq. (*i*), Potential energy

$$V = \phi - \vec{v}.\vec{A} \qquad \qquad ...(v)$$

Hence the Hamiltonian is given by

$$H = T + V = \frac{1}{2m}[p - qA]^2 + q\phi - q(\vec{v}.\vec{A})$$

Taking A and ϕ in terms of co-ordinates r and t we have Hamiltonian

$$H = H(r,p,t) = \frac{i}{2m}\left[p - qA(r,t)\right]^2 + q\phi(r,t) - q(\vec{v}.\vec{A})$$

The canonical equations of motion, therefore, are

$$\dot{p} = -\vec{\nabla} H = -q\,\vec{\nabla}\phi + q\vec{\nabla}(\vec{v}.\vec{A})$$

with $\qquad\qquad v = \frac{1}{m}(p - qA)$

If the electromagnetic field is not changing *i.e.* A and ϕ do not involve t explicitly, then

$$\Sigma\,p_j\,\dot{q}_j = 2T + q\,(\vec{v}.\vec{A})$$

so that $\qquad\qquad H = \Sigma\,p_j\,\dot{q}_j - L$

$$= 2T + q\,(\vec{v}.\vec{A}) - \left[T - q\phi + q\,(\vec{v}.\vec{A})\right]$$

$$= T + q\phi = \frac{1}{2}\,mv^2 + q\phi$$

so that H can be interpreted as the sum of the kinetic energy and electrostatic potential energy of the particle.

Note : In this question q represents charge and q_j (and $\dot{q}_j$) represent respective generalised co-ordinates.

Q. 14.21. State and prove the principle of least action. *(P.U. 2001)*

Ans. Principle of least action. In Mechanics *action is defined as time integral of twice the kinetic energy.*

$\therefore$ Action $\qquad\qquad A = \int\limits_{t_1}^{t_2} 2T\,dT$

But $\qquad\qquad 2T = \Sigma\,p_j\,\dot{q}_j \quad\therefore\; A = \int\limits_{t_1}^{t_2}\Sigma\,p_j\,\dot{q}_j\,dt$

The principle of least action states that for a system for which Hamiltonian is constant.

$$\Delta\int\limits_{t_1}^{t_2}\Sigma\,p_j\,\dot{q}_j\,dt = 0$$

where Δ represents a variation of path which allows a change in time as well as position co-ordinates.

Proof. To prove the principle of least action we shall first distinguish between two types of variation δ and Δ.

In δ variation time remains constant and there is variation only in position co-ordinates.

In Δ variation both time and position co-ordinates vary. Further time t varies even at end points where the position co-ordiantes q_j are zero.

If α is the variational parameter, then in δ-variation t is independent of α, so that

$$\delta q_j = d\alpha\,\frac{\partial q_j}{\partial \alpha} \qquad\qquad\qquad ...(i)$$

In Δ variation $t = t\,(\alpha)$. Thus in Δ variation the function q_j depends upon t and α and therefore $q_j = q_j\,(t,\alpha)$

Δ variation is defined as

$$\Delta q_j = dq_j = d\alpha\left[\frac{dq_j\,(\alpha,t)}{d\alpha}\right]$$

$$= d\alpha\left[\frac{\partial q_j}{\partial \alpha}\frac{d\alpha}{d\alpha} + \frac{\partial q_j}{\partial t}\frac{dt}{d\alpha}\right]$$

$$= d\alpha \left[\frac{\partial q_j}{\partial \alpha} + \dot{q}_j \frac{dt}{d\alpha} \right]$$

$$= d\alpha \frac{\partial q_j}{\partial \alpha} + \dot{q}_j \frac{dt}{d\alpha} \, d\alpha \qquad \qquad \ldots (ii)$$

Since change in t occurs as a result of Δ-variation

$$d\alpha \frac{dt}{d\alpha} = \Delta t \qquad \qquad \ldots (iii)$$

Substituting the values from Eq. (i) and (iii) in Eq. (ii), we get

$$\Delta q_j = \delta q_j + \dot{q}_j \, \Delta t \qquad \qquad \ldots (iv)$$

Action $\qquad A = \int_{t_1}^{t_2} \Sigma \, p_j \, \dot{q}_j \, dt = \int_{t_1}^{t_2} (L + H) \, dt \qquad \qquad [\because L + H = 2 T]$

$$= \int_{t_1}^{t_2} L \, dt + \int_{t_1}^{t_2} H \, dt = \int_{t_1}^{t_2} L \, dt + H \, (t_2 - t_1) \qquad \qquad \ldots (v)$$

Since H is conserved along the actual path.

$\therefore \ \Delta$ variation of action $\Delta A = \Delta \int_{t_1}^{t_2} L \, dt + H \, \Delta t \big|_{t_1}^{t_2} \qquad \qquad \ldots (vi)$

since $H(t_2 - t_1) = H \, \Delta t \big|_{t_1}^{t_2}$

To solve the integral $\Delta \int_{t_1}^{t_2} L \, dt$ where the limits t_1 and t_2 are also subject to change in the variation, we put

$$\int_{t_1}^{t_2} L \, dt = I \, (t_2) - I \, (t_1)$$

where $I \, (t_2)$ and $I \, (t_1)$ represent $\int_{t_1}^{t_2} I \, dt$ at t_2 and t_1 respectively.

Making use of Eq. (iv), we have

$$\Delta \int_{t_1}^{t_2} L \, dt = \delta I \, (t_2) + \dot{I}(t_2) \, \Delta t_2 - \delta I \, (t_1) - \dot{I}(t_1) \Delta t_1$$

$$= \delta I \, (t_2) - \delta I \, (t_1) + \dot{I} \, (t_2) \Delta t_2 - \dot{I}(t_1) \Delta t_1$$

$$= \delta \big[I(t_2) - I(t_1) \big] + \dot{I} \, (t_2) \, \Delta t_2 - \dot{I} \, (t_1) \Delta t_1$$

$$= \delta \int_{t_1}^{t_2} L \, dt + L \, \Delta t \big|_{t_1}^{t_2} \qquad \qquad \ldots (vii)$$

To find the value of $\delta \int_{t_1}^{t_2} L \, dt$, we have

$$\delta \int_{t_1}^{t_2} L \, dt = \int_{t_1}^{t_2} \Sigma \left[\frac{\partial L}{\partial q_j} \delta q_j + \frac{\partial L}{\partial \dot{q}_j} \delta \dot{q}_j \right] dt \qquad \ldots (viii) \, [\text{See Eq. } (i), \text{Q. 14.18}]$$

According to Lagrange's equation

$$\frac{d}{dt}\left[\frac{\partial L}{\partial \dot{q}_j}\right] - \frac{\partial L}{\partial q_j} = 0 \quad \text{or} \quad \frac{\partial L}{\partial q_j} = \frac{d}{dt}\left[\frac{\partial L}{\partial \dot{q}_j}\right]$$

Substituting in Eq. (*viii*), we get

$$\delta \int_{t_1}^{t_2} L\, dt = \int_{t_1}^{t_2} \sum \left\{ \frac{d}{dt}\left[\frac{\partial L}{\partial \dot{q}_j}\right]\delta q_j + \frac{\partial L}{\partial \dot{q}_j}\frac{d}{dt}\,\delta q_j \right\} dt$$

$$= \sum \int_{t_1}^{t_2} \frac{d}{dt}\left[\frac{\partial L}{\partial \dot{q}_j}\,\delta q_j\right] dt \qquad\qquad ... (ix)$$

From Eq. (*iv*) $\qquad\qquad \delta q_j = \Delta q_j - \dot{q}_j\, \Delta t$

Substituting in Eq. (*ix*), we get.

$$\delta \int_{t_1}^{t_2} L\, dt = \sum \int_{t_1}^{t_2} \frac{d}{dt}\left[\frac{\partial L}{\partial \dot{q}_j}\,\Delta q_j - \frac{\partial L}{\partial \dot{q}_j}\,\dot{q}_j\Delta t\right] dt$$

$$= \sum \left[\frac{\partial L}{\partial \dot{q}_j}\,\Delta q_j - \frac{\partial L}{\partial \dot{q}_j}\,\dot{q}_j\, \Delta t\right]_{t_1}^{t_2} \qquad\qquad ... (x)$$

At the end points $\qquad \Delta q_j = 0$

$\therefore$ Eq. (*x*) becomes

$$\delta \int_{t_1}^{t_2} L\, dt = \left[-\sum \frac{\partial L}{\partial \dot{q}_j}\,\dot{q}_j\, \Delta t\right]_{t_1}^{t_2}$$

Substituting in Eq. (*vii*), we get

$$\Delta \int_{t_1}^{t_2} L\, dt = \left[-\sum \frac{\partial L}{\partial \dot{q}_j}\,\dot{q}_j\, \Delta t + L\Delta t\right]_{t_1}^{t_2}$$

$$= \left[(-\sum p_j\, \dot{q}_j + L)\Delta t\right]_{t_1}^{t_2} \qquad\qquad ... (xi)$$

Substituting the value of $\Delta \int_{t_1}^{t_2} L\, dt$ from Eq. (*xi*) in Eq. (*vi*), we get

$$\Delta A = \left[\left(-\sum p_j\, \dot{q}_j + L\right)\Delta t\right]_{t_1}^{t_2} + \left[H\, \Delta t\right]_{t_1}^{t_2}$$

$$= \left[\left(-\sum p_j\, \dot{q}_j + L + H\right)\Delta t\right]_{t_1}^{t_2} \qquad\qquad ... (xii)$$

But $\qquad\qquad \sum p_j . \dot{q}_j = 2T = L + H$

Substituting in Eq. (*xii*), we have $\Delta A = 0$

or $\qquad\qquad \Delta \int_{t_1}^{t_2} \sum p_j\, \dot{q}_j\, dt = 0$

This verifies the principle of least action.

Q. 14.22. (*a*) **Define generalised co-ordinate. Obtain an expression for generalised momentum.**

(b) **Define cyclic co-ordinate. Show that generalised momentum conjugate to a cyclic co-ordinate is conserved.** *(P.U. 2001, 2000; Gharwal U. 2000)*

Ans. (a) **Generalised co-ordinate.** See Q. 14.3.

Generalised momentum. Lagrange's equation for a system of n degrees of freedom consists of n equations which require $2n$ constants for their solution. These are n generalised co-ordinates q_1, q_2 ...q_n and n generalised velocities $\dot{q}_1, \dot{q}_2.....\dot{q}_n$. Taken together these constitute $2n$ independent parameters which can describe the motion of the system.

We can also build similar formulation with generalised velocity and generalised momentum as two independent variables.

The Lagrangian equation of motion for a conservative system is given by

$$\frac{d}{dt}\left(\frac{\partial L}{\partial \dot{q}_j}\right) - \frac{\partial L}{\partial q_j} = 0$$

where
$$\frac{\partial L}{\partial \dot{q}_j} = \frac{\partial (T - V)}{\partial \dot{q}_j} = \frac{\partial T}{\partial \dot{q}_j} - \frac{\partial V}{\partial \dot{q}_j}$$

Since potential V depends only on generalised position co-ordinate q_j and not on generalised velocity $\dot{q}_j$, $\dfrac{\partial V}{\partial \dot{q}_j} = 0$

$$\therefore \qquad \frac{\partial L}{\partial \dot{q}_j} = \frac{\partial T}{\partial \dot{q}_j}$$

The kinetic energy T of a system is given by

$$T = \Sigma \frac{1}{2} m_j \dot{q}_j^2$$

$$\therefore \qquad \frac{\partial L}{\partial \dot{q}_j} = \frac{\partial T}{\partial \dot{q}_j} = \frac{\partial}{\partial \dot{q}_j} \Sigma \frac{1}{2} m_j \dot{q}_j^2$$

$$= m_j \dot{q}_j = \text{mass} \times \text{generalised velocity}$$

$$= \text{generalised momentum } (p_j)$$

$$\therefore \text{Generalised momentum } p_j = \frac{\partial L}{\partial \dot{q}_j}$$

p_j will have dimensions MLT^{-1} of linear momentum if q_j has dimensions of length. If q_j is an angular co-ordinate θ, then p_j will have dimension ML^2T^{-1} of angular momentum.

(b) **Cyclic co-ordinates.** The Lagrangian L of a system is a function of generalised co-ordinates q_j, generalised velocity $\dot{q}_j$ and time t. If the Lagrangian of a system does not contain a given co-ordinate, say q_j, then for such a system $\dfrac{\partial L}{\partial q_j} = 0$. Such a co-ordinate is known as ignorable or cyclic co-ordinate.

Hence *a generalised co-ordinate q_j is said to be cyclic if it does not appear explicitly in the Lagrangian of the system.*

Conservation of generalised momentum. For a conservative system Lagrange's equation is given by

$$\frac{d}{dt}\left[\frac{\partial T}{\partial \dot{q}_j}\right] - \frac{\partial L}{\partial q_j} = 0$$

If the generalised co-ordinate q_j is cyclic, then $\dfrac{\partial L}{\partial q_j} = 0$

$$\therefore \quad \frac{d}{dt}\left[\frac{\partial L}{\partial \dot{q}_j}\right] = 0$$

Integrating, we get $\dfrac{\partial L}{\partial \dot{q}_j} = $ a constant

But $\dfrac{\partial L}{\partial \dot{q}_j} = p_j$ the generalised momentum

$$\therefore \qquad\qquad p_j = \text{a constant.}$$

Thus, the *generalised momentum of the system conjugate to a cyclic co-ordinate is conserved.*

Q. 14.23. Show that if Lagrangian does not depend upon time explicitly the total energy of the system is conserved. *(P.U. 2001)*

Ans. Conservation of total energy. The Lagrangian L of a system is, in general, a function of q_j, $\dot{q}_j$ and t but if it does not depend upon time explicitly, then it is only a function of q_j and $\dot{q}_j$ i.e.

$$L = L\left(q_j, \dot{q}_j\right)$$

$$\therefore \qquad \frac{dL}{dt} = \Sigma \frac{\partial L}{\partial q_j}\frac{\partial q_j}{\partial t} + \Sigma \frac{\partial L}{\partial \dot{q}_j}\frac{\partial \dot{q}_j}{\partial t}$$

$$= \Sigma \frac{\partial L}{\partial q_j}\dot{q}_j + \Sigma \frac{\partial L}{\partial \dot{q}_j}\ddot{q}_j \qquad\qquad ...(i)$$

The Lagrange's equation for a conservative system is given by

$$\frac{d}{dt}\left[\frac{\partial L}{\partial \dot{q}_j}\right] - \frac{\partial L}{\partial q_j} = 0 \text{ or } \frac{\partial L}{\partial q_j} = \frac{d}{dt}\left(\frac{\partial L}{\partial \dot{q}_j}\right) \qquad\qquad ...(ii)$$

Substituting the value of $\dfrac{\partial L}{\partial q_j}$ from Eq. (*ii*) in Eq. (*i*), we get

$$\frac{dL}{dt} = \Sigma \frac{d}{dt}\left[\frac{\partial L}{\partial \dot{q}_j}\right]\dot{q}_j + \Sigma \frac{\partial L}{\partial \dot{q}_j}\ddot{q}_j = \Sigma\frac{d}{dt}\left[\dot{q}_j\frac{\partial L}{\partial \dot{q}_j}\right]$$

or $\quad \dfrac{dL}{dt} - \Sigma \dfrac{d}{dt}\left[\dot{q}_j\dfrac{\partial L}{\partial \dot{q}_j}\right] = 0$ or $\dfrac{d}{dt}\left[L - \Sigma \dot{q}_j\dfrac{\partial L}{\partial \dot{q}_j}\right] = 0$

Integrating both sides, we get

$$L - \Sigma\dot{q}_j\frac{\partial L}{\partial \dot{q}_j} = \text{constant} \qquad\qquad ...(iii)$$

But $\qquad\qquad L = T - V$

$$\therefore \qquad \frac{\partial L}{\partial \dot{q}_j} = \frac{\partial}{\partial \dot{q}_j}(T-V) = \frac{\partial T}{\partial \dot{q}_j} - \frac{\partial V}{\partial \dot{q}_j} \qquad\qquad ...(iv)$$

Again V, the potential depends only on q_j and not on $\dot{q}_j$.

Therefore, $\qquad \dfrac{\partial V}{\partial \dot{q}_j} = 0$

Eq. (*iv*) now reduces to

$$\frac{\partial L}{\partial \dot{q}_j} = \frac{\partial T}{\partial \dot{q}_j} \qquad\qquad ...(v)$$

But $\qquad\qquad T = \Sigma\dfrac{1}{2}m_j\dot{q}_j^2 \qquad\qquad ...(vi)$

$\therefore$ Eq. (v) becomes $\qquad \dfrac{\partial L}{\partial \dot{q}_j} = \dfrac{\partial}{\partial \dot{q}_j}\left[\,\Sigma\dfrac{1}{2}m_j\,\dot{q}_j^2\,\right] = m_j\,\dot{q}_j$

Substituting in Eq. (iii), we get

$\qquad\qquad L - \Sigma\dot{q}_j \times m_j\,\dot{q}_j = \text{a constant}$

or $\qquad\qquad L - \Sigma m_j\,\dot{q}_j^{\,2} = \text{a constant}$ $\qquad\qquad\qquad$ ... (vii)

But $\Sigma m_j\,\dot{q}_j^2 = 2T$ according to Eq. (vi)

Putting in Eq. (vii), we have

$\qquad\qquad\qquad L - 2T = \text{a constant or } T - V - 2T = \text{ a constant}$

or $\qquad -(T+V) = \text{a constant or } T+V = \text{ constant}$

But $\qquad\qquad T+V \doteq E$ the total energy $\quad \therefore E = \text{ a constant}$

Hence, we conclude that *if the Lagrangian does not depend upon time explicitly, the total energy of the conservative system remains conserved i.e. is a constant.*

Q. 14.24. State and prove law of conservation of linear momentum and angular momentum for a system of particles. $\qquad$ *(M.D.U. 2003; G.N.D.U. 2004)*

Ans. Law of conservation of linear momentum. Let us consider a system of particles with generalised co-ordinate q_j and its derivative dq_j The Lagrangian for the system is given by

$$L = T - V$$

where T is the kinetic energy. q_j does not appear in T because it depends upon velocity $(\dot{q}_j)$. T is therefore, not affected by the change of position or shift in origin.

V is the potential energy. It does not depend upon $\dot{q}_j$ as in a conservative system $\dfrac{\partial V}{\partial \dot{q}_j} = 0$. So only $\dfrac{\partial V}{\partial q_j}$ exists.

For a conservative system, Lagrangian equation of motion is given by

$$\dfrac{d}{dt}\left(\dfrac{\partial L}{\partial \dot{q}_j}\right) - \dfrac{\partial L}{\partial q_j} = 0$$

which under the above conditions becomes

$$\dfrac{d}{dt}\left(\dfrac{\partial T}{\partial \dot{q}_j}\right) + \dfrac{\partial V}{\partial q_j} = 0$$

or $\qquad\qquad\qquad \dot{p}_j = -\dfrac{\partial V}{\partial q_j} = Q_j \qquad\qquad\qquad\qquad$ ... (i)

where Q_j is the component of the total force along the direction of translation of q_j and p_j is the component of total linear momentum along the same direction.

Equation (i), therefore, represents the equation of motion for the total linear momentum.

Generalised force is given by

$$Q_j = \sum_i \vec{F}_i \cdot \dfrac{\partial \vec{r}_i}{\partial q_j}$$

where $\dfrac{\partial \vec{r}_i}{\partial q_j} = \hat{n}$ is the unit vector along the direction of translation

$\therefore \qquad\qquad\qquad Q_j = \Sigma_i \vec{F}_i \cdot \hat{n}$

or $$Q_j = \hat{n} \cdot \vec{F} \qquad \qquad \dots (ii)$$

which represents the component of total force along the direction of $\hat{n}$ *i.e.* translation

The kinetic energy is given by

$$T = \frac{1}{2} \sum_i m_i \, \dot{r}_i^2$$

and generalised momentum is given by

$$p_j = \frac{\partial T}{\partial \dot{q}_j} = \sum_i m_i \, \vec{\dot{r}}_i \cdot \frac{\partial \vec{\dot{r}}_i}{\partial \dot{q}_j} = \sum_i m_i \, \vec{v}_i \cdot \frac{\partial \vec{r}_i}{\partial q_j}$$

$$= \sum_i m_i \, \vec{v}_i \cdot \hat{n}$$

$$\therefore \qquad p_j = \hat{n} \cdot \sum_i m_i \, \vec{v}_i \qquad \qquad \dots (iii)$$

which gives the component of total linear momentum along the direction of translation.

Thus Eq. (*i*) *i.e.* $\dot{p}_j = Q_j$ is the equation of motion for the total linear momentum of the system.

Now, if q_j is cyclic co-ordinate, then $-\dfrac{\partial V}{\partial q_j} = Q_j = 0$

$\therefore$ From Eq. (*i*), we have

$$\dot{p}_j = Q_j = 0$$

or $$\dot{p}_j = 0$$

$$\therefore \qquad p_j = \text{a constant}$$

Thus, *if a given component of the total applied force vanishes, the corresponding component of the linear momentum is conserved.*

This proves the principle of conservation of linear momentum.

(*ii*) **Law of conservation of angular momentum.** To prove the conservation of angular momentum for a system of particles, consider a generalised co-ordinate q_j and its derivative dq_j.

The Lagrangian is given by $L = T - V$

T is the kinetic energy which does not depend upon q_j because it only depends upon the velocity $(\dot{q}_j)$.

V is the potential energy which depends upon q_j but does not depend upon $\dot{q}_j$.

For a conservative system, the Lagrangian equation is given by

$$\frac{d}{dt}\left(\frac{\partial L}{\partial \dot{q}_j}\right) + \frac{\partial L}{\partial q_j} = 0$$

which under the above conditions becomes

$$\frac{d}{dt}\left(\frac{\partial T}{\partial \dot{q}_j}\right) + \frac{\partial V}{\partial q_j} = 0$$

or $$\dot{p}_j = -\frac{\partial V}{\partial q_j} = Q_j \qquad \qquad \dots (i)$$

If q_j is a rotation co-ordinate, then the generalised force Q_j is the component of the total applied torque about the axis of rotation and p_j is the component of total angular momentum along the same axis so that Eq. (*i*) represents the equation of motion for the total angular momentum.

The generalised force is given by

$$Q_j = \sum_i \vec{F}_i \cdot \frac{\partial \vec{r}_i}{\partial q_j}$$

Now from Fig. 14.9 the magnitude of $\left| d\vec{r_i} \right| = AB\,dq_j$

[dq_j is infinitesimal rotation]

But $\quad \dfrac{AB}{OA} = \sin\theta \;\text{ or }\; AB = OA\sin\theta$

$$= \vec{r_i}\sin\theta$$

$\therefore \qquad \left| d\vec{r_i} \right| = \vec{r_i}\sin\theta\,dq_j$

so that $\qquad \left| \dfrac{\partial \vec{r_i}}{\partial q_j} \right| = \vec{r_i}\sin\theta$

$$= \hat{n} \times \vec{r_i} \qquad \ldots(ii)$$

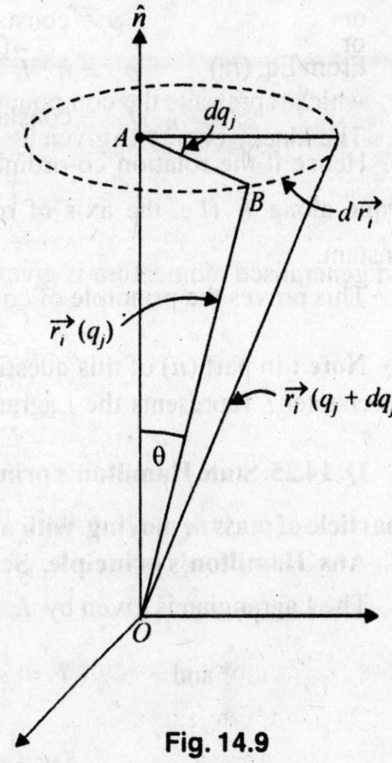

where $\hat{n}$ is a unit vector along OA the axis of rotation.

Thus $\dfrac{\partial \vec{r_i}}{\partial q_j} = \hat{n} \times \vec{r_i}$ shows that $\dfrac{\partial \vec{r_i}}{\partial q_j}$ is perpendicular both

to $\hat{n}$ and $\vec{r_i}$.

Now $\qquad\qquad Q_j = \sum_i \vec{F_i} \cdot \dfrac{\partial \vec{r_i}}{\partial q_j}$

Fig. 14.9

$$= \sum_i \vec{F_i} \cdot \hat{n} \times \vec{r_i} \qquad\qquad \left[\because \dfrac{\partial \vec{r_i}}{\partial q_j} = \hat{n} \times \vec{r_i} \right]$$

$$= \sum_i \hat{n} \cdot \vec{r_i} \times \vec{F_i} = \sum_i \hat{n} \cdot N_i \qquad \left[\text{where } \vec{N_i} \text{ is the torque} = \hat{r_i} \times \vec{F_i} \right]$$

$$= \hat{n} \cdot \sum_i \vec{N_i}$$

or $\qquad Q_j = \hat{n} \cdot \vec{N} \qquad\qquad \ldots(iii)\;[\text{ where } N \text{ is total torque.}]$

Equation (iii) represents that Q_j is the component of total torque about the axis of rotation.

Now $\qquad p_j = \dfrac{\partial T}{\partial \dot{q}_j} = \sum_i m_i\, \vec{r_i} \cdot \dfrac{\partial \vec{r_i}}{\partial \dot{q}_j} = \sum_i m_i \vec{v_i} \cdot \dfrac{\partial \vec{r_i}}{\partial q_j}$

$$= \sum_i m_i \vec{v_i} \cdot \hat{n} \times \vec{r_i} \qquad\qquad [\text{ From Eq. }(ii)\,]$$

$$= \sum_i \hat{n} \cdot \vec{r_i} \times m_i \vec{v_i}$$

$$= \hat{n} \sum_i \vec{r_i} \times m_i \vec{v_i}$$

$$= \hat{n} \sum_i \vec{L_i} \qquad\qquad [\, \vec{r_i} \times m_i \vec{v_i} = \vec{L_i} \text{ the angular momentum vector }]$$

or $\qquad p_j = \hat{n} \cdot \vec{L} \qquad\qquad \ldots(iv)$

Eq. (iv) shows that p_j is the component of total angular momentum along the axis of rotation and hence Eq. (i) represents the equation of motion for the total angular momentum of the system.

Now if q_j is a cyclic co-ordinate, then $-\dfrac{\partial V}{\partial q_j} = Q_j = 0$ and hence from Eq. (i)

$$\dot{p}_j = 0$$

or p_j = constant.

From Eq. (iv) $p_j = \hat{n} \cdot \vec{L}$

∴ $\hat{n} \cdot \vec{L}$ = constant.

Hence if the rotation co-ordinate q_j is cyclic, then Q_j which is the component of the applied torque along $\hat{n}$ (i.e. the axis of rotation) vanishes and thus the component of $\vec{L}$ along $\hat{n}$ is a constant.

This proves the principle of conservation of angular momentum.

Note : In part (ii) of this question $\vec{L}$ represents the total angular momentum vector whereas in this chapter L represents the Lagrangian.

Q. 14.25. State Hamilton's principle and use it to obtain the equation of motion $ma = -\dfrac{dV}{dx}$ for a particle of mass m moving with acceleration a in a potential V.   (P.U. 2001)

Ans. Hamilton's principle. See **Q. 14.17**

The Lagrangian is given by $L = T - V$

and $T = \dfrac{1}{2}m\dot{x}^2$

∴ $L = \dfrac{1}{2}m\dot{x}^2 - V$

Now $P_x = \dfrac{\partial L}{\partial \dot{x}} = m\dot{x}$ [∵ V is not a function of $\dot{x}$.]

∴ $\dot{x} = \dfrac{P_x}{m} = \dfrac{p}{m}$ ... (i) [where p = momentum]

The Hamiltonian is given by

$$H = T + V \text{ and } T = \dfrac{1}{2}m\dot{x}^2$$

or $H = \dfrac{1}{2}m\dot{x}^2 + V$ ... (ii)

$$= \dfrac{1}{2}m\left(\dfrac{p}{m}\right)^2 + V$$

$$= \dfrac{p^2}{2m} + V$$ ... (iii)

From Eq. (ii) $-\dfrac{\partial H}{\partial x} = -\dfrac{\partial V}{\partial x}$ ... (iv)

From Eq. (iii) $\dfrac{\partial H}{\partial p} = \dfrac{p}{m}$ [∵ V is not a function of p]

$$= \dot{x}$$ [using Eq. (i)]

or $\ddot{x} = \dfrac{\dot{p}}{m}$ ... (v)

Using Hamilton's equation $\dfrac{\partial H}{\partial q_j} = -\dot{p}_j$ we have $\dot{p} = -\dfrac{\partial H}{\partial x} = -\dfrac{\partial V}{\partial x}$ [From Eq. (iv)]

Putting $\dot{p} = -\dfrac{\partial V}{\partial x}$ in Eq. (v), we get

$$\ddot{x} = -\dfrac{1}{m}\dfrac{\partial V}{\partial x}$$

$$\text{or} \qquad m\ddot{x} = -\frac{\partial V}{\partial x}$$

$$\text{or} \qquad ma = -\frac{\partial V}{\partial x}$$

Q. 14.26. Show that if a given co-ordinate is cyclic in Lagrangian it will also be cyclic in Hamiltonian. *(P. U. 2001)*

Ans. Hamiltonian is a function of q, p and t and is given by

$$H = H(q_j, p_j, t)$$

The differential of H is

$$dH = \sum_j \frac{\partial H}{\partial q_j} dq_j + \sum_j \frac{\partial H}{\partial p_j} dp_j + \frac{\partial H}{\partial t} dt \qquad \qquad \dots(i)$$

The Hamiltonian H is given by

$$H = \sum_j p_j \dot{q}_j - L$$

$$\therefore \qquad dH = \sum_j \dot{q}_j \, dp_j + \sum_j p_j \, d\dot{q}_j - dL \qquad \qquad \dots(ii)$$

Now Lagrangian L is a function of q, $\dot{q}$ and t and is given by

$$L = L(q_j, \dot{q}_j, t)$$

$$\therefore \qquad dL = \sum_j \frac{\partial L}{\partial q_j} dq_j + \sum_j \frac{\partial L}{\partial \dot{q}_j} d\dot{q}_j + \frac{\partial L}{\partial t} dt \qquad \qquad \dots(iii)$$

Substituting the above value of dL in Eq. (ii), we have

$$dH = \sum_j \dot{q}_j \, dp_j + \sum_j p_j \, d\dot{q}_j - \sum_j \frac{\partial L}{\partial q_j} dq_j - \sum_j \frac{\partial L}{\partial \dot{q}_j} d\dot{q}_j - \frac{\partial L}{\partial t} dt \qquad \dots(iv)$$

But

$$\frac{\partial L}{\partial \dot{q}_j} = p_j \text{ and } \frac{\partial L}{\partial q_j} = \dot{p}_j$$

Substituting $\dfrac{\partial L}{\partial \dot{q}_j} = p_j$ in Eq. (iv), we get

$$dH = \sum_j \dot{q}_j \, dp_j - \sum_j \frac{\partial L}{\partial q_j} dq_j - \frac{\partial L}{\partial t} dt \qquad \qquad \dots(v)$$

Now substituting $\dfrac{\partial L}{\partial q_j} = \dot{p}_j$ in Eq. (v), we get

$$dH = \sum_j \dot{q}_j \, dp_j - \sum_j \dot{p}_j \, dq_j - \frac{\partial L}{\partial t} dt \qquad \qquad \dots(vi)$$

Comparing co-efficients of Eq. (i) and (vi), we get

$$\dot{q}_j = \frac{\partial H}{\partial p_j} \qquad \qquad \dots(vii)(a)$$

and

$$\dot{p}_j = -\frac{\partial H}{\partial q_j} \qquad \qquad \dots(vii)(b)$$

The above equations constitute a set of $2n$ first order equations of motion.

Now, if q is a cyclic co-ordinate in Lagrangian *i.e.* q_j does not appear in L, then we have

$$\frac{\partial L}{\partial q_j} = \dot{p}_j = 0 \text{ or } p_j = \text{a constant}$$

From Eq. (*vii*) (*b*), we have

$$-\frac{\partial H}{\partial q_j} = \dot{p}_j = 0 \text{ or } \frac{\partial H}{\partial q_j} = 0$$

It means q also does not appear in H i.e. q is also cyclic co-ordinate in Hamiltonian.

Q. 14.27. Show that the transformation

$$Q = \sqrt{2q} \; e^a \cos p$$
$$P = \sqrt{2q} \; e^{-a} \sin p$$

is canonical.   (*Gharwal U.* 2000)

Ans. The given transformation is canonical if it satisfies the *exact differential condition*

$$P \, dQ - p \, dq = df \qquad\qquad ...(i)$$

where f is a function.

Now
$$dQ = \frac{1}{2}(2q)^{-\frac{1}{2}} 2 \, e^a \cos p \, dq - (2q)^{\frac{1}{2}} e^a \sin p \, dp$$

$$\therefore \quad PdQ = (\sqrt{2q} \; e^{-a} \sin p)\left[(2q)^{-\frac{1}{2}} e^a \cos p \, dq - (2q)^{\frac{1}{2}} e^a \sin p \, dp \right]$$

$$= \sin p \cos p \, dq - 2q \sin^2 p \, dp \qquad\qquad ...(ii)$$

or
$$PdQ - p \, dq = \sin p \cos p \, dq - 2q \sin^2 p \, dp - p \, dq$$

$$= (\sin p \cos p - p) \, dq - 2q \sin^2 p \, dp$$

$$= \left(\frac{1}{2}.2\sin p \cos p - p\right) dq - 2q \sin^2 p \, dp$$

$$= \left(\frac{1}{2}\sin 2p - p\right) dq - 2q \sin^2 p \, dp$$

$$= \frac{\partial}{\partial q}\left[\frac{1}{2}q\sin 2p - pq\right] dq + \frac{\partial}{\partial p}\left[\frac{1}{2}q\sin 2p - pq\right] dp \qquad ...(iii)$$

because $\frac{\partial}{\partial q}\left[\frac{1}{2}q\sin 2p - pq\right] = \frac{1}{2}\sin 2p - p$

and $\frac{\partial}{\partial p}\left[\frac{1}{2}q\sin 2p - pq\right] = \frac{1}{2}q\cos 2p \times 2 - q$

$$= q(1 - 2\sin^2 p) - q = -2q\sin^2 p$$

Now let $f = \frac{1}{2}q \sin 2p - pq$

$$\therefore \quad PdQ - pdq = \frac{\partial}{\partial q}f \, dq + \frac{\partial}{\partial p} f \, dp = df$$

$\therefore$ $PdQ - pdq = df$ i.e. the condition for the transformation to be canonical is satisfied. Hence the transformation is canonical.

Q. 14.28. Use the variational method to show that the shortest curve joining two fixed points is a straight line.   (*M.D.U.* 2007; *G.N.D.U.* 2004)

Ans. Condition for a function to have stationary value. Consider the integral

$\int_{x_1}^{x_2} f(y, \dot{y}, x)\, dx$ where $f(y, \dot{y}, x)$ is a function of dependent variable y, independent variable

x and $\dot{y} = \dfrac{dy}{dx}$. If this integral is to have a stationary value (*i.e.* a maximum or a minimum), then

$$\delta \int_{x_1}^{x_2} f(y, \dot{y}, x)\, dx = 0$$

where δ is known as the *variation*. It can be proved that the condition that should be satisfied by the function f for the integral to have an extremum value is

$$\frac{\partial f}{\partial y} - \frac{\partial}{\partial x}\left(\frac{\partial f}{\partial \dot{y}}\right) = 0 \qquad\qquad\qquad \dots (i)$$

A straight line is defined as the shortest distance between two points in a plane. Thus, straight line is an extremum path of a particle in a plane. For an element of small arc length or curve ds in a plane, we have

$$ds = \sqrt{dx^2 + dy^2} = \sqrt{dx^2\left[1 + \left(\frac{dy}{dx}\right)^2\right]} = dx\sqrt{1 + \dot{y}^2}$$

$\therefore$ The total length of the curved path between any two points in a plane is given by

$$I = \int_1^2 ds = \int_1^2 \sqrt{(1 + \dot{y}^2)}\, dx$$

For the curve to be the shortest path, $\delta I = 0$ and the function $f = \sqrt{1 + \dot{y}^2}$ must satisfy the condition

$$\frac{\partial f}{\partial y} - \frac{\partial}{\partial x}\left(\frac{\partial f}{\partial \dot{y}}\right) = 0 \qquad\qquad\qquad \dots (ii)$$

Now $\qquad\qquad \dfrac{\partial f}{\partial y} = 0$ and $\dfrac{\partial f}{\partial \dot{y}} = \dfrac{\dot{y}}{\sqrt{1 + \dot{y}^2}}$

Substituting in Eq. (*ii*), we have

$$\frac{\partial}{\partial x}\left(\frac{\dot{y}}{\sqrt{1 + \dot{y}^2}}\right) = 0$$

or $\qquad\qquad \dfrac{\dot{y}}{\sqrt{1 + \dot{y}^2}} = a$ (A constant)

or $\qquad\qquad \dfrac{\dot{y}^2}{1 + \dot{y}^2} = a^2$ or $\dot{y}^2 = a^2 + a^2 \dot{y}^2$ or $\dot{y}^2 (1 - a^2) = a^2$

or $\qquad\qquad \dot{y} = \sqrt{\dfrac{a^2}{1 - a^2}} = m$ (another constant.)

or $\qquad\qquad \dfrac{dy}{dx} = m \;\; \therefore y = mx + c$ (where c is also a constant)

This is the equation representing a straight line. The values of m and c can be calculated in terms of end point co-ordinates of the curve.

SECTION–II
WAVES, VIBRATIONS AND E.M. THEORY

Simple Harmonic Motion

SECTION-II
WAVES, VIBRATIONS AND
E.M. THEORY

1 Simple Harmonic Motion

Q. 1.1. (*a*) **Differentiate between simple harmonic motion and oscillatory motion. Define simple harmonic motion.** (*H.P.U.*, 2001; *Bang.U.*, 2000; *Gauhati U.*, 2000)

(*b*) **Derive a general differential equation of motion of a simple harmonic oscillator and obtain its various solutions.** (*Meerut. U.*, 2006; *G.N.D.U.*, 1999; *Kan. U.*, 1995; *C.U.*, 1992; *Vidya Sagar U.* 1992; *Burdwan U.*, 1992)

Ans. (*a*) **Oscillatory motion.** A motion which repeats itself after regular intervals of time is called a *periodic motion*.

If a body in periodic motion executes to and fro motion about a fixed reference point, it is said to have an oscillatory motion.

The term oscillatory motion is not restricted only to '*displacement*' of a mechanical oscillator, but it may be any physical quantity. For example, in electrical system an oscillatory variation of charge, current or voltage may take place.

Simple harmonic motion. *When a body moves such that its acceleration is always directed towards a certain fixed point and varies directly as its distance from that point, the body is said to execute simple harmonic motion.*

For such a motion to take place the force acting on the body should be directed towards the fixed point and should also be proportional to the *displacement*, *i.e.*, the distance from the fixed point. The function of the force is to bring the body back to its equilibrium position and hence this force is often known as *restoring force*.

(*b*) **Differential equation of simple harmonic oscillator.** Consider a particle of mass m executing simple harmonic motion. If y be the displacement of the particle from equilibrium position at any instant t, the restoring force F acting on the particle is given by

$$F \propto y \quad \text{or} \quad F = -sy$$

where s is the *force constant* of proportionality or *stiffness* or *spring constant*. The negative sign is used to indicate that the direction of the force is opposite to the direction of increasing displacement.

Force constant s is defned as the restoring force per unit displacement

or
$$s = \frac{F}{y}.$$

Its unit is *Newton per metre*.

If $\dfrac{d^2 y}{dt^2}$ is the acceleration of the particle at time t, then

$$m \frac{d^2 y}{dt^2} = -sy \quad \text{or} \quad \frac{d^2 y}{dt^2} + \frac{s}{m} y = 0$$

3

Substituting $\dfrac{s}{m} = \omega^2$, we get $\dfrac{d^2y}{dt^2} + \omega^2 y = 0$ ...(i)

This is the general *differential* equation of motion of a *simple harmonic oscillator*.

Solution of differential equation. To find the solution of differential equation

$$\frac{d^2y}{dt^2} + \omega^2 y = 0$$

Multiply by $2\dfrac{dy}{dt}$ and we get

$$2\frac{dy}{dt}\frac{d^2y}{dt^2} + \omega^2\, 2y\,\frac{dy}{dt} = 0$$

Integrating, we have

$$\left(\frac{dy}{dt}\right)^2 = -\omega^2 y^2 + C$$ ...(ii)

where C is the constant of integration.

When the displacement is maximum, *i.e.*, at $y = a$

where a is the amplitude of the oscillating particle, $\dfrac{dy}{dt} = 0$

i.e., the particle is momentarily at rest in the *extreme* position and begins its journey in the backward direction.

Substituting $y = a$ and $\dfrac{dy}{dt} = 0$ in equation (ii), we have

$$C = a^2\omega^2$$

Substituting this value of C in Eq. (ii), we get

$$\left(\frac{dy}{dt}\right)^2 = \omega^2 (a^2 - y^2)$$

or $\dfrac{dy}{dt} = \omega\sqrt{a^2 - y^2}$ ...(iii)

This equation gives the *velocity* of the particle executing simple harmonic motion at a time t, when the displacement $= y$

$$\therefore \qquad \frac{dy}{\sqrt{a^2 - y^2}} = \omega\, dt$$

Integrating, we have

$$\sin^{-1}\frac{y}{a} = \omega t + \phi$$

or $\qquad\qquad y = a \sin (\omega t + \phi)$ ...(iv)

where ϕ is another constant of integration.

The term $(\omega t + \phi)$ represents the total *phase* of the particle at time t and ϕ is known as the *initial phase* or *phase constant*. If the time is recorded from the instant when $y = 0$ and increasing then $\phi = 0$.

Other solutions. The equation $y = a \sin (\omega t + \phi)$ is just one solution of the differential equation $\dfrac{d^2y}{dt^2} + \omega^2 y = 0$.

An equally valid solution of this equation is

$$y = a \cos (\omega t + \phi)$$ ...(v)

Expanding $y = a \sin (\omega t + \phi)$, we have

$$y = a \cos \phi \sin \omega t + a \sin \phi \cos \omega t$$
$$= A \sin \omega t + B \cos \omega t \qquad \qquad ...(vi)$$

which is another valid solution, in which

$$A = a \cos \phi \text{ and } B = a \sin \phi$$

i.e., $a = \sqrt{A^2 + B^2}$ and $\phi = \tan^{-1}\left(\dfrac{B}{A}\right)$

Similarly, by expanding $y = a \cos (\omega t + \phi)$, we have

$$y = a \cos \phi \cos \omega t - a \sin \phi \sin \omega t$$
$$= A \sin \omega t + B \cos \omega t$$

where $A = - a \sin \phi$ and $B = a \cos \phi$

i.e., $a = \sqrt{A^2 + B^2}$ and $\phi = \tan^{-1}\left(\dfrac{-A}{B}\right)$

The various general solutions of differential equation :

(*i*) In **sine – cosine form** are

$$y = a \sin (\omega t + \phi)$$
$$y = a \cos (\omega t + \phi)$$
$$y = A \sin \omega t + B \cos \omega t$$

(*ii*) **Exponential form.** We can put differential equation (*i*) in the operator form by substituting

$$\frac{d}{dt} = D$$

or $\dfrac{d^2}{dt^2} = D^2$ and we get

$$D^2 y + \omega^2 y = 0$$

or $D^2 = - \omega^2$

∴ $D = \pm i \omega$

Hence the general solution of equation (*i*) becomes

$$y = A e^{i\omega t} + B e^{-i\omega t}$$

In order that this solution may give a real value of y, A and B must be complex conjugates of each other, *i.e.*,

$$A = a + ib \text{ and } B = a - ib$$

A second form of the general solution of equation (*i*) is

$$y = a\, e^{i (\omega t + \phi)}$$

It has two constants a and ϕ and satisfies differential equation (*i*).

Thus the solutions of differential equation (*i*) in **exponential form** are

$$y = A e^{i\omega t} + B e^{- i\omega t}$$

and $y = a\, e^{i(\omega t + \phi)}$

All these alternative ways of writing the solution of differential equation (*i*) have their own advantages. For a particular problem we select the form most convenient for the purpose. We shall use the solution $y = a \sin (\omega t + \phi)$ in general.

Q. 1.2. (*a*) **Explain how interaction of inertia and elasticity account for simple harmonic motion.**   (*G.N.D.U.*, 2007; *P.U.*, 2007, 2002; *Pbi.U.*,1999)

(*b*) **Simple harmonic motion is called sinusoidal or co-sinusoidal. Justify.**

(*G.N.D.U.*, 1999; *P.U.*, 1990)

Ans. (*a*) **Inertia and elasticity for simple harmonic motion.** When an oscillator is displaced from its position of equilibrium by the application of a force and thus doing work on it, a restoring force comes into play tending to bring it back to its equilibrium position. According to Hooke's law this restoring force is proportional to displacement and depends upon the *elastic properties* or *elasticity* of the system. As soon as the restoring force tries to bring the system back to its equilibrium position, the property of *inertia* opposes this change in velocity. Further, when the system reaches the equilibrium position, it overshoots the mark and moves beyond the mean position again due to *inertia* of motion. The motion continues till the restoring force brings the system to rest and then again sets the oscillator into motion back towards the equilibrium position. *This oscillatory motion is simple harmonic in character and continues due to the interaction of inertia and elasticity.*

(*b*) **Simple harmonic motion is sinusoidal or co-sinusoidal.** A simple harmonic motion can be represented by the relations

$$y = a \sin(\omega t + \phi) \qquad \qquad ...(i)$$

or $\qquad\qquad y = a \cos(\omega t + \phi) \qquad \qquad ...(ii)$

where y is the displacement at a time t, a the amplitude, ω the angular frequency and ϕ the phase constant.

From Eq. (*i*), we have

$$\frac{dy}{dt} = a\omega \cos(\omega t + \phi) \quad \text{and} \quad \frac{d^2y}{dt^2} = -a\omega^2 \sin(\omega t + \phi)$$
$$= -\omega^2 y \qquad ...(iii)$$

Similarly, from Eq. (*ii*), we have

$$\frac{dy}{dt} = -a\omega \sin(\omega t + \phi) \quad \text{and} \quad \frac{d^2y}{dt^2} = -a\omega^2 \cos(\omega t + \phi)$$
$$= -\omega^2 y \qquad ...(iv)$$

Thus according to relation (*iii*) and (*iv*) the acceleration $\left(\dfrac{d^2y}{dt^2}\right)$ is proportional to displacement y and is directed towards the mean position which proves that the motion represented by Eq. (*i*) and (*ii*) is simple harmonic.

This is why a simple harmonic motion is called sinusoidal or co-sinusoidal.

Q. 1.3. (*a*) **An oscillatory motion of a body is represented by $y = ae^{i\omega t}$ where symbols have usual meaning. Show that the motion is simple harmonic.** (*P.U.*, 1995)

(*b*) **The displacement of a moving particle at any time t is given by $y = a \cos \omega t + b \sin \omega t$. Show that the motion is simple harmonic.** (*Luck.U.*, 1994)

Ans. (*a*) Given $y = ae^{i\omega t}$

Differentiating with respect to 't' we get

$$\frac{dy}{dt} = ae^{i\omega t} \times i\omega = ia\omega e^{i\omega t}$$

Differentiating again, we get

$$\frac{d^2y}{dt^2} = ia\omega e^{i\omega t} \times i\omega = -a\omega^2 e^{i\omega t} = -\omega^2 y$$

or $\qquad\qquad \dfrac{d^2y}{dt^2} + \omega^2 y = 0$

This is differential equation of S.H.M. Hence $y = ae^{i\omega t}$ represents a S.H.M.

(*b*) $y = a \cos \omega t + b \sin \omega t$

$\therefore \qquad\qquad \dfrac{dy}{dt} = -a\omega \sin \omega t + b\omega \cos \omega t$

and $\qquad\qquad \dfrac{d^2y}{dt^2} = -a\omega^2 \cos \omega t - b\omega^2 \sin \omega t$
$$= -\omega^2 (a \cos \omega t + b \sin \omega t)$$
$$= -\omega^2 y$$

or
$$\frac{d^2 y}{dt^2} + \omega^2 y = 0$$

Hence $y = a \cos \omega t + b \sin \omega t$ is the equation of simple harmonic motion.

Q. 1.4. What are the dimensions of force constant (or stiffness) of vibrating spring?

(G.N.D.U., 2009, 2007; Pbi. U., 2002; H.P.U., 2000; P.U., 1991)

Ans. Dimensions of force constant. Consider a mass m attached to a spring executing S.H.M. If y is the displacement of the mass from its equilibrium position at any instant of time t, then the restoring force F acting on the mass is given by

$$F = - sy$$

where s is the *force constant* or *stiffness* of the spring.

$\therefore$ Dimensions of s are $= \dfrac{F}{y} = \dfrac{Force}{Displacement} = \dfrac{\left[M^1 \, L^1 \, T^{-2} \right]}{\left[L^1 \right]} = \left[M^1 T^{-2} \right]$

Stiffness is expressed in newton per metre (Nm^{-1}).

Q. 1.5. (a) (i) Find an expression for the velocity of a simple harmonic oscillator.

(Nagpur U., 2003; Bang. U., 2000)

(ii) A particle executes simple harmonic motion with a time period of 2 seconds and amplitude 5 cm. Find the maximum magnitude of velocity. *(P. U., 2009)*

(b) Velocity of simple harmonic oscillator at any time t leads the displacement by a phase angle $\dfrac{\pi}{2}$ radian. Explain why ? *(Nagpur U. 2003; G.N.D.U., 1993)*

Ans. (a) (i) Velocity of simple harmonic oscillator. *A particle (or a system) which executes simple harmonic motion is called a simple harmonic oscillator.*

The displacement of a simple harmonic oscillator at any instant of time t is given by

$$y = a \sin (\omega t + \phi) \qquad \qquad \text{... (i)}$$

The velocity is defined as the time rate of change of displacement.

$\therefore$ Velocity $v = \dfrac{dy}{dt} = \dot{y} = a\omega \cos(\omega t + \phi)$

$$= a\omega \sin\left(\omega t + \phi + \frac{\pi}{2} \right) \qquad \qquad \text{... (ii)}$$

As $\sin(\omega t + \phi) = \dfrac{y}{a}, \ \cos(\omega t + \phi) = \sqrt{1 - \dfrac{y^2}{a^2}} = \sqrt{\dfrac{a^2 - y^2}{a}}$

$\therefore$ $v = \omega \sqrt{a^2 - y^2}$ ... (iii)

Maximum velocity. The velocity of the oscillator is maximum when $\sin\left(\omega t + \phi + \dfrac{\pi}{2} \right) = 1$

$\therefore$ $v_{max} = a\omega$

The value of $v = v_{max}$ when $y = 0$, *i.e.*, the particle executing S.H.M. is in its mean position.

(ii) Maximum velocity $v_{max} = a\omega$

Here $T = 2$ sec. $\therefore \ \omega = 2\pi\nu = \dfrac{2\pi}{T} = \dfrac{2\pi}{2} = \pi \, \text{rad s}^{-1}$

Amplitude $a = 5 \text{ cm} = .05 \text{m}$

$\therefore$ $v_{max} = a\omega = .05 \times \pi \text{ m/s} = 0.157 \text{ m/s}$

(b) Comparing equations (*i*) and (*ii*) in part *a* we find that the velocity of simple harmonic oscillator at any instant of time t *leads* the displacement by a phase difference $\dfrac{\pi}{2}$ (radian) or 90°, *i.e.*, the two are in *quadrature.*

The velocity varies harmonically with the same frequency ω.

Q. 1.6. (a) The frequency of S.H.M. is 150 H. What is time period? (*G.N.D. U.,* 2006)

(b) A particle executes S.H.M. of period 10 sec. and amplitude 5 cm. Calculate the maximum amplitude of velocity. (*Gauhati U.,* 2002)

Ans. (*a*) Frequency $\qquad\qquad\qquad\qquad \nu = 150\,H$

$\therefore$ Time period $\qquad\qquad\qquad T = \dfrac{1}{\nu} = \dfrac{1}{150}\,S = 6.67 \times 10^{-3}s = 0.00667\,s$

(*b*) Here displacement amplitude $a = 5$ cm; Time period $T = 10$ sec.

$\therefore$ Angular frequency $\qquad\qquad \omega = \dfrac{2\pi}{T} = \dfrac{2\pi}{10}s^{-1}$

Maximum amplitude of velocity $\quad = a\omega = \dfrac{5 \times 2\pi}{10}$ cm/s

$\qquad\qquad\qquad\qquad\qquad\qquad = \pi$ cm/sec or 3.14 cm/sec.

Q. 1.7. (a) Find an expression for the acceleration of a simple harmonic oscillator.

(b) Show that for the body executing simple harmonic motion the acceleration leads the velocity by $\dfrac{\pi}{2}$ and displacement by π. (*P.U.,* 1991)

(c) A block of mass 2 kg attached to a spring of force constant 50 *N/m* executes simple harmonic motion. If the initial velocity is 3 m/s and initial displacement is 0.8 m, what is the amplitude of motion of block ? (*P. U.,* 2005)

Ans. (*a*) Acceleration of a simple harmonic oscillator. *Acceleration is defined as the time rate of change of velocity.*

Now velocity $\qquad\qquad\qquad v = a\,\omega\,\cos(\omega\,t + \phi)$ $\qquad\qquad\qquad\qquad\qquad$ ...(*i*)

$\therefore$ Acceleration

$\qquad\qquad\qquad\qquad = \dfrac{dv}{dt} = \ddot{y} = -a\omega^2\,\sin(\omega t + \phi)$

$\qquad\qquad\qquad\qquad = a\,\omega^2\,\sin(\omega\,t + \phi + \pi)$ $\qquad\qquad\qquad\qquad$ ...(*ii*)

Maximum acceleration. The acceleration of the oscillator is maximum when $\sin(\omega\,t + \phi + \pi) = 1$

and is given by $\left(\dfrac{d^2 y}{dt^2}\right)_{max} = a\omega^2.$

(b) The velocity $v = a\omega\cos(\omega t + \phi) = a\omega\sin\left(\omega t + \phi + \dfrac{\pi}{2}\right)$ $\qquad\qquad\qquad$ ... (*iii*)

Comparing (*ii*) and (*iii*), we find that the acceleration of a simple harmonic oscillator leads the velocity by $\dfrac{\pi}{2}$ radian in phase.

The displacement $y = a\sin(\omega\,t + \phi)$ $\qquad\qquad\qquad\qquad\qquad\qquad\qquad\qquad$ ...(*iv*)

Comparing (*ii*) and (*iv*), we find that the acceleration of a simple harmonic oscillator leads the displacement by π radian or (180°) in phase, *i.e.*, the acceleration and displacement are in *antiphase.*

(c) The equation of S.H.M. is

$\qquad\qquad\qquad y = a\,sin\,(\omega t + \phi)$

$\therefore$ $\qquad\qquad\qquad v = \dfrac{dy}{dt} = a\omega\,\cos(\omega t + \phi)$

or
$$\frac{v}{\omega} = a \cos{(\omega t + \phi)}$$

$$\therefore \quad y^2 + \frac{v^2}{\omega^2} = a^2 \sin^2{(\omega t + \phi)} + a^2 \cos^2{(\cot + \phi)} = a^2$$

Now frequency
$$v = \frac{1}{2\pi}\sqrt{\frac{s}{m}}$$
(where s is the constant of the spring and m the mass of the block).

$$= \frac{1}{2\pi}\sqrt{\frac{50}{2}} = \frac{5}{2\pi}$$

$$\therefore \quad \omega = 2\pi v = 2\pi \times \frac{5}{2\pi} = 5$$

Now initial velocity $v = 3 \text{ ms}^{-1}$ and initial displacement $y = 0.8$ m

$$\therefore \quad a^2 = y^2 + \frac{v^2}{\omega^2} = (0.8)^2 + \left(\frac{3}{5}\right)^2 = 0.64 + 0.36 = 1$$

$\therefore$ Amplitude of motion of the block $a = 1 m \; s^{-1}$

Q. 1.8. (*a*) **What is the phase relationship between displacement velocity and acceleration in S.H.M.?** (*P. U.*, 2007)

(*b*) **Velocity of a particle executing S.H.M. is minimum at some instant. What can be said about acceleration at that instant?** (*P. U.*, 2008)

(*c*) **Show the phase relation between the displacement velocity and acceleration diagrammatically, given displacement $y = A \sin{(\omega t + \phi)}$.** (*G.N.D.U.*, 1999)

Ans. (*a*) The velocity of a simple harmonic oscillator leads the displacement by a phase difference $\frac{\pi}{2}$ (radian).

The acceleration leads the velocity by a phase difference $\frac{\pi}{2}$ (radian) and, therefore, it leads the displacement by phase difference π (radian).

For proof **see Q 1.5.**

(*b*) For a particle executing S.H.M. displacement is given by the relation
$$y = A \sin{(\omega t + \phi)}$$

$\therefore$ velocity
$$v = \frac{dy}{dt} = A\omega \cos{(\omega t + \phi)}$$

and acceleration
$$a = \frac{dy}{dt} = \frac{d^2 y}{dt^2} = -A\omega^2 \sin{(\omega t + \phi)}$$

The velocity v is minimum when $\cos{(\omega t + \phi)} = \frac{\pi}{2}$ so that $\cos{\frac{\pi}{2}} = 0$ and therefore $v = 0$

When $(\omega t + \phi) = \frac{\pi}{2}$; $\sin{(\omega t + \phi)} = 1$ and, therefore, acceleration has the maximum value $= -A\omega^2$.

(*c*) Given displacement $y = A \sin{(\omega t + \phi)}$

$\therefore$ velocity
$$v = \frac{dy}{dt} = A\omega \cos{(\omega t + \phi)}$$

and acceleration $\qquad a = \dfrac{d^2y}{dt^2} = -A\omega^2 \sin(\omega t + \phi)$

Hence for $\qquad y = 0, \qquad v = +A\omega, \quad a = 0$

$\qquad\qquad\qquad y = +A, \qquad v = 0, \qquad a = -\omega^2 A$

$\qquad\qquad\qquad y = -A, \qquad v = 0, \qquad a = +\omega^2 A$

The same is shown graphically as under

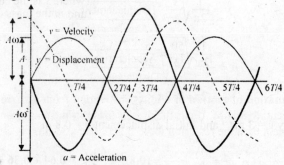

Fig. 1.1

Q. 1.9. (*a*) **Find an expression for the periodic time and frequency of a simple harmonic oscillator.**

(*b*) **A mass m suspended from a spring of stiffness s executes S.H.M. Set up the differential equations of motion and calculate its time period. If we use a stiffer spring without changing the mass, how will the period of oscillation change ?** (*Gauhati U.*, 2000; *H.P.U.*, 1992, *P.U.* 1991)

Ans. (*a*) **Periodic time.** A simple harmonic motion is represented by the equation

$$y = a \sin(\omega t + \phi)$$

In this equation if we increase t by $\dfrac{2\pi}{\omega}$, then

$$y = a \sin\left[\omega\left(t + \dfrac{2\pi}{\omega}\right) + \phi\right]$$

$$= a \sin[\omega t + 2\pi + \phi]$$

$$= a \sin(\omega t + \phi)$$

i.e., the displacement of the particle after a time $T = \dfrac{2\pi}{\omega}$ is the same.

Hence T gives the periodic time of the simple harmonic oscillator.

$$\therefore \qquad\qquad T = \dfrac{2\pi}{\omega}$$

and Frequency $\qquad\qquad n = \dfrac{1}{T} = \dfrac{\omega}{2\pi}$

Thus $\omega = 2\pi n$ = angular velocity of the harmonic oscillator. The acceleration of a simple harmonic oscillator is given by the relation

$$\dfrac{d^2y}{dt^2} = -\omega^2 y$$

Neglecting the negative sign, we have

$$\omega^2 = \frac{\frac{d^2 y}{dt^2}}{y} = \frac{\text{Acceleration}}{\text{Displacement}}$$

$$\therefore \quad \omega = \sqrt{\frac{\text{Acceleration}}{\text{Displacement}}}$$

and

$$T = \frac{2\pi}{\omega} = 2\pi \sqrt{\frac{\text{Displacement}}{\text{Acceleration}}}$$

Also

$$n = \frac{1}{T} = \frac{1}{2\pi} \sqrt{\frac{\text{Acceleration}}{\text{Displacement}}}.$$

(b) **Differential equation of motion of a mass suspended from a spring.** Consider a mass m attached to a spring executing S.H.M. If y is the displacement of the mass from its equilibrium position at any instant of time t, then the restoring force F acting on the mass is given by

$$F = -sy$$

where s is the *force constant* or *stiffness* of the spring. If $\frac{d^2 y}{dt^2}$ is the acceleration of the mass at the time t, then

$$m \frac{d^2 y}{dt^2} = -sy$$

or

$$\frac{d^2 y}{dt^2} = -\frac{s}{m} y \quad \text{or} \quad \frac{d^2 y}{dt^2} + \frac{s}{m} y = 0. \qquad \qquad \dots (i)$$

This is the differential equation of the mass suspended from the spring.

Time period. From Eq. (i)

$$\frac{\text{Displacement } (y)}{\text{Acceleration} \left(\dfrac{d^2 y}{dt^2} \right)} = \frac{m}{s} \qquad \qquad \text{(ignoring the negative sign)}$$

Hence

$$T = 2\pi \sqrt{\frac{\text{Displacement}}{\text{Acceleration}}} = 2\pi \sqrt{\frac{m}{s}}$$

and Frequency

$$n = \frac{1}{T} = \frac{1}{2\pi} \sqrt{\frac{s}{m}}$$

Stiffer spring. When we use a *stiffer* spring of spring constant $s' > s$

then

$$T' = 2\pi \sqrt{\frac{m}{s'}}$$

As $s' > s$; T' is $< T$, i.e., the time period will decrease.

Q. 1.10. (a) **A mass of 1 kg is attached to a spring of stiffness constant 16 Nm^{-1}. Find its natural frequency.** (H.P.U., 2001)

(b) **A particle of mass 100 gm is placed in a field of potential $U = 5x^2 + 10$ ergs / gm. Find the frequency.** (Meerut U., 2001)

(c) **The potential energy of a mass of 1 kg executing S.H.M. is given by $U_p = 2x^2 + 4x + 4$ Joule. Find the equilibrium position, force constant and frequency of oscillation.** (Pbi.U., 2008)

Ans. (a) Here stiffness constant $s = 16 \text{ Nm}^{-1}$,   mass $m = 1$ kg

$\therefore$ Freqency $n = \dfrac{1}{2\pi}\sqrt{\dfrac{s}{m}} = \dfrac{1}{2\pi}\sqrt{\dfrac{16}{1}} = \dfrac{2}{\pi} = 0.64$ Hz

Exercise : *A mass of 2 kg is attached to a spring of stiffness constant 18 Nm^{1}. Find its natural frequency.*   (*P. U.*,2006)

Hint. $n = \dfrac{1}{2\pi}\sqrt{\dfrac{s}{m}} = \dfrac{1}{2\pi}\sqrt{\dfrac{18}{2}} = \dfrac{3}{2\pi} = 0.48 \, Hz$

(b) Here potential energy $U = 5x^2 + 10$ ergs/gm ; $m = 100$ gm

Now $F = -\dfrac{dU}{dx}$ $\therefore$ $F = -\dfrac{d}{dx}(5x^2 + 10) = -10\,x$

Taking x as the displacement, we have $F = m\dfrac{d^2x}{dt^2}$

$\therefore$ $m\dfrac{d^2x}{dt^2} = -10\,x$ or $\dfrac{d^2x}{dt^2} = -\dfrac{10}{m}x$

This is the equation of a simple harmonic motion with force constant $s = 10$ dyne/cm.

$\therefore$ Frequency $n = \dfrac{1}{2\pi}\sqrt{\dfrac{s}{m}} = \dfrac{1}{2\pi}\sqrt{\dfrac{10}{100}} = \dfrac{1}{2\pi\sqrt{10}} = 0.05$ Hz

(c) Potential energy $U_p = 2x^2 + 4x + 4$ Joule

The force F is related to potential energy by the relation $F = -\dfrac{dU}{dx}$

Here $\dfrac{dU}{dx} = 4x + 4 = 4\,(x+1)$ or $F = -4\,(x+1)$

But $F = m\dfrac{d^2x}{dt^2};$ $\therefore$ $m\dfrac{d^2x}{dt^2} = -4\,(x+1)$ ... (*i*)

Now put $x + 1 = y$; $\therefore$ $\dfrac{dx}{dt} = \dfrac{dy}{dt}$ and $\dfrac{d^2x}{dt^2} = \dfrac{d^2y}{dt^2}$

Putting $x + 1 = y$ and $\dfrac{d^2x}{dt^2} = \dfrac{d^2y}{dt^2}$ in (*i*), we have

$$m\dfrac{d^2y}{dt^2} = -4y$$

This is the equation of simple harmonic motion with force constant $s = 4 \text{ Nm}^{-1}$

Also $\omega = \sqrt{\dfrac{s}{m}} = \sqrt{\dfrac{4}{1}} = 2 \text{ rad s}^{-1}$

Hence frequency $n = \dfrac{1}{2\pi}\sqrt{\dfrac{s}{m}} = \dfrac{2}{2\pi} = \dfrac{1}{\pi} = 0.318 \, Hz$

For stable equilibrium $F = 0$

$\therefore$ $4\,(x+1) = 0$ or $4x = -4$ or $x = -1$ m

or $x = -1$m is the position of x for stable equilibrium.

Q. 1.11. (*a*) **A lift is ascending at acceleration of 3 ms^{-2}. What is the period of oscillation of a simple pendulum of length one metre suspended in the lift?**   (*P.U.*, 1995)

(b) A spring when compressed by 10 cm develops a restoring force of 10 N. A body of mass 4 kg is attached to it. Calculate the compression of the spring due to the weight of the body and calculate the period of oscillation. (Pbi.U., 2001)

Ans. (a) The time period of a simple pendulum is given by

$$T = 2\pi \sqrt{\frac{l}{g}}$$

where l is the length of the pendulum and g the acceleration due to gravity.

As the lift is ascending with an acceleration of 3 ms^{-2}, acceleration due to gravity $g = 9.8 + 3 = 12.8$ ms^{-2}. Length of the pendulum $l = 1$ metre

∴ Time period $\qquad T = 2\pi \sqrt{\frac{l}{g}} = 2\pi \sqrt{\frac{1}{12.8}} = 1.756$ sec.

(b) Here restoring force $F = 10$ N; displacement $y = 10$ cm $= 0.1$ m

∴ Force constant $\qquad s = \frac{F}{y} = \frac{10}{0.1} = 100$ Nm^{-1}

Mass attached $m = 4$ kg

∴ Force applied $F = 4$ kg wt $= 4 \times 9.8 = 38.2$ N

∴ Displacement $\qquad y' = \frac{F'}{s} = \frac{39.2}{100}$ m $= 39.2$ cm

Time period $\qquad T = 2\pi \sqrt{\frac{m}{s}} = 2\pi \sqrt{\frac{4}{100}} = \frac{2}{5}\pi = 1.26$ sec.

Q. 1.12. The displacement of a simple harmonic oscillator is given by

$$x = a \sin(\omega t + \phi)$$

If the oscillations started at time $t = 0$ from a position x_0 with velocity $\dot{x} = v_0$, show that

$$\tan \phi = \frac{\omega x_0}{v_0} \text{ and } a = \left[x_0^2 + \frac{v_0^2}{\omega^2} \right]^{\frac{1}{2}}. \qquad (G.N. \ D.U., 2009; \ P.U., 1999, 1995)$$

Ans. Given

∴ $\qquad\qquad\qquad x = a \sin(\omega t + \phi) \ ; \text{ at } t = 0, \ x = x_0$
$\qquad\qquad\qquad x_0 = a \sin \phi$

Also

∴ $\qquad\qquad\qquad \dot{x} = a \omega \cos(\omega t + \phi); \text{ at } t = 0, \ \dot{x} = v_0$
$\qquad\qquad\qquad v_0 = a \omega \cos \phi$

Hence $\qquad\qquad \tan \phi = \frac{\sin \phi}{\cos \phi} = \frac{x_0}{a} \times \frac{a\omega}{v_0} = \frac{\omega x_0}{v_0}$

and $\qquad\qquad a^2 \sin^2 \phi + a^2 \cos^2 \phi = x_0^2 + \frac{v_0^2}{\omega^2}$

or $\qquad\qquad a = \left[x_0^2 + \frac{v_0^2}{\omega^2} \right]^{\frac{1}{2}}$

Q. 1.13. A man stands on a platform which vibrates simple harmonically in a vertical direction at a frequency of 5 Hertz. Show that the mass loses contact with the platform when the displacement exceeds 10^{-2} metres.

Ans. The mass loses contact with the platform when the upward force acting on it exceeds its weight mg.

The mass vibrates simple harmonically given by

$$x = a \sin(\omega t + \phi)$$

$\therefore$ Acceleration $\ddot{x} = a\,\omega^2 \sin(\omega t + \phi) = -\,\omega^2 x$

Upward force $= -\,m\,\omega^2 x$

In the limiting case $mg = m\omega^2 x$

or $x = \dfrac{g}{\omega^2} = \dfrac{9.81}{4\pi^2 5^2} = .01\,m = 10^{-2}\ \text{metre}$

Q. 1.14. A body executing S. H. M. has velocities 80 cm/s and 60 cm/s when displacements are 3 cm and 4 cm respectively. Calculate the amplitude of vibration and the time taken to travel 2.5 cm from positive extremity of the oscillation. (*P.U.*, 1992)

Ans. Velocity $v = \omega\sqrt{a^2 - y^2}$

where ω = angular velocity; a = amplitude and y = displacement from the mean position

$\therefore$ $80\ \text{cm s}^{-1} = \omega\sqrt{a^2 - 3^2}$ ...(i)

$60\ \text{cm s}^{-1} = \omega\sqrt{a^2 - 4^2}$ ...(ii)

$\therefore$ $\dfrac{80}{60} = \dfrac{4}{3} = \dfrac{\sqrt{a^2 - 3^2}}{\sqrt{a^2 - 4^2}}$ or $\dfrac{16}{9} = \dfrac{a^2 - 9}{a^2 - 16}$

or $a = 5\ \text{cm}$

Substituting $a = 5$ cm in (i), we get

$80 = \omega\sqrt{5^2 - 3^2}$

or $\omega = 20\ \text{rad. s}^{-1}$

Now $y = a \sin \omega t$

$\therefore$ Time taken to reach the positive extremity is given by

$5 = 5 \sin \omega t$

or $\sin \omega t = 1$

or $\omega t = \pi/2$

$\therefore$ $t = \dfrac{\pi}{2\omega} = \dfrac{\pi}{40}\ s$

Distance of the point 2.5 cm from positive extremity, from the mean position = 5 − 2.5 = 2.5 cm
Time taken to reach a point 2.5 cm from the mean position is given by

$2.5 = 5 \sin \omega t$

or $\sin \omega t = \dfrac{1}{2}$

or $\omega t = \pi/6$

$\therefore$ $t = \dfrac{\pi}{6\omega} = \dfrac{\pi}{120}\ \text{sec}$

Time taken to travel from a point 2.5 cm from the positive extremity to the positive extremity

$= \dfrac{\pi}{40} - \dfrac{\pi}{120} = \dfrac{\pi}{60} = .052\ \text{sec}$

Hence time taken to travel from positive extremity to a point 2.5 cm away = .052 sec.

Q. 1.15. A tunnel is dug across the earth passing through its centre. If a body of mass 1 kg is dropped into it, will it come out at the other end? If not, then what type of motion does it execute? If radius of earth is 6400 km and g on the surface of earth is 9.8 ms^{-2}, then calculate the possible time period of the body.

(*Kerala U.*, 2001; *G.N.D.U.*, 1994; *P.U.* 1999, 1991; *Vidya Sagar U.*, 1992)

Ans. The acceleration due to gravity g' at a point within the earth is given by $g' = \dfrac{g}{R} \times$ distance from the centre of the earth where g is the acceleration due to gravity on the surface of the earth and R its radius.

If we dig a tunnel along a diameter of the earth and drop a body in it, then let it be at a distance y from the centre and have an acceleration

$$g' = \frac{d^2 y}{dt^2}$$

$$\therefore \quad g' = \frac{d^2 y}{dt^2} = \frac{g}{R} y = ky$$

when k is a constant $= g / R$.

Thus the acceleration is proportional to the displacement from the centre and is directed towards it. The body, therefore **executes simple harmonic motion.**

Time period $\quad T = 2\pi \sqrt{\dfrac{\text{displacement}}{\text{acceleration}}} = 2\pi \sqrt{\dfrac{1}{k}} = 2\pi \sqrt{\dfrac{R}{g}}$

Now $\qquad\qquad R = 6400 \text{ km} = 6400 \times 10^3 \text{ m and } g = 10 \ ms^{-2}$

$$\therefore \qquad T = 2\pi \sqrt{\frac{6400 \times 10^3}{9.8}} = 5078.2 \text{ sec}$$

$$= 84.64 \text{ minutes}$$

Q. 1.16. Show that the frequency of oscillation of a body of mass M suspended from a uniform spring of force constant k and mass m is given by $\dfrac{1}{2\pi} \sqrt{\dfrac{k}{M + \dfrac{m}{3}}}$. It is given that the velocity of any small element of the spring is proportional to its distance from the fixed end of the spring. *(P.U., 2002)*

Ans. Let the length of uniform spring of mass m be L.

$\therefore$ Mass per unit length of the spring $= \dfrac{m}{L}$

Consider a small element of length dl at a distance l from the fixed end, then

Mass of the small element $= \dfrac{m}{L} dl$

When the spring is displaced vertically downward, each element of the spring is elongated by a different amount. The lowest element to which mass M is attached will undergo maximum extension.

Let v be the velocity of the lowest end at any instant. As the velocity of an element of length dl is proportional to its distance l from the fixed end of the spring.

Velocity of this element at a distance l from the fixed end $= v \dfrac{l}{L}$

$\therefore$ Kinetic energy of the element of length dl and mass $\dfrac{m}{L} dl$ is given by

$$K.E = \frac{1}{2}\left(\frac{m}{L} dl\right)\left(v\frac{l}{L}\right)^2 = \frac{1}{2}\frac{mv^2}{L^3} l^2 \, dl$$

Hence $K.E.$ of the spring $= \displaystyle\int_0^L \frac{1}{2}\frac{mv^2}{L^3} l^2 \, dl = \frac{1}{2}\frac{mv^2}{L^3}\left[\frac{l^3}{3}\right]_0^L$

$$= \frac{1}{2} \frac{mv^2}{L^3} \cdot \frac{L^3}{3} = \frac{1}{6} mv^2$$

K.E. of the mass $\qquad M = \frac{1}{2} M v^2$

∴ Total kinetic energy of the whole system $= \frac{1}{2} Mv^2 + \frac{1}{6} mv^2$

$$= \frac{1}{2} v^2 \left[M + \frac{m}{3} \right]$$

If the instantaneous displacement of the mass m is y at a time t, then its potential energy

$$P.E. = \int_0^y ky \, dy = \frac{1}{2} ky^2$$

Thus total energy of the system $E = K.E. + P.E$

or $\qquad\qquad E = \frac{1}{2} \left(M + \frac{m}{3} \right) v^2 + \frac{1}{2} k y^2$

$$= \frac{1}{2} \left(M + \frac{m}{3} \right) \left(\frac{dy}{dt} \right)^2 + \frac{1}{2} ky^2$$

Since the total energy of the system is conserved, $\frac{dE}{dt} = 0$

or $\qquad \frac{d}{dt} \left[\frac{1}{2} \left(M + \frac{m}{3} \right) \left(\frac{dy}{dt} \right)^2 + \frac{1}{2} k y^2 \right] = 0$

or $\qquad \frac{1}{2} \left(M + \frac{m}{3} \right) 2 \frac{dy}{dt} \cdot \frac{d^2y}{dt^2} + \frac{1}{2} k \, 2y \frac{dy}{dt} = 0$

or $\qquad \left(M + \frac{m}{3} \right) \frac{d^2y}{dt^2} + ky = 0$

or $\qquad \frac{d^2y}{dt^2} = - \frac{k}{\left(M + \frac{m}{3} \right)} y$

which represents a simple harmonic motion of time period

$$T = 2\pi \sqrt{\frac{M + \frac{m}{3}}{k}}$$

or frequency $\qquad n = \frac{1}{2\pi} \sqrt{\frac{k}{M + \frac{m}{3}}}$

Q. 1.17. What is a compound pendulum ? Derive an expression for its time period. What is the condition for the time period to be minimum ?

(*Pbi.U.*, 2007, 2005; *G.N.D.U.*, 2006; *P.U.*, 2007, 2004, 2003; *Meerut.U.*, 2007)

Ans. Compound pendulum. *A compound pendulum consists of a rigid body which can oscillate freely about a horizontal axis passing through it.*

Time period of a compound pendulum. Consider a rigid body of any shape and mass m capable of oscillating freely about a horizontal axis passing through it perpendicular to its plane.

Let O be the **centre of suspension** of the body and G its centre of gravity vertically below O at a distance l in the position of rest. When the body is displaced through a small angle θ to the dotted position, the centre of gravity is shifted to the position G' and its weight mg acts vertically downward at G'.

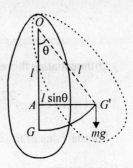

If the pendulum is now released, a restoring couple acts on it and brings it back to the initial position. But due to inertia, it overshoots the mark and hence starts oscillating about the mean position.

The moment of the restoring couple or torque

$$\tau = -mg \times G'A = -mg\,l \sin\theta = -mg\,l\,\theta \quad ...(i)$$

since the angle θ through which the pendulum is displaced is small so that $\sin\theta = \theta$.

Fig. 1.2

This restoring couple gives rise to an angular acceleration α in the pendulum. If I is the moment of inertia of the rigid body (pendulum) about an axis passing through its centre of suspension, then restoring couple (torque) is given by

$$\tau = I\frac{d^2\theta}{dt^2} \quad ...(ii)$$

Comparing equations (i) and (ii), we have

$$I\frac{d^2\theta}{dt^2} = -mg\,l\,\theta$$

or

$$\frac{d^2\theta}{dt^2} = -\frac{mgl}{I}\theta \quad ...(iii)$$

$$\therefore \quad \frac{d^2\theta}{dt^2} \propto \theta \qquad \left[\because -\frac{mgl}{I} = \text{constant}\right]$$

As the angular acceleration is proportional to angular displacement, the motion of the compound pendulum is simple harmonic and its time period T is given by

$$T = 2\pi\sqrt{\frac{\text{Angular displacement}}{\text{Angular acceleration}}} = 2\pi\sqrt{\frac{\theta}{\frac{mgl\theta}{I}}} = 2\pi\sqrt{\frac{I}{mgl}} \quad ...(iv)$$

If I_G is the moment of inertia of the body (or compound pendulum) about an axis parallel to the given axis but passing through C.G. (G), then according to the theorem of parallel axes, we have

$$I = I_G + ml^2$$

Now, $\qquad I_G = mK^2$ where K is the radius of gyration

$$\therefore \qquad I = mK^2 + ml^2 = m(K^2 + l^2)$$

Substituting the value of I in relation (iv), we get

$$T = 2\pi\sqrt{\frac{mK^2 + ml^2}{mgl}} = 2\pi\sqrt{\frac{K^2 + l^2}{lg}} \quad ...(v)$$

Minimum time period. The time period of the compound pendulum is **minimum** when the distance of the point of suspension from C. G. is equal to the radius of gyration.

To prove this put the relation for the time period

$$T = 2\pi\sqrt{\frac{K^2 + l^2}{lg}} \quad \text{as}$$

$$T^2 = \frac{4\pi^2}{g}\left(\frac{K^2 + l^2}{l}\right) = \frac{4\pi^2}{g}\left(\frac{K^2}{l} + l\right)$$

Differentiating this expression with respect to l, we get

$$2T\frac{dT}{dl} = \frac{4\pi^2}{g}\left(-\frac{K^2}{l^2} + 1\right)$$

For the value of time period T to be minimum $\dfrac{dT}{dl} = 0$

or $\qquad\qquad\qquad\qquad 1 - \dfrac{K^2}{l^2} = 0 \quad$ or $\quad l = \pm K.$

Q. 1.18. Work out the time period of a torsional pendulum.   (*G.N.D.U.*, 2006)

Ans. Torsional pendulum. *A torsional pendulum is a heavy circular disc attached symmetrically to the lower end of a fine, long and thin wire, the upper end of which is clamped in a torsion head.* [Fig 1.2 (a)]

It is called a *torsional pendulum* because if the disc is turned slightly from its equilibrium position so as to twist the wire, then on releasing it, it executes torsional vibrations on account of the restoring torque developed in the wire.

Time period. Suppose the disc is turned through an angle θ from the equilibrium position in the horizontal plane and released, then the wire also gets twisted and exerts a torque on the disc to bring it back to the mean position.

The torque acting on the disc is given by

$$\tau = -C\theta \qquad\qquad ... (i)$$

where C is the restoring torque per unit angular twist or *torsional rigidity* of the suspension wire. The negative sign shows that the torque is directed opposite to the angular displacement and tends to restore the pendulum to its equilibrium position.

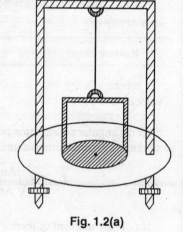

Fig. 1.2(a)

The value of C is given by $C = \dfrac{\pi\eta r^4}{2l}$ where η is the *modulus*

of rigidity of the material of the wire, r the radius and l the length of the suspension wire. This torque produces an angular acceleration

$\alpha = \dfrac{d^2\theta}{dt^2}$ in the disc. If I is the moment of inetia of the disc about the wire as axis, then

$$\tau = I\alpha = I\frac{d^2\theta}{dt^2} \qquad\qquad ... (ii)$$

Comparing equations (*i*) and (*ii*), we get

$$I\frac{d^2\theta}{dt^2} = -C\theta$$

or $\qquad\qquad\qquad\qquad \dfrac{d^2\theta}{dt^2} = -\dfrac{C}{I}\theta \qquad\qquad\qquad ...(iii)$

or $\qquad\qquad\qquad\qquad \alpha = -\dfrac{C}{I}\theta$

i.e., the angular acceleration is directly proportional to angular displacement and is directed towards the equilibruim position.

Thus the motion of the torsional pendulum is *simple harmonic*. The *time period* of oscillation of the torsional pendulum is, therefore, given by

$$T = 2\pi \sqrt{\frac{\text{Angular displacement}}{\text{Angular acceleration}}} = 2\pi \sqrt{\frac{\theta}{\alpha}}$$

$$= 2\pi \sqrt{\frac{\theta}{\left(\dfrac{C}{I}\right)\theta}} = 2\pi, \sqrt{\frac{I}{C}}$$

Q. 1.19 (a) Derive an expression for the total energy of a simple harmonic oscillator and show that it is constant and proportional to the square of the amplitude.
(*P.U.*, 2009, 2008; *G.N.D.U.*, 2007; *Pbi.U.*, 2005; *Meerut U.* 2002)

(b) When the displacement is one half of the maximum amplitude, what fraction of the total energy is kinetic and what fraction is potential in simple harmonic motion? Explain the graphical representation of energy. (*Pbi.U.*, 2005; *Luck. U.*, 1993)

(c) A simple pendulum of length 3m and amplitude .06m has energy 0.6J. Find the energy when amplitude becomes 0.12 m, length remaining unchanged. (*P.U.*, 2007)

Ans. (a) Energy of a simple harmonic oscillator . The total energy of a simple harmonic oscillator at any time t is the sum of its kinetic energy and potential energy at that instant of time.

$$\therefore \qquad E_{total} = K.E. + P.E.$$

Kinetic energy. The general equation of a simple harmonic oscillator is given by

$$y = a \sin(\omega t + \theta)$$

where y is the displacement of the oscillator at any time t, a is the amplitude, ω the angular velocity and θ the initial phase or epoch.

$\therefore$ The velocity at any instant

$$v = \frac{dy}{dt} = \dot{y} = a\omega \cos(\omega t + \phi)$$

$\therefore$ Kinetic energy of the oscillator $= \dfrac{1}{2} m \left(\dfrac{dy}{dt}\right)^2 = \dfrac{1}{2} m \dot{y}^2$

$$= \frac{1}{2} m a^2 \omega^2 \cos^2(\omega t + \phi)$$

Potential energy. The potential energy is equal to the amount of work done in overcoming the restoring force from the mean position through a displacement y.

Now, acceleration $= \dfrac{d^2 y}{dt^2} = -a\omega^2 \sin(\omega t + \phi)$

$$= -\omega^2 y$$

The negative sign indicates that the acceleration is directed towards the mean position.

$\therefore$ Restoring force $= m\omega^2 y = sy$ where s is the force constant of proportionality or *stiffness*.
Hence total work done by the force through a displacement y

$$= \int_0^y sy \, dy = \frac{1}{2} sy^2 = \frac{1}{2} m\omega^2 y^2 \quad :$$

or $\qquad\qquad P.E. = \dfrac{1}{2} sy^2 = \dfrac{1}{2} m\omega^2 y^2 = \dfrac{1}{2} m\omega^2 a^2 \sin^2(\omega t + \phi)$

Total Energy.
$$E = K.E. + P.E. = \frac{1}{2}m\dot{y}^2 + \frac{1}{2}sy^2$$

$$= \frac{1}{2}ma^2\omega^2\cos^2(\omega t + \phi) + \frac{1}{2}ma^2\omega^2\sin^2(\omega t + \phi)$$

$$= \frac{1}{2}ma^2\omega^2$$

but
$$\omega^2 = \frac{s}{m} \qquad\qquad (\because m\,\omega^2 = s)$$

Hence
$$E = \frac{1}{2}sa^2$$

Also $\omega = 2\pi n$ $\qquad \therefore E = \frac{1}{2}ma^2\,4\pi^2n^2 = 2ma^2\pi^2n^2$

Thus total energy of the harmonic oscillator is a constant and proportional to the square of the amplitude.

Maximum K.E. The maximum value of $K.E.$ for $\cos(\omega t + \phi) = 1$ is given by
$$K.E.\,(max) = \frac{1}{2}ma^2\omega^2$$

Maximum P.E. The maximum value of $P.E.$ for $\sin(\omega t + \phi) = 1$ is given by
$$P.E.\,(max) = \frac{1}{2}ma^2\omega^2$$

$\therefore$ $K.E.\,(max) = P.E.\,(max) = $ Total energy $E = \frac{1}{2}ma^2\omega^2$

(b) Total energy $= \frac{1}{2}ma^2\omega^2$

Potential energy $= \frac{1}{2}m\omega^2y^2$

but $y = \frac{a}{2}$

$\therefore$ Potential energy $= \frac{1}{2}m\omega^2\frac{a^2}{4} = \frac{1}{8}m\omega^2a^2 = \frac{1}{4} \times \frac{1}{2}ma^2\omega^2$

Now Kinetic energy $=$ Total energy $-$ Potential energy

$$= \frac{1}{2}ma^2\omega^2 - \frac{1}{8}ma^2\omega^2 = \frac{3}{8}ma^2\omega^2 = \frac{3}{4} \times \frac{1}{2}ma^2\omega^2$$

$\therefore$ $\frac{1}{4}$ of the total energy is potential and $\frac{3}{4}$ is kinetic.

Graphical representation of energy. The variation of total energy, kinetic energy and potential energy of a harmonic oscillator with displacement y is shown in Fig. 1.3.

(i) Kinetic energy. The kinetic energy is given by $\frac{1}{2}m\dot{y}^2$ where $\dot{y}$ is the velocity of the oscillator. The velocity and hence the kinetic enrgy is zero at the extreme positions $y = \pm a$ and maximum in the mean position $y = 0$. The velocity and hence the $K.E.$ decreases as the oscillator moves away from the mean position and finally becomes zero at the extreme positions as shown by the curve marked $K.E.$

(*ii*) **Potential energy.** The potential energy is given by $\frac{1}{2}sy^2$ where s is the *stiffness*. For $y = 0$, *P.E.*

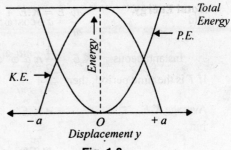

Fig. 1.3

= 0 and for $y = \pm a$, the *P.E.* is maximum = $\frac{1}{2}sa^2$. Thus potential energy goes on increasing as the oscillator moves away from its mean position and becomes maximum at the extreme positions $y = \pm a$ as shown by the curve marked *P.E.*

(*iii*) **Total energy.** The total energy is given by

$\frac{1}{2}sa^2$ which is a constant. This is represented by the straight line marked '*Total energy*' parallel to the displacement axis.

(*c*) Total energy of a harmonic oscillator $E = \frac{1}{2}ma^2\omega^2$ where a is the amplitude and ω the

angular velocity. The time period of a simple pendulum (which is a harmonic oscillator) $T = 2\pi\sqrt{\frac{l}{g}}$

$$\therefore \quad \omega = \frac{2\pi}{T} = \frac{2\pi}{2\pi\sqrt{\frac{l}{g}}} = \sqrt{\frac{g}{l}}$$

When the length remains constant, ω remains constant.

$$\therefore \quad \frac{1}{2}m\omega^2 = \text{a constant}$$

and total energy is proportional to a^2.

When the amplitude changes from 0.06 *m* to 0.12 *m*, it is doubled and hence the energy becomes $2^2 = 4$ times and becomes $4 \times 0.6 = 2.4$ J.

Q. 1.20. Derive a relation between restoring force of a spring and potential energy.

(*H.P.U.*, 2003; *P.U.*, 1999)

Ans. Relation between restoring force and potential energy. For a spring or a simple harmonic oscillator, if y is the displacement from the mean position, then restoring force $F = -sy$ where s is the *force constant* or *stiffness*. The negative sign only indicates that the restoring force is directed towards the mean position. Hence total work done by the force to produce the displacement

$$y = \int_0^y sy\,dy = \frac{1}{2}sy^2.$$ This work is stored in the oscillator as its potential energy.

Hence $P.E. = \frac{1}{2}sy^2 = \frac{1}{2}$ restoring force × (displacement)^2.

Q. 1.21. Show that for a particle executing S.H.M. the average value of kinetic and potential energy is the same and each is equal to half the total energy.

(*Pbi.U.* 2007, 2006, 2003; *Luck. U.* 2002; *G.N.D.U.*, 1999, 1994; *H.P.U.*, 1994)

Ans. Average kinetic energy. Kinetic energy at any instant

$$= \frac{1}{2}mv^2 = \frac{1}{2}m\dot{y}^2 = \frac{1}{2}m\left(\frac{dy}{dt}\right)^2$$

For a S.H.M. $y = a\sin(\omega t + \phi)$

and $\dfrac{dy}{dt} = a\omega\cos(\omega t + \phi)$

$\therefore$ Instantaneous $K.E. = \dfrac{1}{2}m a^2 \omega^2 \cos^2(\omega t + \phi)$

If T is the time period, then

Average K.E.

$$= <K.E.> = \dfrac{1}{T}\int_0^T \dfrac{1}{2}m a^2 \omega^2 \cos^2(\omega t + \phi)\,dt$$

$$= \dfrac{m a^2 \omega^2}{2T}\int_0^T \cos^2(\omega t + \phi)\,dt$$

$$= \dfrac{m a^2 \omega^2}{2T}\int_0^T \dfrac{1}{2}[1 + \cos 2(\omega t + \phi)]\,dt$$

$$= \dfrac{m a^2 \omega^2}{4T}\left[\int_0^T dt + \int_0^T \cos 2(\omega t + \phi)\,dt\right]$$

$$= \dfrac{m a^2 \omega^2}{4T}T \qquad\qquad \left[\because \int_0^T \cos(2\omega t + \phi)\,dt = 0\right]$$

$$= \dfrac{1}{4}m a^2 \omega^2 \qquad\qquad\qquad\qquad\qquad\qquad \dots(i)$$

Average potential energy. Instantaneous potential energy is given by

$$P.E. = \dfrac{1}{2}s y^2 = \dfrac{1}{2}s a^2 \sin^2(\omega t + \phi)$$

$\therefore$ Average P.E. $= <P.E.> = \dfrac{1}{T}\int_0^T \dfrac{1}{2}s a^2 \sin^2(\omega t + \phi)]\,dt$

$$= \dfrac{s a^2}{2T}\int_0^T \dfrac{1}{2}[1 - \cos 2(\omega t + \phi)]\,dt$$

$$= \dfrac{s a^2}{4T}\left[\int_0^T dt - \int_0^T \cos 2(\omega t + \phi)\,dt\right]$$

$$= \dfrac{s a^2}{4T}T = \dfrac{1}{4}s a^2 \qquad\qquad \left[\because \int_0^T \cos 2(\omega t + \phi)\,dt = 0\right]$$

But $\omega^2 = \dfrac{s}{m}$ $\therefore s = m\omega^2$

$\therefore$ Average $P.E. = \dfrac{1}{4}m a^2 \omega^2$ $\qquad\qquad\qquad\qquad\qquad$ $\dots(ii)$

Total Energy. The total energy $= \dfrac{1}{2}m a^2 \omega^2$ $\qquad\qquad\qquad$ $\dots(iii)$

Thus it is clear from Equations (i), (ii) and (iii) that the average kinetic energy of a harmonic oscillator is equal to the average potential energy and is equal to *half* the total energy *i.e.*,

$$<K.E.> = <P.E.> = \dfrac{1}{2}E_{Total}$$

Q. 1.22. Derive the equation for simple harmonic motion from energy considerations.

Ans. Equation of S.H.M. from energy considerations. Consider a particle executing S.H.M.

When the particle is displaced away from the mean position along the Y-axis through a distance $\vec{y}$, a restoring force $\vec{F} = -s\vec{y}$ opposes its motion.

Hence the applied force $\vec{F} = s\vec{y}$ where s is the *force constant* or *stiffness*.

Suppose now the particle is displaced further through a small distance $d\vec{y}$, then

Work done dW for displacement $d\vec{y} = \vec{F}.d\vec{y}$

∴ Total work done to move the particle from the mean position through a displacement $\vec{y}$.

$$W = \int_0^y \vec{F}.d\vec{y} = \int_0^y s\vec{y}.d\vec{y} = s\int_0^y \vec{y}.d\vec{y} = s\int_0^y y\,dy$$

as the angle between $\vec{y}$ and $d\vec{y}$ is zero.

∴
$$W = s\int_0^y y\,dy = \frac{1}{2}sy^2$$

This work done is stored as potential energy.

∴
$$P.E. = \frac{1}{2}sy^2$$

Kinetic energy of the particle $\dfrac{1}{2}mv^2 = \dfrac{1}{2}m\dot{y}^2 = \dfrac{1}{2}m\left(\dfrac{dy}{dt}\right)^2$

∴ Total energy $\quad E = \dfrac{1}{2}sy^2 + \dfrac{1}{2}m\left(\dfrac{dy}{dt}\right)^2$ ...(i)

Differentiating Eq. (i) with respect to 't', we get

$$\frac{dE}{dt} = \frac{1}{2}s\,2y\frac{dy}{dt} + \frac{1}{2}m2\frac{dy}{dt}\left(\frac{d^2y}{dt^2}\right)$$

According to the law of conservation of energy, E is a constant.

∴
$$\frac{dE}{dt} = 0$$

or
$$s\,y\frac{dy}{dt} + m\frac{dy}{dt}\left(\frac{d^2y}{dt^2}\right) = 0$$

or
$$\frac{dy}{dt}\left(sy + m\frac{d^2y}{dt^2}\right) = 0$$

But
$$\frac{dy}{dt} \neq 0$$

∴
$$sy + m\frac{d^2y}{dt^2} = 0$$

Substituting $\quad \dfrac{s}{m} = \omega^2$, we have

$$\frac{d^2y}{dt^2} + \omega^2 y = 0$$

This is the equation of S.H.M. derived from energy considerations.

Q. 1.23. Prove that if at any instant of motion kinetic energy is suddenly increased by a blow in the ratio $(1 + \beta) : 1$, the amplitude of the swing is increased in the ratio

$$\sqrt{1 + \frac{\beta v^2}{a^2 \omega^2}} : 1.$$

Ans. If m is the mass of particle and v the corresponding velocity before the blow, then

$$K.E. = \frac{1}{2}mv^2 \text{ and } P.E. = \frac{1}{2}m\omega^2 y^2.$$

Total energy before the blow $= \frac{1}{2}mv^2 + \frac{1}{2}m\omega^2 y^2 = \frac{1}{2}ma^2\omega^2$

where a is the initial amplitude.

Kinetic energy after the blow $= \frac{1}{2}mv^2(1 + \beta)$

If A is the amplitude after blow, then

Total energy after the blow $= \frac{1}{2}mA^2\omega^2$

$\therefore$

$$\frac{1}{2}mA^2\omega^2 = \frac{1}{2}mv^2(1 + \beta) + \frac{1}{2}m\omega^2 y^2$$

$$= \frac{1}{2}mv^2 + \frac{1}{2}m\omega^2 y^2 + \frac{1}{2}mv^2\beta$$

$$= \frac{1}{2}ma^2\omega^2 + \frac{1}{2}mv^2\beta$$

$\therefore$

$$\frac{A^2}{a^2} = 1 + \frac{\beta v^2}{a^2\omega^2}$$

or

$$\frac{A}{a} = \sqrt{1 + \frac{\beta v^2}{a^2\omega^2}}$$

Hence

$$A : a :: \sqrt{1 + \frac{\beta v^2}{a^2\omega^2}} : 1.$$

Q. 1.24. (a) Calculate the displacement to amplitude ratio for a S. H. M. when K. E. is 90% of total energy. (P.U., 1995)

(b) What is the ratio of kinetic energy at displacement one fourth to one third of the amplitude in case of simple harmonic motion? (P.U., 1995)

Ans. (a) If m is the mass of the particle executing S.H.M., a the amplitude and ω the angular velocity, then

Total energy $= \frac{1}{2}ma^2\omega^2$

Let y be the displacement when $K. E. = 90\%$ of total energy,

As $K.E.$ is 90% of total energy,

Potential energy = Total energy – Kinetic energy = 10% of total energy

Now potential energy $= \dfrac{1}{2} m\omega^2 y^2$

$\therefore \quad \dfrac{\dfrac{1}{2} m\omega^2 y^2}{\dfrac{1}{2} m\omega^2 a^2} = \dfrac{y^2}{a^2} = \dfrac{10}{100} = 0.1$

or $\qquad \dfrac{\text{Displacement}}{\text{Amplitude}} = \dfrac{y}{a} = \sqrt{0.1} = 0.316$

(*b*) If m is the mass of the particle executing S.H.M., a the amplitude and ω the angular velocity, then

Total energy $\qquad\qquad\qquad\qquad = \dfrac{1}{2} m\omega^2 a^2$

When the displacement is y, Potential energy $= \dfrac{1}{2} m\omega^2 y^2$

$\therefore$ Kinetic energy = Total energy – Potential energy $= \dfrac{1}{2} m\omega^2 (a^2 - y^2)$

At displacement $y = \dfrac{a}{4}$, Kinetic energy $E_1 = \dfrac{1}{2} m\omega^2 \left(a^2 - \dfrac{a^2}{16}\right) = \dfrac{15}{32} m\omega^2 a^2$

At displacement $y = \dfrac{a}{3}$, Kinetic energy $E_2 = \dfrac{1}{2} m\omega^2 \left(a^2 - \dfrac{a^2}{9}\right) = \dfrac{8}{18} m\omega^2 a^2$

$\therefore \qquad\qquad\qquad \dfrac{E_1}{E_2} = \dfrac{15}{32} \times \dfrac{18}{8} = \dfrac{135}{128} = 1.055$

Q. 1.25. A simple harmonic oscillator is characterised by $y = a \cos \omega t$. **Calculate the displacement at which kinetic energy is equal to its potential energy.**

(Nagpur U. 2003; Pbi.U., 2000; P.U., 2007, 1996)

Or

At what displacement from the mean position the total energy of a simple harmonic oscillator is half kinetic and half potential ? *(G.N.D.U., 2001)*

Ans. Let y be the displacement at which kinetic energy of the simple harmonic oscillator is equal to its potential energy.

Now $\qquad\qquad y = a \cos \omega t \qquad \therefore \dfrac{dy}{dt} = -a\omega \sin \omega t$

The kinetic energy of a simple harmonic oscillator is given by

$$K.E. = \dfrac{1}{2} mv^2 = \dfrac{1}{2} m\left(\dfrac{dy}{dt}\right)^2 = \dfrac{1}{2} m(-a\omega \sin \omega t)^2$$

$$= \dfrac{1}{2} m a^2 \omega^2 \sin^2 \omega t = \dfrac{1}{2} m a^2 \omega^2 (1 - \cos^2 \omega t)$$

$$= \dfrac{1}{2} m\omega^2 (a^2 - a^2 \cos^2 \omega t) = \dfrac{1}{2} m\omega^2 (a^2 - y^2)$$

$$P.E. = \dfrac{1}{2} s y^2 \text{ where } s = \text{stiffness and } \dfrac{s}{m} = \omega^2 \text{ or } s = m\omega^2$$

$$\therefore \qquad P.E. = \frac{1}{2}\, m\,\omega^2 y^2$$

when $\qquad K.E. = P.E.$

$$\frac{1}{2}\, m\,\omega^2 (a^2 - y^2) = \frac{1}{2} m\,\omega^2 y^2$$

or $\qquad a^2 - y^2 = y^2 \qquad$ or $\qquad a^2 = 2\,y^2$

$\therefore$ Displacement $\quad y = \pm \dfrac{a}{\sqrt{2}}$

In other words, for a displacement $y = \pm \dfrac{a}{\sqrt{2}}$ from the mean position $P.E. = \dfrac{1}{4}\, m\,\omega^2 a^2$,

$K.E. = \dfrac{1}{4}\, m\,a^2 \omega^2$ and total energy $= \dfrac{1}{2} m\,\omega^2 a^2$

i.e., half of the total energy is kinetic and half potential.

Q. 1.26. A hollow sphere is filled with water, used as pendulum bob. If water trickles out slowly through a hole made at the bottom, how will the time period be effected? (*H.P.U.*, 1991)

Ans. The time period of a simple pendulum is given by

$$T = 2\pi \sqrt{\frac{l}{g}}$$

where l is the length of the pendulum and g the acceleration due to gravity.

When the water trickles out slowly through a hole made at the bottom of the hollow sphere used as bob of the pendulum, the mass of the bob goes on slowly decreasing. As time period does not depend upon the mass of the bob, there is no change in time period.

Q. 1.27. Derive the differential equation of S. H. M. for an electrical circuit. Can it be realised in practice?

Ans. Differential equation of an electrical oscillator. Consider an electrical circuit in which an inductor of inductance L and negligible resistance is connected to a capacitor of capacitance C. When the capacitor is first charged by a high tension battery, the electrostatic energy resides in the dielectric medium of the capacitor. As the capacitor begins to discharge through the inductor, a current begins to flow through the inductor coil. This sets up a magnetic field around the coil. As the capacitor discharges, the electrostatic energy of the capacitor is converted into magnetic energy of the inductor. There is thus a continuous exchange of energy between the inductor and the capacitor. As the resistance is negligible, there is no dissipation of energy in the form of heat etc.

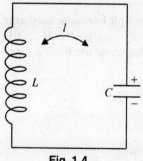

Fig. 1.4

If L is the co-efficient of self inductance of the coil and $\dfrac{dI}{dt}$ the rate of growth of current, then voltage across the inductor

$$= -L\frac{dI}{dt} = -L\frac{d^2 q}{dt^2}$$

and voltage across the capacitor $= \dfrac{q}{C}$

As there is no source of *e.m.f.* in the circuit

$$L\frac{d^2 q}{dt^2} + \frac{q}{C} = 0$$

or
$$\frac{d^2q}{dt^2} + \frac{q}{LC} = 0$$

This equation is similar to the differential equation

$$\frac{d^2y}{dt^2} + \omega^2 y = 0 \text{ where}$$

$$\omega^2 = \frac{1}{LC}$$

Hence this equation is the differential equation of S.H.M. for an electrical circuit. Its solution is

$$q = q_0 \sin(\omega t + \phi)$$

where q_0 is the maximum value of the charge and is known as the *amplitude of the charge.*

Electrical oscillator in practice. The inductance L always has some ohmic resistance due to which there is a continuous loss of energy and the amplitude of S.H.M. slowly dies down to zero. If, however, corresponding amount of energy is supplied to the circuit from an external source, the amplitude of S.H.M. can be maintained. This is done by using a valve or transistor circuit. In this way simple harmonic electrical oscillations can be realised in practice.

Q. 1.28. Discuss the points of similarity between mechanical and electrical oscillations.

(P.U., 2007; G.N.D.U., 2007)

Ans. Points of similarity between mechanical and electrical oscillations. The equation of motion of a simple harmonic mechanical oscillator is given by

$$\frac{d^2y}{dt^2} + \frac{s}{m} y = 0 \qquad \qquad ...(i)$$

where y is the displacement, s the force constant of proportionality or stiffness and m the mass of oscillator.

The angular frequency is given by

$$\omega^2 = \frac{s}{m} \text{ or } \omega = \sqrt{\frac{s}{m}}$$

or frequency
$$v = \frac{1}{2\pi} \sqrt{\frac{s}{m}}.$$

The equation for displacement is given by
$$y = a \sin(\omega t + \phi)$$

where a and ϕ are constants, known as amplitude and initial phase angle.

The total energy of the mechanical oscillator

$$E = \frac{1}{2} m v^2 + \frac{1}{2} s y^2 = \frac{1}{2} m \dot{y}^2 + \frac{1}{2} s y^2$$

where $\frac{1}{2} m \dot{y}^2$ is the K.E. and $\frac{1}{2} s y^2$ the P.E.

The equation of motion of a simple harmonic electrical oscillator is given by

$$\frac{d^2q}{dt^2} + \frac{1}{LC} q = 0$$

where q is the charge, L the inductance and C the capacitance of the electrical circuit.

The angular frequency is given by

$$\omega = \sqrt{\frac{1}{LC}}$$

or frequency $v = \dfrac{1}{2\pi \sqrt{LC}}$

The charge on the capacitance varies harmonically and is represented by an equation similar to displacement equation, *i.e.*,

$$q = q_0 \sin(\omega t + \phi)$$

where q_0 is the amplitude of charge and ϕ the phase difference.

The current $I = \dfrac{dq}{dt}$ corresponds to velocity $v = \dfrac{dy}{dt}$ and is given by

$$I = \omega q_0 \cos(\omega t + \phi).$$

The voltage across the capacitor $V = \dfrac{q}{C} = \dfrac{q_0}{C} \sin(\omega t + \phi)$

Both I and V, therefore, vary harmonically with the same angular velocity ω.

The total energy of an electrical oscillator is the sum of the magnetic energy and electric energy.

The magnetic energy can be calculated from the current I and potential $V = L \dfrac{dI}{dt}$ across the inductance and is given by

$$\int VI\, dt = \int L \frac{dI}{dt} I\, dt = \int LI\, dI = \frac{1}{2} LI^2 = \frac{1}{2} L\dot{q}^2$$

Compare it with kinetic energy in a mechanical oscillator given by $\dfrac{1}{2} m\dot{y}^2$. Thus mass in a mechanical circuit corresponds to inductance in an electrical circuit and velocity to electric current.

The electrostatic energy can be calculated from the voltage across the capacitor and is given by

$$\frac{1}{2} CV^2 = \frac{1}{2} C\left(\frac{q}{C}\right)^2 = \frac{1}{2} \frac{q^2}{C}$$

Compare it with potential energy in a mechanical oscillator given by $\dfrac{1}{2} sy^2$. Thus stiffness s in a mechanical circuit corresponds to $\dfrac{1}{C}$ in an electrical circuit or pliability $\dfrac{1}{s}$ corresponds to capacitance C.

Q. 1.29. What oscillates in a simple harmonic electrical oscillator? Can we realise it in practice?

Ans. An oscillating electrical circuit consists of an inductance L and a capacitance C. In the electrical oscillator it is the charge on the capacitance that oscillates. In other words, *the charge on the capacitor is the harmonically varying quantity which gives rise to electrical oscillations*. In an electrical oscillator *charge* corresponds to *displacement* in a mechanical oscillator. The inductance L is the electrical counterpart of mass m (inertia) and the reciprocal of capacitance $(1/C)$ is the counterpart of stiffness s. The frequency is given by

$$v = \frac{1}{2\pi \sqrt{LC}}$$

We can realise an LC circuit in practice and obtain simple harmonic oscillations if the circuit has *zero* (ohmic) resistance and there is no loss of energy. In practice, however, it is not possible to have a circuit with zero resistance. Hence energy is supplied to the LC circuit to make up for this small inevitable loss by electronic devices like thermionic valves or transistors.

Q. 1.30. Calculate the resultant of two simple harmonic vibrations of the same frequency acting along the same line but differing in phase. What is the amplitude when the phase difference is $0, \dfrac{\pi}{2}$ and π ?

(P.U., 2005; Bhopal U. 2004; C.U., 1991)

Ans. Resultant of two simple harmonic vibrations in the same direction. Let the two simple harmonic vibrations of angular frequency ω acting along the X-axis and having initial phases ϕ_1 and ϕ_2 amplitudes a_1 and a_2 be given by

$$x_1 = a_1 \sin(\omega t + \phi_1) \qquad \text{...(i)}$$
and
$$x_2 = a_2 \sin(\omega t + \phi_2) \qquad \text{...(ii)}$$

The resultant can be calculated analytically as well as geometrically.

Analytical method. The resultant displacement due to the two simple harmonic vibrations is given by

$$x = x_1 + x_2 = a_1 \sin(\omega t + \phi_1) + a_2 \sin(\omega t + \phi_2)$$
$$= \sin \omega t \, (a_1 \cos \phi_1 + a_2 \cos \phi_2) + \cos \omega t \, (a_1 \sin \phi_1 + a_2 \sin \phi_2)$$

Put
$$a_1 \cos \phi_1 + a_2 \cos \phi_2 = R \cos \theta$$
and
$$a_1 \sin \phi_1 + a_2 \sin \phi_2 = R \sin \theta$$

Then
$$x = R \sin \omega t \cos \theta + R \cos \omega t \sin \theta = R \sin(\omega t + \theta)$$

which gives the equation of the resultant simple harmonic vibration of amplitude R and initial phase θ where

$$R^2 = R^2 \cos^2 \theta + R^2 \sin^2 \theta = a_1^2 + a_2^2 + 2a_1 a_2 (\sin \phi_1 \sin \phi_2 + \cos \phi_1 \cos \phi_2)$$
$$= a_1^2 + a_2^2 + 2a_1 a_2 \cos(\phi_2 - \phi_1)$$
$$= a_1^2 + a_2^2 + 2a_1 a_2 \cos \phi \qquad \text{...(iii)}$$

where the phase difference
$$\phi = \phi_2 - \phi_1$$
and
$$\tan \theta = \frac{R \sin \theta}{R \cos \theta} = \frac{a_1 \sin \phi_1 + a_2 \sin \phi_2}{a_1 \cos \phi_1 + a_2 \cos \phi_2}$$

Geometrical method (vector method). Let us represent the vibration

$$x_1 = a_1 \sin(\omega t + \phi_1)$$

as the vector $\overrightarrow{OA}$ where the vector $\overrightarrow{OA} = a_1$ makes an angle θ, with the X-axis and the vibration $\quad x_2 = a_2 \sin(\omega t + \phi_2)$

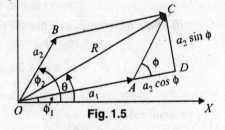

Fig. 1.5

as the vector $\overrightarrow{OB}$ where $\overrightarrow{OB} = a_2$ makes an angle θ_2 with the X-axis as shown in Fig. 1.5

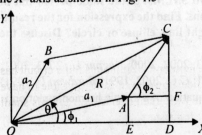

Fig. 1.6

The resultant is given by the vector $R = OC$
and $\qquad \angle BOA = \phi_2 - \phi_1 = \phi$
$\therefore \qquad R^2 = (a_1 + a_2 \cos \phi)^2 + (a_2 \sin \phi)^2$

$$= a_1^2 + a_2^2 + 2a_1 a_2 \cos \phi$$

which is the same result as obtained in *(iii)*.

If θ is the angle that the resultant R makes with the x-axis, then referring to Fig. 1.6, we have

$$\tan \theta = \frac{CD}{OD} = \frac{FD + CF}{OE + ED}$$

$$= \frac{AE + CF}{OE + AF}$$

$$= \frac{a_1 \sin \phi_1 + a_2 \sin \phi_2}{a_1 \cos \phi_1 + a_2 \cos \phi_2}$$

The resulting vibration is, therefore, given by

$$x = R \sin (\omega t + \theta)$$

(*i*) **Phase difference (0).** When the phase difference

$$\phi = (\phi_2 - \phi_1) = 0$$

$$R^2 = a_1^2 + a_2^2 + 2a_1 a_2 \cos(o)$$

$$= a_1^2 + a_2^2 + 2a_1 a_2$$

or amplitude $R = a_1 + a_2$

Let $\phi_1 = 0$ and $\phi_2 = 0$, then

$$\tan \theta = \frac{a_1 \sin \theta_1 + a_2 \sin \theta_2}{a_1 \cos \theta_1 + a_2 \cos \theta_2}$$

$$= 0$$

(*ii*) **Phase difference, $\pi / 2$.** When the phase difference

$$\phi = (\phi_2 - \phi_1) = \pi / 2$$

$$R^2 = a_1^2 + a_2^2 + 2a_1 a_2 \cos \pi/2 = a_1^2 + a_2^2$$

or amplitude $R = \sqrt{a_1^2 + a_2^2}$

Let $\phi_1 = 0$ and $\phi_2 = \pi / 2$, then

$$\tan \theta = \frac{a_1 \sin \phi_1 + a_2 \sin \phi_2}{a_1 \cos \phi_1 + a_2 \cos \phi_2} = \frac{a_1 \sin 0 + a_2 \sin \pi/2}{a_1 \cos 0 + a_2 \cos \pi/2} = \frac{a_2}{a_1}$$

(*iii*) **Phase difference, π.** When the phase difference

$$\phi = (\phi_2 - \phi_1) = \pi$$

$$R^2 = a_1^2 + a_2^2 + 2a_1 a_2 \cos \pi$$

$$= a_1^2 + a_2^2 - 2a_1 a_2$$

or amplitude $R = a_1 - a_2$

Again $\tan \theta = 0$

Q. 1.31. A particle is subjected simultaneously to two S.H.Ms. of the same period but of different amplitudes and phases in perpendicular directions. Find the expression for the resultant motion. For what condition the path may be a straight line, ellipse or circle? Discuss the different important cases.

(*G.N.D.U.*, 2007; *Calicut U.* 2003; *Merrut U.*, 2003, 2002, 2000; *Nagpur U.*, 2003, 2001; *Luck.U.* 1994; *Vidya Sagar U.* 1991; *C.U.* 2002, 1991; *Burdwan U.* 1991)

Ans. Resultant of two S.H.M. at right angles. The equation of a simple harmonic motion is given by

$$x = a \sin (\omega t + \phi)$$

where x is the displacement of the vibrating particle at any instant t, a the amplitude of vibration, ω the angular velocity and ϕ the initial phase.

Let the displacements of two perpendicular simple harmonic motions of the same period (or frequency ω) taking place along the X-axis and Y-axis respectively be represented by

$$x = a \sin (\omega t + \phi_1) \qquad \qquad \text{...(i)}$$

and
$$y = b \sin (\omega t + \phi_2) \qquad \qquad \text{...(ii)}$$

where a is the amplitude of the vibration along the X-axis, b is the amplitude of the vibration along the Y-axis, ϕ_1 and ϕ_2 the initial phases of X and Y vibrations respectively. The phase difference between the two vibrations, then

$$\phi = \phi_2 - \phi_1$$

From (i) we have

$$\frac{x}{a} = \sin \omega t \cos \phi_1 + \cos \omega t \sin \phi_1 \qquad \qquad \text{...(iii)}$$

From (ii) we have

$$\frac{y}{b} = \sin \omega t \cos \phi_2 + \cos \omega t \sin \phi_2 \qquad \qquad \text{...(iv)}$$

Multiplying (iii) by $\sin \phi_2$ and (iv) by $\sin \phi_1$ and subtracting, we have

$$\left(\frac{x}{a} \sin \phi_2 - \frac{y}{b} \sin \phi_1 \right) = \sin \omega t (\cos \phi_1 \sin \phi_2 - \cos \phi_2 \sin \phi_1)$$

$$= \sin \omega t \sin (\phi_2 - \phi_1) \qquad \qquad \text{...(v)}$$

Similarly, multiplying (iv) by $\cos \phi_1$ and (iii) by $\cos \phi_2$ and subtracting, we have

$$\left(\frac{y}{b} \cos \phi_1 - \frac{x}{a} \cos \phi_2 \right) = \cos \omega t (\sin \phi_2 \cos \phi_1 - \sin \phi_1 \cos \phi_2)$$

$$= \cos \omega t \sin (\phi_2 - \phi_1) \qquad \qquad \text{...(vi)}$$

Squaring (v) and (vi) and adding, we get

$$\left(\frac{x}{a} \sin \phi_2 - \frac{y}{b} \sin \phi_1 \right)^2 + \left(\frac{y}{b} \cos \phi_1 - \frac{x}{a} \cos \phi_2 \right)^2$$

$$= \sin^2 (\phi_2 - \phi_1) [\sin^2 \omega t + \cos^2 \omega t]$$
$$= \sin^2 (\phi_2 - \phi_1)$$

or
$$\frac{x^2}{a^2} + \frac{y^2}{b^2} - \frac{2xy}{ab} (\sin \phi_2 \sin \phi_1 + \cos \phi_2 \cos \phi_1) = \sin^2 (\phi_2 - \phi_1)$$

or
$$\frac{x^2}{a^2} + \frac{y^2}{b^2} - \frac{2xy}{ab} \cos (\phi_2 - \phi_1) = \sin^2 (\phi_2 - \phi_1)$$

Substituting $\phi_2 - \phi_1 = \phi$, we get

$$\frac{x^2}{a^2} + \frac{y^2}{b^2} - \frac{2xy}{ab} \cos \phi = \sin^2 \phi \qquad \qquad \text{...(vii)}$$

This is the equation giving the expression for resultant motion and represents the equation of an ellipse whose major and minor axes are inclined to the co-ordinate axes. This ellipse can be inscribed in a rectangle whose sides are $2a$ and $2b$.

Important cases. (i) Straight line. When $\phi = 0$, $\cos \phi = 1$ and $\sin \phi = 0$

The relation (vii) is, then, reduced to

$$\frac{x^2}{a^2} + \frac{y^2}{b^2} - \frac{2xy}{ab} = 0$$

or
$$\left(\frac{x}{a} - \frac{y}{b}\right)^2 = 0$$

This represents a pair of coincident straight lines lying in the *first* and *third* quadrants as

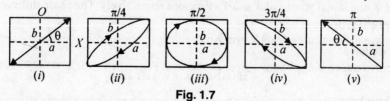

Fig. 1.7

shown in Fig. 1.7 (*i*). The straight line is inclined to the X-axis at angle θ given by $\theta = \tan^{-1}\left(\frac{b}{a}\right)$.

(*ii*) **Oblique ellipse.** When $\phi = \frac{\pi}{4}$, $\cos\frac{\pi}{4} = \frac{1}{\sqrt{2}}$ and $\sin\frac{\pi}{4} = \frac{1}{\sqrt{2}}$
The relation (*vii*) is, then, reduced to

$$\frac{x^2}{a^2} + \frac{y^2}{b^2} - \frac{\sqrt{2}\,xy}{ab} = \frac{1}{2}$$

This represents an *oblique ellipse* lying in *first* and *third* quadrant as shown in Fig. 1.7 (*ii*).

(*iii*) (*a*) **Symmetrical ellipse.** When $\phi = \frac{\pi}{2}$, $\cos\frac{\pi}{2} = 0$ and $\sin\frac{\pi}{2} = 1$
The relation (*vii*) is reduced to

$$\frac{x^2}{a^2} + \frac{y^2}{b^2} = 1$$

This represents a symmetrical ellipse whose major and minor axes coincide with the co-ordinate axes as shown in Fig. 1.7 (*iii*).

(*b*) **Circle.** If $a = b$, the resultant vibration is circular and is represented by
$$x^2 + y^2 = a^2$$

(*iv*) **Oblique ellipse.** When $\phi = \frac{3\pi}{4}$, $\cos\frac{3\pi}{4} = -\frac{1}{\sqrt{2}}$ and $\sin\frac{3\pi}{4} = \frac{1}{\sqrt{2}}$.

The relation (*vii*) is reduced to

$$\frac{x^2}{a^2} + \frac{y^2}{b^2} + \frac{\sqrt{2}\,xy}{ab} = \frac{1}{2}$$

This again represents an oblique ellipse lying in *second* and *fourth* quadrants as shown in Fig. 1.7 (*iv*).

(*v*) **Straight line.** When $\phi = \pi$, $\cos\phi = -1$ and $\sin\phi = 0$
The relation (*vii*) is reduced to

$$\frac{x^2}{a^2} + \frac{y^2}{b^2} + \frac{2xy}{ab} = 0$$

or
$$\left(\frac{x}{a} + \frac{y}{b}\right)^2 = 0$$

This represents a pair of coincident straight lines lying in the *second* and *fourth* quadrants as shown in Fig. 1.7 (*v*). The straight line is inclined to the X-axis at an angle θ which is given by

$$\theta = \tan^{-1}\left(-\frac{b}{a}\right)$$

(*vi*) When φ lies between π and 2 π.

As the phase difference exceeds π, the whole cycle is repeated in the reverse order, *i.e.*, for

$\phi = \frac{5\pi}{4}$ the curve traced is an oblique ellipse as shown in Fig. 1.7 (*iv*), for $\phi = \frac{3\pi}{2}$, it is a symmetri-

cal ellipse as shown in Fig. 1.7 (*iii*) and for $\phi = \frac{7\pi}{4}$ the curve is again an oblique ellipse as shown in

Fig. 1.7 (*ii*). For φ = 2 π the curve is a straight line as shown in Fig. 1.7 (*i*), *i.e.*, for φ = 0.

Q. 1.32. (*a*) **Show that the resultant of two simple harmonic motions at right angles to each other and having equal periods and amplitudes but phase difference 90° is a circle.**

(*Nagpur U.*, 2003, 2002)

(*b*) **Two mutually perpendicular S.H.Ms. are represented by equations x = 4 sin ω*t*; y = 3 cos ω*t*. Find the semi-major and semi-minor axis of an ellipse formed by their superposition.**

(*Nagpur U.*, 2001)

Ans. (*a*) The resultant of two simple harmonic motions at right angles to each other *i.e.* one along the X-axis and the other along the Y-axis, having different amplitudes a and b but equal periods (*T*) or

angular frequencies $\omega = \frac{2\pi}{T}$ and phase difference φ is given by

$$\frac{x^2}{a^2} + \frac{y^2}{b^2} - \frac{2xy}{ab}\cos\phi = \sin^2\phi \qquad \text{[For proof see Q. 1.31 Eq. (*vii*)]}$$

When $a = b$ and $\phi = 90°$; sin φ = sin 90° = 1, cos φ = cos 90° = 0

This equation becomes $\frac{x^2}{a^2} + \frac{y^2}{a^2} = 1$ or $x^2 + y^2 = a^2$ which represents a *circle*.

(*b*) Given x = 4 sin ω *t*; y = 3 cos ω *t* = 3 sin (ω *t* + π/2)

The superposition of these two mutually perpendicular S.H.Ms. gives rise to a *symmetrical ellipse* represented by

$$\frac{x^2}{a^2} + \frac{y^2}{b^2} = 1 \quad \text{or} \quad \frac{x^2}{4^2} + \frac{y^2}{3^2} = 1 \quad \text{or} \quad \frac{x^2}{16} + \frac{y^2}{9} = 1$$

∴ Semi-major axis a = 4 units and semi-minor axis b = 3 units

Q. 1.33. What are Lissajous figures? How will you trace graphically the Lissajous figures

when (*i*) the periods are equal and the phase difference is $\frac{\pi}{4}$ and (*ii*) the periods are in the ratio of 2 : 1 and phase difference is (*a*) zero and (*b*) a quarter of the smaller period ?

(*Meerut.U.*, 2007; *G.N.D.U.*, 2006; *K.U.*, 1991)

Ans. Lissajous figures. *When a particle is acted upon simultaneously by two simple harmonic motions at right angles to each other, the resultant path traced out by the particle is called* **Lissajous figures.**

The nature of the resultant path or the curve traced out depends upon

(*i*) the amplitudes,

(*ii*) the periods (or frequencies), and

(*iii*) the phase difference between the two component vibrations.

Graphical method of tracing Lissajous figures

(*i*) **Amplitudes different, periods same and phase difference** $\frac{\pi}{4}$ **(45°).** Let the simple harmonic vibration along the X-axis have an amplitude a and the vibration along the Y-axis an amplitude b.

Draw two circles of reference of radii a and b equal to the amplitude b.

Draw two circles of reference of radii a and b equal to the amplitudes of the corresponding

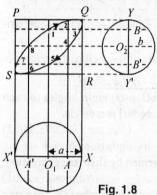

Fig. 1.8

simple harmonic motions taking place along the X-axis and the Y-axis respectively. In the circle of radius a draw a diameter XX' parallel to the X-axis and in the circle of radius b draw a diameter YY' parallel to the Y-axis. As the *periods* are *equal*, divide both the circles into an equal number of parts, say 8, so that each part is travelled in the *same* time. Draw lines through these points perpendicular to the lines XX' and YY' respectively, so as to enclose a rectangle $PQRS$ as shown in Fig. 1.8. It is supposed that the particle O_1 vibrating along XX' (X- vibration) first begins its journey *towards the right* and the particle O_2 vibrating along YY' (Y- vibration) first begins its journey in the *upward direction*.

Let the Y-vibration be ahead of the X-vibration by an angle $\pi/4$. It means that when the particle O_1 starts from its mean position along the X-axis, the particle O_2 has already completed 1/8th of its vibration along the Y-axis, *i.e.*, it is at B. The resultant position of a particle when both the vibrations act on it is represented by the point marked 1.

When the particle O_1 reaches A, the particle O_2 reaches Y and the resultant position is represented by the point marked 2. Proceeding in this manner the positions as indicated by the points 3, 4....8 are marked. Joining all these points by a free hand curve an oblique ellipse as shown in Fig. 1.8 is obtained.

(*ii*) (*a*) **Amplitudes different, periods in the ratio of 1 : 2 and phase difference zero.** Let the simple harmonic vibration along the X-axis have an amplitude a and the vibration along the Y-axis an amplitude b. The period of the Y-vibration is taken to be *double* that of the X-vibration.

Draw two circles of reference of radii a and b equal to the amplitudes of the corresponding simple harmonic motions taking place along the X-axis and Y-axis respectively. In the circle of radius a draw a line XX' parallel to the X-axis and in the circle of radius b draw a line YY' parallel to the Y-axis. As the periods are in the ratio 2 : 1, divide the circle YY' into 8 equal parts and the circle XX' into 4 equal parts (*i.e.*, in the ratio of their corresponding periods) so that each part is travelled in the same time. Draw lines through these points perpendicular to the lines XX' and YY' respectively so as to enclose a rectangle $PQRS$ as shown in Fig. 1.9.

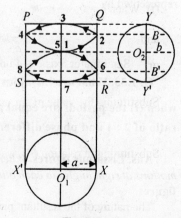

Fig. 1.9

Since the two vibrations are in phase, the particles O_1 and O_2 start simultaneously from their mean positions and the resultant position of a particle when both the vibrations act on it is represented by the point 1. When the particle O_1 is at X the particle O_2 is at B and the resultant position is represented by the point 2. Similarly, when the particle O_1 is in position O_1, X' and again at O_1 the particle O_2 is in the position Y, B and O_2 respectively. The resultant position is represented by the points 3, 4 and 5 respectively.

The particle O_1 now begins its second vibration and when it is at X, O_1 and X', the particle O_2 is at B', Y' and B'. The resultant position is represented by the points 6, 7 and 8 respectively. Joining all these points by a free hand curve the figure as shown in Fig. 1.9 is obtained.

(*ii*) (*b*) **Amplitude different, periods in the ratio of 1 : 2 and phase difference a quarter of the smaller period.** Draw two circles of reference of radii a and b and divide the circle YY' into *eight* equal parts and the circle XX' into *four* equal parts, *i.e.*, in the ratio of their corresponding periods as explained in (*ii*) (*a*).

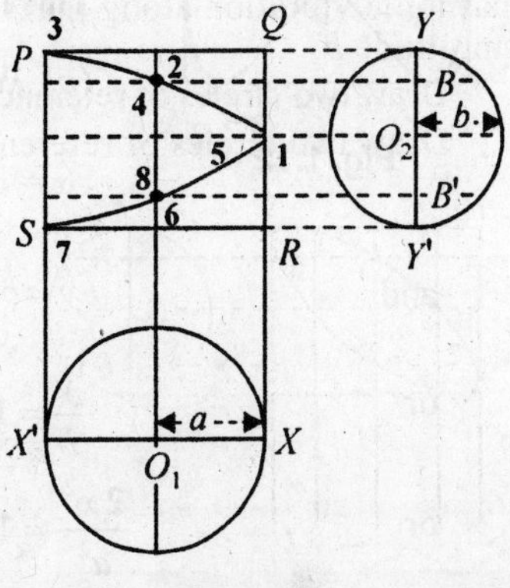

Since the X-vibration (of shorter period) is ahead of the Y-vibration by a quarter period, the particle O_1 will be in the position X when the particle O_2 starts from its mean position. Therefore, the resultant position of a particle when both the vibrations act on it is represented by the point 1. When the particle O_1 comes back to the mean position, the particle O_2 is at B and the resultant position is represented by the point 2. Similarly, when the particle O_1 is in position X', O_1 and back again at X, the particle O_2 is in the position Y, B and back again to O_2 respectively. The resultant position is represented by the points 3, 4 and 5 respectively. The particle O_1 now begins its second vibration and when it is at O_1, X, O_1 and X', the particle O_2 is at B', Y', B' and O_2 respectively. The resultant is represented by the points 6, 7, 8 and 1 respectively. Joining all these points by a free hand curve, the figure of a parabola symmetrical about the X-axis as shown in Fig. 1.10 is obtained.

Fig. 1.10

If, however, amplitudes are different, periods in the ratio 1 : 2 and the phase difference is *one eight* of the smaller period, then proceeding exactly as in (*ii*) (*b*), we get the curve as shown in Fig. 1.11

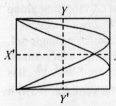

Fig. 1.11

Q. 1.34. Calculate the resultant of two simple harmonic vibrations at right angles when their periods are in the ratio of 2 : 1 and there is a phase difference 0 or $\pi/2$.

(*G.N.D.U.,* 2006; *Meerut U.,* 2005, 2001; *Lucknow U.,* 1996; *K.U.,* 1991)

Ans. Periods in the ratio 2 : 1. Let the two vibrations be represented by

$$x = a \sin \omega t$$

and
$$y = b \sin (2 \omega t + \phi)$$

This shows that the frequency of the Y-vibration is double that of the X-vibration, or the period of Y-vibration is half that of the X-vibration. The Y-vibration is also *ahead* in phase by ϕ.

(*i*) When $\phi = 0$, we have

$$x = a \sin \omega t \qquad \qquad ...(i)$$

and
$$y = b \sin 2 \omega t = 2 b \sin \omega t \cos \omega t$$

or
$$\frac{y}{b} = 2 \sin \omega t \cos \omega t \qquad \qquad ...(ii)$$

Substituting the value of $\sin \omega t = \dfrac{x}{a}$ from (*i*), we get

$$\cos \omega t = \sqrt{1 - x^2 / a^2}$$

Substituting in relation (*ii*), we get

$$\frac{y}{b} = \frac{2x}{a} \left(1 - \frac{x^2}{a^2} \right)^{\frac{1}{2}}$$

Squaring, we get $\quad \dfrac{y^2}{b^2} = \dfrac{4x^2}{a^2}\left(1 - \dfrac{x^2}{a^2}\right)$

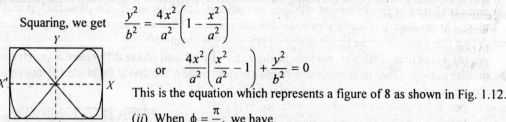

Fig. 1.12

or $\quad \dfrac{4x^2}{a^2}\left(\dfrac{x^2}{a^2} - 1\right) + \dfrac{y^2}{b^2} = 0$

This is the equation which represents a figure of 8 as shown in Fig. 1.12.

(ii) When $\phi = \dfrac{\pi}{2}$, we have

$$x = a \sin \omega t \text{ or } \dfrac{x}{a} = \sin \omega t$$

and $\qquad y = b \sin\left(2\omega t + \dfrac{\pi}{2}\right) = b \cos 2\omega t$

or $\qquad \dfrac{y}{b} = 1 - 2\sin^2 \omega t = 1 - \dfrac{2x^2}{a^2}$

or $\qquad \dfrac{2x^2}{a^2} = 1 - \dfrac{y}{b} = -\left(\dfrac{y-b}{b}\right)$

or $\qquad 2x^2 = -\dfrac{a^2}{b}(y-b)$

or $\qquad x^2 = -\dfrac{a^2}{2b}(y-b)$

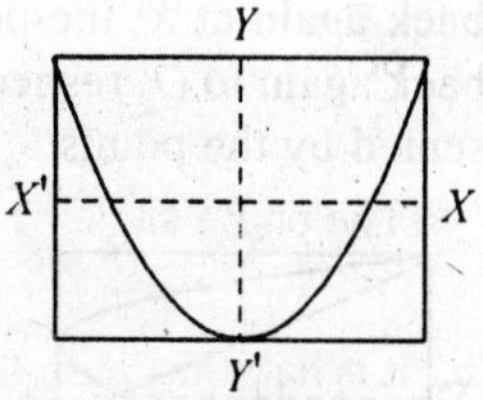

Fig. 1.13

This is the equation of a parabola symmetrical about the Y-axis having its vertex at $(0, b)$ as shown in Fig. 1.13.

Note 1. It should be noted carefully that in the graphical method of obtaining Lissajous figure, the period of the Y-vibration has been taken to be double that of the X-vibration whereas in the analytical method, the frequency of the Y-vibration has been taken to be twice that of the X-vibration, i.e., the period of Y-vibration is half that of the X-vibration. This is why the two halves of the figure of 8 obtained in the latter case are symmetrical about the Y-axis whereas in the former case the two halves are symmetrical about the X-axis. For the same reason the parabola is symmetrical about the Y-axis in the second case and about the X-axis in the first case.

Q. 1.35. Discuss the superposition of a large number of simple harmonic vibrations of equal amplitude and equal successive phase difference.

Ans. Resultant of a large number of simple harmonic vibrations. To find the resultant of a large number of simple harmonic vibrations having the same amplitude 'a', but constant phase difference δ with its predecessor, we represent the various simple harmonic vibrations as $a \sin \omega t$, $a \sin (\omega t + \delta)$, $a \sin (\omega t + 2\delta)$, $a \sin [\omega t + (n-1)$

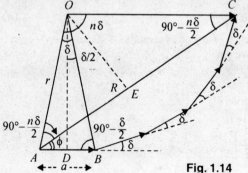

Fig. 1.14

$\delta]$. If R is the amplitude of the resultant vibration and ϕ its phase difference with respect to the first component $a \sin \omega t$, then

$$R \sin (\omega t + \phi) = a \sin \omega t + a \sin (\omega t + \delta) + a \sin (\omega t + 2\delta) \ldots\ldots + a \sin [\omega t + (n-1)\, \delta]$$

To find the value of R and ϕ, the various amplitudes are represented in magnitude and direction by different sides of the polygon. The resultant amplitude is represented by the closing side of the polygon.

If O is the centre of the circle enclosing the (incomplete) polygon of n sides each of magnitude a and external angle δ, then

Radius of the circle r $= OA = OC$

In triangle AOB $\qquad \angle AOB = \delta$ and $\angle OAB = \angle OBA = 90 - \dfrac{\delta}{2}$

Draw $OD \perp AB$, then

$$a = AB = AD + DB = r \sin \frac{\delta}{2} + r \sin \frac{\delta}{2}$$

$$= 2r \sin \frac{\delta}{2}$$

or $\qquad\qquad 2r = a / \sin \dfrac{\delta}{2}$

In $\triangle AOC$ $\qquad \angle AOC = n\delta$ and $\angle OAC = \angle OCA = 90 - \dfrac{n\delta}{2}$

Draw $OE \perp AC$, then

$$R = AC = AE + EC = r \sin \frac{n\delta}{2} + r \sin \frac{n\delta}{2} = 2r \sin \frac{n\delta}{2}$$

or $\qquad\qquad R = a \dfrac{\sin n\delta/2}{\sin \delta/2}$

The phase angle $\qquad \phi = \left(90 - \dfrac{\delta}{2}\right) - \left(90 - \dfrac{n\delta}{2}\right) = (n-1)\dfrac{\delta}{2}$

i.e., it is half the phase difference between the first and the last vibration.

$$\therefore \qquad R \sin(\omega t + \phi) = a \frac{\sin n\delta/2}{\sin \delta/2} \sin\left\{\omega t + (n-1)\frac{\delta}{2}\right\}$$

or $\qquad\qquad R = a \dfrac{\sin n\delta/2}{\sin \delta/2}$

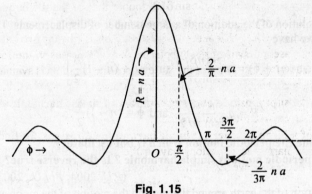

Fig. 1.15

When n is very large, δ is very small and in such a case ϕ is very nearly equal to $n\delta/2$ or $(n-1)\dfrac{\delta}{2}$ and

as $\qquad\qquad \sin \dfrac{\delta}{2} \to \dfrac{\delta}{2} \approx \dfrac{\phi}{n}$

$\therefore \qquad\qquad R = a \dfrac{\sin n\delta/2}{\sin \delta/2} = \dfrac{a \sin \phi}{\phi/n} = na \dfrac{\sin \phi}{\phi}$.

If we plot a graph between $R = na \dfrac{\sin \phi}{\phi}$ and ϕ, it is as shown in Fig. 1.15.

The pattern obtained is symmetrical about $\phi = 0$. The value of R is maximum when $\phi = 0$ so that $\frac{\sin \phi}{\phi} = 1$ and $R = na$.

When $\phi = \frac{\pi}{2}$, $\sin \phi = 1$ and $R = \frac{2}{\pi} na$

When $\phi = \pi$, $\sin \phi = 0$ and $R = 0$

When $\phi = \frac{3\pi}{2}$, $\sin \phi = -1$ and $R = -\frac{2}{3\pi} na$

Q. 1.36. By using exponential series find the resultant of 'n' number of S.H. vibrations of equal amplitude but successive phase angle δ.

Ans. Let us represent the successive simple harmonic motions by exponential functions

$$ae^{i\omega t},\ ae^{i(\omega t + \delta)},\ ae^{i(\omega t + 2\delta)} \ldots \ldots \ldots ae^{i\{\omega t + (n-1)\delta\}}$$

Let the resultant simple harmonic motion be represented by

$$Re^{i(\omega t + \phi)} = ae^{i\omega t} + ae^{i(\omega t + \delta)} + ae^{i(\omega t + 2\delta)} + \ldots\ldots + ae^{i\{\omega t + (n-1)\delta\}}$$

$$= ae^{i\omega t} [1 + e^{i\delta} + e^{i2\delta} + \ldots + e^{i(n-1)\delta}]$$

The expression within brackets is a geometrical series with common ratio $e^{i\delta}$ and

$$= \frac{1 - e^{in\delta}}{1 - e^{i\delta}}$$

$\therefore$
$$Re^{i(\omega t + \phi)} = ae^{i\omega t} \frac{1 - e^{in\delta}}{1 - e^{i\delta}}$$

$$= ae^{i\omega t} \frac{e^{in\delta/2}}{e^{i\delta/2}} \left[\frac{e^{-in\delta/2} - e^{in\delta/2}}{e^{-i\delta/2} - e^{i\delta/2}} \right]$$

$$= ae^{i[\omega t + (n-1)\delta/2]} \frac{\sin n\delta/2}{\sin \delta/2}$$

It is a complex solution of the addition of a large number of displacements. Taking only the real part of the solution, we have

$$R \sin(\omega t + \phi) = a \frac{\sin n\delta/2}{\sin \delta/2} \sin \left[\omega t + (n-1)\frac{\delta}{2} \right]$$

$\therefore$
$$R = a \frac{\sin n\delta/2}{\sin \delta/2} \text{ and } \phi = (n-1)\frac{\delta}{2}$$

Q. 1.37. (*a*) **Name the periodic motion which is not oscillatory.**   (*P.U.*, 1991)

(*b*) **Are all the periodic motions simple harmonic ? Is the reverse true? Explain.**

(*P.U.* 2004; *Pbi.U.*, 2003; *G.N.D.U.*, 1998)

Ans. (*a*) The motion of the earth around the sun and the motion of the moon around the earth are periodic but not oscillatory.

(*b*) No, all the periodic motions are not simple harmonic. As stated in (*a*), the motion of the earth around the sun and the motion of the moon around the earth is periodic but not simple harmonic.

However, the *reverse is true i.e.* all Simple Harmonic motions are periodic. A S.H.M has a definite frequency and hence a fixed time period which makes it a periodic motion.

Q. 1.38. The amplitude of a simple harmonic oscillator is doubled. How does this effect the time period, total energy and maximum velocity of the oscillator ?

(*P.U.*, 2003, 1998; *Pbi., U.* 2000; *H. P. U.*, 1998)

Ans. When the displacement y of a simple harmonic oscillator is given by $y = A \sin(\omega t + \phi)$

velocity $v = \dfrac{dy}{dt} = A\omega \cos(\omega t + \phi)$

and acceleration $a = \dfrac{d^2 y}{dt^2} = -A\omega^2 \sin(\omega t + \phi) = -\omega^2 y$

Now time period $T = 2\pi \sqrt{\dfrac{\text{Displacement}}{\text{Acceleration}}} = 2\pi \sqrt{\dfrac{y}{\omega^2 y}} = \dfrac{2\pi}{\omega}$ (ignoring the negative sign)

As $\dfrac{2\pi}{\omega}$ is a constant, the time period does not depend upon amplitude but remains constant .

Maximum velocity $v_{max} = A\omega$ when $\cos(\omega t + \phi) = 1$

When amplitude A is doubled, the maximum velocity is also doubled.

Total energy $= \dfrac{1}{2} m A^2 \omega^2$

When the amplitude A is doubled, the total energy becomes four times.

Q. 1.39. Mark the correct answer.

(*i*) Which of the following is not essential for S.H.M.?

(*a*) Inertia   (*b*) Restoring force   (*c*) Elasticity   (*d*) Gravity   (*G.N.D.U.*, 1993)

(*ii*) The velocity of a particle executing S.H.M. is minimum at a point where displacement is

(*a*) zero   (*b*) maximum   (*c*) midway between zero and maximum

(*iii*) For a particle executing S.H.M. the phase difference between displacement and velocity is

(*a*) $\pi/2$ (*b*) π (*c*) 0   (*d*) $-\pi/2$ (*H.P.U.*, 1994)

(*iv*) The S.I. unit of force constant or spring constant is

(*a*) Nm   (*b*) Nm^{-1} (*c*) Nm^{-2} (*H.P.U.*, 1993)

(*v*) The potential energy of a particle executing S.H.M. is equal to its kinetic energy when the displacement of the particle is

(*a*) $\pm a$ (*b*) $\pm a/2$ (*c*) $\pm \dfrac{a}{\sqrt 2}$ where a is the amplitude.

(*vi*) In simple harmonic motion the amplitude is 5 cm and time period is 31.4 sec. The maximum velocity is

(*a*) 1   (*b*) 2   (*c*) 1.4   (*d*) 2.4 units   (*Meerut U.*, 2000)

(**Hint.** Take 31.4 sec = 10π sec)

(*vii*) The Lissajous figures make a figure of eight (8) if the frequency ratio is

(*a*) 1 : 2   (*b*) 2 : 1   (*c*) 1 : 1   (*d*) 1 : 3   (*Meerut U.*, 2000)

(*viii*) The potential energy of a simple harmonic oscillator is maximum when its displacement is equal to

(*a*) Zero   (*b*) Amplitude   (*c*) $\dfrac{\text{Amplitude}}{2}$ (*d*) $\dfrac{\text{Amplitude}}{\sqrt 2}$

Ans. (*i*) *d*   (*ii*) *b*   (*iii*) *a*   (*iv*) *b*   (*v*) *c*

(*vi*) *a*   (*vii*) *a*   (*viii*) *b*

EXERCISE

1. A particle executing simple harmonic motion along a straight line has a velocity 4 cm s^{-1} at a distance of 3 cm from the mean position and 3 cm s^{-1} at a distance of 4 cm from it. Find the time it takes to travel 2.5 cm from positive extremity of the oscillation.   [**Ans.** 2.19 sec.]

2 Damped Simple Harmonic Motion

Q. 2.1. What do you mean by damping? Prove that the damping force is independent of acceleration or displacement and is proportional to velocity.

(H.P.U. 2003, 2000, 1993; G.N.D.U. 2009, 2000; P.U. 2006, 1999; Pbi.U. 2007, 1991)

Ans. Damping. The amplitude of a vibrating string, a sounding tuning fork and an oscillating pendulum goes on gradually decreasing and ultimately these bodies stop vibrating, It is because some energy is inevitably lost due to resistive or viscous forces. For example, in the case of a simple pendulum, energy is lost due to friction at the supports and resistance of air. The resistance offered by a damping force is known as *damping*. When the damping is small, it does not produce any significant change in the undamped motion of the vibrating body. In such a case, *the damping force is proportional to the velocity of the vibrating body.*

Proof. To prove the same, consider a body executing simple harmonic motion given by

$$y = a \sin \omega t,$$

and acted upon by a *small* damping force $\vec{f}$.

As a general case, suppose that $\vec{f}$ is a function of displacement, velocity and acceleration and is given by

$$\vec{f} = A + B\vec{y} + C\frac{d\vec{y}}{dt} + D\frac{d^2\vec{y}}{dt^2}$$

The work done by the damping force $\vec{f}$ in displacing the body through a small displacement $d\vec{y}$ is given by

$$dW = \vec{f}.d\vec{y} = \vec{f}.\frac{d\vec{y}}{dt}dt = \vec{f}.\vec{v}\,dt$$

If T is the time period of the vibrating body, then

Work done per cycle $W = \int_0^T dW$

$$= \int_0^T \left(A + B\vec{y} + C\frac{d\vec{y}}{dt} + D\frac{d^2\vec{y}}{dt^2} \right)\left(\frac{d\vec{y}}{dt} \right)dt$$

As $y = a \sin \omega t$; $\dfrac{dy}{dt} = a\omega \cos \omega t$ and $\dfrac{d^2y}{dt^2} = -a\omega^2 \sin \omega t$

$$\therefore \quad W = \int_0^T A\,a\omega \cos \omega t\, dt + \int_0^T (B - D\omega^2)\,a^2\,\omega \sin \omega t \cos \omega t\, dt$$

$$+ \int_0^T C a^2\,\omega^2 \cos^2 \omega t\, dt$$

Now $\quad \displaystyle\int_0^T A a\omega \cos \omega t\, dt = Aa[\sin \omega t\,]_0^T = 0$

$$\int_0^T (B - D\omega^2)\,a^2\omega \sin \omega t \cos \omega t\, dt = \frac{(B - D\omega^2)\,a^2\,\omega}{2}\int_0^T \sin 2\omega t\, dt$$

$$= \frac{(B - D\omega^2)\,a^2\,\omega}{2}[- \frac{\cos 2\omega t}{2\omega}\,]_0^T = 0$$

and $\quad \displaystyle\int_0^T C a^2\,\omega^2 t^2 \cos^2 \omega t\, dt$

$$= C a^2 \omega^2 \int_0^T \frac{1 + \cos 2\,\omega t}{2}\, dt = \frac{1}{2} C a^2 \omega^2 \left[\int_0^T dt + \int_0^T \cos 2\,\omega t\, dt\right]$$

$$= \frac{1}{2} C a^2 \omega^2\, T = \pi\, C a^2\, \omega \qquad\qquad [\because \int_0^T \cos 2\,\omega t\, dt = 0 \ \text{ and } \int_0^T dt = T]$$

The damping force being a frictional force is a non-conservative force and work done against it over a full time period cannot be zero.

Hence work is done only *by* that term of the damping force which is *proportional to velocity* of the vibrating body, the work done due to all other terms being zero. In other words, *the damping force is independent of displacement as well as acceleration and depends only upon velocity.*

Q. 2.2. What are damped vibrations? Establish the differential equation of motion for a damped harmonic oscillator and obtain an expression for displacement. Discuss the case of heavy damping.

(*P.U.* 2007, 2006, 2005, 2003; *Nagpur U.* 2002, 2001; *Kerala U.* 2001; *Pbi.U.* 2001; *H.P.U.* 2000; *Kanpur U.* 1994; *K.U.* 1991; *Luck.U.* 1991)

Ans. Damped vibrations. In an ideal simple harmonic motion, the displacement follows a sine curve for an infinite time. This is because the total energy remains constant. In actual practice, the simple harmonic oscillator always experiences frictional or resistive forces due to which some energy is lost and the oscillations get *damped*. The amplitude of vibration decreases gradually and ultimately the body comes to rest.

The decay of amplitude with time is called damping. Those simple harmonic vibrations where amplitude decreases with the passage of time are called damped simple harmonic vibrations.

Differential equation of motion of damped simple harmonic system. If the velocity of the vibrating body is small, then the retarding force due to the medium is proportional to the first power of velocity. In such a case there are two forces acting on the vibrating particle.

(*i*) The restoring force proportional to displacement y given by $-sy$ where s is a constant known as *stiffness constant* or *spring constant*. The negative sign shows that the direction of the restoring force is opposite to that of displacement, and

(*ii*) A retarding force proportional to velocity given by $-r\,\dfrac{dy}{dt}$ where r is another constant known as *damping constant*. The negative sign again shows that the retarding force also acts opposite to the direction of motion of the body.

If m is the mass of the vibrating particle and its acceleration $\dfrac{d^2 y}{dt^2}$ when it has a displacement y

and is moving with a velocity $\dfrac{dy}{dt}$, then

$$m \frac{d^2 y}{dt^2} = -r \frac{dy}{dt} - sy$$

or

$$m \frac{d^2 y}{dt^2} + r \frac{dy}{dt} + sy = 0 \qquad \ldots(i)$$

The equation represents the motion of the particle under various forces mentioned above and the vibrations are *damped*.

Dividing (i) by m and putting $\dfrac{r}{m} = 2k$ and $\dfrac{s}{m} = \omega_0^2$, we get

$$\frac{d^2 y}{dt^2} + 2k \frac{dy}{dt} + \omega_0^2\, y = 0 \qquad \ldots(ii)$$

In this case k is called the *damping coefficient* and $2k$ give *the force due to resistance of the medium per unit mass per unit velocity.*

Eq. (ii) is known as *differential equation* of damped simple harmonic motion.

Displacement equation. Let a solution of differential equation (ii) be

$$y = Ae^{\alpha t}$$

$\therefore$

$$\frac{dy}{dt} = A\alpha e^{\alpha t} \quad \text{and} \quad \frac{d^2 y}{dt^2} = A\alpha^2 e^{\alpha t}$$

Substituting these values in (ii), we have

$$A\alpha^2 e^{\alpha t} + 2kA\alpha e^{\alpha t} + \omega_0^2 Ae^{\alpha t} = 0$$

or

$$\alpha^2 + 2k\alpha + \omega_0^2 = 0$$

$\therefore$

$$\alpha = \frac{-2k \pm \sqrt{4k^2 - 4\omega_0^2}}{2}$$

$$= k \pm \sqrt{k^2 - \omega_0^2}$$

Hence a general solution of the differential equation (ii) is

$$y = A_1 e^{(-k + \sqrt{k^2 - \omega_0^2})t} + A_2 e^{(-k - \sqrt{k^2 - \omega_0^2})t} \qquad \ldots(iii)$$

where A_1 and A_2 are arbitrary constants whose values are determined from boundary conditions. As we are considering a second order differential equation, there should be two arbitrary constants.

Eq. (iii) can be part in the form

$$y = e^{-kt}\left[A_1 e^{\sqrt{k^2 - \omega_0^2}\,t} + A_2 e^{-\sqrt{k^2 - \omega_0^2}\,t} \right] \qquad \ldots(iv)\,(a)$$

$$= e^{-\frac{r}{2m}t}\left[A_1 e^{\sqrt{\frac{r^2}{4m^2} - \frac{s}{m}}\,t} + A_2 e^{-\sqrt{\frac{r^2}{4m^2} - \frac{s}{m}}\,t} \right] \qquad \ldots(iv)\,(b)$$

This is the *displacement equation* of mass m executing damped simple harmonic motion. The nature of motion depends upon the relative values of k and ω_0, *i.e.*, whether

$$\sqrt{k^2 - \omega_0^2} \quad \text{or} \quad \sqrt{\frac{r^2}{4m^2} - \frac{s}{m}}$$

is positive, zero or negative. When $k > \omega_0$, it is a case of heavy damping.

Heavy damping. When $k > \omega_0$. In this case $k^2 - \omega_0^2 = \dfrac{r^2}{4m^2} - \dfrac{s}{m} = a\ positive$ quantity. Hence

$\sqrt{k^2 - \omega_0^2}$ is real.

Substituting $\sqrt{k^2 - \omega_0^2} = p$ in equation (iv), (a), we have

$$y = e^{-kt}[A_1\, e^{pt} + A_2\, e^{-pt}]$$

Let $\qquad A = A_1 + A_2 \quad and \quad B = A_1 - A_2$

then $\qquad A_1 = \dfrac{A + B}{2} \quad and \quad A_2 = \dfrac{A - B}{2}$

$\therefore \qquad y = e^{-kt}\left[\dfrac{A + B}{2}\, e^{pt} + \dfrac{A - B}{2}\, e^{-pt}\right]$

$$= e^{-kt}\left[A\, \dfrac{e^{pt} + e^{-pt}}{2} + B\, \dfrac{e^{pt} - e^{-pt}}{2}\right]$$

$$= e^{-kt}\,[A \cosh pt + B \sinh pt]$$

The displacement consists of two terms both dying off exponentially to zero. The values of A and B depend upon the initial conditions. If $y = 0$ at $t = 0$, then

$$A = 0 \quad and \quad y = Be^{-kt} \sinh pt$$

$$= Be^{-kt} \sinh \sqrt{(k^2 - \omega_0^2)}\ t$$

$$= Be^{-\frac{r}{m}t} \sinh \sqrt{\left(\dfrac{r^2}{4m^2} - \dfrac{s}{m}\right)}t$$

As the above function is not a periodic function of time, such a motion is called *aperiodic* or *overdamped*. It is neither *dead beat* nor *oscillatory*. It only takes a long time to return to equilibrium position.

Under *very heavy damping*, there is no vibration at all and the particle passes its equilibrium position at the most once before returning asymptotically to rest. This is met with in a dead beat moving coil galvanometer or a pendulum vibrating in a viscous liquid like oil.

The variation of displacement (y) with time (t) for a highly damped simple harmonic oscillator is shown in Fig. 2.1. The oscillator is disturbed by giving it a jerk at $t = 0$ and the system starts moving. At this stage the term e^{-kt} is very nearly equal to *one* ($e^0 = 1$). The displacement increases with time up to $t = t_0$ when the system has maximum displacement. Thereafter the factor e^{-kt} dominates and the displacement decreases exponentially with time.

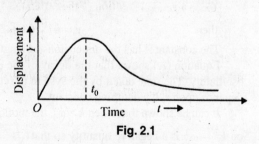

Fig. 2.1

Q. 2.3. **Using the general solution of equation of damped simple harmonic motion discuss the case of critical damping.** *(Pbi. U.*, 2007; *Nagpur. U.* 2001; *P.U.*, 1993; *Kan.U.*, 1990)

Ans. Equation of damped simple harmonic motion. The differential equation for damped simple harmonic motion is given by

$$\frac{d^2y}{dt^2} + 2k\,\frac{dy}{dt} + \omega_0^2\,y = 0 \qquad \qquad \text{...}(i)$$

where $2k = \dfrac{r}{m}$; r being the *damping constant*, m the mass of the vibrating particle and $\omega_0^2 = \dfrac{s}{m}$; s being the *stiffness* or *spring constant*.

The general solution of differential equation (i) is given by

$$y = e^{-kt}\left[A_1\,e^{\sqrt{k^2 - \omega_0^2}\,t} + A_2\,e^{-\sqrt{k^2 - \omega_0^2}\,t}\right] \qquad \qquad \text{...}(ii)$$

where A_1 and A_2 are arbitrary constants the value of which can be determined from boundary conditions. [For proof See **Q. 2.2 Eq. (iv a)**]

Critical damping. The oscillator is said to be *critically damped* if

$$k^2 - \omega_0^2 = 0$$

or
$$\frac{r^2}{4m^2} - \frac{s}{m} = 0$$

In this case the damping term and stiffness term try to balance each other's effect. Substituting $k^2 - \omega_0^2 = 0$ in equation (ii), the displacement y is given by

$$y = e^{-kt}\,(A_1 + A_2) = Ge^{-kt} \qquad \qquad \text{...}(iii)$$

where $\quad G = (A_1 + A_2) = $ a constant.

This shows that the displacement decays to zero exponentially and the system returns to the initial state in the minimum time.

The solution of differential equation (i) given by equation (iii) contains only one constant. But the solution of a second degree differential equation must contain two constants. Thus the solution given by equation (iii) is only a partial solution. To find the complete solution suppose k^2 is *slightly greater than* ω_0^2 and $\sqrt{k^2 - \omega_0^2} = \delta$ a small quantity. Then, equation (ii) becomes

$$y = e^{-kt}\left[A_1\,e^{+\delta t} + A_2\,e^{-\delta t}\right]$$
$$= e^{-kt}\left[A_1\,(1 + \delta t + ...) + A_2\,(1 - \delta t + ...)\right]$$

As δ is very small, terms containing squares and higher powers of δ are being neglected.

Hence
$$y = e^{-kt}\left[(A_1 + A_2) + \delta\,(A_1 - A_2)t\right]$$

Put
$$A_1 + A_2 = A \text{ and } \delta\,(A_1 - A_2) = B,$$

then
$$y = e^{-kt}\,(A + Bt) \qquad \qquad \text{...}(iv)$$

The constant A has the dimensions of length and constant B that of velocity.

Equation (iv) shows that the decay of the displacement y is exponential but the change is non-oscillatory. The time taken by the system to return to the initial state depends upon k which in turn depends upon r, the damping constant.

It can be shown that when $k > \omega_0$, the motion of the oscillator is *highly damped* and when $k < \omega_0$ or $k^2 - \omega_0^2$ is a negative quantity so that $\sqrt{k^2 - \omega_0^2}$ is imaginary, the particle undergoes a *damped simple harmonic motion*.

Therefore, for $k = \omega_0$ the motion is neither overdamped nor oscillatory and is said to be *critically damped*. The property of critical damping is made use of in measuring instruments like ballistic galvanometers.

Q. 2.4. Show that $x = (A + Bt)\, e^{\frac{-r}{2m}t}$ **is the solution of the differential equation**

$\dfrac{d^2 x}{dt^2} + \dfrac{r}{m}\dfrac{dx}{dt} + \dfrac{s}{m}x = 0$ **for the critically damped oscillations.** *(H.P.U., 1995)*

Ans. When the displacement is along the X-axis, the differential equation of damped simple harmonic motion is given by

$$\frac{d^2 x}{dt^2} + \frac{r}{m}\frac{dx}{dt} + \frac{s}{m}x = 0$$

where the symbols have their usual meaning.

Given
$$x = (A + Bt)\, e^{\frac{-r}{2m}t}.$$

Substituting $\dfrac{r}{m} = 2k$ and $\dfrac{s}{m} = \omega_0^2$, we have

$$x = (A + Bt)e^{-kt}$$

$\therefore$
$$\frac{dx}{dt} = -k(A + Bt)e^{-kt} + Be^{-kt}$$

and
$$\frac{d^2 x}{dt^2} = k^2(A + Bt)e^{-kt} - kBe^{-kt} - kBe^{-kt}$$

$$= k^2(A + Bt)e^{-kt} - 2kBe^{-kt}$$

Substituting the values of x, $\dfrac{dx}{dt}$ and $\dfrac{d^2 x}{dt^2}$ in the differential equation

$$\frac{d^2 x}{dt^2} + \frac{r}{m}\frac{dx}{dt} + \frac{s}{m}x = 0$$

or
$$\frac{d^2 x}{dt^2} + 2k\frac{dx}{dt} + \omega_0^2 x = 0$$

we have

$$k^2(A + Bt)e^{-kt} - 2kBe^{-kt} - 2k^2(A + Bt)e^{-kt} + 2kBe^{-kt} + \omega_0^2(A + Bt)e^{-kt} = 0$$

or
$$(\omega_0^2 - k^2)(A + Bt)e^{-kt} = 0$$

or
$$(\omega_0^2 - k^2)x = 0$$

But x is not always zero.

$\therefore$
$$\omega_0^2 - k^2 = 0$$

or
$$k^2 = \omega_0^2 \quad \text{or} \quad \frac{r^2}{4m^2} = \frac{s}{m}$$

This is the condition for critical damping of the oscillation. Hence $x = (A + Bt)\, e^{\frac{-r}{2m}t}$ is the solution of the given differential equation for the critically damped oscillations.

Q. 2.5. Write down the equation of damped simple harmonic oscillator. Find the expression for displacement and discuss the case of (i) heavy damping, (ii) critical damping and (iii) light damping. When do we get oscillatory damped simple harmonic motion ?

(P.U. 2006, 2003; Luck. U. 2002; Nagpur U. 2001; Indore U. 2001; Kan. U. 1995; G.N.D.U. 2009, 2008; Pbi.U. 2007, 2006; H.P.U. 2000)

Ans. Damped simple harmonic oscillator. The differential equation of motion of a damped simple harmonic oscillator is

$$\frac{d^2 y}{dt^2} + 2k\,\frac{dy}{dt} + \omega_0^2\, y = 0 \qquad\qquad\qquad ...(i)$$

and its general solution of displacement is

$$y = e^{-kt}\left[A_1\, e^{\sqrt{k^2 - \omega_0^2}\,t} + A_2\, e^{-\sqrt{k^2 - \omega_0^2}\,t}\right] \qquad\qquad ...(ii)$$

where the symbols have their usual meaning. For derivation of the differential equation and displacement see **Q. 2.2**, Eq. (ii) and Eq. (iv) (a).

The nature of motion represented by equation (ii) depends upon the relative values of k and ω_0. Three different cases arise

(i) *Heavy damping* when $k > \omega_0$. In this case $k^2 - \omega_0^2 = \dfrac{r^2}{4\,m^2} - \dfrac{s}{m} = a$ positive quantity.

Hence $\sqrt{k^2 - \omega_0^2}$ is *real*. Under heavy damping the motion is *aperiodic* or *overdamped*.

(ii) *Critical damping* when $k = \omega_0$. In this case

$$k^2 - \omega_0^2 = \frac{r^2}{4\,m^2} - \frac{s}{m} = 0$$

The motion is neither *overdamped* nor *oscillatory* and is said to be *critically damped*.

(iii) *Light damping* when $k < \omega_0$. In this case $k^2 - \omega_0^2 = \dfrac{r^2}{4\,m^2} - \dfrac{s}{m} = a$ *negative quantity*.

Hence $\sqrt{k^2 - \omega_0^2}$ is an *imaginary quantity*.

Let

$$\sqrt{k^2 - \omega_0^2} = i\omega' \quad \text{or} \quad \omega' = \sqrt{\omega_0^2 - k^2}$$

$$\therefore \qquad y = e^{-kt}\left[A_1\, e^{i\omega' t} + A_2\, e^{-i\omega' t}\right]$$

Put

$$A_1 = \frac{A_0}{2i}\, e^{i\phi} \quad \text{and} \quad A_2 = \frac{A_0}{2i}\, e^{-i\phi}$$

where A_0 and ϕ are also constants the value of which depends upon the state of motion at $t = 0$.

$$\therefore \qquad y = e^{-kt}\, A_0\left[\frac{e^{i(\omega' t + \phi)} - e^{-i(\omega' t + \phi)}}{2i}\right]$$

$$= A_0\, e^{-kt}\, \sin(\omega' t + \phi) \qquad\qquad\qquad ...(iii)$$

This is the equation of a *damped oscillatory simple harmonic* motion with amplitude Ae^{-kt} which goes on decreasing with time and a *new angular* frequency $\omega' = \sqrt{\omega_0^2 - k^2}$ which is less than $\omega_0 = \sqrt{\dfrac{s}{m}}$.

To find the value of A_0 and ϕ. Let the displacement $y = y_0$ (maximum) at time $t = 0$ so that the velocity $\dfrac{dy}{dt} = 0$.

Substituting in equation (iii), we have

$$y_0 = A_0\, \sin\phi \qquad\qquad\qquad ...(iv)$$

Differentiating equation (iii) and putting

$$\frac{dy}{dt} = 0 \text{ at } t = 0, \text{ we get}$$

$$\frac{dy}{dt} = -A_0\, k e^{-kt}\, \sin(\omega' t + \phi) + A_0\, \omega' e^{-kt}\, \cos(\omega' t + \phi)$$

$$\therefore \qquad 0 = -A_0\, k \sin\phi + A_0\, \omega' \cos\phi$$

Hence
$$\tan \phi = \frac{\omega'}{k} = \frac{\sqrt{\omega_0^2 - k^2}}{k}$$

$$\sin \phi = \frac{\omega'}{\sqrt{\omega'^2 + k^2}}$$

∴

Substituting the values of $\sin \phi$ in (iv), we get

$$y_0 = \frac{A_0 \omega'}{\sqrt{\omega'^2 + k^2}} = \frac{A_0 \omega'}{\omega_0} \qquad [\because \omega'^2 = \omega_0^2 - k^2]$$

$$A_0 = \frac{y_0 \omega_0}{\omega'} = \frac{y_0 \omega_0}{\sqrt{\omega_0^2 - k^2}}$$

∴

Substituting the values in (iii), we have

$$y = \frac{y_0 \omega_0 e^{-kt}}{\omega'} \sin(\omega't + \phi)$$

$$= \frac{y_0 \omega_0}{\sqrt{\omega_0^2 - k^2}} e^{-kt} \sin\left(\sqrt{\omega_0^2 - k^2}\, t + \phi\right)$$

or
$$y = A_0 e^{-kt} \sin\left(\sqrt{\omega_0^2 - k^2}\, t + \phi\right)$$

where
$$A_0 = \frac{y_0 \omega_0}{\sqrt{\omega_0^2 - k^2}}$$

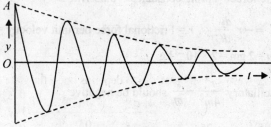

Fig. 2.2

The amplitude of the oscillations, therefore, goes on decreasing with time in accordance with the relation

$$A = A_0 e^{-kt}$$

This is the case of *oscillatory damped simple harmonic motion.*

The graph showing the displacement y with time is given in Fig. 2.2. The time period T' is given by

$$T' = \frac{2\pi}{\omega'} = \frac{2\pi}{\sqrt{\omega_0^2 - k^2}}$$

$$= \frac{2\pi}{\sqrt{\dfrac{s}{m} - \dfrac{r^2}{4m^2}}}$$

The frequency of damped oscillations is given by

$$f' = \frac{\omega'}{2\pi} = \frac{1}{2\pi}\sqrt{\frac{s}{m} - \frac{r^2}{4m^2}}$$

The frequency of natural undamped oscillations is given by

$$f_0 = \frac{1}{2\pi}\sqrt{\frac{s}{m}}$$

Thus f' is less than f_0. The difference depends upon the damping factor r. Larger the value of r, higher is the difference between f_0 and f'.

Exercise. 1. *What do you mean by critical damping ?*   (*G.N.D.U.*, 2008)

Hint See Q. 2.3 and Q. 2.5 under the head 'critical damping'

Exercise 2. *Discuss briefly various types of damping.*   (*G.N.D.U.*, 2007)

Hint (*i*)   *Heavy damping.* See **Q. 2.2**

     (*ii*)   *Critical damping.* See **Q. 2.3**

     (*iii*)   *Light damping.* See **Q. 2.5**

Q. 2.6. (*a*) **A 2gm particle is subjected to an elastic force of 0.03 Nm⁻¹ and a frictional force of 0.005 N per (ms⁻¹). If it is displaced through 2 cm. and then released, find whether the resulting motion is oscillatory or not. If so, find its period.**   (*G.N.D.U.*, 2008)

(*b*) **A mass of 1 kg is suspended from a spring of stiffness constant 25 Nm⁻¹. If the undamped (or natural) frequency is** $\dfrac{2}{\sqrt{3}}$ **times the damped frequency, calculate the damping factor (or constant).**   (*Pbi.U.* 1999; *H.P.U.*, 1991)

(*c*) **A mass of 25 × 10⁻² kg is suspended from the lower end of a vertical spring having a force constant 25 Nm⁻¹. What should be the damping constant of the system so that the motion is critically damped?**   (*Nagpur U.* 2001)

Ans. (*a*) Here elastic force = spring constant $s = 0.03$ Nm⁻¹

$$\text{Frictional force} = -r\frac{dy}{dt} \quad \therefore r = \text{Frictional force per unit velocity} = 0.005\ \text{N per (ms}^{-1})$$

$$m = 2\ \text{gm} = 2\times10^{-3}\ \text{kg}$$

For motion to be oscillatory $\dfrac{r^2}{4m^2} - \dfrac{s}{m}$ should be negative

Now $\dfrac{r^2}{4m^2} = \dfrac{(.005)^2}{4\times(2\times10^{-3})^2} = \dfrac{25}{16}$ and $\dfrac{s}{m} = \dfrac{.03}{2\times10^{-3}} = 15$

As $\dfrac{r^2}{4m^2}$ is less than $\dfrac{s}{m}$, $\dfrac{r^2}{4m^2} - \dfrac{s}{m}$ is a negative quantity. Hence the motion is oscillatory.

Angular velocity $\omega' = \sqrt{\omega_0^2 - k^2} = \sqrt{\dfrac{s}{m} - \dfrac{r^2}{4m^2}}$

$$= \sqrt{15 - \frac{25}{16}} = 3.67\ rad\,s^{-1}$$

Now $\omega' = \dfrac{2\pi}{T}$ $\therefore$ $T = \dfrac{2\pi}{\omega'} = \dfrac{2\times22}{7\times3.67} = 1.71S.$

(*b*) Damped frequency $f' = \dfrac{1}{2\pi}\sqrt{\dfrac{s}{m} - \dfrac{r^2}{4m^2}}$

and undamped frequency $\quad f_0 = \dfrac{1}{2\pi}\sqrt{\dfrac{s}{m}}$

Now $\qquad\qquad\qquad \dfrac{f_0}{f'} = \dfrac{2}{\sqrt{3}}$

or $\qquad \dfrac{\sqrt{\dfrac{s}{m}}}{\sqrt{\dfrac{s}{m} - \dfrac{r^2}{4m^2}}} = \dfrac{2}{\sqrt{3}} \quad$ or $\quad \dfrac{\dfrac{s}{m}}{\dfrac{s}{m} - \dfrac{r^2}{4m^2}} = \dfrac{4}{3}$

or $\qquad\qquad \dfrac{3}{4}\dfrac{s}{m} = \dfrac{s}{m} - \dfrac{r^2}{4m^2}$

or $\qquad\qquad \dfrac{r^2}{4m^2} = \dfrac{1}{4}\dfrac{s}{m}$

$\therefore \qquad\qquad\qquad r^2 = sm$

Given $\qquad\qquad s = 25\ \text{Nm}^{-1} \quad$ and $\quad m = 1\ \text{kg}$

$\qquad\qquad\qquad r^2 = 25\ \text{Nm}^{-1}\ \text{kg} = 25\ \text{kg}^2\ \text{s}^{-2} \qquad\qquad [\because\ N = \text{kg ms}^{-2}]$

$\therefore \qquad\qquad\qquad r = 5\ \text{kg s}^{-1}$

(c) Here $m = 25 \times 10^{-2}$ kg; Force (spring constant) $s = 25\ \text{Nm}^{-1}$
Damping constant $r = ?$

For critical damping $\quad \dfrac{r^2}{4m^2} - \dfrac{s}{m} = 0$

or $\qquad\qquad r^2 = 4ms$ or $r = 2\sqrt{ms} = 2\sqrt{25 \times 10^{-2} \times 25}$

$\qquad\qquad\qquad = 2 \times 25 \times 10^{-1} = 5\ \text{kg s}^{-1}$

Q. 2.7. (a) Show that the unit of damping term (or damping co-efficient) k is s^{-1}.

(G.N.D.U. 2006, 2001; P.U. 2006, 1999; H.P.U. 2002; 1995)

(b) Write the units of damping constant of mechanical and electrical oscillator.

(P.U., 2006)

Ans. (a) For a damped harmonic oscillator the equation of motion is

$$m\frac{d^2y}{dt^2} + r\frac{dy}{dt} + sy = 0$$

or

$$\frac{d^2y}{dt^2} + \frac{r}{m}\frac{dy}{dt} + \frac{s}{m}y = 0$$

Substituting $\qquad \dfrac{r}{m} = 2k \;$ and $\; \dfrac{s}{m} = \omega_0^2$, we get

$$\frac{d^2y}{dt^2} + 2k\frac{dy}{dt} + \omega_0^2\, y = 0$$

$\therefore$ The unit of $r\dfrac{dy}{dt}$ is that of force, $i.e.$, Newton

$\therefore$ Unit of damping constant r is $\dfrac{\text{Force}}{\text{velocity}} = \text{Nm}^{-1}\text{s} = \text{kg ms}^{-2}\,\text{m}^{-1}\text{s} = \text{kg s}^{-1}$

Hence unit of damping (co-efficient) or term $k = \dfrac{r}{m} = \dfrac{kg\,s^{-1}}{kg} = s^{-1}$ *i.e.* k has the dimensions of frequency.

(b) **Unit of damping constant of mechanical oscillator.** The unit of damping constant r of mechancial oscillator is $Nm^{-1}s$. For detail see part (a).

Unit of damping constant of electrical oscillator. For an electrical oscillator

$$L\dfrac{d^2q}{dt^2} + R\dfrac{dq}{dt} + \dfrac{q}{c} = 0 \text{ (See Q. 2.8)}$$

In this equation the resistive force is $R\dfrac{dq}{dt}$ which represents voltage, $\dfrac{dq}{dt}$ is the current and R is the damping constant which has dimensions of voltage/current, *i.e.*, Resistance.

Electrical damping constant is, therefore, defined as voltage per unit current and has units of resistance, i.e., ohm or volt per ampere.

Q. 2.8. A charged capacitor discharges through an inductance and resistance in series. Discuss possible solutions and represent these by graphs. Deduce the condition under which the discharge is (i) critically damped and (ii) oscillatory obtain expression for the frequency. Does the presence of resistance effect the amplitude and frequency of damped oscillations?

(G.N.D.U., 2009; P.U., 2007, 2005, 2003, 1999, 1995, 1994, 1992; H.P.U. 2002, 2000)

OR

Write and solve differential equation for damped LCR series circuit and discuss oscillatory discharge of the condenser.   (P.U., 2009; 2008; G.N.D.U., 2007)

Ans. Discharge of a capacitor through inductance and resistance. Consider an electrical circuit containing a resistance R, an inductance L and a capacitance C as shown in Fig. 2.3 connected to a battery and a key K. When the key K is pressed downward the capacitor C is charged. Let q_0 be the charge on it. When the key K is released the capacitor circuit is completed through the inductance L and resistance R. The capacitor slowly loses its charge due to which

there is a current I at any instant. The current varies at the rate $\dfrac{dI}{dt}$. If

q is the charge on tne capacitor at any instant t, then

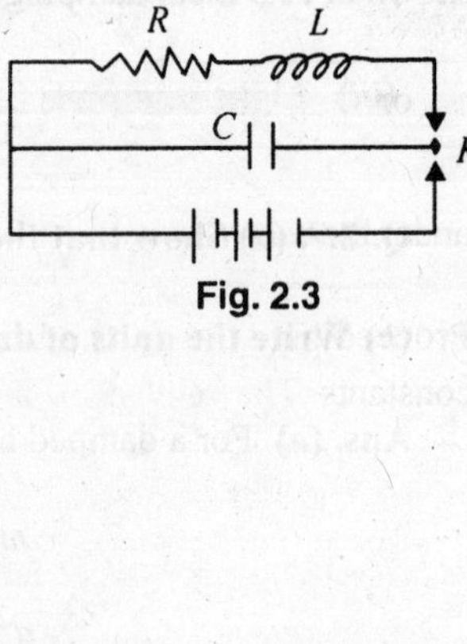

Potential difference across the capacitor $C = \dfrac{q}{C}$

Potential difference across the resistor $R = RI$

Fig. 2.3

Back *e.m.f.* in the inductor $L = -L\dfrac{dI}{dt}$

$$\therefore \qquad \dfrac{q}{C} + RI = -L\dfrac{dI}{dt} \text{ or } \dfrac{q}{C} + RI + L\dfrac{dI}{dt} = 0$$

But as $\quad I = \dfrac{dq}{dt}$ and $\dfrac{dI}{dt} = \dfrac{d^2q}{dt^2} \qquad \therefore \ L\dfrac{d^2q}{dt^2} + R\dfrac{dq}{dt} + \dfrac{q}{C} = 0$

or $\qquad\qquad \dfrac{d^2q}{dt^2} + \dfrac{R}{L}\dfrac{dq}{dt} + \dfrac{I}{LC}q = 0 \qquad\qquad\qquad\qquad\qquad ...(i)$

Put $\qquad\qquad \dfrac{R}{L} = 2k$ and $\dfrac{1}{LC} = \omega_0^2$, then

$$\dfrac{d^2q}{dt^2} + 2k\dfrac{dq}{dt} + \omega_0^2 q = 0 \qquad\qquad\qquad\qquad ...(ii)$$

This equation is similar to equation (ii) of **Q.2.2**, where the displacement y has been replaced by charge q.

Proceeding as in **Q.2.2**, we obtain a general solution of the above equation similar to **Eq. (iv a)** **Q. 2.2** as

$$q = e^{-kt} \left[A_1 e^{+\sqrt{k^2 - \omega_0^2}\, t} + A_2 e^{-\sqrt{k^2 - \omega_0^2}\, t} \right] \qquad \ldots(iii)$$

where A_1 and A_2 are arbitrary constants having dimensions of charge. The values of A_1 and A_2 can be determined from the boundary conditions of the circuit.

The nature of motion represented by equation (iii) depends upon the relative values of k and ω_0. Now three different cases arise.

(i) Heavy damping. When $k^2 > \omega_0^2$, or $\dfrac{R^2}{4L^2} > \dfrac{1}{LC}$. The quantity under the root sign is *positive*

and therefore the co-efficient of t is *real*. The charge on the capacitor decreases rapidly with time and decays to zero in the minimum time. The discharge is known as *aperiodic*, *dead beat* or *non-oscillatory* as shown in Fig. 2.4 (curve 1).

(ii) Critical damping. When $k^2 = \omega_0^2$ or $\dfrac{R^2}{4L^2} = \dfrac{1}{LC}$

The charge at any instant is given by

$$q = e^{-kt} [A + Bt] \qquad \ldots(iv)$$

For proof See **Q. 2.3** Eq. (iv) where y is replaced by q.

The constant A has the dimensions of charge and B has the dimensions of current. The rate of decay of charge depends upon the damping constant k which in turn depends upon the resistance R. The discharge is said to be *critically damped*, *i.e.*, it is neither *oscillatory* nor *non-oscillatory* as shown in Fig. 2.4. (curve 2).

(iii) Light damping (Oscillatory discharge). When $k^2 < \omega_0^2$ or $\dfrac{R^2}{4L^2} < \dfrac{1}{LC}$. The quantity

under the root sign $\sqrt{k^2 - \omega_0^2} = \sqrt{\dfrac{R^2}{4L^2} - \dfrac{1}{LC}}$ is *negative* or $\sqrt{k^2 - \omega_0^2}$ is an *imaginary quantity*.

Proceeding as in **Q. 2.5** we get $q = A_0 e^{-kt} \sin(\omega' t + \phi)$ where $\omega' = \sqrt{\omega_0^2 - k^2}$ and A_0 and ϕ are constants. The value of A_0 and ϕ can be calculated as in **Q. 2.5** and is given by

$$\tan \phi = \frac{\omega'}{k} = \frac{\sqrt{\omega_0^2 - k^2}}{k} = \frac{\sqrt{\dfrac{1}{LC} - \dfrac{R^2}{4L^2}}}{\dfrac{R}{2L}}$$

and

$$A_0 = \frac{q_0 \,\omega_0}{\sqrt{\omega_0^2 - k^2}} = \frac{q_0 \sqrt{\dfrac{1}{LC}}}{\sqrt{\dfrac{1}{LC} - \dfrac{R^2}{4L^2}}}$$

Hence

$$q = A_0 e^{-\left(\frac{R}{2L}\right)t} \sin \left[\left(\sqrt{\dfrac{1}{LC} - \dfrac{R^2}{4L^2}} \right) t + \phi \right] \qquad \ldots(v)$$

The amplitude of the oscillation, therefore, goes on decreasing with time in accordance with the relation

$$A = A_0 e^{-kt} = A_0 e^{-\left(\frac{R}{2L}\right)t}$$

Equation (v) shows that the discharging of the capacitor is damped oscillatory. *Hence the condition for the discharge to be oscillatory is*

$$k^2 < \omega_0^2 \quad \text{or} \quad \frac{R^2}{4L^2} < \frac{1}{LC}$$

The oscillatory discharge is shown in Fig. 2.4, curve (3).

Time period and frequency. The time period

$$T = \frac{2\pi}{\omega'} = \frac{2\pi}{\sqrt{\omega_0^2 - k^2}} = \frac{2\pi}{\sqrt{\frac{1}{LC} - \frac{R^2}{4L^2}}}$$

The frequency

$$n = \frac{1}{T} = \frac{1}{2\pi}\sqrt{\frac{1}{LC} - \frac{R^2}{4L^2}}$$

If R is negligible, then $\frac{R^2}{4L^2} = 0$ and

$$n = \frac{1}{2\pi\sqrt{LC}}$$

Effect of Resistance on amplitude and frequency. The amplitude of damped oscillations is given by

$$A = A_0 e^{-\left(\frac{R}{2L}\right)t}$$

Higher the values of R, smaller is the value of

the factor $e^{-\left(\frac{R}{2L}\right)t}$.

Hence as R increases, the amplitude corresponding to a particular value of t decreases.

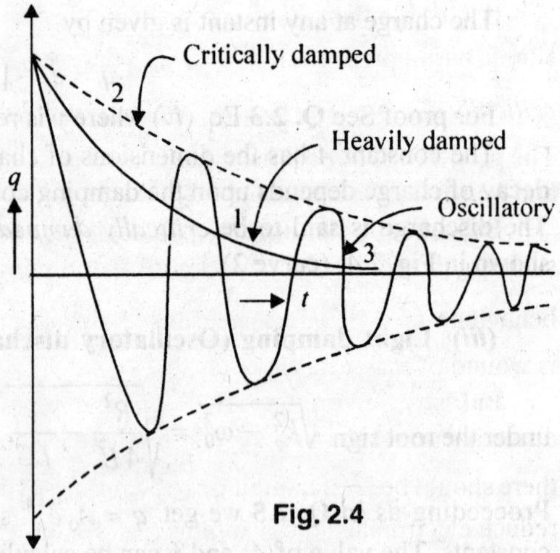

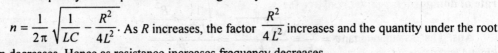

Fig. 2.4

The frequency of damped oscillations is given by

$$n = \frac{1}{2\pi}\sqrt{\frac{1}{LC} - \frac{R^2}{4L^2}}.$$ As R increases, the factor $\frac{R^2}{4L^2}$ increases and the quantity under the root sign decreases. Hence as resistance increases frequency decreases.

Q. 2.9. In an oscillatory circuit $L = 0.5$ H, $C = 1.8$ µfd. What is the maximum value of resistance to be connected so that the circuit may produce oscillations ?   (*H.P.U.*, 1996)

Ans. $L = 0.5$ H $C = 1.8$ µfd $= 1.8 \times 10^{-6}$ F.

Let R be the maximum resistance for which the discharge is oscillatory. For the circuit to produce oscillations,

$$\frac{R^2}{4L^2} = \frac{1}{LC}$$

or

$$R = 2\sqrt{\frac{L}{C}} = 2 \times \sqrt{\frac{0.5}{1.8 \times 10^{-6}}} = 1054 \text{ ohm}$$

Q. 2.10. Explain how the conditions of critical damping are used in designing of electrical instruments. (*H.P.U.*, 1995; *K.U.* 1991; *P.U.*, 1991)

Ans. Use of critical damping. The general solution of the differential equation of a damped simple harmonic motion is

$$y = e^{-kt} \left[A_1 \, e^{\sqrt{k^2 - \omega_0^2}\, t} + A_2 \, e^{-\sqrt{k^2 - \omega_0^2}\, t} \right]$$

where A_1 and A_2 are arbitrary constants, the values of which can be determined from boundary conditions.

$k = \dfrac{r}{2m}$ and $\omega_0^2 = \dfrac{s}{m}$ where r is the damping constant, m the mass of the oscillator and s the spring constant.

Critical damping. If $\quad k = \omega_0, k^2 - \omega_0^2 = \dfrac{r^2}{4m^2} - \dfrac{s}{m} = 0$

The displacement $\qquad y = (A_1 + A_2) e^{-kt}$

This is the limiting case of behaviour shown by the differential equation of motion of a damped simple harmonic oscillator.

If $k < \omega_0$, then $k^2 - \omega_0^2$ is a *negative* quantity and the particle undergoes an *oscillatory* damped simple harmonic motion. For $k = \omega_0$, the motion is neither overdamped nor oscillatory. It is said to be *critically damped.* For $k > \omega_0, k^2 - \omega_0^2$ is positive and the motion is *overdamped* or *non-oscillatory.* The property of critical damping is used in designing electrical measuring instruments like *dead beat* and *ballistic galvanometers.*

Dead beat galvanometer. A dead beat galvanometer is used for measuring *steady current.* In such a galvanometer the motion of the moving coil should be non-oscillatory. For non-oscillatory behaviour $k^2 > \omega_0^2$. To increase the value of k and, therefore, the electromagnetic damping, the coil is wound over a metallic core.

Ballistic galvanometer. Such a galvanometer is used for measuring charge which flows not as a steady current but as a sudden discharge. The motion of the moving coil should be oscillatory and there should be least damping, *i.e.*, $k^2 < \omega_0^2$. The coil is, therefore, wound over a non-metallic core to reduce electromagnetic damping.

Q. 2.11. Show that in case of a damped oscillator the rate of loss of energy is equal to the rate of doing work against resistive force.

(*Pbi.U.*, 2007; *G.N.D.U.* 2002, 2000; *P.U.* 2004, 1999; *H.P.U* 1999)

Ans. The instantaneous total energy in case of a simple harmonic oscillator is the sum of its kinetic and potential energies and is given by

$$E = \frac{1}{2} m \left(\frac{dy}{dt} \right)^2 + \frac{1}{2} s y^2$$

where m is the mass and s the force constant of proportionality or stiffness of the oscillator.

$\therefore \qquad$ Rate of loss of energy $\dfrac{dE}{dt} = \dfrac{d}{dt} \left[\dfrac{1}{2} m \left(\dfrac{dy}{dt} \right)^2 + \dfrac{1}{2} s y^2 \right]$

$$= m \, \frac{dy}{dt} \cdot \frac{d^2 y}{dt^2} + s y \, \frac{dy}{dt}$$

$$= \frac{dy}{dt} \left[m \, \frac{d^2 y}{dt^2} + s y \right] \qquad \qquad ...(i)$$

For mechanical damped harmonic motion

$$m \frac{d^2 y}{dt^2} + r \frac{dy}{dt} + sy = 0$$

$$\therefore \qquad m \frac{d^2 y}{dt^2} + sy = -r \frac{dy}{dt}$$

$\therefore$ Damping or retarding force $F_d = r \frac{dy}{dt} = -\left[m \frac{d^2 y}{dt^2} + sy \right]$

Substituting in equation (i), we have

$$\frac{dE}{dt} = - F_d \frac{dy}{dt} = -\frac{F_d dy}{dt} = -\frac{dW}{dt}$$

because $F_d \, dy$ gives the work done dW for a small displacement dy and $-\dfrac{dW}{dt}$ gives the work done

per unit time or the rate of doing work against resistive force. Thus in the case of a damped oscillator,

Rate of loss of energy $\dfrac{dE}{dt}$ = Rate of doing work against the resistive force $\dfrac{dW}{dt}$.

Q. 2.12. Show that the energy of damped vibrations of a damped simple harmonic oscillator decreases exponentially with time.   (*G.N.D.U.* 2004, 2003; *H.P.U.* 1992; *Luck.U.* 1996)

Ans. Energy decreases exponentially. The equation of motion of a damped simple harmonic oscillator is given by

$$y = \frac{y_0 \, \omega_0}{\sqrt{\omega_0^2 - k^2}} \, e^{-kt} \sin \left(\sqrt{\omega_0^2 - k^2} \, t + \phi \right) \qquad \qquad ...(i)$$

where $\omega_0^2 = \dfrac{s}{m}$ and $2k = \dfrac{r}{m}$; s being the constant of proportionality for the restoring force given by

sy, r the constant of proportionality for the retarding or resistive force given by $r \dfrac{dy}{dt}$, m the mass of

the oscillator and ϕ, the phase angle given by

$$\tan \phi = \frac{\sqrt{\omega_0^2 - k^2}}{k}$$

The amplitude of the oscillations is given by

$$A = \frac{y_0 \, \omega_0}{\sqrt{\omega_0^2 - k^2}} e^{-kt} = A_0 \, e^{-kt}$$

where $A_0 = \dfrac{y_0 \, \omega_0}{\sqrt{\omega_0^2 - k^2}}$ when $t = 0$ and $e^{-kt} = 1$

The total energy for damped motion $E = \dfrac{1}{2} m A^2 \omega^2$

$$= \frac{1}{2} m \omega^2 \, A_0^2 \, e^{-2kt} = E_0 \, e^{-2kt}$$

where $E_0 = \dfrac{1}{2} m \omega^2 \, A_0^2$

It is clear from the equation $A = A_0 \, e^{-kt}$ and $E = E_0 \, e^{-2kt}$ that the amplitude of vibration and total energy goes on decreasing exponentially with time as the terms e^{-kt} as well as e^{-2kt} decay exponentially with time.

Q. 2.13. Define logarithmic decrement and derive a relation for it for a mechanical oscillator and an electrical oscillator. How can you determine experimentally the value of logarithmic decrement and damping co-efficient? *(P.U., 2009, 2008, 2005, 2003, 2002, 1994;*
Meerut U. 2001; G.N.D.U. 2009, 2008, 2007, 2006, 2004, 2000, 1996;
H.P.U. 1996, 1994; Pbi.U. 2008, 2007, 2006, 2005, 2000;1991)

Ans. Logarithmic decrement. The amplitude of the damped oscillations at any time t is given by

$$A = A_0\, e^{-kt}$$

where $k = \dfrac{r}{2m}$, r being the *damping constant* and m the mass of the oscillator. Let us consider the oscillations to start from the mean position, then after a time $t = \dfrac{T}{4}$ where T is the time period, the oscillating particle goes to the extreme position. Let the first amplitude be denoted by A_1, then

$$A_1 = A_0\, e^{-\frac{kT}{4}}$$

The particle will come to the mean position and then go to the extreme position on the *other* side, again come back to the mean position and go to extreme position on the *same* side after a time T, i.e., $\left(T + \dfrac{T}{4}\right)$ from start.

Let the second amplitude be A_2, then

$$A_2 = A_0\, e^{-k\left(T + \frac{T}{4}\right)}$$

Similarly, the successive amplitudes of the 3rd, 4th, 5th etc. oscillations will be given by

$$A_3 = A_0\, e^{-k\left(2T + \frac{T}{4}\right)}$$

$$A_4 = A_0\, e^{-k\left(3T + \frac{T}{4}\right)}$$

$$\cdots\cdots\cdots\cdots\cdots\cdots\cdots\cdots$$

$$\cdots\cdots\cdots\cdots\cdots\cdots$$

$$A_n = A_0\, e^{-k\left((n-1)T + \frac{T}{4}\right)}$$

Hence $\qquad \dfrac{A_1}{A_2} = \dfrac{A_2}{A_3} = \dfrac{A_3}{A_4} = \cdots\cdots = \dfrac{A_{n-1}}{A_n} = e^{kT}$

Taking natural logarithms (to the base e), we have

$$\log_e \frac{A_1}{A_2} = \log_e \frac{A_2}{A_3} = \ldots = kT = \lambda \text{ (say)}$$

where λ is the *logarithmic decrement*.

It is defined as the natural logarithm of the ratio between the two successive amplitudes on the same side of the mean position of a damped oscillation separated by one full period.

Knowing the value of logarithmic decrement λ, we can find the value of A_0.

To find the value of A_0. The amplitude A_0 which could be obtained if damping force were absent can be calculated from the relation

$$A_1 = A_0\, e^{-\frac{kT}{4}} = A_0\, e^{-\frac{\lambda}{4}} \qquad \therefore\ A_0 = A_1\, e^{\lambda/4} = A_1\left[1 + \frac{\lambda}{4}\right]$$

neglecting square and higher powers of λ as the logarithmic decrement λ is a very small quantity as compared to 1.

We shall calculate the relation for logarithmic decrement separately for a mechanical oscillator and an electrical oscillator.

For a mechanical oscillator. For a mechanical oscillator the time period

$$T = \frac{2\pi}{\sqrt{\omega_0^2 - k^2}} = \frac{2\pi}{\omega'}$$

where $2k = \dfrac{r}{m}$, r being the *damping constant* and m the mass of the oscillator; $\omega_0^2 = \dfrac{s}{m}$, s being the *stiffness constant*.

$$\therefore \text{ Logarithmic decrement } \lambda = kT = \frac{r}{2m} T$$

$$= \frac{r}{2m} \frac{2\pi}{\omega'} = \frac{\pi r}{m\omega'}$$

$$= \frac{\pi r}{m\sqrt{\omega_0^2 - k^2}} = \frac{\pi r}{m\sqrt{\dfrac{s}{m} - \dfrac{r^2}{4m^2}}}$$

Damping co-efficient k. As $\lambda = kT$, the logarithmic decrement gives a method of finding the damping co-efficient k. As $k = \dfrac{r}{2m}$, the value of r the constant of proportionality for retarding force can also be determined.

For electrical oscillator. For electrical oscillator also

$$T = \frac{2\pi}{\sqrt{\omega_0^2 - k^2}} = \frac{2\pi}{\omega'}$$

where $2k = \dfrac{R}{L}$, R being the resistance and L the inductance and $\omega_0^2 = \dfrac{1}{LC}$, C being the capacitance of the electrical circuit.

$$\therefore \text{ Logarithmic decrement } \lambda = kT = \frac{R}{2L} T$$

$$= \frac{R}{2L} \frac{2\pi}{\omega'} = \frac{\pi R}{L\omega'}$$

$$= \frac{\pi R}{L\sqrt{\omega_0^2 - k^2}} = \frac{\pi R}{L\sqrt{\dfrac{1}{LC} - \dfrac{R^2}{4L^2}}}$$

Damping co-efficient k. As $\lambda = kT$, the logarithmic decrement gives a method of finding the damping co-efficient k and hence $\dfrac{R}{2L}$.

Experimental determination. Starting from $A = A_0 e^{-kt}$, we have proved that

$$\frac{A_1}{A_2} = \frac{A_2}{A_3} = \frac{A_3}{A_4} \ldots = \frac{A_{n-1}}{A_n} = e^{kt}$$

$$\therefore \qquad \log_e \frac{A_{n-1}}{A_n} = kT = \lambda$$

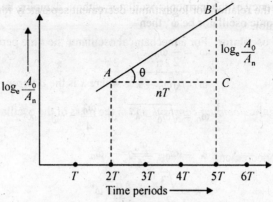

Fig. 2.5

where λ is the logarithmic decrement. The value of λ is determined by comparing two amplitudes which are n periods apart so that

$$\frac{A_0}{A_n} = e^{n\lambda}$$

or

$$\log_e \frac{A_0}{A_n} = n\lambda$$

If, therefore, a graph is plotted between $\log_e \frac{A_0}{A_n}$ and n, it is a straight line.

Thus to find λ experimentally, the values of amplitudes are found at each time period interval. A graph is plotted between time period intervals T, $2T$, $3T$ ... etc. and the corresponding value of $\log_e \frac{A_0}{A_1}, \log_e \frac{A_0}{A_2}, \log_e \frac{A_0}{A_3}$ ...etc.

The graph is a straight line as shown in Fig. 2.5.

$$\therefore \qquad \lambda = \frac{\log_e \frac{A_0}{A_n}}{n} = \frac{BC}{AC} = \tan\theta$$

Q. 2.14. (a) What is physical significance of logarithmic decrement of a damped oscillatory system? (G.N.D.U., 1994)

(b) How logarithmic decrement is related to damping co-efficient of a damped oscillator? (G.N.D.U., 2006)

Ans.(a) Physical significance of logarithmic decrement. The logarithmic decrement of a damped oscillatory system gives the measure of the rate at which the amplitude of vibration decays.

As logarithmic decrement $\lambda = \frac{\pi r}{m\omega'} = \frac{r}{2m} T$ it gives a method of evaluating r the damping co-efficient.

(b) Logarithmic decrement $\lambda = kT$ where k is the damping co-efficient given by $k = \frac{r}{2m}$, k being the damping constant.

Q. 2.15. The frequency of an underdamped harmonic oscillator is adjusted to be equal to half the frequency experienced by the oscillator without damping. Calculate the logarithmic decrement of the system. (Pbi. U., 1995)

Ans. Let the frequency of the harmonic oscillator without damping be ω_0 and the frequency of the underdamped harmonic oscillator be ω', then

$$\omega' = \frac{1}{2}\,\omega_0$$

Now

$$\omega' = \sqrt{\omega_0^2 - k^2} \quad \text{where } k \text{ is the } damping\ co\text{-}efficient.$$

$\therefore$

$$\frac{1}{2}\,\omega_0 = \sqrt{\omega_0^2 - k^2} \quad \text{or} \quad \frac{\omega_0^2}{4} = \omega_0^2 - k^2$$

or

$$k^2 = \omega_0^2 - \frac{\omega_0^2}{4} = \frac{3}{4}\,\omega_0^2$$

$$k = \frac{\sqrt{3}}{2}\,\omega_0 = \sqrt{3}\ \omega'$$

Now logarithmic decrement $\lambda = kT$ and $T = \dfrac{2\pi}{\omega'}$

$\therefore$

$$\lambda = \sqrt{3}\ \omega'.\frac{2\pi}{\omega'} = 2\pi\sqrt{3}$$

Q. 2.16. (*a*) **In a ballistic galvanometer the coil is wound over a non-metallic frame. Comment.**   (*Pbi.U.* 2002; *G.N.D.U.* 1996, 1995; *H.P.U.* 1998, 1997)

(*b*) **Why the coil of a moving coil galvanometer, ammeter and voltmeter is wound over a metallic frame?**   (*Pbi.U.* 2006, 2001, 1999)

Ans. (*a*) **Ballistic galvanometer coil.** A ballistic galvanometer is used for measuring *charge* which flows not as a steady current but as a sudden discharge. The motion of the moving coil should, therefore, be oscillatory and there should be least damping *i.e.* $k^2 < \omega_0^2$.

The coil is wound over a non-metallic frame so that it is non-conducting. This reduces the effect of eddy currents and makes the electromagnetic damping as small as possible. The time period, therefore, becomes large with low value of logarithmic decrement.

(*b*) **Ammeter-voltmeter coil.** A moving coil galvanometer used as an ammeter or voltmeter is a *dead beat* galvanometer which measures *steady current* or *steady voltage*. In such a galvanometer the motion of the moving coil should be non-oscillatory or dead beat. For non-oscillatory behaviour $k^2 > \omega_0^2$. To increase the value of k the damping factor and therefore the electromagnetic damping, the coil is wound over a metallic frame. To further increase electromagnetic damping the core about which the coil rotates is also made metallic. The eddy currents set up in the coil, metallic frame and the metal core create a very high damping and make the motion of the coil dead beat.

Q. 2.17. **A damped vibrating system, starting from rest, reaches a first amplitude of 500 mm which reduces to 50 mm in that direction after 100 oscillations each of period 2.3 secs. Find the damping constant, relaxation time and the correction for the first displacement for damping [$\log_e^{10} = 2.3$].**   (*Indore U.* 2001; *Pbi.U.,* 1991)

Ans. The damping constant k is given by the relation

$$\log_e \frac{A_1}{A_2} = \log_e \frac{A_2}{A_3} = \ldots\ldots = k$$

where A_1, A_2, A_3 etc. are the successive amplitudes and T the time period. The amplitude n vibrations after the first, *i.e.*, $n + 1$th vibration is A_{n+1}, then

$$\log_e \frac{A_1}{A_{n+1}} = \log_e \frac{A_1}{A_2} \times \log_e \frac{A_2}{A_3} \times \ldots \log_e \frac{A_n}{A_{n+1}} = nkT$$

Now $A_1 = 500$ mm; $A_{101} = 50$ mm; $n = 100$; $T = 2.3$ sec

$\therefore$ $$\log_e \frac{500}{50} = 100\,k \times 2.3$$

or $$2.3\,\log_{10}^{10} = 2.3 \times 100\,k$$

or $$100\,k = 1$$

$\therefore$ Damping constant $\qquad k = \dfrac{1}{100} = .01$

Relaxation time $\qquad t_r = \dfrac{1}{k} = \dfrac{1}{.01} = 100$ sec .

Logarithmic decrement $\lambda = kT = .01 \times 2.3 = 0.023$

The amplitude A_0, which could be obtained if the damping force were absent, is given by

$$A_0 = A_1\left(1 + \frac{\lambda}{4}\right) = 500\left(1 + \frac{1}{4} \times .01 \times 2.3\right)$$

$$= 502.875$$

$\therefore$ Correction for the first displacement $= 2.875$ mm.

Exercise. *A damped vibrating system starting from rest reaches the first amplitude of 300mm which reduces to 30 mm in that direction after 100 vibrations each of period 1.5 sec. Find the damping co-efficient.* (P.U., 2006)

Hint. $\log_e \dfrac{300}{30} = 100\,k \times 1.5$

or $\qquad 2.302 = 150\,k$

or $\qquad k = \dfrac{2.302}{150} = .0153$

Q. 2.18. Define relaxation time of damped oscillatory system. Show that it varies inversely as damping constant. Derive an expression for relaxation period of (*i*) a mechanical oscillator, (*ii*) electrical oscillator. How is it useful in determining the logarithmic decrement of a system? What is the relation between logarithmic decrement and relaxation time?

(*P.U.* 2009, 2007, 2005, 2004; *H.P.U.* 2001, 1999, 1994; *Pbi.U.*, 2008, 2006, 2000, 1993; *G.N.D.U.* 2008, 2001)

Ans. Relaxation time or modulus of decay. *The relaxation time is defined as the time in which the amplitude of the damped oscillations falls to $\dfrac{1}{e}$ of its original value.*

If A_0 is the original amplitude of a damped oscillator, which becomes $A = \dfrac{A_0}{e}$ in time t_r, then t_r is said to be the *relaxation time*. As $1/e = 0.368$, the amplitude of a damped oscillator falls to 36.8% of its initial value in a time $t_r =$ relaxation time. Higher is the relaxation time slower is the rate of fall of amplitude and hence slower is the rate of dissipation of energy.

The amplitude of the damped oscillator at any time t is given by

$$A = A_0\,e^{-kt}$$

where k is the *damping co-efficient.*

If t is the relaxation time, then

$$A = A_0\,e^{-kt_r} = A_0\,\frac{1}{e} = A_0\,e^{-1}$$

$$e^{-kt_r} = e^{-1}$$

or $\qquad\qquad\qquad\qquad kt_r = 1$

or $\qquad\qquad$ relaxation time $\qquad t_r = \dfrac{1}{k}$ $\qquad\qquad\qquad\qquad\qquad$ ...(i)

It is clear from equation (i) that *relaxation time varies inversely as the damping co-efficient.*

(i) **Mechanical oscillator.** For a mechanical oscillator $2k = \dfrac{r}{m}$ where r is the damping constant.

$$\therefore \qquad\qquad\qquad k = \dfrac{r}{2m}$$

Hence relaxation time for a mechanical oscillator $= \dfrac{1}{k} = \dfrac{2m}{r}$

Thus relaxation time is inversely proportional to damping constant.

(ii) **Electrical oscillator.** For an electrical oscillator

$$q = q_0 e^{-kt}$$

$\therefore$ For $\qquad t = t_r = \dfrac{1}{k}, q = q_0 e^{-1} = \dfrac{q_0}{e}$

For an electrical oscillator $2k = \dfrac{R}{L}$ where R is the resistance and L the inductance of the circuit.
Hence relaxation time for an electrical oscillator

$$= \dfrac{1}{k} = \dfrac{2L}{R}$$

Thus relaxation time is inversely proportional to the resistance of the oscillator circuit.

Relation between logarithmic decrement and relaxation time. Relaxation time $t_r = \dfrac{1}{k}$ and logarighmic decrement $\lambda = kT$

$$\therefore \qquad\qquad\qquad \lambda = \dfrac{T}{t_r}$$

Thus the logarithmic decrement may also be defined as the ratio of the time period of vibration T to the modulus of decay (or relaxation time).

A knowledge of relaxation time and the time period, therefore, helps in the determination of logarithmic decrement according to the relation

$$\lambda = \dfrac{T}{t_r}$$

Q. 2.19. (a) **Define quality factor of a damped oscillator. Deduce an expression for it for a mechanical oscillator and an electrical oscillator.**

(b) **Show that (i) lower the damping, higher will be the quality factor.**

(ii) **For large quality factor damping has little or no effect on the frequency.**

(G.N.D.U., 2009, 2007, 2006, 2002; H.P.U. 2001, 1999, 1996, 1995; Pbi. U., 2008, 2007, 2006, 2000, 1995; P.U., 2009, 2008, 2006, 1995)

Ans. (a) **Quality factor or Q value.** (i) The quality factor measures the rate of decay of energy of the damped harmonic oscillator. For an undamped simple harmonic oscillator the total energy (kinetic + potential) at any time is given by

$$E = \dfrac{1}{2} m \omega_0^2 A^2$$

In the case of damped oscillations the work done against the retarding or resistive force is not stored as potential energy. As a result, as the particle oscillates, the total energy goes on decreasing. The amplitude of the damped oscillations is given by

$$A = A_0\, e^{-kt}$$

and ω_0 is replaced by $\sqrt{\omega_0^2 - k^2} = \omega'$.

∴ Energy of the damped oscillator is given by

$$E = \frac{1}{2} m\omega'^2 A_0^2\, e^{-2kt} = E_0\, e^{-2kt} \qquad \qquad ...(i)$$

where $$E_0 = \frac{1}{2} m\omega'^2 A_0^2$$

When $$t = \frac{1}{2k}$$

$$E = E_0\, e^{-2k/2k} = E_0\, e^{-1} = \frac{E_0}{e}$$

∴ In time $t = \dfrac{1}{2k} = \dfrac{1}{2}\dfrac{2m}{r} = \dfrac{m}{r}$

where r is the damping constant and m the mass of the oscillator, the energy of the oscillator decays to $\dfrac{1}{e} E_0$ from E_0. During this time the oscillator will have vibrated through an angle θ given by

$$\theta = \omega't = \omega' \times \frac{m}{r} = \frac{\omega'm}{r} \text{ radians.}$$

The quantity $\dfrac{\omega'm}{r} = Q$ gives the *quality factor or Q-value. Thus quality factor is defined as the angle (in radians) through which the damped oscillator oscillates as its energy decays to* $\dfrac{E_0}{e}$ *from* E_0.

∴ Quality factor for a *mechanical* oscillator

$$Q = \frac{\omega'm}{r} = \frac{\omega'}{2k} \qquad \qquad ...(ii)$$

The quality factor is, therefore, inversely proportional to damping co-efficient. The relation $Q = \dfrac{\omega'm}{r}$ gives the value of quality factor in terms of ω' the frequency of displacement resonance and r the damping constant.

For an **electrical** oscillator $2k = \dfrac{R}{L}$ where L is the inductance and R the resistance of the electrical circuit.

∴ Quality factor for an **electrical** oscillator

$$= \frac{\omega'}{2k} = \frac{\omega'L}{R}$$

(ii) The energy of the damped oscillator according to equation (i) is given by

$$E = E_0\, e^{-2kt}$$

∴ Power dissipation P = Rate of loss of total energy with time

$$= -\frac{dE}{dt} \text{ is given by}$$

$$P = -\frac{dE}{dt} = 2k E_0\, e^{-2kt} = 2k E$$

or $$-dE = 2k \, E \, dt = 2\frac{r}{2m} E \, dt = \frac{r}{m} E \, dt$$

If $dT = T$ the time period of the oscillator, then

$$dT = T = \frac{2\pi}{\omega'}$$

Hence loss of energy during the time of one time period or loss of energy per cycle

$$-dE_T = \frac{r}{m} ET = \frac{r}{m} E \frac{2\pi}{\omega'}$$

$$\therefore \qquad \frac{\omega' m}{r} = -\frac{2\pi E}{d \, E_T}$$

But $\dfrac{\omega' m}{r}$ is the quality factor as proved in (ii).

$$\therefore \quad \text{Quality factor} \quad Q = 2\pi \times \frac{\text{Energy of the oscillator}}{\text{Energy lost per cycle}}$$

(b) (i). The quality factor $Q = \dfrac{\omega'}{2k}$ where $2k = \dfrac{r}{m}$ for a mechanical oscillator and $2k = \dfrac{R}{L}$ for an electrical oscillator.

The quality factor Q is *large* if the damping co-efficient k is *small* and Q is *small* if the damping co-efficient k is *large*. The quality factor, therefore, represents the efficiency of the oscillator. *Hence lower the damping, higher is the quality factor.*

(ii). The value of ω' is given by $\omega' = \sqrt{\omega_0^2 - k^2}$, when the damping is small (or in other words the quality factor Q is large) k^2 is negligible as compared to ω_0^2 and hence $\omega' = \omega_0$.

$$\therefore \quad \text{Quality factor} \quad Q = \frac{m\omega'}{r} = \frac{m\omega_0}{r} = \frac{m}{r}\left(\frac{s}{m}\right)^{\!\!1/2}$$

where $\sqrt{\dfrac{s}{m}} = \omega_0$, s being the spring constant and m the mass of a S.H. oscillator.

As $\dfrac{m}{r}\left(\dfrac{s}{m}\right)^{\!\!1/2} = a$ constant, the quality factor is a constant. As $\omega' = \omega_0 = a$ *constant*, *a large quality factor has little or no effect on the frequency.*

Q. 2.20. Express amplitude, energy, logarithmic decrement and relaxation time in terms of Q the quality factor.   (*P.U.*, 2007; *G.N.D.U.*, 2007, 2006; *Pbi.U.* 2002, 1999; *H.P.U.* 2000)

Ans. (i) Amplitude. The amplitude A at any time t is given by

$$A = A_0 \, e^{-kt}$$

and $$Q = \frac{\omega'}{2k} \qquad\qquad\qquad \left[\because k = \frac{\omega'}{2Q}\right]$$

Substituting we have

$$A = A_0 \, e^{-\frac{\omega' t}{2Q}}$$

(ii) **Energy.** The energy of the oscillator

$$E = \frac{1}{2} m\omega'^2 A_0^2 \, e^{-2kt}$$

$$= \frac{1}{2} m\omega'^2 A_0^2 \, e^{-2\frac{\omega'}{2Q}t} = E_0 \, e^{-\frac{\omega' t}{Q}} \qquad\qquad \left[\because E_0 = \frac{1}{2} m\omega'^2 A_0^2\right]$$

$$\therefore \qquad E = E_0 \, e^{-\omega' t/Q}$$

(iii) **Logarithmic decrement.** The logarithmic decrement

$$\lambda = kT = \frac{k2\pi}{\omega'} = \frac{\pi}{Q} \qquad\qquad\qquad \left[\because \; Q = \frac{\omega'}{2k} \right]$$

(iv) **Relaxation time.** The relaxation time

$$t_r = \frac{1}{k} = \frac{2Q}{\omega'} \qquad\qquad\qquad \left[\because \; Q = \frac{\omega'}{2k} \right]$$

Q. 2.21 (*a*) In LCR circuit if $L = 1$ mH, $C = 10\ \mu$F and $R = 0.4\ \Omega$, calculate Q factor.
(*P.U.*, 1992)

(*b*) Deduce the frequency and quality factor of an LCR circuit with $L = 2$mH, $C = 5\mu$F and $R = 0.2$ ohm. (*P.U.* 2004, 2003)

Ans. (*a*) For an *LCR* circuit the quality factor

$$Q = \frac{\omega' L}{R} \qquad\qquad\qquad\qquad\qquad ...(i)$$

and

$$\omega' = \sqrt{\frac{1}{LC} - \frac{R^2}{4L^2}} \qquad\qquad\qquad\qquad ...(ii)$$

Substituting
$$L = 1\,\text{mH} = 10^{-3}\ \text{H}$$
$$C = 10\ \mu\text{F} = 10 \times 10^{-6} = 10^{-5}\ \text{F}$$
$$R = 0.4\ \Omega = 4 \times 10^{-1}\ \Omega$$

in Eq. (*ii*), we have

$$\omega' = \sqrt{\frac{1}{10^{-3} \times 10^{-5}} - \frac{4 \times 4 \times 10^{-2}}{4 \times 10^{-6}}}$$

$$= \sqrt{10^8 - 4 \times 10^4} = 10^4 \ \text{rad s}^{-1} \ (\text{approx})$$

$\therefore$ Quality factor $\quad Q = \dfrac{\omega' L}{R} = \dfrac{10^4 \times 10^{-3}}{4 \times 10^{-1}} = 25$

(*b*) Here $L = 2mH = 2 \times 10^{-3}\ H; \ C = 5\mu F = 5 \times 10^{-6}\ F$
$$R = 0.2\ \Omega = 2 \times 10^{-1}\ \Omega$$

Angular frequency $\omega' = \sqrt{\dfrac{1}{LC} - \dfrac{R^2}{4L^2}}$

$$= \sqrt{\frac{1}{2 \times 10^{-3} \times 5 \times 10^{-6}} - \frac{2 \times 2 \times 10^{-2}}{4 \times 4 \times 10^{-6}}}$$

$$= \sqrt{10^8 - 25 \times 10^2} = 10^4 \ \text{rad s}^{-1} \qquad (\text{approx})$$

Frequency $\nu = \dfrac{\omega'}{2\pi} = \dfrac{10^4}{2\pi} = \dfrac{10}{2\pi} \times 10^3 = 1.59 \times 10^3 = 1590$ Hz

and quality factor $Q = \dfrac{L\omega'}{R} = \dfrac{2 \times 10^{-3} \times 10^4}{2 \times 10^{-1}} = 10^2 = 100$

Q. 2.22. A simple pendulum has a period of 1 sec. and an amplitude of 10°. After 10 complete oscillations its amplitude is reduced to 5°. What is the relaxation time of the pendulum and quality factor? *(P.U., 1995)*

Ans. For a damped simple harmonic oscillator, the amplitude is given by

$$A = A_0 e^{-kt} = A_0 e^{-\frac{r}{2m}t} \qquad \qquad ...(i)$$

Here $\qquad\qquad A_0 = 10°; \; A = 5°$

after 10 complete oscillations *i.e.*, after a time = $10 \times$ Times period = $10 \times 1 = 10$ sec. Substituting in (i)

$$5 = 10 \, e^{-10k}$$

$$\therefore \qquad e^{-10k} = \frac{1}{2} \quad \therefore \quad e^{10k} = 2$$

or $\qquad\qquad k = \dfrac{\log_e 2}{10} = \dfrac{0.6931}{10} = 0.06931$

The relaxation time $\quad t_r = \dfrac{1}{k} = \dfrac{1}{0.06931} = 14.428$ sec

Quality factor $\quad Q = \omega \dfrac{m}{r} = \dfrac{\omega}{2k}$ where $\omega = \dfrac{2\pi}{T} = 2\pi$ $\qquad\qquad [\because T = 1s]$

$$\therefore \qquad Q = \frac{2\pi}{T \times 2k} = \frac{\pi}{kT} = \frac{\pi}{k} = \frac{\pi}{0.06931} = 45.33$$

Q. 2.23. Show that the fractional change in the natural frequency of a damped simple harmonic oscillator is $\dfrac{1}{8Q^2}$ where Q is the quality factor.

(H.P.U. 2000; G.N.D.U., 1996, 1993; P.U., 1996)

Ans. Let ω_0 be the angular frequency of the undamped oscillator and ω' that of the damped S.H. oscillator, then

$$\omega' = \sqrt{\omega_0^2 - k^2} \text{ where } k \text{ is the } damping \; co\text{-}efficient$$

given by $\quad k = \dfrac{r}{2m}$ where r is the *damping constant*

Hence $\qquad\qquad \omega' = \left(\omega_0^2 - \dfrac{r^2}{4m^2} \right)^{\frac{1}{2}}$

$$= \omega_0 \left(1 - \frac{r^2}{4m^2 \omega_0^2} \right)^{\frac{1}{2}}$$

When r is small, $\dfrac{r^2}{4m^2 \omega_0^2}$ is a very-very small quantity. Therefore applying Binomial theorem

and neglecting higher powers, we have

$$\omega' = \omega_0 \left(1 - \frac{1}{2} \frac{r^2}{4m^2 \omega_0^2} + ... \right)$$

or $\qquad \dfrac{\omega'}{\omega_0} = 1 - \dfrac{1}{8} \dfrac{r^2}{m^2 \omega_0^2}$

or $\qquad 1 - \dfrac{\omega'}{\omega_0} = \dfrac{1}{8} \dfrac{r^2}{m^2 \omega_0^2}$

or $\qquad \dfrac{\omega_0 - \omega'}{\omega_0} = \dfrac{1}{8} \dfrac{r^2}{m^2 \omega_0^2}$

Now quality factor $\qquad Q = \dfrac{m \omega_0}{r}$

$\therefore \qquad\qquad \dfrac{\omega_0 - \omega'}{\omega_0} = \dfrac{1}{8Q^2}$

But $\dfrac{\omega_0 - \omega'}{\omega_0}$ represents the fractional change in the natural (angular) frequency of the oscillator.
Hence the fractional change in the natural frequency of a damped simple harmonic oscillator is
$\dfrac{1}{8Q^2}$ where Q is the quality factor.

Q. 2.24. Show that the ratio of energy lost per cycle to the energy stored in a damped oscillator is $\dfrac{2\pi}{Q}$ where Q is the quality factor.

(*P.U.*, 2008, 2006, 1995; *Pbi. U.*, 1993; *H.P.U.* 2003, 1993, 1992)

Ans. The total energy stored in a damped oscillator at a time t is given by

$$E_t = E_0 \, e^{-2kt}$$

where k is the damping co-efficient $= \dfrac{r}{2m}$, r being the *damping constant* and m the mass of the oscillator. The rate of loss of total energy,

$$\dfrac{dE_t}{dt} = -2k \, E_0 \, e^{-2kt} = -2kE$$

or $\qquad dE_t = -2k \, E \, dt = -2 \dfrac{r}{2m} E \, dt = -\dfrac{r}{m} E \, dt$

Let T' be the time period of damped oscillator, then

$$T' = \dfrac{2\pi}{\omega'}$$

where ω' is the angular frequency of the damped oscillator.

$\therefore$ Energy lost per cycle

$$d \, E_T = \dfrac{-r}{m} ET = -\dfrac{r}{m} E \dfrac{2\pi}{\omega'} = -2\pi E \dfrac{r}{m\omega'}$$

Now $\qquad \dfrac{m\omega'}{r} = Q$ the quality factor

$\therefore \qquad\qquad dE_T = -\dfrac{2\pi}{Q} E$

or $\qquad\qquad \dfrac{d \, E_T}{E} = -\dfrac{2\pi}{Q} = \dfrac{2\pi}{Q}$ (neglecting the negative sign)

The negative sign only indicates that the energy is decreasing.

Hence the ratio of the energy lost per cycle to the energy stored in a damped oscillator $= \dfrac{2\pi}{Q}$.

The ratio is a constant.

Q. 2.25. Show that the Q factor represents the change in phase during which the energy of a damped oscillator reduces to $\dfrac{1}{e}$ of its initial value.   (*G.N.D.U.* 2000; *H.P.U.*, 2001, 1995)

Ans. The energy of a damped oscillator is given by

$$E = E_0\, e^{-2kt}$$

where k is the *damping coefficient* $= \dfrac{r}{2m}$, r being the *damping constant* and m the mass of the oscillator.

Suppose the energy of the damped oscillator is reduced to $\dfrac{1}{e}$ of its initial value in a time t_r, then

$$E = \frac{E_0}{e} = E_0\, e^{-2kt_r}$$

$$\therefore \qquad 2k\, t_r = 1$$

or $$t_r = \frac{1}{2k} = \frac{1}{2} \cdot \frac{2m}{r} = \frac{m}{r}$$

$\therefore$ If ω' is the angular frequency of the damped oscillator, then change in phase angle during the time t_r is given by

$$d\phi = \omega' t_r = \omega' \frac{m}{r}$$

But $$\frac{\omega' m}{r} = Q \text{ the quality factor}$$

$$\therefore \qquad d\phi = Q.$$

Thus Q factor represents the change in phase during which the energy of a damped oscillator reduces to $\dfrac{1}{e}$ of its initial value.

Q. 2.26. (*a*) **Deduce the frequency and quality factor of an LCR circuit with $L = 2$ mH, $C = 5\,\mu F$ and $R = 0.2$ ohm.**   (*G.N.D.U.* 2003; *H.P.U.*, 1992)

(*b*) **A condenser of capacity 1 μF, an inductance of 0.2 Henry and a resistance of 800 ohm are connected in series. Is the circuit oscillatory? If yes, calculate the frequency and quality factor of the circuit.**   (*G.N.D.U.* 2002; *H.P.U.* 2002; *P.U.* 1998)

Ans. (*a*) For an *LCR* circuit, the frequency of damped oscillations is given by

$$f' = \frac{\omega'}{2\pi} \quad \text{where}\ \omega' = \sqrt{\frac{1}{LC} - \frac{R^2}{4L^2}}$$

Substituting

$$L = 2\,\text{mH} = 2 \times 10^{-3}\,\text{H}$$

$$C = 5\,\mu F = 5 \times 10^{-6}\,\text{F}$$

$$R = 0.2\ \text{ohm} = 2 \times 10^{-1}\ \text{ohm}$$

we have $$\omega' = \sqrt{\frac{1}{2 \times 10^{-3} \times 5 \times 10^{-6}} - \frac{2 \times 2 \times 10^{-2}}{4 \times 4 \times 10^{-6}}}$$

$$= 10^4\ \text{rad s}^{-1}\ (\text{App.})$$

$$\therefore \qquad f' = \frac{10^4}{2\pi} \text{ Hertz or } \omega' = 2\pi f' = 10^4$$

or Quality factor $\quad Q = \dfrac{L\omega'}{R} = \dfrac{10^4 \times 2 \times 10^{-3}}{2 \times 10^{-1}} = 100$

(b) Here $C = 1\ \mu F = 10^{-6}$ F; $L = 0.2$ H; $R = 800\ \Omega$

For the circuit to be oscilatory $\dfrac{R^2}{4L^2} < \dfrac{1}{LC}$

Now $\quad \dfrac{R^2}{4L^2} = \dfrac{800 \times 800}{4 \times 0.2 \times 0.2} = 4 \times 10^6$

and $\quad \dfrac{1}{LC} = \dfrac{1}{0.2 \times 10^{-6}} = 5 \times 10^6$

As $\dfrac{R^2}{4L^2} < \dfrac{1}{LC}$, the circuit is oscillatory.

The angular frequency $\quad \omega' = \sqrt{\dfrac{1}{LC} - \dfrac{R^2}{4L^2}} = \sqrt{5 \times 10^6 - 4 \times 10^6}$

$$= 10^3 \text{ rad s}^{-1}$$

Hence frequency $\quad f' = \dfrac{\omega'}{2\pi} = \dfrac{10^3}{2\pi} = 159\text{ s}^{-1}$

and quality factor $\quad Q = \dfrac{L\omega'}{R} = \dfrac{0.2 \times 10^3}{800} = 0.25$

Exercise. *Examine whether the discharge of a capacitor of capacity 1 μF through resistance of 400Ω and inductor of 0.1 H is oscillatory or not.* (*P.U., 2007; Pbi. U., 2007*)

Hint. $\dfrac{R^2}{4L^2} = \dfrac{400 \times 400}{4 \times 0.1 \times 0.1} = 4 \times 10^{-6}$

$$\dfrac{1}{LC} = \dfrac{1}{0.1 \times 1 \times 10^{-6}} = 10^7$$

As $\dfrac{R2}{4L2} < \dfrac{1}{LC}$ the discharge is oscillatory.

Q. 2.27. If the quality factor of an undamped tuning fork of frequency 256 is 10^3, calculate the time in which its energy is reduced to 1/e of its energy in the absence of damping. How many oscillations the tuning fork will make in this time?

Ans. The time t in which the energy decays to 1/e of its original value is given by

$$t = Q/\omega'$$

where Q is the quality factor and $\omega' = \sqrt{\omega_0^2 - k^2}$

ω_0 the frequency without damping and k is the damping co-efficient.

In this case $\omega' = \omega_0 = 2\pi \times 256$

$$\therefore \qquad t = \dfrac{Q}{\omega_0} = \dfrac{10^3}{2\pi \times 256} = 0.62 \text{ sec}$$

The number of oscillations made by the tuning fork in this time $= 256 \times t$

$$= \dfrac{256 \times 10^3}{2\pi \times 256} = \dfrac{1000}{2\pi} = 159$$

Q. 2.28. The radiated power from an electron (damped oscillator) is given by

$$P = \frac{e^2 \, \omega^4 \, x_0^2}{12 \pi \varepsilon_0 \, c^3} \text{ watts}$$

at a wavelength of 0.6 microns, where the different symbols have the values:–

e = **electronic charge** $(1.6 \times 10^{-19} \text{ C})$

$$\frac{1}{4 \pi \varepsilon_0} = 9 \times 10^9 \text{ metre farad}^{-1}$$

m = **electronic mass** $(9.0 \times 10^{-31} \text{ kg})$

c = **velocity of light for free space** = $3 \times 10^8 \text{ ms}^{-1}$

and x_0 = **maximum amplitude of oscillator.**

Show that Q value of the atom is $\cong 10^7$ and its free radiation lifetime $\cong 10^{-8}$ sec. (The life time is the time for its energy to decay to $\dfrac{1}{e}$-th of its initial value.)

Ans. Let T be the time period and ν the frequency corresponding to the wavelength λ $(0.6 \times 10^{-6} \text{ m})$ at which power is radiated by the electron, then

$$Q = \frac{2\pi \times \text{Energy of the oscillator}}{\text{Energy lost per second} \times \text{time period}} = \frac{2\pi E}{-\dfrac{dE}{dt} T}$$

Energy of the oscillator $E = \dfrac{1}{2} m \omega^2 x_0^2$

Radiated power $\qquad P = \dfrac{dE}{dt} = \dfrac{e^2 \omega^4 x_0^2}{12 \pi \varepsilon_0 c^3} \text{ watts}$

$$\therefore \quad Q = \frac{2\pi \dfrac{1}{2} m \omega^2 x_0^2}{\dfrac{e^2 \omega^4 x_0^2 T}{12 \pi \varepsilon_0 c^3}} = \frac{12 \pi^2 m \varepsilon_0 c^3}{e^2 \omega^2 T} = \frac{12 \pi^2 m \varepsilon_0 c^2 \nu}{e^2 \omega^2}$$

But $\qquad\qquad \omega = 2\pi\nu$

$$\therefore \quad Q = \frac{3 m \varepsilon_0 c^3}{e^2 \nu} = \frac{3 m \varepsilon_0 c^2 \lambda}{e^2} \qquad\qquad \left[\because \lambda = \frac{c}{\nu} \right]$$

$$= \frac{3 \times 9 \times 10^{-31} \times (3 \times 10^8)^2 \times 0.6 \times 10^{-6}}{(1.6 \times 10^{-19})^2 \times 4\pi \times 9 \times 10^9} = 5 \times 10^7 \approx 10^7$$

The lifetime of the oscillator $= \dfrac{Q}{\omega} = \dfrac{Q\lambda}{2\pi c}$

$$= \frac{5 \times 10^7 \times 0.6 \times 10^{-6}}{2\pi \times 3 \times 10^8} = 1.59 \times 10^{-8} \text{ sec} \approx 10^{-8} \text{ sec}$$

Q. 2.29. Discuss the methods (logarithmic decrement, relaxation time and quality factor) for quantitative measurement of damping effect in a damped simple harmonic oscillator.

(*P.U.*, 1996; *H.P.U.*, 1992; *Pbi.U.*, 1991; *G.N.D.U.*, 1990)

OR

Explain how the quantitative measurement of damping effect in a damped simple harmonic oscillator can be used to determine the damping force per unit mass per unit velocity experimentally in three different ways.

(*Pbi.U.*, 2005;)

Ans. Quantitative measurement of damping effect. The equation of motion of a damped simple harmonic oscillator is given by

$$m\frac{d^2y}{dt^2} + r\frac{dy}{dt} + sy = 0$$

or

$$\frac{d^2y}{dt^2} + \frac{r}{m}\frac{dy}{dt} + \frac{s}{m}y = 0$$

or

$$\frac{d^2y}{dt^2} + 2k\frac{dy}{dt} + \omega_0^2 y = 0$$

where

$$2k = \frac{r}{m} \text{ and } \omega_0^2 = \frac{s}{m}$$

The factor $2k$ is defined as the damping force per unit mass per unit velocity and is called the *damping co-efficient* or damping factor and is a quantitative measure of damping. The valur of k can be determined experimentally by the following methods:

(i) By logarithmic decrement. For a damped oscillator the amplitude decays exponentially with time in accordance with the relation

$$A = A_0 e^{-kT}$$

If $A_1, A_2 .... A_{n-1}, A_n$ are the successive amplitudes, then

$$\frac{A_1}{A_2} = \frac{A_2}{A_3} .... = \frac{A_{n-1}}{A_n} = e^{kt}$$

$$\therefore \quad \log_e \frac{A_{n-1}}{A_n} = kT = \lambda$$

λ is a constant known as logarithmic decrement. The value of λ is determined by comparing two amplitudes which are n periods apart so that

$$\frac{A_0}{A_n} = e^{n\lambda}$$

or

$$n\lambda = \log_e \frac{A_0}{A_n}$$

The value of k is calculated from the value of λ and T which can be determined experimentally.

(ii) By relaxation time. The value of damping co-efficient k can be determined by finding the relaxation time t_r *i.e.*, the time in which the amplitude of a damped oscillator falls to $1/e$ of its original value by using the relation $k = \dfrac{1}{t_r}$.

The value of t_r is experimentally determined by plotting a graph between amplitude and time and finding from the graph the value of time $t = t_r$ in which the amplitude falls to $1/e = 0.368$ of its original value.

(iii) By quality factor Q. The quality factor Q is given by

$$Q = \frac{\omega' m}{r} = \frac{\omega'}{2k}$$

But $\omega' = \dfrac{2\pi}{T}$ where T is the time period.

$$\therefore \quad Q = \frac{2\pi}{T}\frac{1}{2k} = \frac{\pi}{kT}$$

from which we have damping co-efficient

$$k = \frac{\pi}{QT}.$$

The quality factor Q and time period T can be determined experimentally.

Q 2.30. (a) What is damping? On what factors the damping depends?   (*H.P.U.* 1999)

(b) **What is the effect of damping on the natural frequency of an oscillator?**

(*G.N.D.U.* 2007; *Pbi.U.* 2003)

(c) **Does viscous damping remain proportional to velocity under all conditions?**

(*Pbi.U.* 2000)

(d) **Write unit of damping constant and damping co-efficient for mechanical and electrical oscillator.**   (*H.P.U.* 2002)

Ans. (a) **Damping.** *The decay of amplitude of a damped harmonic oscillator with time is called damping.*

Factors on which damping depends. In the case of real vibratory systems damping depends upon (*i*) *resistive or viscous forces e.g., resistance of air,* (*ii*) structural conditions e.g., *friction at the supports* of a vibratory system like a simple pendulum and (*iii*) *velocity* — The damping force is independent of displacement or acceleration but is proportional to velocity.

(b) **Effect of damping on natural frequency.** The frequency of natural undamped oscillations of a mechanical oscillator is given by

$$f_0 = \frac{1}{2\pi}\sqrt{\frac{s}{m}}$$

where s is a constant known as *stiffness constant* or *spring constant* and m the *mass* of vibrating particle.

The frequency of damped oscillations is given by

$$f' = \frac{1}{2\pi}\sqrt{\frac{s}{m} - \frac{r^2}{4m^2}}$$

where r is also a constant known as *damping constant*. Thus f' is less than f_0 *i.e. the* presence of damping reduces the natural frequency of the oscillator. The difference depends upon the damping factor. Larger is the value of r, higher is the difference between f' and f_0 and smaller is the frequency of the damped oscillator as compared to the natural frequency of the oscillator.

(c) No. Viscous damping is proportional to velocity only for small values of velocity.

(d) **Unit of damping constant and damping co-efficient.** For a mechanical oscillator the unit of damping constant r is Nm^{-1} s or Kg s^{-1} and of damping co-efficient $k = \frac{r}{2m}$ is s^{-1}.

For electrical oscillator the unit of damping constant R is an ohm and damping co-efficient $\frac{R}{2L}$ is s^{-1}, the same as for a mechanical oscillator.

Q. 2.31. Mark the correct answer.

(*i*) The angular frequency of a damped oscillator is

(a) $2\pi\left(\frac{s}{m} - \frac{r^2}{4m}\right)$ (b) $\frac{1}{2\pi}\frac{\sqrt{s}}{m}$ (c) $\frac{1}{2\pi}\left(\frac{s}{m} - \frac{r^2}{4m^2}\right)^{\frac{1}{2}}$ (d) $\left(\frac{s}{m} - \frac{r^2}{4m^2}\right)^{\frac{1}{2}}$

where r = damping constant

 s = force or stiffness constant   (*H.P.U.,* 1993)

 m = mass of damped oscillator

(*ii*) The unit of force constant or spring constant in S.I. system is

  (*a*) N-m   (*b*) Nm^{-1} (*c*) Nm^{-2} (*d*) Nm^2 (*H.P.U.*, 1993)

(*iii*) Relaxation time is defined as the time during which the amplitude of the damped oscillator

  (*a*) Grows to *e* times the initial value

  (*b*) Decays to 1/*e* times the initial value

  (*c*) Grows to e^2 times the initial value

  (*d*) Decays to $1/e^2$ times the initial value   (*H.P.U.*, 1993)

(*iv*) The relaxation time τ for a mechanical oscillator is related to damping constant *r* as

  (*a*) $\tau = \dfrac{r}{2m}$ (*b*) $\tau = \dfrac{2m}{r}$ (*c*) $\tau = 2\,m\,r$ (*d*) $\tau = \dfrac{r}{m}$ (*H.P.U.*, 1992)

(*v*) The quality factor *Q* of an electrical oscillator is

  (*a*) $\dfrac{\omega R}{L}$ (*b*) $\dfrac{LR}{\omega}$ (*c*) $\dfrac{\omega L}{R}$ (*d*) $\dfrac{\omega}{LR}$ (*H.P.U.*, 1991)

(*vi*) In which of the following oscillations the amplitude varies with time?

  (*a*) Undamped oscillator   (*b*) Damped oscillator

  (*c*) Forced oscillator   (*d*) None of the above.   (*H.P.U.*, 2003)

(*vii*) If ω_0 is natural frequency and *k* represents damping then damped motion will be oscillatory if

  (*a*) $k = \omega_0$ (*b*) $k > \omega_0$ (*c*) $k < \omega_0$ (*d*) none of these   (*Meerut U.* 2000)

(*viii*) Differential equation of a damped harmonic oscillator is

$$\frac{d^2x}{dt^2} + 0.2\frac{dx}{dt} + 36x = 0,$$ its time period is nearly

  (*a*) $\pi/3$ (*b*) $\pi/2$ (*c*) $\pi/6$ (*d*) $\pi/4$ (*Luck.U.* 2001)

(*ix*) In electrical damped oscillator $\dfrac{R}{2L}$ has the units of

  (*a*) displacement   (*b*) time

  (*c*) reciprocal of time   (*d*) reciprocal of frequency   (*H.P.U.* 2003)

Ans. (*i*) *d*   (*ii*) *b*   (*iii*) *b*   (*iv*) *b*   (*v*)   *c*

        (*vi*) *b*   (*vii*) *c*   (*viii*) *a*   (*ix*) *c*

EXERCISES

1. Examine if the discharge of a capacitor is oscillatory, given that $R = 500\Omega$, $L = 0.1$ H and $C = 1$ μ F.   (*G.N.D.U.*, 1991)

    [**Ans.** oscillatory]

2. In an oscillatory circuit $L = 0.2$ H; $C = .0012$ μ F. What is the maximum value of resistance to be connected so that the circuit may produce oscillations?   (*H.P.U.*, 1994)

    [**Ans.** $2.58 \times 10^4\ \Omega$]

3. Deduce the frequency and quality factor of a circuit with $L = 5$ m H; $C = 2$ μ F; $R = 0.1$ ohm.

                                                     (*H.P.U.*, 1993)

    $$\left[\textbf{Ans.}\ \frac{10^4}{2\pi}\ \text{Hz; } 500\right]$$

4. If the energy of a note of frequency 100 Hz decreases to one half of its original value in one second, calculate the Q-value.

[Hint.

$$E = E_0 \, e^{-\omega' t/Q}$$

Here

$$\frac{E}{E_0} = \frac{1}{2}, \; \omega' = \omega = 2\pi \times 100, \; t = 1 \text{ sec}$$

∴

$$Q = \frac{2\pi \times 100}{2.3026 \log_{10} \dfrac{1}{2}} = 906.3$$

[Note. For electromagnetic damping and damping due to eddy currents as well as damping correction to be applied to a ballistic galvanometer see **Electricity and Magnetism** by the same author.]

3 Forced Oscillator and Resonance

Q. 3.1. (*a*) **Explain free vibrations, damped vibrations, forced vibrations and resonance, giving one example of each.**   (*P.U. 2008; G.N.D.U. 2008, 2007, 2006; Meerut U.*, 2003, 2002, 2001; *Calicut U.* 2003; *Nagpur U.*, 2002, 2001; *Pbi.U.*, 2001; *H.P.U.*, 1992)

(*b*) **What is the significance of '*i*' as a vector operator?**

Ans. (*a*) **Free vibrations.** When a body is displaced from its position of equilibrium and then released, it begins to vibrate. The time period or the frequency of vibration depends upon the dimensions, moment of inertia and elastic constants of the vibrating system.

Such vibrations are called free vibrations and the frequency with which a body vibrates when left free to itself is called its natured frequency.

Example. If a simple pendulum is displaced towards one side and then left free, it vibrates with a time period *t* given by

$$t = 2\pi\sqrt{\frac{l}{g}}$$

If the length *l* and the acceleration due to gravity *g* remain constant the pendulum will have the same time period and the same frequency.

Damped vibrations. In case of free vibrations the amplitude of vibrations remains constant. But free vibrations with constant amplitude is an ideal concept. In actual practice the amplitude of an oscillator goes on decreasing with every subsequent vibration due to loss of energy on account of work done against various types of damping forces.

These vibrations in which the amplitude of subsequent vibrations goes on decreasing due to the effect of damping forces are known as damped vibrations.

Example. A simple (or compound) pendulum vibrating in air and electromagnetic oscillations set up in an *LCR* circuit.

Forced vibrations. If we hold the pendulum bob in the hand, the pendulum can be given any number of swings per second by moving the hand. The pendulum vibrates with the frequency of the motion of the hand and not with its own natural frequency.

The phenomenon of setting a body into vibrations with the help of a strong periodic force having a frequency different from the natural frequency of the body is called forced vibrations.

If this frequency of the applied force is not equal to the natural frequency of the body, then the body tends to vibrate with its own period. The applied force some time helps and some times opposes the motion of the body. Hence there is a tussle and the body is unable to attain a large amplitude. Finally, the body is forced to vibrate with the period of the applied force. A body can be forced to vibrate with any frequency depending upon that of the applied force, but the vibrations die out as soon as the applied force is removed.

Example. Strike a tuning fork and hold its stem in the hand. The intensity of sound produced is low. The prongs of the tuning fork set only a small volume of air near them into vibrations and energy is dissipated slowly. If the stem of the fork is pressed on the table it is set into forced vibrations. The sound becomes very loud as now a large volume of air is set into vibrations by the table. Intensity of sound now dies off quickly.

Resonance. When a periodic force of a frequency equal to the natural frequency of a body is applied, the body slowly gains in amplitude and finally begins to vibrate with a very large amplitude. This is known as sympathetic vibrations or resonance and is defined as the *phenomenon of setting a body into vibrations with its natural frequency by the application of a periodic force of the same frequency.*

When the frequency of the applied force is equal to the natural frequency of the body the applied force helps to increase the amplitude of the body at each step as the force is always in phase with it. Every new impulse adds to the effect of all the previous impulses and the accumulated effect is to make the body vibrate with a large amplitude.

Example. Strike a tuning fork and hold it over a tube containing water. If the level of water in the tube is gradually lowered the length of the air column increases. When the natural frequency of the air column equals the frequency of the tuning fork a very loud sound is produced. This is a case of resonance.

(b) **'*i*' as a vector operator.** The vector operator '*i*' is in no way different from $\sqrt{-1}$ in mathematics. The *physical significance* of this vector operator is as given below.

If '*i*' precedes a vector, it is said to operate on that vector and the direction of that vector on which it operates is turned through $+\dfrac{\pi}{2}$ radians. In other words the phase of that vector is *advanced* through 90°.

If '$-i$' operates on a vector, the direction of the vector is turned through $-\dfrac{\pi}{2}$ radians. In other words the phase of that vector is *retarded* through 90°.

Q. 3.2. Define and explain the impedance of an electrical circuit. Derive an expression for it and give its units. *(H.P.U., 2002; G.N.D.U., 2002, 2000)*

Ans. Impedance of an electrical circuit. In an electrical circuit having a pure resistance R, the applied voltage and the current are in phase. Then according to Ohm's law

$$V = RI \qquad \qquad ...(i)$$

where V and I are the root mean square values of the applied voltage and current respectively. The relation (*i*) is basically a scalar relation.

If the voltage is alternating given by $V = V_0 \sin(\omega t + \phi)$ or $V = V_0 \cos(\omega t + \phi)$ or $V = V_0 e^{i(\omega t + \phi)}$, the current also has the same frequency or ω and the same phase and is, therefore, given by

$I = I_0 \sin(\omega t + \phi)$ or $I = I_0 \cos(\omega t + \phi)$ or $I = I_0 e^{i(\omega t + \phi)}$ where V_0 and I_0 are the maximum values of the voltage and current respectively.

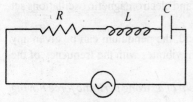

Fig. 3.1

However, when an inductance L and a capacitance C are introduced in the circuit in series with the resistance R, the applied voltage is given by

$$V = RI + L\frac{dI}{dt} + \frac{q}{C} \qquad \qquad ...(ii)$$

where $RI = V_R$ is the voltage across R, $L\dfrac{dI}{dt} = V_L$. The voltage across L and $\dfrac{q}{C} = V_C$ the voltage across C (q being the charge).

Electrical reactance due to inductance. Suppose the current through the circuit is given by

$$I = I_0 e^{i\omega t}$$

then
$$V_L = L\frac{dI}{dt} = L\frac{d}{dt}I_0 e^{i\omega t} = i\omega L I_0 e^{i\omega t} = i\omega L I$$

The quantity ωL has the dimensions of resistance. It is known as *reactance due to inductance* and is denoted by X_L. The presence of the vector operator i indicates that the phase of the voltage across the inductance is $90° \left(\dfrac{\pi}{2}\right)$ ahead of the current through the circuit or the voltage *leads* the current.

Electrical reactance due to capacitance. The voltage across the capacitance

$$V_C = \frac{q}{C} = \frac{1}{C}\int I dt = \frac{I_0}{C}\int e^{i\omega t}\, dt$$

$$= \frac{1}{i\omega C}I_0 e^{i\omega t} = -i\frac{1}{\omega C}$$

The quantity $\dfrac{1}{\omega C}$ also has the dimensions of resistance. It is known as *reactance due to capacitance* and is denoted by X_C. The presence of the vector operator $-i$ indicates that the voltage across the capacitance *lags* the current by $90° \left(\dfrac{\pi}{2}\right)$.

Electrical impedance. The voltage and current across the resistance R are in phase with each other and given by

$$V_R = RI_0 e^{i\omega t} = RI$$

The total voltage drop in the circuit is given by

$$V = RI + i\omega L I - i\frac{1}{\omega C}I$$

or
$$\frac{V}{I} = R + i\left(\omega L - \frac{1}{\omega C}\right)$$

or
$$Z_e = R + i\left(\omega L - \frac{1}{\omega C}\right)$$

Z_e is the electrical impedance of the circuit.

Hence the electrical impedance is defined as the ratio of the voltage to the current or the voltage required to produce a unit current in the circuit.

$$Z_e = \frac{V}{I}$$

Unit of impedance. The unit of electrical impedance is an ohm.

Electrical impedance as a vector. The electrical impedance can be shown in a vector diagram as in Fig. 3.2.

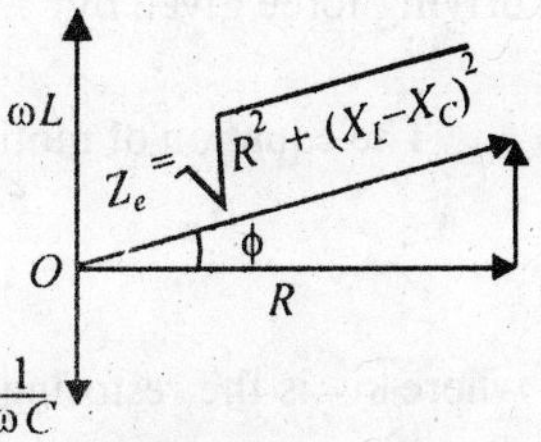

$$\omega L = X_L$$

is shown as a vector ahead of R by $90° \left(\dfrac{\pi}{2}\right)$ and $\dfrac{1}{\omega C} = X_C$ is

shown as a vector behind R in phase by $90° \left(\dfrac{\pi}{2}\right)$.

Fig. 3.2

$$\therefore \text{ Magnitude of } Z_e = \sqrt{R^2 + (X_L - X_C)^2} = \sqrt{R^2 + \left(\omega L - \frac{1}{\omega C}\right)^2}$$

The quantity $X_L - X_C = X_e$ given the net electrical reactance of the circuit.

∴   Ohm's law can be stated in the vector form

$$\vec{I} = \frac{\vec{V}}{\vec{Z_e}}$$

The phase angle ϕ by which the voltage leads or lags the current is given by

$$\tan \phi = \frac{X_e}{R} = \frac{X_L - X_C}{R} = \frac{\omega L - \dfrac{1}{\omega C}}{R}$$

The vector impedance $\vec{Z_e}$ can be supposed to be made up of two components. Referring to Fig. 3.2.,

$$R = Z_e \cos \phi \text{ and } X_e = Z_e \sin \phi$$

∴   Vectorially $\vec{Z_e} = Z_e \cos \phi + i Z_e \sin \phi$

$$= Z_e (\cos \phi + i \sin \phi)$$

$$= Z_e e^{i\phi}$$

∴   The voltage is given by the relation

$$V = V_0 e^{i (\omega t + \phi)}$$

If $\omega L > \dfrac{1}{\omega C}$ *i.e.*; the reactance due to inductance is greater than the reactance due to capacitance

ϕ is *positive* and the voltage leads the current. If $\omega L < \dfrac{1}{\omega C}$ *i.e.*, the reactance due to inductance is less than the reactance due to capacitance, ϕ is *negative* and the voltage lags the current.

The magnitude of Z_e depends upon the frequency of the applied voltage. When

$$\omega L = \frac{1}{\omega C} \quad \text{or} \quad \omega = \frac{1}{\sqrt{LC}}$$

The impedance Z_e has the minimum value which is $= R$.

Q. 3.3. (a) Derive the value of the mechanical impedance of a physical system subjected to driving forces.

(b) What is the physical significance of mechanical impedance of a forced oscillator?

(*G.N.D.U.*, 2006, 2002, 2000, 1993; *H.P.U.*, 2002, 1999, 1992; *Pbi.U.*, 2007, 2001, 1995; *P.U.*, 2008, 2001, 2000,1993)

Ans. (a) Impedance of a mechanical system. Consider a mechanical oscillatory system having a mass m, stiffness constant s and damping constant r acted upon by an external periodic driving force given by

$$F = F_0 e^{i \omega t}$$

The equation of motion is given by

$$m\frac{d^2 y}{dt^2} + r\frac{dy}{dt} + sy = F_0 e^{i\omega t} \qquad \qquad ....(i)$$

where sy is the restoring force proportional to displacement and $r\dfrac{dy}{dt}$ is the resisting force being directly proportional to the velocity of the oscillator.

Let the displacement be given by

$$y = A e^{i \omega t}$$

∴

$$\frac{dy}{dt} = i\omega A e^{i\omega t} \quad \text{and} \quad \frac{d^2 y}{dt^2} = -\omega^2 A e^{i\omega t}$$

Substituting in (i), we have

$$-m\omega^2 A e^{i\omega t} + ir\omega A e^{i\omega t} + s A e^{i\omega t} = F_0 e^{i\omega t} = F$$

or

$$i A\omega e^{i\omega t}\left[im\omega + r - i\frac{s}{\omega}\right] = F$$

but $i A\omega e^{i\omega t} = \dfrac{dy}{dt} = v$ the velocity of the oscillator

$$\therefore \quad v\left[r + i\left(m\omega - \frac{s}{\omega}\right)\right] = F$$

or

$$\frac{F}{v} = r + i\left(m\omega - \frac{s}{\omega}\right)$$

or

$$Z_m = r + i\left(m\omega - \frac{s}{\omega}\right).$$

Z_m is the mechanical impedance of the oscillator.

Hence the mechanical impedance is defined as the ratio of the instantaneous force exerted by the external periodic force to the instantaneous velocity of the oscillator or the external force required to produce a unit velocity in the oscillator.

$$\therefore \quad Z_m = \frac{F}{v}$$

Units. The unit of mechanical impedance Z_m is $\dfrac{N}{ms^{-1}} = N m^{-1} s$

or

$$\frac{kg\,m\,s^{-2}}{m\,s^{-1}} = kg\,s^{-1}$$

Mechanical impedance $Z_m = r + i\left(\omega m - \dfrac{s}{\omega}\right)$

$$= r + X_m$$

where X_m is known as *mechanical reactance* and consists of two components.

(i) ωm the reactance due to mass or inertia and

(ii) $\dfrac{s}{m}$ the reactance due to stiffness or elasticity.

Magnitude of the impedance

$$Z_m = \sqrt{r^2 + X_m^2} = \sqrt{r^2 + \left(\omega m - \frac{s}{\omega}\right)^2}$$

The phase angle is given by

$$\tan\phi = \frac{X_m}{r} = \frac{\omega m - \dfrac{s}{\omega}}{r}$$

where ϕ is the phase difference between the external force and velocity of the oscillator.

Mechanical impedance as a vector. The vector

impedance $\vec{Z}_m$ can be supposed to be made up of two components $r = Z_m \cos\phi$ and $X_m = Z_m \sin\phi$ as shown in Fig. 3.3.

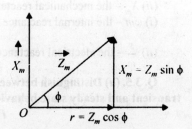

Fig. 3.3

Vectorially $\vec{Z}_m = Z_m \cos\phi + i Z_m \sin\phi$

$$= Z_m (\cos \phi + i \sin \phi)$$
$$= Z_m \, e^{i \phi}.$$

(*b*) **Physical significance.** Mechanical impedance of an oscillatory system opposes a change in displacement or velocity of the oscillator. $Z_m = \dfrac{F}{v}$. In other words $F = Z_m \, v$. Hence greater the impedance smaller is the velocity produced in the oscillator by a given external force.

$$\vec{Z}_m = r + i \left(m\omega - \frac{s}{\omega} \right)$$

The presence of reactance $\left(m\omega - \dfrac{s}{\omega} \right)$ and resistance r introduces a phase difference between

applied force and velocity of the oscillator given by $\tan \phi = \dfrac{m\omega - \dfrac{s}{\omega}}{r}$.

The presence of vector operator i introduces an additional phase difference of $\pi/2$ or $90°$.

Q. 3.4. (*a*) **What is mechanical reactance? What are its two important constituents?**

(*Pbi.U.*, 2000, 1999; *G.N.D.U.*, 1995)

(*b*) **What is mechanical impedance of a forced oscillator ? On what factors its value depends?**

(*P.U.* 2008)

Ans. (*a*) **Mechanical reactance.** Mechanical reactance is the resistance offered by the combined effect of mass or inertia and stiffness or elasticity to the motion of the damped oscillator. It is given by

$$X_m = \omega m - \frac{s}{\omega}$$

where m is the mass and s the stiffness constant of the oscillator, ω is the frequency of the external periodic force.

Mechanical reactance has two important constituents.

(*i*) ωm, the inertial reactance,

and (*ii*) $\dfrac{s}{\omega}$, the elastic reactance.

There is a phase difference of π between the inertial reactance and elastic reactance.

(*b*) **Mechanical impedance Z_m.** See Q. 3.3

Factor on which Z_m depends. Mechanical impedance

$$Z_m = \sqrt{r^2 + \left(w\omega - \frac{s}{\omega} \right)^2} = \sqrt{r^2 + X_m^2}$$

Therefore, mechanical impedance depends upon

(*i*) r – the damping constant and

(*ii*) X_m – the mechanical reactance which in turn depends upon two factors

(*i*) ωm – the internal reactance and

(*ii*) $\dfrac{s}{\omega}$ – the electrical reactance [For details see part (*a*)]

Q. 3.5. (*a*) **Distinguish between transient and steady state in a forced oscillator. Explain the transient and steady state behaviour of a mechanical oscillator driven by a force**

$$F = F_0 \, e^{i \omega t}$$

Discuss the case when $F = F_0 \cos \omega t$ and when $F = F_0 \sin \omega t$ and show that the driven oscillator is always behind the driving force in phase.

(*Nagpur U.* 2003; *H.P.U.*, 2003, 2002, 2000, 1999, 1994; *P.U.*, 2009, 2007, 2005, 2004, 2003, 2002, 2000, 1995; *G.N.D.U*; 2009, 2007, 2003; *Luck.U.*, 2001; *Pbi.U.*, 2007, 2006, 2005, 2002, 2000; *Meerut U.*, 2007, 2002; *Kan.U.*, 1995,1992)

Ans. Mechanical forced oscillator. *An oscillator which is driven continuously by an external periodic force to maintain its oscillations is called forced oscillator.*

The equation of motion of a damped simple harmonic oscillator is given by

$$m\frac{d^2 y}{dt^2} + r\frac{dy}{dt} + sy = 0$$

where (*i*) sy is the restoring force proportional to displacement from the mean position and (*ii*) $r\frac{dy}{dt}$ is the resisting force being directly proportional to the velocity of the particle $\frac{dy}{dt}$.

Equation of motion. Now suppose an external periodic force $F = F_0 e^{i\omega t}$ where F_0 is the maximum value of the applied force or force amplitude and ω is its angular frequency, is applied to the oscillating system. The equation of motion is then given by

$$m\frac{d^2 y}{dt^2} + r\frac{dy}{dt} + sy = F_0 e^{i\omega t} \qquad \qquad ...(i)$$

The complete solution of this equation will consist of two parts.

(*i*) **Transient state.** The first part is known as the *transient term* which dies away with time. The transient behaviour persists only for a short interval of time. During this time the natural oscillations of the system will prevail and the system will behave as if no external force is acting.

The displacement of the oscillations is, therefore, given by the solution of the equation

$$m\frac{d^2 y}{dt^2} + r\frac{dy}{dt} + sy = 0 \qquad \qquad ...(ii)$$

Dividing equation (*ii*) by m and substituting

$$\frac{s}{m} = \omega_0^2 \text{ and } \frac{r}{m} = 2k \text{ we have}$$

$$\frac{d^2 y}{dt^2} + 2k\frac{dy}{dt} + \omega_0^2 y = 0.$$

The oscillatory solution of this equation is

$$y = A_0 e^{-kt} \sin\left(\sqrt{\omega_0^2 - k^2}\; t + \phi\right)$$
$$= A_0 e^{-kt} \sin\left(\omega' t + \phi\right)$$

where $\omega' = \sqrt{\omega_0^2 - k^2}, \quad A_0 = \dfrac{y_0 \,\omega_0}{\sqrt{\omega_0^2 - k^2}}$

and $\tan\phi_0 = \dfrac{\sqrt{\omega_0^2 - k^2}}{k}$

The amplitude $A_0 e^{-kt}$ decays with time due to the presence of the term e^{-kt}. The quantity ω_0 is known as the natural frequency of the oscillator in the absence of dissipative as well as driving forces.

(*ii*) **Steady state.** The second part is known as the *steady state term* which describes the behaviour of the oscillator after the transient term has died away.

To begin with both the terms contribute to the motion of the oscillator but later on the transient term becomes almost negligible and the ultimate behaviour of the oscillator will be given by the steady state term. During the transient stage the oscillator neither oscillates with its natural frequency nor with the frequency of the impressed force. During the steady state the oscillator oscillates with the frequency of the external driving force.

The external driving force is a periodic force which may be given by $F = F_0 \cos \omega t$ or $F = F_0 \sin \omega t$ or by a complex quantity $F = F_0 e^{i\omega t}$ as $F_0 e^{i\omega t} = F_0 (\cos \omega t + i \sin \omega t)$ is a combination of the two forces. If the external driving force is $F_0 \cos \omega t$, then it is the real part of the complex quantity $F_0 e^{i\omega t}$. If the force is $F_0 \sin \omega t$, then it is that part of the complex quantity $F_0 e^{i\omega t}$ which is preceded by i. We shall, therefore consider a general case of the external force given by $F = F_0 e^{i\omega t}$ and derive from it the particular cases of $F = F_0 \cos \omega t$ or $F = F_0 \sin \omega t$.

Equation (i) may now be written as

$$m\frac{d^2y}{dt^2} + r\frac{dy}{dt} + sy = F_0 e^{i\omega t} \qquad ...(iii)$$

In the steady state let one particular solution of the equation be

$$y = A e^{i\omega t}$$

where A is a complex quantity.

$$\therefore \qquad \frac{dy}{dt} = i\omega A e^{i\omega t}$$

and

$$\frac{d^2y}{dt^2} = -\omega^2 A e^{i\omega t}$$

Substituting in equation (iii), we have

$$A(-\omega^2 m + i\omega r + s) e^{i\omega t} = F_0 e^{i\omega t}$$

This relation is true for all values of t.

$$\therefore \qquad A = \frac{F_0}{i\omega r + (s - \omega^2 m)}$$

$$= \frac{-iF_0}{\omega r - i(s - \omega^2 m)}$$

$$= \frac{-iF_0}{\omega\left[r + i\left(\omega m - \frac{s}{\omega}\right)\right]} = \frac{-iF_0}{\omega \vec{Z}_m}$$

where $\vec{Z}_m$ is the mechanical impedance given by

$$\vec{Z}_m = r + i\left(\omega m - \frac{s}{\omega}\right)$$

Putting $r = Z_m \cos\phi$ and $\omega m - \frac{s}{\omega} = Z_m \sin\phi$ where Z_m is the modulus of the complex impedance

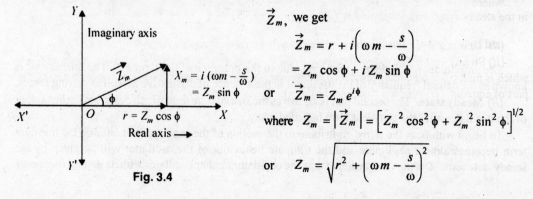

$\vec{Z}_m$, we get

$$\vec{Z}_m = r + i\left(\omega m - \frac{s}{\omega}\right)$$
$$= Z_m \cos\phi + i Z_m \sin\phi$$
$$\text{or} \quad \vec{Z}_m = Z_m e^{i\phi}$$
where $Z_m = |\vec{Z}_m| = \left[Z_m^2 \cos^2\phi + Z_m^2 \sin^2\phi\right]^{1/2}$

or $Z_m = \sqrt{r^2 + \left(\omega m - \frac{s}{\omega}\right)^2}$

Fig. 3.4

and $\quad\quad\quad \tan\phi = \dfrac{Z_m \sin\phi}{Z_m \cos\phi} = \dfrac{\omega m - \dfrac{s}{\omega}}{r} = \dfrac{X_m}{r}$

ϕ being the phase difference between displacement y and applied force F

$\therefore \quad\quad\quad y = A e^{i\omega t} = \dfrac{-iF_0}{\omega \vec{Z}_m} e^{i\omega t}$

$\quad\quad\quad\quad = \dfrac{-iF_0}{\omega Z_m e^{i\phi}} e^{i\omega t} = \dfrac{-iF_0}{\omega Z_m} e^{i(\omega t - \phi)}$ ...(iv)

Discussion. (*i*) **Driving force** $F = F_0 \cos\omega t$. (*i*) **Transient State.** The transient state solution remains the same as already discussed as it does not involve the external force F. The system behaves as if no external force is applied.

(*ii*) **Steady State.** If the external driving force is $F_0 \cos\omega t$, then it is the real part of the complex function $F_0 e^{i\omega t}$. Therefore, the steady state term will *only* consist of the real part of equation (*iv*), which may be put in the form

$\quad\quad\quad y = \dfrac{-iF_0}{\omega Z_m}[\cos(\omega t - \phi) + i\sin(\omega t - \phi)]$

$\quad\quad\quad\quad = \dfrac{F_0}{\omega Z_m}[-i\cos(\omega t - \phi) + \sin(\omega t - \phi)]$ ...(v)

$\quad\quad\quad\quad = \dfrac{-iF_0}{\omega Z_m}\cos(\omega t - \phi) + \dfrac{F_0}{\omega Z_m}\sin(\omega t - \phi)$

and the real part of the above equation gives

$\quad\quad\quad y = \dfrac{F_0}{\omega Z_m}\sin(\omega t - \phi)$ ...(vi)

$\quad\quad\quad\quad = \dfrac{F_0}{\omega Z_m}\cos\left[\omega t - \left(\phi + \dfrac{\pi}{2}\right)\right]$

The driving applied force is $F_0 \cos\omega t$ which is the real part of

$\quad\quad\quad\quad F_0 e^{i\omega t} = F_0 \cos\omega t + iF_0 \sin\omega t$

Comparing $\quad\quad\quad\quad y = \dfrac{F_0}{\omega Z_m}\cos\left[\omega t - \left(\phi + \dfrac{\pi}{2}\right)\right]$

with $\quad\quad\quad\quad F = F_0 \cos\omega t$

We find that the total phase difference between the displacement y and the applied force F is $-\left(\phi + \dfrac{\pi}{2}\right)$

in the steady state. The amplitude is $\dfrac{F_0}{\omega Z_m}$.

(*ii*) **Driving force** $F = F_0 \sin\omega t$. (*i*) **Transient State.** Same as for $F = F_0 \cos\omega t$.

(*ii*) **Steady state.** The external driving force $F_0 \sin\omega t$ is that part of the complex function $F_0 e^{i\omega t}$ which is multiplied by vector operator i. Therefore, the steady state term will now *only* consist of that part of equation (*iv*) which is multiplied by i, which from equation (*v*), we get

$\quad\quad\quad y = \dfrac{-F_0}{\omega Z_m}\cos(\omega t - \phi)$ ...(vii)

$\quad\quad\quad\quad = \dfrac{F_0}{\omega Z_m}\sin\left[\omega t - \left(\phi + \dfrac{\pi}{2}\right)\right]$

The driving force is $F_0 \sin \omega t$.

Comparing
$$y = \frac{F_0}{\omega Z_m} \sin\left[\omega t - \left(\phi + \frac{\pi}{2}\right)\right] \text{ with}$$

$$F = F_0 \sin \omega t$$

We again find that the total phase difference between the displacement y and applied force F is $-(\phi + \pi/2)$ in the steady state. The amplitude is also $\dfrac{F_0}{\omega Z_m}$.

(b) **Phase difference between driven oscillator and driving force.** We have proved above that when the driving force $F = F_0 \cos \omega t$, the displacement $y = \dfrac{F_0}{\omega Z_m} \cos[\omega t - (\phi + \pi/2)]$ and when $F = F_0 \sin \omega t$, $y = \dfrac{F_0}{\omega Z_m} \sin[\omega t - (\phi + \pi/2)]$. In both the cases we find that the driven oscillator is always behind the driving force in phase. The value of the difference in phase is $-(\phi + \pi/2)$.

Q. 3.6. Discuss the behaviour of displacement versus driving force frequency in case of a forced oscillator. Show that (i) The displacement at low frequency is independent of frequency (ii) The resonant frequency of driving force is slightly less than the natural frequency of the oscillator

(iii) Maximum amplitude $A_{max} = \dfrac{F_0}{r\omega'}$ where r is damping constant and $\omega' = \sqrt{\dfrac{s}{m} - \dfrac{r^2}{4m^2}}$.

(H.P.U., 2003, 2001, 1999, 1993; Pbi.U., 2007, 2006, 2003; P.U., 2007, 2006, 2002, 2000, 1999; G.N.D.U., 2006, 2001, 1994; Meerut U., 2000)

Ans. Behaviour of displacement versus driving force frequency. When a periodic driving force $F = F_0 \cos \omega t$ is applied to a damped oscillator and a steady state is reached, the displacement is given by

$$y = \frac{F_0}{\omega Z_m} \sin(\omega t - \phi) \qquad \text{...(i)}$$

where Z_m is the mechanical impedance offered by the oscillator and its magnitude is given by

$$Z_m = \sqrt{r^2 + \left(\omega m - \frac{s}{\omega}\right)^2} \qquad \text{...(ii)}$$

and
$$\tan \phi = \frac{\omega m - \dfrac{s}{m}}{r}$$

r being the *damping constant*, m the *mass* and s the stiffness or *spring constant* of the oscillator. [For proof see Q. 3.5 Eq. (vi)]

Substituting $\quad 2k = \dfrac{r}{m} \quad$ and $\quad \omega_0^2 = \dfrac{s}{m} \quad$ in (ii) we get

$$Z_m = \frac{m}{\omega} \sqrt{4k^2 \omega^2 + (\omega^2 - \omega_0^2)^2}$$

ω_0 being the natural frequency of the oscillator.

$$\therefore \qquad y = \frac{F_0}{\omega \dfrac{m}{\omega} \sqrt{4k^2 \omega^2 + (\omega^2 - \omega_0^2)^2}} \sin(\omega t - \phi)$$

$$= \frac{f_0}{\sqrt{4k^2 \omega^2 + (\omega^2 - \omega_0^2)^2}} \sin(\omega t - \phi)$$

where $\qquad f_0 = \dfrac{F_0}{m}$ and $\tan\phi = \dfrac{\omega m - \dfrac{s}{m}}{r} = \dfrac{\omega^2 - \omega_0^2}{2k\omega}$

Substituting $\qquad \dfrac{f_0}{\sqrt{4k^2\omega^2 + (\omega^2 - \omega_0^2)^2}} = a$, the *displacement amplitude* we have

$$y = a\sin(\omega t - \phi) \qquad\qquad ...(iii)$$

We shall study the behaviour of *displacement amplitude* versus driving force frequency in three stages of frequencies *i.e.*, low frequency, resonant frequency and high frequency.

(*i*) **At low driving frequencies** ($\omega << \omega_0$) *i.e.*, the driving force frequency is very much less than the natural frequency of oscillations. The displacement amplitude

$$a = \dfrac{f_0}{\sqrt{4k^2\omega^2 + (\omega^2 - \omega_0^2)^2}}$$

When $\omega \to 0$, ω^2 can be neglected as compared to ω_0^2, $4k^2\omega^2$ as compared to $(\omega_0^2)^2$ and we get

$$a = \dfrac{f_0}{\omega_0^2} = \dfrac{F_0/m}{s/m} = \dfrac{F_0}{s}$$

Thus at very low driving force frequencies, the amplitude of forced oscillations depends upon the driving force F_0 and stiffness constant s but is independent of frequency.

Thus the amplitude of forced oscillator and also the impedance is *stiffness controlled*.

(*ii*) **At high driving force frequency** ($\omega >> \omega_0$) *i.e.*, the driving force frequency is very much greater than the natural frequency of the oscillator. For large values of ω, ω^2 is very much greater than ω_0^2 so that ω_0^2 can be neglected as compared to ω^2 and then

$$a = \dfrac{f_0}{\sqrt{4k^2\omega^2 + (\omega^2 - \omega_0^2)^2}} = \dfrac{f_0}{\sqrt{4k^2\omega^2 + \omega^4}} = \dfrac{f_0}{\omega^2}$$

If k the damping is very small so that $4k^2\omega^2$ can be neglected as compared to ω^4.

As $\omega \to \infty$; $a \to 0$ *i.e.*, the amplitude almost approaches zero as the driving force frequency becomes very large.

(*iii*) **At frequency of displacement resonance** ($\omega = \omega_0$) *i.e.*, the driving force frequency is equal to the natural frequency of the oscillator. This is the case of *amplitude resonance*. At this stage the amplitude is given by

$$a = \dfrac{f_0}{\sqrt{4k^2\omega^2 + (\omega^2 - \omega_0^2)^2}} = \dfrac{f_0}{2k\omega}$$

Thus at a driving force frequency equal to the resonant frequency the maximum amplitude is inversely proportional to damping coefficient k. For small damping, amplitude is large and for large damping, amplitude is small. Theoretically for $k = 0$, $a = \infty$.

When, however, damping is present the displacement resonance takes place at a frequency $\omega = \sqrt{\omega_0^2 - 2k^2}$ as proved below.

For amplitude a to be a maximum $\dfrac{da}{d\omega} = 0$

Now displacement amplitude $a = \dfrac{f_0}{\sqrt{4k^2\,\omega^2 - (\omega^2 - \omega_0^2)^2}}$

$$\therefore \quad \frac{d}{d\omega}\left[\frac{f_0}{\sqrt{4k^2\,\omega^2 + (\omega^2 - \omega_0^2)^2}}\right] = \frac{-f_0[4\omega)(\omega^2 - \omega_0^2) + 8k^2\,\omega]}{2[4k^2\,\omega^2 + (\omega^2 - \omega_0^2)^2]^{3/2}} = 0$$

$$\therefore \quad 4\omega(\omega^2 - \omega_0^2) + 8k^2\,\omega = 0$$

or $\qquad \omega^2 - \omega_0^2 = -2k^2$

$$\therefore \quad \omega^2 = \omega_0^2 - 2k^2$$

or $\qquad \omega = \sqrt{\omega_0^2 - 2k^2} = \omega_0\sqrt{1 - \dfrac{2k^2}{\omega_0^2}}$

$$= \omega_0\sqrt{1 - \frac{r^2}{2m^2\,\omega_0^2}}$$

Thus the *maximum displacement amplitude or displacement resonance takes place at a frequency slightly less than* ω_0 *the natural frequency of the oscillator and is given by*

$$\omega = \sqrt{\omega_0^2 - 2k^2} = \omega_0\sqrt{1 - \frac{r^2}{2m^2\,\omega_0^2}}$$

In other words the resonant frequency of driving force ω *is slightly less than the natural frequency of displacement* ω_0.

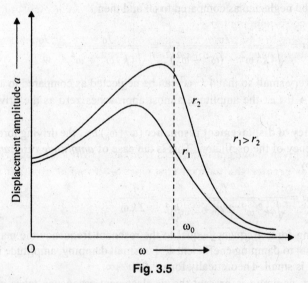

Fig. 3.5

Maximum value of displacement amplitude. The displacement amplitude is given by

$$a = \frac{f_0}{\sqrt{4k^2\,\omega^2 - (\omega^2 - \omega_0^2)^2}}$$

The displacement amplitude is maximum at frequency of resonance $\omega = \sqrt{\omega_0^2 - 2k^2}$.

Substituting this value of ω in the expression for a we have

$$a_{max} = \frac{f_0}{\sqrt{4k^2(\omega_0^2 - 2k^2) + (\omega_0^2 - 2k^2 - \omega_0^2)^2}}$$

$$= \frac{f_0}{\sqrt{4k^2(\omega_0^2 - 2k^2) + 4k^4}} = \frac{f_0}{2k\sqrt{\omega_0^2 - k^2}}$$

$$= \frac{f_0}{\frac{r}{m}\sqrt{\omega_0^2 - \frac{r^2}{4m^2}}} = \frac{F_0}{r\sqrt{\omega_0^2 - \frac{r^2}{4m^2}}} = \frac{F_0}{r\omega'}$$

where $\qquad \omega' = \sqrt{\omega_0^2 - \frac{r^2}{4m^2}} = \sqrt{\frac{s}{m} - \frac{r^2}{4m^2}}$ = natural frequency of damped oscillator.

Graphical representation. We have seen that amplitude of forced vibrations at low frequencies

is $\dfrac{F_0}{s}$ and almost becomes zero at very high frequencies. The maximum value of displacement

amplitude $a_{max} = \dfrac{F_0}{r\omega'}$. Thus higher the damping smaller is the amplitude at resonance as shown in

Fig. 3.5. As $r_1 > r_2$ the value of a_{max} corresponding to r_1 is less than that corresponding to r_2. The

frequency for maximum displacement resonance amplitude $\omega' = \sqrt{\omega_0^2 - \dfrac{r^2}{4m^2}}$. Hence, as r decreases

ω' comes closer to ω_0. As shown in Fig. 3.5 $r_1 > r_2$. Therefore a_{max} corresponding to r_2 is closer to ω_0
as compared to a_{max} corresponding to r_1.

Exercise. *Show that the maximum displacement of a forced damped oscillator with driving
force* $F = F_0 \cos \omega t$ *and having damping constant* (r) *is given by*

$$a_{max} = \frac{F_0}{r\omega'}$$

where $\qquad \omega' = \sqrt{\dfrac{s}{m} - \dfrac{r^2}{4m^2}}$ $\qquad\qquad\qquad\qquad\qquad\qquad$ (P.U. 2006)

Hint. See Q. 3.6 given above under the head **'Maximum value of displacement amplitude'**.

**Q. 3.7. Which is greater the natural frequency of damped oscillations or frequency of
displacement resonance?** $\qquad\qquad\qquad\qquad\qquad\qquad\qquad\qquad\qquad\qquad\qquad$ (P.U., 1995)

Ans. The displacement resonance occurs at an angular frequency ω given by

$$\omega = \sqrt{\omega_0^2 - 2k^2} = \sqrt{\frac{s}{m} - \frac{r^2}{2m^2}} \qquad\qquad\qquad\qquad ...(i)$$

$$\left(\text{since } \omega_0^2 = \frac{s}{m} \text{ and } 2k = \frac{r}{m} \right)$$

The natural (angular) frequency of damped oscillations is

$$\omega' = \sqrt{\omega_0^2 - k^2} = \sqrt{\frac{s}{m} - \frac{r^2}{4m^2}} \qquad\qquad\qquad\qquad ...(ii)$$

Comparing (i) and (ii) we find that $\omega' > \omega$

Hence natural frequency of damped oscillations is greater than the frequency at which displacement resonance occurs.

Q. 3.8. Prove that displacement resonant frequency of driving force is less than the natural frequency of the undamped oscillator. *(P.U., 1999; H.P.U., 1995)*

Ans. It has been proved in **Q. 3.6** that displacement resonance takes place at a frequency

$$\omega = \sqrt{\omega_0^2 - 2k^2}$$

where $\omega_0^2 = \dfrac{s}{m}$ and $2k = \dfrac{r}{m}$

This shows that displacement resonance occurs at a frequency ω slightly less than ω_0 the frequency of free oscillations (or natural frequency of undamped oscillator) as $\sqrt{\omega_0^2 - 2k^2}$ is less than ω_0, k^2 being a positive quantity.

Q. 3.9. For a mechanical oscillator driven by a force $F = F_0 \cos \omega t$, discuss the variation of phase difference between displacement and driving force with driving force frequency. What is the phase difference between displacement and force at very high frequency?

(G.N.D.U., 2002; H.P.U., 2001, 2000; P.U., 1995; Kan.U., 1995)

Ans. Variation of phase difference between displacement and driving force frequency. When a periodic driving force $F = F_0 \cos \omega t$ is applied to a damped oscillator and a steady state is reached the displacement is given by

$$y = \frac{F_0}{\omega Z_m} \sin (\omega t - \phi) \qquad \qquad ...(i)$$

Where Z_m is the mechanical impedance offered by the oscillator and its magnitude is given by

$$Z_m = \sqrt{r^2 + \left(\omega m - \frac{s}{\omega}\right)^2}$$

r being the *damping constant*, m the *mass* and s the stiffness or *spring constant* of the oscillator.

$$\tan \phi = \frac{\omega m - \dfrac{s}{\omega}}{r} = \frac{\omega^2 - \dfrac{s}{m}}{\dfrac{r}{m}\omega} = \frac{\omega^2 - \omega_0^2}{2k\omega}$$

where $\omega_0^2 = \dfrac{s}{m}$ and $2k = \dfrac{r}{m}$

The driving force $F = F_0 \cos \omega t$ ...(ii)

Relation (i) can be put in the form

$$y = \frac{F_0}{\omega Z_m} \cos\left[\omega t - \left(\phi + \frac{\pi}{2}\right)\right] \qquad \qquad ...(iii)$$

From Eq. (iii) and (ii), we find that displacement lags behind the driving force by an angle $\left(\phi + \dfrac{\pi}{2}\right)$. The value of ϕ or $\tan \phi$ varies with ω. Thus phase difference between displacement y and driving force F will also vary with ω. Let the phase difference between y and F be denoted by θ, then

$$\theta = -\left(\frac{\pi}{2} + \phi\right)$$

We shall study the variation of θ (or ϕ) versus ω in three stages of frequencies *i.e.*, low frequency, high frequency and resonant frequency.

(i) Low frequency. When $\omega << \omega_0$. At $\omega = 0$

$$\tan \phi = \frac{\omega - \omega_0^2}{2k\omega} = -\infty$$

$$\therefore \qquad \phi = -\pi/2$$

The total phase difference $\theta = -\left(\dfrac{\pi}{2} + \phi\right) = -\left(\dfrac{\pi}{2} - \dfrac{\pi}{2}\right) = 0$

Thus at $\omega = 0$ the driving force and resulting displacement are in *phase*. As ω increases a slight phase difference is introduced, θ having a small but positive value indicating that the displacement lags the force.

(ii) Resonant frequency. When $\omega = \omega_0$ where ω_0 is the natural frequency of undamped oscillations

$$\tan \phi = \frac{\omega^2 - \omega_0^2}{2k\omega} = 0$$

$$\therefore \qquad \phi = 0$$

$\therefore$ Total phase difference $\theta = -\left(\dfrac{\pi}{2} + \phi\right) = -\pi/2$

Thus at $\omega = \omega_0$ the resultant displacement lags behind the driving force by an angle $\dfrac{\pi}{2}$.

(iii) High frequency. When $\omega >> \omega_0$. As $\omega \to \infty$

$$\tan \phi = \frac{\omega^2 - \omega_0^2}{2k\omega} = +\infty$$

$$\therefore \qquad \phi = \frac{\pi}{2}$$

$\therefore$ Total phase difference $\theta = -\left(\dfrac{\pi}{2} + \phi\right)$

$$= -\left(\frac{\pi}{2} + \frac{\pi}{2}\right) = -\pi$$

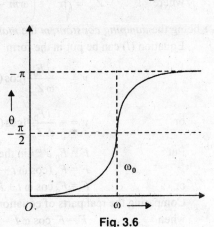

Fig. 3.6

Thus when ω increases beyond ω_0 the displacement lags behind the driving force by an angle greater than

$\dfrac{\pi}{2}$ *and finally when* $\omega \to \infty$ *the phase angle increases to* π *i.e., displacement lags behind by* π.

The variation of total phase difference θ with ω is shown in Fig. 3.6.

Q. 3.10. (a) What causes the phase difference ϕ between the applied force and displacement?
(Pbi.U., 2000)

(b) Complete the sentence "At resonance the displacement ——— the driving force by an angle ———".
(P.U., 1996)

Ans. (a) Cause of phase difference. The phase difference ϕ between the applied force and

displacement is caused by the mechanical impedance $\vec{Z}_m = r + i\left(m\omega - \dfrac{s}{\omega}\right)$ where r is the resistance

or *damping constant*, m the *mass* of the vibrating particle and s the *spring constant*. The presence of

reactance $\left(m\omega - \dfrac{s}{\omega}\right)$ and *resistance r* introduces a phase difference given by

$$\tan \phi = \frac{m\omega - \dfrac{s}{\omega}}{r}$$

The presence of vector operator i introduces an additional phase difference of $\pi/2$.

(b) At resonance the displacement *lags behind* the driving force by an *angle* $\dfrac{\pi}{2}$ *radian.*

Q. 3.11. (a) Derive an expression for the velocity amplitude of a forced oscillator. Discuss the variation of velocity amplitude with driving force frequency and show its behaviour graphically and that it is stiffness controlled at low frequency whereas it is mass controlled at high frequency.

Show that velocity amplitude at velocity resonance is frequency independent.

(b) Discuss the variation of phase difference between velocity and driving force frequency.

(*P.U.*, 2009, 2008, 2007, 2005, 2004, 2003, 1999, 1996; *G.N.D.U.* 2006;
Luck.U., 2001; *H.P.U.*, 2000)

Ans. (*a*) **Velocity of a forced oscillator.** When a periodic driving force $F = F_0\, e^{i\omega t}$ is applied to a damped oscillator and a steady state is reached the displacement is given by

$$y = -\frac{i F_0}{\omega Z_m} e^{i(\omega t - \phi)} \qquad\qquad\qquad ...(i)$$

where $\qquad Z_m = \sqrt{r^2 + \left(\omega m - \dfrac{s}{\omega}\right)^2}\qquad$ and $\qquad \tan\phi = \dfrac{\omega m - \dfrac{s}{\omega}}{r}$

r being the *damping constant*, m the *mass* and s the stiffness or spring constant.

Equation (*i*) can be put in the form

$$y = -\frac{i F_0}{\omega Z_m}[\cos(\omega - \phi) + i\sin(\omega t - \phi)]$$

or $\qquad\qquad y = -\dfrac{i F_0}{\omega Z_m}[\cos(\omega t - \phi) + \dfrac{F_0}{\omega Z_m}\sin(\omega t - \phi) \qquad\qquad ...(ii)$

Put $\qquad\qquad F = F_0\, e^{i\omega t}$ in the form

$$F = F_0\,(\cos\omega t + i\sin\omega t)$$

or $\qquad\qquad F = F_0\cos\omega t + i F_0 \sin\omega t \qquad\qquad\qquad ...(iii)$

Comparing the real parts of equations (*ii*) and (*iii*) we have

when $\qquad\qquad F = F_0 \cos\omega t \qquad\qquad\qquad\qquad\qquad ...(iv)$

$$y = \frac{F_0}{\omega Z_m}\sin(\omega t - \phi) \qquad\qquad\qquad ...(v)$$

Similarly comparing the imaginary parts of equations (*ii*) and (*iii*), we have

when $\qquad\qquad F = F_0 \sin\omega t \qquad\qquad\qquad\qquad\qquad ...(vi)$

$$y = \frac{F_0}{\omega Z_m}\cos(\omega t - \phi) \qquad\qquad\qquad ...(vii)$$

The velocity of a forced oscillator is defined as the rate of change of displacement with time. We shall calculate the value of velocity

(*i*) When the driving force is $F_0 \cos\omega t$ and

(*ii*) When the driving force is $F_0 \sin\omega t$.

(*i*) **Driving force $F_0 \cos\omega t$.** When the driving force is given by $F = F_0 \cos\omega t$, the displacement of the forced oscillations in the steady state is given by

$$y = \frac{F_0}{\omega Z_m} \sin(\omega t - \phi)$$

$\therefore$ velocity $v = \dfrac{dy}{dt} = \dfrac{F_0}{\omega Z_m} \omega \cos(\omega t - \phi)$

$$= \frac{F_0}{Z_m} \cos(\omega t - \phi) = v_0 \cos(\omega t - \phi) \qquad \qquad ...(viii)$$

$$= v_0 \sin\left[(\omega t - \phi) + \frac{\pi}{2}\right] \qquad \qquad ...(ix)$$

where $v_0 = F_0/Z_m$

Comparing equation (ix) with (v), we find that velocity always leads the displacement by a phase angle $\dfrac{\pi}{2}$. Comparing equation (viii) with (iv), we find that velocity lags behind the driving force by a phase angle ϕ.

   (ii) Driving force $F_0 \sin \omega t$. When the driving force is $F = F_0 \sin \omega t$, the displacement is given by

$$y = \frac{F_0}{\omega Z_m} \cos(\omega t - \phi)$$

$\therefore$ velocity $v = \dfrac{dy}{dt} = \dfrac{-F_0}{\omega Z_m} (-\omega)\sin(\omega t - \phi)$

$$= \frac{F_0}{Z_m} \sin(\omega t - \phi) = v_0 \sin(\omega t - \phi) \qquad \qquad ...(x)$$

$$= v_0 \cos\left[(\omega t - \phi) + \frac{\pi}{2}\right] \qquad \qquad ...(xi)$$

where $v_0 = \dfrac{F_0}{Z_m}$

Comparing equation (xi) with (vii), we again find that velocity always leads the displacement by a phase angle $\dfrac{\pi}{2}$.

   Comparing equation (x) with (vi) we again find that velocity lags behind the driving force by a phase angle ϕ.

   Variation of velocity amplitude with driving force frequency. We have seen in the above discussion that when the applied force is $F = F_0 \cos \omega t$ the velocity of forced vibrations is $v = v_0 \cos(\omega t - \phi)$ and when the applied force is $F = F_0 \sin \omega t$ the velocity of forced vibrations is $v = v_0 \sin(\omega t - \phi)$ where $v_0 = F_0/Z_m$.

   The amplitude of the velocity in each case

$$v_0 = \frac{F_0}{Z_m} = \frac{F_0}{\sqrt{r^2 + X_m^2}} = \frac{F_0}{\sqrt{r^2 + \left(\omega m - \dfrac{s}{\omega}\right)^2}} \qquad \qquad ...(xii)$$

   We shall discuss the behaviour of velocity amplitude versus driving force frequency in three stages *i.e.*, low frequency, high frequency and resonant frequency.

   (i) Low frequency. According to equation (xii), the mechanical impedance

$$Z_m = \sqrt{r^2 + \left(\omega m - \frac{s}{\omega}\right)^2}$$

$\left(\omega m - \dfrac{s}{\omega}\right) = X_m$ is known as mechanical reactance. It consists two parts ωm and $\dfrac{s}{\omega}$. For *low*

frequencies $\dfrac{s}{\omega}$ is a large quantity. In such a case the impedance Z_m depends upon s and is said to be *stiffness controlled*.

When $\qquad\qquad \omega \to 0, \; m\omega \to 0 \text{ and } \dfrac{s}{\omega} \to \infty$

$$\therefore \qquad Z_m = \left(r^2 + \frac{s^2}{\omega^2}\right)^{\frac{1}{2}} = \frac{s}{\omega}$$

As $\dfrac{s}{\omega}$ is a very large quantity and r^2 can be neglected as compared to $\dfrac{s^2}{\omega^2}$.

$$\therefore \qquad v_0 = \frac{F_0}{Z_m} = \frac{F_0}{s/\omega} = F_0 \frac{\omega}{s}$$

when $\qquad\qquad \omega \to 0, \; v_0 \to 0$

(*ii*) **High frequency.** At high frequencies ωm is a large quantity. In such a case the impedance Z_m depends upon m and is said to be *mass controlled* or *inertia* controlled.

When $\qquad \omega \to \infty, \; m\omega \to \infty \text{ but } \dfrac{s}{\omega} \to 0$

$$\therefore \qquad Z_m = \left[r^2 + \left(m\omega - \frac{s}{\omega}\right)^2\right]^{1/2} = \left[r^2 + m^2\omega^2\right]^{1/2} = m\omega$$

[because $(m\omega)$ is very large, r^2 can be neglected as compared to $m^2\omega^2$.]

$$\therefore \qquad v_0 = \frac{F_0}{Z_m} = \frac{F_0}{m\omega}$$

when $\qquad\qquad \omega \to \infty, \; v_0 \to 0$

(*iii*) **Resonant frequency.** For a frequency ω_0 at which $\omega_0 m = \dfrac{s}{\omega_0}$ the reactance

$X_m = \omega_0 m - \dfrac{s}{\omega_0} = 0, Z_m$ has its minimum value given by $Z_m = r$. It is a real quantity with zero

reactance. At this frequency the velocity amplitude has its maximum value $v_0 = \dfrac{F_0}{Z_m} = \dfrac{F_0}{r}$. This

frequency ω_0 is known as the *frequency of velocity resonance*.

Thus at frequency of velocity resonance, the velocity amplitude depends upon the driving force F_0 and r the resisting force per unit velocity but is independent of frequency.

Velocity resonance occurs at natural frequency of the oscillator. For velocity resonance

$\omega = \omega_0 = \sqrt{\dfrac{s}{m}}$ = natural frequency of the oscillator. This can be proved as follows.

$\because \qquad v_0 = \dfrac{F_0}{Z_m}, v_0$ has maximum value when Z_m is a minimum. Now Z_m is minimum for a frequency

given by $\dfrac{dZ_m}{d\omega} = 0$.

As
$$Z_m = \left[r^2 + \left(\omega m - \frac{s}{\omega} \right)^2 \right]^{\frac{1}{2}}$$

$$\frac{dZ_m}{d\omega} = \frac{1}{2} \left[r^2 + \left(\omega m - \frac{s}{\omega} \right)^2 \right]^{-\frac{1}{2}} 2 \left(\omega m - \frac{s}{\omega} \right) \left(m + \frac{s}{\omega^2} \right) = 0$$

$$\therefore \qquad \left(\omega m - \frac{s}{\omega} \right) \left(m + \frac{s}{\omega^2} \right) = \frac{1}{\omega} \left(\omega m - \frac{s}{\omega} \right) \left(\omega m + \frac{s}{\omega} \right) = 0$$

or
$$\omega^2 m^2 - \frac{s^2}{\omega^2} = 0$$

$$\therefore \qquad \omega^4 = \frac{s^2}{m^2}$$

or
$$\omega = \sqrt{\frac{s}{m}} = \omega_0$$

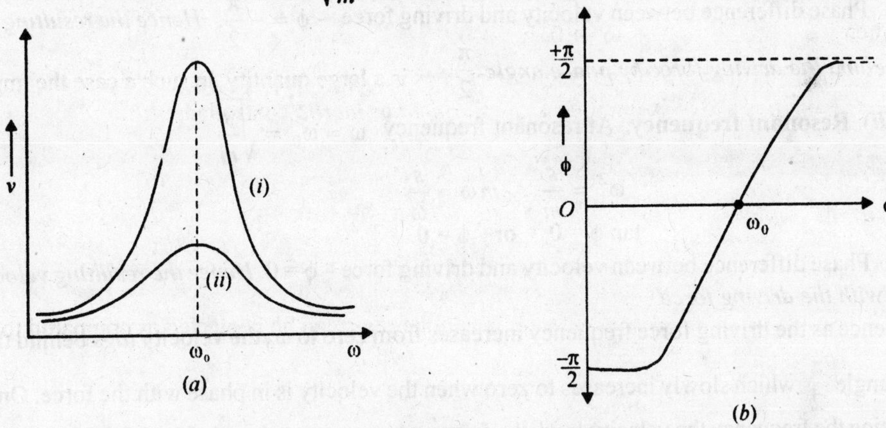

Fig. 3.7

The variation of magnitude of velocity with frequency of the driving force is shown in Fig. 3.7 (a).

At resonance $v_0 = \dfrac{F_0}{r}$. The height and sharpness of the peak at resonance depends upon r. For small value of r, the velocity at resonance is very large, curve (i) and for large values of r the velocity has a smaller value, curve (ii).

(b) Variation of phase difference between velocity and driving force frequency. The velocity for a forced oscillator is given by

$$v = \frac{F_0}{Z_m} \cos(\omega t - \phi)$$

When the driving force is given by
$$F = F_0 \cos \omega t$$

Thus the phase difference between velocity and driving force is $- \phi$ *i.e.*, the velocity *lags behind* the driving force by an angle ϕ given by

$$\tan \phi = \frac{\omega m - \dfrac{s}{\omega}}{r}$$

(*i*) **Low frequency.** At low frequencies $\omega \to 0$

$$m\omega \to 0 \text{ and } \frac{s}{\omega} \to \infty$$

$\therefore$

$$\tan \phi = -\infty$$

or

$$\phi = -\frac{\pi}{2}$$

$\therefore$ Phase difference between velocity and driving force $-\phi = +\frac{\pi}{2}$. *Hence the resulting velocity leads the driving force by phase angle* $\frac{\pi}{2}$.

(*ii*) **High frequency.** At high frequencies $\omega \to \infty$

$\therefore$

$$m\omega \to \infty \text{ and } \frac{s}{\omega} \to 0$$

$\therefore$

$$\tan \phi = +\infty$$

or

$$\phi = +\frac{\pi}{2}$$

$\therefore$ Phase difference between velocity and driving force $-\phi = -\frac{\pi}{2}$. *Hence the resulting velocity lags behind the driving force by phase angle* $\frac{\pi}{2}$.

(*iii*) **Resonant frequency.** At resonant frequency $\omega = \omega_0 = \sqrt{\dfrac{s}{m}}$

or

$$\omega^2 = \frac{s}{m} \quad \therefore \quad m\omega = \frac{s}{\omega}$$

$\therefore$

$$\tan \phi = 0 \quad \text{or} \quad \phi = 0.$$

$\therefore$ Phase difference between velocity and driving force $-\phi = 0$. *Hence the resulting velocity is in phase with the driving force.*

Hence as the driving force frequency increases from zero to ω_0 the velocity *lags* behind the force by an angle $\frac{\pi}{2}$ which slowly increases to zero when the velocity is in phase with the force. On further increasing the frequency the velocity *leads* the force and as ω approaches ∞ the angle of lead approaches $\frac{\pi}{2}$. This is shown in Fig. 3.7 (*b*).

Q. 3.12. Why is there large amplitude, when frequency of external periodic force is same as natural frequency of the body?   (*P.U.*, 1991)

Ans. When the frequency of external periodic force is equal to the natural frequency of the body the external periodic force helps to increase the amplitude of vibration of the body at each step as the external applied force is always in phase with the vibrations of the body. Every new impulse adds to the effect of all the previous impulses as the successive impulses always arrive in phase and the accumulated effect is to make the body vibrate with a large amplitude.

Q. 3.13. (*a*) Draw a graph between velocity amplitude and driving force frequency of a forced oscillator.   (*H.P.U.*, 2001)

(*b*) **Show that whereas at resonance displacement lags behind the driving force by $\pi/2$, the velocity is in phase with driving force.**   (*G.N.D.U.*, 2002)

Ans. (*a*) **Graph between velocity amplitude and driving force frequency.** For a forced oscillator of natural frequency ω_0, when a driving force of frequency ω acts on it, the velocity amplitude v is given by

$$v = \frac{F_0}{\sqrt{r^2 + \left(\omega m - \dfrac{s}{\omega}\right)^2}}$$

For *large values* of ω, $\dfrac{s}{\omega} \to 0$ and ωm has a large values so that r^2 can be neglected as compared to ωm and

$$v = \frac{F_0}{\omega m}$$

For frequency ω_0 at resonance $\omega m = \dfrac{s}{\omega}$ or $\omega m - \dfrac{s}{\omega} = 0$

$$\therefore \qquad v = \frac{F_0}{r}$$

For *small values* of ω, $\dfrac{s}{\omega}$ is very large and ωm as well as r^2 can be neglected as compared to s/ω and

$$v = \frac{F_0 \omega}{s}$$

The variation of velocity amplitude with ω the driving force frequency is shown in **Fig. 3.7 (a)**, **Q. 3.11**.

(b) Phase difference at displacement resonance and velocity resonance. When a periodic force

$$F = F_0 \cos \omega t \qquad \qquad \qquad ...(i)$$

is applied to a damped oscillator and a steady state is reached the displacement is given by

$$y = \frac{F_0}{\omega Z_m} \sin (\omega t - \phi) \qquad \qquad ...(ii)$$

where $Z_m = \sqrt{r^2 + \left(\omega m - \dfrac{s}{\omega}\right)^2}$, r is the *damping constant*, m the *mass* and s the *stiffness* or *spring constant*.

The phase difference between the driving force and displacement of forced oscillator is given by

$$\tan \phi = \frac{\omega m - s/\omega}{r}$$

Equation (*ii*) can be put in the form

$$y = \frac{F_0}{\omega Z_m} \cos \left[\omega t - (\phi + \pi/2)\right] \qquad \qquad ...(iii)$$

Comparing Eqs. (*i*) and (*iii*) we find that displacement lags behind the driving force by an angle $\phi + \pi/2$.

At displacement resonance $\omega m = s/\omega$ or $\omega m - s/\omega = 0$

$$\therefore \qquad \tan \phi = 0 \qquad \text{or} \qquad \phi = 0$$

$\therefore$ *At resonance displacement lags behind the driving force by an angle* $\pi/2$.

For the same periodic force $F = F_0 \cos \omega t$ the velocity of the forced oscillator is given by

$$v = \frac{F_0}{Z_m} \cos (\omega t - \phi)$$

and phase difference $\qquad \tan\phi = \dfrac{\omega m - s/\omega}{r}$

At velocity resonance again $\;\omega m = s/\omega\;$ or $\;\omega m - s/\omega = 0$

$\therefore \qquad\qquad\qquad\qquad \tan\phi = 0 \quad$ or $\quad \phi = 0.$

$\therefore$ *At resonance, velocity is in phase with the driving force.*

Q. 3.14. Show that the displacement resonance occurs at a frequency slightly less than the frequency of velocity resonance. *(P.U., 2007, 2006, 2002; H.P.U., 2001)*

Ans. The velocity resonance occurs at a frequency

$$\omega = \omega_0$$

where ω_0 is the frequency of free oscillations of the forced oscillator.

The displacement resonance takes place at a frequency

$$\omega' = \omega_0\sqrt{1 - \dfrac{r^2}{2m^2\omega_0^2}}$$

since r, m and ω_0 are all positive quantities (being squares) the displacement resonance occurs at a frequency ω' slightly less than ω the frequency of velocity resonance.

Q. 3.15. (a) Discuss the variation of acceleration amplitude with driving force frequency of a forced mechanical oscillator and show that

(i) Acceleration amplitude at high frequency is frequency independent and

(ii) When damping constant is very small the acceleration amplitude at resonance frequency equals the natural frequency of the forced oscillator. *(Pbi. U. 2008; P.U., 2003; G.N.D.U., 2008, 2003)*

(b) Prove that if $r = \sqrt{sm}$ then acceleration amplitude at frequency of velocity resonance is equal to limit of acceleration amplitude at high frequency, where s is stiffness, m the mass of mechanical oscillator and r the force per unit velocity. *(G.N.D.U. 2008; Pbi. U. 2005)*

Ans. Variation of acceleration amplitude with driving force frequency. When the driving force is given by

$$F = F_0 \cos\omega t$$

the displacement of the forced oscillations in the steady state is given by

$$y = \dfrac{F_0}{\omega Z_m}\sin(\omega t - \phi)$$

and velocity $\qquad v = \dot{y} = \dfrac{dy}{dt} = \dfrac{F_0}{Z_m}\cos(\omega t - \phi)$

$\therefore$ acceleration $\qquad \ddot{y} = \dfrac{d^2 y}{dt^2} = -\dfrac{F_0\,\omega}{Z_m}\sin(\omega t - \phi)$

where $\qquad\qquad Z_m = \sqrt{r^2 + \left(\omega m - \dfrac{s}{\omega}\right)^2}$

$\therefore$ Acceleration amplitude $= \dfrac{F_0\,\omega}{\left[r^2 + \left(\omega m - \dfrac{s}{\omega}\right)^2\right]^{1/2}}$

$$= \frac{F_0}{\left[\dfrac{r^2}{\omega^2} + \left(m - \dfrac{s}{\omega^2}\right)^2\right]^{1/2}}$$

Now three cases arise :

(*i*) *At low frequency.* At low frequency $\omega \to 0$, therefore the term s/ω^2 dominates provided r is

small. In such a case the oscillator is said to be *stiffness controlled.* When r is small and $\omega \to 0$, $Z_m = \dfrac{s}{\omega}$

and hence acceleration amplitude $= \dfrac{F_0\,\omega}{s/\omega} = \dfrac{F_0\,\omega^2}{s}$. But $\omega \to 0$

Hence acceleration amplitude is zero.

(*ii*) *At high frequency.* For large values of ω, $\dfrac{s}{\omega}$ can be neglected as compared to $\omega\,m$ and r^2 as

compared to $\omega^2\,m^2$ so that we get $Z_m = \omega\,m$. In such a case the oscillator is said to be *inertia controlled.*

$\therefore$ For large frequencies acceleration amplitude

$$= \frac{F_0\,\omega}{Z_m} = \frac{F_0\,\omega}{\omega\,m} = \frac{F_0}{m}$$

i.e., the acceleration amplitude depends upon the driving force F_0 and mass m but is independent of frequency.

(*iii*) **Maximum value of acceleration amplitude.** The acceleration amplitude becomes maximum

when $\dfrac{\omega}{Z_m}$ is minimum or $\dfrac{Z_m}{\omega}$ is a maximum *i.e.*

$$\frac{d}{d\omega}\left(Z_m\,\omega^{-1}\right) = \frac{d}{d\omega}\left\{\omega^{-1}\left[r^2 + \left(\omega m - \frac{s}{\omega}\right)^2\right]^{1/2}\right\}$$

$$= \frac{d}{d\omega}\left[r^2/\omega^2 + \left(m - \frac{s}{\omega^2}\right)^2\right]^{1/2}$$

$$= \frac{1}{2}\left[r^2/\omega^2 + \left(m - \frac{s}{\omega^2}\right)^2\right]^{-1/2}\left[\left(-2\frac{r^2}{\omega^3}\right) + 2\left(m - \frac{s}{\omega^2}\right)\left(\frac{2s}{\omega^3}\right)\right]$$

$$= \frac{-\dfrac{r^2}{\omega^3} + \dfrac{2\,sm}{\omega^3} - \dfrac{2s^2}{\omega^5}}{\left[r^2/\omega^2 + \left(m - \dfrac{s}{\omega^2}\right)^2\right]^{1/2}} = 0$$

or $$-\frac{r^2}{\omega^3} + \frac{2\,sm}{\omega^3} - \frac{2s^2}{\omega^5} = 0$$

or $$-r^2 + 2\,sm - \frac{2s^2}{\omega^2} = 0$$

or $$2\,sm - r^2 = \frac{2s^2}{\omega^2}$$

or
$$\omega^2 = \frac{2s^2}{2sm - r^2}$$

or
$$\omega = \sqrt{\frac{2s^2}{2sm - r^2}}$$

Thus the acceleration amplitude is maximum when

$$\omega = \sqrt{\frac{2s^2}{2sm - r^2}}$$

ω is, therefore called the *frequency of maximum acceleration amplitude.*
Taking this value of ω as ω', we have

Maximum acceleration amplitude $= \dfrac{F_0\,\omega'}{\left[r^2 + \left(\omega'm - \dfrac{s}{\omega'} \right)^2 \right]^{1/2}}$

(*i*) Maximum acceleration amplitude at high frequency

The acceleration amplitude $= \dfrac{F_0\,\omega}{Z_m}$ where

$$Z_m = \sqrt{r^2 + \left(\omega m - \frac{s}{\omega} \right)^2}$$

For large value of $\omega, \dfrac{s}{\omega}$ can be neglected as compared to $\omega\,m$, r^2 as compared to $\omega^2\,m^2$ and we
get $Z_m = \omega\,m$.

$\therefore$ For large frequencies maximum acceleration amplitude

$$= \frac{F_0\,\omega}{Z_m} = \frac{F_0\,m}{\omega\,m} = \frac{F_0}{m}$$

i.e., the maximum acceleration amplitude depends upon the driving force and the mass m but is

independent of frequency. Thus $\dfrac{F_0}{m}$ *gives the limit of acceleration amplitude at high frequency.*

(*ii*) When damping constant is very small

The acceleration amplitude resonance frequency is given by

$$\omega' = \sqrt{\frac{2s^2}{2sm - r^2}}$$

When damping constant r is very small, r^2 can be neglected as compared to $2\,sm$ and we get

$$\omega' = \sqrt{\frac{2s^2}{2sm}} = \sqrt{\frac{s}{m}} = \text{natural frequency of forced oscillator.}$$

*Hence when damping constant is very small the acceleration amplitude at resonance frequency
equals the natural frequency of the forced oscillator.*

(*b*) At velocity resonance $\omega m - \dfrac{s}{\omega} = 0$

or
$$\omega \left(m - \frac{s}{\omega^2} \right) = 0$$

The acceleration amplitude $= \dfrac{F_0}{\left[\dfrac{r^2}{\omega^2} + \left(m - \dfrac{s}{\omega^2}\right)^2\right]^{1/2}}$.

Substituting $\left(m - \dfrac{s}{\omega^2}\right) = 0$, we get

Acceleration amplitude $= \dfrac{F_0}{r/\omega}$

Again at velocity resonance $\omega m = \dfrac{s}{\omega}$ or $\omega^2 = \dfrac{s}{m}$ or $\omega = \sqrt{\dfrac{s}{m}}$

Also $\qquad\qquad r = \sqrt{sm}$ (given) $\qquad \therefore \quad \dfrac{r}{\omega} = \dfrac{\sqrt{sm}}{\sqrt{\dfrac{s}{m}}} = m$

Hence acceleration amplitude $\dfrac{F_0}{r/\omega} = \dfrac{F_0}{m}$

But $\dfrac{F_0}{m}$ gives the limit of acceleration amplitude at high frequency. Therefore, we conclude that

if $r = \sqrt{sm}$ the acceleration amplitude at the frequency of velocity resonance is equal to the limit of acceleration amplitude at high frequency.

Exercise. *Write the expression for frequency at resonance for displacement, velocity and acceleration.* (*Pbi. U.* 2005)

Hint. The frequency at resonance

(*i*) *For displacement* $= \omega' = \sqrt{\omega_0^2 - 2k^2}$

where $\qquad\qquad \omega_0 = \sqrt{\dfrac{s}{m}} \qquad$ and $\qquad 2k = \dfrac{r}{m}$

ω_0 is the *natural frequency* of the forced oscillator
s is the *stiffness constant* (or spring constant)
m is the *mass* of the vibrating particle

(*ii*) *For velocity* $= \omega = \sqrt{\dfrac{s}{m}} = \omega_0$ the natural frequency of the forced oscillator

(*iii*) *For acceleration* $= \omega = \sqrt{\dfrac{2s^2}{2sm - r^2}} \qquad$ where $r =$ damping constant

When damping constant r is very small r^2 can be neglected as compared to $2sm$ and we get

$\omega = \sqrt{\dfrac{s}{m}} =$ natural frequency of forced oscillator.

Q. 3.16. What is sharpness of resonance? What factors govern sharpness of resonance ? Explain the effect of damping on sharpness of resonance. (*Meerut U.*, 2007, 2003, 2001; *Nagpur U.*, 2003, 2002; *G.N.D.U.*, 2006, 2003; *P.U.*, 2007, 1995; *Pbi. U.* 2005; *Luck.U.*, 2002, 1992; *K.U.*, 1991)

Ans. Sharpness of resonance. The displacement amplitude of a forced oscillator is given by

$$a = \dfrac{f_0}{\sqrt{4k^2\omega^2 - (\omega^2 - \omega_0^2)^2}}$$

At resonance the frequency of the applied force is equal to the frequency of the oscillator i.e.

$$\omega = \omega_0 \quad \text{or} \quad (\omega^2 - \omega_0^2) = 0$$

∴ Amplitude of forced vibration at resonance $= \dfrac{f_0}{2k\omega}$ where f_0 is the applied force per unit

mass, $\dfrac{\omega}{2\pi}$ the frequency of the applied force and k the damping coefficient.

As the frequency of the applied force ω is increased or decreased from its resonant value ω_0 the value of the amplitude always decreases.

When the amplitude at resonance falls rapidly as the frequency ω of the applied force is changed slightly from its resonant value the resonance is said to be *sharp*.

When the amplitude at resonance falls gradually as the frequency ω of the applied force is changed slightly from its resonant value the resonance is said to be flat.

The sharpness of resonance depends upon damping.

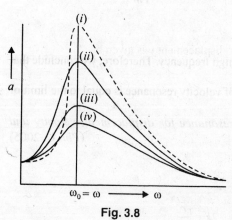

Fig. 3.8

Effect of damping on sharpness of resonance.

(*i*) When $k = 0$ *i.e.*, there is no damping, the amplitude at resonance becomes infinite as shown in Fig. 3.8. (*i*).

(*ii*) When damping is small the amplitude is sufficiently large but falls off rapidly as the frequency of the applied force becomes slightly different from the natural frequency of the body.

(*iii*) As the value of k increases the amplitude at resonance decreases but the curves in Fig. 3.6 (*iii*) and (*iv*) fall of gradually and even when the frequency of the applied force is a little different from the natural frequency of the body the amplitude is nearly the same. *In other words, when damping is small resonance is sharp and when damping is large resonance is flat.*

Q. 3.17. Why should two tuning forks be very accurately in unison to show resonance while a tuning fork and an air column require to be only approximately tuned? (*K.U.*, 1991)

Ans. The amplitude of the forced oscillator at resonance becomes very large. This is because resonance is due to the accumulated effect of a number of successive impulses. Each impulse imparts energy to the forced oscillator at the proper time in the right direction *i.e.*, the forced oscillator and the applied force *are in phase*. This happens when there is almost zero damping.

If the damping is large as *in the case of an air column* the natural vibrations die out quickly and by the time the effect of, say, the 10th impulse is coming that of the first almost disappears. It means there is no chance for the impulse to go out of phase and decrease the amplitude. For maximum amplitude in such a case the impressed force should be in phase for 10 vibrations only and slight amount of mistuning will have no effect.

If the damping is small *as in the case of tuning fork* the natural vibrations die out very slowly and when the 10th impulse comes the effect of the first still persists. The impulses will get out of phase and destroy each other's effect even if there is a small difference in frequency. The tuning, therefore, should be sharp so that the impressed force and the natural vibrations remain practically in phase.

Q. 3.18. (a) Derive an expression for the average power supplied to a forced oscillator in the steady state by an external driving force

$$F = F_0 \cos \omega t.$$

(*Pbi. U.* 2008, 2006, 2005; *P.U.*, 2000, 1991; *H.P.U.*, 1994)

(b) Derive an expression for the average power supplied to an electrical oscillator.

(G.N.D.U. 2007)

Ans. (a) Power supplied by driving force. When an oscillator is set into forced vibrations by an external driving force some energy is dissipated in every cycle due to damping resistance r. To maintain the steady state of the forced oscillator this energy loss has to be supplied by the driving force.

When a damped simple harmonic mechanical oscillator is acted upon by an external periodic driving force $F = F_0 \cos \omega t$, the velocity of the forced oscillator is given by

$$\frac{dy}{dt} = v = \frac{F_0}{Z_m} \cos(\omega t - \phi)$$

where

$$Z_m = \sqrt{r^2 + \left(\omega m - \frac{s}{\omega}\right)^2}$$

and

$$\tan \phi = \frac{\left(\omega m - \frac{s}{\omega}\right)}{r}$$

The work done by the driving force F in producing a displacement y is given by

$$W = Fy$$

∴ The instantaneous power supplied to the oscillator

$$P = \frac{dW}{dt} = F\frac{dy}{dt} = Fv$$

$$= \text{Instantaneous force} \times \text{instantaneous velocity}$$

$$= F_0 \cos \omega t \times \frac{F_0}{Z_m} \cos(\omega t - \phi)$$

∴ Work done in a time $dt = \dfrac{F_0^2}{Z_m} \cos \omega t \cos(\omega t - \phi)\, dt$

or Work done in a time T where T is the time period of the oscillator

$$= \frac{F_0^2}{Z_m} \int_0^T \cos \omega t \cos(\omega t - \phi)\, dt$$

∴ Average power over one complete cycle

$$P_{(av)} = \frac{F_0^2}{Z_m T} \int_0^T [\cos \omega t \cos(\omega t - \phi)\, dt$$

$$= \frac{F_0^2}{Z_m T} \int_0^T [\cos^2 \omega t \cos \phi + \cos \omega t \sin \omega t \sin \phi]\, dt$$

$$= \frac{F_0^2}{Z_m T}\left[\cos \phi \int_0^T \cos^2 \omega t\, dt + \sin \phi \int_0^T \cos \omega t \sin \omega t\, dt\right]$$

$$= \frac{F_0^2}{2 Z_m} \cos \phi$$

$$\because \quad \frac{1}{T}\int_0^T \cos^2 \omega t\, dt = \frac{1}{T}\int_0^T \frac{\cos 2\omega t + 1}{2}\, dt$$

$$= \frac{1}{T}\int_0^T \frac{\cos 2\omega t}{2}\, dt + \frac{1}{T}\int_0^T \frac{1}{2}\, dt = \frac{1}{2}$$

because
$$\left[\int_0^T \frac{\cos 2\omega t}{2}\, dt = 0\right]$$

and
$$\int_0^T (\cos \omega t \sin \omega t)\, dt = \int_0^T \frac{\cos 2\omega t}{2} = 0$$

$$\therefore \quad \sin \phi \int_0^T \cos \omega t \sin \omega t\ dt = 0$$

∴ Average power supplied by the driving force to the oscillator

$$P_{(av)} = \frac{F_0^2}{2 Z_m} \cos \phi$$

In the above expression $\cos \phi$ is known as *'power factor'*.

(b) **Power supplied to an electrical oscillator.** Let $E = E_0 \cos \omega t$ be the external voltage (or driving force) applied to a damped electrical oscillator circuit consisting of a resistance R, an inductance L and a capacitance C in series. Then,

Current in the circuit
$$I = \frac{dQ}{dt} = \frac{E}{Z_e} = \frac{E_0}{Ze} \cos(\omega t - \phi)$$

where
$$Z_e = \sqrt{R^2 + \left(L\omega - \frac{1}{C\omega}\right)^2}$$

and
$$\tan \phi = \frac{L\omega - \dfrac{1}{C\omega}}{R} \qquad \text{[For proof See Q. 3.34]}$$

Then, proceeding as in part (a), we get
Instantaneous power supplied to the oscillator

$$P = EI = E_0 \cos \omega t\ \frac{E_0}{Z_e} \cos (\omega t - \phi)$$

which gives,
Average power over one complete cycle

$$P_{(av)} = \frac{E_0^2}{Z_e T} \int_0^T \cos \omega t \cos (\omega t - \phi)\, dt$$

and finally
$$P_{(av)} = \frac{E_0^2}{2 Z_e} \cos \phi$$

Q. 3.19. (a) **Show graphically the variation of average power of a forced oscillator with driving force frequency.** (P.U., 2007, 2000, 1995, 1994)

(b) **Show that the average power absorbed by the oscillator is given by** $\frac{1}{2} r v_0^2$ **where** v_0 **is the velocity amplitude attained by a driven oscillator.** (Pbi. U. 2008)

Ans. *(a)* **Graphical representation of average power of forced oscillator with driving force frequency.** The average power supplied to the forced oscillator is given by

$$P_{(av)} = \frac{F_0^2}{2 Z_m} \cos \phi$$

where $\quad Z_m = \sqrt{r^2 + \left(\omega m - \dfrac{s}{\omega} \right)^2} \quad$ and $\quad \cos \phi = \dfrac{r}{Z_m} = \dfrac{r}{\sqrt{r^2 + \left(\omega m - \dfrac{s}{\omega} \right)^2}}$

when $\quad \cos \phi = 1 \ $ *i.e.,* when $\left(\omega m - \dfrac{s}{\omega} \right) = 0, \ \omega^2 = \dfrac{s}{m} = \omega_0^2$

which is the case of resonance, the average power $P_{(av)}$ is maximum. The average power $P_{(av)}$ depends upon Z_m and in turn on frequency ω. We shall consider the variation of $P_{(av)}$ with ω in three different cases.

1. At low frequency. At low frequency $\omega \to 0$

$$\therefore \qquad m\omega \to 0, \frac{s}{\omega} \to \infty$$

$\therefore$ Z_m tends to be very large and hence the average power $P_{(av)}$ is small.

For $\qquad \omega = 0, \ Z_m = \infty$ and $P_{(av)} = 0$

2. At high frequency. At high frequency $\omega \to \infty$

$$\therefore \qquad m\omega \to \infty, \frac{s}{\omega} \to 0$$

$\therefore$ Z_m again tends to be very large and hence the average power $P_{(av)}$ is small.

3. At resonant frequency. At resonant frequency $\omega = \omega_0$

$$\therefore \qquad Z_m = r \ \text{ and } \ \cos \phi = \frac{r}{Z_m} = \frac{r}{r} = 1$$

Thus the average power at resonant frequency is maximum and given by

$$P_{(av)} = \frac{F_0^2}{2 Z_m} = \frac{F_0^2}{2r}$$

The variation of $P_{(av)}$ with driving force frequency is shown in Fig. 3.9. At $\omega = 0$, $P_{(av)} = 0$ and when ω is very large $P_{(av)}$ again tends to zero. The peak occurs at $\omega = \omega_0$. At this frequency, the power supplied to the forced oscillator by the driving force is maximum and equal to $\dfrac{F_0^2}{2r}$. Thus height of the peak and sharpness of its peak at resonance is determined by the damping constant r. The variation of $P_{(av)}$ with ω determines the response of the oscillator to the driving force.

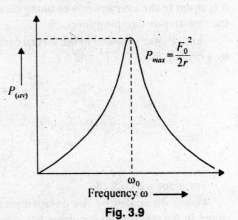

Fig. 3.9

$P_{max} = \dfrac{F_0^2}{2r}$

The graph between $P_{(av)}$ and ω is known as *absorption curve of the oscillator.*

(b) The average power at velocity resonant frequency

$$P_{(av)} = \frac{F_0^2}{2 Z_m} = \frac{Z_m}{2} \cdot \frac{F_0^2}{Z_m^2}$$

But $\dfrac{F_0}{Z_m} = v_0$ the velocity amplitude attained by a driven oscillator.

[For proof see Eq. (*ix*) Q. 3.11]

$$\therefore \qquad P_{(av)} = \frac{Z_m}{2} v_0^2$$

But $Z_m = r$ at resonant frequency [See No. 3 in part (*a*)]

$$\therefore \qquad P_{(av)} = \frac{1}{2} r v_0^2$$

This gives the average power absorbed by the oscillator.

Q. 3.20. (*a*) **When is the power supplied to an oscillator by the driving force maximum?**

(*H.P.U.*, 1993)

OR

What is the average power delivered by driving force at resonance ?   (*P.U.* 2008)

Ans. The power supplied to an oscillator by the driving force is maximum at resonant frequency *i.e.*, when the frequency of the driving force ω is equal to the natural frequency of oscillation ω_0 of the

oscillator. The average power supplied to the oscillator $P_{av} = \dfrac{F_0^2}{2Z_m} \cos\phi$

where $\qquad Z_m = \sqrt{r^2 + \left(\omega m - \dfrac{s}{\omega}\right)^2}$ and $\cos\phi = \dfrac{r}{\sqrt{r^2 + \left(\omega m - \dfrac{s}{\omega}\right)^2}}$

when $\qquad\qquad \omega^2 = \omega_0^2 = \dfrac{s}{m}, \left(\omega m - \dfrac{s}{\omega}\right) = 0$ and $\cos\phi = 1$,

the average power is maximum and given by $\dfrac{F_0^2}{2Z_m} = \dfrac{F_0^2}{2r}$. This gives the average power delivered by driving force at resonance.

Q. 3.21. Derive an expression for the power supplied to the forced oscillator and show that it is equal to the average power being dissipated. or the average work done per second against the resistive or damping force.   (*P.U.*, 2003, 2000, 1996, 1994; *Pbi.U.*, 2006, 2002)

Ans. Power supplied to the forced oscillator. The average power supplied to a forced oscillator by a driving force $F = F_0 \cos\omega t$

$$P_{(av)} = \frac{F_0^2}{2Z_m} \cos\phi \qquad\qquad\qquad ...(i)$$

where $\qquad Z_m = \sqrt{r^2 + \left(\omega m - \dfrac{s}{\omega}\right)^2}$ and $\cos\phi = \dfrac{r}{Z_m} = \dfrac{r}{\sqrt{r^2 + \left(\omega m - \dfrac{s}{\omega}\right)^2}}$

For proof see **Q. 3.18.**

Power dissipated by the damped oscillator. The power supplied by the driving force is not stored in the mechanical oscillator but is used up in doing work against the dissipative frictional resisting forces. If r is the frictional force per unit velocity, then total frictional force $= rv = r\dfrac{dy}{dt}$.

The rate of working by the oscillator against the frictional force

$$= \text{frictional force} \times \text{instantaneous velocity}$$

$$= \left(r\frac{dy}{dt}\right)\frac{dy}{dt} = r\left(\frac{dy}{dt}\right)^2 = rv^2$$

$$= r\frac{F_0^2}{Z_m^2}\cos^2(\omega t - \phi)$$

as $\qquad v = \dfrac{F_0}{Z_m}\cos(\omega t - \phi)$ when driving force is $F = F_0 \cos \omega t$.

The average value of $\cos^2(\omega t - \phi)$ over one period is given by

$$\frac{1}{T}\int_0^T \cos^2(\omega t - \phi)\,dt = \frac{1}{T}\int_0^T \frac{[1 - \cos 2(\omega t - \phi)]}{2}\,dt$$

$$= \frac{1}{T}\left[\frac{1}{2}\int_0^T dt - \frac{1}{2}\int_0^T \cos 2(\omega t - \phi)\right] = \frac{1}{2}$$

$\therefore$ Average loss of power $= \dfrac{1}{2}\dfrac{F_0^2}{Z_m^2}r$ ...(ii)

But $\qquad\qquad \cos\phi = \dfrac{r}{Z_m}$

Substituting in (ii), we have

Average loss of power $\qquad = \dfrac{1}{2}\dfrac{F_0^2}{Z_m}\cos\phi$ ...(iii)

Comparing (i) and (iii), we have

'*Average power supplied by the driving force to the oscillator is equal to the average power dissipated against the frictional force or the average work done per second against the resistive or damping force*'.

Note. The students are well advised to compare the above result with the power in an alternating current circuit which is given by $VI \cos \phi$ where V and I are the r.m.s. values of voltage and current respectively and $\cos \phi$ is the power factor.

As $\qquad\qquad I = \dfrac{V}{Z_e}$, we have $\quad VI \cos\phi = \dfrac{V^2}{Z_e}\cos\phi$

Moreover $\qquad\qquad V_{r.m.s.} = \dfrac{V_0}{\sqrt{2}}$

$\therefore \qquad\qquad \dfrac{V^2}{Z_e}\cos\phi = \dfrac{V_0^2}{2Z_e}\cos\phi$

Thus applied e.m.f. in the electric circuit corresponds to the applied driving force and electric impedance Z_e to the mechanical impedance Z_m.

Q. 3.22. Show that in the steady state the amplitude and phase of a driven oscillator adjust themselves so that average power supplied by the driving force just equals that being dissipated by the frictional force. (*P.U.*, 2001; *G.N.D.U.*, 1995)

Ans. Steady state. When a damped simple harmonic oscillator is acted upon by an external driving force $F = F_0 \cos \omega t$, then in the steady state

The average power supplied to the oscillator

$$P_{(av)} = \frac{F_0^2}{2 Z_m} \cos\phi \qquad\qquad \text{[For proof see Q. 3.18]} \qquad ...(i)$$

where $\dfrac{F_0}{Z_m}$ is the velocity amplitude and ϕ the phase.

The average power dissipated by the oscillator

$$P_{(av)} = \frac{F_0^2}{2 Z_m} \cos\phi \qquad\qquad \text{[For proof see Q. 3.21]} \qquad ...(ii)$$

which has the same velocity amplitude and phase.

We find from relation (i) and (ii)

"*In a steady state the amplitude and phase of the driven oscillator adjust themselves so that the average power supplied by the driving force just equals that being dissipated by the frictional force.*"

Q. 3.23. **Show that power dissipated per cycle by the frictional force $r\,\dot{y}$ is given by**

$\pi r \omega\, y_{max}^2$ **where** $y_{max} = \dfrac{F_0}{\omega (Z_m)_{min}}$.   *(G.N.D.U., 1991)*

Ans. Average loss of power $= \dfrac{F_0^2}{2 Z_m} \cos\phi$ but $\cos\phi = \dfrac{r}{Z_m}$

$\therefore$ Average loss of power $= \dfrac{F_0^2}{2 Z_m^2} r$

Loss of power in one complete cycle

$$= \frac{1}{2}\frac{F_0^2}{Z_m^2} r\, T = \frac{1}{2}\frac{F_0^2}{Z_m^2} r\, \frac{2\pi}{\omega}$$

$$= \pi r \omega \left(\frac{F_0}{\omega Z_m}\right)^2$$

But $y_0 = \dfrac{F_0}{\omega Z_m}$

$\therefore$ $y_{0(max)} = \dfrac{F_0}{(\omega Z_m)_{min}}$

$\therefore$ Loss of power in one complete cycle $= \pi r \omega\, y_0^2$ (max).

Exercise. *Show that the total energy dissipated over one cycle in a forced oscillator is proportional to square of the amplitude.*

                                                  (P.U. 2006)

Hint. The total energy dissipated over one complete cycle in a forced oscillator is equal to the total loss of power in one complete cycle which is equal to $\pi r \omega y_0^2$(max). As y_0(max) represents the amplitude the total energy dissipated per cycle is also proportional to the square of the amplitude.

Q. 3.24. Is the energy stored in a forced oscillator? Explain and justify.

                        (P.U., 2006, 2003; Pbi. U., 2001, 2000, 1993)

Ans. No. Energy is not stored in the forced oscillator. The energy supplied by the external periodic force is exactly the same as that lost per cycle due to damping resistance. The energy supplied by the external periodic force helps in the maintenance of the oscillations of forced oscillator. Thus, in the steady state, the amplitude and period of the forced oscillator are so adjusted that the power supplied by the external periodic force is equal to the energy dissipated against the frictional forces.

Q. 3.25. A damped oscillator consists of a mass 200 gm attached to a spring of constant 100 Nm^{-1} and damping constant 5 Nm^{-1}s. It is driven by a force $F = 6 \cos \omega t$ Newton, where $\omega = 30$ s^1. If displacement in steady state is $x = A \sin(\omega t - \phi)$ metre, find A and ϕ. Also calculate the power supplied to the oscillator. *(Pbi.U., 2003; P.U., 2001, 2000, 1994)*

Ans. Amplitude of the driving force $F_0 = 6$ N

Frequency of the driving force $\qquad \omega = 30$ s^{-1}

Mass of damped oscillator $\qquad\qquad m = 200$ gm $= 0.2$ kg

Spring constant $\qquad\qquad\qquad\qquad s = 100$ N m^{-1}

Damping constant $\qquad\qquad\qquad r = 5$ N m^{-1} s

When an external force $F = F_0 \cos \omega t$ acts on a damped oscillator the steady state is given by
$$x = A \sin(\omega t - \phi)$$

where $A = \dfrac{F_0}{\omega Z_m}$, Z_m being the 'impedance' of the mechanical system given by

$$Z_m = \sqrt{r^2 + \left(\omega m - \frac{s}{\omega}\right)^2}$$

and $\qquad\qquad \tan \phi = \dfrac{\omega m - \dfrac{s}{\omega}}{r}$

$\therefore \qquad\qquad \tan \phi = \dfrac{30 \times 0.2 - \dfrac{100}{30}}{5} = 0.534$

$\therefore \qquad\qquad \phi = 28° \, 6'$ and $\cos \phi = 0.8821$

$$Z_m = \sqrt{(5 \times 5) + \left(30 \times 0.2 - \frac{100}{30}\right)^2} = 5.67 \, \text{N m}^{-1} \text{s}$$

$\therefore \qquad\qquad A = \dfrac{F_0}{\omega Z_m} = \dfrac{6}{30 \times 5.67} = 0.0352 \, \text{m} = 3.52 \, \text{mm}$

Average power supplied $= \dfrac{F_0^2}{2 Z_m} \cos \phi = \dfrac{6 \times 6}{2 \times 5.67} \times 0.8821 = 2.8$ watt

Exercise. *A damped oscillator of mass 0.2 kg damping constant 4 Nm^{-1}s, spring constant 80 Nm^{-1} is driven by a force $F = 6 \cos 30t$ Newton. Calculate the average power supplied.*
(Pbi. U. 2007)

Hint. $F_0 = 6$ N; $\omega = 30$ s^{-1}; $m = 0.2$ kg; $r = 4$ Nm^{-1}s; $s = 80$ Nm^{-1}

$\therefore \qquad Z_m = \sqrt{r^2 + \left(\omega m - \frac{s}{\omega}\right)^2} = \sqrt{4 \times 4 + \left(30 \times 0.2 - \frac{80}{30}\right)^2}$

$\qquad\qquad\qquad = 5.2$ Nm^{-1}s

$\qquad\qquad \tan \phi = \dfrac{\omega m - \dfrac{s}{\omega}}{r} = \dfrac{30 \times 0.2 - \dfrac{80}{30}}{4} = 0.8333$

or $\qquad\qquad \phi = 39.8° \qquad \therefore \qquad \cos \phi = 0.7682$

Average power supplied $\dfrac{F_0^2}{2 Z_m} \cos \phi = \dfrac{6 \times 6}{2 \times 5.2} \times 0.7682 = 2.66$ Watt

Q. 3.26. (*a*) **What is absorption resonance curve? Draw it for a forced oscillator. Why is it so called?**   (*G.N.D.U.* 2006; *P.U.*, 2001, 2000, 1999)

(*b*) **What is meant by resonance absorption band width? Define it and show it on a *P-ω* graph. Explain how the damping of the medium effects the band width? How it is related to damping constant ?**   (*G.N.D.U.* 2008, 2007; *P.U.* 2007; *Pbi.U.*, 2007, 2003;

Nagpur U., 2001; *H.P.U.*, 2000)

Ans. (*a*) **Absorption resonance curve.** The average power supplied to the forced oscillator by the driving force is given by

$$P_{(av)} = \frac{F_0^2}{2 Z_m} \cos\phi = \frac{F_0^2 r}{2 Z_m^2}$$

where

$$Z_m = \sqrt{r^2 + \left(\omega m - \frac{s}{\omega}\right)^2}$$

and

$$\cos\phi = \frac{r}{Z_m} = \frac{r}{\sqrt{r^2 + \left(\omega m - \frac{s}{\omega}\right)^2}}$$

The quantity $P_{(av)}$ *i.e.*, the average power thus depends upon Z_m and in turn on ω. It has a maximum value when $\cos\phi = 1$ which gives $\left(\omega m - \frac{s}{\omega}\right) = 0$ so that $\phi = 0$ and $Z_m = r$.

When $\omega m - \frac{s}{\omega} = 0, \omega^2 = \frac{s}{m} = \omega_0^2$ which is the case of *velocity resonance*. Hence $P_{(av)}$ has a maximum value at velocity resonance. It is because when $\phi = 0$, velocity and the applied periodic force are always in phase and hence maximum power is supplied to the oscillator.

∴ $$P_{(av.max)} = \frac{F_0^2}{2 Z_m} = \frac{F_0^2}{2r}$$ $[\because Z_m = r]$

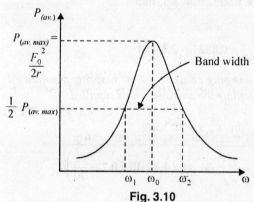

Fig. 3.10

The variation of $P_{(av)}$ with ω the frequency of the driving force for a forced oscillator is shown in Fig. 3.10. It is known as a $P_{(av)} - \omega$ graph.

The graph between $P_{(av)}$ and ω is called the *absorption resonance curve* of the forced oscillator.

It is so called because the power absorbed by the oscillator is maximum at the frequency of velocity resonance.

(*b*) **Resonance absorption band width.** From Fig. 3.10, it is seen that $P_{(av)}$ has a maximum value for $\omega = \omega_0$ as proved above, its value decreases on either side of the maxima.

Let ω_1 and ω_2 be the frequencies for which $P_{(av)} = \frac{1}{2} P_{(av.max)}$.

The condition for $P_{(av)} = \frac{1}{2} P_{(av.max)}$

gives $$\frac{F_0^2 r}{2 Z_m^2} = \frac{1}{2} \frac{F_0^2}{2r}$$

$$Z_m^2 = 2r^2$$

or $$r^2 + \left(\omega m - \frac{s}{\omega}\right)^2 = 2r^2$$

or $$\omega m - \frac{s}{\omega} = \pm r$$

Let ω_1 be less than ω_0 and ω_2 greater than ω_0, then

$$\omega_2 m - \frac{s}{\omega_2} = + r$$

or $$\omega_2^2 - \frac{s}{m} = + \frac{r}{m}\omega_2 \qquad \qquad \text{...}(i)$$

and $$\omega_1 m - \frac{s}{\omega_1} = - r$$

or $$\omega_1^2 - \frac{s}{m} = - \frac{r}{m}\omega_1 \qquad \qquad \text{...}(ii)$$

Subtracting (ii) from (i), we have

$$\omega_2^2 - \omega_1^2 = \frac{r}{m}(\omega_2 + \omega_1)$$

or $$\omega_2 - \omega_1 = \frac{r}{m} \qquad \qquad \text{...}(iii)$$

where r is the *damping constant*.

$$= 2k$$

where k is the *damping coefficient*.

The angular frequency difference $\omega_2 - \omega_1$ *is called the bandwidth of the response curve. It is defined as the difference in the angular frequencies below and above the frequency of velocity resonance for which the average power drops to half the maximum value.*

The *band width* is shown on a $P - \omega$ graph in Fig. 3.10.

Effect of damping. As band width $(\omega_2 - \omega_1)$ is directly proportional to r the damping constant, the band width increases as the damping constant increases.

Q. 3.27. (*a*) **Derive an expression for the Q-value of a forced oscillator in terms of resonance absorption band width. If the Q-value of an oscillator is increased how is band width of the absorption curve affected. Prove that band width $= \dfrac{\omega_0}{Q}$ where the symbols have their usual meaning.**

(*Pbi.U.*, 2001, 1991; *P.U.* 2009, 2007, 2006, 2004, 2001; *Nagpur U.* 2003, 2001; *G.N.D.U.*, 2007, 2006, 2000; *H.P.U.*, 1999, 1994)

(*b*) **If the resonant (angular) frequency of acoustic system is 280 Hz and half power frequencies are 200 Hz and 360 Hz respectively, calculate the quality factor.**

(*Nagpur U.*, 2002)

Ans. (*a*) **Quality factor Q in terms of band width.** The quality factor Q of a mechanical oscillator is given by $Q = \dfrac{m\omega_0}{r}$ where ω_0 is the (angular) frequency of velocity resonance, m the mass and r the damping constant. [For proof See **Q. 2.19** (*b*) (*ii*)]

Resonance absorption band width $\omega_2 - \omega_1 = \dfrac{r}{m}$ where ω_1 is less than ω_0 and ω_2 greater than ω_0 for which the average power drops to half the maximum value. [For proof See **Q. 3.26 (b) Eq. (iii)**]

Hence quality factor $\qquad Q = \dfrac{m\omega_0}{r} = \dfrac{\omega_0}{\omega_2 - \omega_1} \qquad\qquad \left[\because \omega_2 - \omega_1 = \dfrac{r}{m} \right]$

$$= \frac{\text{Frequency at resonance}}{\text{Full band width at half maximum power}}$$

∴   *Q-value of an oscillator is the ratio of frequency of maximum velocity response to the band width at half maximum power.*

Effect of increase in Q-value. As $Q = \dfrac{\omega_0}{\omega_2 - \omega_1} = \dfrac{\omega_0}{\text{band width}}$, when Q-value of an oscillator is increased $(\omega_2 - \omega_1)$ *i.e.*, band width decreases because ω_0 is a constant quantity.

As $Q = \dfrac{\omega_0}{\text{band width}}$, $\qquad$ band width $= \dfrac{\omega_0}{Q}$

Note. For an electric oscillator quality factor $Q = \dfrac{L\omega_0}{R}$ See **Eq. (i) Q. 3.37.**

(b) Here $\omega_0 = 280$ Hz, $\qquad \omega_1 = 200$ Hz, $\qquad \omega_2 = 360$ Hz

∴   Quality factor $Q = \dfrac{\omega_0}{\omega_2 - \omega_1} = \dfrac{280}{360 - 200} = \dfrac{280}{160} = 1.75$

Exercise. *Calculate the band width of an acoustic system having $Q = 1.75$ and resonant frequency* 280 Hz.   *(Nagpur U., 2001)*
Ans. 160 Hz.

Q. 3.28. (a) Find the Q-value of an oscillator in terms of the energy decay.

(b) What is figure of merit of an oscillator and how is it defined in terms of bandwidth? The quality factor Q is a measure of sharpness of resonance in case of a forced oscillator. Explain.
                                           (P.U., 2009, 2000; G.N.D.U., 2009, 1995; H.P.U., 1993)

Ans. (a) Q in terms of energy decay. The quality factor of a forced oscillator

$$Q = \frac{2\pi \times \text{Average energy stored}}{\text{Energy dissipated per cycle}} = \frac{2\pi\, E_{av}}{T \times P_{av}}$$

The instantaneous value of energy = K.E. + P.E. at any time.

The $\qquad\qquad K.E. = \dfrac{1}{2} m \left(\dfrac{dy}{dt} \right)^2$

and $\qquad\qquad P.E. = \displaystyle\int_0^y sy\, dy = \dfrac{1}{2} sy^2$

∴   Total energy $E = \dfrac{1}{2} m \left(\dfrac{dy}{dt} \right)^2 + \dfrac{1}{2} sy^2$

If the applied driving force is represented by $F = F_0 \cos \omega t$, then for the forced oscillator

$$y = \frac{F_0}{\omega Z_m} \sin (\omega t - \phi)$$

and
$$\frac{dy}{dt} = \frac{F_0}{Z_m}\cos(\omega t - \phi)$$

$$\therefore \quad E = \frac{1}{2}m\left(\frac{F_0}{Z_m}\right)^2\cos^2(\omega t - \phi) + \frac{1}{2}\frac{s}{\omega^2}\left(\frac{F_0}{Z_m}\right)^2\sin^2(\omega t - \phi)$$

For a complete cycle the average value of $\cos^2(\omega t - \phi)$

$$= \frac{1}{T}\int_0^T\cos^2(\omega t - \phi)\,dt = \frac{1}{2}$$

and the average value of $\sin^2(\omega t - \phi)$

$$= \frac{1}{T}\int_0^T\sin^2(\omega t - \phi)\,dt = \frac{1}{2}$$

$$\therefore \quad E_{(av)} = \frac{1}{4}m\left(\frac{F_0}{Z_m}\right)^2 + \frac{1}{4}\frac{s}{\omega^2}\left(\frac{F_0}{Z_m}\right)^2$$

$$= \frac{1}{4}m\left(\frac{F_0}{Z_m}\right)^2\left[1 + \frac{s}{m\omega^2}\right]$$

$$= \frac{1}{4}m\left(\frac{F_0}{Z_m}\right)^2\left[1 + \frac{\omega_0^2}{\omega^2}\right]$$

and
$$P_{(av)} = \frac{F_0^2}{2Z_m}\cos\phi = \frac{F_0^2}{2Z_m}\frac{r}{Z_m} = \frac{F_0^2}{Z_m^2}\frac{r}{2}$$

$$\therefore \quad Q = 2\pi\frac{E_{(av)}}{T \times P_{(av)}} = \frac{2\pi}{T}\frac{m}{2r}\left(1 + \frac{\omega_0^2}{\omega^2}\right)$$

At resonance
$$\omega_0 = \omega \quad \therefore \quad 1 + \frac{\omega_0^2}{\omega^2} = 2$$

and
$$\frac{2\pi}{T} = \omega = \omega_0$$

$$\therefore \quad Q = \frac{m\omega_0}{r}$$

Hence quality factor $Q = \dfrac{2\pi \times \text{Average energy stored}}{\text{energy dissipated per cycle}}$ gives the definition of Q in terms of energy decay.

(b) Figure of merit. *It is defined as the ratio of the frequency at velocity resonance (maximum velocity response) to the full bandwidth at half maximum power.*

If ω_0 is the frequency of velocity resonance and $\omega_2 - \omega_1$ the full bandwidth at half maximum power, then

$$\text{Figure of merit} = \frac{\text{Frequency at velocity resonance}}{\text{Full bandwidth at half maximum power}}$$

$$= \frac{\omega_0}{\omega_2 - \omega_1} = \frac{\omega_0\, m}{r} = Q \qquad\qquad [\because \omega_2 - \omega_1 = r/m]$$

where Q is the quality factor.

Quality factor a measure of sharpness of resonance. The figure of merit (or quality factor) measures the *sharpness of tuning*. Higher the figure of merit for a given resonance frequency smaller is the bandwidth *i.e.*, sharper is the tuning. This fact is used to increase the '*selectivity*' of radio sets. The sharpness of response of a circuit allows radio signals to be reproduced without any interference from signals of frequencies close to it.

Q. 3.29. What is physical significance of Q-value of a forced oscillator? (*P.U.*, 2009, 1993)

Ans. Q-value represents the sharpness of absorption curve. The larger the value of quality factor Q sharper is the peak value of absorption curve.

Q-value also measures the amplification factor. Thus at displacement resonance the displacement at low frequency is amplified by Q times.

Q. 3.30. Light of wavelength 6×10^{-5} cm is emitted by an electron in an atom (a damped simple harmonic oscillator) with a quality factor 3×10^6. Find the width of the spectral line from such an atom from resonance bandwidth.

Ans. The quality factor Q is given by

$$Q = \frac{\omega_0}{\omega_2 - \omega_1}$$

where ω_0 is the angular frequency of maximum velocity response (resonance) and $\omega_2 - \omega_1$ is the bandwidth in terms of angular frequency at half maximum power.

Quality factor in terms of wavelength. The above relation can be put in terms of wavelength as under. Let v_1, v_2 and v_0 be the frequencies and λ_1, λ_2 and λ_0 the wavelengths corresponding to angular frequencies ω_1, ω_2 and ω_0, then

$$\frac{\omega_0}{\omega_2 - \omega_1} = \frac{2\pi v_0}{2\pi v_2 - 2\pi v_1} = \frac{v_0}{v_2 - v_1}$$

$$= \frac{\dfrac{c}{\lambda_0}}{\dfrac{c}{\lambda_2} - \dfrac{c}{\lambda_1}} = \frac{\dfrac{1}{\lambda_0}}{\dfrac{1}{\lambda_2} - \dfrac{1}{\lambda_1}} \qquad\qquad \left[\because v = \frac{c}{\lambda}\right]$$

$$= \frac{1}{\lambda_0}\frac{\lambda_1\lambda_2}{\lambda_1 - \lambda_2} = \frac{\lambda_0}{\lambda_1 - \lambda_2}$$

since $\lambda_1\lambda_2 = \lambda_0^2$ (approx.). Hence $Q = \dfrac{\lambda_0}{\lambda_1 - \lambda_2}$

$$\therefore \quad \text{Bandwidth} \qquad \lambda_1 - \lambda_2 = \frac{\lambda_0}{Q}$$

Now $\qquad \lambda_0 = 6 \times 10^{-5}$ cm $= 6 \times 10^{-7}$ m and $Q = 3 \times 10^6$

$$\therefore \quad \text{Bandwidth} \quad = \frac{\lambda_0}{Q} = \frac{6 \times 10^{-7}}{3 \times 10^6} = 2 \times 10^{-13} \text{ m} = 2 \times 10^{-3} \text{ Å}$$

Q. 3.31. The line width of orange line of Kr^{86} at $\lambda = 6058$ Å is found to be 5.50×10^{-3} Å. Calculate (*a*) line frequency (*ii*) line width in Hertz. (*G.N.D.U.*, 1995)

Ans. Line wavelength $\lambda_0 = 6058$ Å $= 6058 \times 10^{-10}$ m

$\therefore$ Line frequency $v_0 = \dfrac{c}{\lambda_0} = \dfrac{3 \times 10^8}{6058 \times 10^{-10}} = 4.95 \times 10^{14}$ Hertz

Line width in wavelength $\lambda_1 - \lambda_2 = 5.50 \times 10^{-3}$ Å $= 5.50 \times 10^{-13}$ m

$\therefore$ Line width in terms of frequency $= \dfrac{c}{\lambda_1 - \lambda_2}$

$$= \dfrac{3 \times 10^8}{5.50 \times 10^{-13}} = 5.45 \times 10^{20}$$ Hz

Q. 3.32. If the displacement at resonance is given by

$$A_{max} = \dfrac{F_0}{\omega' r} \quad \text{where} \quad \omega' = \sqrt{\dfrac{s}{m} - \dfrac{r^2}{4m^2}}$$

show that the displacement at low frequencies is amplified by a factor Q at displacement resonance. *(P.U. 2006, 2005, 2004; G.N.D.U., 2008, 2006, 1994; H.P.U., 1991)*

Or

Find Q value of the oscillatory system as an amplification factor.
(Pbi.U., 2002, 2000, 1999; P.U., 2009, 2004, 2002, 2001, 1999, 1994; H.P.U., 2000, 1993)

Or

Prove that in the case of a forced oscillator the amplification factor is equal to its Q-value.
(Pbi. U. 2007, 2006)

Ans. Q value as amplification factor. The displacement at resonance is given by

$$A_{max} = \dfrac{F_0}{\omega' r}$$

where

$$\omega' = \sqrt{\dfrac{s}{m} - \dfrac{r^2}{4m^2}}$$

The amplitude

$$A = \dfrac{f_0}{\sqrt{4k^2 \omega^2 + (\omega^2 - \omega_0^2)^2}} \qquad \left[where \ f_0 = \dfrac{F_0}{m} \right]$$

when $\omega \to 0$, the amplitude $A_0 = \dfrac{f_0}{\omega_0^2} = \dfrac{f_0}{\dfrac{s}{m}} = \dfrac{F_0}{s}$.

The ratio of the maximum displacement at resonance to the maximum displacement when the frequency of the applied force approaches zero is known as amplification factor.

Now $\left(\dfrac{A_{max}}{A_0} \right)^2 = \dfrac{F_0^2}{\omega'^2 r^2} \times \dfrac{s^2}{F_0^2}$

$$= \dfrac{s^2}{\omega'^2 r^2} = \dfrac{m^2 \omega_0^4}{r^2 \left(\omega_0^2 - \dfrac{r^2}{4m^2} \right)} \qquad \left[\because \dfrac{s}{m} = \omega_0^2 \right]$$

$$= \dfrac{m^2 \omega_0^2}{r^2 \left(1 - \dfrac{r^2}{4m^2 \omega_0^2} \right)}$$

but $\quad Q = \dfrac{m\,\omega_0}{r}$

$\therefore \qquad \left(\dfrac{A_{max}}{A_0}\right)^2 = \dfrac{Q^2}{1 - \dfrac{1}{4Q^2}}$

or $\qquad \dfrac{A_{max}}{A_0} = \dfrac{Q}{\left(1 - \dfrac{1}{4Q^2}\right)^{\frac{1}{2}}} = \dfrac{Q}{\left(1 + \dfrac{1}{8Q^2}\right)}$

If Q is very large, then $\dfrac{1}{8Q^2}$ is very small as compared to 1 and thus can be neglected.

$\therefore \qquad \dfrac{A_{max}}{A_0} = Q$

Hence Q value of an oscillatory system (or in the case of a forced oscillator) is equal to the amplification factor.

In other words, the displacement at low frequencies is amplified by a factor Q at displacement resonance.

Q. 3.33. Prove that the band width of the resonance absorption curve defines the phase angle range $\tan\phi = \pm 1$. (*Pbi. U.* 2006; *H.P.U.*, 2003, 2002, 2000, 1995; *P.U.*, 2005, 2000, 1995; *G.N.D.U.*, 1996)

Ans. If ω_0 is the resonance frequency of the driving force, then at this frequency the driving force will deliver the maximum power. Now

Maximum average power $(P_{av})_{max} = \dfrac{F_0^2}{2r}$

The sharpness of the peak depends only on the damping constant r.

Now *band width of the curve is defined as the difference of two frequencies* $(\omega_2 - \omega_1)$ *corresponding to which power absorbed is half of maximum power.*

Average power $\quad P_{av} = \dfrac{F_0^2}{2Z_m}\cos\phi$

$\qquad\qquad\qquad = \dfrac{r\,F_0^2}{2Z_m^2} \qquad\qquad\qquad\qquad \left(\because \cos\phi = \dfrac{r}{Z_m}\right)$

$\therefore \qquad \dfrac{r\,F_0^2}{2Z_m^2} = \dfrac{1}{2}\dfrac{F_0^2}{2r}$

or $\qquad Z_m^2 = 2r^2$

Now $\quad Z_m = \sqrt{r^2 + \left(m\omega - \dfrac{s}{\omega}\right)^2}$

$\therefore \qquad r^2 + \left(m\omega - \dfrac{s}{\omega}\right)^2 = 2r^2 \qquad\qquad\qquad\qquad ...(i)$

or $\qquad m\omega - \dfrac{s}{\omega} = \pm r$

Phase angle ϕ is given by

$$\tan \phi = \frac{m\omega - \dfrac{s}{\omega}}{r} = \frac{\pm r}{r} = \pm 1$$

This shows that the bandwidth of resonance absorption curve defines the phase angle range. $\tan \phi = \pm 1$.

Q. 3.34. An electric oscillator is driven by an *e.m.f.* $E = E_0\, e^{j\omega t}$. Discuss the transient and steady state. Derive an expression for the current in the electric circuit in the steady state and find its value when the applied *e.m.f.* is

(i) $E = E_0 \cos \omega t$ **(ii) $E_0 \sin \omega t$**   (G.N.D.U. 2006; P.U., 2005, 2001, 2000; H.P.U., 1992)

Or

Set up the differential equation of a forced electrical oscillator and solve it. Discuss the transient and steady state solution.   (G.N.D.U. 2007)

Ans. Current in an electric circuit. Consider an electric oscillator consisting of an electric circuit containing a resistance R, an inductance L and a capacitance C in series as shown in Fig. 3.11 connected to an *A.C.* source for which the *e.m.f.* is represented by

$$E = E_0\, e_m^{j\omega t}$$

ω being the angular frequency of the applied alternating *e.m.f.*
Such a circuit behaves as a driven oscillator. The loss of energy
in the resistance is compensated by the supply of energy from
the *A.C.* source just as the loss of energy due to friction in a
mechanical driven oscillator is compensated by the driving
force.

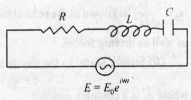

$$E = E_0 e^{iWt}$$

Fig. 3.11

If I is the current at any instant, then
Fall of potential across the resistance $R = RI$

If the current varies at the rate $\dfrac{dI}{dt}$, then the voltage required to overcome the back *e.m.f.* in the inductance $= L\dfrac{dI}{dt}$.

If q is the charge accumulated on the capacitor at that instant, then

Fall of potential across the capacitor $= \dfrac{q}{C}$

Hence the voltage equation is given by

$$RI + L\frac{dI}{dt} + \frac{q}{C} = E = E_0\, e^{i\omega t}$$

Now $I = \dfrac{dq}{dt}$ and $\dfrac{dI}{dt} = \dfrac{d^2q}{dt^2}$

Hence $R\dfrac{dq}{dt} + L\dfrac{d^2q}{dt^2} + \dfrac{q}{C} = E_0\, e^{i\omega t}$

or $L\dfrac{d^2q}{dt^2} + R\dfrac{dq}{dt} + \dfrac{q}{C} = E_0\, e^{i\omega t}$ ...(i)

(i) Transient state. The first part of Eq. (i) is known as the transient term which dies away with time. The transient behaviour persists only for a short interval of time. During this time, the natural oscillations of the system will prevail and the system will behave as if no external force is acting. The variation of charge is, therefore, given by the solution of the equation

$$L\frac{d^2q}{dt^2} + R\frac{dq}{dt} + \frac{q}{C} = 0 \qquad\qquad ...(i)(a)$$

Dividing by L and substituting $\frac{R}{L} = 2k$ and $\frac{1}{LC} = \omega_0^2$, we get

$$\frac{d^2q}{dt^2} + 2k\frac{dq}{dt} + \omega_0^2 q = 0$$

The oscillatory solution of this equation is

$$q = A_0 e^{-kt} \sin\left(\sqrt{\omega_0^2 - k^2}\, t + \phi\right)$$

$$= A_0 e^{-kt} \sin(\omega't + \phi)$$

where $\omega' = \sqrt{\omega_0^2 - k^2}$, $A_0 = \frac{q_0\omega_0}{\sqrt{\omega_0^2 - k^2}}$ and $\tan\phi = \frac{\sqrt{\omega_0^2 - k^2}}{k}$

[For proof See Q. 2.8]

The amplitude $A_0 e^{-kt}$ decays with time due to the presence of the term e^{-kt}. The quantity

$\omega_0 = \frac{1}{\sqrt{LC}}$ is known as the natural frequency of the electrical oscillator in the absence of the dissipative as well as driving forces.

(ii) Steady state. In the steady state let one particular solution of the equation be

$$q = q_0\, e^{i\omega t}$$

where q_0 is a complex quantity.

$\therefore$ $\qquad \frac{dq}{dt} = i\omega q_0\, e^{i\omega t}$ and $\frac{d^2q}{dt^2} = -\omega^2 q_0\, e^{i\omega t}$

Substituting in equation (i), we have

$$\left(-\omega^2 L + i\omega R + \frac{1}{C}\right) q_0\, e^{i\omega t} = E_0\, e^{i\omega t}$$

This relation is true for all values of t.

$\therefore$ $\qquad q_0 = \dfrac{E_0}{i\omega R + \left(\dfrac{1}{C} - \omega^2 L\right)} = \dfrac{-E_0}{\omega R - i\left(\dfrac{1}{C} - \omega^2 L\right)}$

$$= \dfrac{-iE_0}{\omega\left[R + i\left(L\omega - \dfrac{1}{C\omega}\right)\right]} = \dfrac{-iE_0}{\omega \vec{Z}_e} \qquad\qquad ...(ii)$$

where $\vec{Z}_e$ is a complex quantity called the *electric impedance* (or effective resistance) of the circuit, given by

$$\vec{Z}_e = R + i\left(L\omega - \frac{1}{C\omega}\right)$$

R is the *ohmic* resistance of the circuit and $\left(L\omega - \dfrac{1}{C\omega}\right) = X$ is called the *total reactance*, $L\omega = X_L$

represents the *reactance due to inductance* and $\dfrac{1}{C\omega} = X_C$ represents the *reactance due to capacitance*.

Now,   put $R = Z_e \cos \phi$

and $\left(L\omega - \dfrac{1}{C\omega} \right) = Z_e \sin \phi$

so that $Z_e = \sqrt{R^2 + \left(L\omega - \dfrac{1}{C\omega} \right)^2}$

and $\tan \phi = \dfrac{\left(L\omega - \dfrac{1}{C\omega} \right)}{R}$

$\therefore$ $\vec{Z_e} = Z_e \cos \phi + i Z_e \sin \phi$

$= Z_e (\cos \phi + i \sin \phi) = Z_e e^{i\phi}$

Substituting in equation (ii), we get

$$q_0 = \dfrac{-i E_0}{\omega Z_e e^{i\phi}}$$

But $q = q_0 e^{i\omega t}$

$\therefore$ $q = \dfrac{-i E_0 e^{i\omega t}}{\omega Z_e e^{i\phi}} = \dfrac{-i E_0}{\omega Z_e} e^{i(\omega t - \phi)}$ ...(iii)

The current I in the electric circuit (similar to velocity v in a mechanical **oscillator**) is given by

$$I = \dfrac{dq}{dt}$$

$\therefore$ $I = \dfrac{dq}{dt} = \dfrac{-i E_0 e^{i(\omega t - \phi)}}{\omega Z_e} \times i\omega = \dfrac{E_0}{Z_e} e^{i(\omega t - \phi)}$

$= I_0 e^{i(\omega t - \phi)}$ ...(iv)

where $I_0 = \dfrac{E_0}{Z_e}$

The current I and the applied e.m.f. E are not in phase. There is a phase difference of ϕ between applied e.m.f. and current.

(iii) Applied e.m.f. $E = E_0 \cos \omega t$. The applied e.m.f. $E = E_0 e^{i\omega t}$ can be put in the form
$E = E_0 (\cos \omega t + i \sin \omega t)$
$= E_0 \cos \omega t + i E_0 \sin \omega t$ ...(v)
Thus $E = E_0 \cos \omega t$ is the real part of the complex quantity $E = E_0 e^{i\omega t}$.
Therefore the steady state solution for the current I will be the real part of equation (iv) which may be put in the from
$I = I_0 e^{i(\omega t - \phi)} = I_0 [\cos(\omega t - \phi) + i \sin(\omega t - \phi)]$ ...(vi)
The real part is $I = I_0 \cos(\omega t - \phi)$
Thus when the applied e.m.f. is $E = E_0 \cos \omega t$, the current is

$$I = I_0 \cos(\omega t - \phi) = \dfrac{E_0}{Z_e} \cos(\omega t - \phi)$$ ...(vii)

where $\tan \phi = \dfrac{L\omega - \dfrac{1}{C\omega}}{R}$ and $Z_e = \sqrt{R^2 + \left(L\omega - \dfrac{1}{C\omega} \right)^2}$

(iv) **Applied e.m.f.** $E = E_0 \sin \omega\, t$. When the applied *e.m.f.* is $E = E_0 \sin \omega\, t$, it is that part of equation (v) which is preceded by vector operator *i*. Therefore, the steady state term for the current *I* will also be that part of equation (vi) which is preceded by vector operator *i*.

$$\therefore \qquad I = I_0 \sin(\omega t - \phi) = \frac{E_0}{Z_e} \sin(\omega t - \phi)$$

The value of Z_e and ϕ are given in part *(i)* above.

Q. 3.35. Discuss the variation of electric current amplitude and phase with frequency of applied e.m.f. in an *LCR* circuit. At what frequency will the current be maximum? What is the phase difference between voltage and current at resonance?   (*G.N.D.U.* 2006; *Pbi. U.* 2005; *P.U.*, 2001; *H.P.U.*, 1993, 1992)

Ans. Variation of current amplitude and phase with frequency of applied e.m.f. When an *e.m.f.* $E = E_0\, e^{i\omega t}$ is applied to a circuit containing a resistance *R*, an inductance *L* and a capacitance *C* in series (*LCR* circuit) the current is given by

$$I = I_0\, e^{i(\omega t - \phi)}$$

where $\quad I_0 = \dfrac{E_0}{Z_e} = \dfrac{E_0}{\sqrt{R^2 + \left(L\omega - \dfrac{1}{C\omega}\right)^2}}$

and $\quad \tan\phi = \dfrac{L\omega - \dfrac{1}{C\omega}}{R}$

Note. If the applied *e.m.f.* is $E = E_0 \cos \omega\, t$ the current is $I = I_0 \cos(\omega t - \phi)$ and when the applied *e.m.f.* is $E = E_0 \sin \omega\, t$, $I = I_0 \sin(\omega t - \phi)$

As $\quad Z_e = \sqrt{R^2 + \left(L\omega - \dfrac{1}{C\omega}\right)^2}$, three cases arise

(i) $\;L\omega < \dfrac{1}{C\omega}\quad$ *(ii)* $\;L\omega > \dfrac{1}{C\omega}\;$ and $\quad$ *(iii)* $\;L\omega = \dfrac{1}{C\omega}$

We shall study these three cases separately.

(i) **Low driving frequency.** When ω is small $L\omega < \dfrac{1}{C\omega}$ *i.e.*, the *reactance due to inductance* X_L *is less than reactance due to capacitance.* The net reactance is *capacitative* and the impedance is said to be *capacitance controlled.*

Now $\quad Z_e = \sqrt{R^2 + \left(L\omega - \dfrac{1}{C\omega}\right)^2}$

As $\quad \omega \to 0;\; L\omega \to 0$ and $\dfrac{1}{C\omega} \to \infty$

$$\therefore \qquad I_0 = \frac{E_0}{\sqrt{R^2 + \left(L\omega - \dfrac{1}{C\omega}\right)^2}} = \frac{E_0}{1/C\omega} = 0 \qquad [\because R\text{ is small}]$$

Thus at low frequency the peak value of current in the forced electric oscillator is zero.

The phase difference ϕ between current and applied *e.m.f.* is given by

$$\tan\phi = \frac{L\omega - \dfrac{1}{C\omega}}{R}$$

As $\omega \to 0;\ L\omega \to 0; \dfrac{1}{C\omega} \to \infty$

$$\tan\phi = -\infty \text{ or } \phi = -\frac{\pi}{2}$$

Hence the phase difference between current and voltage $= -\phi = +\dfrac{\pi}{2}$

Thus for very low driving frequencies *the current leads the applied voltage* by $\dfrac{\pi}{2}$. In other words, the *voltage lags behind* the current. As the impedance Z_e is very large the current I is very small.

(ii) High driving frequencies. When ω is large $L\omega > \dfrac{1}{C\omega}$ *i.e* ., the *reactance due to induc-tance* X_L *is greater than reactance due to capacitance*. The net reactance is *inductive* and the impedance is said to be *inductance controlled*.

As $\omega \to \infty;\ L\omega \to \infty; \dfrac{1}{C\omega} \to 0$

$\therefore$ Current amplitude $I_0 = \dfrac{E_0}{\sqrt{R^2 + \left(L\omega - \dfrac{1}{C\omega}\right)^2}} = \dfrac{E_0}{L\omega} = 0$ [$\because R$ is very small]

Thus at high frequencies also the current amplitude is very small and finally becomes zero at $\omega = \infty$.

$$\tan\phi = \frac{L\omega - \dfrac{1}{C\omega}}{R} = +\infty$$

$\therefore$ $\phi = +\dfrac{\pi}{2}$

Thus at very high driving frequencies the *current lags behind the applied* voltage by $\dfrac{\pi}{2}$. In other words, the external voltage leads the current in the circuit. The impedance again becomes very large and hence for high frequency of the applied voltage the current becomes very small.

(iii) Resonant frequency. When $L\omega = \dfrac{1}{C\omega}$, the impedance

$$Z_e = \sqrt{R^2 + \left(L\omega - \frac{1}{C\omega}\right)^2} = R$$

the ohmic resistance of the circuit and has a minimum value.

The current amplitude $I_0 = \dfrac{E_0}{\sqrt{R^2 + \left(L\omega - \dfrac{1}{C\omega}\right)^2}} = \dfrac{E_0}{R}$

This is the *maximum* value of current and it is a case of *resonance*.

The resonant frequency is given by

$$L\omega = \frac{1}{C\omega}$$

or

$$\omega^2 = \frac{1}{LC}$$

Denoting the resonant angular frequency by ω_0, we have

$$\omega_0^2 = \frac{1}{LC}$$

or

$$\omega_0 = \frac{1}{\sqrt{LC}}$$

$\therefore$ Resonant frequency $v_0 = \dfrac{\omega_0}{2\pi} = \dfrac{1}{2\pi\sqrt{LC}}$

As $L\omega = \dfrac{1}{C\omega}$ $\tan\phi = \dfrac{L\omega - \dfrac{1}{C\omega}}{R} = 0$

$\therefore$ $\phi = 0$

Thus the current in the circuit is in phase with the applied *e.m.f.*

To conclude. At low frequencies of applied *e.m.f.* the current in the circuit is very small and tends to zero. As the frequency is increased the current amplitude increases and becomes a maximum at $\omega = \omega_0$ where ω_0 is the natural frequency of the electric circuit given by $\omega_0 = \dfrac{1}{\sqrt{LC}}$. The maximum value of $I = \dfrac{E_0}{R}$. The variation of current amplitude I_0 with frequency ω for values of $R = 0$, R having a low value and R having a high value is shown in Fig. 3.12.

As $\omega = 0$, the phase angle $\phi = -\dfrac{\pi}{2}$. The phase angle increases as ω increases. As $\omega = \omega_0$, the phase angle $\phi = 0$. As ω further increases ϕ increases and as $\omega \to \infty$ phase angle $\phi = +\dfrac{\pi}{2}$ as shown in Fig. 3.13.

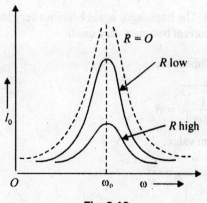

Fig. 3.12

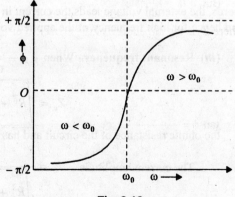

Fig. 3.13

From the above discussion we find that the current amplitude is maximum at resonance *i.e.,* when the frequency of the applied *e.m.f.* $\dfrac{\omega}{2\pi} = \dfrac{\omega_0}{2\pi} = \dfrac{1}{2\pi\sqrt{LC}}$ the natural frequency of the electric circuit.

The phase difference between voltage and current at resonance is zero *i.e.,* at resonance the applied *e.m.f.* and current are in *phase*.

Q. 3.36. Find the frequency of a circuit containing inductance of 100 μ H and capacity of 0.01 μ F. To which wavelength (of radio wave) its response will be maximum? (*P.U.,* 2001, 2000)

Ans. Here $L = 100\ \mu\,H = 100 \times 10^{-6} = 10^{-4}\ H;\ \ C = .01\ \mu\,F = .01 \times 10^{-6} = 10^{-8}\ F$

$\therefore$ Frequency of the circuit $\nu = \dfrac{1}{2\pi\sqrt{LC}}$

$$= \dfrac{1}{2 \times 3.142 \times \sqrt{10^{-4} \times 10^{-8}}} = \dfrac{10^6}{6.284} = 1.59 \times 10^5\ Hz$$

Velocity of radio waves $c = 3 \times 10^8\ ms^{-1}$

$\therefore$ Wavelength of maximum response $\lambda = \dfrac{c}{\nu} = \dfrac{3 \times 10^8}{1.59 \times 10^5}$

$$= 1.89 \times 10^3 = 1890\ m$$

Q. 3.37. (*a*) **Find the Q-value of a resonating *LCR* circuit.**   (*P.U.,* 2004, 2004, 2001, 1995)

(*b*) **In *LCR* circuit at resonance maximum potential drop across inductance is equal to Q-times the applied *E.M.F.* How ?**   (*G.N.D.U.* 2007; *P.U.,* 2000, 1999)

Ans. (*a*) **Quality factor.** The quality factor of a forced oscillator

$$Q = \dfrac{2\pi \times \text{Average energy stored}}{\text{Energy dissipated per cycle}}$$

$$= \dfrac{2\pi E_{av}}{T \times P_{av}}$$

where T is the time period of the oscillator and P_{av} the average power.

Q-value of a resonating *LCR* circuit. In an electrical circuit average power dissipated is given by $\dfrac{1}{2} E_0 I_0 \cos\phi$ where E_0 and I_0 are the maximum values of applied *A.C.* voltage and current respectively and $\cos\phi$ is the power factor.

But $I_0 = \dfrac{E_0}{Z_e}$ and $\cos\phi = \dfrac{R}{Z_e}$

where Z_e is the impedance of the electrical circuit given by

$$Z_e = \sqrt{R^2 + \left(L\omega - \dfrac{1}{C\omega}\right)^2} \quad \text{and}$$

$$\tan\phi = \dfrac{L\omega - \dfrac{1}{C\omega}}{R} \quad \text{or} \quad \cos\phi = \dfrac{R}{\sqrt{R^2 + \left(L\omega - \dfrac{1}{C\omega}\right)^2}} = \dfrac{R}{Z_e}$$

$\therefore$ $$P_{av} = \dfrac{1}{2}\dfrac{E_0^2}{Z_e}\cos\phi = \dfrac{1}{2}\dfrac{E_0^2 R}{Z_e^2}$$

To find the average energy stored in an electrical LCR circuit, we have total energy E at any time.

$$E = \frac{1}{2} Li^2 + \frac{1}{2} \frac{q^2}{C}$$

[In an electrical circuit L corresponds to m and $1/C$ corresponds to s. Similarly i corresponds to v or $\frac{dy}{dt}$ and q corresponds to displacement y in a mechanical oscillator.]

As the applied e.m.f. is represented by $E = E_0 \sin \omega t$, by comparison with mechanical case

$$q = -\frac{E_0}{\omega Z_e} \cos(\omega t - \phi)$$

and

$$i = \frac{dq}{dt} = \frac{E_0}{Z_e} \sin(\omega t - \phi)$$

$\therefore$

$$E = \frac{1}{2} L \left(\frac{E_0}{Z_e}\right)^2 \sin^2(\omega t - \phi) + \frac{1}{2C} \left(\frac{E_0}{\omega Z_e}\right)^2 \cos^2(\omega t - \phi)$$

The average value of $\sin^2(\omega t - \phi)$ as well as $\cos^2(\omega t - \phi)$ for complete cycle is $\frac{1}{2}$.

$\therefore$

$$E_{av} = \frac{1}{4} L \left(\frac{E_0}{Z_e}\right)^2 + \frac{1}{4C} \left(\frac{E_0}{\omega Z_e}\right)^2$$

Replacing $\frac{1}{LC} = \omega_0^2$, we have

$$E_{av} = \frac{1}{4} L \left[\left(\frac{E_0}{Z_e}\right)^2 + \omega_0^2 \left(\frac{E_0}{\omega Z_e}\right)^2 \right]$$

Quality factor

$$Q = 2\pi \frac{E_{av}}{T \times P_{av}}$$

$$= 2\pi \frac{\frac{1}{4} L \left[\left(\frac{E_0}{Z_e}\right)^2 + \frac{\omega_0^2}{\omega^2} \left(\frac{E_0}{Z_e}\right)^2 \right]}{T \times \frac{E_0^2 R}{2 Z_e^2}}$$

$$= \frac{2\pi}{T} \frac{L}{2R} \left[1 + \frac{\omega_0^2}{\omega^2} \right]$$

At resonance $\omega_0 = \omega$

and $\frac{2\pi}{T} = \omega = \omega_0$

$\therefore$

$$Q = \frac{1}{2} \frac{L\omega_0}{R} \times 2 = \frac{L\omega_0}{R}$$

(b) Quality factor $Q = \dfrac{L\omega_0}{R}$ [*Voltage amplification factor*]   ...(i)

If I_0 is the value of current, when current resonance occurs at a frequency ω_0, then
Maximum potential difference across the inductance $= I_0 L\omega_0$

Also at resonance $L\omega_0 = \dfrac{1}{C\omega_0}$

or $\quad I_0 L\omega_0 = \dfrac{I_0}{C\omega_0}\quad$ or $\quad I_0 L\omega_0 - \dfrac{I_0}{C\omega_0} = 0$

i.e., the potential difference across the inductance coil and capacitor are equal and have a phase difference of 180° so that net potential drop across L and C is zero. In such a case

Potential drop across $R = I_0 R = $ Applied e.m.f. E

Multiplying and dividing the right hand side of Eq. (i) by I_0, we get

$$Q = \frac{I_0 L\omega_0}{I_0 R} = \frac{\text{Maximum potential difference across inductance}}{\text{Applied } e.m.f. \text{ in the circuit}}$$

or *Maximum potential drop across inductance is Q times the applied e.m.f.*

Quality factor Q is, therefore, also known as *voltage amplification factor.*

Exercise 1. *What is significance of quality factor of a series LCR circuit ?* (G.N.D.U. 2008)

Hint. The significance of quality factor Q of a series *LCR* circuit lies in the fact that the maximum potential drop across the inductance L is Q-times the applied *e.m.f. i.e. Q gives the voltage amplification factor of the circuit.*

Q. 3.38. Prove that in *LCR* circuit at resonance the maximum potential difference occurs across the capacitor at a frequency

$$\omega = \omega_0 \left(1 - \frac{1}{2Q^2}\right)^{\frac{1}{2}}$$

where $\qquad \omega_0 = \dfrac{1}{\sqrt{LC}}$ **and** $Q = \dfrac{L\omega_0}{R}$. (G.N.D.U. 2009; P.U., 2001, 1995)

Ans. Maximum potential difference across the capacitor. If $E = E_0 \sin \omega t$ is an alternating voltage applied to *LCR* circuit, then steady state solution is given by

$$q = \frac{E_0}{\omega Z_e} \cos(\omega t - \phi)$$

where $\qquad Z_e = \sqrt{R^2 + \left(L\omega - \dfrac{1}{C\omega}\right)^2}$

is the electrical impedance of the circuit and

$$\tan\phi = \frac{L\omega - \dfrac{1}{C\omega}}{R}$$

The potential across the capacitor $\dfrac{q}{C}$ is maximum when q is maximum *i.e.*, the denominator ωZ_e of the amplitude $\dfrac{E_0}{\omega Z_e}$ is a minimum. In other words

$$\frac{d}{d\omega}(\omega Z_e) = 0$$

or $\qquad \dfrac{d}{d\omega}\left[\omega\left\{R^2 + \left(L\omega - \dfrac{1}{C\omega}\right)^2\right\}^{\frac{1}{2}}\right] = 0$

or
$$\frac{d}{d\omega}\left[\omega^2 R^2 + \omega^4 L^2 + \frac{1}{C^2} - \frac{2L\omega^2}{C}\right]^{\frac{1}{2}} = 0$$

or
$$\frac{1}{2}\left(\omega^2 R^2 + \omega^4 L^2 + \frac{1}{C^2} - \frac{2L\omega^2}{C}\right)^{-\frac{1}{2}}\left(2\omega R^2 + 4\omega^3 L^2 - \frac{4L\omega}{C}\right) = 0$$

or
$$\frac{2\omega R^2 + 4\omega^3 L^2 - 4\dfrac{L\omega}{C}}{2\left[\omega^2 R^2 + \omega^4 L^2 + \dfrac{1}{C^2} - \dfrac{2L\omega^2}{C}\right]^{\frac{1}{2}}} = 0$$

or
$$2\omega R^2 + 4\omega^3 L^2 - 4\frac{L\omega}{C} = 0$$

or
$$R^2 + 2\omega^2 L^2 - 2\frac{L}{C} = 0$$

or
$$\omega^2 = \frac{1}{LC} - \frac{R^2}{2L^2}$$

Now $\dfrac{1}{LC} = \omega_0^2$ where ω_0 is the natural frequency of the LC circuit and quality factor $Q = \dfrac{L\omega_0}{R}$.

$\therefore$
$$\omega^2 = \omega_0^2 - \frac{\omega_0^2}{2Q^2}$$

or
$$\omega = \omega_0\left(1 - \frac{1}{2Q^2}\right)^{\frac{1}{2}}$$

Q. 3.39. Show that in the resonant *LCR* circuit the maximum potential drop across the inductor

occurs when $\omega = \dfrac{\omega_0}{\left[1 - \dfrac{1}{2Q^2}\right]^{1/2}}$ where $\omega_0 = \dfrac{1}{\sqrt{LC}}$, $Q_0 = \dfrac{L\omega_0}{R}$ and symbols have their usual

meaning.   *(P.U.*, 2007, 2006, 2002, 2001; *G.N.D.U.* 2009)

Ans. Maximum potential difference across inductor. If $E = E_0 \sin \omega t$ is an alternating voltage applied to *LCR* circuit, then steady state solution is given by

$$q = \frac{E_0}{\omega Z_e}\cos(\omega t - \phi)$$

where $Z_e = \sqrt{R^2 + \left(L\omega - \dfrac{1}{C\omega}\right)^2}$ is the electrical impedance of the circuit and $\tan\phi = \dfrac{L\omega - \dfrac{1}{C\omega}}{R}$.

Now $I = \dfrac{dq}{dt} = -\dfrac{E_0}{\omega Z_e}\omega \sin(\omega t - \phi) = -\dfrac{E_0}{Z_e}\sin(\omega t - \phi)$

and $\dfrac{dI}{dt} = -\dfrac{E_0}{Z_e}\omega\cos(\omega t - \phi) = -\dfrac{E_0}{Z_e/\omega}\cos(\omega t - \phi)$

The potential drop across the inductor $= L\dfrac{dI}{dt}$

It has a maximum value when $\dfrac{dI}{dt}$ is maximum and $\dfrac{dI}{dt}$ is maximum when $\dfrac{E_0}{Z_e/\omega}$ is maximum or

when $\dfrac{Z_e}{\omega}$ is minimum $i.e.$, when $\dfrac{d}{d\omega}\left(\dfrac{Z_e}{\omega}\right) = 0$

Now
$$\dfrac{Z_e}{\omega} = \dfrac{1}{\omega}\left[R^2 + \left(L\omega - \dfrac{1}{C\omega}\right)^2\right]^{1/2} = \left[R^2\omega^{-2} + \left(L - \dfrac{1}{C}\omega^{-2}\right)^2\right]^{1/2}$$

∴
$$\dfrac{d}{d\omega}(Z_e/\omega) = \dfrac{1}{2}\left[R^2\omega^{-2} + \left(L - \dfrac{1}{C}\omega^{-2}\right)^2\right]^{-1/2}$$
$$\times\left(-2R^2\omega^{-3} + 2\left(L - \dfrac{1}{C}\omega^{-2}\right)\left(\dfrac{2}{C}\omega^{-3}\right)\right)$$
$$= \left(\dfrac{Z_e}{\omega}\right)^{-1/2}\left[-R^2\omega^{-3} + \dfrac{2}{C}\omega^{-3}\left(L - \dfrac{1}{C\omega}\omega^{-2}\right)\right]$$

But
$$\left(\dfrac{Z_e}{\omega}\right)^{-1/2} \neq 0$$

∴
$$-R^2\omega^{-3} + \dfrac{2}{C}\omega^{-3}\left(L - \dfrac{1}{C}\omega^{-2}\right) = 0$$

or
$$-R^2 + \dfrac{2}{C}\left(L - \dfrac{1}{C\omega^2}\right) = 0$$

or
$$-R^2 + 2\dfrac{L}{C} - \dfrac{2}{C^2\omega^2} = 0$$

or
$$\dfrac{2}{C^2\omega^2} = \dfrac{2L}{C} - R^2$$

or
$$\dfrac{1}{\omega^2} = LC - \dfrac{R^2C^2}{2} \qquad\qquad\qquad ...(i)$$

Now $\omega_0 = \dfrac{1}{\sqrt{LC}}$ or $LC = \dfrac{1}{\omega_0^2}$ ∴ $L = \dfrac{1}{\omega_0^2 C}$

and $Q = \dfrac{L\omega_0}{R} = \dfrac{\omega_0}{R}\left(\dfrac{1}{\omega_0^2 C}\right) = \dfrac{1}{\omega_0 RC}$

$i.e.$, $RC = \dfrac{1}{\omega_0 Q}$

Substituting in Eq. (i), we have

$$\dfrac{1}{\omega^2} = \dfrac{1}{\omega_0^2} - \dfrac{1}{2\omega_0^2 Q^2} = \dfrac{1}{\omega_0^2}\left[1 - \dfrac{1}{2Q^2}\right]$$

$$\therefore \qquad \omega = \frac{\omega_0}{\left[1 - \dfrac{1}{2Q^2}\right]^{1/2}}$$

Q. 3.40. Considering the circuit given below determine the value of ω that produces maximum power dissipation through the resistor R.   (*Pbi.U.*, 1995)

Ans. Maximum power dissipation through R. The circuit given is an *LCR* series circuit connected to an *A.C.* supply

$$E = E_0 \sin \omega t$$

In such a circuit the current is given by

$$I = I_0 \sin(\omega t - \phi)$$

$$= \frac{E_0}{Z_e} \sin(\omega t - \phi)$$

where Z_e is the electrical impedance

$$= \sqrt{R^2 + \left(L\omega - \frac{1}{C\omega}\right)^2}$$

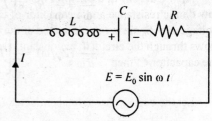

Fig. 3.14

and ϕ the phase difference between current and voltage given by

$$\tan \phi = \frac{L\omega - \dfrac{1}{C\omega}}{R}$$

The power dissipation through the resistor $R = I^2 R$.

It is maximum when I is maximum. For I to be maximum Z_e is a minimum

or

$$\frac{dZ_e}{d\omega} = 0$$

Now

$$\frac{dZ_e}{d\omega} = \frac{d}{d\omega}\left[R^2 + \left(L\omega - \frac{1}{C\omega}\right)^2\right]^{\frac{1}{2}}$$

$$= \frac{d}{d\omega}\left[R^2 + L^2\omega^2 + \frac{1}{C^2\omega^2} - 2\frac{L}{C}\right]^{\frac{1}{2}}$$

$$= \frac{1}{2}\left[R^2 + L^2\omega^2 + \frac{1}{C^2\omega^2} - 2\frac{L}{C}\right]^{-\frac{1}{2}}\left[2L^2\omega - \frac{2}{C^2\omega^3}\right] = 0$$

$$= \frac{2L^2\omega - \dfrac{2}{C^2\omega^3}}{2\left[R^2 + L^2\omega^2 + \dfrac{1}{C^2\omega^2} - 2\dfrac{L}{C}\right]^{\frac{1}{2}}} = 0$$

$$\therefore \qquad 2L^2\omega - \frac{2}{C^2\omega^3} = 0$$

or $\qquad \omega^4 = \dfrac{1}{L^2 C^2}$ or $\quad \omega = \dfrac{1}{\sqrt{LC}}$

Hence the power dissipation in R is a maximum when the value of $\omega = \dfrac{1}{\sqrt{LC}} = $ natural angular frequency of the LC circuit.

Q. 3.41. A parallel L-C circuit is connected to an $A.C.$ source of voltage $E = E_0 \sin \omega t$. Calculate the current in the circuit at any instant. *(P.U., 1995)*

Ans. Current in a parallel LC circuit. In a parallel L-C circuit an inductance L having a very low ohmic resistance and a capacitor of capacitance C are connected in parallel. An $A.C.$ source of voltage $E = E_0 \sin \omega t$ is connected at the points A and B as shown in Fig. 3.15. Suppose a current i flows through the circuit at any instant. Let i_1 be the current through the inductance L and i_2 through the capacitor C, then

$$i = i_1 + i_2 \qquad \qquad ...(i)$$

Let the current through the inductor L vary at the rate $\dfrac{di_1}{dt}$, then

$$E - L\dfrac{di_1}{dt} = 0$$

or $\qquad\qquad L\dfrac{di_1}{dt} = E = E_0 \sin \omega t$

$\therefore \qquad\qquad i_1 = \dfrac{E_0}{L} \int \sin \omega t \, dt$

$$= -\dfrac{E_0}{\omega L} \cos \omega t$$

Let the charge on the capacitor at any instant be q, then

$$q = CE = C\,E_0 \sin \omega t$$

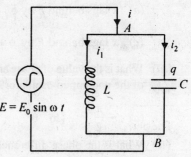

Fig. 3.15

$\therefore$ Current throught the capacitor $i_2 = \dfrac{dq}{dt} = C\omega E_0 \cos \omega t$

Substituting the values of i_1 and i_2 in (i), we have

$$i = i_1 + i_2 = C\omega E_0 \cos \omega t - \dfrac{E_0}{\omega L} \cos \omega t$$

$$= \left(C\omega - \dfrac{1}{\omega L} \right) E_0 \cos \omega t$$

If $C\omega = \dfrac{1}{\omega L}$ the current in the circuit will be zero. This will happen when

$$C\omega = \dfrac{1}{\omega L} \quad \text{or} \quad \omega = \dfrac{1}{\sqrt{LC}} \quad \text{or} \quad n = \dfrac{1}{2\pi\sqrt{LC}}$$

i.e., the frequency of the applied $A.C.$ voltage is equal to the natural frequency of the $L.C.$ circuit.

Q. 3.42. A voltage of 200 volts is applied to series LCR circuit with $L = 10\ \mu H$, $R = 20\ \Omega$ and $C = 0.01\ \mu F$. Calculate bandwidth. *(P.U. 2009)*

Ans. $L = 10\ \mu H = 10 \times 10^{-6}\ H;\quad C = 0.01\ \mu F = 10^{-8}\ F$

$\therefore \qquad\qquad \omega_0 = \dfrac{1}{\sqrt{LC}} = \dfrac{1}{\sqrt{10 \times 10^{-6} \times 10^{-8}}} = \dfrac{10^7}{\sqrt{10}}$

Quality factor $Q = \dfrac{L\omega_0}{R} = \dfrac{10 \times 10^{-6} \times 10^7}{20 \times \sqrt{10}} = \dfrac{5}{\sqrt{10}}$

Also $Q = \dfrac{\omega_0}{\omega_2 - \omega_1}$ where $\omega_2 - \omega_1$ is the bandwidth

$\therefore$ Bandwidth $\omega_2 - \omega_1 = \dfrac{\omega_0}{Q} = \dfrac{10^7}{\sqrt{10}} \times \dfrac{\sqrt{10}}{5} = 0.2 \times 10^6$ rad s^{-1}

Q. 3.43. Mark the correct answer.

(i) A damped mechanical oscillator of frequency ω' is acted upon by an external force $F = F_0 \sin \omega\, t$. If the natural frequency of free oscillations be ω_0, the frequency of oscillations of forced oscillations in steady state will be

(a) ω_0 (b) ω' (c) ω (d) $\omega - \omega'$ (H.P.U., 2002; P.U., 1996)

(ii) Which of the following is the phase relationship between the displacement x of the forced oscillator and the applied force?

(a) x lags behind F by ϕ (b) x leads F by ϕ

(c) x lags behind F by $\phi + \dfrac{\pi}{2}$ (d) x leads F by $\phi + \dfrac{\pi}{2}$ (H.P.U., 1992)

(iii) What is the value of phase angle ϕ when driving force frequency is equal to natural frequency of the undamped oscillator?

(a) $-\dfrac{\pi}{2}$ (b) 0 (c) $+\dfrac{\pi}{2}$ (d) π

(iv) What is the phase difference between driving force and velocity of forced oscillator?

(a) ϕ (b) $\dfrac{\pi}{2} + \phi$ (c) $\phi - \dfrac{\pi}{2}$ (d) $\dfrac{\pi}{2} - \phi$ (H.P.U., 1995)

(v) The quality factor is

(a) directly proportional to the damping resistance (r)

(b) directly proportional to the square of the damping resistance r

(c) inversely proportional to the damping resistance r

(d) inversely proportional to the square of the damping resistance r

(vi) The quality factor of an electric oscillator is given by

(a) $Q = \dfrac{L}{\omega_0 R}$ (b) $Q = \dfrac{R}{\omega_0 L}$ (c) $Q = \dfrac{\omega_0 L}{R}$ (d) $Q = \omega_0 LR$ (H.P.U., 1991)

(vii) In a forced oscillator at very low and very high frequencies the value of which of the following variables tends to zero ?

(a) charge   (b) current   (c) phase   (d) driving e.m.f.   (H.P.U., 1994)

(viii) The resonant frequency of an electric oscillator is given by

(a) $v = 2\pi\sqrt{LC}$ (b) $v = \dfrac{2\pi}{\sqrt{LC}}$ (c) $v = \dfrac{1}{2\pi\sqrt{LC}}$ (d) $v = \dfrac{2\pi}{LC}$

Ans. (i) c   (ii) c   (iii) b   (iv) a   (v) c   (vi) c   (vii) b
(viii) c

EXERCISES

1. A root mean square voltage of 100 volts is applied to a series LCR circuit, having $R = 10$ ohm, $L = 10$ mH and $C = 1\,\mu$ F. Calculate
   - (i) The natural frequency
   - (ii) Current at resonance
   - (iii) Q value of the circuit at resonance
   - (iv) Bandwidth of the circuit.

Hint.

   (i) Natural frequency $v = \dfrac{1}{2\pi\sqrt{LC}} = 1592\,\text{Hz}$

   (ii) Current at Resonance $I_{max} = \dfrac{V_{max}}{R} = \dfrac{\sqrt{2}\,V_{rms}}{R} = \dfrac{\sqrt{2}\times 100}{10} = 14.14\,\text{A}.$

   (iii) Q value $= \omega_0 \dfrac{L}{R} = \dfrac{1}{\sqrt{LC}}\dfrac{L}{R} = \sqrt{\dfrac{L}{C}}\dfrac{1}{R} = \sqrt{\dfrac{10\times 10^{-3}}{1\times 10^{-6}}}\times\dfrac{1}{10} = 10$

   (iv) Bandwidth $\omega_2 - \omega_1$

   $$Q = \dfrac{\omega_0}{\omega_2 - \omega_1}$$

   $$\therefore\quad \omega_2 - \omega_1 = \dfrac{\omega_0}{Q} = \dfrac{1}{\sqrt{LC}}\cdot\dfrac{1}{Q} = \sqrt{\dfrac{1}{10\times 10^{-3}\times 10^{-6}}}\times\dfrac{1}{10}$$

   $$= 1000\,\text{rad s}^{-1}$$

4

Coupled Oscillators

Q. 4.1. (*a*) **Explain the meaning of coupled oscillator.** (*P.U.*, 2001)

(*b*) **Define and explain normal co-ordinates, degrees of freedom and normal modes of vibration of an oscillatory system.** (*Pbi.U.*, 2006, 2002; *H.P.U.*, 2000, 1995, 1994; *P.U.*, 2006, 2005, 2000, 1999; *G.N.D.U.*, 2009, 2008, 2007, 2006, 2000, 1999)

Ans. (*a*) **Coupled oscillator.** In a forced oscillator it is assumed that the external driving force is practically not affected by the forced oscillations of the driven system *i.e.* the flow of energy between the driving agency and the driven system is only in one direction — from the driving agency to the driven system. But in actual practice there is always some feed back of energy, however small.

The two or more oscillators linked together in such a way that an exchange of energy transfer takes place between them are called coupled oscillators.

(*b*) **Normal co-ordinates.** Normal co-ordinates are those co-ordinates which help us to express the equations of motion of the harmonic oscillators of a coupled system in the form of a set of *linear differential equations with constant co-efficients* and in which each equation contains only *one variable.*

Normal modes of vibration. *The manner in which a coupled system oscillates is called a mode.* The mode of a coupled system may be harmonic or non-harmonic.

The harmonic modes of a coupled system are called normal modes.

Normal modes have definite characteristics and are represented by linear differential equations with constant coefficients and only one dependent variable or normal co-ordinates. A normal mode has its own frequency known as *normal frequency. In each* normal mode all the components of the system vibrate with the same normal frequency. The normal modes of vibration are *entirely independent of each other* since the energy associated with a normal mode is never exchanged with the energy associated with another normal mode. The total energy of the oscillator is equal to the sum of the energies of all the normal modes. If at any time only one mode is excited and vibrates the other modes will always be at rest and unexcited and these will acquire no energy from the vibrating mode.

Degrees of freedom. A degree of freedom of a system is the *independent way* by which the system may *acquire energy.* A degree of freedom is assigned its own particular normal co-ordinates. The *number* of degrees of freedom and the number of normal co-ordinates of a system is the number of different ways in which the system can acquire energy. Each harmonic oscillator has two degrees of freedom as it may have *both kinetic* as well as *potential energy.*

The kinetic energy of a simple harmonic oscillator of mass m and having displacement co-ordinate x is given by $\frac{1}{2}m\dot{x}^2 = a\dot{x}^2$ where $a = \frac{1}{2}m$. The potential energy is given by $\frac{1}{2}sx^2 = bx^2$ where s is the stiffness constant.

If the normal modes of a harmonic oscillator are represented by normal co-ordinates X and Y, then the total energy corresponding to the two modes will be

$$E_X = a\dot{X}^2 + bX^2$$

and
$$E_Y = c\dot{Y}^2 + dY^2$$

where a, b, c and d are constants, $a\dot{X}^2$ and $c\dot{Y}^2$ give the kinetic energy and bX^2 and dY^2 the potential energy.

Q. 4.2. (a) What is meant by coupling of two oscillators? Discuss completely the oscillations of two identical stiffness coupled pendulums and write the equation of motion of the system in different cases in terms of normal co-ordinates, X and Y. Differentiate between inphase and out of phase mode.

(G.N.D.U. 2007, 2006; Pbi. U. 2007; H.P.U., 2002, 2001, 1999, 1996; P.U., 2008, 2002)

(b) Give example of normal co-ordinates. *(G.N.D.U. 2007)*

(c) What determines the number of modes of a system of coupled oscillators? *(Pbi. U. 2008)*

Ans. Coupled Oscillators. *Two or more oscillators linked together in such a way that an exchange of energy transfer takes place between them are called coupled oscillators.*

Stiffness coupled system of two pendulums. Consider a coupled system of two identical pendulums each having a pendulum bob of mass m suspended by a light weightless, rigid rod of length l. The bobs are connected by a light spring of stiffness s, whose normal length is equal to the distance between the bobs when none of the two pendulums is displaced from its equilibrium position. Such pendulums are known as **stiffness coupled.**

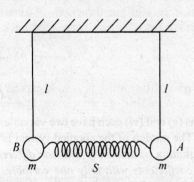

Fig. 4.1

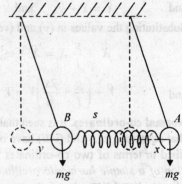

Fig. 4.2

Let the two pendulums A and B be set into vibrations with a *small* amplitude in the plane of the paper and let x and y be the displacements (in the same direction) of the pendulums marked A and B respectively as shown in Fig. 4.1 and Fig. 4.2 then the spring is elongated by a length $(x - y)$ and the corresponding force called into play is $s(x - y)$. The component of the force due to gravity tending to bring the bobs of the pendulums back to its mean position

$$= -\frac{mgx}{l} \text{ for the pendulum } A$$

and
$$= -\frac{mgy}{l} \text{ for the pendulum } B.$$

∴ The equations of motion for the pendulums A and B respectively, are

$$m\ddot{x} = -mg\frac{x}{l} - s(x - y) \qquad \qquad ...(i)$$

and
$$m\ddot{y} = -mg\frac{y}{l} + s(x - y) \qquad \qquad ...(ii)$$

The first term in each equation is the normal simple harmonic motion term and the second term is due to the *coupling of the spring*. If $x > y$ the spring is extended beyond its normal length and will, therefore, apply a force against the acceleration of x but in favour of the acceleration of y. Dividing equations (*i*) and (*ii*) by m and substituting $\frac{g}{l} = \omega_0^2$, we have

$$\ddot{x} + \frac{g}{l}x = \ddot{x} + \omega_0^2 x = -\frac{s}{m}(x - y) \qquad \qquad ...(iii)$$

and

$$\ddot{y} + \frac{g}{l}y = \ddot{y} + \omega_0^2 y = -\frac{s}{m}(y - x) \qquad \qquad ...(iv)$$

Adding (*iii*) and (*iv*), we get

$$\ddot{x} + \ddot{y} + \frac{g}{l}(x + y) = \ddot{x} + \ddot{y} + \omega_0^2(x + y) = 0 \qquad \qquad ...(v)$$

Subtracting (*iv*) from (*iii*), we get

$$\ddot{x} - \ddot{y} + \frac{g}{l}(x - y) = \ddot{x} - \ddot{y} + \left(\omega_0^2 + \frac{2s}{m}\right)(x - y) = 0 \qquad \qquad ...(vi)$$

Let us choose two new co-ordinates X and Y so that

$$X = x + y \qquad \text{and} \qquad Y = x - y$$

then

$$\dot{X} = \dot{x} + \dot{y} \qquad \text{and} \qquad \dot{Y} = \dot{x} - \dot{y}$$

and

$$\ddot{X} = \ddot{x} + \ddot{y} \qquad \text{and} \qquad \ddot{Y} = \ddot{x} - \ddot{y}$$

Substituting the values in (*v*) and (*vi*), we get

$$\ddot{X} + \frac{g}{l}X = \ddot{X} + \omega_0^2 X = 0 \qquad \qquad ...(vii)$$

and

$$\ddot{Y} + \left(\frac{g}{l} + \frac{2s}{m}\right)Y = \ddot{Y} + \left(\omega_0^2 + \frac{2s}{m}\right)Y = 0 \qquad \qquad ...(viii)$$

Normal co-ordinates. It is seen that whereas equations (*v*) and (*vi*) each have two variables, we find that equations (*vii*) and (*viii*) have only one variable. The motion of the coupled system is thus described in terms of two co-ordinates X and Y. *Each equation of motion is a linear differential equation of a simple harmonic oscillator with constant coefficients with only one variable.* The co-ordinates X and Y are therefore *normal co-ordinates* of the coupled system.

Thus the coupled system of two simple pendulums has *two normal modes*, one described by *normal co-ordinate X* and the other by the *normal co-ordinate Y.*

Normal modes (*i*) In phase mode. $Y = 0$. When normal co-ordinate $Y = 0$, $x - y = 0$ *i.e.*, $x = y$ for all times. The motion is completely described by

$$\ddot{X} + \frac{g}{l}X = \ddot{X} + \omega_0^2 X = 0$$

As the relative displacement of the two pendulum always remain the same ($\because x = y$), *the stiffness of the coupling has no effect.* The spring always remains at its normal length. The frequency of oscillations is the same as that of either pendulum in isolation *i. e.*, $\omega_0^2 = \frac{g}{l}$. Both pendulums are always swinging in the same phase. Such vibrations are called *in-phase vibrations* and the corresponding mode is known as *in-phase mode.*

(*ii*) **Out of phase mode :** $X = 0$. When normal co-ordinate $X = 0$, $x + y = 0$ or $x = -y$ for all times. The motion is completely described by

$$\ddot{Y} + \left(\frac{g}{l} + \frac{2s}{m}\right)Y = \ddot{Y}\left(\omega_0^2 + \frac{2s}{m}\right)Y = 0$$

When the displacement (x) of the pendulum A is *positive* that of B (y) is *negative* but equal to that of A $(x = -y)$. At zero displacement the two pendulums will be moving in opposite directions. Thus the periodic motion of the two pendulums will be 180° out of phase. Such vibrations are called *out of phase vibrations* and the corresponding mode is known as *out of phase mode.*

(b) **Example.** As discussed in part (a) under the head **'Normal co-ordinates'** the coupled system of two simple pendulums has two *normal modes*, one described by *normal co-ordinate X* and the other by *normal co-ordinate Y*.

(c) **Number of normal modes.** The number of normal modes of a system of coupled oscillators is equal to the number of particles or number of oscillators linked together to form the coupled system.

Q 4.3. Derive an expression for the total energy of a stiffness coupled system of identical pendulums and show that the total energy of the system remains constant.

(*H.P.U.*, 2003, 2002, 1999, 1995; *P.U.*, 2007, 2005, 1995)

Ans. Total energy of two identical stiffness coupled pendulums. The equation of motion of a stiffness coupled system of two identical pendulums A and B is given by

$$\ddot{X} + \omega_0^2 X = 0 \qquad\qquad ...(i)$$

$$\ddot{Y} + \left(\omega_0^2 + \frac{2s}{m}\right)Y = 0 \qquad\qquad ...(ii)$$

where $X = x + y$ and $Y = x - y$ are the *normal co-ordinates of the system x* and y are the displacement (in the same direction) of the pendulums A and B respectively as shown in Fig. 4.2. in Q. 4.2 $\omega_0^2 = \frac{g}{l}$ where l is the length of the pendulum and s is the stiffness constant. Solving equations (i) and (ii), we get

$$X = x + y = X_0 \cos(\omega_1 t - \phi_1) \qquad\qquad ...(iii)$$

and $$Y = x - y = Y_0 \cos(\omega_2 t - \phi_2) \qquad\qquad ...(iv)$$

X_0 and Y_0 are the *normal mode amplitudes* and $\omega_1 = \omega_0 = \left(\frac{g}{l}\right)^{\frac{1}{2}}$ and

$$\omega_2 = \left(\omega_0^2 + \frac{2s}{m}\right)^{\frac{1}{2}} = \left(\frac{g}{l} + \frac{2s}{m}\right)^{\frac{1}{2}} \text{ are } \textit{normal mode frequencies.}$$

To simplify further discussions, let

$$X_0 = Y_0 = 2a$$

and $$\phi_1 = \phi_2 = 0$$

∴ Equations (iii) and (iv) give

$$X = x + y = 2a \cos \omega_1 t \qquad\qquad ...(v)$$

and $$Y = x - y = 2a \cos \omega_2 t \qquad\qquad ...(vi)$$

Adding (v) and (vi), we get

$$2x = X + Y = 2a \cos \omega_1 t + 2a \cos \omega_2 t$$

$$\therefore \quad x = \frac{1}{2}(X + Y) = a\cos\omega_1 t + a\cos\omega_2 t$$

Subtracting (vi) from (v), we get

$$y = \frac{1}{2}(X - Y) = a\cos\omega_1 t - a\cos\omega_2 t$$

The corresponding velocities are given by

$$\dot{x} = -a\omega_1 \sin\omega_1 t - a\omega_2 \sin\omega_2 t$$

and

$$\dot{y} = -a\omega_1 \sin\omega_1 t + a\omega_2 \sin\omega_2 t.$$

Now let the system be set in motion by displacing the bob x to the right by a distance $x = 2a$ keeping $y = 0$ and both the bobs be released from rest so that $\dot{x} = \dot{y} = 0$ at a time $t = 0$. The motion of pendulum A is given by

$$x = a\cos\omega_1 t + a\cos\omega_2 t = 2a\cos\frac{(\omega_2 - \omega_1)t}{2}\cos\frac{(\omega_1 + \omega_2)t}{2}$$

and the motion of pendulum B is given by

$$y = a\cos\omega_1 t - a\cos\omega_2 t = -2a\sin\frac{(\omega_2 - \omega_1)t}{2}\sin\frac{(\omega_1 + \omega_2)t}{2}$$

$\frac{\omega_2 - \omega_1}{2} = \omega_m$ is called the *modulated* or beat frequency and $\frac{\omega_1 + \omega_2}{2} = \omega_a$ is called the *average* frequency.

Hence the modulated amplitude of pendulum $A = A = 2a\cos\omega_m t$

and $x = A\cos\omega_a t$

The modulated amplitude of pendulum $B = B = 2a\sin\omega_m t$

and $y = -B\sin\omega_a t$

If we assume that the spring is very weak and does not store any energy we can consider the modulated amplitude $2a\cos\omega_m t$ and $2a\sin\omega_m t$ to remain constant over one cycle of average frequency.

$\therefore$ Energy of pendulum A ; $E_A = \dfrac{1}{2}mv^2 = \dfrac{1}{2}m(A\omega_a)^2$

$$= \frac{1}{2}m(2a\cos\omega_m t)^2\,\omega_a^2 = 2ma^2\,\omega_a^2\cos^2\omega_m t$$

Energy of pendulum B; $E_B = \dfrac{1}{2}mv^2 = \dfrac{1}{2}m(B\omega_a)^2$

$$= \frac{1}{2}m(2a\sin\omega_m t)^2\,\omega_a^2 = 2ma^2\,\omega_a^2\sin^2\omega_m t$$

Hence total energy $E = E_A + E_B = 2ma^2\omega_a^2$

Evidently, the total energy $E = E_A + E_B$ is constant as m, a and ω_a are constants.

Also $E_A - E_B = 2ma^2\omega_a^2[\cos^2\omega_m t - \sin^2\omega_m t]$

$$= E\cos 2\omega_m t = E\cos(\omega_2 - \omega_1)t$$

$\therefore$ $E_A = \dfrac{1}{2}E[1 + \cos(\omega_2 - \omega_1)t]$

and $E_B = \dfrac{1}{2}E[1 - \cos(\omega_2 - \omega_1)t].$

This shows that total energy is *constant* but *it flows back* and *forth between the pendulums at the modulated* (or beat) *frequency.*

Thus we see that after drawing aside the bob of the first pendulum by a distance $2a$ and releasing it the pendulum shows the cosine behaviour at a frequency ω_a which is the average of the two normal mode frequencies and its amplitude also varies according to the cosine law at a low frequency of half the difference between the normal mode frequencies. On the other hand pendulum 2 starts from zero and vibrates according to the sine law with the same average frequency and its amplitude builds up to $2a$ and then decays according to sine law at the same low frequency of half the difference between the normal mode frequencies.

The initial configuration $x = 2a$, $y = 0$ can be decomposed into X and Y modes as shown in Fig. 4.3. The X mode i.e., $x = y = a$ so that $X_0 = x + y = 2a$ is known as the 'in phase' mode and the Y mode i.e., $x = a, y = -a$ so that $Y_0 = x - y = 2a$ is known as the out of phase mode.

As the Y-mode has a higher frequency it will gain half a vibration (phase difference π radian) on the X-mode after a number of vibrations and the combination of X and Y mode then will give $x = 0$ and

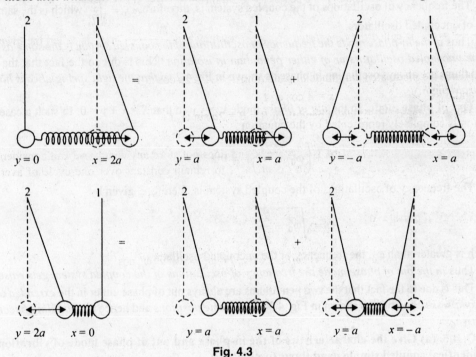

Fig. 4.3

$y = 2a$ as shown in the lower Fig. 4.3. After some time when Y gains another half a vibration $x = 2a$ and $y = 0$. Thus the pendulums only exchange energy the normal modes do not. The 'in phase' mode remains 'in phase' mode and 'out of phase mode' remains 'out of phase' mode.

Q. 4.4. Which different types of coupling are used for coupling two oscillators? Show that in the in phase mode, the frequency of oscillations is the same as of uncoupled oscillators whereas in the out of phase mode, the frequency of oscillations gets raised. (Pbi.U., 1990)

Ans. Types of coupling. Two oscillators are coupled together to bring about an exchange of energy between them. The common coupling components for mechanical oscillators may be 'stiffness' or 'mass' and in case of electrical oscillators it may be 'capacitance' or 'inductance'. Capacitance and inductance are energy storing electrical components and coupling through them consumes no power, there by making it possible for the energy transfer to take place over a number of oscillations. Coupling may also be done through the 'resistance' component but this causes an inevitable loss of energy so that the amplitude goes on rapidly falling.

In phase mode. The differential equations of motion of coupled system of two identical (mechanical) oscillators say two simple pendulums in terms of normal co-ordinates X and Y are given by

$$\ddot{X} + \frac{g}{l} X = \ddot{X} + \omega_0^2 X = 0$$

and

$$\ddot{Y} + \left(\frac{g}{l} + \frac{2s}{m} \right) Y = \ddot{Y} + \left(\omega_0^2 + \frac{2s}{m} \right) Y = 0$$

where $X = x + y$ and $Y = x - y$; x and y being the displacements of the two (mechanical) oscillators, s the stiffness and m the *mass*. For proof see **Q. 4.2** Eq. (*vii*) and (*viii*).

In the *in-phase* mode $x = y$ so that $Y = x - y = 0$. In such a case the motion is completely represented by the equation

$$\ddot{X} + \frac{g}{l} X = \ddot{X} + \omega_0^2 X = 0$$

The frequency of oscillations of the coupled system is, therefore, $\omega_0 = \sqrt{\dfrac{g}{l}}$ which is the same as that of uncoupled oscillators.

Thus *in the in-phase mode the frequency of oscillations of the coupled system is the same as that of the uncoupled oscillators or of either pendulum in isolation.* This is due to the fact that the two pendulums are always oscillating in phase as shown in Fig 4.2 *so that the light spring always has its natural length.*

Out of phase mode. In the *out of phase* mode $x = -y$ so that $X = x + y = 0$. In such a case the motion is completely represented by the equation

$$\ddot{Y} + \left(\omega_0^2 + \frac{2s}{m} \right) Y = 0$$

The frequency of oscillations of the coupled system is, therefore, given by

$$\omega' = \sqrt{\omega_0^2 + \frac{2s}{m}}$$

which is greater than ω_0, the frequency of the uncoupled oscillators.

Thus *in the out of phase mode the frequency of oscillations of the coupled system gets raised.*

This is due to the fact that the two pendulums are always out of phase either in the *extended* or in the *compressed* position as shown in Fig. 4.3 *i.e. extreme positions* and hence the *coupling becomes effective.*

Q. 4.5. (a) Give the characteristics of the in-phase and out of phase mode of vibration of two identical coupled simple pendulums (oscillators).

(*G.N.D.U.*, 2003, 2002, 2001; *Pbi.U.*, 2003; *H.P.U.*, 2000; *P.U.*, 2000, 1999)

(b) What is the value of ratio of displacements for in-phase and out of phase mode ?

(*P.U.* 2007)

Ans. (a) Two oscillating, identical coupled simple pendulums have two normal modes of vibration

(*i*) In-phase mode and (*ii*) Out of phase mode, each having its own characteristics.

(*i*) **Characteristics of in phase mode.** (*i*) The in-phase mode can be excited by displacing the bobs of the two pendulums to the same side by the same amount and then letting them oscillate purely on their own.

(*ii*) The equation of the in-phase mode is

$$\ddot{X} + \omega_0^2 X = 0 \qquad \qquad ...(i)$$

It describes the oscillatory behaviour of the system when

$$Y = (x - y) = 0 \quad \text{or} \quad x = y$$

(iii) The displacement of both the (bobs) or masses is the *same in magnitude* as well as in *direction* and both the masses continuously oscillate in the *same phase*. It means that both the pendulums pass through their mean position or through either of the extreme positions simultaneously.

(iv) The amplitude of the two simple pendulums is the same *i.e. a.*

(v) The shape or configuration of the mode is $\dfrac{x}{y} = +1$

(vi) Each pendulum executes simple harmonic oscillation at frequency $\omega_0 = \sqrt{g/l}$ which is the natural frequency of free oscillations of either pendulum in isolation.

(vii) In the in-phase mode there is no effect of the stiffness term s of the coupling on the motion of the two masses because the spring always has its natural length — it is neither stretched nor compressed.

(viii) A solution of Eq. (i) gives

$$X = X_0 \cos (\omega_0 t - \phi).$$

If the maximum value of x and y be a, then $X_0 = 2a$ is the *normal mode amplitude.*

(ii) **Characteristics of out of phase mode** (i) The out of phase mode can be excited by displacing the bobs of the two pendulums in opposite directions by the same amount and then let them oscillate freely on their own.

(ii) The equation of the out of phase mode is

$$\ddot{Y} + \left(\omega_0^2 + \frac{2s}{m} \right) Y = 0 \qquad \qquad \text{...(ii)}$$

It describes the oscillatory behaviour of the system when

$$X = (x + y) = 0 \quad \text{or} \quad x = -y$$

(iii) The displacement of either mass (bob) is equal in magnitude but opposite in direction to the other mass and the two masses continuously oscillate *out of phase* by an angle of 180° or π-radian with respect to each other.

It means that both the pendulums pass through their mean position (in opposite directions) or are at their (opposite) extreme positions simultaneously.

(iv) The amplitude of the two simple pendulums is the same *i.e., 'a'*

(v) The shape or configuration of the mode is $\dfrac{x}{y} = -1$.

(vi) Each pendulum executes simple harmonic oscillations at a frequency

$$\omega' = \sqrt{\frac{g}{l} + \frac{2s}{m}} = \sqrt{\omega_0^2 + \frac{2s}{m}}$$

which is higher than the natural frequency of the free oscillations of either pendulum.

(vii) In the out of phase mode the coupling term s dominates the motion of the two masses and raises the frequency of oscillation. It is because the coupling spring is either in the stretched or in the compressed state. Only once in one time period or oscillation the spring acquires its normal length when the masses pass through their mean positions.

(viii) A solution of Eq. (ii) gives

$$Y = Y_0 \cos (\omega' t - \phi')$$

If the maximum value of x and y be a, then $Y_0 = 2a$ is the normal mode amplitude.

NOTE. X_0 and Y_0 are purely mathematical quantities and do not represent the amplitude of the oscillation of either pendulum which has a value $a = \dfrac{X_0}{2}$ for the in-phase mode and $a = \dfrac{Y_0}{2}$ for the out of phase mode.

(b) For **in-phase mode** $x = y$ or $\dfrac{x}{y} = +1$

For **out of phase mode** $x = -y$ or $\dfrac{x}{y} = -1$

For details See part (a).

Q. 4.6. (a) **One of the pendulums of a coupled oscillator is clamped while the other is free to oscillate. Show that the frequency of the single pendulum is given by**

$$\nu = \frac{1}{2\pi}\sqrt{\frac{g}{l} + \frac{s}{m}} .$$ (G.N.D.U., 1999)

(b) **Two identical pendulums are connected by a light spring attached to their bobs. The mass of each bob is 10 gm and the stiffness constant of the spring is 8×10^{-3} Nm^{-1}. When one pendulum is clamped the period of the other is found to be 1.20 sec. Find the periods of the normal modes.**

(H.P.U., 2001)

Ans. (a) **Frequency when one pendulum is clamped.** Suppose the two pendulums A and B of length l and having bobs of mass m are coupled together by a light spring of stiffness constant s as shown in Fig. 4.1, **Q. 4.2.** Then, as proved in **Q. 4.2** the equations of motion of the pendulums A and B respectively, when the coupled system is set into oscillation are

$$m\frac{d^2x}{dt^2} = -mg\frac{x}{l} - s(x - y)$$

and

$$m\frac{d^2y}{dt^2} = -mg\frac{y}{l} + s(x - y)$$

When the pendulum B is clamped, $y = 0$ and the equation of motion of A is given by

$$m\frac{d^2x}{dt^2} = -mg\frac{x}{l} - sx$$

or

$$\frac{d^2x}{dt^2} = -\left(\frac{g}{l} + \frac{s}{m}\right)x$$

This is the equation of motion of a simple harmonic oscillator and the angular frequency of oscillation ω_1 is given by

$$\omega_1 = \sqrt{\frac{g}{l} + \frac{s}{m}} .$$

and frequency

$$\nu_1 = \frac{1}{2\pi}\sqrt{\frac{g}{l} + \frac{s}{m}} .$$

When the pendulum A is clamped $x = 0$ and the equation of motion of B is given by

$$m\frac{d^2y}{dt^2} = -mg\frac{y}{l} + s(-y)$$

or

$$\frac{d^2y}{dt^2} = -\left(\frac{g}{l} + \frac{s}{m}\right)y$$

This is again the equation of motion of a simple harmonic oscillator and the angular frequency of oscillation ω_2 is given by $\omega_2 = \sqrt{\dfrac{g}{l} + \dfrac{s}{m}}$

and frequency $$\nu_2 = \frac{1}{2\pi} \sqrt{\frac{g}{l} + \frac{s}{m}}$$

Thus whether the pendulum A is clampled or the pendulum B, the frequency of oscillation of the unclamped single pendulum is given by

$$\nu = \frac{1}{2\pi} \sqrt{\frac{g}{l} + \frac{s}{m}}$$

or $$\omega = \sqrt{\frac{g}{l} + \frac{s}{m}}$$

(b) When one of the pendulums is clamped the angular frequency ω of the other is given by

$$\omega = \sqrt{\frac{g}{l} + \frac{s}{m}}$$

But $\frac{g}{l} = \omega_0^2$ where ω_0 is the normal mode frequency of the in-phase mode.

$\therefore$ $$\omega = \sqrt{\omega_0^2 + \frac{s}{m}}$$

or $$\omega^2 = \omega_0^2 + \frac{s}{m} \qquad \qquad \qquad ...(i)$$

Here $T = 1.20$ sec. $\therefore$ $\omega = \frac{2\pi}{T} = \frac{2\pi}{1.20} = 5.237 \ s^{-1}$

$$s = 8 \times 10^{-3} \ Nm^{-1} ; \quad m = 10 \ gm = 10^{-2} \ kg$$

Substituting in Eq. (i), we have

$$(5.237)^2 = \omega_0^2 + \frac{8 \times 10^{-3}}{10^{-2}}$$

or $$\omega_0^2 = (5.237)^2 - 0.8 = 26.626$$

$\therefore$ $$\omega_0 = 5.16 \ sec^{-1}$$

and $$T_0 = \frac{2\pi}{\omega_0} = 1.218 = 1.22 \ sec.$$

This is the time period of the in-phase mode.

The normal mode frequency of the out of phase mode is given by

$$\omega_2 = \sqrt{\omega_0^2 + \frac{2s}{m}}$$

$\therefore$, $$\omega_2^2 = 26.626 + \frac{2 \times 8 \times 10^{-3}}{10^{-2}} = 26.626 + 1.6$$

$$= 28.226$$

$$\omega_2 = 5.312$$

or

Hence $$T_2 = \frac{2\pi}{\omega_2} = 1.18 \ sec.$$

This is the time period of the out of phase mode.

Exercise. *Two identical pendulums are coupled together with light spring of stiffness constant 0.12 Nm^{-1} and mass of each bob is 0.15 kg. When one pendulum is clamped the period of the other is 1.25 s. Find the normal mode time periods.*

(*P.U.* 2007)

Hint. When one pendulum is clamped, period of the other

$$T = 1.25 \text{ s}$$

$$\therefore \qquad \omega = \frac{2\pi}{T} = \frac{2\pi}{1.25} = 5.03 \text{ s}^{-1}$$

$s = 0.12$ Nm^{-1} ; $m = 0.15$ kg

$$\therefore \qquad (5.03)^2 = \omega_0^2 + \frac{0.12}{0.15}$$

or $$\omega_0^2 = (5.03)^2 - \frac{0.12}{0.15} = 25.3 - 0.8 = 24.5$$

or $$\omega_0 = 4.95 \text{ s}^{-1}$$

$$\therefore \qquad T_0 = \frac{2\pi}{\omega_0} = 1.27 \text{ s} \qquad \text{(This is the time period of in-phase mode)}$$

$$\omega_2 = \sqrt{\omega_0^2 + \frac{2s}{m}} = \sqrt{24.5 + \frac{0.24}{0.15}} = 5.11 \text{ s}^{-1}$$

and $$T_2 = \frac{2\pi}{5.11} = 1.23 \text{ s} \text{ (This is the time period of out of phase mode)}$$

Q. 4.7. Give a general method of finding normal mode frequencies and obtain expression for the normal mode frequencies of stiffness coupled pendulums.

(*Pbi. U.* 2005; *G.N.D.U.*, 2002, *P.U.*, 2000; *H.P.U.*, 1994, 1993)

Ans. General method of finding normal mode frequencies. Consider a system of two coupled simple pendulums of the same length coupled by a spring of stiffness s, then their equations of motion are

$$m\ddot{x} + \frac{mg}{l}x + s(x - y) = 0 \qquad \qquad ...(i)$$

and $$m\ddot{y} + \frac{mg}{l}y - s(x - y) = 0 \qquad \qquad ...(ii)$$

where x and y are the displacements of the bobs of the two pendulums respectively from their mean positions; l is the length of each pendulum, m the mass of each pendulum bob as proved in Eq. (*i*) and (*ii*) Q. 4.2.

Now, when a coupled system oscillates in a *single normal mode* each component of the system vibrates with the frequency of that mode. Therefore, supposing that the system of the coupled pendulums vibrates only in one of its normal modes, let the frequency be ω, then the solutions of the above equations are

$$x = A \cos \omega t$$
and $$y = B \cos \omega t$$

where A and B are the displacement amplitude of x and y at the frequency ω.

$$\therefore \qquad \ddot{x} = -A\omega^2 \cos\omega t \text{ and } \ddot{y} = -B\omega^2 \cos\omega t$$

Substituting in (*i*) and (*ii*), we have

$$\left[-m\omega^2 A + \frac{mg}{l}A + s(A - B) \right] \cos\omega t = 0 \qquad \qquad ...(iii)$$

and $$\left[-m\omega^2 B + \frac{mg}{l}B - s(A - B) \right] \cos\omega t = 0 \qquad \qquad ...(iv)$$

First normal mode frequency. Adding (*iii*) and (*iv*), we get

$$(A + B)\left(-m\omega^2 + \frac{mg}{l}\right) = 0 \qquad \qquad ...(v)$$

This equation is satisfied when $\omega^2 = \frac{g}{l}$.

Thus this gives the *first normal mode frequency (or frequency of in-phase mode)* $\omega = \sqrt{\frac{g}{l}}$.

Second normal mode frequency. Subtracting (*iv*) from (*iii*), we get

$$(A - B)\left(-m\omega^2 + \frac{mg}{l} + 2s\right) = 0 \qquad \qquad ...(vi)$$

This equation is satisfied when

$$\omega^2 = \frac{g}{l} + \frac{2s}{m}$$

This gives the *second normal mode, frequency, (or frequency of out of phase mode)*

$$\omega = \sqrt{\frac{g}{l} + \frac{2s}{m}}$$

In phase conditions. Substituting $\omega^2 = \frac{g}{l}$ in (*vi*), we have

$$(A - B) \, 2s = 0$$

or $$A - B = 0$$

∴ $$A = B$$

which gives the *in phase* condition.

Out of phase condition. Substituting $\omega^2 = \frac{g}{l} + \frac{2s}{m}$ in (*v*), we have

$$(A + B) \, 2s = 0$$

∴ $$A + B = 0$$

or $$A = -B$$

which gives the *out of phase* or (antiphase) condition.

Q. 4.8. (*a*) Do normal modes exchange energy with each other ?

(*b*) Show that normal modes are independent of each other and there is no exchange of energy between two coupled pendulums. What do you mean by the statement that normal co-ordinates are independent of each other? (*P.U.*, 2006, 2003, 2000, 1999, 1995; *Pbi.U.*, 2002, 2000, 1999, 1991; *H.P.U.*, 2003, 2002, 2000, 1993, 1992)

(*c*) What is the significance of normal modes of a coupled system ? (*G.N.D.U.* 2008, *P.U.* 2007)

Ans. (*a*) There is no exchange of energy between two normal modes of a coupled system of two oscillators.

(*b*) No exchange of energy between normal modes. The equation of motion of a stiffness coupled system of two identical simple pendulums A and B is given by

$$\ddot{X} + \omega_0^2 \, X = 0 \qquad \qquad ...(i)$$

and $$\ddot{Y} + \left(\omega_0^2 + \frac{2s}{m}\right) Y = 0 \qquad \qquad ...(ii)$$

where $X = x + y$ and $Y = x - y$ are the normal co-ordinates of the system. x and y are the displacements (in the same direction) of the pendulums A and B respectively, $\omega_0^2 = \frac{g}{l}$ where l is the length of the pendulum and s the stiffness constant. For proof see **Q. 4.2** Eq. (*vii*) and (*viii*)

Solving equation (*i*) and (*ii*), we get

$$X = x + y = X_0 \cos(\omega_1 t - \phi_1)$$

and

$$Y = x - y = Y_0 \cos(\omega_2 t - \phi_2)$$

where X_0 and Y_0 are the normal mode amplitudes, $\omega_1 = \omega_0 = \left(\dfrac{g}{l}\right)^{\frac{1}{2}}$ and $\omega_2 = \left(\omega_0^2 + \dfrac{2s}{m}\right)^{\frac{1}{2}} = \left(\dfrac{g}{l} + \dfrac{2s}{m}\right)^{\frac{1}{2}}$

are normal mode frequencies.

Putting

$$X_0 = Y_0 = 2a, \text{ we have}$$

$$X = 2 a \cos(\omega_1 t - \phi_1)$$

and

$$Y = 2 a \cos(\omega_2 t - \phi_2)$$

As $X = x + y$, X mode is known as *in-phase* mode. The total energy of the system in X-mode is given by

$$E_x = \frac{1}{2} m \omega_1^2 (2a)^2 = 2 m a^2 \omega_1^2$$

As $Y = x - y$, Y-mode is known as *out of phase* mode. The total energy of the system in Y-mode is given by

$$E_y = \frac{1}{2} m \omega_2^2 (2a)^2 = 2 m a^2 \omega_2^2$$

Both E_x and E_y do not vary with time. They are constant quantities. Therefore, we conclude that no exchange of energy takes place from one normal mode to another. In other words, normal modes are independent of each other.

When we say that normal co-ordinates are independent of each other, we mean that between the in-phase mode represented by the normal co-ordinate X and the out of phase mode represented by the normal co-ordinate Y there is no exchange of energy and hence the two are independent of each other.

(c) **Significance of normal modes.** A coupled system can be set into oscillations in an infinite number of ways and the oscillations may not be periodic in all such cases. The normal modes i.e. *in-phase mode* and *out of phase mode* are the only possible ways in which each component of the coupled system executes simple harmonic oscillations with the same frequency and the same amplitude.

The significance of the normal modes lies in the fact that the general motion of the coupled system is given by the superposition of the normal modes.

Thus, if we know the details of the normal modes, we can obtain the general motion of the oscillating system from the initial conditions.

Suppose [as discussed in part (*b*)] the normal co-ordinates of the two oscillating systems A and B are given by

$$X = x + y = X_0 \cos(\omega_1 t - \phi_1)$$

and

$$Y = x - y = Y_0 \cos(\omega_2 t - \phi_2)$$

where X_0 and Y_0 are the normal mode amplitudes, x and y are the displacements in the *same direction* of coupled system A and B respectively, then

$$x = \frac{X + Y}{2} = \frac{1}{2} X_0 \cos(\omega_1 t - \phi_1) + \frac{1}{2} Y_0 \cos(\omega_2 t - \phi_2)$$

and

$$y = \frac{X - Y}{2} = \frac{1}{2} X_0 \cos(\omega_1 t - \phi_1) - \frac{1}{2} Y_0 \cos(\omega_2 t - \phi_2)$$

Here X_0, Y_0, ϕ_1 and ϕ_2 are the four unknown quantities. When these quantities are known the general motion of the system is completely known. In this lies the significance of studying the normal modes of a coupled system.

Q. 4.9. Two masses m_1 and m_2 are coupled by a spring of stiffnes s. The masses are pulled apart and released. Show that their motion is simple harmonic. Prove that the system will oscillate with a frequency

$$\sqrt{\frac{s}{\mu}} \quad \textbf{where} \quad \mu = \frac{m_1 m_2}{m_1 + m_2}. \qquad \text{(\textit{P.U.}, 2001, 2000, 1996, 1995)}$$

Ans. Frequency of a two body coupled oscillator. Consider two masses m_1 and m_2 connected by a spring of stiffness or force constant s. When the two masses are displaced from their equilibrium positions, the spring either contracts or extends, depending upon the displacement of the masses. This causes a linear restoring force to be produced in the spring and both masses begin to vibrate harmonically about their equilibrium position. Such a system is known as a *two body oscillator* or *coupled oscillator*. A familiar example is a diatomic molecule in which the two atoms are connected by some internal force known as '*bond*'.

As no external force acts on the system, the centre of mass either remains stationary or moves with constant velocity. If we consider the motion in the centre of mass frame supposed stationary, the two masses will move in opposite directions.

Let l be the normal length of the spring. If x_1 and x_2 are the co-ordinates of the ends of the spring at any instant, then elongation of the spring $x = (x_1 - x_2) - l$.

The value of x will be *positive* if the spring is stretched, *zero* if it has normal length and *negative* when the spring is compressed. Let us suppose x is positive. The forces exerted by the spring on m_1 and m_2 are equal and opposite and their magnitude is sx.

The equations of motion of m_1 and m_2 are

$$m_1 \frac{d^2 x_1}{dt^2} = -sx \qquad \text{...(i)}$$

$$m_2 \frac{d^2 x_2}{dt^2} = sx \qquad \text{...(ii)}$$

Multiplying (i) by m_2 and (ii) by m_1 and subtracting (ii) from (i), we have

$$m_1 m_2 \frac{d^2 x_1}{dt^2} - m_1 m_2 \frac{d^2 x_2}{dt^2} = -s(m_1 + m_2)x$$

or

$$\frac{m_1 m_2}{m_1 + m_2} \frac{d_2}{dt^2}(x_1 - x_2) = -sx \qquad \text{...(iii)}$$

As $\quad x = (x_1 - x_2) - l$

$$\frac{dx}{dt} = \frac{d}{dt}(x_1 - x_2) \qquad\qquad [\because l = \text{a constant}]$$

and

$$\frac{d^2 x}{dt^2} = \frac{d^2}{dt^2}(x_1 - x_2)$$

Substituting in (iii), we have

$$\frac{m_1 m_2}{m_1 + m_2} \frac{d^2 x}{dt^2} = -sx \qquad \text{...(iv)}$$

Now $\dfrac{m_1 m_2}{m_1 + m_2} = \mu$ the reduced mass of the system

$\therefore$ From relation (iv)

$$\mu \frac{d^2 x}{dt^2} = -sx \quad \text{or} \quad \mu \frac{d^2 x}{dt^2} + sx = 0$$

This is the equation of a *simple harmonic motion*. The time period T is given by

$$T = 2\pi \sqrt{\frac{\mu}{s}}$$

Both the masses m_1 and m_2 execute simple harmonic motion with time period T along the same straight line, but the two motions differ in phase by π.

Frequency. The frequency n of the two body coupled oscillator is given by

$$n = \frac{1}{T} = \frac{1}{2\pi} \sqrt{\frac{s}{\mu}}$$

or   Angular frequency $\omega = 2\pi n = \sqrt{\frac{s}{\mu}}$

Q. 4.10. The angular vibrational frequency of CO molecule is 0.6×10^{15} s^{-1}. Calculate the amount of work required for stretching it by 0.5 Å from the equilibrium position.   (*P.U.*, 1990)

Ans. Reduced mass of CO molecule

$$\mu = \frac{m_1 \times m_2}{m_1 + m_2} = \frac{12 \times 16}{12 + 16} \text{ a.m.u} = 6.85 \times 1.67 \times 10^{-27} \text{ kg}$$

(where 1 a.m.u. $= 1.67 \times 10^{-27}$ kg)

Angular vibrational frequency $\omega = 2\pi n = 0.6 \times 10^{15}$ s^{-1}

Now $\omega = \sqrt{\frac{s}{\mu}}$

∴   Inter-atomic force constant $s = \omega^2 \mu$
$$= (0.6 \times 10^{15})^2 \times 6.85 \times 1.67 \times 10^{-27}$$
$$= 4.118 \times 10^3 \text{ Nm}^{-1}$$

Work done for stretching by $x = 0.5$ Å $= 0.5 \times 10^{-10}$ m

$$W = \frac{1}{2} sx^2 = \frac{1}{2} \times 4.118 \times 10^3 \times 0.5 \times 0.5 \times 10^{-20} = 5.15 \times 10^{-18} \text{ J}$$

Q. 4.11. Sodium chloride molecule vibrates with natural frequency 1.14×10^{13} Hz. Calculate the interatomic force constant for the molecule. Given mass of sodium atom = 23 a.m.u. and that of chlorine atom is 35 a.m.u. (1 a.m.u. = 1.67×10^{-27} kg).   (*P.U.*, 1993)

Ans. The vibrations of sodium chloride molecule are similar to the vibrations of a mechanical system of two masses coupled by a spring of force constant s, the frequency of which is given by

$$n = \frac{1}{2\pi} \sqrt{\frac{s}{\mu}}$$

where μ is the reduced mass equal to $\frac{m_1 m_2}{m_2 + m_2}$.

∴   Reduced mass of sodium chloride molecule

$$\mu = \frac{23 \times 35}{23 + 35} = 13.88 \text{ a.m.u.} = 13.88 \times 1.67 \times 10^{-27} = 23.18 \times 10^{-27} \text{ kg}$$

Now frequency $n = \frac{1}{2\pi} \sqrt{\frac{s}{\mu}}$

$$\therefore \qquad n^2 = \frac{1}{4\pi^2} \cdot \frac{s}{\mu}$$

or
$$s = 4\pi^2 n^2 \mu = 4 \times \left(\frac{22}{7}\right)^2 \times (1.14 \times 10^{13})^2 \times 23.18 \times 10^{-27}$$
$$= 118.9 \ \text{Nm}^{-1}.$$

Q. 4.12. Explain the inductance coupling of two electrical oscillators and define co-efficient of coupling.(*G.N.D.U.*, 2007, 2006, 2001, 1991; *P.U.*, 2004, 2001; *H.P.U.*, 2001, 1999, 1994; *Pbi.U.*, 1993)

Ans. Inductively coupled circuits. Two electrical circuits are said to be inductively coupled when the magnetic flux due to the current flowing in one circuit threads the second circuit. The two circuits are then said to have a *mutual inductance*. According to Faraday's law of electro-magnetic induction, whenever the magnetic flux in one circuit changes an induced *e.m.f.* is set up in the other which is proportional to the time rate of change of magnetic flux and lasts only for the time the change is taking place. The most familiar example is that of a transformer whose working depends on the mutual induction between its primary and secondary coils.

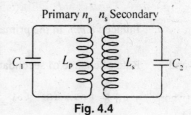

Fig. 4.4

The power source is connected to the primary and the secondary is wound over the primary in the *same sense*.

Two inductively coupled electrical circuits are shown in Fig. 4.4.

Let n_p represent the number of turns in the primary coil. If ϕ is the magnetic flux set up in the *primary* when a unit current flows through a single turn of the primary coil, then assuming that there is no leakage of flux outside the coil,

Flux linked with *each* primary turn $= n_p \phi$

$\therefore$ Total flux linked with primary coil $= n_p \cdot n_p \phi$

or
$$L_p = n_p^2 \phi$$

where L_p is the coefficient of self-induction of the primary. Similarly, if a unit current flowing through a single turn of the secondary coil also produces a magnetic flux ϕ, then

Flux linked with *each* secondary turn $= n_s \phi$

or
$$L_s = n_s^2 \phi$$

where L_s is the coefficient of self-induction of the secondary.

If we suppose that all the lines of magnetic flux due to a unit current in the primary, thread all the turns of the secondary, then

Total flux lines linking the secondary $= n_s (n_p \phi)$

or
$$M = n_s n_p \phi = \sqrt{L_p L_s}$$

where M is the coefficient of mutual induction between the two coils.

Co-efficient of coupling. The above result is true only when there is no leakage of magnetic flux. In practice, however, some leakage of flux does take place and $M < \sqrt{L_p L_s}$.

The ratio $\dfrac{M}{\sqrt{L_p L_s}} = k$ is called the *coefficient of coupling.*

For *small* value of k the two circuits have a *loose coupling* and are said to be *lightly coupled.*

Q. 4.13. Explain transfer of energy between two resistance free electric circuits which are inductively coupled. When is the coupling loose or tight? Obtain an expression for the normal mode frequencies and show that they are almost equal for loose coupling.

(*P.U.*, 2009, 2007, 2006, 2004, 2003, 2002, 2001, 2000; *Pbi.U.*, 2007, 2006, 2005, 2003, 2002, 1999; *H.P.U.*, 2001, 2000, 1999, 1996, 1994; *G.N.D.U.*, 2009, 2008, 2006, 1996)

Ans. Energy transfer. To consider the *energy transfer* between the two inductively coupled circuits as shown in Fig. 4.4, let the two circuits be made to oscillate with a frequency ω and let $I_p = I_1 e^{i\omega t}$ and $I_s = I_2 e^{i\omega t}$ be the currents in the two circuits respectively, then

$$\text{Rate of change of primary current} = \frac{dI_p}{dt}$$

$$= \frac{d}{dt} I_1 e^{i\omega t} = i\omega I_1 e^{i\omega t} = i\omega I_p$$

$\therefore$ Induced *e.m.f.* in the primary coil $= -L_p \dfrac{dI_p}{dt} = -i\omega L_p I_p$

and   Rate of change of secondary current $= \dfrac{dI_s}{dt}$

$$= \frac{d}{dt} I_2 e^{i\omega t} = i\omega I_2 e^{i\omega t} = i\omega I_s$$

$\therefore$ Induced *e.m.f.* in the secondary coil $= -L_s \dfrac{dI_s}{dt} = -i\omega L_s I_s$

and   Potential difference across the capacitor C_1 (Fig. 4.4) in the primary circuit $= \dfrac{\int I_p \, dt}{C_1}$

$$= \frac{\int I_1 e^{i\omega t} \, dt}{C_1} = \frac{I_1 e^{i\omega t}}{i\omega C_1} = -\frac{i I_p}{\omega C_1}$$

Potential difference across the capacitor C_2 (Fig. 4.4) in the secondary circuit $= \dfrac{\int I_s \, dt}{C_2}$

$$= \frac{\int I_2 e^{i\omega t} \, dt}{C_2} = \frac{I_2 e^{i\omega t}}{i\omega C_2} = -\frac{i I_s}{\omega C_2}$$

If the two circuits are considered free from resistance and have inductance and capacitance only, then the *e.m.f.* equations for the primary and the secondary respectively are

$$-L_p \frac{dI_p}{dt} + \frac{\int I_p \, dt}{C_1} - M \frac{dI_s}{dt} = 0$$

and

$$-L_s \frac{dI_s}{dt} + \frac{\int I_s \, dt}{C_2} - M \frac{dI_p}{dt} = 0$$

Substituting the values of various quantities, we have

$$i\omega L_p I_p - \frac{i}{\omega C_1} I_p + i\omega M I_s = 0 \qquad \ldots(i)$$

and

$$i\omega L_s I_s - \frac{i}{\omega C_2} I_s + i\omega M I_p = 0 \qquad \ldots(ii)$$

Multiplying (i) by $\dfrac{\omega}{i L_p}$ and (ii) by $\dfrac{\omega}{i L_s}$, we have

$$\omega^2 I_p - \frac{I_p}{L_p C_1} + \frac{M}{L_p}\omega^2 I_s = 0$$

and

$$\omega^2 I_s - \frac{I_s}{L_s C_2} + \frac{M}{L_s}\omega^2 I_p = 0$$

Now $\dfrac{1}{L_p C_1} = \omega_1^2$ where ω_1 is the *natural frequency* of the *primary circuit* containing inductance

L_p and capacitance C_1 and $\dfrac{1}{L_s C_2} = \omega_2^2$ where ω_2 is the *natural frequency* of the *secondary* circuit containing inductance L_s and capacitance C_2.

Substituting $\dfrac{1}{L_p C_1} = \omega_1^2$ and $\dfrac{1}{L_s C_2} = \omega_2^2$, we get

$$I_p(\omega_1^2 - \omega^2) = \frac{M}{L_p}\omega^2 I_s$$

and

$$I_s(\omega_2^2 - \omega^2) = \frac{M}{L_s}\omega^2 I_p$$

Multiplying we have

$$I_p I_s (\omega_1^2 - \omega^2)(\omega_2^2 - \omega^2) = \frac{M^2}{L_p L_s}\omega^4 I_s I_p$$

or

$$(\omega_1^2 - \omega^2)(\omega_2^2 - \omega^2) = \frac{M^2}{L_p L_s}\omega^4 = k^2\omega^4$$

where $k = \dfrac{M}{\sqrt{L_p L_s}}$ is the coefficient of coupling.

To simplify put $\omega_1 = \omega_2 = \omega_0$, then

$$(\omega_0^2 - \omega^2)^2 = k^2\omega^4$$

or

$$\omega_0^2 - \omega^2 = \pm k \omega^2$$

$$\therefore \quad \omega = \pm\frac{\omega_0}{\sqrt{1 \pm k}}$$

The negative sign on the right hand side has no meaning as ω cannot be negative.
The positive sign gives two frequencies

$$\omega_a = \frac{\omega_0}{\sqrt{1 + k}} \quad \text{and} \quad \omega_b = \frac{\omega_0}{\sqrt{1 - k}}.$$

These are the *normal mode frequencies*.

In phase and out of phase normal modes. From the relation

$$I_p\left(\omega_1^2 - \omega^2\right) = \frac{M}{L_p}\omega^2 I_s$$

We have

$$\frac{I_s}{I_p} = \frac{\omega_1^2 - \omega^2}{\omega^2} \cdot \frac{L_p}{M} = \frac{\omega_0^2 - \omega^2}{\omega^2} \cdot \frac{L_p}{M} \qquad [\because \omega_1 = \omega_0]$$

$$= \left(\frac{\omega_0^2}{\omega^2} - 1\right) \frac{L_p}{M} \qquad\qquad\qquad\qquad ...(i)$$

Selecting the value of $\omega = \dfrac{\omega_0}{\sqrt{1 + k}}$, we have

$$\frac{\omega_0^2}{\omega^2} = 1 + k \ \text{ or } \ \frac{\omega_0^2}{\omega^2} - 1 = +k$$

Substituting in Eq. (i), we get

$$\frac{I_s}{I_p} = +k \ \frac{L_p}{M}$$

It is clear that the right hand side of the above equation is positive i.e. I_s and I_p are in phase.

Hence $\omega = \dfrac{\omega_0}{\sqrt{1 + k}} = \omega_a$ represents the frequency of the in-phase mode.

Similarly selecting $\omega = \dfrac{\omega_0}{\sqrt{1 - k}}$, we find that

$$\frac{I_s}{I_p} = -k \ \frac{L_s}{M}$$

i.e. I_s and I_p are out of phase. Hence $\omega = \dfrac{\omega_0}{\sqrt{1 - k}} = \omega_s$ represents the frequency of out of phase mode.

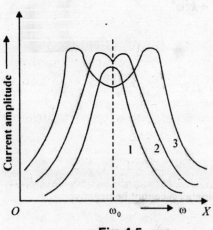

Fig. 4.5

Loose and tight coupling. In loose (weak) coupling k is small ($\ll 1$) and both the systems behave almost independently. In this case ω_a and ω_b are very nearly equal to ω_0. In tight (strong) coupling k is large (very nearly equal to unity) so that ω_a and ω_b differ from ω_0 by a large quantity, the peak values of current are displaced and the dip between the peaks is more pronounced. The variation of current amplitude with driving force frequency ω for different values of k is shown in Fig. 4.5. The three cases shown are

(1) for k small

(2) for k having intermediate value and (3) for k large.

It may be noted that for k small (loose coupling) bandwidth is negligible i.e., resonance occurs at one frequency. For large k (tight coupling) bandwidth is large i.e., resonance occurs at two widely apart frequencies.

Exercise. *Write the relation for coupling constant k in terms of self inductances and mutual inductance. What do you infer from k = 0 ?* (*P.U.* 2006)

Hint. $k = \dfrac{M}{\sqrt{L_1 L_2}}$; $k = 0$, means $M = 0$ i.e. there is no mutual inductance between the two primary coils and hence there is absolutely no coupling between them.

Q. 4.14. In a transformer the mutual inductance of two coils is 0.3 H where as the self inductance of primary and secondary are 0.28 H and 0.36 H respectively. Is the transformer loose or tight coupled.(*Pbi. U. 2008, 2007; G.N.D.U. 2004, P.U.*, 2006, 2002, 2000, 1999; *H.P.U.*, 2003, 1996)

Ans. Co-efficient of coupling, $k = \dfrac{M}{\sqrt{L_p L_s}} = \dfrac{0.3}{\sqrt{0.28 \times 0.36}} = 0.95$

As the coefficient of coupling k is nearly equal to unity, the transformer is almost *tight coupled.*

Exercise. *Find the co-efficient of coupling in case of a transformer in which self inductance of the primary is 0.02 H and that of the secondary is 0.18 H and mutual inductance is 0.04 H.*

(*P.U. 2008; Pbi. U. 2005*)

Hint. $K = \dfrac{M}{\sqrt{L_1 L_2}} = \dfrac{.04}{\sqrt{.18 \times .02}} = 0.67 \text{ or } 67\%$

Q. 4.15. Mark the correct answer.

(*i*) The stiffness of coupling has no effect when
  (*a*) both oscillators move out of phase
  (*b*) both oscillators move in phase
  (*c*) none of these

(*ii*) Which of the following is correct for tight coupling of two inductively coupled oscillators?
  (*a*) $L_1 C_1 = L_2 C_2$ (*b*) $\omega_1 = \omega_2$
  (*c*) $k = 0$ (*d*) none of these   (*G.N.D.U.*, 1994)

(*iii*) The co-efficient of coupling of coupled electrical oscillator is given by

  (*a*) $k = M L_p L_s$ (*b*) $k = \dfrac{M}{L_p L_s}$ (*c*) $k = \dfrac{M}{\sqrt{L_p L_s}}$ (*d*) $k = \dfrac{\sqrt{L_p L_s}}{M}$ (*H.P.U.*, 1991)

(*iv*) For tight coupling of the oscillators resonance occurs at
  (*a*) two widely separated frequencies   (*b*) two close frequencies
  (*c*) single low frequency   (*d*) single high frequency

(*v*) The normal mode beat frequency of two identical coupled pendulums is 5 Hz. The time interval between two maximum displacements of the pendulum will be
  (*a*) 0.1 sec   (*b*) 0.2 sec   (*c*) 1 sec   (*d*) 5 sec   (*H.P.U.*, 1995)

(*vi*) A stiffness coupled system consists of 4 simple pendulums. In how many normal modes a system can oscillate at a time ?
  (*a*) 1   (*b*) 2   (*c*) 3   (*d*) 4   (*H.P.U.*, 2003, 1997)

(*vii*) If L_1 and L_2 be the co-efficients of self induction of primary and secondary of a transformer and if M is the mutual inductance of the two coils then for perfect coupling

  (*a*) $M = L_1 L_2$ (*b*) $M = \sqrt{L_1 L_2}$

  (*c*) $M = \dfrac{1}{L_1 L_2}$ (*d*) $M = \dfrac{1}{\sqrt{L_1 L_2}}$ (*H.P.U.*, 2002)

Ans. (*i*) b   (*ii*) d   (*iii*) c   (*iv*) a   (*v*) a   (*vi*) a   (*vii*) b

5

Transverse Waves

Q. 5.1. (*a*) **What is wave motion? What are transverse and longitudinal waves? Give the condition regarding the direction of oscillation and direction of propagation of longitudinal and transverse waves.** (*P.U.*, 2001, 2000, 1999; *G.N.D.U.*, 1999)

(*b*) **State the characteristics of progressive wave. Derive an equation for the progressive wave of wavelength λ and amplitude a moving with a velocity v in the positive X-direction.**

(*G.N.D.U.* 2007; *Pbi. U.* 2005; *Mithila U.*, 1999; *Luck. U.,* 1993; *Burd. U.*, 1991)

(*c*) **What is a plane wave ?** (*G.N.D.U.* 2007, 2006)

Ans. (*a*) Wave motion. *Wave motion is a form of disturbance which travels through a medium due to the repeated periodic motion of the particles of the medium about their mean positions, the disturbance being handed on from one particle to the next particle of the medium.*

It may be noted that there is no bodily transfer of the medium through which the wave propagates, but it is only the disturbance which travels forward.

Transverse wave motion *is that wave motion in which the particles of the medium vibrate about their mean positions in a direction at right angle to the direction of propagation of the wave.*

Longitudinal wave motion *is that wave motion in which the particles of the medium vibrate about their mean positions in the same direction in which the wave is propagated.*

Mathematically, if the displacement vector of the vibrating particles of the medium is denoted by $\vec{y}$ and the vectorial distance along the direction of propagation of the wave by $\vec{x}$, then

For *transverse wave* $\quad \hat{x}.\hat{y} = 0 \quad$ but $\quad \hat{x} \times \hat{y} \neq 0$ and

For *longitudinal wave* $\quad \hat{x}.\hat{y} \neq 0 \quad$ but $\quad \hat{x} \times \hat{y} = 0$.

Characteristics of wave motion. A progressive simple harmonic wave is that whose amplitude remains constant with time. Its characteristics are

(*i*) A wave is a form of disturbance which propagates in a medium.

(*ii*) When the wave propagates the particles of the medium simply oscillate about their mean position.

(*iii*) There is a definite phase difference between every two consecutive particles.

(*iv*) The velocity of the wave is different from the velocity of the particles. The velocity of the wave is a constant for a given medium but the velocity of the particle goes on changing, being maximum in the mean position and minimum in the extreme position.

(*v*) Wave motion is possible only in media which have the property of inertia and elasticity.

(*vi*) The energy of the vibrating particle at the extreme position is wholly potential and in the mean position wholly kinetic.

(*vii*) When a wave travels in a medium, there is a flow of energy without any transfer of matter.

(*b*) **Equation of a progressive wave.** *In a wave motion, the particles of the medium execute simple harmonic vibrations about their mean position along or perpendicular to the direction of propagation of the wave according as it is a longitudinal or a transverse wave. The disturbance is handed on from particle to particle after a definite time and there is a gradual fall of phase in the direction of motion.*

Consider a transverse wave in a string propagating from left to right along the positive *X*-direction starting from *A* as shown in Fig. 5.1. A particle on the right will begin its vibrations a certain time later than the one on the left.

As each particle of the medium executes simple harmonic motion the equation of motion of any particle, say *A*, is given by

$$y = a \sin \omega t$$

where *a* is the amplitude of the vibrating particle, *y* the displacement after a time *t* and ω the angular velocity.

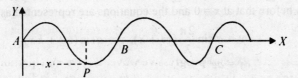

Fig. 5.1

If *n* is the frequency of vibration, then ω = 2 π *n*.

∴ $$y = a \sin 2 \pi n t$$

When the particle *A* passes through its mean position, the particles like *B*, *C*, etc., also pass through their mean positions in the same direction.

Hence the particles *A*, *B*, *C* ... etc. are in the *same phase*.

The distance *AB* between the two consecutive particles in the same phase is called the *wavelength* and denoted by λ. The phase changes by 2π in going from *A* to *B*.

Therefore, in going from the point *A* to any point *P* at a distance *x* from *A* the phase changes by ϕ and is given by

$$\phi = \frac{2\pi}{\lambda} x$$

Hence the displacement of *P* is given by

$$y = a \sin (\omega t - \phi)$$

$$= a \sin \left(2 \pi n t - \frac{2\pi}{\lambda} x \right)$$

$$= a \sin \left(2 \pi \frac{v}{\lambda} t - \frac{2\pi}{\lambda} x \right)$$

or $$y = a \sin \frac{2\pi}{\lambda} (v t - x) \qquad \qquad ...(i)$$

The equation is quite general and gives the displacement of any particle whose distance *x* from the fixed point *A* at any time is known.

Hence this is the equation of a progressive simple harmonic wave.

The number of wavelengths in a unit distance is called *wave number*. It is denoted by $\bar{v}$.

∴ $$\bar{v} = \frac{1}{\lambda}$$

The quantity $\dfrac{2\pi}{\lambda} = k$ is called *propagation constant*.

Other forms. Equation (*i*) can also be written as

$$y = a\sin\left(\dfrac{2\pi v}{\lambda}t - \dfrac{2\pi}{\lambda}x\right)$$

$$= a\sin(\omega t - kx) \qquad ...(ii) \qquad \left[\because \dfrac{2\pi v}{\lambda} = 2\pi n = \omega\right]$$

In exponential form

$$y = a\,e^{i(\omega t - kx)} \qquad\qquad ...(iii)$$

The equations $y = a\sin\dfrac{2\pi}{\lambda}(vt - x)$, $y = a\sin(\omega t - kx)$ and $y = ae^{i(\omega t - kx)}$ denote a wave moving to the right along $+X$ axis.

If the wave is moving to the left (along $-X$-direction) the sign of ϕ is changed because the oscillations at x begin before that at $x = 0$ and the equations are represented as

$$y = a\sin\dfrac{2\pi}{\lambda}(vt + x), \quad y = a\sin(\omega t + kx)$$

and $y = ae^{i(\omega t + kx)}$.

(*c*) **Plane wave.** If we consider a plane perpendicular to the direction in which a wave is propagated, then all oscillators lying in that plane of the medium have the same phase. A plane of common phase progressing through the medium can be regarded as a *plane wave*.

Q. 5.2. If a wave of frequency 500 Hz is travelling with a velocity of 200 ms^{-1}, then find the change in phase at a given point in space between a time interval of 10^{-3} sec. Also find the path difference between two points which differ in phase by $\dfrac{\pi}{2}$ radian. (*P.U.*, 1993)

Ans. At a given point in space, the change in phase is 2π during a time interval T, the time period of wave motion.

$\therefore$ For a time interval t, phase change $\phi = \dfrac{2\pi}{T}t$

Here frequency of the wave $n = 500$ Hz

$\therefore$ Time period $T = \dfrac{1}{n} = \dfrac{1}{500}$ sec

Hence phase change in a time interval 10^{-3} sec, $\phi = \dfrac{2\pi}{T}t$

$$= 2\pi \times 10^{-3} \times 500 = \pi \text{ radian}$$

At a given time, the phase difference between two points separated by a distance λ, the wavelength of the wave $= 2\pi$.

$\therefore$ For two points separated by a distance x, phase difference

$$\phi = \dfrac{2\pi}{\lambda}x$$

Here $\phi = \dfrac{\pi}{2}$; $\lambda = \dfrac{v}{n} = \dfrac{200\,\text{ms}^{-1}}{500\,\text{s}^{-1}} = 0.4\,\text{m}$

$\therefore$ $\dfrac{\pi}{2} = \dfrac{2\pi}{0.4}x$ or path difference $x = 0.1$ m

Q. 5.3. A simple harmonic wave travelling along X-axis is given by

$$y = 5\sin 2\pi\,(0.2\,t - 0.5\,x).$$

Calculate the amplitude, frequency, wavelength, wave velocity, particle velocity, velocity amplitude, particle acceleration and acceleration amplitude (x is in metres and t in seconds).

(*P.U.*, 1992)

Ans. The given equation is

$$y = 5 \sin 2\pi (0.2\, t - 0.5\, x) \text{ m}$$

Comparing with the equation

$$y = a \sin \frac{2\pi}{\lambda} (vt - x)$$

$$= a \sin 2\pi \left(\frac{vt}{\lambda} - \frac{x}{\lambda} \right) = a \sin 2\pi \left(nt - \frac{x}{\lambda} \right)$$

We have

Amplitude $a = 5$ m

Frequency $n = 0.2 \text{ s}^{-1}$

Now $\dfrac{x}{\lambda} = 0.5\,x$

$\therefore$ Wave length $\lambda = \dfrac{1}{0.5} = 2 \text{ m}$

Wave velocity $v = n\,\lambda = 0.2 \times 2 = 0.4 \text{ m s}^{-1}$

Particle velocity $= \dfrac{dy}{dt} = 5 \cos 2\pi (0.2t - 0.5x) \times 0.2$

$$= \cos 2\pi (0.2\, t - 0.5\, x) \text{ m s}^{-1}$$

Particle velocity amplitude $= 1 \text{ m s}^{-1}$

Particle acceleration $= \dfrac{d^2 y}{dt^2} = -\sin 2\pi (0.2t - 0.5x) \times 0.2$

$$= -0.2 \sin 2\pi (0.2\, t - 0.5\, x) \text{ m s}^{-2}$$

Particle acceleration amplitude $= -0.2 \text{ ms}^{-2}$

Exercise. *Find the amplitude, frequency, velocity and wavelength of the transverse wave in a string represented by*

$$y = 5 \sin 2\pi (t - 0.04\, x) \text{ in } S.I. \text{ units.} \qquad (P.U., 2001)$$

Hint. Compare with Eq. $y = a \sin 2\pi \left(nt - \dfrac{x}{\lambda} \right)$

Amplitude $a = 5$ m;

Frequency $n = 1 \text{ s}^{-1}$

Wave length $\lambda = \dfrac{1}{0.04} = 25$ m

Velocity $v = n\,\lambda = 25 \text{ m s}^{-1}$

Q. 5.4. Write down the equation of wave travelling in the negative direction along X-axis and having an amplitude 0.01 m, a frequency 550 Hz and speed 330 m/s.   (*Luck.U.*, 1995)

Ans. The equation of a wave travelling in the negative X-direction is

$$y = a \sin \frac{2\pi}{\lambda} (vt + x)$$

Now $a = 0.01$ m, $v = 330$ m s^{-1}, $n = 550$ Hz

$\therefore$ $\lambda = \dfrac{v}{n} = \dfrac{330}{550} = \dfrac{3}{5}$ m

Substituting, we get

$$y = 0.01 \sin\left[2\pi \times \frac{5}{3}(330t + x)\right]$$

or $y = 0.01 \sin 2\pi\left(550\,t + \dfrac{5}{3}x\right)$

Q. 5.5. (*a*) **Show that the slope of the displacement curve for a wave gives the volumetric strain in the medium in which it travels.**

(*b*)   **Derive a relation between v (wave velocity), $\dfrac{dy}{dt}$ (particle velocity) and $\dfrac{dy}{dx}$ (volumetric strain).**   (*Mithila U.*, 1999; *Kan. U.*, 1990; *Vid. S. U.*, 1990)

Ans. (*a*) **Volumetric strain.** Consider a displacement curve *ABCDE* of a wave set up in a cylinder having unit area of cross-section and its axis coincident with the direction of propagation of the wave

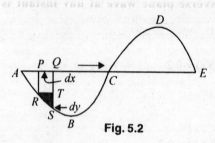

Fig. 5.2

ACE. Consider two neighbouring points *P* and *Q* distance *dx* apart. The displacement at *P* is *PR* and that at *Q* is *QS*. The volume of the gas between the points *P* and *Q* is given by

$$PQ \times 1 = PQ$$

When the wave is in the position shown, the particle *P* is displaced by *PR* and the particle *Q* is displaced by *QS*. Hence the change in volume between *P* and *Q* is given by

$$QS - PR = ST = dy$$

$\therefore$ Volumetric strain $= \dfrac{\text{change in volume}}{\text{original volume}}$

$$= \frac{ST}{PQ} = \frac{ST}{RT} = \frac{dy}{dx}$$

= the slope of the displacement curve.

Thus the slope of the displacement curve at any point measures the volumetric strain at that point.

(*b*) **Relation between wave velocity, particle velocity and volumetric strain.** The equation of a wave motion is given by

$$y = a\sin\frac{2\pi}{\lambda}(vt - x) \qquad \qquad ...(i)$$

Differentiating (*i*) with respect to *x*, we have

$$\frac{dy}{dx} = -a\frac{2\pi}{\lambda}\cos\frac{2\pi}{\lambda}(vt - x) \qquad \qquad ...(ii)$$

Now $\dfrac{dy}{dx}$ represents the strain or compression in the medium. When $\dfrac{dy}{dx}$ is positive a rarefaction takes place and when $\dfrac{dy}{dx}$ is negative a compression takes place.

Differentiating (i) with respect to t, we have

$$\frac{dy}{dt} = a\frac{2\pi v}{\lambda}\cos\frac{2\pi}{\lambda}(vt - x) \qquad\qquad ...(iii)$$

Here $\frac{dy}{dt}$ represents the velocity of the particle or *particle velocity*.

Comparing (ii) and (iii), we have

$$\frac{dy}{dt} = -v\frac{dy}{dx} \qquad\qquad ...(iv)$$

or   Particle velocity = Wave velocity × Slope of the displacement curve or strain

From relation (iv) we find that when $\frac{dy}{dx}$ is positive *i.e.*, it is a rarefaction $\frac{dy}{dt}$ is negative *i.e.*,

the particles are moving in the backward direction (towards the mean position). Similarly, when $\frac{dy}{dx}$

is negative *i.e.*, it is a compression $\frac{dy}{dt}$ is positive *i.e.*, the particle are moving in the forward direction

(away from the mean position).

Q. 5.6. The displacement equation for a transverse plane wave at any instant is
$y(x, t) = 0.03 \sin(3\pi t - 0.03\pi x)$ **where x and t are in metres and seconds. Calculate wavelength, frequency and velocity of the wave. Also calculate phase difference between two particles 0.05 metre apart at same instant.** (*P.U.*, 1991)

Ans. The general displacement equation for a transverse plane wave is given by

$$y = a\sin\frac{2\pi}{\lambda}(vt - x) = a\sin\left(2\pi\frac{v}{\lambda}t - \frac{2\pi}{\lambda}x\right)$$

$$= a\sin\left(2\pi nt - \frac{2\pi}{\lambda}x\right)$$

Comparing with the given equation

$$y(x, t) = 0.03 \sin(3\pi t - 0.03\pi x)$$

we have $2\pi n = 3\pi$

or $n = \frac{3}{2} = 1.5$ Hertz

$$\frac{2\pi}{\lambda} = 0.03\pi$$

or $\lambda = \frac{2}{0.03} = 66\frac{2}{3}$ m

Velocity $v = n\lambda = \frac{3}{2} \times \frac{200}{3} = 100\,\text{ms}^{-1}$

Phase difference between two particles $x = 0.05$ m apart

$$\phi = \frac{2\pi}{\lambda}x = 0.03\pi \times 0.05 = .0015\pi$$

Exercise. *Equation of a plane progressive wave is given below*
$$y = 10 \sin \pi [0.01 x - 2.00 t]$$
where y and x are expressed in cm and t in seconds. Determine (i) amplitude of the wave (ii) frequency of the wave (iii) phase difference at an instant between two points 40 cm apart.
(*Indore U.*, 2001)

Hint. The given equation can be written as

$$y = -10 \sin 2\pi [1.00\, t - 0.005\, x]$$

∴   Amplitude $a = 10$ cm

Frequency $n = 1\, s^{-1}$.

$$\lambda = \frac{1}{.005} = 200\,\text{cm}$$

Hence phase difference $\phi \quad = \frac{2\pi}{\lambda} x = \frac{2\pi}{200} \times 40 = \frac{2}{5}\pi$ rad.

Q. 5.7. A wave of frequency 400 Hz is travelling with a velocity 800 m/s. How far are two points situated whose displacements differ in phase by $\frac{\pi}{4}$?   (*P.U.*, 1996)

Ans.   Frequency of the wave $n = 400$ Hz .

Velocity of the wave $v = 800$ ms^{-1}

∴   Wavelength $\lambda = \frac{v}{n} = \frac{800}{400} = 2\,\text{m}$

Phase difference between two points a distance x apart

$$\phi = \frac{2\pi}{\lambda} x$$

∴   For the displacements to differ in phase by $\frac{\pi}{4}$

$$\phi = \frac{\pi}{4} = \frac{2\pi}{2} x$$

or $x = \frac{1}{4} m = 0.25\,\text{m} = 25$ cm

Exercise. *A wave has frequency of 400 Hz and velocity 320 ms^{-1}. Find the distance between points which are 45° out of phase.*   (*Pbi. U.* 2008)

Hint. · $\lambda = \frac{v}{n} = \frac{320}{400} = 0.8$ m

$$\phi = \frac{2\pi}{\lambda} x \quad \text{or} \quad 45° = \frac{\pi}{4} = \frac{2\pi}{0.8} x$$

∴ $x = \frac{0.8}{8} = 0.1$ m $= 10$ cm

Q. 5.8. (a) Show that for a transverse wave in a string $T/\rho = c^2$ where T is the tension with which the string is stretched, ρ the mass per unit length of the string and c the velocity of the wave produced in it. Hence find the frequency of the fundamental note and the first octave of the vibrating string fixed at both ends.   (*Meerut U.* 2006, 2005; *Indore U.*, 2001; *Pbi.U.*, 2000; *G.N.D.U.*, 2006, 2000)

(b)   The wave velocity in a string is a function of elasticity and inertia of the medium. Comment.   (*P.U.*, 1999)

(c) Find the speed of propagation of transverse wave on a 0.8 mm wire which is under a tension of 700 N. The density of steel is 7.9×10^3 kg/m^3.   (*Pbi. U.* 2008)

Ans. (a) Transverse waves in a string. A string is a cord whose length is very large as compared to its diameter and which is perfectly uniform and flexible. When a string is stretched between two points and is plucked in a direction at right angles to its length *transverse vibrations* are produced in it. The particles vibrate perpendicular to its length and movement is handed on from particle to particle. A transverse wave travels along the string with a velocity depending upon certain constants of the string.

Velocity of transverse waves. Consider a part of the wave AB travelling in the string from left to right with a velocity c. If the string is pulled from right to left with the same velocity the wave AB will remain stationary with respect to the paper in space. A small part PQ of the wave AB can be considered to be the arc of a circle. As the string moves along the circular arc PQ a centripetal force acts on it along the radius towards the centre O.

A uniform tension or stretching force T acts in the string throughout. This tension T acts along CP at P and along CQ at Q, where CP and CQ are tangents to the arc PQ at P and Q respectively. Draw PO and QO perpendiculars to the arc at P and Q meeting at O the centre of the circular arc having a radius r.

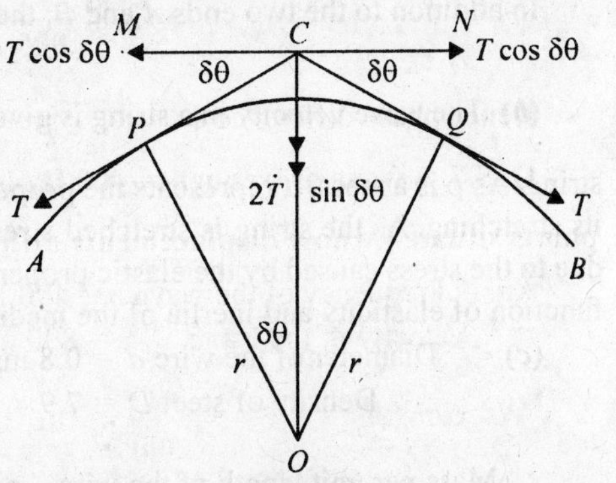

Let the angle POQ be denoted by $2\,\delta\theta$. Join OC; then OC is the bisector of the angle POQ.

$\therefore$ Arc $PQ = r \times 2\,\delta\theta$

Let ρ be the mass per unit length of the string, then

$$\text{Mass of the part } PQ = \rho \times PQ = 2\,\rho r \delta\theta$$

Fig. 5.3

The centripetal force acting on $PQ = \dfrac{2\rho r \delta\theta c^2}{r} = 2\rho c^2 \delta\theta$ ...(i)

The tension T can be resolved into two rectangular components. The horizontal component $T\cos\delta\theta$ along CM and $T\cos\delta\theta$ along CN, cancel each other being equal and opposite. The vertical components of tension act in the same direction and total force along CO

$$= 2\,T\sin\delta\theta = 2\,T\delta\theta \qquad\qquad [\because \delta\theta \text{ is small}] \quad ...(ii)$$

This provides the necessary centripetal force. Equating (i) and (ii), we have

$$2T\delta\theta = 2\,\rho c^2\,\delta\theta$$

or $T = \rho\,c^2$ or $c^2 = \dfrac{T}{\rho}$

$\therefore$ Velocity of the transverse wave $c = \sqrt{\dfrac{T}{\rho}}$

Frequency of the fundamental note. When a string is fixed at both ends, it is said to produce a *fundamental note*, if it vibrates as a whole in one segment. In such a case the length l of the string is equal to $\dfrac{\lambda}{2}$ where λ is the wavelength of the note.

$\therefore$ $\lambda = 2\,l$

Now frequency $n = \dfrac{c}{\lambda} = \dfrac{1}{2l}\sqrt{\dfrac{T}{\rho}}$

This is the frequency of the fundamental note.

Fundamental note   First octave

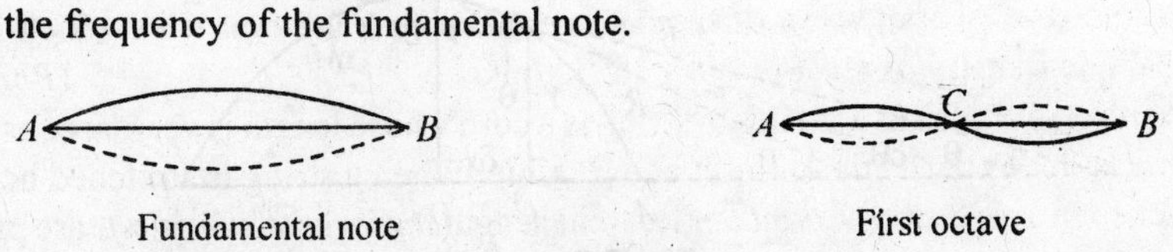

Fig. 5.4

The two fixed ends A and B of the string act as nodes.

156

Waves, Vibrations and E.M. Theory

Frequency of first octave. When the string vibrates in two segments, it is said to produce *first octave*. In such a case $\lambda = l$.

$\therefore$ Frequency of the first octave $= n_1 = \dfrac{c}{\lambda} = \dfrac{1}{l}\sqrt{\dfrac{T}{\rho}}$

In addition to the two ends A and B, there is a node at the mid point C.

(b) The wave velocity in a string is given by $c = \sqrt{\dfrac{T}{\rho}}$ where ρ is the mass per unit length of the string. As ρ is a mass; it represents the property of *inertia*, Again T is the tension in the string due to its stretching. As the string is stretched a restoring force is called into play. This restoring force is due to the stress caused by the elastic properties of the string. Thus the wave velocity in a string is a function of elasticity and inertia of the medium or the string.

(c) Diameter of the wire $d = 0.8$ mm $= 0.8 \times 10^{-3}$ m $= 8 \times 10^{-4}$ m

Density of steel $D = 7.9 \times 10^3$ kg/m^3

$\therefore$ Mass per unit length of the wire $\rho = \dfrac{\pi d^2}{4} \times D = \dfrac{\pi}{4} \times 8 \times 8 \times 10^{-8} \times 7.9 \times 10^3$

$= 397 \times 10^{-5}$ kg/m $= 3.97 \times 10^{-3}$ kg/m

Tension T = 700 N

$\therefore$ Speed (velocity) of propagation of transverse wave in the string

$$c = \sqrt{\dfrac{T}{\rho}} = \sqrt{\dfrac{700}{3.97 \times 10^{-3}}} = 4.2 \times 10^2 = 420 \text{ m/s}$$

Q. 5.9. (a) Prove that the wave equation for a transverse wave in a string is given by

$$\dfrac{\delta^2 y}{\delta x^2} = \dfrac{1}{c^2}\dfrac{\delta^2 y}{\delta t^2}$$

where $c = \sqrt{\dfrac{T}{\rho}}$, **$T$ being the tension and ρ the linear density of the string. What are its possible solutions?** (*Pbi.U.*, 2007, 2003, 2002, 1999; *P.U.*, 2002, 2001, 2000, 1999; *Kerala U.*, 2001; *Cal. U.* 2003; *H. P.U.*, 1996; *G.N.D.U.*, 1994)

(b) A plane wave travelling in a string along X-axis is represented by

$$y = 5 \cos \dfrac{\pi}{2}\left(\dfrac{x}{60} - \dfrac{t}{0.03}\right)$$

where x and y are in metres and t in seconds. Find the speed of the wave. (*P.U.* 2008)

Ans. (a) Wave equation for transverse wave in a string. Consider a string AB plucked in the middle so that when left to itself it begins to vibrate. The components of the tension T at right angles

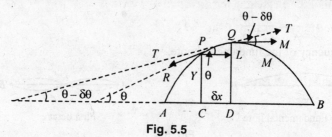

Fig. 5.5

to the length of the string tend to bring the string back to equilibrium position. Consider a small element PQ of the string.

The tension T at P acts along the tangent PR and at Q along the tangent QT. It is supposed that the gradient of the curve formed by the string in the displaced position is very small so that the tension T acts uniformly along the string and the normal position of the string coincides with the X-axis of the co-ordinate system.

The small element PQ of the string executes simple harmonic motion and undergoes a vertical displacement which varies with the position of the element as well as with time.

From P and Q draw PL and QM respectively parallel to AB. The tangent at P is inclined to the X-axis and the line PL at an angle θ and the tangent at Q is inclined to X-axis and the line QM at an angle $\theta - \delta\theta$. The angle $\delta\theta$ is very small as the amplitude of string is small.

The components of tension T acting at P are

$$T\cos\theta \text{ in the horizontal direction}$$

and $T\sin\theta$ in the vertically downward direction.

Similarly, the components of tension T acting at Q are

$$T\cos(\theta - \delta\theta) \text{ in the horizontal direction}$$

and $T\sin(\theta - \delta\theta)$ in the vertically upward direction.

As θ and $(\theta - \delta\theta)$ differ by a very small value $\delta\theta$

$$T\cos\theta = T\cos(\theta - \delta\theta)$$

Hence the two horizontal components cancel each other as they act almost in the same line in opposite directions. The resultant force F acting in the vertically downward direction

$$= T\sin\theta - T\sin(\theta - \delta\theta)$$
$$= T\sin\theta - T\sin\theta\ \cos\delta\theta + T\cos\theta\ \sin\delta\theta$$

But $\delta\theta$ is very small.

$\therefore$ $\cos\delta\theta = 1$ and $\sin\delta\theta = \delta\theta$

Hence the resultant force $F = T\sin\theta - T\sin\theta + T\cos\theta\ \delta\theta$

$$= T\delta(\sin\theta)$$

As θ is small, $\sin\theta = \tan\theta = \dfrac{dy}{dx}$

where $\dfrac{dy}{dx}$ is the slope of the curve

$\therefore$ $F = T\delta\left(\dfrac{dy}{dx}\right) = T\left[\dfrac{d}{dx}\left(\dfrac{dy}{dx}\right)\right]\delta x$

$$= T\dfrac{d^2 y}{dx^2}\ \delta x \qquad\qquad\qquad ...(i)$$

If ρ is the mass per unit length of the string, then mass of the element PQ of length $\delta x = \rho\,\delta x$.

The acceleration of the element in the direction of Y-axis $= \dfrac{d^2 y}{dt^2}$

If we neglect the effect of gravity, then

Force on the element $= \rho\delta x \times \dfrac{d^2 y}{dt^2}$ \qquad\qquad\qquad ...(ii)

Comparing (i) and (ii), we have

$$\rho\,\delta x\,\dfrac{d^2 y}{dt^2} = T\dfrac{d^2 y}{dx^2}\,\delta x$$

or

$$\dfrac{d^2 y}{dt^2} = \dfrac{T}{\rho}\dfrac{d^2 y}{dx^2}$$

or
$$\frac{d^2y}{dt^2} = c^2 \frac{d^2y}{dx^2}$$ ...(iii)

Where $\sqrt{\dfrac{T}{\rho}} = c = a$ constant. The dimensions of c are those of velocity $[L^1 T^{-1}]$.

The equation (iii) is the differential equation of wave motion and can be put in the form

$$\frac{d^2y}{dx^2} = \frac{1}{c^2} \frac{d^2y}{dt^2}$$

The wave equation $\dfrac{d^2y}{dt^2} = c^2 \dfrac{d^2y}{dx^2}$ has been derived by considering the vibrating string as a proto type. Any partial differential equation of the form

$$\frac{\partial^2 \psi}{\partial t^2} = c^2 \frac{\partial^2 \psi}{\partial x^2}$$

or
$$\frac{\partial^2 \psi}{\partial x^2} = \frac{1}{c^2} \frac{\partial^2 \psi}{\partial t^2}$$

represents a general wave equation where ψ is a function of space and time co-ordinates and c the velocity with which the wave travels without any change of form. The wave variable ψ represents the transverse displacement y in the case of a string, pressure in the case of sound waves in a gas and electric field vector $\vec{E}$ in the case of electro-magnetic waves and so on. For plane waves in one dimension only it is a function of x but in the case of waves in two or three dimensions it is a function of two or three space co-ordinates.

Solution of the wave equation. We shall consider the wave equation in the form

$$\frac{d^2y}{dt^2} = c^2 \frac{d^2y}{dx^2}$$

It is clear from the form of the wave equation that the solution of this equation must be a linear function of the variables x and t. A function of the form

$$y = f_1 (ct - x) \text{ or } y = f_2 (ct + x)$$

is one of its solutions. Therefore, a general solution is given by

$$y = f_1 (ct - x) + f_2 (ct + x)$$

To show that $y = f_1 (ct - x)$ is a solution of the wave equation, we have

$$\frac{dy}{dt} = c f_1' (ct - x)$$

and
$$\frac{d^2y}{dt^2} = c^2 f_1'' (ct - x)$$

Where f_1' and f_1'' are the first and second derivatives of f_1 respectively with respect to $(ct - x)$.
Similarly

$$\frac{dy}{dx} = -f_1'(ct - x)$$

and
$$\frac{d^2y}{dx^2} = f_1'' (ct - x)$$

Hence
$$\frac{d^2 y}{dt^2} = c^2 \frac{d^2 y}{dx^2}.$$

Similarly it can be shown that $y = f_2 (ct + x)$ as well as $y = f_1 (ct - x) + f_2 (ct + x)$ is a solution of the wave equation.

In a harmonic progressive wave each particle of the medium executes simple harmonic motion which may be represented by a sine or a cosine function.

For a wave travelling along the positive x direction, we have

For sine function $y = f(ct - x) = a \sin k (ct - x)$ ...(i)

where a is the amplitude and k a constant. The wave profile repeats itself regularly at a distance $\frac{2\pi}{k}$ because $a \sin k\left(ct - x + \frac{2\pi}{k} \right) = a \sin k (ct - x)$. The distance $2 \pi/k$, therefore, gives the wavelength λ.

Hence $\lambda = \dfrac{2\pi}{k}$ or $k = \dfrac{2\pi}{\lambda}$

Substituting in (i), we have

$$y = a \sin \frac{2\pi}{\lambda} (ct - x) = a \sin \left(\frac{2\pi ct}{\lambda} - \frac{2\pi}{\lambda} x \right)$$

$$= a \sin 2\pi \left(vt - \frac{x}{\lambda} \right) = a \sin (\omega t - kx)$$

where $\omega = 2\pi v$ (v = frequency) and $k = \dfrac{2\pi}{\lambda} = 2\pi \bar{v}$ and $\bar{v}$ is the wave number $i.e.$, the reciprocal of the wavelength or *the number of waves contained in a unit length*. The constant k is known as *propagation constant*.

For cosine function $y = a \cos \dfrac{2\pi}{\lambda} (ct - x) = a \cos 2\pi \left(vt - \dfrac{x}{\lambda} \right)$

$$= a \cos (\omega t - kx)$$

Exponential form. The exponential form of the equation $y = ae^{i(\omega t - kx)}$ is equally valid solution of the differential equation as it contains both the sine and cosine functions. The real part of the expression is the cosine function and the part multiplied by ($i = \sqrt{-1}$) is the sine function.

$y = a \sin \dfrac{2\pi}{\lambda} (ct - x)$ or $y = a \cos \dfrac{2\pi}{\lambda} (ct - x)$ or $y = ae^{i(\omega t - kx)}$

represents a wave moving to the right whereas

$y = a \sin \dfrac{2\pi}{\lambda} (ct + x)$ or $y = a \cos \dfrac{2\pi}{\lambda} (ct + x)$ or $y = ae^{i(\omega t + kx)}$

represents a wave moving to the left in the negative $(- x)$ direction.

(b) Given $y = 5 \cos \dfrac{\pi}{2} \left(\dfrac{x}{60} - \dfrac{t}{0.03} \right)$

$$= 5 \cos \frac{\pi}{120} \left(x - \frac{60t}{0.03} \right) = 5 \cos \frac{2\pi}{240} (x - 2000t)$$

$$= 5 \cos \left[\frac{-2\pi}{240} \right] (2000t - x)$$

Comparing this with standard equation for a progressive wave in cosine form $y = a \cos \dfrac{2\pi}{\lambda}(ct - x)$,

we have

$$c = 2000 \text{ m/s}$$

as x and y are in metres and t is in seconds.

Q. 5.10. Prove that $\psi = Ae^{i(\omega t - kx)}$ is the solution of wave equation.   (*G.N.D.U.*, 1994)

Ans. $\psi = Ae^{i(\omega t - kx)}$ where ω is the angular frequency $= 2\pi n$, k the propagation constant $= \dfrac{2\pi}{\lambda}$

$$\therefore \qquad \frac{d\psi}{dt} = i\omega Ae^{i(\omega t - kx)} \quad \text{and} \quad \frac{d^2\psi}{dt^2} = -\omega^2 Ae^{i(\omega t - kx)}$$

$$= -\omega^2 \psi$$

$$\frac{d\psi}{dx} = -ik Ae^{i(\omega t - kx)} \quad \text{and} \quad \frac{d^2\psi}{dx^2} = k^2 Ae^{i(\omega t - kx)}$$

$$= k^2 \psi$$

$$\therefore \qquad \frac{d^2\psi}{dt^2} = \frac{\omega^2}{k^2}\frac{d^2\psi}{dx^2}$$

Now $\dfrac{\omega}{k} = \dfrac{2\pi n\lambda}{2\pi} = n\lambda = c$ the velocity of the wave

$$\therefore \qquad \frac{\omega^2}{k^2} = c^2$$

and $\dfrac{d^2\psi}{dt^2} = c^2 \dfrac{d^2\psi}{dx^2}$

or $\dfrac{d^2\psi}{dx^2} = \dfrac{1}{c^2}\dfrac{d^2\psi}{dt^2}$

which represents a general wave equation where ψ is a function of space and time co-ordinates (x and t) and c the velocity with which the wave travels without any change in form.

Hence $\psi = Ae^{i(\omega t - kx)}$ is the solution of the wave equation.

Q. 5.11. If a wave is represented by $y = a \sin k(vt - x)$

Prove that $\dfrac{d^2y}{dt^2} = v^2 \dfrac{d^2y}{dx^2}$.   (*P.U.*, 1992)

Ans. $y = a \sin k(vt - x)$

$$\therefore \qquad \frac{dy}{dt} = kva\cos k(vt - x) \qquad \text{and} \qquad \frac{d^2y}{dt^2} = -k^2v^2\, a\sin k(vt - x)$$

$$\therefore \qquad \frac{dy}{dx} = -ka\cos k(vt - x) \qquad \text{and} \qquad \frac{d^2y}{dx^2} = -k^2\, a\sin k(vt - x)$$

Hence $\dfrac{d^2y}{dt^2} = v^2 \dfrac{d^2y}{dx^2}$.

Q. 5.12. (*a*) Show that $y = x^2 + c^2 t^2$ is a solution of one dimensional wave equation.

(*P.U.*, 2008, 1994)

(*b*) Prove that $10 \sin kx \cos ct$ cannot be a solution to the one dimensional wave equation (*k* and *c* are constants).   (*P.U.*, 2007, 2001, 2000)

Ans. $y = x^2 + c^2 t^2$

$\therefore$ $\dfrac{dy}{dt} = 2c^2 t$ and $\dfrac{d^2 y}{dt^2} = 2c^2$

Again $\dfrac{dy}{dx} = 2x$ and $\dfrac{d^2 y}{dx^2} = 2$

Hence $\dfrac{d^2 y}{dt^2} = c^2 \dfrac{d^2 y}{dx^2}$

which is the one dimensional wave equation for a wave travelling along *x*-axis with a velocity *c*. Hence $y = x^2 + c^2 t^2$ is a solution of one dimensional wave equation.

(*b*) $y = 10 \sin kx \cos ct$

$\therefore$ $\dfrac{dy}{dt} = -10 c \sin kx \sin ct$ and $\dfrac{d^2 y}{dt^2} = -10 c^2 \sin kx \cos ct = -c^2 y$

Again $\dfrac{dy}{dx} = 10 k \cos kx . \cos ct$ and $\dfrac{d^2 y}{dx^2} = -10 k^2 \sin kx \cos ct = -k^2 y$

$\therefore$ $\dfrac{d^2 y}{dt^2} = \dfrac{c^2}{k^2} \dfrac{d^2 y}{dx^2}$

This equation does not satisfy one dimensional wave equation.

$\therefore$ $y = 10 \sin kx \cos ct$ cannot be a solution to one dimensional wave equation.

Q. 5.13. A string 1.3 metre in length is divided into three segments such that their frequencies are in the ratio 2 : 3 : 4. Find the length of each segment.   (*P.U.*, 1991)

Ans. The frequency $n = \dfrac{1}{2l} \sqrt{\dfrac{T}{\rho}}$

As *T* and ρ are constants, the frequency $n \propto \dfrac{1}{l}$

As the frequencies are in the ratio 2 : 3 : 4, the lengths of the segments, l_1, l_2, l_3 are in the ratio

$\dfrac{1}{2} : \dfrac{1}{3} : \dfrac{1}{4}$ or 6 : 4 : 3.

Also total length $l = l_1 + l_2 + l_3 = 1.3$ m

$\therefore$ $l_1 = \dfrac{1.3}{6+4+3} \times 6 = 0.6$ m

$l_2 = \dfrac{1.3}{6+4+3} \times 4 = 0.4$ m

$l_3 = \dfrac{1.3}{6+4+3} \times 3 = 0.3$ m

Q. 5.14. A string is stretched by suspending a load of 5 kg. The mass per unit length of the string is 5 gm m^{-1}. The travelling waves are sent through the string by oscillating one of the ends with a frequency of 250 Hz and amplitude 5 mm. Calculate the velocity and the length of the wave. Also write the equation of the travelling wave. Take $g = 10$ ms^{-2} (*P.U.*, 2002)

Ans. Load suspended = 5 kg.; $g = 10 \ ms^{-2}$

$\therefore$ Tension $\quad T = 5 \times 10 = 50 \ N$

Mass per unit length $\rho = 5 \ gm \ m^{-1} = 5 \times 10^{-3} \ kg \ m^{-1}$

$\therefore$ Velocity $\quad c = \sqrt{\dfrac{T}{\rho}} = \sqrt{\dfrac{50}{5 \times 10^{-3}}} = 100 \ ms^{-1}$

Frequency $\quad\quad \nu = 250 \ Hz$

$\therefore$ Wavelength $\quad \lambda = \dfrac{100}{250} = 0.4 \ m$

Amplitude $\quad a = 5 \ mm = 5 \times 10^{-3} \ m$

Wave equation is given by

$$y = a \sin \frac{2\pi}{\lambda}(ct - x) = 5 \times 10^{-3} \sin \frac{2\pi}{0.4}(100t - x)$$

$$= 5 \times 10^{-3} \sin 5\pi \, (100 \, t - x)$$

Exercise. *Consider a rope 10 metres long with a mass of 0.05 kg. One end of the rope is given a transverse motion of small amplitude with a frequency of 10 s^{-1}. If the tension in the rope is 200 N, what is the wave length of the wave created in the rope.* (*Meerut U.* 2006)

Hint. $\quad\quad\quad\quad\quad \rho = \dfrac{.05}{10} = .005 \ kg/m$

$\quad\quad\quad\quad\quad\quad T = 200 \ N$

$\therefore \quad\quad\quad\quad c = \sqrt{\dfrac{T}{\rho}} = \sqrt{\dfrac{200}{.005}} = 200 \ m/s$

Frequency $\quad\quad \nu = 10 \ s^{-1}$

$\therefore$ Wavelength $\quad \lambda = \dfrac{c}{\nu} = \dfrac{200}{10}$

$\quad\quad\quad\quad\quad\quad\quad = 20 \ m$

Q. 5.15. Two wires of steel of the same length are stretched on a sonometer. The tension of the first and second are 8 kg wt and 2 kg wt respectively. Find the ratio of the fundamental notes emitted by the two wires when the diameter of cross section of the first wire is half that of the second. (*Cal. U.*, 1990)

Ans. Let d be the density of steel.

Diameter of the second wire = D

$\therefore$ Diameter of the first wire $= \dfrac{D}{2}$

Mass per unit length of the first wire $\rho_1 = \dfrac{\pi}{4}\left(\dfrac{D}{2}\right)^2 d = \dfrac{\pi}{16}D^2 d$

Mass per unit length of the second wire $\rho_2 = \dfrac{\pi}{4} D^2 d = \dfrac{\pi}{4} D^2 d$

$\therefore \quad\quad\quad\quad\quad\quad\quad \dfrac{\rho_2}{\rho_1} = 4$

Tension for first wire $T_1 = 8 \ kg \ wt = 8 \ g \ Newton$

Tension for the second wire $T_2 = 2 \ kg \ wt = 2g \ Newton$

Let l be the length of each wire, then

Frequency of the fundamental note of first wire $n_1 = \dfrac{1}{2l}\sqrt{\dfrac{T_1}{\rho_1}}$

Frequency of the fundamental note of second wire $n_2 = \dfrac{1}{2l}\sqrt{\dfrac{T_2}{\rho_2}}$

$$\therefore \quad \frac{n_1}{n_2} = \sqrt{\frac{T_1}{\rho_1}\cdot\frac{\rho_2}{T_2}} = \sqrt{\frac{8}{2}}.4 = 4$$

Q. 5.16. A string AB of length 100 cm is kept under uniform tension. A bridge is kept at C such that $BC = 60$ cm. When the string is subjected to vibration BC part vibrates with frequency 252 Hz. Find the frequency of both parts of the string when the bridge is moved through 10 cm towards A. *(Vid. S. U., 1991)*

Ans. The position of the bridge in the first and second case is shown in Fig. 5.6 (*a*) and (*b*) respectively.

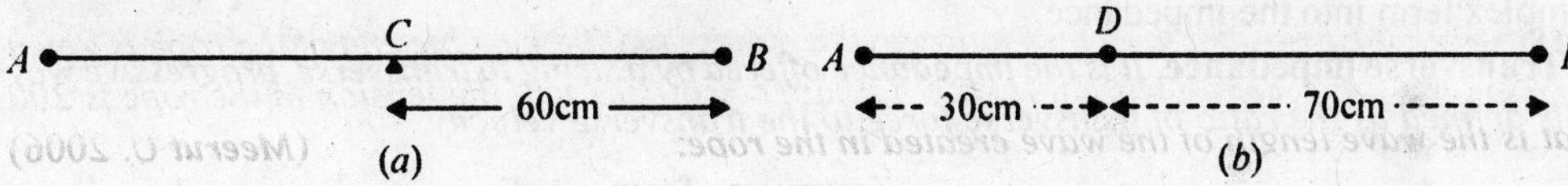

Fig. 5.6

When $BC = 60$ cm, frequency of BC part, $n = \dfrac{1}{2l}\sqrt{\dfrac{T}{\rho}}$

or $\qquad 252 = \dfrac{1}{120}\sqrt{\dfrac{T}{\rho}}$

$$\therefore \quad \sqrt{\frac{T}{\rho}} = 252 \times 120$$

When the bridge is moved 10 cm towards A from C to D
$$BD = 70 \text{ cm and } DA = 30 \text{ cm}$$

$\therefore$ Frequency of part BD, $n_1 = \dfrac{1}{2\times70}\sqrt{\dfrac{T}{\rho}} = \dfrac{1}{140}\times252\times120 = 216$ Hz

Frequency of part DA, $n_2 = \dfrac{1}{2\times30}\sqrt{\dfrac{T}{\rho}} = \dfrac{1}{60}\times252\times120 = 504$ Hz

Q. 5.17. A stretched string is observed to vibrate with a frequency 30 c.p.s in the fundamental note when the length of the string is 60 cm. The string has a mass of 0.5 gm/cm. Find the velocity of propagation of the transverse wave and compute the tension of the string.
(Burd. U., 1990)

Ans. Frequency of the fundamental note $n = 30$ c.p.s.
Length of the string $l = 60$ cm
Mass per unit length $\rho = 0.5$ gm/cm
Let T be the tension of the string, then

$$n = \frac{1}{2l}\sqrt{\frac{T}{\rho}}$$

or
$$30 = \frac{1}{2 \times 60} \times \sqrt{\frac{T}{0.5}}$$

$\therefore$
$$T = 30 \times 30 \times 2 \times 2 \times 60 \times 60 \times 0.5 = 6.48 \times 10^6 \text{ dynes/cm}$$

Velocity of propagation $v = \sqrt{\dfrac{T}{\rho}} = n \times 2l = 30 \times 2 \times 60$

$$= 3600 \text{ cm/sec}$$

Q. 5.18. Derive the relation for the characteristic impedance of a string. Explain the factors on which it depends. (*G.N.D.U.* 2008, 2007, 2004; *P.U.,* 2009, 2006, 2005, 2001, 2000, 1999; *Pbi. U.,* 2008, 1993)

Ans. Characteristic impedance of a string. A wave of any type-mechanical, electrical or electro-magnetic experiences an impedance while propagating through a medium. When there is no resistive or dissipating mechanism, the impedance is determined by two energy storing parameters *i.e.*, inertia and elasticity for mechanical waves and inductance and capacitance in the case of electrical waves. The impedance in such a case is a real quantity. The presence of a loss mechanism introduces a complex term into the impedance.

Transverse impedance. *It is the impedance offered by a string to transverse, progressive waves and is defined as the ratio of transverse force to the transverse velocity.*

$\therefore$
$$\text{Impedance, } Z = \frac{\text{Transverse force}}{\text{Transverse velocity}} = \frac{F}{v}$$

Suppose we have a continuous string stretching from left to right with the left end at $x = 0$. Consider a progressive wave on the string which is generated by an impressed oscillating force $F = F_0 \, e^{i\omega t}$ acting at this end. The force acts only in the plane of the paper in a *transverse* direction *i.e.*, perpendicular to the equilibrium position of the string.

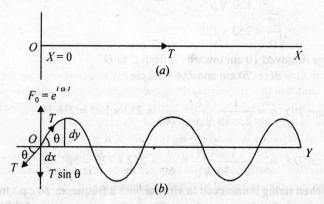

Fig. 5.7

If the string has a constant tension T, then at the end of the string ($x = 0$) the applied force $F_0 \, e^{i\omega t}$ and the $T \sin \theta$ component of T always balance each other.

$\therefore$
$$F = F_0 \, e^{i\omega t} = - T \sin \theta$$

As θ is small, then as shown in Fig. 5.7 (*b*)

$$\sin \theta = \tan \theta = \frac{dy}{dx}$$

$\therefore$
$$F_0 \, e^{i\omega t} = -T \left(\frac{dy}{dx} \right)_{x=0}$$

The displacement of the progressive wave is represented in the exponential form by the equation

$$\vec{y} = \vec{A}\, e^{i(\omega t - kx)}$$

where $\vec{A}$ is the amplitude and may be a *complex* quantity due to its phase relation with F and

$k = \dfrac{2\pi}{\lambda} = \dfrac{\omega}{c}$, ω being the angular frequency of the applied periodic force and c the wave velocity.

Hence at the end of the string where $x = 0$.

$$F_0\, e^{i\omega t} = -\, T\left(\dfrac{dy}{dx}\right)_{x=0} = ik\, T\vec{A}\, e^{i\omega t}$$

$$\therefore \qquad \vec{A} = \dfrac{F_0}{ikT}$$

and

$$\vec{y} = \dfrac{F_0}{iT} \times \dfrac{c}{\omega}\, e^{i(\omega t - kx)}$$

$\therefore$ Transverse velocity

$$\vec{v} = \dfrac{d\vec{y}}{dt}$$

$$= F_0\, \dfrac{c}{T}\, e^{i(\omega t - kx)} = v e^{i(\omega t - kx)}$$

where v is the *velocity amplitude* $= \dfrac{F_0\, c}{T}$

According to definition, impedance $Z = \dfrac{F_0}{v}$

$$\therefore \qquad Z = \dfrac{F_0}{v} = \dfrac{T}{c}$$

Now for a string $\quad c = \sqrt{\dfrac{T}{\rho}}\ $ or $\ T = \rho\, c^2$

where ρ is the mass per unit length or the linear density of the string.

$\therefore$ Characteristic impedance $Z = \rho\, c$.

Factors on which characteristic impedance depends. The characteristic impedance depends upon ρ the mass per unit length of the string. It also depends upon the value of the velocity of the wave c. The value of velocity c depends upon inertia and elasticity of the medium. Therefore, the impedance also depends upon these two *energy storing* factors.

Q. 5.19. (*a*) **What happens if incident waves fall at a common boundary of two strings having different impedances but joined in such a way that tension is the same throughout?**

(*b*) **Define reflection coefficient and transmission coefficient of amplitude. What is the amplitude of transverse waves reflected at the dense medium (*i.e.*, $Z_2 \cong \infty$)?**

(*G.N.D.U.,* 2009, 2007, 2006; *P.U.,* 2009, 1995)

Ans. (*a*) **Reflection and transmission of a wave on a string at a discontinuity.** A string offers a characteristic impedance $\rho\, c$ to the waves travelling along it. Whenever there is a *sudden* change in impedance due to a *discontinuity* at the junction of two media the wave suffers reflection at the boundary. This applies to all types of waves whether they are sound waves along a string, voltage or current waves along a transmission line or electromagnetic waves in a medium.

Let us suppose that the string consists of two parts smoothly joined at the point P, $x = 0$ and has a constant tension

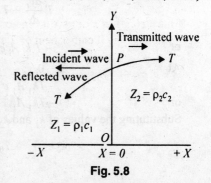

Fig. 5.8

T along the whole string. The two sections have different linear densities ρ_1 and ρ_2 and, therefore, different wave velocities c_1 and c_2 given by

$$c_1 = \sqrt{\frac{T}{\rho_1}} \quad \text{and} \quad c_2 = \sqrt{\frac{T}{\rho_2}}$$

The specific or characteristic impedances respectively are $Z_1 = \rho_1 c_1$ and $Z_2 = \rho_2 c_2$. If the incident wave is represented by the real part of the displacement equation

$$y_1 = A_1 e^{i(\omega t - k_1 x)}$$

where A_1 is the amplitude of the incident wave travelling in the *positive X-direction* with velocity c_1 and $k_1 = \dfrac{\omega}{c_1}$, then the reflected and transmitted waves are represented by the real part of the equations.

$$y_r = B_1 e^{i(\omega t + k_1 x)}$$

and
$$y_t = A_2 e^{i(\omega t - k_2 x)}$$

where B_1 is the amplitude of the reflected wave travelling in the *negative X-direction* with velocity c_1 and A_2 is the amplitude of the transmitted wave travelling in the *positive X*-direction with velocity c_2 and $k_2 = \dfrac{\omega}{c_2}$. The value of B_1 and A_2 can be determined with the help of two boundary conditions which must be satisfied at the point of impedance discontinuity at $x = 0$. The boundary conditions are:—

(1) The displacement y is the same immediately to the left and to the right of $x = 0$ for all times so that there is *no discontinuity of displacement*. This is the *geometrical condition* and is stated as

$$y_i + y_r = y_t$$

or
$$A_1 e^{i(\omega t - k_1 x)} + B_1 e^{i(\omega t + k_1 x)} = A_2 e^{i(\omega t - k_2 x)}$$

At
$$x = 0$$
$$A_1 e^{i\omega t} + B_1 e^{i\omega t} = A_2 e^{i\omega t}$$

or
$$A_1 + B_1 = A_2 \qquad \qquad ...(i)$$

(2) The transverse force $T\left(\dfrac{dy}{dx}\right)$ at $x = 0$ is *continuous across the boundary*. This means that the gradient $\dfrac{dy}{dx}$ *must have the same value on both sides.* If it is not so a finite transverse force will act on an infinitesimally small mass of the string producing an infinite acceleration which is physically an absurd statement. This is the *dynamical condition* and is stated as

$$T\frac{dy_i}{dx} + T\frac{dy_r}{dx} = T\frac{dy_t}{dx}$$

or
$$-T k_1 A_1 e^{i(\omega t - k_1 x)} + T k_1 B_1 e^{i(\omega t + k_1 x)} = -T k_2 A_2 e^{i(\omega t - k_2 x)}$$

At
$$x = 0$$
$$-T k_1 A_1 e^{i\omega t} + T k_1 B_1 e^{i\omega t} = -T k_2 A_2 e^{i\omega t}$$

or
$$-T k_1 A_1 + T k_1 B_1 = -T K_2 A_2$$

Substituting the values of k_1 and k_2, we have

$$-\omega\frac{T}{c_1} A_1 + \omega\frac{T}{c_1} B_1 = -\omega\frac{T}{c_2} A_2$$

Now $\quad \dfrac{T}{c_1} = \rho_1 c_1 = Z_1 \quad$ and $\quad \dfrac{T}{c_2} = \rho_2 c_2 = Z_2$

$\therefore \qquad\qquad\qquad\qquad (A_1 - B_1) Z_1 = A_2 Z_2 \qquad\qquad\qquad\qquad\qquad ...(ii)$

(b) Reflection coefficient of amplitude. The reflection coefficient

$$= \dfrac{\text{Amplitude of reflected wave}}{\text{Amplitude of incident wave}} = \dfrac{B_1}{A_1}$$

Now from (ii)

$$\dfrac{A_2}{A_1 - B_1} = \dfrac{A_1 + B_1}{A_1 - B_1} = \dfrac{Z_1}{Z_2}$$

$\therefore \quad$ Reflection co-efficient $\dfrac{B_1}{A_1} = \dfrac{Z_1 - Z_2}{Z_1 + Z_2}$

Transmission coefficient of amplitude. The transmission coefficient

$$= \dfrac{\text{Amplitude of transmitted wave}}{\text{Amplitude of incident wave}} = \dfrac{A_2}{A_1}$$

Substituting $B_1 = A_2 - A_1$ in (ii), we have

$$(A_1 - A_2 + A_1) Z_1 = A_2 Z_2$$

or $\qquad\qquad 2 A_1 Z_1 = A_2 (Z_1 + Z_2)$

$\therefore \qquad\qquad\qquad \dfrac{A_2}{A_1} = \dfrac{2 Z_1}{Z_1 + Z_2}$

It is clear from the above expression that both these coefficients are independent of ω i.e., these hold for waves of all the frequencies. These are real quantities and, therefore, are free from phase changes except the phase change of π when reflection takes place at a fixed end.

Amplitude after reflection at dense medium $(Z_2 \cong \infty)$

If $Z_2 = \infty$ i.e., $x = 0$ is a *fixed* end, then $A_2 = 0$ and there is no transmitted wave. This also gives

$$\dfrac{B_1}{A_1} = \dfrac{Z_1/Z_2 - 1}{Z_1/Z_2 + 1} = -1$$

so that the incident wave is completely reflected with a phase change of π i.e., the phase is reversed. This condition is necessary for standing waves to exist. A group of waves having a number of component frequencies will *retain* its shape on reflection.

Amplitude after reflection at rarer medium $(Z_2 \cong 0)$

If $Z_2 = 0$ i.e., $x = 0$ is a *free* end, then

$$\dfrac{B_1}{A_1} = 1 \quad \text{and} \quad \dfrac{A_2}{A_1} = 2$$

i.e., the amplitude of the transmitted wave A_2 is twice that of the incident wave A_1. It is due to this reason that there is 'flick' at the end of a whip or the free end of a string when a wave reaches it.

As $B_1 = A_1$, the incident wave is completely reflected without any phase change.

Q. 5.20. Explain why we hear a 'flick' at the end of a string.

(P.U. 2007, 2001; Pbi U., 2001; G.N.D.U., 1995)

Ans. There is a *'flick'* at the end of a whip or the free end of a string because when a wave travelling through the string reaches the free end it meets a highly rare medium for which the characteristic impedance $Z_2 \cong 0$. The transmission coefficient of amplitude A_2 is given by

$$\frac{A_2}{A_1} = \frac{2Z_1}{Z_1 + Z_2}$$

when $Z_2 = 0, \dfrac{A_2}{A_1} = 2$ or $A_2 = 2A_1$

The amplitude at the free end is thus doubled and hence the intensity of the wave becomes four times. The sound becomes very loud and is called '*flick*'.

Q. 5.21. Obtain an expression for the energy of a transversely vibrating string. Hence derive the expression for the rate of flow of energy along the stretched string.

(*P.U.*, 2003; *Gauhati U.*, 2000)

Ans. Energy of a vibrating string. When a transverse wave is propagated through a string, the displacement of the particles of the string is given by $y = A\, e^{i\,(\omega t - kx)}$.

We shall, however, assume that the displacement varies as a sine function and is given by the imaginary part of the above equation *i.e.*,

$$y = A \sin(\omega t - kx)$$

where $\omega = 2\pi \nu$, ν being the frequency and $k = \dfrac{2\pi}{\lambda}$, λ being the wave length of the wave travelling through the string.

$\therefore$ Particle velocity $v = \dfrac{dy}{dt} = A\omega \cos(\omega t - kx)$

and acceleration $a = \dfrac{d^2 y}{dt^2} = -A\omega^2 \sin(\omega t - kx) = -\omega^2 y$

Consider a very small element of length dx of the string of mass m, then

Potential energy of the element $E_p = -\displaystyle\int_0^y m\, \dfrac{d^2 y}{dt^2}\, dy$

$$= m\omega^2 \int_0^y y\, dy = \frac{1}{2} m\, \omega^2 y^2$$

$$= \frac{1}{2} m\omega^2 A^2 \sin^2(\omega t - kx)$$

and Kinetic energy of the element $E_k = \dfrac{1}{2} mv^2 = \dfrac{1}{2} m\left(\dfrac{dy}{dt}\right)^2$

$$= \frac{1}{2} m\omega^2 A^2 \cos^2(\omega t - kx)$$

$\therefore$ Total energy of the element $E = E_p + E_k$

$$= \frac{1}{2} m\omega^2 A^2 \left[\sin^2(\omega t - kx) + \cos^2(\omega t - kx)\right]$$

$$= \frac{1}{2} m\omega^2 A^2$$

If ρ is the mass per unit length (or linear density) of the string, then $m = \rho\, dx$

$\therefore$ $E = \dfrac{1}{2} \rho\, \omega^2 A^2\, dx$ ...(*i*)

Hence total energy per unit length $E_1 = \dfrac{1}{2} \rho \omega^2 A^2$ ...(ii)

Rate of flow of energy. The rate of flow of energy across any cross-section of the string is given by

$$I = \frac{dE}{dt} = \frac{1}{2} \rho \omega^2 A^2 \frac{dx}{dt}$$

From Eq (i).

But $\dfrac{dx}{dt} = c$, the velocity of propagation of the wave in the string.

$$\therefore \qquad I = \frac{1}{2} \omega^2 A^2 (\rho c)$$

$$= \frac{1}{2} \omega^2 A^2 Z \qquad (\because Z = \rho\, c) \qquad \qquad ...(iii)$$

From relation (iii), we find that

(i) The rate of flow of energy through the string when a wave propagates through it is proportional to Z-the characteristic impedance of the string

(ii) It is independent of x and t.

(iii) The rate of flow of energy is the same everywhere in the string and at all instants of time.

Q. 5.22. Show that all energy arriving at the boundary in the incident wave leaves the boundary in the reflected and transmitted wave. Define reflection and transmission coefficients of energy. Show that the sum of the reflection and transmission co-efficients of energy is always unity. (*P.U.*, 2004, 2001, 2000, 1994; *Pbi.U.*, 2006, 2001; *G.N.D.U.*, 2009, 2007, 2006, 2000, 1993)

Ans. Reflection and transmission of energy. When a wave meets a boundary between two media having different impedance values a part of it is reflected and a part transmitted. If A_1 is the amplitude of the incident wave in the medium of impedance Z_1 (linear density ρ_1, wave velocity c_1), B_1 the amplitude of the reflected wave and A_2 the amplitude of the transmitted wave in the medium of impedance Z_2 (linear density ρ_2, wave velocity c_2), then

The reflection coefficient $\dfrac{B_1}{A_1} = \dfrac{Z_1 - Z_2}{Z_1 + Z_2}$ ...(i)

and transmission coefficient $\dfrac{A_2}{A_1} = \dfrac{2Z_1}{Z_1 + Z_2}$ ...(ii)

In a general case, the total energy per unit length of a string of linear density ρ, amplitude A and angular frequency ω is given by

$$E = \frac{1}{2} \rho\, \omega^2 A^2 \qquad \qquad \text{[For proof See } \textbf{Q. 5.21}, \text{ Eq } (ii)\text{]}$$

As the wave travels along the string with a velocity c each unit length of the string takes up its oscillation with the passage of the wave.

$\therefore$ Rate of flow of energy along the string = energy $\times$ velocity $= \dfrac{1}{2} \rho\, \omega^2 A^2 c$

If the point at which reflection takes place is at $x = 0$, then the rate of energy arriving at the boundary $x = 0$, with the incident wave

$$= \frac{1}{2} \rho_1\, \omega^2 A_1^2\, c_1 = \frac{1}{2} Z_1 \omega^2 A_1^2 \qquad \qquad [\because \rho_1 c_1 = Z_1]$$

The energy leaves the boundary *via* the reflected and the transmitted waves.

∴   Rate at which energy leaves the boundary

$$= \frac{1}{2} \rho_1 \omega^2 B_1^2 c_1 + \frac{1}{2} \rho_2 \omega^2 A_2^2 c_2$$

$$= \frac{1}{2} Z_1 \omega^2 B_1^2 + \frac{1}{2} Z_2 \omega^2 A_2^2$$

Substituting the values of B_1 and A_2 from (*i*) and (*ii*) the above expression

$$= \frac{1}{2} \omega^2 A_1^2 \frac{Z_1 (Z_1 - Z_2)^2 + 4 Z_1^2 Z_2}{(Z_1 + Z_2)^2} = \frac{1}{2} Z_1 \omega^2 A_1^2$$

which is equal to the energy arriving with the incident wave.

This shows that all the energy arriving at the boundary in the incident wave leaves the boundary in the reflected and transmitted wave.

Reflected and transmitted energy coefficients. The reflected and transmitted energy coefficients are defined as

$$\text{Reflected energy coefficient} = \frac{\text{Reflected energy}}{\text{Incident energy}}$$

$$= \frac{\frac{1}{2} Z_1 \omega^2 B_1^2}{\frac{1}{2} Z_1 \omega^2 A_1^2} = \frac{B_1^2}{A_1^2} = \left(\frac{Z_1 - Z_2}{Z_1 + Z_2} \right)^2 \qquad ...(iii)$$

$$\text{Transmitted energy coefficient} = \frac{\text{Transmitted energy}}{\text{Incident energy}}$$

$$= \frac{\frac{1}{2} Z_2 \omega^2 A_2^2}{\frac{1}{2} Z_1 \omega^2 A_1^2} = \frac{Z_2 A_2^2}{Z_1 A_1^2} = \frac{4 Z_1 Z_2}{(Z_1 + Z_2)^2} \qquad ...(iv)$$

∴   Reflected energy co-efficient + transmitted energy co-efficient $= \left(\frac{Z_1 - Z_2}{Z_1 + Z_2} \right)^2 + \frac{4 Z_1 Z_2}{(Z_1 + Z_2)^2} = 1$

Q. 5.23. Explain the term impedance matching. State the conditions for perfect impedance matching between two media. What are the uses of impedance matching? Give application for anti-reflection films.

(*P.U.*, 2006, 2005, 2001, 1996, 1994, 1990; *G.N.D.U.*, 2007, 2006, 2004, 1993)

Ans. Impedance matching. When a wave meets a boundary between two media having different impedance values, a part of it is reflected and a part transmitted. The reflection energy coefficient is given by

$$\frac{\text{Reflected energy}}{\text{Incident energy}} = \left(\frac{Z_1 - Z_2}{Z_1 + Z_2} \right)^2$$

If $Z_1 = Z_2$, the reflected energy = 0
The transmitted coefficient of energy is given by

$$\frac{\text{Transmitted energy}}{\text{Incident energy}} = \frac{4 Z_1 Z_2}{(Z_1 + Z_2)^2}$$

If $Z_1 = Z_2$, the transmitted coefficient of energy = 1. In such a case
Transmitted energy = Incident energy

This shows that when $Z_1 = Z_2$, no energy is reflected and all energy is transmitted. *In such a case the impedances are said to be perfectly matched.*

Conditions for impedance matching when $Z_1 \neq Z_2$. When the impedances of the two media are not equal. As for example, in the case of two strings of different characteristic impedance $(Z_1 \neq Z_2)$, it can be shown that '*impedance matching*' can be brought about by 'coupling' a piece of string of impedance Z and length l between the two strings of impedance Z_1 and Z_2, such that

$$Z = \sqrt{Z_1 Z_2}$$

and
$$l = \lambda / 4$$

where λ is the wavelength of the incident wave in the material of the coupling element.

Thus the conditions are

(*i*) The impedance of the coupling element is the geometric mean of the impedances of the media to be matched.

(*ii*) The coupling element has length $l = \dfrac{\lambda}{4}$ where λ is the wavelength of the incident wave in the medium of the coupling element.

Uses of impedance matching. What has been stated above for matching of impedance of two strings is equally applicable to all types of waves travelling through two wave conducting media of different impedances. The principle of '*impedance matching*', therefore, finds wide application in many fields. Some of these are

(*i*) The transfer of power from a generator to a load is maximum when the impedances of the generator and the load are matched.

(*ii*) In electronic appliances, like the power amplifier or the radio set the impedance of the output circuit is matched to the impedance of the loud speaker with the help of a suitable coupling transformer.

(*iii*) **Anti-reflection films.** Lenses of optical instruments are coated with a dielectric layer of thickness $\dfrac{\lambda}{4}$ (quarter wave layer) and refractive index $n = \sqrt{n_1 n_2}$ where n_1 is the refractive index of air and n_2 that of the material of the lens. The application of the anti-reflection coating is known as '*blooming*' and is brought about by evaporating a dielectric substance of suitable refractive index on the surface of the lens. For example, magnesium oxide ($n = 1.38$) is used for impedance matching between air ($n_1 = 1$) and glass $n_2 = (1.38)^2 = 1.9$. It is not possible to have an exact matching because a material of the required refractive index may not be available. Moreover, a quarter wave impedance may give a perfect match for waves of light of a particular wavelength say in the middle of the visible spectrum but may give appreciable reflection in the extreme blue and red regions. The coating, therefore, gives a '*purple*' appearances by reflected light.

(*iv*) Two transmission lines of different impedances are matched by inserting quarter wavelength stubs of the line between them.

Q. 5.24. Two electric transmission cables are joined at a point. What special care should be taken for proper transmission of power? *(G.N.D.U., 1994)*

Ans. When two electric transmission cables are joined at a point, proper transmission of power takes place only when the impedance of the two cables is the same *i.e.*, $Z_1 = Z_2$. If it is not so *i.e.*, the transmission lines are of different impedance, then the impedances are matched by inserting a *quarter wavelength* stub of the line between them such that the impedance of the stub Z is given by

$$Z = \sqrt{Z_1 Z_2}$$

Q. 5.25. What does the term 'the matching of impedance' imply? Show that for perfect matching the impedance of the coupling element is the geometric mean of the impedances of the media to be matched when the impedances of the two media are not equal.

(*G.N.D.U.* 2006; *P.U.*, 2003)

Ans. Impedance matching See Q. 5.23.

Impedance of the coupling element. Two media of characteristic impedance Z_1 and Z_2 ($Z_1 \neq Z_2$) coupled through an element of impedance Z and length l is shown in Fig.5.9. The boundaries of the coupling element are located at $x = 0$ and $x = l$. The wave enters the coupling medium at $x = 0$ and leaves it at $x = l$. The value of wave numbers for the three media are k_1, k and k_2 respectively. The incident reflected and transmitted waves in all the three media are as shown in the figure.

For maximum transfer of power the two boundary conditions that must be satisfied are

(*i*) The displacement y is continuous at the interfaces $x = 0$ and $x = l$

and (*ii*) The transverse force $T \dfrac{dy}{dx}$ is also continuous at these two points.

At $x = 0$ According to first condition at $x = 0$

$$y_{i1} + y_{r1} = y_i + y_r$$

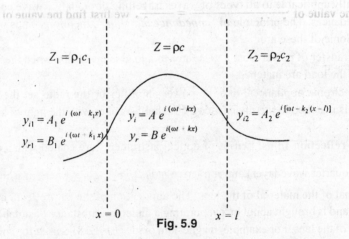

$$Z_1 = \rho_1 c_1 \qquad\qquad Z = \rho c \qquad\qquad Z_2 = \rho_2 c_2$$

$$y_{i1} = A_1 e^{i(\omega t - k_1 x)} \qquad y_i = A e^{i(\omega t - kx)} \qquad y_{i2} = A_2 e^{i[\omega t - k_2(x - l)]}$$

$$y_{r1} = B_1 e^{i(\omega t + k_1 x)} \qquad y_r = B e^{i(\omega t + kx)}$$

$$x = 0 \qquad\qquad x = l$$

Fig. 5.9

or $$A_1 e^{i(\omega t - k_1 x)} + B_1 e^{i(\omega t + k_1 x)} = A e^{i(\omega t - kx)} + B e^{i(\omega t + kx)}$$

Putting $x = 0$, we get

$$A_1 e^{i\omega t} + B_1 e^{i\omega t} = A e^{i\omega t} + B e^{i\omega t}$$

or $$A_1 + B_1 = A + P \qquad\qquad\qquad ...(i)$$

According to the second condition at $x = 0$

$$T[-i k_1 A_1 + i k_1 B_1] = T[-i k A + i k B]$$

or $$-i[A_1 T k_1 - B_1 T k_1] = -i[A T k - B T k]$$

Now $$Tk = T \frac{2\pi}{\lambda} = T \frac{2\pi v}{c} = \frac{T}{c}\omega = Z\omega \qquad\qquad \text{since } \frac{T}{c} = Z$$

∴ Substituting $T k_1 = Z_1 \omega$ and $T k = Z \omega$ in the above equation we get

$$Z_1 \omega (A_1 - B_1) = Z \omega (A - B)$$

or $$Z_1 (A_1 - B_1) = Z (A - B) \qquad\qquad\qquad ...(ii)$$

At $x = l$ At the boundary of the coupling medium and the medium into which the wave is finally transmitted, we have, according to the first condition

$$y_i + y_r = y_{i2}$$

or
$$A e^{i(\omega t - kx)} + B e^{i(\omega t + kx)} = A_2 e^{i[\omega t - k_2(x-l)]}$$

At $x = l$, we have

$$A e^{i(\omega t - kl)} + B e^{i(\omega t + kl)} = A_2 e^{i\omega t}$$

or
$$e^{i\omega t}[A e^{-ikl} + B e^{ikl}] = A_2 e^{i\omega t}$$

or
$$A e^{-ikl} + B e^{+ikl} = A_2 \qquad \qquad ...(iii)$$

Similarly according to second condition at $x = l$

$$-i A T k e^{i(\omega t - kl)} + i B T k e^{i(\omega t + kl)} = -i A_2 T k_2 e^{i\omega t}$$

or
$$-A T k e^{-ikl} + B T k e^{+ikl} = -A_2 T k_2$$

Substituting $T k = Z \omega$ and $T k_2 = Z_2 \omega$, we get

$$\omega [A Z e^{-ikl} - B Z e^{+ikl}] = \omega A_2 Z_2$$

or
$$Z [A e^{-ikl} - B e^{+ikl}] = A_2 Z_2 \qquad \qquad ...(iv)$$

To find the value of $\dfrac{\text{transmitted energy}}{\text{Incident energy}} = \dfrac{Z_2 A_2^2}{Z_1 A_1^2}$, we first find the value of $\dfrac{A_2}{A_1}$.

From Eq. (i) $\qquad B_1 = A + B - A_1$

Substituting in Eq. (ii), we get

$$Z_1 (A_1 - A - B + A_1) = Z (A - B)$$

or
$$2 Z_1 A_1 = Z_1 (A + B) + Z (A - B)$$

or
$$2 A_1 = (A + B) + \frac{Z}{Z_1}(A - B)$$

$$= A\left[1 + \frac{Z}{Z_1}\right] + B\left[1 - \frac{Z}{Z_1}\right]$$

or
$$A_1 = \frac{1}{2}A\left[1 + \frac{Z}{Z_1}\right] + \frac{1}{2}B\left[1 - \frac{Z}{Z_1}\right] \qquad ...(v)$$

To find the value of A and B in terms of A_2 we have, from Eq. (iv)

$$A e^{-ikl} - B e^{+ikl} = \frac{Z_2}{Z} A_2 \qquad \qquad ...(vi)$$

Adding Eqs. (iii) and (vi), we get

$$2 A e^{-ikl} = A_2\left(1 + \frac{Z_2}{Z}\right)$$

or
$$A = \frac{A_2}{2}\left(1 + \frac{Z_2}{Z}\right)e^{+ikl}$$

Subtracting (vi) from (iii), we get

$$2 B e^{+ikl} = A_2\left(1 - \frac{Z_2}{Z}\right)$$

or
$$B = \frac{A_2}{2}\left(1 - \frac{Z_2}{Z}\right)e^{-ikl}$$

Substituting these values of A and B in eq. (v), we get

$$A_1 = \frac{A_2}{4}\left(1 + \frac{Z}{Z_1}\right)\left(1 + \frac{Z_2}{Z}\right)e^{+ikl} + \frac{A_2}{4}\left(1 - \frac{Z}{Z_1}\right)\left(1 - \frac{Z_2}{Z}\right)e^{-ikl}$$

or

$$\frac{A_1}{A_2} = \frac{1}{4}\left(1 + \frac{Z}{Z_1} + \frac{Z_2}{Z} + \frac{Z_2}{Z_1}\right)e^{+ikl} + \frac{1}{4}\left(1 - \frac{Z}{Z_1} - \frac{Z_2}{Z} + \frac{Z_2}{Z_1}\right)e^{-ikl}$$

$$= \frac{1}{2}\left(1 + \frac{Z_2}{Z_1}\right)\frac{e^{ikl} + e^{-ikl}}{2} + \frac{1}{2}\left(\frac{Z}{Z_1} + \frac{Z_2}{Z}\right)\frac{e^{ikl} - e^{-ikl}}{2}$$

$$= \frac{1}{2}\left(1 + \frac{Z_2}{Z_1}\right)\cos kl + i\frac{1}{2}\left(\frac{Z}{Z_1} + \frac{Z_2}{Z}\right)\sin kl$$

$\therefore$

$$\frac{\text{Transmitted energy}}{\text{Incident energy}} = \frac{E_T}{E_i} = \frac{Z_2(A_2)^2}{Z_1(A_1)^2} = \frac{Z_2}{Z_1}\left(\frac{A_2}{A_1}\right)\left(\frac{A_2}{A_1}\right)$$

$$= \frac{Z_2}{Z_1}\frac{4}{\left(1 + \frac{Z_2}{Z_1}\right)^2 \cos^2 kl + \left(\frac{Z}{Z_1} + \frac{Z_2}{Z}\right)^2 \sin^2 kl}$$

If $l = \dfrac{\lambda}{4}$, then $\cos kl = \cos\dfrac{k\lambda}{4} = \cos\dfrac{2\pi}{\lambda}\cdot\dfrac{\lambda}{4} = \cos\dfrac{\pi}{2} = 0$ and $\sin kl = \sin\dfrac{\pi}{2} = 1$.

$\therefore$

$$\frac{E_T}{E_i} = \frac{Z_2}{Z_1}\frac{4}{\left(\dfrac{Z}{Z_1} + \dfrac{Z_2}{Z}\right)^2}$$

For maximum transfer of power $\dfrac{E_T}{E_i} = 1$

$\therefore$

$$\frac{Z_2}{Z_1} \times \frac{4}{\left(\dfrac{Z}{Z_1} + \dfrac{Z_2}{Z}\right)^2} = 1$$

or

$$4\frac{Z_2}{Z_1} = \left(\frac{Z}{Z_1} + \frac{Z_2}{Z}\right)^2 = \left(\frac{Z}{Z_1}\right)^2 + \left(\frac{Z_2^2}{Z}\right) + 2\frac{Z_2}{Z_1}$$

or

$$\left(\frac{Z}{Z_1}\right)^2 + \left(\frac{Z_2}{Z}\right)^2 - 2\frac{Z_2}{Z_1} = \left(\frac{Z}{Z_1} - \frac{Z_2}{Z}\right)^2 = 1$$

or

$$\frac{Z}{Z_1} - \frac{Z_2}{Z} = 1$$

or $Z^2 = Z_1 Z_2$ or $Z = \sqrt{Z_1 Z_2}$

Thus perfect matching is achieved and all the incident energy is transmitted when the following two conditions are satisfied :

1. The impedance of the coupling element is given by $Z = \sqrt{Z_1 Z_2}$ i.e. it is the geometric mean of the impedances of the media to be matched.

2. The coupling element has a length $l = \dfrac{\lambda}{4}$ where λ is the wavelength of the incident wave in the medium of the coupling element.

Q. 5.26. Two strings of linear densities 0.25 gm/cm and 1.0 gm/cm are joined together and stretched with a force of 100 N. Calculate the coefficients of reflection and transmission of amplitude. (*P.U.* 2002, 2000 (*modified*), 1995)

Ans. $\rho_1 = 0.25$ gm/cm $= 0.025$ kg m^{-1}

$\rho_2 = 1.0$ gm/cm $= 0.1$ kg m^{-1}, $T = 100$ N

$\therefore \qquad c_1 = \sqrt{\dfrac{T}{\rho_1}} = \sqrt{\dfrac{100}{0.025}} = 63.25$ m s^{-1}

and $\qquad c_2 = \sqrt{\dfrac{T}{\rho_2}} = \sqrt{\dfrac{100}{0.1}} = 31.622$ m s^{-1}

Now $\quad Z_1 = \rho_1 c_1 = 0.025 \times 63.25 = 1.581$

and $\quad Z_2 = \rho_2 c_2 = 0.1 \times 31.622 = 3.162$

Reflection coefficient of amplitude $\qquad = \dfrac{B_1}{A_1} = \dfrac{Z_1 - Z_2}{Z_1 + Z_2}$

$$= \dfrac{1.581 - 3.162}{1.581 + 3.162} = -0.333$$

Transmission coefficient of amplitude $\dfrac{A_2}{A_1} = \dfrac{2Z_1}{Z_1 + Z_2}$

$$= \dfrac{2 \times 1.581}{1.581 + 3.162} = 0.667$$

Exercise. *Two strings of linear densities* 5×10^{-4} *kg/m and* 2×10^{-3} *kg/m are joined together and stretched by a force of* 50 N. *Calculate the co-efficient of reflection and transmission.*

(*G.N.D.U.*, 2001)

Ans. $- 0.333$ and 0.667.

Q. 5.27. Two strings of linear densities 0.5 gm m^{-1} and 1.5 gm m^{-1} are joined together and stretched with a certain force. Calculate

(*i*) Ratio of wave speeds in two strings

(*ii*) Reflection and transmission coefficients of energy. (*G.N.D.U.*, 1993; *P.U.*, 2007)

Ans. $\rho_1 = 0.5$ gm m$^{-1} = 0.5 \times 10^{-3}$ kg m^{-1};

$\rho_2 = 0.5$ gm m$^{-1} = 1.5 \times 10^{-3}$ kg m^{-1}

(*i*) $\dfrac{c_1}{c_2} = \sqrt{\dfrac{T}{\rho_1}} \times \sqrt{\dfrac{\rho_2}{T}} = \sqrt{\dfrac{\rho_2}{\rho_1}} = \sqrt{\dfrac{1.5 \times 10^{-3}}{0.5 \times 10^{-3}}} = \sqrt{3} = 1.732$

(*ii*) $\dfrac{Z_1}{Z_2} = \dfrac{\rho_1 c_1}{\rho_2 c_2} = \dfrac{\rho_1}{\rho_2} \cdot \dfrac{c_1}{c_2} = \dfrac{0.5 \times 10^{-3}}{1.5 \times 10^{-3}} \times 1.732 = 0.577$

or $\quad Z_1 = 0.577 \, Z_2$

Reflected energy coefficient $\quad = \left(\dfrac{Z_1 - Z_2}{Z_1 + Z_2}\right)^2 = \left(\dfrac{0.577 Z_2 - Z_2}{0.577 Z_2 + Z_2}\right)^2 = \left(\dfrac{-0.423}{1.577}\right)^2$

$$= 0.072$$

Transmitted energy coefficient $= \dfrac{4 Z_1 Z_2}{(Z_1 + Z_2)^2} = \dfrac{4 \times 0.577 Z^2}{(0.577 + 1)^2 Z^2} = \dfrac{4 \times 0.577}{(1.577)^2}$

$$= 0.928$$

Exercise. *Two strings whose linear densities are in the ratio of* 1 : 4 *are stretched and joined together. A transverse wave is incident at the boundary. Calculate the reflection and transmission co-efficient of amplitude.*   *(G.N.D.U., 2002)*

Hint. $\dfrac{\rho_1}{\rho_2} = \dfrac{1}{4}; \dfrac{c_1}{c_2} = \sqrt{\dfrac{T}{\rho_1} \times \dfrac{\rho_2}{T}} = \sqrt{\dfrac{\rho_2}{\rho_1}} = \sqrt{\dfrac{4}{1}} = 2$

$\dfrac{Z_1}{Z_2} = \dfrac{\rho_1}{\rho_2} \dfrac{c_1}{c_2} = \dfrac{1}{4} \times 2 = \dfrac{1}{2}$

Amplitude reflection co-efficient $= \dfrac{Z_1 - Z_2}{Z_1 + Z_2} = \dfrac{\dfrac{Z_1}{Z_2} - 1}{\dfrac{Z_1}{Z_2} + 1} = \dfrac{\dfrac{1}{2} - 1}{\dfrac{1}{2} + 1} = -\dfrac{1}{3}$

Amplitude transmission co-efficient $= \dfrac{2Z_1}{Z_1 + Z_2} = \dfrac{2\dfrac{Z_1}{Z_2}}{\dfrac{Z_1}{Z_2} + 1} = \dfrac{2 \times \dfrac{1}{2}}{\dfrac{1}{2} + 1} = \dfrac{2}{3}$

Q. 5.28. A wave travelling in a rod meets a metallic joint where the Young's modulus is twice the value but density remains the same. Calculate the reflection and transmission coefficients of amplitude.   *(P.U., 1996)*

Ans. Let ρ be the density, Y the young's modulus of the rod and $2Y$ of the metallic joint.

Velocity of the wave in the rod $c_1 = \sqrt{\dfrac{Y}{\rho}}$

Velocity of the wave in the metallic joint $c_2 = \sqrt{\dfrac{2Y}{\rho}}$

Impedance of the rod $Z_1 = \rho c_1 = \rho \sqrt{\dfrac{Y}{\rho}} = \sqrt{\rho Y}$

Impedance of the metallic joint $Z_2 = \rho c_2 = \rho \sqrt{\dfrac{2Y}{\rho}} = \sqrt{2\rho Y}$

$\therefore$ $\dfrac{Z_2}{Z_1} = \sqrt{2}$ or $Z_2 = \sqrt{2}\, Z_1$

Reflection coefficient of amplitude $\dfrac{B_1}{A_1} = \dfrac{Z_1 - Z_2}{Z_1 + Z_2} = \dfrac{Z_1 - \sqrt{2}\, Z_1}{Z_1 + \sqrt{2}\, Z_1}$

$= \dfrac{1 - 1.4142}{1 + 1.4142} = \dfrac{0.4142}{2.4142} = 0.17$

Transmission coefficient of amplitude $\dfrac{A_2}{A_1} = \dfrac{2Z_1}{Z_1 + Z_2} = \dfrac{2Z_1}{Z_1 + \sqrt{2}\, Z_1}$

$= \dfrac{2}{2.414} = 0.83$

Q. 5.29. Discuss analytically the formation of standing waves in a string of fixed length. What are its eigen frequencies? How does the position of nodal points change with eigen frequencies?   *(G.N.D.U. 2007, 2006; Pbi. U. 2006; P.U. 1995)*

Ans. Standing waves in a string of fixed length. Consider a string of fixed length l clamped rigidly at both ends. Consider a monochromatic wave *i.e.*, a wave of only one (angular) frequency ω and amplitude a travelling in a positive X-direction, then the wave equation is given by

$$y_1 = a\, e^{i\,(\omega\, t - kx)}$$

where $\quad k = \dfrac{2\pi}{\lambda} = \dfrac{\omega}{c}$

This wave is reflected from the fixed end and if the amplitude of the reflected wave travelling along the *negative X*-direction is b, then the equation of the reflected wave is given by

$$y_2 = b\, e^{i\,(\omega\, t + kx)}$$

The displacement of a point on the string due to both these waves is given by

$$y = y_1 + y_2 = a\, e^{i(\omega\, t - kx)} + b\, e^{i(\omega\, t + kx)} \qquad ...(i)$$

The boundary condition to be satisfied at all times are

(a) At $x = 0$, displacement $y = 0$

(b) At $x = l$, displacement $y = 0$

Applying the boundary condition (a) we have from (i)

$$0 = a\, e^{i\,\omega\, t} + b\, e^{i\,\omega\, t}$$

or $\quad\quad a = -b$

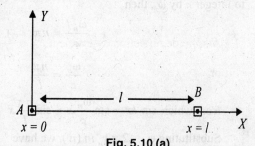

Fig. 5.10 (a)

This condition implies that the wave is completely reflected at either end which offers infinite impedance with a *reversal of phase* or a phase change of π.

Substituting $b = -a$ in (i), we have

$$y = a\, e^{i\,\omega\, t}\,[e^{-ikx} - e^{+ikx}]$$

$$= (-2i)\, a e^{i\omega t}\,\frac{e^{-ikx} - e^{+ikx}}{-2i}$$

or $\qquad\qquad y = -2\, i\, a\, e^{i\,\omega\, t} \sin kx \qquad\qquad\qquad ...(ii)$

This equation satisfies the *standing wave time independent* form of the wave equation

$$\frac{d^2 y}{dt^2} + k^2 y = 0, \text{ because from Eq } (ii)$$

$$\frac{dy}{dt} = (-2i)a(i\omega)e^{i\omega t} \sin kx$$

and

$$\frac{d^2 y}{dt^2} = (-2i)a(-\omega^2)e^{i\omega t} \sin kx = -\omega^2 y$$

$$\therefore \qquad \frac{1}{c^2}\cdot\frac{d^2 y}{dt^2} = -\frac{\omega^2}{c^2}y = -k^2 y$$

Substituting in the differential form of wave equation

$$\frac{d^2 y}{dx^2} = \frac{1}{c^2}\frac{d^2 y}{dt^2}, \text{ we have}$$

$$\frac{d^2 y}{dx^2} + k^2 y = 0$$

Thus equation (ii) gives a general result for all wave shapes and frequencies.

Applying the boundary condition (b), we have from (ii)

$$0 = -2\, ia\, e^{i\,\omega\, t} \sin kl$$

or $\qquad \sin k\,l = \sin \dfrac{\omega}{c}\,l = 0$ $\qquad\qquad\qquad\qquad \left[\because k = \dfrac{\omega}{c}\right]$

or $\qquad\qquad\qquad \dfrac{\omega l}{c} = n\pi$ $\qquad\qquad\qquad\qquad\qquad\qquad\qquad$ ...(iii)

where n is an integer.

This condition limits the value of *allowed* frequencies. If we denote the value of ω corresponding to integer n by ω_n, then

$$\dfrac{\omega_n\,l}{c} = n\pi$$

or $\qquad\qquad\qquad \dfrac{\omega_n}{c} = \dfrac{n\pi}{l}$ $\qquad\qquad\qquad\qquad\qquad\qquad$ ...(iv)

from which $\sin kx = \sin \dfrac{\omega_n}{c} x = \sin \dfrac{n\pi}{l} x$ $\qquad\qquad\qquad$ ...(iv) (a)

Substituting $\omega_n = 2\pi v_n$ *in* (iv), we have

$$\dfrac{2\pi v_n}{c} = \dfrac{n\pi}{l}$$

or $\qquad\qquad\qquad v_n = \dfrac{nc}{2l}$ $\qquad\qquad\qquad\qquad\qquad\qquad\qquad$ ...(v)

If λ_n is the corresponding wavelength, then

$$\lambda_n = \dfrac{c}{v_n} = \dfrac{2l}{n}$$

or $\qquad\qquad\qquad l = \dfrac{n\lambda_n}{2}$ $\qquad\qquad\qquad\qquad\qquad\qquad\qquad$ ...(vi)

Hence we find that *the allowed frequencies define the length of the string as an exact number of half wavelengths.*

Eigen frequencies. The frequencies given by equation (v) for various integral values of n are the *normal frequencies* or *normal modes of vibration* and are often called *Eigen frequencies*. The term Eigen frequencies is commonly used in *wave-mechanics*.

The lowest frequency corresponding to $n = 1$ is called the *fundamental* and those corresponding to $n > 1$ are known as *harmonics*. The first three harmonics for $n = 2, 3, 4$ are shown in Fig. 5.10 (b). In general all normal modes may be present at the same time. The general displacement is the superposition of all the displacements due to different allowed frequencies.

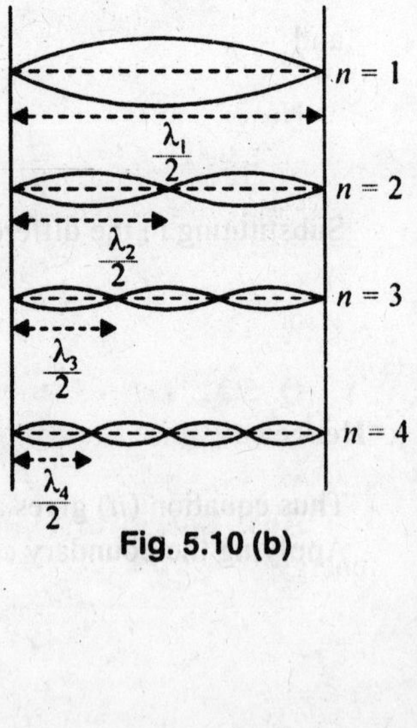

Nodes and antinodes. From equation (iv) (a), we find that for values of n greater than 1, there are a number of positions along the string which are always at rest. These positions are given by

$$\sin \dfrac{\omega_n}{c} x = \sin \dfrac{n\pi}{l} x = 0$$

$\qquad\qquad\qquad\qquad$ or $\qquad\qquad \dfrac{n\pi x}{l} = r\pi$

where $\qquad\qquad\qquad r = 0, 1, 2, 3 \dots n$

Fig. 5.10 (b)

The position of the two fixed ends is given by $r = 0$ and $r = n$ because $r = 0$ gives $x = 0$ and $r = n$ gives $x = l$. Between these two positions there are $n - 1$ positions for the nth harmonic which are equally spaced along the string where the displacement is zero for all times. These positions are known as *nodes* or *nodal points* and give the positions of zero motion in a *system of standing waves*. These standing waves are produced by the superposition of the incident and the reflected waves travelling in the opposite directions. The nodal points will exist if the reflection is complete so that the amplitude of the incident and the reflected progressive waves are equal and opposite. For $n = 4$, the number of nodes $= n - 1 = 3$. In between two consecutive nodes and equally spaced are the positions having maximum displacement. These points are known as *antinodes*.

Equations for standing waves. Equation (*ii*) for nth harmonic can be expressed as

$$y_n = -2\,a\,i\,e^{i\omega_n t}\sin\frac{\omega_n}{c}x$$

$$= 2\,a(-i)(\cos\omega_n t + i\sin\omega_n t)\sin\frac{\omega_n}{c}x$$

$$= (A_n\cos\omega_n t + B_n\sin\omega_n t)\sin\frac{\omega_n}{c}x \qquad\qquad ...(vii)$$

where $A_n = -2\,ai$ and $B_n = 2\,a$.

Equation (*vii*) gives the equation of standing wave, along the string.

Q. 5.30. A wire of linear density 0.01 gm/cm is stretched with a tension of 10 N. It resonates at a frequency of 200 Hz. The next higher frequency at which it resonates is 240 Hz. Find the length of the wire. (*P.U.*, 1993)

Ans. Let the string be vibrating in p segments corresponding to 200 Hz frequency and $(p + 1)$ segemnts corresponding to the frequency 240 Hz. If T is the tension and ρ the density, then

$$200 = \frac{p}{2l}\sqrt{\frac{T}{\rho}} \qquad\qquad ...(i)$$

and

$$240 = \frac{p+1}{2l}\sqrt{\frac{T}{\rho}} \qquad\qquad ...(ii)$$

From (*i*) and (*ii*), we get

$$\frac{240}{200} = \frac{p+1}{p}$$

or

$$p = \frac{200}{240 - 200} = 5$$

Now

$$T = 10\text{ N}, \rho = 0.01\text{ gm/cm} = 0.001\text{ kg/m}$$

∴

$$200 = \frac{5}{2l}\sqrt{\frac{10}{0.001}} = \frac{500}{2l}$$

or

$$l = \frac{500}{400} = 1.25\text{ m}$$

Q. 5.31. Derive an expression for the potential and kinetic energy of a vibrating string. Hence calculate the energy in each normal mode of a vibrating string.

(*P.U.*, 2001; *G.N.D.U.*, 2006, 1995, 1994, 1991)

Ans. Energy of a vibrating string. A vibrating string possess both kinetic as well as potential energy.

Kinetic energy. Consider a small element of length dx of a stretched vibrating string of total length l and mass per unit length ρ. If $\dot{y}$ is the velocity of the element, then

$$\text{K.E. of the element} = \frac{1}{2}\rho\,dx\,\dot{y}^2$$

$$\therefore\quad \text{Total } K.E. \text{ of the string} = \frac{1}{2}\int_0^l \rho\,\dot{y}^2\,dx$$

Potential energy. It is the work done by tension T in extending an element of length dx in the normal position of the string to a new element of length ds in the vibrating position.

$\therefore$ Potential energy of the element $= T(ds - dx)$

$$= T\left[(dx^2 + dy^2)^{1/2} - dx\right]$$

$$= T\left\{\left[1 + \left(\frac{dy}{dx}\right)^2\right]^{\frac{1}{2}} - 1\right\}dx$$

$$= \frac{1}{2}T\left(\frac{dy}{dx}\right)^2 dx$$

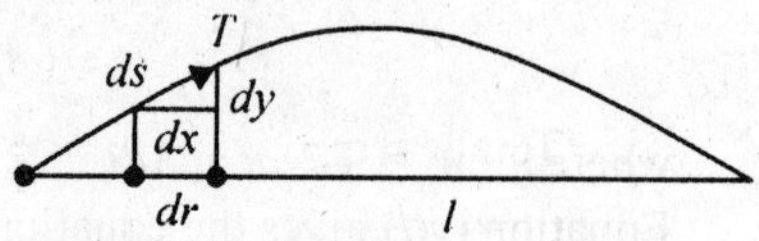

as $\left[1 + \left(\frac{dy}{dx}\right)^2\right]^{\frac{1}{2}} = 1 + \frac{1}{2}\left(\frac{dy}{dx}\right)^2$

neglecting higher power of $\frac{dy}{dx}$ and also assuming T to be a constant.

$$\therefore\quad \text{Total P.E. of the string} = \frac{1}{2}T\int_0^l \left(\frac{dy}{dx}\right)^2 dx$$

Fig. 5.11

Energy in each normal mode. When a string vibrates in a pure normal mode, every point in the string vibrates with the same frequency and at any moment all parts move either in the same or in the opposite phase. In a normal mode the total displacement y in the string is the superposition of the displacements y_n of the individual harmonics and the total energy of the resultant vibration is obtained by adding the energy of each mode as if it existed independently of other modes. Thus the kinetic energy of the nth mode

$$E_n \text{ (kinetic)} = \frac{1}{2}\int_0^l \rho\,\dot{y}_n^2\,dx$$

and potential energy E_n (potential) $= \frac{1}{2}T\int_0^l \left(\frac{dy_n}{dx}\right)^2 dx$

The displacement for the nth harmonic is given by

$$y_n = (A_n\cos\omega_n t + B_n\sin\omega_n t)\sin\frac{\omega_n}{c}x \qquad \text{[Eq. (vii) Q. 5.29]}$$

where $A_n = -2\,ai$ and $B_n = 2\,a$

$\therefore$

$$\dot{y}_n = (-A_n\omega_n\sin\omega_n t + B_n\omega_n\cos\omega_n t)\sin\frac{\omega_n}{c}x$$

and $\qquad \dfrac{dy_n}{dx} = \dfrac{\omega_n}{c}\,(A_n \cos\omega_n\,t + B_n \sin\omega_n\,t)\cos\dfrac{\omega_n}{c}\,x$

$\therefore \qquad$ Total Energy $= E_n$ (kinetic) $+ E_n$ (potential)

$$= \dfrac{1}{2}\,\rho\omega_n{}^2(-A_n\sin\omega_n\,t + B_n\cos\omega_n t)^2 \int_0^l \sin^2\dfrac{\omega_n}{c}\,x\,dx$$

$$+ \dfrac{1}{2}\,T\dfrac{\omega_n{}^2}{c^2}(A_n\cos\omega_n t + B_n\sin\omega_n\,t)^2 \int_0^l \cos^2\dfrac{\omega_n}{c}\,x\,dx$$

Now $\quad \dfrac{T}{c^2} = \rho,\ \ \displaystyle\int_0^l \sin^2\dfrac{\omega_n}{c}\,x\,dx = \dfrac{1}{2}l,\ \ \int_0^l \cos^2\dfrac{\omega_n}{c}\,x\,dx = \dfrac{1}{2}\,l$

and $\quad (-A_n\sin\omega_n\,t + B_n\cos\omega_n\,t)^2 + (A_n\cos\omega_n\,t + B_n\sin\omega_n\,t)^2$

$$= (A_n^2 + B_n^2)$$

$\therefore \quad$ Total energy $\quad = \dfrac{1}{4}\,\rho l\omega_n^2\,(A_n^2 + B_n^2)$

$$= \dfrac{1}{4}\,m\omega_n^2(A_n^2 + B_n^2)$$

where $m = \rho\,l =$ mass of the whole string.

As mass m, normal mode frequency ω_n, and normal mode amplitudes A_n and B_n are constants, the total energy in the normal mode vibration of the string remains constant.

Q. 5.32. When a rod is clamped at the end horizontally and free end is pressed down and released, show that for the smallest frequency of vibration, the wavelength is four times the length of the rod. (*P.U.*, 1991)

Ans. When a rod is clamped at one end horizontally and the free end is pressed and released, the free end moves up and down with maximum amplitude as shown in Fig. 5.12. Various portions of the rod from the free end A to the clamped end N vibrate with smaller and smaller amplitude. The clamped end N does not vibrate at all. In other words the free end A is the antinode and the clamped end N a node.

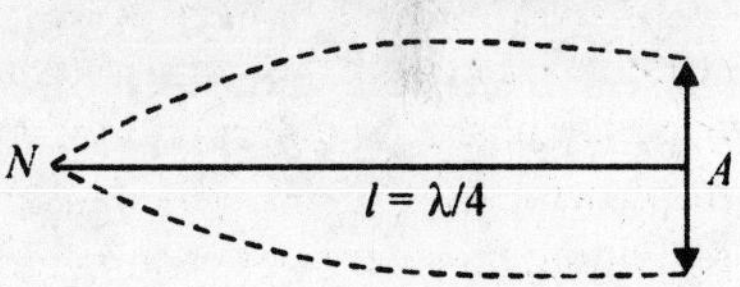

$\therefore$ Length of the rod $l =$ Minimum distance between a

node and an antinode $= \dfrac{\lambda}{4}$, where λ is the wavelength.

Fig. 5.12

$\therefore \qquad\qquad \lambda = 4\,l$

This is the maximum wavelength and the frequency corresponding to it is the smallest.

Q. 5.33. Mark the correct answer.

(*i*) The differential equation of wave motion is

(*a*) $\quad \dfrac{d^2y}{dx^2} = \dfrac{1}{c}\dfrac{d^2y}{dt^2}$

(*b*) $\quad \dfrac{d^2y}{dx^2} = c^2\dfrac{d^2y}{dt^2}$

(*c*) $\quad \dfrac{d^2y}{dx^2} = \dfrac{1}{c^2}\dfrac{d^2y}{dt^2}$

(*d*) $\quad \dfrac{d^2y}{dx^2} = c\dfrac{d^2y}{dt^2}$

(*ii*) The relation between path difference x and phase difference ϕ is

(*a*) $\phi = 2\pi\lambda x$

(*b*) $\phi = \dfrac{2\pi}{\lambda}x$

(*c*) $\phi = \dfrac{2\pi}{x}\lambda$

(*d*) $\phi = \dfrac{2\pi}{x\lambda}$

(*iii*) The velocity of transverse waves in a string is given by

(*a*) $v = \dfrac{\sqrt{T}}{\rho}$ $\qquad$ (*b*) $v = \dfrac{T}{\sqrt{\rho}}$ $\qquad$ (*c*) $v = \sqrt{\dfrac{T}{\rho}}$ $\qquad$ (*d*) $v = \dfrac{T}{\rho}$

(*iv*) Impedances are said to be matched when

(*a*) $Z_1 = Z_2$ $\qquad$ (*b*) $Z_1 > Z_2$ $\qquad$ (*c*) $Z_1 < Z_2$ $\qquad$ (*d*) $Z_2 = 0$

Ans. (*i*) *c* $\qquad\qquad$ (*ii*) *b* $\qquad\qquad$ (*iii*) *c* $\qquad\qquad$ (*iv*) *a*

EXERCISES

1. Equation of a progressive wave is given by

$$y = \sin\left(500\pi t - \frac{\pi}{70}x\right) \text{ units.}$$

What are the amplitude, frequency and wavelength of the wave? $\qquad$ (*Vid. S.U.*, 1992, 1990)

[**Ans.** Amplitude = 1 unit, Frequency = 250 units, Wavelength = 140 units]

2. Write down the equation of a simple harmonic progressive wave of amplitude 0.001 m and frequency 5 Hz travelling in the negative *x*-direction with a velocity 3000 m/s. $\qquad$ (*Luck. U.*, 1996)

$$\left[\textbf{Ans. } y = 0.001 \sin 2\pi\left(5t + \frac{x}{600}\right)\right]$$

6 Longitudinal Waves

Q. 6.1. Show that the velocity of sound in a solid medium is $\sqrt{\dfrac{Y}{\rho}}$ **where Y and ρ denote respectively the Young's modulus and density of the solid.**

(*Luck. U.*, 2001; *Gauhati U.*, 2000 ; *Cal. U.*, 1992)

Ans. Velocity of sound in a solid medium. Sound is a form of longitudinal wave motion. Longitudinal vibrations can be set up in a solid medium in the form of a rod whose thickness is small as compared to its length. To set up longitudinal vibrations in a rod it is either stroked at one end with a hammer or rubbed along its length by a resined cloth. The longitudinal vibrations travel along the rod with a velocity which depends upon the Young's modulus Y and density ρ of the material of the rod.

Consider a rod of uniform area of cross-section a. Let the axis of the rod be along the X-axis. Suppose longitudinal sound waves are travelling in the solid medium of the rod from left to right along the X-axis OX. Take two planes perpendicular to OX at A and B a small distance δx apart. When sound waves travel through the medium let at any instant the plane A be displaced to A' and plane B to B'. Suppose the displacement of the plane at $A = AA' = y$ and the rate of change of displacement

$$= \frac{dy}{dx}$$

$\therefore$ Displacement of the plane at $B = BB' = y + \left(\dfrac{dy}{dx}\right)\delta x$

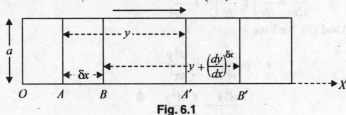

Fig. 6.1

As the displacement of the plane B is greater than the displacement of the plane A, the distance $B'A'$ is greater than BA by an amount given by

$$y + \left(\frac{dy}{dx}\right)\delta x - y = \left(\frac{dy}{dx}\right)\delta x$$

$\therefore$ Change of distance between the planes A and $B = \left(\dfrac{dy}{dx}\right)\delta x$

183

Original distance between the planes A and $B = \delta x$

$\therefore$ Longitudinal strain $= \dfrac{\text{Change in length}}{\text{Original length}}$

$$= \frac{\text{Change of distance between the planes } A \text{ and } B}{\text{Original distance between the planes } A \text{ and } B} = \frac{\left(\dfrac{dy}{dx}\right)\delta x}{\delta x}$$

or   Longitudinal strain $= \dfrac{dy}{dx}$

When the rod is under strain elastic forces automatically come into play.

Let F be the force per unit area on the plane A and $\dfrac{dF}{dx}$ the rate of change of force, then

Force on the plane $A = aF$

and Force on the plane $B = aF + a\left(\dfrac{dF}{dx}\right)\delta x$

Hence net force on the layer $AB = a\left(\dfrac{dF}{dx}\right)\delta x$

Mass of the medium in the layer $AB = a\,\delta x\,\rho$ where ρ is the density of the medium.

If $\dfrac{d^2 y}{dt^2}$ represents the acceleration of the particles in the layer, then

$$a\left(\frac{dF}{dx}\right)\delta x = a\,\delta x\,\rho\,\frac{d^2 y}{dt^2} \quad \text{or} \quad \frac{dF}{dx} = \rho\,\frac{d^2 y}{dt^2} \qquad \ldots(i)$$

Now, Young's modulus (or Longitudinal elasticity) of the medium

$$Y = \frac{\text{Stress (Force per unit area)}}{\text{Longitudinal strain}} = \frac{F}{\dfrac{dy}{dx}}$$

$\therefore$

$$F = Y\,\frac{dy}{dx}$$

or

$$\frac{dF}{dx} = \frac{d}{dx}\left(Y\,\frac{dy}{dx}\right) = Y\,\frac{d^2 y}{dx^2} \qquad \ldots(ii)$$

Comparing (i) and (ii), we have

$$\rho\,\frac{d^2 y}{dt^2} = Y\,\frac{d^2 y}{dx^2}$$

or

$$\frac{d^2 y}{dt^2} = \frac{Y}{\rho}\,\frac{d^2 y}{dx^2}$$

This expression represents the differential equation of longitudinal wave propagation along the rod. Comparing it with standard equation of wave motion

$$\frac{d^2 y}{dt^2} = v^2\,\frac{d^2 y}{dx^2}$$

we get the velocity of the wave

$$v^2 = \frac{Y}{\rho}$$

or $$v = \sqrt{\frac{Y}{\rho}}$$

This shows that the velocity of longitudinal waves travelling through a rod depends upon Young's modulus Y and density ρ. It is independent of the applied force and area of cross-section.

Q. 6.2. Derive an expression for the velocity of longitudinal waves in a gaseous medium.

(*Luck .U.*, 2001, 1993 ; *Burd. U.*, 1991 ; *H.P.U.*, 1991)

Ans. Velocity of longitudinal waves in a gas. The velocity of longitudinal waves in a fluid is given by the relation

$$v = \sqrt{\frac{E}{\rho}}$$

Where E is the coefficient of volume elasticity (bulk modulus) of the medium and ρ its density.

To prove this suppose longitudinal sound waves are travelling in a gaseous medium from *left* to right. Due to these longitudinal waves *rarefactions* and *condensations* will be formed in the medium. Let these rarefractions and condensations travel from left to right with a velocity v along the X-axis OX in a tube of area of cross-section a.

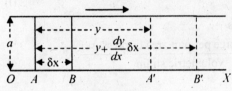

Fig. 6.2

Consider two planes perpendicular to OX at A and B a small distance δx apart. When sound waves travel through the medium let at any instant the plane A be displaced to the position A' and plane B to the position B'.

Suppose the displacement of the plane at $A = AA' = y$ and the rate of change of displacement $= \dfrac{dy}{dx}$

$\therefore$ Displacement at $B = BB' = y + \left(\dfrac{dy}{dx}\right)\delta x$

As the displacement of the plane B is greater than the displacement of the plane A, the distance $B'A'$ is greater than BA by an amount given by

$$y + \left(\frac{dy}{dx}\right)\delta x - y = \left(\frac{dy}{dx}\right)\delta x$$

$\therefore$ Change in volume $= a\left(\dfrac{dy}{dx}\right)\delta x$

Original volume of the layer $AB = a\,\delta x$

$\therefore$ Volumetric strain $= \dfrac{a\left(\dfrac{dy}{dx}\right)\delta x}{a\,\delta x} = \dfrac{dy}{dx}$

Let P be the excess of pressure over the atmosphere at the plane A. Suppose the excess pressure varies with distance x at the rate $\dfrac{dP}{dx}$, then

Excess pressure at the plane $B = P + \left(\dfrac{dP}{dx}\right)\delta x$

The excess of pressure at A and B act in *opposite* directions.

$\therefore$ The resultant pressure acting on the element AB

$$= P + \left(\frac{dP}{dx} \right) \delta x - P = \left(\frac{dP}{dx} \right) \delta x$$

Hence force acting on the element $AB = a \left(\frac{dP}{dx} \right) \delta x$

As ρ is the density of the gaseous medium, the mass of the element $AB = a \, \delta x \, \rho$

If $\frac{d^2 y}{dt^2}$ is the acceleration of the mass of the element AB, then according to Newton's second law of motion

$$a \, \delta x \, \rho \, \frac{d^2 y}{dt^2} = a \left(\frac{dP}{dx} \right) \delta x$$

or
$$\rho \, \frac{d^2 y}{dt^2} = \frac{dP}{dx} \qquad \qquad ...(i)$$

Now Bulk modulus (or volume elasticity) of the gas

$$E = \frac{\text{Stress (force per unit area or pressure)}}{\text{volumetric strain}}$$

$$= - \frac{P}{\dfrac{dy}{dx}} \qquad \qquad ...(ii)$$

or
$$P = E \, \frac{dy}{dx} \text{ (numerically)}$$

$\therefore$
$$\frac{dP}{dx} = \frac{d}{dx} \left(E \, \frac{dy}{dx} \right) = E \, \frac{d^2 y}{dx^2} \qquad \qquad ...(ii)(a)$$

Comparing (i) and (ii) we have

$$\rho \, \frac{d^2 y}{dt^2} = E \, \frac{d^2 y}{dx^2}$$

or
$$\frac{d^2 y}{dt^2} = \frac{E}{\rho} \frac{d^2 y}{dx^2}$$

This represents the differential equation of a longitudinal (or sound) wave propagating in a gaseous (fluid) medium. Comparing it with standard equation of wave motion

$$\frac{d^2 y}{dt^2} = v^2 \frac{d^2 y}{dx^2}, \text{ we get}$$

$$v^2 = \frac{E}{\rho}$$

or
$$v = \sqrt{\frac{E}{\rho}}$$

This shows that the velocity of sound waves through a gas depends upon volume elasticity and density of the gas.

Q. 6.3. What is specific acoustic impedance ? In what units is it measured ?

(Os. U. 2004, 1997)

Ans. Specific acoustic impedance. *It is defined as the ratio of excess of pressure to the particle velocity in the wave motion.* It is denoted by Z.

$$\therefore \qquad Z = \dfrac{P}{\dfrac{dy}{dt}}$$

But $\qquad\qquad P = -E\dfrac{dy}{dx}$ [Eq. (ii) Q 6.2]

and $\qquad\qquad y = a \sin \dfrac{2\pi}{\lambda}(vt - x)$

$\therefore \qquad\qquad \dfrac{dy}{dt} = a \dfrac{2\pi v}{\lambda} \cos \dfrac{2\pi}{\lambda}(vt - x)$

and $\qquad\qquad \dfrac{dy}{dx} = -a \dfrac{2\pi}{\lambda} \cos \dfrac{2\pi}{\lambda}(vt - x)$

$\therefore \qquad Z = \dfrac{Ea \dfrac{2\pi}{\lambda} \cos \dfrac{2\pi}{\lambda}(vt - x)}{a \dfrac{2\pi}{\lambda} v \cos \dfrac{2\pi}{\lambda}(vt - x)} = \dfrac{E}{v}$

$\therefore$ *Specific acoustic impedance may also be defined as the ratio of the elasticity of the medium to the velocity of the wave.*

Units. The unit of Z are that of $\dfrac{P}{\dfrac{dy}{dx}} = \dfrac{\text{Force}}{\text{area}} \times \dfrac{\text{time}}{\text{length}} = \text{Newton sec/ m}^3$

Q. 6.4. Obtain the expression for total mechanical (kinetic and potential) energy per unit volume of the medium when a wave is travelling through it. Prove that in a progressive wave half the energy is kinetic and half potential. Also show that maximum kinetic energy is equal to maximum potential energy.   *(Bang. U.* 2004; *Pbi.U.,* 2007, 2001 ; *H.P.U.,* 1992 ; *P.U.,* 1991)

Ans. Energy of a progressive wave. When a wave travels through a medium, it means transfer of energy from one place to another in the direction of propagation of the wave. If v is the velocity of the wave, then energy transferred per second is equal to the energy possessed by the particles of the medium in a length v. The energy of the progressive wave at any instant is paritally potential and partially kinetic. As the particles of the medium execute simple harmonic motion, the kinetic energy is maximum at the mean position where the displacement is zero and particle velocity is maximum. The potential energy is maximum at the extreme position where the displacement is maximum and particle velocity is zero. It means that at the mean position entire energy of the wave is kinetic (potential energy is zero) and at the extreme position entire energy of the wave is potential (kinetic energy is zero).

It should be clearly noted that there is no transfer of the medium in the direction of propagation of the progressive wave but there is only a transfer of energy in the direction of propagation of the wave.

A progressive wave of wavelength λ travelling with a velocity v along the positive direction of X-axis is represented by the expression

$$y = a \sin \dfrac{2\pi}{\lambda}(vt - x)$$

where y is the displacement at a point distant x from the origin at any time t and a the amplitude. The velocity of the particle

$$\dfrac{dy}{dt} = a 2\pi \dfrac{v}{\lambda} \cos \dfrac{2\pi}{\lambda}(vt - x)$$

and acceleration $\qquad \dfrac{d^2 y}{dt^2} = - \dfrac{4 \pi^2 v^2}{\lambda^2} \sin \dfrac{2\pi}{\lambda} (vt - x)$

The negative sign suggests that the acceleration of the particles is always directed towards the mean position.

Kinetic energy. Consider a unit volume of the medium of mass ρ equal to the density of the medium, then

$$K.E. \text{ per unit volume} = \frac{1}{2} \text{ mass} \times (\text{velocity})^2$$

$$= \frac{1}{2} \rho \cdot \left\{ a \frac{2\pi v}{\lambda} \cos \frac{2\pi}{\lambda} (vt - x) \right\}^2$$

$$= \frac{2 \pi^2 v^2 \rho}{\lambda^2} a^2 \cos^2 \left[\frac{2\pi}{\lambda} (vt - x) \right]$$

$$= 2 \pi^2 a^2 n^2 \rho \cos^2 \left[\frac{2\pi}{\lambda} (vt - x) \right]$$

where $\qquad n = \dfrac{v}{\lambda}$

Potential energy. To find the potential energy per unit volume of the medium, we have

Force on a unit volume = mass × acceleration

$$= - \rho \, a \frac{4 \pi^2 v^2}{\lambda^2} \sin \frac{2\pi}{\lambda} (vt - x)$$

$$= - \rho \frac{4 \pi^2 v^2}{\lambda^2} y$$

The negative sign only indicates that the force is directed towards the mean position opposite to the displacement. Hence work done to produce a small displacement dy

$$= \rho \frac{4 \pi^2 v^2}{\lambda^2} y dy$$

$\therefore$ Work done during the whole displacement from 0 to y

$$= \int_0^y \rho \frac{4 \pi^2 v^2}{\lambda^2} y dy = \frac{4 \pi^2 v^2 \rho}{\lambda^2} \frac{y^2}{2}$$

$$= \frac{2 \pi^2 v^2 \rho}{\lambda^2} a^2 \sin^2 \left[\frac{2\pi}{\lambda} (vt - x) \right]$$

$$= 2 \pi^2 n^2 a^2 \rho \sin^2 \left[\frac{2\pi}{\lambda} (vt - x) \right].$$

This work is stored in a unit volume of the medium as potential energy of the wave.

$\therefore$ Potential energy per unit volume $= 2 \pi^2 a^2 n^2 \rho \sin^2 \left[\dfrac{2\pi}{\lambda} (vt - x) \right]$

Total Energy. Total energy per unit volume = Kinetic energy per unit volume + Potential energy per unit volume

$$= 2 \pi^2 n^2 a^2 \rho \left\{ \sin^2 \left[\frac{2\pi}{\lambda} (vt - x) \right] + \cos^2 \left[\frac{2\pi}{\lambda} (vt - x) \right] \right\}$$

$$= 2\pi^2 n^2 a^2 \rho$$

or   Total energy per unit volume $E = 2\pi^2 n^2 a^2 \rho$ ...(i)

Average kinetic energy density. Now consider a cylindrical column of the medium of unit area of cross-section with its axis parallel to the direction of propagation. If we take an element of length dx, then its volume $= dx \times 1 = dx$.

The K.E. of this volume

$$= 2\pi^2 a^2 n^2 \rho \cos^2\left[\frac{2\pi}{\lambda}(vt - x)\right] dx \qquad\qquad ...(ii)$$

The different elements of the column will have different kinetic energies. The total kinetic energy of a column of length λ equal to the wavelength of the wave can be calculated by integrating equation (ii) between $x = 0$ and $x = \lambda$. Dividing the result by λ we get the **average kinetic energy per unit volume** or **average kinetic energy density.**

$\therefore$ Average K.E. per unit volume

$$= 2\pi^2 a^2 n^2 \rho \frac{1}{\lambda} \int_0^\lambda \cos^2 \frac{2\pi}{\lambda}(vt - x)\, dx$$

$$= 2\pi^2 a^2 n^2 \rho \frac{1}{\lambda} \frac{\lambda}{2} = \pi^2 a^2 n^2 \rho \qquad \left[\because \int_0^\lambda \cos^2 \frac{2\pi}{\lambda}(vt - x)\, dx = \frac{\lambda}{2}\right]$$

Again $2\pi n = \omega$

$\therefore$ $\pi^2 n^2 = \dfrac{1}{4}\omega^2$

Hence average kinetic energy per unit volume $= \dfrac{1}{4}\rho a^2 \omega^2$

Average potential energy density. The potential energy per unit volume

$$= 2\pi^2 a^2 n^2 \rho \sin^2\left[\frac{2\pi}{\lambda}(vt - x)\right]$$

$\therefore$ Potential energy for a volume dx

$$= 2\pi^2 a^2 n^2 \rho \sin^2\left[\frac{2\pi}{\lambda}(vt - x)\right] dx$$

and the **average potential energy per unit volume** or **Average potential energy density**

$$= 2\pi^2 a^2 n^2 \rho \frac{1}{\lambda} \int_0^\lambda \sin^2 \frac{2\pi}{\lambda}(vt - x)\, dx$$

$$= 2\pi^2 a^2 n^2 \rho \frac{1}{\lambda} \frac{\lambda}{2} \qquad\qquad \left[\because \int_0^\lambda \sin^2 \frac{2\pi}{\lambda}(vt - x)\, dx = \frac{\lambda}{2}\right]$$

$$= \pi^2 a^2 n^2 \rho = \frac{1}{4}\rho a^2 \omega^2$$

$\therefore$ **Average total energy per unit volume** or **Average total energy density**

$$E = \pi^2 a^2 n^2 \rho + \pi^2 a^2 n^2 \rho = 2\pi^2 a^2 n^2 \rho$$

$$= \frac{1}{2}\rho a^2 \omega^2$$

$\therefore$ Average kinetic energy per unit volume $(K.E.)_{av}$
                        = Average potential energy per unit volume $(P.E.)_{av}$

$$= \frac{1}{2} \times \text{Average total energy per unit volume.}$$

Hence average kinetic energy per unit volume is equal to the average potential energy per unit volume and is equal to half the total energy per unit volume of the progressive wave.

Maximum potential energy. It should be noted that both potential and kinetic energies of the wave depend upon the position and time *i.e.*, the values of x and t, but the total energy is independent of both these quantities.

The potential energy at a point is **maximum** when

$$\sin \frac{2\pi}{\lambda} (vt - x) = 1$$

or
$$y = a \qquad \left[\because \; y = a \sin \frac{2\pi}{\lambda} (vt - x) \right]$$

i.e., when the point is at extreme end of its displacement on either side of its mean position. The value of maximum potential energy

$$= 2\pi^2 \, a^2 \, n^2 \, \rho = \frac{1}{2} \, \rho \, a^2 \, \omega^2$$

Maximum kinetic energy. The kinetic energy at a point is maximum when

$$\cos \frac{2\pi}{\lambda} (vt - x) = 1$$

or
$$\sin \frac{2\pi}{\lambda} (vt - x) = 0$$

$$\therefore \qquad y = 0$$

i.e., when the point is passing through its mean position.

The value of maximum kinetic energy

$$= 2\pi^2 \, n^2 \, a^2 \, \rho = \frac{1}{2} \, \rho \, a^2 \, \omega^2$$

Thus the maximum value of the potential energy is the same as the maximum value of kinetic energy and is equal to the average total energy per unit volume of the medium. Further at a time, when the potential energy at a point is maximum, the kinetic energy is zero and *vice versa*.

The kinetic energy is maximum when the particle is at its mean position, and is gradually converted into potential energy as the particle moves towards the extreme position. At the extreme position the energy is wholly potential. When the particle again moves backward to the mean position the potential energy is gradually converted into kinetic energy till the particle reaches the mean position where the energy is wholly kinetic.

Q. 6.5. A plane progressive wave of frequency 256 Hz and amplitude 1/1000 mm is propagating through air of density 1.29 kg/m³. Calculate the energy density in the wave.

(*Kerla.U.*, 2001)

Ans. Here $\rho = 1.29$ kg/m³ ; $a = 1/1000$ mm $= 10^{-6}$ m ; $\omega = 2\pi \times 256$ rad s^{-1}

Average energy density $= \dfrac{1}{2} \, \rho \, a^2 \, \omega^2 = \dfrac{1}{2} \times 1.29 \times 10^{-12} \times 4\pi^2 \times 256 \times 256$

$$= 1.67 \times 10^{-6} \text{ Jm}^{-3}$$

Q. 6.6. Explain the term intensity of an acoustic wave. Obtain expression for intensity of the wave using expression for total energy possesssed by a wave in terms of density of the medium, frequency, amplitude and velocity of the wave.

(*Pbi.U.*, 1999 ; *G.N.D.U.*, 1996 ; *Cal. U.*, 1992 ; *P.U.*, 1991)

Ans. Intensity of the wave. *The intensity of an acoustic wave is defined as the amount of energy flowing through the medium per unit area per unit time.* It is denoted by I.

In an advancing wave train a new length v equal to the velocity of the wave is set in motion every second. Hence the energy transferred per unit area per unit time is equal to the energy contained in a length v.

Now the total energy contained in a unit volume of the medium or energy density $E = 2\pi^2 n^2 a^2 \rho$ (For proof see **Q. 6.4. Eq. (i)** where ρ is the density of the medium, n the frequency and a the amplitude of the wave

$\therefore$ Intensity of the wave $I = Ev = 2\pi^2 n^2 a^2 \rho v$ ...(i)

Hence intensity of the wave is equal to the product of the energy density and velocity of the wave. It is, therefore, known as *energy current*.

Now $I = 2\pi^2 n^2 a^2 \rho v = \dfrac{1}{2}\rho a^2 \omega^2 v$ ...(ii) $[\because \omega = 2\pi n]$

This shows that intensity of a wave is

(*i*)   proportional to the density of the medium

(*ii*) velocity of the wave

(*iii*) square of frequency of the wave and

(*iv*) square of amplitude of the wave

Q. 6.7. Show that the total energy and intensity of a progressive wave are independent of space and time co-ordinates (x and t).   (*G.N.D.U.*, 2000 ; *H.P.U.*, 1996)

Ans. Total energy and intensity independent of space and time co-ordinates. The average total energy per unit volume of a progressive wave is given by

$$E = \frac{1}{2}\rho a^2 \omega^2 = 2\pi^2 n^2 a^2 \rho \qquad\qquad ...(i)$$

[For proof see **Q. 6.4. Eq. (*i*)**]

The intensity of the wave is given by

$$I = 2\pi^2 n^2 a^2 \rho v = \frac{1}{2}\rho a^2 \omega^2 v \qquad\qquad ...(ii)$$

[For proof see **Q. 6.6. Eq. (*i*)**]

From (*i*) and (*ii*) it is clear that average total energy per unit volume and intensity of a progressive wave are independent of space and time co-ordinates (x and t).

Q. 6.8. (*a*) Show that the intensity of the wave at a point is given by

$$I = \frac{P^2_{rms}}{\rho v}$$

where p_{rms} is the root mean square value of the excess pressure.

(*b*) Calculate the increase in pressure when a sound wave produces an energy 10^{-7} Watt/cm^2. Velocity of sound = 340 m/sec. and density of air = 0.001293 gm/c.c. (*Kan.U.*, 1990)

Ans. (*a*) Intensity and excess pressure. The intensity I of a progressive wave is given by

$$I = 2\pi^2 n^2 a^2 \rho v$$

where the symbols have their usual meanings.

The velocity of sound v in a medium of bulk modulus E and density ρ is given by

$$v = \sqrt{\frac{E}{\rho}}$$

Now $E = -\dfrac{p}{dV/V}$

where p is the excess pressure and $\dfrac{dV}{V}$ the volumetric strain.

For a longitudinal wave

$$\text{Volumetric strain } \quad \frac{dV}{V} = \frac{dy}{dx} \quad \text{[For proof See Q 6.2]}$$

$$\therefore \qquad v = \sqrt{-\frac{p}{\dfrac{dy}{dx}}\,\frac{1}{\rho}}$$

or

$$p = -v^2\,\rho\,\frac{dy}{dx}$$

Now $\quad \dfrac{dy}{dx} = -a\,\dfrac{2\pi}{\lambda}\cos\dfrac{2\pi}{\lambda}(vt - x)$ $\qquad\qquad \left[\because y = a\sin\dfrac{2\pi}{\lambda}(vt - x)\right]$

$$\therefore \qquad \text{Excess pressure } \quad p = \frac{2\pi\,a\,v^2\,\rho}{\lambda}\cos\frac{2\pi}{\lambda}(vt - x)$$

$$= 2\pi\,a\,n\,v\,\rho\cos\frac{2\pi}{\lambda}(vt - x)$$

The maximum value of the excess pressure

$$p_{max} = \frac{2\pi\,a\,v^2\,\rho}{\lambda} = 2\pi\,a\,n\,v\,\rho$$

Now $\quad I = 2\,\pi^2\,n^2\,a^2\,\rho\,v = \dfrac{4\pi^2\,n^2\,a^2\,\rho^2\,v^2}{2\,\rho\,v} = \dfrac{P_{max}^2}{2\,\rho\,v}$

or

$$P_{max} = \sqrt{2\,\rho\,v\,I}$$

Also $\quad p^2 = 4\pi^2\,a^2\,n^2\,v^2\,\rho^2\cos^2\dfrac{2\pi}{\lambda}(vt - x)$

The mean value of p^2 for a wavelength λ is given by

$$P_{rms}^2 = 4\pi^2\,a^2\,n^2\,v^2\,\rho^2\,\frac{1}{\lambda}\int_0^\lambda\cos^2\frac{2\pi}{\lambda}(vt - x)$$

$$= 4\pi^2\,a^2\,n^2\,v^2\,\rho^2\,\frac{1}{\lambda}\frac{\lambda}{2} = 2\pi^2\,a^2\,n^2\,v^2\,\rho^2$$

$$\therefore \qquad I = \frac{P_{rms}^2}{\rho\,v}$$

(b) Energy flow or intensity $I = 10^{-7}$ Watt/cm^2

$$= 10^{-7} \text{ Joule/sec/cm}^2$$

$$= 10^{-3} \text{ Joule/sec/m}^2$$

Velocity of sound $\quad v = 340$ m/sec

Density of air $\qquad \rho = 0.001293$ gm/c.c.

$$= 0.001293 \times 10^3 \text{ kg/m}^2$$

$\therefore \quad$ Excess pressure $\quad P_{max} = \sqrt{2\,I\,\rho\,v}$

$$= \sqrt{2 \times 10^{-3} \times 0.001293 \times 10^3 \times 340}$$

$$= 0.9376 \text{ Newton/sq m.}$$

Q. 6.9. A tuning fork has a frequency of 256 and an amplitude of 0.5 cm. If the velocity of sound is 340 m/s, calculate the energy current. Density of air is 0.001293 gm/c.c.

(Kan. U., 1990)

Ans. Given $n = 256$, $a = 0.5$ cm $= 0.5 \times 10^{-2}$ m

$$v = 340 \text{ m/s}, \rho = 0.001293 \text{ gm/c.c.}$$

$$= 0.001293 \times 10^3 \text{ kg/m}^3$$

Energy current = Intensity $I = 2\pi^2 n^2 a^2 \rho v$

$$= \left[2 \times \frac{22}{7} \times \frac{22}{7} \times 256 \times 256 \times 0.5 \times 0.5 \times 10^{-4} \times 0.001293 \times 10^3 \times 340 \right]$$

$$= 119 \text{ J/s/m}^2 = 119 \text{ watt/m}^2$$

Q. (a) 6.10. Define the terms wave velocity and group velocity. Find a relation connecting the two. (G.N.D.U. 2008, 2007, 2006, 2004, 2002, 2000; Bhopal U. 2004; P.U., 2009, 2007, 2006, 2005, 2002, 2001, 2000, 1999; Pbi.U., 2006, 2005, 2000, 1991; Luck.U., 2001; H.P.U., 1992)

(b) Phase velocity of a deep water wave is given by $v = \sqrt{\dfrac{9\lambda}{2\pi}}$. Show that group velocity of such a wave is one half of the phase velocity (P.U., 2008)

Ans. (a)**Wave motion.** Wave motion is a form of disturbance which travels through a medium due to the repeated periodic motion of the particles of the medium about their mean positions, the motion being handed over from one particle to the next. The individual oscillators which make up the medium only execute simple harmonic motion about their mean positions and do not themselves travel through the medium with the wave. Every particle begins its vibrations a little later than its predecessor and there is a progressive change of phase as we travel from one particle to the next. *It is the phase relationship of these particles that we observe as a wave and not their progressive motion through the medium.* There are three distinct velocities connected with the wave motion.

(*i*) **The particle velocity.** It is the velocity of the simple harmonic motion of the oscillating particle about its equilibrium position.

(*ii*) **The wave or phase velocity.** It is the velocity with which the plane of equal phase (crest or trough) travels through the medium.

The equation of a plane progressive wave is given by

$$y = a \sin \frac{2\pi}{\lambda} (vt - x) = a \sin (\omega t - k x)$$

where $\omega = 2 \pi n$ and $k = \dfrac{2\pi}{\lambda}$

$$\therefore \quad \frac{\omega}{k} = \frac{2\pi n}{2\pi/\lambda} = n\lambda = v$$

This v is the *phase velocity or the wave velocity.* Hence '*phase velocity is the velocity with which a plane progressive wave front travels forward and which has a constant phase given by* ($\omega t - k x$)'.

Thus $\omega t - kx =$ a constant

Differentiating with respect to t, we get

$$\omega - k\,\frac{dx}{dt} = 0$$

or $\qquad\qquad \dfrac{dx}{dt} = \dfrac{\omega}{k} = v$ (phase velocity) $\hspace{3cm}$ ...(i)

The group velocity. A group consists of a number of waves of different frequencies superimposed upon each other. For example, white light consists of a continuous visible wave length spectrum ranging from about 3000Å in the violet to about 7000Å in the red region. The motion of such a pulse is described by its group velocity.

The wave velocity of each component of such a group would be different in all media except vacuum. Hence such a group of waves will *disperse* with time when it is travelling through a medium.

The importance of the group velocity lies in the fact that *this is the velocity with which the maximum amplitude and thus the energy of the wave group is transmitted.*

For *monochromatic wave* the group velocity and wave velocity are identical.

Wave groups. Let us consider a group of waves consisting of only two components of equal amplitudes and having frequencies ω_1 and ω_2, differing by a *small* amount and represented by the equation

$$y_1 = a \cos (\omega_1 t - k_1 x)$$

and $\qquad\qquad y_2 = a \cos (\omega_2 t - k_2 x)$

where $\dfrac{\omega_1}{k_1}$ and $\dfrac{\omega_2}{k_2}$ represent their respective velocities, k is known as wave number and is $= 2\pi/\lambda$.

It is further supposed that $\dfrac{\omega_1}{k_1} \neq \dfrac{\omega_2}{k_1}$ *i.e.*, it is a *dispersive medium.*

The resultant amplitude is given by

$$y = y_1 + y_2 = a \left[\cos (\omega_1 t - k_1 x) + \cos (\omega_2 t - k_2 x) \right]$$

$$= 2a \cos \left[\frac{(\omega_1 + \omega_2)}{2} t - \frac{(k_1 + k_2)}{2} x \right] \cos \left[\frac{(\omega_1 - \omega_2)}{2} t - \frac{(k_1 - k_2)}{2} x \right]$$

$$\therefore \qquad\qquad y = 2a \cos (\omega t - kx) \cos \left(\frac{\Delta \omega t}{2} - \frac{\Delta k x}{2} \right) \hspace{2cm} ...(ii)$$

where $\qquad\qquad \omega = \dfrac{\omega_1 + \omega_2}{2}$ and $k = \dfrac{k_1 + k_2}{2}$

and $\qquad\qquad \Delta\omega = (\omega_1 - \omega_2)$ and $\Delta k = (k_1 - k_2)$.

The resultant wave has two parts

(a) A wave of angular frequency ω, propagation constant k and velocity

$$v = \frac{\omega}{k}$$

(b) A second wave of angular frequency $\dfrac{\Delta\omega}{2}$, propagtion constant $\dfrac{\Delta k}{2}$ and velocity $v_g = \dfrac{\Delta\omega}{\Delta k}$.

The first type of wave has a maximum amplitude $2a$. It is modulated in space and time by the second wave which consists of a group of waves of the first type and is a very slowly varying envelope of frequency $\dfrac{\Delta\omega}{2}$ and propagation constant $\dfrac{\Delta k}{2}$. The modulated pattern moves with a velocity $v_g = \dfrac{\Delta\omega}{\Delta k}$ known as the group velocity.

∴   **Group velocity** $v_g = \dfrac{\Delta \omega}{\Delta k} = \dfrac{d\omega}{dk}$ ...(iii)

If the waves are sound waves, the intensity is maximum whenever the amplitude is maximum $= 2a$. This occurs twice in every period of the modulating frequency *i.e.*, at a frequency

$$2\,\frac{\Delta \omega}{2.2\pi} = \frac{\omega_1 - \omega_2}{2\pi} = v_1 - v_2$$

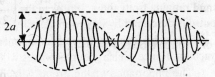

where v_1 and v_2 are the frequencies corresponding to ω_1 and ω_2. Thus the *beats* of maximum intensity fluctuations have a frequency equal to the difference $v_1 - v_2$ of the two components. If the two components have equal amplitudes, the amplitude of the envelope will vary between 0 and $2a$. In such a case the modulation is said to be complete or 100%.

Fig.6.3

Relation between group velocity and wave velocity. Suppose the two frequency components have different phase velocities $\dfrac{\omega_1}{k_1}$ and $\dfrac{\omega_2}{k_2}$ so that $\dfrac{\omega_1}{k_1} \neq \dfrac{\omega_2}{k_2}$, then the velocity $v_g = \dfrac{\omega_1 - \omega_2}{k_1 - k_2} = \dfrac{\Delta \omega}{\Delta k}$ will be different from each of the phase velocities. In such a case the superposition of the two waves will no longer remain constant and hence the group profile will change with time. Such a medium in which the phase velocity depends upon frequency is called a *dispersive medium*. The variation of ω as a function of k represents a *dispersion relation*.

If the group of waves consists of a number of component velocities very close to each other, we can write

$$\frac{\Delta \omega}{\Delta k} = \frac{d\omega}{dk} = v_g$$ ...(iv)

If the phase velocity is represented by v, then

$$v = \frac{\omega}{k} \quad \text{or} \quad \omega = k v$$

$$\therefore \quad \frac{d\omega}{dk} = v + k\,\frac{dv}{dk}$$

But $\dfrac{d\omega}{dk} = v_g$

∴ $v_g = v + \dfrac{k}{dk}\,dv$ ...(v)

Also $k = \dfrac{\omega}{v} = \dfrac{2\pi n}{v} = \dfrac{2\pi}{\lambda}$

$$\frac{dk}{d\lambda} = -\frac{2\pi}{\lambda^2} = -\frac{1}{\lambda}\,k$$

or $\dfrac{k}{dk} = -\dfrac{\lambda}{d\lambda}$

Substituting the above value of $\dfrac{k}{dk}$ in (v), we have

$$v_g = v - \lambda\,\frac{dv}{d\lambda}$$ ...(vi)

The group velocity v_g may be $< = >$ v where v is the wave or phase velocity.

(*b*) **Phase velocity**

$$v = \sqrt{\frac{9\lambda}{2\pi}} = \left(\frac{9}{2\pi}\right)^{\frac{1}{2}} \lambda^{\frac{1}{2}}$$

$$\therefore \quad \frac{dv}{d\lambda} = \left(\frac{9}{2\pi}\right)^{\frac{1}{2}} \frac{1}{2} \lambda^{-\frac{1}{2}}$$

and

$$\lambda \frac{dv}{d\lambda} = \left(\frac{9}{2\pi}\right)^{\frac{1}{2}} \frac{1}{2} \lambda^{\frac{1}{2}}$$

or Group velocity $v_g = v - \lambda \dfrac{dv}{d\lambda}$

$$= \left(\frac{9}{2\pi}\right)^{\frac{1}{2}} \lambda^{\frac{1}{2}} - \left(\frac{9}{2\pi}\right)^{\frac{1}{2}} \frac{1}{2} \lambda^{\frac{1}{2}}$$

$$= \frac{1}{2}\left(\frac{9}{2\pi}\right)^{\frac{1}{2}} \lambda^{\frac{1}{2}} = \frac{1}{2} v$$

Q. 6.11. Is group velocity less than wave velocity or greater than wave velocity ? Comment. Prove that if the phase velocity is the same for all the component waves, group velocity of the wave obtained by their superposition is equal to the wave velocity.

(*G.N.D.U., 2006; Luck.U., 2001 ; P.U., 1995, 1990 ; Pbi.U.,1991*)

Ans. Group velocity and wave velocity. If v_g is group velocity, v the wave velocity (or phase velocity), λ the wavelength and $\dfrac{dv}{d\lambda}$ the rate of change of velocity with wavelength, then

$$v_g = v - \lambda \frac{dv}{d\lambda}$$ [For proof see **Q. 6.10.** Eq. (*vi*)]

Now three cases arise :

(*i*) $\dfrac{dv}{d\lambda}$ is a positive quantity. In such a case $v_g < v$ *i.e.*, group velocity is less than wave velocity.

(*ii*) $\dfrac{dv}{d\lambda} = 0$. In such a case $v_g = v$ *i.e.*, group velocity is equal to wave velocity or phase velocity. In other words if the phase velocity is the same for all the component waves, the group velocity of the wave obtained by their superposition is equal to wave (or phase) velocity.

(*iii*) $\dfrac{dv}{d\lambda}$ is *a negative* quantity. In such a case

$$v_g = v + \lambda \frac{dv}{d\lambda}$$

and $v_g > v$ *i.e.*, group velocity is greater than wave velocity.

Hence group velocity is less than, equal to or greater than wave velocity according as $\dfrac{dv}{d\lambda}$ is positive, zero or negative.

Q. 6.12. (*a*) What is dispersion of waves ? Discuss and distinguish between normal dispersion, non-dispersion and anomalous dispersion. Give dispersion relations for them. Also give examples.   (*P.U., 2009, 2007, 2006, 2004, 2001, 1998, 1992; Pbi.U., 2006, 2000;*

G.N.D.U., 2006, 1995)

(*b*) **Show that group velocity is equal to wave velocity in a non-dispersive medium.**

(*Meerut U., 2007*)

Ans. (a) Dispersion. Group velocity and wave velocity of a group of waves is connected by the relation

$$v_g = v - \lambda \frac{dv}{d\lambda} \qquad \qquad ...(i)$$

where the symbols have their usual meanings. When $\frac{dv}{d\lambda}$ is zero i.e., the wave velocity does not vary with wavelength group velocity v_g = wave velocity v i.e. all the waves in the group even of different wavelengths (or frequencies) travel with the same velocity and remain together. The most familiar example is that of white light travelling through vacuum. Such a medium is non-dispersive medium.

A medium is which $\frac{dv}{d\lambda} \neq 0$, the group velocity depends upon wavelength (or frequencies). As a result waves of different wavelengths travel with different velocities and separate out. *The process of separation of waves of different wavelengths (or frequencies) while passing through a medium is known as dispersion.* Such a medium is called a *dispersive medium.*

The dispersion of white light into its consituent colours while passing through a prism is a familiar example.

Dispersion relation

(i) **Normal dispersion.** If $\frac{dv}{d\lambda}$ is a positive quantity, in relation (i) $v_g < v$ i.e., group velocity is less than wave velocity. This is the case of *normal dispersion*. In this case $v_g = v - \lambda \frac{dv}{d\lambda}$ gives the dispersion relation.

(ii) **Non-dispersion.** If $\frac{dv}{d\lambda} = 0$, $v_g = v$ i.e., group velocity is equal to the wave velocity. This is the case of *non-dispersive medium*. In such a case $v_g = v$ gives the dispersion relation. Hence group velocity is equal to wave velocity in a non-dispersive medium.

(iii) **Anomalous dispersion.** If $\frac{dv}{d\lambda}$ is a negative quantity, $v_g > v$ i.e., group velocity is greater than wave velocity. This is the case of *anomalous* dispersion. In this case $v_g = v + \lambda \frac{dv}{d\lambda}$ gives the dispersion relation.

Examples. Electromagnetic wave in vacuum are non-dispersive. In dielectric media (glass, water etc.) there is normal dispersion except at the natural resonant frequency of its atoms and $v_g < v$. In electrical conductors $v_g > v$ and there is anomalous dispersion.

(b) See part (a) (ii) Non-dispersion

Q. 6.13. Explain why there is no difference in wave velocity and group velocity when light travels in vacuum. *(H.P.U., 1993)*

Ans. Group velocity v_g and wave velocity v are connected by the relation

$$v_g = v - \lambda \frac{dv}{d\lambda}$$

where λ is the wavelength and $\frac{dv}{d\lambda}$ the rate of change of wave velocity with wavelength. When light travels through vacuum all the waves of different wavelengths travel with the same velocity i.e., there is no change in wave velocity with wavelength or $\frac{dv}{d\lambda} = 0$. Vacuum is, therefore, a *non-dispersive medium*

$$\therefore \qquad v_g = v$$

This explains why there is no difference in wave velocity and group velocity when light travels in vacuum.

Q. 6.14. (*a*) **How dispersive medium is distinguished from a non-dispersive medium ?**

(*G.N.D.U.*, 2003, 2001, 1993 ; *P.U.*, 2008, 2002 ; *Pbi.U.*, 2007, 2003, 2002, 2001)

(*b*) **The wave velocity *v* of a transverse wave in a crystal of atomic separation (*a*) is given**

by $v = c \left[\dfrac{\sin \dfrac{ka}{2}}{k \dfrac{a}{2}} \right]$ **where *k* is the wave number and *c* is a constant. Show that the value of group**

velocity is $c \left[\dfrac{\cos ka}{2} \right]$ (*G.N.D.U.*, 2008)

Ans. (*a*) In a non-dispersive medium group velocity v_g is equal to wave velocity v.

According to the dispersion relation

$$v_g = v - \lambda \frac{dv}{d\lambda}$$

For a non-dispersive medium $\dfrac{dv}{d\lambda} = 0$

$\therefore$ $v_g = v$

For a dispersive medium $\dfrac{dv}{d\lambda} \neq 0$. If $\dfrac{dv}{d\lambda}$ is positive, $v_g < v$

If $\dfrac{dv}{d\lambda}$ is negative, $v_g > v$

$\therefore$ For a dispersive medium $v_g < v$ or $v_g > v$

(*b*) Group velocity $v_g = v + k \dfrac{dv}{dk}$

where v is the wave velocity and k the wave number.

Now $v = c \left[\dfrac{\sin \dfrac{ka}{2}}{\dfrac{ka}{2}} \right] = c \left[\dfrac{ka}{2} \right]^{-1} \sin \dfrac{ka}{2}$

$\therefore$ $\dfrac{dv}{dk} = c \left[\dfrac{ka}{2} \right]^{-1} \dfrac{a}{2} \cos \dfrac{ka}{2} - \sin \dfrac{ka}{2} c \left[\dfrac{ka}{2} \right]^{-2} \dfrac{a}{2}$

$= \dfrac{c}{k} \cos \dfrac{ka}{2} - \dfrac{c}{k^2 \dfrac{a}{2}} \sin \dfrac{ka}{2}$

or $k \dfrac{dv}{dk} = c \cos \dfrac{ka}{2} - c \dfrac{\sin \dfrac{ka}{2}}{k \dfrac{a}{2}} = c \cos \dfrac{ka}{2} - v$

$\therefore$ group velocity $v_g = v + k \dfrac{dv}{dk} = c \cos \dfrac{ka}{2}$

Q. 6.15. (*a*) **What do you understand by phase and group velocity ? Obtain expression for them in terms of angular frequency and propagation number.**   (*Luck. U.*, 1995, 1993, 1991)

(*b*) **The phase velocity of waves under the combined effect of surface tension and gravity is**

given by $v = \sqrt{\dfrac{1}{k} \left(g + k^2 \dfrac{T}{\rho} \right)}$ **where *k* is the wave number, *g* the acceleration due to gravity.**

T the surface tension and ρ the density. Calculate the velocity group velocity. (*G.N.DU.* 2008)

Ans. (a) Phase and group velocity. See **Q. 6.10**

Phase velocity in terms of ω and k. The phase velocity or wave velocity $v = n\lambda$ where n is the frequency and λ the wavelength of the wave.

$$\therefore \qquad v = n\lambda = 2\pi n \frac{\lambda}{2\pi} = \frac{\omega}{k}$$

where k is the propagation number given by $k = \dfrac{2\pi}{\lambda}$ and ω the angular frequency.

Group velocity. Group velocity $v_g = \dfrac{\Delta\omega}{\Delta k} = \dfrac{d\omega}{dk}$ i.e., it is the rate of change of angular frequency ω with respect to propagation number k.

For proof See **Q. 6.10.**

(b) Wave velocity $v = \dfrac{\omega}{k} = \sqrt{\dfrac{1}{k}\left(g + \dfrac{k^2 T}{\rho}\right)} = \dfrac{1}{k}\sqrt{kg + \dfrac{k^3 T}{\rho}}$

$$\therefore \qquad \omega = \sqrt{kg + \frac{k^3 T}{\rho}} = \left(kg + \frac{k^3 T}{\rho}\right)^{\frac{1}{2}}$$

Group velocity $\qquad v_g = \dfrac{d\omega}{dk} = \dfrac{d}{dk}\left(kg + \dfrac{k^3 T}{\rho}\right)^{\frac{1}{2}}$

$$= \frac{1}{2}\left(kg + \frac{k^3 T}{\rho}\right)^{-\frac{1}{2}}\left(g + \frac{3k^2 T}{\rho}\right)$$

$$= \frac{1}{2}\frac{\left(g + \dfrac{3k^2 T}{\rho}\right)}{\omega}$$

Q. 6.16. Two sinusoidal waves

$$y_1 = 0.03 \cos (7t - 10x) \text{ m and}$$
$$y_2 = 0.03 \cos (5t - 8x) \text{ m}$$

were superimposed. Calculate the group velocity.

(P.U., 2000, 1999; G.N.D.U., 2003, 2000, 1996)

Ans. Comparing with the wave equation $y = a \cos (\omega t - kx)$ we have,

Amplitude $\qquad\qquad a = 0.03$ m

Angular frequency $\qquad \omega_1 = 7; \qquad \omega_2 = 5$

Propagation constant $\ k_1 = 10; \qquad k_2 = 8$

$\therefore$ Group velocity $\ v_g = \dfrac{\Delta\omega}{\Delta k} = \dfrac{\omega_1 - \omega_2}{k_1 - k_2} = \dfrac{7 - 5}{10 - 8} = 1 \text{ ms}^{-1}.$

Q. 6.17. Calculate the group velocity when the two waves

$$y_1 = 10 \sin (2\pi t - 5x)$$
$$y_2 = 15 \sin (5\pi t + 5x)$$

superimpose. y_1 and y_2 are in metres. (P.U; 1994)

Ans. Comparing with the wave equation $y = a \sin (\omega t - kx)$ we have,

Angular frequency $\ \omega_1 = 2\pi, \qquad \omega_2 = 5\pi$

Propagation number (constant) $\quad k_1 = +5; \qquad k_2 = -5$

$\therefore$ Group velocity $v_g = \dfrac{\Delta \omega}{\Delta k} = \dfrac{\omega_1 - \omega_2}{k_1 - k_2} = \dfrac{2\pi - 5\pi}{+5 - (-5)}$

$$= -\dfrac{3}{10}\pi = -0.3\pi \text{ ms}^{-1}$$

Q. 6.18. Show that in a conducting medium

$$v_g = v \left[1 + \dfrac{\lambda}{2\varepsilon_r} \dfrac{d\varepsilon_r}{d\lambda} \right]$$

where ε_r = relative permittivity $\dfrac{\varepsilon}{\varepsilon_0}$ and $\mu = 1$. Comment on the type of dispersion.

Ans. The wave velocity is given by

$$v = \dfrac{1}{\sqrt{\varepsilon_r \mu}} = \dfrac{1}{\sqrt{\varepsilon_r}} = \varepsilon_r^{-1/2} \qquad\qquad [\because \mu = 1]$$

$\therefore$
$$\dfrac{dv}{d\lambda} = -\dfrac{1}{2}\varepsilon_r^{-3/2} \dfrac{d\varepsilon_r}{d\lambda} = -\dfrac{1}{2\varepsilon_r}\varepsilon_r^{-1/2}\dfrac{d\varepsilon_r}{d\lambda}$$

$$= -v\dfrac{1}{2\varepsilon_r}\dfrac{d\varepsilon_r}{d\lambda}$$

Now $v_g = v - \lambda \dfrac{dv}{d\lambda}$

$$= v + \lambda v \dfrac{1}{2\varepsilon_r}\dfrac{d\varepsilon_r}{d\lambda} = v\left[1 + \dfrac{\lambda}{2\varepsilon_r}\dfrac{d\varepsilon_r}{d\lambda} \right]$$

As the quantity within brackets is greater than one, $v_g > v$ i.e., it is the case of *anomalous dispersion.*

Q. 6.19. Do the molecules actually flow from the speaker to the audience. Discuss what happens in reality.   (*Pbi.U.*, 1999)

Ans. No, the molecules of the medium do not actually flow from the speaker to the listener. The molecules only oscillate about their mean positions. Each molecule receives energy from the neighbouring molecule immediately preceeding it and is itself set into oscillation. In the process it further transfers energy to its immediate next neighbouring moleclue. In this way it is the energy that flows from the speaker to the audience in the form longitudinal sound waves due to the repeated periodic motion of the molecules of the medium about their mean positions.

Q. 6.20. (*a*) Why a monochromatic wave cannot be utilised for the transmission of signal ?
                                                                  (*Pbi.U.*, 2001, 1999).

(*b*) Can a sinusoidal wave be used for transmission of a signal ?   (*Pbi.U.*, 2008).

Ans. (*a*) A monochromatic wave prevades in all directions without limit both in space and time i.e., it neither has a beginning nor an end. Its characteristics like frequency, amplitude, wavelength etc. always remain the same. In order to transmit a signal, the signal has to be bounded by space and time in order to demarcate the beginning or the end. This can be accompalished by changing the amplitude of one of the waves as in amplitude modulation or the frequency of one of the waves as in frequency modulation of a radio signal. The radio reception of the enhanced amplitude or modified frequency marks the arrival of the signal. Obviously a monochromatic wave having a constant amplitude or frequency can not be utilised for transmission of a signal.

(*b*) A sinusoidal wave is a pure sine wave. It has only a single frequency i.e. it is monochromatic. It cannot therefore, be used for transmission of a signal as explained in **part (*a*).**

Q. 6.21. Mark the correct answer.
(*i*) In a non-dispersive medium the group velocity is
    (*a*) greater than phase velocity   (*b*) less than phase velocity
    (*c*) independent of phase velocity   (*d*) equal to phase velocity   (*H.P.U.*, 1992)
(*ii*) In a normal dispersive medium the group velocity c_g and phase velocity c are related as
    (*a*) $c_g > c$ (*b*) $c_g = c$ (*c*) $c_g = c^{-1}$ (*d*) $c_g < c$ (*H.P.U.*, 1994)
(*iii*) The phase velocity c and group velocity c_g are related as

    (*a*) $c_g = c - \lambda \dfrac{dc}{d\lambda}$ (*b*) $c_g = c + \lambda \dfrac{d\lambda}{dc}$

    (*c*) $c = c_g + \lambda \dfrac{dc_g}{d\lambda}$ (*d*) $c = c_g - \lambda \dfrac{dc_g}{d\lambda}$ (*H.P.U.*, 1996)

Ans. (*i*) *d*   (*ii*) *d*   (*iii*) *a*

EXERCISE

1. Two waves $y_1 = 0.07 \cos (3\,t - 4\,x)$ m
    and $y_2 = 0.07 \cos (t - 2\,x)$ m
    are superimposed. Calculate the group velocity.   (*P.U.*, 2000)   [**Ans.** 1 ms^{-1}]

Interference, Beats, Stationary Waves, Doppler Effect and Ultrasonics

7

Q. 7.1. (*a*) **What is interference of sound? What are silence zones and how do you explain their existence in the neighbourhood of a powerful source of sound?** (*Cal. U.*, 1991)

(*b*) **In a very big hall an observer receives sound waves directly from a source of sound placed at 120 metre. He also receives waves reflected from mid point of 25 metre high ceiling. What should be the wave length of the waves for maximum intensity?** (*Luck. U.*, 2001)

Ans. (*a*) Interference of sound. When two wave trains of sound are travelling along the same straight line in a medium, each particle of the medium is acted upon by both these waves simultaneously. If the two waves arrive at a point in the same phase *i.e.*, the *two crests or two troughs* (*two condensation or two rarefactions*) superimpose then the resultant amplitude is equal to the sum of the two amplitudes of the respective waves, while at some other points where they arrive in opposite phase, *i.e.*, the crest of one falls over the *trough* of the other or the *condensation* due to one falls over the *rarefaction* due to the other the resultant amplitude is equal to the difference of the individual amplitudes. The resultant amplitudes at points where the two waves meet in phase is maximum and hence the intensity of sound is maximum whereas the points where the two waves meet in opposite phase, resultant amplitude is minimum and the intensity is minimum. *This redistribution of energy when two sound waves superimpose upon each other is known as interference.*

Examples. (*i*) A typical case in which the two waves of nearly the same amplitude superimpose is represented in Fig. 7.1. The resultant form of the waves is shown by a thick line. In this case the crest of one falls over the crest of the other and the trough falls over the trough of the other. The resultant wave has an amplitude equal to the sum of the amplitudes of the component waves. This is a case of *constructive interference.*

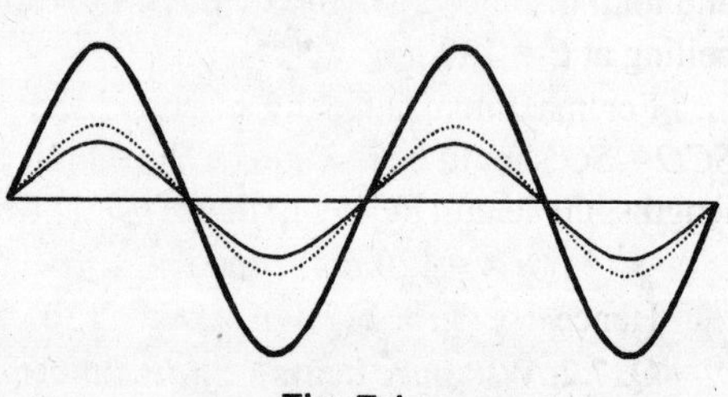

Fig. 7.1

(*ii*) When the two waves of the same amplitude reach in opposite phase the crest of one falls over the trough of the other and the resultant intensity is zero. This is represented in Fig. 7.2. This is a case of *destructive interference.*

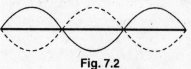

Fig. 7.2

Silence zones. The phenomenon of interference explains the existence of silence zones. When a powerful source of sound is placed at a distance from the observer, he not only receives waves directly from the sounding body but also receives reflected waves from some big surfaces, the intensity of which is almost the same. As the distances travelled by these waves are not the same, it is possible that these may reach the observer in the same phase or in opposite phase. If these waves reinforce the resultant sound is maximum, but if these are in opposite phase these cancel the effect due to each other and hence practically no sound is heard. This will happen *if the path difference between the two waves is equal to an odd multiple of half a wavelength.* This explains the existence of *silence zones.* If the observer moves towards or away from the source the sound is again heard. Its intensity increases and becomes maximum when the path difference is equal to an *even multiple of half a wavelength.* It again becomes minimum or zero when the path difference is an *odd multiple of half a wavelength.*

The presence of silence zones has been observed in the case of a ship which approaches a fog siren installed on a high cliff or rock. As shown in Fig. 7.3 (*a*) the sound from the siren *A* reaches the ship by two paths

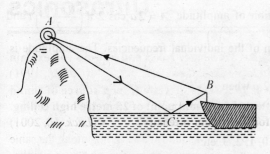

Fig. 7.3 (a)

(*i*) directly along *AB,* and

(*ii*) along *ACB* after reflection from the surface of water.

When the path difference is $\frac{\lambda}{2}$ or odd multiple of $\frac{\lambda}{2}$ no sound is heard but if the ship moves inwards or outwards the path difference changes and the sound becomes audible.

The sound will be maximum when the path difference is $\lambda\left(2\frac{\lambda}{2}\right)$ or any even multiple of $\frac{\lambda}{2}$.

(*b*) The observer *O* receives the sound from the source *S* directly. These sound waves travel a distance of 120 m.

The ceiling is 25 m high.

∴   *CD* = 25 m

As *C* is the mid point of the hall, *SD* = *DO* = 60 m

∴ $SC = CO = \sqrt{60^2 + 25^2} = 65\,\text{m}.$

and total distance travelled by the wave reflected from the ceiling at *C* = 130 m.

For maximum intensity of sound the path difference *SCO* – *SO* should be = λ *i.e.,* If the length *SO* has *n* wave lengths, the length *SCO* will have (*n* + 1) wave lengths.

∴   *n* λ = 120 m   and   (*n* + 1) λ = 130 m

Hence   (*n* + 1) λ – *n* λ = λ = 130 – 120 = 10 m or wave length = 10 m

Q. 7.2. What are beats? Show that the number of beats produced per second is equal to the difference in the frequencies of the two sounding bodies. How can this phenomenon be used to determine the frequency of a tuning fork?   (*Cal. U.* 2003, *Kerala U.,* 2001; *Gauhati U.,* 2000; *Vid. S. U.,* 1990, 1992; *Burd. U.,* 1991; *Osm. U.,* 1997)

Ans. Beats. *When two wave-trains of nearly the same frequency travel along the same straight line in the same direction the resultant displacement at a point alternately waxes and wanes in amplitude as many times per second as the difference in their frequencies. This phenomenon is known as* **beats.** The explanation is as follows :

The displacement *y* of a particle at any time *t* when a harmonic wave of frequency *n* is moving with a velocity *v* is given by

$$y = a \sin 2\pi n t$$

where a is the amplitude of the vibration.

If we consider two wave motions of slightly different frequencies of values n and m per second, then the displacement of a particle due to these waves is given by

$$y_1 = a \sin 2\pi n t \quad \text{and} \quad y_2 = a \sin 2\pi m t$$

When the two waves superimpose the resultant displacement Y is given by

$$Y = y_1 + y_2 = a \sin 2\pi n t + a \sin 2\pi m t$$

$$= 2a \cos 2\pi \left(\frac{n-m}{2} \right) t \, \sin 2\pi \left(\frac{n+m}{2} \right) t$$

$$= A \sin 2\pi \left(\frac{n+m}{2} \right) t$$

This equation represents a periodic vibration of amplitude $A = 2a \cos 2\pi \left(\dfrac{n-m}{2} \right) t$ and frequency $\dfrac{n+m}{2}$, which is the arithmetic mean of the individual frequencies. The amplitude is, however, not constant as it changes with time.

The maximum value of the amplitude $A = \pm 2a$ when

$$\cos 2\pi \left(\frac{n-m}{2} \right) t = \pm 1$$

or $\pi (n-m) t = k\pi$ where $k = 0, 1, 2, 3,$ etc.

or $t = \dfrac{k}{n-m} = 0, \dfrac{1}{n-m}, \dfrac{2}{n-m}, \dfrac{3}{n-m} \cdots$

and so on, i.e., t is an integral multiple of $\dfrac{1}{n-m}$.

∴   Time interval between two consecutive maxima

$$= \frac{1}{n-m}$$

or   The frequency of maxima $= n - m$

The minimum value of the amplitude $A = 0$ when

$$\cos 2\pi \left(\frac{n-m}{2} \right) t = 0$$

or $\pi (n-m) t = k\pi + \pi/2$ where $k = 0, 1, 2, 3,$ etc.

or $t = \dfrac{k}{n-m} + \dfrac{1}{2(n-m)}$

$$= \dfrac{1}{2(n-m)}, \dfrac{3}{2(n-m)}, \dfrac{5}{2(n-m)} \cdots \quad \text{for } k = 0, 1, 2, 3 \ldots$$

and so on, i.e., t is an odd multiple of $\dfrac{1}{2(n-m)}$.

The minima are, therefore, regularly timed between the maxima. The time interval between two consecutive minima

$$= \frac{1}{n-m}$$

or   The frequency of minima $= n - m$

Since one maximum and one minimum sound constitutes a beat, the number of beats = $n - m$.
The intensity of the resultant sound rises and falls $n - m$ times per second.

The resultant wave is thus a simple harmonic wave whose frequency is equal to the arithmetic mean of the component frequencies and whose amplitude varies alternately from $2a$ or the sum of the amplitudes of the component waves, to zero or their difference. The vibration has a frequency equal to the difference of the component frequencies.

Determination of frequency. The phenomenon of beats is used to determine the frequency of a tuning fork. The number of beats produced by two tuning forks of nearly the same frequencies is equal to the difference in frequencies of the two forks. Thus if n is the frequency of a tuning fork A and b the number of beats produced, then the unknown frequency m of the tuning fork B is given by

$$m = n \pm b$$

To decide about the *positive* or *negative* sign proceed as follows :

Attach a little of wax to the prong of the tuning fork B of unknown frequency and again find out the number of beats produced. *If the number of beats decreases, then take* **positive** *sign and if the number of beats increases take* **negative** *sign.*

The effect of attaching a little of wax to the prongs of B is to make it heavy and so its frequency will decrease. Thus if the frequency of this tuning fork of unknown frequency was already greater, the difference between the two frequencies will decrease and so the number of beats will also decrease, hence *positive sign should be taken.* If the frequency of the unknown tuning fork, *i.e.*, of B had been less than that of A, the effect of loading the prongs of B is to increase the frequency difference and so the number of beats will increase, hence *negative sign* should be taken.

Q. 7.3. A fork of unknown frequency gives 4 beats per second when sounded with another of frequency 256. The fork is now loaded with a piece of wax and again 4 beats per second are heard. Calculate the frequency of the unknown fork.

Ans. Number of beats produced = 4

Frequency of one tuning fork = 256

∴   Frequency of the other = $256 \pm 4 = 252$ or 260

When the tuning fork is loaded with wax its frequency decreases. If the frequency is taken to be 252 it should decrease further and the number of beats should always increase.

If the frequency is taken to be 260 the number of beats should decrease when the tuning fork is loaded with a very small quantity of wax. If the quantity used is large the value of frequency will fall below 256. In the present case it falls to 252 thus making the difference again 4 and producing 4 beats per second. Hence

The frequency before loading = 260.

Q. 7.4. What is the difference between interference and beats?

(Cal. U., 1991; Vid. S.U., 1991)

Ans. Interference and beats. To produce stationary interference the two sources must have exactly the same frequencies. The positions of maximum and minimum sound remain fixed at their places so long as the sound from the two sources is maintained.

To produce beats the two sources must have slightly different frequencies. The positions of maximum and minimum sound do not remain fixed at their places but travel onward and can be heard at all places at different times.

Q. 7.5. Two tuning forks produce 4 beats per second when sounded together. One of them is in unison with 1.20 m length of wire and the other with 1.25 m of it. Calculate the frequencies of the forks.

(Kan.U., 1990)

Ans. Let n_1 and n_2 be the frequencies of the forks, then

$$n_1 - n_2 = 4 \qquad\qquad ...(i)$$

If the string is stretched by a tension T and has mass per unit length ρ, then

$$n_1 = \frac{1}{2 \times 1.20}\sqrt{\frac{T}{m}} \quad \text{and} \quad n_2 = \frac{1}{2 \times 1.25}\sqrt{\frac{T}{m}}$$

$$\therefore \quad \frac{n_1}{n_2} = \frac{1.25}{1.20} = \frac{25}{24}$$

or $$n_1 = n_2 \times \frac{25}{24}$$

Substituting in (i), we get

$$n_2 \frac{25}{24} - n_2 = 4$$

∴ $n_2 = 96$ cycle s^{-1} and $n_1 = 96 + 4 = 100$ cycles s^{-1}.

Q. 7.6. Calculate the velocity of sound in a gas in which the waves of wavelength 50 cm and 50.5 cm produce 6 beats per second.   (*Vid. S.U.*, 1992)

Ans. Let v be the velocity of sound in the gas

$$\lambda_1 = 50 \text{ cm} = 0.500 \text{ m}, \quad \lambda_2 = 50.5 \text{ cm} = 0.505 \text{ m}$$

$$\therefore \quad \frac{v}{\lambda_1} - \frac{v}{\lambda_2} = 6 \quad \text{or} \quad \frac{v}{0.500} - \frac{v}{0.505} = 6$$

or $$(0.505 - 0.500)\, v = 6 \times 0.500 \times 0.505$$

$$\therefore \quad v = \frac{6 \times 0.500 \times 0.505}{0.005} = 303 \text{ ms}^{-1}$$

Q. 7.7. (*a*) **Explain the term standing waves. Investigate theoretically the formation of stationary (standing) waves and discuss their characteristic properties.**

(*G.N.D.U.*, 2008, 2006; *Cal. U.*, 2001, 1990; *Luck. U.*, 1994)

(*b*) **How does the wave function of a progressive wave differ from that of a stationary wave ?**

(*Pbi. U.*, 2006)

Ans. (*a*) **Stationary waves (Standing waves).** Stationary waves (or Standing waves) are produced when two wave trains of the same period, wavelength amplitude and velocity travelling along the same straight line in opposite directions superimpose upon each other.

The analytical expression for a progressive wave of wavelength λ, amplitude a travelling with a velocity v along the positive direction of X-axis is given by

$$y_1 = a\sin\frac{2\pi}{\lambda}(vt - x) \qquad \qquad ...(i)$$

where y_1 is the displacement at any time t and x is the distance of the particle from the origin ($x = 0$).

For a wave travelling in the opposite direction with the same velocity the distance of a particle in the negative direction of X-axis is $- x$, hence the displacement y_2 of this particle at the same time t is given by

$$y_2 = a\sin\frac{2\pi}{\lambda}(vt + x) \qquad \qquad ...(ii)$$

These displacement equations actually refer to the incident and the reflected waves in the case of an open pipe or a string free at the other end, when the boundary where reflection taken place is taken as the origin $x = 0$.

The resultant displacement y at the same time is given by

$$y = y_1 + y_2$$

Hence the resultant displacement equation is

$$y = y_1 + y_2 = a\sin\frac{2\pi}{\lambda}(vt - x) + a\sin\frac{2\pi}{\lambda}(vt + x)$$

$$= 2a\sin\frac{2\pi}{\lambda}vt\cos\frac{2\pi}{\lambda}x \qquad \qquad ...(iii)$$

$$\left[\because \sin A + \sin B = 2\sin\frac{A+B}{2}\cos\frac{A-B}{2} \right]$$

or $$y = A\sin\frac{2\pi}{\lambda}vt \qquad \qquad ...(iv)$$

where $$A = 2a\cos\frac{2\pi}{\lambda}x$$

Equation (iv) represents a simple harmonic motion of the same wavelength and velocity as the individual components. Its amplitude is not constant but varies with x the position of the particle.

Velocity. The velocity of the particles due to the resultant wave motion is obtained by differentiating the displacement y with respect to time t (Keeping x constant) in equation (iii).

$$\therefore \qquad \text{Velocity} \quad \frac{dy}{dt} = \frac{4\pi v}{\lambda}\cos\frac{2\pi}{\lambda}x\cos\frac{2\pi}{\lambda}vt \qquad \qquad ...(v)$$

Compression or strain. The compression or strain of the resultant vibration at any point is obtained by differentiating the displacement y with respect to x (keeping t constant) in equation (iii).

$$\therefore \qquad \text{Strain} \quad \frac{dy}{dx} = -\frac{4\pi a}{\lambda}\sin\frac{2\pi}{\lambda}x\sin\frac{2\pi}{\lambda}vt \qquad \qquad ...(vi)$$

The equations (iii), (v) and (vi) show that the displacement, velocity and strain at a given point change with time and at a given time are different at different points.

Changes with respect to position

At positions where $$\frac{2\pi}{\lambda}x = 0, \pi, 2\pi...., m\pi$$

or $$x = 0, \frac{\lambda}{2}, ..., m\frac{\lambda}{2}$$

$$\sin\frac{2\pi}{\lambda}x = 0 \quad \text{and} \quad \cos\frac{2\pi}{\lambda}x = \pm 1$$

At positions where $$\frac{2\pi}{\lambda}x = \frac{\pi}{2}, \frac{3\pi}{2},....(2m+1)\frac{\pi}{2}$$

or $$x = \frac{\lambda}{4}, \frac{3\lambda}{4},....(2m+1)\frac{\lambda}{4}$$

$$\sin\frac{2\pi}{\lambda}x = \pm 1 \quad \text{and} \quad \cos\frac{2\pi}{\lambda}x = 0$$

(i) Displacement (Antinodes and Nodes). The displacement is given by

$$y = 2a\sin\frac{2\pi}{\lambda}vt\cos\frac{2\pi}{\lambda}x$$

This is maximum when $$\cos\frac{2\pi}{\lambda}x = \pm 1$$

or At points where $$x = 0, \frac{\lambda}{2}, \lambda....\frac{m\lambda}{2}$$

the displacement is maximum. These points are called the **antinodes**.

The displacement is minimum when $\cos\dfrac{2\pi}{\lambda} = 0$

or   At points where $x = \dfrac{\lambda}{4}, \dfrac{3\lambda}{4}, \ldots\ldots, (2m+1)\dfrac{\lambda}{4}$

These points are called **nodes**.

Hence the interface $x = 0$ is an *antinode* and other antinodes lie at distance $\dfrac{\lambda}{2}, \lambda, \dfrac{3\lambda}{2}, \ldots\ldots,$ from this point.

The *nodes* lie in between the *antinodes* at distances $\dfrac{\lambda}{4}, \dfrac{3\lambda}{4}$ etc.

At points other than nodes and antinodes the displacement decreases gradually from their maximum value at the antinode to zero value at the node.

(*ii*) **Velocity.** From (*v*) we find that velocity is maximum when

$$\cos\frac{2\pi}{\lambda}x = \pm 1$$

or   At points where $x = 0, \dfrac{\lambda}{2}, \lambda\ldots\ldots, \dfrac{m\lambda}{2}$

i.e., the velocity is maximum at the antinodes where the displacement is also maximum.

The velocity is minimum (zero) when $\cos\dfrac{2\pi}{\lambda}x = 0$

or   At points where $x = \dfrac{\lambda}{4}, \dfrac{3\lambda}{4}\ldots., (2m+1)\dfrac{\lambda}{4}$

i.e., the velocity is minimum (zero) at the nodes where the displacement is also minimum.

(*iii*) **Strain.** From (*vi*), we find that strain is maximum when

$$\sin\frac{2\pi}{\lambda}x = \pm 1$$

or   At points where $x = \dfrac{\lambda}{4}, \dfrac{3\lambda}{4}, \ldots\quad (2m+1)\dfrac{\lambda}{4}$

i.e., the strain is maximum at the nodes where displacement and velocity are zero.

It is minimum when $\sin\dfrac{2\pi}{\lambda}x = 0$

or   At points where $x = 0, \dfrac{\lambda}{2}, \lambda\ldots., m\dfrac{\lambda}{2}$

i.e., the strain is minimum at the antinodes where the displacement and velocity are maximum.

Changes with respect to time. If T is the period of vibration of a particle due to either wave and v its velocity, then the distance travelled in time T is given by

$$\lambda = v\,T$$

or $\dfrac{v}{\lambda} = \dfrac{1}{T}$

Substituting the value of $\dfrac{v}{\lambda}$ in (*iii*), (*v*) and (*vi*), we have

Displacement $y = 2\,a\sin\dfrac{2\pi t}{T}\cos\dfrac{2\pi}{\lambda}x$ ...(*vii*)

Velocity

$$\frac{dy}{dt} = \frac{4\,a\pi v}{\lambda}\cos\frac{2\pi}{\lambda}x\cos\frac{2\pi t}{T}$$ ...(viii)

and Strain

$$\frac{dy}{dx} = -\frac{4\pi a}{\lambda}\sin\frac{2\pi}{\lambda}x\sin\frac{2\pi t}{T}$$ ...(ix)

At times when

$$\frac{2\pi t}{T} = 0, \pi, 2\pi...., m\pi$$

or   when

$$t = 0, \frac{T}{2}, T,...., m\frac{T}{2}$$

$$\sin\frac{2\pi t}{T} = 0 \text{ and } \cos\frac{2\pi t}{T} = \pm 1$$

At times when

$$\frac{2\pi t}{T} = \frac{\pi}{2}, \frac{3\pi}{2},....,(2m+1)\frac{\pi}{2}$$

or

$$t = \frac{T}{4}, \frac{3T}{4}.....,(2m+1)\frac{T}{4}$$

$$\sin\frac{2\pi t}{T} = \pm 1 \text{ and } \cos\frac{2\pi t}{T} = 0$$

(i) Displacement. From (vii) displacement is maximum when

$$\sin\frac{2\pi t}{T} = \pm 1$$

or   when

$$t = \frac{T}{4}, \frac{3T}{4}, ...,(2m+1)\frac{T}{4}$$

Being alternately maximum positive or negative.
The displacement is minimum, when

$$\sin\frac{2\pi t}{T} = 0$$

or   when $t = 0, \dfrac{T}{2}, T,.....,m\dfrac{T}{2}$

(ii) Velocity. From (viii) the velocity is maximum, when

$$\sin\frac{2\pi t}{T} = \pm 1$$

or   when $t = 0, \dfrac{T}{2}, T,.....,m\dfrac{T}{2}$

The velocity is minimum, when

$$\cos\frac{2\pi t}{T} = 0$$

or   when $t = \dfrac{T}{4}, \dfrac{3T}{4},.....,(2m+1)\dfrac{T}{4}$

Hence when the displacement is maximum, *i.e.*, the particles are at their extreme positions, the velocity is zero and when the displacement is zero, *i.e.*, the particles are passing through their mean positions, the velocity is maximum.

(*iii*) **Strain.** From (*ix*) the strain is maximum, when

$$\sin \frac{2\pi t}{T} = \pm 1$$

or   when $t = \dfrac{T}{4}, \dfrac{3T}{4}, \ldots, (2m+1)\dfrac{T}{4}$

The strain is minimum, when

$$\sin \frac{2\pi t}{T} = 0$$

or   when $t = 0,\; \dfrac{T}{2},\; T, \ldots, m\dfrac{T}{2}$

Hence the strain is maximum at times when the displacement is maximum and the velocity is zero. The strain is minimum when the displacement is zero and velocity is maximum.

Characteristic properties

1. The stationary waves are not progressive, *i.e.*, the condensations (crests) or rarefactions (troughs) do not travel forward or backward. Hence *there is no transfer of energy from one particle to the other*. The displacement and velocity at a point continuously change from maximum positive to maximum negative value and *vice versa*.

2. Every particle except at the nodes, executes simple harmonic motion with the same period as the component waves. The particles *at the nodes always have zero displacement, zero velocity and undergo the maximum changes in strain*. The displacement increases as we proceed from the nodes on either side and becomes maximum at the antinodes which is midway between the two nodes. *At the antinodes the displacement and velocity are maximum and the strain is zero*.

3. The distance between two consecutive nodes or antinodes is equal to *half the wave* length of the stationary wave, which is the same as that of component waves.

4. Twice in one vibration at intervals of $\dfrac{T}{2}$ all the particles have maximum displacement and are momentarily at rest having zero velocity. After a time $T/2$ the particles having maximum positive displacement have maximum negative displacement and *vice versa*.

5. Twice in one vibration all the particles pass through their mean positions and have maximum velocity. After a time $T/2$ they again pass through their mean positions in the opposite directions with maximum velocity.

The medium splits up into segments. For half a time period all the particles in a segment between any two consecutive nodes move in one direction and in the next half in the opposite direction. At any particular instant the direction of motion of the particles in one segment is opposite to that of the particles in the segment next to it or just behind it.

Exercise. *What do you mean by nodes and antinodes in a stationary wave.*   (*P.U. 2008*)

Hint: See **Q.** given above under the head (*i*) **Displacement (Antinodes and nodes)**

(*b*) The equation of a progressive wave is given by $y = a \sin \dfrac{2\pi}{\lambda}(vt - x)$ where λ is the wave length and v the velocity of the wave.

The equation of a stationary wave is given by

$$y = a \sin \frac{2\pi}{\lambda} vt \ \cos \frac{2\pi}{\lambda} x$$

Thus the wave function of a progressive wave is a composite function of x and t *i.e.*, $y = f(x, t)$. On the other hand, the wave function of a standing wave is the product two separate functions, one of time t containing $\sin \dfrac{2\pi}{\lambda} vt$ and the second of distance x containing $\cos \dfrac{2\pi}{\lambda} x$. Thus $y = f_1(x) f_2(t)$

Q. 7.8. Distinguish between progressive and stationary waves.

(*Cal. U.* 2001; *Pbi. U.*, 1993; *Vid. S.U.*, 1992; *P.U.*, 2009, 1991)

Ans. The distinction between progressive and stationary waves is given below in a tabular form.

Progressive waves	*Stationary waves*
1. The disturbance travels forward, *i.e.*, it is handed over from one particle to the next after some time.	1. The disturbance is fixed, *i.e.*, no particle transfers its motion to the next at any time.
2. Each particle has the same constant amplitude. The phase varies along the wave, *i.e.*, a particle reaches any stage of its displacement at a time different from that of the last and the next particle.	2. The amplitude of each particle is not the same. It is maximum at an antinode and decreases gradually from an antinode to the node according to the cosine law. All the particles between two consecutive nodes are in the same phase, *i.e.*, they reach their maximum or minimum displacement at the same time. The phase of particles in one segment is opposite to that of the particles in the next or the last segment.
3. No particle is permanently at rest. Every particle is momentarily at rest at the extreme positions of its displacement. Different particles reach this position at different times.	3. Particles at the nodes are permanently at rest. Other particles are also momentarily at rest at the extreme position of their displacements. All the particles reach this position at the same time. This condition is repeated after half a period.
4. All the particles have the same maximum velocity which they have on passing through their mean positions one after the other.	4. The velocity at the nodes is always zero. It increases gradually as we go to the antinodes and is maximum at the antinodes. All the particles have their maximum velocity when they pass through their mean positions at the same time.
5. Every region passes successively through conditions of compression, normal density and rarefaction and these conditions travel forward.	5. The condensation, regions of normal density and rarefactions are fixed. In any region the same condition appears and disappears alternately.

6. The displacement, velocity and strain equations are represented by $$y = a \sin \frac{2\lambda}{\lambda}(vt - x)$$ $$\frac{dy}{dt} = \frac{2\pi a v}{\lambda}\cos\frac{2\pi}{\lambda}(vt - x)$$ $$\frac{dy}{dx} = \frac{-2\pi a}{\lambda}\cos\frac{2\pi}{\lambda}(vt - x)$$ A particle has its maximum velocity and maximum strain (change of pressure) at the same time and has its maximum displacement a quarter period later. The velocity and the pressure curves, therefore, agree and are $T/4$ ahead of the displacement curve.	6. The displacement, velocity and strain equation are represented by $$y = 2a \cos\frac{2\pi}{\lambda}x \sin\frac{2\pi}{\lambda}vt$$ $$\frac{dy}{dt} = \frac{4\pi a v}{\lambda}\cos\frac{2\pi}{\lambda}x \cos\frac{2\pi}{\lambda}vt$$ $$\frac{dy}{dx} = \frac{-4\pi a}{\lambda}\sin\frac{2\pi}{\lambda}x \sin\frac{2\pi}{\lambda}vt$$ A particle has its maximum displacement and maximum strain at the same time but has its maximum velocity a quarter period later. No two curves agree in this case.
7. There is a transmission of energy across every plane.	7. There is no flow of energy across any plane. This is due to the fact that condensation and velocity curves differ in phase by $T/4$.

Q. 7.9. What is meant by Doppler effect ? Derive an expression for the change in frequency of a note due to relative motion of the observer, source and medium. Hence give the relation for the following special cases :

    (*i*) **Source moves towards the observer and observer moves away from the source both in the direction of sound**

    (*ii*) **Source and observer move towards each other**

    (*iii*) **Source and observer move away from each other**

    (*iv*) **Source moves away from observer and the observer moves towards the source.**

(Cal. U. 2003; Nagpur U., 2003, 2002, 2001)

    Ans. Doppler effect. When a sounding body produces a note of frequency n, a listener at a distance receives n waves per second if he is at rest. If there is a relative motion between them due to the motion of the source or the listener or both the number of waves received by the listener per second or the apparent frequency of the sound changes and is not the same as that of the source. The pitch of the note heard appears to rise if the two are approaching each other and appears to fall if the two are receding away from each other.

    The apparent change in frequency due to a relative motion between the source and the listener is known as **Doppler's principle.**

    Example 1. If a railway engine travelling with a high speed with its whistle blowing is approaching an observer, the pitch appears to rise. The pitch of the note appears to fall just as the engine passes the observer on the platform.

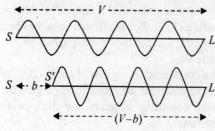

Fig. 7.4

    Example 2. If a tuning fork mounted on a resonance box is moved in a circle, then to a listener who places himself in the plane of the fork, the pitch seems to be higher as the fork is moving towards him than when it is moving away from him.

    Expression for change in frequency. 1. Source in motion, listener and medium at rest. Let the frequency of the note produced by the source be n and V be the velocity of sound. The number of waves emitted by the source per second is n and these would occupy a length V if the source is stationary at S. If *the source now moves towards the listener* (in the same direction in which the sound is travelling) with a velocity b, then after one second it will be at S'. The n waves produced per second will now be crowded in the space $S'L$ instead of SL and occupy a length $(V - b)$ as shown in Fig. 7.4.

$\therefore$ Reduced wavelength $= \dfrac{V - b}{n}$

Remember : *The motion of the source causes a change in wavelength.*

Hence the apparent pitch of the sound heard by the listener

$$n' = \frac{\text{Velocity}}{\text{Wavelength}} = \frac{V}{(V - b)} n \qquad \qquad ...(i)$$

Since $(V - b) < V$, hence $n' > n$. This shows that the apparent frequency, as heard by the listener, is **higher** than the actual frequency of the note when the source moves towards the listener.

If the source instead of moving towards the listener *moves away from him* (in a direction opposite to that of the sound), then b is negative and the new frequency n' is given by

$$n' = \frac{V}{V + b} . n. \qquad \qquad ...(ii)$$

Since $(V + b) > V$, hence $n' < n$. This shows that the apparent frequency as heard by the listener, is **lower** than the actual frequency of the note when the source moves away from the listener.

2. Listener in motion, source and medium at rest. When the listener is at rest the length of the block of waves passing him per second is V containing n waves. Hence the wavelength of sound

$$\lambda = \frac{V}{n}.$$

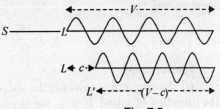

If the listener moves away from the source with a velocity c, then it will be at L' after one second. The length of the block of waves which has now passed the observer is $(V - c)$ as shown in Fig. 7.5.

Fig. 7.5

Remember : *The motion of the listener causes a change in the number of waves received per second.*

$\therefore$ Apparant frequency $n'' = \dfrac{\text{length of block of waves}}{\text{wavelength}}$

$$= \frac{V - c}{\lambda} = \frac{V - c}{V} n \qquad \qquad ...(iii)$$

When the listener is moving towards the source, c is negative and the apparent frequency is given by

$$n'' = \frac{V + c}{V} n \qquad \qquad ...(iv)$$

It may be carefully noted that in this case the wavelength of the note emitted by the source remains unchanged and the apparent change in the frequency or pitch of the note is due to the change in the rate at which the waves are received by the listener.

3. Source and listener both in motion and medium at rest. When the source and the listener are both in motion, the former causes a change in wavelength and the latter a change in the number of waves received. If both are moving in the **same** direction in which the sound is travelling, then

Reduced wavelength due to motion of the source

$$= \frac{V - b}{n}$$

Length of the block of waves received due to motion of the listener

$$= V - c$$

$\therefore$ Apparent frequency $n'' = \dfrac{\text{Length of the block of waves}}{\text{Reduced wavelength}}$

$$= \frac{V - c}{V - b} n \qquad\qquad\qquad ...(v)$$

This relation covers all possible cases, with appropriate signs given to c and b. Thus if the listener is at rest $c = 0$ and we get the relation as in (1). If the source is at rest $b = 0$ and we get the same relation as in (2) for the apparent frequencies.

If $c = b$ i.e., the source and the listener move with the same velocity in the same direction, then

$$n'' = n$$

i.e., there is no change in the frequency of the note, in such a case there is no relative motion between the source and the listener. A familiar example of this case is that of the whistle of the engine as listened by the observer sitting in the train carried by the engine.

4. Effect of motion of the medium. When the medium is in motion i.e., there is a wind blowing from S to L with velocity w, the apparent velocity of sound increases from V to $(V + w)$.

$$\therefore \qquad n'' = \frac{(V + w) - c}{(V + w) - b} n$$

If the wind is blowing with the same velocity in the opposite direction, i.e., from L to S, w is negative and

$$n'' = \frac{(V - w) - c}{(V - w) - b} n$$

Special cases

(i) **Source moves towards the observer and observer moves away from the source both in the direction of sound.** In this case as proved in relation (v),

Apparent frequency $n'' = \dfrac{V - c}{V - b} n$ \qquad\qquad ...(vi)

(ii) **Source and observer move towards each other.** In this case c is negative and relation (vi) becomes

Apparent frequency $n'' = \dfrac{V - (- c)}{V - b} n = \dfrac{V + c}{V - b} n$ \qquad\qquad ...(vii)

(iii) **Source and observer move away from each other.** In this case b is negative and relation (vi) becomes

Apparent frequency $n'' = \dfrac{V - c}{V - (- b)} n = \dfrac{V - c}{V + b} n$ \qquad\qquad ...(viii)

(iv) **Source moves away from observer and observer moves towards the source.** In this case both b and c are negative and relation (vi) becomes

Apparent frequency $n'' = \dfrac{V - (- c)}{V - (- b)} n = \dfrac{V + c}{V + b} n$ \qquad\qquad ...(ix)

Q. 7.10. Two trains are approaching each other with speeds of 60 Km/hr. and 45 Km/hr. A whistle of frequency 512 Hz is sounded in the first train. Calculate the frequency of the note heard by a listener in the second train (i) before and (ii) after the trains pass each other. (speed of sound 332 m/s)

(*Nagpur U.*, 2001)

Ans. Velocity of sound $V = 332$ m/s.

Velocity of first train (source) $b = 60$ Km/hr $= \dfrac{60 \times 1000}{60 \times 60}$

$$= \dfrac{100}{6} = 16.67 \, \text{m/sec.}$$

Velocity of second train (listener) $c = 45$ Km/hr $= \dfrac{45 \times 1000}{60 \times 60}$

$$= \dfrac{50}{4} = 12.5 \, \text{m/sec.}$$

(*i*)   **Before the trains pass each other.** In this case source and the listener are moving towards each other

$\therefore$ Apparent frequency $n' = \dfrac{V + c}{V - b} \times n$

$$= \dfrac{332 + 12.5}{332 - 16.67} \times 512 = \dfrac{344.5}{315.33} \times 512 = 559.3 \, \text{Hz}$$

(*ii*)   **After the trains pass each other.** In this case source and listener are moving away from each other.

Apparent frequency $n' = \dfrac{V - c}{V + b} \times n$

$$= \dfrac{332 - 12.5}{332 + 16.67} \times 512 = \dfrac{319.5}{348.67} \times 512 = 469.1 \, \text{Hz}$$

Q. 7.11. Calculate the velocity with which a source of frequency 10,000 Hz should approach an observer at rest in order to produce a Doppler shift of 200 Hz. Velocity of sound 332 m/s.

(Nagpur U., 2002)

Ans. Velocity of sound $V = 332$ m/s; Frequency of source $n = 10,000$ Hz

Doppler shift = change in frequency = 200 Hz.

As the source is in motion and listener is at rest,

Apparent frequency $n' = \dfrac{V}{V - b} n$

As $(V - b) < b$, hence $n' > n$

$\therefore$ $n' = 10,000 + 200$ Hz

or $10,200 = \dfrac{332}{332 - b} \times 10,000$

or $10,200 \times 332 - 10200 \, b = 332 \times 10,000$

or $(10,200 - 10,000) \, 332 = 10200 \, b$

or $b = \dfrac{200 \times 332}{10200} = 6.5 \, \text{m/s}$

$$= \dfrac{6.5 \times 60 \times 60}{1000} = 23.4 \, \text{Km/hour.}$$

Exercise. *A train sounding a whistle of frequency 500 approaches a stationary observer at a speed of 72 Km/hr. Find the frequency of sound heard by the listener. (velocity of sound = 340 m/s)*

(Nagpur U., 2003, 2001)

Hint. $72 \, \text{Km/hr} = \dfrac{72 \times 1000}{60 \times 60} = 20 \, \text{ms}^{-1}$

$$n' = \frac{V}{V - b} n = \frac{332}{332 - 20} \times 500 = 532\,\text{Hz}$$

Q. 7.12. What are ultrasonic waves? Describe two methods of producing ultrasonic waves and briefly describe their detection and uses.

(*Meerut U.*, 2007, 2006, 2003, 2001, 2000; *Mithila U.*, 1999)

Ans. Ultrasonic waves. Human ear is sensitive to sounds of frequency lying between 20 and 20,000 cycles per second. The ear is unable to hear sounds of frequency less than 20 Hz and more than 20,000 Hz. The sounds of frequency less than 20 are called *infrasonics* whereas those of frequency more than 20,000 are called *ultrasonics*. In other words ultrasonics are longitudinal mechanical waves of frequency beyond the highest audible frequency (*i.e.*, 20,000 Hz). As their frequency is very high, the wave length is very low (about 1.6 cm).

The important methods of producing ultrasonic waves are

(*i*) *Mechanical method.* The most commonly used mechanical generator of ultrasonics is Galton's whistle. It produces frequencies upto 100 kilo-cycles with a constant amplitude.

(*ii*) *Magnetostriction oscillator* and

(*iii*) *Piezo-electric oscillator.* We shall describe in detail the last two methods.

(*i*) **Magnetostriction oscillator.** When a bar of a ferro magnetic material like iron or Nickel is suddenly magnetised with the help of a strong magnetic field applied parallel to its length it undergoes a slight change in length. This is known as *magnetic-striction effect*.

If a rod of *invar* (36% Ni + 64% Fe) or *monel* (65% Ni + 31% Cu + 4% Fe, Si, Mn and C) is placed inside a coil parallel to its axis and a high frequency current is passed through the coil, the rod is magnetised and demagnetised with the current. The length of the rod changes accordingly and its free ends produce high frequency vibrations or ultrasonics. If the length of the rod is so adjusted that its natural frequency of vibration is the same as the frequency of the applied alternating current, *resonance* takes place and the amplitude of vibrations becomes very large.

As the rod vibrates longitudinally its fundamental frequency of vibration is given by

$$n = \frac{1}{2l} \sqrt{\frac{Y}{\rho}}$$

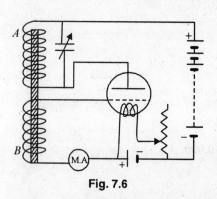

Fig. 7.6

where l is the length, Y the Young's modulus of the material and ρ the density.

A circuit showing the working of a magnetostriction oscillator is shown in Fig. 7.6. The high frequency current is obtained from a valve oscillator. The best results are, however, obtained if the rod AB is previously magnetised by means of a second coil wound over it and carrying a direct current.

(*ii*) **Piezo electric oscillator.** When a slab of quartz, tourmaline, Zinc blende or Rochelle salt cut with its faces perpendicular the optic axis is subjected to a mechanical pressure on one pair of parallel faces, electric charges are developed on the other pair of parallel faces perpendicular to the first pair. The quantity of charge developed is proportional to the applied pressure. The sign of charge is reversed when the pressure is changed into tension.

This phenomenon is known as *piezo-electric effect*.

On the other hand when an electric potential difference is applied across the faces of a crystal, the crystal undergoes a strain. If the direction of applied potential difference is reversed the direction of strain is also reversed *i.e.*, if in the first case it is a compression strain now it will be an extension strain and vice-versa. Hence if a *high frequency alternating voltage* is applied to the crystal slab rapid alternation of compression and extension takes place in two perpendicular directions resulting in the forced vibrations of the crystal.

This phenomenon is known as *inverse piezo-electric effect.*

When the frequency of these forced vibrations becomes equal to the natural frequency of the *slab, resonance* takes place and the amplitude of vibration becomes sufficiently large.

When an alternating voltage is applied to the slab along its *thickness* there are alternating changes in its length and thickness *i.e.*, when the length increases, the thickness decreases and *vice-versa* with the same frequency as that of the applied A.C. voltage. When the frequency of the applied A.C. voltage becomes equal to the natural frequency of the slab, resonant vibrations take place in the slab.

The natural frequency of vibration of the slab is given by

$$n = \frac{1}{2d} \sqrt{\frac{E}{\rho}}$$

where d = distance between the opposite faces of the crystal slab

E = Bulk modulus of quartz (material of the slab) = 8×10^{10} N/m^2

ρ = density of quartz = 2.65×10^3 kg/m^3

$$\therefore \quad n = \frac{1}{2d} \sqrt{\frac{8 \times 10^{10}}{2.65 \times 10^3}} = \frac{2.75 \times 10^3}{d} \text{ Hz}$$

If $d = 1$ mm $= 10^{-3}$ m, then

$$n = \frac{2.75 \times 10^3}{10^{-3}} = 2.75 \times 10^6 \text{ Hz} = 2.75 \text{ MHz}$$

The crystal is placed between two metal plates A and B so as to form a parallel plate condenser with crystal C as the dielectric. The plates are connected to the primary of a transformer which is coupled inductively to the oscillatory circuit of a valve as shown in Fig. 7.7.

When the valve oscillates high frequency alternating voltages are impressed on the plates A and B. Inverse Piezo-electric effect takes place and the crystal contracts and expands periodically thereby producing compressions and rarefactions in the surrounding medium. When the frequency of the oscillations produced by the valve is equal to the natural frequency of the crystal resonance occurs and the amplitude of the vibrations becomes very large.

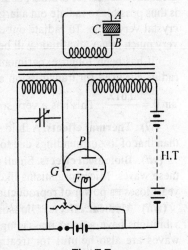

Fig. 7.7

Detection of ultrasonic waves.

(*i*) **Kundt's tube method.** Kundt's tube can be used to detect ultrasonic waves in a similar way as for ordinary sound waves.

(*ii*) **Sensitive flame.** Since very high frequency sound waves change the intensity of the flame, a flame can be used to detect the presence of ultrasonics.

(*iii*) **Thermal detectors.** A *probe* of fine platinum wire is placed in the region to be tested for ultrasonic waves. At a node compression and rarefactions occur very rapidly and cause adiabatic changes. The platinum probe is, therefore, alternately heated or cooled and the resistance changes accordingly which can be detected by suitable methods. No such changes occur at an antinode.

(*iv*) **Piezo electric detectors.** When one pair of faces of a piezo-electric crystal like quartz is subjected to ultrasonic waves opposite charges are developed on the other pair perpendicular to the first. These changes are amplified by an electronic amplifier and then detected by suitable means.

Applications (or uses)

(*i*) **Velocity of sound in liquids and gases.** Ultrasonics have been used to find velocity of sound in liquids and gases, particularly when available in small quantities. This determination reveals many physical and chemical properties of the substances.

To find the velocity stationary waves are set up in the liquid or gas similar to the Kundt's tube method and the wavelength of the wave λ is determined. The velocity $V = n\lambda$ where n is the frequency of oscillations. Changes in velocity with frequency and temperature can also be determined by this method.

The velocity of ultrasonic waves can also be determined by using an *acoustic grating*. For details See **Q 7.14.**

(*ii*) **Elastic symmetries of crystals.** When ultrasonic waves are passed through a solid or a liquid and a beam of light is made to travel in a direction at right angles the ultrasonic wave system acts like a grating. The compressions act as lines of greater density or *opacities* and rarefactions like lines of lesser density or *transparencies.*

If ultrasonic waves are applied to an isotropic crystal they give rise to interference fringes from which the elastic symmetry of the crystal can be determined.

(*iii*) **Depth sounding.** Ultrasonic waves are used for signalling, for finding the depth of sea and to detect the positions of submerged rocks, submarines and ice bergs.

A strong beam of ultrasonic waves is transmitted and received, after reflection from the submerged object. By noting the time taken the distance can be calculated.

(*iv*) **Chemical effects.** Ultrasonic waves have been used to form stable emulsions of immiscible liquids like water and oil; to liquify *gells* like aluminium hydroxide in the same manner as they are liquified by shaking; to coagulate *aerosols i.e.*, dispersed fine particles of a solid or a liquid in a gas, *e.g.,* dust, smoke, mist, etc. to accelerate crystallisation and to produce oxidation.

(*v*) **Sound signalling.** Ultrasonic waves have been used for directional signalling. Because of their high frequency these waves can be sent out in the form of a narrow beam and therefore have a great advantage over ordinary sound waves in the audible range which spread out in all directions. It is thus possible to radiate out a large amount of energy without making the amplitude of the vibrating crystal very large. To radiate out energy at the same rate using ordinary audible sound frequency a very much larger amplitude will be required.

It has been found experimentally that if a vibrating crystal in the form of a circular disc of radius r is used for transmission of signal, the angle of the core containing the waves is given by $\sin\theta = \dfrac{0.61\lambda}{r}$. This has a very small value for short wavelength.

(*vi*) **Thermal effects.** A fluid subjected to ultrasonic waves shows a slightly higher temperature than that of its surroundings due to the absorption of waves.

(*vii*) **Biological effects.** Small animals like frog, fish, etc., are maimed or killed when exposed to these waves. Micro-organisms like bacteria are torn to pieces or burnt or otherwise destroyed and yeast loses its power of reproduction.

(*viii*) **Medical effects.** Ultrasonics are now widely used for medical purposes. The ultrasonic vibrations have a good massaging effect and can be used for treatment of muscular pains. These waves are also helpful for treatment of neuro-patients where other conventional method like psychotherapy, drug treatment or electric shock treatment fail. These waves have been used for location of the position of eye tumour and for extraction of broken teeth.

(*ix*) **Other effects.** The ultrasonic waves are used to detect cracks or other defects in homogeneity noticeable by reflection or absorption and washing of silk and delicate fabrics.

Q. 7.13. Calculate the fundamental frequency of ultrasonics produced by a quartz crystal of thickness 0.5 mm. The value of Young's modulus for quartz is 8×10^{11} dynes/cm² and density 2.65 gm/cm³.   (*Nagpur U.*, 2002)

Ans. Here thickness of quartz crystal $d = 0.5$ mm $= 0.05$ cm.

Density of quartz $\rho = 2.65$ gm/cm³

Young's modulus of quartz $Y = 8 \times 10^{11}$ dynes/cm²

∴   Frequency of fundamental note produced

$$n = \frac{1}{2d}\sqrt{\frac{Y}{\rho}} = \frac{1}{2 \times 0.05}\sqrt{\frac{8 \times 10^{11}}{2.65}}$$

$$= 5.49 \times 10^6 \text{ Hz} = 5.49 \text{ MHz}.$$

Q. 7.14. What are ultrasonics ? How ultrasonics are produced? Describe a method of measurement of velocity of ultrasonic waves.   (*Nag. U.* 2002; *Gauhati U.*, 2000)

Ans. For 'what are ultrasonic waves and how these are produced' see Q. 7.12.

Velocity of ultrasonic waves. To measure the velocity of ultrasonic waves we use a piezo electric oscillator which consists of a quartz crystal set into high frequency resonant vibrations with the help of a variable radio frequency electronic oscillator.

Radio frequency oscillator. A radio frequency oscillator produces *A.C. voltages* of frequency of the order of a few megacycles per second. Its input is connected to the *A.C.* mains and the out put to the quartz slab as shown in Fig. 7.8. The frequency of the *R.F.* out put can be varied by rotating a knob which in turn changes the capacitance of the oscillating *LC* circuit. The value of out put frequency is read on a calibrated dial fixed on the panel known as *Frequency meter.* It has normally a range from 0–10 MHz.

Acoustic grating. The velocity of ultrasonic waves set up in a liquid can be determined with the help of the *acoustic grating* formed by them. When plane ultrasonic waves are produced in a liquid the pressure varies periodically with the distance from the ultrasonic source being higher at a compression and lower at a rarefaction. The density of the medium and the refractive index also show a periodic variation with distance from the source along the direction of propagation of the wave. Under such a condition, if monochromatic light from a slit is passed through the liquid in a direction at right angles to the wave propagation the liquid behaves as a diffraction grating with grating element (width of opacity + width of transparency) equal to the wave length of ultrasonic waves, λ_u. Such a grating is known as *acoustic grating*. The light which suffers diffraction at the grating shows a number of diffraction images of the slit when seen through a telescope eye-piece. The arrangement of the apparatus is shown in Fig. 7.9.

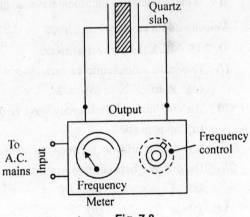

Fig. 7.8

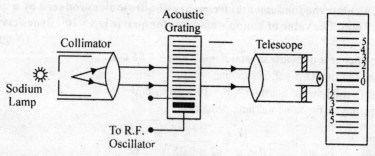

Fig. 7.9

The acoustic grating is mounted on the prism table of a spectrometer. A parallel beam of monochromatic sodium light rendered parallel by the collimator is incident normally on the acoustic grating. The diffracted light is viewed through the telescope. The diffraction pattern consists of a central maxima (0-order) and a number of principal maxima on either side (1, 2, 3, 4, 5...).

If λ is the wavelength of sodium light which suffers diffraction at the acoustic grating of grating element $(a + b) = \lambda_u$ and θ_n is the angle of diffraction for the nth order maxima, then

$$\lambda_u \sin \theta_n = n \lambda$$

$\therefore$ Wavelength of ultrasonic wave $\lambda_u = \dfrac{n\lambda}{\sin \theta_n}$

If D is the distance between the telescope objective and the eye piece cross wire (which is equal to the focal length of the objective), and d_n the distance of the nth order diffraction maxima from the central zero order diffraction maxima, then

$$\sin \theta_n = \tan \theta_n = \dfrac{d_n}{D}$$

Hence $\lambda_u = \dfrac{n\lambda D}{d_n}$

If ν is the frequency of ultrasonic waves as given by the frequency meter of the R.F. oscillator, then

Velocity of ultrasonic waves $= \nu \lambda_u = \dfrac{\nu n \lambda D}{d_n}$

Q. 7.15. Mark the correct answer.

(*i*)   Two wave trains reinforce each other when the phase difference between them is

    (*a*) Zero   (*b*) $\pi/2$ (*c*) π (*d*) any value

(*ii*)   The amplitude of a stationary wave is zero at

    (*a*) an antinode   (*b*) node

    (*c*) a point midway between the node and antinode   (*d*) no where

(*iii*)   The distance between two nearest antinodes is

    (*a*) λ (*b*) $\lambda/2$ (*c*) $\lambda/4$ (*d*) Zero

Ans. (*i*) *a*   (*ii*) *b*   (*iii*) *b*

EXERCISE

1.   Two organ pipes when sounded together produce 4 beats per second. Find their frequencies if one of them is 75 cm long and the other 80 cm long.

                                                                  (*Kan. U.*, 1990)

                                                                   [Ans. 64 and 60]

8 Electromagnetic Waves

Q. 8.1. Write Maxwell's equations in electromagnetic theory. Explain the physical significance of each of these equations giving the basic laws from which these are derived.

(*P.U.* 2007, 2005; *M.D.U.*, 2003, 2002, 2001; *G.N. D.U.* 2007, 2004, 2002, 2001, 2000, 1999; *Kerala U.*, 2001; *Luck. U.* 2002; *K.U.*, 2000, 1995; *Pbi.U.*, 2000, 1995; *H.P.U.*, 1996, 1994; *Gharwal U.*, 1999)

Ans. Maxwell's equations. There are four Maxwell's equations in electromagnetic theory. The first two are known as *steady state equations* and the last two are known as *time varying equations.* These equations have been stated below in *differential form.*

First steady state equation. (*i*) In *vector* notation Maxwell's *first* steady state equation is given by

$$div\,\vec{D} = \varepsilon\,div\,\vec{E} = \vec{\nabla}\cdot\vec{D} = \varepsilon\vec{\nabla}\cdot\vec{E} = \rho \qquad ...(i)$$

where $\vec{D}$ is the electric displacement vector $= \varepsilon\vec{E}, \varepsilon$ the permittivity of the medium; $\vec{E}$ the electric field vector, ρ the charge density and $\vec{\nabla}$ an operator called *Del operator.* $\vec{\nabla}$ is the three dimensional operator.

Its value is $\vec{\nabla} = \hat{i}\dfrac{\partial}{\partial x} + \hat{j}\dfrac{\partial}{\partial y} + \hat{k}\dfrac{\partial}{\partial z}$

$$\therefore \quad \vec{\nabla}\cdot\vec{D} = \varepsilon\left[\frac{\partial\vec{E}_x}{\partial x} + \frac{\partial\vec{E}_y}{\partial y} + \frac{\partial\vec{E}_z}{\partial z}\right]$$

Physical significance. It is a time independent or steady state equation which relates the spatial variation or divergence of electric field with charge density. This equation is a restatement of Gauss's law in electrostatics. Putting equation (*i*) in the form $\vec{\nabla}\cdot\vec{E} = \dfrac{\rho}{\varepsilon}$ and integrating over a volume V, we get

$$\iiint \vec{\nabla}\cdot\vec{E}\,dV = \frac{1}{\varepsilon}\iiint \rho\,dV \qquad ...(ii)$$

According to divergence theorem in vector analysis

$$\iiint \vec{\nabla}\cdot\vec{E}\,dV = \oiint_s \vec{E}\cdot d\vec{S} \qquad ...(iii)$$

where $\oiint_s$ represents integration over a closed surface.

Comparing (*ii*) and (*iii*), we have

$$\oiint_s \vec{E} \cdot d\vec{S} = \frac{1}{\varepsilon} \iiint \rho \, dV$$

Now $\oiint_s \vec{E} \cdot d\vec{S}$ represents the electric flux through a closed surface and $\iiint \rho \, dV = q$ the total charge within the closed surface.

$$\therefore \qquad \oiint \vec{E} \cdot d\vec{S} = \frac{q}{\varepsilon}$$

Thus the electric flux through the charged surface is equal to the total charge inside the volume divided by ε. This is **Gauss's law in electrostatics.**

Second steady state equation. In vector notation Maxwell's *second steady state* equation is given by

$$\vec{\nabla} \cdot \vec{B} = 0 \qquad \qquad ...(iv)$$

where $\vec{B}$ is the magnetic induction vector.

or $\qquad \mu \left(\dfrac{\partial H_x}{\partial x} + \dfrac{\partial H_y}{\partial y} + \dfrac{\partial H_z}{\partial z} \right) = 0 \qquad \qquad ...(iv)(a)$

Physical significance. It is a time independent or steady state equation which gives the spatial variation or divergence of magnetic induction. The equation $\vec{\nabla} \cdot \vec{B} = 0$ is a restatement of Gauss's law in magnetism coupled with the fact that magnetic poles exist in pairs.

For a closed surface $\iiint \vec{\nabla} \cdot \vec{B} \, dV = 0$

Applying divergence theorem in vector analysis, we have

$$\iiint \vec{\nabla} \cdot \vec{B} \, dV = \oiint \vec{B} \cdot d\vec{S}$$

$$\therefore \qquad \oiint \vec{B} \cdot d\vec{S} = 0$$

Now $\oiint \vec{B} \cdot d\vec{S}$ represent the magnetic flux through a closed surface. Thus the magnetic flux through a closed surface is zero. In other words, the equation shows that the magnetic flux entering into the volume is equal to the magnetic flux leaving the volume. It means that there is no *source* or *sink* in the volume or *isolated magnetic pole (or monopole) cannot exist.*

First time varying equation. In vector form Maxwell's *first time* varying equation is given by

$$Curl \, \vec{E} = \vec{\nabla} \times \vec{E} = -\frac{\partial B}{\partial t} = -\mu \frac{\partial \vec{H}}{\partial t} \qquad \qquad ...(v)$$

Physical significance. It is a time varying or time dependent equation which relates the spatial variation of electric field with time variation of magnetic field. This equation is a restatement of Faraday's law of electromagnetic induction (including Lenz's law).

Integrating the equation $\vec{\nabla} \times \vec{E} = -\dfrac{\partial B}{\partial t}$ over any surface bounding the path C we have

$$\int_s (\vec{\nabla} \times \vec{E}) \cdot d\vec{S} = -\oint_s \frac{\partial \vec{B}}{\partial t} \cdot d\vec{S} \qquad \qquad ...(vi)$$

According to Stoke's theorem in vector analysis

$$\int_s (\vec{\nabla} \times \vec{E}) \cdot d\vec{S} = \oint_c \vec{E} \cdot d\vec{l}$$

Hence Eq. (*vi*) becomes $\oint_c \vec{E}.d\vec{l} = -\oint_s \dfrac{\partial \vec{B}}{\partial t}.d\vec{S}$

$\oint_c \vec{E}.d\vec{l}$ represents the induced *e.m.f.* in a closed circuit and $-\oint_s \dfrac{\partial \vec{B}}{\partial t}.d\vec{S}$ represents the negative of the rate of change of magnetic flux through the circuit which is Faraday's law of electromagnetic induction. It shows that the time variation of magnetic induction $\vec{B}$ or field $\vec{H}$ generates the electric field $\vec{E}$.

Second time varying equation. In *vector* form Maxwell's *second time varying* equation is given by

$$Curl \ \vec{H} = \vec{\nabla} \times \vec{H} = \vec{J} + \dfrac{\partial \vec{D}}{\partial t}$$

where $\vec{J}$ is the conduction current density given by $\vec{J} = \sigma \vec{E}, \sigma$ being the conductivity of the medium and $\dfrac{\partial \vec{D}}{\partial t}$ the displacement current density.

Physical significance. It is a time varying or time dependent equation which relates the spatial variation of magnetic field with current density and displacement current density. This equation is a restatement of Ampere's law combined together for conduction current and displacement current. This equation tells us that a changing electric field produces a changing magnetic field. We already know that a changing magnetic field produces a changing electric field. Hence we conclude that '*a changing electric field produces a changing magnetic field and a changing magnetic field produces a changing electric field and the alternate production of electric and magnetic field gives rise to propagation of electromagnetic waves.*'

Q 8.2 (*a*) **Write Maxwell's equations for free space.**   (*Pbi.U.* 2000)

     (*b*) **Which law indicates the absence of magnetic monopole?** (*Pbi. U.* 2007, 2003, 2002)

OR

Show from Maxwell's equations that magnetic monopoles do not exist.   (*G.N.D.U.* 2007)

Ans. (*a*) **Maxwell's equations for free space.** Maxwell's equations for free space are

1. **Steady state equations**   (*i*) $\vec{\nabla}.\vec{D} = 0$

                                   (*ii*) $\vec{\nabla}.\vec{B} = 0$

2. **Time varying equations**   (*iii*) $\vec{\nabla} \times \vec{E} = -\dfrac{\partial \vec{B}}{\partial t}$ and

                                 (*iv*) $\vec{\nabla} \times \vec{H} = \dfrac{\partial D}{\partial t}$

(*b*) Maxwell's steady state equation $\vec{\nabla}.\vec{B} = 0$ or $\mu\left(\dfrac{\partial H_x}{\partial x} + \dfrac{\partial H_y}{\partial y} + \dfrac{\partial H_z}{\partial z}\right) = 0$ is a restatement of Gauss's law in magnetism. This law in integral form becomes $\oiint \vec{B}.\vec{dS} = 0$. It shows that the magnetic flux entering into a volume is equal to the magnetic flux leaving the volume. It means that there is *no source* or *sink* in *the volume* or *isolated magnetic poles* i.e. *magnetic monopoles* cannot exist.

Q. 8.3. State Maxwell's equations in electromagnetic theory and derive them from basic laws of physics these equations represent.

(*Bang. U.* 2004; *Nagpur U.* 2002, 2000; *K.U.* 2002; *Indore U.* 2001;
Gharwal U. 2000, 1999; *G.N.D.U.* 1999, 1996)

Ans. Maxwell's equations. There are *four* Maxwell's equations in electromagnetic theory. The first two are known as *steady state equations* and the last two are known as *time varying equations.*

Steady state equations. (*i*) In *vector* notation Maxwell's *first steady state* equation is given by

$$Div \ \vec{D} = \varepsilon \ div \ \vec{E} = \vec{\nabla}.\vec{D} = \varepsilon \ \vec{\nabla}.\vec{E} = \rho$$

where $\vec{D}$ is the displacement vector $= \varepsilon \vec{E}$, ε the permittivity of the medium, $\vec{E}$ the electric field vector and ρ the charge density.

Derivation. This equation is a restatement of Gauss's law in electrostatics.

In S. I. units Gauss's law can be stated in the vector integral form as

$$\varepsilon \oiint \vec{E}.\vec{dS} = q$$

where ε is the permittivity of the medium, $\vec{E}$ the electric field vector at a point on the closed surface, dS a differential area element around the vector $\vec{E}$. The surface integral $\oiint$ indicates that the surface in question is to be divided into infinitesimal elements of area $\vec{dS}$ and that the *scalar* quantity $\vec{E}.\vec{dS}$ is to be evaluated for each element and the sum taken for the entire surface. Now consider a rectangular parallelopiped of sides dx, dy and dz containing point P located at one of its corners having co-ordinates x, y, z in an electric field.

The area of the front surface of the parallelopiped is given by

$$\vec{dS} = + \hat{i} \ dy \ dz$$

and the area of the back surface containing the point P is given by

$$\vec{dS} = - \hat{i} \ dy \ dz$$

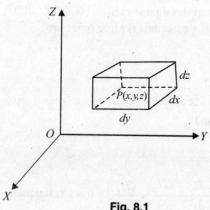

Fig. 8.1

The *minus* sign is used in this case because $\vec{dS}$ is *positive* in the direction of outward drawn normal to the surface which is along $+ i$ direction for the front surface and $- \hat{i}$ direction for the back surface, $\hat{i}$ being a unit vector along the positive direction of X-axis.

Let the electric field at the point P on the back surface be $\vec{E}$ and let it vary at the rate $\dfrac{\partial \vec{E}}{\partial x}$ along the X-axis.

∴ The electric field at a point on the front surface

$$= \vec{E} + \frac{\partial \vec{E}}{\partial x} \ dx$$

The contribution to electric flux by these two surfaces is given by

$$\vec{E}.(-\hat{i} \ dy \ dz) + \left(\vec{E} + \frac{\partial \vec{E}}{\partial x} \ dx \right).(+ \hat{i} \ dy \ dz)$$

$$= dx \ dy \ dz \left(\frac{\partial \vec{E}}{\partial x}.\hat{i} \right) = dx \ dy \ dz \ \frac{\partial}{\partial x} (\vec{E}.\hat{i}) = dx \ dy \ dz \ \frac{\partial E_x}{\partial x}$$

where E_x is the component of $\vec{E}$ along the X-axis.

Similarly the contribution of the pair of faces of area $dxdz$

$$= dx\, dy\, dz\, \frac{\partial E_y}{\partial y}$$

where E_y is the component of $\vec{E}$ along the Y-axis and contribution by the pair of faces of area $dy\, dx$

$$= dx\, dy\, dz\, \frac{\partial E_z}{\partial z}$$

were E_z is the components of $\vec{E}$ along the Z-axis.

$\therefore$ Total electric flux for the whole of the surface

$$\oiint \vec{E}.\vec{ds} = dx\, dy\, dz \left(\frac{\partial E_x}{\partial x} + \frac{\partial E_y}{\partial y} + \frac{\partial E_z}{\partial z} \right)$$

but

$$\frac{\partial E_x}{\partial x} + \frac{\partial E_y}{\partial y} + \frac{\partial E_z}{\partial z} = \vec{\nabla}.\vec{E} = div\, \vec{E}$$

If q is the charge within the surface and ρ the charge density *i.e.*, the charge per unit volume, then

$$q = dx\, dy\, dz\, \rho$$

Hence Gauss's theorem in differential form can be stated as

$$\varepsilon\, (dx\, dy\, dz)(\vec{\nabla}.\vec{E}) = (dx\, dy\, dz)\, \rho$$

or

$$\varepsilon\, \vec{\nabla}.\vec{E} = \rho \ \text{ or }\ \vec{\nabla}.\vec{E} = \frac{\rho}{\varepsilon}$$

or

$$\vec{\nabla}.\varepsilon\vec{E} = \rho \ \text{ or }\ \vec{\nabla}.\vec{D} = \rho$$

which is Maxwell's first steady state equation.

It can be seen that $\vec{D}$ has the dimensions of charge per unit area, because

$$\vec{D} = \varepsilon\vec{E} = \frac{\text{Farads}}{\text{Metre}} \times \frac{\text{Volts}}{\text{Metre}} = \frac{\text{Coulomb}}{\text{Metre} \times \text{Metre}} = \frac{\text{Charge}}{\text{area}}$$

$\therefore$ $\vec{\nabla}.\vec{D}$ has the dimensions of $\dfrac{\text{charge}}{\text{volume}}$ since dimensions of $\vec{\nabla}$ are $\dfrac{1}{\text{length}}$.

(*ii*) In *vector* notation Maxwell's *second* steady state equation is given by

$$\vec{\nabla}.\vec{B} = 0$$

where $\vec{B}$ is magnetic induction. This equation is a restatement of Gauss's law in magnetism coupled with the fact that magnetic poles exist in pairs.

Derivation. It is a well known fact in magnetism that isolated magnetic poles do not exist. Thus the total magnetic flux through any closed surface in a magnetic field must be zero.

$$\oint \vec{B}.\vec{dS} = 0$$

This equation can also be changed into differential form in the same manner as for Gauss's law in electrostatics and therefore, gives

$$\vec{\nabla}.\vec{B} = 0$$

This is Maxwell's second steady state equation.

Time varying equations. We shall first derive Maxwell's second time varying equation.

(*iii*) In vector form Maxwell's *second* time varying equation is given by

$$Curl\, \vec{H} = \vec{\nabla} \times \vec{H} = \vec{J} + \frac{\partial \vec{D}}{\partial t}$$

where $\vec{J}$ is the conduction current density and $\dfrac{\partial \vec{D}}{\partial t}$ the displacement current density.

This equation is a restatement of Ampere's law combined together for conduction current and displacement current.

Derivation. In S.I. units the magnetic field intensity at a point distant r from an infinitely long straight conductor carrying current i is given by

$$H = \frac{i}{2\pi r}$$

or

$$B = \mu H = \frac{\mu i}{2\pi r}$$

$$\therefore \qquad B(2\pi r) = \mu i$$

Suppose the current i is emerging at the point O out of the paper, then $\vec{B}$ the magnetic induction at a distance r from O will act along a circular path of radius r. If we take a small length $\vec{dl}$ of the path at P, then at this point $\vec{B}$ as well as $\vec{dl}$ are in the same direction. As $\vec{B}$ is constant all along the circle

$$\oint \vec{B} \cdot \vec{dl} = \oint B\, dl = B \oint dl = (B)(2\pi r)$$

$\therefore$ Ampere's law can be stated as

$$\oint \vec{B} \cdot \vec{dl} = \mu i$$

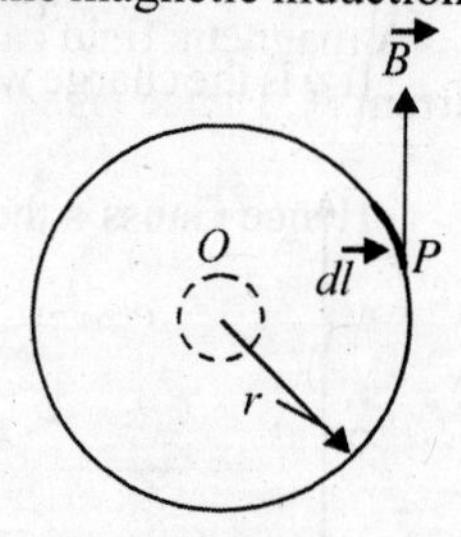

Fig. 8.2

Displacement current. Consider a circuit containing a battery, a key and a capacitor C as shown in Fig. 8.3 (a). As soon as the current is switched on, the battery begins to charge the capacitor, and an electric field say E is set up in the cylindrical region between the circular plates of the parallel plate capacitor. Let E increase at a steady rate $\dfrac{dE}{dl}$ so long as the charge is being supplied by the battery to the capacitor plates. Thus a steady current i flows into the positive plate and an equal steady current

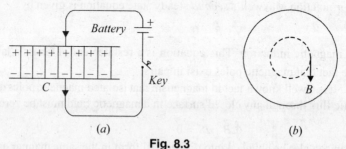

(a)   (b)

Fig. 8.3

i flows out of the negative plate. A magnetic compass or a device to detect a magnetic field placed near the leads will show the presence of the magnetic field associated with the current. If a sufficiently delicate experiment is performed it will be observed that a magnetic field is also set up in the region between the capacitor plates due to the changing electric field although no ohmic or conduction current is flowing. Thus a changing electric field gives rise to a current known as *displacement current*. The concept of displacement current is necessary as current is continuous. We have seen that a current i enters the positive plate and leaves the negative plate. The conduction current is itself not continuous across the capacitor gap as no charge is transported across the gap. This continuity is maintained by the displacement current i_d which is exactly equal to i.

In S.I. units the electric field within the plates of the capacitor is given by

$$E = \frac{q}{\varepsilon A}$$

where q is the charge on the plate, A its area and ε the permittivity of the medium between the plates

$$\therefore \qquad \frac{dE}{dt} = \frac{1}{\varepsilon A} \frac{dq}{dt} = \frac{i}{\varepsilon A}$$

or $$\varepsilon A \frac{dE}{dt} = i$$

The displacement $D = \varepsilon E =$ charge per unit area $= \dfrac{q}{A}$

$\therefore$ Displacement current $i_d = \dfrac{dq}{dt} = A \dfrac{d}{dt}(\varepsilon E) = A\varepsilon \dfrac{dE}{dt} = i$

A magnetic field can, therefore, be created by the conduction current i as well as displacement current i_d. Hence when both the currents are present. Ampere's law can be modified as

$$\oint \vec{B} \cdot \vec{dl} = \mu\,(i + i_d)$$

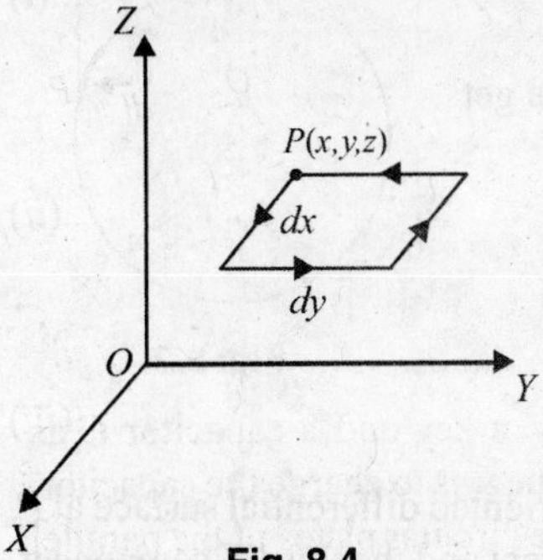

Fig. 8.4

Now consider a rectangular element of sides dx and dy containing a point P located at one of its corners having co-ordinates x, y, z in a magnetic field. Let $\vec{B}$ be the value of magnetic induction at P and let the rate of change of magnetic induction be $\dfrac{\partial \vec{B}}{\partial x}$ along X-axis and $\dfrac{\partial \vec{B}}{\partial y}$ along Y-axis. To find the value of $\oint \vec{B} \cdot \vec{dl}$ starting from P and going round the path as shown by the arrow heads, we have

$$\oint \vec{B} \cdot \vec{dl} = \vec{B} \cdot (\hat{i}\,dx) + \left(\vec{B} + \frac{\partial \vec{B}}{dx}\,dx \right) \cdot (\hat{j}\,dy)$$

$$+ \left(\vec{B} + \frac{\partial \vec{B}}{dy}\,dy \right) \cdot (-\hat{i}\,dx) + \vec{B} \cdot (-\hat{j}\,.dy)$$

$$= dx\,dy \left(\frac{\partial \vec{B}}{\partial x} \cdot \hat{j} - \frac{\partial \vec{B}}{\partial y} \cdot \hat{i} \right) = dx\,dy \left[\frac{\partial}{\partial x}(\vec{B}.\hat{j}) - \frac{\partial}{\partial y}(\vec{B}.\hat{i}) \right]$$

$$= dx\,dy \left(\frac{\partial}{\partial x} B_y - \frac{\partial}{\partial y} \cdot B_x \right) = dx\,dy \left[\frac{\partial B_y}{\partial x} - \frac{\partial B_x}{\partial y} \right]$$

where B_y is the component of $\vec{B}$ along the Y-axis and B_x the component along X-axis.

If $\vec{J}$ represents the current density and area $dx\,dy = \vec{ds}$, then

$$i = \vec{J}.\vec{ds} = \vec{J}.(\hat{k}\,dx\,dy) = dx\,dy\,(\vec{J}.\hat{k}) = dx\,dy\,J_z$$

where J_z is the component of $\vec{J}$ along Z-axis.

The displacement current $i_d = \varepsilon A \dfrac{\partial \vec{E}}{\partial t}$. Representing A by a small vector element $\vec{ds}$, then the value of i_d in vector form is given by

$$i_d = \varepsilon \frac{\partial \vec{E}}{\partial t} \cdot \vec{ds}$$

$$= \varepsilon \frac{\partial \vec{E}}{\partial t} \cdot (\hat{k}\ dx\ dy)$$

$$= \varepsilon\ dx\ dy \left(\frac{\partial \vec{E}}{\partial t} \cdot \hat{k} \right) = \varepsilon\ dx\ dy\ \frac{\partial E_z}{\partial t}$$

Substituting the value of i, i_d and $\oint \vec{B} \cdot \vec{dl}$ in the equation for Ampere's law, we have

$$dx\ dy \left(\frac{\partial B_y}{\partial x} - \frac{\partial B_x}{\partial y} \right) = \mu\ dx\ dy \left(J_z + \varepsilon \frac{\partial E_z}{\partial t} \right)$$

or $\qquad\qquad \dfrac{\partial B_y}{\partial x} - \dfrac{\partial B_x}{\partial y} = \mu \left(J_z + \varepsilon \dfrac{\partial E_z}{\partial t} \right)$ ...(i)

If we start with a rectangular element parallel to the yz plane, we get

$$\frac{\partial B_z}{\partial y} - \frac{\partial B_y}{\partial z} = \mu \left(J_x + \varepsilon \frac{\partial E_x}{\partial t} \right)$$ ...(ii)

and for a rectangular element parallel to the zx plane, we have

$$\frac{\partial B_x}{\partial z} - \frac{\partial B_z}{\partial x} = \mu \left(J_y + \varepsilon \frac{\partial E_y}{\partial t} \right)$$ ...(iii)

Each rectangle gives us a different component of an arbitrarily oriented differential surface at P. The first equation represents the Z-component, the second X-component and the third Y-component.

Therefore, multiplying first by $\hat{k}$, second by $\hat{i}$ and third by $\hat{j}$ and adding, we get

$$\hat{i} \left(\frac{\partial B_z}{\partial y} - \frac{\partial B_y}{\partial z} \right) + \hat{j} \left(\frac{\partial B_x}{\partial z} - \frac{\partial B_z}{\partial x} \right) + \hat{k} \left(\frac{\partial B_y}{\partial x} - \frac{\partial B_x}{\partial y} \right)$$

$$= \mu \left\{ \left(J_x + \varepsilon \frac{\partial E_x}{\partial t} \right) \hat{i} + \left(J_y + \varepsilon \frac{\partial E_y}{\partial t} \right) \hat{j} + \left(J_z + \varepsilon \frac{\partial E_z}{\partial t} \right) \hat{k} \right\}$$

or $\qquad\qquad \vec{\nabla} \times \vec{B} = \mu \left(\vec{J} + \varepsilon \dfrac{\partial \vec{E}}{\partial t} \right)$

or $\qquad\qquad \mu \vec{\nabla} \times \vec{H} = \mu \left(\vec{J} + \dfrac{\partial \vec{D}}{\partial t} \right)$ $\qquad\qquad$ [$\because B = \mu H$ and $D = \varepsilon E$]

$\therefore \qquad\qquad Curl\ \vec{H} = \vec{\nabla} \times \vec{H} = \vec{J} + \dfrac{\partial \vec{D}}{\partial t}$

This is Maxwell's **second** *time varying equation*.

(iv) In vector form Maxwell's *first* time varying equation is given by

$$Curl\ \vec{E} = \vec{\nabla} \times \vec{E} = -\frac{\partial \vec{B}}{\partial t} = -\mu \frac{\partial \vec{H}}{\partial t}$$

Derivation. This equation is a restatement of Faraday's law in electricity.

Faraday's law of electromagnetic induction states that whenever the magnetic flux ϕ linked with a circuit changes an induced electromotive force is set up. If the rate of change of magnetic flux is in webers/sec, the *e.m.f.* will be in volts

$$\therefore \quad V = -\frac{\partial \phi}{dt}$$

Now consider a uniform magnetic field of induction $\vec{B}$ at right angles

to the plane of the paper. Let $\dfrac{d\vec{B}}{dt}$ be the rate of increase of the field at

every point. This can be achieved by suitably varying the current in the electromagnet producing the field.

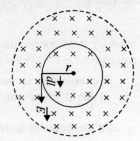

Fig. 8.5

Imagine a circle of radius r in the magnetic field and let ϕ be the magnetic flux linked with it at any time, then the induced *e.m.f.* round the circular loop

$$V = -\frac{d\phi}{dt}$$

It is supposed that this *e.m.f.* sets up an electric field $\vec{E}$ which will be tangential to the circle at every point. The work done in taking a unit positive charge once round the circuit

$$= \oint \vec{E} . \vec{dl} = E\,2\pi r = V$$

But $\qquad V = -\dfrac{d\phi}{dt}$

$$\therefore \qquad = \oint \vec{E} . \vec{dl} = -\frac{d\phi}{dt}$$

which is another form of Faraday's law.

If we consider a differential element of area $\vec{ds}$ in the magnetic field, then

$$\phi = \vec{B} . \vec{ds}$$

and

$$-\frac{\partial \phi}{dt} = -\frac{\partial \vec{B}}{dt} . \vec{ds}$$

Proceeding as in the last case, we have

$$\hat{i}\left(\frac{\partial E_z}{\partial y} - \frac{\partial E_y}{\partial z}\right) + \hat{j}\left(\frac{\partial E_z}{\partial x} - \frac{\partial E_x}{\partial z}\right) + \hat{k}\left(\frac{\partial E_y}{\partial x} - \frac{\partial E_x}{\partial y}\right)$$

$$= -\left(\frac{\partial B_x}{\partial t}\hat{i} + \frac{\partial B_y}{\partial t}\hat{j} + \frac{\partial B_z}{\partial t}\hat{k}\right)$$

or

$$\vec{\nabla} \times \vec{E} = -\frac{\partial \vec{B}}{\partial t} = -\mu\frac{\partial \vec{H}}{dt}$$

$$\therefore \qquad Curl\ \vec{E} = -\mu\frac{\partial \vec{H}}{dt}$$

This is Maxwell's **first** time varying equation in vector form.

Q. 8.4 (a). Explain the concept of displacement current. Distinguish between conduction and displacement current. What made Maxwell suggest the presence of displacement current?

(*G.N.D.U.* 2009, 2006; *Pbi.U.* 2005; *K.U.* 2000; *H.P.U.*, 1993)

(b) Determine the displacement current across two circular plates each of radius 12 cm. and separated by 5.00 mm. The rate of change of potential difference across the plates is 1.87 × 10⁹ Volt/s.

(*P.U.* 2007)

Ans (a). Conduction current. Conduction current is the electric current which actually flows through a conducting medium and obeys Ohm's law $i = \dfrac{V}{R}$ as well as its vector form $\vec{J} = \sigma \vec{E}$

where $\vec{J}$ is the conduction current density, σ the conductivity of the medium and $\vec{E}$ the electric field intensity.

Displacement current. Displacement current is the current which is set up in a dielectric medium ($\sigma = 0$) due to the variation of induced displacement charge produced by the changing electric field applied across the dielectric. Displacement charge density is given by $\dfrac{\partial \vec{D}}{\partial t} = \varepsilon \dfrac{\partial \vec{E}}{\partial t}$. It also has the units of current per unit area as given in **Q 8.6.**

To explain 'What made Maxwell to suggest the presence of displacement current' and concept of displacement current see **Q. 8.3 'Displacement current'.**

(b). Displacement current density $J_D = \dfrac{\partial D}{\partial t} = \varepsilon \dfrac{\partial E}{\partial t} \; [\because D = \varepsilon \, E]$

$\therefore$ Displacement current $i_d = A \in \dfrac{\partial E}{\partial t}$

Here $\in = \dfrac{1}{36\pi \times 10^9}$ coul^2 sec^2/kg m^3

Radius of the plates $r = 12$ cm $= 12 \times 10^{-2}$m

$\therefore$ Area of the plates $A = \pi r^2 = \pi \times 144 \times 10^{-4}$ m^2

Distance between the plates $x = 5.00$ m.m $= 5 \times 10^{-3}$ m

Rate of change of potential difference $\dfrac{dV}{dt} = 1.87 \times 10^9$ V/s

$\therefore \quad \dfrac{\partial E}{\partial t} = \dfrac{1}{x} \dfrac{\partial V}{\partial t} = \dfrac{1}{5 \times 10^{-3}} \times 1.87 \times 10^9 V / s = 0.374 \times 10^{12} V / s / m$

Displacement current $i_d = A \varepsilon \dfrac{\partial E}{\partial t} = \pi \times 144 \times 10^{-4} \times \dfrac{1}{36\pi \times 10^9} \times 0.347 \times 10^{12}$

$= 4 \times 0.374 \times 10^{-1} = 0.1496 \, A$

$= 0.15 \, A \, (APP)$

Q. 8.5. What is the chief contribution of Maxwell to electromagnetic wave theory? How does this contribution explain the radiative process? (*Pbi. U.,* 2005; *P.U.* 2001, 2000)

Ans. Chief contribution of Maxwell. The chief contribution of Maxwell to the electromagnetic wave theory is the introduction of the idea of '*displacement vector*' in a polarizable dielectric medium corresponding to the electric field vector in vacuum or free space. The displacement vector $\vec{D}$ is related to the electric field vector $\vec{E}$ by the relation

$$\vec{D} = \varepsilon \, \vec{E}$$

where ε is the permittivity of the medium.

Further, according to Maxwell a changing electric field gives rise to a '*displacement current.*'

Hence displacement current density $= \dfrac{\partial \vec{D}}{\partial t} = \dfrac{\partial}{\partial t} (\varepsilon \vec{E}) = \varepsilon \dfrac{\partial \vec{E}}{\partial t}$

Thus Maxwell's second time varying equation for electromagnetic waves is modified to

$$\vec{\nabla} \times \vec{H} = \vec{J} + \dfrac{\partial \vec{D}}{\partial t} = \sigma \vec{E} + \varepsilon \dfrac{\partial \vec{E}}{\partial t}$$

Radiative process. It is the term $\dfrac{\partial \vec{D}}{\partial t} = \varepsilon \dfrac{\partial \vec{E}}{\partial t}$ which accounts for all the radiative processes from a charge undergoing an acceleration (positive and negative). Various ways in which it happens are:

When an electron

(*i*) moves from a higher energy level in an atom to a lower energy level due to de-excitation of the atom

(*ii*) suffers a collision due to which its path gets curved and hence it has an acceleration and

(*iii*) undergoes an oscillatory motion in an alternating field as in a wireless antenna.

Q. 8.6. Show that the displacement term in Maxwell's equations has the dimensions of current per unit area. (*Pbi, U.* 2005; *G.N.D.U.* 2002)

Ans. Maxwell's second time varying equation for an electromagnetic field states

$$\vec{\nabla} \times \vec{H} = \vec{J} + \dfrac{\partial \vec{D}}{\partial t}$$

where $\vec{J} = \sigma \vec{E}$; σ being the conductivity of the medium, $\vec{D} = \varepsilon \vec{E}$, ε being the permittivity of the medium having units Farads/metre; $\vec{E}$ being the electric field vector having units volt/metre. The terms $\dfrac{\partial D}{\partial t}$ is known as the *displacement term* and $\vec{D}$ is the *electric displacement vector*.

$$\therefore \quad \text{Dimensions of } D = \dfrac{\text{Farads}}{\text{metre}} \times \dfrac{\text{Volt}}{\text{metre}} = \dfrac{\text{coulomb}}{(\text{metre})^2}$$

and Dimensions of $\dfrac{\partial D}{\partial t} = \dfrac{\text{coulomb}}{(\text{metre})^2} \cdot \dfrac{1}{\text{sec}} = \dfrac{\text{Ampere}}{\text{metre}^2}$

Hence the dimensions of displacement term are that of current per unit area or current density.

Q. 8.7. State Maxwell's equations in electromagnetic theory for a non-conducting medium. Derive the component form of the four relations. (*G.N. D.U.* 2004; *P.U.,* 1993)

Ans. Maxwell's equation in electromagnetic theory. The electromagnetic theory can be developed with the help of four vector relations known as Maxwell's equations. Two of these relations are independent of time and are known as *steady state equations*. The other two relations depend upon time and are, therefore, known as *time varying equations*. The two time varying equations are mathematically sufficient to produce separate wave equations for the electric field vector $\vec{E}$ and magnetic field vector $\vec{H}$. The steady state equations help to identify that the wave nature is **transverse.**

Steady state equation. (1) In *vector* notation Maxwell's *first* steady state equation is given by

$$div\ \vec{D} = \varepsilon\ div\ \vec{E} = \vec{\nabla} . \vec{D} = \varepsilon\ \vec{\nabla} . \vec{E} = \rho \qquad \qquad ...(i)$$

where $\vec{D}$ is the displacement vector $= \varepsilon \vec{E}$, ε the permittivity of the medium, $\vec{E}$ the electric field vector and ρ the charge density (charge per unit volume).

Since the equation involves a *scalar* (dot) produce of $\vec{\nabla}$ and $\vec{D}$, the result is a scalar quantity ρ.

(2) In *vector* notation Maxwell's *second* steady state equation is given by

$$div\ \vec{B} = \vec{\nabla} . \vec{B} = \mu\ \vec{\nabla} . \vec{H} = 0 \qquad \qquad ...(ii)$$

where $\vec{B}$ is the magnetic induction field and $\vec{H}$ the magnetic intensity $= \dfrac{B}{\mu}$, μ being the permeability of the medium.

This equation also involves the *scalar* product of $\vec{\nabla}$ and $\vec{B}$ and the result is a scalar quantity.

Time varying equation. (1) In *vector* notation Maxwell's *first* time varying equation is given by

$$\text{curl } \vec{E} = \vec{\nabla} \times \vec{E} = -\frac{\partial \vec{B}}{\partial t} = -\mu \frac{\partial \vec{H}}{\partial t} \qquad \qquad ...(iii)$$

This equation involves the *vector* (cross) product of $\vec{\nabla}$ and $\vec{E}$ and the result is a *vector* quantity.

(2) In *vector* notation Maxwell's *second* time varying equation is given by

$$\vec{\nabla} \times \vec{B} = \mu \left(\vec{J} + \frac{\partial \vec{D}}{\partial t} \right)$$

or

$$\vec{\nabla} \times \mu \vec{H} = \mu \left(\vec{J} + \frac{\partial \vec{D}}{\partial t} \right)$$

or

$$\vec{\nabla} \times \vec{H} = \vec{J} + \frac{\partial \vec{D}}{\partial t} = \vec{J} + \varepsilon \frac{\partial \vec{E}}{\partial t}$$

Now $\vec{J} = \sigma \vec{E}$ where σ is the conductivity (reciprocal of resistivity) of the medium. For non-conducting medium $\sigma = 0$. Hence Maxwell's second time varying equation for a non-conducting medium becomes

$$\vec{\nabla} \times \vec{H} = \frac{\partial \vec{D}}{\partial t} = \varepsilon \frac{\partial \vec{E}}{\partial t} \qquad \qquad ...(iv)$$

Component form of Maxwell's relations

1. $\qquad \vec{\nabla} . \vec{D} = \rho$ or $\vec{\nabla} . \varepsilon \vec{E} = \rho$

Now $\qquad \vec{E} = \hat{i}\, E_x + \hat{j}\, E_y + \hat{k}\, E_z$

$\therefore \qquad \left(\hat{i} \frac{\partial}{\partial x} + \hat{j} \frac{\partial}{\partial y} + \hat{k} \frac{\partial}{\partial z} \right) . \varepsilon \left(\hat{i}\, E_x + \hat{j}\, E_y + \hat{k}\, E_z \right) = \rho$

or $\qquad \varepsilon \left(\frac{\partial E_x}{\partial x} + \frac{\partial E_y}{\partial y} + \frac{\partial E_z}{\partial z} \right) = \rho \qquad \qquad ...(v)\,(a)$

If charge density $\rho = 0$

$\qquad \varepsilon \left(\frac{\partial E_x}{\partial x} + \frac{\partial E_y}{\partial y} + \frac{\partial E_z}{\partial z} \right) = 0$

or $\qquad \frac{\partial E_x}{\partial x} + \frac{\partial E_y}{\partial y} + \frac{\partial E_z}{\partial z} = 0 \qquad \qquad ...(v)\,(b)$

2. $\qquad \vec{\nabla} . \vec{B} = 0$ or $\vec{\nabla} . (\mu \vec{H}) = 0$

Now $\qquad \vec{H} = \hat{i}\, H_x + \hat{j}\, H_y + \hat{k}\, H_z$

$\therefore \qquad \left(\hat{i} \frac{\partial}{\partial x} + \hat{j} \frac{\partial}{\partial y} + \hat{k} \frac{\partial}{\partial z} \right) . \mu \left(\hat{i}\, H_x + \hat{j}\, H_y + \hat{k}\, H_z \right) = 0$

or $\qquad \mu \left(\frac{\partial H_x}{\partial x} + \frac{\partial H_y}{\partial y} + \frac{\partial H_z}{\partial z} \right) = 0$

or $\qquad \frac{\partial H_x}{\partial x} + \frac{\partial H_y}{\partial y} + \frac{\partial H_z}{\partial z} = 0 \qquad \qquad ...(vi)$

3. $\vec{\nabla} \times \vec{E} = - \dfrac{\partial \vec{B}}{\partial t} = - \mu \dfrac{\partial \vec{H}}{\partial t}$

Now $\vec{\nabla} \times \vec{E} = \left(\hat{i} \dfrac{\partial}{\partial x} + \hat{j} \dfrac{\partial}{\partial y} + \hat{k} \dfrac{\partial}{\partial z} \right) \times (\hat{i} E_x + \hat{j} E_y + \hat{k} E_z)$

$$= \begin{vmatrix} \hat{i} & \hat{j} & \hat{k} \\ \dfrac{\partial}{\partial x} & \dfrac{\partial}{\partial y} & \dfrac{\partial}{\partial z} \\ E_x & E_y & E_z \end{vmatrix}$$

$$= \hat{i} \left(\dfrac{\partial E_z}{\partial y} - \dfrac{\partial E_y}{\partial z} \right) + \hat{j} \left(\dfrac{\partial E_x}{\partial z} - \dfrac{\partial E_z}{\partial x} \right) + \hat{k} \left(\dfrac{\partial E_y}{\partial x} - \dfrac{\partial E_x}{\partial y} \right) \qquad \text{...(vii)}$$

and $-\mu \dfrac{\partial \vec{H}}{\partial t} = -\mu \left(\hat{i} \dfrac{\partial H_x}{\partial t} + \hat{j} \dfrac{\partial H_y}{\partial t} + \hat{k} \dfrac{\partial H_z}{\partial t} \right) \qquad \text{...(viii)}$

Equating the components along the corresponding co-ordinate axes of equation (*vii*) and (*viii*), we have

$$-\mu \dfrac{\partial H_x}{\partial t} = \dfrac{\partial E_z}{\partial y} - \dfrac{\partial E_y}{\partial z} \qquad \text{(ix) (a)}$$

$$-\mu \dfrac{\partial H_y}{\partial t} = \dfrac{\partial E_x}{\partial z} - \dfrac{\partial E_z}{\partial x} \qquad \text{(ix) (b)}$$

$$-\mu \dfrac{\partial H_z}{\partial t} = \dfrac{\partial E_y}{\partial x} - \dfrac{\partial E_x}{\partial y} \qquad \text{(ix) (c)}$$

4. $\vec{\nabla} \times \vec{H} = - \dfrac{\partial \vec{D}}{\partial t} = - \varepsilon \dfrac{\partial \vec{E}}{\partial t}$ [For a non conducting medium]

Now $\vec{\nabla} \times \vec{H} = \left(\hat{i} \dfrac{\partial}{\partial x} + \hat{j} \dfrac{\partial}{\partial y} + \hat{k} \dfrac{\partial}{\partial z} \right) \times (\hat{i} H_x + \hat{j} H_y + \hat{k} H_z)$

$$= \begin{vmatrix} \hat{i} & \hat{j} & \hat{k} \\ \dfrac{\partial}{\partial x} & \dfrac{\partial}{\partial y} & \dfrac{\partial}{\partial z} \\ H_x & H_y & H_z \end{vmatrix}$$

$$= \hat{i} \left(\dfrac{\partial H_z}{\partial y} - \dfrac{\partial H_y}{\partial z} \right) + \hat{j} \left(\dfrac{\partial H_x}{\partial z} - \dfrac{\partial H_z}{\partial x} \right) + \hat{k} \left(\dfrac{\partial H_y}{\partial x} - \dfrac{\partial H_x}{\partial y} \right) \qquad \text{...(x)}$$

and $\varepsilon \dfrac{\partial \vec{E}}{\partial t} = \varepsilon \left[\hat{i} \dfrac{\partial E_x}{\partial t} + \hat{j} \dfrac{\partial E_y}{\partial t} + \hat{k} \dfrac{\partial E_z}{\partial t} \right] \qquad \text{...(xi)}$

Equating the components along the corresponding co-ordinate axes, of equation (*x*) and (*xi*) we have

$$\varepsilon \dfrac{\partial E_x}{\partial t} = \dfrac{\partial H_z}{\partial y} - \dfrac{\partial H_y}{\partial z} \qquad \text{...(xii) (a)}$$

$$\varepsilon \frac{\partial E_y}{\partial t} = \frac{\partial H_x}{\partial z} - \frac{\partial H_z}{\partial x} \quad \text{...(xii) (b)}$$

$$\varepsilon \frac{\partial E_z}{\partial t} = \frac{\partial H_y}{\partial x} - \frac{\partial H_x}{\partial y} \quad \text{...(xii) (c)}$$

Q. 8.8. (*a*) A changing electric field induces magnetic field. Write the mathematical relation to this effect. (*H.P.U., 1995*)

(*b*) When do Maxwell's equation's become uncoupled? What is the consequence? (*Pbi.U.,* 1999)

Ans. Maxwell's equation $\vec{\nabla} \times \vec{H} = \vec{J} + \frac{\partial \vec{D}}{\partial t} = \vec{J} + \varepsilon \frac{\partial \vec{E}}{\partial t}$ for a conducting medium and $\vec{\nabla} \times \vec{H} = \frac{\partial \vec{D}}{\partial t} = \varepsilon \frac{\partial \vec{E}}{\partial t}$ for a non-conducting medium, are the mathematical relations which show that a changing electric field $\left(\frac{\partial \vec{E}}{\partial t}\right)$ induces a space variating magnetic field $(\vec{\nabla} \times \vec{H})$.

(*b*) **Coupled Equations.** Maxwell's two time varying equations are

$$\vec{\nabla} \times \vec{E} = -\frac{\partial \vec{B}}{\partial t} = -\mu \frac{\partial \vec{H}}{\partial t} \quad \text{...(i)}$$

and

$$\vec{\nabla} \times \vec{H} = \vec{J} + \frac{\partial \vec{D}}{\partial t} = \vec{J} + \frac{\in \vec{H}}{\partial t} \quad \text{...(ii)}$$

According to first equation, the time variation of $\vec{B}$ (or magnetic field $\vec{H}$) produces a space varying electric field $\vec{E}$ and according to second equation the time variation of $\vec{D}$ (or electric field $\vec{E}$) produces a space varying magnetic field $\vec{H}$. The two equations are, therefore, said to be *coupled.*

Uncoupled Equations. These Maxwell's equations become uncoupled when there is no time variation of $\vec{B}$ (or $\vec{H}$) or $\vec{D}$ (or $\vec{E}$) *i.e.* $\frac{\partial \vec{B}}{\partial t} = 0$ and $\frac{\partial \vec{D}}{\partial t} = 0$. In such a case Maxwell's two time varying equations become

$$\vec{\nabla} \times \vec{E} = 0$$

$$\vec{\nabla} \times \vec{H} = \vec{J}$$

The two steady state equations $\vec{\nabla} \cdot \vec{D} = \in \vec{\nabla} \cdot \vec{E} = \rho$ and $\vec{\nabla} \cdot \vec{B} = \mu \, \vec{\nabla} \cdot \vec{H} = 0$ remain as before.

In other words, the electric and magnetic effects can be treated separately and independently and we can make separate study of 'Electrostatics' and 'Magnetostatics'.

Q. 8.9. Write Maxwell's equations of E.M. Theory and hence derive the general wave equation for electric vector and magnetic vector for E.M. waves in a medium with finite permeability μ and permittivity ε but no conductivity (σ = 0). What important conclusions can you draw from it? (*P.U.* 2008, 2007, 2005, 2004, 2003, 2001, 2000, 1999; *Pbi.U.* 2007, 2006, *M.D.U.* 2001; *K.U.* 1995; *H.P.U.* 2002, 1999; *G.N.D.U.* 2009; 1994)

Ans. Wave equation. As $\sigma = 0$, we consider a *non-conducting* medium (or insulating medium or dielectric) having finite permeability μ and permittivity ε. If the medium is free from a charge source, charge density $\rho = 0$, In such a case Maxwell's equation for the vectors $\vec{E}$ and $\vec{H}$ are

$$\varepsilon \vec{\nabla} \cdot \vec{E} = 0 \text{ or } \vec{\nabla} \cdot \vec{E} = 0 \quad \text{...(1)}$$

$$\mu \, \vec{\nabla} \cdot \vec{H} = 0 \quad \text{or} \quad \vec{\nabla} \cdot \vec{H} = 0 \qquad \qquad \dots(2)$$

$$\vec{\nabla} \times \vec{E} = \frac{-\partial \vec{B}}{\partial t} = -\mu \frac{\partial \vec{H}}{\partial t} \qquad \qquad \dots(3)$$

$$\vec{\nabla} \times \vec{H} = \vec{J} + \varepsilon \frac{\partial \vec{E}}{\partial t} \quad \text{or} \quad \vec{\nabla} \times \vec{H} = \sigma \vec{E} + \varepsilon \frac{\partial \vec{E}}{\partial t} \qquad \dots(4) \ (a)$$

As $\sigma = 0$, the above equation for a non-conducting medium becomes

$$\vec{\nabla} \times \vec{H} = \frac{\partial \vec{D}}{\partial t} = \varepsilon \frac{\partial \vec{E}}{\partial t} \qquad \qquad \dots 4 \ (b)$$

For electric field $\vec{E}$. Taking the curl of equation (3), and substituting the value of $\vec{\nabla} \times \vec{H}$ from (4) (b) we have

$$\vec{\nabla} \times (\vec{\nabla} \times \vec{E}) = \vec{\nabla} \times \left(-\mu \frac{\partial \vec{H}}{\partial t} \right) = -\mu \left(\vec{\nabla} \times \frac{\partial \vec{H}}{\partial t} \right) = -\mu \frac{\partial}{\partial t} (\vec{\nabla} \times \vec{H})$$

$$= -\mu \frac{\partial}{\partial t} \left(\varepsilon \frac{\partial \vec{E}}{\partial t} \right) = -\mu \varepsilon \frac{\partial^2 \vec{E}}{\partial t^2} \qquad \qquad \dots(i)$$

Applying the triple vector identity

$$\vec{A} \times (\vec{B} \times \vec{C}) = \vec{B} \, (\vec{A} \cdot \vec{C}) - \vec{C} (\vec{A} \cdot \vec{B}) \text{ to } \vec{\nabla} \times (\vec{\nabla} \times \vec{E}), \text{ we have}$$

$$\vec{\nabla} \times (\vec{\nabla} \times \vec{E}) = \vec{\nabla} \, (\vec{\nabla} \cdot \vec{E}) - \vec{E}(\vec{\nabla} \cdot \vec{\nabla}) = -\nabla^2 \vec{E} \qquad \qquad \dots(ii)$$

since $\vec{\nabla} \cdot \vec{E} = 0$ according to equation (1) and $- \vec{E} \, (\vec{\nabla} \cdot \vec{\nabla}) = -\nabla^2 \vec{E}$

From (i) and (ii), we have

$$-\mu \varepsilon \frac{\partial^2 \vec{E}}{\partial t^2} = -\nabla^2 \vec{E}$$

or

$$\nabla^2 \vec{E} = \mu \varepsilon \frac{\partial^2 \vec{E}}{\partial t^2} \qquad \qquad \dots(iii)$$

This is the general wave equation for the vector field $\vec{E}$ in a non-conducting medium.

For free space. For free space $\mu = \mu_0$ and $\in = \in_0$

$$\therefore \qquad \nabla^2 \vec{E} = \mu_0 \in_0 \frac{\partial^2 \vec{E}}{\partial t^2}$$

For magnetic field $\vec{H}$. Taking curl of equation 4 (b) and substituting the value of $\vec{\nabla} \times \vec{E}$ from (3), we have

$$\vec{\nabla} \times (\vec{\nabla} \times \vec{H}) = \vec{\nabla} \times \left(\varepsilon \frac{\partial \vec{E}}{\partial t} \right) = \varepsilon \left(\vec{\nabla} \times \frac{\partial \vec{E}}{\partial t} \right) = \varepsilon \frac{\partial}{\partial t} (\vec{\nabla} \times \vec{E})$$

$$= \varepsilon \frac{\partial}{\partial t} \left(-\mu \frac{\partial \vec{H}}{\partial t} \right) = -\mu \varepsilon \frac{\partial^2 \vec{H}}{\partial t^2} \qquad \qquad \dots(iv)$$

Applying the triple vector identity

$$\vec{A} \times (\vec{B} \times \vec{C}) = \vec{B} \, (\vec{A} \cdot \vec{C}) - \vec{C} \, (\vec{A} \cdot \vec{B}) \quad \text{to } \vec{\nabla} \times (\vec{\nabla} \times \vec{H}), \text{ we have}$$

$$\vec{\nabla} \times (\vec{\nabla} \times \vec{H}) = \vec{\nabla} \, (\vec{\nabla} \cdot \vec{H}) - \vec{H} \, (\vec{\nabla} \cdot \vec{\nabla}) = -\nabla^2 \vec{H} \qquad \qquad \dots(v)$$

since $\vec{\nabla} . \vec{H} = 0$ according to equation (2) and

$$- \vec{H} \, (\vec{\nabla} . \vec{\nabla}) = - \nabla^2 \vec{H}$$

From (iv) and (v), we have

$$- \mu\varepsilon \, \frac{\partial^2 \vec{H}}{\partial t^2} = - \nabla^2 \vec{H}$$

or

$$\nabla^2 \vec{H} = \mu\varepsilon \, \frac{\partial^2 H}{\partial t^2} \qquad \qquad ...(vi)$$

This is the general wave equation for the vector field $\vec{H}$ in a non-conducting medium.

Conclusions *(i)* **Wave velocity.** The velocity of the E.M. wave in free space is a constant $= 3 \times 10^8$ ms^{-1} which is identical with the velocity of light. This suggests that light is also a form of electromagnetic wave.

For proof and calculations **see Q. 8.12.**

(ii) Both the electric and magnetic fields satisfy the same wave equation. It means that the oscillations of both the electric as well as magnetic field are *in phase.*

(iii) As the velocity of E.M. waves in vacuum $c = \dfrac{1}{\sqrt{\mu_0 \varepsilon_0}}$ is the same for all wave lengths, the electric as well as magnetic waves are non-dispersive in vacuum.

Q. 8.10. State Maxwell's equations for electromagnetic waves in a conducting medium. Hence derive the wave equation. Which is the dissipative term?

(Pbi. U. 2008; G.N.D.U. 2006; Cal. U. 2003; Gauhati U. 2000; H.P.U., 1993; P.U., 1992)

Ans. Wave equation. Consider a *conducting* medium having finite permeability μ, permittivity ε, and conductivity σ. If the medium is free from a charge source $\rho = 0$. In such a case Maxwell's equation for the vectors $\vec{E}$ and $\vec{H}$ are

$$\varepsilon \vec{\nabla} . \vec{E} = 0 \quad \text{or} \quad \vec{\nabla} . \vec{E} = 0 \qquad \qquad ...(1)$$

$$\mu \vec{\nabla} . \vec{H} = 0 \quad \text{or} \quad \vec{\nabla} . \vec{H} = 0 \qquad \qquad ...(2)$$

$$\vec{\nabla} \times \vec{E} = - \mu \, \frac{\partial \vec{H}}{\partial t} \qquad \qquad ...(3)$$

$$\vec{\nabla} \times \vec{H} = \vec{J} + \varepsilon \, \frac{\partial \vec{E}}{\partial t} \quad \text{or} \quad \vec{\nabla} \times \vec{H} = \sigma \vec{E} + \varepsilon \, \frac{\partial \vec{E}}{\partial t} \qquad \qquad ...(4)$$

As $\vec{J} = \sigma \vec{E}$

For electric field $\vec{E}$. Taking curl of equation (3) and substituting the value of $(\vec{\nabla} \times \vec{H})$ from (4), we have

$$\vec{\nabla} \times (\vec{\nabla} \times \vec{E}) = \vec{\nabla} \times \left(- \mu \, \frac{\partial \vec{H}}{\partial t} \right) = - \mu \left(\vec{\nabla} \times \frac{\partial \vec{H}}{\partial t} \right)$$

$$= - \mu \, \frac{\partial}{\partial t} \, (\vec{\nabla} \times \vec{H}) = - \mu \, \frac{\partial}{\partial t} \left(\sigma \vec{E} + \varepsilon \, \frac{d \vec{E}}{\partial t} \right)$$

$$= - \mu \, \sigma \, \frac{\partial \vec{E}}{\partial t} - \mu\varepsilon \, \frac{\partial^2 \vec{E}}{\partial t^2} \qquad \qquad ...(i)$$

Applying the triple vector identity

$$\vec{A} \times (\vec{B} \times \vec{C}) = \vec{B}\,(\vec{A}.\vec{C}) - \vec{C}\,(\vec{A}.\vec{B})\ to\ \vec{\nabla} \times (\vec{\nabla} \times \vec{E}),\ \text{we have}$$

$$\vec{\nabla} \times (\vec{\nabla} \times \vec{E}) = \vec{\nabla}\,(\vec{\nabla}.\vec{E}) - \vec{E}\,(\vec{\nabla}.\vec{\nabla}) = -\nabla^2\vec{E} \qquad ...(ii)$$

since $\vec{\nabla}.\vec{E} = 0$ according to equation (1) and $-\vec{E}\,(\vec{\nabla}.\vec{\nabla}) = -\nabla^2\vec{E}$

From (i) and (ii), we have

$$-\nabla^2\vec{E} = -\mu\sigma\frac{\partial\vec{E}}{\partial t} - \mu\varepsilon\frac{\partial^2\vec{E}}{\partial t^2}$$

or

$$\nabla^2\vec{E} = \mu\sigma\frac{\partial\vec{E}}{\partial t} + \mu\varepsilon\frac{\partial^2\vec{E}}{\partial t^2} \qquad (iii)$$

If the medium is non-conducting, $\sigma = 0$ and we have

$$\nabla^2\vec{E} = \mu\varepsilon\frac{\partial^2\vec{E}}{\partial t^2} \qquad ...(iv)$$

Comparing (iii) and (iv), we find that $\mu\sigma\frac{\partial\vec{E}}{\partial t}$ is the *dissipative term* which allows the current to flow.

For magnetic field $\vec{H}$. Taking curl of equation (4) and substituting the value of $\vec{\nabla} \times \vec{E}$ from (3), we have

$$\vec{\nabla} \times (\vec{\nabla} \times \vec{H}) = \vec{\nabla} \times \left(\sigma\vec{E} + \varepsilon\frac{\partial\vec{E}}{\partial t}\right) = \sigma\,(\vec{\nabla} \times \vec{E}) + \varepsilon\frac{\partial}{\partial t}(\vec{\nabla} \times \vec{E})$$

$$= -\mu\sigma\frac{\partial\vec{H}}{\partial t} - \varepsilon\mu\frac{\partial^2\vec{H}}{\partial t^2} \qquad ...(v)$$

Applying the triple vector identity

$$\vec{A} \times (\vec{B} \times \vec{C}) = \vec{B}\,(\vec{A}.\vec{C}) - \vec{C}\,(\vec{A}.\vec{B})\ \text{to}\ \vec{\nabla} \times (\vec{\nabla} \times \vec{H}),\ \text{we have}$$

$$\vec{\nabla} \times (\vec{\nabla} \times \vec{H}) = \vec{\nabla}\,(\vec{\nabla}.\vec{H}) - \vec{H}\,(\vec{\nabla}.\vec{\nabla}) = -\nabla^2\vec{H} \qquad ...(vi)$$

since $\vec{\nabla}.H = 0$ according to equation (2) and

$$-\vec{H}\,(\vec{\nabla}.\vec{\nabla}) = -\nabla^2\vec{H}$$

From (v) and (vi), we have

$$-\nabla^2\vec{H} = -\mu\sigma\frac{\partial\vec{H}}{\partial t} - \varepsilon\mu\frac{\partial^2\vec{H}}{\partial t^2}$$

or

$$\nabla^2\vec{H} = \mu\sigma\frac{\partial\vec{H}}{\partial t} + \mu\varepsilon\frac{\partial^2\vec{H}}{\partial t^2} \qquad ...(vii)$$

If the medium is non-conducting, $\sigma = 0$ and we have

$$\nabla^2\vec{H} = \mu\varepsilon\frac{\partial^2\vec{H}}{\partial t^2} \qquad ...(viii)$$

Comparing (*vii*) and (*viii*), we find that $\mu\sigma \dfrac{\partial^2 \vec{H}}{\partial t^2}$ is the *dissipative term* which allows the current to flow.

Q. 8.11. State Maxwell's equations in electromagnetic theory. Show by mathematical treatment that e.m. waves are transverse in nature with electric and magnetic field vectors at right angles to the direction of propagation.

(*Pbi. U.* 2006, 2005; *Nagpur U.* 2003; *Gauhati U.* 2002; *G.N.D.U.* 2007, 2006, 1999; *M.D.U.* 2002; *P.U.* 1994, 1991; *H.P.U.* 1994, 1993.)

Ans. Maxwell's equations. For a charge free ($\rho = 0$) non-conducting medium ($\sigma = 0$) having permeability μ and permittivity ε, Maxwell's equations in vector form are

$$\vec{\nabla}.\vec{E} = 0$$

$$\vec{\nabla}.\vec{H} = 0$$

$$\vec{\nabla} \times \vec{E} = -\mu \frac{\partial \vec{H}}{\partial t}$$

$$\vec{\nabla} \times \vec{H} = \varepsilon \frac{\partial \vec{E}}{\partial t}$$

In component form the equations are restated as under

1. $$\frac{\partial E_x}{\partial x} + \frac{\partial E_y}{\partial y} + \frac{\partial E_z}{\partial z} = 0 \qquad \qquad ...(1)$$

2. $$\frac{\partial H_x}{\partial x} + \frac{\partial H_y}{\partial y} + \frac{\partial H_z}{\partial z} = 0 \qquad \qquad ...(2)$$

3. $$-\mu \frac{\partial H_x}{\partial t} = \frac{\partial E_z}{\partial y} - \frac{\partial E_y}{\partial z} \qquad \qquad ...(3)\,(i)$$

$$-\mu \frac{\partial H_y}{\partial t} = \frac{\partial E_x}{\partial z} - \frac{\partial E_z}{\partial x} \qquad \qquad ...(3)\,(ii)$$

$$-\mu \frac{\partial H_z}{\partial t} = \frac{\partial E_y}{\partial x} - \frac{\partial E_x}{\partial y} \qquad \qquad ...(3)\,(iii)$$

4. $$\varepsilon \frac{\partial E_x}{\partial t} = \frac{\partial H_z}{\partial y} - \frac{\partial H_y}{\partial z} \qquad \qquad ...(4)\,(i)$$

$$\varepsilon \frac{\partial E_y}{\partial t} = \frac{\partial H_x}{\partial z} - \frac{\partial H_z}{\partial x} \qquad \qquad ...(4)\,(ii)$$

$$\varepsilon \frac{\partial E_z}{\partial t} = \frac{\partial H_y}{\partial x} - \frac{\partial H_x}{\partial y} \qquad \qquad ...(4)\,(iii)$$

We shall first consider a system of plane waves and assume that these waves are propagated in the positive Z direction. For such waves the wave properties are constant in the *XY* plane. In other words the vector fields $\vec{E}$ and $\vec{H}$ are independent of x and y and their partial derivatives with respect to x and y are zero

$$\therefore \qquad \frac{\partial \vec{E}}{\partial x} = \frac{\partial \vec{E}}{\partial y} = \frac{\partial \vec{H}}{\partial x} = \frac{\partial \vec{H}}{\partial y} = 0$$

Now $\qquad \vec{E} = E_x\,\hat{i} + E_y\,\hat{j} + E_z\,\hat{k}$

and $\qquad \vec{H} = H_x\,\hat{i} + H_y\,\hat{j} + E_z\,\hat{k}$

$$\therefore \quad \frac{\partial E_x}{\partial x} = \frac{\partial E_x}{\partial y} = \frac{\partial E_y}{\partial x} = \frac{\partial E_y}{\partial y} = 0 \ \text{ and } \ \frac{\partial H_x}{\partial x} = \frac{\partial H_x}{\partial y} = \frac{\partial H_y}{\partial x} = \frac{\partial H_y}{\partial y} = 0$$

As $\dfrac{\partial E_x}{\partial x} = 0$ and $\dfrac{\partial E_y}{\partial y} = 0$ Maxwell first relation becomes

$$\frac{\partial E_z}{\partial z} = 0 \qquad\qquad\qquad\qquad ...(i)$$

As $\dfrac{\partial H_x}{\partial x} = 0$ and $\dfrac{\partial H_y}{\partial y} = 0$, Maxwell second relaion becomes

$$\frac{\partial H_z}{\partial z} = 0 \qquad\qquad\qquad\qquad ...(ii)$$

Considering the Z-component 3 (*iii*) of Maxwell's third relation and 4 (*iii*) of Maxwell's fourth relation, we have

$$-\mu\,\frac{\partial H_z}{\partial t} = 0 \ \text{ or } \ \frac{\partial H_z}{\partial t} = 0 \qquad ...(iii) \left[\because \ \frac{\partial E_y}{\partial x} = \frac{\partial E_x}{\partial y} = 0 \right.$$

and $$\varepsilon\,\frac{\partial E_z}{\partial t} = 0 \ \text{ or } \ \frac{\partial E_z}{\partial t} = 0 \qquad ...(iv) \left. \because \ \frac{\partial H_y}{\partial x} = \frac{\partial H_x}{\partial y} = 0 \right]$$

From equation (*i*), (*ii*), (*iii*) and (*iv*) we find that the Z-components of either $\vec{E}$ or $\vec{H}$ do not vary with space (Z-co-ordinate) or time *i.e.*, E_z and H_z are constant. Since we are considering only the oscillatory nature of either $\vec{E}$ or $\vec{H}$ a constant E_z or H_z will have no effect on the wave propagation. We can, therefore, put $E_z = H_z = 0$ and substituting these values in equations 3 (*i*), 3 (*ii*), 4 (*i*) and 4 (*ii*), we have

$$-\mu\,\frac{\partial H_x}{\partial t} = -\frac{\partial E_y}{\partial z} \qquad\qquad\qquad ...(v)$$

$$-\mu\,\frac{\partial H_y}{\partial t} = -\frac{\partial E_x}{\partial z} \qquad\qquad\qquad ...(vi)$$

$$\varepsilon\,\frac{\partial E_x}{\partial t} = -\frac{\partial H_y}{\partial z} \qquad\qquad\qquad ...(vii)$$

or $$\varepsilon\,\frac{\partial E_y}{\partial t} = \frac{\partial H_x}{\partial z} \qquad\qquad\qquad ...(viii)$$

Electromagnetic waves are transverse. As the wave propagates along the Z-direction and $E_z = H_z = 0$ the electromagnetic waves have no longitudinal component. Further the variation of $\vec{H}$ or $\vec{E}$ occurs only in a direction perpendicular to Z-axis and from equation (*v*) to (*viii*) we see that neither the time derivative nor the Z-derivative of H_x and H_y (or E_x and E_y) vanishes. *This means that the waves are transverse in nature.*

This can also be proved mathematically as under. Dividing equation (v) by equation (vi), we get

$$\frac{-\mu \dfrac{\partial H_x}{\partial t}}{-\mu \dfrac{\partial H_y}{\partial t}} = -\frac{\dfrac{\partial E_y}{\partial z}}{\dfrac{\partial E_x}{\partial z}} \quad \text{or} \quad \frac{\partial H_x}{\partial H_y} = -\frac{\partial E_y}{\partial E_x}$$

or

$$\frac{H_x}{H_y} = -\frac{E_y}{E_x} \quad \text{or} \quad H_x E_x + H_y\,E_y = 0$$

Now $\vec{E}.\vec{H} = EH \cos\theta$ where θ is the angle between the electric field vector $\vec{E}$ and magnetic field vector $\vec{H}$.

$\therefore\quad (E_x\hat{i} + E_y\hat{j} + E_z\hat{k})\cdot(H_x\hat{i} + H_y\hat{j} + H_z\hat{k}) = E_x\,H_x + E_y\,H_y + E_z\,H_z = EH\cos\theta$

But $E_z = 0$ and $H_z = 0$ $\therefore$ $E_z H_z = 0$

Hence $EH\cos\theta = E_x H_x + E_y\,H_y = 0$

or $\cos\theta = 0$ $\therefore$ $\theta = \dfrac{\pi}{2}$

This shows that $\vec{E}$ and $\vec{H}$ are at right angles to each other. Moreover, the X-component of $\vec{H}$ is related to the Y-component of $\vec{E}$ and vice-versa. Therefore, if $\vec{E}$ acts along the X-axis, $\vec{H}$ will act along the Y-axis and vice-versa. As the wave propagates along the Z-axis, $\vec{E}$ and $\vec{H}$ act in directions at right angles to the direction of propagation of the wave.

Q. 8.12. (a) Prove that the velocity of an e.m. wave in a medium of magnetic permeability μ, electric susceptibility ε and conductivity $\sigma = 0$ is given by $c = \sqrt{\dfrac{1}{\mu\varepsilon}}$.

(Pbi.U. 2006; G.N.D.U., 1996; P.U., 1995, 1991; H.P.U., 1992)

(b) If for vacuum $\mu_0 = 4\pi \times 10^{-7}$ kg m/coul^2 and $\varepsilon_0 = \dfrac{1}{36\pi \times 10^9}$ coul^2 sec^2/kg m^3 find the velocity of elecromagnetic waves and show that it is equal to the speed of light.

(Pbi. U., 2002)

Ans. (a) Velocity of electromagnetic waves. The wave equation for an electromagnetic wave for a non-conducting medium ($\sigma = 0$) with magnetic permeability μ and electric susceptibility ε in terms of electric field vector $\vec{E}$ is given by

$$\nabla^2 \vec{E} = \mu\,\varepsilon\,\frac{\partial^2 \vec{E}}{\partial t^2} \qquad\qquad \text{[For proof see \textbf{Q 8.9} Eq. (\textit{iii})] ...(\textit{i})}$$

and in terms of magnetic field vector $\vec{H}$ is given by

$$\nabla^2 \vec{H} = \mu\,\varepsilon\,\frac{\partial^2 \vec{H}}{\partial t^2} \qquad\qquad \text{[For proof see \textbf{Q 8.9} Eq. (\textit{vi})] ...(\textit{ii})}$$

The general wave equation in three dimensions is given by

$$\nabla^2 \psi = \frac{1}{c^2}\frac{\partial^2 \psi}{\partial t^2} \qquad\qquad\qquad ...(\textit{iii})$$

where ψ is the '*disturbance*' or '*wave function*' and is a function of x, y, z and t, c is the wave velocity.

Comparing equation (i) or (ii) with (iii), we have

Velocity of the electromagnetic wave $c = \sqrt{\dfrac{1}{\mu \varepsilon}}$

Equation (i) gives the wave equation for the vector $\vec{E}$ and equation (ii) for the vector $\vec{H}$. Hence

the velocity of the vector $\vec{E}$ and $\vec{H}$ in electro magnetic waves propagating through free space is

$\sqrt{\dfrac{1}{\mu_0 \, \varepsilon_0}}$.

It can be seen that $\sqrt{\dfrac{1}{\mu \varepsilon}}$ has dimensions of velocity.

Taking the dimensions of μ and ε we have

$$\mu\varepsilon = \frac{\text{kg metre}}{\text{coulomb}^2} \times \frac{\text{coulomb}^2 \, \text{sec}^2}{\text{kg. metre}^3} = \frac{\text{sec}^2}{\text{m}^2}$$

$\therefore \qquad \sqrt{\dfrac{1}{\mu \varepsilon}} = \dfrac{\text{metre}}{\text{sec}} = \text{m/sec}$

(b) $\mu_0 = 4\,\pi \times 10^{-7}$ kg m/coul^2 ; $\varepsilon_0 = \dfrac{1}{36\,\pi \times 10^9}$ coul^2 sec^2 /kg m^3

$\therefore \qquad c = \sqrt{\dfrac{1}{\mu_0\,\varepsilon_0}} = \sqrt{\dfrac{1}{4\,\pi \times 10^{-7}} \times 36\,\pi \times 10^9} = 3 \times 10^8 \ \text{ms}^{-1}$

Thus the velocity of E.M waves in vacuum is equal to the velocity of light.

Q. 8.13. **Using Maxwell's equations in electromagnetic theory, derive the wave equation for a plane polarised electro magnetic wave having finite values of permeability and permittivity**

(*a*) **For a charge free non conducting medium**

$$\rho = 0, \ \sigma = 0$$

(*b*) **For a charge free conucting medium**

$$\rho = 0, \ \sigma \neq 0.$$

(*H.P.U.* 2003, 1993; *P.U.* 2009, 2000; *Pbi.U.* 2003, 2001; *M.D.U.* 2002 ; *G.N.D.U.* 2001, 1994)

Ans. (*a*) **Charge free, non-conducting medium.** For a charge free ($\rho = 0$) non-conducting medium ($\sigma = 0$) having permeability μ and permittivity ε, Maxwell's equation in component form are

1. $\dfrac{\partial E_x}{\partial x} + \dfrac{\partial E_y}{\partial y} + \dfrac{\partial E_z}{\partial z} = 0$ \hfill ...(1)

2. $\dfrac{\partial H_x}{\partial x} + \dfrac{\partial H_y}{\partial y} + \dfrac{\partial H_z}{\partial z} = 0$ \hfill ...(2)

3. $-\,\mu\,\dfrac{\partial H_x}{\partial t} = \dfrac{\partial E_z}{\partial y} - \dfrac{\partial E_y}{\partial z}$ \hfill ...(3) (i)

$-\,\mu\,\dfrac{\partial H_y}{\partial t} = \dfrac{\partial E_x}{\partial z} - \dfrac{\partial E_z}{\partial x}$ \hfill ...(3) (ii)

$-\,\mu\,\dfrac{\partial H_z}{\partial t} = \dfrac{\partial E_y}{\partial x} - \dfrac{\partial E_x}{\partial y}$ \hfill ...(3) (iii)

4. $\varepsilon \dfrac{\partial E_x}{\partial t} = \dfrac{\partial H_z}{\partial y} - \dfrac{\partial H_y}{\partial z}$ ...(4) (i)

        $\varepsilon \dfrac{\partial E_y}{\partial t} = \dfrac{\partial H_x}{\partial z} - \dfrac{\partial H_z}{\partial x}$ ...(4) (ii)

        $\varepsilon \dfrac{\partial E_z}{\partial t} = \dfrac{\partial H_y}{\partial x} - \dfrac{\partial H_x}{\partial y}$ ...(4) (iii)

Plane wave. We shall first consider a system of plane waves and assume that these waves are propagated in the positive Z-direction. For such waves the wave properties are constant in the XY plane. In other words, the vector fields $\vec{E}$ and $\vec{H}$ are independent of x and y and their partial derivatives with respect to x and y are zero.

$\therefore$
$$\frac{\partial \vec{E}}{\partial x} = \frac{\partial \vec{E}}{\partial y} = \frac{\partial \vec{H}}{\partial x} = \frac{\partial \vec{H}}{\partial y} = 0$$

Now $\vec{E} = E_x \hat{i} + E_y \hat{j} + E_z \hat{k}$

and $\vec{H} = H_x \hat{i} + H_y \hat{j} + H_z \hat{k}$

$\therefore$
$$\frac{\partial E_x}{\partial x} = \frac{\partial E_x}{\partial y} = \frac{\partial E_y}{\partial x} = \frac{\partial E_y}{\partial y} = 0 \text{ and } \frac{\partial H_x}{\partial x} = \frac{\partial H_x}{\partial y} = \frac{\partial H_y}{\partial x} = \frac{\partial H_y}{\partial y} = 0$$

As $\dfrac{\partial E_x}{\partial x} = 0$ and $\dfrac{\partial E_y}{\partial y} = 0$, Maxwell's first relation becomes

$$\frac{\partial E_z}{\partial z} = 0 \qquad\qquad\qquad\qquad\qquad ...(i)$$

As $\dfrac{\partial H_x}{\partial x} = 0$ and $\dfrac{\partial H_y}{\partial y} = 0$, Maxwell's second relation becomes

$$\frac{\partial H_z}{\partial z} = 0 \qquad\qquad\qquad\qquad\qquad ...(ii)$$

Considering the Z-component 3 (iii) of Maxwell's third relation and 4 (iii) of Maxwell's fourth relation, we have

$$-\mu \frac{\partial H_z}{\partial t} = 0 \text{ or } \frac{\partial H_z}{\partial t} = 0 \qquad ...(iii) \left[\because \frac{\partial E_y}{\partial x} = \frac{\partial E_x}{\partial y} = 0 \right]$$

and $\varepsilon \dfrac{\partial E_z}{\partial t} = 0$ or $\dfrac{\partial E_z}{\partial t} = 0$ $...(iv) \left[\because \dfrac{\partial H_y}{\partial x} = \dfrac{\partial H_x}{\partial y} = 0 \right]$

From equations (i), (ii), (iii) and (iv) we find that the Z-components of either $\vec{E}$ or $\vec{H}$ do not vary with space (Z-co-ordinate) or time i.e., E_z and H_z are constant. Since we are considering only the oscillatory nature of either $\vec{E}$ or $\vec{H}$ a constant E_z or H_z will have no effect on the wave propagation. We can, therefore, put $E_z = H_z = 0$ and substituting these values in equations (3) (i), (3) (ii), (4) (i) and (4) (ii), we have

$$-\mu \frac{\partial H_x}{\partial t} = -\frac{\partial E_y}{\partial z} \qquad\qquad\qquad\qquad ...(v)$$

$$-\mu \frac{\partial H_y}{\partial t} = \frac{\partial E_x}{\partial z} \qquad\qquad\qquad\qquad ...(vi)$$

$$\varepsilon \, \frac{\partial E_x}{\partial t} = \frac{-\partial H_y}{\partial z} \qquad \qquad \qquad ...(vii)$$

$$\varepsilon \, \frac{\partial E_y}{\partial t} = \frac{\partial H_x}{\partial z} \qquad \qquad \qquad ...(viii)$$

Plane polarised wave. For a *plane polarised wave* travelling along the + Z direction, we can choose the electric field vector $\vec{E}$ to be zero either along the X-axis or Y-axis. If we take $\vec{E}$ along the X-axis then $E_y = 0$. In this case the magnetic field vector will be zero along X-axis *i.e.*, $H_x = 0$.

Substituting $H_x = E_y = 0$ in equations (v) to (viii), we have

$$- \mu \, \frac{\partial H_y}{\partial t} = \frac{\partial E_x}{\partial z} \qquad \qquad \qquad ...(ix)$$

and

$$\varepsilon \, \frac{\partial E_x}{\partial t} = - \frac{\partial H_y}{\partial z} \qquad \qquad \qquad ...(x)$$

Taking $\dfrac{\partial}{\partial z}$ of (ix) and $\dfrac{\partial}{\partial t}$ of (x), we have

$$- \mu \, \frac{\partial^2 H_y}{\partial t \partial z} = \frac{\partial^2 E_x}{\partial z^2} \qquad \qquad \qquad ...(xi)$$

and

$$\varepsilon \, \frac{\partial^2 E_x}{\partial t^2} = - \frac{\partial^2 H_y}{\partial z \partial t} \qquad \qquad \qquad ...(xii)$$

From (xi) and (xii) we have

$$\frac{\partial^2 E_x}{\partial z^2} = \mu \, \varepsilon \, \frac{\partial^2 E_x}{\partial t^2} \qquad \qquad \qquad ...(xii)\,(a)$$

This is the wave equation for E_x for a charge free non-conducting medium.

Similarly taking $\dfrac{\partial}{\partial t}$ of (ix) and $\dfrac{\partial}{\partial z}$ of (x), we have

$$- \mu \, \frac{\partial^2 H_y}{\partial t^2} = \frac{\partial^2 E_x}{\partial z \partial t} \qquad \qquad \qquad ...(xiii)$$

and

$$\varepsilon \, \frac{\partial^2 E_x}{\partial t \partial z} = - \frac{\partial^2 H_y}{\partial z^2} \qquad \qquad \qquad ...(xiv)$$

From (xiii) and (xiv) we have

$$\frac{\partial^2 H_y}{\partial z^2} = \mu \, \varepsilon \, \frac{\partial^2 H_y}{\partial t^2} \qquad \qquad \qquad ...(xiv)\,(a)$$

This is the wave equation for H_y for a charge free non-conducting medium.

It is clear form the two wave equations (xii) (a) and (xiv) (a) that both the vectors E_x and H_y obey the same wave equation.

(b) Charge free conducting medium. For a charge free ($\rho = 0$) conducting medium ($\sigma \neq 0$), the first three Maxwell's relations in component form are the same but Maxwell's fourth relation will include an additional term due to a conducting current given by $\vec{J} = \sigma \vec{E}$ where σ is the conductivity of the medium. Since $\vec{J} = \sigma \vec{E} = \sigma \vec{E_x} + \sigma \vec{E_y} + \sigma \vec{E_z}$, equations (4) (i), (ii) and (iii) will then become

$$\sigma E_x + \varepsilon \frac{\partial E_x}{\partial t} = \frac{\partial H_z}{\partial y} - \frac{\partial H_y}{\partial z} \qquad \text{...(4) (i)}$$

$$\sigma E_y + \varepsilon \frac{\partial E_y}{\partial t} = \frac{\partial H_x}{\partial z} - \frac{\partial H_z}{\partial x} \qquad \text{...(4) (ii)}$$

$$\sigma E_z + \varepsilon \frac{\partial E_z}{\partial t} = \frac{\partial H_y}{\partial x} - \frac{\partial H_x}{\partial y} \qquad \text{...(4) (iii)}$$

Putting $E_z = H_z = 0$ as explained in part (a) under the head *plane wave* in 4 (i) and 4 (ii), we have

$$\sigma E_x + \varepsilon \frac{\partial E_x}{\partial t} = - \frac{\partial H_y}{\partial z}$$

$$\sigma E_y + \varepsilon \frac{\partial E_y}{\partial t} = + \frac{\partial H_x}{\partial z}$$

Putting $H_x = E_y = 0$ as explained in part (a) under the head *plane polarised wave,* the second of the above equations vanishes and we have only

$$\sigma E_x + \varepsilon \frac{\partial E_x}{\partial t} = - \frac{\partial H_y}{\partial z} \qquad \text{...(xv)}$$

Taking $\dfrac{\partial}{\partial z}$ of (ix) from part (a) and $\dfrac{\partial}{\partial t}$ of (xv), we have

$$- \mu \frac{\partial^2 H_y}{\partial t \partial z} = \frac{\partial^2 E_x}{\partial z^2} \qquad \text{...(xvi)}$$

and $$\sigma \frac{\partial E_x}{\partial t} + \varepsilon \frac{\partial^2 E_x}{\partial t^2} = - \frac{\partial^2 H_y}{\partial z \partial t}$$

$$\therefore \qquad \frac{\partial^2 E_x}{\partial z^2} = \mu \varepsilon \frac{\partial^2 E_x}{\partial t^2} + \mu \sigma \frac{\partial E_x}{\partial t} \qquad \text{...(xvii)}$$

This is the wave equation for E_x for a charge free conducting medium.

Similarly taking $\dfrac{\partial}{\partial t}$ of (x) from part (a) and $\dfrac{\partial}{\partial z}$ of (xv), we have

$$- \mu \frac{\partial^2 H_y}{\partial t^2} = \frac{\partial^2 E_x}{\partial z \partial t}$$

and $$\sigma \frac{\partial E_x}{\partial z} + \varepsilon \frac{\partial^2 E_x}{\partial t \partial z} = - \frac{\partial^2 H_y}{\partial z^2}$$

$$\therefore \qquad - \mu \varepsilon \frac{\partial^2 H_y}{\partial t^2} = - \frac{\partial^2 H_y}{\partial z^2} - \sigma \frac{\partial E_x}{\partial x}$$

But from (ix) in part (a) $\dfrac{\partial E_x}{\partial z} = - \mu \dfrac{\partial H_y}{\partial t}$

Substituting we have

$$- \mu \varepsilon \frac{\partial^2 H_y}{\partial t^2} = - \frac{\partial^2 H_y}{\partial z^2} + \mu \sigma \frac{\partial H_y}{\partial t}$$

$$\text{or} \qquad \frac{\partial^2 H_y}{\partial z^2} = \mu\,\varepsilon\,\frac{\partial^2 H_y}{\partial t^2} + \mu\,\sigma\,\frac{\partial H_y}{\partial t} \qquad\qquad ...(xviii)$$

This is the wave equation for H_y for a charge free conducting medium.

Q. 8.14. *(a)* *(i)* **What is plane polarised e.m. wave?**   *(G.N.D.U.* 2006)

(ii) **Write the wave equations for plane polarised electromagnetic waves in a dielectric medium having finite values of μ and ε but $\sigma = 0$ and write solutions to these equations.**

What is the phase difference between E and H ? Explain.   *(G.N.D.U.* 2001; *P.U.,* 1994)

(b) **For propagation of uniform plane wave in free space prove that** $\dfrac{\vec{E}}{\vec{H}} = \sqrt{\dfrac{\mu}{\varepsilon}}$

(Nagpur, U. 2003)

Ans. *(a)* *(i)* **Plane polarised e.m., wave.** An electromagnetic wave in which the electric and magnetic field oscillate only in one plane perpendicular to the direction of propagation of the wave is called *plane polarised.*

(ii) **Wave equation.** For a plane polarised electromagnetic wave travelling along the direction of Z-axis and polarised in such a way that $E_y = 0$ and $H_x = 0$, the wave equations for a dielectric (non-conducting) medium with $\sigma = 0$ are

For E_x $\qquad \dfrac{\partial^2 E_x}{\partial z^2} = \mu\,\varepsilon\,\dfrac{\partial^2 E_x}{\partial t^2}$ $\qquad$ [For proof see **Q. 8.13** Eq. *(xii)* *(a)*]   ...*(i)*

and for H_y $\qquad \dfrac{\partial^2 H_y}{\partial z^2} = \mu\,\varepsilon\,\dfrac{\partial^2 H_y}{\partial t^2}$ $\qquad$ [For proof see **Q. 8.13** Eq. *(xiv)* *(a)*]   ...*(ii)*

The solution of equation *(i)* is

$$E_x = E_0 \sin\frac{2\pi}{\lambda}\,(vt - z) \qquad\qquad ...(iii)$$

and solution of equaiton *(ii)* is

$$H_y = H_0 \sin\frac{2\pi}{\lambda}\,(vt - z) \qquad\qquad ...(iv)$$

where E_0 and H_0 are the maximum values of $\vec{E}$ and $\vec{H}$ respectively, v is the velocity with which the wave is propagating in the positive Z direction given by $v = \sqrt{\dfrac{1}{\mu\varepsilon}}$.

The sine solution of the wave equation indicates that there is no conductance or ohmic current. We can choose a cosine solution also.

Phase difference between E and H. The electric and magnetic vectors are shown in Fig. 8.6. It is clear from the figure that the electric and magnetic vectors are in phase *i.e.,* at the time $\vec{E}$ attains the maximum value E_0, $\vec{H}$ attains the maximum value H_0. Similarly when $\vec{E} = 0$, $\vec{H} = 0$.

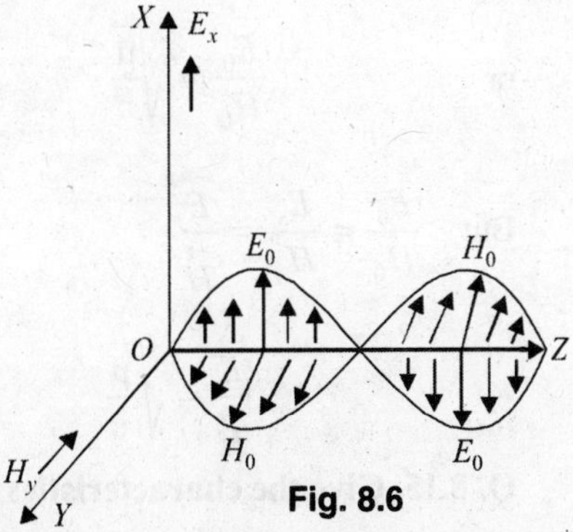

It is also clear from equations *(iii)* and *(iv)*, when

$$\sin\frac{2\pi}{\lambda}\,(vt - z) = 1 \; i.e., \; \frac{2\pi}{\lambda}\,(vt - z) = \frac{\pi}{2},$$

$E_x = E_0$ and at the same time $H_y = H_0$ *i.e.,*

Fig. 8.6

$\vec{E}$ and $\vec{H}$ have their maximum values at the same time. When $\sin\dfrac{2\pi}{\lambda}\,(vt - z) = 0 \; i.e.,$

$\frac{2\pi}{\lambda}(vt - z) = 0$, $E_x = 0$ and at the same time $H_y = 0$ i.e., $\vec{E}$ and $\vec{H}$ have their zero values at the same time.

$\therefore$ $\vec{E}$ and $\vec{H}$ are in phase.

The direction of propagation of the wave is given by the cross product of $\vec{E}$ and $\vec{H}$. As in our discussion $\vec{E}$ is along the X-axis $(\vec{E_x})$ and $\vec{H}$ along Y-axis $(\vec{H_y})$, the wave will propagate along the Z-axis and the magnitude of the velocity $\vec{E} \times \vec{H} = E_x H_y$.

(b)   For a plane polarised electromagnetic wave travelling along the + Z direction, the electric vector $\vec{E}$ is taken along the X-axis (E_x) and the magnetic vector $\vec{H}$ along the Y-axis (H_y), then

$$-\mu \frac{\partial H_y}{\partial t} = \frac{\partial E_x}{\partial z} \quad \text{[For proof See Q. 8.13 Eq. (ix)]} \qquad \text{...(v)}$$

The equation of a plane polarised electro-magnetic wave in such a case is given by

$$E_x = E_0 \sin \frac{2\pi}{\lambda}(vt - z)$$

and $$H_y = H_0 \sin \frac{2\pi}{\lambda}(vt - z)$$

[For proof see Q. 8.14 Eq. (iii) and (iv)]

$\therefore$
$$\frac{\partial E_x}{\partial z} = -E_0 \frac{2\pi}{\lambda} \cos \frac{2\pi}{\lambda}(vt - z) \text{ and}$$

$$\frac{\partial H_y}{\partial t} = H_0 \frac{2\pi v}{\lambda} \cos \frac{2\pi}{\lambda}(vt - z)$$

Substituting in Eq. (v), we have

$$-\mu H_0 \frac{2\pi v}{\lambda} \cos \frac{2\pi}{\lambda}(vt - z) = -E_0 \frac{2\pi}{\lambda} \cos \frac{2\pi}{\lambda}(vt - z)$$

or $\mu v H_0 = E_0$

But for an electro magnetic wave $v = \sqrt{\dfrac{1}{\mu\varepsilon}}$

$\therefore$
$$E_0 = \frac{\mu}{\sqrt{\mu\varepsilon}} H_0$$

or
$$\frac{E_0}{H_0} = \sqrt{\frac{\mu}{\varepsilon}}$$

But $\dfrac{E_0}{H_0} = \dfrac{E_x}{H_y} = \dfrac{\vec{E}}{\vec{H}}$

$\therefore$
$$\frac{\vec{E}}{\vec{H}} = \sqrt{\frac{\mu}{\varepsilon}} \qquad \text{... (vi)}$$

Q. 8.15. Give the characteristics of electromagnetic waves in free space.
(P.U. 2009; Pbi. U., 2006; H.P.U., 1996)

Ans. Characteristics of electromagnetic waves in free space (*i*) The electromagnetic waves are *transverse* in nature. The electric field vector $\vec{E}$ and the magnetic field vector $\vec{H}$ are mutually perpendicular to each other as well as prependilion to the direction of propagation of the wave.

(*ii*) The rate of flow of electromagnetic energy per unit area along the direction of propagation of the wave is given by Poynting vector $\vec{E} \times \vec{H}$ or $\dfrac{\vec{E} \times \vec{B}}{\mu}$.

(*iii*) The wave velocity in free space is given by $\sqrt{\dfrac{1}{\varepsilon_0 \mu_0}}$ and in a dielectric medium is $\sqrt{\dfrac{1}{\varepsilon \mu}}$.

(*iv*) The vectors $\vec{E}$ and $\vec{H}$ are in phase with each other *i.e.*, at the time $\vec{E}$ attains the maximum value $\vec{E_0}$, $\vec{H}$ attains the maximum value $\vec{H_0}$.

(*v*) The electrostatic energy density U_e is equal to the magnetic energy density U_m

$$\frac{U_e}{U_m} = \frac{\dfrac{1}{2} \varepsilon\, E^2}{\dfrac{1}{2} \mu H^2} = \frac{\varepsilon}{\mu}\frac{E^2}{H^2}$$

but $\dfrac{E}{H} = \sqrt{\dfrac{\mu}{\varepsilon}}$ $\therefore$ $\dfrac{E^2}{H^2} = \dfrac{\mu}{\varepsilon}$ ...(*i*)

Hence $\dfrac{U_e}{U_m} = \dfrac{\varepsilon}{\mu} \cdot \dfrac{\mu}{\varepsilon} = 1$

or $U_e = U_m$

(*vi*) The total energy U is the sum of the electrostatic and magnetic energy densities

$$U = U_e + U_m$$

Note. The energy density in a dielectric is ε_r times the energy density of the same waves in vacuum.

$$U = U_e + U_m = \frac{1}{2} \varepsilon\, E^2 + \frac{1}{2} \mu H^2$$

$$= \frac{1}{2} \varepsilon E^2 + \frac{1}{2} \varepsilon E^2 = \varepsilon E^2$$

$$= \varepsilon_r\, (\varepsilon_0\, E^2) = \varepsilon_r \times [\text{energy density in free space}]$$

Q. 8.16. (*a*) **According to e.m. theory, what factors vary at right angles to the direction of propagation of the light wave.**   (*G.N.D.U.*, 1996)

(*b*) **Differentiate between mechanical and e.m. waves.**   (*P.U.*, 2009, 2005)

Ans. According to electro magnetic theory the electric field vector $\vec{E}$ and the magnetic field vector $\vec{H}$ oscillate or vary at right angles to the direction of propagation of the wave. The vectors $\vec{E}$ and $\vec{H}$ are also at right angles to each other. If the wave propagates along the Z-direction and $\vec{E}$ is directed along X-direction, then $\vec{H}$ is directed along the Y-direction. If $\vec{E}$ is directed along the Y-direction $\vec{H}$ is directed along the X-direction.

(b) Differentiation or comparison between mechanical and _e.m._ waves.

_e.m._ waves	Mechanical waves
1. The e.m. waves are transverse in nature	1. The mechanical waves can be transverse as well as longitudinal.
2. They do not require any material medium to propagate and can even travel through vacuum.	2. They require a material medium for propagation.
3. The velocity of propagation depends upon permeability μ and permittivity $\in$ and is given by $\dfrac{1}{\sqrt{\in \mu}}$.	3. The velocity of propagation depends upon tension and mass per unit length. For example, the velocity of transverse waves in a string $v = \sqrt{\dfrac{T}{\rho}}$
4. It is the electric and magnetic field vectors $\vec{E}$ and $\vec{H}$ which cause oscillation _i.e._, the variables are E and H (or B).	4. It is the particles of the medium which execute oscillations and the variable is particle displacement.
5. The total energy $U = U_e + U_m = \dfrac{1}{2}\in E^2 + \dfrac{1}{2}\mu H^2$ where U_e is the electrostatic energy density and U_m the magnetic energy density.	5. For mechanical waves such as those in a stretched string kinetic energy is proportional to ρ the mass per unit length and potential energy is proportional to T, the tension.
6. The frequency of _e.m._ waves is equal to the number of times the electric and magnetic fields associated with the wave oscillate in one second.	6. The frequency of mechanical wave is equal to the frequency of vibration of the particle of the medium (about their mean position) through which the wave is travelling.

Q. 8.17. A light wave is characterised by its electric vector $\vec{E}$ although it has a magnetic vector $\vec{B}$. Explain why.   (_P.U._ 2006, 2000, 1999; _G.N.D.U._, 1994; _H.P.U._, 1993)

OR

Why does the eletric field of electromagnetic wave determine the polarisation rather than magnetic field?   (_H.P.U._, 1994, 1991)

Ans. A light wave is an electromagnetic wave. The force exerted by its electric vector $\vec{E}$ on a particle of charge q is given by $q\,\vec{E}$ (magnitude $q\,E$). If the particle is moving with a velocity $\vec{v}$, then the force exerted by its magnetic vector $\vec{B}$ is given by $q\,(\vec{v} \times \vec{B})$ and the magnitude of the maximum value is given by $q\,v\,B$. For an electromagnetic wave

$$\frac{|\vec{E}|}{|\vec{H}|} = \sqrt{\frac{\mu}{\varepsilon}} = \mu \sqrt{\frac{1}{\mu\varepsilon}} = \mu c \qquad \text{[For proof see Q. 8.14 Eq. (_vi_)]}$$

or $\qquad\qquad \dfrac{|\vec{E}|}{|\vec{B}|} = c \quad \text{or} \quad B = \dfrac{E}{c}$

$\therefore \qquad\qquad qvB = \dfrac{v}{c}\, qE$

The magnetic force is therefore v/c of the electric force. The value of c being very large as compared to v, the electric force is much greater than the magnetic force. This is the reason why a light wave is characterised by its electric vector.

An idea of their relative values is given by the following example. The intensity of bright sun-light on the surface of the earth is about 1 kW per square metre which gives the amplitude of electric vector 1 kV/m. This is reasonably modest value and can be easily measured. The corresponding magnetic field amplitude is about $3\mu\, T$. (micro-Tesla). This is a very weak field being about 1/10 of the earth's field and cannot be conveniently measured. Although the wave cannot exist unless both $\vec{E}$ and $\vec{B}$ are present, $\vec{E}$ is much more important than $\vec{B}$ from the point of view of the effects produced by the wave when it passes through matter as the effect due to $\vec{B}$ can be easily ignored.

Polarisation of electromagnetic waves is caused when the waves pass through certain polarising materials e.g., when light passes through quartz or calcite crystal. As the effect of electric field vector is very much greater than that of the magnetic field vector, the polarisation is determined by the electric field vector.

Q. 8.18. **An electromagnetic wave in empty space has a maximum electric field of 1000 V/m. What is the maximum value of magnetic field ?**   *(H.P.U., 1993)*

Ans. $E_0 = 1000$ V/m

Now $B_0 = \mu_0\, H_0$ But $\dfrac{E}{H} = \mu c$ or $\dfrac{E_0}{H_0} = \mu_0\, c$

$\therefore \qquad B_0 = \mu_0\, H_0 = \dfrac{E_0}{c}$ $\left[\because\ \mu_0\, \varepsilon_0 = \dfrac{1}{c^2} \right]$

$\therefore$ Magnetic field vector $H_0 = \dfrac{B_0}{\mu_0} = \dfrac{E_0}{\mu_0\, c}$

$= \dfrac{1000}{4\pi \times 10^{-7} \times 3 \times 10^8} = \dfrac{25}{3\pi}$ units $= 2.65$ units

Q. 8.19. (*a*) **Define Poynting vector for E.M. waves. What does it (measures) represent? What are its units? Show that Poynting vector measures the flow of energy per unit area per second in an electro magnetic wave.**

(*G.N.D.U.* 2008, 2007, 2006, 2004, 2003, 1999, 1994; *Pbi. U.* 2007, 2003, 1999; *P.U.* 2009, 2008, 2007, 2006, 2004, 2003, 2001; *H.P.U.* 2001, 1999, 1995; *Osm. U.* 2004; *K.U.* 1995)

(*b*) **State and derive Poynting's theorem or derive expression for the flow of E.M. energy in a medium.**

(*K.U.* 2002, 2000; *M.D.U.* 2003, 2000, 1999; *Cal. U.* 2003; *G.N.D.U.* 1999; *Pbi.U.* 1999; *H.P.U.* 1996, 1995)

Ans. (*a*) Poynting vector. The cross product of the electric field vector $\vec{E}$ and the magnetic field vector $\vec{H}$ is known as a Poynting vector. It is denoted by S. Mathematically

$$\text{Poynting vector } \vec{S} = \vec{E} \times \vec{H}$$

For an electromagnetic wave the direction of propagation of the wave is always in the direction given by $\vec{E} \times \vec{H}$ *i.e.*, the direction of Poynting vector.

Units of S $\quad \vec{S} = \vec{E} \times \vec{H} = \dfrac{\text{Volts}}{\text{Length}} \times \dfrac{\text{Current}}{\text{Length}} = \dfrac{\text{Power}}{\text{Area}}$

$$= \left[V\,m^{-1} \right] \left[A\,m^{-1} \right] = VA\ m^{-2} = Js^{-1}\ m^{-2} = Wm^{-2}$$

The S.I unit of Poynting vector is (Wm^{-2}) or Watt per square metre. *The Poynting vector measures electrical power per unit area.*

If we consider a plane polarised electro-magnetic wave travelling along the Z-axis and take the electric vector $\vec{E}$ along the X-axis, E_x, then magnetic vector $\vec{H}$ will be along the Y-axis, H_y because in an *E.M.* wave electric and magnetic vectors are at right angles to each other and also at right angles to the direction of propagation of the *E.M.* wave. ·

∴   Poynting vector $\vec{S} = \vec{E} \times \vec{H} = \hat{i}\ E_x \times \hat{j}\ H_y = \hat{k}\ E_x\ H_y$

Taking magnitudes only $S = E_x\ H_y$

Thus *poynting vector measures the flow of electric energy per unit time per unit area held perpendicular to the direction of propagation of the electro-magnetic wave. It is also called the flux vector or power flux.*

(*b*) **PoyntingTheorem.** As the electromagnetic wave propagates from one point to another, there is a transfer of electromagnetic energy.

Maxwell's curl equations state

$$\vec{\nabla} \times \vec{E} = -\frac{\partial \vec{B}}{\partial t} = -\mu \frac{\partial \vec{H}}{\partial t} \qquad \qquad ...(i)$$

and $$\vec{\nabla} \times \vec{H} = \vec{J} + \frac{\partial \vec{D}}{\partial t} = \vec{J} + \varepsilon \frac{\partial \vec{E}}{\partial t} \qquad \qquad ...(ii)$$

Taking the scalar product of equation (*i*) with $\vec{H}$ and of equation (*ii*) with $\vec{E}$, we have

$$\vec{H} \cdot (\vec{\nabla} \times \vec{E}) = -\mu \frac{\partial \vec{H}}{\partial t} \cdot \vec{H} = -\frac{1}{2}\mu \frac{\partial H^2}{\partial t} \qquad \qquad ...(iii)$$

and $$\vec{E} \cdot (\vec{\nabla} \times \vec{H}) = \vec{E} \cdot \vec{J} + \vec{E} \cdot \varepsilon \frac{\partial \vec{E}}{\partial t} = \vec{E} \cdot \vec{J} + \frac{1}{2}\varepsilon \frac{\partial E^2}{\partial t} \qquad \qquad ...(iv)$$

Subtracting equation (*iii*) from equation (*iv*), we have

$$\vec{E} \cdot (\vec{\nabla} \times \vec{H}) - \vec{H} \cdot (\vec{\nabla} \times \vec{E}) = \vec{E} \cdot \vec{J} + \frac{1}{2}\varepsilon \frac{\partial E^2}{\partial t} + \frac{1}{2}\mu \frac{\partial H^2}{\partial t}$$

$$= \vec{E} \cdot \vec{J} + \frac{1}{2}\frac{\partial}{\partial t}[\varepsilon E^2 + \mu H^2] \qquad \qquad ...(v)$$

Now $\vec{A} \cdot (\vec{\nabla} \times \vec{B}) - \vec{B} \cdot (\vec{\nabla} \times \vec{A}) = \vec{\nabla} \cdot (\vec{B} \times \vec{A}) = -\vec{\nabla} \cdot (\vec{A} \times \vec{B})$

Equation (*v*) can, therefore, be put as

$$-\vec{\nabla} \cdot (\vec{E} \times \vec{H}) = \vec{E} \cdot \vec{J} + \frac{\partial}{\partial t}\left(\frac{\varepsilon E^2}{2} + \frac{\mu H^2}{2}\right)$$

But $\vec{E} \times \vec{H} = \vec{S}$ the Poynting vector

∴ $$\vec{\nabla} \cdot \vec{S} + \frac{\partial}{\partial t}\left(\frac{\varepsilon E^2}{2} + \frac{\mu H^2}{2}\right) = -\vec{E} \cdot \vec{J} \qquad \qquad ...(vi)$$

Integrating equation (*vi*) over a volume V bounded by the closed surface, we have

$$\iiint\limits_{V} \vec{\nabla} \cdot \vec{S}\ dV + \frac{\partial}{\partial t}\iiint\limits_{V}\left(\frac{\varepsilon E^2}{2} + \frac{\mu H^2}{2}\right) dV = -\iiint\limits_{V} \vec{E} \cdot \vec{J}\ dV \qquad \qquad ...(vii)$$

According to Gauss's divergence theorem in vector analysis

$$\iint \vec{S} . d\vec{A} = \iiint_V \vec{\nabla} . \vec{S}\, dV \qquad\qquad ...(vii)\,(a)$$

where $d\vec{A}$ is a small area element of the surface.

Substituting the above value of $\iiint_V \vec{\nabla} . \vec{S}\, dV$ in Equation (vii), we get

$$\iint \vec{S} . d\vec{A} + \frac{\partial}{\partial t} \iiint_V \left(\frac{\varepsilon E^2}{2} + \frac{\mu H^2}{2} \right) dV = - \iiint_V \vec{E} . \vec{J}\, dV \qquad\qquad ...(viii)$$

Now $\iint \vec{S} . d\vec{A}$ = Flow of energy per unit time across the boundary of the volume V.

$\dfrac{\partial}{\partial t} \iiint_V \left(\dfrac{\varepsilon E^2}{2} + \dfrac{\mu H^2}{2} \right) dV$ = Rate of change of total energy (Electric + magnetic) of the electromagnetic field.

$-\iiint \vec{E} . \vec{J}\, dV$ = work done by the field on the source because $\vec{E} . \vec{J}$ is the energy consumed per unit volume due to Joule heating.

Equation $(viii)$ is the statement of Poynting theorem. It gives the law of conservation of energy.

In free space $\vec{J} = 0$ and equation $(viii)$ becomes

$$\iint \vec{S} . d\vec{A} = - \frac{\partial}{\partial t} \iiint_V \left(\frac{\varepsilon E^2}{2} + \frac{\mu H^2}{2} \right) dV \qquad\qquad ...(ix)$$

This equation shows that the flow of energy per unit time across the boundary of the closed volume is equal to the rate of change of total energy of the electromagnetic field.

Equation of Continuity. Again substituting in Eq. (ix)

$$\iint \vec{S} . d\vec{A} = \iiint_V \vec{\nabla} . \vec{S}\, dV \text{ from Eq } (vii)\,(a)$$

and $\left(\dfrac{\varepsilon E^2}{2} + \dfrac{\mu H^2}{2} \right) = U_E + U_M = U$

where U_E is electric energy per unit volume, U_M the magnetic energy per unit volume and U the total energy per unit volume, we have

$$\iiint_V \vec{\nabla} . \vec{S}\, dV = - \iiint_V \frac{\partial}{\partial t} U\, dV$$

or $\qquad \iiint_V \vec{\nabla} . \vec{S}\, dV + \iiint_V \frac{\partial}{\partial t} U\, dV = 0$

which gives $\vec{\nabla} . \vec{S} + \dfrac{\partial U}{\partial t} = 0$.

This is called the *equation of continuity*

Q. 8.20. The electric and magnetic fields are varying sinusoidally in time as

$$E = E_0 \sin \omega t \text{ and } \vec{H} = H_0 \sin \omega t \cdot$$

Show that the average value of Poynting vector

$$<S> = \frac{\vec{E_0}}{\sqrt{2}} \times \frac{\vec{H_0}}{\sqrt{2}} = E_{r.m.s.} \times H_{r.m.s.} = \frac{1}{2} (\vec{E_0} \times \vec{H_0}).$$

(Kerala U. 2001; P.U., 1996, 1994, 1992, 1990; Pbi.U.,1990)

Ans. Average value of Poynting vector. The average value of Poynting vector *is defined as the average over one complete period of the wave*. If T is the time period of the wave, then

$$<S> = \frac{1}{T} \int_0^T (\vec{E} \times \vec{H}) \, dt$$

$$= \frac{1}{T} \int_0^T (\vec{E_0} \sin \omega t) \times (\vec{H_0} \sin \omega t) \, dt$$

$$= \frac{1}{T} (\vec{E_0} \times \vec{H_0}) \int_0^{2\pi/\omega} \sin^2 \omega t \, dt$$

$$= \frac{\omega}{2\pi} (\vec{E_0} \times \vec{H_0}) \int_0^{2\pi/\omega} \frac{1 - \cos 2\omega t}{2} \, dt$$

$$= \frac{\omega}{4\pi} (\vec{E_0} \times \vec{H_0}) \left[t - \frac{\sin 2\omega t}{2\omega} \right]_0^{2\pi/\omega} \qquad \left[\because \left\{ t - \frac{\sin 2\omega t}{2\omega} \right\}_0^{2\pi/\omega} = \frac{2\pi}{\omega} \right]$$

$$= \frac{\vec{E_0} \times \vec{H_0}}{2} = \frac{\vec{E_0}}{\sqrt{2}} \times \frac{\vec{H_0}}{\sqrt{2}} = \frac{1}{2} (\vec{E_0} \times \vec{H_0}) = \vec{E}_{r.m.s.} \times \vec{H}_{r.m.s.}$$

Q. 8.21. Show that for a plane electromagnetic wave

(i) The average value of Poynting vector

$$S_{AV} = \frac{1}{2} c\varepsilon E_0^2 = \frac{1}{2} c\mu H_0^2$$

OR

Find the average value of Poynting vector of a plane harmonic wave in a medium of absolute permittivity ϵ_0.

(Pbi.U. 2008)

(ii) The flow of energy in a homogeneous isotropic medium is in the direction of wave propagation.

(P.U. 2002, 2001, 1999; Gharwal U. 2000; H.P.U., 1996, 1995)

Ans. (i) Average value of Poynting vector. Consider a plane electromagentic wave travelling along the Z-axis with its electric and magnetic vectors E_x and H_y given by

$$E_x = E_0 \sin \frac{2\pi}{\lambda} (ct - z)$$

and

$$H_y = H_0 \sin \frac{2\pi}{\lambda} (ct - z)$$

For such a wave

$$\frac{E_0}{H_0} = \frac{E_x}{H_y} = \mu c$$

As the electric and magnetic vectors are in the *same phase* the ratio of the magnitudes of the two vectors at any time can be put in the form

$$\frac{|\vec{E}|}{|\vec{H}|} = \mu c$$

The electric vector $\vec{E}$ and the magnetic vector $\vec{H}$ being at right angles to each other, if $\hat{n}$ is a *unit normal* in the dirction at right angles to both, then $\hat{n}$ is a *unit vector* in the direction of propagation of the wave and the direction of the cross product $(\hat{n} \times \vec{E})$ is the same as that of $\vec{H}$.

$$\text{Now} \quad |\vec{H}| = \frac{|\vec{E}|}{\mu c}.$$

$$\therefore \qquad \vec{H} = \frac{\hat{n} \times \vec{E}}{\mu c}$$

Poynting vector $\vec{S} = \vec{E} \times \vec{H} = \dfrac{\vec{E} \times (\hat{n} \times \vec{E})}{\mu c}$

But $\quad \vec{E} \times (\hat{n} \times \vec{E}) = \hat{n} (\vec{E} . \vec{E}) - \vec{E} (\vec{E} . \hat{n})$

Now $\vec{E} . \vec{E} = E^2$ and $\vec{E} . \hat{n} = 0$ because $\vec{E}$ and $\hat{n}$ are at right angles to each other.

$$\therefore \qquad \vec{S} = \frac{E^2}{\mu c} \hat{n} = \frac{\varepsilon c}{\varepsilon \mu c^2} E^2 \hat{n} = \varepsilon c E^2 \hat{n} \qquad \left[\because c^2 = \frac{1}{\varepsilon \mu} \right]$$

Hence average value of Poynting vector

$$< \vec{S} > = \varepsilon c < E^2 > \hat{n} \qquad \qquad \text{...(i)}$$

but $\quad < E^2 > = E_0^2 < \left[\sin \dfrac{2\pi}{\lambda} (ct - z) \right]^2 > = \dfrac{E_0^2}{2}$

$$\therefore \qquad < \vec{S} > = \frac{1}{2} c \varepsilon E_0^2 \hat{n} \qquad \qquad \text{...(ii)}$$

The magnitude of the average Poynting vector

$$S_{AV} = \frac{1}{2} c \varepsilon E_0^2 \qquad \qquad \text{...(iii)}$$

Average Poynting vector in terms of H_0. As stated above

$$\frac{E_0}{H_0} = \mu c \quad \text{or} \quad E_0 = H_0 \mu c$$

$$\therefore \qquad S_{AV} = \frac{1}{2} c \varepsilon E_0^2 = \frac{1}{2} c \varepsilon \mu^2 c^2 H_0^2 = \frac{1}{2} \frac{c^3 \mu}{\frac{1}{\varepsilon \mu}} H_0^2$$

$$= \frac{1}{2} \frac{c^3 \mu}{c^2} H_0^2 = \frac{1}{2} c \mu H_0^2$$

For air or free space

$$S_{AV} = \frac{1}{2} c \varepsilon_0 E_0^2 = \frac{1}{2} c \mu_0 H_0^2$$

$\therefore$ The average value of poynting vector of a plane harmonic wave in a medium of absolute permittivity ϵ_0 is $\qquad S_{AV} = \dfrac{1}{2} c \epsilon_0 E_0^2$

$S_{AV} = I$ is known as the *intensity of the electromagnetic wave.*

(ii) **Flow of energy is in the direction of wave propagation.** It has been proved in (ii) above that

$$< \vec{S} > = c \varepsilon \frac{E_0^2}{2} \hat{n}$$

but $\qquad c\varepsilon = \dfrac{1}{Z}$ $\qquad \left[\because Z = \sqrt{\dfrac{\mu}{\varepsilon}} \text{ as proved in Eq. (iv) } \textbf{Q.8.38 } \dfrac{1}{Z} = \sqrt{\dfrac{\varepsilon}{\mu}} = \dfrac{\varepsilon}{\sqrt{\mu\varepsilon}} = \varepsilon c \right]$

where Z is the impedance of the medium to electromagnetic waves and

$$\frac{E_0}{\sqrt{2}} = E_{rms} \quad \text{or} \quad \frac{E_0^{\,2}}{2} = E_{rms}^2$$

$$\therefore \qquad <\vec{S}> = \frac{E_{rms}^{\,2}}{Z}\,\hat{n}$$

As $\dfrac{E_{rms}^{\,2}}{Z}$ represents energy and $\hat{n}$ is a unit vector in direction of propagation of the wave the flow of energy in a plane wave is in the direction of wave propagation.

Q. 8.22. Show that the energy flux for a travelling plane ploarised E.M wave in free space is simply the energy density times the velocity of the wave.(*P.U.* 2003 ; *Pbi.U.* 2005, 2000, 1995)

Ans. Energy flux in a travelling wave. Consider a plane polarised electromagnetic wave travelling in the +Z direction with electric and magnetic field vectors E_x and H_y respectively, then

$$\vec{E} = E_x\,\hat{i} + E_y\,\hat{j} + E_z\,\hat{k} = E_x\,\hat{i} \qquad\qquad [E_y = E_z = 0]$$

and $\qquad \vec{H} = E_x\,\hat{i} + H_y\,\hat{j} + H_z\,\hat{k} = H_y\,\hat{j} \qquad\qquad [H_x = H_z = 0]$

Let $\qquad E_x = E_0 \sin \dfrac{2\pi}{\lambda}(vt - z) = E_0 \sin(\omega t - kz)$

where $\qquad k = \dfrac{2\pi}{\lambda}$ and $\omega = \dfrac{2\pi v}{\lambda}$

Now energy flux is given by the magnitude of the Poynting vector

$$S = |\vec{S}| = |\vec{E} \times \vec{H}| = |E_x \times H_y|$$

$$= E_0 H_0 \sin^2(\omega t - k z)$$

Energy density $\quad U = \dfrac{1}{2}\varepsilon E^2 + \dfrac{1}{2}\mu H^2 = \dfrac{1}{2}\varepsilon E^2 + \dfrac{1}{2}\varepsilon E^2 \qquad \left[\because \dfrac{1}{2}\varepsilon E^2 = \dfrac{1}{2}\mu H^2 \right]$

$$= \varepsilon E^2 = \varepsilon E_0^{\,2} \sin^2(\omega t - k z)$$

Hence $\qquad \dfrac{S}{U} = \dfrac{E_0 H_0}{\varepsilon E_0^{\,2}} = \dfrac{H_0}{\varepsilon E_0}$

But $\qquad \dfrac{H_0}{E_0} = \sqrt{\dfrac{\varepsilon}{\mu}}$

$$\frac{S}{U} = \frac{1}{\varepsilon}\sqrt{\frac{\varepsilon}{\mu}} = \frac{1}{\sqrt{\varepsilon\mu}} = v \text{ the velocity of the wave}$$

or $\qquad\qquad S = Uv$

Hence energy flux for a travelling wave in free space is equal to the product of total energy density and velocity of the wave.

Q. 8.23. (*i*) **Show that in a conductor the average value of Poynting vector is given by**

$$S_{AV} = \frac{1}{2} E_0 H_0 \cos 45° = \frac{1}{2} H_0^2 (R_e Z_e).$$

(*Pbi.U.* 2007, 2003, 1991; *G.N.D.U.* 2000)

(*ii*) **Relate Poynting vector to the impedance of a dielectric to** *e.m.* **waves**   (*P.U.* 2006)

Ans. (*i*) **Average value of Poynting vector.** The average value of Poynting vector is given by

$$\vec{S}_{AV} = \frac{1}{T} \int_0^T (\vec{E} \times \vec{H}) \, dt$$

Now, for a plane polarised electro magnetic wave travelling in the +Z direction

$$E = E_x \hat{i} \text{ and } H = H_y \hat{j}$$

$$\therefore \qquad S_{AV} = \frac{1}{T} \int_0^T E_x H_y \, dt \qquad\qquad\qquad\qquad ...(i)$$

The expression for E_x and H_y for a plane polarised electro magnetic wave through a conductor are

$$E_x = E_0 e^{i\omega t - \gamma z} \text{ and } H_y = H_0 e^{i(\omega t - \phi) - \gamma z} \qquad \text{[See Eq. (iv) Q. 8.29]}$$

where $\qquad\qquad \phi = \frac{\pi}{4}.$ $\qquad\qquad$ [For proof see **Q 8.40** Eq. (*ii*) and Eq. (*iv*) (*a*)]

At the point $z = 0$, $E_x = E_0 e^{i\omega t}$ and $H_y = H_0 e^{i(\omega t - \phi)}$

The real part of these expressions are

$$E_x = E_0 \cos \omega t \quad \text{and} \quad H_y = H_0 \cos (\omega t - \phi)$$

$$\therefore S_{AV} = \frac{1}{T} \int_0^T E_0 \cos \omega t \, H_0 \cos (\omega t - \phi) \, dt = \frac{E_0 H_0}{T} \int_0^T \cos \omega t \cos (\omega t - \phi) \, dt$$

Now $\quad \cos (\omega t - \phi) \cos \omega t = (\cos \omega t \cos \phi - \sin \omega t \sin \phi) \cos \omega t$

$$= \cos^2 \omega t \cos \phi - \cos \omega t \sin \omega t \sin \phi = \frac{1}{2} (1 + \cos 2 \omega t) \cos \phi - \frac{1}{2} \sin 2 \omega t \sin \phi$$

$$= \frac{1}{2} \cos \phi + \frac{1}{2} \cos \phi \cos 2 \omega t - \frac{1}{2} \sin \phi \sin 2\omega t$$

Again $\qquad \int_0^T \cos 2 \omega t \, dt = 0 \text{ and } \int_0^T \sin 2 \omega t \, dt = 0$

or $\frac{1}{2} \cos \phi \int_0^T \cos 2 \omega t \, dt = 0$ and $\frac{1}{2} \sin \phi \int_0^T \sin \omega t \, dt = 0$

$$\therefore \qquad \int_0^T \cos \omega t \cos (\omega t - \phi) \, dt = \frac{1}{2} \cos \phi \int_0^T dt = \frac{T}{2} \cos \phi$$

and $\qquad S_{AV} = \frac{E_0 H_0}{T} \cdot \frac{T}{2} \cos \phi = \frac{1}{2} E_0 H_0 \cos \phi = \frac{1}{2} E_0 H_0 \cos 45°$

$$= \frac{1}{2} E_0 H_0 \cos \frac{\pi}{4}$$

Since impedance of the conductor (or dielectric) $Z_e = \dfrac{E_x}{H_y} = \dfrac{E_0 e^{(i\omega t - \gamma z)}}{H_0 e^{i(\omega t - \phi) - \gamma z}} = \dfrac{E_0}{H_0} e^{i\phi}$

or
$$Z_e = \frac{E_0}{H_0} (\cos \phi + i \sin \phi)$$

$\therefore$ Real part of $Z_e = R_e \, Z_e = \dfrac{E_0}{H_0} \cos \phi$

or $E_0 \cos \phi = H_0 \, (R_e \, Z_e)$

$\therefore$ $S_{AV} = \dfrac{1}{2} H_0^2 \, (R_e \, Z_e)$

This equation relates the Poynting vector S_{AV} to the (real part of) impedance of the dielectric Z_e.

Q. 8.24. **If a 500 watt laser beam is concentrated by a lens into a cross-sectional area of 10^{-10} m², find the value of Poynting vector and the amplitude of electric field.**

Given $\varepsilon_0 = 9 \times 10^{-12}$ S.I. units.   (*H.P.U.*, 1996)

Ans. Poynting vector $\vec{S} = \dfrac{\text{Power}}{\text{area}} = \dfrac{500}{10^{-10}}$

$$= 5 \times 10^{12} \text{ W/m}^2$$

Now average poynting vector

$$S_{AV} = \frac{1}{2} c \varepsilon \, E_0^2$$

or   Electric field $E_0 = \left[\dfrac{2 \, S_{AV}}{c \varepsilon} \right]^{\frac{1}{2}}$

Now $\varepsilon = 9 \times 10^{-12}$ Farad/m and $c = 3 \times 10^8$ ms^{-1}

$\therefore$ $E_0 = \left(\dfrac{2 \times 5 \times 10^{12}}{3 \times 10^8 \times 9 \times 10^{-12}} \right)^{1/2}$

$$= 0.609 \times 10^8 \text{ volt/m}$$

The dimensions of $E_0 = \left[\dfrac{W}{m^2} \times \dfrac{s}{m} \times \dfrac{m}{\text{Farad}} \right]^{\frac{1}{2}}$

$$= \left[\frac{W \times s}{m^2} \times \frac{\text{Volt}}{\text{coulomb}} \right]^{1/2} = \left[\frac{\text{Coulomb} \times \text{volt} \times \text{volt}}{m^2 \times \text{coulomb}} \right]^{\frac{1}{2}}$$

$$= \text{Volt / metre.}$$

Exercise. *If a 2 KW laser beam is concentrated by a lens into a cross-sectional area of 10^{-10} m², find the value of Poynting vector and the amplitude of electric field.*   (*P.U.* 2000, 1999)

Ans. $\vec{S} = 2 \times 10^{13}$ W/m² ; $E_0 = 1.21 \times 10^8$ volt/m

Q. 8.25. Calculate the value of Poynting vector for a 100 watt lamp at a distance of 1.0 m from it.   (*H.P.U.* 2000, 1999; *Pbi.U.* 2002; *G.N.D.U.*, 1993)

Ans. Total average power emitted by the lamp

$$P = 100 \text{ watts}$$

The light emitted by the lamp will spread out in the form of a sphere, the radius of which is equal to the distance from it.

$\therefore$ Radius of sphere $r = 1.0$ m

Let S_{AV} denote the average Poynting vector over the surface of the sphere, then

$$S_{AV} = \frac{P}{4\pi r^2} = \frac{100}{4\pi \times (1)^2} = 7.958 \text{ Wm}^{-2}$$

Q. 8.26. A radio station radiates power of 10^5 watts uniformly over a hemisphere concentric with the station. Find the magnitude of Poynting vector and the amplitude of electric and magnetic fields at a point 10 kms from the radio station. $\varepsilon_0 = 9 \times 10^{-12}$ farads per metre and $\mu_0 = 4\pi \times 10^{-7}$ henry per metre. **[G.N.D.U. 2004 (similar)]**

Ans. Total average power radiated by the radio station

$$P = 10^5 \text{ W}$$

Radius of the hemisphere = 10 kms = 10^4 m

Let S_{AV} denote the average Poynting vector over the surface of the hemisphere, then

$$S_{AV} = \frac{P}{2\pi r^2} = \frac{10^5}{2\pi \times 10^8} = 1.592 \times 10^{-4} \text{ W/m}^2$$

For free space, average Poynting vector

$$S_{AV} = \frac{1}{2} c \varepsilon_0 E_0^2$$

$$\therefore \quad E_0 = \left[\frac{2S_{AV}}{c\varepsilon_0}\right]^{\frac{1}{2}} = \left[\frac{2 \times 1.592 \times 10^{-4}}{3 \times 10^8 \times 9 \times 10^{-12}}\right]^{\frac{1}{2}}$$

$$= 0.3434 \text{ volt/metre}$$

Now $$\vec{H_0} = \frac{\vec{B_0}}{\mu_0} = \frac{\vec{E_0}}{\mu_0 c}$$

or $$H_0 = \frac{E_0}{\mu_0 c} = \frac{0.3434}{4\pi \times 10^{-7} \times 3 \times 10^8} = 9.1 \times 10^{-4} \text{ ampere turns per metre}$$

Exercise : *A radio station is broadcasting at 10^9 watts. Find the value of poynting vector at a location 30 km away.* **(P.U. 2006)**

Hint: Assuming that the power spreads over hemisphere of radius 30km

$$S_{AV} = \frac{P}{2\pi r^2} = \frac{10^9}{2\pi \times 900 \times 10^6}$$

$$= 0.177 \text{ W/m}^2$$

Q. 8.27. Calculate the value of Poynting vector on the surface of the sun if the power radiated by it is 3.8×10^{26} watts (radius of sun = 7×10^8) m. If the average distance between the sun and the earth is 1.5×10^{11} m show that the value of solar constant is 1.34×10^3 watts/ m^2 sec. or 2 cals/cm^2 minute **(G.N.D.U. 2009; H.P.U. 2001; M.D.U. 2000)**

Ans. Total average power radiated by the sun

$$P = 3.8 \times 10^{26} \text{ W}$$

Radius of the sun $r = 7 \times 10^8$ m

Let S_{AV} denote the average Poynting vector over the surface of the sun, then

$$S_{AV} = \frac{P}{4\pi r^2} = \frac{3.8 \times 10^{26}}{4\pi \times (7 \times 10^8)^2} = 6.17 \times 10^7 \text{ W/m}^2$$

Solar constant is the average solar energy received per second per square metre of earth's surface = Average value of Poynting vector on the surface of earth

Average distance between sun and earth

$$R = 1.5 \times 10^{11} \text{ m}$$

$\therefore$ Solar constant = Average value of Poynting vector on the surface of earth (S_E)

or   Solar constant $S_E = \dfrac{3.8 \times 10^{26}}{4 \, \pi \, (1.5 \times 10^{11})^2} = 1.34 \times 10^3 \text{ Watt/m}^2 = \dfrac{1.34 \times 10^3 \times 60}{10^4}$

$$= 8.04 \text{ Joules /cm}^2/\text{min}$$

$$= \dfrac{8.04}{4.2} \text{ cal/cm}^2/\text{min}$$

$$= \text{ nearly 2 cals /cm}^2/\text{min}$$

Q. 8.28. On the surface of earth the energy received is 1.33 kW/m^2 from the sun. Calculate the electric field associated with sunlight (on surface of earth) assuming that it is essentially monochromatic (λ = 6000Å). Given ε = 9 × 10^{-12} S.I. units.

Ans. Energy received per second per square metre on the surface of the earth = Average value of Poynting vector on Earth's surface

Now $S_{AV} = \dfrac{1}{2} \, c \varepsilon \, E_0^2$

$\therefore$ $E_0 = \left(\dfrac{2 S_{AV}}{c \varepsilon} \right)^{\frac{1}{2}} = \left(\dfrac{2 \times 1.33 \times 10^3}{3 \times 10^8 \times 9 \times 10^{-12}} \right)^{\frac{1}{2}}$

$$= 992.6 \text{ volt/m}$$

Q. 8.29. (a) Derive the equation for a plane polarised electromagnetic wave in a conducting medium having finite values of μ, ε, and σ. Find the solution for the electric field vector.

(b) (i) Show that in a conducting medium the displacement current leads the conduction current by 90°.   *(Pbi.U. 2006; H.P.U. 2001, 1999; G.N.D.U. 2000, 2007, 1995, 1993)*

(ii) The amplitude of the wave gets attenuated with distance inside the conducting medium.

(H.P.U., 1993)

Ans. Wave equation. For a plane polarised electromagnetic wave travelling along the direction of Z-axis and polarised in such a way that $E_y = 0$ and $H_x = 0$, the wave equations for a conducting medium are

For E_x $\dfrac{\partial^2 E_x}{\partial z^2} = \mu \varepsilon \, \dfrac{\partial^2 E_x}{\partial t^2} + \mu \sigma \, \dfrac{\partial E_x}{\partial t}$ ...(i)

For H_y $\dfrac{\partial^2 H_y}{\partial z^2} = \mu \varepsilon \, \dfrac{\partial^2 H_y}{\partial t^2} + \mu \sigma \, \dfrac{\partial H_y}{\partial t}$ ...(ii)

For proof see **Q. 8.13.** Eq. (xvii) and (xviii).

Comparing these equations to those for a non-conducting dielectric medium we find that in this case an additional resistive or dissipative term $\mu \sigma \, \dfrac{\partial E_x}{\partial t} \left[\text{or} \ \ \mu \sigma \, \dfrac{\partial H_y}{\partial t} \right]$ is present. This term allows the conduction current to flow. It is similar to the diffusion term and the product $\dfrac{1}{\mu \sigma}$ is called the *magnetic diffusivity* and has the dimensions of $L^2 \, T^{-1}$.

In our discussion we shall confine ourselves to the wave equation for the electric field vector as it plays a very important role in electromagnetic waves.

Equation (*i*) can be put in the form

$$\frac{\partial^2 E_x}{\partial z^2} - \mu\sigma \frac{\partial E_x}{\partial t} - \mu\varepsilon \frac{\partial^2 E_x}{\partial t^2} = 0 \qquad \qquad ...(iii)$$

Assuming that time variation of E_x is simple harmonic, *i.e.*

$$E_x = E_0 e^{i\omega t}, \text{ we get}$$

$$\frac{\partial E_x}{dt} = i\omega E_0 e^{i\omega t} = i\omega E_x$$

and $\quad \dfrac{\partial^2 E_x}{\partial t^2} = -\omega^2 E_0 e^{i\omega t} = -\omega^2 E_x$

Substituting in (*iii*), we have

$$\frac{\partial^2 E_x}{\partial z^2} - (i\omega\mu\sigma - \omega^2\mu\varepsilon) E_x = 0$$

or $\qquad \dfrac{\partial^2 E_x}{\partial z^2} - \gamma^2 E_x = 0 \qquad\qquad$ [where $\gamma^2 = i\omega\mu\sigma - \omega^2\mu\varepsilon$]

The solution of this equation is

$$E_x = E_0 e^{i\omega t} e^{-\gamma z} = E_0 e^{(i\omega t - \gamma z)} \qquad\qquad ...(iv)$$

The solution with the term $e^{+\gamma z}$ is ignored because we are considering the propagation of the wave along the positive direction of Z-axis. The value of γ will depend upon the nature of the medium.

If the medium is a dielectric only displacement currents due to the factor $\mu\varepsilon \dfrac{\partial E_x}{\partial t^2}$ will flow. If the medium is a conductor the ohmic current due to the factor $\mu\sigma \dfrac{\partial E_x}{\partial t}$ will be dominant.

(b) (i) Displacement current leads the conduction current. The ratio of the conduction current density to the displacement current density is given by

$$\frac{\text{Conduction current density}}{\text{Displacement current density}} = \frac{J}{\dfrac{\partial D}{\partial t}}$$

Now $J = \sigma E_x$, as the components E_y and E_z are zero and $\dfrac{\partial D}{\partial t} = \dfrac{\partial}{\partial t}(\varepsilon E_x)$

$$\therefore \quad \frac{J}{\dfrac{\partial D}{\partial t}} = \frac{\sigma E_x}{\dfrac{\partial}{\partial t}(\varepsilon E_x)} = \frac{\sigma E_x}{\dfrac{\partial}{\partial t}(\varepsilon E_0 e^{i\omega t})} = \frac{\sigma E_x}{i\omega\varepsilon E_x} = \frac{\sigma}{i\omega\varepsilon}$$

The presence of the factor i in the denominator indicates that the displacement current is *ahead* of the conduction current *i.e.*, leads *by a phase angle of* $\dfrac{\pi}{2}$ (90°).

(ii) Amplitude of the wave. For a conductor the conduction current is very much greater than the displacement current *i.e.*,

$$\frac{J}{\dfrac{\partial D}{\partial t}} >> 1$$

or $\qquad\qquad\qquad\qquad \sigma \gg \omega\varepsilon$

or $\qquad\qquad\qquad\qquad \omega\mu\sigma \gg \omega^2\mu\varepsilon$

$\therefore\ \omega^2\mu\varepsilon$ can be neglected as compared to $\omega\mu\sigma$ in the expression for γ^2. Hence in such a case

$$\gamma^2 = i\omega\mu\sigma$$

To evaluate γ, let $\qquad \gamma = \alpha + i\beta$

$\therefore \qquad\qquad\qquad \gamma^2 = \alpha^2 - \beta^2 + 2i\alpha\beta = i\omega\mu\sigma$

Comparing real and imaginary terms

$$\alpha^2 - \beta^2 = 0 \qquad\qquad\qquad\qquad\qquad\qquad ...(iv)$$

and $\qquad\qquad\qquad\qquad \alpha\beta = \dfrac{\omega\mu\sigma}{2} \qquad\qquad\qquad\qquad\qquad ...(v)$

From (iv) $\alpha = \beta$ and from (v) $\alpha^2 = \beta^2 = \dfrac{\omega\mu\sigma}{2}$

or $\qquad\qquad\qquad\qquad \alpha = \beta = \left[\dfrac{\omega\mu\sigma}{2}\right]^{\frac{1}{2}}$

$\therefore \qquad\qquad\qquad\qquad \gamma = \left[\dfrac{\omega\mu\sigma}{2}\right]^{\frac{1}{2}} (1 + i)$

Hence $\qquad E_x = E_0\, e^{i\omega t}\, e^{-(1 + i)\left(\frac{\omega\mu\sigma}{2}\right)^{\frac{1}{2}} z}$

$$= E_0\, e^{-\left(\frac{\omega\mu\sigma}{2}\right)^{\frac{1}{2}} z}\, e^{i\left[\omega t - \left(\frac{\omega\mu\sigma}{2}\right)^{\frac{1}{2}} z\right]}.$$

This represents a progressive wave in the positive Z-direction with an amplitude decaying with

the factor $e^{-\left(\frac{\omega\mu\sigma}{2}\right)^{\frac{1}{2}} z}$. The presence of z in the power of the external term indicates that the amplitude of the wave gets attenuated with distance inside the conducting medium. The dimensions of the product $\omega\mu\sigma$ are L^{-2}.

Q. 8.30. Define skin depth of a conductor in case of E.M. wave. On what factors does it depend and how? Prove that as frequency increases skin depth decreases. What is its value for a perfect conductor ? Explain skin effect and the electric shielding properties of a conductor.

(P.U. 2009, 2007, 2006, 2005, 2004, 2003, 2001, 2000, 1999; H.P.U 2000, 1992; Pbi.U. 2006, 2005, 2000, 1991; G.N.D.U. 2007, 2004, 1999, 1995; Cal. U. 2003)

Ans. Skin depth. *Skin depth is defined as the distance in the conductor over which the electric*

field vector of the wave propagation in the medium decays to $\dfrac{1}{e}$ *times its value at the surface.*

For a wave propagating in the Z-direction the amplitude of the electric field vector is given by

$$E_0\, e^{-\left(\frac{\omega\mu\sigma}{2}\right)^{\frac{1}{2}} z}$$

where ω is the angular frequency of the wave, μ the permeability and σ the conductivity of the

conductor in which the wave is propagating. Therefore, over a distance $z = \left(\dfrac{2}{\omega\mu\sigma}\right)^{\frac{1}{2}}$ the amplitude

decays to

$$E_0 e^{-1} = \frac{1}{e} E_0$$

$\therefore$ The distance $\left(\dfrac{2}{\omega\mu\sigma}\right)^{\frac{1}{2}} = \delta$ is called the *skin depth* or *penetration depth*.

Factors (*i*) Effect of frequency. The skin depth $\delta = \left(\dfrac{2}{\omega\mu\sigma}\right)^{\frac{1}{2}}$. It is a function of ω *i.e.*, the frequency of the electromagnetic waves. Thus skin depth is inversely proportional to the square root of the frequency. Therefore for waves of high frequency δ is small and for those of low frequency δ is large. *Hence as frequency increases, skin depth decreases and vice-versa.*

Skin effect. The value of skin depth δ is very small for very high frequency electromagnetic waves. This is why high frequency electromagnetic waves experience a very high impedance and travel a very small distance in a conductor and hence the electric field is confined to a very small region on the surface of the conductor. This is called *skin effect.*

Skin effect for a perfect conductor. For a perfect conductor $\sigma = \infty$, skin depth $\delta = 0$.

Shielding by a conductor. The comparative value of δ for *Cu*, $\mu = \mu_0 = 4\,\pi \times 10^{-7}$ henry/m and $\sigma = 5.8 \times 10^7$ siemens/ metre for various values of frequency are

Frequency 60 Hertz	$\delta = 9$ mm
Frequency 1 Mega Hertz	$\delta = 6.6 \times 10^{-5}$ metre
Frequency 30,000 M Hertz	$\delta = 3.8 \times 10^{-7}$ metre

This is clear from the above data that high frequency electromagnetic waves have a very small skin depth *i.e.*, the conductor acts as *shield* for high frequency electro magnetic waves.

The above data also shows that it is possible that a medium which behaves as a good conductor for low frequency electro magnetic waves may behave as a bad conductor for high frequency electro magnetic waves.

(*ii*) **Permeability.** Skin depth is inversely proportional to the square root of the permeability of the medium.

(*iii*) **Conductivity.** Skin depth is inversely proportional to the square root of conductivity of the medium.

Q. 8.31 (*a*). When is a medium a conductor or a dielectric?

OR

Distinguish between perfect dielectric and perfect conductor. A good conductor like Cu behaves like a good conductor up to a frequency of 10^{16} hertz, the frequency of ultra violet light and as a dielectric at a frequency of 10^{20} hertz, the frequency of X-rays. Justify.(*G.N.D.U.* 2009)

(*b*) **Show that conduction current is not applicable for an e.m. wave in a medium of $\sigma = 10^{-15}$ mho per metre and $\epsilon = 10^{-11}$ Farad per metre.**   (*G.N.D.U.* 2008)

Ans (*a*). Distinction between a conductor and dielectric. The ratio of the *ohmic current density* $\vec{J}$ to the *displacement current density* $\delta\vec{D}/\delta t$ for a medium having finite values of μ, ε and σ is given by

$$\frac{J}{\delta D/\delta t} = \frac{\sigma}{\omega\varepsilon}$$

which is a non-dimensional quantity. It is possible to represent the medium by a simple circuit shown in Fig. 8.7. The total current is divided into two branches containing a capacitance of reactance $\dfrac{1}{\omega\varepsilon}$ ohm-metre and the other branch containing a resistance of conductivity σ siemens/metre.

If σ is large (*i.e.,* resistivity is small) a large fraction of the current flows through the σ branch and the medium is said to be **conducting.**

If $\omega\varepsilon$ is large *i.e.,* $\dfrac{1}{\omega\varepsilon}$ the capacitance reactance is small, most of the current flows as displacement current through the reactance branch and the medium is said to behave as a **dielectric.**

If $\dfrac{\sigma}{\omega\varepsilon} > 100$, the conduction current dominates and the medium is a conductor, On the other

hand if $\dfrac{\omega\varepsilon}{\sigma} > 100$, the displacement current dominates

and the medium is a dielectric.

In between these values the medium is said to be a *quasi or semi-conductor.*

For copper $\sigma = 5.8 \times 10^7$ siemens/metre

and $\varepsilon = \varepsilon_0 = 9 \times 10^{-12}$ Farads/metre

$$\therefore \qquad \frac{\sigma}{\omega\varepsilon} = \frac{\sigma}{2\pi\varepsilon\,\text{frequency}} = \frac{10^{18}}{\text{frequency}}$$

For a frequency less than 10^{16} Hertz, $\dfrac{\sigma}{\omega\varepsilon} > 100$

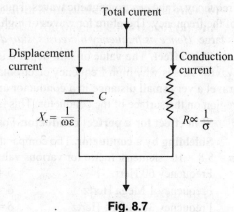

Fig. 8.7

For a frequency greater than 10^{20} Hertz, $\dfrac{\omega\varepsilon}{\sigma} > 100$

So upto a frequency 10^{16} Hertz, the frequency of ultra violet light, copper is a conductor and above a frequency of 10^{20} Hertz, the frequency of X–rays, copper behaves like a dielectric. This is why X–rays can travel a distance of many wavelengths in copper.

(*b*) For an insulating medium having σ of the order of 10^{-15} siemens per metre and ε of the order

of 10^{-11} Farads per metre $\dfrac{\omega\varepsilon}{\sigma} > 10^4\,\omega$ or $\dfrac{J}{\delta D/\delta t} = \dfrac{\sigma}{\omega\varepsilon} = \dfrac{10^{-4}}{\omega}$.

so that conduction current J is almost negligible at all frequencies. In other words, conduction current is not applicable for *e.m.* waves in such an insulating medium.

Exercise. *Distinguish between dielectric and conducting media. What happens to the amplitude of an e.m. wave when it travels through each of them?* (*Pbi.U.* 2008)

Hint: (*i*) For distinction between dielectric and conducting medium see **Q. 8.31** under the head '**Distinction between a conductor and dielectric**'.

(*ii*) For what happens to the amplitude of an e.m. wave when it travels through each of then see **Q. 8.29 (*b*) (*ii*)** under the head '**Amplitude of the wave**'

Q. 8.32. Calculate the skin depth for a frequency of 10^6.

Given $\mu = 4\pi \times 10^{-7}$ Am^{-2} and $\sigma = 5.8 \times 10^7$ mho m^{-1} (*H.P.U.,* 1993)

Ans.   Skin depth $\delta = \left(\dfrac{2}{\omega\mu\sigma}\right)^{\frac{1}{2}}$

Here $\omega = 2\pi \times 10^6$, $\mu = 4\pi \times 10^{-7}$ Am^{-2} and $\sigma = 5.8 \times 10^7$ mho m^{-1}

$$\therefore \qquad \delta = \left(\frac{2}{2\pi \times 10^6 \times 4\pi \times 10^{-7} 5.8 \times 10^7}\right)^{\frac{1}{2}} = 6.61 \times 10^{-5}\,\text{m}$$

Exercise. *Calculate the skin depth for copper with* $\mu = 4\pi \times 10^{-7}\,Am^{-2}$ *and* $\sigma = 5.8 \times 10^7\,mho\,m^{-1}$ *at a frequency of 60Hz*   *(Pbi.U. 2008)*

Hint: $\delta = \left(\dfrac{2}{\omega\mu\sigma}\right)^{1/2} = \left[\dfrac{2}{2\pi \times 60 \times 4\pi \times 10^{-7} \times 5.8 \times 10^7}\right]^{1/2} = 8.53 \times 10^{-3}\,m = 8.53\,mm.$

Q. 8.33 (a). Calculate the frequency at which the skin depth in sea water is one metre. Given that conductivity $\sigma = 4.3$ mhos/m and permeability $\mu = 4\pi \times 10^{-7}$ henries per meter.

(H.P.U., 1994)

(b) Why is radio-communication difficult for sub-marines?   *(G.N.D.U 2008)*

Ans. (a) Here $\sigma = 4.3$ mho/m, $\mu = \mu_0 = 4\pi \times 10^{-7}\,Hm^{-1}$

Now   Skin depth $\delta = \left(\dfrac{2}{\omega\mu\sigma}\right)^{\frac{1}{2}}$

or $\delta^2 = \dfrac{2}{\omega\mu\sigma} = \dfrac{2}{2\pi\nu\mu\sigma}$

$\therefore$ $\nu = \dfrac{2}{2\pi\mu\sigma\delta^2} = \dfrac{2}{2\pi \times 4\pi \times 10^{-7} \times 4.3 \times 1^2}$

$= 5.891 \times 10^4\,Hz = 58.91\,KHz.$

(b) It has been proved in part (a) that at a frequency 58.91 KHz the skin depth of sea water is

only 1 metre. This means that the energy of the e.m. wave is reduced to $\dfrac{1}{e}$ *i.e.*, about 43% at a depth

of only one metre. At a greater depth where submarines normally ply the energy of the *e.m.* wave will be still less. So a radio transmitter of high power (or wattage) is required to communicate with the submarine even at very low frequencies of the order of 60KHz. This is why radio-communication is difficult for submarines.

Q. 8.34. Calculate the skin depth for a frequency 10^{10} Hz for silver. Given.

$\sigma = 2 \times 10^7\,Sm^{-1}$ **and** $\mu = 4\pi \times 10^{-7}\,Hm^{-1}$

(Pbi.U. 2007, 2003, 2001, 1999; H.P.H. 2002, 2000; P.U. 2001)

Ans. Given $\sigma = 2 \times 10^7\,Sm^{-1}$ $\mu = \mu_0 = 4\pi \times 10^{-7}\,Hm^{-1}$

$\omega = 2\pi \times 10^{10}$

Now skin depth $\delta = \left[\dfrac{2}{\omega\mu\sigma}\right]^{1/2} = \left[\dfrac{2}{2\pi \times 10^{10} \times 4\pi \times 10^{-7} \times 2 \times 10^7}\right]^{1/2}$

$= 1.12 \times 10^{-6}\,m$

Q. 8.35. Discuss the behaviour of copper to e.m. waves of frequency 0.5×10^{16} Hz and 7.0×10^{20} Hz. Given the conductivity of coper $\sigma = 5.8 \times 10^7$ mho m^{-1} and permittivity $\varepsilon = 9 \times 10^{-12}\,C^2/Nm^2$.   *(P.U. 2008; G.N.D.U., 1993)*

Ans. Here $\sigma = 5.8 \times 10^7$ mho m^{-1}, $\varepsilon = 9 \times 10^{-12}\,C^2/Nm^2$

(i) For frequency $\nu = 0.5 \times 10^{16}$ Hz

or $\omega = 2\pi \times 0.5 \times 10^{16}$

$\dfrac{\sigma}{\omega\varepsilon} = \dfrac{5.8 \times 10^7}{2\pi \times 0.5 \times 10^{16} \times 9 \times 10^{-12}} = 205$

As $\dfrac{\sigma}{\omega\varepsilon} > 100$, the conduction current dominates. Hence for frequency 0.5×10^{16} copper is a conductor.

(ii) For frequency $\nu = 7 \times 10^{20}$ Hz, $\omega = 2\pi \times 7 \times 10^{20}$

$$\therefore \quad \frac{\sigma}{\omega\varepsilon} = \frac{5.8 \times 10^7}{2\pi \times 2 \times 10^{20} \times 9 \times 10^{-12}} = 0.00147$$

As $\dfrac{\sigma}{\omega\varepsilon} < 100$, the displacement current dominates. Hence for a frequency 7×10^{20}, copper is a dielectric.

Exercise. *Given that for a medium $\sigma = 0.1\ Sm^{-1}$, $\mu_r = 1$, and $\varepsilon_r = 40$. Does the medium behave as a conductor or dielectric at*

(i) *50 KHz and* (ii) *10^4 MHz ? Explain.* (P.U. 2001)

Hint (i) $\dfrac{\sigma}{\omega\varepsilon} = \dfrac{0.1}{2\pi \times 50 \times 10^3 \times 40 \times 9 \times 10^{-12}} = 885$. It will behave as a conductor because

$$\frac{\sigma}{\omega\varepsilon} > 100$$

(ii) $\dfrac{\sigma}{\omega\varepsilon} = \dfrac{0.1}{2\pi \times 10^{10} \times 40 \times 9 \times 10^{-12}} = 0.004425$. It will behave as a dielectric because

$$\frac{\sigma}{\omega\varepsilon} < 100.$$

Q. 8.36. Explain the behaviour of pure water to e.m. waves of frequency 200 Hz and 100 MHz, when dielectric constant of water is 80 and $\sigma = 10^{-3}$ mho m^{-1}. (G.N.D.U., 1994)

Ans. For water $k = \dfrac{\varepsilon}{\varepsilon_0} = 80$ or $\varepsilon = 80\ \varepsilon_0$

$\sigma = 10^{-3}$ mho m^{-1} and $\varepsilon_0 = 9 \times 10^{-12}$ farad m^{-1}

$$\therefore \quad \frac{\sigma}{\varepsilon} = \frac{10^{-3}}{80 \times 9 \times 10^{-12}} = 1.39 \times 10^6$$

(i) For frequency $\nu = 200\ Hz$, $\omega = 2\pi \times 200$

$$\frac{\sigma}{\omega\varepsilon} = \frac{1.39 \times 10^6}{2\pi \times 200} = 1106$$

As $\dfrac{\sigma}{\omega\varepsilon}$ is greater than 100, water acts as a conductor.

(ii) For frequency $\nu = 100$ MHz, $\omega = 2\pi \times 10^8$

$$\therefore \quad \frac{\sigma}{\omega\varepsilon} = \frac{1.39 \times 10^6}{2\pi \times 10^8} = 0.0022$$

As $\dfrac{\sigma}{\omega\varepsilon}$ is less than 100, water acts as dielectric.

Q. 8.37. Show that high frequency electromagnetic waves propagate only a small distance in a conductor. (P.U. 2008; Pbi.U. 2007; G.N.D.U. 2002, 1994; Cal. U. 2003; H.P.U., 1995, 1991)

Ans. Propagation of electromagnetic waves through a conductor. The equation of a progressive wave travelling in the $+Z$ direction in a conducting medium is given by

$$E_x = E_0 \, e^{\left(\frac{-\omega\mu\sigma}{2}\right)^{\frac{1}{2}} z} \, e^{i\left[\omega t - \left(\frac{\omega\mu\sigma}{2}\right)^{\frac{1}{2}} z\right]}$$

Therefore, the phase velocity of the wave is given by

$$v = \frac{\omega}{k} \text{ where } k = \left(\frac{\omega\mu\sigma}{2}\right)^{\frac{1}{2}} \text{ the coefficient of } z \text{ in the second term.}$$

Also $\left(\dfrac{\omega\mu\sigma}{2}\right)^{\frac{1}{2}} = \dfrac{1}{\delta}$ where δ is the skin depth.

$$\therefore \qquad\qquad v = \frac{\omega}{k} = \omega\,\delta$$

If λ_c is the wavelength of electromagnetic waves in the conductor and v the corresponding frequency, then

velocity $\quad v = \nu$ (frequency) $\lambda_c = \omega\,\delta = 2\,\pi\,\nu\,\delta$

$$\therefore \qquad\qquad \lambda_c = 2\,\pi\,\delta \qquad \text{or (skin depth)} = \frac{\lambda c}{2\pi}$$

The amplitude of the electromagnetic wave is given by

$$E_0 \, e^{-\left(\frac{\omega\mu\sigma}{2}\right)^{\frac{1}{2}} z} = e^{-\frac{z}{\delta}}$$

The amplitude will, therefore, fall to 1% of its surface value in a distance z, given by

$$0.01 = e^{-\frac{z}{\delta}}$$

or $\qquad\qquad \log_e 0.01 = -\dfrac{z}{\delta}$

or $\qquad\qquad z = -\,\delta \log_e 0.01 = -\,\delta \times 2.3 \times \log_{10} 0.01$

$$= 4.6\,\delta = \frac{4.6}{2\,\pi} \times \lambda_c = \frac{3}{4}\,\lambda_c.$$

Hence electromagnetic waves effectively travel about three quarters of a wavelength in a conductor. The amplitude of the wave falls below 1% thereafter and the wave becomes ineffective. Hence it cannot be detected.

High frequency waves. For high frequency waves λ_c the wavelength of electromagnetic waves in a conductor is a very small quantity. Hence such waves propagate only a small distance in a conductor.

Q. 8.38. Define characteristic impedance of a dielectric to electromagnetic waves and calculate the characteristic (intrinsic) impedance of free space. Show that electric and magnetic fields are in phase and the value of electric field vector at any instant is 377 times the value of magnetic field vector in free space.

(*H.P.U.* 2003, 2002, 2001, 2000, 1999; *P.U.* 2007, 2006, 2003, 2001, 2000, 1999, 1995; *G.N.D.U.* 2006, 2002, 1995; *M.D.U.* 2002 ; *Pbi.U.* 2007, 2006, 1999)

Ans. Impedance of a dielectric. For an electric circuit impedance Z is defined as the ratio of the voltage applied to the circuit to the current flowing through it, *i.e.*,

$$Z = \frac{V}{I}$$

In the case of electromagnetic waves, the ratio of the *instantaneous electric field intensity* to the *instantaneous magnetic field intensity* gives the impedance of the dielectric medium.

$\because$ For electromagnetic waves $Z = \dfrac{E}{H}$

The dimensions of E are $\dfrac{\text{volts}}{\text{metre}}$ and of H are $\dfrac{\text{amperes}}{\text{metre}}$.

$$\therefore \quad \frac{E}{H} = \frac{\text{volts}}{\text{metre}} \times \frac{\text{metre}}{\text{ampere}} = \frac{\text{volts}}{\text{ampere}} = \text{ohms}$$

For a plane polarised electromagnetic wave travelling in the positive direction of Z-axis and polarised such that $E_y = 0$ and $H_x = 0$, the wave equation for electric and magnetic field vectors are

$$E_x = E_0 \sin \frac{2\pi}{\lambda} (vt - z) \qquad \qquad \text{...}(i)$$

and

$$H_y = H_0 \sin \frac{2\pi}{\lambda} (vt - z) \qquad \qquad \text{...}(ii)$$

Now $\qquad -\mu \dfrac{\partial H_y}{\partial t} = \dfrac{\partial E_x}{\partial z}$ $\qquad\qquad\qquad\qquad\qquad$ **[Q. 8.13 Eq. (ix)]**

From (i) $\qquad \dfrac{\partial E_x}{\partial z} = -E_0 \dfrac{2\pi}{\lambda} \cos \dfrac{2\pi}{\lambda} (vt - z)$

From (ii) $\qquad \dfrac{\partial H_y}{\partial t} = H_0 \dfrac{2\pi v}{\lambda} \cos \dfrac{2\pi}{\lambda} (vt - z)$

$$\therefore \qquad -\mu H_0 \frac{2\pi v}{\lambda} = -E_0 \frac{2\pi}{\lambda}$$

or $\qquad\qquad \mu H_0 v = E_0$

or $\qquad\qquad \dfrac{E_0}{H_0} = \mu v$

but $\qquad\qquad v = \sqrt{\dfrac{1}{\mu \varepsilon}}$

$$\therefore \qquad \frac{E_0}{H_0} = \frac{\mu}{\sqrt{\mu \varepsilon}} = \sqrt{\frac{\mu}{\varepsilon}} \qquad \qquad \text{...}(iii)$$

$$\therefore \qquad Z = \frac{E_0}{H_0} = \frac{E_x}{H_y} = \sqrt{\frac{\mu}{\varepsilon}} \qquad \qquad \text{...}(iv)$$

or $\qquad\qquad \left| \dfrac{\vec{E}}{\vec{H}} \right| = \sqrt{\dfrac{\mu}{\varepsilon}}$

Electric and magnetic fields are in phase As the ratio $\left| \dfrac{\vec{E}}{\vec{H}} \right|$ is real and positive, the electric and magnetic fields are in phase with each other.

$\therefore$ Characteristic impedance of a dielectric medium to electromagnetic waves $Z = \sqrt{\dfrac{\mu}{\varepsilon}}$

Characteristic impedance of free space. For free space

$$\mu_0 = 4\pi \times 10^{-7} \text{ kg m coulomb}^2$$

$$\varepsilon_0 = \frac{1}{36\pi \times 10^9} \text{ coulomb}^2 \text{ sec}^2/\text{kg m}^3 \quad \text{and}$$

$$\therefore \quad \sqrt{\frac{\mu_0}{\varepsilon_0}} = \sqrt{4\pi \times 10^{-7} \times 36\pi \times 10^9} = 377 \text{ ohm}$$

$\vec{E} = 377 \, \vec{H}$. In free space $\left|\dfrac{\vec{E}}{\vec{H}}\right| = \sqrt{\dfrac{\mu_0}{\varepsilon_0}} = 377 \quad \text{or} \quad \left|\vec{E}\right| = 377 \left|\vec{H}\right|$

∴   In free space the value of $\left|\vec{E}\right|$ the electric field vector at any instant is 377 time, the value of $\left|\vec{H}\right|$ the magnetic field vector.

Q. 8.39. Show that electrostatic energy per unit volume in an electromagnetic wave is equal to magnetic energy per unit volume and total energy density in the dielectric = ε_r × total energy density in free space.

Ans. Electrostatic and magnetic energy. It has been proved in **Q. 8.14 Eq.** (*vi*) that

$$\frac{E_x}{H_y} = \sqrt{\frac{\mu}{\varepsilon}}$$

$$\therefore \qquad \varepsilon E_x^2 = \mu H_y^2$$

or

$$\frac{1}{2}\varepsilon E_x^2 = \frac{1}{2}\mu H_y^2$$

Now the quantity εE_x^2 has the dimensions of $\dfrac{\text{Farads}}{\text{metre}} \times \dfrac{\text{volts}^2}{\text{metre}^2} = \dfrac{\text{Joule}}{\text{metre}^3}$ *i.e.*, Energy per unit volume.

The quantity $\dfrac{1}{2}\varepsilon E_x^2$ is the electrostatic energy per unit volume for a dielectric and $\dfrac{1}{2}\mu H_y^2$ is the magnetic energy per unit volume. The total energy is the sum of the two energies and is given by

$$U_{\text{Total}} = \frac{1}{2}\varepsilon E_x^2 + \frac{1}{2}\mu H_y^2$$

$$= \varepsilon E_x^2 \qquad \qquad \left[\because \frac{1}{2}\mu H_y^2 = \frac{1}{2}\varepsilon E_x^2\right]$$

$$= \varepsilon_0 \, \varepsilon_r \, E_x^2 .$$

For a plane polarised electromagnetic wave travelling in the +Z direction

$$E_x = E$$

$$\therefore \qquad U_{\text{Total}} = \varepsilon_0 \, \varepsilon_r \, E^2 = \varepsilon_r \, (\varepsilon_0 E^2)$$

where $\varepsilon_0 E^2$ is the total energy per unit volume in free space.

Hence total energy density in dielectric = ε_r × Total energy density in free space.

8.40. (*a*) Calculate the impedance of a conducting medium to electromagnetic waves. Name the constants which determine the characteristic impedance of a medium. What is the phase diffience between electric and magnetic field vectors?

(*Cal. U.* 2003; *Pbi. U.* 2003; *H.P.U.* 2003; *P.U.* 2009, 2000, 1995)

(b) Show that (i) when the impedance is small the conductor behaves as a short circuit to the electric field and

(ii) For a conductor the magnetic field energy increases as the electric field energy decreases.

(P.U. 2006; G.N.D.U., 1993)

Ans. (a) Impedance of a conducting medium to electromagnetic waves. For an electromagnetic wave in a dielectric or a loss less medium, impedance $\vec{Z} = \dfrac{\vec{E_x}}{\vec{H_y}} = \sqrt{\dfrac{\mu}{\varepsilon}}$ and is a real quantity. In this case $\vec{E_x}$ and $\vec{H_y}$ are in the *same phase i.e.,* E_x and H_y have their maximum (or zero) value at the *same time*.

Now consider a conducting medium having finite values of μ, ε and σ. The wave equation in such a medium is given by

$$E_x = E_0 \, e^{i\omega t} \, e^{-\gamma z} \qquad \qquad ...(i)$$

where

$$\gamma = (1+i)\left(\dfrac{\omega\mu\sigma}{2}\right)^{\frac{1}{2}}$$

Let the impedance of the conducting medium be a complex quantity for the sake of generality. This implies that there is a *phase difference* between the two field vectors. If we assume that H_y lags behind E_x by a phase angle ϕ, then

$$H_y = H_0 \, e^{i(\omega t - \phi)} \, e^{-\gamma z} \qquad \qquad ...(ii)$$

For a plane polarised electromagnetic wave travelling in the positive direction of Z-axis and polaised so that $E_y = 0$ and $H_x = 0$, we have

$$-\mu \dfrac{\partial H_y}{\partial t} = \dfrac{\partial E_x}{\partial z} \qquad \qquad ...(iii)$$

From (i),

$$\dfrac{\partial E_x}{\partial z} = -\gamma \, E_0 \, e^{i\omega t} \, e^{-\gamma z} = -\gamma E_x$$

From (ii),

$$-\mu \dfrac{\partial H_y}{\partial t} = -\mu i \omega H_0 \, e^{(i\omega t - \phi)} \, e^{-\lambda z} = -\mu i \omega H_y$$

Substituting in (iii), we have

$$-\gamma E_x = -\mu i \omega H_y$$

$$\therefore \qquad Z_c = \dfrac{E_x}{H_y} = \dfrac{i\omega\mu}{\gamma} = \dfrac{i(\omega\mu)}{(1+i)\left(\dfrac{\omega\mu\sigma}{2}\right)^{\frac{1}{2}}} \qquad \qquad ...(iii)\,(a)$$

$$= \dfrac{i(1-i)}{(1+i)(1-i)}\left(\dfrac{2\omega\mu}{\sigma}\right)^{\frac{1}{2}} = \dfrac{(1+i)}{2}\left(\dfrac{2\omega\mu}{\sigma}\right)^{\frac{1}{2}}$$

$$= \dfrac{1+i}{\sqrt{2}}\left(\dfrac{\omega\mu}{\sigma}\right)^{\frac{1}{2}} = \left(\dfrac{\omega\mu}{\sigma}\right)^{\frac{1}{2}}\left(\dfrac{1}{\sqrt{2}} + \dfrac{i}{\sqrt{2}}\right) \qquad \qquad ...(iv)$$

But $\dfrac{1}{\sqrt{2}} + \dfrac{i}{\sqrt{2}} = \cos 45° + i \sin 45° = e^{i\phi}$ where $\phi = 45° = \dfrac{\pi}{4}$ radian $\qquad ...(iv)\,(a)$

$$\therefore \qquad \vec{Z_c} = \left(\frac{\omega\mu}{\sigma}\right)^{\frac{1}{2}} e^{i\phi} = \left(\frac{\omega\mu}{\sigma}\right)^{\frac{1}{2}} e^{i\pi/4}$$

Hence magnitude of $\vec{Z_c}$ or Real part of Z_c.

$$|\vec{Z_c}| = \left(\frac{\omega\mu}{\sigma}\right)^{\frac{1}{2}} \qquad \qquad \qquad ...(v)$$

and its direction is $45° = \dfrac{\pi}{4}$ radian behind the direction of $\vec{E_x}$.

Phase difference between $\vec{E}$ and $\vec{H}$. As magnetic field vector H_y lags behind electric field vector E_x by a phase angle ϕ, and $\phi = \dfrac{\pi}{4}$ the magnetic field $\vec{H}$ lags behind electric field vector $\vec{E}$ by an angle $\pi/4$. Thus phase difference between electric and magnetic field vector is $\pi/4$.

Exercise. *Show that magnetic field in e.m. waves lags behind electric field by $\dfrac{\pi}{4}$ while propagating in a conducting medium.* (P.U. 2008)

Hint: See above under the head **phase difference between $\vec{E}$ and $\vec{H}$**.

Z_c **in terms of** ω, ε **and** σ. Now

$$\frac{\omega\mu}{\sigma} = \frac{\omega}{\sigma} \cdot \frac{\varepsilon}{\varepsilon} \cdot \frac{\varepsilon_0}{\varepsilon_0} \cdot \frac{\mu_0}{\mu_0} \cdot \mu$$

$$= \frac{\omega\varepsilon}{\sigma} \cdot \frac{\varepsilon_0}{\varepsilon} \cdot \frac{\mu}{\mu_0} \cdot \frac{\mu_0}{\varepsilon_0}$$

$$\therefore \qquad \left(\frac{\omega\mu}{\sigma}\right)^{\frac{1}{2}} = \sqrt{\frac{\omega\varepsilon}{\sigma}} \cdot \sqrt{\frac{\mu_r}{\varepsilon_r}} \cdot \sqrt{\frac{\mu_0}{\varepsilon_0}}$$

where μ_r is the permeability of the conductor and ε_r the permittivity relative to vacuum. But

$$\sqrt{\frac{\mu_0}{\varepsilon_0}} = 377 \text{ ohms}.$$

$$\therefore \qquad |\vec{Z_c}| = \left(\frac{\omega\mu}{\sigma}\right)^{\frac{1}{2}} = 377 \sqrt{\frac{\mu_r}{\varepsilon_r}} \cdot \sqrt{\frac{\omega\varepsilon}{\sigma}}$$

We can also write relation (*iv*) as

$$\vec{Z_c} = R + iX = \frac{1+i}{\sqrt{2}} \left(\frac{\omega\mu}{\sigma}\right)^{\frac{1}{2}} = \left(\frac{\omega\mu}{2\sigma}\right)^{\frac{1}{2}} + i\left(\frac{\omega\mu}{2\sigma}\right)^{\frac{1}{2}}$$

where R is the real part of complex impedance $\vec{Z_c}$ and X the imaginary part.

Constants which determine impedance. The impedance of a dielectric medium $Z = \sqrt{\dfrac{\mu}{\varepsilon}}$. Therefore, the impedance of a dielectric is

(*i*) directly proportional to the square root of permeability μ.

and (*ii*) inversely proportional to the square root of permittivity ε.

The impedance of a conducting medium $Z_c = \sqrt{\dfrac{\omega \mu}{\sigma}}$. Therefore, the impedance of a conducting medium is

(*i*)   directly proportional to the square root of frequency ω and permeability μ and (*ii*) inversely proportional to the square root of conductivity σ.

(*b*) (*i*) **When the impedance is small or zero.** For a wavelength $\lambda = \dfrac{1}{10}$ metre, frequency $v = $ 3000 M Hertz

$$\frac{\omega \mu}{\sigma} \text{ for } Cu = 2.9 \times 10^{-9} \text{ and } \mu_r = \varepsilon_r = 1$$

$$Z_c = 377 \times (2.9 \times 10^{-9})^{\frac{1}{2}} = 0.02 \text{ ohm}$$

For $\sigma = \infty$, $Z_c = 0$ and the electric field vector $E_x = 0$. When σ is high Z_c is small.

Hence when Z_c is small or zero the σ is high or infinite and therefore, conductor behaves as a short circuit to the electric field. Due to this there is a large conduction current which increases the magnetic field.

(*ii*) **Increase in magnetic field energy.** For a dielectric

$$Z = \frac{E_x}{H_y} = \sqrt{\frac{\mu}{\varepsilon}}$$

$$\therefore \qquad \frac{1}{2} \varepsilon E_x^2 = \frac{1}{2} \mu H_y^2$$

i.e., Electric field energy density = Magnetic field energy density

For a conductor $Z_c = \dfrac{E_x}{H_y} = \left(\dfrac{\omega \mu}{\sigma}\right)^{\frac{1}{2}}$ [From equation v]

$$\therefore \qquad \frac{\dfrac{1}{2} \varepsilon E_x^2}{\dfrac{1}{2} \mu H_y^2} = \frac{\dfrac{1}{2} \varepsilon \omega \mu}{\dfrac{1}{2} \mu \sigma} = \frac{\varepsilon \omega}{\sigma}$$

or $\qquad \dfrac{\text{Magnetic field energy density}}{\text{Electric field energy density}} = \dfrac{\sigma}{\varepsilon \omega}$

But the expression $\dfrac{\sigma}{\varepsilon \omega}$ measures the ratio of conduction current density to displacement current density. For a conductor the conduction current density is large. Hence in a conductor the magnetic field energy dominates the electric field energy *i.e.,* the magnetic field energy increases and the electric field energy decreases.

Q. 8.41. (*a*) **Show that**

(*i*) **Refractive index of a dielectric** $n = \sqrt{\varepsilon_r}$. **Hence find the refractive index of one medium with respect to another.**

(*ii*) **Refractive index of a conducting medium**

$$n = (1 - i) \left(\frac{\sigma}{2 \omega \varepsilon_0} \right)^{\frac{1}{2}}.$$

Ans. (*i*) **Refractive index of dielectric.** The refractive index of a medium

$$n = \frac{\text{velocity of light in vacuum or free space}}{\text{velocity of light in the medium}}$$

$$= \frac{c}{v} = \sqrt{\frac{\mu \varepsilon}{\mu_0 \varepsilon_0}} = \sqrt{\varepsilon_r \, \mu_r}$$

but μ_r is very nearly equal to unity *i.e.*, $\mu_r = \dfrac{\mu}{\mu_0} = 1$

Hence $\qquad n = \sqrt{\varepsilon_r}$

Relation between refractive index and impedance.

Again $\dfrac{Z \text{ free space}}{Z \text{ dielectric}} = \dfrac{\sqrt{\dfrac{\mu_0}{\varepsilon_0}}}{\sqrt{\dfrac{\mu}{\varepsilon}}} = \dfrac{\sqrt{\dfrac{\varepsilon}{\varepsilon_0}}}{\sqrt{\dfrac{\mu}{\mu_0}}} = \sqrt{\dfrac{\varepsilon_r}{\mu_r}}$

$$= \sqrt{\varepsilon_r} \qquad\qquad\qquad \left[\because \frac{\mu}{\mu_0} = \mu_r = 1 \right]$$

$\therefore$ For a dielectric $n = \sqrt{\varepsilon_r}$

$$= \frac{Z \text{ free space}}{Z \text{ dielectric}}$$

If, however, the electromagnetic waves travel from a medium of refractive index n_1 and impedance Z_1 to a medium of refractive index n_2 and impedance Z_2, then

$$n_1 = \frac{Z \text{ free space}}{Z_1}, \ n_2 = \frac{Z \text{ free space}}{Z_2}$$

$\therefore$ Refractive index of one medium with respect to another $n = \dfrac{n_2}{n_1} = \dfrac{Z_1}{Z_2}.$

(*ii*) **Refractive index of a conductor.** If Z_2 is the impedance of a conductor and Z_1 of free space then

$$Z_2 = | \vec{Z}_2 | = i \frac{(\omega \mu)}{\gamma} = \frac{i (\omega \mu)}{(1 + i) \left(\dfrac{\omega \mu \sigma}{2} \right)^{\frac{1}{2}}} \qquad\qquad \text{[See Eq. (}iii\text{) (}a\text{) Q. 8.40]}$$

and
$$Z_1 = |\vec{Z_1}| = \left(\frac{\mu_0}{\varepsilon_0}\right)^{\frac{1}{2}}$$

$$\therefore \quad n = \frac{Z_1}{Z_2} = \frac{\left(\frac{\mu_0}{\varepsilon_0}\right)^{\frac{1}{2}}(1+i)\left(\frac{\omega\mu\sigma}{2}\right)^{\frac{1}{2}}}{i(\omega\mu)}$$

Now
$$\frac{(1+i)}{i} = \frac{1}{i} + 1 = (1-i)$$

and
$$\left[\frac{\mu_0\,\omega\mu\sigma}{2\varepsilon_0\,\mu^2\,\omega^2}\right]^{\frac{1}{2}} = \frac{(\mu\,\mu_0)^{\frac{1}{2}}}{\mu}\left(\frac{\sigma}{2\omega\varepsilon_0}\right)^{\frac{1}{2}}$$

$$\therefore \quad n = \frac{(\mu\,\mu_0)^{1/2}}{\mu}(1-i)\left(\frac{\sigma}{2\omega\varepsilon_0}\right)^{\frac{1}{2}}$$

but $\dfrac{(\mu\,\mu_0)^{1/2}}{\mu}$ is very nearly equal to unity.

$$\therefore \quad n = (1-i)\left(\frac{\sigma}{2\omega\varepsilon_0}\right)^{\frac{1}{2}} = \left(\frac{\sigma}{2\omega\varepsilon_0}\right)^{\frac{1}{2}} - i\left(\frac{\sigma}{2\omega\,\varepsilon_0}\right)^{\frac{1}{2}}$$

Q. 8.42. (a) Explain the reflection and transmission of an electromagnetic wave incident normally on a plane between media of impedance Z_1 and Z_2. Find out the expressions for the reflection and transmission coefficients and express these in terms of the refractive index of the two media.

(*Meerut.U.* 2007; *P.U.* 2007, 2005, 2004, 2003, 2001; *G.N.D.U.*, 2008, 2006, 2004, 1993, 1991; *Pbi. U.*, 1993; *H.P.U.*, 1991)

(b) (i) Prove that a perfect conductor is a perfect reflector of electromagnetic waves.

(*P.U.* 2007, 2006; *G.N.D.U.*, 1995, 1994, 1993; *Pbi. U.*, 1995, 1993; *H.P.U.*, 1994)

(ii) There is a change of phase by π radian for a wave on reflection from a discontinuity of infinite conductance. Explain.   (*P.U.* 2006, 2002)

Ans. (a) Reflection and transmission of electromagnetic waves. Consider an electromagnetic wave incident normally on an infinite plane boundary separating two media of impedances Z_1 and Z_2. These impedances will be real for dielectric media and complex quantities for conducting media. The electric field vectors for the incident, reflected and transmitted waves are indicated as E_i, E_r and E_t and the corresponding values for the magnetic field vectors H_i, H_r and H_t respectively. The vector direction of $\vec{E_r} \times \vec{H_r}$ must be opposite to that of $\vec{E_i} \times \vec{H_i}$ to satisfy the energy flow condition of Poynting vector. Therefore, if the incident wave is travelling along the positive direction of Z-axis, the reflected wave will travel in the negative direction of Z-axis, *i.e.*, the incident wave will be reflected normally backward. If Z_2 is less than Z_1 it is the electric vector which is reversed and if Z_2 is greater than Z_1, the magnetic vector will be reversed. We are considering a case $Z_2 < Z_1$.

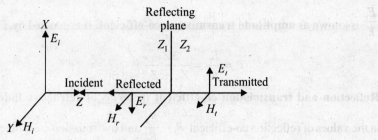

Fig. 8.8

According to boundary conditions from electromagnetic theory the components of field vectors $\vec{E}$ and $\vec{H}$ tangential or parallel to the boundary are continuous across the boundary.

$\therefore$ $\qquad\qquad$ $E_i + E_r = E_t$ $\qquad\qquad\qquad\qquad\qquad\qquad\qquad\qquad$ ...(i)

and $\qquad\qquad$ $H_i + H_r = H_t$ $\qquad\qquad\qquad\qquad\qquad\qquad\qquad\qquad$ ...(ii)

Again $\qquad$ $Z_1 = \dfrac{E_i}{H_i}, \; -Z_1 = \dfrac{E_r}{H_r}$ and $Z_2 = \dfrac{E_t}{H_t}$

or $\qquad\qquad$ $H_i = \dfrac{E_i}{Z_1}, \; H_r = -\dfrac{E_r}{Z_1}$ and $H_t = \dfrac{E_t}{Z_2}$

Substituting in (ii) we have

$$\frac{E_i}{Z_1} - \frac{E_r}{Z_1} = \frac{E_t}{Z_2}$$

or $\qquad\qquad$ $E_i - E_r = E_t \dfrac{Z_1}{Z_2}$ $\qquad\qquad\qquad\qquad\qquad\qquad\qquad$ ...(iii)

Dividing (i) by (iii), we have

$$\frac{E_i + E_r}{E_i - E_r} = \frac{Z_2}{Z_1} \qquad\qquad\qquad\qquad\qquad\qquad ...(iv)$$

By componendo and dividendo

$$\frac{E_r}{E_i} = \frac{Z_2 - Z_1}{Z_2 + Z_1} \qquad\qquad\qquad\qquad\qquad\qquad ...(v)$$

Adding 1 to both sides, we have

$$\frac{E_r}{E_i} + 1 = \frac{Z_2 - Z_1}{Z_2 + Z_1} + 1 \text{ or } \frac{E_r + E_i}{E_i} = \frac{2Z_2}{Z_2 + Z_1}$$

or $\qquad\qquad$ $\dfrac{E_t}{E_i} = \dfrac{2Z_2}{Z_2 + Z_1}$ $\qquad\qquad\qquad$ ...(vi) $[\because E_r + E_i = E_t]$

$\dfrac{E_r}{E_i}$ is known as **amplitude reflection co-efficient.** It is denoted by R and is given by

$$R = \frac{E_r}{E_i} = \frac{Z_2 - Z_1}{Z_2 + Z_1}$$

$\dfrac{E_t}{E_i}$ is known as **amplitude transmission co-efficient.** It is denoted by T and is given by

$$T = \frac{E_t}{E_i} = \frac{2Z_2}{Z_2 + Z_1}$$

Reflection and transmission co-efficient in terms of refractive index. For two dielectric media the values of reflection co-efficient $R = \dfrac{E_r}{E_i}$ and transmission co-efficient $T = \dfrac{E_t}{E_i}$ can also be put in terms of refractive indices of the two media.

From relation (*iv*), we have

$$\frac{E_i + E_r}{E_i - E_r} = \frac{Z_2}{Z_1} = \frac{n_1}{n_2}$$

$\therefore$ Reflection co-efficient $R = \dfrac{E_r}{E_i} = \dfrac{n_1 - n_2}{n_1 + n_2}$ ...(*vii*)

If n is the refractive index of the second medium with respect to the first, then $n = \dfrac{n_2}{n_1}$. Now, equation (*vii*) can be put as

$$R = \frac{1 - \dfrac{n_2}{n_1}}{1 + \dfrac{n_2}{n_1}} = \frac{1 - n}{1 + n}$$ ...(*vii*) (*a*)

Adding 1 to both sides of (*vii*), we have

$$\frac{E_r + E_i}{E_i} = \frac{E_t}{E_i} = \frac{2n_1}{n_1 + n_2}$$

$\therefore$ Transmission co-efficient $T = \dfrac{E_t}{E_i} = \dfrac{2n_1}{n_1 + n_2}$ ...(*viii*)

or $$T = \frac{2}{1 + \dfrac{n_2}{n_1}} = \frac{2}{1 + n}$$ ...(*viii*) (*a*)

Reflected energy co-efficient. The reflected energy co-efficient is given by

$$R_E = \frac{E_r H_r}{E_i H_i}$$

If the incident electro magnetic wave is travelling in air or free space and strikes a dielectric normally, then

$$\frac{E_i}{H_i} = \frac{E_r}{H_r} = Z_1 = \left(\frac{\mu_0}{\varepsilon_0}\right)^{\frac{1}{2}}$$

and $$\frac{E_t}{H_t} = Z_2 = \left(\frac{\mu}{\varepsilon}\right)^{\frac{1}{2}}$$

where μ is the permeability and ε the permittivity of the second medium.

$$\therefore \quad H_i = \left(\frac{\varepsilon_0}{\mu_0}\right)^{\frac{1}{2}} E_i ; \ H_r = \left(\frac{\varepsilon_0}{\mu_0}\right)^{\frac{1}{2}} E_r \text{ and } H_t = \left(\frac{\varepsilon}{\mu}\right)^{\frac{1}{2}} E_t$$

$$\therefore \quad \text{Reflected energy co-efficient } R_E = \frac{E_r H_r}{E_i H_i} = \frac{E_r \left(\dfrac{\varepsilon_0}{\mu_0}\right)^{\frac{1}{2}} E_r}{E_i \left(\dfrac{\varepsilon_0}{\mu_0}\right)^{\frac{1}{2}} E_i} = \frac{E_r^2}{E_i^2}$$

$$= \left(\frac{n_1 - n_2}{n_1 + n_2}\right)^2 = \left(\frac{1-n}{1+n}\right)^2$$

For an air glass interface $n_1 = 1$ and $n_2 = 1.5$, we have

$$R_E = \left(\frac{0.5}{2.5}\right)^2 = 0.04 = 4\% \qquad \qquad \text{...(ix)}$$

Transmitted energy co-efficient. The transmitted energy co-efficient is given by

$$T_E = \frac{E_t H_t}{E_i H_i} = \frac{E_t \left(\dfrac{\varepsilon}{\mu}\right)^{\frac{1}{2}} E_t}{E_i \left(\dfrac{\varepsilon_0}{\mu_0}\right)^{\frac{1}{2}} E_i} = \left(\frac{\varepsilon_r}{\mu_r}\right)^{\frac{1}{2}} \frac{E_t^2}{E_i^2}$$

For a non-magnetic substance $\mu_r = 1$. In such a case

$$n = \sqrt{\varepsilon_r}$$

$$\therefore \quad T_E = n \frac{E_t^2}{E_i^2} = n \left(\frac{2}{1+n}\right)^2 = \frac{4n}{(1+n)^2}$$

For an air glass interface $n = 1.5$, and we have

$$T_E = \frac{4 \times 1.5}{(1+1.5)^2} = \frac{6}{6.25} = 0.96 = 96\% \qquad \qquad \text{...(x)}$$

Exercise I. *of the first medium is free space, second medium is glass of refractive index 1.5 find the percentage value of R and T when e.m., waves travel from free space to glass.* (P.U. 2005)

Hint: Amplitude reflection co-efficient $R = \dfrac{1-n}{1+n} = \dfrac{1-1.5}{1+1.5} = -0.2$

Amplitude transmission co-efficient $T = \dfrac{2}{1+n} = \dfrac{2}{1+1.5} = 0.8$

Reflection energy co-efficient $R_E =$ See **Eq. (ix)**
Transmission energy co-efficient T_E see **Eq. (x)**.

(b) (i) Good conductors are good reflectors. If the wave is travelling in air and strikes a

perfect conductor of $\sigma = \infty$, then $Z_2 = \sqrt{\dfrac{\mu \omega}{\sigma}} = 0$ at normal incidence, and

$$R = \frac{E_r}{E_i} = \frac{Z_2 - Z_1}{Z_2 + Z_1} = -1$$

or $\qquad E_r = -E_i$

i.e., the wave is reflected completely.

In such a case $\qquad \dfrac{E_t}{E_i} = \dfrac{2Z_2}{Z_2 + Z_1} = 0$

i.e., there is no transmitted wave.

Thus good conductors are very good reflectors of electromagnetic waves. This is why light waves are very well reflected from polished metal surfaces. *In other words a perfect conductor is a perfect reflector of electromagnetic waves.*

(*ii*) **Phase change on reflection.** As proved above when reflection takes place from a discontinuity of infinite conduction $\dfrac{E_r}{E_i} = -1$, *i.e.,* the incident wave travels in the opposite direction as a fully reflected wave which implies a phase reversal or phase change of π-radian.

Q. 8.43. Calculate the characteristic impedance of copper to e.m. waves of wavelength 1m. Given conductivity of copper is 5.8×10^7 Sm^{-1}. What is the value for a perfect conductor?

(*H.P.U.,* 1995)

Ans. Wavelength λ = 1 m

∴ Frequency, $\nu = \dfrac{c}{\lambda} = 3 \times 10^8$ Hz

Characteristic impedance $\qquad Z_c = \left(\dfrac{\omega\mu}{\sigma}\right)^{\frac{1}{2}} e^{i\phi}$

$$= \left(\dfrac{\omega\mu}{\sigma}\right)^{\frac{1}{2}} (\cos\phi + i\sin\phi) \text{ where } \phi = \dfrac{\pi}{4}$$

Real part of $Z_c \qquad = \left(\dfrac{\omega\mu}{\sigma}\right)^{\frac{1}{2}} \cos\phi = \left(\dfrac{\omega\mu}{\sigma}\right)^{\frac{1}{2}} \cos\dfrac{\pi}{4}$

$$= \left(\dfrac{\omega\mu}{\sigma}\right)^{\frac{1}{2}} \dfrac{1}{\sqrt{2}} = \left(\dfrac{\omega\mu}{2\sigma}\right)^{\frac{1}{2}} = \left(\dfrac{2\pi\nu\mu}{2\sigma}\right)^{\frac{1}{2}}$$

$$= \left(\dfrac{\pi\nu\mu}{\sigma}\right)^{\frac{1}{2}} = \left(\dfrac{\pi\nu\mu_0\mu_r}{\sigma}\right)^{\frac{1}{2}}$$

Since copper is a good conductor, for it $\mu_r = 1$.

∴ Real part of impedance $R_e(Z_c) = \left(\dfrac{\pi\nu\mu_0}{\sigma}\right)^{\frac{1}{2}}$

Now $\qquad \mu_0 = 4\pi \times 10^{-7}$ Hm^{-1}

∴ $$R_e(Z_c) = \left[\dfrac{3.142 \times 3 \times 10^8 \times 4 \times 3.142 \times 10^{-7}}{5.8 \times 10^7}\right]^{\frac{1}{2}}$$

$$= 4.51 \times 10^{-3} \text{ ohm}$$

For a perfect conductor σ = ∞

∴ $\qquad Z_c = 0$

Q. 8.44. **Show that radar waves of frequency 1 MHz get reflected from metallic surface of the aeroplane for which $\mu = 4\pi \times 10^{-7}$ H/m and $\sigma = 5.8 \times 10^7$ mho/m.** *(P.U., 1996)*

Ans. Characteristic impedance of the metallic surface of the aeroplane

$$\text{Real part of } Z_c = \left(\frac{\pi \nu \mu_0 \mu_r}{\sigma}\right)^{\frac{1}{2}}$$ [For proof see **Q 8.43**]

For a metal $\mu_r = 1$

$\therefore$ $\text{Real part of } Z_c = \left(\frac{\pi \nu \mu_0}{\sigma}\right)^{\frac{1}{2}} = \left(\frac{3.142 \times 10^6 \times 4 \times 3.14 \times 10^{-7}}{5.8 \times 10^7}\right)^{\frac{1}{2}}$

or $Z_2 = Z_c = 2.6 \times 10^{-4}$ ohm = 0.00026 ohm

Characteristic impedance of free space or air $Z_1 = 377$ ohm

$\therefore$ Reflection co-efficient $R = \dfrac{Z_2 - Z_1}{Z_2 + Z_1} = \dfrac{0.00026 - 377}{0.00026 + 377}$

$$= -1 \text{ (very nearly)}$$

Now $R = \dfrac{E_r}{E_i} = -1$

Thus $E_r = -E_i$ i.e., the wave gets reflected almost completely.

Q. 8.45. Calculate the co-efficient of reflection and transmission of energy of the normally incident E.M. wave on surface of

(i) **a medium with $\varepsilon_r = 81$** (ii) **glass having $\varepsilon_r = 2.89$**

  (P.U. 2004, 2003, 2001, 1999; H.P.U. 2003, 2001; Pbi.U. 2007, 2002; G.N.D.U. 2001, 2000)

Ans. (i) Here $\varepsilon_r = 81$

$\therefore$ Refractive index $n = \sqrt{\varepsilon_r} = \sqrt{81} = 9$

Reflection energy co-efficient $R_E = \left(\dfrac{1-n}{1+n}\right)^2 = \left(\dfrac{1-9}{1+9}\right)^2 = 0.64$

Transmission energy co-efficient $T_E = \dfrac{4n}{(1+n)^2} = \dfrac{4 \times 9}{(1+9)^2} = 0.36$

(ii) $\varepsilon_r = 2.89 \therefore n = \sqrt{2.89} = 1.7$

$$R_E = \left(\frac{1-n}{1+n}\right)^2 = \left(\frac{0.7}{2.7}\right)^2 = 0.067$$

$$T_E = \frac{4n}{(1+n)^2} = \frac{4 \times 1.7}{(2.7)^2} = .933$$

Exercise. *An e.m. wave travelling in vacuum is incident normally on the plane surface of a material whose refractive index is 1.7. Find the reflection and transmission co-efficient of energy.*
                                                                                (P.U. 2007)

Hint: Same as (ii) given above.

Q. 8.46 (a). Prove the laws of reflection and refraction for a plane electromagnetic wave when it travels obliquely from a dielectric medium of permittivity $\in_1$ and permeability μ_1 into a dielectric medium of permittivity $\in_2$ and permeability μ_2.

(b) show that $\dfrac{E_r^2}{E_i^2} = 1 - \dfrac{\sqrt{\in_2}\, E_t^2 \cos\theta_2}{\sqrt{\in_1}\, E_i^2 \cos\theta_1}$

where E_i is the amplitude of the incident, E_r of the reflected and E_t that of the transmitted electric field vector, θ_1 the angle of incidence and θ_2 the angle of refraction.

Ans. (*a*) Consider a plane electromagnetic wave incident obliquely on a plane surface *XY* of a dielectric.

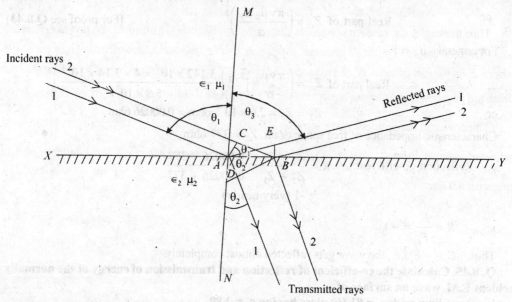

Fig. 8.9

A part of the plane wave will be transmitted and a part of it reflected. The transmitted wave will also be refracted i.e., its direction of propagation will be altered.

In Fig. 8.9 the incident ray marked (2) travels the distance *CB* when the reflected ray marked (1) travels the distance *AE* in the first medium of permittivity ϵ_1 and permeability μ_1 and the transmitted ray marked (1) travels the distance *AD* in the second medium of permittivity ϵ_2 and permeability μ_2.

If v_1 is the velocity of the wave in the *first* medium and v_2 that in the *second* medium, then

$$\frac{CB}{AD} = \frac{v_1}{v_2}$$

Now, $CB = AB \sin \theta_1$ and $AD = AB \sin \theta_2$.

$\therefore$
$$\frac{CB}{AD} = \frac{\sin \theta_1}{\sin \theta_2} = \frac{v_1}{v_2}$$

But
$$v_1 = \frac{1}{\sqrt{\mu_1 \epsilon_1}} = \frac{1}{\sqrt{\mu_0 \epsilon_1}}$$

and
$$v_2 = \frac{1}{\sqrt{\mu_2 \epsilon_2}} = \frac{1}{\sqrt{\mu_0 \epsilon_2}}$$

where μ_0 is the permeability of free space so that $\mu_1 = \mu_2 = \mu_0$

Therefore,
$$\frac{\sin \theta_1}{\sin \theta_2} = \sqrt{\frac{\epsilon_2}{\epsilon_1}} = n$$

where n is the refractive index of the second medium with respect to the first medium. This proves the **law of refraction** or **Snell's law.**

Further
$$AE = CB$$
$\therefore$
$$\sin\theta_1 = \sin\theta_3$$
or
$$\theta_1 = \theta_3$$

Thus the angle of incidence is equal to the angle of reflection. This proves the **law of reflection.**

(b) According to Poynting's theorem, the power transmitted per square metre is given by $\vec{E}\times\vec{H}$ where $\vec{E}$ is the electric and $\vec{H}$ the magnetic field vector. Since $\vec{E}$ and $\vec{H}$ are at right agles to each other the power transmitted per square metre is $\dfrac{E^2}{Z}$ where Z is the impedance of the dielectric.

The power in the incident wave striking AB will be proportional to $\dfrac{E_i^2}{Z_1}\cos\theta_1$ and that in the reflected wave will be $\dfrac{E_r^2}{Z_1}\cos\theta_1$. Further the power transmitted through the boundary will be proportional to $\dfrac{E_t^2}{Z_2}\cos\theta_2$.

By the principle of conservation of energy

$$\frac{E_i^2}{Z_1}\cos\theta_1 = \frac{E_r^2}{Z_1}\cos\theta_1 + \frac{E_t^2}{Z_2}\cos\theta_2$$

or
$$E_i^2 - E_r^2 = \frac{Z_1 E_t^2 \cos\theta_2}{Z_2 \cos\theta_1}$$

or
$$E_r^2 = E_i^2 - \frac{Z_1 E_t^2 \cos\theta_2}{Z_2 \cos\theta_1}$$

Dividing both sides by E_i^2, we get

$$\frac{E_r^2}{E_i^2} = 1 - \frac{Z_1 E_t^2 \cos\theta_2}{Z_2 E_t^2 \cos\theta_1}$$

or
$$\frac{E_r^2}{E_i^2} = 1 - \frac{\sqrt{\epsilon_2}\, E_t^2 \cos\theta_2}{\sqrt{\epsilon_1}\, E_i^2 \cos\theta_1} \qquad \left[\because \frac{Z_1}{Z_2} = \sqrt{\frac{\epsilon_2}{\epsilon_1}} = \frac{\sqrt{\epsilon_2}}{\sqrt{\epsilon_1}}\right]$$

Q. 8.47. Calculate the reflection co-efficient R when a perpendicularly polarised electromagnetic wave (horizontal polarisation) is reflected at the surface of a plane dielectric medium.

Ans. Horizontal Polarisation. In this case the electric field vector $\vec{E}$ of the electromagnetic wave is perpendicular to the plane of incidence and parallel to the reflecting surface.

Let the electric field strength of the incident wave be E_i in the positive X-direction, then applying boundry condition that the tangential component of $\vec{E}$ is continuous across the boundary, we have
$$E_i + E_r = E_t \qquad\qquad ...(i)$$
where E_r is the electric field strength of the reflected and E_t that of the transmitted (or refracted) electromagnetic wave

Dividing Eq. (i) by E_i, we get
$$\frac{E_t}{E_i} = 1 + \frac{E_r}{E_i} \qquad\qquad ...(ii)$$

It has been proved in Q. 8.46 that

$$\frac{E_r^2}{E_i^2} = 1 - \frac{\sqrt{\epsilon_2}\, E_t^2 \cos\theta_2}{\sqrt{\epsilon_1}\, E_i^2 \cos\theta_1} \qquad \qquad ... (iii)$$

where θ_1 is the angle of incidence and θ_2 the angle of refraction (Fig. 8.9)

Substituting the value of $\dfrac{E_t}{E_i}$ from Eq. (ii) in Eq. (iii), we get

$$\frac{E_r^2}{E_i^2} = 1 - \sqrt{\frac{\epsilon_2}{\epsilon_1}} \left[1 + \frac{E_r}{E_i} \right]^2 \frac{\cos\theta_2}{\cos\theta_1} \qquad ... (iv)$$

or

$$1 - \frac{E_r^2}{E_i^2} = \sqrt{\frac{\epsilon_2}{\epsilon_1}} \left[1 + \frac{E_r}{E_i} \right]^2 \frac{\cos\theta_2}{\cos\theta_1}$$

or

$$\left(1 - \frac{E_r}{E_i} \right)\left(1 + \frac{E_r}{E_i} \right) = \sqrt{\frac{\epsilon_2}{\epsilon_1}} \left[1 + \frac{E_r}{E_i} \right]^2 \frac{\cos\theta_2}{\cos\theta_1}$$

or

$$\frac{1 - \dfrac{E_r}{E_i}}{1 + \dfrac{E_r}{E_i}} = \frac{\sqrt{\epsilon_2}\,\cos\theta_2}{\sqrt{\epsilon_1}\,\cos\theta_1}$$

or

$$\frac{E_i - E_r}{E_i + E_r} = \frac{\sqrt{\epsilon_2}\,\cos\theta_2}{\sqrt{\epsilon_1}\,\cos\theta_1}$$

By componendo and dividendo, we have

$$\frac{-2\,E_r}{2E_i} = \frac{\sqrt{\epsilon_2}\,\cos\theta_2 - \sqrt{\epsilon_1}\,\cos\theta_1}{\sqrt{\epsilon_1}\,\cos\theta_1 + \sqrt{\epsilon_2}\,\cos\theta_2}$$

or

$$\frac{E_r}{E_i} = \frac{\sqrt{\epsilon_1}\,\cos\theta_1 - \sqrt{\epsilon_2}\,\cos\theta_2}{\sqrt{\epsilon_1}\,\cos\theta_1 + \sqrt{\epsilon_2}\,\cos\theta_2}$$

Now

$$\sqrt{\epsilon_2}\,\cos\theta_2 = \sqrt{\epsilon_2\,(1 - \sin^2\theta_2)}$$

$$= \sqrt{\epsilon_2 - \epsilon_2\sin^2\theta_2}$$

$$= \sqrt{\epsilon_2 - \epsilon_1\sin^2\theta_1} \qquad \left(\because \epsilon_2\sin^2\theta_2 = \epsilon_1\sin^2\theta_1 \right)$$

$\therefore$

$$\frac{E_r}{E_i} = \frac{\sqrt{\epsilon_1}\,\cos\theta_1 - \sqrt{\epsilon_2 - \epsilon_1\sin^2\theta_1}}{\sqrt{\epsilon_1}\,\cos\theta_1 + \sqrt{\epsilon_2 - \epsilon_1\sin^2\theta_1}}$$

$$= \frac{\cos\theta_1 - \sqrt{\dfrac{\epsilon_2}{\epsilon_1} - \sin^2\theta_1}}{\cos\theta_1 + \sqrt{\dfrac{\epsilon_2}{\epsilon_1} - \sin^2\theta_1}} \qquad ... (v)$$

Thus, reflector co-efficient is given by

$$R = \frac{E_r}{E_i} = \frac{\cos\theta_1 - \sqrt{\left(\dfrac{\epsilon_2}{\epsilon_1}\right) - \sin^2\theta_1}}{\cos\theta_1 + \sqrt{\left(\dfrac{\epsilon_2}{\epsilon_1}\right) - \sin^2\theta_1}}$$

Equation (*vi*) gives the ratio of reflected to incident electric field strength for the case of a perpendicularly polarised waves. This is known as **Reflection co-efficient.**

Q. 8.48. Calculate the reflection co-efficient R when an electromagnetic wave polarised in a plane parallel to the plane of incidence (vertical polarisation) is reflected at the surface of a plane dielectric medium.

Ans. Vertical Polarisation. In the case of vertical polarisation the electric field $\overline{E}$ of the electromagnetic wave is parallel to the plane of incidence and perpendicular to the reflecting surface.

Therefore, applying the boundary condition that the tangential component of $\overline{E}$ is continuous across the boundary, we have

$$(E_i - E_r)\cos\theta_1 = E_t \cos\theta_2$$

where E_i is the electric field strength of the incident wave, E_r of the reflected wave and E_t of the transmitted (or refracted) wave, θ_1 is the angle of incidence and θ_2 the angle of refraction (Fig. 8.9)

$$\therefore \qquad E_t = (E_i - E_r)\frac{\cos\theta_1}{\cos\theta_2}$$

$$= E_i\left(1 - \frac{E_r}{E_i}\right)\frac{\cos\theta_1}{\cos\theta_2}$$

or $$\frac{E_t}{E_i} = \left(1 - \frac{E_r}{E_i}\right)\frac{\cos\theta_1}{\cos\theta_2} \qquad \ldots (i)$$

It has been proved in *Q* 8.46 that

$$\frac{E_r^2}{E_i^2} = 1 - \frac{\sqrt{\epsilon_2}E_t^2\cos\theta_2}{\sqrt{\epsilon_2}E_i^2\cos\theta_1} \qquad \ldots (ii)$$

Substituting the value of $\frac{E_t}{E_i}$ from Eq. (*i*) in Eq. (*ii*), we have

$$\frac{E_r^2}{E_i^2} = 1 - \frac{\sqrt{\epsilon_2}}{\sqrt{\epsilon_2}}\left(1 - \frac{E_r}{E_i}\right)^2\frac{\cos^2\theta_1}{\cos^2\theta_2}\cdot\frac{\cos\theta_2}{\cos\theta_1}$$

$$= 1 - \sqrt{\frac{\epsilon_2}{\epsilon_1}}\left(1 - \frac{E_r}{E_i}\right)^2\frac{\cos\theta_1}{\cos\theta_2}$$

or $$1 - \frac{E_r^2}{E_i^2} = \sqrt{\frac{\epsilon_2}{\epsilon_1}}\left(1 - \frac{E_r}{E_i}\right)^2\frac{\cos\theta_1}{\cos\theta_2}$$

or $$\left(1 - \frac{E_r}{E_i}\right)\left(1 + \frac{E_r}{E_i}\right) = \sqrt{\frac{\epsilon_2}{\epsilon_1}}\left(1 - \frac{E_r}{E_i}\right)^2\frac{\cos\theta_1}{\cos\theta_2}$$

or $$1 + \frac{E_r}{E_i} = \sqrt{\frac{\epsilon_2}{\epsilon_1}}\left(1 - \frac{E_r}{E_i}\right)\frac{\cos\theta_1}{\cos\theta_2}$$

$$= \frac{\sqrt{\epsilon_2}\cos\theta_1}{\sqrt{\epsilon_1}\cos\theta_2} - \frac{\sqrt{\epsilon_2}E_r\cos\theta_1}{\sqrt{\epsilon_1}E_i\cos\theta_2}$$

or $$\frac{E_r}{E_i}\left(1 + \frac{\sqrt{\epsilon_2}\cos\theta_1}{\sqrt{\epsilon_1}\cos\theta_2}\right) = \frac{\sqrt{\epsilon_2}}{\sqrt{\epsilon_1}}\frac{\cos\theta_1}{\cos\theta_2} - 1$$

or $\qquad \dfrac{E_r}{E_i}\left(\dfrac{\sqrt{\epsilon_1}\,\cos\theta_2 + \sqrt{\epsilon_2}\,\cos\theta_1}{\sqrt{\epsilon_1}\,\cos\theta_2}\right) = \dfrac{\sqrt{\epsilon_2}\,\cos\theta_1 - \sqrt{\epsilon_1}\,\cos\theta_2}{\sqrt{\epsilon_1}\,\cos\theta_2}$

$\therefore \qquad \dfrac{E_r}{E_i} = \dfrac{\sqrt{\epsilon_2}\,\cos\theta_1 - \sqrt{\epsilon_1}\,\cos\theta_2}{\sqrt{\epsilon_2}\,\cos\theta_1 + \sqrt{\epsilon_1}\,\cos\theta_2}$

$\qquad\qquad = \dfrac{\sqrt{\epsilon_2}\,\cos\theta_1 - \sqrt{\epsilon_1}\,\sqrt{1-\sin^2\theta_2}}{\sqrt{\epsilon_2}\,\cos\theta_1 + \sqrt{\epsilon_1}\,\sqrt{1-\sin^2\theta_2}}$

But $\qquad\qquad \sin^2\theta_2 = \dfrac{\epsilon_1\,\sin^2\theta_1}{\epsilon_2}$

$\therefore \qquad \dfrac{E_r}{E_i} = \dfrac{\sqrt{\epsilon_2}\,\cos\theta_1 - \sqrt{\epsilon_1}\,\sqrt{1-\dfrac{\epsilon_1\,\sin^2\theta_1}{\epsilon_2}}}{\sqrt{\epsilon_2}\,\cos\theta_1 + \sqrt{\epsilon_1}\,\sqrt{1-\dfrac{\epsilon_1\,\sin^2\theta_1}{\epsilon_2}}}$

$\qquad\qquad = \dfrac{\sqrt{\epsilon_2}\,\cos\theta_1 - \sqrt{\epsilon_1}\,\sqrt{\dfrac{\epsilon_1}{\epsilon_2}\left(\dfrac{\epsilon_2}{\epsilon_1}-\sin^2\theta_1\right)}}{\sqrt{\epsilon_2}\,\cos\theta_1 + \sqrt{\epsilon_1}\,\sqrt{\dfrac{\epsilon_1}{\epsilon_2}\left(\dfrac{\epsilon_2}{\epsilon_1}-\sin^2\theta_1\right)}}$

$\qquad\qquad = \dfrac{\sqrt{\epsilon_2}\,\cos\theta_1 - \dfrac{\epsilon_1}{\sqrt{\epsilon_2}}\,\sqrt{\left(\dfrac{\epsilon_2}{\epsilon_1}-\sin^2\theta_1\right)}}{\sqrt{\epsilon_2}\,\cos\theta_1 + \dfrac{\epsilon_1}{\sqrt{\epsilon_2}}\,\sqrt{\dfrac{\epsilon_2}{\epsilon_1}-\sin^2\theta_1}}$

$\qquad\qquad = \dfrac{\sqrt{\epsilon_2}\,\dfrac{\sqrt{\epsilon_2}}{\epsilon_1}\,\cos\theta_1 - \sqrt{\left(\dfrac{\epsilon_2}{\epsilon_1}-\sin^2\theta_1\right)}}{\sqrt{\epsilon_2}\,\dfrac{\sqrt{\epsilon_2}}{\epsilon_1}\,\cos\theta_1 + \sqrt{\left(\dfrac{\epsilon_2}{\epsilon_1}-\sin^2\theta_1\right)}}$

$\therefore$ Reflection co-efficient $\qquad R = \dfrac{E_r}{E_i}$

$\qquad\qquad = \dfrac{\left(\dfrac{\epsilon_2}{\epsilon_1}\right)\cos\theta_1 - \sqrt{\left(\dfrac{\epsilon_2}{\epsilon_1}-\sin^2\theta_1\right)}}{\left(\dfrac{\epsilon_2}{\epsilon_1}\right)\cos\theta_1 - \sqrt{\left(\dfrac{\epsilon_2}{\epsilon_1}-\sin^2\theta_1\right)}}$ $\qquad$ ... (iii)

Equation (iii) gives the reflection co-efficient for vertical polarisation.

Note : *The students are advised to compare the values of reflection co-efficient R in the case of horizontal polarisation and vertical polarisation.*

Q. 8.49 (a). Explain the phenomenon of dispersion of electromagnetic waves in a conductor.
(P.U. 2003, 2001, 2000; Gauhati U. 2000; G.N.D.U., 1993)

(b) Does refractive index of a medium depend upon frequency of the wave? Explain.
(Pbi.U. 2008)

Ans. Phase velocity of electromagnetic waves in vacuum $c = \sqrt{\dfrac{1}{\mu_0 \varepsilon_0}}$ ...(i)

and phase velocity of electromagnetic waves in a medium $v = \sqrt{\dfrac{1}{\mu \varepsilon}}$ ...(ii)

Squaring (i) and (ii) and dividing, we get

$$\frac{c^2}{v^2} = \frac{\mu \varepsilon}{\mu_0 \varepsilon_0} = \mu_r \varepsilon_r$$

where μ_r and ε_r are the relative values of permeability and permittivity respectively. For a conducting medium $\mu_r = 1$

$$c^2 = \varepsilon_r v^2 \qquad ...(iii)$$

Now, for a conductor ε_r and v are functions of wavelength λ, but c is a constant.

∴ Differentiating eq. (iii), with respect to λ, we get

$$\varepsilon_r \, 2v \, \frac{dv}{d\lambda} + v^2 \, \frac{d\varepsilon_r}{d\lambda} = 0$$

or $$\frac{dv}{d\lambda} = - \frac{v}{2\varepsilon_r} \cdot \frac{d\varepsilon_r}{d\lambda} \qquad ...(iv)$$

The group velocity v_g and phase velocity v are related as

$$v_g = v - \lambda \frac{dv}{d\lambda}$$

Substituting the value of $\dfrac{dv}{d\lambda}$ from (iv), we have

$$v_g = v + \frac{v}{2\varepsilon_r} \frac{d\varepsilon_r}{d\lambda}$$

or $$v_g = v\left[1 + \frac{1}{2\varepsilon_r} \frac{d\varepsilon_r}{d\lambda}\right]$$

i.e. $v_g > v$. When group velocity is greater than phase velocity, it is a case of *anomalous* dispersion.

Thus electro magnetic waves suffer *anomalous* dispersion in conductors.

(b) Yes. The refractive index of a medium depends upon frequency of the wave. For example, refractive index of a transparent medium for light waves of shorter wave length (higher frequency is greater than that for waves of longer wave length (lower frequency). For example, the refractive index is greater for violet rays (shorter wave length–higher frequency) than that of red rays (longer wave length-lower frequency.

Q. 8.50. Mark the correct answer

(i)   Which of the following has coulomb as the unit?   (H.P.U., 1996)

(a) $\oint \vec{H}.\vec{dl}$ (b) $\oint \vec{E}.\vec{dl}$ (c) $\iint \vec{D}.\vec{ds}$ (d) $\iint \vec{E}.\vec{ds}$

(ii)   Maxwell's equation involving $\dfrac{\partial \vec{B}}{\partial t}$ is obtained from   (H.P.U., 1995)

(a) Ampere's law   (b) Gauss's law
(c) Biot and Savart's law   (d) Faraday's law.

(iii)   During the propagation of e.m. waves in a medium   (H.P.U., 1993)
(a) Electric energy density is double of the magnetic energy density
(b) Electric energy density is half of the magnetic energy density
(c) Both electric and magnetic energy densities are equal
(d) Both electric and magnetic energy densities are zero

(iv)   The velocity of plane e.m. wave in vacuum is given by

(a) $c = \dfrac{1}{\sqrt{\mu_0 \varepsilon_0}}$ (b) $c = \sqrt{\mu_0 \varepsilon_0}$ (c) $c = \left(\dfrac{\varepsilon_0}{\mu_0}\right)^{\frac{1}{2}}$ (d) $c = \left(\dfrac{\mu_0}{\varepsilon_0}\right)^{\frac{1}{2}}$

(H.P.U. 2003, 1996, 1994, 1991)

(v)   The S.I. unit of Poynting vector is
(a) $W\,m^2$ (b) $W\,m$ (c) $W\,m^{-1}$ (d) $J\,s^{-1}\,m^{-2}$

(vi)   Skin depth for a conductor in reference to e.m. waves varies   (H.P.U., 1993)
(a) Inversely as square root of frequency
(b) Inversely as frequency
(c) Directly as frequency
(d) Directly as square of frequency

(vii)   The magnitude of impedance in a conducting medium to e.m. waves is

(a) $Z_0 = \sqrt{\dfrac{\sigma}{\omega\mu}}$ (b) $Z_0 = \sqrt{\dfrac{\mu\sigma}{\omega}}$ (c) $Z_0 = \sqrt{\dfrac{\omega\sigma}{\mu}}$ (d) $Z_0 = \sqrt{\dfrac{\mu\omega}{\sigma}}$

(H.P.U., 1992)

(viii)   The phase difference between electric and magnetic field vectors in a conductor is

(a) π rad   (b) $\dfrac{\pi}{2}$ rad   (c) $\dfrac{\pi}{4}$ rad   (d) zero

(G.N.D.U., 1993, 1994; H.P.U., 2002, 1996)

(ix)   The characteristic impedance for a perfect conductor to e.m. wave is

(H.P.U., 1994; G.N.D.U., 1993)

(a) Zero   (b) 1   (c) ∞ (d) none of these

(x)   During propagation of e.m. waves in a conductor

(a) magnetic field vector lags behind the electric field vector by an angle $\dfrac{\pi}{4}$ radian

(b) Magnetic field vector leads the electric field vector by an angle $\dfrac{\pi}{4}$ radian

(c) Magnetic field vector lags behind the electric field vector by an angle $\dfrac{\pi}{2}$ radian

(d) Magnetic field vector leads the electric field vector by an angle $\dfrac{\pi}{2}$ radian

(xi) In a conductor the phase difference between displacement and conduction current is

    (a) $\pi/4$ (b) $\pi/2$ (c) π (d) zero   (H.P.U. 2002)

Ans. (i) c (ii) d (iii) c (iv) a (v) d (vi) a (vii) d (viii) c (ix) a (x) a (xi) b

EXERCISES

1. What will be the skin depth of a medium having conductance 2×10^7 Sm^{-1} (S is the symbol for Siemen, the unit of conductance) for e.m. waves of frequency 10 kHz. Given $\mu = 4\pi \times 10^{-7}$ Hm^{-1}. **[Ans. 1.126 mm]**

2. Show that the conduction current is not appreciable for an e.m. wave in a medium of $\sigma = 10^{-15}$ mho/metre and $\varepsilon = 10^{-11}$ farad/metre.

   [**Hint.** Here $\dfrac{\omega\varepsilon}{\sigma} = \dfrac{10^{-11}}{10^{-15}}\omega = 10^4\,\omega$]

   As , $\dfrac{\omega\varepsilon}{\sigma} > 100$ the displacement current dominates and the conduction current is not appreciable.

3. What will be the skin depth in a medium having conductivity 2×10^7 siemens per metre for electromagnetic waves of frequency 1 MHz? Given $\mu = 4\pi \times 10^{-7}$ Hm^{-1}. *(Pbi. U., 1991)* **[Ans. 1126 mm]**

4. If a 200 Watt laser beam is concentrated by a lens into a cross-section area of about 10^{-4} sq.cm, find the value of Poynting vector and amplitude of electric field.

$$\left[\textbf{Ans.}\quad \begin{array}{l} 2 \times 10^{10}\ \text{W/m}^2 \\ 3.85 \times 10^6\ \text{volt/m} \end{array}\right]$$

9

Fourier Analysis

Q. 9.1. (*a*) **What is a periodic function?**

(*b*) **State Fourier's theorem. Describe the complex form of Fourier's theorem. Explain how you will evaluate various co-efficients a_0, a_n and b_n in Fourier series.**

(*H.P.U.*, 2003, 2000, 1996; *K.U.*, 2002,1996; *M.D.U.*, 2007, 2006, 2001, 2000, 1999; *R.M.L.AV. U.*, 1996)

Ans. (*a*) **Periodic Function.** *Any function which repeats itself regularly over a given interval of space or time is called a periodic function.*

Thus $f(t) = f(t \pm T)$ is a periodic function of time where T is the time period. Similarly, $f(x) = f(x \pm \lambda)$ is a periodic function of space (in one dimension).in which λ represents periodic (wave) length. In fact, any function $f(x) = f(x \pm \alpha)$ is a periodic function if α represents the time period T, the wavelength λ, the phase angle 2π (radians) in accordance with the form of x.

(*b*) **Fourier's theorem.** *It states that any single valued finite and continuous periodic function of wavelength λ can be built up by compounding simple harmonic (sine or cosine) vibrations of wavelength λ, $\lambda/2$, $\lambda/3$, $\lambda/4$, ...etc.*

or

A periodic function of time period T can be represented as made up of simple harmonic vibrations of period T, $T/2$, $T/3$, $T/4$,...etc.

However, the most useful form of Fourier's theorem is stated as:

Any complex periodic function of frequency ν may be treated as made up of a series of simple harmonic (sine or cosine) vibrations of frequency ν, 2ν, 3ν, 4ν, ...etc.

Mathematically, Fourier's theorem for a periodic function $f(x)$ may be represented by the sum of harmonic terms as

$$f(x) = \frac{1}{2}a_0 + a_1 \cos x + a_2 \cos 2x + ... + a_n \cos nx + ...$$

$$+ b_1 \sin x + b_2 \sin 2x + ... + b_n \sin nx \qquad ...(i)$$

or $$f(x) = \frac{1}{2}a_0 + \sum_{n=1}^{n=\infty}(a_n \cos nx + b_n \sin nx) \qquad ...(ii)$$

The above series is known as *Fourier series* for periodic function $f(x)$. It must satisfy the condition that it is a convergent series. The co-efficients, a_0, a_n and b_n are called *Fourier co-efficients*.

Complex form. Substituting $a_n = c_n \cos \theta_n$ and $b_n = c_n \sin \theta_n$ we can put Fourier series given in (*ii*) as

$$f(x) = \frac{1}{2} a_0 + \sum_{n=1}^{n=\infty} (c_n \cos \theta_n \cos nx + c_n \sin \theta_n \sin nx)$$

or
$$f(x) = \frac{1}{2} a_0 + \sum_{n=1}^{n=\infty} c_n \cos (nx - \theta_n) \qquad \qquad ...(iii)$$

so that $c_n = \sqrt{a_n^2 + b_n^2}$ and $\theta_n = \tan^{-1} \dfrac{b_n}{a_n}$

Similarly, substituting $\cos nx = \dfrac{e^{inx} + e^{-inx}}{2}$

and $\sin nx = \dfrac{e^{inx} + e^{-inx}}{2i}$, we have

$$f(x) = \frac{1}{2} a_0 + \sum_{n=1}^{n=\infty} a_n \frac{e^{inx} + e^{-inx}}{2} + b_n \frac{e^{inx} - e^{-inx}}{2i}$$

$$= \frac{1}{2} a_0 + \sum_{n=1}^{n=\infty} \frac{a_n - ib_n}{2} e^{inx} + \sum_{n=1}^{n=\infty} \frac{a_n + ib_n}{2} e^{-inx}$$

$$= \frac{1}{2} a_0 + \sum_{n=1}^{n=\infty} \frac{a_n - ib_n}{2} e^{inx} + \sum_{n=-1}^{n=-\infty} \frac{a_n - ib_n}{2} e^{inx}$$

Putting $a_n - ib_n = 2d_n$

and $a_0 = 2d_0$, we have

$$f(x) = \sum_{n=-\infty}^{n=+\infty} d_n e^{inx} \qquad \qquad ...(iv)$$

This is the complex form of Fourier series for $f(x)$. The co-efficient d_n is known as *complex Fourier coefficient*.

Even and odd functions. Now cosine terms are *even functions i.e.*, $\cos x = \cos(-x)$ and sine terms are *odd function i.e.*, $\sin x = - \sin(-x)$

Again $\qquad f(x) = \frac{1}{2} [f(x) + f(-x)] + \frac{1}{2} [f(x) - f(-x)]$

in which the *first* is an *even* function and *second* an *add* function. Thus in Fourier series the cosine terms represent the even part of $f(x)$ and the sine terms the odd part. Conversely if $f(x)$ is an even function it is represented by Fourier series having only cosine terms and if $f(x)$ is an odd function it is represented by Fourier series having only sine terms.

Value of co-efficients. (i) To find the value of a_0 integrate both sides of equation (ii) with respect to x over the period 0 to 2π, so that

$$\int_0^{2\pi} f(x) \, dx = \frac{1}{2} a_0 \int_0^{2\pi} dx + \sum_{n=1}^{n=\infty} a_n \int_0^{2\pi} \cos nx \, dx + \sum_{n=1}^{n=\infty} b_n \int_0^{2\pi} \sin nx \, dx$$

$$= \pi a_0 \left[\because \int_0^{2\pi} \cos nx \, dx = 0 \text{ and } \int_0^{2\pi} \sin nx \, dx = 0 \right]$$

$$\therefore \quad a_0 = \frac{1}{\pi} \int_0^{2\pi} f(x) \, dx$$

or $\quad \dfrac{1}{2} a_0 = \dfrac{1}{2\pi} \displaystyle\int_0^{2\pi} f(x) \, dx$ ...(v)

i.e., $\dfrac{1}{2} a_0$ is the average of the function over the interval 2π.

(ii) To find the value of a_n, multiply both sides of equation (i) by $\cos nx$ and integrate over the period of x from 0 to 2π so that

$$\int_0^{2\pi} f(x) \cos nx \, dx = \frac{1}{2} a_0 \int_0^{2\pi} \cos nx \, dx$$

$$+ a_1 \int_0^{2\pi} \cos x \cos nx \, dx + a_2 \int_0^{2\pi} \cos 2x \cos nx \, dx + \dots + a_n \int_0^{2\pi} \cos nx \cos nx \, dx + \dots$$

$$+ b_1 \int_0^{2\pi} \sin x \cos nx \, dx + b_2 \int_0^{2\pi} \sin 2x \cos nx \, dx + \dots + b_n \int_0^{2\pi} \sin x \cos nx \, dx + \dots$$

Now $\qquad \displaystyle\int_0^{2\pi} \cos nx \, dx = 0$

$$\int_0^{2\pi} \cos mx \cos nx \, dx \begin{cases} = 0, \text{ if } m \neq n \\ = \pi, \text{ if } m = n \end{cases}$$

and $\qquad \displaystyle\int_0^{2\pi} \sin mx \cos nx \, dx = 0$, for all values of m and n

$\therefore \qquad \displaystyle\int_0^{2\pi} f(x) \cos nx \, dx = a_n \int_0^{2\pi} \cos nx \cos nx \, dx$

$$= a_n \int_0^{2\pi} \cos^2 nx \, dx = \frac{a_n}{2} \int_0^{2\pi} (1 + \cos 2nx) \, dx = \frac{a_n}{2} 2\pi$$

$$= \pi a_n$$

or $\quad a_n = \dfrac{1}{\pi} \displaystyle\int_0^{2\pi} f(x) \cos nx \, dx$ ...(vi)

Thus a_n represents twice the average value of $f(x) \cos nx$ over the interval 2π.

(iii) To evaluate b_n, multiply both sides of equation (i) by $\sin nx$ and integrate over the interval 0 to 2π, so that

$$\int_0^{2\pi} f(x) \sin nx \, dx = \frac{1}{2} a_0 \int_0^{2\pi} \sin nx \, dx + a_1 \int_0^{2\pi} \cos x \sin nx \, dx$$

$$+ a_2 \int_0^{2\pi} \cos 2x \sin nx dx + \dots \dots + a_n \int_0^{2\pi} \cos nx \sin nx \, dx$$

$$+ \dots + b_1 \int_0^{2\pi} \sin x \sin nx \, dx + b_2 \int_0^{2\pi} \sin 2x \sin nx \, dx + \dots + b_n \int_0^{2\pi} \sin nx \sin nx \, dx + \dots$$

Now

$$\int_0^{2\pi} \sin nx \, dx = 0$$

$$\int_0^{2\pi} \sin mx \sin nx \, dx \begin{cases} = 0, \text{ if } m \neq n \\ = \pi, \text{ if } m = n \end{cases}$$

and

$$\int_0^{2\pi} \cos mx \sin nx \, dx = 0 \text{ for all values of } m \text{ and } n.$$

$$\therefore \qquad \int_0^{2\pi} f(x) \sin nx \, dx = b_n \int_0^{2\pi} \sin nx \sin nx \, dx$$

$$= b_n \int_0^{2\pi} \sin^2 nx \, dx = \frac{b_n}{2} \int_0^{2\pi} (1 - \cos 2nx) \, dx = \frac{b_n}{2} \cdot 2\pi$$

$$= \pi b_n$$

or
$$b_n = \frac{1}{\pi} \int_0^{2\pi} f(x) \sin nx \, dx \qquad \qquad \dots (vii)$$

Thus b_n represents twice the average value of $f(x) \sin nx$ over the interval 2π.

Note. In the Fourier series given in (i) x is assumed to be in radians. If x represents a length, then the argument of cosine and sine factors must be phase angle and therefore, represented as

$\cos \left(\dfrac{2\pi x}{\lambda} \right)$ and $\sin \left(\dfrac{2\pi x}{\lambda} \right)$ where λ is the periodic (wave) length.

If, however, x represents time *i.e.* the periodic function is $f(t)$ a function of time, then the cosine factors are represented as $\cos \left(\dfrac{2\pi t}{T} \right)$, $\cos 2\pi vt$, $\cos \omega t$ and, similarly, the sine factors where T is the time period, v the frequency and ω the angular frequency.

In such a case to find the value of a_0, integrate both sides with respect to t over the period 0 to T and we get

$$a_0 = \frac{2}{T} \int_0^T f(t) \, dt$$

To evaluate a_n multiply both sides by $\cos (n\omega t)$ and integrate over the period 0 to T so that

$$a_n = \frac{2}{T} \int_0^T f(t) \cos (n\omega t) \, dt$$

Similarly to evaluate b_n multiply both sides by $\sin (n \omega t)$ and integrate over the period 0 to T so that

$$b_n = \frac{2}{T} \int_0^T f(t) \sin (n\omega t) \, dt$$

In general, we have

$$a_n = \frac{1}{\text{Half interval}} \int_0^T f(t) \cos{(n\omega t)} \, dt$$

and

$$b_n = \frac{1}{\text{Half interval}} \int_0^T f(t) \sin{(n\omega t)} \, dt$$

Q. 9.2. Write down the values of constants a_0, a_n and b_n in Fourier theorem for a function $y = f(\omega t)$.   (*Meerut U.* 2001)

Ans. The constants a_0, a_n and b_n in terms of x for a function $f(x)$ are given by

$$a_0 = \frac{1}{\pi} \int_0^{2\pi} f(x) \, dx; \; a_n = \frac{1}{\pi} \int_0^{2\pi} f(x) \cos nx \, dx \quad \text{and}$$

$$b_n = \frac{1}{\pi} \int_0^{2\pi} f(x) \sin nx \, dx$$

For a function $y = f(\omega t)$, $x = \omega t$

$$\therefore \; 2\pi = \omega T \text{ where } T \text{ is the time period and } T = \frac{2\pi}{\omega}$$

Also $dx = d(\omega t)$ and $\dfrac{1}{\pi} = \dfrac{2}{\omega T}$

Now

$$a_0 = \frac{1}{\pi} \int_0^{2\pi} f(x) \, dx = \frac{2}{\omega T} \int_0^{2\pi} f(\omega t) \, d(\omega t)$$

$$a_n = \frac{1}{\pi} \int_0^{2\pi} f(x) \cos nx \, dx = \frac{2}{\omega T} \int_0^{2\pi} f(\omega t) \cos n(\omega t) \, d(\omega t)$$

and

$$b_n = \frac{1}{\pi} \int_0^{2\pi} f(x) \sin nx \, dx = \frac{2}{\omega T} \int_0^{2\pi} f(\omega t) \sin n(\omega t) \, d(\omega t)$$

Q. 9.3. State Dirichlet's theorem. What are Dirichlet conditions? State the limitations of Fourier's theorem.

(*Nagpur U.* 2002, 2001; *Meerut U.* 2002, 2000; *K.U.* 2001, 2000; *Gharwal U.* 2000; *H.P.U.* 1996, 1995)

Ans. Dirichlet theorem. Dirichlet's theorem states that *"A function $f(x)$ can be expanded as a Fourier series*

$$f(x) = \frac{1}{2} a_0 + \sum_{n=1}^{n=\infty} a_n \cos nx + \sum_{n=1}^{n=\infty} b_n \sin nx$$

where a_0, a_n and b_n are constants if it satisfies the following conditions known as Dirichlet's conditions."

Dirichlet's conditions.

(*i*) $f(x)$ is periodic, single valued and finite

(*ii*) $f(x)$ is piece wise continuous *i.e.*, has a finite number of discontinuities in any one period. A function $f(x)$ is said to have a discontinuity at $x = x_0$ if the right handed limit of $f(x)$ at $x = x_0$ and the left handed limit of $f(x)$ at $x = x_0$ are not equal *i.e.* $f(x_0^-) \neq f(x_0^+)$. Such a discontinuity is shown in Fig. 9.1 for function $f(x)$ at $x = x_0$. The function depicted by the graph is called piece wise continuous.

(*iii*) $f(x)$ has only a finite number of maxima and minima

(*iv*) $f(x) = f(x + 2\pi)$ for values of x outside of $(-\pi, +\pi)$

Limitations of Fourier's theorem. A function can be expressed in the form of Fourier's series under the conditions known as Dirichlet's conditions given above. These conditions, therefore, impose limitations on the application of Fourier theorem to a given function.

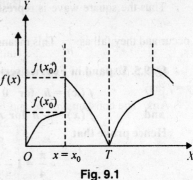

Fig. 9.1

Q. 9.4. Completely analyse the square wave periodic vibration and obtain the expression for the Fourier co-efficients.

(*M.D.U.*, 2008; *Meerut U.* 2002; *Nagpur U.* 2001; *Ranchi U.* 1991)

Ans. Square wave. A square wave of height h is shown in Fig. 9.2.

Mathematically it is represented as

$$f(x) = 0, \ -\pi < x < 0$$

$$= h, \ 0 < x < \pi$$

as the limits of x are in terms of π, x is in radians. Therefore, according to Fourier series

$$f(x) = \frac{1}{2} a_0 + \sum_{n=1}^{n=\infty} (a_n \cos nx + b_n \sin nx) \qquad \ldots(i)$$

Now
$$a_0 = \frac{1}{\pi} \int_{-\pi}^{+\pi} f(x) \, dx = \frac{1}{\pi} \left[\int_{-\pi}^{0} f(x) \, dx + \int_{0}^{\pi} f(x) \, dx \right]$$

But
$$f(x) = 0 \text{ for } -\pi < x < 0$$

$\therefore$
$$a_0 = \frac{1}{\pi} \int_{0}^{\pi} h \, dx = h \qquad\qquad\qquad [\because f(x) = h, \ 0 < x < \pi]$$

Also
$$a_n = \frac{1}{\pi} \int_{-\pi}^{+\pi} f(x) \cos nx \, dx = \frac{1}{\pi} \int_{0}^{\pi} f(x) \cos nx \, dx$$

$$= \frac{1}{\pi} \int_{0}^{\pi} h \cos nx \, dx = 0$$

Similarly
$$b_n = \frac{1}{\pi} \int_{0}^{\pi} h \sin nx \, dx = \frac{h}{n\pi} (1 - \cos n\pi)$$

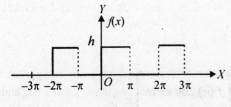

Fig. 9.2

$\therefore \qquad b_n = \dfrac{2h}{n\pi}$ when n is odd

and $\quad b_n = 0$ when n is even

Hence Fourier series (*i*) becomes

$$f(x) = \frac{h}{2} + 0 + \sum_{n=1}^{n=\infty} \frac{2h}{n\pi} \sin nx \ [\text{where } n \text{ is odd}]$$

or
$$f(x) = \frac{h}{2} + \frac{2h}{\pi} \left[\frac{\sin x}{1} + \frac{\sin 3x}{3} + \frac{\sin 5x}{5} + ... \right]$$

Thus the square wave is represented by Fourier sine series. Only odd terms in the sine series occur and they fall as $\frac{1}{n}$. This means that the square wave contains high frequency components.

Q. 9.5. Expand in Fourier series

$$f(x) = h \quad \text{for} \quad 0 < x < \pi$$

and $$f(x) = -h \quad \text{for} \quad \pi < x < 2\pi$$

Hence prove that

$$\frac{\pi}{4} = 1 - \frac{1}{3} + \frac{1}{5} - \frac{1}{7} + ...$$

or

Apply Fourier theorem to analyse a rectangular wave.

(*M.D.U. 2008; Nag. U. 2001; K.U. 2000, 1996*)

Ans. Rectangular wave. The graphical representation of the function is shown in Fig. 9.3. It

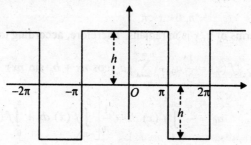

Fig. 9.3

represents a *rectangular wave*. As the limits of x are in terms of π, x is in radians. Therefore, according to Fourier series

$$f(x) = \frac{1}{2} a_0 + \sum_{n=1}^{n=\infty} (a_n \cos nx + b_n \sin nx)$$

Now $$a_0 = \frac{1}{\pi} \int_0^{2\pi} f(x)\, dx = \frac{1}{\pi} \left[\int_0^{\pi} f(x)\, dx + \int_{\pi}^{2\pi} f(x)\, dx \right]$$

$$= \frac{1}{\pi} \left[\int_0^{\pi} h\, dx - \int_{\pi}^{2\pi} h\, dx \right] = \frac{h}{\pi} \left\{ [x]_0^{\pi} - [x]_{\pi}^{2\pi} \right\}$$

$$= 0$$

Again $$a_n = \frac{1}{\pi} \int_0^{2\pi} f(x) \cos nx\, dx$$

$$= \frac{1}{\pi} \left[\int_0^{\pi} f(x) \cos nx\, dx + \int_{\pi}^{2\pi} f(x) \cos nx\, dx \right]$$

$$= \frac{h}{\pi} \left[\int_0^\pi \cos nx \, dx - \int_\pi^{2\pi} \cos nx \, dx \right] = 0$$

Similarly $b_n = \dfrac{1}{\pi} \displaystyle\int_0^{2\pi} f(x) \sin nx \, dx$

$$= \frac{1}{\pi} \left[\int_0^\pi f(x) \sin nx \, dx + \int_\pi^{2\pi} f(x) \sin nx \, dx \right]$$

$$= \frac{h}{\pi} \left[\int_0^\pi \sin nx \, dx - \int_\pi^{2\pi} \sin nx \, dx \right]$$

$$= \frac{h}{n\pi} \left\{ \left[-\cos nx \right]_0^\pi + \left[\cos nx \right]_\pi^{2\pi} \right\}$$

$$= \frac{h}{n\pi} \left\{ (1 - \cos n\pi) + (1 - \cos n\pi) \right\}$$

$$= \frac{2h}{n\pi} (1 - \cos n\pi)$$

For *even* values of n, $\cos n\pi = +1$ and $1 - \cos n\pi = 0$
$\therefore\ b_n = 0$ *i.e.*, b_2, b_4, b_6 etc. are zero.
For *odd values of* n $\cos n\pi = -1$ and $1 - \cos n\pi = 2$

$$\therefore\ b_n = \frac{4h}{n\pi} \ \ i.e.,\ b_1 = \frac{4h}{\pi},\ b_3 = \frac{4h}{3\pi},\ b_5 = \frac{4h}{5\pi}\ ....$$

Thus Fourier series representation is given by

$$f(x) = \frac{4h}{\pi} \left\{ \sin x + \frac{\sin 3x}{3} + \frac{\sin 5x}{5} + ... \right\}$$

It is clear from this expression that
(*i*) The frequencies of the component vibrations are *odd* multiples of the fundamental frequency.
(*ii*) As the frequencies increase in the ratio 1: 3: 5... the amplitude decreases in the ratio 1: 1/3: 1/5....
(*iii*) All the components have the same phase.

For $x = \dfrac{\pi}{2},\ f(x) = h$

$$\therefore\ \ h = \frac{4h}{\pi} \left[\sin \frac{\pi}{2} + \frac{1}{3} \sin \frac{3\pi}{2} + \frac{1}{5} \sin \frac{5\pi}{2} + \frac{1}{7} \sin \frac{7\pi}{2} + ... \right]$$

$$= \frac{4h}{\pi} \left[1 - \frac{1}{3} + \frac{1}{5} - \frac{1}{7} + ... \right]$$

or $\dfrac{\pi}{4} = \left[1 - \dfrac{1}{3} + \dfrac{1}{5} - \dfrac{1}{7} + ... \right]$

Q. 9.6. Apply Fourier's theorem to analyze a saw toothed wave.   (*K.U.*, 1994)
or

Expand in Fourier series

$$f(x) = t \ \text{for} \ -T/2 < t < T/2$$

$$f(t + T) = f(t).$$

(*Nag. U.* 2001; *Os. U.*, 1997)

Ans. **Saw tooth wave.** A graphical representation of the function is shown in Fig. 9.4. It is a

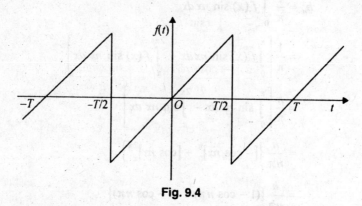

Fig. 9.4

periodic curve and the displacement is linear with time. It represents a *saw tooth wave.*

As the limits are in terms of T, we represent the function as a Fourier series in the form of

$$f(t) = \frac{1}{2} a_0 + \sum_{n=1}^{n=\infty} [a_n \cos (n\omega t) + b_n \sin (n\omega t)]$$

where

$$\omega = 2\pi v = 2\pi/T$$

Now

$$a_0 = \frac{2}{T} \int_0^T f(t) \, dt = \frac{2}{T} \left[\int_{-T/2}^0 f(t) \, dt + \int_0^{+T/2} f(t) \, dt \right]$$

$$= \frac{2}{T} \left[\int_{-T/2}^0 t \, dt + \int_0^{+T/2} t \, dt \right] = 0$$

Again

$$a_n = \frac{2}{T} \int_0^T f(t) \cos (n\omega t) \, dt$$

$$= \frac{2}{T} \left[\int_{-T/2}^0 f(t) \cos (n\omega t) \, dt + \int_0^{+T/2} f(t) \cos (n\omega t) \, dt \right]$$

$$= \frac{2}{T} \left[\int_{-T/2}^0 t \cos (n\omega t) \, dt + \int_0^{+T/2} t \cos (n\omega t) \, dt \right]$$

$$= \frac{2}{T} \left[\int_{-T/2}^{+T/2} t \cos (n\omega t) \, dt \right] = \frac{2}{T} \left[\frac{t \sin (n\omega t)}{n\omega} - \frac{1}{n\omega} \left(\frac{\cos (n\omega t)}{n\omega} \right) \right]_{-T/2}^{+T/2} = 0$$

Similarly

$$b_n = \frac{2}{T} \int_0^T f(t) \sin (n\omega t) \, dt$$

$$= \frac{2}{T} \left[\int_{-T/2}^{0} f(t) \sin(n\omega t)\, dt + \int_{0}^{+T/2} f(t) \sin(n\omega t)\, dt \right]$$

$$= \frac{2}{T} \left[\int_{-T/2}^{+T/2} t \sin(n\omega t)\, dt \right]$$

$$= \frac{2}{T} \left[\frac{-t\cos(n\omega t)}{n\omega} + \frac{1}{n\omega}\left(\frac{\sin(n\omega t)}{n\omega} \right) \right]_{-T/2}^{+T/2}$$

$$= \frac{-2}{T} \left[\frac{T}{2n\omega} \cos(n\pi) + \frac{T}{2n\omega} \cos(-n\pi) \right]_{-T/2}^{+T/2}$$

As

$$\left[\frac{1}{n\omega} \frac{\sin(n\omega t)}{n\omega} \right]_{-T/2}^{+T/2} = 0$$

∴

$$b_n = \frac{-2}{T}\left[\frac{T}{n\omega} \cos(n\pi) \right] = \frac{-2T}{n\omega T} \cos(n\pi)$$

$$= \mp \frac{T}{n\pi} \text{ according as } n \text{ is even or odd}$$

or

$$b_n = (-1)^{n+1} \frac{T}{n\pi}$$

Hence

$$f(t) = \frac{T}{\pi} \sum_{n=1}^{n=\infty} \frac{(-1)^{n+1}}{n} \sin(n\omega t)$$

or

$$f(t) = \frac{T}{\pi}\left[\sin \omega t - \frac{1}{2}\sin 2\omega t + \frac{1}{3}\sin 3\omega t - \frac{1}{4}\sin 4\omega t + ... \right]$$

When the number of terms in the series is increased sufficiently the resultant curve resembles more and more the saw tooth wave.

Q. 9.7. Find the Fourier series for $f(x) = x$ in the closed interval $(-\pi, \pi)$.

(H.P.U. 2003; M.D.U. 1999)

Ans. The function $f(x) = x$ in the closed interval $(-\pi, \pi)$ represents a saw tooth wave form shown in Fig. 9.4.

The Fourier series expansion for $f(x)$ is given by

$$f(x) = \frac{1}{2} a_0 + \sum_{n=1}^{n=\infty} (a_n \cos nx + b_n \sin nx) \qquad ...(i)$$

The given function $f(x) = x$ is clearly an *odd* function.

Now

$$\frac{1}{2} a_0 = \frac{1}{2\pi} \int_{0}^{2\pi} f(x)\, dx = \frac{1}{2\pi} \int_{-\pi}^{\pi} f(x)\, dx$$

$$= \frac{1}{2\pi} \int_{-\pi}^{\pi} x\, dx = 0 \qquad \text{[As } f(x) = x \text{ is an odd function of } x]$$

and $\quad a_n = \dfrac{1}{\pi} \displaystyle\int_0^{2\pi} f(x) \cos nx\, dx = \dfrac{1}{\pi} \int_{-\pi}^{\pi} f(x) \cos nx\, dx$

$$= \frac{1}{\pi} \int_{-\pi}^{\pi} x \cos nx\, dx = 0$$

[As $f(x) = x$ is an odd function, $\cos nx$ an even function, therefore $x \cos nx$ is an odd function of x.]

Also $\quad b_n = \dfrac{1}{\pi} \displaystyle\int_0^{2\pi} f(x) \sin ndx = \dfrac{1}{\pi} \int_{-\pi}^{\pi} x \sin nx\, dx$

$$= \frac{2}{\pi} \int_0^{\pi} x \sin nx\, dx$$

Integrating by parts, we have

$$b_n = \frac{2}{\pi} \left[\frac{x\,(-\cos nx)_0^{\pi}}{n} - \int_0^{\pi} 1 \left(\frac{-\cos nx}{n} \right) dx \right]$$

$$= \frac{2}{\pi n} \left[-\pi \cos n\pi + \frac{(\sin nx)_0^{\pi}}{n} \right]$$

$$= \frac{2}{\pi n} \left[-\pi\,(-1)^n + 0 \right]$$

$$= \frac{-2}{n} (-1)^n = \frac{2}{n}(-1)^{n+1}$$

$$= \frac{2}{n} \qquad \text{when } n \text{ is an } odd \text{ integer}$$

and $\qquad\qquad\qquad\qquad = \dfrac{-2}{n} \qquad \text{when } n \text{ is an } even \text{ integer}$

Substituting the values of $\dfrac{1}{2} a_0 = 0$, $a_n = 0$ and b_n as calculated above in Eq. (i), we get

$$f(x) = 2 \sum_{n=1}^{\infty} \frac{-(1)^{n+1}}{n} \sin nx$$

$$= 2 \left[\sin x - \frac{1}{2} \sin 2x + \frac{1}{3} \sin 3x - \frac{1}{4} \sin 4x + \ldots \right]$$

Q. 9.8. (*a*) **How will you represent a function given over a half interval Fourier series?**

(*b*) **Derive the half interval Fourier expansion of a function $f(x)$ in the interval** $\left(0, \dfrac{l}{2} \right)$. **Obtain also the Fourier co-efficients.** (*H.P.U.*, 1994, 1992)

Ans. (*a*) **Half interval series.** A function over a limited range of a variable can also be expressed in terms of a Fourier series. For example, if we wish to expand a function given over a half period of the lowest term we may represent it either in terms of sines or in terms of cosines. If we represent the function given in the half period interval by a Fourier cosine series the repetition outside the interval will be that of an *even* function and if we represent it as a Fourier sine series the repetition will be that of an *odd* function.

For a function defined over half interval 0 to π, the value of various co-efficients is given by

$$a_0 = \frac{1}{1/2 \text{ interval}} \int_0^\pi f(x)\, dx$$

$$a_n = \frac{1}{1/2 \text{ interval}} \int_0^\pi f(x) \cos nx\, dx$$

$$b_n = \frac{1}{1/2 \text{ interval}} \int_0^\pi f(x) \sin nx\, dx$$

The expression $f(x)$ as an even function $f_e(x)$ in cosine terms is given by

$$f(x) = f_e(x) = \frac{a_0}{2} + \sum_{n=1}^{n=\infty} a_n \cos(nx)$$

The expresseion $f(x)$ as an odd function $f_0(x)$ in sine terms is given by

$$f(x) = f_0(x) = \sum_{n=1}^{n=\infty} b_n \sin(nx)$$

(b) Half interval Fourier expansion of $f(x)$. The half interval is from 0 to $l/2$. The arguments of sine or cosine are the phase angles and when the interval is represented as a distance, the variable becomes $2\pi \dfrac{x}{l}$, so that as x changes by l, the phase changes by 2π.

Cosine series. If we choose an even function, it will be represented as a cosine series given by

$$f(x) = f_e(x) = \frac{a_0}{2} + \sum_{n=1}^{n=\infty} a_n \cos 2\pi n \frac{x}{l} \qquad \qquad ...(i)$$

Fourier co-efficient a_n. The Fourier co-efficient a_n is given by

$$a_n = \frac{1}{\text{half interval}} \int_{-l/2}^{+l/2} f(x) \cos \frac{2\pi nx}{l}\, dx$$

$$= \frac{2}{l} \left[\int_{-l/2}^0 f_e(x) \cos \frac{2\pi nx}{l}\, dx + \int_0^{+l/2} f_e(x) \cos \frac{2\pi nx}{l}\, dx \right]$$

$$= \frac{4}{l} \int_0^{l/2} f_e(x) \cos \frac{2\pi nx}{l}\, dx$$

as $\qquad\qquad f(x) = f_e(x)$ for $0 < x < l/2$

and $\qquad\qquad f(x) = f(-x) = f_e(x)$ for $0 < x < l/2$

Sine series. If we choose an *odd* function, it will be represented as a sine series given by

$$f(x) = f_0(x) = \frac{a_0}{2} + \sum_{n=1}^{n=\infty} b_n \sin \frac{2\pi nx}{l} \qquad \qquad ...(ii)$$

Fourier co-efficient b_n. Fourier co-efficient b_n is given by

$$b_n = \frac{1}{\text{half interval}} \int_{-l/2}^{+l/2} f(x) \sin \frac{2\pi nx}{l}\, dx$$

$$= \frac{2}{l}\left[\int_{-l/2}^{0} f_0(x) \sin\frac{2\pi nx}{l}\,dx + \int_{0}^{+l/2} f_0(x)\sin\frac{2\pi nx}{2}\,dx \right]$$

as $f(x) = f_0(x)$ in the range $0 < x < l/2$

Now $\int_{-l/2}^{0} f_0(x)\sin\frac{2\pi nx}{l}\,dx = \int_{l/2}^{0} f_0(-x)\sin\frac{2\pi nx}{l}\,dx$

$$= -\int_{l/2}^{0} f_0(x)\sin\frac{2\pi nx}{l}\,dx = \int_{0}^{l/2} f_0(x)\sin\frac{2\pi nx}{l}\,dx$$

$$= \int_{0}^{l/2} f(x)\sin\frac{2\pi nx}{l}\,dx$$

∴ $b_n = \frac{2}{l}\left[\int_{0}^{l/2} f(x)\sin\frac{2\pi nx}{l}\,dx + \int_{0}^{l/2} f(x)\sin\frac{2\pi nx}{l}\,dx \right]$

or $b_n = \frac{4}{l}\int_{0}^{l/2} f(x)\sin\frac{2\pi nx}{l}\,dx$

These representations hold good only in the half interval 0 to $l/2$. Outside the half interval 0 to $l/2$ these representations will not represent $f(x)$.

Q. 9.9. If $f(x) = x\ (0 < x < \pi/2)$

and $f(x) = \pi - x\ (\pi/2 < x < \pi)$

express the function as a sine and a cosine series and show that

$$\frac{\pi^2}{8} = 1 - \frac{1}{3^2} + \frac{1}{5^2} - \frac{1}{7^2} + \ldots\ldots$$ (K.U 2000; H.P.U., 1993)

Ans. Triangular function. A graphical representation of the function is shown in Fig. 9.5 by *thick* line. It represents a plucked string. The function is defined over only half interval 0 to π and

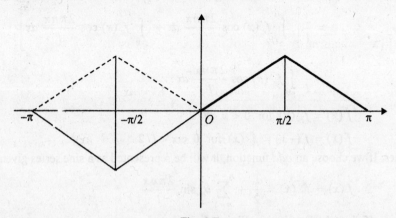

Fig. 9.5

can, therefore, be represented by either cosine or sine series. When represented as a sine series the function repeated outside say in the range $-\pi$ to 0 is shown by *full thin line* curve *i.e.* as an *odd* function given by

$$f(x) = -f(-x)$$

Similarly, if we represent it as a Fourier cosine series, it will repeat outside this interval say in the range $-\pi$ to 0 by the *dotted line curve i.e.*, as an *even* function given by

$$f(x) = f(-x)$$

(*i*) **Cosine series expansion.** The cosine series expansion over the half interval 0 to π is given by

$$f(x) = \frac{a_0}{2} + \sum_{n=1}^{n=\infty} a_n \cos nx$$

Now $\quad a_0 = \dfrac{1}{1/2\pi} \int_0^\pi f(x)\,dx = \dfrac{2}{\pi}\left[\int_0^{\pi/2} f(x)\,dx + \int_{\pi/2}^{\pi} f(x)\,dx \right]$

$$= \frac{2}{\pi}\left[\int_0^{\pi/2} x\,dx + \int_{\pi/2}^{\pi} (\pi - x)\,dx \right]$$

$$= \frac{2}{\pi}\left[\frac{1}{2}(x^2)_0^{\pi/2} + (\pi x)_{\pi/2}^{\pi} - \frac{1}{2}(x^2)_{\pi/2}^{\pi} \right] = \frac{2}{\pi}\left[\frac{\pi^2}{8} + \pi^2 - \frac{\pi^2}{2} - \frac{\pi^2}{2} + \frac{\pi^2}{8} \right]$$

$$= \frac{2}{\pi}\cdot\frac{\pi^2}{4} = \frac{\pi}{2}$$

or $\quad \dfrac{1}{2}a_0 = \pi/4$

Again $\quad a_n = \dfrac{1}{\pi/2}\left[\int_0^\pi f(x)\,(\cos nx)\,dx \right]$

$$= \frac{2}{\pi}\left[\int_0^{\pi/2} x\,(\cos nx)\,dx + \int_{\pi/2}^{\pi} (\pi - x)\,(\cos nx)\,dx \right]$$

But $\quad \displaystyle\int_0^{\pi/2} x(\cos nx)\,dx = \frac{(x \sin nx)_0^{\pi/2}}{n} - \int_0^{\pi/2} \frac{1.\sin nx\,dx}{n}$

$$= \frac{\pi}{2n}\sin\left(\frac{n\pi}{2}\right) - \frac{1}{n}\frac{(-\cos nx)_0^{\pi/2}}{n} = \frac{\pi}{2n}\sin\left(\frac{n\pi}{2}\right) + \frac{1}{n^2}\left[\cos\left(\frac{n\pi}{2}\right) - 1\right]$$

Also $\quad \displaystyle\int_{\pi/2}^{\pi} (\pi - x)\cos nx\,dx = \pi \int_{\pi/2}^{\pi} \cos nx\,dx - \int_{\pi/2}^{\pi} x\cos nx\,dx$

$$= \frac{\pi(\sin nx)_{\pi/2}^{\pi}}{n} - \left[\frac{x(\sin nx)_{\pi/2}^{\pi}}{n} - \int_{\pi/2}^{\pi}\frac{1.\sin nx}{n}\,dx \right]$$

$$= \frac{\pi}{n}\left[0 - \sin\frac{n\pi}{2} \right] - \frac{1}{n}\left[0 - \frac{\pi}{2}\left(\sin\frac{n\pi}{2}\right) \right] - \frac{1}{n}\frac{(-\cos nx)_{\pi/2}^{\pi}}{n}$$

$$= -\frac{\pi}{2n}\sin\frac{n\pi}{2} - \frac{1}{n^2}\left[\cos n\pi - \cos\left(\frac{n\pi}{2}\right) \right]$$

or $\quad a_n = \dfrac{2}{\pi}\left[\dfrac{\pi}{2n}\sin\left(\dfrac{n\pi}{2}\right) + \dfrac{1}{n^2}\left\{ \cos\left(\dfrac{n\pi}{2}\right) - 1 \right\} - \dfrac{\pi}{2n}\sin\left(\dfrac{n\pi}{2}\right) \right.$

$$\left. - \frac{1}{n^2}\left\{ \cos n\pi - \cos\left(\frac{n\pi}{2}\right) \right\} \right]$$

$$= \frac{2}{\pi n^2}\left[\cos\left(\frac{n\pi}{2}\right) - 1 - \cos n\pi + \cos\left(\frac{n\pi}{2}\right)\right]$$

$$= \frac{-2}{\pi n^2}\left[1 + (-1)^2 - 2\cos\left(\frac{n\pi}{2}\right)\right]$$

Using $n = 1, 2, 3, 4, 5$.......etc. in the expression for a_n,
we get

$$a_1 = 0 \qquad\qquad\qquad a_2 = \frac{-8}{2^2 \pi}$$

$$a_3 = 0 \qquad\qquad\qquad a_4 = 0$$

$$a_5 = 0 \qquad\qquad\qquad a_6 = \frac{-8}{6^2 \pi}$$

$$a_7 = 0 \qquad\qquad\qquad a_8 = 0$$

$$a_9 = 0 \qquad\qquad\qquad a_{10} = \frac{-8}{10^2 \pi}$$

i.e. a_n = zero for all odd values of n and for all values of n which are multiples of 4 *i.e* $a_n = \frac{-8}{n^2 \pi}$ for all even values of n except those even values which are multiples of 4.

Substituting the values of a_0 and a_n in the expression

$$f(x) = \frac{1}{2} a_0 + \sum_{n=1}^{\infty} a_n \cos nx, \quad \text{we get}$$

$$f(x) = \frac{\pi}{4} - \frac{8}{\pi}\left[\frac{1}{2^2}\cos 2x + \frac{1}{6^2}\cos 6x + \frac{1}{10^2}\cos 10x + ...\right]$$

(*ii*) **Sine series expansion.** The sine series expansion over the half interval 0 to π is given by

$$f(x) = \sum_{n=1}^{n=\infty} b_n \sin nx$$

Now

$$b_n = \frac{1}{\pi/2}\left[\int_0^{\pi} f(x)(\sin nx)\, dx\right]$$

or

$$b_n = \frac{2}{\pi}\left[\int_0^{\pi/2}(x)(\sin nx)\, dx + \int_{\pi/2}^{\pi}(\pi - x)\sin nx\, dx\right]$$

but

$$\int_0^{\pi/2} x \sin nx\, dx = -\frac{(x\cos nx)_0^{\pi/2}}{n} - \int_0^{\pi/2}\frac{(-\cos nx)}{n}\, dx$$

$$= -\frac{1}{n}\left[\frac{\pi}{2}\cos\left(\frac{n\pi}{2}\right) - 0\right] + \frac{1}{n}\frac{(\sin nx)_0^{\pi/2}}{n}$$

$$= -\frac{\pi}{2n}\cos\left(\frac{n\pi}{2}\right) + \frac{1}{n^2}\sin\left(\frac{n\pi}{2}\right)$$

Also $\displaystyle\int_{\pi/2}^{\pi}(\pi - x)\sin nx\, dx = \pi\int_{\pi/2}^{\pi}\sin nx\, dx + \int_{\pi/2}^{\pi}x\,(-\sin nx)\, dx$

$$= \frac{\pi(-\cos nx)_{\pi/2}^{\pi}}{n} + \frac{(x \cos nx)_{\pi/2}^{\pi}}{n} - \int_{\pi/2}^{\pi} \frac{1 . \cos nx}{n} \, dx$$

$$= \frac{-\pi}{n} \left[\cos n\pi - \cos \left(\frac{n\pi}{2} \right) \right] + \frac{1}{n} \left[\pi \cos n\pi - \frac{\pi}{2} \cos \left(\frac{n\pi}{2} \right) \right] - \frac{1}{n} \frac{(\sin nx)_{\pi/2}^{\pi}}{n}$$

$$= \frac{-\pi}{n} \cos n\pi + \frac{\pi}{n} \cos \frac{n\pi}{2} + \frac{\pi}{n} \cos n\pi - \frac{\pi}{2n} \cos \left(\frac{n\pi}{2} \right) - \frac{1}{n^2} \left[\sin n\pi - \sin \frac{n\pi}{2} \right]$$

$$= \frac{\pi}{2n} \cos \left(\frac{n\pi}{2} \right) + \frac{1}{n^2} \sin \left(\frac{n\pi}{2} \right)$$

$$\therefore \quad b_n = \frac{2}{\pi} \left[\frac{-\pi}{2n} \cos \left(\frac{n\pi}{2} \right) + \frac{1}{n^2} \sin \left(\frac{n\pi}{2} \right) + \frac{\pi}{2n} \cos \left(\frac{n\pi}{2} \right) + \frac{1}{n^2} \sin \left(\frac{n\pi}{2} \right) \right]$$

$$= \frac{2}{\pi n^2} \times 2 \sin \left(\frac{n\pi}{2} \right) = \frac{4}{\pi n^2} \sin \left(\frac{n\pi}{2} \right)$$

For *even* values of n, $\sin \dfrac{n\pi}{2} = 0$ and $b_n = 0$

For *odd* values of n

$$n = 1, \quad \sin \frac{n\pi}{2} = \sin \frac{\pi}{2} = 1$$

$$n = 3, \quad \sin \frac{3\pi}{2} = -1, \; n = 5, \sin \frac{5\pi}{2} = 1$$

$$n = 7, \quad \sin \frac{7\pi}{2} = -1$$

$\therefore$ The sine expansion in Fourier series is given by

$$f(x) = \frac{4}{\pi} \left[\frac{\sin x}{1^2} - \frac{\sin 3x}{3^2} + \frac{\sin 5x}{5^2} - \frac{\sin 7x}{7^2} + \ldots \right]$$

When $x = \pi/2$, $f(x) = x = \dfrac{\pi}{2} = \dfrac{4}{\pi} \left[\dfrac{\sin \pi/2}{1^2} - \dfrac{\sin 3\pi/2}{3^2} + \dfrac{\sin 5\pi/2}{5^2} - \ldots \right]$

or

$$\frac{\pi^2}{8} = \frac{1}{1^2} - \frac{1}{3^2} + \frac{1}{5^2} - \frac{1}{7^2} + \ldots$$

Q. 9.10. (a) Find the Fourier series for a function
$$f(x) = x^2 \text{ for } -\pi < x < \pi. \qquad \text{(H.P.U., 1996)}$$
(b) Hence show that

$$\frac{\pi^2}{6} = \sum_{n=1}^{n=\infty} \frac{1}{n^2}.$$

Ans. Fourier series for $f(x) = x^2$. Fourier series of a function $f(x)$ is given by

$$f(x) = \frac{a_0}{2} + \sum_{n=1}^{n=\infty} [a_n \cos nx + b_n \sin nx]$$

Calculation of co-efficients (*i*) a_0

Now
$$a_0 = \frac{1}{\pi} \int_{-\pi}^{+\pi} f(x) \, dx$$

$$= \frac{1}{\pi} \int_{-\pi}^{+\pi} x^2 \, dx = \frac{1}{\pi} \left[\frac{x^3}{3} \right]_{-\pi}^{+\pi}$$

$$= \frac{1}{\pi} \left[\frac{\pi^3}{3} + \frac{\pi^3}{3} \right] = \frac{2\pi^2}{3}$$

(*ii*)
$$a_n = \frac{1}{\pi} \int_{-\pi}^{+\pi} x^2 \, (\cos nx) \, dx = \frac{2}{\pi} \int_0^{\pi} x^2 \, (\cos nx) \, dx$$

as the function is even.

$$= \frac{2}{n\pi} \left[x^2 \sin nx \right]_0^{\pi} - \frac{4}{n\pi} \int_0^{\pi} x \, (\sin nx) \, dx$$

$$= 0 + \frac{4}{\pi n^2} \left[x \cos nx \right]_0^{\pi} - \frac{4}{\pi n^2} \int_0^{\pi} (\cos nx) \, dx$$

$$= \frac{4}{n^2} \cos n\pi - \frac{4}{\pi n^2} \left[\sin nx \right]_0^{\pi}$$

$$= (-1)^n \frac{4}{n^2}$$

(*iii*)
$$b_n = \frac{1}{\pi} \int_{-\pi}^{+\pi} x^2 \sin nx \, dx = 0$$

as the function is an odd function.

$$\therefore \qquad x^2 = \frac{\pi^2}{3} + \sum (-1)^n \frac{4}{n^2} \cos nx$$

$$= \frac{\pi^2}{3} - 4 \left[\frac{1}{1^2} \cos x - \frac{1}{2^2} \cos 2x + \frac{1}{3^2} \cos 3x + \ldots \right] \qquad \ldots(i)$$

(*b*)   Putting $x = \pi$ in Eq. (*i*), we have

$$\pi^2 = \frac{\pi^2}{3} + 4 \left[\frac{1}{1^2} + \frac{1}{2^2} + \frac{1}{3^2} + \ldots \right]$$

or
$$\frac{\pi^2}{6} = \frac{1}{1^2} + \frac{1}{2^2} + \frac{1}{3^2} + \ldots$$

$$= \sum_{n=1}^{n=\infty} \frac{1}{n^2}$$

Q. 9.11. Analyse a triangular wave into its simple harmonic components with the help of Fourier theorem. (*K.U.* 2001; *Gharwal U.* 2000)

Ans. Triangular wave. A triangular wave can be represented by the function

$$f(x) = \begin{cases} kx & \text{for } 0 < x < \pi \\ -kx & \text{for } -\pi < x < 0 \end{cases}$$

where k is a *positive* constant. A triangular wave is shown in Fig. 9.6. The Fourier series expansion of $f(x)$ is given by

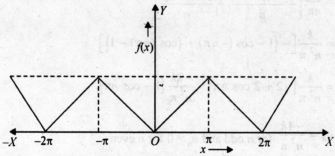

Fig. 9.6

$$f(x) = \frac{1}{2} a_0 + \sum_{n=1}^{\infty} [a_n \cos nx + b_n \sin nx] \qquad ...(i)$$

Now $\quad a_0 = \frac{1}{\pi} \int_{-\pi}^{+\pi} f(x)\, dx = \frac{1}{\pi} \left[\int_{-\pi}^{0} f(x)\, dx + \int_{0}^{\pi} f(x)\, dx \right]$

$$= \frac{1}{\pi} \left[\int_{-\pi}^{0} (-kx)\, dx + \int_{0}^{\pi} (kx)\, dx \right] = \frac{1}{\pi} \left[\frac{-k\,(x^2)_{-\pi}^{0}}{2} + \frac{k\,(x^2)_{0}^{\pi}}{2} \right]$$

$$= \frac{1}{\pi} \left[\frac{+k\pi^2}{2} + \frac{k\pi^2}{2} \right] = k\pi$$

Hence $\quad \dfrac{1}{2} a_0 = \dfrac{k\pi}{2}$

Again $\quad a_n = \frac{1}{\pi} \int_{-\pi}^{\pi} f(x) \cos nx\, dx = \frac{1}{\pi} \left[\int_{-\pi}^{0} f(x) \cos nx\, dx + \int_{0}^{\pi} f(x) \cos nx\, dx \right]$

$$= \frac{1}{\pi} \left[\int_{-\pi}^{0} (-kx) \cos nx\, dx + \int_{0}^{\pi} kx \cos nx\, dx \right]$$

$$= \frac{k}{\pi} \left[\int_{-\pi}^{0} (-x) \cos nx\, dx + \int_{0}^{\pi} x \cos nx\, dx \right]$$

Integrating both the integrals by parts, we get

$$a_n = \frac{k}{\pi} \left[\left\{ \frac{-x \sin x}{n} \right\}_{-\pi}^{0} - \int_{-\pi}^{0} (-1) \frac{\sin nx}{n}\, dx + \left[\left\{ \frac{x \sin x}{n} \right\}_{0}^{\pi} - \int_{0}^{\pi} \frac{1 . \sin nx}{n}\, dx \right] \right]$$

$$= \frac{k}{\pi} \left[0 + \frac{1}{n} \int_{-\pi}^{0} \sin nx\, dx \right] + \left[0 - \frac{1}{n} \int_{0}^{\pi} \sin nx\, dx \right]$$

$$= \frac{k}{n\pi} \left[\frac{-(\cos nx)_{-\pi}^{0}}{n} + \frac{(\cos nx)_{0}^{\pi}}{n} \right]$$

$$= \frac{k}{n^2 \pi} \left[-\{1 - \cos(-n\pi)\} + \{\cos(n\pi) - 1\} \right]$$

$$= \frac{k}{n^2 \pi} [-2 + 2\cos n\pi] = \frac{-2k}{n^2 \pi} [1 - \cos n\pi]$$

$\therefore$ $a_n = \dfrac{-4k}{n^2 \pi}$ for n odd and $a_n = 0$ for n even

Also $b_n = \dfrac{1}{\pi} \displaystyle\int\limits_{-\pi}^{\pi} f(x) \sin nx \, dx$

$$= \frac{1}{\pi} \left[\int_{-\pi}^{0} (-kx) \sin nx \, dx + \int_{0}^{\pi} kx \sin nx \, dx \right]$$

$$= \frac{k}{\pi} \left[\int_{-\pi}^{0} x(-\sin x) \, dx - \int_{0}^{\pi} x(-\sin x) \, dx \right]$$

$$= \frac{k}{\pi} \left[\left\{ \frac{x \cos nx}{n} \right\}_{-\pi}^{0} - \int_{-\pi}^{0} \frac{1 . \cos nx}{n} \, dx - \left\{ \frac{x \cos nx}{n} \right\}_{0}^{\pi} + \int_{0}^{\pi} \frac{1 . \cos nx}{n} \, dx \right]$$

$$= \frac{k}{\pi} \left[\left\{ 0 + \frac{\pi \cos(-n\pi)}{n} \right\} - \frac{1}{n^2} (\sin nx)_{-\pi}^{0} - \left\{ \frac{\pi \cos nx}{n} - 0 \right\} + \frac{1}{n^2} (\sin nx)_{0}^{\pi} \right]$$

$$= \frac{k}{\pi} \left\{ \frac{\pi}{n} \cos n\pi - 0 - \frac{\pi}{n} \cos n\pi + 0 \right\} = 0$$

Thus the co-efficients of all sine terms are zero. Substituting the values of a_0, a_n (for odd values of n only) and $b_n = 0$, in Eq. (i) we get

$$f(x) = \frac{k\pi}{2} - \frac{4k}{\pi} \sum_{n_{odd}}^{\infty} \frac{\cos nx}{n^2} = \frac{k\pi}{2} - \frac{4k}{\pi} \left[\frac{\cos x}{1^2} + \frac{\cos 3x}{3^2} + \frac{\cos 5x}{5^2} + \ldots \right]$$

For $k = 1$, $f(x) = \dfrac{\pi}{2} - \dfrac{4}{\pi} \left[\cos x + \dfrac{1}{3^2} \cos 3x + \dfrac{1}{5^2} \cos 5x + \ldots \right]$

Q. 9.12. Find the Fourier series for $f(x)$ in the interval $(-\pi, \pi)$ when

$$f(x) = (\pi + x) \text{ for } -\pi < x < 0$$

and $f(x) = (\pi - x)$ for $0 < x < \pi$.

(*M.D.U.* 2003)

Ans. The graph of the given function $f(x)$ in the interval $(-\pi, \pi)$ is shown in Fig. 9.7. The periodic extension beyond $(-\pi)$ and $(+\pi)$ is indicated by dotted curve. It is clear from the figure that in the given interval function $f(x)$ is an *even* function.

The Fourier series for the function $f(x)$ is given by

$$f(x) = \frac{1}{2} a_0 + \sum_{n=1}^{\infty} [a_n \cos nx + b_n \sin nx] \quad ...(i)$$

To find the value of Fourier co-efficients a_0, a_n and b_n we have,

$$\frac{1}{2} a_0 = \frac{1}{2\pi} \int_{-\pi}^{\pi} f(x) \, dx = \frac{2}{2\pi} \int_{0}^{\pi} f(x) \, dx \qquad [\because f(x) \text{ is an even function}]$$

$$= \frac{1}{\pi} \int_0^\pi (\pi - x) \, dx = \frac{1}{\pi}\left[\pi \int_0^\pi dx - \int_0^\pi x dx \right]$$

$$= \frac{1}{\pi}\left[\pi \, [x]_0^\pi - \frac{[x^2]_0^\pi}{2} \right] = \frac{1}{\pi}\left[\pi \, (\pi - 0) - \frac{(\pi^2 - 0)}{2} \right]$$

$$= \frac{1}{\pi}\left[\frac{\pi^2}{2} \right] = \frac{\pi}{2}$$

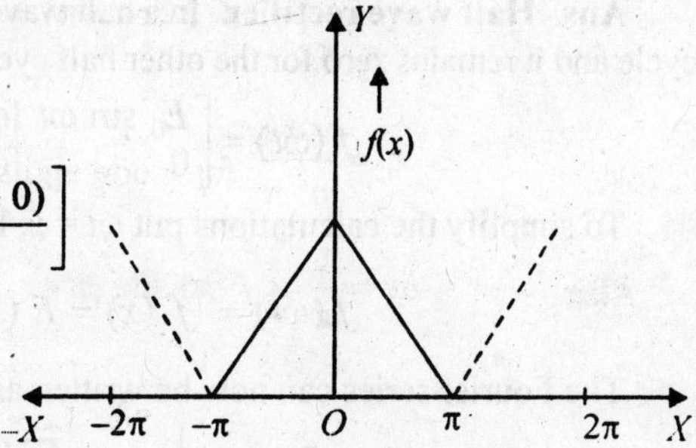

Fig. 9.7

Again $\quad a_n = \frac{1}{\pi} \int_{-\pi}^{\pi} f(x) \cos nx \, dx = \frac{2}{\pi} \int_0^\pi f(x) \cos nx \, dx$

$$[\because f(x) \text{ is an even function}, f(x) \cos nx \text{ is also an even function.}]$$

$$\therefore \qquad a_n = \frac{2}{\pi} \int_0^\pi (\pi - x) \cos nx \, dx = \frac{2}{\pi}\left[\pi \int_0^\pi \cos nx \, dx - \int_0^\pi x \cos nx \, dx \right]$$

Solving the first integral directly and second by the method of integration by parts, we get

$$a_n = \frac{2}{\pi}\left[\left\{ \pi \, \frac{(\sin nx)_0^\pi}{n} - \frac{(x \sin nx)_0^\pi}{n} \right\} + \int_0^\pi 1 \cdot \frac{\sin nx}{n} \, dx \right]$$

$$= \frac{2}{\pi}\left[\frac{1}{n} \int_0^\pi \sin nx \, dx \right] \qquad\qquad [\because \text{The expression within } \{ \} = 0]$$

$$= \frac{2}{\pi n}\left[\frac{(-\cos nx)_0^\pi}{n} \right] = \frac{-2}{\pi n^2} (\cos n\pi - 1)$$

$$= \frac{-2}{\pi n^2}\left[(-1)^n - 1 \right]$$

$$= \frac{4}{\pi n^2} \text{ when } n \text{ is odd and zero when } n \text{ is even.}$$

Also $\quad b_n = \frac{1}{\pi} \int_{-\pi}^{\pi} f(x) \sin nx \, dx$

Now $f(x)$ is an even function but $\sin x$ is an odd function. Therefore, $f(x) \sin nx$ is an odd function.

$$\therefore \qquad \int_{-\pi}^{\pi} f(x) \sin nx \, dx = 0$$

Hence $b_n = 0$ *i.e.,* the amplitude of all the sine terms is zero. Substituting the values of Fourier co-efficients a_0 and a_n (for n odd only) in Eq. (*i*), we have

$$f(x) = \frac{\pi}{2} + \frac{4}{\pi n^2} \sum_{n \text{ odd}}^{\infty} \cos nx$$

$$= \frac{\pi}{2} + \frac{4}{\pi} \left[\cos x + \frac{1}{3^2} \cos 3x + \frac{1}{5^2} \cos 5x + \ldots \right]$$

Q. 9.13. Apply Fourier theorem to analyse the out put of a half wave rectifier.

(M.D.U. 2006, 2002, 2000; K.U. 2002, 2000)

Ans. Half wave rectifier. In a half wave rectifier the output voltage is obtained only for one half cycle and it remains zero for the other half cycle (Fig. 9.8.) The output voltage is given by the equation

$$f(\omega t) = \begin{bmatrix} E_0 \sin \omega t & \text{for } 0 < \omega t < \pi \\ 0 & \text{for } \pi < \omega t < 2\pi \end{bmatrix}$$

To simplify the calculations put $\omega t = x$, keeping the limits from 0 to 2π so that

$$f(\omega t) = f(x) = E(x) = \begin{bmatrix} E_0 \sin x & \text{for } 0 < x < \pi \\ 0 & \text{for } \pi < x < 2\pi \end{bmatrix}$$

The Fourier series can now be written as

$$E(x) = \frac{1}{2} a_0 + \sum_{n=1}^{\infty} \left[a_n \cos nx + b_n \sin nx \right] \qquad \ldots(i)$$

where
$$a_0 = \frac{1}{\pi} \int_0^{2\pi} f(x) \, dx = \frac{1}{\pi} \int_0^{2\pi} E(x) \, dx$$

$$= \frac{1}{\pi} \left[\int_0^{\pi} E_0 \sin x \, dx + \int_\pi^{2\pi} E_0 \sin x \, dx \right]$$

$$= \frac{1}{\pi} \left[E_0 \left(-\cos x \right)_0^{\pi} + 0 \right]$$

$$= \frac{2 E_0}{\pi}$$

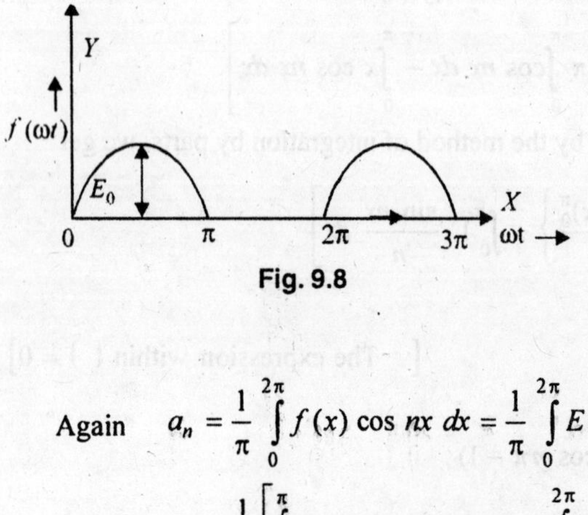

Fig. 9.8

Hence $\quad \dfrac{1}{2} a_0 = \dfrac{E_0}{\pi}$

Again $\quad a_n = \dfrac{1}{\pi} \int_0^{2\pi} f(x) \cos nx \, dx = \dfrac{1}{\pi} \int_0^{2\pi} E(x) \cos nx \, dx$

$$= \frac{1}{\pi} \left[\int_0^{\pi} E_0 \sin x \cos nx \, dx + \int_\pi^{2\pi} (0) \cos nx \, dx \right]$$

$$= \frac{1}{\pi} \int_0^{\pi} E_0 \sin x \cos nx \, dx = \frac{E_0}{2\pi} \int_0^{\pi} \left[\sin (n+1) x - \sin (n-1) x \right] dx$$

$$\{ [\because \sin (nx + x) - \sin (nx - x)] = \sin nx \cos x + \cos nx \sin x - \sin nx \cos x$$
$$+ \cos nx \sin x = 2 \sin x \cos nx \}$$

$$= \frac{E_0}{2\pi} \left[\frac{-\{ \cos (n+1) x \}_0^{\pi}}{n+1} - \frac{-\{ \cos (n-1) x \}_0^{\pi}}{n-1} \right]$$

$$= \frac{-E_0}{2\pi} \left[\frac{\cos (n+1) \pi - 1}{n+1} - \frac{\cos (n-1) \pi - 1}{n-1} \right]$$

$$= \frac{-E_0}{2\pi}\left[\{\cos(n-1)\pi - 1\}\left\{\frac{1}{n+1} - \frac{1}{n-1}\right\}\right]$$

$$\{\because \ \cos(n+1)\pi = \cos(n-1)\pi\}$$

$$= \frac{-E_0}{2\pi}\{(-1)^{n-1} - 1\}\left\{\frac{-2}{n^2-1}\right\} = \frac{E_0}{\pi}\frac{(-1)^{n-1}-1}{n^2-1} \qquad \ldots(ii)$$

When n is odd $\dfrac{(-1)^{n-1}-1}{n^2-1} = 0$

$$\therefore \qquad a_n = \frac{-2E_0}{\pi(n^2-1)} \text{ For } n \text{ even only}$$

Also $b_n = \dfrac{1}{\pi}\displaystyle\int_0^{2\pi} f(x)\sin nx\ dx = \dfrac{1}{\pi}\displaystyle\int_0^{2\pi} E(x)\sin nx\ dx$

$$= \frac{1}{\pi}\left[\int_0^\pi E_0 \sin x \sin nx\ dx + \int_\pi^{2\pi}(0)\sin nx\ dx\right]$$

$$= \frac{E_0}{\pi}\int_0^\pi \sin x \sin nx\ dx$$

For $n=1$, $b_1 = \dfrac{E_0}{\pi}\displaystyle\int_0^\pi \sin^2 x\ dx = \dfrac{E_0}{2\pi}\displaystyle\int_0^\pi (1-\cos 2x)\ dx$

$$= \frac{E_0}{2\pi}\left[x - \frac{\sin 2x}{2}\right]_0^\pi = \frac{E_0}{2\pi}(\pi - 0) = \frac{E_0}{2} \qquad \ldots(iii)$$

For $n>1$, $b_n = \dfrac{E_0}{\pi}\displaystyle\int_0^\pi \sin x \sin nx\ dx$

$$= \frac{E_0}{2\pi}\int_0^\pi \left[\cos(n-1)x - \cos(n+1)x\right]dx$$

$$[\because \ \cos(nx-x) - \cos(nx+x) = \cos nx \cos x + \sin nx \sin x - \cos nx \cos x + \sin nx \sin x$$
$$= 2\sin nx \sin x]$$

$$= \frac{E_0}{2\pi}\left[\frac{[\sin(n-1)x]_0^\pi}{n-1} - \frac{[\sin(n+1)x]_0^\pi}{n+1}\right] = 0 \qquad \ldots(iv)$$

Substituting the values of a_0, a_n (for even values of n only) and b_n (for $n=1$ only) in Eq. (i), we have

$$E_{(x)} = \frac{E_0}{\pi} - \frac{2E_0}{\pi}\sum_{n=1}^\infty \frac{\cos nx}{(n^2-1)} + \frac{E_0}{2}\sin x$$

$$= \frac{E_0}{\pi} + \frac{E_0}{2}\sin x - \frac{2E_0}{\pi}\left[\frac{\cos 2x}{3} + \frac{\cos 4x}{15} + \frac{\cos 6x}{35} + \ldots\right]$$

Putting $x = \omega t$, we get

$$E(\omega t) = \frac{E_0}{\pi} + \frac{E_0}{2} \sin \omega t - \frac{2 E_0}{\pi} \left[\frac{\cos 2\, \omega t}{3} + \frac{\cos 4\, \omega t}{15} + \frac{\cos 6\, \omega t}{35} + ... \right]$$

The first term $\dfrac{E_0}{\pi}$ represents the *d.c.* or average value of voltage output of half wave rectifier *i.e.*

$E_{d.c} = \dfrac{E_0}{\pi}$. Other components represent output voltage of frequency ω, 2 ω, 4 ω, 6 ω ......etc.

Ripple factor. Ripple factor of a rectifier is given by

$$\gamma = \frac{r.m.s \text{ value of } A.C \text{ component in output}}{D.C \text{ component}}$$

In a half wave rectifier *r.m.s* value of the output voltage

$$E_{r.m.s} = \frac{E_0}{2}$$

$\therefore$ *r.m.s* value of *A.C* component only $= E'_{r.m.s.} = \sqrt{E_{r.m.s}^2 - E_{d.c}^2}$

$$= \sqrt{\left(\frac{E_0}{2} \right)^2 - \left(\frac{E_0}{\pi} \right)^2} = 0.386\ E_0$$

Hence ripple factor $\gamma = \dfrac{E'_{r.m.s}}{E_{d.c}} = \dfrac{0.386\ E_0}{E_0 / \pi} = 0.386\,\pi = 1.21$

Q. 9.14. Analyse the out put of a full wave rectifier using Fourier series method. Prove that the rectifier removes undesirable ripples.

(*M.D.U* 2005, 2001, 1998; *Gharwal U.* 1999; *K.U.* 1995; *H.P.U.* 1992)

Ans. Full wave rectifier. A full wave rectifier passes the positive peak of incoming input sine wave signal and inverts the negative peak of the input sine wave signal.

The output voltage is given by the equation

$$f(\omega t) = \left[\begin{array}{l} E_0 \sin \omega t \ \text{ for } \ 0 < \omega t < \pi \\ -E_0 \sin \omega t \ \text{ for } \ \pi < \omega t < 2\pi \end{array} \right.$$

It is shown in Fig. 9.9.

To simplify the calculations put $\omega t = x$ keeping the limits the same from 0 to 2π, so that

$$f(\omega t) = f(x) = E(x) = \left[\begin{array}{l} E_0 \sin x \ \text{for} \ 0 < x < \pi \\ -E_0 \sin x \ \text{for} \ \pi < x < 2\pi \end{array} \right.$$

The Fourier series can now be written as

$$E(x) = \frac{1}{2}\, a_0 + \sum_{n=1}^{\infty} \left[a_n \cos nx + b_n \sin nx \right]$$

...(i)

where $a_0 = \dfrac{1}{\pi} \displaystyle\int_0^{2\pi} f(x)\, dx = \dfrac{1}{\pi} \displaystyle\int_0^{2\pi} E(x)\, dx$

$$= \frac{1}{\pi} \left[\int_0^\pi E_0 \sin x \, dx + \int_\pi^{2\pi} (-E_0) \sin x \, dx \right]$$

$$= \frac{E_0}{\pi} \left[(-\cos x)_0^\pi + (\cos x)_\pi^{2\pi} \right]$$

$$= \frac{E_0}{\pi} \left[-(\cos \pi - 1) + (\cos 2\pi - \cos \pi) \right]$$

$$= \frac{E_0}{\pi} \quad (4)$$

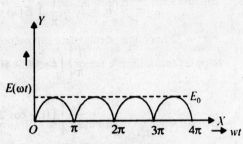

Fig. 9.9

Hence $\dfrac{1}{2} a_0 = \dfrac{2E_0}{\pi}$

Again $a_n = \dfrac{1}{\pi} \displaystyle\int_0^{2\pi} f(x) \cos nx \, dx = \dfrac{1}{\pi} \int_0^{2\pi} E(x) \cos nx \, dx$

$$= \frac{1}{\pi} \left[\int_0^\pi E_0 \sin x \cos nx \, dx + \int_\pi^{2\pi} (-E_0 \sin x) \cos nx \, dx \right]$$

$$= \frac{E_0}{\pi} \left[\int_0^\pi \sin x \cos nx \, dx - \int_\pi^{2\pi} \sin x \cos nx \, dx \right] \qquad \dots(ii)$$

But $\displaystyle\int_0^\pi \sin x \cos nx \, dx = \dfrac{(-1)^{n-1} - 1}{n^2 - 1}$

[For proof See Q. 9.13 Eq. (ii)]
Similarly it can be proved that

$$\int_\pi^{2\pi} \sin x \cos nx \, dx = - \frac{(-1)^{n-1} - 1}{n^2 - 1}$$

Substituting the values of the integrals in Eq. (ii) we have

$$a_n = \frac{E_0}{\pi} \left[\frac{(-1)^{n-1} - 1}{n^2 - 1} + \frac{(-1)^{n-1} - 1}{n^2 - 1} \right]$$

When n is an even integer > 1

$$a_n = \frac{4E_0}{\pi(n^2 - 1)}$$

When n is an odd integer > 1

$$a_n = 0$$

Also $b_n = \dfrac{1}{\pi} \displaystyle\int_0^{2\pi} E(x) \sin x \, dx$

$$= \frac{1}{\pi} \left[\int_0^\pi E_0 \sin x \sin nx \, dx + \int_\pi^{2\pi} (-E_0) \sin x \sin nx \, dx \right]$$

But $\displaystyle\int_0^\pi E_0 \sin x \sin nx \, dx = 0$ (For $n > 1$)

[For proof see **Q. 9.13.** Eq. (*iv*)]

Similarly it can be proved that $\int_{\pi}^{2\pi}(-E_0)\sin x \sin nx dx = 0$

For $n = 1$

$$b_n = b_1 = \frac{1}{\pi}\int_0^{2\pi} E(x)\sin x dx$$

$$= \frac{1}{\pi}\left[\int_0^{\pi} E_0 \sin x \sin x dx + \int_{\pi}^{2\pi}(-E_0)\sin x \sin x\, dx\right]$$

$$= \frac{E_0}{2\pi}\left[\int_0^{\pi}(1-\cos 2x)\,dx - \int_{\pi}^{2\pi}(1-\cos 2x)\,dx\right]$$

$$= \frac{E_0}{2\pi}\left[(x)_0^{\pi} - \frac{(\sin 2x)_0^{\pi}}{2} - (x)_{\pi}^{2\pi} + \frac{(\sin 2x)_{\pi}^{2\pi}}{2}\right]$$

$$= \frac{E_0}{2\pi}[\pi - 0 - \pi - 0] = 0$$

Thus $b_n = 0$ for all values of n.

Substituting the value of a_0, a_n (for even values fo n only) in Eq. (*i*), we get

$$E(x) = \frac{2 E_0}{\pi} - \frac{4 E_0}{\pi (n^2 - 1)}\sum_{n=1}^{\infty}\cos nx \qquad\qquad \text{[For } n \text{ even only]}$$

$$= \frac{2 E_0}{\pi} - \frac{4 E_0}{\pi}\left[\frac{\cos 2x}{3} + \frac{\cos 4x}{15} + \frac{\cos 6x}{35} + ...\right]$$

Putting $x = \omega t$, we get

$$E(\omega t) = \frac{2 E_0}{\pi} - \frac{4 E_0}{\pi}\left[\frac{\cos 2\,\omega t}{3} + \frac{\cos 4\,\omega t}{15} + \frac{\cos 6\,\omega t}{35} + ...\right] \qquad ...(iii)$$

The first term $\dfrac{2 E_0}{\pi}$ represents the *D.C.* or average value of voltage output of the full wave

rectifier *i.e.* $E_{d.c.} = \dfrac{2 E_0}{\pi}$. Other components represent output voltage of frequency $2\omega, 4\omega, 6\omega$ ....etc.

Ripple factor. Ripple factor γ of a rectifier is given by

$$\gamma = \frac{r.m.s. \text{ value of } A.C. \text{ component of the output}}{D.C. \text{ component}}$$

In a full wave rectifier *r.m.s* value of the output voltage $E_{r.m.s.} = \dfrac{E_0}{\sqrt{2}}$

$\therefore$ *r.m.s* value of *A.C.* out put only $E'_{r.m.s.} = \sqrt{(E_{r.m.s.})^2 - (E_{d.c.})^2}$

$$= \sqrt{\left(\frac{E_0}{\sqrt{2}}\right)^2 - \left(\frac{2 E_0}{\pi}\right)^2} = 0.308\, E_0$$

Hence ripple factor of a full wave rectifier

$$\gamma = \frac{E'_{r.m.s.}}{E_{d.c.}} = \frac{0.308\, E_0}{\dfrac{2\, E_0}{\pi}} = \frac{0.308 \times \pi}{2} = 0.48$$

Rectifier removes undesirable ripples. From Eq. (*iii*), we find that the frequency (ω) of the input sine wave signal *i.e.*, input voltage $E_0 \sin \omega t$ has been eliminated. The lowest frequency of the voltage oscillation is 2 ω. The high frequency components fall off as ($n^2 - 1$) indicating that the out put voltage gets depleted of the high frequency components at a vey fast rate. Thus a full wave rectifier does a fairly good job of approximating direct current with a ripple factor of only 0.48.

Q. 9.15. State Fourier's theorem and give some of its applications.
(*Gharwal U.* 1999; *Os. U.*, 1997; *Ranchi U.*, 1991)

Ans. Fourier's theorem. See **Q. 9.1 (b).**

Applications. (*i*) It is used to analyse a complex note into its con .ituent simple harmonic vibrations.

The terms required to build up a periodic curve may be limited or may be infinite in number. Any term, even the first, may be absent. For example, if we have a complex vibration due to two tones, say 100 and 101, then Fourier analysis of this complex vibration will give only the components of frequency 100 and 101 and none else. How do they form the harmonic series? The answer is simple. These are in fact 100th and 101st terms of the series, all other terms being absent. The frequency of the compound vibration is 1, because in one second (not earlier) each of the constituents will have completed an exact number of vibrations. The fundamental in this case has a frequency *one* but with *zero* amplitude.

If a complex curve to be analysed has only a slight curvature, everywhere, the lower members of its constituents have a greater amplitude. For points on a curve having large curvature the higher terms are more important. A curve with sharp corners possesses an infinite number of terms of the series.

In case of two harmonic vibrations whose frequencies are incommensurable such as 100 and 100 π or 100 $\sqrt{2}$, the theorem does not apply because the *compound vibration is not periodic.*

(*ii*) It is also used to synthesise a complex periodic vibration from its simple harmonic constituents.

(*iii*) It has a wide field of application not only in the study of sound but also in various other branches of Physics such as magnetic storms and rise and fall of potential in electrical machines. It has been also used successfully to analyse periodic phenomenon in nature such as sun spots and rise and fall of tides.

9.16. What are Fourier integrals? Explain. Obtain Fourier integral for (*i*) even function (*ii*) odd function and (*iii*) in complex form. (*K.U.* 2002; *M.D.U.* 2000, 1999)

Ans. Fourier integral. If a function $f(x)$ is (*i*) defined in the interval ($-L, L$) (*ii*) is periodic with a period 2 L, (*iii*) is differentiable (*iv*) is integrable in the limit $-\infty$ to $+\infty$ and (*v*) $f(x)$ as well as $f'(x)$ or $\dfrac{df(x)}{dx}$ are piece wise continuous in the interval ($-L, L$), then the function can be expressed in the form

$$f(x) = \frac{1}{2\pi} \int_{-\infty}^{+\infty} f(t) \left[\int_{-\infty}^{+\infty} \cos \omega \, (x - t)\, d\omega \right] dt \qquad \text{...(i)}$$

The *double integral* on the right hand side of Eq. (*i*) is known as *Fourier integral.*

Proof. The given function $f(x)$ can be written in the form of Fourier series as

$$f(x) = \frac{1}{2}\, a_0 + \sum_{n=1}^{n=\infty} a_n \cos\left(\frac{n\pi x}{L}\right) + \sum_{n=1}^{n=\infty} b_n \sin\left(\frac{n\pi x}{L}\right) \qquad \text{...(ii)}$$

[As x represents a length, the argument of sine and cosine must be phase angle and represented as

$$\frac{2\pi x}{\lambda} = \frac{2\pi x}{2L} = \frac{\pi x}{L}]$$

Now $\qquad \dfrac{1}{2} a_0 = \dfrac{1}{2L} \displaystyle\int_{-L}^{L} f(\lambda)\,dx; \quad a_n = \dfrac{1}{L} \displaystyle\int_{-L}^{L} f(x) \cos\left(\dfrac{n\pi x}{L}\right) dx$ and

$$b_n = \frac{1}{L} \int_{-L}^{L} f(x) \sin\left(\frac{n\pi x}{L}\right) dx$$

As the variable in Fourier integral [given in (*i*)] is t we shall change the variable in the values of a_0, a_n and b_n from x to t. This will not change the value of the integrals because a_0, a_n and b_n are independent of x.

$$\therefore \qquad \frac{1}{2} a_0 = \frac{1}{2L} \int_{-L}^{L} f(t)\,dt \qquad\qquad\qquad\qquad ...(iii)$$

$$a_n = \frac{1}{L} \int_{-L}^{L} f(t) \cos\left(\frac{n\pi t}{L}\right) dt \qquad\qquad\qquad ...(iv)$$

and $\qquad b_n = \dfrac{1}{L} \displaystyle\int_{-L}^{-L} f(t) \sin\left(\dfrac{n\pi t}{L}\right) dt \qquad\qquad\qquad ...(v)$

Substituting the values of a_0, a_n and b_n from relations (*iii*), (*iv*) and (*v*) in Eq. (*ii*), we get

$$f(x) = \frac{1}{2L} \int_{-L}^{L} f(t)\,dt + \sum_{n=1}^{\infty} \left[\left\{ \frac{1}{L} \int_{-L}^{L} f(t) \cos\left(\frac{n\pi t}{L}\right) dt \right\} \cos\left(\frac{n\pi x}{L}\right) \right.$$

$$\left. + \left\{ \frac{1}{L} \int_{-L}^{L} f(t) \sin\left(\frac{n\pi t}{L}\right) dt \right\} \sin\left(\frac{n\pi x}{L}\right) \right] dt$$

$$= \frac{1}{2L} \int_{-L}^{L} f(t)\,dt + \sum_{n=1}^{\infty} \frac{1}{L} \int_{-L}^{L} f(t) \left[\cos\left(\frac{n\pi t}{L}\right) \cos\left(\frac{n\pi x}{L}\right) + \sin\left(\frac{n\pi t}{L}\right) \sin\left(\frac{n\pi x}{L}\right) \right] dt$$

$$= \frac{1}{2L} \int_{-L}^{L} f(t)\,dt + \sum_{n=1}^{\infty} \frac{1}{L} \int_{-L}^{L} f(t) \cos\left\{ \frac{n\pi (x-t)}{L} \right\} dt$$

$$= \frac{1}{2\pi} \left[\frac{\pi}{L} \int_{-L}^{L} f(t)\,dt + \sum_{n=1}^{\infty} \frac{2\pi}{L} f(t)\cos\left\{ \frac{n\pi (x-t)}{L} \right\} dt \right]$$

$$= \frac{1}{2\pi} \int_{-L}^{L} f(t) \left[\frac{\pi}{L} + \sum_{n=1}^{\infty} \frac{2\pi}{L} \cos\left\{ \frac{n\pi (x-t)}{L} \right\} \right] dt$$

$$= \frac{1}{2\pi} \int_{-L}^{L} f(t) \left[\frac{\pi}{L} \cos\left\{ 0 \times \frac{\pi}{L} (x-t) \right\} + \sum_{n=1}^{\infty} \frac{\pi}{L} \cos\left\{ \frac{n\pi (x-t)}{L} \right\} \right.$$

$$\left. + \sum_{n=1}^{\infty} \frac{\pi}{L} \cos\left\{ \frac{n\pi (x-t)}{L} \right\} \right] dt$$

$$\left[\because \cos\left\{0 \times \frac{\pi}{L}(x-t)\right\} = 1 \text{ and } \frac{2\pi}{L}\int_{-L}^{L}\cos\left\{\frac{n\pi(x-t)}{L}\right\} \text{ has been split into two parts.}\right]$$

$$= \frac{1}{2\pi}\int_{-L}^{L}f(t)\left[\frac{\pi}{L}\cos\left\{0\times\frac{\pi}{L}(x-t)\right\} + \sum_{n=1}^{\infty}\frac{\pi}{L}\cos\left\{\frac{n\pi(x-t)}{L}\right\} + \sum_{n=1}^{\infty}\frac{\pi}{L}\cos\left\{\frac{-n\pi(x-t)}{L}\right\}\right]dt$$

$$\left[\because \cos\left\{\frac{n\pi(x-t)}{L}\right\} = \cos\left\{\frac{-n\pi(x-t)}{L}\right\}\right]$$

$$= \frac{1}{2\pi}\int_{-L}^{L}f(t)\left[\sum_{n=0}^{\infty}\frac{\pi}{L}\cos\left\{\frac{n\pi(x-t)}{L}\right\} + \sum_{n=-1}^{-\infty}\frac{\pi}{L}\cos\left\{\frac{n\pi(x-t)}{L}\right\}\right]dt$$

$$\left[\because \frac{\pi}{L}\cos\left\{0\times\frac{\pi}{L}(x-t)\right\} + \sum_{n=1}^{\infty}\frac{\pi}{L}\cos\left\{\frac{n\pi(x-t)}{L}\right\} = \sum_{n=0}^{\infty}\frac{\pi}{L}\cos\left\{\frac{2\pi(x-t)}{L}\right\}\right]$$

or $$f(x) = \frac{1}{2\pi}\int_{-L}^{L}f(t)\left[\sum_{n=-\infty}^{+\infty}\frac{\pi}{L}\cos\left\{\frac{n\pi(x-t)}{L}\right\}\right]dt \qquad ...(vi)$$

When $L \to \infty$ or $\dfrac{L}{\pi} \to \infty$, Then $\dfrac{\pi}{L} = \Delta\omega \to 0$

and $\displaystyle\sum_{n=-\infty}^{+\infty}\frac{\pi}{L}\cos\left\{\frac{n\pi(x-t)}{L}\right\}$ becomes $\displaystyle\sum_{n=-\infty}^{+\infty}\Delta\omega\cos\{n(x-t)\Delta\omega\}$.

Changing the summation into integration and substituting $\Delta\omega = d\omega$ and $n\Delta\omega = \omega$, we get

$$\sum_{n=-\infty}^{+\infty}\Delta\omega\cos\{n(x-t)\Delta\omega\} = \int_{-\infty}^{+\infty}\cos\omega(x-t)\,d\omega$$

Substituting $$\sum_{n=-\infty}^{+\infty}\frac{\pi}{L}\cos\left\{n\pi\frac{x-t}{L}\right\} = \int_{-\infty}^{+\infty}\cos\omega(x-t)\,d\omega \text{ in Eq. } (vi)$$

we get

$$f(x) = \frac{1}{2\pi}\int_{-\infty}^{+\infty}f(t)\left[\int_{-\infty}^{+\infty}\cos\omega(x-t)\,d\omega\right]dt \qquad ...(vii)$$

Thus we have obtained Fourier integral for $f(x)$ from the Fourier series expansion of $f(x)$. Relation (vii) can be further simplified to

$$f(x) = \frac{1}{2\pi}\int_{-\infty}^{+\infty}d\omega\left[\int_{-\infty}^{+\infty}f(t)\cos\{\omega(x-t)\}dt\right]$$

$$= \frac{1}{\pi}\int_{0}^{\infty}d\omega\int_{-\infty}^{+\infty}f(t)\cos\{\omega(x-t)\}dt \qquad ...(viii)$$

For even functions. When $f(x)$ is an even function of x, then $f(-x) = f(x)$ and the term

$$\int_{-\infty}^{+\infty}f(t)\cos\omega(x-t)\,dt = \int_{-\infty}^{0}f(t)\cos\omega(x-t)\,dt + \int_{0}^{\infty}f(t)\cos\omega(x-t)\,dt \qquad ...(ix)$$

Changing t to $-t$ in the first integral of relation (ix), we have

$$\int\limits_{-\infty}^{0} f(t) \cos \omega (x - t)\, dt = \int\limits_{\infty}^{0} f(-t) \cos \omega (x + t)\, (-dt)$$

$$= -\int\limits_{\infty}^{0} f(t) \cos \omega (x + t)\, dt$$

$$[\because f(-t) = f(t) \text{ when } x \text{ is even}]$$

$$= \int\limits_{0}^{\infty} f(t) \cos \omega (x + t)\, dt$$

$$\therefore \int\limits_{-\infty}^{+\infty} f(t) \cos \omega (x - t)\, dt = \int\limits_{0}^{\infty} f(t) \cos \omega (x + t)\, dt + \int\limits_{0}^{\infty} f(t) \cos \omega (x - t)\, dt$$

$$= \int\limits_{0}^{\infty} f(t) \left[\cos \omega (x + t) + \cos \omega (x - t)\right] dt$$

$$= \int\limits_{0}^{\infty} f(t)\, (2 \cos \omega x \cos \omega t)\, dt$$

Substituting in Eq. (*viii*), we get

$$f(x) = \frac{1}{\pi} \int\limits_{0}^{\infty} d\omega \int\limits_{0}^{\infty} f(t)\, (2 \cos \omega x \cos \omega t)\, dt$$

$$= \frac{2}{\pi} \int\limits_{0}^{\infty} \cos \omega x\, d\omega \int\limits_{0}^{\infty} f(t) \cos \omega t\, dt \qquad \ldots(x)$$

This form of Fourier integral for even function is known as *Fourier cosine integral formula*.

For odd functions. When $f(x)$ is an odd function of x, then $f(-x) = -f(x)$. In such a case the first integral on the right hand side of Eq. (*ix*) *i.e.* $\int\limits_{-\infty}^{0} f(t) \cos \omega (x - t)\, dt$ on changing t to $(-t)$

becomes $\int\limits_{+\infty}^{0} f(-t) \cos \omega (x + t)\, (-dt)$

$$= -\int\limits_{+\infty}^{0} \{-f(t)\} \cos \omega (x + t)\, dt = \int\limits_{\infty}^{0} f(t) \cos \omega (x + t)\, dt$$

$$= -\int\limits_{0}^{\infty} f(t) \cos \omega (x + t)\, dt$$

$\therefore$ From Eq. (*ix*), we have

$$\int\limits_{-\infty}^{+\infty} f(t) \cos \omega (x - t)\, dt = -\int\limits_{0}^{\infty} f(t) \cos \omega (x + t)\, dt + \int\limits_{0}^{\infty} f(t) \cos \omega (x - t)\, dt$$

$$= \int\limits_{0}^{\infty} f(t) [\cos \omega (x - t) - \cos \omega (x + t)]\, dt = \int\limits_{0}^{\infty} f(t) [2 \sin \omega x \sin \omega t]\, dt$$

Substituting in Eq. (*viii*), we get

$$f(x) = \frac{1}{\pi} \int\limits_{0}^{\infty} d\omega \int\limits_{0}^{\infty} f(t)(2 \sin \omega x \sin \omega t)\, dt$$

$$= \frac{2}{\pi} \int\limits_{0}^{\infty} \sin \omega x\, d\omega \int\limits_{0}^{\infty} f(t) \sin \omega t\, dt \qquad \ldots(xi)$$

This form of Fourier integral for odd function is known as *Fourier sine integral formula*.

Complex form. We know that sin $\omega \, (x - t)$ is an odd function of ω

$$\therefore \qquad \int\limits_{-\infty}^{\infty} \sin \omega \, (x - t) \, d\omega = 0 \text{ and therefore}$$

$$\frac{1}{2\pi} \int\limits_{-\infty}^{\infty} f(t) \left[\int\limits_{-\infty}^{\infty} \sin \omega \, (x - t) \, d\omega \right] dt = 0$$

Multiplying above equation by $i = \sqrt{-1}$ and adding Eq. (*vii*), we get

$$f(x) = \frac{1}{2\pi} \int\limits_{-\infty}^{\infty} f(t) \left[\int\limits_{-\infty}^{\infty} \cos \omega \, (x - t) \, d\omega + i \sin \omega \, (x - t) \, d\omega \right] dt$$

or

$$f(x) = \frac{1}{2\pi} \int\limits_{-\infty}^{\infty} f(t) \left[\int\limits_{-\infty}^{+\infty} e^{i\omega(x - t)} \, d\omega \right] dt$$

$$= \frac{1}{2\pi} \int\limits_{-\infty}^{+\infty} d\omega \int\limits_{-\infty}^{+\infty} f(t) \, e^{i\omega(x - t)} \, dt \qquad \qquad \text{...(xii)}$$

This is the complex form of **Fourier integral formula.**

Q. 9.17 (a) What are Fourier transforms? Explain.

(*K.U.* 2002, 2001; *M.D.U.* 2008, 2006, 2003, 2000, 1999)

(b) Define infinte and finite Fourier sine and cosine transforms. (*M.D.U.* 2000)

Ans. (a) Fourier transforms. If we have a function $f(x)$ of variable x, then Fourier transform of $f(x)$ denoted as $F(k)$ is given by the integral

$$F(k) = \frac{1}{\sqrt{2\pi}} \int\limits_{-\infty}^{+\infty} e^{-ikx} f(x) \, dx \qquad \qquad \text{...(i)}$$

The function $f(x)$ can be written in the form of complex Fourier integral as

$$f(x) = \frac{1}{2\pi} \int\limits_{-\infty}^{\infty} dk \int\limits_{-\infty}^{\infty} f(t) \, e^{ik(x - t)} \, dt$$

(Eq. (*xii*) **Q. 9.16** replacing k by ω)

Rearranging right hand side of the above equation, we have

$$f(x) = \frac{1}{\sqrt{2\pi}} \int\limits_{-\infty}^{\infty} dk \, e^{ikx} \left[\frac{1}{\sqrt{2\pi}} \int\limits_{-\infty}^{\infty} f(t) \, e^{-ikt} \, dt \right] \qquad \qquad \text{...(ii)}$$

Substituting variable t for x in Fourier transform [Eq. (*i*)], we have

$$F(k) = \frac{1}{\sqrt{2\pi}} \int\limits_{-\infty}^{\infty} e^{-ikt} f(t) \, dt$$

$\therefore$ Eq. (*ii*) becomes

$$f(x) = \frac{1}{\sqrt{2\pi}} \int\limits_{-\infty}^{\infty} dk \, e^{ikx} F(k) \qquad \qquad \text{...(iii)}$$

Eq (*iii*) expresses $f(x)$ as *inverse Fourier transform* of $F(k)$. This equation is known as *Fourier inversion formula*.

(*b*) **Fourier sine transforms.** For an *odd* function Fourier integral is given by

$$f(x) = \frac{2}{\pi} \int\limits_{0}^{\infty} \sin kx \, dk \int\limits_{0}^{\infty} f(t) \sin kt \, dt \qquad \qquad \text{...(iv)}$$

[Eq. (*xi*) **Q. 9.16** replacing ω by k)]

or
$$f(x) = \sqrt{\frac{2}{\pi}} \int_0^\infty \sin kx \, dk \, F_S(k) \qquad ...(v)$$

where
$$F_S(k) = \sqrt{\frac{2}{\pi}} \int_0^\infty f(t) \sin kt \, dt \qquad ...(vi)$$

In terms of variable x, Eq. (vi) written as

$$F_S(k) = \sqrt{\frac{2}{\pi}} \int_0^\infty f(x) \sin kx \, dx$$

is known as *Infinite Fourier sine transform* of $f(x)$ in the range $0 < x < \infty$.

Eq. (v) which gives $f(x)$ in terms of Fourier sine transform $F_s(k)$ is known as *Inverse infinite Fourier sine transform.*

Finite Fourier sine transforms. When $f(x)$ is an odd function of x, defined in the interval $(-L, L)$ and has a period $2L$, it can be written in the form of Fourier sine series as

$$f(x) = \sum_{n=1}^\infty b_n \sin \frac{n\pi x}{L} \qquad ...(vii)$$

[For an odd function $a_0 = 0$ and $a_n = 0$]

Now
$$b_n = \frac{2}{L} \int_0^L f(x) \sin \left(\frac{n\pi x}{L}\right) dx$$

$$\therefore \quad f(x) = \sum_{n=1}^\infty \frac{2}{L} \int_0^L f(x) \sin \left(\frac{n\pi x}{L}\right) dx \sin \left(\frac{n\pi x}{L}\right)$$

$$= \sqrt{\frac{2}{L}} \sum_{n=1}^\infty F_s(n) \sin \left(\frac{n\pi x}{L}\right) \qquad ...(viii)$$

where
$$F_s(n) = \sqrt{\frac{2}{L}} \int_0^L f(x) \sin \left(\frac{n\pi x}{L}\right) dx \qquad ...(ix)$$

The term $F_s(n)$ given by Eq. (ix) is known as *Finite Fourier sine transform* of $f(x)$ for x between 0 and L.

Eq. $(viii)$ which gives $f(x)$ in terms of $F_s(n)$ is known as *Inverse finite Fourier transform.*

Fourier cosine transforms. For an *even* function Fourier integral is given by

$$f(x) = \frac{2}{\pi} \int_0^\infty \cos kx \, dx \int_0^\infty f(t) \cos kt \, dt$$

[Eq (x) Q. 9.16 replacing ω by k]

or
$$f(x) = \sqrt{\frac{2}{\pi}} \int_0^\infty \cos kx \, dk \, F_c(k) \qquad ...(x)$$

where
$$F_c(k) = \sqrt{\frac{2}{\pi}} \int_0^\infty f(t) \cos kt \, dt \qquad ...(xi)$$

In terms of variable x Eq. (xi) written as

$$F_c(k) = \sqrt{\frac{2}{\pi}} \int_0^\infty f(x) \cos kx \, dx$$

is known as *infinite Fourier cosine transform* of $f(x)$. Eq. (x) which gives $f(x)$ in terms of *Fourier cosine transform* $F_c(k)$ is known as *Inverse infinite Fourier cosine transform* of $F_c(k)$.

Finite Fourier cosine transforms. When $f(x)$ is an even function of x defined in the interval $(-L, L)$ and has a period $2L$, it can be written in the form of Fourier series as

$$f(x) = \frac{1}{2} a_0 + \sum_{n=1}^{\infty} a_n \cos\left(\frac{n\pi x}{L}\right)$$

(As $b_n = 0$)

$$\frac{1}{2} a_0 = \frac{1}{L} \int_0^L f(x)\, dx \; ; \; a_n = \frac{2}{L} \int_0^L f(x) \cos\left(\frac{n\pi x}{L}\right) dx$$

$$\therefore \quad f(x) = \frac{1}{L} \int_0^L f(x)\, dx + \sum_{n=1}^{\infty} \frac{2}{L} \int_0^L f(x) \cos\left(\frac{n\pi x}{L}\right) dx \cos\left(\frac{n\pi x}{L}\right)$$

$$= \sqrt{\frac{1}{2L}}\, F_c(o) + \sqrt{\frac{2}{L}} \sum_{n=1}^{\infty} F_c(n) \cos\left(\frac{n\pi x}{L}\right) \qquad \ldots(xii)$$

where $F_c(o) = \sqrt{\frac{2}{L}} \int_0^L f(x)\, dx$ and $F_c(n) = \sqrt{\frac{2}{L}} \int_0^L f(x) \cos\left(\frac{n\pi x}{L}\right) dx$ $\qquad \ldots(xiii)$

The term $F_c(n)$ given by Eq. $(xiii)$ is known as *Finite Fourier cosine transform* of $f(x)$ for x between 0 and L.

Eq. (xii) which gives $f(x)$ in terms of $F_c(n)$ is known as *inverse finite Fourier transform*.

Q. 9.18. Find the Fourier transform of the Gaussian function $f(x) = e^{-x^2/2}$. Show that the Fourier transform of a Gaussian distribution is also a Gaussian distribution.

(*K.U.* 2002; *M.D.U.* 2006, 2005, 2003, 2002)

Ans. Fourier transform of $f(x) = e^{-x^2/2}$. The Fourier transform of a function $f(x)$ is given by

$$f(k) = \frac{1}{\sqrt{2\pi}} \int_{-\infty}^{\infty} f(x)\, e^{-ikx}\, dx \qquad \ldots(i)$$

Substituting the value of $f(x) = e^{-x^2/2}$ in (i), we have

$$f(k) = \frac{1}{\sqrt{2\pi}} \int_{-\infty}^{\infty} e^{-x^2/2}\, e^{-ikx}\, dx = \frac{1}{\sqrt{2\pi}} \int_{-\infty}^{\infty} e^{-(x^2/2 + ikx)}\, dx$$

Now

$$\frac{x^2}{2} + ikx = \left[\left(\frac{x}{\sqrt{2}}\right)^2 + 2i\,\frac{k}{\sqrt{2}}\,\frac{x}{\sqrt{2}} + \left(\frac{ik}{\sqrt{2}}\right)^2\right] + \frac{k^2}{2}$$

$$= \left(\frac{x}{\sqrt{2}} + \frac{ik}{\sqrt{2}}\right)^2 + \frac{k^2}{2}$$

$$\therefore \quad F(k) = \frac{1}{\sqrt{2\pi}} \int_{-\infty}^{\infty} e^{-\left(\frac{x}{\sqrt{2}} + \frac{ik}{\sqrt{2}}\right)^2 - \frac{k^2}{2}}\, dx = \frac{1}{\sqrt{2\pi}} e^{-k^2/2} \int_{-\infty}^{\infty} e^{-\left(x/\sqrt{2} + \frac{ik}{\sqrt{2}}\right)^2}\, dx$$

$$= \frac{1}{\sqrt{2\pi}} e^{-k^2/2}\, I \qquad \ldots(ii) \left[\text{where } I = \int_{-\infty}^{\infty} e^{-\left(\frac{x}{\sqrt{2}} + \frac{ik}{\sqrt{2}}\right)^2}\, dx\right] \qquad \ldots(iii)$$

Now put $\dfrac{x}{\sqrt{2}} + \dfrac{ik}{\sqrt{2}} = y$ so that when $x \to \infty$, $y \to \infty$ and when $x \to -\infty$, $y \to -\infty$

Then differentiating we get $\dfrac{dx}{\sqrt{2}} = dy$ or $dx = \sqrt{2}\ dy$

Substituting in Eq. (*iii*), we get

$$I = \int\limits_{-\infty}^{\infty} e^{-y^2} \sqrt{2}\ dy = \sqrt{2} \int\limits_{-\infty}^{\infty} e^{-y^2}\ dy = 2\sqrt{2} \int\limits_{0}^{\infty} e^{-y^2}\ dy$$

Now put $y^2 = z$ so that when $y = 0$, $z = 0$ and when $y \to \infty$, $z \to \infty$

Then differentiating we get $2y\ dy = dz$ or $dy = \dfrac{dz}{2y} = \dfrac{dz}{2z^{1/2}} = \dfrac{1}{2} \dfrac{dz}{z^{1/2}}$

$$\therefore \qquad I = 2\sqrt{2} \int\limits_{0}^{\infty} e^{-z}\ \dfrac{1}{2} \dfrac{dz}{z^{1/2}} = \sqrt{2} \int\limits_{0}^{\infty} e^{-z}\ z^{-1/2}\ dz$$

But $\int\limits_{0}^{\infty} e^{-z} z^{-1/2}\ dz$ is a standard integral the value of which $= \sqrt{\pi}$

$$\therefore \qquad I = \sqrt{2}\ \sqrt{\pi} = \sqrt{2\pi}$$

and $\qquad f(k) = \dfrac{1}{\sqrt{2\pi}}\ e^{-k^2/2}\ I = \dfrac{1}{\sqrt{2\pi}}\ e^{k^2/2}\ \sqrt{2\pi} = e^{k^2/2}$

Thus the Fourier transform of $e^{-x^2/2} = e^{-k^2/2}$

In other words, '*The Fourier transform of a Gaussian distribution is also a Gaussian distribution*'.

Q. 9.19. **Find the Fourier transform of function**

$$f(x) = \begin{vmatrix} (1 - x^2) & \text{for } |x| < 1 \\ 0 & \text{for } |x| > 1 \end{vmatrix}$$

(*M.D.U.* 2001; *K.U.* 2001)

Ans. The Fourier transform of a function $f(x)$ is given by

$$F(k) = \dfrac{1}{\sqrt{2\pi}} \int\limits_{-\infty}^{+\infty} f(x)\ e^{-ikx}\ dx \qquad\qquad ...(i)$$

Substituting the value of $f(x) = (1 - x^2)$ in (*i*), we have

$$F(k) = \dfrac{1}{\sqrt{2\pi}} \int\limits_{-1}^{1} (1 - x^2)\ e^{-ikx}\ dx$$

[The limits have been changed from $(-\infty$ to $+\infty)$ to $(-1$ to $+1)$ as $f(x) = 0$ for $|x| > 1$.]
Integrating by parts, we get

$$F(k) = \dfrac{1}{\sqrt{2\pi}} \left[\left\{ (1 - x^2) \dfrac{e^{-ikx}}{(-ik)} \right\}_{-1}^{1} - \int\limits_{-1}^{1} (-2x) \dfrac{e^{-ikx}}{(-ik)}\ dx \right]$$

Now $\left\{ (1 - x^2) \dfrac{e^{-ikx}}{(-ik)} \right\} = 0$ for $x = 1$ and for $x = -1$

$$\therefore \quad F(k) = \frac{1}{\sqrt{2\pi}} \left[-\frac{2}{ik} \int_{-1}^{1} x\, e^{-ikx}\, dx \right]$$

$$= -\frac{1}{\sqrt{2\pi}} \times \frac{2}{ik} \left[\left\{ x \frac{e^{-ikx}}{(-ik)} \right\}_{-1}^{1} - \int_{-1}^{1} 1 \frac{e^{-ikx}}{(-ik)}\, dx \right]$$

$$= -\frac{1}{\sqrt{2\pi}} \times \frac{2}{ik} \left[\frac{e^{-ik} - (-e^{-ik})}{(-ik)} + \frac{1}{ik} \int_{-1}^{1} e^{-ikx}\, dx \right]$$

$$= -\frac{1}{\sqrt{2\pi}} \times \frac{2}{(ik)^2} \left[-2\cos k + \frac{\{ e^{-ikx} \}_{-1}^{1}}{(-ik)} \right]$$

$$= \sqrt{\frac{2}{\pi}} \frac{1}{k^2} \left[\frac{-2k\cos k}{k} + \frac{1}{k} \frac{e^{ik} - e^{-ik}}{i} \right]$$

$$= \sqrt{\frac{2}{\pi}} \frac{1}{k^3} \left[-2k\cos k + 2\sin k \right]$$

$$= \sqrt{\frac{2}{\pi}} \frac{2}{k^3} \left[\sin k - k\cos k \right]$$

The above expression gives the Fourier transform $F(k)$ of $f(x) = (1 - x^2)$. When $f(x) = 0$, $F(k) = 0$.

Q. 9.20. Find the Fourier transform of the function

$$f(x) = \begin{cases} 1 ; |x| < a \\ 0 ; |x| > a \end{cases}.$$

(M.D.U. 2007, 2002)

Ans. The Fourier transform of a function $f(x)$ is given by

$$F(k) = \frac{1}{\sqrt{2\pi}} \int_{-\infty}^{\infty} f(x)\, e^{-ikx}\, dx \qquad \qquad ...(i)$$

Given $f(x) = 0$ for $|x| > a$ *i.e.* for x from a to ∞
and also from $-\infty$ to $-a$ and $f(x) = 1$ for $|x| < a$ *i.e.* for x from $-a$ to $+a$

$$\therefore \int_{-\infty}^{\infty} f(x)\, e^{-ikx}\, dx = \int_{-\infty}^{-a} (0)\, e^{-ikx}\, dx + \int_{-a}^{a} (1)\, e^{-ikx}\, dx + \int_{a}^{\infty} (0)\, e^{-ikx}\, dx = \int_{-a}^{a} e^{-ikx}\, dx$$

Hence

$$F(k) = \frac{1}{\sqrt{2\pi}} \int_{-a}^{a} e^{-ikx}\, dx = \frac{1}{\sqrt{2\pi}} \frac{[e^{-ikx}]_{-a}^{a}}{(-ik)}$$

$$= \frac{1}{\sqrt{2\pi}} \frac{e^{ika} - e^{-ika}}{ik} = \frac{1}{\sqrt{2\pi}} \frac{2\sin ka}{k}$$

$$= \sqrt{\frac{2}{\pi}} \frac{\sin ka}{k} \qquad \qquad ...(ii)\ [\text{For } k \neq 0]$$

For $k = 0$, $\int\limits_{-a}^{a} e^{-ikx} dx = \int\limits_{-a}^{a} e^{0} dx = \int\limits_{-a}^{a} dx = [x]_{-a}^{a} = 2a$

$\therefore$

$$F(k) = \frac{1}{\sqrt{2\pi}} \cdot 2a = \sqrt{\frac{2}{\pi}} \, a \qquad \qquad ...(iii)$$

Relation (ii) gives the Fourier transform for $k \neq 0$ and relation (iii) for $k = 0$.

9.21. Fourier transform of function $f(x)$ is $F(k)$. Prove that Fourier transform of $f(x-2)$ would be $F(k) e^{-2ik}$.

(K.U. 2000)

Ans. The Fourier transform of a function $f(x)$ is given by

$$F(k) = \frac{1}{\sqrt{2\pi}} \int\limits_{-\infty}^{+\infty} f(x) e^{-ikx} \, dx \qquad \qquad ...(i)$$

$\therefore$ Fourier transform of $f(x-2)$

$$= \frac{1}{\sqrt{2\pi}} \int\limits_{-\infty}^{+\infty} f(x-2) \, e^{-ikx} \, dx$$

Let $x - 2 = t$ or $x = 2 + t$ $\therefore dx = dt$
and $f(x-2) = f(t)$.

$\therefore$ Fourier transform of $f(x-2) = \dfrac{1}{\sqrt{2\pi}} \int\limits_{-\infty}^{\infty} f(t) \, e^{-ik(2+t)} \, dt$

$$= \frac{1}{\sqrt{2\pi}} \int\limits_{-\infty}^{+\infty} f(t) \, e^{-2ik} e^{-ikt} \, dt$$

$$= e^{-2ik} \frac{1}{\sqrt{2\pi}} \int\limits_{-\infty}^{\infty} f(t) \, e^{-ikt} \, dt \qquad \qquad ...(ii)$$

Using Eq. (i) and replacing x by t, we have

$$F(k) = \frac{1}{\sqrt{2\pi}} \int\limits_{-\infty}^{\infty} f(t) \, e^{-ikt} \, dt$$

$\therefore$ Fourier transform of $f(x-2) = e^{-2ik} F(k) = F(k) e^{-2ik}$.

EXERCISES

1. A function is defined as

$$f(x) = \begin{cases} -5 \text{ for } -\pi < x < 0 \\ +5 \text{ for } 0 < x < \pi \end{cases}.$$

Express it as Fourier series and hence prove

$$\frac{\pi}{4} = 1 - \frac{1}{3} + \frac{1}{5} - \frac{1}{7} + ...$$

(K.U. 2000)

Hint. Fourier series is given by

$$f(x) = \frac{a_0}{2} + \sum_{n=1}^{\infty} a_n \cos nx + \sum_{n=1}^{\infty} b_n \sin nx$$

$$a_0 = \frac{1}{\pi} \int_{-\pi}^{\pi} f(x)\, dx = \frac{1}{\pi} \int_{-\pi}^{0} f(x)\, dx + \int_{0}^{\pi} f(x)\, dx$$

$$= \frac{1}{\pi} \int_{-\pi}^{0} -5\, dx + \int_{0}^{\pi} 5\, dx = \frac{1}{\pi} \left[-5(x)_{-\pi}^{0} + 5(x)_{0}^{\pi} \right]$$

$$= \frac{1}{\pi} \left[-5(0 + \pi) + 5(\pi - 0) \right] = 0$$

$$a_n = \frac{1}{\pi} \int_{-\pi}^{\pi} f(x) \cos nx\, dx = \frac{1}{\pi} \left[\int_{-\pi}^{0} f(x) \cos nx\, dx + \int_{0}^{\pi} f(x) \cos nx\, dx \right]$$

$$= \frac{1}{\pi} \left[-5 \int_{-\pi}^{0} \cos nx\, dx + 5 \int_{0}^{\pi} \cos nx\, dx \right]$$

$$= \frac{1}{\pi} \left[-5 \left(\frac{\sin nx}{n} \right)_{-\pi}^{0} + 5 \left(\frac{\sin nx}{n} \right)_{0}^{\pi} \right]$$

$$= \frac{1}{\pi} \left[-5 \times 0 + 5 \times 0 \right] = 0$$

$$b_n = \frac{1}{\pi} \int_{-\pi}^{\pi} f(x) \sin nx\, dx = \frac{1}{\pi} \left[\int_{-\pi}^{0} f(x) \sin nx\, dx + \int_{0}^{\pi} f(x) \sin nx\, dx \right]$$

$$= \frac{1}{\pi} \left[-5 \int_{-\pi}^{0} \sin nx\, dx + 5 \int_{0}^{\pi} \sin nx\, dx \right]$$

$$= \frac{1}{\pi} \left[-5 \left(\frac{-\cos nx}{n} \right)_{-\pi}^{0} + 5 \left(\frac{-\cos nx}{n} \right)_{0}^{\pi} \right]$$

$$= \frac{1}{\pi} \left[\frac{5}{n} (\cos 0 - \cos n\pi) - \frac{5}{n} (\cos n\pi - \cos 0) \right]$$

$\cos n\pi = -1$ for n odd ; and $= 1$ for n even

$$\therefore \quad b_n = \frac{1}{\pi} \left[\frac{5}{n}(2) - \frac{5}{n}(-2) \right] = \frac{20}{\pi n} \text{ for } n \text{ odd and } = 0 \text{ for } n \text{ even}$$

$$\therefore \quad f(x) = \frac{20}{\pi} \left[\sin x + \frac{\sin 3x}{3} + \frac{\sin 5x}{5} + \dots \right]$$

Put $x = \pi/2$, then

$$f\left(\frac{\pi}{2}\right) = \frac{20}{\pi} \left[1 - \frac{1}{3} + \frac{1}{5} - \frac{1}{7} + \dots \right]$$

But $\quad f\left(\frac{\pi}{2}\right) = 5 \quad [\because f(x) = +5 \text{ for } 0 < x < \pi] \quad \therefore 5 = \frac{20}{\pi} \left[1 - \frac{1}{3} + \frac{1}{5} - \frac{1}{7} + \dots \right]$

or $\quad \frac{5\pi}{20} = 1 - \frac{1}{3} + \frac{1}{5} - \frac{1}{7} + \dots \qquad$ or $\qquad \frac{\pi}{4} = 1 - \frac{1}{3} + \frac{1}{5} - \frac{1}{7} + \dots$

SECTION–III
ELECTRICITY AND MAGNETISM

Vector Calculus

Note. Students are advised to read **Chapter 1** of **'Mechanics and Properties of Matter'** portion Art 1.9 'Differentiation of a vector with respect to a scalar' and Q. 1.28 and 1.29. Some results are given below for ready reference.

(i) $\dfrac{d\vec{A}}{dt} = \underset{\delta t \to 0}{Lim} \dfrac{\vec{A}(t+\delta t) - \vec{A}(t)}{\delta t}$

(ii) $\dfrac{d}{dt}(\vec{A} + \vec{B}) = \dfrac{d\vec{A}}{dt} + \dfrac{d\vec{B}}{dt}$

(iii) $\dfrac{d\vec{A}}{dt} = \dfrac{d\vec{A}}{ds}\dfrac{ds}{dt}$

(iv) $\dfrac{d(u\vec{A})}{dt} = \dfrac{du}{dt}\vec{A} + u\dfrac{d\vec{A}}{dt}$

(v) $\dfrac{d\vec{A}}{dt} = \dfrac{\partial A_x}{\partial t}\hat{i} + \dfrac{\partial A_y}{\partial t}\hat{j} + \dfrac{\partial A_z}{\partial t}\hat{k}$

(vi) $\dfrac{d(\vec{A}.\vec{B})}{dt} = \dfrac{d\vec{A}}{dt}.\vec{B} + \vec{A}.\dfrac{d\vec{B}}{dt}$

(vii) $\dfrac{d(\vec{A} \times \vec{B})}{dt} = \dfrac{d\vec{A}}{dt} \times \vec{B} + \vec{A} \times \dfrac{d\vec{B}}{dt}$

(viii) $\dfrac{d}{dt}\left(\vec{A} \times \dfrac{d\vec{A}}{dt}\right) = \vec{A} \times \dfrac{d^2\vec{A}}{dt^2}$

(ix) The derivative of a vector of constant direction is parallel to that vector.

(x) The derivative of a vector of constant magnitude is perpendicular to the vector itself.

(xi) $\dfrac{d}{dt}\left(\vec{A}.\vec{B} \times \vec{C}\right) = \dfrac{d\vec{A}}{dt}.\vec{B} \times \vec{C} + \vec{A}.\dfrac{d\vec{B}}{dt} \times \vec{C} + \vec{A}.\vec{B} \times \dfrac{d\vec{C}}{dt}$

(xii) $\dfrac{d}{dt}\left(\vec{A} \times \vec{B} \times \vec{C}\right) = \dfrac{d\vec{A}}{dt} \times \left(\vec{B} \times \vec{C}\right) + \vec{A} \times \left(\dfrac{d\vec{B}}{dt} \times \vec{C}\right) + \vec{A} \times \left(\vec{B} \times \dfrac{d\vec{C}}{dt}\right)$

Note. In the derivation of the product of vector, the order of placement of vectors should not be ordinarily changed.

Q. 1.1. (*a*) **What is a field ? What are scalar and vector fields ? Explain. Give one example of each.**(*Pbi. U.*, 2006; 2003, 2002; *M.D.U.* 2002, 1999; *H.P.U.* 2001, 1999, 1994; *Ranchi U.* 1991)

(*b*) **A quantity possesses both magnitude and direction. Is it necessarily a vector? Explain.**
(*Pbi. U.*, 2008; *H.P.U.* 2001)

Ans. (*a*) **Field.** A *field is a region in space in which a function u is defined at all points.* Thus in Cartesian co-ordinates $u = f(x, y, z)$ specifies a field.

Scalar field. *A region in space in which a scalar quantity is continuous and is defined by a single value at every point of the position variable is called a scalar field.*

If ϕ is a scalar function of position variable $\vec{r}$ with a set of co-ordinates (x, y, z) then we denote the scalar field as $\phi = (\vec{r}) = \phi\,(x, y, z)$.

Examples. (*i*) Variation of temperature at various points along a metal rod one end of which is heated while the other end is kept cold is an example of *scalar temperature field.*

(*ii*) Variation of electric potential at various points surrounding a charged body is an example of *scalar potential field.*

It should be noted that a surface passing through all such points which have the same value of scalar field are called *level surfaces*, as for example *equipotential surfaces.*

Vector field. *A region in space in which a vector quantity is continuous and is defined by a single value (in magnitude and direction) at every point of the position variable is called a vector field.*

If *V* is vector function of position variable *r* with a set of co-ordinates (x, y, z) then we denote the vector field as

$$V\,(r) = \vec{V}\,(x, y, z)$$

Examples. (*i*) An *electric field* is an example of a vector field. The force experienced by a unit positive charge placed at any point in the field gives the *magnitude* of the vector field and the direction in which the unit positive charge moves, if free to do so gives the *direction* of the vector field.

A vector field is represented by *flux lines* or *lines of flow.*

(*ii*) The *gravitational field* acting on a body is another example of vector field.

(*b*) A quantity which possesses both magnitude and direction is *not necessarily a vector.* A vector besides possessing magnitude and direction must obey rules of addition and multiplication according to vector algebra. For example, it should add according to parallelogram law of vectors.

As an example, '*finite rotation*' has a magnitude and direction but is not a vector quantity. Similarly, *electric current* possesses both magnitude and direction but is not a vector.

Q. 1.2. (*a*) **Define equal vectors, negative vectors, null vector, unit vector, free vector, localised vector, position vector, polar vector and axial vector.** (*H.P.U.*, 2006)

(*b*) **What should be the orientation between unit vectors, $\hat{A}$ and $\hat{B}$ such that their sum has unit magnitude?** (*G.N.D.U.* 2003)

(*c*) **If unit vector $\hat{A}$ and $\hat{B}$ are inclined at an angle θ then prove that $\left| \hat{A} - \hat{B} \right| = 2\sin\theta/2$.**

(*M.D.U.* 2003)

Ans. (*a*) **Equal vectors.** *Two vectors $\vec{A}$ and $\vec{B}$ are said to be equal, if they have equal magnitude and the same direction.*

Example Two vectors $\vec{A}$ and $\vec{B}$ as shown in Fig. 1.1 (a) are equal vector, or $\vec{A} = \vec{B}$

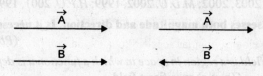

Fig. 1.1 (a)   Fig. 1.1 (b)

Negative vectors. *The negative vector of a given vector is that vector the magnitude of which is equal to that of the given vector but direction is just opposite.*

Example. The vector $\vec{B}$ which is equal in magnitude to the vector $\vec{A}$ but opposite in direction to that of $\vec{A}$ as shown in Fig. 1.1 (b) is a negative vector of $\vec{A}$ or $\vec{B} = -\vec{A}$

Null vector. *A vector whose magnitude is zero is called a null vector (or zero vector)*

Unit vector. *A vector whose magnitude is unity and direction is the same as that of the given vector is called a unit vector.*

A unit vector is written as $\hat{A}$ and it is given by $\hat{A} = \dfrac{\vec{A}}{\left|\vec{A}\right|}$ where $\left|\vec{A}\right|$ represents the magnitude of the vector $\vec{A}$

$$\vec{A} = |\vec{A}|\,\hat{A}$$

Localised (or line) vector. *A vector is said to be localised vector, if it is restricted to pass through a given origin.*

Position vector. *A vector drawn from the origin of the co-ordinate system to any point in space is called the position vector of the point with respect to the origin.*

If (x, y, z) are the co-ordinates of the point P w.r.t. the origin O of the co-ordinate system, then the vector $\overrightarrow{OP}$ drawn from the origin O to the point P is called the position vector.

It is represented by

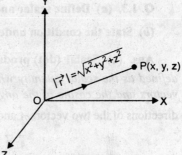

$$\overrightarrow{OP} = \vec{r} = x\hat{i} + y\hat{j} + z\hat{k}$$

where $\hat{i}$, $\hat{j}$ and $\hat{k}$ are the unit vectors along X, Y and Z directions respectively. The magnitude of the position vector

Fig. 1.1 (c)

$\vec{r}$ is given by $\left|\vec{r}\right| = (x^2 + y^2 + z^2)^{\frac{1}{2}}$

Polar vector. *A vector the direction of which is along the direction of motion of a body (or a system) is known as a polar vector.*

Examples. Displacement, velocity, acceleration, force, linear momentum etc.

Now, consider a right handed co-ordinate system and let x, y, z be the co-ordinates, of a point in this right handed system. If we put $x' = -x$, $y' = -y$ and $z' = -z$ the co-ordinate transformation is known as *parity transformation.*

If a vector changes sign under parity transformation it is a polar vector.

Axial vector. *A line vector representing a vector quantity where the action of rotation takes place about an axis, drawn parallel to the axis of rotation such that the magnitude of the quantity is given by the length of the vector and its direction by the right hand screw rule is called an axial vector.*

Examples. Angular velocity, angular acceleration, angular momentum, torque etc.

(b) If $\hat{A}$ and $\hat{B}$ are two vectors inclined at an angle θ, then magnitude $\left|\vec{R}\right|$ of the resultant is given by

$$|\vec{R}| = |\vec{A} + \vec{B}| = \sqrt{A^2 + B^2 + 2AB\cos\theta}$$

Where A and B are the magnitudes of $\hat{A}$ and $\hat{B}$ respectively.

If $\hat{A}$ and $\hat{B}$ are unit vectors, then magnitude of each = 1. When their sum has unit magnitude $|\vec{R}| = 1$

$$\therefore \qquad 1 = \sqrt{1+1+2\cos\theta} \quad \text{or} \quad 1 = 2(1+\cos\theta)$$

or $\qquad 1 + \cos\theta = \dfrac{1}{2}$ or $\cos\theta = -\dfrac{1}{2}$ $\therefore \theta = 120°$

Hence the orientation between the two vectors should be 120°,

(c) $$|\vec{A} - \vec{B}| = \sqrt{A^2 + B^2 - 2AB\cos\theta}$$

For unit vectors $\qquad |\hat{A} - \hat{B}| = \sqrt{1 + 1 - 2\cos\theta} = \sqrt{2(1-\cos\theta)}$ or

$$|\hat{A} - \hat{B}|^2 = 2(1-\cos\theta) = 2 \times 2\sin^2\theta/2$$

$$\therefore \qquad |\hat{A} - \hat{B}| = 2\sin\theta/2$$

Q. 1.3. (*a*) **Define scalar and vector product of two vectors.**

(*b*) **State the condition under which $\vec{A}.\vec{B}$ is negative.** (*G.N.D.U.* 2003)

Ans. (*a*) **Scalar (dot) product of two vectors.** *The scalar product of two vectors $\vec{A}$ and $\vec{B}$ is defined as the scalar quantity which is equal to the product of the magnitudes of the given two vectors and the cosine of the angle between their directions.* Thus if θ be the angle between the directions of the two vectors $\vec{A}$ and $\vec{B}$ then,

$$\vec{A}.\vec{B} = AB\cos\theta$$

Vector (cross) product of two vectors . *The cross product of two vectors $\vec{A}$ and $\vec{B}$ whose directions are inclined at an angle θ is the vector whose magnitude is AB sin θ and direction is perpendicular to the plane containing $\vec{A}$ and $\vec{B}$.*

Thus $\vec{A} \times \vec{B} = AB$ sin $\theta\hat{n}$ where $\hat{n}$ is unit vector perpendicular to the vectors $\vec{A}$ and $\vec{B}$. The unit vector $\hat{n}$ is called *unit normal*

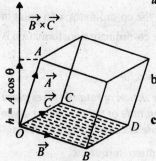

Fig. 1.1 (*d*)

(*b*) $\vec{A}.\vec{B} = AB\cos\theta$

For $\vec{A}.\vec{B}$ to be negative cos θ must be negative *i.e.*, θ should be between $\dfrac{\pi}{2}$ and $\dfrac{3\pi}{2}$.

Q. 1.4. Define scalar triple product of vectors. Explain its physical significance and give its two important features.

(*P.U.*, 2007; *Meerut. U.* 2003, 2002; *H.P.U.* 2002)

Ans. Scalar triple product. *The scalar product of vector $\vec{A}$ with a vector which is itself the vector product of two vectors $\vec{B}$ and $\vec{C}$ is known as scalar triple product.*

$\therefore$ Scalar triple product $= \vec{A}.(\vec{B} \times \vec{C})$

We know that $\vec{B} \times \vec{C}$ is a vector normal to the plane of $\vec{B}$ and $\vec{C}$ and its magnitude is equal to the area of a parallelogram having the sides represented by $\vec{B}$ and $\vec{C}$ as shown.

The scalar product of $\vec{A}$ and $(\vec{B} \times \vec{C})$ is the product of this area and the projection of $\vec{A}$ along the direction of the vector $(\vec{A} \times \vec{B})$ which is given by $h = A \cos \theta$

$\therefore$ $= \vec{A}.(\vec{B} \times \vec{C}) =$ Area of parallelogram $OCDB \times h$

        $=$ Volume of the parallelopiped enclosed by the vectors $\vec{A}, \vec{B}$ and $\vec{C}$ as its edges :

Scalar triple product in rectangular components. The scalar triple product in terms of rectangular components is written as

$$\vec{A}.(\vec{B} \times \vec{C}) = (A_x \hat{i} + A_y \hat{j} + A_z \hat{k}) . \left[(B_x \hat{i} + B_y \hat{j} + B_z \hat{k}) \times (C_x \hat{i} + C_y \hat{j} + C_z \hat{k} \right]$$

$$= (A_x \hat{i} + A_y \hat{j} + A_z \hat{k}). \begin{vmatrix} \hat{i} & \hat{j} & \hat{k} \\ B_x & B_y & B_z \\ C_x & C_y & C_z \end{vmatrix}$$

$$= (A_x \hat{i} + A_y \hat{j} + A_z \hat{k}).\left[(B_y C_z - B_z C_y)\hat{i} + (B_z C_x - B_x C_z)\hat{j} + (B_x C_y - C_x B_y)\hat{k} \right]$$

$$= A_x(B_y C_z - B_z C_y) + A_y(B_z C_x - B_x C_z) + A_z(B_x C_y - C_x B_y)$$

$$= \begin{vmatrix} A_x & A_y & A_z \\ B_x & B_y & B_z \\ C_x & C_y & C_z \end{vmatrix}$$

Physical significance and important features (*i*) The scalar triple product $\vec{A}.(\vec{B} \times \vec{C})$ represents the volume of the parallelopiped enclosed by the vectors $\vec{A}, \vec{B}$ and $\vec{C}$ as its edges.

(*ii*) As any face of the parallelogram enclosed by two of the three vectors can be taken as the base, there are three equivalent expressions for volume as

$$\text{Volume } V = \vec{A}.(\vec{B} \times \vec{C}) = \vec{B}.(\vec{C} \times \vec{A}) = \vec{C}.(\vec{A} \times \vec{B})$$

(*iii*) In scalar triple product, the position of 'dot' and 'cross' may be interchanged without changing the value of the product, provided the *cyclic order* is maintained.

(*iv*) If $\vec{A}.(\vec{B} \times \vec{C}) = 0$, the volume of the parallelopiped formed by the vectors $= 0$. Hence, the three vectors are co-planar.

Q. 1.5. (*a*) If $\vec{A} + \vec{B} + \vec{C} = 0$ prove that $\vec{A}.(\vec{B} \times \vec{C}) = 0$ (*Meerut. U.* 2003)

(*b*) **Prove that** $\vec{A}.(\vec{A} \times \vec{C}) = 0$ (*M. D. U.,* 2008)

Ans. (*a*) If $\vec{A} + \vec{B} + \vec{C} = 0$, the three vectors $\vec{A}, \vec{B}$ and $\vec{C}$ are co-planar. As $\vec{A}.(\vec{B} \times \vec{C})$ represents the volume of the parallelopiped enclosed by the vectors $\vec{A}, \vec{B}$ and $\vec{C}$ as its edges and the three vectors are co-planar, the volume of the parallelopiped is zero.

$\therefore$ $\vec{A}.(\vec{B} \times \vec{C}) = 0$

(b) It has been proved in **Q. 1.4** that

$$\vec{A}.(\vec{B} \times \vec{C}) = A_x(B_yC_z - B_zC_y) + A_y(B_zC_x - B_xC_z) + A_z(B_xC_y - C_xB_y)$$

In this equation put $\vec{B} = \vec{A}$ or $B_x = A_x$, $B_y = A_y$, and $B_z = A_z$

Substituting, we get

$$\vec{A}.(\vec{A} \times \vec{C}) = A_x(A_yC_z - A_zC_y) + A_y(A_zC_x - A_xC_z) + A_z(A_xC_y - C_xA_y)$$

$$= A_xA_yC_z - A_xA_zC_y + A_yA_zC_x - A_yA_xC_z + A_zA_xC_y - A_zC_xA_y$$

$$= (A_xA_yC_z - A_yA_xC_z) + (A_yA_zC_x - A_zC_xA_y) + (A_zA_xC_y - A_xA_zC_y) = 0$$

as each term is zero.

Q. 1.6. Define vector product of three vectors. Show that $\vec{A} \times (\vec{B} \times \vec{C}) = \vec{B}(\vec{A}.\vec{C}) - \vec{C}(\vec{A}.\vec{B})$

(M.D.U. 2007; Meerut. U. 2003)

Ans. Vector triple product. The cross product of a vector $\vec{A}$ with the cross product of other two vectors $\vec{B}$ and $\vec{C}$ is called the vector product of three vectors or vector triple product and is denoted as $\vec{A} \times (\vec{B} \times \vec{C})$.

Vector triple product $\vec{A} \times (\vec{B} \times \vec{C})$. To evaluate this expression we shall first find the value of $\vec{B} \times \vec{C}$ which in terms of rectangular components is given by

$$\vec{B} \times \vec{C} = \begin{vmatrix} \hat{i} & \hat{j} & \hat{k} \\ B_x & B_y & B_z \\ C_x & C_y & C_z \end{vmatrix}$$

$$= (B_yC_z - B_zC_y)\hat{i} + (B_zC_x - B_xC_z)\hat{j} + (B_xC_y - B_yC_x)\hat{k}$$

Now $$\vec{A} \times (\vec{B} \times \vec{C}) = (A_x\hat{i} + A_y\hat{j} + A_z\hat{k}) \times [(B_yC_z - B_zC_y)\hat{i}$$

$$+ (B_zC_x - B_xC_z)\hat{j} + (B_xC_y - B_yC_x)\hat{k}]$$

$$= \begin{vmatrix} \hat{i} & \hat{j} & \hat{k} \\ A_x & A_y & A_z \\ (B_yC_z - B_zC_y) & (B_zC_x - B_xC_z) & (B_xC_y - B_yC_x) \end{vmatrix}$$

The first term of the above determinant

$$= [A_y(B_xC_y - B_yC_x) - A_z(B_zC_x - B_xC_z)]\hat{i}$$

$$= [A_yB_xC_y - A_yB_yC_x - A_zB_zC_x + A_zB_xC_z]\hat{i}$$

Add and subtract $A_xB_xC_x$, collect positive and negative terms and arrange, then we get

First term $= [(A_yB_xC_y + A_zB_xC_z + A_xB_xC_x) - (A_yB_yC_x + A_zB_zC_x + A_xB_xC_x]\hat{i}$

$$= [B_x(A_xC_x + A_yC_y + A_zC_z) - C_x(A_xB_x + A_yB_y + A_zB_z)]\hat{i}$$

$$= B_x(\vec{A}.\vec{C})\hat{i} - C_x(\vec{A}.\vec{B})\hat{i}$$

Similarly, the second and third terms of the determinant are

2nd term $= B_y(\vec{A}.\vec{C})\hat{j} - C_y(\vec{A}.\vec{B})\hat{j}$

3rd term $= B_z(\vec{A}.\vec{C})\hat{k} - C_z(\vec{A}.\vec{B})\hat{k}$

Adding all these terms, we get

$$\vec{A}\times(\vec{B}\times\vec{C}) = (B_x\hat{i} + B_y\hat{j} + B_z\hat{k})(\vec{A}.\vec{C}) - (C_x\hat{i} + C_y\hat{j} + C_z\hat{k})(\vec{A}.\vec{B})$$

$$= \vec{B}(\vec{A}.\vec{C}) - \vec{C}(\vec{A}.\vec{B})$$

As the vector $(\vec{B}\times\vec{C})$ is perpendicular to the plain containing $\vec{B}$ and $\vec{C}$, the vector $\vec{A}\times(\vec{B}\times\vec{C})$ will be perpendicular to the plane containing $\vec{A}$ and $(\vec{B}\times\vec{C})$ i.e., it will be in the plane of $\vec{B}$ and $\vec{C}$ the vectors inside the brackets. This is also clear from the result $(\vec{A}.\vec{C})$ and $(\vec{A}.\vec{B})$ being scalar quantities the resultant lies in the plane of $\vec{B}$ and $\vec{C}$.

Also $\qquad \vec{A}\times(\vec{B}\times\vec{C}) = -(\vec{B}\times\vec{C})\times\vec{A}$

Q. 1.7. Prove that $\vec{A}\times(\vec{B}\times\vec{C}) + \vec{B}\times(\vec{C}\times\vec{A}) + \vec{C}\times(\vec{A}\times\vec{B}) = 0$

(*Meerut. U.* 2002; *K.U.* 1992)

Ans. According to triple vector product

$$\vec{A}\times(\vec{B}\times\vec{C}) = \vec{B}(\vec{A}.\vec{C}) - \vec{C}(\vec{A}.\vec{B})$$

$$\vec{B}\times(\vec{C}\times\vec{A}) = \vec{C}(\vec{B}.\vec{A}) - \vec{A}(\vec{B}.\vec{C})$$

$$\vec{C}\times(\vec{A}\times\vec{B}) = \vec{A}(\vec{C}.\vec{B}) - \vec{B}(\vec{C}.\vec{A})$$

Now $\qquad \vec{A}.\vec{C} = \vec{C}.\vec{A},\ \vec{A}.\vec{B} = \vec{B}.\vec{A},\ \vec{B}.\vec{C} = \vec{C}.\vec{B}$

$\therefore \qquad \vec{A}\times(\vec{B}\times\vec{C}) + \vec{B}\times(\vec{C}\times\vec{A}) + \vec{C}\times(\vec{A}\times\vec{B}) = 0$

Q. 1.8. Prove that $(\vec{A}+\vec{B}).[\vec{B}+\vec{C})\times(\vec{C}+\vec{A})] = 2\vec{A}.(\vec{B}\times\vec{C})$

Ans. $(\vec{A}+\vec{B}).[(\vec{B}+\vec{C})\times(\vec{C}+\vec{A})]$

$$= (\vec{A}+\vec{B}).[(\vec{B}\times\vec{C}) + (\vec{B}\times\vec{A}) + (\vec{C}\times\vec{C}) + (\vec{C}\times\vec{A})]$$

$$= \vec{A}.(\vec{B}\times\vec{C}) + \vec{A}.(\vec{B}\times\vec{A}) + \vec{A}.(\vec{C}\times\vec{C}) + \vec{A}.(\vec{C}\times\vec{A})$$

$$+ \vec{B}.(\vec{B}\times\vec{C}) + \vec{B}.(\vec{B}\times\vec{A}) + \vec{B}.(\vec{C}\times\vec{C}) + \vec{B}.(\vec{C}\times\vec{A})$$

Now $\qquad \vec{A}.(\vec{B}\times\vec{A}) = 0;\ \vec{A}.(\vec{C}\times\vec{C}) = 0;\ \vec{A}.(\vec{C}\times\vec{A}) = 0$

$$\vec{B}.(\vec{B}\times\vec{C}) = 0;\ \vec{B}.(\vec{B}\times\vec{A}) = 0;\ \vec{B}.(\vec{C}\times\vec{C}) = 0$$

$\therefore (\vec{A}+\vec{B}).[(\vec{B}+\vec{C})\times(\vec{C}+\vec{A})] = \vec{A}.(\vec{B}\times\vec{C}) + \vec{B}.(\vec{C}\times\vec{A})] = 2\vec{A}.(\vec{B}\times\vec{C})$

Q. 1.9. *(a)* **Describe gradient of a scalar field in Cartesian co-ordinates. Explain its physical significance. Show that the gradient of a scalar function at any point is directed normally to the surface in the scalar field over which the value of scalar function is constant.**

(b) **The gradient of a scalar field is a vector. Hence explain how you can produce a vector from a scalar field.** (*Meerut. U.* 2003; *M.D.U.* 2003; *H.P.U.* 2003; 2000; *K.U.* 2001; *P.U.* 2000; 1995; *Pbi. U.* 2000; 1995, *G.N.D.U.* 2007, 2006, 1997; *Osm. U.* 1997)

Ans. (a) Gradient of a scalar field in Cartesian co-ordinates. Consider a point P in the scalar field having position vector. $\vec{r} = x\hat{i} + y\hat{j} + z\hat{k}$ and let the value of the scalar field at this point be $\phi(\vec{r}) = \phi(x, y, z)$ where $\phi(xyz)$ is continuous differentiable function of three independent space co-ordinates x, y, z.

The partial derivative of ϕ with respect to x (keeping y and z constant) $= \dfrac{\partial \phi}{\partial x}$. It measures the rate of change of ϕ at the point P along the X-direction. Similarly, $\dfrac{\partial \phi}{\partial y} =$ rate of change of ϕ at the point P along the Y-direction and $\dfrac{\partial \phi}{\partial z} =$ rate of change of ϕ at the point P along the Z-direction. The function ϕ, therefore, has different rates of variation along different directions. With the partial derivatives $\dfrac{\partial \phi}{\partial x}, \dfrac{\partial \phi}{\partial y}, \dfrac{\partial \phi}{\partial z}$ we can construct at every point in space a vector whose components along the X, Y and Z directions are equal to the respective partial derivatives of the scalar function ϕ. This vector is known as the *gradient of* ϕ *or grad* ϕ.

$$\therefore \qquad grad\ \phi = \frac{\partial \phi}{\partial x}\hat{i} + \frac{\partial \phi}{\partial y}\hat{j} + \frac{\partial \phi}{\partial z}\hat{k} \qquad\qquad ...(i)$$

$$= \left(\frac{\partial}{\partial x}\hat{i} + \frac{\partial}{\partial y}\hat{j} + \frac{\partial}{\partial z}\hat{k} \right)\phi = \vec{\nabla}\phi \qquad\qquad ...(ii)$$

The symbol $\vec{\nabla}$ (read as Del) is called vector differential operator or Del operator. It should be clearly noted that $\vec{\nabla}$ is not a vector but an operator which obeys laws of vectors

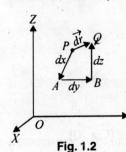

$$\vec{\nabla} = \frac{\partial}{\partial x}\hat{i} + \frac{\partial}{\partial y}\hat{j} + \frac{\partial}{\partial z}\hat{k}$$

Physical significance of grad ϕ. Consider a point P having position co-ordinates x, y, z, and point Q very close to it having position co-ordinates $x + dx, y + dy, z + dz$ as shown in Fig. 1.2. The vector distance between the two points P and Q is

Fig. 1.2

$$\vec{dr} = dx\,\hat{i} + dy\,\hat{j} + dz\,\hat{k}.$$

Let ϕ be the value of a scalar function at P and $\phi + d\phi$ its value at Q, then the change in value of $\phi = d\phi$ in known as the *total differential of* ϕ.

Now rate of change of ϕ along X-axis $= \dfrac{\partial \phi}{\partial x}$

$$\therefore \qquad \text{Value of } \phi \text{ at } A = \phi + \frac{\partial \phi}{\partial x}dx$$

The rate of change of ϕ along Y-axis $= \dfrac{\partial \phi}{\partial y}$

$$\therefore \qquad \text{Value of } \phi \text{ at } B = \phi + \frac{\partial \phi}{\partial x}dx + \frac{\partial}{\partial y}\left(\phi + \frac{\partial \phi}{\partial x}dx \right)dy$$

$$= \phi + \frac{\partial \phi}{\partial x}dx + \frac{\partial \phi}{\partial y}dy + \frac{\partial^2 \phi}{\partial x \partial y}dx\,dy$$

$$= \phi + \frac{\partial \phi}{\partial x} dx + \frac{\partial \phi}{\partial y} dy$$

because the terms $\frac{\partial^2 \phi}{\partial x \partial y} dx\, dy$ contains the product of two very small quantities and can be neglected.

The rate of change of ϕ along Z-axis $= \frac{\partial \phi}{\partial z}$

$\therefore$ Value of ϕ at $Q = \phi + \frac{\partial \phi}{\partial x} dx + \frac{\partial \phi}{\partial y} dy + \frac{\partial}{\partial z}\left(\phi + \frac{\partial \phi}{\partial x} dx + \frac{\partial \phi}{\partial y} dy\right) dz$

$$= \phi + \frac{\partial \phi}{\partial x} dx + \frac{\partial \phi}{\partial y} dy + \frac{\partial \phi}{\partial z} dz$$

Neglecting the terms $\frac{\partial^2 \phi}{\partial x \partial z} dx\, dz$ and $\frac{\partial^2 \phi}{\partial y \partial z} dy\, dz$

$\therefore$

$$d\phi = \frac{\partial \phi}{\partial x} dx + \frac{\partial \phi}{\partial y} dy + \frac{\partial \phi}{\partial z} dz$$

$$= \left(\frac{\partial \phi}{\partial x}\hat{i} + \frac{\partial \phi}{\partial y}\hat{j} + \frac{\partial \phi}{\partial z}\hat{k}\right) \cdot (dx\,\hat{i} + dy\,\hat{j} + dz\,\hat{k})$$

or

$$d\phi = \vec{\nabla}\phi \cdot \vec{dr} = \vec{\nabla}\phi \cdot \hat{r}\, dr$$

$\therefore$

$$\frac{d\phi}{dr} = \vec{\nabla}\phi \cdot \hat{r}$$

where $\hat{r}$ is a unit vector along PQ the direction of displacement. Thus $\frac{d\phi}{dr}$ is the directional derivative of ϕ. The rate of change is maximum if $\hat{r}$ is along $\vec{\nabla}\phi$ *i.e.*, the angle between $\vec{\nabla}\phi$ and $\hat{r}$ is zero.

Hence gradient of a scalar field ϕ defines a vector field the magnitude of which is equal to the maximum rate of change of ϕ and the direction of which is the same as the direction of displacement along which the rate of change is maximum.

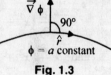

Fig. 1.3

Geometrical interpretation. The value of $\frac{d\phi}{dr} = 0$ when we move in a direction perpendicular to the direction $\vec{\nabla}\phi$ *i.e.*, when the angle between $\hat{r}$ in the direction of displacement and $\vec{\nabla}\phi = 90°$ as shown in Fig. 1.3. In such a case because $d\phi = 0$, $\phi = $ a constant. This defines a three dimensional surface and $\vec{\nabla}\phi$ a vector normal to the surface.

A unit vector normal to the surface $\phi\,(x, y, z) = $ a constant is given by

$$\frac{\vec{\nabla}\phi}{|\vec{\nabla}\phi|}$$

In other words, *the gradient of a scalar function at any point is directed normally to the surface in the scalar field over which the value of scalar function is constant.*

(*b*) **Gradient of scalar field is a vector.** From relation (*i*) we have

$$\text{grad } \phi = \vec{\nabla}\phi = \frac{\partial \phi}{\partial x}\hat{i} + \frac{\partial \phi}{\partial y}\hat{j} + \frac{\partial \phi}{\partial z}\hat{k}$$

This shows that grad ϕ is a vector whose x, y, z components are

$$\frac{\partial \phi}{\partial x} \hat{i}, \ \frac{\partial \phi}{\partial y} \hat{j} \text{ and } \frac{\partial \phi}{\partial z} \hat{k}$$

Hence the gradient of scalar field is a vector.

For example, electric potential V is a scalar function but $-\vec{\nabla} V = \vec{E}$ the electric field intensity is a vector which shows how V varies in the neighbourhood of a point in space.

Vector from a scalar field. The gradient of a scalar field (function) grad $\phi = \vec{\nabla} \phi$ is a vector. Thus by considering gradient of a scaler field we get a vector field starting from a scalar field.

Q. 1.10. Give physical interpretation of grad V.   (G.N.D.U. 2003)

Ans. See Q. 1.9 'Physical singnificance of grad ϕ' and 'Geometrical interpretation'

Q. 1.11. Calculate grad r where $\vec{r} = x\hat{i} + y\hat{j} + z\hat{k}$

Ans. $\text{grad } r = \vec{\nabla} r = \left(\hat{i} \frac{\partial}{\partial x} + \hat{j} \frac{\partial}{\partial y} + \hat{k} \frac{\partial}{\partial z} \right) (x^2 + y^2 + z^2)^{\frac{1}{2}}$

because $r = |\vec{r}| = (x^2 + y^2 + z^2)^{\frac{1}{2}}$

Now $\hat{i} \frac{\partial}{\partial x} (x^2 + y^2 + z^2)^{\frac{1}{2}} = \hat{i} \left[\frac{1}{2} (x^2 + y^2 + z^2)^{1/2} 2x \right] = \hat{i} \left[x(x^2 + y^2 + z^2)^{-1/2} \right]$

$$= \hat{i} \frac{x}{(x^2 + y^2 + z^2)^{1/2}} = \hat{i} \frac{x}{r}$$

Similarly,

$$\hat{j} \frac{\partial}{\partial y} (x^2 + y^2 + z^2)^{1/2} = \hat{j} \frac{y}{r}$$

and $\hat{k} \frac{\partial}{\partial z} (x^2 + y^2 + z^2)^{1/2} = \hat{k} \frac{z}{r}$

$$\therefore \qquad \vec{\nabla} r = \frac{x}{r} \hat{i} + \frac{y}{r} \hat{j} + \frac{z}{r} \hat{k} = \frac{x\hat{i} + y\hat{j} + z\hat{k}}{r}$$

$$= \frac{\vec{r}}{r} = \frac{\vec{r}}{|\vec{r}|} = \hat{r}$$

Q. 1.12. Find the value of $\vec{\nabla} r^n$ where $\vec{r} = x\hat{i} + y\hat{j} + z\hat{k}$.   (Ranchi U. 1991)

Ans. $\vec{\nabla} r^n = \left(\hat{i} \frac{\partial}{\partial x} + \hat{j} \frac{\partial}{\partial y} + \hat{k} \frac{\partial}{\partial z} \right) (x^2 + y^2 + z^2)^{\frac{n}{2}}$

$$= \left[\frac{n}{2} (x^2 + y^2 + z^2)^{\frac{n}{2}-1} 2x \right] \hat{i} + \left[\frac{n}{2} (x^2 + y^2 + z^2)^{\frac{n}{2}-1} 2y \right] \hat{j}$$

$$+ \left[\frac{n}{2} (x^2 + y^2 + z^2)^{\frac{n}{2}-1} 2z \right] \hat{k}$$

$$= n\left(x^2 + y^2 + z^2\right)^{\frac{n}{2}-1} \left(x\hat{i} + y\hat{j} + z\hat{k}\right)$$

$$= n r^{n-2}\, \vec{r}$$

Exercises. (*i*) *Calculate* $\vec{\nabla} r$

Hint. Put $n = 1$, then $\vec{\nabla} r = r^{-1}\,\vec{r} = \dfrac{\vec{r}}{r} = \hat{r}$ [Also see **Q. 1.11**] [**Ans.** $\hat{r}$]

(*ii*) *Calculate* $\vec{\nabla} r^2$

Hint. Put $n = 2$ [**Ans.** $2\vec{r}$]

(*iii*) *Calculate* $\vec{\nabla} r^3$ (*G.N.D.U.*, 2007)   [**Ans.** $3 r\, \vec{r}$]

Hint. Put $n = 3$

(*iv*) *Calculate* $\vec{\nabla}\left(\dfrac{1}{r}\right)$ (*P.U.*, 2007, *Meerut. U.*, 2007, *H.P.U.*, 2006) $\left[\textbf{Ans.} -\dfrac{\vec{r}}{r^3}\right]$

Hint. Put $n = -1$

(*v*) *Calculate* $\vec{\nabla}\left(\dfrac{1}{r^n}\right)$ $\left[\textbf{Ans.} -\dfrac{n}{r^{n+2}}\,\vec{r}\right]$

Hint. Put $n = -n$ [Also see **Q. 1.13**]

(*vi*) *Calculate* $\vec{\nabla}\left(\dfrac{1}{r^3}\right)$ (*G.N.D.U.*, 2009, 2007) $\left[\textbf{Ans.} -\dfrac{3}{r^5}\,\vec{r}\right]$

Hint. Put $n = -3$.

Q. 1.13. Prove that $\vec{\nabla}\left(\dfrac{1}{r^n}\right) = \dfrac{-n}{r^{n+2}}\,\vec{r}$ **where** $r = \sqrt{x^2 + y^2 + z^2}$

(*P. U.* 2003; *G.N.D.U.*, 1990)

Ans. $\vec{\nabla}\left(\dfrac{1}{r^n}\right) = \left(\hat{i}\dfrac{\partial}{\partial x} + \hat{j}\dfrac{\partial}{\partial y} + \hat{k}\dfrac{\partial}{\partial z}\right)\left(x^2 + y^2 + z^2\right)^{-\frac{n}{2}}$

$$= \left[-\dfrac{n}{2}\left(x^2 + y^2 + z^2\right)^{-\frac{n}{2}-1} 2x\right]\hat{i} + \left[-\dfrac{n}{2}\left(x^2 + y^2 + z^2\right)^{-\frac{n}{2}-1} 2y\right]\hat{j}$$

$$+ \left[-\dfrac{n}{2}\left(x^2 + y^2 + z^2\right)^{-\frac{n}{2}-1} 2z\right]\hat{k}$$

$$= -n\left(x^2 + y^2 + z^2\right)^{-\frac{(n+2)}{2}} \left(x\hat{i} + y\hat{j} + z\hat{k}\right)$$

$$= -\dfrac{n}{r^{n+2}}\,\vec{r}$$

Q. 1.14. Given $\phi = x^4 + y^4 + z^4$ **determine** $\vec{\nabla}\phi$ (*P. U.* 1994)

Ans. $\vec{\nabla}\phi = \left(\dfrac{\partial}{\partial x}\hat{i} + \dfrac{\partial}{\partial y}\hat{j} + \dfrac{\partial}{\partial z}\hat{k}\right)\left(x^4 + y^4 + z^4\right)$

$$= \left(\dfrac{\partial}{\partial x}x^4\right)\hat{i} + \left(\dfrac{\partial}{\partial y}y^4\right)\hat{j} + \left(\dfrac{\partial}{\partial z}z^4\right)\hat{k}$$

$$= 4x^3\,\hat{i} + 4y^3\,\hat{j} + 4z^3\,\hat{k}$$
$$= 4\,(x^3\,\hat{i} + y^3\,\hat{j} + z^3\,\hat{k})$$

Ex. *If* $\phi = x^{3/2} + y^{3/2} + z^{3/2}$ *find* $\vec{\nabla}\phi$ (*Pbi. U.* 2002, 2001)

Hint. $\vec{\nabla}\phi = \dfrac{3}{2}\left[x^{1/2}\,\hat{i} + y^{1/2}\,\hat{j} + z^{1/2}\,\hat{k}\right]$

Q. 1.15. If $\phi\,(x, y, z) = 3x^2\,y - y^3\,x^2$ be any scalar function of x, y, z, find out grad ϕ at 1, 2, 2.

Ans. $$grad\ \ \phi = \vec{\nabla}\phi = \frac{\partial\phi}{\partial x}\hat{i} + \frac{\partial\phi}{\partial y}\hat{j} + \frac{\partial\phi}{\partial z}\hat{k}$$

Now $$\phi = 3x^2\,y - y^3\,x^2$$

$\therefore$ $$\frac{\partial\phi}{\partial x} = 6xy - 2xy^3;\ \frac{\partial\phi}{\partial y} = 3x^2 - 3y^2x^2;\ \frac{\partial\phi}{\partial z} = 0$$

$\therefore$ $$grad\ \ \phi = (6xy - 2xy^3)\hat{i} + (3x^2 - 3y^2x^2)\hat{j}$$

At the point 1, 2, 2

$$6xy - 2xy^3 = 12 - 16 = -4;\ 3x^2 - 3y^2\,x^2 = 3 - 12 = -9$$

$\therefore$ $grad\ \ \phi = -4\hat{i} - 9\hat{j}$

Ex. *If* $\phi\,(x, y, z) = 3x^2\,y - y\,z^2$ *find grad* ϕ *at the point* $(1, 2, -1)$ (*M.D.U.* 2001)

Hint. $$\frac{\partial\phi}{\partial x} = 6xy;\ \frac{\partial\phi}{\partial y} = 3x^2 - z^2;\ \frac{\partial\phi}{\partial z} = -2\,yz$$

$\therefore$ $$\vec{\nabla}\phi = 6xy\hat{i} + (3x^2 - z^2)\hat{j} - 2\,yz\,\hat{k}$$

At point $(1, 2, -1)$, $grad\ \phi = 12\hat{i} + 2\hat{j} + 4\hat{k}$

Q. 1.16. Given a vector $\vec{r} - \vec{r}' = (x - x')\hat{i} + (y - y')\hat{j} + (z - z')\hat{k}$. Prove that

$$\vec{\nabla}\left(\frac{1}{|\vec{r} - \vec{r}'|}\right) + \vec{\nabla}'\left(\frac{1}{|\vec{r} - \vec{r}'|}\right) = 0$$

(*H.P.U.* 1994)

Ans. $$|\vec{r} - \vec{r}'| = [(x - x')^2 + (y - y')^2 + (z - z')^2]^{1/2}$$

$\therefore$ $$\vec{\nabla}\left(\frac{1}{|\vec{r} - \vec{r}'|}\right) = \left(\hat{i}\frac{\partial}{\partial x} + \hat{j}\frac{\partial}{\partial y} + \hat{k}\frac{\partial}{\partial z}\right)[(x - x')^2 + (y - y')^2 + (z - z')^2]^{-\frac{1}{2}}$$

Now $\hat{i}\dfrac{\partial}{\partial x}[(x - x')^2 + (y - y')^2 + (z - z')^2]^{-\frac{1}{2}}$

$$= \left\{-\frac{1}{2}[(x - x')^2 + (y - y')^2 + (z - z')^2]^{-3/2}\,2(x - x')\right\}\hat{i}$$

$$= -\left\{[(x - x')^2 + (y - y')^2 + (z - z')^2]^{-3/2}\,(x - x')\right\}\hat{i}$$

$$= -[\,|\vec{r} - \vec{r}'|^{-3}\,(x - x')]\hat{i}$$

Similarly, $\hat{i}\dfrac{\partial}{\partial y}[(x - x')^2 + (y - y')^2 + (z - z')^2]^{-1/2}$

$$= -[\,|\vec{r} - \vec{r}'|^{-3}\,(y - y')]\hat{j}$$

and $\hat{i}\dfrac{\partial}{\partial z}[(x - x')^2 + (y - y')^2 + (z - z')^2]^{-1/2}$

$$= - [|\vec{r} - \vec{r'}|^{-3} (z - z')]\hat{k}$$

$$\therefore \quad \vec{\nabla}\left(\frac{1}{|\vec{r} - \vec{r'}|}\right) = -\left\{|\vec{r} - \vec{r'}|^{-3}[(x - x')\hat{i} + (y - y')\hat{j} + (z - z')\hat{k}]\right\}$$

$$= -\left\{|\vec{r} - \vec{r'}|^{-3}(\vec{r} - \vec{r'})\right\} \qquad \ldots(i)$$

Again $\quad \vec{\nabla'}\left(\left|\dfrac{1}{\vec{r}} - \dfrac{1}{\vec{r'}}\right|\right) = \left(\hat{i}\dfrac{\partial}{\partial x'} + \hat{j}\dfrac{\partial}{\partial y'} + \hat{k}\dfrac{\partial}{\partial z'}\right)[(x - x')^2 + (y - y')^2 + (z - z')^2]^{-1/2}$

Now $\hat{i}\dfrac{\partial}{\partial x'}[(x - x')^2 + (y - y')^2 + (z - z')^2]^{-1/2}$

$$= \left\{-\frac{1}{2}[(x - x')^2 + (y - y')^2 + (z - z')^2]^{-3/2}\, 2(x - x') \times -1\right\}\hat{i}$$

$$= [(x - x')^2 + (y - y')^2 + (z - z')^2]^{-3/2}(x - x')]\hat{i}$$

$$= [|\vec{r} - \vec{r'}|^{-3}(x - x')]\hat{i}$$

Similarly, $\hat{i}\dfrac{\partial}{\partial y'}[(x - x')^2 + (y - y')^2 + (z - z')^2]^{-1/2}$

$$= [|\vec{r} - \vec{r'}|^{-3}(y - y')]\hat{j}$$

and $i\dfrac{\partial}{\partial z'}[(x - x')^2 + (y - y')^2 + (z - z')^2]^{-1/2}$

$$= [|\vec{r} - \vec{r'}|^{-3}(z - z')]\hat{k}$$

$$\vec{\nabla'}\left(\frac{1}{|\vec{r} - \vec{r'}|}\right) = \left\{|\vec{r} - \vec{r'}|^{-3}[(x - x')\hat{i} + (y - y')\hat{j} + (z - z')\hat{k}]\right\}$$

$$= |\vec{r} - \vec{r'}|^{-3}(\vec{r} - \vec{r'}) \qquad \ldots(ii)$$

Adding (i) and (ii), we have

$$\vec{\nabla}\left(\frac{1}{|\vec{r} - \vec{r'}|}\right) + \vec{\nabla'}\left(\frac{1}{|\vec{r} - \vec{r'}|}\right) = -[|\vec{r} - \vec{r'}|^{-3}(\vec{r} - \vec{r'})] + [|\vec{r} - \vec{r'}|^{-3}(\vec{r} - \vec{r'})]$$

$$= 0$$

Q. 1.17. Find a unit normal to the surface $x^2y + 2xz = 4$ at point $(2, -2, 3)$

(*P.U.*, 2005; *G.N.D.U.* 1991)

Ans. The point $(2, -2, 3)$ satisfies the equation $x^2y + 2xz = 4$

Therefore, the point $(2, -2, 3)$ lies on the surface represented by the equation $x^2y + 2xz = 4$

A unit normal to the surface of $\phi(x, y, z) =$ a constant is given by $\dfrac{\vec{\nabla}\phi}{|\vec{\nabla}\phi|}$

Here ϕ is $\qquad x^2y + 2xz = 4$

$\therefore \qquad \vec{\nabla}\phi = \vec{\nabla}(x^2y + 2xz)$

$$= \hat{i}\frac{\partial\phi}{\partial x} + \hat{j}\frac{\partial\phi}{\partial y} + \hat{k}\frac{\partial\phi}{\partial z}$$

$$\frac{\partial\phi}{\partial x} = 2xy + 2z; \; \frac{\partial\phi}{\partial y} = x^2; \; \frac{\partial\phi}{\partial z} = 2x$$

At the point $(2, -2, 3)$ $\dfrac{\partial \phi}{\partial x} = -2; \dfrac{\partial \phi}{\partial y} = 4; \dfrac{\partial \phi}{\partial z} = 4$

$\therefore$ $\vec{\nabla}\phi = -2\,\hat{i} + 4\,\hat{j} + 4\,\hat{k}$

Also $|\vec{\nabla}\phi| = \sqrt{(-2)^2 + (4)^2 + (4)^2} = \sqrt{36} = 6$

$\therefore$ Unit normal to the surface $x^2 y + 2xz = 4$ at the point $(2, -2, 3)$

$$\dfrac{-2\hat{i} + 4\hat{j} + 4\hat{k}}{6} = -\dfrac{1}{3}\hat{i} + \dfrac{2}{3}\hat{j} + \dfrac{2}{3}\hat{k}$$

Q. 1.18. What is a lamellar field?   (Pbi.U., 2006; H.P.U. 1995)

Ans. Lamellar field. *A vector field which can be expressed as the gradient of a scalar field is known as a lamellar (or laminar) vector field.*

Electric field is an example of a lamellar field since

$$\vec{E} = -\vec{\nabla}V$$

where V is the electrical potential which is a scalar function.

The word lamellar (or laminar) means that the field can be divided into laminas or layers over which the value of the scalar function whose gradient gives the vector field $\vec{E}$ remains constant.

Equipotential surfaces in the electric field are an example of such laminae.

Q. 1.19. (a) Define divergence of a vector field. What is its physical meaning? Give two examples.   (P.U., 2006)

(b) Divergence of a vector field is a scalar quantity. Hence explain how you can produce a scalar field from a vector field. (Pbi. U., 2007, 2003, 2001, 2000, 1999, H.P.U. 2001, 1999, 1996; G.N.D.U. 2008, 2001, 1996; K.U. 2000, 1996; Osm. U. 1997; P. U. 1995; Ranchi U. 1991)

Ans. Divergence of a vector field. Just as we can get a vector field starting from a scalar field we can get a scalar field starting from a vector field.

Consider a vector field $\vec{A}$, the magnitude and direction of which is a function of the position co-ordinates at a point, then the scalar product of the differential operator $\vec{\nabla}$ and the vector $\vec{A}$ is a *scalar* function of position co-ordinates x, y, z and is known as the *divergence of the vector $\vec{A}$*.

$\therefore$ $div.\ \vec{A} = \vec{\nabla} \cdot \vec{A}$

where $\vec{\nabla} = \left(\hat{i}\dfrac{\partial}{\partial x} + \hat{j}\dfrac{\partial}{\partial y} + \hat{k}\dfrac{\partial}{\partial z} \right)$

and $\vec{A} = (\hat{i}\,A_x + \hat{j}\,A_y + \hat{k}\,A_z)$

$\therefore$ $\vec{\nabla} \cdot \vec{A} = \left(\hat{i}\dfrac{\partial}{\partial x} + \hat{j}\dfrac{\partial}{\partial y} + \hat{k}\dfrac{\partial}{\partial z} \right) \cdot (\hat{i}\,A_x + \hat{j}\,A_y + \hat{k}\,A_z)$

$$= \dfrac{\partial A_x}{\partial x} + \dfrac{\partial A_y}{\partial y} + \dfrac{\partial A_z}{\partial z}$$

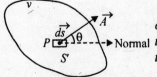

Physical meaning. *The divergence of a vector is the limiting value of the net outward flow of some physical quantity like a fluid or electric flux through the surface area of a unit volume as the volume tends to approach zero.*

Consider a closed volume v having a surface area S in a vector field as shown in Fig. 1.4. Let the vector field at a point P on the

Fig. 1.4

surface be $\vec{A}$ and let $\vec{ds}$ be a vector representing a small area surrounding the point P, its direction being that of the outward drawn normal to the surface. If θ is the angle between the direction of the field vector and outward drawn normal to the surface at P, then

Flux of the field out of the area $\vec{ds} = A\,ds\,\cos\theta = \vec{A}\,.\,\vec{ds}$

∴ Total flux of the field out of the whole surface

$$= \iint_s \vec{A}\,.\,\vec{ds}$$

If v the volume enclosed by the surface is vanishingly small then the outward flux per unit volume gives the divergence of $\vec{A}$ $(div.\ \vec{A})$.

∴ $$div.\ \vec{A} = \lim_{v \to 0} \frac{1}{v} \iint_s \vec{A}\,.\,\vec{ds} \qquad\qquad ...(i)$$

Examples. (*i*) Let a vector $\vec{A}$ represent the velocity $\vec{V}$ of a liquid in motion then $div\ \vec{V}$ at a point will represent the volume of the liquid flowing out per second per unit volume enclosed, through a small closed surface surrounding it. If $div\ \vec{V}$ at a point is *negative*, it shows that the liquid is flowing towards the point *i.e.*, it is a *sink* and if $div\ \vec{V}$ at a point is *positive*, it indicates that the liquid is flowing away from the point *i.e.*, it is a *source* of the liquid.

(*ii*) For an electric field the divergence of the field vector $\vec{E}$ over the surface of a unit volume element surrounding a point in an electric field is given by

$$div\ \vec{E} = \lim_{v \to 0} \frac{1}{v} \iint_s \vec{E}\,.\,\vec{ds}$$

where s is the closed surface surrounding the point and v the volume of the element surrounding it.

The divergence of an electric field at any point gives the charge density at that point as

$$\vec{\nabla}\,.\,\vec{E} = \frac{\rho}{\varepsilon_0}$$

which is a scalar function.

(*b*) **Divergence of a vector is a scalar.** According to relation (*i*)

$$div\ \vec{A} = \lim_{v \to 0} \frac{1}{v} \oiint_s \vec{A}\,.\,\vec{ds}$$

Hence divergence of a vector field at a point is equal to flux per unit volume through a closed surface drawn around the point as the volume enclosed by the surface approaches zero. Thus $div\ \vec{A}$ is the volume flux density at the point and is a scalar quantity.

Scalar from a vector field. The divergence of a vector field $div\ \vec{A} = \vec{\nabla}\,.\,\vec{A}$ is a scalar quantity. Thus by considering the divergence of a vector field we get a scalar field starting from a vector field.

Q. 1.20. Derive an expression for divergence of a vector field in Cartesian co-ordinates from first principles. (*K.U.*, 1996, 1994; *P.U.*, 1995, 1991; *Pbi. U.*, 2007, 1995)

Ans. Divergence of a vector in Cartesian co-ordinates. To find the value of $div\ \vec{A}$ using cartesian co-ordinates draw a rectangular parallelopiped with a point P having co-ordinates x, y, z at its centre and with edges of length Δx, Δy, and Δz parallel to the three respective co-ordinate axes as shown in

Fig. 1.5. Resolve the vector $\vec{A}$ at the point P into three rectangular components A_x, A_y, A_z parallel to the three respective axes. The value of *div* $\vec{A}$ is then equal to the total outflow of the vector quantity over the surface of the parallelopiped.

The outflow over the front face (marked 1) of the block perpendicular to the X-axis will be entirely due to A_x; the component of $\vec{A}$ parallel to OX

The co-ordinates of P_1 the centre of the face marked 1 are $\left(x + \dfrac{\Delta x}{2} \right)$, y, z because P lies at the centre of the block and the length of the edge $= \Delta x$, therefore $PP_1 = \dfrac{\Delta x}{2}$. Similarly the co-ordinates of P_2 the centre of the opposite face marked 2 are $\left(x - \dfrac{\Delta x}{2} \right), y, z$

Let $\dfrac{\partial A_x}{\partial x}$ be the space rate of variation of A_x with x, then

Magnitude of A_x at P_1 the centre of the front face 1

$$= A_x + \frac{\partial A_x}{\partial x} \cdot \frac{\Delta x}{2}$$

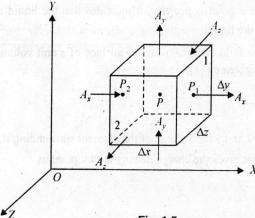

Fig. 1.5

According to the definition of divergence, in the limit $v = 0$. Hence Δy and Δz are vanishingly small in the limit and therefore the value of A_x at every point on the front face may be taken to be

$$= A_x + \frac{\partial A_x}{\partial x} \frac{\Delta x}{2}$$

$\therefore$ Total flow of the vector on the front face 1

$$= \left(A_x + \frac{\partial A_x}{\partial x} \frac{\Delta x}{2} \right) \Delta y\, \Delta z$$

in the outward direction and for the opposite face 2 it is

$$= \left(A_x - \frac{\partial A_x}{\partial x} \frac{\Delta x}{2} \right) \Delta y\, \Delta z$$

in the inward direction.

$\therefore$ Net flow of the vectors A_y and A_z in the direction parallel to OX

$$= \left(A_x + \frac{\partial A_x}{\partial x} \frac{\Delta x}{2} \right) \Delta y\, \Delta z - \left(A_x - \frac{\partial A_x}{\partial x} \frac{\Delta x}{2} \right) \Delta y\, \Delta z$$

$$= \frac{\partial A_x}{\partial x} \Delta x\, \Delta y\, \Delta z$$

Similarly, the net outflow of the vectors A_y and A_z over the faces perpendicular to OY and OZ will be

$$\frac{\partial A_y}{\partial y} \Delta x\, \Delta y\, \Delta z \quad \text{and} \quad \frac{\partial A_z}{\partial z} \Delta x\, \Delta y\, \Delta z$$

$\therefore$ Total outflow of the vector over the entire surface of the block is given by

$$\iint_{\substack{\text{surface of the}\\\text{parallelopiped}}} \vec{A} \cdot \vec{ds} = \left(\frac{\partial A_x}{\partial x} + \frac{\partial A_y}{\partial y} + \frac{\partial A_z}{\partial z} \right) \Delta x \, \Delta y \, \Delta z$$

where $\Delta x \, \Delta y \, \Delta z$ is the volume of the block.

∴ Net outward flow of the vector per unit volume or

$$\underset{v \to 0}{\text{Lim}} \frac{1}{v} \iint_S \vec{A} \cdot \vec{ds} = \frac{1}{\Delta x \, \Delta y \, \Delta z} \left[\frac{\partial A_x}{\partial x} + \frac{\partial A_y}{\partial y} + \frac{\partial A_z}{\partial z} \right] \Delta x \, \Delta y \, \Delta z$$

$$= \frac{\partial A_x}{\partial x} + \frac{\partial A_y}{\partial y} + \frac{\partial A_z}{\partial z}$$

Hence in Cartesian co-ordinates the divergence of a vector field $\vec{A}$ is given by

$$\frac{\partial A_x}{\partial x} + \frac{\partial A_y}{\partial y} + \frac{\partial A_z}{\partial z} = \vec{\nabla} \cdot \vec{A}$$

Q. 1.21. (a) If ϕ is a scalar field and $\vec{A}$ a vector field find the value of div $\phi(\vec{A})$

(*Meerut U.* 2003)

(b) Prove that $\vec{\nabla} \cdot (\vec{A} + \vec{B}) = \vec{\nabla} \cdot \vec{A} + \vec{\nabla} \cdot \vec{B}$ **where** $\vec{A}$ **and** $\vec{B}$ **are differentiable vector functions.**
(*H.P.U.* 2007, 2003; 2001)

Ans. (a) If ϕ is a scalar field and $\vec{A}$ a vector field, then *div.* $(\phi \vec{A}) = \vec{\nabla} \cdot (\phi \vec{A})$

$$= \left(\frac{\partial}{\partial x} \hat{i} + \frac{\partial}{\partial y} \hat{j} + \frac{\partial}{\partial z} \hat{k} \right) \cdot (\phi A_x \hat{i} + \phi A_y \hat{j} + \phi A_z \hat{k})$$

$$= \frac{\partial}{\partial x} (\phi A_x) + \frac{\partial}{\partial y} (\phi A_y) + \frac{\partial}{\partial z} (\phi A_z)$$

$$= \frac{\partial \phi}{\partial x} A_x + \phi \frac{\partial A_x}{\partial x} + \frac{\partial \phi}{\partial y} A_y + \phi \frac{\partial A_y}{\partial y} + \frac{\partial \phi}{\partial z} dz + \phi \frac{\partial A_z}{\partial z}$$

$$= \left(\frac{\partial \phi}{\partial x} A_x + \frac{\partial \phi}{\partial y} A_y + \frac{\partial \phi}{\partial z} A_z \right) + \phi \left(\frac{\partial A_x}{\partial x} + \frac{\partial A_y}{\partial y} + \frac{\partial A_z}{\partial z} \right)$$

$$= \left(\frac{\partial \phi}{\partial x} \hat{i} + \frac{\partial \phi}{\partial y} \hat{j} + \frac{\partial \phi}{\partial z} \hat{k} \right) \cdot (A_x \hat{i} + A_y \hat{j} + A_z \hat{k}) + \phi \left(\frac{\partial A_x}{\partial x} + \frac{\partial A_y}{\partial y} + \frac{\partial A_z}{\partial z} \right)$$

$$= \vec{\nabla} \phi \cdot \vec{A} + \phi (\vec{\nabla} \cdot \vec{A})$$

or $\qquad div (\phi \vec{A}) = grad \, \phi \cdot \vec{A} + \phi \, div (\vec{A})$ or $\vec{\nabla} \cdot (\phi \vec{A}) = \vec{\nabla} \phi \cdot \vec{A} + \phi \vec{\nabla} \cdot \vec{A}$

(b) Let vector $\qquad \vec{A} = A_x \hat{i} + A_y \hat{j} + A_z \hat{k}$

and vector $\qquad \vec{B} = B_x \hat{i} + B_y \hat{j} + B_z \hat{k}$ then

$$(\vec{A} + \vec{B}) = (A_x + B_x)\hat{i} + (A_y + B_y)\hat{j} + (A_z + B_z)\hat{k}$$

Taking divergence on both sides we have

$$\vec{\nabla} \cdot (\vec{A} + \vec{B}) = \left(\hat{i} \frac{\partial}{\partial x} + \hat{j} \frac{\partial}{\partial y} + \hat{k} \frac{\partial}{\partial z} \right) \left[(A_x + B_x)\hat{i} + (A_y + B_y)\hat{j} + (A_z + B_z)\hat{k} \right]$$

$$= \frac{\partial}{\partial x}(A_x + B_x) + \frac{\partial}{\partial y}(A_y + B_y) + \frac{\partial}{\partial z}(A_z + B_z)$$

$$= \left(\frac{\partial A_x}{\partial x} + \frac{\partial A_y}{\partial y} + \frac{\partial A_z}{\partial z}\right) + \left(\frac{\partial B_x}{\partial x} + \frac{\partial B_y}{\partial y} + \frac{\partial B_z}{\partial z}\right)$$

$$= \vec{\nabla}.\vec{A} + \vec{\nabla}.\vec{B}$$

or $\vec{\nabla}.(\vec{A} + \vec{B}) = \vec{\nabla}.\vec{A} + \vec{\nabla}.\vec{B}$

Q. 1.22. (a) What do you mean by a solenoidal vector field ? Give one example. What is the meaning of $\vec{\nabla}.\vec{E} \neq 0$.   (*G.N.D.U.*, 2007; *Pbi, U.* 2006, 2001, 1999;

H.P.U. 2001, 1999, 1997, *M.D.U.* 1999)

(b) Prove that $\vec{A} = 3y^2z^2\hat{i} + 3x^2z^2\hat{j} + 3x^2y^2\hat{k}$ is a solenoidal vector.   (*P.U.* 2001, 2000)

(c) Find the value of the constant b so that the vector field

$$\vec{A} = x^2\hat{i} + (y - 2xy)\hat{j} + (x + bz)\hat{k} \text{ is solenoidal}$$ (*Pbi. U.* 1999)

Ans. (a) Solenoidal field. *A vector field whose divergence vanishes (= 0) is known as a solenoidal field.* Magnetic induction field is an example of a solenoidal field since.

$$div\,\vec{B} = \vec{\nabla}.\vec{B} = 0$$

$\vec{\nabla}.\vec{E} \neq 0$, means the divergence of electric field is not equal to zero *i.e.*, the *electric field is not solenoidal*

(b) $\vec{A} = 3y^2z^2\hat{i} + 3x^2z^2\hat{j} + 3x^2y^2\hat{k}$

$$\vec{\nabla}.\vec{A} = \left(\frac{\partial}{\partial x}\hat{i} + \frac{\partial}{\partial y}\hat{j} + \frac{\partial}{\partial z}\hat{k}\right).(3y^2z^2\hat{i} + 3x^2z^2\hat{j} + 3x^2y^2\hat{k})$$

$$= \frac{\partial}{\partial x}(3y^2z^2) + \frac{\partial}{\partial y}(3x^2z^2) + \frac{\partial}{\partial z}(3x^2y^2) = 0$$

As the divergence of vector field $\vec{A} = 0$, the vector field $\vec{A}$ is solenoidal

(c) Given $\vec{A} = x^2\hat{i} + (y - 2xy)\hat{j} + (x + bz)\hat{k}$

$\therefore$ $div\,\vec{A} = \vec{\nabla}.\vec{A} = \left(\frac{\partial}{\partial x}\hat{i} + \frac{\partial}{\partial y}\hat{j} + \frac{\partial}{\partial z}\hat{k}\right).\left[x^2\hat{i} + (y - 2xy)\hat{j} + (x + bz)\hat{k}\right]$

$$= \frac{\partial}{\partial x}x^2 + \frac{\partial}{\partial y}(y - 2xy) + \frac{\partial}{\partial z}(x + bz)$$

$$= 2x + 1 - 2x + b = 0 \text{ or } b = -1$$

Hence if $b = -1$, the vector $\vec{A}$ is solenoidal because then $div\,\vec{A} = 0$

Ex. *Find the constant 'a' so that the vector $\vec{A} = (x + 3y)\hat{i} + (2y + 3z)\hat{j} + (x + az)\hat{k}$ is a solenoidal vector.*   (*P.U.*, 2007; *H.P.U.* 1999; *M.D.U.* 1999; *G.N.D.U.* 2001)

Hint. $\vec{\nabla}.\vec{A} = \frac{\partial}{\partial x}(x + 3y) + \frac{\partial}{\partial y}(2y + 3z) + \frac{\partial}{\partial z}(x + az) = 1 + 2 + a = 0$

$\therefore$ $a = -3$

Q. 1.23. If the vector $\vec{A} = 3xyz\hat{i} + 2xy^2\hat{j} - x^2yz\hat{k}$ and scalar function $\phi = 3x^2 - yz$, evaluate div $(\phi\vec{A})$ at position (1, –1, 1).

Ans. $div\,(\phi\,\vec{A}) = \vec{\nabla}\,\phi\,.\,\vec{A} + \phi\,div\,(\vec{A})$

Here $\phi = 3x^2 - yz$ and $\vec{A} = 3xyz\,\hat{i} + 2xy^2\,\hat{j} - x^2yz\,\hat{k}$

$\therefore$ $grad\,\phi = \vec{\nabla}\,\phi = \left(\dfrac{\partial\phi}{\partial x}\hat{i} + \dfrac{\partial\phi}{\partial y}\hat{j} + \dfrac{\partial\phi}{\partial z}\hat{k}\right) = 6x\hat{i} - z\,\hat{j} - y\,\hat{k}$

$\therefore$ $grad\,\phi\,.\,\vec{A} = \vec{\nabla}\,\phi\,.\,\vec{A} = (6x\hat{i} - z\,\hat{j} - y\,\hat{k})\,.\,(3xyz\,\hat{i} + 2xy^2\,\hat{j} - x^2yz\,\hat{k})$

$= 18x^2yz - 2xy^2z + x^2y^2z$

$= xyz\,(18x - 2y + xy)$

$div\,\vec{A} = \vec{\nabla}\,.\,\vec{A} = \dfrac{\partial A_x}{\partial x} + \dfrac{\partial A_y}{\partial y} + \dfrac{\partial A_z}{\partial z} = 3yz + 4xy - x^2y$

$\therefore$ $\phi\,(div\,\vec{A}) = \phi\,(\vec{\nabla}\,.\,\vec{A}) = (3x^2 - yz)\,(3yz + 4xy - x^2y)$

At the point $1, -1, 1$

$grad\,\phi\,.\,\vec{A} = \vec{\nabla}\,\phi\,.\,\vec{A} = -1(18 + 2 - 1) = -19$

$\phi\,(div\,\vec{A}) = (4)\,(-6) = -24$

$\therefore$ $(div\,\phi\,\vec{A}) = \phi\,(\vec{\nabla}\,.\,\vec{A}) = grad\,\phi\,.\,\vec{A} + \phi\,(div\,\vec{A})$

or $\vec{\nabla}\,.\,(\phi\,\vec{A}) = \vec{\nabla}\,\phi\,.\,\vec{A} + \phi\,(\vec{\nabla}\,.\,\vec{A})$

$= -19 - 24 = -43$

Q. 1.24. If $\vec{r} = x\hat{i} + y\hat{j} + z\hat{k}$ find div $r^n\,\vec{r}$.   *(Pbi. U. 1991)*

Ans. $div\,r^n\,\vec{r} = \vec{\nabla}\,.\,r^n\,\vec{r}$

$= \left(\dfrac{\partial}{\partial x}\hat{i} + \dfrac{\partial}{\partial y}\hat{j} + \dfrac{\partial}{\partial z}\hat{k}\right).(x^2 + y^2 + z^2)^{n/2}\,(x\hat{i} + y\hat{j} + z\hat{k})$

$= \dfrac{\partial}{\partial x}[x(x^2 + y^2 + z^2)^{n/2}] + \dfrac{\partial}{\partial y}[y(x^2 + y^2 + z^2)^{n/2}] + \dfrac{\partial}{\partial z}[z(x^2 + y^2 + z^2)^{n/2}]$

Now $\dfrac{\partial}{\partial x}[x(x^2 + y^2 + z^2)^{n/2}] = x\dfrac{n}{2}(x^2 + y^2 + z^2)^{n/2-1}\,2x + (x^2 + y^2 + z^2)^{n/2}$

$= nx^2\,(x^2 + y^2 + z^2)^{n/2-1} + (x^2 + y^2 + z^2)^{n/2}$

Similarly, $\dfrac{\partial}{\partial y}[y(x^2 + y^2 + z^2)^{n/2}] = ny^2\,(x^2 + y^2 + z^2)^{n/2-1} + (x^2 + y^2 + z^2)^{n/2}$

and $\dfrac{\partial}{\partial z}[z(x^2 + y^2 + z^2)^{n/2}] = nz^2\,(x^2 + y^2 + z^2)^{n/2-1} + (x^2 + y^2 + z^2)^{n/2}$

$\therefore$ $\vec{\nabla}\,.\,r^n\,\vec{r} = n(x^2 + y^2 + z^2)\,(x^2 + y^2 + z^2)^{n/2-1} + 3(x^2 + y^2 + z^2)^{n/2}$

$= n(x^2 + y^2 + z^2)^{n/2} + 3(x^2 + y^2 + z^2)^{n/2}$

$= (n + 3)\,r^n$

Exercises. *Calculate the value of*

(i) $\vec{\nabla}\,.\,\vec{r}$ (ii) $\vec{\nabla}\,.\,\hat{r}$ *(H.P.U., 1996)*   (iii) $\vec{\nabla}\,.\,\dfrac{\hat{r}}{r^2}$ *(P.U., 1991)*

(iv) $\vec{\nabla}\,.\,(r^3\,\vec{r})$ *(H.P.U., 1995)*

Hint. (*i*) $\vec{\nabla} \cdot \vec{r} = \vec{\nabla} \cdot r^0 \vec{r}$

$\therefore$ Put $n = 0$ in the relation $(n + 3) r^n$

and we get $\qquad\qquad \vec{\nabla} \cdot \vec{r} = 3$ $\qquad\qquad\qquad$ [Also see **Q. 1.25** For complete solution]

(*ii*) $\vec{\nabla} \cdot \hat{r} = \vec{\nabla} \cdot \dfrac{\vec{r}}{r} = \vec{\nabla} \cdot r^{-1} \vec{r}$

Put $n = -1$ in the relation $(n + 3) r^n$

and we get $\vec{\nabla} \cdot \hat{r} = \dfrac{2}{r}$ $\qquad\qquad\qquad$ [Also see **Q. 1.26** For complete solution]

(*iii*) $\vec{\nabla} \cdot \dfrac{\hat{r}}{r^2} = \vec{\nabla} \cdot \dfrac{\vec{r}}{r^3} = \vec{\nabla} \cdot r^{-3} \vec{r}$

Put $n = -3$ in the relation $(n + 3) r^n$

and we get $\qquad\qquad \vec{\nabla} \cdot \dfrac{\vec{r}}{r^3} = 0$ $\qquad\qquad$ [Also see **Q. 1.29** For complete solution]

(*iv*) $\vec{\nabla} \cdot (r^3 \vec{r})$

Put $n = 3$ in the relation $(n + 3) r^n$

and we get $\vec{\nabla} \cdot (r^3 \vec{r}) = 6r^3$ $\qquad\qquad\qquad$ [Also see **Q. 1.30** For complete solution]

Q. 1.25. If $\vec{R} = x\hat{i} + y\hat{j} + z\hat{k}$ **find the value of** *div* $\vec{R}$. $\qquad$ (*P.U.*, 2009; *Os. U.*, 1997)

Ans. $\qquad\qquad\qquad\qquad \vec{R} = x\hat{i} + y\hat{j} + z\hat{k}$

$\therefore \qquad\qquad div \ \vec{R} = \vec{\nabla} \cdot \vec{R} = \left(\dfrac{\partial}{\partial x}\hat{i} + \dfrac{\partial}{\partial y}\hat{j} + \dfrac{\partial}{\partial z}\hat{k} \right) \cdot (x\hat{i} + y\hat{j} + z\hat{k})$

$\qquad\qquad 1 + 1 + 1 = 3$

as $\qquad\qquad \dfrac{\partial x}{\partial x}\hat{i} \cdot \hat{i} = 1; \dfrac{\partial y}{\partial y}\hat{j} \cdot \hat{j} = 1 \ \text{and} \ \dfrac{\partial z}{\partial z}\hat{k} \cdot \hat{k} = 1$

all other terms are zero.

Q. 1.26. If $\vec{R} = (x\hat{i} + y\hat{j} + z\hat{k})$ **find the value of** *div* $\hat{R}$. $\qquad$ (*Pbi.U.*, 2006; *H.P.U.* 1996)

Ans. $\qquad\qquad\qquad\qquad \hat{R} = \dfrac{\vec{R}}{R}$

$\therefore \ \vec{\nabla} \cdot \dfrac{\vec{R}}{R} = \left(\hat{i}\dfrac{\partial}{\partial x} + \hat{j}\dfrac{\partial}{\partial y} + \hat{k}\dfrac{\partial}{\partial z} \right) \cdot (x^2 + y^2 + z^2)^{-\frac{1}{2}} (x\hat{i} + y\hat{j} + z\hat{k})$

$\qquad\quad = \dfrac{\partial}{\partial x}[x(x^2 + y^2 + z^2)^{-1/2}] + \dfrac{\partial}{\partial y}[y(x^2 + y^2 + z^2)^{-1/2}] + \dfrac{\partial}{\partial z}[z(x^2 + y^2 + z^2)^{-1/2}]$

Now $\quad \dfrac{\partial}{\partial x}[x(x^2 + y^2 + z^2)^{-1/2}] = x\left[-\dfrac{1}{2}(x^2 + y^2 + z^2)^{-3/2} 2x \right] + (x^2 + y^2 + z^2)^{-1/2}$

$\qquad = -x^2 (x^2 + y^2 + z^2)^{-3/2} + (x^2 + y^2 + z^2)^{-1/2}$

$\qquad = \dfrac{-x^2}{R^3} + \dfrac{1}{R}$

Similarly $\dfrac{\partial}{\partial y}[y(x^2 + y^2 + z^2)^{-1/2}] = -\dfrac{y^2}{R^3} + \dfrac{1}{R}$

and $\dfrac{\partial}{\partial z}[z(x^2 + y^2 + z^2)^{-1/2}] = -\dfrac{z^2}{R^3} + \dfrac{1}{R}$

$\therefore \qquad \vec{\nabla}.\dfrac{\vec{R}}{R} = -\dfrac{(x^2 + y^2 + z^2)}{R^3} + \dfrac{3}{R} = -\dfrac{R^2}{R^3} + \dfrac{3}{R} = \dfrac{2}{R}$

or $\qquad\qquad div\,\hat{R} = \vec{\nabla}.\hat{R} = \dfrac{2}{R}$

Alternate solution

$$div\,\hat{R} = \vec{\nabla}.\hat{R} = \vec{\nabla}.\dfrac{1}{R}\vec{R}$$

Put $\dfrac{1}{R} = u$, then

$$\vec{\nabla}.\hat{R} = \vec{\nabla}.u\vec{R} = u\vec{\nabla}.\vec{R} + \vec{R}.\vec{\nabla}u$$

But $\qquad \vec{\nabla}.\vec{R} = 3$

and $\qquad \vec{\nabla}u = \left(\dfrac{\partial}{\partial x}\dfrac{1}{R}\right)\hat{i} + \left(\dfrac{\partial}{\partial y}\dfrac{1}{R}\right)\hat{j} + \left(\dfrac{\partial}{\partial z}\dfrac{1}{R}\right)\hat{k}$

As $\qquad \dfrac{1}{R} = (x^2 + y^2 + z^2)^{-1/2}; \dfrac{\partial}{\partial x}\dfrac{1}{R} = -\dfrac{1}{2}(x^2 + y^2 + z^2)^{-3/2}\,2x$

$$= \dfrac{x}{(x^2 + y^2 + z^2)^{3/2}} = -\dfrac{x}{R^3}$$

Similarly $\qquad \dfrac{\partial}{\partial y}\dfrac{1}{R} = -\dfrac{y}{R^3}$ and $\dfrac{\partial}{\partial z}\dfrac{1}{R} = -\dfrac{z}{R^3}$

$\therefore \qquad \vec{\nabla}u = -\dfrac{1}{R^3}(x\hat{i} + y\hat{j} + z\hat{k}) = -\dfrac{\vec{R}}{R^3}$

$\therefore \qquad \vec{\nabla}.\hat{R} = \dfrac{1}{R}.3 - \dfrac{\vec{R}.\vec{R}}{R^3}$

$$= \dfrac{3}{R} - \dfrac{R^2}{R^3}(\hat{R}.\hat{R}) = \dfrac{3}{R} - \dfrac{1}{R} = \dfrac{2}{R}$$

Q. 1.27. If $\vec{A} = \dfrac{x}{r}\hat{i} + \dfrac{y}{r}\hat{j} + \dfrac{z}{r}\hat{k}$ calculate $div\,\vec{A}$ where $\vec{r}$ is the position vector.

(*H.P.U.*, 1996)

Ans. $\qquad \vec{A} = \dfrac{x}{r}\hat{i} + \dfrac{y}{r}\hat{j} + \dfrac{z}{r}\hat{k} = \dfrac{x\hat{i} + y\hat{j} + z\hat{k}}{r}$

$$\dfrac{\vec{r}}{r} = \hat{r}$$

$\therefore \qquad div\,\vec{A} = div\,\hat{r} = \vec{\nabla}.\hat{r} = \dfrac{2}{r}$ \qquad [For complete solution see **Q. 1.26**]

Q. 1.28. If $\vec{A} = \dfrac{\vec{r}}{r}$ find grad div $\vec{A}$. \qquad\qquad (*P.U.*, 1991)

Ans. $\qquad div\,\vec{A} = \vec{\nabla}.\dfrac{\vec{r}}{r} = \vec{\nabla}.\hat{r} = \dfrac{2}{r}$ \qquad [For proof see **Q. 1.26**]

$$\therefore \qquad grad\ div\ \vec{A} = grad\frac{2}{r} = \vec{\nabla}\left(\frac{2}{r}\right)$$

$$= 2\ \vec{\nabla}\left(\frac{1}{r}\right) = 2\left(\hat{i}\frac{\partial}{\partial x} + \hat{j}\frac{\partial}{\partial y} + \hat{k}\frac{\partial}{\partial z}\right)(x^2 + y^2 + z^2)^{-1/2}$$

$$= 2\left\{\left[-\frac{1}{2}(x^2 + y^2 + z^2)^{\frac{-3}{2}}\ 2x\right]\hat{i} + \left[-\frac{1}{2}(x^2 + y^2 + z^2)^{\frac{-3}{2}}\ 2y\right]\hat{j} + \left[-\frac{1}{2}(x^2 + y^2 + z^2)^{\frac{-3}{2}}\ 2z\right]\hat{k}\right\}$$

$$= -2\left[\frac{x}{r^3}\hat{i} + \frac{y}{r^3}\hat{j} + \frac{z}{r^3}\hat{k}\right]$$

$$= -\frac{2}{r^3}(x\hat{i} + y\hat{j} + z\hat{k}) = -\frac{2}{r^3}\vec{r}$$

Q. 1.29. The electric field due to a point charge Q is expressed as $\vec{E} = \dfrac{Q}{4\pi\varepsilon_0}\dfrac{\hat{r}}{|r^2|}$. Show that div. $\vec{E} = \vec{\nabla}.\vec{E} = 0$

(G.N.D.U., 2008; P.U. 1991)

OR

A given vector $\vec{r} = x\hat{i} + y\hat{j} + z\hat{k}$ show that $\vec{\nabla}.\left(\dfrac{\vec{r}}{r^3}\right) = 0.$

(Pbi.U., 2007; P.U. 2001, 2000; H.P.U. 2001, 1997; M.D.U. 2001)

Ans.
$$\frac{\hat{r}}{|r^2|} = \frac{\vec{r}}{r^3} = (x\hat{i} + y\hat{j} + z\hat{k})(x^2 + y^2 + z^2)^{-3/2}$$

$$\therefore \qquad \vec{\nabla}.\frac{\vec{r}}{r^3} = \left(\frac{\partial}{\partial x}\hat{i} + \frac{\partial}{\partial y}\hat{j} + \frac{\partial}{\partial z}\hat{k}\right).(x\hat{i} + y\hat{j} + z\hat{k})(x^2 + y^2 + z^2)^{-3/2}$$

$$= \frac{\partial}{\partial x}\left[x(x^2 + y^2 + z^2)^{-3/2}\right] + \frac{\partial}{\partial y}\left[y(x^2 + y^2 + z^2)^{-3/2}\right] + \frac{\partial}{\partial z}\left[z(x^2 + y^2 + z^2)^{-3/2}\right]$$

Now $\dfrac{\partial}{\partial x}\left[x(x^2 + y^2 + z^2)^{-3/2}\right] = x\left[-\dfrac{3}{2}(x^2 + y^2 + z^2)^{-5/2}\ 2x\right] + (x^2 + y^2 + z^2)^{-3/2}$

$$= -3x^2(x^2 + y^2 + z^2)^{-5/2} + (x^2 + y^2 + z^2)^{-3/2}$$

$$= \frac{-3x^2}{r^5} + \frac{1}{r^3}$$

Similarly $\dfrac{\partial}{\partial y}[y(x^2 + y^2 + z^2)^{-3/2}] = \dfrac{-3y^2}{r^5} + \dfrac{1}{r^3}$

and $\dfrac{\partial}{\partial z}[z(x^2 + y^2 + z^2)^{-3/2}] = \dfrac{-3z^2}{r^5} + \dfrac{1}{r^3}$

$$\therefore \qquad \vec{\nabla}.\frac{\hat{r}}{|r^2|} = \frac{-3(x^2 + y^2 + z^2)}{r^5} + \frac{3}{r^3} = -\frac{3r^2}{r^5} + \frac{3}{r^3} = \frac{3}{r^3} - \frac{3}{r^3} = 0$$

$$\therefore \qquad \vec{\nabla}.\vec{E} = \vec{\nabla}.\left[\frac{Q}{4\pi\varepsilon_0}\frac{\hat{r}}{|r^2|}\right] = \frac{Q}{4\pi\varepsilon_0}\left[\vec{\nabla}.\frac{\hat{r}}{|r^2|}\right] = 0$$

Q. 1.30. Calculate the value of $\vec{\nabla} \cdot (r^3 \vec{r})$ where $\vec{r} = (x\hat{i} + y\hat{j} + z\hat{k})$.   *(H.P.U, 1995)*

Ans. $\vec{\nabla} \cdot (r^3 \vec{r}) = \left(\dfrac{\partial}{\partial x}\hat{i} + \dfrac{\partial}{\partial y}\hat{j} + \dfrac{\partial}{\partial z}\hat{k} \right) \cdot (x^2 + y^2 + z^2)^{3/2}(x\hat{i} + y\hat{j} + z\hat{k})$

$$= \dfrac{\partial}{\partial x}[x(x^2 + y^2 + z^2)^{3/2}] + \dfrac{\partial}{\partial y}[y(x^2 + y^2 + z^2)^{3/2}] + \dfrac{\partial}{\partial z}[z(x^2 + y^2 + z^2)^{3/2}]$$

Now $\dfrac{\partial}{\partial x}[x(x^2 + y^2 + z^2)^{3/2}] = x\left[\dfrac{3}{2}(x^2 + y^2 + z^2)^{1/2} 2x \right] + (x^2 + y^2 + z^2)^{3/2}$

$$= 3x^2 r + r^3$$

Similarly $\dfrac{\partial}{\partial y}[y(x^2 + y^2 + z^2)^{3/2}] = 3y^2 r + r^3$

and $\dfrac{\partial}{\partial z}[z(x^2 + y^2 + z^2)^{3/2}] = 3z^2 r + r^3$

$\therefore$ $\vec{\nabla} \cdot (r^3 \vec{r}) = 3(x^2 + y^2 + z^2) r + 3r^3 = 3r^2 r + 3r^3 = 6r^3$

Q. 1.31. (a) Show that $\vec{\nabla} \cdot \vec{\nabla} \phi = \nabla^2 \phi$ *(P.U. 2003, 2001)*

(b) If $\phi = x^2 - y^2 + 2z$ find div. grad ϕ *(K.U. 1991)*

Ans. (a) $\vec{\nabla}\phi = \dfrac{\partial\phi}{\partial x}\hat{i} + \dfrac{\partial\phi}{\partial y}\hat{j} + \dfrac{\partial\phi}{\partial z}\hat{k}$

$\therefore$ $\vec{\nabla}\cdot\vec{\nabla}\phi = \left(\dfrac{\partial}{\partial x}\hat{i} + \dfrac{\partial}{\partial y}\hat{j} + \dfrac{\partial}{\partial z}\hat{k} \right)\cdot\left(\dfrac{\partial\phi}{\partial x}\hat{i} + \dfrac{\partial\phi}{\partial y}\hat{j} + \dfrac{\partial\phi}{\partial z}\hat{k} \right)$

$$= \dfrac{\partial}{\partial x}\left(\dfrac{\partial\phi}{\partial x}\right) + \dfrac{\partial}{\partial y}\left(\dfrac{\partial\phi}{\partial y}\right) + \dfrac{\partial}{\partial z}\left(\dfrac{\partial\phi}{\partial z}\right)$$

$$= \dfrac{\partial^2\phi}{\partial x^2} + \dfrac{\partial^2\phi}{\partial y^2} + \dfrac{\partial^2\phi}{\partial z^2} = \nabla^2\phi$$

where $\left(\dfrac{\partial^2}{\partial x^2} + \dfrac{\partial^2}{\partial y^2} + \dfrac{\partial^2}{\partial z^2} \right) = \nabla^2$

(b)   div. grad $\phi = \vec{\nabla}\cdot\vec{\nabla}\phi$

Now $\vec{\nabla}\phi = \left(\hat{i}\dfrac{\partial}{\partial x} + \hat{j}\dfrac{\partial}{\partial y} + \hat{k}\dfrac{\partial}{\partial z} \right)(x^2 - y^2 + 2z)$

$$= 2x\hat{i} - 2y\hat{j} + 2\hat{k}$$

$\therefore$ $\vec{\nabla}\cdot\vec{\nabla}\phi = \vec{\nabla}\cdot(2x\hat{i} - 2y\hat{j} + 2\hat{k})$

$$= \left(\hat{i}\dfrac{\partial}{\partial x} + \hat{j}\dfrac{\partial}{\partial y} + \hat{k}\dfrac{\partial}{\partial z} \right)\cdot(2x\hat{i} - 2y\hat{j} + 2\hat{k})$$

$$= 2 - 2 = 0$$

Exercise. If $\phi = 4x^3 y^2 z^4$ find div. grad ϕ.   *(M.D.U., 2008)*

Hint. grad $\phi = \vec{\nabla}\phi = \left(\hat{i}\frac{\partial}{\partial x} + \hat{j}\frac{\partial}{\partial y} + \hat{k}\frac{\partial}{\partial z}\right)(4x^3 y^2 z^4)$

$= (12x^2 y^2 z^4)\,\hat{i} + (8x^3 y z^4)\,\hat{j} + (16\,x^3 y^2 z^3)\,\hat{k}$

$\therefore$ div. grad $\phi = \vec{\nabla}.\vec{\nabla}\phi = \left(\hat{i}\frac{\partial}{\partial x} + \hat{j}\frac{\partial}{\partial y} + \hat{k}\frac{\partial}{\partial z}\right).\left[(12x^2 y^2 z^4)\hat{i} + (8x^3 y z^4)\hat{j} + (16x^3 y^2 z^3)\hat{k}\right]$

$= \frac{\partial}{\partial x}(12x^2 y^2 z^4) + \frac{\partial}{\partial y}(8x^3 y z^4) + \frac{\partial}{\partial z}(16x^3 y^2 z^3)$

$= 24x\,y^2 z^4 + 8x^3 z^4 + 48x^3 y^2 z^2$

Q. 1.32. State and prove Gauss's divergence theorem.   (*P.U.* 2009, 2007, 2001, 2000;
K.U. 2003; *H.P.U.* 2006, 2003, 2001, 2000; *M.D.U.* 2008, 2007,
2001; *Gharwal.U.* 2000; *Pbi.U.* 2006, 1999; *G.N.D.U.* 2009, 2007,
2006, 1999, 1997, 1994; *K.U.* 1995; *Ranchi.U.* 1991; *Meerut.U.* 2007, 2006)

Ans. Gauss's divergence theorem. Gauss's divergence theorem states that if a closed surface

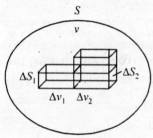

Fig. 1.6

$\vec{S}$ encloses a volume v in a vector field $\vec{A}$, then the surface integral of the normal component of $\vec{A}$ over the entire surface $\vec{S}$ is equal to the volume integral of divergence $\vec{A}$ over the volume v enclosed by the surface $\vec{S}$.

or $\iint_S \vec{A}.\vec{ds} = \iiint_v (div\,\vec{A})\,dv$

or $\iint_S \vec{A}.\vec{ds} = \iiint_v (\vec{\nabla}.\vec{A})\,dv$

Proof. Suppose a surface $\vec{S}$ encloses a volume v in a vector field $\vec{A}$. Let the volume v be divided into a large number of small elements of volume $\Delta v_1, \Delta v_2 \dots \Delta v_i \dots$ etc. by enclosing surface areas $\Delta \vec{S_1}, \Delta \vec{S_2}, \dots \Delta \vec{S_i}, \dots$ etc. respectively. Taking the *outward flux* of the vector field through a closed surface as positive and the *inward flux* as *negative* we find that the outward flux from one face of a small element of volume say Δv_1 wil be equal and opposite to the outward flux from the common face of a neighbouring element say Δv_2 and the two will cancel each other. As a result, the sum of all the outward fluxes from the elements of volume such as $\Delta v_1, \Delta v_2, \dots \Delta v_i, \dots$ etc. will be equal to the total outward flux from the whole volume v because all parts of the outwards flux from the small elements of volume will cancel out except for those parts which are through the outer bounding surface $\vec{S}$.

$\therefore$ Total outward flux through the closed surface $\vec{S}$ *i.e.*, the surface integral of the vector $\vec{A}$ over the surface $\vec{S}$ is equal to the sum of the outward fluxes over the surfaces $\Delta \vec{S_1}, \Delta \vec{S_2}, \dots \Delta \vec{S_i}$ etc.

or $\iint_S \vec{A}.\vec{ds} = \sum \iint_{\Delta S_i} \vec{A}.\vec{ds}$ ...(i)

The value of *div* $\vec{A}$ in a small element like Δv_i having a surface area ΔS_i is given by

$$div \vec{A} = \lim_{\Delta v_i \to 0} \frac{1}{\Delta v_i} \iint_{\Delta S_i} \vec{A} \cdot \vec{ds}$$

or
$$\iint_{\Delta S_i} \vec{A} \cdot \vec{ds} = (div \vec{A}) \Delta v_i$$

∴
$$\sum \iint_{\Delta S_i} \vec{A} \cdot \vec{ds} = \sum (div \vec{A}) \Delta v_i$$

When $\Delta v_i = dv$ i.e., an infinite number of small volume elements are involved and $\Delta v_i \to 0$, we have

$$\sum (div \vec{A}) \Delta v_i = \iiint_v (div \vec{A}) dv$$

∴
$$\sum \iint_{\Delta S_i} \vec{A} \cdot \vec{ds} = \iiint_v (div \vec{A}) dv \qquad \qquad ...(ii)$$

Comparing (i) and (ii), we get

$$\iint_S \vec{A} \cdot \vec{ds} = \iiint_v (div \vec{A}) dv = \iiint_v (\vec{\nabla} \cdot \vec{A}) dv$$

The importance of this theorem lies in the fact that *it helps us to convert a surface integral into a volume integral and vice versa.*

Q. 1.33. Prove that the volume integral of the divergence of a vector field $\vec{A}$ taken over any volume is equal to the surface integral of $\vec{A}$ over the closed surface surrounding the volume. (*H.P.U.* 2006, 2002, 2000, 1997, 1994)

Ans. According to the statement

$$\iiint_v (\vec{\nabla} \cdot \vec{A}) dv = \oiint_S \vec{A} \cdot \vec{ds}$$

This is the statement of Gauss's divergence theorem. [For proof see **Q. 1.32**]

Q. 1.34. Using Gauss's divergence theorem evaluate

$$\iint_S xdydz + ydzdx + zdxdy$$

where S is the sphere $x^2 + y^2 + z^2 = 1$.

Ans. The sphere $x^2 + y^2 + z^2 = 1$ has a radius unity and its centre is at the origin. As a general case, consider a sphere of radius r, with centre at the origin, then Gauss's divergence theorem can be put in the form

$$\oiint_S \vec{r} \cdot \vec{ds} = \iiint_v (\vec{\nabla} \cdot \vec{r}) dv$$

where $\vec{r}$ is the radius vector, $\vec{ds}$ a small vector area element and dv a small volume element.

Now for the given sphere

$$\vec{r} = x\hat{i} + y\hat{j} + z\hat{k}$$

and
$$\vec{ds} = dydz\,\hat{i} + dxdz\,\hat{j} + dxdy\,\hat{k}$$

∴
$$\vec{r} \cdot \vec{ds} = (x\hat{i} + y\hat{j} + z\hat{k}) \cdot (dydz\,\hat{i} + dxdz\,\hat{j} + dxdy\,\hat{k})$$
$$= xdydz + ydxdz + zdxdy$$

and
$$\iint_S \vec{r} \cdot \vec{ds} = \iint x \, dy \, dz + y \, dx \, dz + z \, dx \, dy$$

Also
$$\vec{\nabla} \cdot \vec{r} = \left(\frac{\partial}{\partial x} \hat{i} + \frac{\partial}{\partial y} \hat{j} + \frac{\partial}{\partial z} \hat{k} \right) \cdot (x\hat{i} + y\hat{j} + z\hat{k})$$

$$= \frac{\partial}{\partial x} x + \frac{\partial}{\partial y} y + \frac{\partial}{\partial z} z = 3$$

∴
$$\iint_S \vec{r} \cdot \vec{ds} = \iiint_v (\vec{\nabla} \cdot \vec{r}) \, dv = \iiint_v 3 \, dv = 3V$$

$$= 3 \times \frac{4}{3} \pi r^3 = 4 \pi r^3 = 4\pi \qquad\qquad [\because r = 1]$$

or
$$\iint_S x \, dy \, dz + y \, dx \, dz + z \, dx \, dy = 4\pi$$

where S is given by $x^2 + y^2 + z^2 = 1$.

Q. 1.35. Evaluate $\iiint_v \vec{\nabla} \cdot \vec{A} \, dv$ where V is the volume of the cubical box bounded by the planes $x = 0, x = 1; y = 0, y = 1; z = 0, z = 1$.

Ans. To evelute the integral $\iiint_v \vec{\nabla} \cdot \vec{A} \, dv$ we make use of Gauss's theorem in vector analysis *i.e.*,

$$\iiint_v (\vec{\nabla} \cdot \vec{A}) \, dv = \oiint_S \vec{A} \cdot \vec{ds} = \oiint_S (x^2 \hat{i} + y^2 \hat{j} + z^2 \hat{k}) \cdot \vec{ds}$$

The surface S' of the cubical box consists of **six surfaces**

S_1 = Surface *OADB* represented by the plane $x = 0$

S_2 = Surface *CFEG* represented by the plane $x = 1$

S_3 = Surface *OBGC* represented by the plane $y = 0$

S_4 = Surface *AFED* represented by the plane $y = 1$

S_5 = Surface *OAFC* represented by the plane $z = 0$

S_6 = Surface *BGED* represented by the plane $z = 1$

On the surface S_1, $x = 0$

∴ $\vec{A} = y^2 \hat{j} + z^2 \hat{k}$

The outward unit normal $\hat{n}$ is along the *negative x*-direction

∴ $\hat{n} = -\hat{i}$

Hence $\vec{ds} = \hat{n} \, ds = -ds \hat{i}$

∴ $\iint_{S_1} \vec{A} \cdot \vec{ds} = \iint_{S_1} (y^2 \hat{j} + z^2 \hat{k}) \cdot ds \hat{i} = 0$

On the surface S_2, $x = 1$

∴ $\vec{A} = \hat{i} + y^2 \hat{j} + z^2 \hat{k}$

The outword unit normal is along the *positive x*-direction

∴ $\hat{n} = +\hat{i}$ and $\vec{ds} = \hat{n} \, ds = ds \hat{i}$

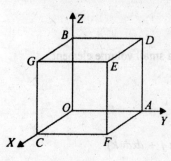

Fig. 1.7

$$\therefore \qquad \iint\limits_{S_2} \vec{A} \cdot \vec{ds} = \iint\limits_{S_2} (\hat{i} + y^2\,\hat{j} + z^2\,\hat{k}) \cdot ds\,\hat{i} = \iint\limits_{S_2} ds = S_2$$

The area of the surface S_2 $(y = 1, z = 1) = 1$

Hence
$$\iint\limits_{S_1} \vec{A} \cdot \vec{ds} + \iint\limits_{S_2} \vec{A} \cdot \vec{ds} = 1$$

Similarly
$$\iint\limits_{S_3} \vec{A} \cdot \vec{ds} + \iint\limits_{S_4} \vec{A} \cdot \vec{ds} = 1$$

and
$$\iint\limits_{S_5} \vec{A} \cdot \vec{ds} + \iint\limits_{S_6} \vec{A} \cdot \vec{ds} = 1$$

$$\therefore \qquad \iint\limits_{S} \vec{A} \cdot \vec{ds} = \iint\limits_{S_1} \vec{A} \cdot \vec{ds} + \iint\limits_{S_2} \vec{A} \cdot \vec{ds} + \iint\limits_{S_3} \vec{A} \cdot \vec{ds} + \iint\limits_{S_4} \vec{A} \cdot \vec{ds}$$

$$+ \iint\limits_{S_5} \vec{A} \cdot \vec{ds} + \iint\limits_{S_6} \vec{A} \cdot \vec{ds} = 1 + 1 + 1 = 3$$

Q. 1.36. A vector $\vec{r} = x\hat{i} + y\hat{j} + z\hat{k}$. Prove that $\iint\limits_{S} \vec{r} \cdot \vec{ds} = 3V$ where V is the volume enclosed by the surface S.

Ans. According to Gauss's divergence theorem

$$\oiint\limits_{S} \vec{A} \cdot \vec{ds} = \iiint\limits_{V} (\vec{\nabla} \cdot \vec{A})\,dv$$

Here
$$\vec{A} = \vec{r}$$

$$\therefore \qquad \oiint\limits_{S} \vec{r} \cdot \vec{ds} = \iiint\limits_{V} (\vec{\nabla} \cdot \vec{r})\,dv$$

Now
$$\vec{\nabla} \cdot \vec{r} = \left(\frac{\partial}{\partial x}\hat{i} + \frac{\partial}{\partial y}\hat{j} + \frac{\partial}{\partial z}\hat{k} \right) \cdot (x\hat{i} + y\hat{j} + z\hat{k})$$

$$= 1 + 1 + 1 = 3$$

$$\therefore \qquad \iint\limits_{S} \vec{r} \cdot \vec{ds} = \iiint\limits_{V} 3\,dv = 3\iiint\limits_{V} dv = 3V$$

Q. 1.37. Define curl of a vector field and give its physical significance. Show that curl of a vector field is a vector quantity.   *(P.U. 2007, 2000, 1994; G.N.D.U. 2009, 2004, 2000, 1999, 1993, Pbi.U. 2008, 2006, 2000, 1995; Meerut.U. 2005, Osm.U. 1997; H.P.U. 2003, 1995; K.U. 1995)*

Ans. Curl of a vector field. Consider a vector field $\vec{A}$ the magnitude and direction of which is a function of position co-ordinates at a point, then the vector (cross) product of the differential operator $\vec{\nabla}$ and the vector $\vec{A}$ is a *vector* function of position co-ordinates x, y, z and is known as the *curl* of the vector $\vec{A}$.

$$\therefore \qquad Curl\ \vec{A} = \vec{\nabla} \times \vec{A}$$

Now
$$\vec{\nabla} = \left(\frac{\partial}{\partial x}\hat{i} + \frac{\partial}{\partial y}\hat{j} + \frac{\partial}{\partial z}\hat{k} \right)$$

and $$\vec{A} = (A_x \,\hat{i} + A_y \,\hat{j} + A_z \,\hat{k})$$

$\therefore$
$$\vec{\nabla} \times \vec{A} = \left(\frac{\partial}{\partial x}\,\hat{i} + \frac{\partial}{\partial y}\,\hat{j} + \frac{\partial}{\partial z}\,\hat{k}\right) \times (A_x \,\hat{i} + A_y \,\hat{j} + A_z \,\hat{k})$$

$$= \frac{\partial A_y}{\partial x}\,\hat{i} \times \hat{j} + \frac{\partial A_z}{\partial x}\,\hat{i} \times \hat{k} + \frac{\partial A_x}{\partial y}\,\hat{j} \times \hat{i} + \frac{\partial A_z}{\partial y}\,\hat{j} \times \hat{k} + \frac{\partial A_x}{\partial z}\,\hat{k} \times \hat{i} + \frac{\partial A_y}{\partial z}\,\hat{k} \times \hat{j}$$

$$= \left(\frac{\partial A_z}{\partial y} - \frac{\partial A_y}{\partial z}\right)\hat{i} + \left(\frac{\partial A_x}{\partial z} - \frac{\partial A_z}{\partial x}\right)\hat{j} + \left(\frac{\partial A_y}{\partial x} - \frac{\partial A_x}{\partial y}\right)\hat{k}$$

The above expression can be put in determinant form as under

$$\text{Curl } \vec{A} = \begin{vmatrix} \hat{i} & \hat{j} & \hat{k} \\ \dfrac{\partial}{\partial x} & \dfrac{\partial}{\partial y} & \dfrac{\partial}{\partial z} \\ A_x & A_y & A_z \end{vmatrix}$$

Physical significance. Consider a vanishingly small area $\Delta \vec{S}$ enclosed by a closed path which forms its boundary. Let $\vec{A}$ be a vector field defined everywhere in the region and $\vec{dl}$ a vector representing a small element of the path, its direction being that of the tangent to the path at the element $\vec{dl}$. If θ is the angle between the vector $\vec{A}$ at any point on the curve and the direction of the element, then

$$\vec{A} \cdot \vec{dl} = A dl \cos \theta$$

As $A \cos \theta$ is the component of the vector $\vec{A}$ along the element $\vec{dl}$, the line integral of the vector field $\vec{A}$ for the closed path

$$= \oint A \, dl \cos \theta = \oint \vec{A} \cdot \vec{dl}$$

where the symbol $\oint$ represents the integration over the entire closed path. It is a scalar quantity. The path encloses an area $\Delta \vec{S}$.

$\therefore$ Line integral per unit area $= \dfrac{1}{\Delta S} \oint \vec{A} \cdot \vec{dl}$

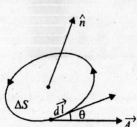

Now consider a unit vector $\hat{n}$ in a direction perpendicular to the area

Fig. 1.8 S, the positive direction of $\hat{n}$ being related to the direction of the line integral by the right handed screw rule. *The curl of the vector field $\vec{A}(curl\ \vec{A})$ is defined as the vector, the magnitude of whose component in the direction of the unit vector $\hat{n}$ is given by the line integral of the vector $\vec{A}$ for the closed path per unit area enclosed by it when the area becomes vanishingly small.* As the magnitude of the component of a vector in the direction of the unit vector is given by the scalar product of the vector and the unit vector $\hat{n}$.

$\therefore$
$$\text{Curl } \vec{A} \cdot \hat{n} = \underset{\Delta S \to 0}{Lim}\ \frac{1}{\Delta S} \oint \vec{A} \cdot \vec{dl}$$

As $\Delta S \to 0$ let it be denoted by dS, then

$$\text{Curl } \vec{A} \cdot \hat{n}\ dS = \oint \vec{A} \cdot \vec{dl}$$

$\therefore$ $Curl\ \vec{A}.\ \vec{dS} = \oint \vec{A}.\ \vec{dl}$

or $Curl\ \vec{A} = \dfrac{1}{\vec{dS}} \oint \vec{A}.\ \vec{dl}$ ...(i)

Curl of a vector field is a vector. Curl of a vector field $\vec{A}$ is given by the cross (vector) product of the operator $\vec{\nabla}$ which behaves as a vector and $\vec{A}$ i.e.,

$$Curl\ \vec{A} = \vec{\nabla} \times \vec{A}$$

$\therefore$ $Curl\ \vec{A}$ is a *vector*.

Relation (i) also shows that curl $\vec{A}$ is a vector.

Q. 1.38. (*a*) **Calculate the value of the curl of a vector in terms of Cartesian co-ordinates.**
(*Pbi.U. 1995; H.P.U. 1995; K.U. 1995, 1994, 1991;*
P.U. 2007, 1994, 1992; G.N.D.U. 1993, 1991, 1990)

(*b*) **If $\vec{E} = (x + y)\hat{i} + (y - 2x)\hat{j} - 2z\hat{k}$, prove that $Curl\ \vec{E} = -3\hat{k}$ and $div\ \vec{E} = 0$**
(*Pbi.U. 2000*)

(*c*) **Prove that $Curl\ \left|r^n\right| \vec{r} = 0$ where $\vec{r} = x\hat{i} + y\hat{j} + z\hat{k}$ is the position vector.** (*H.P.U. 2007*)

Ans. (*a*) **Curl of a vector in Cartesian co-ordinates.** To calculate the value of the curl of a vector we use the definition

$$Curl\ \vec{A} = \underset{\Delta S \to 0}{Limit}\ \dfrac{1}{\Delta \vec{S}} \oint \vec{A}.\ \vec{dl}$$

where $\oint \vec{A}.\ \vec{dl}$ is the line integral of the vector field $\vec{A}$ for the closed path enclosing a vanishingly small area $\Delta \vec{S}$. To find the value of $Curl\ \vec{A}$ in Cartesian co-ordinates we shall take up one component at a time. Consider a point P having co-ordinates x, y, z. For simplicity, with P at its centre draw a rectangular path $ABCD$ of surface parallel to XY plane having its surface AB of length Δx parallel to X-axis and surface BC of length Δy parallel to Y-axis.

In such a case the unit vector $\hat{n}$ = unit vector $\hat{k}$ parallel to Z-axis and we shall get the Z-component of the $curl\ \vec{A}$ denoted as $curl_z\ \vec{A}$.

According to right hand screw rule the direction of line integral around the closed rectangular path must be clockwise as seen by some one looking **up** in the direction $\hat{n}$. Let A_x, A_y, A_z be the components of the vector $\vec{A}$ in the direction of X, Y, Z, axes respectively at the point x, y, z.

The co-ordinates of a point at the centre of AB are

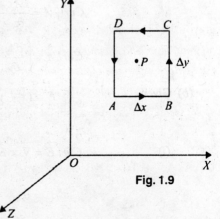

Fig. 1.9

$x, \left(y - \dfrac{\Delta y}{2}\right), z$. If the rate of change of A_x along the

Y-axis is $\dfrac{\partial A_x}{\partial y}$ then the value of A_x at the centre of AB

$$= A_x - \dfrac{\partial A_x}{\partial y}\ \dfrac{\Delta y}{2}$$

Similarly the value of A_x at the centre of CD

$$= A_x + \frac{\partial A_x}{\partial y} \frac{\Delta y}{2}$$

The co-ordinates of a point at the centre of BC are $\left(x + \dfrac{\Delta x}{2}\right)$, y, z. If the rate of change of A_y along the X-axis is $\left(\dfrac{\partial A_y}{\partial x}\right)$ then the value of A_y at the centre of BC

$$= A_y + \frac{\partial A_y}{\partial x} \frac{\Delta x}{2}$$

Similarly the value of A_y at the centre of DA

$$= A_y - \frac{\partial A_y}{\partial x} \frac{\Delta x}{2}$$

Hence $\quad \oint \vec{A} \cdot \vec{dl} = \left(A_x - \dfrac{\partial A_x}{\partial y} \dfrac{\Delta y}{2}\right) \Delta x + \left(A_y + \dfrac{\partial A_y}{\partial x} \dfrac{\Delta x}{2}\right) \Delta y$

$$- \left(A_x + \frac{\partial A_x}{\partial y} \frac{\Delta y}{2}\right) \Delta x - \left(A_y - \frac{\partial A_y}{\partial x} \frac{\Delta x}{2}\right) \Delta y$$

$$= \frac{\partial A_y}{\partial x} \Delta x \, \Delta y - \frac{\partial A_x}{\partial y} \Delta x \, \Delta y$$

$$= \left(\frac{\partial A_y}{\partial x} - \frac{\partial A_x}{\partial y}\right) \Delta x \, \Delta y$$

$\therefore \quad Curl_z \, A = \underset{\Delta S \to 0}{Lim} \dfrac{1}{\vec{\Delta S}} \oint \vec{A} \cdot \vec{dl}$

$$= \frac{\partial A_y}{\partial x} - \frac{\partial A_x}{\partial y} \qquad \qquad ...[\because \Delta S = \Delta x \, \Delta y]$$

Similarly x and y components of the $curl \, \vec{A}$ are

$$Curl_x \, A = \frac{\partial A_z}{\partial y} - \frac{\partial A_y}{\partial z}$$

$$Curl_y \, A = \frac{\partial A_x}{\partial z} - \frac{\partial A_z}{\partial x}$$

$\therefore \quad Curl \, \vec{A} = \left(\dfrac{\partial A_z}{\partial y} - \dfrac{\partial A_y}{\partial z}\right) \hat{i} + \left(\dfrac{\partial A_x}{\partial z} - \dfrac{\partial A_z}{\partial x}\right) \hat{j} + \left(\dfrac{\partial A_y}{\partial x} - \dfrac{\partial A_x}{\partial y}\right) \hat{k} = \vec{\nabla} \times \vec{A}$

(b) Given $\qquad \vec{E} = (x + y)\hat{i} + (y - 2x)\hat{j} - 2z \, \hat{k}$

(i) $\qquad Curl \, \vec{E} = \vec{\nabla} \times \vec{E} = \begin{vmatrix} \hat{i} & \hat{j} & \hat{k} \\ \dfrac{\partial}{\partial x} & \dfrac{\partial}{\partial y} & \dfrac{\partial}{\partial z} \\ (x + y) & (y - 2x) & (-2z) \end{vmatrix}$

$$= \hat{i}\left[\frac{\partial}{\partial y}(-2z) - \frac{\partial}{\partial z}(y - 2x)\right] + \hat{j}\left[\frac{\partial}{\partial z}(x + y) - \frac{\partial}{\partial x}(-2z)\right]$$

$$+ \hat{k}\left[\frac{\partial}{\partial x}(y - 2x) - \frac{\partial}{\partial y}(x + y)\right]$$

$$= \hat{k}(-2 - 1) = -3\hat{k}$$

(ii) $div\,\vec{E} = \vec{\nabla}\cdot\vec{E} = \left(\frac{\partial}{\partial x}\hat{i} + \frac{\partial}{\partial y}\hat{j} + \frac{\partial}{\partial z}\hat{k}\right)\cdot\left[(x + y)\hat{i} + (y - 2x)\hat{j} + (-2z)\hat{k}\right]$

$$= \frac{\partial}{\partial x}(x + y) + \frac{\partial}{\partial y}(y - 2x) + \frac{\partial}{\partial z}(-2z)$$

$$= 1 + 1 - 2 = 0$$

(c) $\vec{r} = x\hat{i} + y\hat{j} + z\hat{k}$ and

$$\left|\vec{r}\right| = [x^2 + y^2 + z^2]^{\frac{1}{2}} \text{ or } \left|\vec{r}\right|^n = [x^2 + y^2 + z^2]^{\frac{n}{2}}$$

Now $curl \left|\vec{r}\right|^n \vec{r} = \vec{\nabla}\times\left|\vec{r}\right|^n \vec{r} = \left(\hat{i}\frac{\partial}{\partial x} + \hat{j}\frac{\partial}{\partial y} + \hat{k}\frac{\partial}{\partial z}\right)\times\left|\vec{r}\right|^n (x\hat{i} + y\hat{j} + z\hat{k})$

or

$$\vec{\nabla}\times\left|\vec{r}\right|^n \vec{r} = \begin{vmatrix} \hat{i} & \hat{j} & \hat{k} \\ \dfrac{\partial}{\partial x} & \dfrac{\partial}{\partial y} & \dfrac{\partial}{\partial z} \\ \left|\vec{r}\right|^n x & \left|\vec{r}\right|^n y & \left|\vec{r}\right|^n z \end{vmatrix}$$

$$= \hat{i}\left[\frac{\partial}{\partial y}\left|\vec{r}\right|^n z - \frac{\partial}{\partial z}\left|\vec{r}\right|^n y\right] + \hat{j}\left[\frac{\partial}{\partial z}\left|\vec{r}\right|^n x - \frac{\partial}{\partial x}\left|\vec{r}\right|^n z\right] + \hat{k}\left[\frac{\partial}{\partial x}\left|\vec{r}\right|^n y - \frac{\partial}{\partial y}\left|\vec{r}\right|^n x\right]$$

$$= \hat{i}\left[\frac{\partial}{\partial y}(x^2 + y^2 + z^2)^{\frac{n}{2}} z - \frac{\partial}{\partial z}(x^2 + y^2 + z^2)^{\frac{n}{2}} y\right]$$

$$+ \hat{j}\left[\frac{\partial}{\partial z}(x^2 + y^2 + z^2)^{\frac{n}{2}} x - \frac{\partial}{\partial x}(x^2 + y^2 + z^2)^{\frac{n}{2}} z\right]$$

$$+ \hat{k}\left[\frac{\partial}{\partial y}(x^2 + y^2 + z^2)^{\frac{n}{2}} y - \frac{\partial}{\partial y}(x^2 + y^2 z^2)^{\frac{n}{2}} x\right]$$

$$= \hat{i}\left[n(x^2 + y^2 + z^2)^{\frac{n}{2}-1} yz - n(x^2 + y^2 + z^2)^{\frac{n}{2}-1} yz\right]$$

$$+ \hat{j} \left[n(x^2 + y^2 + z^2)^{\frac{n}{2}-1} xz - n(x^2 + y^2 + z^2)^{\frac{n}{2}-1} xz \right]$$

$$+ \hat{k} \left[n(x^2 + y^2 + z^2)^{\frac{n}{2}-1} xy - n(x^2 + y^2 + z^2)^{\frac{n}{2}-1} xy \right]$$

= 0 [Since each term with in square brackets is zero.

Exercise *If* $\vec{A} = \dfrac{\vec{r}}{r}$ *then prove that* $\vec{A}$ *is irrotational.*   (*G.N.D.U.* 2006)

Hint. A vector $\vec{A}$ is irrotational if $\vec{\nabla} \times \vec{A} = 0$

Given $\vec{A} = \dfrac{\vec{r}}{r} = r^{-1} \vec{r} = \left| \vec{r} \right|^{-1} \vec{r}$

It has been proved in **Q. 1.38** (c) given above that $\vec{\nabla} \times \left| \vec{r} \right|^{n} \vec{r} = 0$. Here $n = -1$. Therefore, substituting $n = -1$, we get

$$\vec{\nabla} \times \left| \vec{r} \right|^{-1} \vec{r} = 0$$

As $\vec{\nabla} \times \vec{A} = 0$, the vector $\vec{A} = \dfrac{\vec{r}}{r}$ is irrotational

Q. 1.39. (a) What is an irrotational (vector) field? Give one example.
                    (*Pbi.U.* 2006, 2001; *H.P.U.* 1997, 1994, 1992; *G.N.D.U.* 2007, 2003, 1990)

(b) Show that the vector field $\vec{A} = \dfrac{-2z^2 y}{x^3} \hat{i} + \dfrac{z^2}{x^2} \hat{j} + \dfrac{2yz}{x^2} \hat{k}$ **is irrotational.**
                    (*G.N.D.U.* 2009, 2002; *H.P.U.* 1997)

Ans. (a) **Irrotational field.** *A vector field whose curl vanishes* (= 0) *is called irrotational field*
If $\vec{A}$ represents on irrotational field, then *curl* $\vec{A} = \vec{\nabla} \times \vec{A} = 0$
Example. Electric field $\vec{E}$ is an example of an irrotational field since

$$\vec{\nabla} \times \vec{E} = 0$$

[**Note.** A vector field whose curl is not equal to zero is called a *rotational vector field*. Magnetic field $\vec{B}$ is an example of rotational vector field since $\vec{\nabla} \times \vec{B} \neq 0$]

(b) A vector field is irrotational if *curl* $\vec{A} = \vec{\nabla} \times \vec{A} = 0$

$$\text{Now } \vec{\nabla} \times \vec{A} = \begin{vmatrix} \hat{i} & \hat{j} & \hat{k} \\ \dfrac{\partial}{\partial x} & \dfrac{\partial}{\partial y} & \dfrac{\partial}{\partial z} \\ \dfrac{-2z^2 y}{x^3} & \dfrac{z^2}{x^2} & \dfrac{2yz}{x^2} \end{vmatrix}$$

$$= \hat{i}\left[\frac{\partial}{\partial y}\left(\frac{2yz}{x^2}\right) - \frac{\partial}{\partial z}\left(\frac{z^2}{x^2}\right)\right] + \hat{j}\left[\frac{\partial}{\partial z}\left(\frac{-2z^2 y}{x^3}\right) - \frac{\partial}{\partial x}\left(\frac{2yz}{x^2}\right)\right] + \hat{k}\left[\frac{\partial}{\partial x}\left(\frac{z^2}{x^2}\right) - \frac{\partial}{\partial y}\left(\frac{-2z^2 y}{x^3}\right)\right]$$

or $\qquad \vec{\nabla} \times \vec{A} = \hat{i}\left(\frac{2z}{x^2} - \frac{2z}{x^2}\right) + \hat{j}\left(\frac{-4zy}{x^3} + \frac{4yz}{x^3}\right) + \hat{k}\left(\frac{-2z^2}{x^3} + \frac{2z^2}{x^3}\right) = 0$

As $\vec{\nabla} \times \vec{A} = 0$, the *curl* of the vector field vanishes. The field is, therefore, *irrotational*.

Ex. *Show that the field* $\vec{E} = 6xy\hat{i} + (3x^2 - 3y^2)\hat{j}$ *is irrotational.* $\qquad$ *(H.P.U. 2002, 2000)*

Hint. $\qquad \vec{\nabla} \times \vec{E} = \begin{vmatrix} \hat{i} & \hat{j} & \hat{k} \\ \frac{\partial}{\partial x} & \frac{\partial}{\partial y} & \frac{\partial}{\partial z} \\ 6xy & (3x^2 - 3y^2) & 0 \end{vmatrix} = \hat{k}\left[\frac{\partial}{\partial x}(3x^2 - 3y^2) - \frac{\partial}{\partial y}(6xy)\right]$
$\qquad\qquad\qquad\qquad\qquad\qquad\qquad\qquad\qquad\qquad\qquad\qquad = 6x - 6x = 0$

As *curl* $\vec{E} = \vec{\nabla} \times \vec{E} = 0$, the field is irrotational.

Q. 1.40. Consider a vector field $\vec{A} = x^2\hat{i} + y^2\hat{j} + z^2\hat{k}$**. (*i*) Is the field solenoidal? Is the field irrotational?**
$\qquad\qquad\qquad\qquad\qquad\qquad\qquad\qquad\qquad\qquad\qquad\qquad\qquad\qquad\qquad$ *(Pbi. U. 1993)*

Ans. (*i*) The rectangular components of the vector field $\vec{A}$ are

$$A_x = x^2 \quad A_y = y^2 \quad A_z = z^2$$

$\therefore \qquad\qquad \frac{\partial A_x}{\partial x} = 2x; \frac{\partial A_y}{\partial y} = 2y; \frac{\partial A_z}{\partial z} = 2z$

Now $\qquad\qquad \vec{\nabla} . \vec{A} = \frac{\partial A_x}{\partial x} + \frac{\partial A_y}{\partial y} + \frac{\partial A_z}{\partial z} = 2x + 2y + 2z$

Since the divergence of the vector field $\vec{A}$ does not vanish (is not equal to zero), the field is *not solenoidal*.

(*ii*) $\qquad\qquad \vec{\nabla} \times \vec{A} = \begin{vmatrix} \hat{i} & \hat{j} & \hat{k} \\ \frac{\partial}{\partial x} & \frac{\partial}{\partial y} & \frac{\partial}{\partial z} \\ x^2 & y^2 & z^2 \end{vmatrix} = 0$

Since *curl* of the vector field $\vec{A}$ vanishes (= 0) *the field is irrotational.*

Q. 1.41. What do you understand by irrotational vector (field)? Show that the motion is irrotational if the body is moving with a velocity $\vec{V} = (2x\hat{i} + 2y\hat{j})$. **ms**$^{-1}$**.**
$\qquad\qquad\qquad\qquad\qquad\qquad$ *(G.N.D.U. 2007; H.P.U. 1991; Meerut U. 2002)*

Ans. Irrotational vector. *A vector whose curl vanishes (= 0) is called an irrotational vector.*
If $\vec{A}$ is an irrotational vector, then *Curl* $\vec{A} = \vec{\nabla} \times \vec{A} = 0$
Velocity of the body $\vec{V} = (2x\hat{i} + 2y\hat{j})\,\text{ms}^{-1}$

$$\text{Curl } \vec{V} = \vec{\nabla} \times \vec{V} = \begin{vmatrix} \hat{i} & \hat{j} & \hat{k} \\ \frac{\partial}{\partial x} & \frac{\partial}{\partial y} & \frac{\partial}{\partial z} \\ 2x & 2y & 0 \end{vmatrix} = 0$$

As curl $\vec{V} = 0$, the motion is irrotational.

Q. 1.42. (*a*) A vector field is given by $\vec{A} = yz\,\hat{i} + xz\,\hat{j} + xy\,\hat{k}$. **Show that it is both irrotational and solenoidal.**   (*M.D.U.*, 2002)

(*b*) **If the vector field** $\vec{A}$ **is irrotational show that** $\vec{A} \times \vec{r}$ **is solenoidal where** $\vec{r} = x\,\hat{i} + y\,\hat{j} + z\,\hat{k}$.   (*G.N.D.U.*, 2006)

Ans.(*a*) (*i*) The rectangular components of the vector field $\vec{A}$ are

$$A_x = yz;\ A_y = xz;\ A_z = xy$$

$$\therefore \qquad \frac{\partial A_x}{\partial x} = 0;\ \frac{\partial A_y}{\partial y} = 0;\ \frac{\partial A_z}{\partial z} = 0$$

Hence $\qquad \vec{\nabla}\cdot\vec{A} = \dfrac{\partial A_x}{\partial x} + \dfrac{\partial A_y}{\partial y} + \dfrac{\partial A_z}{\partial z} = 0$

As the divergence of the vector field $\vec{A} = 0$, *the field is solenoidal.*

(*ii*)

$$\vec{\nabla}\times\vec{A} = \begin{vmatrix} \hat{i} & \hat{j} & \hat{k} \\ \dfrac{\partial}{\partial x} & \dfrac{\partial}{\partial y} & \dfrac{\partial}{\partial z} \\ yz & xz & xy \end{vmatrix}$$

$$= \hat{i}\left[\frac{\partial}{\partial y}xy - \frac{\partial}{\partial z}xz\right] + \hat{j}\left[\frac{\partial}{\partial z}.yz - \frac{\partial}{\partial x}xy\right]$$

$$+ \hat{k}\left[\frac{\partial}{\partial x}xz - \frac{\partial}{\partial y}yz\right]$$

$$= \hat{i}\,[x - x] + \hat{j}\,[y - y] + \hat{k}\,[z - z] = 0$$

Since curl of the vector field $\vec{A}$ vanishes (= 0) *the field is irrotational.*

(*b*) As the vector field $\vec{A}$ is irrotational, it means $\vec{\nabla}\times\vec{A} = 0$

Now, consider the vector identify,

$$\vec{\nabla}\cdot\left(\vec{A}\times\vec{B}\right) = \vec{B}.\vec{\nabla}\times\vec{A} - \vec{A}.\vec{\nabla}\times\vec{B}$$

Substituting $\vec{B} = \vec{r}$ in the identify, we get

$$\vec{\nabla}\cdot\left(\vec{A}\times\vec{r}\right) = \vec{r}.\vec{\nabla}\times\vec{A} - \vec{A}.\vec{\nabla}\times\vec{r}$$

But $\qquad \vec{\nabla}\times\vec{A} = 0$

$$\therefore \qquad \vec{\nabla}\cdot\left(\vec{A}\times\vec{r}\right) = -\vec{A}.\vec{\nabla}\times\vec{r}$$

Now
$$\vec{\nabla} \times \vec{r} = \begin{vmatrix} \hat{i} & \hat{j} & \hat{k} \\ \dfrac{\partial}{\partial x} & \dfrac{\partial}{\partial y} & \dfrac{\partial}{\partial z} \\ x & y & z \end{vmatrix}$$

or
$$\vec{\nabla} \times \vec{r} = \hat{i}\left(\frac{\partial}{\partial y}z - \frac{\partial}{\partial z}y\right) + \hat{j}\left(\frac{\partial}{\partial z}x - \frac{\partial}{\partial x}z\right) + \hat{k}\left(\frac{\partial}{\partial x}y - \frac{\partial}{\partial y}x\right) = 0$$

Since each term with in the brackets is zero.

$$\therefore \qquad \vec{\nabla}.\left(\vec{A} \times \vec{r}\right) = 0$$

This means $\vec{A} \times \vec{r}$ is *solenoidal*

Q. 1.43. What do you conclude from

(i)   *Curl* $\vec{F} \neq 0$ and *div* $\vec{F} = 0$

(ii)   *Curl* $\vec{F} = 0$ and *div* $\vec{F} \neq 0$

(iii)   *Curl* $\vec{F} = 0$ and *div* $\vec{F} = 0$ or $\vec{\nabla} \times \vec{F} = 0$ and $\vec{\nabla}.\vec{F} = 0$ *(Pbi.U.* 2003)

(iv)   *Curl* $\vec{F} \neq 0$ and *div* $\vec{F} \neq 0$ *(G.N.D.U.* 1991)

Ans. *div* $\vec{F} = 0$ means $\vec{\nabla}.\vec{F} = 0$

Compare it with the relation
$$\vec{\nabla}.(\vec{\nabla} \times \vec{A}) \equiv 0$$

We find that a vector field $\vec{F}$ whose divergence is zero $[div \ \vec{F} = \vec{\nabla}.\vec{F} = 0]$ can be written as
$$\vec{F} = \vec{\nabla} \times \vec{A}$$

i.e., it is the *curl* of another vector field $\vec{A}$. Vector fields for which divergence vanishes or $\vec{\nabla}.\vec{F} = 0$ are known as *solenoidal*.

As *curl* $\vec{F} \neq 0$ the field is *rotational* as also *non-conservative*.

(ii) *Curl* $\vec{F} = 0$ means $\vec{\nabla} \times \vec{F} = 0$ compare it with the relation
$$\vec{\nabla} \times \vec{\nabla}\phi = 0$$

We find that a vector field $\vec{F}$ whose *curl* is zero $[\ Curl \ \vec{F} = 0 \ $ or $\ \vec{\nabla} \times \vec{F} = 0\ ]$ can be written as
$$\vec{F} = \vec{\nabla}\phi$$

i.e., it is the gradient of a scalar field ϕ. Vector fields for which *curl* vanishes or $\vec{\nabla} \times \vec{F} = 0$ are known as *irrotational as well as conservative*.

As *div* $\vec{F} \neq 0$ the field is non-solenoidal

(iii) As *curl* $\vec{F} = 0$ the field is *irrotational* as well as *conservative*.

As *div* $\vec{F} = 0$ the field is also *solenoidal*.

(vi) As *curl* $\vec{F} \neq 0$ the field is *rotational* as well as *non-conservative*.

As *div* $\vec{F} \neq 0$ the field is *non-solenoidal*.

Q. 1.44. (a) Prove that $Curl\ (\phi \vec{A}) = \phi\ curl\ \vec{A} + grad\ \phi \times \vec{A}$ (Indore. U. 2001)

(b) **Calculate the value of the divergence of a vector product of two vectors or prove that**
div $(\vec{A} \times \vec{B}) = \vec{B}.\ Curl\ \vec{A} - \vec{A}.\ curl\ \vec{B}$.

(Indore. U. 2001; Gharwal. U. 2000; H.P.U. 1995; Meerut. U. 2002, M.D.U. 2002)

(c) **If $\vec{A}$ and $\vec{B}$ are irrotational, then prove that $\vec{A} \times \vec{B}$ solenoidal**   (H.P.U. 1995)

Ans. (a) The vector $\vec{A} = A_x \hat{i} + A_y \hat{j} + A_z \hat{k}$

$\therefore$ $\phi \vec{A} = \phi A_x \hat{i} + \phi A_y \hat{j} + \phi A_z \hat{k}$

$$Curl\ (\phi \vec{A}) = \vec{\nabla} \times \phi \vec{A} = \left(\frac{\partial}{\partial x}\hat{i} + \frac{\partial}{\partial y}\hat{j} + \frac{\partial}{\partial z}\hat{k} \right) \times (\phi A_x \hat{i} + \phi A_y \hat{j} + \phi A_z \hat{k})$$

$$= \begin{vmatrix} \hat{i} & \hat{j} & \hat{k} \\ \frac{\partial}{\partial x} & \frac{\partial}{\partial y} & \frac{\partial}{\partial z} \\ \phi A_x & \phi A_y & \phi A_z \end{vmatrix} = \hat{i}\left[\frac{\partial}{\partial y}(\phi A_z) - \frac{\partial}{\partial z}(\phi A_y) \right]$$

$$+ \hat{j}\left[\frac{\partial}{\partial z}(\phi A_x) - \frac{\partial}{\partial x}(\phi A_z) \right] + \hat{k}\left[\frac{\partial}{\partial x}(\phi A_y) - \frac{\partial}{\partial y}(\phi A_x) \right]$$

$$= \hat{i}\left(\phi\frac{\partial A_z}{\partial y} + \frac{\partial \phi}{\partial y}A_z - \phi\frac{\partial A_y}{\partial z} - \frac{\partial \phi}{\partial z}A_y \right)$$

$$+ \hat{j}\left(\phi\frac{\partial A_x}{\partial z} + \frac{\partial \phi}{\partial z}A_x - \phi\frac{\partial A_z}{\partial x} - \frac{\partial \phi}{\partial x}A_z \right)$$

$$+ \hat{k}\left(\phi\frac{\partial A_y}{\partial x} + \frac{\partial \phi}{\partial x}A_y - \phi\frac{\partial A_x}{\partial y} - \frac{\partial \phi}{\partial y}A_x \right)$$

$$= \phi\left[\hat{i}\left(\frac{\partial A_z}{\partial y} - \frac{\partial A_y}{\partial z} \right) + \hat{j}\left(\frac{\partial A_x}{\partial z} - \frac{\partial A_z}{\partial x} \right) + \hat{k}\left(\frac{\partial A_y}{\partial x} - \frac{\partial A_x}{\partial y} \right) \right]$$

$$+ \left[\hat{i}\left(\frac{\partial \phi}{\partial y}A_z - \frac{\partial \phi}{\partial z}A_y \right) + \hat{j}\left(\frac{\partial \phi}{\partial z}A_x - \frac{\partial \phi}{\partial x}A_z \right) + \hat{k}\left(\frac{\partial \phi}{\partial x}A_y - \frac{\partial \phi}{\partial y}A_x \right) \right]$$

$$= \phi\begin{vmatrix} \hat{i} & \hat{j} & \hat{k} \\ \frac{\partial}{\partial x} & \frac{\partial}{\partial y} & \frac{\partial}{\partial z} \\ A_x & A_y & A_z \end{vmatrix} + \begin{vmatrix} \hat{i} & \hat{j} & \hat{k} \\ \frac{\partial \phi}{\partial x} & \frac{\partial \phi}{\partial y} & \frac{\partial \phi}{\partial z} \\ A_x & A_y & A_z \end{vmatrix}$$

$$= \phi\ \vec{\nabla} \times \vec{A} + \vec{\nabla}\phi \times \vec{A}$$

$$= \phi\ Curl\ \vec{A} + grad\ \phi \times \vec{A} \quad \textbf{OR} \quad \vec{\nabla} \times (\phi\vec{A}) = \phi(\vec{\nabla} \times \vec{A}) + \vec{\nabla}\phi \times \vec{A}$$

(b) **Divergence of a vector product.** Let the two vectors be A and B then

$$divergence\ (\vec{A} \times \vec{B}) = \vec{\nabla}.\ (\vec{A} \times \vec{B})$$

Now
$$(\vec{A} \times \vec{B}) = \begin{vmatrix} \hat{i} & \hat{j} & \hat{k} \\ A_x & A_y & A_z \\ B_x & B_y & B_z \end{vmatrix}$$

$$= (A_y B_z - A_z B_y)\hat{i} + (A_z B_x - A_x B_z)\hat{j} + (A_x B_y - A_y B_x)\hat{k}$$

$$\therefore \quad \vec{\nabla} \cdot (\vec{A} \times \vec{B}) = \left(\frac{\partial}{\partial x}\hat{i} + \frac{\partial}{\partial y}\hat{j} + \frac{\partial}{\partial z}\hat{k} \right) \cdot [(A_y B_z - A_z B_y)\hat{i}$$

$$+ (A_z B_x - A_x B_z)\hat{j} + (A_x B_y - A_y B_x)\hat{k}]$$

$$= \frac{\partial}{\partial x}(A_y B_z - A_z B_y) + \frac{\partial}{\partial y}(A_z B_x - A_x B_z) + \frac{\partial}{\partial z}(A_x B_y - A_y B_x)$$

$$= \frac{\partial A_y}{\partial x}B_z + A_y\frac{\partial B_z}{\partial x} - \frac{\partial A_z}{\partial x}B_y - \frac{\partial B_y}{\partial x}A_z$$

$$+ \frac{\partial A_z}{\partial y}B_x + A_z\frac{\partial B_x}{\partial y} - \frac{\partial A_x}{\partial y}B_z - \frac{\partial B_z}{\partial y}A_x$$

$$+ \frac{\partial A_x}{\partial z}B_y + A_x\frac{\partial B_y}{\partial z} - \frac{\partial A_y}{\partial z}B_x - \frac{\partial B_x}{\partial z}A_y$$

Rearranging we get

$$B_x\left(\frac{\partial A_z}{\partial y} - \frac{\partial A_y}{\partial z} \right) + B_y\left(\frac{\partial A_x}{\partial z} - \frac{\partial A_z}{\partial x} \right) + B_z\left(\frac{\partial A_y}{\partial x} - \frac{\partial A_x}{\partial y} \right)$$

$$- A_x\left(\frac{\partial B_z}{\partial y} - \frac{\partial B_y}{\partial z} \right) - A_y\left(\frac{\partial B_x}{\partial z} - \frac{\partial B_z}{\partial x} \right) - A_z\left(\frac{\partial B_y}{\partial x} - \frac{\partial B_x}{\partial y} \right)$$

$$= \vec{B} \cdot (\vec{\nabla} \times \vec{A}) - \vec{A} \cdot (\vec{\nabla} \times \vec{B})$$

(c) As $\vec{A}$ and $\vec{B}$ are *irrotational* $\vec{\nabla} \times \vec{A} = 0$ and $\vec{\nabla} \times \vec{B} = 0$

Also $\vec{\nabla} \cdot (\vec{A} \times \vec{B}) = \vec{B} \cdot (\vec{\nabla} \times \vec{A}) - \vec{A} \cdot (\vec{\nabla} \times \vec{B}) = 0$

because $\vec{\nabla} \times \vec{A} = 0$ and $\vec{\nabla} \times \vec{B} = 0$

As $\vec{\nabla} \cdot (\vec{A} \times \vec{B}) = 0$, $(\vec{A} \times \vec{B})$ is *solenoidal*.

Q. 1.45. What is meant by circulation of a vector field ?   (*P.U.* 1994)

Ans. Circulation. *The line integral of a vector function $\vec{A}$ along a closed path is called* circulation.

$$\therefore \qquad \text{Circulation} = \oint \vec{A} \cdot \vec{dl}$$

where $\vec{dl}$ is an elementary vector length along the closed

path and $\oint$ denotes integral over a closed path.

Direction of circulation. The direction of circulation is determined by the *right hand screw rule* which is used for finding the direction of angular quantities.

Let P be a point in the X-Y plane having position vector $\vec{r}$ in a vector field $\vec{A}$ parallel to X-axis and $abcd$ an

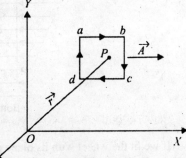

Fig. 1.10

elementary rectangular area drawn about the point P in the same plane, then circulation of $\vec{A}$ along the path $abcd$ is given by

$$\text{Circulation} = \oint_{abcd} \vec{A} \cdot \vec{dl}$$

The direction of circulation when the path $abcd$ is traversed in the *clockwise* direction i.e., "*a to b to c to d to a*" will be along the $-Z$ axis and when the path $abcd$ is traversed in the *anti-clockwise* direction i.e., "*d to c to b to a to d*" will be along the $+Z$ axis according to the right hand screw rule.

Thus

$$\oint_{abcd} \vec{A} \cdot \vec{dl} = - \oint_{dcba} \vec{A} \cdot \vec{dl}$$

The path $abcd$ may not be a rectangle. It can have any contour or shape and may not even lie in a plane.

Curl of the vector field. *The ratio of the circulation to the surface area when the area tends to zero is called the curl of the vector field.*

$$\therefore \quad Curl\ \vec{A} = \lim_{s \to 0} \frac{1}{S} \oint_C \vec{A} \cdot \vec{dl}$$

$$\therefore \quad Curl = \text{circulation density.}$$

Circulation and curl. When the area tends to zero, the contour of the area approaches the nearest neighborhood of a point and the circulation also tends to zero but the curl or circulation density may not be zero and may have a finite value.

Q. 1.46. Explain how curl of a vector quantity is related with rotation ? (*G.N.D.U.* 1990)

Ans. Relation between curl and rotation. Curl of a vector quantity is a vector directed along the perpendicular to the plane of maximum rotation.

Consider the stream line flow of water in a canal. The velocity (vector) of flow of water is maximum at the top and minimum (zero) at the bottom and there exists a velocity gradient.

If we fit a toothed wheel with its plane in which it can rotate along the direction of flow as shown in Fig. 1.11 (*a*) the wheel will begin to rotate about the axis passing through its centre and perpendicular to the direction of flow. The rotation of the wheel will be in the clockwise direction because the velocity of flow of water at the top is greater than that at the bottom of the wheel.

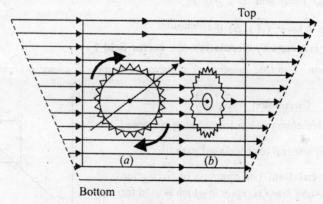

Fig. 1.11

If we fit the wheel with its plane perpendicular to the direction of flow as shown in Fig. 1.11(*b*) the wheel will not rotate. The rotation of the wheel in position (*a*) is maximum and in position (*b*) zero or minimum. If the wheel is fitted in any intermediate position, the *rotation* will be in between the maximum and the minimum values.

The rotation of maximum value is called curl. When the rotation is clockwise as in the above case curl is directed into the plane of the paper according to right hand screw rule.

Q. 1.47. (*a*) **If** $\vec{r} = x\hat{i} + y\hat{j} + z\hat{k}$ **find the value of curl** $\vec{r}$.   (*Osm.U.* 1997)

(*b*) **For a position vector** $\vec{r} = \hat{i}x + \hat{j}y + \hat{k}z$ **show that Curl** $\left[\dfrac{\hat{k}}{r}\right] = \dfrac{-\hat{i}y + \hat{j}x}{r^3}$

(*M.D.U.* 2000)

Ans. (*a*) $Curl \; \vec{r} = \vec{\nabla} \times \vec{r} = \left(\dfrac{\partial}{\partial x}\hat{i} + \dfrac{\partial}{\partial y}\hat{j} + \dfrac{\partial}{\partial z}\hat{k}\right) \times (x\hat{i} + y\hat{j} + z\hat{k})$

$$= \begin{vmatrix} \hat{i} & \hat{j} & \hat{k} \\ \dfrac{\partial}{\partial x} & \dfrac{\partial}{\partial y} & \dfrac{\partial}{\partial z} \\ x & y & z \end{vmatrix} = 0$$

(*b*) $\vec{r} = \hat{i}x + \hat{j}y + \hat{k}z$

$\therefore$ $r = (x^2 + y^2 + z^2)^{1/2}$ and $\dfrac{\hat{k}}{r} = (x^2 + y^2 + z^2)^{-1/2}\,\hat{k}$

and $Curl \left[\dfrac{\hat{k}}{r}\right] = \vec{\nabla} \times \left[(x^2 + y^2 + z^2)^{\frac{-1}{2}}\,\hat{k}\right]$

$$= \left(\hat{i}\dfrac{\partial}{\partial x} + \hat{j}\dfrac{\partial}{\partial y} + \hat{k}\dfrac{\partial}{\partial z}\right) \times \left[(x^2 + y^2 + z^2)^{\frac{-1}{2}}\,\hat{k}\right]$$

$$= \begin{vmatrix} \hat{i} & \hat{j} & \hat{k} \\ \dfrac{\partial}{\partial x} & \dfrac{\partial}{\partial y} & \dfrac{\partial}{\partial z} \\ 0 & 0 & (x^2 + y^2 + z^2)^{\frac{-1}{2}} \end{vmatrix} = \hat{i}\dfrac{\partial}{\partial y}(x^2 + y^2 + z^2)^{\frac{-1}{2}} - \hat{j}\dfrac{\partial}{\partial x}(x^2 + y^2 + z^2)^{\frac{-1}{2}}$$

$$= \hat{i}\left[-\dfrac{1}{2}(x^2 + y^2 + z^2)^{-3/2}\,2y\right] - \hat{j}\left[-\dfrac{1}{2}(x^2 + y^2 + z^2)^{-3/2}\,2x\right]$$

$$= \dfrac{-\hat{i}y}{(x^2 + y^2 + z^2)^{-3/2}} + \dfrac{-\hat{j}x}{(x^2 + y^2 + z^2)^{3/2}} = \dfrac{-\hat{i}y + \hat{j}x}{r^3}$$

Q. 1.48. (*a*) **Find the curl of the vector field**

$$H_x = x^2 - z^2 \; ; \; H_y = 2 \; ; \; H_z = 2xz$$ (*G.N.D.U.* 2002; *P.U.* 1995)

(*b*) **Given** $\vec{A} = x^2 y\hat{i} + (x - y)\hat{k}$ **find (*i*)** $\vec{\nabla} \cdot \vec{A}$ **and (*ii*)** $\vec{\nabla} \times \vec{A}$ (*P.U.* 1999)

Ans. (*a*) *Curl* of a vector $\vec{H}$ is given by

$$Curl \; \vec{H} = \vec{\nabla} \times \vec{H} = \left(\dfrac{\partial H_z}{\partial y} - \dfrac{\partial H_y}{\partial z}\right)\hat{i} + \left(\dfrac{\partial H_x}{\partial z} - \dfrac{\partial H_z}{\partial x}\right)\hat{j} + \left(\dfrac{\partial H_y}{\partial x} - \dfrac{\partial H_x}{\partial y}\right)\hat{k}$$

Now $\dfrac{\partial H_z}{\partial y} = 0$; $\dfrac{\partial H_z}{\partial x} = 2z$; $\dfrac{\partial H_y}{\partial z} = 0$; $\dfrac{\partial H_y}{\partial x} = 0$; $\dfrac{\partial H_x}{\partial z} = -2z$, $\dfrac{\partial H_x}{\partial y} = 0$

$\therefore$ $Curl \; \vec{H} = 0 + (-2z - 2z)\hat{j} + 0 = -4z\hat{j}$

(b) $\vec{A} = x^2 y\,\hat{i} + (x - y)\hat{k}$

(i) $div \; \vec{A} = \vec{\nabla} \cdot \vec{A} = \left(\dfrac{\partial}{\partial x}\hat{i} + \dfrac{\partial}{\partial y}\hat{j} + \dfrac{\partial}{\partial z}\hat{k} \right) \cdot \left[x^2 y\,\hat{i} + (x - y)\hat{k} \right]$

$$= \dfrac{\partial}{\partial x}(x^2 y) + \dfrac{\partial}{\partial y}(0) + \dfrac{\partial}{\partial z}(x - y)$$

$\therefore$ $\vec{\nabla} \cdot \vec{A} = 2xy$

(ii) $Curl \; \vec{A} = \vec{\nabla} \times \vec{A} = \left(\dfrac{\partial}{\partial x}\hat{i} + \dfrac{\partial}{\partial y}\hat{j} + \dfrac{\partial}{\partial z}\hat{k} \right) \times \left[x^2 y\,\hat{i} + (x - y)\hat{k} \right]$

$$= \begin{vmatrix} \hat{i} & \hat{j} & \hat{k} \\ \dfrac{\partial}{\partial x} & \dfrac{\partial}{\partial y} & \dfrac{\partial}{\partial z} \\ x^2 y & 0 & (x - y) \end{vmatrix}$$

or $\vec{\nabla} \times \vec{A} = \hat{i}\left[\dfrac{\partial}{\partial y}(x - y) - \dfrac{\partial}{\partial z}(0) \right] + \hat{j}\left[\dfrac{\partial}{\partial z}(x^2 y) - \dfrac{\partial}{\partial x}(x - y) \right]$

$$+ \hat{k}\left(\dfrac{\partial}{\partial x}(0) - \dfrac{\partial}{\partial y}(x^2 y) \right)$$

$$= \hat{i}(-1) + \hat{j}(-1) - \hat{k}(x^2)$$

$\therefore$ $\vec{\nabla} \times \vec{A} = -\hat{i} - \hat{j} - x^2\,\hat{k}$

Q. 1.49. (a) Find the curl of the vector field   (P.U. 1995)

$$\vec{B} = a\left[\dfrac{y\,\hat{i}}{(x^2 + y^2)^{3/2}} - \dfrac{x\,\hat{j}}{(x^2 + y^2)^{3/2}} \right]$$

Ans. $Curl \; \vec{B} = \vec{\nabla} \times \vec{B} = \left(\dfrac{\partial B_z}{\partial y} - \dfrac{\partial B_y}{\partial z} \right)\hat{i} + \left(\dfrac{\partial B_x}{\partial z} - \dfrac{\partial B_z}{\partial x} \right)\hat{j} + \left(\dfrac{\partial B_y}{\partial x} - \dfrac{\partial B_x}{\partial y} \right)\hat{k}$

Now $B_x = \dfrac{ay}{(x^2 + y^2)^{3/2}}; B_y = -\dfrac{ax}{(x^2 + y^2)^{3/2}}; B_z = 0$

$\therefore$ $\dfrac{\partial B_z}{\partial y} = 0, \dfrac{\partial B_y}{\partial z} = 0; \dfrac{\partial B_x}{\partial z} = 0, \dfrac{\partial B_z}{\partial x} = 0$

Now $\dfrac{\partial B_y}{\partial x} = -ax\left[-\dfrac{3}{2}(x^2 + y^2)^{-5/2} 2x \right] - \dfrac{a}{(x^2 + y^2)^{3/2}}$

$$= \dfrac{3ax^2}{(x^2 + y^2)^{5/2}} - \dfrac{a}{(x^2 + y^2)^{3/2}}$$

$$\dfrac{\partial B_x}{\partial y} = ay\left[-\dfrac{3}{2}(x^2 + y^2)^{-5/2} 2y \right] + \dfrac{a}{(x^2 + y^2)^{3/2}}$$

$$= -\frac{3ay^2}{(x^2 + y^2)^{5/2}} + \frac{a}{(x^2 + y^2)^{3/2}}$$

$$\therefore \quad \vec{\nabla} \times \vec{B} = \left[\frac{3ax^2}{(x^2 + y^2)^{5/2}} - \frac{a}{(x^2 + y^2)^{3/2}} + \frac{3ay^2}{(x^2 + y^2)^{5/2}} - \frac{a}{(x^2 + y^2)^{3/2}} \right] \hat{k}$$

$$= \left[\frac{3a(x^2 + y^2)}{(x^2 + y^2)^{5/2}} - \frac{2a}{(x^2 + y^2)^{3/2}} \right] \hat{k} = \frac{a}{(x^2 + y^2)^{3/2}} \hat{k}$$

Q. 1.50. Find the constants a, b, c in the equation

$\vec{A} = (x + by + 4z)\hat{i} + (3x - 4y + cz)\hat{j} + (ax - 2y + 3z)\hat{k}$ such that $\vec{\nabla} \times \vec{A} = 0$.

(P.U. 1992)

Ans. For $\vec{\nabla} \times \vec{A} = 0$ each component must be zero in the expression

$$\vec{\nabla} \times \vec{A} = \left(\frac{\partial A_z}{\partial y} - \frac{\partial A_y}{\partial z} \right)\hat{i} + \left(\frac{\partial A_x}{\partial z} - \frac{\partial A_z}{\partial x} \right)\hat{j} + \left(\frac{\partial A_y}{\partial x} - \frac{\partial A_x}{\partial y} \right)\hat{k}$$

Now $\qquad A_x = x + by + 4z;\ A_y = 3x - 4y + cz;\ A_z = ax - 2y + 3z$

Hence $\qquad \left(\dfrac{\partial A_z}{\partial y} - \dfrac{\partial A_y}{\partial z} \right) = -2 - c = 0 \quad$ or $\quad c = -2$

Again $\qquad \left(\dfrac{\partial A_x}{\partial z} - \dfrac{\partial A_z}{\partial x} \right) = 4 - a = 0 \quad$ or $\quad a = +4$

Also $\qquad \left(\dfrac{\partial A_y}{\partial x} - \dfrac{\partial A_x}{\partial y} \right) = 3 - b = 0 \quad$ or $\quad b = +3$

Q. 1.51. Calculate the curl and divergence of the following.

(i) $\quad F_x = x + y, \quad F_y = x + y, \quad F_z = -2z$

(ii) $\quad H_x = x^2 - z^2;\ H_y = 2;\ H_z = 2xz$ $\qquad\qquad$ *(G.N.D.U. 2002)*

Ans. *(i)* $Curl\ \vec{F} = \vec{\nabla} \times \vec{F} = \left[\dfrac{\partial F_z}{\partial y} - \dfrac{\partial F_y}{\partial z} \right]\hat{i} + \left[\dfrac{\partial F_z}{\partial x} - \dfrac{\partial F_x}{\partial z} \right]\hat{j} + \left[\dfrac{\partial F_y}{\partial x} - \dfrac{\partial F_x}{\partial y} \right]\hat{k}$

Now $\qquad \dfrac{\partial F_z}{\partial y} = 0;\ \dfrac{\partial F_z}{\partial x} = 0;$

$$\frac{\partial F_y}{\partial x} = 1;\ \frac{\partial F_y}{\partial z} = 0$$

$$\frac{\partial F_x}{\partial y} = 1;\ \frac{\partial F_x}{\partial z} = 0$$

$\therefore \qquad\qquad Curl\ \vec{F} = 0$

$$Div\ \vec{F} = \vec{\nabla} \cdot \vec{F} = \frac{\partial F_x}{\partial x} + \frac{\partial F_y}{\partial y} + \frac{\partial F_z}{\partial z}$$

Now
$$\frac{\partial F_x}{\partial x} = 1, \frac{\partial F_y}{\partial y} = 1; \frac{\partial F_z}{\partial z} = -2$$

$\therefore$ Div $\vec{F} = 1 + 1 - 2 = 0$

(ii) For $Curl\ \vec{H}$ see **Q. 1.48 (a)**

$$Div\ \vec{H} = \vec{\nabla} . \vec{H} = \frac{\partial H_x}{\partial x} + \frac{\partial H_y}{\partial y} + \frac{\partial H_z}{\partial z}$$

Now
$$\frac{\partial H_x}{\partial x} = 2x; \frac{\partial H_y}{\partial y} = 0; \frac{\partial H_z}{\partial z} = 2x$$

$\therefore$ $Div\ \vec{H} = 4x$

Q. 1.52. (a) Prove that the curl of linear velocity of the particles of a rigid body rotating about an axis passing through it is twice the angular velocity.

(G.N.D.U. 1995; K.U. 1991; Ranchi U. 1997)

OR

If $\vec{\omega} \times \vec{r} = \vec{V}$, prove that $\vec{\omega} = \frac{1}{2}$ Curl V where $\vec{\omega}$ is a constant vector.   (Kan.U. 1997)

(b) If $\vec{V}$ represents the velocity vector of a solid body rotating about an axis show that Curl $\vec{V} = 2\vec{\omega}$ and div $\vec{V} = 0$ (P.U. 2007)

Ans. (a) Let $\vec{V}$ be the linear velocity of a particle having position vector $\vec{r}$ on the rigid body and $\vec{\omega}$ its angular velocity. If x, y and z are the co-ordinates of the point having position vector $\vec{r}$ then

$$\vec{r} = x\hat{i} + y\hat{j} + z\hat{k}$$

If ω_x, ω_y and ω_z are the x, y and z-components of $\vec{\omega}$ then

$$\vec{\omega} = \omega_x \hat{i} + \omega_y \hat{j} + \omega_z \hat{k}$$

Now
$$\vec{V} = \vec{\omega} \times \vec{r} = \begin{vmatrix} \hat{i} & \hat{j} & \hat{k} \\ \omega_x & \omega_y & \omega_z \\ x & y & z \end{vmatrix}$$

or
$$\vec{V} = \hat{i}(\omega_y z - \omega_z y) + \hat{j}(\omega_z x - \omega_x z) + \hat{k}(\omega_x y - \omega_y x) \qquad ...(i)$$

$\therefore$
$$Curl\ \vec{V} = \vec{\nabla} \times \vec{V} = \begin{vmatrix} \hat{i} & \hat{j} & \hat{k} \\ \frac{\partial}{\partial x} & \frac{\partial}{\partial y} & \frac{\partial}{\partial z} \\ (\omega_y z - \omega_z y) & (\omega_z x - \omega_x z) & (\omega_x y - \omega_y x) \end{vmatrix}$$

$$= \hat{i}\left[\frac{\partial}{\partial y}(\omega_x y - \omega_y x) - \frac{\partial}{\partial z}(\omega_z x - \omega_x z)\right]$$

$$+ \hat{j}\left[\frac{\partial}{\partial z}(\omega_y z - \omega_z y) - \frac{\partial}{\partial x}(\omega_x y - \omega_y x)\right] + \hat{k}\left[\frac{\partial}{\partial x}(\omega_z y - \omega_x z) - \frac{\partial}{\partial y}(\omega_y z - \omega_z y)\right]$$

As the angular velocity $\vec{\omega}$ for all the particles of a rigid body rotating about an axis passing through it is the same $\vec{\omega}$ is a constant. Hence all the derivatives $\dfrac{\partial}{\partial x}, \dfrac{\partial}{\partial y}$ and $\dfrac{\partial}{\partial z}$ for the components

of $(\omega_x, \omega_y$ and $\omega_z)$ are zero. Also $\left(\dfrac{\partial y}{\partial x}, \dfrac{\partial z}{\partial x}\right); \left(\dfrac{\partial x}{\partial y}, \dfrac{\partial z}{\partial y}\right); \left(\dfrac{\partial x}{\partial z}, \dfrac{\partial y}{\partial z}\right)$ are all zero.

Hence
$$curl\ \vec{V} = \hat{i}(\omega_x + \omega_x) + \hat{j}(\omega_y + \omega_y) + \hat{k}(\omega_z + \omega_z)$$

$$= 2(\omega_x \hat{i} + \omega_y \hat{j} + \omega_z \hat{k}) = 2\vec{\omega} \qquad ...(ii)$$

Therefore, when a body is in rotation the curl of its linear velocity at any point is twice its angular velocity (both in direction as well as magnitude).

(b) To prove $curl\ V = 2\vec{\omega}$ See **part (a) Eq (ii)**

To prove div $\vec{V} = 0$. As proved in **part (a) Eq (i)**

$$\vec{V} = \vec{\omega} \times \vec{r} = \hat{i}(\omega_y z - \omega_z y) + \hat{j}(\omega_z x - \omega_x z) + \hat{k}(\omega_x y - \omega_y x)$$

$$\therefore \quad \vec{\nabla} \cdot \vec{V} = \left(\hat{i}\dfrac{\partial}{\partial x} + \hat{j}\dfrac{\partial}{\partial y} + \hat{k}\dfrac{\partial}{\partial z}\right) \cdot \left[\hat{i}(\omega_y z - \omega_z y) + \hat{j}(\omega_z x - \omega_x z) + \hat{k}(\omega_x y - \omega_y x)\right]$$

$$= \dfrac{\partial}{\partial x}(\omega_y z - \omega_z y) + \dfrac{\partial}{\partial y}(\omega_z x - \omega_x z) + \dfrac{\partial}{\partial z}(\omega_x y - \omega_y x)$$

$$= 0$$

as each term in brackets is individually zero, $\omega_x, \omega_y, \omega_z$ being rectangular components of $\vec{\omega}$ are constants.

Q. 1.53. If $\vec{A}$ and $\vec{B}$ are two differentiable vectors, then show that

$$\vec{\nabla} \times (\vec{A} + \vec{B}) = \vec{\nabla} \times \vec{A} + \vec{\nabla} \times \vec{B} \qquad \text{(H.P.U. 2003)}$$

Ans. The vector
$$\vec{A} = A_x \hat{i} + A_y \hat{j} + A_z \hat{k}$$

and
$$\text{vector } \vec{B} = B_x \hat{i} + B_y \hat{j} + B_z \hat{k}$$

$$\therefore \qquad \vec{A} + \vec{B} = (A_x + B_x)\hat{i} + (A_y + B_y)\hat{j} + (A_z + B_z)\hat{k}$$

and
$$\vec{\nabla} \times (\vec{A} + \vec{B}) = \left(\hat{i}\dfrac{\partial}{\partial x} + \hat{j}\dfrac{\partial}{\partial y} + \hat{k}\dfrac{\partial}{\partial z}\right) \times \left[(A_x + B_x)\hat{i} + (A_y + B_y)\hat{j} + (A_z + B_z)\hat{k}\right]$$

$$= \begin{vmatrix} \hat{i} & \hat{j} & \hat{k} \\ \dfrac{\partial}{\partial x} & \dfrac{\partial}{\partial y} & \dfrac{\partial}{\partial z} \\ (A_x + B_x) & (A_y + B_y) & (A_z + B_z) \end{vmatrix}$$

$$= \hat{i}\left[\dfrac{\partial}{\partial y}(A_z + B_z) - \dfrac{\partial}{\partial z}(A_y + B_y)\right] + \hat{j}\left[\dfrac{\partial}{\partial z}(A_x + B_x) - \dfrac{\partial}{\partial x}(A_z + B_z)\right]$$

$$+ \hat{k} \left[\frac{\partial}{\partial x}(A_y + B_y) - \frac{\partial}{\partial y}(A_x + B_x) \right]$$

$$= \hat{i} \left[\frac{\partial A_z}{\partial y} + \frac{\partial B_z}{\partial y} - \frac{\partial A_y}{\partial z} - \frac{\partial B_y}{\partial z} \right] + \hat{j} \left[\frac{\partial A_x}{\partial z} + \frac{\partial B_x}{\partial z} - \frac{\partial A_z}{\partial x} - \frac{\partial B_z}{\partial x} \right]$$

$$+ \hat{k} \left[\frac{\partial A_y}{\partial x} + \frac{\partial B_y}{\partial x} - \frac{\partial A_x}{\partial y} - \frac{\partial B_x}{\partial y} \right]$$

$$= \left[\hat{i} \left(\frac{\partial A_z}{\partial y} - \frac{\partial A_y}{\partial z} \right) + \hat{j} \left(\frac{\partial A_x}{\partial z} - \frac{\partial A_z}{\partial x} \right) + \hat{k} \left(\frac{\partial A_y}{\partial x} - \frac{\partial A_x}{\partial y} \right) \right]$$

$$+ \left[\hat{i} \left(\frac{\partial B_z}{\partial y} - \frac{\partial B_y}{\partial z} \right) + \hat{j} \left(\frac{\partial B_x}{\partial z} - \frac{\partial B_z}{\partial x} \right) + \hat{k} \left(\frac{\partial B_y}{\partial x} - \frac{\partial B_x}{\partial y} \right) \right]$$

$$= \vec{\nabla} \times \vec{A} + \vec{\nabla} \times \vec{B}$$

Hence $\vec{\nabla} \times (\vec{A} + \vec{B}) = \vec{\nabla} \times \vec{A} + \vec{\nabla} \times \vec{B}$

Q. 1.54. (*a*) **Show by actual computation that curl gradient of a scalar function is always zero or curl grad $\phi = 0$.** (*G.N.D.U.* 2008, 2006; *P.U.* 2001; *H.P.U.* 2001; *M.D.U.* 2001)

(*b*) **Show that the curl of a uniform electric field is zero.**

(*Meerut. U.* 2005; *H.P.U.* 2003; *P.U.* 2003)

Ans. Let ϕ be a scalar function, then

$$Grad \ \phi = \vec{\nabla} \phi = \hat{i} \frac{\partial \phi}{\partial x} + \hat{j} \frac{\partial \phi}{\partial y} + \hat{k} \frac{\partial \phi}{\partial z}$$

and $\qquad Curl \ Grad \ \phi = \vec{\nabla} \times (\vec{\nabla} \phi)$

$$= \left(\hat{i} \frac{\partial}{\partial x} + \hat{j} \frac{\partial}{\partial y} + \hat{k} \frac{\partial}{\partial z} \right) \times \left(\hat{i} \frac{\partial \phi}{\partial x} + \hat{j} \frac{\partial \phi}{\partial y} + \hat{k} \frac{\partial \phi}{\partial z} \right)$$

$$= \begin{vmatrix} \hat{i} & \hat{j} & \hat{k} \\ \dfrac{\partial}{\partial x} & \dfrac{\partial}{\partial y} & \dfrac{\partial}{\partial z} \\ \dfrac{\partial \phi}{\partial x} & \dfrac{\partial \phi}{\partial y} & \dfrac{\partial \phi}{\partial z} \end{vmatrix}$$

$$= \hat{i} \left(\frac{\partial}{\partial y} \frac{\partial \phi}{\partial z} - \frac{\partial}{\partial z} \frac{\partial \phi}{\partial y} \right) + \hat{j} \left(\frac{\partial}{\partial z} \frac{\partial \phi}{\partial x} - \frac{\partial}{\partial x} \frac{\partial \phi}{\partial z} \right) + \hat{k} \left(\frac{\partial}{\partial x} \frac{\partial \phi}{\partial y} - \frac{\partial}{\partial y} \frac{\partial \phi}{\partial x} \right) \quad ...(i)$$

If ϕ is finite, single valued and continuous function and its first derivatives are also continuous, then

$$\frac{\partial}{\partial y} \frac{\partial \phi}{\partial z} = \frac{\partial}{\partial z} \frac{\partial \phi}{\partial y}; \ \frac{\partial}{\partial z} \frac{\partial \phi}{\partial x} = \frac{\partial}{\partial x} \frac{\partial \phi}{\partial z}; \ \frac{\partial}{\partial x} \frac{\partial \phi}{\partial y} = \frac{\partial}{\partial y} \frac{\partial \phi}{\partial x}$$

because the order of partial differentiation is immaterial.

Substituting in Equation (*i*), we have

$$Curl \ grad \ \phi = \vec{\nabla} \times (\vec{\nabla} \phi) = 0$$

(b) The electric field $\vec{E}$ is negative gradient of the scalar function '*electric potential* ϕ'

or
$$\vec{E} = -\vec{\nabla}\phi = -\,grad\;\phi$$
$$\therefore\; Curl\;\vec{E} = \vec{\nabla} \times \vec{E} = \vec{\nabla} \times (-\vec{\nabla}\phi) = 0$$

because curl grad
$$\phi = \vec{\nabla} \times (\vec{\nabla}\phi) = 0$$

Q. 1.55. Show that a vector field whose curl is everywhere zero can be expressed as the gradient of another suitable scalar field. What is this type of field called?

(*G.N.D.U.* 2004, 1992)

Ans. Let $\vec{F}$ be a vector field whose curl is everywhere zero, then

$$\vec{\nabla} \times \vec{F} = 0 \qquad\qquad\qquad ...(i)$$

We know that if ϕ is a scalar field

$$curl\;grad\,\phi = \vec{\nabla} \times \vec{\nabla}\phi \equiv 0 \qquad\qquad\qquad ...(ii)$$

Comparing (*i*) and (*ii*), we get

$$\vec{F} = \vec{\nabla}\phi$$

i.e., the vector field $\vec{F}$ whose *curl* is everywhere zero can be expressed as the gradient of a suitable scalar field ϕ.

Vector fields for which *curl* vanishes or $\vec{\nabla} \times \vec{F} = 0$ are called *irrotational*. Such fields are also *conservative*.

Q. 1.56. Prove that div curl $\vec{A} = 0$ or $\vec{\nabla}.(\vec{\nabla} \times \vec{A}) = 0$ where $\vec{A} = Ax\,\hat{i} + Ay\,\hat{j} + Az\,\hat{k}$

OR

If a vector $\vec{B}$ is curl of another vector $\vec{A}$, then the divergence of such a vector is zero.

(*Pbi.U.* 2003; *Meerut. U.* 2003, 2002; *P.U.* 2007, 2001, 2000, *H.P.U.* 2002, 2000, 1997; *K.U.* 1991; *G.N.D.U.* 2007, 2006)

Ans. Suppose
$$\vec{B} = curl\;\vec{A}$$

then
$$div\;\vec{B} = div\,(curl\;\vec{A}) = \vec{\nabla}.(\vec{\nabla} \times \vec{A})$$

If the components of the vector $\vec{A}$ are A_x, A_y and A_z, then

$$\vec{\nabla}.(\vec{\nabla} \times \vec{A}) = \left(\hat{i}\frac{\partial}{\partial x} + \hat{j}\frac{\partial}{\partial y} + \hat{k}\frac{\partial}{\partial z}\right).\left\{\left(\frac{\partial A_z}{\partial y} - \frac{\partial A_y}{\partial z}\right)\hat{i} + \left(\frac{\partial A_x}{\partial z} - \frac{\partial A_z}{\partial x}\right)\hat{j} + \left(\frac{\partial A_y}{\partial x} - \frac{\partial A_x}{\partial y}\right)\hat{k}\right\}$$

$$= \frac{\partial^2 A_z}{\partial x \partial y} - \frac{\partial^2 A_y}{\partial x \partial z} + \frac{\partial^2 A_x}{\partial y \partial z} - \frac{\partial^2 A_z}{\partial y \partial x} - \frac{\partial^2 A_x}{\partial y \partial z} + \frac{\partial^2 A_y}{\partial x \partial z} = 0$$

Thus we see that $\vec{\nabla}.(\vec{\nabla} \times \vec{A}) = 0$ or *div curl* $\vec{A} = 0$.

It, therefore, means that if a vector $\vec{B}$ is curl of another vector $\vec{A}$, then the divergence of such a vector is zero. Also see **Q 1.57.**

Q. 1.57. Show that a vector field whose divergence is everywhere zero can be expressed as curl of some other suitable vector field. (*G.N.D.U.* 1994)

Ans. Let $\vec{F}$ be a vector field whose divergence is everywhere zero, then

$$\vec{\nabla}.\vec{F} = 0. \qquad\qquad\qquad ...(i)$$

We know that if $\vec{A}$ is another vector field, then

$$div\ curl\ \vec{A} = \vec{\nabla} \cdot (\vec{\nabla} \times \vec{A}) = 0 \qquad \qquad ...(ii)$$

Comparing (i) and (ii), we get

$$\vec{F} = \vec{\nabla} \times \vec{A}$$

Hence a vector field $\vec{F}$ whose divergence is everywhere zero can be expressed as the curl of some other suitable vector field $\vec{A}$.

Q. 1.58. Prove that $\vec{\nabla} \times (\vec{\nabla} \times \vec{E}) = -\nabla^2 \vec{E} + \vec{\nabla}(\vec{\nabla} \cdot \vec{E})$ (G.N.D.U. 1990)

Ans.

$$(\vec{\nabla} \times \vec{E}) = \begin{vmatrix} \hat{i} & \hat{j} & \hat{k} \\ \dfrac{\partial}{\partial x} & \dfrac{\partial}{\partial y} & \dfrac{\partial}{\partial z} \\ E_x & E_y & E_z \end{vmatrix}$$

$$= \hat{i}\left(\frac{\partial E_z}{\partial y} - \frac{\partial E_y}{\partial z}\right) + \hat{j}\left(\frac{\partial E_x}{\partial z} - \frac{\partial E_z}{\partial x}\right) + \hat{k}\left(\frac{\partial E_y}{\partial x} - \frac{\partial E_x}{\partial y}\right)$$

$$\therefore \quad \vec{\nabla} \times (\vec{\nabla} \times \vec{E}) = \begin{vmatrix} \hat{i} & \hat{j} & \hat{k} \\ \dfrac{\partial}{\partial x} & \dfrac{\partial}{\partial y} & \dfrac{\partial}{\partial z} \\ \left(\dfrac{\partial E_z}{\partial y} - \dfrac{\partial E_y}{\partial z}\right) & \left(\dfrac{\partial E_x}{\partial z} - \dfrac{\partial E_z}{\partial x}\right) & \left(\dfrac{\partial E_y}{\partial x} - \dfrac{\partial E_x}{\partial y}\right) \end{vmatrix}$$

OR

$$= \hat{i}\left[\frac{\partial}{\partial y}\left(\frac{\partial E_y}{\partial x} - \frac{\partial E_x}{\partial y}\right) - \frac{\partial}{\partial z}\left(\frac{\partial E_x}{\partial z} - \frac{\partial E_z}{\partial x}\right)\right]$$

$$+ \hat{j}\left[\frac{\partial}{\partial z}\left(\frac{\partial E_z}{\partial y} - \frac{\partial E_y}{\partial z}\right) - \frac{\partial}{\partial x}\left(\frac{\partial E_y}{\partial x} - \frac{\partial E_x}{\partial y}\right)\right]$$

$$+ \hat{k}\left[\frac{\partial}{\partial x}\left(\frac{\partial E_x}{\partial z} - \frac{\partial E_z}{\partial x}\right) - \frac{\partial}{\partial y}\left(\frac{\partial E_z}{\partial y} - \frac{\partial E_y}{\partial z}\right)\right]$$

$$= \hat{i}\left[\frac{\partial^2 E_y}{\partial y \partial x} - \frac{\partial^2 E_x}{\partial y^2} - \frac{\partial^2 E_x}{\partial z^2} + \frac{\partial^2 E_z}{\partial z \partial x}\right] + \hat{j}\left[\frac{\partial^2 E_z}{\partial z \partial y} - \frac{\partial^2 E_y}{\partial z^2} - \frac{\partial^2 E_y}{\partial x^2} + \frac{\partial^2 E_x}{\partial x \partial y}\right]$$

$$+ \hat{k}\left[\frac{\partial^2 E_x}{\partial x \partial z} - \frac{\partial^2 E_z}{\partial x^2} - \frac{\partial^2 E_z}{\partial y^2} + \frac{\partial^2 E_y}{\partial y \partial z}\right]$$

Adding $\dfrac{\partial^2 E_x}{\partial x^2} - \dfrac{\partial^2 E_x}{\partial x^2}$ (which is equal to zero) to the $\hat{i}$ component, we get

$$\hat{i}\left[\left(\frac{\partial^2 E_y}{\partial y \partial x} + \frac{\partial^2 E_z}{\partial z \partial x} + \frac{\partial^2 E_x}{\partial x^2}\right) - \left(\frac{\partial^2 E_x}{\partial y^2} + \frac{\partial^2 E_x}{\partial z^2} + \frac{\partial^2 E_x}{\partial x^2}\right)\right]$$

$$= \hat{i}\left[\frac{\partial}{\partial x}(\vec{\nabla}.\vec{E}) - \nabla^2 E_x\right]$$

Similarly the $\hat{j}$ components becomes

$$\hat{j}\left[\frac{\partial}{\partial y}(\vec{\nabla}.\vec{E}) - \nabla^2 E_y\right]$$

and $\hat{k}$ component becomes

$$\hat{k}\left[\frac{\partial}{\partial z}(\vec{\nabla}.\vec{E}) - \nabla^2 E_z\right]$$

Hence $\vec{\nabla} \times (\vec{\nabla} \times \vec{E}) = \left(\hat{i}\dfrac{\partial}{\partial x} + \hat{j}\dfrac{\partial}{\partial y} + \hat{k}\dfrac{\partial}{\partial z}\right)(\vec{\nabla}.\vec{E}) - \nabla^2\,(E_x\,\hat{i} + E_y\,\hat{j} + E_z\,\hat{k})$

$$= \vec{\nabla}\,(\vec{\nabla}.\vec{E}) - \nabla^2\vec{E}$$

$$= -\nabla^2\vec{E} + \vec{\nabla}(\vec{\nabla}.\vec{E})$$

Alternative proof. Using the following relation for triple vector product

$$\vec{A} \times (\vec{B} \times \vec{C}) = \vec{B}(\vec{A}.\vec{C}) - \vec{C}(\vec{A}.\vec{B}) \text{ we can write}$$

$$\vec{\nabla} \times (\vec{\nabla} \times \vec{A}) = \vec{\nabla}(\vec{\nabla}.\vec{A}) - \vec{A}(\vec{\nabla}.\vec{\nabla})$$

$$= \vec{\nabla}\,(\vec{\nabla}.\vec{A}) - \nabla^2\vec{A}$$

Q. 1.59. If $\vec{A} = 2x^2z^2\,\hat{i} - 2xy^2\,\hat{j} + 2x^2\,y^2\,\hat{k}$ find the value of curl $\vec{A}$ at the point (1, 1, 1).

(*Pbi. U.* 1993)

Ans. $Curl\ \vec{A} = \vec{\nabla} \times \vec{A} = \begin{vmatrix} \hat{i} & \hat{j} & \hat{k} \\ \dfrac{\partial}{\partial x} & \dfrac{\partial}{\partial y} & \dfrac{\partial}{\partial z} \\ 2x^2z^2 & -2xy^2 & 2x^2y^2 \end{vmatrix}$

$$= \hat{i}\left[\frac{\partial}{\partial y}(2x^2y^2) - \frac{\partial}{\partial z}(-2xy^2)\right] + \hat{j}\left[\frac{\partial}{\partial z}(2x^2z^2) - \frac{\partial}{\partial x}(2x^2y^2)\right] + \hat{k}\left[\frac{\partial}{\partial x}(-2xy^2) - \frac{\partial}{\partial y}(2x^2z^2)\right]$$

$$= \hat{i}[4x^2y] + \hat{j}[4x^2z - 4xy^2] + \hat{k}[-2y^2]$$

Putting $x = 1, y = 1$, and $z = 1$, we get

$$\vec{\nabla} \times \vec{A} = 4\hat{i} + 0\hat{j} - 2\hat{k} = 4\hat{i} - 2\hat{k}$$

Q. 1.60. (*a*) State and prove Stoke's theorem. Give its importance.

(*Pbi.U.* 2008, 2007, 2001, 2000, 1999; *P.U.* 2001; *M.D.U.* 2003, 2000; *G.N.D.U.* 2009, 2000, 1995; *H.P.U.* 2007, 2003, 1999, 1997, 1996; *Meerut.U.* 2003)

(*b*) Using Stoke's theorem show that curl $\vec{E} = 0$.   (*Pbi.U.* 2007, 2006)

Ans.(a) Stoke's theorem. *Stoke's theorem states that the surface integral of the curl of a vector $\vec{A}$ over a surface $\vec{S}$ of any shape is equal to the line integral of the vector field $\vec{A}$ over the boundary of that surface*

or
$$\iint_S (curl\ \vec{A}) . \vec{dS} = \oint \vec{A} . \vec{dl}$$

where $\oint$ represents the line integral over the closed path enclosing the surface $\vec{S}$.

The sense of integration is related with the positive normal to the surface S according to the right hand screw rule.

Stoke's theorem may also be stated in the form *'Stoke's theorem states that the line integral of a vector field $\vec{A}$ around any closed curve C is equal to the surface integral of the curl of $\vec{A}$ over an open surface S bounded by the curve C'* Mathematically.

$$\oint_C \vec{A} . \vec{dl} = \iint_S (Curl\ A). \vec{ds} = \iint_S \vec{\nabla} \times \vec{A}) . \vec{ds}$$

we shall prove the theorem given in the form

$$\iint_S (Curl\ \vec{A}) . \vec{ds} = \oint \vec{A} . \vec{dl}$$

Suppose a smooth closed curve l encloses vector area $\vec{S}$ in a vector field $\vec{A}$. Let the area $\vec{S}$ be divided into a large number of small areas $\Delta S_1, \Delta S_2, ...\Delta S_i, ...$ etc. having perimeters $\Delta l_1, \Delta l_2... \Delta l_i$ etc. respectively. The line integrals of the vector $\vec{A}$ around each of the small paths $\Delta l_1, \Delta l_2 ... \Delta l_i$ etc. will be in the same sense. Therefore the line integral along the common boundary of two small areas like ΔS_1 and ΔS_2 will cancel each other being in the opposite direction. Hence, the sum of all these line integrals will be equal to the line integral around l the boundary enclosing the whole area $\vec{S}$ because in traversing the small areas all parts of the line integral will cancel out except for those parts which are along the outer boundary l. Thus the line integral around the closed curve l is equal to the sum of the line integrals around the paths $\Delta l_1, \Delta l_2, ... \Delta l_i ...$ etc.

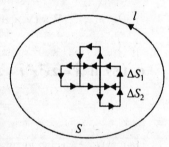

Fig. 1.12

or
$$\oint_l \vec{A} . \vec{dl} = \sum_{\Delta l_i} \oint \vec{A} . \vec{dl} \qquad ...(i)$$

Any one of the small areas ΔS_i will have a *curl* of the vector field of which the normal component

$$Curl_n\ \vec{A} = \lim_{\Delta S_i \to 0} \frac{1}{\Delta S_i} \oint_{\Delta l_i} \vec{A} . \vec{dl}$$

or
$$\oint_{\Delta l_i} \vec{A} . \vec{dl} = (Curl_n\ \vec{A})\ \Delta S_i$$

$\therefore$
$$\sum_{\Delta l_i} \oint \vec{A} . \vec{dl} = \sum (Curl_n\ \vec{A})\ \Delta S_i$$

When $\Delta S_i = ds$ i.e., an infinite number of small volume elements are involved and $\Delta S_i \to 0$, then
$$\sum (Curl_n\ \vec{A})\ \Delta S = \iint_S (Curl_n\ \vec{A}) . \vec{ds} = \iint_S Curl\ \vec{A} . \vec{ds}$$

$$\therefore \qquad \sum_{\Delta l_i} \oint \vec{A} \cdot \vec{dl} = \iint_S Curl \ \vec{A} \cdot \vec{ds} \qquad \qquad ....(ii)$$

From (*i*) and (*ii*), we get

$$\iint_S Curl \ \vec{A} \cdot \vec{ds} = \oint_l \vec{A} \cdot \vec{dl}$$

or

$$\iint_S (\vec{\nabla} \times \vec{A}) \cdot \vec{ds} = \oint_l \vec{A} \cdot \vec{dl}$$

Importance. The importance of Stoke's theorem lies in the fact that it helps us to convert the line integral of a vector into the surface integral of the *curl* of that vector and vice-versa.

e.g. to prove Ampere's law in differential form $\vec{\nabla} \times \vec{B} = \mu_0 \vec{J}$ we convert $\oint \vec{B} \cdot \vec{dl}$ into

$\iint_S (\vec{\nabla} \times \vec{B}) \cdot \vec{ds}$ using Stoke's theorem and equate it to $\mu_0 \iint_S \vec{J} \cdot \vec{ds}$, so that $\vec{\nabla} \times \vec{B} = \mu_0 \vec{J}$.

(*b*) According to Stoke's theorem

$$\iint_S Curl \ \vec{A} \cdot \vec{ds} = \oint_l \vec{A} \cdot \vec{dl}$$

where $\oint_l$ is the line, integral over a closed path

If $\vec{A} = \vec{E}$, the electrostatic field, then

$$\iint_S Curl \ \vec{E} \cdot \vec{ds} = \oint_l \vec{E} \cdot \vec{dl}$$

but $\oint_l \vec{E} \cdot \vec{dl}$ is the integral of the electric field $\vec{E}$ over a closed path and is zero.

$$\therefore \qquad \iint_S Curl \ \vec{E} \cdot \vec{ds} = 0 \ or \ Curl \ \vec{E} = 0$$

Q. 1.61. If the line integral of a vector *A* around a closed curve is equal to the surface integral of the vector $\vec{B}$ taken over the surface bounded by the given closed curve show that $\vec{B} = curl \ \vec{A}$.

Ans. Let a closed curve be bounded by the surface *S*, then

$$\oint \vec{A} \cdot \vec{dl} = \oiint_S \vec{B} \cdot \vec{ds} \qquad \qquad ...(i)$$

According to Stoke's theorem,

$$\oint \vec{A} \cdot \vec{dl} = \oiint_S Curl \ \vec{A} \cdot \vec{ds} \qquad \qquad ...(ii)$$

$\therefore$ From (*i*) and (*ii*), we have

$$\oiint \vec{B} \cdot \vec{ds} = \oiint Curl \, \vec{A} \cdot \vec{ds}$$

Hence $\vec{B} = Curl \, \vec{A}$

Q. 1.62. A vector $\vec{r} = x\hat{i} + y\hat{j} + z\hat{k}$. Show that $\oint \vec{r} \cdot \vec{dr} = 0$.

Ans. According to Stoke's theorem

$$\oint \vec{A} \cdot \vec{dl} = \iint_S (\vec{\nabla} \times \vec{A}) \cdot \vec{ds}$$

Here $\vec{A} = \vec{r}$ and $\vec{dl} = $ a line element $= \vec{dr}$

$\therefore$ $\oint \vec{A} \cdot \vec{dl} = \oint \vec{r} \cdot \vec{dr}$

$\therefore$ $\oint \vec{r} \cdot \vec{dr} = \iint_S (\vec{\nabla} \times \vec{r}) \cdot \vec{dr}$

But $\vec{\nabla} \times \vec{r} = \left(\dfrac{\partial}{\partial x}\hat{i} + \dfrac{\partial}{\partial y}\hat{j} + \dfrac{\partial}{\partial z}\hat{k} \right) \times (x\hat{i} + y\hat{j} + z\hat{k})$

$$= \begin{vmatrix} \hat{i} & \hat{j} & \hat{k} \\ \dfrac{\partial}{\partial x} & \dfrac{\partial}{\partial y} & \dfrac{\partial}{\partial z} \\ x & y & z \end{vmatrix} = 0$$

$\therefore$ $\oint \vec{r} \cdot \vec{dr} = 0$

Q. 1.63. It the vector $\vec{A} = K(-y\hat{i} + x\hat{j})$, calculate (*i*) curl $\vec{A}$ (*ii*) $\oint \vec{A} \cdot \vec{dl}$ for closed curve $x^2 + y^2 = r^2, z = 0$ and hence (*iii*) verify Stokes' law.   (*H.P.U.* 1992)

Ans. (*i*) Vector $\vec{A}$

$$= K(-y\hat{i} + x\hat{j})$$

$\therefore$ $Curl \, \vec{A} = \vec{\nabla} \times \vec{A} = \begin{vmatrix} \hat{i} & \hat{j} & \hat{k} \\ \dfrac{\partial}{\partial x} & \dfrac{\partial}{\partial y} & \dfrac{\partial}{\partial z} \\ -Ky & +Kx & 0 \end{vmatrix}$

$$= [+ K - (-K)] \hat{k} = + 2K \, \hat{k}$$

(*ii*) $\oint \vec{A} \cdot \vec{dl}$ for the closed curve $x^2 + y^2 = r^2, z = 0$

$$\vec{A} \cdot \vec{dl} = K(-y\hat{i} + x\hat{j}) \cdot (dx\hat{i} + dy\hat{j} + dz\hat{k})$$
$$= K(-y\,dx + x\,dy)   \qquad ...(i)$$

The closed curve $x^2 + y^2 = r^2$ is satisfied if

we put $x = r \cos\theta$ and $y = r \sin\theta$

because $\qquad\qquad x^2 + y^2 = r^2 \cos^2 \theta + r^2 \sin^2 \theta = r^2$

Hence $\qquad\qquad dx = -r \sin \theta \, d\theta$ and $dy = r \cos \theta \, d\theta$

Substituting in (i), we have

$$\vec{A} \cdot \vec{dl} = K[r^2 \sin^2 \theta \, d\theta + r^2 \cos^2 \theta \, d\theta] = Kr^2 \, d\theta$$

$$\therefore \qquad \oint \vec{A} \cdot \vec{dl} = \oint Kr^2 \, d\theta = Kr^2 \oint d\theta = 2\pi \, Kr^2 \qquad\qquad ...(ii)$$

because a closed curve extends an angle 2π at its centre.

(iii) According to Stoke's theorem

$$\oint \vec{A} \cdot \vec{dl} = \iint_S Curl \ \vec{A} \cdot \vec{dS}$$

A closed curve $x^2 + y^2 = r^2$, $z = 0$ lies in the x-y plane and hence the area vector is directed along the z-axis

$$\therefore \qquad\qquad \vec{dS} = dS\,\hat{k}$$

Hence $\qquad \iint_S Curl \ \vec{A} \cdot \vec{dS} = \iint_S + 2K\,\hat{k} \cdot dS\,\hat{k} = 2K \iint_S dS$

Now $\iint_S dS$ for the closed curve $x^2 + y^2 = r^2$ which represents a circle of radius $r = \pi \, r^2$

$$\therefore \qquad\qquad \iint_S Curl \ \vec{A} \cdot \vec{ds} = 2K \pi r^2 \qquad\qquad ...(iii)$$

As $\oint \vec{A} \cdot \vec{dl}$ as calculated in relation (ii) and $\iint_S curl \ \vec{A} \cdot \vec{dl}$ as calculated in relation (iii) are both equal to $2\pi \, Kr^2$, Stoke's theorem is verified.

Q. 1.64. State and prove Green's theorem in a plane. *(G.N.D.U. 2009; Pbi. U. 2008;*
P.U. 2006; Gauhati. U. 2000; H.P.U. 1997, 1996; K.U. 1991)

Ans. Green's theorem in a plane. Green's theorem in a plane is a special case of Stoke's theorem. It states

'If S is a closed region in xy plane bounded by a simple closed curve C and M and N are continuous functions of x and y having continuous derivatives, then

$$\oint_C M \, dx + N \, dy = \iint_S \left(\frac{\partial N}{\partial x} - \frac{\partial M}{\partial y} \right) dx \, dy$$

where the curve C is traversed in the anticlockwise direction.

Proof. Let S be a closed region in x-y plane bounded by a closed curve C. Suppose $\vec{A}$ is a vector field having M and N as its x and y-components respectively, then

$$\vec{A} = M\,\hat{i} + N\,\hat{j} \qquad\qquad ...(i)$$

In the x-y plane a displacement vector $\vec{dr}$ is given by

$$\vec{dr} = dx\,\hat{i} + dy\,\hat{j} \qquad\qquad ...(ii)$$

According to Stoke's theorem

$$\oint_C \vec{A} \cdot \vec{dr} = \iint_S (\vec{\nabla} \times \vec{A}) \cdot \vec{dS} \qquad\qquad ...(iii)$$

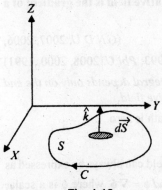

Fig. 1.13

From (i), (ii) and (iii) $\vec{A} \cdot \vec{dr} = (M\,\hat{i} + N\,\hat{j}) \cdot (dx\,\hat{i} + dy\,\hat{j}) = Mdx + Ndy \qquad\qquad ...(iv)$

Also

$$\vec{\nabla} \times \vec{A} = \begin{vmatrix} \hat{i} & \hat{j} & \hat{k} \\ \dfrac{\partial}{\partial x} & \dfrac{\partial}{\partial y} & \dfrac{\partial}{\partial z} \\ M & N & 0 \end{vmatrix}$$

$$= \hat{i}\left[-\frac{\partial N}{\partial Z}\right] + \hat{j}\left[\frac{\partial M}{\partial Z}\right] + \hat{k}\left[\frac{\partial N}{\partial x} - \frac{\partial M}{\partial y}\right] \qquad ...(v)$$

Consider a small area element $\vec{dS}$ on the surface S. As S lies in the x-y plane the area vector will point in the $+z$-direction. As the curve C is traversed in the anticlockwise direction.

$$\therefore \qquad \vec{dS} = dS\,\hat{k} \qquad ...(vi)$$

From (v) and (vi)

$$(\vec{\nabla} \times \vec{A}) . \vec{ds} = \left[-\hat{i}\frac{\partial N}{\partial Z} + \hat{j}\frac{\partial M}{\partial Z} + \hat{k}\left(\frac{\partial N}{\partial x} - \frac{\partial M}{\partial y}\right)\right] . [dS\,\hat{k}]$$

$$= \left(\frac{\partial N}{\partial x} - \frac{\partial M}{\partial y}\right)dS \qquad ...(vii)$$

As $\qquad \hat{i}.\hat{k} = \hat{j}.\hat{k} = 0 \quad$ and $\quad \hat{k}.\hat{k} = 1$

Also $\qquad dS = dx\,dy \qquad ...(viii)$

as the area element dS lies in the x-y plane.

Substituting the value of $\vec{A}.\vec{dr}$ from Eq. (iv), $(\vec{\nabla} \times \vec{A}).\vec{dS}$ from Eq. (vii) and dS from Eq. $(viii)$ in Stoke's theorem [Eq. (iii)], we get

$$\oint_C M\,dx + N\,dy = \iint_S \left(\frac{\partial N}{\partial x} - \frac{\partial M}{\partial y}\right)dS$$

$$= \iint_S \left(\frac{\partial N}{\partial x} - \frac{\partial M}{\partial y}\right)dx\,dy$$

This equation is known as Green's theorem in a plane.

Q. 1.65. (*a*) **What is a conservative field? Show that a conservative field is the gradient of a scalar field and curl of such a field is zero.**

(*b*) **Show that electric field is conservative and curl $\vec{E} = 0$.**   (*G.N.D.U.* 2007, 2006, 2004, 1999, 1996; *H.P.U.* 2001, 1997, 1996, 1993; *Pbi.U.* 2008, 2000, 1991)

Ans. (*a*) **Conservative field.** *A vector field for which the line integral depends only on the end points but is independent of the actual path, is known as a conservative field.*

In other words, the integral of a conservative field for a closed path is zero.

Thus if $\oint \vec{A}.\vec{dl} = 0$, $\vec{A}$ represents a conservative field.

Conservative field as gradient of scalar field. A conservative field can always be expressed as the gradient of a scalar field. For example, if a vector field $\vec{A} = grad\,\phi = \vec{\nabla}\phi$ where ϕ is a scalar field, then the vector field $\vec{A}$ is a conservative field.

To prove, consider two points A and B and let $\vec{A}$ be a vector field, then the line integral $\int \vec{A}.\vec{dr}$ where $\vec{dr}$ is an infinitesimally small displacement gives a scalar function, say ϕ

$$\therefore \qquad \int_A^B \vec{A} \cdot \vec{dr} = \phi_B - \phi_A$$

and
$$\underset{\Delta x \to 0}{Lt} \frac{1}{\Delta x} \int_A^B \vec{A} \cdot \vec{dr} = \frac{\phi(x + \Delta x, y, z) - \phi(x, y, z)}{\Delta x} = \frac{\partial \phi}{\partial x} \qquad \ldots(i)$$

Now $\int_A^B \vec{A} \cdot \vec{dr}$ depends only on the initial and final values of ϕ at points A and B and is therefore independent of the path.

If we choose the *straight line* path from A to B, then $\vec{dr} = dx\, i$ for this path since it is parallel to x-axis.

$$\therefore \qquad \underset{\Delta x \to 0}{Lt} \frac{1}{\Delta x} \int_A^B \vec{A} \cdot \vec{dr} = \underset{\Delta x \to 0}{Lt} \frac{1}{\Delta x} \int_A^B \vec{A} \cdot dx\, \hat{i}$$

$$= \underset{\Delta x \to 0}{Lt} \frac{1}{\Delta x} \int_A^B A_x\, dx$$

As the length of the path approaches zero in the limit $A_x = $ constant

$$\therefore \qquad \underset{\Delta x \to 0}{Lt} \frac{1}{\Delta x} \int_A^B A_x\, dx = \frac{A_x}{\Delta x} \int_A^B dx = \frac{A_x}{\Delta x} \Delta x = A_x \qquad \ldots(ii)$$

Form (i) and (ii) we have

$$A_x = \frac{\partial \phi}{\partial x}$$

similarly we can prove that

$$A_y = \frac{\partial \phi}{\partial y} \quad \text{and} \quad A_z = \frac{\partial \phi}{\partial z}$$

Hence
$$\vec{A} = A_x\, \hat{i} + A_y\, \hat{j} + A_z\, \hat{k}$$

$$= \frac{\partial \phi}{\partial x}\hat{i} + \frac{\partial \phi}{\partial y}\hat{j} + \frac{\partial \phi}{\partial z}\hat{k} = \vec{\nabla} \phi$$

Thus for a *conservative field*

$$\vec{A} = \vec{\nabla} \phi = grad\, \phi$$

i.e., *a conservative field is gradient of a scalar field.*

Curl of conservative field is zero. A conservative field is always given by the gradient of a scalar field (or function). If $\vec{A}$ is a conservative field and ϕ a scalar function, then

$$\vec{A} = grad\, \phi = \vec{\nabla} \phi$$

and
$$Curl\, \vec{A} = \vec{\nabla} \times \vec{A} = \vec{\nabla} \times \vec{\nabla} \phi = 0$$

because curl of gradient of a scalar function is zero.

(b) Electric field is conservative. An electric field is the example of a conservative field because an electric field is the negative of gradient of scalar potential (ϕ)

or
$$\vec{E} = - grad\, \phi = - \vec{\nabla} \phi$$

The curl of an electric field is given by

$$Curl \ \vec{E} = - \ curl \ grad \ \phi = - \ \vec{\nabla} \times \vec{\nabla} \phi = 0$$

We summarise below various conditions for a vector field to be *conservative*.

(*i*) *A vector field for which the line integral depends only on the end points and is independent of the actual path taken is conservative field.*

(*ii*) *The line integral of a conservative field over a closed path is zero.* If $\vec{A}$ is a conservative field

$$\oint \vec{A} \cdot \vec{dl} = 0$$

(*iii*) *A conservative field can always be represented as the gradient of a scalar field.* If $\vec{A}$ is a conservative field and ϕ the corresponding scalar field, then

$$\vec{A} = \vec{\nabla} \phi = grad \ \phi$$

(*iv*) The *curl* of a conservative field is zero. If $\vec{A}$ is a conservative field

$$Curl \ \vec{A} = \vec{\nabla} \times \vec{A} = 0$$

Q. 1.66. What is the difference between a conservative field and a non-conservative field? Give one example of each   (*P.U.* 2007, 2001; *G.N.D.U.* 2000; *K.U.* 2000; *Pbi.U.* 2000, 1993)

Ans. Conservative field. A vector field for which the line integral depends only on the end points but is independent of the actual path is a conservative field. For a conservative field the line integral for a closed path is zero. If $\vec{A}$ is a conservative field $\oint \vec{A} \cdot \vec{dl} = 0$.

A conservative field is always the gradient of a scalar function. If $\vec{A}$ is a conservative field and ϕ the corresponding scalar function, then

$$\vec{A} = grad \ \phi = \vec{\nabla} \phi$$

The curl of a conservative field is zero, or $\vec{\nabla} \times \vec{A} = 0$.

Non-conservative field. A vector field for which the line integral depends upon the path and for which the integral for a closed path is not equal to zero is called a non-conservative field. For a non-conservative field

$$Curl \ \vec{A} \neq 0 \quad \text{or} \quad \vec{\nabla} \times \vec{A} \neq 0$$

Examples. Electric field due to a stationary charge is conservative. Magnetic field is non-conservative

Q. 1.67. Check whether the electrostatic field represented by $\vec{E} = axy^2 \ (y\hat{i} + x\hat{j})$ **is conservative or not?**
                                                                                              (*G.N.D.U.* 1995)

Ans. The electrostatic field $\vec{E}$ is conservative if $\vec{\nabla} \times \vec{E} = 0$

Now $$\vec{\nabla} = \frac{\partial}{\partial x} \hat{i} + \frac{\partial}{\partial y} \hat{j} + \frac{\partial}{\partial z} \hat{k}$$

Hence $$\vec{\nabla} \times \vec{E} = \left(\frac{\partial}{\partial x} \hat{i} + \frac{\partial}{\partial y} \hat{j} + \frac{\partial}{\partial z} \hat{k} \right) \times (axy^3 \ \hat{i} + ax^2 y^2 \ \hat{j})$$

or $$\vec{\nabla} \times \vec{E} = \begin{vmatrix} \hat{i} & \hat{j} & \hat{k} \\ \dfrac{\partial}{\partial x} & \dfrac{\partial}{\partial y} & \dfrac{\partial}{\partial z} \\ axy^3 & ax^2 y^2 & 0 \end{vmatrix}$$

or $$\vec{\nabla} \times \vec{E} = \hat{k}\left[\frac{\partial}{\partial x}(ax^2y^2) - \frac{\partial}{\partial y}(axy^3)\right]$$

$$= \hat{k}(2axy^2 - 3axy^2) = -axy^2\,\hat{k}$$

As $\vec{\nabla} \times \vec{E} \neq 0$ the field is not conservative.

Exercise. *Prove that the vector field* $\vec{A} = xy^2\,\hat{i} + x^3\,y\,\hat{j}$ *is non-conservative.*   (P.U. 2009)

Hint. $$\vec{\nabla} \times \vec{A} = \begin{vmatrix} \hat{i} & \hat{j} & \hat{k} \\ \dfrac{\partial}{\partial x} & \dfrac{\partial}{\partial y} & \dfrac{\partial}{\partial z} \\ xy^2 & x^3y & 0 \end{vmatrix}$$

$$= \hat{k}\left[\frac{\partial}{\partial x}x^3 y - \frac{\partial}{\partial y}xy^2\right]$$

$$= 3x^2y - 2xy \neq 0$$

As $\vec{\nabla} \times \vec{A}$ is not equal to zero the field $\vec{A}$ is not conservative.

Q. 1.68. Prove that the electric field given by $\vec{E} = \hat{i}\,x + \hat{j}\,y + \hat{k}\,z$ is conservative.

(P.U. 1992; H.P.U. 1991)

Ans. The field $$\vec{E} = \hat{i}\,x + \hat{j}\,y + \hat{k}\,z$$

Now $$\vec{\nabla} \times \vec{E} = \begin{vmatrix} \hat{i} & \hat{j} & \hat{k} \\ \dfrac{\partial}{\partial x} & \dfrac{\partial}{\partial y} & \dfrac{\partial}{\partial z} \\ x & y & z \end{vmatrix}$$

$$= \hat{i}\left(\frac{\partial z}{\partial y} - \frac{\partial y}{\partial z}\right) + \hat{j}\left(\frac{\partial x}{\partial z} - \frac{\partial z}{\partial x}\right) + \hat{k}\left(\frac{\partial y}{\partial x} - \frac{\partial x}{\partial y}\right)$$

But each term $\dfrac{\partial z}{\partial y}, \dfrac{\partial y}{\partial z}, \dfrac{\partial x}{\partial z}, \dfrac{\partial z}{\partial x}, \dfrac{\partial y}{\partial x}, \dfrac{\partial x}{\partial y}$ is zero.

$\therefore$ $$\vec{\nabla} \times \vec{E} = 0.$$

Hence $\vec{E}$ is a conservative field.

Ex. *Determine whether the electric field* $\vec{E} = xy\,\hat{i} + y^3\,\hat{j}$ *is conservative or not.*(H.P.U. 1999)

Hint. $$\vec{\nabla} \times \vec{E} = \begin{vmatrix} \hat{i} & \hat{j} & \hat{k} \\ \dfrac{\partial}{\partial x} & \dfrac{\partial}{\partial y} & \dfrac{\partial}{\partial z} \\ xy & y^3 & 0 \end{vmatrix} = \hat{k}(-x) = -\hat{k}\,x$$

As $\vec{\nabla} \times \vec{E} \neq 0$, the field is not conservative

Q. 1.69. If $\vec{A} = x^2 y \hat{i} - 2xz \hat{j} + 2yz \hat{k}$ find curl curl $\vec{A}$ (K.U. 2002)

Ans. $\vec{A} = x^2 y \hat{i} - 2xz \hat{j} + 2yz \hat{k}$

$\therefore$ $Curl \; \vec{A} = \vec{\nabla} \times \vec{A} = \begin{vmatrix} \hat{i} & \hat{j} & \hat{k} \\ \dfrac{\partial}{\partial x} & \dfrac{\partial}{\partial y} & \dfrac{\partial}{\partial z} \\ x^2 y & -2xz & 2yz \end{vmatrix}$

$\therefore$ $= \hat{i}(2z + 2x) + \hat{j}(0) + \hat{k}(-2z - x^2)$

$= \hat{i}(2z + 2x) - \hat{k}(2z + x^2)$

$\therefore$ $curl \; curl \; \vec{A} = \vec{\nabla} \times \left(\vec{\nabla} \times \vec{A} \right) = \begin{vmatrix} \hat{i} & \hat{j} & \hat{k} \\ \dfrac{\partial}{\partial x} & \dfrac{\partial}{\partial y} & \dfrac{\partial}{\partial z} \\ 2(z + x) & 0 & -(2z + x^2) \end{vmatrix}$

$= \hat{i}(0) + \hat{j}(2 + 2x) + \hat{k}(0) = 2(x + 1)\hat{j}$

Q. 1.70. What is physical significance of the line integral of a vector field ? Explain with examples.

Ans. **Line integral of a vector field.** Consider a path ACB between two points A and B in a vector field F. Divide the path ACB into a very large number of small elements $dl_1, dl_2, dl_3 ... dl_i ...$ etc. such that the corresponding values of the vector field are $\vec{F_1}, \vec{F_2}, \vec{F_3} ... \vec{F_i}$ etc. respectively.

Each element $\vec{dl}$ is also a vector element as it has a magnitude dl and the direction at the point say P is parallel (tangent) to the path while going from A to B.

The summation of the scalar products

$\vec{F_1} . \vec{dl_1} + \vec{F_2} . \vec{dl_2} + \vec{F_3} . \vec{dl_3} + ... \vec{F_i} . \vec{dl_i} + ... = \sum \vec{F_i} . \vec{dl_i}$

for all elements in the limit $\vec{dl_i} \to 0$ is known as the *line integral* of the vector field $\vec{F}$.

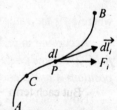

Fig. 1.15

$\therefore$ Line integral of a vector field $= \int\limits_{A}^{B} \vec{F} . \vec{dl}$
along ACB

Line integral of an electrostatic field. As an example, let us now suppose that the vector field is an electric field $\vec{E}$ then a *small* test charge q_0 placed at P experiences a force

$$\vec{F} = q_0 \vec{E}$$

$\therefore$ Work done by the field when the test charge moves through a small vector distance dl

$$dW = \vec{F} . \vec{dl} = q_0 \vec{E} . \vec{dl}$$

Total work done when the test charge moves from A to B

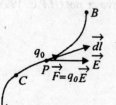

Fig. 1.16

$$W = \int\limits_{A}^{B} dW = \int\limits_{A}^{B} \vec{F} . \vec{dl} = \int\limits_{A}^{B} q_0 \vec{E} . \vec{dl} = q_0 \int\limits_{A}^{B} \vec{E} . \vec{dl}$$

∴ Work done by the field per unit charge

$$= \frac{W}{q_0} = \int_A^B \vec{E} . \, \vec{dl}$$

In other words *line integral of an electrostatic field from a point A to point B gives the work done by the field when a unit positive charge moves from A to B under the effect of the field.*

Q. 1.71. Show that the line integral of a conservative field taken between two points in the region is independent of the path and the line integral over a closed path is zero.

(*G.N.D.U.* 1993; *K.U.* 1992, 1990; *P.U.* 1991)

OR

Show that the line integral of a vector over a closed path is always zero if the vector field is gradient of a scalar. (*M.D.U.* 2002)

Ans. Line integral of a conservative vector field. A conservative vector field can be expressed as the gradient of a scalar field.

For example, if a vector field $\vec{A} = grad \, \phi = \vec{\nabla} \phi$ where ϕ is a scalar field, then the vector field $\vec{A}$ is a conservative field.

The line integral of the vector field $\vec{A}$ between two points A and B is given by $\int_A^B \vec{A} . \, \vec{dr}$ where $\vec{dr}$ is a small vector element of distance.

∴

$$\int_A^B \vec{A} . \, \vec{dr} = \int_A^B \vec{\nabla} \phi . \, \vec{dr} = \int_A^B d\phi$$

because

$$\vec{\nabla} \phi . \, \vec{dr} = \left(\frac{\partial \phi}{\partial x} \hat{i} + \frac{\partial \phi}{\partial y} \hat{j} + \frac{\partial \phi}{\partial z} \hat{k} \right) . (dx \, \hat{i} + dy \, \hat{j} + dz \, \hat{k})$$

$$= \frac{\partial \phi}{\partial x} dx + \frac{\partial \phi}{\partial y} dy + \frac{\partial \phi}{\partial z} dz = d\phi$$

∴

$$\int_A^B \vec{A} . \, \vec{dr} = \int_A^B d\phi = \phi_B - \phi_A \qquad \qquad ...(i)$$

where ϕ_B is the value of scalar function ϕ at B and ϕ_A its value at A.

According to relation (*i*) *the line integral of the conservative vector field $\vec{A}$ depends only on the values of scalar field at the initial and final positions A and B and is independent of the path joining A and B.*

Now consider a closed path *ACBDA*. The line integral along the closed path *ACBDA* is the sum of the line integrals from *A* to *B* along the path *ACB* and from *B* to *A* along the path *BDA*.

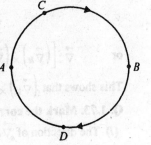

Fig. 1.17

∴

$$\oint_{ACBDA} \vec{A} . \, \vec{dr} = \underset{\text{along } ACB}{\int_A^B \vec{A} . \, \vec{dr}} + \underset{\text{along } BDA}{\int_B^A \vec{A} . \, \vec{dr}}$$

To evaluate $\underset{\text{along } ACD}{\int_A^B \vec{A} . \, \vec{dr}}$ all vector segments are taken pointing in the direction A to B and to evaluate

$\int\limits_{\substack{B \\ \text{along } BDA}}^{A} \vec{A} \cdot \vec{dr}$ all the vector segments are taken pointing in the opposite direction form B to A.

$$\therefore \qquad \int\limits_{\substack{A \\ \text{along } ACB}}^{B} \vec{A} \cdot \vec{dr} = - \int\limits_{\substack{B \\ \text{along } BDA}}^{A} \vec{A} \cdot \vec{dr}$$

$$\therefore \qquad \oint\limits_{ACBDA} \vec{A} \cdot \vec{dr} = \int\limits_{\substack{A \\ \text{along } ACB}}^{B} \vec{A} \cdot \vec{dr} - \int\limits_{\substack{A \\ \text{along } ACB}}^{B} \vec{A} \cdot \vec{dr} = 0$$

Hence the line integral of a conservative field (OR a vector field which is gradient of a scalar field) over a closed path is zero.

Q. 1.72. If u and ϕ are differentiable scalar field functions, then show that $(\vec{\nabla}u) \times (\vec{\nabla}\phi)$ is solenoidal.

(*P.U.* 2002; 2000)

Ans. Let $\qquad (\vec{\nabla}u) \times (\vec{\nabla}\phi) = \vec{A}$, then

$$\text{div } \vec{A} = \vec{\nabla} \cdot \vec{A} = \vec{\nabla} \cdot \left[\left(\vec{\nabla}u\right) \times \left(\vec{\nabla}\phi\right) \right] \qquad ...(i)$$

According to the vector identity

$$\vec{\nabla} \cdot \left(\vec{A} \times \vec{B}\right) = \vec{B} \cdot \left(\vec{\nabla} \times \vec{A}\right) - \vec{A} \cdot (\vec{\nabla} \times \vec{B})$$

we have, by substituting $\vec{A} = \vec{\nabla}u$ and $\vec{B} = \vec{\nabla}\phi$ in Eq (i)

$$\vec{\nabla} \cdot \left[\left(\vec{\nabla}u\right) \times \left(\vec{\nabla}\phi\right) \right] = \vec{\nabla}\phi \cdot \left(\vec{\nabla} \times \vec{\nabla}u\right) - \vec{\nabla}u \cdot \left(\vec{\nabla} \times \vec{\nabla}\phi\right)$$

or $\qquad \vec{\nabla} \cdot \vec{A} = \vec{\nabla}\phi \cdot \left(\vec{\nabla} \times \vec{\nabla}u\right) - \vec{\nabla}u \cdot \left(\vec{\nabla} \times \vec{\nabla}\phi\right)$

But $\qquad \vec{\nabla} \times \vec{\nabla}u = 0 \quad$ and $\quad \vec{\nabla} \times \vec{\nabla}\phi = 0$

$\therefore \qquad \vec{\nabla} \cdot \vec{A} = 0$

or $\qquad \vec{\nabla} \cdot \left[\left(\vec{\nabla}u\right) \times \left(\vec{\nabla}\phi\right) \right] = 0$

This shows that $\left(\vec{\nabla}u\right) \times \left(\vec{\nabla}\phi\right)$ is a solenoidal vector as its divergence is equal to zero.

Q. 1.73. Mark the correct answer.

(*i*) The direction of $\vec{\nabla}\phi$ (or gradient ϕ) is always

   (*a*) $\perp$ to the surface ϕ = a constant

   (*b*) $||$ to the surface ϕ = a constant

   (*c*) $\perp$ or $||$ depending upon the shape of the surface

   (*d*) none of these.   (*H.P.U.* 1994, 1993)

(*ii*) The function $\vec{\nabla} \cdot \vec{A}$ represents

   (*a*) The total flux of $\vec{A}$ over any arbitrary closed surface.

   (*b*) The outward flux density at the point (x, y, z)

(c) The inward flux density at the point (x, y, z)

(d) None of these   (H.P.U. 1999)

(iii) If a vector field can be expressed as the gradient of a scalar, then the vector field is called

(a) solenoidal   (b) irrotational

(c) lamellar   (d) none of these.   (H.P.U. 1995)

(iv) The vector field is solenoidal if

(a) $\vec{\nabla} \times \vec{A} = 0$ (b) $\vec{\nabla} \cdot \vec{A} = 0$

(c) $\vec{A} = 0$ (d) none of these   (H.P.U. 1995)

(v) The vector field is irrotational if

(a) $\vec{\nabla} \times \vec{A} = 0$ (b) $\vec{\nabla} \cdot \vec{A} = 0$

(c) $\vec{\nabla} \times \vec{A} = 1$ (d) $\vec{\nabla} \cdot \vec{A} = 1$ (H.P.U. 1991)

(vi) A vector field A is conservative if

(a) $\vec{A} = \vec{\nabla} \cdot \phi$ (b) $\vec{A} = \vec{\nabla} \times \phi$

(c) $\vec{A} = \vec{\nabla} \phi$ (d) $\vec{A} = \nabla^2 \phi$ (HP.U. 2002)

(vii) The z-component of the curl of the field

$E_x = ky$ $E_y = kx$ $E_z = 0$ is

(a) $2k$ (b) $-2k$

(c) zero   (d) $-k$ (P.U. 1994)

(viii) If $\vec{a}$ is a constant vector then $\vec{\nabla} \times (\vec{a} \times \vec{r}) =$

(a) 0 (b) $\vec{a}$

(c) $2\vec{a}$ (d) $\dfrac{\vec{a}}{2}$ (H.P.U. 1995)

(ix) The divergence of curl of a vector is always

(a) 1 (b) 0

(c) $\dfrac{1}{2}$ (d) $\dfrac{\pi}{2}$ (H.P.U. 1997)

(x) The line integral of the vector field around a closed path can always be written as

(a) $\iint\limits_S (\vec{\nabla} \times \vec{A}) \, dS$ (b) $\oiint\limits_S (\vec{\nabla} \cdot \vec{A}) \cdot \vec{dS}$

(c) $\iint\limits_S (\vec{\nabla} \times \vec{A}) \cdot \vec{dS}$ (d) $\oiint (\vec{\nabla} \times \vec{A}) \cdot \vec{dS}$ (H.P.U. 1994)

(xi) For a conservative field

(a) $\oint \vec{E} \cdot \vec{dl} = 0$ (b) $\oint \vec{E} \cdot \vec{dl} = 1$

(c) $\oint \vec{E} \cdot \vec{dl} = El$ (d) $\oint \vec{E} \cdot \vec{dl} = Edl \cos \theta$ (H.P.U. 1996)

(xii) Which of the following is not a vector

(a) $(\vec{A} \cdot \vec{\nabla}) \vec{E}$ (b) $(\vec{A} \times \vec{\nabla}) \times \vec{E}$

(c) $(\vec{A} \cdot \vec{\nabla}) V$ (d) $(\vec{A} \times \vec{\nabla}) V$ (H.P.U. 2001)

(xiii) Which type of field can be expressed as the gradient of a scalar field function.

(a) Lamellar   (b) Solenoidal

(c) Rotational   (d) none of these   (H.P.U. 2003)

Ans.

(i) a	(ii) b	(iii) c	(iv) b
(v) a	(vi) c	(vii) c	(viii) c
(ix) b	(x) c	(xi) a	(xii) c
(xiii) a			

EXERCISES

1. Find the curl of the vector field

   $H_x = x^2 - z^2$; $H_y = 2$; $H_z = 2xz$

   (Ans. $-4z\,\hat{j}$)

2. Given $\vec{A} = x^2\,y\hat{i} + (x - y)\hat{k}$ find

   (a) $div\,\vec{A}$ (b) $curl\,\vec{A}$ at the point (2, 3, 0)   [Ans. (a) 12 (b) $-(\hat{i} + \hat{j} + 4\hat{k})$]

3. Verify Stoke's theorem for the vector field

   $\vec{A} = y\hat{i} - x\hat{j}$ with boundary of a circle of radius 1 unit with centre at the origin in x-y plane.

   (G.N.D.U. 1991)

   Hint. $\vec{A} = y\hat{i} - x\hat{j}$. The equation of the circle is

   $$x^2 + y^2 = 1 \quad curl\,\vec{A} = -2\hat{k}; \quad \int \vec{A} \cdot \vec{dl} = -2\pi$$

   and $$\iint_S curl\,\vec{A} \cdot \vec{ds} = -2\pi$$

4. Show that the electric field $\vec{E} = 6xy - (3x^2 - 3y^2)\hat{j}$ is conservative.   (P.U. 2000)

   Hint. $\vec{\nabla} \times \vec{E} = \begin{vmatrix} \hat{i} & \hat{j} & \hat{k} \\ \dfrac{\partial}{\partial x} & \dfrac{\partial}{\partial y} & \dfrac{\partial}{\partial z} \\ 6xy & -(3x^2 - 3y^2) & 0 \end{vmatrix} = -6x + 6x = 0$

2

Coulomb's Law and Electric Field

Q. 2.1. (*a*) **State Coulomb's law in vector notation.**

(*P.U.,* 2007; *G.N.D.U.* 2004, *Meerut U.* 2002; *H.P.U.,* 2006, 1997)

(*b*) **Write the law for the force between two point charges when their position vectors are given.**

(*c*) **State the law in C.G.S. and S.I. units.**

(*H.P.U.,* 1995, 1993; *A.U.,* 1995, 1994; *P.U.,* 1992)

Ans. (*a*) **Coulomb's law.** For two electric charges at rest, like charges repel each other and unlike charges attract each other. Coulomb's law states that

"*The magnitude of the force between two point charges is directly proportional to the product of the magnitude of the charges and inversely proportional to the square of the distance between them.*'

If q_1 and q_2 are the magnitudes of two charges and r the distance between them, then the force

$$F = K \frac{q_1 q_2}{r^2}$$

where K is the constant of proportionality, the value of which depends upon the nature of the medium separating the two charges and the system of units in which various quantities are expressed.

In the **vector** form Coulomb's law can be stated as

$$\vec{F}_{21} = K \frac{q_1 q_2}{\left|\vec{r}_{21}\right|^2} \hat{r}_{21} \qquad \qquad ...(i)$$

where $\vec{F}_{21}$ is the force on charge q_2 due to charge q_1, $\vec{r}_{21}$ the vector distance of q_2 from q_1 and $\hat{r}_{21}$ a unit vector in the direction of $\vec{r}_{21}$ *i.e., to charge q_2 from charge q_1.*

The unit vector $\qquad \hat{r}_{21} = \dfrac{\vec{r}_{21}}{\left|\vec{r}_{21}\right|}$

$$\therefore \qquad \vec{F}_{21} = K \frac{q_1 q_2 \vec{r}_{21}}{\left|\vec{r}_{21}\right|^3} \qquad \qquad ...(ii)$$

(*b*) **Force between two charges when their position vectors are given.** Let $\vec{r}_1$ and $\vec{r}_2$ represent the position vectors of two point charges q_1 and q_2 respectively, then

$$\vec{r_2} = \vec{r_1} + \vec{r_{21}}$$

or

$$\vec{r_{21}} = \vec{r_2} - \vec{r_1}$$

and

$$|\vec{r_{21}}| = |\vec{r_2} - \vec{r_1}|$$

Substituting in Eq. (*ii*), we get

Force on charge q_2 due to charge q_1

$$\vec{F_{21}} = K\ \frac{q_1 q_2}{|\vec{r_2} - \vec{r_1}|^3}\ (\vec{r_2} - \vec{r_1}) \qquad\qquad ...(iii)$$

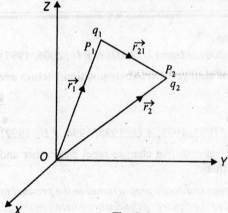

Fig. 2.1

(*c*) **In C.G.S system.** In C.G.S. system, the

constant $K = \dfrac{1}{k}$ and for any medium

$$\vec{F_{21}}\ (\text{medium}) = \frac{1}{k}\ \frac{q_1 q_2}{|\vec{r_{21}}|^2}\ \hat{r}_{21} = \frac{1}{k}\ \frac{q_1 q_2}{|\vec{r_{21}}|^3}\ \vec{r_{21}}$$

$$= \frac{1}{k}\ \frac{q_1 q_2\ (\vec{r_2} - \vec{r_1})}{|\vec{r_2} - \vec{r_1}|^3}$$

k is known as *specific inductive capacity or dielectric constant* of the medium and its value for vacuum or free space is taken to be **unity**. For air at N.T.P. it is also very nearly equal to 1 (1.0059).

∴ For vacuum or free space

$$\vec{F_{21}}\ (\text{vacuum}) = \frac{q_1 q_2}{|\vec{r_{21}}|^2}\ \hat{r}_{21} = \frac{q_1 q_2}{|\vec{r_{21}}|^3}\ \vec{r_{21}}$$

$$= \frac{q_1 q_2\ (\vec{r_2} - \vec{r_1})}{|\vec{r_2} - \vec{r_1}|^3}$$

In the C.G.S. system, the force is measured in dynes, distance in c.m. and charge in *e.s.u.* or stat-coloumb.

In S.I. units. In S.I. units $K = \dfrac{1}{4\pi\varepsilon}$ where ε is the permittivity of the medium.

∴ For any medium $\vec{F_{2i}}\ (\text{medium}) = \dfrac{1}{4\pi\varepsilon}\ \dfrac{q_1 q_2\ (\hat{r}_{21})}{|\vec{r_{21}}|^2} = \dfrac{1}{4\pi\varepsilon}\ \dfrac{q_1 q_2\ \vec{r_{21}}}{|\vec{r_{21}}|^3}$

$$= \frac{1}{4\pi\varepsilon}\ \frac{q_1 q_2\ (\vec{r_2} - \vec{r_1})}{|\vec{r_2} - \vec{r_1}|^3}$$

For vacuum or free space

$$\vec{F_{21}}\ (\text{vacuum}) = \frac{1}{4\pi\varepsilon_0}\ \frac{q_1 q_2}{|\vec{r_{21}}|^2}\ \hat{r}_{21} = \frac{1}{4\pi\varepsilon_0}\ \frac{q_1 q_2\ \vec{r_{21}}}{|\vec{r_{21}}|^3}$$

$$= \frac{1}{4\pi\varepsilon_0} \frac{q_1 q_2 (\vec{r_2} - \vec{r_1})}{|\vec{r_2} - \vec{r_1}|^3}$$

where ε_0 is the permittivity of free space. The value of $\frac{1}{4\pi\varepsilon_0} = 9 \times 10^9$ newton-m^2/coulomb^2 [Nm^{2}C^{-2}] and $\varepsilon_0 = 8.85 \times 10^{-12}$ coulomb^2/Newton m^2 [C^{2}N^{-1}m^{-2}].

Q. 2.2. Define a coulomb and a stat-coulomb. Derive a relation between the two.

(P.U. 2005; Pbi. U., 2002)

Ans. Coulomb. The S.I. unit of charge is a *coulomb*. It is defined from the basic unit of current in S.I. *i.e.*, an *ampere*.

A coulomb is the quantity of charge that passes through any cross-section of a conductor when a current of one ampere flows through it for one second.

Stat-coulomb. The C.G.S. unit of charge is a *stat-coulomb*.

The charge is said to be one stat-coulomb if it experiences a force of repulsion of one dyne when placed in vacuum at a distance of one cm from an equal and similar charge.

Relation between coulomb and stat-coulomb. The magnitude of electrostatic force, between two charges of one coulomb each placed one metre apart in vacuum is given by

$$F = \frac{1}{4\pi\varepsilon_0} \frac{q_1 q_2}{r^2}$$

$$= 9 \times 10^9 \text{ N m}^2 \text{C}^{-2} \times \text{C}^2 \text{ m}^{-2}$$

$$= 9 \times 10^9 \text{ N} = 9 \times 10^{14} \text{ dynes}$$

Now let 1 coulomb = n stat-coulomb

$\therefore$ In C.G.S. units $\qquad F = \frac{q_1 q_2}{r^2} = \frac{n \times n}{100^2} = \frac{n^2}{10^4}$ dynes

or $\qquad\qquad \frac{n^2}{10^4} = 9 \times 10^{14}$

$\therefore \qquad\qquad n^2 = 9 \times 10^{18} \quad$ or $\quad n = 3 \times 10^9$

Hence 1 coulomb = 3×10^9 stat-coulomb

Q. 2.3.(a) Define dielectric constant of a medium. Show that the dielectric constant is equal to relative permittivity. *(H.P.U., 1995)*

(b) Why the force between two charges placed in water is less than that in air at the same distance apart ? *(H.P.U. 2007)*

Ans. (a) Dielectric constant. *The dielectric constant of a medium is defined as the ratio of the magnitude of the force between two charges placed a certain distance apart in vacuum to the force between the same two charges placed the same distance apart in the medium.*

The force between two charges q_1 and q_2 placed at a distance r in a medium in C.G.S. units, taking magnitudes only is given by

$$F_m = \frac{1}{k} \frac{q_1 q_2}{r^2}$$

and in free space $\qquad\qquad F_0 = \frac{q_1 q_2}{r^2}$

$$\therefore \qquad \frac{F_0}{F_m} = k \qquad \qquad \qquad ...(i)$$

where k is the *dielectric constant* of medium.

Similarly in S.I. units, taking magnitudes only

$$F_m = \frac{1}{4\pi\varepsilon}\frac{q_1 q_2}{r^2}$$

and

$$F_0 = \frac{1}{4\pi\varepsilon_0}\frac{q_1 q_2}{r^2}$$

$$\therefore \qquad \frac{F_0}{F_m} = \frac{\varepsilon}{\varepsilon_0} = \varepsilon_r \qquad \qquad \qquad ...(ii)$$

ε_r is known as *relative permittivity and is the ratio of the permittivity of the medium to the permittivity of free space (or vacuum).*

From (i) and (ii), we have

$$k = \varepsilon_r$$

Thus the dielectric constant of a medium is the same as its relative permittivity, both being dimensionless constants.

(**b**) The dielectric constant of water $k = 80$. If F_0 is the force between the two charges in free space (or air) and F_m the force between the same two charges, placed the same distance apart in water,

then

$$\frac{F_0}{F_m} = k$$

$$\therefore \qquad F_m = \frac{1}{k} F_0 = \frac{1}{80} F_0$$

Thus the force between two charges placed in water is $\frac{1}{80}$ of the force between the same two charges placed the same distance apart in air.

Q. 2.4. Prove that Coulomb's law is in accordance with Newton's third law of motion.

(*G.N.D.U.*, 1997, 1996)

OR

Show that electric force between static charges is Newtonian.

Ans. Coulomb's law is in accordance with Newton's third law of motion. Let $\vec{r_1}$ and $\vec{r_2}$ represent the position vectors of two point charges q_1 and q_2 respectively, then the force on charge q_2 due to charge q_1 (in S.I. units) in free space is given by

$$\vec{F_{21}} = \frac{1}{4\pi\varepsilon_0} \frac{q_1 q_2}{|\vec{r_2} - \vec{r_1}|^3} (\vec{r_2} - \vec{r_1}) \qquad \qquad (i)$$

Now

$$(\vec{r_1} - \vec{r_2}) = -(\vec{r_2} - \vec{r_1})$$

and

$$|\vec{r_1} - \vec{r_2}| = |\vec{r_2} - \vec{r_1}|$$

$$\therefore \qquad \vec{F_{12}} = -\frac{1}{4\pi\varepsilon_0} \frac{q_1 q_2}{|\vec{r_2} - \vec{r_1}|^3} (\vec{r_2} - \vec{r_1}) \qquad \qquad ...(ii)$$

Comparing (i) and (ii), we have

$$\vec{F}_{12} = -\vec{F}_{21}$$

This relation shows that *the force $\vec{F}_{21}$ on the charge q_2 due to the charge q_1 is equal and oppo-site to the force $\vec{F}_{12}$ on the charge q_1 due to the charge q_2.* Hence Coulomb's law is in accordance with Newton's third law of motion. In other words, the electric force between two static charges is Newtonian in character.

Q.2.5. What are limitations of Coulomb's law?   (*Pbi. U.*, 2003, 2000; *H.P.U.*, 2002, 1993)

Ans. Limitations of Coulomb's law. (i) Coulomb's law is valid only for point charges, (ii) Coulomb's law is strictly applicable to charges at rest. When a charge is in motion forces other than electrostatic forces come into play and Coulomb's law cannot be used to measure the charges in motion.

Q. 2.6. (*a*) **Two charges + 5 coulomb and + 15 coulomb are located at points (2, – 4, 3) and (–3, 2, 1) metre. Calculate the force on + 15 coulomb.**   (*P.U.*, 1994)

(*b*) **How far should be the two protons if electric force between them is equal to the weight of a proton?**   (*G.N.D.U.*, 1997)

(*c*) **Prove that the period of revolution of a particle carrying a charge – q in the circular orbit of radius R around a fixed charge + Q is given by $T^2 = \dfrac{16\pi^3 \varepsilon_0 m R^3}{qQ}$.**   (*P.U.* 2007)

Ans. (*a*) Here $q_1 = +5\,C$ $q_2 = +15\,C$

$$\vec{r_1} = 2\hat{i} - 4\hat{j} + 3\hat{k} \text{ and } \vec{r_2} = -3\hat{i} + 2\hat{j} + \hat{k}$$

∴ $$\vec{r_2} - \vec{r_1} = -5\hat{i} + 6\hat{j} - 2\hat{k}$$

Force on the charge q_2 (+ 15 C)

$$\vec{F}_{21} = \frac{1}{4\pi\varepsilon_0} \frac{q_1 q_2}{|\vec{r_2} - \vec{r_1}|^3} (\vec{r_2} - \vec{r_1})$$

Now $$|\vec{r_2} - \vec{r_1}| = \sqrt{(-5)^2 + (6)^2 + (-2)^2} = \sqrt{65}$$

∴ $$\vec{F}_{21} = \frac{1}{4\pi\varepsilon_0} \frac{5 \times 15}{65^{3/2}} (5\hat{i} + 6\hat{j} - 2\hat{k})$$

$$= \frac{9 \times 10^9 \times 5 \times 15}{65^{3/2}} (5\hat{i} + 6\hat{j} - 2\hat{k})$$

$$= 1.288 \times 10^9 (-5\hat{i} + 6\hat{j} - 2\hat{k}) \text{ Newton}$$

(*b*) Rest mass of the proton $m = 1.67 \times 10^{-27}$ kg

Charge on the proton $e = 1.6 \times 10^{-19}\,C$

Let r be the distance between the two protons when electric force between them is equal to the weight of a proton $= mg = 1.67 \times 10^{-27} \times 9.8$ Newton

Electrical force between two protons $= \dfrac{1}{4\pi\varepsilon_0} \dfrac{e \times e}{r^2} = \dfrac{9 \times 10^9 \times 1.6 \times 10^{-19} \times 1.6 \times 10^{-19}}{r^2}$

$$\frac{9 \times 10^9 \times 1.6 \times 10^{-19} \times 1.6 \times 10^{-19}}{r^2} = 1.67 \times 10^{-27} \times 9.8$$

$$\therefore \quad r^2 = \frac{9 \times 10^9 \times 1.6 \times 10^{-19} \times 1.6 \times 10^{-19}}{1.67 \times 10^{-27} \times 9.8} = 1.408 \times 10^{-2}$$

$$\therefore \qquad\qquad\qquad\qquad\qquad r = 1.186 \times 10^{-1} \text{ m} = 0.1186 \text{ m}$$

(c) The force of attraction between the particle carrying a charge $- q$ revolving round the fixed charge $+ Q$ in a circular orbit of radius R is given by

$$F = \frac{1}{4\pi\varepsilon_0} \frac{Qq}{R^2}$$

This force is balanced by the centrifugal force acting on the revolving particle given by $m R^2 \omega$ where m is the mass of the revolving particle and ω its angular velocity.

$$\therefore \qquad\qquad m R \omega^2 = \frac{1}{4\pi\varepsilon_0} \frac{Qq}{R^2}$$

If T is the time period of revolution of the charged particle around the fixed charge, then

$$\omega = \frac{2\pi}{T}$$

$$\therefore \qquad\qquad m R . \frac{4\pi^2}{T^2} = \frac{1}{4\pi\varepsilon_0} \frac{Qq}{R^2}$$

or $$\qquad\qquad T^2 = \frac{16\pi^3 \varepsilon_0 m R^3}{Qq}$$

Q. 2.7. Is the Coulomb force that one charge exerts on another charge changed if other charges are brought nearby? Hence find the net force due to a number of discrete charges.

(G.N.D.U., 2000, 1994)

Ans. Coulomb's force between two charges is a two body interaction and is independent of the presence of other charges. Hence the Coulomb's force that one charge exerts on another charge remains unchanged if other charges are brought nearby.

Net force due to a number of discrete charges. To find the net force due to a number of discrete

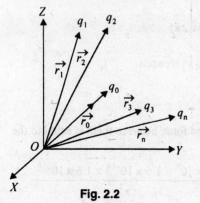

Fig. 2.2

charges q_1, q_2, q_3 ... q_n located at position vectors $\vec{r_1}, \vec{r_2}, \vec{r_3}, ... \vec{r_n}$ on a test charge q_0 located at position vector $\vec{r_0}$, we calculate the force due to each one of the charges on the test charge and add all the forces vectorially. Now force on q_0 due to charge q_1

$$\vec{F_{01}} = \frac{1}{4\pi\varepsilon_0} \frac{q_1 q_0}{|\vec{r_0} - \vec{r_1}|^3} (\vec{r_0} - \vec{r_1})$$

Similarly force on q_0 due to the charge q_2

$$\vec{F}_{02} = \frac{1}{4\pi\varepsilon_0} \frac{q_2\,q_0}{|\vec{r_0} - \vec{r_2}|^3} (\vec{r_0} - \vec{r_2})$$

and so on. And finally the force on q_0 due to the charge q_n

$$\vec{F}_{0n} = \frac{1}{4\pi\varepsilon_0} \frac{q_n\,q_0}{|\vec{r_0} - \vec{r_n}|^3} (\vec{r_0} - \vec{r_n})$$

Thus the net force

$$\vec{F} = \vec{F}_{01} + \vec{F}_{02} + \text{.......} + \vec{F}_{0n}$$

$$= \frac{q_0}{4\pi\varepsilon_0} \left[\frac{q_1}{|\vec{r_0} - \vec{r_1}|^3} (\vec{r_0} - \vec{r_1}) + \frac{q_2}{|\vec{r_0} - \vec{r_2}|^3} (\vec{r_0} - \vec{r_2}) + \text{....} \frac{q_n}{|\vec{r_0} - \vec{r_n}|^3} (\vec{r_0} - \vec{r_n}) \right]$$

$$= \frac{q_0}{4\pi\varepsilon_0} \sum_{i=1}^{n} \frac{q_i}{|\vec{r_0} - \vec{r_i}|^3} (\vec{r_0} - \vec{r_i})$$

Thus when we have a number of charges the force on a particular charge is the vector sum of the *two body Coulomb force* exerted by other charges on it. This is known as *principle of superposition*.

Q. 2.8. Using x, y and z co-ordinates and measuring lengths in metres charges of + 20 coulomb and + 30 coulomb are placed at positions (8, 0, 0) and (0, 8, 0) respectively. Evaluate the force experienced by a charge of + 10 coulomb at the position (4, 4, 0). Use vectors to get your answer.

Ans. Here $\qquad\qquad q_1 = + 20\text{C} \quad \vec{r_1} = 8\hat{i}$

$$q_2 = + 30\text{C} \quad \vec{r_2} = 8\hat{j}$$

$$q_0 = + 10\text{C} \quad \vec{r_0} = 4\hat{i} + 4\hat{j}$$

Force on charge $q_0 = + 10\text{C}$ at $\vec{r_0} = 4\hat{i} + 4\hat{j}$ due to charge $q_1 = + 20\text{C}$ at $\vec{r_1} = 8\hat{i}$ and $q_2 = + 30\text{C}$ at $\vec{r_2} = 8\hat{j}$ is given by $\vec{F} = \vec{F}_{01} + \vec{F}_{02}$

$$= \frac{q_0}{4\pi\varepsilon_0} \left[\frac{q_1}{|\vec{r_0} - \vec{r_1}|^3} (\vec{r_0} - \vec{r_1}) + \frac{q_2}{|\vec{r_0} - \vec{r_2}|^3} (\vec{r_0} - \vec{r_2}) \right] \text{...}(i)$$

Now $\qquad (\vec{r_0} - \vec{r_1}) = - 4\hat{i} + 4\hat{j}$

$\therefore \qquad |\vec{r_0} - \vec{r_1}| = \sqrt{4^2 + 4^2} = \sqrt{32}$

$(\vec{r_0} - \vec{r_2}) = 4\hat{i} - 4\hat{j}$

$\therefore \qquad |\vec{r_0} - \vec{r_2}| = \sqrt{4^2 + 4^2} = \sqrt{32}$

$\dfrac{1}{4\pi\varepsilon_0} = 9 \times 10^9 \text{ Nm}^2\text{C}^{-2}$

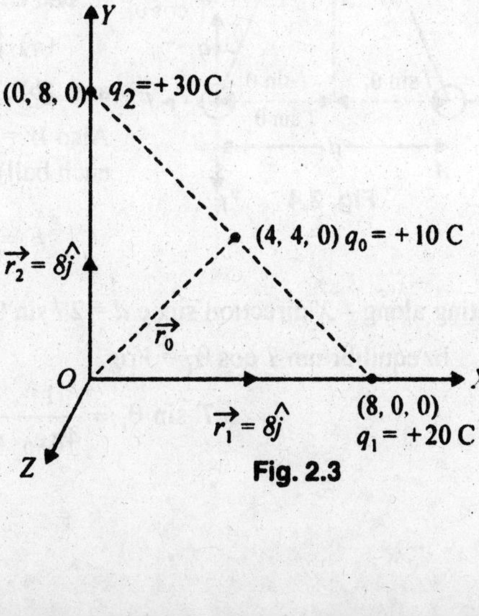

Fig. 2.3

Substituting in (*i*) we get

$$\vec{F} = 10 \times 9 \times 10^9 \left[\frac{20}{32^{3/2}} (-4\hat{i} + 4\hat{j}) + \frac{30}{32^{3/2}} (4\hat{i} - 4\hat{j}) \right]$$

$$= \frac{10 \times 9 \times 10^9}{32^{3/2}} [-20 \times 4 (\hat{i} - \hat{j}) + 30 \times 4 (\hat{i} - \hat{j})]$$

$$= \frac{225 \times 10^9}{8\sqrt{2}} (\hat{i} - \hat{j})$$

∴ Magnitude of the force

$$|\vec{F}| = 10^9 \times \frac{225}{8\sqrt{2}} \sqrt{(1 + 1)} = \frac{225 \times 10^9}{8} = 28.1 \times 10^9 \text{ Newton}$$

Direction. The direction of the force $\vec{F}$ is such that is makes an angle $\tan^{-1}(-1) = 45°$ with $+X$-axis and an angle of 45° with $-Y$-axis.

Q. 2.9. (*a*) Two identical metal balls of density ρ having equal and similar charges are **supported from a common point by means of silk threads each of length *l*. The two threads make an angle $2\theta_1$ with each other in air in equilibrium. The system is then immersed in a dielectric liquid of density σ, when the equilibrium angular separation is $2\theta_2$. Find the relative permittivity of the liquid.**

(*b*) If in the above case the angular separation remains unchanged on immersing in the dielectric liquid and $\dfrac{\rho}{\sigma} = m$, then show that relative permittivity of the liquid is $\dfrac{m}{m-1}$.

(P.U. 1994)

Ans. (*a*) As shown in Fig. 2.4 the charge on the ball *B* is in equilibrium under the action of three forces.

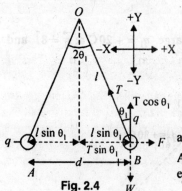

Fig. 2.4

(*i*)   The tension *T* in the silk thread acting along *BO*.

(*ii*) The weight *W* of the charged ball *B* acting vertically downward.

(*iii*) The electrostatic repulsion *F* acting on the charge *q* on *B* due to the charge *q* on *A*.

The tension *T* can be resolved into two components

(*a*) $T \cos \theta_1$ acting along $+Y$-axis

and (*b*) $T \sin \theta_1$ acting along $-X$-axis

Also $W = Mg = V\rho g$ acting along $-Y$-axis (*V* being the volume of each ball)

$$F = \frac{1}{4\pi\varepsilon_0} \frac{q^2}{d^2} = \frac{1}{4\pi\varepsilon_0} \frac{q^2}{4l^2 \sin^2 \theta_1}$$

acting along $-X$ direction since $d = 2\,l \sin \theta_1$

In equilibrium $T \cos \theta_1 = V\rho g$ ...(*i*)

$$T \sin \theta_1 = \frac{1}{4\pi\varepsilon_0} \frac{q^2}{4l^2 \sin^2 \theta_1}$$ ...(*ii*)

Dividing (ii) by (i) we get

$$\tan \theta_1 = \frac{1}{4\pi\varepsilon_0} \frac{q^2}{4l^2 \sin^2\theta_1} \frac{1}{V\rho g}$$

or $\quad \tan\theta_1 \sin^2\theta_1 = \dfrac{1}{4\pi\varepsilon_0} \dfrac{q^2}{4l^2} \dfrac{1}{V\rho g}$ ...(iii)

Let the relative permittivity of the liquid be ε_r. As $2\theta_2$ is the equilibrium angular separation between the two balls when immersed in the liquid of density σ, we have

$$T\cos\theta_2 = V(\rho - \sigma)g \qquad ...(iv)$$

and $\quad T\sin\theta_2 = \dfrac{1}{4\pi\varepsilon_0\varepsilon_r} \dfrac{q^2}{4l^2 \sin^2\theta_2}$ ...(v)

Dividing (v) by (iv), we get

$$\tan\theta_2 = \frac{1}{4\pi\varepsilon_0\varepsilon_r} \frac{q^2}{4l^2\sin^2\theta_2} \frac{1}{V(\rho-\sigma)g}$$

or $\quad \tan\theta_2 \sin^2\theta_2 = \dfrac{1}{4\pi\varepsilon_0\varepsilon_r} \dfrac{q^2}{4l^2} \dfrac{1}{V(\rho-\sigma)g}$ ...(vi)

Dividing (vi) by (iii), we get

$$\frac{\tan\theta_2 \sin^2\theta_2}{\tan\theta_1 \sin^2\theta_1} = \frac{1}{\varepsilon_r} \frac{\rho}{(\rho-\sigma)}$$

or $\quad \varepsilon_r = \dfrac{\rho}{(\rho-\sigma)} \dfrac{\tan\theta_1 \sin^2\theta_1}{\tan\theta_2 \sin^2\theta_2}$

(b) If the angular separation remains unchanged $\theta_2 = \theta_1$, then

$$\varepsilon_r = \frac{\rho}{(\rho-\sigma)} = \frac{\frac{\rho}{\sigma}}{\frac{\rho}{\sigma}-1} = \frac{m}{m-1}$$

since $\quad \dfrac{\rho}{\sigma} = m$

Q. 2.10. Write briefly what you know about quantisation of charge. Why it is not possible for a body to have charge of 1.5 e? (*H.P.U.*, 2000, 1997; *P.U.*, 2007, 1995, 1992)

Ans. Quantisation of charge. All matter is composed of atoms and molecules. An atom consists of a positively charged nucleus with a suitable number of negatively charged electrons revolving round it in suitable orbits so that the isolated atom is on the whole neutral. The nucleus, in turn, is made up of positively charged particles called *protons* and neutral particles called *neutrons*. The charge on a proton though positive is exactly equal in magnitude to the negative charge on the electron. The number of orbital electrons is equal to the number of protons in the nucleus, thus making the atom on the whole, electrically neutral.

Molecules, in general, are larger in size than atoms. A molecule usually contains a few atoms of either the same element or of different elements. The fundamental charge on the electron (or proton) is 1.6×10^{-19} coulomb denoted by e. Thus the charge on the proton is $+e$ and on the electron is $-e$.

Charge of 1.5 e not possible. Since all matter in nature consists of an integral number of fundamental particles (atoms or molecules) and charges add algebraically, the total charge in any given piece of matter must be an integral multiple of e. In other words, we can only have charges $\pm e$, $\pm 2e$, $\pm 3e$, ..., $\pm ne$ where n is an integer.

This fact is known as *principle of quantisation* of charge. According to this principle it is not possible to have a fractional charge like 1.5 *e* or 2.3 *e*, etc.

However, quantisation or atomicity of charge becomes unimportant when we consider matter in bulk. For example, when a glass rod is rubbed with silk electrons are transferred from the surface of one material to the surface of the other. The material that gains the electrons becomes *negatively* charged and the material that loses the electrons becomes *positively* charged. In most situations, the number of electrons transferred is so large that the charge of one electron more or less is unobservable. For this reason the variation of charge is often treated as *continuous*.

A further point regarding quantisation of charge may also be noted. A highly successful model for the substructure of a large number of known elementary particles involves entities called *quarks*. The various quarks that are required for a complete theory are postulated to carry charges of $\pm \frac{1}{3} e$ and $\pm \frac{2}{3} e$. But the combination in which quarks are present in the observed elementary particles are such that net charge is always $+ e$, $- e$, or zero. Although there is strong evidence that quarks exist inside the elementary particles, a free quark has never been detected.

This is again in agreement with quantisation of charge.

Q. 2.11. (*a*) **Define electric field intensity. State its value for a point charge and give its units.** *(Pbi. U.*, 2002; *H.P.U.*, 1992)

(*b*) **A charge of** $10\sqrt{2}$ **Coulomb is located at** $(3\hat{i} + 4\hat{j} + 5\hat{k})$ *m* **calculate the electric field intensity at a point having position vector** $(5\hat{i} + 4\hat{j} + 3\hat{k})m$. *(Pbi. U.*, 2000; *H.P.U.*, 2000, 1997; *P.U.* 2008 similar)

Ans. (*a*) **Electric field intensity.** *The electric field intensity* $\vec{E}$ *at a point is expressed in magnitude and direction by the force* $\vec{E}$ *per unit charge experienced by a small positive test charge q_0 placed at that point*

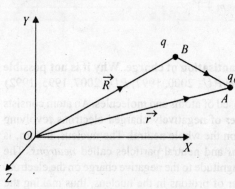

Fig. 2.5

$$\vec{E} = \frac{\vec{F}}{q_0}$$

where $\vec{F}$ is the total experienced by the charge q_0.

The value of q_0 should be so small that it should not disturb the electric field. Therefore, to be more exact, the ratio $\dfrac{\vec{F}}{q_0}$ as the magnitude of the test charge q_0 is made smaller and smaller so that it finally tends to zero *i.e.*, the limiting value of

$$\underset{q_0 \to 0}{Lim} \frac{\vec{F}}{q_0}$$

defines a vector known as electric field at the point.

The S.I. unit of electric field intensity is Newton/coulomb (NC^{-1}).

Electric field due to a point charge. Let a point charge q known as the *source charge* be placed at the point B having a position vector $\vec{r}$ and a test charge q_0 at the point A having the position vector, then $\vec{r}$ the force on the charge q_0 due to the charge q is given by

$$\vec{F} = \frac{1}{4\pi\varepsilon_0} \frac{qq_0}{|\vec{r} - \vec{R}|^3} (\vec{r} - \vec{R})$$

The electric field at A known as the *observation point* is given by

$$\vec{E} = \frac{\vec{F}}{q_0} = \frac{1}{4\pi\varepsilon_0} \frac{q}{|\vec{r} - \vec{R}|^3} (\vec{r} - \vec{R}) \qquad \qquad ...(i)$$

Note. *Note that in the relation (i) in the expression* $(\vec{r} - \vec{R})$, $\vec{r}$ *the position vector of the observation point (test charge) precedes the position vector of the source charge.*

The direction of electric intensity is the same as that of $(\vec{r} - \vec{R})$ and is *from the source charge* to the *observation point* (or test charge).

When the source charge lies at the origin O. Then $R = 0$

In such a case
$$\vec{E} = \frac{1}{4\pi\varepsilon_0} \frac{q}{r^3} \vec{r} \qquad \qquad ...(ii)$$

$$= \frac{1}{4\pi\varepsilon_0} \frac{q}{r^2} \frac{\vec{r}}{r}$$

or
$$\vec{E} = \frac{1}{4\pi\varepsilon_0} \frac{q}{r^2} \hat{r} \qquad \qquad ...(iii)$$

where $\hat{r}$ is a unit vector in the direction of $\vec{r}$ and $\vec{r}$ is the position vector of the observation point.

The magnitude of electric intensity $E = \frac{1}{4\pi\varepsilon_0} \frac{q}{r^2}$

(b) Electric field intensity at a point at the position vector $\vec{r}$ due to a charge q at the position vector $\vec{R}$ is given by

$$\vec{E} = \frac{1}{4\pi\varepsilon_0} \frac{q}{|\vec{r} - \vec{R}|^3} (\vec{r} - \vec{R})$$

Now
$$q = 10\sqrt{2} \text{ C}; \ (\vec{r} - \vec{R}) = [(5\hat{i} + 4\hat{j} + 3\hat{k}) - (3\hat{i} + 4\hat{j} + 5\hat{k})]$$

$$= 2\hat{i} - 2\hat{k}$$

$$\therefore \qquad |\vec{r} - \vec{R}| = \sqrt{4 + 4} = \sqrt{8} = 2\sqrt{2}$$

$$\therefore \qquad E = \frac{1}{4\pi\varepsilon_0} \frac{10\sqrt{2}}{2^3 \times 2^{3/2}} 2(\hat{i} - \hat{k}) = \frac{9 \times 10^9 \times 10(\hat{i} - \hat{k})}{8}$$

$$= 1.125 \times 10^{10} (\hat{i} - \hat{k}) = 11.25 \times 10^9 (\hat{i} - \hat{k}) \text{ NC}^{-1}$$

Exercise. *If a pithball of 1gm is in equilibrium when placed in an electric field of 5 NC^{-1} established between two charged plates, then determine the charge on the pithball.* (H.P.U. 2006)

Hint. Electric field $E = 5 \text{ NC}^{-1}$. Let q be the charge on the pithball, then force on the pithball $F = qE = 5q$ Newton

Mass of the pithball $m = 1\text{gm} = 10^{-3}$ kg

$\therefore$ Downward force on the pithball due to gravity

$$mg = 10^{-3} \times 9.8 \text{ Newton}$$

As the pithball is in equilibrium

$$qE = mg \text{ or } 5\,q = 10^{-3} \times 9.8$$

$$\therefore \qquad q = \frac{10^{-3} \times 9.8}{5} = 1.96 \times 10^{-3}\,C$$

Q. 2.12. Calculate the electric field intensity on the surface of uranium nucleus $Z = 92$. Its nuclear radius is 7×10^{-15} m. *(H.P.U., 1995)*

Ans. Charge on the nucleus $Q = Ze = 92 \times 1.6 \times 10^{-19}$ C

Radius $r = 7 \times 10^{-15}$ m

Magnitude of electric field intensity on the surface

$$E = \frac{1}{4\pi\varepsilon_0}\frac{Q}{r^2} = \frac{9 \times 10^9 \times 92 \times 1.6 \times 10^{-19}}{(7 \times 10^{-15})^2}$$

$$= 27.04 \times 10^{20}\ NC^{-1}\ (\text{Newton/Coulomb})$$

The direction of E is along the outward drawn radius.

Q. 2.13. (a) Two charges are at a certain distance apart. Electric field is zero at one point between them. What do you conclude about the charges? Explain. *(G.N.D.U., 2003, 1995)*

(b) Point charges $-5\,e$ and $+2\,e$ are separated by a distance of 50 cm. Find out the point at which electric field is zero. *(Gharwal. U., 2000)*

Ans. As the electric field is zero at a point *between* the two charges, either both the charges are positive or both of them are negative.

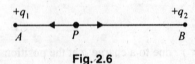

Fig. 2.6

When both the charges say q_1 and q_2 are positive and placed at points A and B and P is a point between them where electric field is zero, then electric field at P due to charge $+q_1$ at A

$$E_1 = \frac{1}{4\pi\varepsilon_0}\frac{q_1}{AP^2} \text{ along } AP \text{ produced}$$

and electric field at P due to charge $+q_2$ at B

$$E_2 = \frac{1}{4\pi\varepsilon_0}\frac{q_2}{BP^2} \text{ along } BP \text{ produced}$$

i.e., E_1 and E_2 act in opposite directions. They will cancel each other and the resultant field will be zero when

$$\frac{1}{4\pi\varepsilon_0}\frac{q_1}{AP^2} = \frac{1}{4\pi\varepsilon_0}\frac{q_2}{BP^2}$$

or

$$\frac{q_1}{q_2} = \frac{AP^2}{BP^2}$$

Similar treatment holds when both the charges are negative.

But if one charge say q_1 is positive and the other charge q_2 is negative, then E_1 and E_2 will both act in the same direction *i.e.*, AP produced and their resultant will never be zero.

(b) As one charge is negative and the other positive the point P where the electric field is zero will lie on the line joining the two charges produced on the side of the smaller charge *i.e.* $+2\,e$. Let the distance of this point from the change $+2\,e$ be x, then its distance from the charge $-5\,e = (0.5 + x)$.

Hence $\dfrac{1}{4\pi\varepsilon_0}\dfrac{2e}{x^2} - \dfrac{1}{4\pi\varepsilon_0}\dfrac{5e}{(0.5+x)^2} = 0$

or $\qquad \dfrac{2}{x^2} = \dfrac{5}{(0.5+x)^2} = \dfrac{5}{0.25+x+x^2}$

$\therefore \qquad 5x^2 = 0.5 + 2x + 2x^2$

or $\qquad 3x^2 - 2x - 0.5 = 0$

$\therefore \qquad x = \dfrac{2 \pm \sqrt{4+6}}{6} = \dfrac{2+\sqrt{10}}{6} = 0.86\ m$

[Ignoring negative sign as it would give a negative value of x which is not correct]

Thus the point will be at a distance of $0.86\ m$ from the charge $+2\ e$ and $(0.86 + 0.5) = 1.36$ m from the charge $-5\ e$.

Q. 2.14. A charge $q_1 = 4$ μC is located at the origin. Another charge $q_2 = 1$ μC is placed at a distance 0.2 m from the origin along the X-axis. Find the location at which the electric field due to these charges is zero. (*H.P.U.*, 1992)

Ans. Let a charge 1 μC be placed at A, 0.2 m from the origin O along the X-axis and B be a point at a distance x where the field is zero, then in S.I. units

$\qquad \dfrac{1}{4\pi\varepsilon_0}\dfrac{4\times10^{-6}}{x^2} = \dfrac{1}{4\pi\varepsilon_0}\dfrac{1\times10^{-6}}{(0.2-x)^2}$

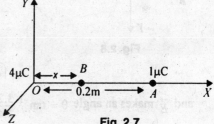

Fig. 2.7

or $\qquad 4(0.2-x)^2 = x^2$

or $\qquad 2(0.2-x) = x$

or $\qquad 0.4 = 3x$

or $\qquad x = \dfrac{0.4}{3} = \dfrac{2}{15}$ m from O.

Q. 2.15. An electron with a velocity of 2.4×10^6 ms^{-1} flies into a uniform electric field of intensity 135 Vm^{-1}. It moves along a field line until it comes to a halt. Calculate the distance travelled by the electron within the field. (*P.U.*, 1994)

Ans. The electron will come to a halt when its kinetic energy is used up in doing work against the electric field. Suppose it travels a distance S before coming to a halt, then

Work done $= Ee\,S = 135 \times 1.6 \times 10^{-19}\,S$ $\qquad$ [e = electronic charge = 1.6×10^{-19} C]

Kinetic energy of the electron $= \dfrac{1}{2}mv^2 = \dfrac{1}{2} \times 9 \times 10^{-31} \times (2.4 \times 10^6)^2$

where $m = 9 \times 10^{-31}$ kg.

$\therefore \qquad 135 \times 1.6 \times 10^{-19}\,S = \dfrac{9 \times 10^{-31} \times 2.4 \times 2.4 \times 10^{12}}{2}$

or $\qquad S = \dfrac{9 \times 10^{-31} \times 2.4 \times 2.4 \times 10^{12}}{2 \times 135 \times 1.6 \times 10^{-19}} = 0.12$ m = 12 cm

Q. 2.16. (a) A charge of 100 coulomb is located at the point 3, 4, 0 (metre). Find the electric field intensity at the origin (0, 0, 0).

(b) Two positive charges of magnitude $+2e$ coulomb each are located at point (0, 6) and (0, -6) respectively, find out

(*i*) $\vec{E}$ at (8, 0) metres

(*ii*) force on a charge of + 10 coulomb placed at (0, 0).   (*G.N.D.U.*, 1991)

Ans. (*a*) Vector distance of the charge from the origin

$$\vec{r} = 3\hat{i} + 4\hat{j}$$

∴ Vector distance of the origin from the charge

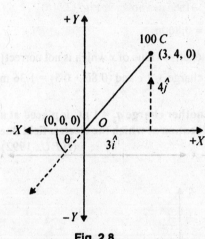

Fig. 2.8

$$-\vec{r} = -3\hat{i} - 4\hat{j}$$

∴ $|\vec{r}| = \sqrt{3^2 + 4^2} = 5\text{m}$

Hence electric field at O

$$\vec{E} = \frac{1}{4\pi\varepsilon_0} \frac{q}{|\vec{r}|^3} \vec{r}$$

$$= 9 \times 10^9 \times \frac{100}{5^3} (-3\hat{i} - 4\hat{j})$$

$$= 9 \times 10^9 \left(-\frac{12}{5}\hat{i} - \frac{16}{5}\hat{j} \right)$$

$$= 9 \times 10^9 (-2.4\hat{i} - 3.2\hat{j})$$

∴

$$|\vec{E}| = 9 \times 10^9 \sqrt{(2.4)^2 + (3.2)^2} = 36 \times 10^9 \text{ NC}^{-1}$$

and $\vec{E}$ makes an angle $\theta = \tan^{-1}\dfrac{3.2}{2.4} = \dfrac{4}{3}$ with the direction of $-\hat{i}$ *i.e.*, negative *X*-axis.

(*b*) Let $q_1 = + 2e$ be the charge at the point (0, 6) and $q_2 = + 2e$ the charge at the point (0, – 6) and *P* the point (8, 0), then

$$q_1 = + 2e; \vec{r_1} = 6\hat{j}$$

$$q_2 = + 2e; \vec{r_2} = - 6\hat{j}$$

Position vector of the observation point $P = \vec{r_0} = 8\hat{i}$

(*i*) Electric field at *P* at the position $\vec{r_0} = 8\hat{i}$ due to the charges q_1 and q_2 [Fig. 2.9(*a*)]

$$\vec{E} = \frac{1}{4\pi\varepsilon_0} \left[\frac{q_1}{|\vec{r_0} - \vec{r_1}|^3} (\vec{r_0} - \vec{r_1}) + \frac{q_2}{|\vec{r_0} - \vec{r_2}|^3} (\vec{r_0} - \vec{r_2}) \right]$$

Now $(\vec{r_0} - \vec{r_1}) = 8\hat{i} - 6\hat{j}$

and $|\vec{r_0} - \vec{r_1}| = \sqrt{8^2 + (-6)^2} = 10$

Also $(\vec{r_0} - \vec{r_2}) = 8\hat{i} + 6\hat{j}$

and $|\vec{r_0} - \vec{r_2}| = \sqrt{8^2 + 6^2} = 10$

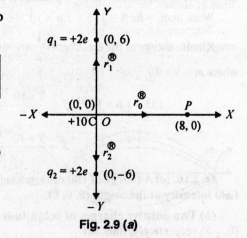

Fig. 2.9 (a)

$$\therefore \quad \vec{E} = \frac{1}{4\pi\varepsilon_0}\left[\frac{2e}{10^3}(8\hat{i}-6\hat{j}) + \frac{2e}{10^3}(8\hat{i}+6\hat{j})\right]$$

$$= \frac{9\times10^9 \times 2e \times 16\hat{i}}{10^3} = 2.88e \times 10^8 \text{ N C}^{-1}$$

acting in the direction of $+X$-axis.

(ii) Let the position vector of the charge of $+10\ C$ be $\vec{r}$, then as shown in Fig. [2.9(b)]

$$\vec{r} = 0\hat{i} + 0\hat{j} = 0$$

Again

$$q_1 = +2e;\ \vec{r_1} = 6\hat{j}$$

$$\therefore \quad (\vec{r_1} - \vec{r}) = 6\hat{j} \text{ and } |\vec{r_1} - \vec{r}| = 6$$

$$q_2 = +2e;\ r_2 = -6j$$

$$\therefore \quad \left(\vec{r_2} - \vec{r}\right) = -6j \text{ and } |\vec{r_2} - \vec{r}| = 6$$

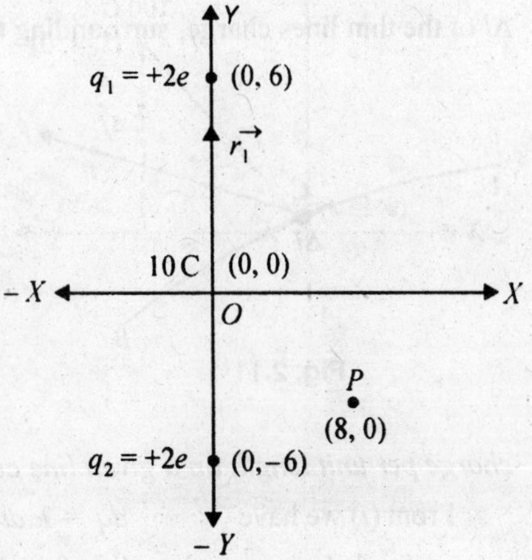

Force on the charge of $10\ C$ due to charges q_1 and q_2

$$F = \frac{10}{4\pi\varepsilon_0}\left[\frac{q_1}{|\vec{r_1} - \vec{r}|^3}(\vec{r_1} - \vec{r}) + \frac{q_2}{|\vec{r_2} - \vec{r}|^3}(\vec{r_2} - \vec{r_1})\right]$$

$$= \frac{10}{4\pi\varepsilon_0}\left[\frac{2e \times 6\hat{j}}{6^3} + \frac{2e \times (-6j)}{6^3}\right] = 0$$

$q_1 = +2e$ • (0, 6)

$\vec{r_1}$

$-X$ ← $10\ C$ | (0, 0) → X

O

P
•
(8, 0)

$q_2 = +2e$ • (0, -6)

$-Y$

Fig. 2.9 (b)

Q. 2.17. (a) **What are electric lines of force?**

(b) **Why two electric lines of force do not cross each other?** (G.N.D.U. 2001)

Ans. (a) **Electric lines of force.** If a small test charge q_0 ($q_0 \to 0$) is placed in an electric field $\vec{E}$, then it will move along a curve such that the tangent to the curve at every point gives the direction of electric field $\vec{E}$ at that point. Such a line (or curve) is known as *line of electric force.*

(i) It is assumed that when a point charge q is placed in a medium of permittivity ε, the number of lines of electric force originating from the point $= \dfrac{q}{\varepsilon}$.

Suppose we have a point charge q and we draw a sphere of radius r around the point, then magnitude of electric field strength at any point on the spherical surface

$$|\vec{E}| = E = \frac{1}{4\pi\varepsilon}\frac{q}{r^2} = \frac{q/\varepsilon}{4\pi r^2} = \frac{\text{Number of lines of electric force}}{\text{Area of the sphere through which the lines cross}}$$

= Number of lines of electric force crossing per unit area.

The strength of the electric field at a point is, therefore, taken to be proportional to the number of lines crossing a unit area around that point.

(ii) The lines of force originate from a positive charge and terminate on a negative charge as shown

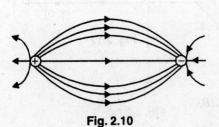

Fig. 2.10

(b) The lines of electric force do not cross each other, because if they cross each other it would mean that there are at least two directions of the electric field $\vec{E}$ at that point i.e. $\vec{E}$ will not be unique which is against the concept of vector field and is an erroneous idea.

Q. 2.18. What is line charge density? Derive an expression for the electric field due to an infinitely long uniformly charged straight wire using Coulomb's law.

(P.U., 2007, 2006, 1994, 1991; K.U., 1994; G.N.D.U., 1993, 1991; H.P.U., 1993)

Ans. Line charge density. Consider a charged thin wire AB. If Δq is the charge on a small length Δl of the thin lines charge, surrounding the point C, then

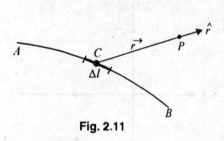

Average charge per unit length $= \dfrac{\Delta q}{\Delta l}$

The limiting value of $\dfrac{\Delta q}{\Delta l}$ as $\Delta l \to 0$ is known as the line charge density λ at the point C on the infinitesimally small element of length Δl.

Fig. 2.11

$$\therefore \qquad \lambda = \operatorname*{Lim}_{\Delta l \to 0} \frac{\Delta q}{\Delta l} = \frac{dq}{dl} \qquad \qquad ...(i)$$

Hence the line charge density may be defined as the charge per unit length on a given line curved or straight.

From (i) we have $\qquad dq = \lambda \, dl$

∴ Total charge on a length l of the line is given by

$$q = \int_l dq = \int_l \lambda \, dl$$

If we have a uniform charge distribution and q is the charge on a length l, then

$$q = \lambda l \quad \text{or} \quad \lambda = \frac{q}{l}$$

Electric field due to a line charge. Let AB be a line element of charge having a uniform line charge density λ. Consider a small length dl of the line element containing the point C having a position vector $\vec{R}$, then

Charge on the element of length $dl = dq = \lambda \, dl$

The electric field intensity $\vec{dE}$ at an observation point P having position vector $\vec{r}$ due to the charge dq on the small line element of length dl in free space is given by

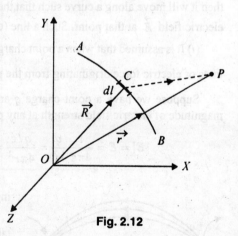

Fig. 2.12

$$\vec{dE} = \frac{1}{4\pi \varepsilon_0} \frac{dq \, (\vec{r} - \vec{R})}{|\vec{r} - \vec{R}|^3} = \frac{1}{4\pi \varepsilon_0} \frac{\lambda \, dl \, (\vec{r} - \vec{R})}{|\vec{r} - \vec{R}|^3}$$

∴ Electric intensity at P due to the whole line charge AB,

$$\vec{E} = \frac{1}{4\pi\varepsilon_0} \int_A^B \frac{\lambda \, dl \, (\vec{r} - \vec{R})}{|\vec{r} - \vec{R}|^3}$$

If the point C on the small line element dl lies at the origin, then $\vec{R} = 0$. In such a case

$$d\vec{E} = \frac{1}{4\pi\varepsilon_0} \frac{dq}{|\vec{r}|^3} \vec{r} = \frac{1}{4\pi\varepsilon_0} \frac{\lambda \, dl \, \vec{r}}{|\vec{r}|^3}$$

$$= \frac{1}{4\pi\varepsilon_0} \frac{\lambda \, dl}{r^2} \frac{\vec{r}}{r} = \frac{1}{4\pi\varepsilon_0} \frac{\lambda \, dl}{r^2} \hat{r}.$$

where $\hat{r}$ is a unit vector drawn from the charge dq at C to the point P i.e., in the direction of $\vec{r}$.

For the whole line charge AB the electric field intensity

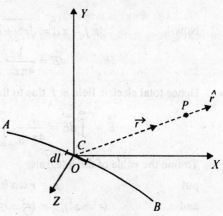

Fig. 2.13

$$\vec{E} = \frac{1}{4\pi\varepsilon_0} \int_A^B \frac{\lambda \, dl \, \vec{r}}{|\vec{r}|^3} = \frac{1}{4\pi\varepsilon_0} \int_A^B \frac{\lambda \, dl \, \hat{r}}{r^2}$$

Electric field due to an infinite line charge. Consider a long straight line charge of infinite length in the form of a uniformly charged straight wire placed along the X-axis and extending from $x = -\infty$ to $x = +\infty$ in the free space. Let P be the point where the electric intensity is to be calculated. Draw PO perpendicular to the line charge and let O represent the origin and OPY the Y-axis of the co-ordinate system.

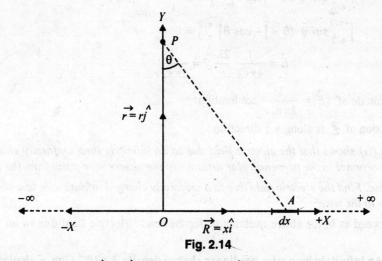

Fig. 2.14

Let $$\vec{OP} = \vec{r} = r\hat{j}$$

Consider a small element of length dx of the line charge at a distance x from O.

Let $$\vec{OA} = \vec{R} = x\hat{i}$$

If λ is the line charge density, then charge on the length $dx = dq = \lambda dx$

Electric field at P due to this charge element at A in S.I. units in free space

$$\vec{dE} = \frac{1}{4\pi\varepsilon_0}\frac{\lambda dx\,(\vec{r} - \vec{R})}{|\vec{r} - \vec{R}|^3} = \frac{1}{4\pi\varepsilon_0}\frac{\lambda dx\,(r\,\hat{j} - x\,\hat{i})}{|r\,\hat{j} - x\,\hat{i}|^3}$$

Now $$|r\,\hat{j} - x\,\hat{i}| = \sqrt{r^2 + (-x)^2} = \sqrt{r^2 + x^2}$$

$\therefore$ $$\vec{dE} = \frac{1}{4\pi\varepsilon_0}\frac{\lambda dx}{(r^2 + x^2)^{3/2}}\,(r\,\hat{j} - x\,\hat{i}) \qquad \text{...(ii)}$$

Hence total electric field at P due to the whole line charge element extending from $-\infty$ to $+\infty$.

$$\vec{E} = \int_{-\infty}^{+\infty} \vec{dE} = \frac{\lambda}{4\pi\varepsilon_0}\int_{-\infty}^{+\infty}\frac{r\,dx}{(r^2 + x^2)^{3/2}}\,\hat{j} - \frac{\lambda}{4\pi\varepsilon_0}\int_{-\infty}^{+\infty}\frac{x\,dx}{(r^2 + x^2)^{3/2}}\,\hat{i} \qquad \text{...(iii)}$$

To find the value of the integrals,

put $$x = r\tan\theta \qquad \therefore\ dx = r\sec^2\theta\,d\theta$$

and $$(r^2 + x^2)^{3/2} = (r^2 + r^2\tan^2\theta)^{3/2} = r^3\,(1 + \tan^2\theta)^{3/2} = r^3\sec^3\theta$$

Also when $x = +\infty$; $\theta = +\dfrac{\pi}{2}$ and when $x = -\infty$; $\theta = -\dfrac{\pi}{2}$

Substituting in (iii), we have

$$\vec{E} = \frac{\lambda}{4\pi\varepsilon_0}\int_{-\pi/2}^{+\pi/2}\frac{r^2\sec^2\theta\,d\theta}{r^3\sec^3\theta}\,\hat{j} - \frac{\lambda}{4\pi\varepsilon_0}\int_{-\pi/2}^{+\pi/2}\frac{r^2\tan\theta\sec^2\theta\,d\theta}{r^3\sec^3\theta}\,\hat{i}$$

$$= \left[\frac{\lambda}{4\pi\varepsilon_0 r}\int_{-\pi/2}^{+\pi/2}\cos\theta\,d\theta\right]\hat{j} - \left[\frac{\lambda}{4\pi\varepsilon_0 r}\int_{-\pi/2}^{+\pi/2}\sin\theta\,d\theta\right]\hat{i}$$

Now $$\int_{-\pi/2}^{+\pi/2}\cos\theta\,d\theta = \left[\sin\theta\right]_{-\pi/2}^{+\pi/2} = 2$$

and $$\int_{-\pi/2}^{+\pi/2}\sin\theta\,d\theta = \left[-\cos\theta\right]_{-\pi/2}^{+\pi/2} = 0$$

$\therefore$ $$\vec{E} = \frac{1}{4\pi\varepsilon_0}\frac{2\lambda}{r}\,\hat{j} = \frac{\lambda}{2\pi\varepsilon_0 r}\,\hat{j} \qquad \text{...(iv)}$$

The magnitude of $|\vec{E}| = \dfrac{\lambda}{2\pi\varepsilon_0 r}$ coulomb/m^2

The direction of $\vec{E}$ is along $+ Y$ direction.

Equation (iv) shows that the electric field due to an infinitely long uniformly charged wire is inversely proportional to the perpendicular distance of the observation point from the wire.

Exercise. *Find the electric field due to a uniformly charged infinite wire at a point on a line perpendicular to the wire.*   (Pbi. U. 2007)

Hint. Proceed as in the above question under the head **'Electric field due to an infinite line charge'.**

Q. 2.19. **An infinitely long wire has linear charge density 2×10^{-6} C/m. Calculate the intensity of the electric field at a point distant 10 cm normal to the length of the wire.**

(K.U., 2002)

Ans. Charge per unit length $\lambda = 2 \times 10^{-6}$ C/m

Distance of the point $r = 10$ cm $= 0.1$ m

Intensity of the electric field $E = \dfrac{\lambda}{2\pi\varepsilon_0 r}$

$$= \dfrac{2 \times 10^{-6}}{2\pi\varepsilon_0 \times 0.1} = \dfrac{2 \times 2 \times 10^{-5}}{4\pi\varepsilon_0}$$

$$= 4 \times 10^{-5} \times 9 \times 10^9 = 36 \times 10^4$$

$$= 3.6 \times 10^5 \text{ N/C}$$

Q. 2.20. (*a*) **A uniformly charged thin wire of length *l* carrying a total charge *q* lies along the X-axis of *x-y* plane. Find the electric field due to this wire at a point having co-ordinates (0, *a*). Choose the origin of the co-ordinate system at the centre of the wire.** (*A.U.*, 1995)

(*b*) **Calculate the electric field 12 cm above the centre of a line charge 10 cm long having 2.6 µC.** (*Kerala. U.*, 2001)

Ans. (*a*) Consider a uniformly charged thin wire of length *l* along the X-axis in the *x-y* plane and charge per unit length $\lambda = q/l$. The origin of the co-ordinate system is at the centre of the wire at *O* so that portion of the wire along $+ X$ axis is $+ l/2$ and along $- X$ axis is $- l/2$. The point *P* having co-ordinates (0, *a*) will be on the Y-axis at a distance *a* from the origin.

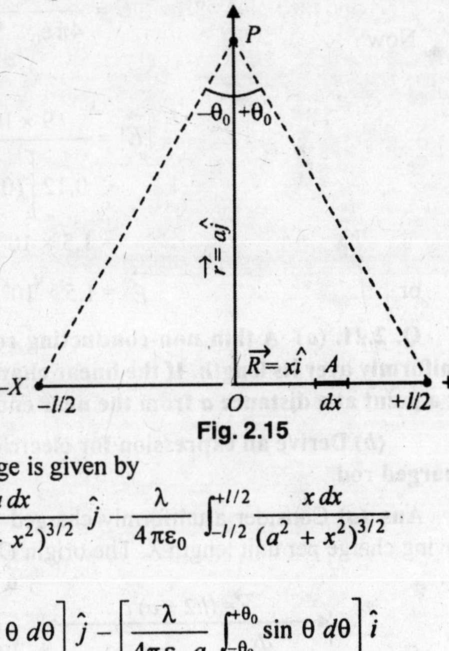

The electric field at *P* having position vector $\vec{r} = a\,\hat{j}$ due to the charge on a length *dx* at *A* at a distance $\vec{R} = x\hat{i}$ from the origin is given by

$$\vec{dE} = \dfrac{1}{4\pi\varepsilon_0} \dfrac{\lambda\,dx}{(a^2 + x^2)^{3/2}}\,(a\hat{j} - x\hat{i})$$

[For proof see **Q. 2.18.** Eq. (*ii*)]

Fig. 2.15

The total electric field due to the whole line charge is given by

$$\vec{E} = \dfrac{\lambda}{4\pi\varepsilon_0} \int_{-l/2}^{+l/2} \dfrac{a\,dx}{(a^2+x^2)^{3/2}}\,\hat{j} - \dfrac{\lambda}{4\pi\varepsilon_0} \int_{-l/2}^{+l/2} \dfrac{x\,dx}{(a^2+x^2)^{3/2}}$$

Proceeding as in **Q. 2.18**, we get

$$\vec{E} = \left[\dfrac{\lambda}{4\pi\varepsilon_0 a} \int_{-\theta_0}^{+\theta_0} \cos\theta\,d\theta \right] \hat{j} - \left[\dfrac{\lambda}{4\pi\varepsilon_0 a} \int_{-\theta_0}^{+\theta_0} \sin\theta\,d\theta \right] \hat{i}$$

where $+ \theta_0$ and $- \theta_0$ are the values of angle θ subtended at *P* by the lengths $+ l/2$ and $- l/2$ respectively.

$$\therefore \qquad \vec{E} = \dfrac{\lambda}{4\pi\varepsilon_0 a} \left\{ \left[\sin\theta \right]_{-\theta_0}^{+\theta_0} \hat{j} + \left[\cos\theta \right]_{-\theta_0}^{+\theta_0} \hat{i} \right\}$$

Now $\qquad \sin\theta_0 = \dfrac{l/2}{\left(a^2 + \dfrac{l^2}{4}\right)^{1/2}}; \quad \sin(-\theta_0) = \dfrac{-l/2}{\left(a^2 + \dfrac{l^2}{4}\right)^{1/2}}$

$$\cos\theta_0 = \dfrac{a}{\left(a^2 + \dfrac{l^2}{4}\right)^{1/2}}; \quad \cos(-\theta_0) = \dfrac{a}{\left(a^2 + \dfrac{l^2}{4}\right)^{1/2}}$$

$\therefore$ The term $\left[\cos\theta \right]_{-\theta_0}^{+\theta_0} = 0$

Hence $\vec{E} = \dfrac{\lambda}{4\pi\varepsilon_0\, a}\left[\dfrac{l/2}{\left(a^2+\dfrac{l^2}{4}\right)^{1/2}}+\dfrac{l/2}{\left(a^2+\dfrac{l^2}{4}\right)^{1/2}}\right]\hat{j} = \dfrac{1}{4\pi\varepsilon_0}\dfrac{\lambda}{a}\dfrac{l}{\left(a^2+\dfrac{l^2}{4}\right)^{1/2}}\hat{j}$

$$= \dfrac{1}{4\pi\varepsilon_0}\dfrac{q}{a\left(a^2+\dfrac{l^2}{4}\right)^{1/2}}\hat{j}$$

(b) Let the line charge be along the X-axis, then the point 12 cm above the centre of the line charge lies along the Y-axis.

Here $l = 10$ cm $= 0.1$ m ; $a = 12$ cm $= 0.12$ m.

$q = 2.6\ \mu C = 2.6\times10^{-6}\,C$

Now $\vec{E} = \dfrac{1}{4\pi\varepsilon_0}\dfrac{q}{a\left(a^2+\dfrac{l^2}{4}\right)^{1/2}}\hat{j}$

$\therefore$ $|\vec{E}| = \dfrac{9\times10^9\times2.6\times10^{-6}}{0.12\left[(0.12)^2+\dfrac{(0.1)^2}{4}\right]^{1/2}} = \dfrac{9\times10^9\times2.6\times10^{-6}}{0.12\times0.13}$

$$= 1.5\times10^6\ \text{N/C}$$

or $\vec{E} = 1.5\times10^6$ N/C along $+\,Y$-axis.

Q. 2.21. (*a*) **A thin non-conducting rod of length *l* carries a positive charge distributed uniformly over its length. If the linear charge density is λ, find the intensity of the electric field at a point at a distance *a* from the near end of the rod and on its axis.**   (*A.U.*, 1995)

(*b*) **Derive an expression for electric field at a point situated on the axis of a uniformly charged rod.**   (*Pbi. U.*, 2008)

Ans. (*a*) Consider a uniformly charged thin non-conducting rod of length l along the X-axis having charge per unit length λ. The origin O of the co-ordinate system is taken at the centre of the wire. The point P also lies on the X-axis at a distance a

Fig. 2.15 (a)

from the near end $\left(+\dfrac{1}{2}\right)$.

$\therefore$ Position vector of the point P

$$= \vec{r} = r\hat{i} = \left(\dfrac{l}{2}+a\right)\hat{i}$$

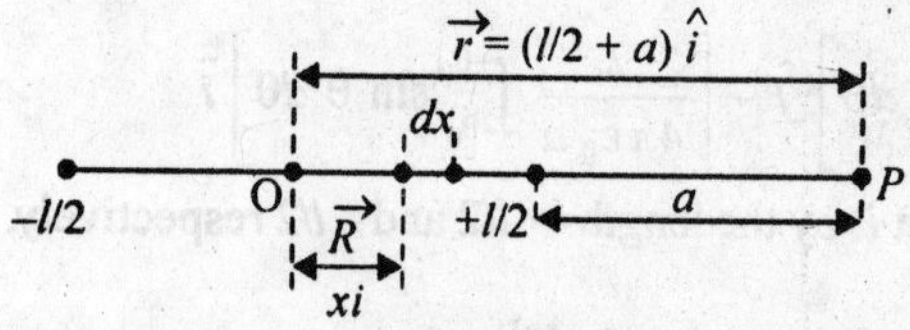

The electric field at P due to charge $\lambda\,dx$ on a small element dx at a vector distance $\vec{R}=x\hat{i}$ is given by

$$\vec{dE} = \dfrac{1}{4\pi\varepsilon_0}\dfrac{\lambda\,dx}{|\vec{r}-\vec{R}|^3}(\vec{r}-\vec{R}) = \dfrac{1}{4\pi\varepsilon_0}\lambda\,dx\dfrac{(r-x)\hat{i}}{|r-x|^3} = \dfrac{\lambda}{4\pi\varepsilon_0}\dfrac{dx}{(r-x)^2}\hat{i}$$

$\therefore$ Electric field at P due to the charge on the whole length l of the wire

$$\vec{E} = \int dE = \dfrac{\lambda\hat{i}}{4\pi\varepsilon_0}\int_{-l/2}^{+l/2}\dfrac{dx}{(r-x)^2} = \dfrac{\lambda\,\hat{i}}{4\pi\varepsilon_0}\left[\dfrac{1}{r-x}\right]_{-l/2}^{+l/2} = \dfrac{\lambda\hat{i}}{4\pi\varepsilon_0}\left[\dfrac{1}{r-\dfrac{l}{2}}-\dfrac{1}{r+\dfrac{l}{2}}\right]$$

Substituting $r = \dfrac{l}{2} + a$, we get

$$\vec{E} = \frac{\lambda \hat{i}}{4\pi\varepsilon_0}\left[\frac{1}{a} - \frac{1}{a+l}\right] = \frac{\lambda \hat{i}}{4\pi\varepsilon_0}\left[\frac{a+l-a}{a(a+l)}\right] = \frac{\lambda l}{4\pi\varepsilon_0\, a\,(a+l)}\,\hat{i}$$

(b) Proceed as in part (a) and derive the relation.

$$\vec{E} = \frac{\lambda \hat{i}}{4\pi\varepsilon_0}\left[\frac{1}{r-\dfrac{l}{2}} - \frac{1}{r+\dfrac{l}{2}}\right]$$

$$= \frac{\lambda \hat{i}}{4\pi\varepsilon_0}\left[\frac{r+\dfrac{l}{2}-r+\dfrac{l}{2}}{\left(r^2 - \dfrac{l^2}{4}\right)}\right]$$

$$= \frac{\lambda}{4\pi\varepsilon_0}\frac{l}{\left(r^2 - \dfrac{l^2}{4}\right)}\,\hat{i}$$

The field acts along the X-axis.

Q. 2.22. Two parallel infinite wires have uniform line charge densities λ_1 and λ_2 separated by a distance x. Calculate electric force per unit length on one wire as a result of the other.

(G.N.D.U., 1995)

Ans. Let A and B be two parallel infinite wires placed parallel to Y-axis as shown in Fig. 2.16. Let λ_1 be the uniform line charge density of wire A and λ_2 that of wire B, then,

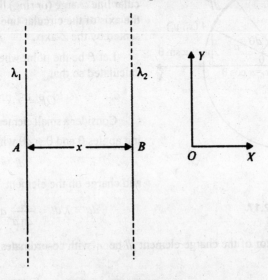

Fig. 2.16

Electric intensity due to the wire A at a distance x from it

$$\vec{E} = \frac{1}{2\pi\varepsilon_0} \frac{\lambda_1}{x}$$

The direction of $\vec{E}$ is perpendicular to the length of the wire A *i.e.* along $+X$ aix.

A small length dl of the wire B carries a charge $dq = \lambda_2 dl$

$\therefore$ Force acting on the length dl of the wire B due to the charge on the wire A

$$= \frac{1}{2\pi\varepsilon_0} \frac{\lambda_1 \lambda_2 \, dl}{x}$$

$\therefore$ Electric force per unit length $= \dfrac{1}{2\pi\varepsilon_0} \dfrac{\lambda_1 \lambda_2}{x}$

The force acts in a direction perpendicular to the length of the wire B *i.e.*, along $+X$-axis. Similarly the force acting on the wire A due to the charge on the wire $B = \dfrac{1}{2\pi\varepsilon_0} \dfrac{\lambda_1 \lambda_2}{x}$ in a direction perpendicular to the length of the wire A *i.e.*, along $-X$-axis.

Q. 2.23. Derive an expression for the electric field due to a circular line charge at a point on its axis.

OR

Derive an expression for electric field at a point situated on the axis of a uniformly charged ring.   *(Pbi. U.,* 2001; *H.P.U.,* 2000)

Ans. Electric field due to a circular charge (or uniformly charged ring). Consider a circular line charge (or uniformly charged ring) of radius a, having total charge q, then line charge density

$$\lambda = \frac{q}{2\pi a}.$$

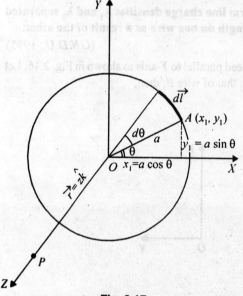

Fig. 2.17

Let the centre of the line charge (or ring) be at the origin O of the co-ordinate system and the circular line charge (or ring) lie in the XY plane so that the axis of the circular line charge or ring is represented by the Z-axis.

Let P be the point where electric field is to be calculated so that

$$\overrightarrow{OP} = \vec{r} = z\,\hat{k}$$

Consider a small element of length $\overrightarrow{dl}$ at A making angles θ and $\theta + d\theta$ with the X-axis, then

$$dl = a\,d\theta$$

and charge on the element

$$dq = \lambda\,dl = \frac{q}{2\pi a}\,a\,d\theta = \frac{q}{2\pi}\,d\theta$$

Let the position vector of the charge element dl be $\vec{r_1}$ with co-ordinates (x_1, y_1) as it lies in the X-Y plane.

[Note. In this question we have taken the position vector of the source charge as $\vec{r_1}$ instead of $\vec{R}$ as in earlier question because we have taken the co-ordinates of the point A as x_1, y_1].

$$\therefore \qquad \vec{r_1} = x_1 \hat{i} + y_1 \hat{j} = a \cos \theta \hat{i} + a \sin \theta \hat{j}$$

Electric field at P due to this charge element at A

$$d\vec{E} = \frac{dq}{4\pi \varepsilon_0} \frac{(\vec{r} - \vec{r_1})}{|\vec{r} - \vec{r_1}|^3} = \frac{q\, d\theta}{2\pi} \frac{1}{4\pi \varepsilon_0} \frac{(\vec{r} - \vec{r_1})}{|\vec{r} - \vec{r_1}|^3} \qquad \ldots(i)$$

Substituting the value of $\vec{r} = z\hat{k}$ and $\vec{r_1} = x\hat{i} + y\hat{j}$, we have

$$(\vec{r} - \vec{r_1}) = z\hat{k} - x_1 \hat{i} - y_1 \hat{j} = z\hat{k} - a \cos \theta \hat{i} - a \sin \theta \hat{j}$$

and $\qquad |\vec{r} - \vec{r_1}| = (z^2 + a^2 \cos^2 \theta + a^2 \sin^2 \theta)^{1/2} = (z^2 + a^2)^{1/2}$ in Eq. (i), we have

$$d\vec{E} = \frac{q}{2\pi} \frac{1}{4\pi \varepsilon_0} \frac{z\hat{k} - a \cos \theta \hat{i} - a \sin \theta \hat{j}}{(z^2 + a^2)^{3/2}} d\theta$$

The total electric field due to the whole circular line charge (or ring) is obtained by integrating the above expression between the limits $\theta = 0$ to $\theta = 2\pi$

$$\therefore \qquad \vec{E} = \int_0^{2\pi} d\vec{E} = \frac{qz\hat{k}}{2\pi (z^2 + a^2)^{3/2}} \frac{1}{4\pi \varepsilon_0} \int_0^{2\pi} d\theta$$

$$- \frac{qa}{2\pi (z^2 + a^2)^{3/2}} \frac{1}{4\pi \varepsilon_0} \left[\hat{i} \int_0^{2\pi} \cos \theta\, d\theta + \hat{j} \int_0^{2\pi} \sin \theta\, d\theta \right]$$

$$= \frac{1}{4\pi \varepsilon_0} \frac{qz\hat{k}\, 2\pi}{2\pi (z^2 + a^2)^{3/2}} = \frac{1}{4\pi \varepsilon_0} \frac{qz}{(z^2 + a^2)^{3/2}} \hat{k} \qquad \ldots(ii)$$

$$= \frac{1}{4\pi \varepsilon_0} \frac{2\pi a \lambda z}{(z^2 + a^2)^{3/2}} \hat{k} \qquad \qquad [\because q = 2\pi a \lambda]$$

$$= \frac{a\lambda}{2\varepsilon_0} \frac{z}{(z^2 + a^2)^{3/2}} \hat{k} \qquad \qquad \ldots(iii)$$

Since $\displaystyle\int_0^{2\pi} \cos \theta\, d\theta = 0$ and $\displaystyle\int_0^{2\pi} \sin \theta\, d\theta = 0$

For positive values of $z\,(z > 0)\ \vec{E}$ is along the $+Z$ axis and for negative values of $z\,(z < 0)\vec{E}$ is along $-Z$-axis.

Q. 2.24. (*a*) **Define surface charge density and volume charge density. State the relation between electric intensity and charge density.**

(*H.P.U.*, 2007, 1999, 1996; *P.U.*, 2003, 1997; *Kerala U.*, 2001)

(*b*) **Is volume charge density invariant (under Lorentz transformations)?**

(*G.N.D.U.*, 2003; *P.U.* 2002; *H.P.U.* 2002, 1999)

Ans. (*a*) **Surface charge density.** Consider a thin charged sheet. If Δq is the charge on a small area ΔS of the charged surface surrounding the point P, then average charge per unit area $= \dfrac{\Delta q}{\Delta S}$

The limiting value of $= \dfrac{\Delta q}{\Delta S}$ as $\Delta S \to 0$ is known as the surface charge density σ at the point P on the infinitesimally small element of area ΔS

$$\therefore \qquad \sigma = \underset{\Delta S \to 0}{\text{Lim}} \frac{\Delta q}{\Delta S} = \frac{dq}{dS}$$

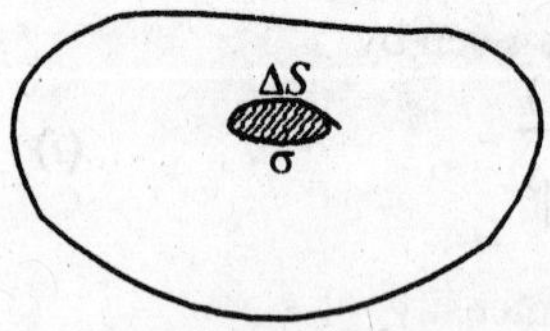

Hence the surface charge density may be defined as the charge per unit area on a given surface plane or curved.

If we have a uniform charge distribution and q is the charge on a surface S, then

Fig. 2.18

$$\sigma = \frac{q}{S}$$

Relation between electric intensity and surface charge density. If σ is the surface charge density on a small area element dS lying at the position vector $\vec{r_1}$, then the electric field intensity $\vec{dE}$ at a point P at the position vector $\vec{r}$ from the origin, in free space is given by

$$\vec{dE} = \frac{1}{4\pi\varepsilon_0} \frac{\sigma\,dS}{|\vec{r} - \vec{r_1}|^3} (\vec{r} - \vec{r_1})$$

For a continuous surface charge distribution the total electric field intensity

$$\vec{E} = \frac{1}{4\pi\varepsilon_0} \iint_S \frac{\sigma\,dS}{|\vec{r} - \vec{r_1}|^3} (\vec{r} - \vec{r_1})$$

If the small area element dS lies at the origin $\vec{r_1} = 0$. In such a case

$$\vec{dE} = \frac{1}{4\pi\varepsilon_0} \frac{\sigma\,dS}{r^3} \vec{r}$$

$$= \frac{1}{4\pi\varepsilon_0} \frac{\sigma\,dS}{r^2} \frac{\vec{r}}{r} = \frac{1}{4\pi\varepsilon_0} \frac{\sigma\,dS}{r^2} \hat{r}$$

where $\hat{r}$ is a unit vector in the direction of $\vec{r}$.

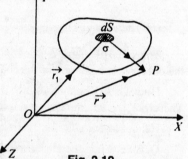

Fig. 2.19

and

$$\vec{E} = \frac{1}{4\pi\varepsilon_0} \iint_S \frac{\sigma\,dS}{r^3} \vec{r} = \frac{1}{4\pi\varepsilon_0} \iint_S \frac{\sigma\,dS}{r^2} \hat{r}$$

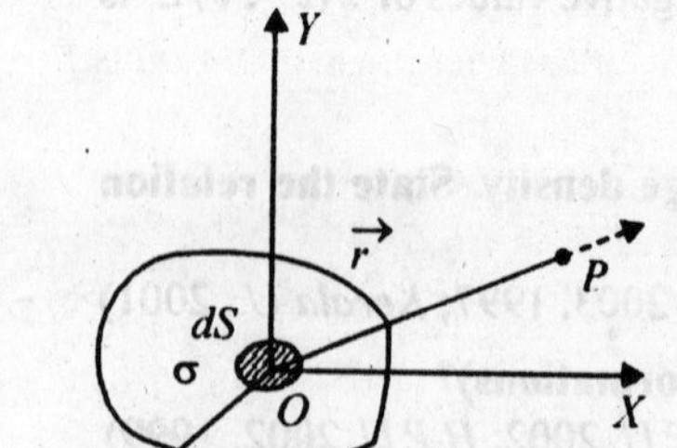

Volume charge density. Consider a three-dimensional volume having a charge. If Δq is the charge in a small volume ΔV, then

$$\text{Average charge per unit volume} = \frac{\Delta q}{\Delta V}$$

The limiting value of $\frac{\Delta q}{\Delta V}$ as $\Delta V \to 0$ is known as the volume charge density ρ at a point P within the infinitesimally small volume ΔV.

Fig. 2.20

$$\rho = \underset{\Delta V \to 0}{\text{Lim}} \frac{\Delta q}{\Delta V} = \frac{dq}{dV} \qquad \qquad ...(ii)$$

Hence the volume charge density may be defined as the charge per unit volume.

If we have a uniform volume charge distribution and q is the charge within volume, V, then

$$\rho = \frac{q}{V}$$

Relation between electric intensity and volume charge density. If ρ is the volume charge density in a small volume element dV lying at the position vector $\vec{r_1}$, then the electric field intensity $\vec{dE}$ at a point P at the position vector $\vec{r}$ from the origin, in free space is given by

$$\vec{dE} = \frac{1}{4\pi\varepsilon_0} \frac{\rho \, dV}{|\vec{r} - \vec{r_1}|^3} (\vec{r} - \vec{r_1})$$

For a continuous volume charge distribution, the total electric field intensity

$$\vec{E} = \frac{1}{4\pi\varepsilon_0} \iiint_V \frac{\rho \, dV}{|\vec{r} - \vec{r_1}|^3} (\vec{r} - \vec{r_1})$$

If the small volume element dV lies at the origin $\vec{r_1} = 0$. In such a case

$$\vec{dE} = \frac{1}{4\pi\varepsilon_0} \frac{\rho \, dV}{r^3} \vec{r} = \frac{1}{4\pi\varepsilon_0} \frac{\rho \, dV}{r^2} \frac{\vec{r}}{r} = \frac{1}{4\pi\varepsilon_0} \frac{\rho \, dV}{r^2} \hat{r}$$

where $\hat{r}$ is a unit vector in the direction of $\vec{r}$

and

$$\vec{E} = \frac{1}{4\pi\varepsilon_0} \iiint_V \frac{\rho \, dV}{r^3} \vec{r} = \frac{1}{4\pi\varepsilon_0} \iiint_V \frac{\rho \, dV}{r^2} \hat{r}$$

(b) The volume charge density $\rho = \lim_{\Delta V \to 0} \frac{\Delta q}{\Delta V}$

The value of charge Δq does not depend upon the state of the observer or the charge *i.e.* whether the observer is in motion or the charge or both.

However, ΔV being a volume (l^3) is different for different observers which are in relative motion. Therefore, the volume charge density ρ will not have the same value in all inertial frames.

Hence *the volume charge density is not invariant under Lorentz transformations.*

Q. 2.25. Find the electric field due to a circular charged disc at a point on a line perpendicular to the disc and passing through its centre. Hence calculate the electric field due to an infinitely large plane conducting sheet of charge. (*Pbi. U.*, 1999; *H.P.U.*, 1992)

OR

Calculate the electric field strength due to a uniformly charged circular sheet on the axis. (*Pbi.U.*, 2002)

Ans. Field due to a circular charged disc. Suppose we have a circular charged disc of radius R in the XY plane as shown in Fig. 2.21 (for convenience). Consider a ring of radius a and thickness da of this disc, then

Surface area of the ring $= 2\pi a \, da$.

If σ is the surface charge density, then

Charge on the ring $q = \sigma 2\pi a \, da$.

Let P be the point on the axis of the disc perpendicular to its surface and passing through its centre O, then OP represents the Z-axis.

Let $\qquad OP = \vec{z}$

$\therefore$ Electric field at P due to the circular element of radius a and thickness da (considering it a line element) according to relation (*ii*) Q. 2.23.

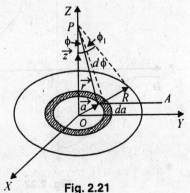

Fig. 2.21

$$\vec{dE} = \frac{1}{4\pi\varepsilon_0} \frac{qz}{(z^2 + a^2)^{3/2}} \hat{k} = \frac{1}{4\pi\varepsilon_0} \frac{\sigma \, 2\pi \, a \, da \, z}{(z^2 + a^2)^{3/2}} \hat{k} = \frac{\sigma \, a \, da \, z}{2\varepsilon_0 \, r^3} \hat{k} \quad [\because (z^2 + a^2)^{1/2} = r]$$

Now in $\triangle \, OAP$

$$a = z \tan \phi \quad \therefore \quad da = z \sec^2 \phi \, d\phi$$

and $$r = z \sec \phi$$

Substituting we have

$$\vec{dE} = \frac{\sigma \, z^3 \sec^2 \phi \tan \phi \, d\phi}{2\varepsilon_0 \, z^3 \sec^3 \phi} \hat{k} = \frac{\sigma \sin \phi \, d\phi}{2\varepsilon_0} \hat{k}$$

Let a point on the extremity of the disc of radius R subtend an angle ϕ_1 at P, then

The electric field at P due to the whole disc

$$\vec{E} = \frac{\sigma}{2\varepsilon_0} \hat{k} \int_0^{\phi_1} \sin \phi \, d\phi = \frac{\sigma}{2\varepsilon_0} \hat{k} \, [- \cos \phi]_0^{\phi_1}$$

$$= \frac{\sigma}{2\varepsilon_0} \hat{k} \, [1 - \cos \phi_1]$$

Now $\cos \phi_1 = \dfrac{|z|}{\sqrt{z^2 + R^2}}$ where $|z|$ is the absolute value of z.

$$\therefore \quad \vec{E} = \frac{\sigma}{2\varepsilon_0} \hat{k} - \frac{\sigma |z|}{2\varepsilon_0 \sqrt{z^2 + R^2}} \hat{k}$$

$$= \frac{\sigma z}{2\varepsilon_0} \left[\frac{1}{|z|} - \frac{1}{\sqrt{z^2 + R^2}} \right] \hat{k} \qquad \qquad ...(i)$$

Variation of electric field with distance. According to relation (i) we find that the electric field due to a uniformly charged disc at a point on its axis is directed along the Z-direction and its magnitude

$$E = \frac{\sigma z}{2\varepsilon_0} \left[\frac{1}{|z|} - \frac{1}{\sqrt{z^2 + R^2}} \right] \qquad \qquad ...(ii)$$

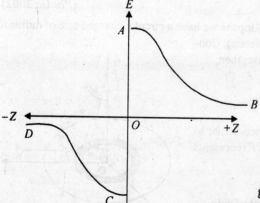

Fig. 2.22

(i) When the point P lies on the $+z$ axis, then

$$|z| = z$$

and relation (ii) becomes

$$E = \frac{\sigma}{2\varepsilon_0} \left[1 - \frac{z}{\sqrt{z^2 + R^2}} \right] \qquad ...(iii)$$

At the centre of the disc $z = 0$

$$\therefore \quad E = \frac{\sigma}{2\varepsilon_0}$$

According to relation (iii) the electric field goes on decreasing as we move away from the centre and becomes zero at $z = \infty$. This is shown in Fig. 2.22 by the portion AB of the curve.

(*ii*) When the point P lies on the $-Z$ axis, then $|z| = -z$ and relation (*iii*) becomes

$$E = -\frac{\sigma}{2\varepsilon_0}\left[1 + \frac{z}{\sqrt{z^2 + R^2}}\right]$$

At the centre of the disc $z = 0$

$$\therefore \qquad E = -\frac{\sigma}{2\varepsilon_0} \qquad \qquad ...(v)$$

As we move away from the centre along $-Z$ axis electric field goes on decreasing and finally becomes zero at $z = \infty$. This is shown by the portion CD of the curve.

Comparing relation (*iv*) and (*v*) we find that the value of electric field at the centre of the disc is $+\dfrac{\sigma}{2\varepsilon_0}$ if we approach the centre from positive side of Z-axis and the value is $-\dfrac{\sigma}{2\varepsilon_0}$ if we approach the centre from negative side of Z-axis. The value of electric field suddenly jumps from $+\dfrac{\sigma}{2\varepsilon_0}$ to $-\dfrac{\sigma}{2\varepsilon_0}$ as we cross the centre of the disc.

Such a point where the electric field shows a sudden jump is called *point of discontinuity. The centre of the disc is, therefore, a point of discontinuity.*

Electric field due to infinite sheet of charge. For an infinite plane sheet of charge $R \to \infty$. In such a case

$$\vec{E} = \frac{\sigma z}{2\varepsilon_0 |z|}\,\hat{k}$$

For a point on the $+Z$ axis $|z| = +z$

and

$$\vec{E} = +\frac{\sigma}{2\varepsilon_0}\,\hat{k}$$

For a point on the $-Z$ axis $|z| = -z$

and

$$\vec{E} = -\frac{\sigma}{2\varepsilon_0}\,\hat{k}$$

The above relations clearly show that electric field is directed normally outward from the infinite sheet of charge. Further, the magnitude of the field is independent of the distance of the point from the infinite plane sheet of charge. This means that an infinite sheet of charge produces a *uniform electric field.*

The value of electric field suddenly jumps from $+\dfrac{\sigma}{2\varepsilon_0}$ to $-\dfrac{\sigma}{2\varepsilon_0}$ as we cross the sheet. Thus for an infinite sheet $z = 0$ *is a point of discontinuity.*

Q. 2.26. Find electric field at the centre of a hemisphere of radius r and charge density σ.
(*P.U.*, 2003)

Ans. Electric field at the centre of a hemisphere. ABC is a hemisphere with centre O and radius r. Consider an element of area ds in the form of a circular strip symmetrically placed over the hemisphere. The radius of the strip is $r \sin \theta$ and its width $r\, d\theta$ where θ is the polar angle.

$$\therefore \quad ds = 2\pi\,(r \sin \theta)\,(r d\theta) = 2\,\pi\,r^2 \sin \theta\,d\theta.$$

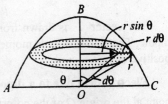

Fig. 2.23

As the surface charge density is σ, the total charge on the strip

$$dq = \sigma \, 2 \, \pi \, r^2 \sin \theta \, d\theta$$

The electric field at O, the centre of the hemisphere due to this circular element of area

$$dE = \frac{dq}{4\pi \varepsilon_0 \, r^2} = \frac{\sigma \, 2 \, \pi \, r^2 \sin \theta \, d\theta}{4 \, \pi \, \varepsilon_0 \, r^2}$$

$$= \frac{\sigma \sin \theta \, d\theta}{2 \, \varepsilon_0}$$

The electric field dE can be resolved into X and Y components. The x-components of the field vanish on integration over the whole hemisphere. The y-component of the field

$$d E_y = dE \cos \theta$$

The total field E due to the whole hemisphere is given by

$$E = \int d E_y = \int_0^{\pi/2} \frac{\sigma \sin \theta \cos \theta \, d\theta}{2 \, \varepsilon_0}$$

$$= \int_0^1 \frac{\sigma \sin \theta \, d \, (\sin \theta)}{2 \, \varepsilon_0}$$

or

$$E = \frac{\sigma}{4\varepsilon_0} \left[\text{as} = \int_0^1 \sin \theta \, d \, (\sin \theta) = \frac{1}{2} \right]$$

The field points along the axis of symmetry and away from the hemisphere.

Q. 2.27. (a) What is an electric dipole? What is dipole moment? Calculate the electric field due to a dipole at a point (i) on the axial line and (ii) on the equatorial line. (H.P.U., 1997)

Show that the value of electric field due to a small dipole at a far off point on the axial line is twice that on the equational line.

(G.N.D.U., 2008, 2007, 2004, 1997, 1996; P.U., 1992, 1991)

(b) Calculate the intensity of the electric field due to an electric dipole of dipole moment 4.5×10^{-10} Coul. metre at a distance of 1 metre from it (i) on its axis and (ii) on the perpendicular axis bisector. (Kan. U., 1997, 1994)

Ans. (a) Electric dipole. *A pair of equal and opposite point charges separated by a small distance is called an electric dipole.*

A molecule made up of a positive and a negative ion is an example of electric dipole in nature.

Electric dipole moment *is defined as the product of one of the charges and the vector distance separating the two charges.*

Thus two equal and opposite charges $+ q$ and $- q$ separated by a small distance $2l$ constitute a dipole. The electric dipole moment is given by

$$\vec{p} = q2\vec{l} = 2q\vec{l}$$

The vector $\vec{l}$ is drawn from the negative to the positive charge and is along the axis of the dipole. The electric dipole moment is a *vector* quantity and its direction is also from negative to the positive charge.

Electric field due to a dipole. Consider an electric dipole lying along the X-axis with its mid point at the origin O of the co-ordinate system. Let the magnitude of each charge be q and $2\vec{l}$ the vector distance between the charges.

Dipole moment of the electric dipole

$$\vec{p} = q2\vec{l} = 2ql\,\hat{i}$$

(i) Point on the axial line. Consider a point P on the axial line of the dipole at a vector distance $\vec{r} = r\hat{i}$ from the origin. Let $\vec{r_+}$ and $\vec{r_-}$ be the position vectors of charges $+q$ and $-q$ respectively then $\vec{r_+} = \vec{l} = l\hat{i}$ and $\vec{r_-} = -\vec{l} = -l\hat{i}$.

Electric field at P due to the charge $+q$

$$\vec{E_+} = \frac{q}{4\pi\varepsilon_0}\frac{(\vec{r}-\vec{r_+})}{|\vec{r}-\vec{r_+}|^3} = \frac{q}{4\pi\varepsilon_0}\frac{(r\hat{i}-l\hat{i})}{|r\hat{i}-l\hat{i}|^3}$$

$$= \frac{q}{4\pi\varepsilon_0}\frac{(r-l)\hat{i}}{(r-l)^3} = \frac{q}{4\pi\varepsilon_0(r-l)^2}\hat{i}$$

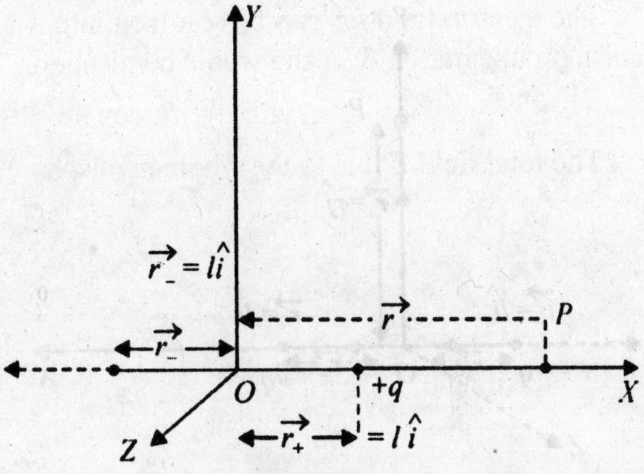

Similarly electric field at P due to the charge $-q$

$$\vec{E_-} = \frac{-q}{4\pi\varepsilon_0}\frac{r\hat{i}+l\hat{i}}{|r\hat{i}+l\hat{i}|^3} = -\frac{q}{4\pi\varepsilon_0(r+l)^2}\hat{i}$$

The resultant electric field at P

Fig. 2.24 (a)

$$\vec{E} = \vec{E_+} + \vec{E_-} = \frac{q\hat{i}}{4\pi\varepsilon_0}\left[\frac{1}{(r-l)^2} - \frac{1}{(r+l)^2}\right]$$

$$= \frac{q\hat{i}}{4\pi\varepsilon_0}\left[\frac{4rl}{(r^2-l^2)^2}\right]$$

Now

$$2lq\,\hat{i} = \vec{p}$$

$$\therefore \qquad \vec{E} = \frac{1}{4\pi\varepsilon_0}\frac{2r\,\vec{p}}{(r^2-l^2)^2} \qquad \qquad ...(i)$$

Equation (i) shows that the electric field $\vec{E}$ acts along the $+X$ direction.

When P lies at a far off point. When the point P lies at a vary large distance as compared to the length of the dipole i.e. $r >> l$, then l^2 can be neglected as compared to r^2 and we get

$$\vec{E} = \frac{1}{4\pi\varepsilon_0}\frac{2\,\vec{p}}{r^3} \qquad \qquad ...(ii)$$

This shows that the electric field due to a dipole at a far off point varies inversely as the cube of the distance from the dipole.

The direction of electric field is along $+X$-axis as the direction $\vec{p}$ is from $-q$ to $+q$ to $+q$ i.e., along $+X$-axis.

(ii) Point on the equatorial line. As the origin of the co-ordinate system lies at the mid point of the dipole, the equatorial line co-incides with the Y-axis.

Consider a point P on the Y-axis (Equatorial line) at a vector distance $\vec{r} = r\,\hat{j}$ from the origin. Then electric field at P due to the charge $+q$

$$\vec{E}_{+} = \frac{q}{4\pi\varepsilon_0}\frac{(\vec{r}-\vec{r}_{+})}{|\vec{r}-\vec{r}_{+}|^3} = \frac{q}{4\pi\varepsilon_0}\frac{r\,\hat{j}-l\,\hat{i}}{|r\,\hat{j}-l\,\hat{i}|^3} = \frac{q}{4\pi\varepsilon_0}\frac{r\,\hat{j}-l\,\hat{i}}{(r^2+l^2)^{3/2}}$$

because $\qquad\qquad |r\,\hat{j}-l\,\hat{i}| = (r^2+l^2)^{1/2}$

Similarly electric field at P due to the charge $-q$

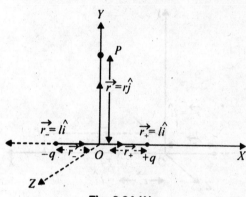

Fig. 2.24 (b)

$$\vec{E}_{-} = \frac{-q}{4\pi\varepsilon_0}\frac{r\,\hat{j}+l\,\hat{i}}{(r^2+l^2)^{3/2}}$$

The resultant electric field at P

$$\vec{E} = \vec{E}_{+} + \vec{E}_{-}$$

$$= \frac{q}{4\pi\varepsilon_0}\left[\frac{r\,\hat{j}-l\,\hat{i}}{(r^2+l^2)^{3/2}} - \frac{r\,\hat{j}+l\,\hat{i}}{(r^2+l^2)^{3/2}}\right]$$

$$= \frac{-q}{4\pi\varepsilon_0}\frac{2\,l\,\hat{i}}{(r^2+l^2)^{3/2}} = \frac{-\vec{p}}{4\pi\varepsilon_0\,(r^2+l^2)^{3/2}}$$

...(iii)

Eq. (iii) shows that the electric field $\vec{E}$ acts along the $-X$ direction.

When P lies at a far off point. For a very far off point l^2 can be neglected as compared to r^2 and we get

$$\vec{E} = -\frac{\vec{p}}{4\pi\varepsilon_0\,r^3}$$

...(iv)

This relation shows that the electric field $\vec{E}$ points in a direction opposite to dipole moment vector $\vec{p}$. As the direction of $\vec{p}$ is from $-q$ to $+q$ i.e., along $+X$ axis, the electric field points along $-X$ axis. This relation also shows that the electric field due to a short dipole varies inversely as the cube of the distance of the point.

Comparing relation (ii) and (iv) we find that

(1) The magnitude of the electric field due to a small dipole at a far off point on the axial line is *twice* the value of the electric field at a far off point on the equatorial line.

(2) The electric field on the axial line is directed along $+X$ axis and on the equatorial line along $-X$ axis.

(b) For a far off point on the axial line, the electric field

$$|\vec{E}| = \frac{1}{4\pi\varepsilon_0}\frac{2p}{r^3}$$

Here $p = 4.5 \times 10^{-10}$ coul metre; $\dfrac{1}{4\pi\varepsilon_0} = 9\times10^9$; $r = 1$ metre

$$\therefore \qquad |\vec{E}| = \frac{2\times4.5\times10^{-10}}{1\times1\times1}\times9\times10^9 = 8.1\ \text{NC}^{-1}$$

When the point lies on the perpendicular axis bisector or equatorial line

$$|\vec{E}| = \frac{1}{4\pi\varepsilon_0}\frac{p}{r^3} = 4.05 \text{ NC}^{-1}$$

Q. 2.28. Calculate the electric field at a far off arbitrary point due to a small point dipole. Hence find the value of the field at a point (i) on the axial line and (ii) on the equatorial line.

(P.U. 2007; H.P.U. 2002, 1999; Kan. U., 1997,1993)

Ans. Electric field at any point due to a short dipole. Consider an electric dipole lying along the X-axis with its mid point O at the origin of the co-ordinate system. Let the magnitude of each charge be q and $2\vec{l}$ the vector distance between the two charges then

Dipole moment of the electric dipole $\vec{p} = 2q\,\vec{l}$

Let the position vector of the charge $+q$ be $\vec{r}_+$ and of the charge $-q$ be $\vec{r}_-$ then $\vec{r}_+ = \vec{l}$ and $\vec{r}_- = -\vec{l}$

Consider a point P having position vector $\vec{r}$. The electric field at P due to the charge $+q$

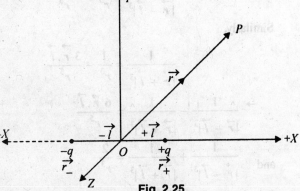

Fig. 2.25

$$\vec{E}_+ = \frac{q}{4\pi\varepsilon_0}\frac{(\vec{r}-\vec{r}_+)}{|\vec{r}-\vec{r}_+|^3} = \frac{q}{4\pi\varepsilon_0}\frac{(\vec{r}-\vec{l})}{|\vec{r}-\vec{l}|^3}$$

Electric field at P due to the charge $-q$

$$\vec{E}_- = -\frac{q}{4\pi\varepsilon_0}\frac{(\vec{r}-\vec{r}_-)}{|\vec{r}-\vec{r}_-|^3} = -\frac{q}{4\pi\varepsilon_0}\frac{(\vec{r}+\vec{l})}{|\vec{r}+\vec{l}|^3}$$

Total electric field at P due to both the charges

$$\vec{E} = \vec{E}_+ + \vec{E}_- = \frac{q}{4\pi\varepsilon_0}\left[\frac{(\vec{r}-\vec{l})}{|\vec{r}-\vec{l}|^3} - \frac{(\vec{r}+\vec{l})}{|\vec{r}+\vec{l}|^3}\right]$$

$$= \frac{q\,\vec{r}}{4\pi\varepsilon_0}\left[\frac{1}{|\vec{r}-\vec{l}|^3} - \frac{1}{|\vec{r}+\vec{l}|^3}\right] - \frac{q\,\vec{l}}{4\pi\varepsilon_0}\left[\frac{1}{|\vec{r}-\vec{l}|^3} + \frac{1}{|\vec{r}+\vec{l}|^3}\right] \qquad ...(i)$$

Now
$$|\vec{r}-\vec{l}|^2 = (\vec{r}-\vec{l})\cdot(\vec{r}-\vec{l}) = r^2 + l^2 - 2\vec{r}\cdot\vec{l}$$

$$= r^2\left[1 - \frac{2\vec{r}\cdot\vec{l}}{r^2} + \frac{l^2}{r^2}\right] = r^2\left[1 - \frac{2\vec{r}\cdot\vec{l}}{r^2}\right]$$

because when $r \gg l$, l^2 can be neglected as compared to r^2 and $\frac{l^2}{r^2}$ tends to zero.

$$\therefore \qquad |\vec{r}-\vec{l}| = r\left[1 - \frac{2\vec{r}\cdot\vec{l}}{r^2}\right]^{1/2}$$

and
$$\frac{1}{|\vec{r} - \vec{l}|^3} = r^{-3}\left(1 - \frac{2\vec{r}\cdot\vec{l}}{r^2}\right)^{-3/2}$$

$$= \frac{1}{r^3}\left(1 - \frac{3\vec{r}\cdot\vec{l}}{r^2} + \dots \text{ terms containing higher powers}\right)$$

As the terms containing higher powers can be neglected,

$$\frac{1}{|\vec{r} - \vec{l}|^3} = \frac{1}{r^3} + \frac{3\vec{r}\cdot\vec{l}}{r^5}$$

Similarly,

$$\frac{1}{|\vec{r} + \vec{l}|^3} = \frac{1}{r^3} - \frac{3\vec{r}\cdot\vec{l}}{r^5}$$

$$\therefore \quad \frac{1}{|\vec{r} - \vec{l}|^3} - \frac{1}{|\vec{r} + \vec{l}|^3} = \frac{6\vec{r}\cdot\vec{l}}{r^5}$$

and
$$\frac{1}{|\vec{r} - \vec{l}|^3} + \frac{1}{|\vec{r} + \vec{l}|^3} = \frac{2}{r^3}$$

Substituting these values in Eq. (*i*), we have

$$\vec{E} = \frac{q\vec{r}}{4\pi\varepsilon_0}\frac{6\vec{r}\cdot\vec{l}}{r^5} - \frac{q\vec{l}}{4\pi\varepsilon_0}\frac{2}{r^3}$$

$$= \frac{3\vec{r}(\vec{r}\cdot 2q\vec{l})}{4\pi\varepsilon_0\,r^5} - \frac{2q\vec{l}}{4\pi\varepsilon_0\,r^3}$$

or
$$\vec{E} = \frac{3\vec{r}(\vec{r}\cdot\vec{p})}{4\pi\varepsilon_0\,r^5} - \frac{\vec{p}}{4\pi\varepsilon_0\,r^3} \qquad \dots(ii)$$

Relation (*ii*) gives the electric field due to a small dipole located at the origin at any point away from it.

(*i*) **When P lies on the axial line.** When the point *P* lies on the axial line

$$\vec{r} = r\hat{i} \text{ and } \vec{l} = l\hat{i}$$

$$\therefore \quad \vec{r}\cdot\vec{p} = \vec{r}\cdot 2q\vec{l} = r\hat{i}\cdot 2ql\hat{i} = r\,2ql = rp$$

$$\therefore \quad \vec{E} = \frac{3r\hat{i}\,r\,p}{4\pi\varepsilon_0\,r^5} - \frac{p\hat{i}}{4\pi\varepsilon_0\,r^3} = \frac{2p}{4\pi\varepsilon_0\,r^3}\hat{i} = \frac{2\vec{p}}{4\pi\varepsilon_0\,r^3}$$

Compare the above result with relation (*ii*). Q. 2.27.

(*ii*) **When P lies on the equatorial line.** When the point *P* lies on the equatorial line

$$\vec{r} = r\hat{j} \text{ and } \vec{l} = l\hat{i}$$

$$\therefore \quad \vec{r}\cdot\vec{p} = r\hat{j}\cdot 2ql\hat{i} = 2qrl(\hat{j}\cdot\hat{i}) = 0$$

$$\therefore \qquad \vec{E} = -\frac{p}{4\pi\varepsilon_0\,r^3}$$

Compare the above result with relation (*iv*) Q. 2.27.

Q. 2.29. A thin rod of length 2*l* having uniform linear charge density λ extends from *x* = − *l* to *x* = + *l*. Find (*a*) monopole moment of the rod (*b*) dipole moment of the rod with respect to the origin.   (*P.U.*, 2003)

Ans. (*a*) **Monopole moment.** Monopole moment of the rod = Total charge on the rod

$$= \lambda \times 2l = 2\lambda l$$

because λ is uniform linear charge density

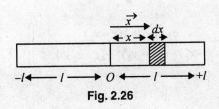

Fig. 2.26

(*b*) **Dipole moment.** Consider a small element *dx* of the rod at a distance *x* from *O* so that the position vector of the element is $\vec{x} = x\hat{i}$.

The charge on the element $dq = \lambda\,dx$

As the element is small, we can treat it as a point charge. The dipole moment of the element with respect to the origin *O*.

$$d\vec{p} = dq\,\vec{x} = \lambda\,dx\,x\hat{i}$$

∴ Total dipole moment of the rod

$$\vec{p} = \int d\vec{p} = \int_{-l}^{+l} \lambda\,x\,dx\,\hat{i} = \hat{i}\,\lambda \int_{-l}^{+l} x\,dx = \hat{i}\,\lambda\left[\frac{x^2}{2}\right]_{-l}^{+l} = 0$$

Thus the rod has no dipole moment about the origin which is the centre of the rod.

Q. 2.30. There are two charges q_1 and q_2 at the position vectors $\vec{r_1}$ and $\vec{r_2}$. Find (*i*) The electric field at $\vec{r}$ and (*ii*) The curl of this vector field.

Ans. (*i*) Let *P* be the point at position vector $\vec{r}$, q_1 the charge at the position vector $\vec{r_1}$ and q_2 the charge at position vector $\vec{r_2}$, then electric field at *P*

$$\vec{E} = \frac{1}{4\pi\varepsilon_0}\left[\frac{q_1\,(\vec{r}-\vec{r_1})}{|\vec{r}-\vec{r_1}|^3} + \frac{q_2\,(\vec{r}-\vec{r_2})}{|\vec{r}-\vec{r_2}|^3}\right]$$

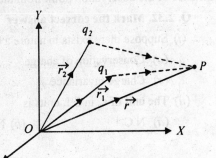

Fig. 2.27

(*ii*) Let the cartesian co-ordinates of *P*, q_1 and q_2 respectively be (*x*, *y*, *z*), (x_1, y_1, z_1); and (x_2, y_2, z_2) then

$$\vec{E} = \frac{1}{4\pi\varepsilon_0}\left[\frac{q_1\{(x-x_1)\hat{i}+(y-y_1)\hat{j}+(z-z_1)\hat{k}\}}{\{(x-x_1)^2+(y-y_1)^2+(z-z_1^2)^2\}^{3/2}} + \frac{q_2\{(x-x_2)\hat{i}+(y-y_2)\hat{j}+(z-z_2)\hat{k}\}}{\{(x-x_2)^2+(y-y_2)^2+(z-z_2)^2\}^{3/2}}\right]$$

$$\text{Now } Curl\ \vec{E} = \frac{1}{4\pi\varepsilon_0}\left[\left(\frac{\partial E_z}{\partial y}-\frac{\partial E_y}{\partial z}\right)\hat{i} + \left(\frac{\partial E_x}{\partial z}-\frac{\partial E_z}{\partial x}\right)\hat{j} + \left(\frac{\partial E_y}{\partial x}-\frac{\partial E_x}{\partial y}\right)\hat{k}\right]$$

and $E_x = \dfrac{1}{4\pi\varepsilon_0}\left[\dfrac{q_1(x-x_1)}{\{(x-x_1)^2+(y-y_1)^2+(z-z_1)^2\}^{3/2}}+\dfrac{q_2(x-x_2)}{\{(x-x_2)^2+(y-y_2)^2+(z-z_2)^2\}^{3/2}}\right]$

Hence $\dfrac{\partial E_x}{\partial y}=\dfrac{1}{4\pi\varepsilon_0}\left[\dfrac{q_1(x-x_1)\left(-\dfrac{3}{2}\right)2(y-y_1)}{\{(x-x_1)^2+(y-y_1)^2+(z-z_1)^2\}^{5/2}}+\dfrac{q_2(x-x_2)\left(-\dfrac{3}{2}\right)2(y-y_2)}{\{(x-x_2)^2+(y-y_2)^2+(z-z_2)^2\}^{5/2}}\right]$

$=\dfrac{1}{4\pi\varepsilon_0}\left\{-3\left[\dfrac{q_1(x-x_1)(y-y_1)}{\{(x-x_1)^2+(y-y_1)^2+(z-z_1)^2\}^{5/2}}+\dfrac{q_2(x-x_2)(y-y_2)}{\{(x-x_2)^2+(y-y_2)^2+(z-z_2)^2\}^{5/2}}\right]\right\}$

Similarly

$\dfrac{\partial E_y}{\partial x}=\dfrac{1}{4\pi\varepsilon_0}\left\{-3\left[\dfrac{q_1(y-y_1)(x-x_1)}{\{(x-x_1)^2+(y-y_1)^2+(z-z_1)^2\}^{5/2}}+\dfrac{q_2(y-y_2)(x-x_2)}{\{(x-x_2)^2+(y-y_2)^2+(z-z_2)^2\}^{5/2}}\right]\right\}$

$\therefore \quad \dfrac{\partial E_y}{\partial x}-\dfrac{\partial E_x}{\partial y}=0$

Similarly $\quad \dfrac{\partial E_x}{\partial z}-\dfrac{\partial E_z}{\partial x}=0$

and $\quad \dfrac{\partial E_z}{\partial y}-\dfrac{\partial E_y}{\partial z}=0$

$\therefore \qquad\qquad Curl\ \vec{E}=0$

Q. 2.31. It is said that the distance between the two charges constituting the electric dipole should be small as compared to what?
(G.N.D.U., 2003)

Ans. In calculating the intensity of the electric field at any arbitrary point at a distance r from the centre of the dipole, it is assumed that $r \gg l$ so that l^2 can be neglected as compared to r^2. Therefore, the distance between the two charges ($2l$) constituting the dipole should be small as compared to r the distance of the observation point from the centre of the dipole.

Q. 2.32. Mark the correct answer

(i) Suppose there exists in nature a body with charge 1.7 e. Will it violate the principle of
   (a) Conservation of charge
   (b) Charge quantisation
   (c) Charge invariance .
   (d) Superposition

(ii) The unit of ε_0 in S.I. units is
   (a) N C^{-1}
   (b) N m^2 C^{-2}
   (c) C^2 N^{-1} m^{-2}
   (d) C S^{-1}
(H.P.U., 2000)

(iii) Two charges + 2 μC and + 5 μC are separated by a distance $d = 10$ cm apart. The ratio of the force acting on the respective charges is
   (a) 2 : 5
   (b) 5 : 2
   (c) 1 : 1
   (d) 4 : 25
(P. U., 1994)

(iv) The direction of electric dipole moment is
   (a) from positive to negative
   (b) from negative to positive
   (c) not known

(v) The electric field due to an infinite charged wire at a point on a line perpendicular to the wire is

(a) $\dfrac{\lambda}{2\pi\varepsilon_0}$ (b) $\dfrac{\lambda}{4\pi\varepsilon_0\,a}$ (c) $\dfrac{2\lambda}{\pi\varepsilon_0\,a}$ (d) $\dfrac{\lambda}{\pi\varepsilon_0\,a}$

Ans. (i) b (ii) c (iii) c (iv) b

(v) a

EXERCISES

1. Two charges +5 coulomb and +15 coulomb are located at points (2, – 4, 3) and (– 3, 2, 1) metres. Calculate the force on + 15 coulomb.

$$\left[\text{Ans. } |\vec{F_{12}}| = 10.38 \times 10^9 \text{ N}; \hat{r}_{12} = \frac{-5\,\hat{i} + 6\,\hat{j} - 2\,\hat{k}}{\sqrt{65}}\right]$$

2. Calculate the net electrical force on a unit positive charge placed at the centre of a square of side 'b' which has charges $q, 2q, -4q$ and $2q$ placed in order at 4 corners.

Hint. Let the square $ABCD$ of each side 'b' have charges $q, +2q, -4q$ and $2q$ at the corners A, B, C and D. Electric intensity at 0 due to $2q$ at B and $2q$ at D cancel each other. Therefore electric intensity at O

$$= \frac{1}{4\pi\varepsilon_0}\left[\frac{q}{b^2/2} + \frac{4q}{b^2/2}\right] = \left[\frac{1}{4\pi\varepsilon_0}\frac{10q}{b^2}\right]$$

$$\left\{\text{Ans. } \left[\frac{1}{4\pi\varepsilon_0}\frac{10q}{b^2}\right]\right\}$$

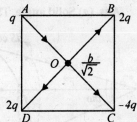

Fig. 2.28

3 Gauss's Theorem and Its Applications

Q. 3.1. (*a*) **Define a solid angle and show that the solid angle subtended by (*i*) a sphere at its centre is 4π (*ii*) a closed surface of any shape at a point inside it is 4π and at a point outside it is zero.** (*P.U.* 2003, 2001, *H.P.U.* 1995)

(*b*) **Calculate the maximum value of a solid angle.** (*P.U.* 2007)

Ans. (*a*) Solid angle. The solid angle $d\omega$ subtended by an elementary surface ares $\vec{dS}$ at a point O at a vector distance $\vec{r}$ from it is given by

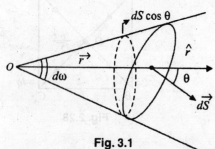

Fig. 3.1

$$d\omega = \frac{\vec{dS}.\hat{r}}{r^2} \qquad ...(i)$$

where $\hat{r}$ is a unit vector in the direction of $\vec{r}$ and is given by

$$\hat{r} = \frac{\vec{r}}{\left|\vec{r}\right|} = \frac{\vec{r}}{r}$$

$$\therefore \qquad d\omega = \frac{\vec{dS}.\vec{r}}{r^3} \qquad ...(ii)$$

But $\vec{dS}.\vec{r} = dS\, r \cos\theta$ where θ is the angle that the area vector $\vec{dS}$ makes with the distance vector $\vec{r}$.

$$\therefore \qquad d\omega = \frac{dS\, r \cos\theta}{r^3} = \frac{dS \cos\theta}{r^2} \qquad ...(iii)$$

$dS \cos\theta$ is the projection of the area $\vec{dS}$ in a direction perpendicular to $\vec{r}$ or it is the normal component of the area of the surface dS.

Hence the solid angle subtended by a surface at a point is measured by the ratio of the normal component of the area of the surface to the square of the distance of the surface from the point.

The unit of solid angle is steradian (*sr*).

(*i*) **Solid angle subtended by a sphere at its centre.** Consider a sphere of radius r. The solid angle subtended by an elementary area $\vec{dS}$ at its centre is given by

$$d\omega = \frac{\vec{dS}.\hat{r}}{r^2} = \frac{dS \cos\theta}{r^2} = \frac{dS}{r^2}$$

because the angle θ between the area vector $\overrightarrow{dS}$ and the radius vector $\overrightarrow{r}$ (or unit vector $\hat{r}$) is zero as both the vectors act in the same direction.

The total solid angle subtended by the whole of the surface of the sphere at the centre

$$\omega = \int d\omega = \iint_{CS} \frac{dS}{r^2} = \frac{1}{r^2} \iint_{CS} dS = \frac{1}{r^2} \times 4\pi r^2 = 4\pi$$

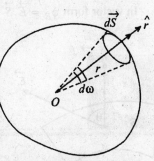

Since the area of the surface of the sphere $= 4\pi r^2$

Hence the surface of sphere subtends a solid angle of 4π steradians at its centre.

(*ii*) **Solid angle subtended by a closed surface of any shape at a point inside it.** Consider a closed surface S_1 of any shape. Let P be a point any where inside it. Draw a sphere S with P as centre.

Now the solid angle subtended by the elementary area dS_1 of the surface S_1 at P is equal to the solid angle subtended by the elementary area dS of the sphere S at P.

Fig. 3.2

Again, corresponding to every elementary area of the surface S_1 there is a surface area of the sphere S. Thus the total solid angle subtended by the surface S_1 at any point inside it is equal to the solid angle subtended by the spherical surface S and is, therefore, equal to 4π.

In other words a closed surface of any shape subtends a solid angle 4π at any point inside it.

Solid angle subtended by a closed surface at any point outside it. Consider a point P outside a closed surface S. As shown the solid angle subtended by the elementary surface area dS_1 and dS_2 are equal in magnitude but opposite in sign because the area vector $\overrightarrow{dS_1}$ makes an acute angle with $\hat{r}$ (or $\overrightarrow{r}$) whereas area vector $\overrightarrow{dS_2}$ makes an obtuse angle with $\hat{r}$ (or $\overrightarrow{r}$). Thus the net solid angle subtended by the two elementary areas taken together is zero.

Fig. 3.3

As corresponding to every area $\overrightarrow{dS_1}$ there is an area $\overrightarrow{dS_2}$, the net solid angle subtended by each pair will be zero. Hence the net solid angle subtended by the whole of the closed surface at any point outside it is zero.

(*b*) **Maximum value of solid angle.** The solid angle subtended by a closed surface of any shape at a point inside it is maximum and its value is 4π steradian.

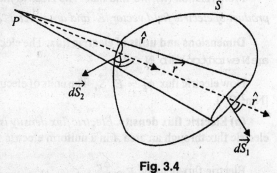

Fig. 3.4

Q.3.2. (*a*) **Explain the meaning of the term electric flux. What are its dimensions and S.I. units?** (*G.N.D.U.* 2003, 2002, 2000 ; *H.P.U.*, 1994 ; *Pbi. U.*, 2006, 1991 ; *Luck. U.*, 1993)

(*b*) **Define electric flux density write its S.I. units.** (*G. N. D.U.* 2006; *M.D.U.* 2000)

Ans. Electric flux. For a *uniform electric field*, the electric flux ϕ_E through an area S is defined as the product of the area and the component of electric field vector $\vec{E}$ normal to the area.

$$\therefore \qquad \phi_E = ES \cos \theta$$

where θ is the angle between the direction of $\vec{E}$ and positive normal to area $\vec{S}$

In vector form $\phi_E = \vec{E}.\vec{S}$

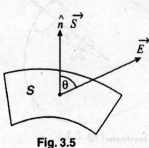

If S is the magnitude of the area vector $\vec{S}$ and $\hat{n}$ a unit vector in the direction of positive normal, then $\vec{S} = S\hat{n}$

The electric flux can, therefore, be written as the scalar product of two vectors

$$\phi_E = \vec{E}.\vec{S} = \vec{E}.S\hat{n}$$

For a *closed surface* the direction of $\hat{n}$ is along the *outward drawn normal to the surface.*

Fig. 3.5

For a non-uniform electric field *i.e.,* if $\vec{S}$ is large or $\vec{E}$ varies from point to point, we divide the surface S into small elementary areas $\Delta\vec{S}$ each, then the electric flux over the elementary area $\Delta\vec{S}$ is given by

$$\Delta\phi_E = \vec{E}.\Delta\vec{S} \qquad\qquad\qquad ...(i)$$

The electric flux over the whole area

$$\phi_E = \sum_s \vec{E}.\Delta\vec{S}$$

As $\Delta\vec{S} \to 0$ we can replace $\Delta\vec{S}$ by $d\vec{S}$ and $\Delta\phi_E$ by $d\phi_E$, then relation (i) can be put as

$$d\phi_E = \vec{E}.d\vec{S} \qquad\qquad\qquad ...(ii)$$

$$\therefore \qquad \phi_E = \iint_s \vec{E}.d\vec{S}$$

where $\iint_s$ represents the surface integral over the area $\vec{S}$.

From relation (ii), we find that '*The electric flux through a vector area* $d\vec{S}$ *is given by the dot product of electric field vector* $\vec{E}$ *and area vector* $d\vec{S}$.

Dimensions and units of electric flux. The electric intensity $\vec{E} = \dfrac{\vec{F}}{q_0}$. The units of $\vec{E}$ therefore, are Newton/coulomb [N C^{-1}]

Now electric flux $\phi_E = \vec{E}.\vec{S}$. The units of electric flux therefore, are Newton metre^2 per coulomb [Nm^2 C^{-1}].

(b) Electric flux density. *Electric flux density is defined as electric flux per unit area.* If ϕ_E is the electric flux through an area A in a uniform electric field, then,

Electric flux density $E = \dfrac{\phi_E}{A}$

Unit. The S.I. unit of electric flux density is [N C^{-1}] *Newton per Coulumb.*

Exercise. *A rectangular surface of area $15m^2$ is placed in a uniform electric field of 3000 N/C making an angle of 60° with the field. Find the electric flux through the sheet.* (P.U. 2006)

Hint. $E = 3000$ N/C; $S = 15$ m^2; $\theta = 60°$

$\therefore$ Electric flux through the sheet $\phi_E = ES \cos \theta$

where θ is the angle between the direction of the field E and positive normal to the area (which gives the direction of area vector)

$\therefore \qquad\qquad \phi_E = 3000 \times 15 \times \cos 60° = 3000 \times 15 \times 0.5 = 22500$ Nm^{2}C^{-1}

Q.3.3. If $\vec{E} = 3\,\hat{i} + 4\,\hat{j} + 8\,\hat{k}$ **calculate the electric flux through surface area 100 units lying in X-Y plane.** *(G.N.D.U., 1993 ; Pbi. U., 1993 ; P.U., 1991)*

Ans. Here $\qquad\qquad \vec{E} = 3\,\hat{i} + 4\,\hat{j} + 8\,\hat{k}$. The field is uniform.

As the surface area lies in the X-Y plane, the area vector is directed in the Z-direction

$\therefore \qquad\qquad$ Area vector $\vec{S} = 100\,\hat{k}$

where $\hat{k}$ is a unit vector along the $+ Z$ axis.

For free space, electric flux $\phi_E = \iint_s \vec{E}.\,d\vec{S} = \vec{E}.\vec{S}$ as the field is uniform.

$\therefore \qquad\qquad \phi_E = \vec{E}.\vec{S} = (3\,\hat{i} + 4\,\hat{j} + 8\,\hat{k}).\,(100\,\hat{k}) = 800$ Nm^2 C^{-1}

Exercise. *If the electric field is given by* $\vec{E} = 6\,\hat{i} + 3\,\hat{j} + 4\,\hat{k}$, *calculate the electric flux through a surface of area 20 units lying in Y-Z plane.* *(M.D.U. 2002)*

Hint. The field is uniform. As surface area lies in Y-Z plane, the area vector is directed in X-direction. $\vec{S} = 20\,\hat{i}$

$$\phi_E = \iint_s \vec{E}.\,d\vec{S} = \vec{E}.\vec{S} = (6\,\hat{i} + 3\,\hat{j} + 4\,\hat{k}).\,(20\hat{i}) = 120$$ Nm^2 C^{-1}

Q.3.4. In a region an electric fields $\vec{E} = 2\,\hat{i} + 3\,\hat{j} + \hat{k}$. **Calculate the electric flux through the surface** $\vec{S} = 10\,\hat{i}$. *(P.U. 2007, H.P.U. 1996)*

Ans. Here $\qquad\qquad \vec{E} = 2\,\hat{i} + 3\,\hat{j} + \hat{k}$. The field is uniform

$$\vec{S} = 10\,\hat{i}$$

$\therefore$ Electric flux $\qquad \phi_E = \vec{E}.\vec{S} = (2\,\hat{i} + 3\,\hat{j} + \hat{k}).\,(10\,\hat{i}) = 20$ Nm^2 C^{-1}

Q.3.5. Under what conditions is the flux of a vector field through a plane surface (*i*) positive (*ii*) negative (*iii*) zero? *(G.N.D.U., 1994)*

Ans. For a vector field through a plane surface *positive flux* implies lines of electric force of the field *emerging out* of the surface, *negative flux* means lines of force of the field are *directed* into the surface. The flux is zero if as many lines of force are directed into the surface as emerge out of it.

Q.3.6. Show that the electric flux over a surface S due to a point charge q is $\dfrac{\omega}{4\pi \varepsilon_0}\,q$ **where q is the charge and ω the solid angle subtended by the surface at the charge.**

Ans. Electric flux over a surface due to a point charge. Consider a point charge q and a surface S in free space. Let r be the distance from the charge to a point P on the surface, $\hat{n}$ the outwardly directed unit normal to the surface at the point P contained by a small element of surface area vectorially represented by $d\vec{S}$. The electric field $\vec{E}$ at the point P on the surface due to the

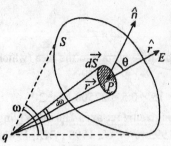

Fig. 3.6

charge q is directed along the line from the charge q to the point P. Let the direction of $\vec{E}$ make an angle θ with the unit normal $\hat{n}$ then the electric flux over the area $\vec{dS}$ is given by

$$d\phi_E = \vec{E} \cdot \vec{dS} = \frac{1}{4\pi\varepsilon_0} \frac{q}{r^2} \hat{r} \cdot \hat{n}\, dS$$

$$= \frac{1}{4\pi\varepsilon_0} \frac{q}{r^2}\, dS \cos\theta$$

as $\hat{r} \cdot \hat{n} = \cos\theta$

Now $\dfrac{dS \cos\theta}{r^2} = d\omega$ the small solid angle subtended by the surface dS at the position of the point charge q

$\therefore$ $$d\phi_E = \frac{1}{4\pi\varepsilon_0}\, q\, d\omega$$

Hence electric flux over the whole of the surface S due to the point charge q

$$\phi_E = \frac{1}{4\pi\varepsilon_0} \iint_s q\, d\omega = \frac{1}{4\pi\varepsilon_0}\, q\omega$$

if q has a constant value and ω is the solid angle subtended by the whole surface S at the point charge q.

Q.3.7. What is Gaussian surface ?   *(Pbi. U. 2006; H.P.U., 1995)*

Ans. Gaussian surface. A hypothetical closed surface of any shape drawn in an electric field for the purpose of solving problems concerning electric flux is called *Gaussian surface*. The shape of the Gaussian surface is decided on the basis of the symmetry of the problem so that the value of electric flux $\phi_E = \oiint \vec{E} \cdot \vec{dS}$ (for free space) can be calculated.

Q.3.8. (a) State and prove Gauss's (law) theorem in electrostatics. Prove that total flux over a surface due to a charge lying outside is zero.

(b) Write the law for a volume distribution of charge.

(Meerut. U. 2006, 2003; P.U. 2001, 2000, 1995 ; Gharwal. U. 2000; Indore. U. 2001; Gauhati. U. 2000; M.D.U. 2001 ; H.P.U. 2007, 2002, 2001, 1999, 1995 ; G.N.D.U. 2008, 2001; Pbi. U. 2007, 1995 ; K.U. 2000, 1994 ; Kan. U. 1997 ; Luck.U. 1995 ; A.U. 1995, 1994 ; Cal.U. 1992, Burd.U. 1990)

Ans. (a) Gauss's theorem. Gauss's theorem states that '*The total electric flux in free space (or vacuum) through a closed surface is equal to $\dfrac{1}{\varepsilon_0}$ times the charge enclosed by the surface*'.

or $$\phi_E = \oiint_s \vec{E} \cdot \vec{dS} = \frac{q}{\varepsilon_0}$$

Consider a charge q situated at O, the origin of the rectangular co-ordinate system. Let S be a Gaussian surface around this charge. Now consider a small elementary area $\vec{dS}$ at a vector distance $\vec{r}$ from the charge q.

The electric flux through the area $\vec{dS}$ is given by

$$d\phi_E = \vec{E} \cdot \vec{dS}$$

where $\vec{E}$ is the electric field vector at $\vec{r}$.

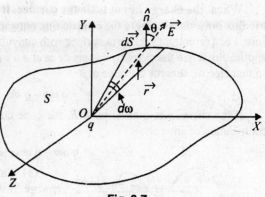

Fig. 3.7

The total electric flux over the (closed) Gaussian surface due to the charge q inside it, in free space is given by

$$\phi_E = \int d\phi_E = \oiint \vec{E} \cdot \vec{dS}$$

Now, the electric intensity $\vec{E}$ at a point on the elementary surface $\vec{dS}$ at the position vector $\vec{r}$ due to the charge q at the origin is given by

$$\vec{E} = \frac{1}{4\pi\varepsilon_0} \frac{q}{r^2} \hat{r}$$

where $\hat{r}$ is a unit vector in the direction of electric intensity $\vec{E}$.

Also $\vec{dS} = dS\,\hat{n}$, where $\hat{n}$ is a unit vector in the direction of positive (outward drawn) normal to the surface $\vec{dS}$

$$\therefore \quad \phi_E = \frac{1}{4\pi\varepsilon_0} \oiint \frac{q}{r^2} \hat{r} \cdot \hat{n}\, dS$$

$$= \frac{1}{4\pi\varepsilon_0} \oiint q \frac{dS \cos\theta}{r^2} \qquad\qquad [\because \hat{r} \cdot \hat{n} = \cos\theta]$$

Now $\dfrac{dS \cos\theta}{r^2} = d\omega$ the small solid angle subtended by the elementary area $\vec{dS}$ at q.

$$\therefore \quad \phi_E = \frac{1}{4\pi\varepsilon_0} \oiint q\, d\omega = \frac{q}{4\pi\varepsilon_0} \oiint d\omega = \frac{q}{\varepsilon_0}$$

as $\oiint d\omega = 4\pi$ i.e., the solid angle subtended by a closed surface at a point inside it is 4π.

Hence $\phi_E = \dfrac{q}{\varepsilon_0}$ where $\phi_E = \oiint \vec{E} \cdot \vec{dS}$

The statement $\oiint \vec{E} \cdot \vec{dS} = \dfrac{q}{\varepsilon_0}$ is known the **integral form of Gauss's law.**

If there are several charges inside, the positive charges give the values $\dfrac{q_1}{\varepsilon_0} + \dfrac{q_2}{\varepsilon_0} + ...$ and the negative charges give the values $\dfrac{-q_1'}{\varepsilon_0} - \dfrac{q_2'}{\varepsilon_0} - ...$ and the total electric flux due to all the charges $= \dfrac{1}{\varepsilon_0}(q_1 + q_2 + ... - q_1' - q_2' ...)$. Thus the total charge inside refers to the algebric sum of the charges.

Hence for a number of point charges within the closed surface, Gauss's theorem can be stated as

$$\phi_E = \oiint \vec{E} \cdot \vec{dS} = \frac{1}{\varepsilon_0} \sum q_i$$

When the charge lies outside the surface. If the charge lies outside a closed surface the electric flux inwards is equal to the electric flux outwards and the resultant flux for the whole surface is zero. For a re-entrant surface (a surface with convulsions) as shown in Fig. 3.8 the theorem is equally applicable. When the charge q lies inside as at A a small cone cuts the surface an **odd** number of times so that electric flux for the cone at A

$$= +q\, d\omega - q\, d\omega + q\, d\omega - q\, d\omega + q\, d\omega = q\, d\omega$$

If the charge lies outside as at B, the cone cuts the surface an even number of times and the contribution of any cone

$$= q\, d\omega - q\, d\omega + q\, d\omega - q\, d\omega = 0.$$

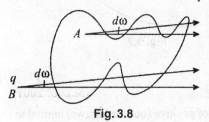

Fig. 3.8

(b) Gauss's theorem for a volume distribution of charge. If we have a volume charge density ρ, then the total charge in a volume space V is given by

$$q = \iiint_V \rho\, dV$$

Gauss's theorem is then stated as

$$\phi_E = \iint \vec{E} \cdot \vec{dS} = \frac{q}{\varepsilon_0} = \frac{1}{\varepsilon_0} \iiint_V \rho\, dV$$

Q.3.9. (a) What is the electric flux through a closed surface surrounding a dipole ?

(*H.P.U.*, 1996)

(b) Can we apply Gauss's law to calculate the electric field due to an electric dipole?

(*P.U.* 2006)

Ans. (a) Electric flux due to a dipole. If a closed surface encloses an electric dipole, the total electric flux through it is zero. It is because an electric dipole consists of two equal and opposite charges separated by a certain distance.

Hence the algebric sum of all the charges within the surface is zero. Hence ϕ_E which is equal to $\dfrac{q}{\varepsilon_0} = 0$.

(b) As explained in part (*a*) the algebraic sum of all the charges (on a dipole) being zero, the electric flux over a closed surface enclosing the dipole is zero. We cannot, therefore apply Gauss's law to calculate the electric field due to a dipole.

Ex. (*i*) *An electric dipole of length 10^{-2} m and dipole moment 4×10^{-6} Cm is enclosed in a cubical box $1m \times 1m \times 1m$. Calculate the electric flux over its surface.* (*Pbi.U.* 2001, 2000, 1999)

(*ii*) *An electric dipole of moment 5×10^{-6} Cm is enclosed in a card board spherical shell of radius 1m. Find the electric flux over the whole surface.* (*Pbi.U.* 2002 ; *H.P.U.* 2001)

Ans. $\phi_E = 0$ in each case as explained above.

Q.3.10. Find the total charge enclosed by a closed surface if number of lines entering is 20,000 and emerging out is 45000. (*Kan.U.*, 1997 ; *G.N.D.U.*, 1996)

Ans. Number of flux lines entering the closed surface

$$\phi_i = 20,000$$

Number of flux lines emerging out of the surface

$$\phi_0 = 45000$$

Net number of flux lines leaving the surface

$$\phi_E = \phi_0 - \phi_i = 45000 - 20,000 = 25000$$

According to Gauss's theorem the net flux emerging out of an arbitrary closed surface is given by

$$\phi_E = \frac{q}{\varepsilon_0}$$

where q is the total charge inside the surface

$$\therefore \quad q = \varepsilon_0 \, \phi_E = 8.85 \times 10^{-12} \times 25000 = 22.125 \times 10^{-8} \text{ C}$$

Ex. (i) *Calculate total charge enclosed by a closed surface if the number of lines of force emerging out from it is 20,000 and those entering is 10,000.*

(G.N.D.U. 2009, 2007 similar; P.U. 2006; G.N.D.U. 2002)

Hint. $\quad\quad\quad\quad \phi_E = \phi_0 - \phi_i = 20,000 - 10,000 = 10,000$

$$q = \varepsilon_0 \, \phi_E = 10,000 \times 8.85 \times 10^{-12} = 8.85 \times 10^{-8} \text{ C}$$

Ex. (2). *If 2000 flux through lines enter a given volume of space and 4000 lines diverge from it, find the total charge within the volume.* *(M.D.U. 2001)*

Hint. $\quad\quad\quad\quad \phi_E = \phi_0 - \phi_i = 4000 - 2000 = 2000$

$$q = \varepsilon_0 \, \phi_E = 2000 \times 8.85 \times 10^{-12} = 17.70 \times 10^{-9} \text{ C}$$

Q.3.11. Show that electric flux through the surface of a sphere due to a point charge lying outside it is zero. *(Pbi. U. 2008; P.U. 2009, 2002)*

Ans. Suppose a point charge $+ q$ lies outside a sphere as shown. From the point charge draw a small cone making a solid angle $d\Omega$. This cone cuts off a surface area dS_1, on the nearer side at a distance r_1 and an area S_2 on the farther side at a distance r_2.

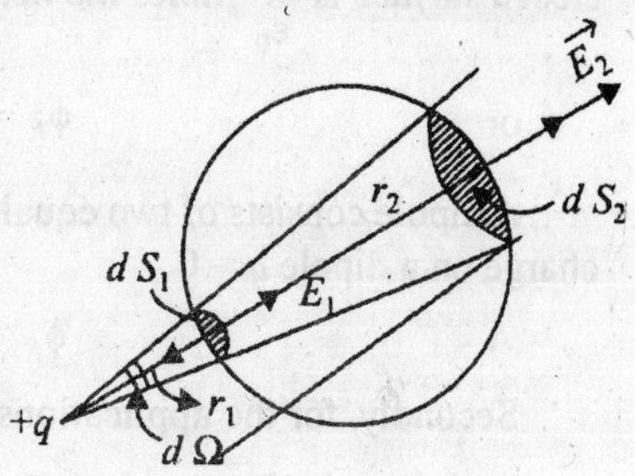

The electric flux through $\vec{dS_1} = d\phi_1 = \vec{E_1} \cdot \vec{dS_1}$

where $\vec{E_1}$ is the electric field at dS_1 due to the charge $+ q$.
It is clear from the figure that $\vec{E_1}$ and $\vec{dS_1}$ point in opposite directions *i.e.* the angle between them $= 180° = \pi$

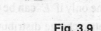

Fig. 3.9

$$\therefore \quad d\phi_1 = \vec{E_1} \cdot \vec{dS_1} = E_1 \, dS_1 \cos 180° = - E_1 \, dS_1 \quad ...(i)$$

The magnitude of $\vec{E_1}$ the electric field at dS_1

$$E_1 = \frac{q}{4\pi \, \varepsilon_0 \, r_1^2}$$

$$\therefore \quad\quad d\phi_1 = \frac{-q}{4\pi \, \varepsilon_0 \, r_1^2} \, dS_1 \quad\quad\quad ...(ii)$$

Now $\dfrac{dS_1}{r_1^2} = d\Omega$ = solid angle subtended by dS_1 at the charge q.

$$\therefore \quad\quad d\phi_1 = - \frac{q}{4\pi \varepsilon_0} \, d\Omega \quad\quad\quad ...(iii)$$

Similarly electric flux through $\vec{dS_2} = d\phi_2 = \vec{E_2} \cdot \vec{dS_2}$

where $\vec{E_2}$ is the electric field at dS_2 due to the charge $+ q$. It is clear from the figure that $\vec{E_2}$ and $\vec{dS_2}$ point in the same direction *i.e.* the angle between them $= 0$ (zero)

$$\therefore \quad\quad d\phi_2 = \vec{E_2} \cdot \vec{dS_2} = E_2 \, dS_2 \cos \theta = E_2 \, dS_2$$

The magnitude of $\vec{E_2}$ the electric field at dS_2

$$E_2 = \frac{q}{4\pi\,\varepsilon_0\,r_2^2}$$

$\therefore$
$$d\phi_2 = \frac{q}{4\pi\,\varepsilon_0\,r_2^2}\,dS_2$$

But $\dfrac{dS_2}{r_2^2} = d\Omega$ = Solid angle subtended by dS_2 at charge q

$\therefore$
$$d\phi_2\,\frac{q}{4\pi\,\varepsilon_0}\,d\Omega \qquad\qquad ...(iv)$$

The total electric flux through the surfaces dS_1 and $dS_2 = d\phi = d\phi_1 + d\phi_2$

$$= \frac{-q}{4\pi\,\varepsilon_0}\,d\Omega + \frac{q}{4\pi\,\varepsilon_0}\,d\Omega = 0$$

The entire surface of the sphere can be divided into such pairs of areas. Each pair will make zero contribution towards electric flux. *Hence the total electric flux through the surface of the sphere due to a point charge lying outside it is zero.*

Q.3.12. Can we apply Gauss's law to calculate the electric field due to electric dipole? Explain. (G.N.D.U. 2003)

Ans. No. Firstly, *'Gauss's theorem states that the total electric flux in free space through a closed surface is* $\dfrac{1}{\varepsilon_0}$ *times the net charge enclosed by the surface.*

or
$$\phi_E = \oiint \vec{E}\cdot\vec{dS} = \frac{q}{\varepsilon_0}$$

A dipole consists of two equal and opposite charges separated by a small distance. Hence the net charge on a dipole $q = 0$

$\therefore$
$$\phi_E = 0$$

Secondly, for the applications of Gauss's law, we have to evaluate the integral $\oiint \vec{E}\cdot\vec{dS}$. This can be done only if $\vec{E}$ can be taken out of the integral sign, which is possible for equifield surface *i.e.* for symmetric charge distribution and the charge distribution for a dipole is not symmetric.

Q.3.13. A Gaussian surface encloses no net charge. Does it mean $E = 0$ on its surface? (Pbi.U. 2003)

Ans. No· E is not zero on the Gaussian surface. For exmple, in the case of electric dipole within a closed serface, total charge inside the surface is zero. But the electric field due to the dipole at every point on the surface has a finite value.

Q.3.14. A sphere of radius 3 cm, has a point charge $q = 7.6\ \mu C$ located at its centre. Find the electric flux through it. (H.P.U. 1994)

Ans. According to Gauss's theorem, the total electric flux through the closed surface of a sphere

$$\phi_E = \frac{q}{\varepsilon_0}$$

Here $q = 7.6\ \mu C = 7.6\times10^{-6}\,C$; $\varepsilon_0 = 8.85\times10^{-12}\,C^2\,N^{-1}\,m^{-2}$

$\therefore$
$$\phi_E = \frac{q}{\varepsilon_0} = \frac{7.6\times10^{-6}}{8.85\times10^{-12}} = 8.59\times10^5\ N\ m^2\ C^{-1}$$

Q.3.15. (a) A point charge q is enclosed at the centre of a cube of side a. Find the electric flux (i) through the whole cube (ii) through one face of the cube. *(Kerala.U. 2001)*

(b) A point charge 17.7 μC is located at the centre of a cube of side 3 cm. Find the electric flux through (i) whole of the cube (ii) each face of the cube.

(P.U., 1991 ; G.N.D.U., 1991 ; H.P.U., 1993)

Ans. The total electric flux through all the six faces of the cube forming a closed surface, according to Gauss's theorem is given by

$$\phi_E = \frac{q}{\varepsilon_0}$$

A cube has 6 faces of equal area and the charge is located at the centre, symmetrically with respect to each face.

∴ Electric flux through each face $= \dfrac{1}{6}\dfrac{q}{\varepsilon_0}$

(b) Here $q = 17.7\ \mu C = 17.7 \times 10^{-6}\ C; \varepsilon_0 = 8.85 \times 10^{-12}\ C^2\ N^{-1}\ m^{-2}$

∴ Electric flux through whole of the cube $\phi_E = \dfrac{q}{\varepsilon_0}$

$$= \frac{17.7 \times 10^{-6}}{8.85 \times 10^{-12}} = 2 \times 10^6\ N\ m^2\ C^{-1}$$

Electric flux through each face $= \phi_E$ per face $= \dfrac{1}{6} \times 2 \times 10^6 = 0.33 \times 10^6\ N m^2\ C^{-1}$

Ex.1 *A point charge of 11 Coulomb is located at the centre of a cube of side 5 cm. Calculate the electric flux through each surface.* *(P.U. 2003 ; 2001)*

Hint. Electric flux through each surface $= \dfrac{1}{6}\dfrac{q}{\varepsilon_0} = \dfrac{1}{6} \times \dfrac{11}{8\cdot 85 \times 10^{-12}} = 0.2 \times 10^{12}\ N m^2\ C^{-1}$

Ex.2 *Calculate the electric flux coming out of a cube of side 0.5m if the charge of 1 μc is placed at its centre.* *(H.P.U. 2007)*

Hint. Electric flux coming out of the whole cube $\phi_E = \dfrac{q}{\varepsilon_0}$

$$= \frac{10^{-6}}{8.85 \times 10^{-12}} = 0.113 \times 10^6 = 1.13 \times 10^5\ N m^2\ C^{-1}$$

Q.3.16. The electric field $\vec{E}$ in a certain region of space is given by $\vec{E} = by\ \hat{j}$ where b is a constant. A cube of side a is placed in this field with one corner at the origin as shown in Fig. 3.10. Find the electric flux over the surface of the cube. Also find the total charge and volume charge density.

Ans. The field $\vec{E}$ is given by $\vec{E} = by\hat{j}$. It acts at right angles to the face *BEFD* and *AOCG* i.e., *XZ* planes at $y = a$ and $y = 0$. The field $\vec{E}$ acts parallel to the pairs of *X-Y* planes and *Y-Z* planes.

The electric flux over a surface $\phi_E = \iint\limits_{s} \vec{E} \cdot \vec{dS}$

On the *BEFD*, $y = a$, the field has a constant value

$$E = by\hat{j} = ba\hat{j}\ \text{and}\ \vec{dS} = dS\ \hat{j}$$

$\therefore$ Electric flux

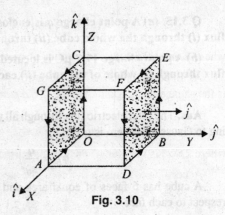

Fig. 3.10

$$= \iint_s \vec{E} \cdot dS = \iint_s ba\,\hat{j} \cdot dS\,\hat{j} = \iint_s ba\,ds$$

$$= ba \iint_s ds = ba \times a^2 = ba^3$$

since the area of the square face $BEFD = \iint_s dS = a^2$

For the face $AOCG$, $y = 0$

$\therefore$ $\vec{E} = by\,\hat{j} = 0$

Hence the electric flux on the face $AOCG = 0$.

As the field $\vec{E} = by\,\hat{j}$ acts along the Y-axis, it is par-
allel to the pairs X-Y and Y-Z planes. Hence the area vector $\vec{dS}$ which has a direction normal to the
faces is perpendicular to $\vec{E}$.

$\therefore$ For all those faces $\vec{E} \cdot \vec{dS} = EdS \cos 90° = 0$

Hence total flux on the surface of the cube $= ba^3$ N m^2 C^{-1} ...(i)

According to Gauss's theorem,

Total electric flux on a closed surface $\phi_E = \dfrac{q}{\varepsilon_0}$ ...(ii)

Comparing Eqs. (i) and (ii), we have

$$\frac{q}{\varepsilon_0} = ba^3 \text{ or } q = \varepsilon_0\, ba^3 \text{ coulomb}$$

Volume charge density $\rho = \dfrac{q}{\text{volume of the cube}} = \dfrac{\varepsilon_0\, b a^3}{a^3} = \varepsilon_0\, b$ C m^{-3}

**Q.3.17. Apply Gauss's theorem to calculate the electric field due to an infinitely long uni-
formly charged straight wire (or infinite line charge).**

(*H.P.U.* 2003, 1996, 1995 ; *M.D.U.* 2003 ; *K.U.* 1994 ; *P.U.* 1991 ; *Kan.U.* 1994)

Ans. Field due to a charged straight wire. Consider an infinitely long straight wire having a
constant line charge density λ. Let P be a point at a distance a from the the straight line charge. The
direction of the electric field due to the electric charge will be *radially outward* due to *symmetry*.

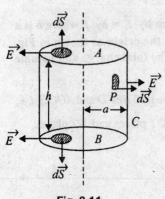

Fig. 3.11

Draw a cylinder of height h and radius a coaxial with the line charge
and closed at both ends by plain caps A and B normal to the axis to
represent the Gaussian surface. The closed surface consists of three
parts A, B and C. Now if we consider a very small area element $\vec{dS}$
on the surface A, then area vector $\vec{dS}$ acts along the *outward drawn
normal* and is at right angles to the electric field vector $\vec{E}$.

$\therefore$ For the surface A ; $\iint_A \vec{E} \cdot \vec{dS} = 0$

Similarly for the surface B ; $\iint_B \vec{E} \cdot \vec{dS} = 0$

For the surface C the area vector $\vec{dS}$ and the electric field vector $\vec{E}$ are parallel and act in the same direction

$$\therefore \qquad \iint_C \vec{E} \cdot \vec{dS} = \iint_C E \, dS$$

where E and dS are the magnitudes of vectors $\vec{E}$ and $\vec{dS}$ respectively.

As all points on the curved surface of the cylinder C are equidistant from the axis, the electric field is the same at every point. Hence $E = a$ constant

$$\therefore \qquad \iint_C E \, dS = E \iint_C dS = 2\pi \, ah \, E \qquad \qquad ...(i)$$

where $2\pi \, ah$ is the area of the curved surface of the cylinder of height h and radius a.

According to Gauss's theorem, the electric flux over whole of the closed surface

$$\phi_E = \oiint \vec{E} \cdot \vec{dS} = \iint_A \vec{E} \cdot \vec{dS} + \iint_B \vec{E} \cdot \vec{dS} + \iint_C \vec{E} \cdot \vec{dS}$$

and is given by
$$\phi_E = \frac{q}{\varepsilon_0}$$

Now the total charge within the Gaussian surface = charge on the wire of height $h = \lambda h$

$$\therefore \qquad \phi_E = \oiint \vec{E} \cdot dS = \frac{\lambda h}{\varepsilon_0} \qquad \qquad ...(ii)$$

Comparing (i) and (ii) we get

$$2\pi a h E = \frac{\lambda}{\varepsilon_0}$$

or
$$E = \frac{1}{2\pi \varepsilon_0} \frac{\lambda}{a}$$

The direction of $\vec{E}$ is perpendicular to the charged wire at every point.

Q.3.18. (*a*) **Apply Gauss's theorem to calculate the electric field due to an infinitely long, uniformly charged, hollow cylinder. Is the result applicable to a hollow conducting cylinder ?**

(*b*) **Find the electric field due to two co-axial cylinders of radii a and b ($a > b$) the inner cylinder having a charge $+\lambda$ and the outer cylinder $-\lambda$ per unit length when the point lies at a distance r**

    (*i*)   **outside the cylinders $r > a$**   (*ii*)   **between the cylinders $a > r > b$**

    (*iii*)   **inside the cylinders $r < b$**   (*A.U.*, 1993 ; *Burd. U.*, 1990)

Ans. (*a*) **Electric field due to a hollow cylinder.**
Consider an *infinitely long, uniformly charged hollow,* circular cylinder of radius a ; having a charge λ per unit length. Let P be a point at a distance r ($r > a$) from the axis of the cylinder where electric field intensity $\vec{E}$ is required. From considerations of cylindrical symmetry we find that the *electric field is radial* and electric field vector is directed along the *outward* drawn normal at every point of the charged cylinder. Further, as the cylinder is *uniformly* charged the electric field intensity is the *same* at all points at the same distance from the axis.

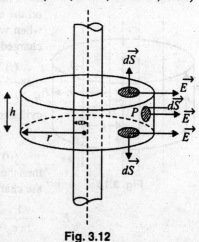

Draw a co-axial cylinder of height h and radius r containing the point P as shown in Fig. 3.12 to represent the Gaussian surface. The electric flux on the top and the bottom surface of the Gaussian cylinder is zero as on these surfaces

Fig. 3.12

the electric field vector $\vec{E}$ and the area vector $\vec{dS}$ are at right angles to each other.

$$\therefore \qquad \oiint \vec{E} \cdot \vec{dS} = 0$$

The electric flux is, therefore, only contributed by the cylindrical surface and is given by

$$\oiint \vec{E} \cdot \vec{dS} = E\, 2\pi\, r h \qquad\qquad ...(i)$$

where $2\pi\, rh$ is the area of the curved surface of the cylinder.

Since the outer cylinder contains a charge λh inside it, therefore, according to Gauss's theorem.

$$\iint \vec{E} \cdot \vec{dS} = \frac{\lambda h}{\varepsilon_0} \qquad\qquad ...(ii)$$

Comparing (i) and (ii), we have

$$E\, 2\pi\, r h = \frac{\lambda h}{\varepsilon_0}$$

$$\therefore \qquad E = \frac{1}{2\pi\varepsilon_0}\, \frac{\lambda}{r} \qquad\qquad ...(iii)$$

If the point P is infinitely close to the charged surface, then $r = a$ and hence

$$E = \frac{1}{2\pi\varepsilon_0}\, \frac{\lambda}{a} \qquad\qquad ...(iv)$$

If σ is the surface charge density then charge per unit length

$$\lambda = 2\pi a\sigma$$

Hence $$E = \frac{1}{2\pi\varepsilon_0}\, \frac{2\pi a\sigma}{a} = \frac{\sigma}{\varepsilon_0}$$

For a point inside the charged cylinder *i.e.*, for $r < a$ no charge is enclosed within the Gaussian surface

$$\therefore \qquad E\, 2\pi\, r h = 0$$

or $$E = 0$$

The results are equally applicable to a hollow conducting cylinder. The surface of the conducting cylinder is an *equipotential surface* and the electric field intensity is everywhere normal to the surface and its directon is, therefore, along the outward drawn normal at every point.

(b) Two co-axial cylinders. Supposee we have two co-axial cylinders of radii a and b where $a > b$ having a charge per unit length $+\lambda$ on the inner cylinder and $-\lambda$ on the outer cylinder. In actual practice we come across such a case when we have two co-axial conducting, hollow cylinders, the inner charged and the outer earthed.

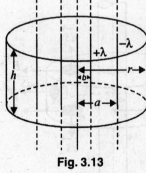

Fig. 3.13

(i) When the point P lies outside the cylinder at a distance r such that $r > a$, the charge enclosed within the Gaussian cylinder of length $h = (+\lambda h - \lambda h) = 0$ due to the inner as well as the outer charged cylinders.

$$\therefore \qquad \text{For } r > a, \quad E = 0$$

(ii) When the point P lies in between the two cylinders $a > r > b$, then the charge $+\lambda h$ is only enclosed within the Gaussian cylinder and the charge $-\lambda h$ is outside it.

$$\therefore \qquad E = +\frac{1}{2\pi\varepsilon_0}\, \frac{\lambda}{r} \qquad\qquad \text{[See Eq. (iii)]}$$

(*iii*) When the point P lies inside the two cylinders $r < b$, no charge is enclosed within the Gaussian surface

$$\therefore \qquad E = 0$$

Q.3.19. Apply Gauss's theorem to calculate the electric field due to a uniformly charged solid cylinder.

Prove that the electric field at a point inside a uniformly charged cylinder of infinite length is proportional to the distance of the point from the axis. *(P.U.* 2002 *; A.U.,* 1995)

Ans. Electric field due to a charged solid cylinder. Consider an infinitely long, *uniformly charged* circular solid cylinder of radius a having a charge ρ per unit volume. Let P be a point at a distance r $(r > a)$ from the axis of the cylinder where the electric field intensity $\vec{E}$ is required.

As proved in **Q.3.18.** [Eq. (*i*)], if we consider Gaussian cylinder of radius r and height h, then

$$\oint \vec{E} . \vec{dS} = E\, 2\pi\, r\, h \qquad\qquad ...(i)$$

where $2\pi\, rh$ is the area of the curved surface of the Gaussian cylinder, the value of $\iint \vec{E} . \vec{dS}$ on the top and bottom surface of the Gaussian cylinder being zero. Since the outer cylinder contains a charge $\pi\, a^2\, h\, \rho$, therefore according to Gauss's theorem

$$\oint \vec{E} . \vec{dS} = \frac{\pi\, a^2\, h\, \rho}{\varepsilon_0} \qquad\qquad ...(ii)$$

Comparing (*i*) and (*ii*), we get

$$E\, 2\pi\, rh = \frac{\pi\, a^2\, h\, \rho}{\varepsilon_0}$$

or

$$E = \frac{a^2\, \rho}{2\varepsilon_0\, r} \qquad\qquad ...(iii)$$

If λ is the charge per unit length of the cylinder, then

$$\lambda = \pi\, a^2\, \rho$$

Hence

$$E = \frac{1}{2\pi\, \varepsilon_0} \frac{\lambda}{r} \qquad\qquad ...(iv)$$

The result is the same as found in **Q. 3.18**, Eq (*iii*).

When the point P lies on the surface. When the point P lies on the surface of the cylinder $r = a$ and we have

$$E = \frac{a\, \rho}{2\varepsilon_0} \qquad\qquad\qquad \text{from Eq. } (iii)$$

and

$$E = \frac{1}{2\pi\varepsilon_0} \frac{\lambda}{a} \qquad\qquad\qquad \text{from Eq. } (iv)$$

This result is again the same as found in **Q.3.18,** Eq. (*iv*).

When the point P lies within the cylinder. When the point P lies within the cylinder $(r < a)$ the total charge inside the Gaussian cylindrical surface of radius r and height $h = \pi\, r^2\, h\, \rho$.

$$\therefore \qquad \oint \vec{E} . \vec{dS} = \frac{q}{\varepsilon_0} = \frac{\pi\, r^2\, h\, \rho}{\varepsilon_0} \qquad\qquad ...(v)$$

Comparing (*i*) and (*v*), we have

$$E\,2\pi\,rh = \frac{\pi r^2\,h\,\rho}{\varepsilon_0}$$

or
$$E = \frac{r\,\rho}{2\varepsilon_0} \qquad\qquad\qquad ...(vi)$$

Thus the electric intensity inside a solid charged cylinder is directly proportional to its distance from the axis of the cylinder or E ∝ r.

Note. This result is not the same as for a hollow charged cylinder as in that case the electric intensity at a point inside the cylinder is zero.

Q. 3.20. Apply Gauss's theorem to find the electric field strength $\vec{E}$ near a plane non-conducting thin sheet of charge of infinite extent. Hence show that the field is independent of the distance of the observation point from the sheet.

(*H.P.U.* 2006, 2003; *G.N.D.U.* 2006, 1999, 1997 ; *K.U.* 2000, 1995, 1994 ; *Pbi. U.* 2003, 1995, 1991;*Gharwal U.* 1999 ; *Kan. U.,* 1996 ; *Luck. U.,* 1995)

Ans. Electric field near a charged infinite plane. Let *AB* be a part of a uniformly charged infinite plane of a non-conducting material having a *uniform* surface charge density σ. From symmetry considerations the electric field is in a direction perpendicular to the sheet and hence everywhere normal to it. Consider a right cylinder *a b c d* with its plane faces *ab* and *cd* each having an area $\vec{dS}$ parallel to the charged plane and its cylindrical curved surface normal to the plane *AB* as shown in Fig. 3.14.

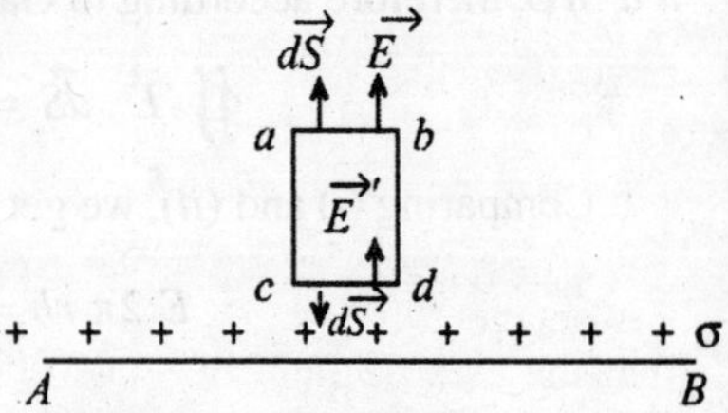

Let $\vec{E}$ and $\vec{E'}$ be the values of electric field on the faces *ab* and *cd* repectively, then,

Eletric flux over the face $ab = \vec{E}\,.\,\vec{dS}$

and Electric flux over the face $cd = -\,\vec{E}\,.\,\vec{dS}$

Fig. 3.14

The negative sign indicates that the direction of electric field vector on *cd* is not along the outward drawn normal but is directed along the inward normal.

The total electric flux over the curved surface of the cylinder is zero because its sides are parallel to the direction of electric field and therefore the electric field vector and area vector are perpendicular to each other.

The electric flux over the whole surface of the cylinder is zero as there is no charge inside it.

$$\therefore \qquad \vec{E}\,.\,\vec{dS} - \vec{E'}\,.\,\vec{dS} = 0$$

or
$$\vec{E} = \vec{E'}$$

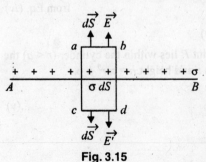

Fig. 3.15

Hence electric field intensity is the same at every point near a charged infinite plane.

Now consider the right cylinder with its ends *ab* and *cd* on the opposite sides of the plane charge *d* sheet as shown in Fig. 3.15. The electric flux over both the sufaces *ab* and *cd* is now positive because the electric field on *ab* as well as on *cd* is directed along the outward drawn normal. The electric flux over the curved surfaces of the cylinder is again zero.

∴ Electric flux over the whole closed surface of the Gaussian cylinder $= \vec{E} \cdot \vec{dS} + \vec{E'} \cdot \vec{dS}$

$$= 2\vec{E} \cdot \vec{ds} \qquad \qquad \qquad ...(i) \; [\because \vec{E'} = \vec{E}]$$

If σ is the surface density of the charge, then

The total charge within the cylinder $q = \sigma \, dS$

According to Gauss's theorem

Total electric flux over the closed surface of the Gaussian cylinder

$$= \frac{\sigma \, dS}{\varepsilon_0} \qquad \qquad \qquad ...(ii)$$

Comparing (i) and (ii), we have

$$2\vec{E} \cdot \vec{ds} = \sigma \, dS / \varepsilon_0$$

or $\qquad \qquad \qquad 2 \, E \, dS = \dfrac{\sigma \, dS}{\varepsilon_0}$

$$[\because \vec{E} \cdot \vec{dS} = E \, dS, \text{ angle between } \vec{E} \text{ and } \vec{dS} \text{ being zero}]$$

∴ $\qquad \qquad \qquad E = \dfrac{\sigma}{2\varepsilon_0} \qquad \qquad \qquad ...(iii)$

The direction of $\vec{E}$ is perpendicular to the charged plane. If the charged sheet lies in the X-Y plane, the direction of $\vec{E}$ will lie along Z-axis. In such a case

$$\vec{E} = \frac{\sigma}{2\varepsilon_0} \hat{k}$$

Electric field independent of distance from charged sheet. It is clear from the relation $E = \dfrac{\sigma}{2\varepsilon_0}$ that the electric field depends only on the surface charge density and ε_0 the permittivity of the medium. It is independent of the distance of the observation point from the charged sheet.

Q.3.21. (*a*) **Apply Gauss's law to calculate**

(*i*) **The electric field at any point due to a plane non-conducting thin sheet of charge of infinite extent.**

(*ii*) **The electric field at any point due to two parallel sheets of charge.**   (*Pbi*. U., 1991)

(*b*) **Calculate the intensity of the electric field at a point between oppositely charged parallel plates.**   (*G.N.D.U.* 2002)

Ans. (*i*) See Q. 3.20.

(*ii*) **Electric field at any point due to two parallel sheets of charge.** Suppose there are two parallel plane sheets A and B having uniform surface charge densities $+ \sigma_1$ and $+ \sigma_2$ respectively.

Let the sheet A be to the left of sheet B.

There are three regions

Region 1 – To the *left* of sheet A.

Region 2 – *Between* the two sheets A and B.

Region 3 – To the *right* of sheet B.

Region 1. Consider a point P_1 in the region 1, then

Electric field at P_1 due to the surface charge density $+ \sigma_1$ on A

$$= \frac{\sigma_1}{2\varepsilon_0} \text{ along } -X \text{ direction}$$

Electric field at P_1 due to the surface charge density $+ \sigma_2$ on B

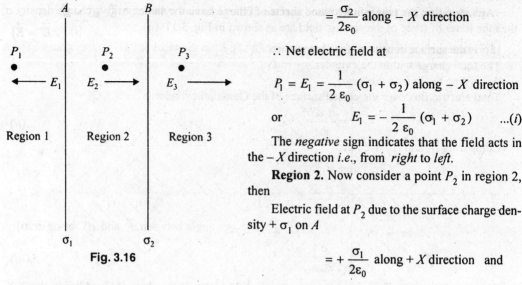

$$= \frac{\sigma_2}{2\varepsilon_0} \text{ along } - X \text{ direction}$$

$\therefore$ Net electric field at

$$P_1 = E_1 = \frac{1}{2\,\varepsilon_0}(\sigma_1 + \sigma_2) \text{ along } - X \text{ direction}$$

or $\qquad E_1 = -\frac{1}{2\,\varepsilon_0}(\sigma_1 + \sigma_2)$ ...(i)

The *negative* sign indicates that the field acts in the $-X$ direction *i.e.*, from *right* to *left*.

Region 2. Now consider a point P_2 in region 2, then

Electric field at P_2 due to the surface charge density $+\sigma_1$ on A

Fig. 3.16

$$= +\frac{\sigma_1}{2\varepsilon_0} \text{ along } + X \text{ direction and}$$

Electric field at P_2 due to the surface charge density $+\sigma_2$ on B

$$= -\frac{\sigma_2}{2\varepsilon_0} \text{ along } -X \text{ direction}$$

$\therefore$ Net electric field at $\qquad P_2 = E_2 = \frac{1}{2\varepsilon_0}(\sigma_1 - \sigma_2)$ ...(ii)

The net electric field will act in the $+X$ direction if $\sigma_1 > \sigma_2$ and in the $-X$ direction if $\sigma_2 > \sigma_1$.

Region 3. Again consider a point P_3 in region 3, then

Electric field at P_3 due to surface charge density $+\sigma_1$ on A

$$= +\frac{\sigma_1}{2\varepsilon_0} \text{ along } + X \text{ direction}$$

and Electric field P_3 due to surface charge density $+\sigma_2$ on $B = +\frac{\sigma_2}{2\varepsilon_0}$ along $+X$ direction.

$\therefore$ Net eletric field at $\qquad P_3 = E_3 = +\frac{1}{2\varepsilon_0}(\sigma_1 + \sigma_2)$ ...(iii)

The *positive* sign indicates that the field acts in the $+X$ direction *i.e.*, from *left* to *right*.

(b) **Oppositely charged parallel plates.** If we have two infinite plane parallel sheets of charge having charge densities $\sigma_1 = +\sigma$ and $\sigma_2 = -\sigma$, then the field is non-zero only in between the two sheets and has value

$$\frac{1}{2\varepsilon_0}(\sigma + \sigma) = \frac{\sigma}{\varepsilon_0}$$

obtained by substituting $\sigma_1 = \sigma$ and $\sigma_2 = -\sigma$ in relation (ii)

The field is *uniform* independent of the distance between the sheets so long as the distance is very small as compared to the size of the sheets. The direction of the field is as shown in Fig. 3.16. (Region 2)

Q.3.22. Sketch the electric field of two infinite plane sheets of charge that intersect each other at right angles.

(G.N.D.U. 1992)

Ans. Suppose the two infinite plane sheets of charge have the same positive charge density σ, then the lilnes of force of the electric field are as shown in Fig. 3.17. (*a*).

It is beacuse a unit charge placed at any opoint say P_1 in the quadrant *XOY* experiences a force

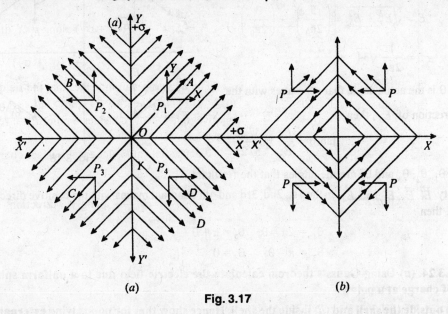

(*a*)   (*b*)

Fig. 3.17

$\dfrac{\sigma}{2\varepsilon_0}$ due to the charge + σ on the sheet *XOX'* along P_1Y and $\dfrac{\sigma}{2\varepsilon_0}$ due to the charge + σ on the sheet

YOY' along P_1X. The resultant field acts along P_1A which makes an angle of 45° both with the *X*-axis and *Y*-axis.

When the point lies in the quadrant *YOX'* the resultant field acts along P_2B and similarly in the quadrant *X'OY'* it acts along the direction P_3C and in the quadrant *Y'OX* the field acts along P_4D.

(*b*) When the sheet *XOX'* is charged positively and has a charge density + σ and *YOY'* is charged negatively and has a charge density − σ, then the lines of force are as shown in Fig. 3.17 (*b*).

(*c*) When the both the sheets are negatively charged the lines of force are again as shown in Fig. 3.17 (*a*) but the arrow heads will point in the opposite directions.

(*d*) When the sheet *XOX'* is charged negatively and *YOY'* positively the lines of force are again as shown in Fig. 3.17 (*b*) but the arrow heads will point in opposite directions.

Q.3.23. Two flat infinite sheets of charge with surface densities + 5 and − 3 units are kept mutually perpendicular to each other. Deduce the electric field in all the regions into which the space is divided due to sheets of charges.

Ans. Let the two flat infinite sheets of charge be placed as shown, the sheet *A* having surface charge density + 5 units and the sheet *B* − 3 units. The electric field $\vec{E}_a$ dut to the sheet *A* and $\vec{E}_b$ due to sheet *B* are perpendicular to each other at every point and have the same magnitude everywhere but their sense of directions is different in each of the four quadrants as shown in Fig. 3.18.

$$\vec{E}_a = \frac{\sigma}{2\varepsilon_0} = +\frac{1}{2\varepsilon_0} \times 5 = \frac{5}{2\varepsilon_0}$$

$$\vec{E}_b = \frac{\sigma}{2\varepsilon_0} = -\frac{1}{2\varepsilon_0} \times 3 = \frac{-3}{2\varepsilon_0}$$

∴ Magnitude of electric intensity $\vec{E}$ in each

quadrant

$$E = \sqrt{E_a^2 + E_b^2} = \left(\frac{5}{2\varepsilon_0}\right)^2 + \left(\frac{3}{2\varepsilon_0}\right)^2$$

$$= \frac{1}{2\varepsilon_0} \sqrt{34}$$

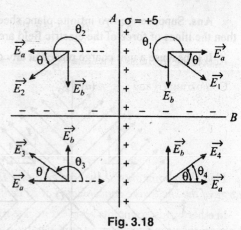

If θ is the actue angle that $\vec{E}$ makes with the

direction of $\vec{E_a}$, then

$$\tan \theta = \frac{E_b}{E_a} = \frac{3/2\varepsilon_0}{5/2\varepsilon_0} = \frac{3}{5}$$

Fig. 3.18

If θ_1, θ_2, θ_3 and θ_4 are the angles that the resultant
intensity $\vec{E_1}, \vec{E_2}, \vec{E_3}$ and $\vec{E_4}$ in the 1st, 2nd, 3rd and 4th quadrant makes with the positive direction of
X-axis, then

$$\theta_1 = 2\pi - \theta; \quad \theta_2 = \pi + \theta$$
$$\theta_3 = \pi - \theta; \quad \theta_4 = \theta$$

Q.3.24. (*a*) **Using Gauss's theorem calculate the electric field due to a uniform spherical
shell of charge at a point.**

(*i*) **outside the shell and (ii) inside the shell. Hence show that for points lying external to it a
uniformaly charged spherical shell behaves as if the entire charge were concentrated at its
centre and for point lying inside it the electric field is zero. Show graphically the variation of
electric field with distance from the centre of the shell.**

(*P.U.* 2009; *G.ND.U.* 2008, 2006, 2004, 2001, 2000;

H.P.U. 2007, 2001; *M.D.U.* 2000 ; *Luck. U.* 1995 ; *K.U.* 1994)

(*b*) **A hollow metallic sphere of radius 0.1 m has 10^{-8} coulomb of charge uniformaly spread over
it. Determine the electric field intensity at points (i) on the surface of the sphere (ii) at points 7 cm
away from the centre and (iii) at points 0.5 m away from the centre.**

(*Indore. U.* 2001)

Ans. (*a*) **Field due to spherical shell.** Consider a spherical shell of radius *a* and having a uniform surface charge density σ, then the total charge on the shell

$$q = 4\pi a^2 \sigma$$

(*i*) **Point outside the shell.** For a point *P* lying outside the charged shell at a distance $R > a$ draw
a sphere of radius *R* concentric with the shell to represent the Gaussian surface. If we consider a small

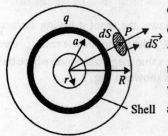

element of surface area $\vec{dS}$, then the area vector $\vec{dS}$ is directed radially
outward. From considerations of spherical symmetry the electric field
vector is also directed radially outwards and has a constant value on
the surface of a sphere concentric with the charged shell. In other
words, the electric field vector $\vec{E}$ and the area vector $\vec{dS}$ are parallel
at all points on the surface of the sphere and *E* has a constant value.

Fig. 3.19

∴ Total electric flux over the spherical surface of radius *R* is
given by

$$\oint \vec{E} \cdot \vec{dS} = E\, 4\pi\, R^2 \qquad \qquad ...(i)$$

According to Gauss's theorem $\oint \vec{E} \cdot \vec{dS} = \dfrac{q}{\varepsilon_0}$ $\qquad ...(ii)$

Comparing (i) and (ii), we have

$$E\, 4\pi\, R^2 = \dfrac{q}{\varepsilon_0} \qquad \qquad ...(iii)$$

or $\qquad E = \dfrac{q}{4\pi\varepsilon_0\, R^2} = \dfrac{I}{4\pi\varepsilon_0}\dfrac{q}{R^2}$

Thus for a point outside the charged spherical shell the electric field is the same as if the entire charge of the shell were concentrated at its centre.

In other words, for points lying external to it a uniformly charged spherical shell behaves as if the whole charge were concentrated at its centre.

E in terms of σ. Substituting $q = 4\pi a^2\, \sigma$ in (iii), we have

$$E = \dfrac{1}{4\pi\varepsilon_0}\dfrac{4\pi a^2\, \sigma}{R^2} = \dfrac{a^2}{R^2}\dfrac{\sigma}{\varepsilon_0} \qquad \qquad ...(iv)$$

For a point just on the surface of the shell $R = a$.

Substituting $R = a$ in (iii), we have

$$E = \dfrac{1}{4\pi\varepsilon_0}\dfrac{q}{a^2}$$

Substituting $R = a$ in (iv), we have

$$E = \dfrac{\sigma}{\varepsilon_0}$$

(ii) **Point inside the shell.** Now consider a point inside the shell at a distance $r < a$. The Gaussian surface is now a sphere of radius r and enclose no charge inside it.

∴ $\qquad \qquad q = 0$

Hence according to Gauss's theorem

$$\oint \vec{E} \cdot \vec{dS} = 0$$

or $\qquad \qquad E\, 4\pi\, r^2 = 0$

∴ $\qquad \qquad E = 0$

This means there is no electric field inside a uniformly charged spherical shell.

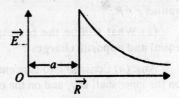

Fig. 3.20

Graphical representation. The variations of electric field $\vec{E}$ with distance $\vec{R}$ from the centre of a charged spherical shell of radius a is shown in Fig. 3.20.

(b) Radius of the hollow sphere $a = 0.1$ m ; Charge on the hollow sphere $q = 10^{-8}$ C

(i) ∴ Electric intensity at a point on the surface of the hollow sphere

$$= \dfrac{1}{4\pi\varepsilon_0}\dfrac{q}{a^2} = \dfrac{9 \times 10^9 \times 10^{-8}}{0.1 \times 0.1} = 9 \times 10^3 \text{ N C}^{-1}$$

(ii) A point 7 cm = .07 m away lies inside the hollow sphere.

∴ At this point $E = 0$

(iii) For a point 0.5 m away, $R = 0.5$ m

and electric intensity $E = \dfrac{1}{4\pi\varepsilon_0}\dfrac{q}{R^2} = \dfrac{9\times10^9\times10^{-8}}{0.5\times0.5} = 0.36\times10^3$ N C^{-1}

Q.3.25. Using Gauss's law show that there is a discontinuity in the magnitude of the electric field at the surface of the shell. (*P.U.* 2007; *Pbi.U. 2007*; *G.N.D.U*, 2002)

Ans. Discontinuity in the magnitude of electric field. For a spherical shell having a total charge q and radius a, the electric intensity at a point distant R from the centre of the shell $(R > a)$

$$E = \dfrac{1}{4\pi\varepsilon_0}\dfrac{q}{R^2}$$

For a point on the surface of the shell $(R = a)$

$$E = \dfrac{1}{4\pi\varepsilon_0}\dfrac{q}{a^2}$$

For a point inside the shell *i.e.* $(R < a)$ the electric field

$$E = 0$$

The variation of electric $\vec{E}$ with distance R from the centre of the shell is shown in Fig. 3.20

(For proof of the relations given above **See Q. 3.24.**)

From the above discussion we find that as we move away from the surface of the shell the intensity of the electric field varies inversely as the square of the distance of the point from the centre of the shell, but there is an abrupt discontinuity in the magnitude of the electric field at the surface of

the shell from $\dfrac{1}{4\pi\varepsilon_0}\dfrac{q}{a^2}$ to zero, when we move to inside the shell.

Q.3.26. (a) Two concentric thin metallic shells of radii R_1 and R_2, where $R_1 < R_2$ bear charges q_1 and q_2 respectively. Using Gauss's law find (i) The electric field intensity at radius $r < R_1$. (ii) The electric field intensity at radius r between R_1 and R_2. (iii) The electric field intensity at radius $r > R_2$.

(b) What will be the corresponding results if the two hollow conducting spheres carry equal and opposite charges ? (*P.U.*, 1994 ; *A.U.*, 1993)

Ans. (a) Consider two concentric spherical shells of radii R_1 and R_2 so that $R_1 < R_2$. The charge on the inner shell is q_1 and on the outer shell is q_2.

(i) For a point outside the outer shell $r > R_2$.

The electric field due to the inner shell $= \dfrac{1}{4\pi\varepsilon_0}\dfrac{q_1}{r^2}$

and electric field due to outer shell $= \dfrac{1}{4\pi\varepsilon_0}\dfrac{q_2}{r^2}$

because as proved in **Q.3.24** '*for a point outside the charged spherical shell the electric field is the same as if the entire charge of the shell were concentrated at its centre*'.

Both the fields are radial.

∴ Total field at a point outside the outer shell $= \dfrac{1}{4\pi\varepsilon_0}\dfrac{q_1+q_2}{r^2}$

When the two concentric metallic shells (or hollow conducting spheres) carry equal and opposite charges

$$q_1 = + q \text{ and } q_2 = - q$$

∴ Total electric field at a point outside the outer shell = 0 ...(i)

(ii) **For a point between the two shells.** $r > R_1$ but $r < R_2$

The electric field due to the inner shell $= \dfrac{1}{4\pi\varepsilon_0} \dfrac{q}{r^2}$ and electric field due to the outer shell = 0.

∴ Net electric field at a point between the two shells $= \dfrac{1}{4\pi\varepsilon_0} \dfrac{q_1}{r^2}$

When $q_1 = + q$ and $q_2 = - q$

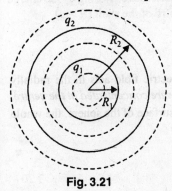

Fig. 3.21

The total electric field $= \dfrac{1}{4\pi\varepsilon_0} \dfrac{q}{r^2}$ ... (ii)

(iii) **For a point inside the inner shell** $r < R_1$.

No charge is contained within the Gaussian surface

∴   Electric field due to the inner shell = 0

and   electric field due to the outer shell = 0

∴   Net electric field at a point inside the inner shell = 0

When $q_1 = + q$ and $q_2 = - q$

the total electric field is also = 0 ...(iii)

(b) When the two hollow conducting spheres carry equal and opposite charge, then

For a point outside the outer shell, electric field $E = 0$ [see Eq. (i)]

For a point between the two shells, electric field at a distance $r = \dfrac{1}{4\pi\varepsilon_0} \dfrac{q}{r^2}$ where q is the charge on the inner hollow sphere [see Eq (ii)]

For a point inside the inner shell, electric field $E = 0$ [see Eq. (iii)]

Q. 3.27. Using Gauss's theorem calculate the electric field due to a uniformly charged non-conducting solid sphere at a point

(i)   **outside the sphere**

(ii) **on the surface of the sphere, and**

(iii) **inside the sphere.**   (G.N.D.U. 2007, 2001 ; Gharwal. U. 2000 ; H.P.U. 2003, 2002 ; Luck. U., 1993, 1992 ; P.U., 1992)

Ans. Electric field due to a uniformly charged non-conducting solid sphere. Consider a non-conducting solid sphere of radius a carrying a total charge q uniformly distributed in its volume.

(i) **Point outside the sphere.** Let the point P be at a distance R from the centre of the sphere so that $R > a$. To find the electric field intensity at P draw a sphere of radius R concentric with the charged sphere and passing through the point P to represent the Gaussian surface. The charged sphere lies completely inside the Gaussian surface so the net charge enclosed by the Gaussian surface is equal to the total charge q of the sphere.

If we consider a small element of the surface area $\vec{dS}$, then the area vector $\vec{dS}$ is directed radially outward. From

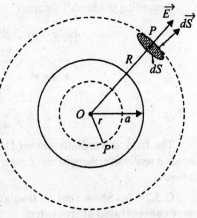

Fig. 3.22

considerations of spherical symmetry the electric field vector is also directed radially outward and has a constant value on the surface of the sphere. In other words, the electric field vector $\vec{E}$ and the area vector $\vec{dS}$ are parallel at all points on the surface of the shpere and $\vec{E}$ has a constant value.

∴ Total electric flux over the spherical surface of radius R

$$= \oint \vec{E} \cdot \vec{dS} = E \oint dS = E\, 4\pi\, R^2$$

According to Gauss's theorem

$$\oint \vec{E} \cdot \vec{dS} = q / \varepsilon_0$$

∴ $$E\, 4\pi\, R^2 = q/\varepsilon_0$$

or $$E = \frac{1}{4\pi\, \varepsilon_0} \frac{q}{R^2}$$

Thus for a point outside the uniformly charged sphere, the electric field acts in the radially outward direction. *The value of E is the same as if the whole charge were concentrated at the centre.*

(*ii*) **Point on the surface of the sphere.** For a point just on the surface of the sphere, the whole charge q, as before, can be supposed to be concentrated at the centre

∴ Eelctric field $$E = \frac{1}{4\pi\, \varepsilon_0} \frac{q}{a^2}$$

acting radially outward.

(*iii*) **Point inside the sphere.** Let the point P' be inside the sphere at a distance r from the centre of the sphere so that $r < a$. We again choose the Gaussian surface as a sphere of radius r with centre O. The spherical shell outside P' will not contribute any electric field at P' since the electric field inside a spherical shell is zero. It is only the charge within sphere of radius r which contributes to the electric intensity at P'.

Let ρ be the volume charge density of the charged sphere, then

$$\rho = \frac{q}{\frac{4}{3}\pi\, a^3}$$

∴ Net charge within the Gaussian surface of radius $r = \frac{4}{3}\pi\, r^3 \rho = \frac{\frac{4}{3}\pi\, r^3}{\frac{4}{3}\pi\, a^3} q = q\, \frac{r^3}{a^3}$

Total electric flux through the Gaussian surface $\oint \vec{E}.\vec{dS} = E \oint dS = E\, 4\pi\, r^2$

According to Gauss's theorem

$$\oint \vec{E} \cdot \vec{dS} = \frac{q}{\varepsilon_0} \frac{r^3}{a^3}$$

or $$E\, 4\pi\, r^2 = \frac{q}{\varepsilon_0} \frac{r^3}{a^3}$$

or $$E = \frac{1}{4\pi\, \varepsilon_0} \frac{qr}{a^3}$$

The field acts radially outward. The above relation shows that the *electric field at any point inside a uniformly charged solid sphere is directly proportional to its distance from the centre of the sphere.*

Q.3.28. (*a*) **Show that an insulated charged conducting sphere acts as if the whole charge were concentrated at its centre.**

(b) **A solid metallic sphere of radius R carries a charge q. What is the value of surface charge density?**   (*Luck. U.*, 1995)

Ans. Charged conducting sphere. Consider an insulated charged conducting sphere of radius a

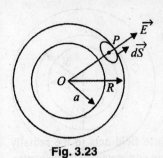

Fig. 3.23

and having a total charge q. For a point P lying outside the charged conducting sphere at a distance $R > a$ draw a spherical shell of radius R concentric with the conducting sphere to represent the Gaussian surface. If we consider a small element of surface area $\vec{dS}$ then the vector $\vec{dS}$ is directed radially outward. As the surface of a conducting sphere is an equipotential surface the electric field vector $\vec{E}$ is also directed radially outwards and from considerations of spherical symmetry has a constant value on the surface of the spherical shell concentric with the charged conducting sphere. In other words, the electric field vector $\vec{E}$ and the area vector $\vec{dS}$ are parallel at all points on the Gaussian surface and $\vec{E}$ has a constant value.

∴ Total electric flux over the spherical surface of radius R

$$\oiint \vec{E} \cdot \vec{dS} = \oiint E\,dS = E \oiint dS = E\,4\pi R^2$$

According to Gauss's theorem

$$\oiint \vec{E} \cdot \vec{dS} = q / \varepsilon_0$$

or $$E = \frac{1}{4\pi \varepsilon_0} \frac{q}{R^2} \qquad\qquad ...(i)$$

Thus for a point outside the charged insulated conducting sphere the electric field is the same if the entire charge were concentrated at its centre.

(b) **Surface charge density.** In terms of surface charge density σ, the electric field close to a conductor is given by

$$E = \frac{\sigma}{\varepsilon_0} \qquad\qquad ....(ii)$$

For proof See Q.3.33 (Eq. (iii)

Comparing (i) and (ii), we have

$$\frac{\sigma}{\varepsilon_0} = \frac{1}{4\pi\varepsilon_0} \frac{q}{R^2}$$

∴ $$\sigma = \frac{q}{4\pi R^2}$$

This relation again shows that the whole charge behaves as if concentrated at the centre.

Q.3.29. A spherical charge distribution is given by $\rho(r) = \rho_0 \left(1 - \dfrac{r}{a}\right)$ for $r \le a$ and $\rho(r) = 0$ for $r \ge a$. Derive an expression for electric field intensity E at a point inside the sphere. For what value of r is E maximum. ρ and a are volume charge density and radius of the spherical charge distribution respectively and r is the distance from its centre.

(*P.U.*, 1995 ; *G.N.D.U.*, 1994 ; *Luck. U.*, 1995)

Ans. According to Gauss's theorem (in S.I. units)

$$\oiint \vec{E} \cdot \vec{dS} = \frac{q}{\varepsilon_0}$$

...(i)

where q is the total charge contained within the Gaussian surface.

To find the value of the charge q contained in a sphere of radius r ($r < a$), consider concentric spheres of radius r and $(r + dr)$ as shown, then volume of the spherical shell of radius r and thickness $dr = 4\pi r^2\, dr$

Charge dq contained in the shell

$$dq = 4\pi r^2\, dr\, \rho = 4\pi r^2\, dr\, \rho_0 \left(1 - \frac{r}{a}\right)$$

$$= 4\pi \rho_0 \left(r^2 - \frac{r^3}{a}\right) dr$$

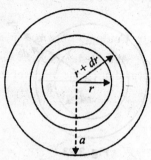

Fig. 3.24

$\therefore$ Total charge contained within the sphere of radius r

$$q = \int_0^r dq = 4\pi \rho_0 \left[\int_0^r r^2\, dr - \frac{1}{a}\int_0^r r^3\, dr\right]$$

$$= 4\pi \rho_0 \left[\frac{r^3}{3} - \frac{r^4}{4a}\right]$$

...(ii)

The value of E at every point on the surface of the sphere of radius r is the same due to symmetry of spherical charge distribution

$\therefore$

$$\oiint \vec{E} \cdot \vec{dS} = \oiint E\, dS = E \oiint dS$$

$$= E\, 4\pi r^2$$

...(iii)

Substituting the value of $\oiint \vec{E} \cdot \vec{dS}$ from (iii) and q from (ii) in (i), we have

$$E\, 4\pi r^2 = 4\pi \frac{\rho_0}{\varepsilon_0}\left[\frac{r^3}{3} - \frac{r^4}{4a}\right]$$

or

$$E = \frac{\rho_0}{\varepsilon_0}\left[\frac{r}{3} - \frac{r^2}{4a}\right]$$

...(iv)

Value of r for maximum value of E.

Now

$$\frac{dE}{dr} = \frac{\rho_0}{\varepsilon_0}\left[\frac{1}{3} - \frac{1}{2}\frac{r}{a}\right]$$

The value of E is maximum for value of r given by $\dfrac{dE}{dr} = 0$

or

$$\frac{\rho_0}{\varepsilon_0}\left[\frac{1}{3} - \frac{1}{2}\frac{r}{a}\right] = 0$$

or

$$r = \frac{2}{3}a$$

For this value of r, the value of E is maximum and is given by putting $r = \dfrac{2}{3}a$ in (iv)

$\therefore$

$$E_{\max} = \frac{\rho_0}{\varepsilon_0}\left[\frac{2}{9}a - \frac{1}{9}a\right] = \frac{1}{9}\frac{\rho_0}{\varepsilon_0}a$$

Q.3.30. Show that Coulomb's law can be deduced from Gauss's law and considerations of symmetry.

(*H.P.U.* 2001, 2000, 1996, 1995 ; *G.N.D.U.*, 2007, 2006, 2000 ; *Gharwal. U.*, 2000 ; *Pbi. U.*, 2008, 2006, 1995 ; *Luck. U.*, 1994)

OR

Coulomb's law is a special case of Gauss's law. Explain.   (*Pbi.U.*, 2003, 1991)

Ans. Deduction of Coulomb's law from Gauss's law. Consider an isolated point charge q located at O, the origin of the co-ordinate system. Draw a sphere of radius r with q as centre to represent a *spherical Gaussian surface*. From considerations of *spherical symmetry* the electric field intensity $\vec{E}$ at any point on the surface must have the same magnitude and must be directed along the outward drawn radius *i.e.*, $\vec{E}$ must be *normal* to the surface.

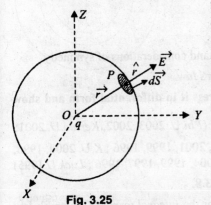

Fig. 3.25

Let P be a point on the surface of the sphere having a position vector $\vec{r}$, then

Electric intensity at P, $\vec{E} = E\hat{r}$ where $\hat{r}$ is a unit vector in the direction of $\vec{r}$.

Now consider a small area element $\vec{dS}$ about the point P. For a spherical surface the area vector $\vec{dS}$ at any point is also directed along the outward drawn normal to the surface.

Therefore, the electric field vector $\vec{E}$ and area vector $\vec{dS}$ at any point on the surface of the sphere are parallel to each other.

Hence $\vec{E} . \vec{dS} = E \, dS$

where E and dS are the magnitudes of vectors $\vec{E}$ and $\vec{dS}$ respectively.

According to Gauss's theorem

$$\oiint_{C.S} \vec{E} . \vec{dS} = \frac{q}{\varepsilon_0} \qquad \qquad ...(i)$$

where $\oiint_{C.S}$ represents integration over a closed surface.

But $\oiint \vec{E} . \vec{dS} = \oiint E \, dS = E \oiint dS = E \, 4\pi \, r^2$ ...(ii)

From (*i*) and (*ii*), we have

$$E \, 4\pi \, r^2 = \frac{q}{\varepsilon_0}$$

or $E = \frac{1}{4\pi \varepsilon_0} \frac{q}{r^2}$

The above relation gives the magnitude of the electric field intensity at any point at a distance r from the isolated point charge q and from considerations of symmetry its direction is along the line joining the charge to the point.

Hence
$$\vec{E} = \frac{1}{4\pi\varepsilon_0} \frac{q}{r^2} \hat{r}$$

If a second charge q' is placed at the point P where the value of $\vec{E}$ has been calculated, then the magnitude of the force that acts on it is given by

$$F = Eq' = \frac{1}{4\pi\varepsilon_0} \frac{qq'}{r^2}$$

Taking the direction of the force also into consideration

$$\vec{F} = \frac{1}{\varepsilon_0} \frac{qq'}{r^2} \hat{r}$$

which is *Coulomb's law*.

Hence Coulomb's law can be deduced from Gauss's law and considerations of symmetry.

In other words, *Coulomb's law is a special case of Gauss's law*.

Q.3.31. State and prove Gauss's (law) theorem. Express it in differential form and show that $\vec{\nabla} \cdot \vec{E} = \dfrac{\rho}{\varepsilon_0}$.   *(Pbi. U.* 2003, 2002, *Kerala. U.* 2001;

Gharwal. U. 2000; *H.P.U.* 2007, 2002, 2001, 1999, 1996 ; *K.U.* 2000, 1996;
P.U. 2003, 2002, 2000 ; *G.N.D.U.* 2009, 2007, 2006, 2004, 1999, 1997, 1996 ; *Luck.U.*1995)

Ans. For statement of Gauss's theorem and proof See Q.3.8.

Differential form of Coulomb's law. Gauss's theorem or the *integral form* of Coulomb's law states that

$$\oiint \vec{E} \cdot \vec{dS} = \frac{q}{\varepsilon_0}$$

To convert it to *differential form* of Coulomb's law or Gauss's law we make use of Gauss's divergence theorem of vector calculus, which states

$$\oiint \vec{A} \cdot \vec{dS} = \iiint_V (\vec{\nabla} \cdot \vec{A}) \, dv$$

For an electrostatic field $\vec{E}$, we have

$$\oiint \vec{E} \cdot \vec{dS} = \iiint_V (\vec{\nabla} \cdot \vec{E}) \, dv$$

∴ Gauss's theorem can be written as

$$\oiint \vec{E} \cdot \vec{dS} = \iiint_V (\vec{\nabla} \cdot \vec{E}) \, dv = \frac{q}{\varepsilon_0} \qquad \qquad ...(i)$$

If ρ is the charge density at a point within the volume V, then

$$q = \iiint_V \rho \, dv \text{ or } \frac{q}{\varepsilon_0} = \frac{1}{\varepsilon_0} \iiint_V \rho \, dv = \iiint_V \frac{\rho}{\varepsilon_0} \, dv \qquad \qquad ...(ii)$$

Comparing (*i*) and (*ii*), we have

∴
$$\vec{\nabla} \cdot \vec{E} = \frac{\rho}{\varepsilon_0} \qquad \qquad ...(iii)$$

This is the differential form of Gauss's law (or Coulomb's law)

Q.3.32. Given the electric field in a region of space $\vec{E} = 2\,x\,\hat{i} + 2\,y\,\hat{j} + z\,\hat{k}$. Calculate the volume charge density.   *(Pbi. U. 2008; H.P.U. 2003 ; P.U. 2003, 2001; G.N.D.U., 1993)*

Ans. According to differential form of Gauss's law $\vec{\Delta}.\vec{E} = \dfrac{\rho}{\varepsilon_0}$

Now $\vec{E} = 2\,x\,\hat{i} + 2\,y\,\hat{j} + z\,\hat{k}$

$\therefore$ $\vec{\nabla}.\vec{E} = \left(\dfrac{\partial}{\partial x}\,\hat{i} + \dfrac{\partial}{\partial y}\,\hat{j} + \dfrac{\partial}{\partial z}\,\hat{k}\right).(2\,x\,\hat{i} + 2\,y\,\hat{j} + z\,\hat{k})$

$$= 2 + 2 + 1 = 5\ \text{N C}^{-1}\,\text{m}^{-1}$$

Hence volume density of charge

$$\rho = \varepsilon_0\,(\vec{\nabla}.\vec{E})$$
$$= 8.85 \times 10^{-12}\ \text{C}^2\,\text{N}^{-1}\,\text{m}^{-2} \times 5\ \text{N C}^{-1}\,\text{m}^{-1}$$
$$= 44.25 \times 10^{-12}\ \text{Cm}^{-3}$$

Ex.1. *Electric field in a given region of space is $\vec{E} = 5\,x\,\hat{i} + 6\,y\,\hat{j} + 3z\,\hat{k}$. Find volume charge density. Given $\varepsilon_0 = 8.85 \times 10^{-12}\ C^2\,N^{-1}\,m^{-2}$.*   *(K.U. 2000 ; M.D.U. 1999)*

Hint. $\vec{\nabla}.\vec{E} = \left(\dfrac{\partial}{\partial x}\,\hat{i} + \dfrac{\partial}{\partial y}\,\hat{j} + \dfrac{\partial}{\partial z}\,\hat{k}\right).(5\,x\,\hat{i} + 6\,y\,\hat{j} + 3\hat{k}) = 5 + 6 + 3 = 14\ \text{N C}^{-1}\,\text{m}^{-1}$

$\rho = \varepsilon_0\,(\vec{\nabla}.\vec{E}) = 14 \times 8.85 \times 10^{-12} = 123.9 \times 10^{-12}\ \text{Cm}^{-3}$

Ex.2. Given $\vec{E} = k\,\vec{r}$, *calculate the volume charge density where k is a constant.*   *(P.U. 2007)*

Hint. $\vec{E} = k\,\vec{r} = k(x\,\hat{i} + y\,\hat{j} + z\,\hat{k})$

$\therefore$ $\vec{\nabla}.\vec{E} = \left(\dfrac{\partial}{\partial x}\,\hat{i} + \dfrac{\partial}{\partial y}\,\hat{j} + \dfrac{\partial}{\partial z}\,\hat{k}\right).(x\,\hat{i} + y\,\hat{j} + z\,\hat{k})\,k = (1 + 1 + 1)\,k = 3k$

But $\vec{\nabla}.\vec{E} = \dfrac{\rho}{\varepsilon_0}$ $\therefore$ $\rho = \varepsilon_0\left(\vec{\nabla}.\vec{E}\right) = 3\,\varepsilon_0\,k$

Q.3.33. *(a)* Prove that the electric field on the surface of a conductor is $\dfrac{\sigma}{\varepsilon_0}$ where σ is the surface charge density. Hence show that the electric field near a charged conducting sheet is twice as great as near a non-conducting sheet with the same surface density of charge.

                                    (G.N.D.U. 2002 ; Luck.U., 1996 ; Cal. U., 1993, 1991)

(b) Show that any excess charge placed on a conductor must be entirely on its surface.

Ans. *(a)* **Electric field on the surface of a conductor.** Let C be a point very close to a charged conducting surface AB having a local surface charge density σ. Draw through C a small Gaussian cylinder CD whose sides are perpendicular to the charged surface and the ends C and D are parallel to the surface such that the end C lies just outside the charged surface and the end D just inside it. If ΔS is the area of the charged surface enclosed within the cylinder, then charge within the cylinder

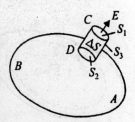

Fig. 3.26

$$= \sigma \, \Delta S$$

∴ According to Gauss's theorem total electrical flux over the surface of the closed cylinder

$$= \sigma \, \Delta S / \varepsilon_0 \qquad \qquad ...(i)$$

The surface of the conductor AB is an equipotential surface. The direction of the electric field intensity at every point is, therefore, along the outward drawn normal. The closed cylinder has three surfaces S_1, S_2, and S_3.

∴ Electric flux over the surface S_1 at $C = \iint\limits_{S_1} \vec{E} \cdot \vec{dS}$

where $\vec{E}$ is the electric field just outside the cylinder.

The electric field over the area S_2 at D is zero as *the electric field intensity inside a charged conductor is zero*. The electric flux over the curved surface S_3 of the cylinder is also zero as the direction of electric field intensity is parallel to the surface.

∴ Total electric flux over the closed surface of the cylinder CD

$$= \oiint \vec{E} \cdot \vec{dS} = \iint\limits_{S_1} \vec{E} \cdot \vec{dS} + \iint\limits_{S_2} \vec{E} \cdot \vec{dS} + \iint\limits_{S_3} \vec{E} \cdot \vec{dS}$$

$$= \iint\limits_{S_1} \vec{E} \cdot \vec{dS} = \iint\limits_{S_1} E \, dS = E \iint\limits_{S_1} dS = E \, \Delta S \qquad \qquad ...(ii)$$

From (*i*) and (*ii*) we have

$$E \, \Delta S = \sigma \, \Delta S / \varepsilon_0$$

or

$$E = \frac{\sigma}{\varepsilon_0} \qquad \qquad ...(iii)$$

Thus the *local field* at a point on the surface of a conductor is equal to $\dfrac{1}{\varepsilon_0}$ times the *surface charge density* σ at that point.

Electric field near a non-conducting sheet. The electric field near a plane non-conducting thin sheet of charge is $\dfrac{\sigma}{2\varepsilon_0}$ $\qquad \qquad ...(iv)$

For proof See **Q.3.20.** Eq. (*iii*)

Comparing equations (*iii*) and (*iv*), we find that the electric field near a charged conducting sheet is twice as great as near a non-conducting sheet with the same surface density of charge.

(b) Excess charge lies on the surface of a conductor. Consider a conductor carrying a charge q. The electric field intensity $\vec{E}$ at any point inside it is zero.

Now consider a Gaussian surface just inside the conductor infinitely close to the actual surface as shown by dotted line in Fig. 3.27.

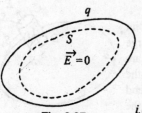

Fig. 3.27

The total electric flux through this surface

$$\oiint \vec{E} \cdot \vec{dS} = 0 \text{ since } \vec{E} = 0$$

According to Gauss's theorem $\oiint \vec{E} \cdot \vec{dS} = \dfrac{q}{\varepsilon_0} = 0$ or $q = 0$

Thus there is no charge any where within the surface of the conductor i.e., *the excess charge lies on the surface of the conductor*.

Q.3.34. The electric field near earth's surface is 300 volt/metre directed downward. What is the surface charge density of earth's surface? *(M.D.U., 2000)*

Ans. Here $E = 300$ Vm^{-1} = 300 J C^{-1} m^{-1} = 300 N m C^{-1} m^{-1} = 300 NC^{-1}

Earth being a conductor, the surface charge density of earth's surface σ is given by $E = \dfrac{\sigma}{\varepsilon_0}$

or $$\sigma = \varepsilon_0 E = 4\pi\, \varepsilon_0\, \frac{E}{4\pi}$$

But $$\frac{1}{4\pi\,\varepsilon_0} = 9 \times 10^9 \text{ N C}^{-2} \text{ m}^2$$

∴ $$\sigma = \frac{1}{9 \times 10^9}\,\frac{300}{4\pi} = \frac{1}{12\pi} \times 10^{-7} \text{ Cm}^{-2}$$

Q.3.35. Prove that the mechanical force per unit area on the surface of a charged conductor acting normally to the surface is given by

$$F = \frac{\sigma^2}{2\varepsilon_0} = \frac{1}{2}\,\varepsilon_0\, E^2 \text{ Nm}^{-2}$$

where symbols have their usual meanings. Hence deduce the total outward pressure on a charged soap bubble. *(P.U. 2006, 2001 ; M.D.U. 2007, 2002, 1999 ; Kan.U. 1996 ;*
K.U. 2002, 1995, 1994 ; A.U. 1995,1994 ; H.P.U. 1991)

Ans. Mechanical force per unit area on the surface of a charged conductor. The charge on any small area of a conductor experiences an outward mechanical force due to the repulsion of the charge on the rest of the area. Let AB represent a charged conducting surface. Consider a small element of area dS and

let P be a point just outside it. If σ is the surface density of

charge, then electric field at P, $E = \dfrac{\sigma}{\varepsilon_0}$.

The electric field at P may be regarded as made up of two parts :

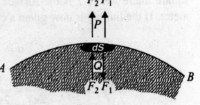

Fig. 3.28

(*i*) An *outward force* F_1 due to the charge on the small area dS very close to P and

(*ii*) An *outward force* F_2 due to the charge on the rest of the surface.

∴ $$F_1 + F_2 = E = \sigma/\varepsilon_0$$

Now consider a point Q *just inside* the charged surface.

Since Q lies inside the conductor,

∴ Electric field at $Q = 0$.

The field at Q may again be regarded as made up of two parts. As the point Q lies on the opposite side of P, but still very close to it, the force F_1 due to the charge on the small area dS will be equal in magnitude but opposite in direction.

Since Q lies very near P the force at Q due to the rest of the charged surface will be the same and in the same direction as at P

∴ $$-F_1 + F_2 = 0 \qquad\qquad\qquad ...(ii)$$

Comparing (*i*) and (*ii*), we have $F_1 = F_2 = \sigma/2\varepsilon_0$

The charge on area dS is $\sigma \, dS$ and a unit charge on it experiences an outward force $F = \dfrac{\sigma}{2\varepsilon_0}$ due to the charge on the rest of the surface.

$\therefore$ Outward force on the area $dS = \sigma \, dS \, \dfrac{\sigma}{2\varepsilon_0} = \dfrac{\sigma^2 \, dS}{2 \, \varepsilon_0}$

$\therefore$ Outward force per unit area (or outward pressure) $= \dfrac{\sigma^2}{2\varepsilon_0}$ ...(iii)

Now $\qquad\qquad\qquad E = \dfrac{\sigma}{\varepsilon_0} \quad \text{or} \quad \sigma = \varepsilon_0 \, E$

$\therefore$ Outward force per unit area or electrostatic pressure acting along the outward drawn normal to the surface

$$= \frac{\varepsilon_0^2 \, E^2}{2\varepsilon_0} = \frac{1}{2} \, \varepsilon_0 \, E^2 \qquad\qquad\qquad ...(iv)$$

when the conductor lies in a medium of relative permittivity ε_r the outward force per unit area

$$= \frac{1}{2} \, \varepsilon_r \, \varepsilon_0 \, E^2$$

Total outward pressure on a charged soap bubble. The existence of outward mechanical force or outward pressure on the surface of a charged conductor can be shown with the help of a soap bubble.

The pressure inside a soap bubble is greater than that outside by an amount $\dfrac{4T}{r}$ Newton per square metre where T is the surface tension in Newton per metre and r the radius of the bubble in metre. If the bubble is now given a charge q, then surface charge density

$$\sigma = \frac{q}{4\pi r^2}$$

$\therefore$ Outward pressure $= \dfrac{\sigma^2}{2\varepsilon_0} = \dfrac{1}{2\varepsilon_0} \dfrac{q^2}{16 \, \pi^2 \, r^4} = \dfrac{q^2}{32 \, \varepsilon_0 \, \pi^2 \, r^4}$

The bubble expands due to this external pressure until the excess pressure falls to a value given by

$$P = \frac{4T}{r} - \frac{q^2}{32 \, \varepsilon_0 \, \pi^2 \, r^4}$$

Exercise. *Prove that the surface tension of a soap bubble of radius r decreases by an amount*

$\dfrac{q^2}{128 \, \pi^2 \, r^3 \, \varepsilon_0}$ *when it is given a charge $\pm q$.* (P.U. 2005)

Hint. For an uncharged soap bubble excess pressure inside the soap bubble $= \dfrac{4T}{r}$ Nm^{-2}

For a soap bubble given a charge $\pm q$ the excess pressure falls to a value

$$\frac{4T}{r} - \frac{q^2}{32\varepsilon_0 \, \pi^2 r^4} = \frac{4}{r}\left[T - \frac{q^2}{128 \, \pi^2 r^3 \, \varepsilon_0} \right]$$

This shows that the value of surface tension decreases by an amount $\dfrac{q^2}{128 \, \pi^2 \, r^3 \, \varepsilon_0}$

Q.3.36. A soap bubble of radius 5 mm is formed at the end of an open glass tube. What charge should be given to the bubbles so that it is in equilibrium? Surface tension = 0.033 Nm^{-1}

(*P.U.* 2000)

Ans. The soap bubble will be in equilibrium when

$$\frac{4T}{r} = \frac{q^2}{32\,\varepsilon_0\,\pi^2\,r^4}$$

∴ $\qquad q^2 = 4\,T \times 32\,\varepsilon_0\,\pi^2\,r^3 = 4\,\pi\,\varepsilon_0 \times 32\,\pi\,T\,r^3$

Now $\qquad T = 0.033$ Nm^{-1} = 33×10^{-3} Nm^{-1}, $r = 5$ mm = 5×10^{-3} m

$$\frac{1}{4\pi\varepsilon_0} = 9 \times 10^9 \text{ Nm}^2 \text{ C}^{-2}$$

∴ $\quad q^2 = \dfrac{1}{9 \times 10^9} \times 32 \times \dfrac{22}{7} \times 33 \times 10^{-3} \times (5 \times 10^{-3})^3 = 46.095 \times 10^{-18}$

or $\qquad q = 6.79 \times 10^{-9}$ C.

Q.3.37. Find the surface density of charge of a horizontal charged plate so that the gold foil weighing 40 mg/cm^2 when placed on the plate will rise.   (*Kerala. U.* 2001 ; *H.P.U.*, 1991)

Ans. Suppose the surface density of charge required to raise the gold foil = σ

∴ Upward pressure on the gold foil $= \dfrac{\sigma^2}{2\varepsilon_0}$ Newton m^{-2}

Downward weight of the foil per sq metre = $40 \times 10^{-6} \times 10^4 \times 9.8$ Newton m^{-2}

For the foil to rise $\qquad \dfrac{\sigma^2}{2\varepsilon_0} = 40 \times 10^{-6} \times 10^4 \times 9.8$

or $\qquad \sigma^2 = 2\,\varepsilon_0 \times 40 \times 10^{-6} \times 10^4 \times 9.8$

$\qquad\qquad = 2 \times 8.85 \times 10^{-12} \times 40 \times 10^{-6} \times 10^4 \times 9.8$

$\qquad \sigma = 8.33 \times 10^{-6}$ coulomb m^{-2}

Q.3.38. Two parallel discs *A* and *B* are placed a short distance apart in air. *A* is charged with positive electricity and *B* is earthed. If the field between the plates is uniform find the force per unit area.

Ans. (*i*) Let *A* and *B* be the two plates placed a short distance apart in air. *A* is charged positively and *B* is earth connected.

A negative charge is induced on the inner side of the plate *B* and positive goes to the earth. If + σ is the surface density of charge on the plate *A*, then that on the plate *B* will be – σ.

Electric field at a point near a charged conducting plane is $\dfrac{\sigma}{2\varepsilon_0}$

∴ A unit charge on the plate *A* is attracted by the plate *B* with a force $\dfrac{\sigma}{2\varepsilon_0}$

Hence force of attraction per unit area $= \dfrac{\sigma}{2\varepsilon_0} \times \sigma = \dfrac{1}{2\varepsilon_0}\sigma^2$ ...(*i*)

This gives the force of attraction per unit area in terms of the surface density of charge.

(*ii*) The electric field *E* at any point *P* between the two plates is given by

$$E = \frac{\sigma}{\varepsilon_0} \qquad\qquad ∴ \ \sigma = \varepsilon_0 E$$

Hence force of attraction per unit area $= \dfrac{1}{2\varepsilon_0}\varepsilon_0^2\,E^2 = \dfrac{1}{2}\varepsilon_0\,E^2$ ...(*ii*)

This gives the force of attraction per unit area in terms of electric field intensity between the two plates.

(*iii*) The work done in taking a unit positve charge from B to A against the electrical forces

$= \dfrac{\sigma}{\varepsilon_0} d$ where d is the distance between the two plates.

$\therefore$ Potential difference between the two plates

$$V = \frac{\sigma}{\varepsilon_0} d \quad \text{or} \quad \sigma = \frac{\varepsilon_0 V}{d}$$

Substituting the value of σ in (*i*), we have

Force of attraction per unit area $= \dfrac{1}{2\varepsilon_0} \dfrac{\varepsilon_0^2 V^2}{d^2} = \dfrac{1}{2} \varepsilon_0 \dfrac{V^2}{d^2}$ ...(*iii*)

This gives the force of attraction per unit area in terms of potential difference between the two plates.

Q.3.39. Obtain an expression for energy density stored in an electric field. (*G.N.D.U.* 2004)

Ans. Energy density in electric field. The outward force per unit area of a charged surface is given by

$$F = \frac{1}{2} \varepsilon_0 E^2$$

where $\vec{E}$ is the electric field intensity [For proof See **Q. 3.35 Eq. (*iv*)**]

If this force causes a *unit area* of the charged surface to move a distance dx inwards along the direction of the electric field $\vec{E}$ *in a direction perpendicular to the area without changing the potential of the charged surface* then,

Work done by the force $= \dfrac{1}{2} \varepsilon_0 E^2 \, dx$

In this process, a volume dx of the medium has been swept by the unit area and work done is stored in the volume dx of the medium as energy of the electric field.

$\therefore$ Energy stored in the electric field per unit volume of the medium $= \dfrac{1}{2} \varepsilon_0 E^2 \dfrac{dx}{dx} = \dfrac{1}{2} \varepsilon_0 E^2$

Hence energy density stored in the electric field $= \dfrac{1}{2} \varepsilon_0 E^2$.

Q. 3.40. Mark the correct answers.

(*i*) The solid angle subtended at a point at the centre of closed sphere is

    (*a*) zero   (*b*) π

    (*c*) 2π (*d*) 4π (*H.P.U.* 1996)

(*ii*) The unit of electric flux is

    (*a*) Weber   (*b*) $N \, m^2 \, C^{-1}$

    (*c*) $N \, C^{-1}$ (*d*) Gauss

(*iii*) A charge of 15 μC is placed at one corner of a cube. The electric flux will be

    (*a*) Zero through each face   (*b*) Same through each face

    (*c*) Zero through three faces meeting at the location   (*P.U.,* 1994)

(*iv*) The electric field intensity E inside a uniformly charged sphere varies with distance r of the observation point as

    (*a*) $E \propto r$ (*b*) $E \propto 1/r$

    (*c*) $E \propto r^2$ (*d*) $E \propto 1/r^2$ (*H.P.U.,* 1994)

(v) The electric field between two oppositely charged plates having equal charge density σ is given by

(a) σ/ε_0 (b) $\sigma/2\varepsilon_0$

(c) zero   (d) $2\sigma/\varepsilon_0$ (H.P.U. 1995)

(vi) The variation of electric field intensity $\vec{E}$ with distance $|\vec{r}|$ from the centre of a hollow spherical shell of radius R is given by

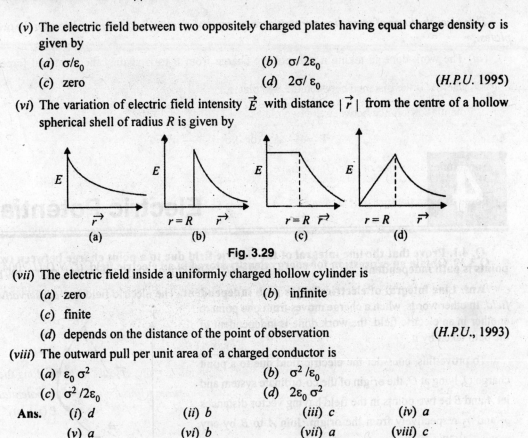

Fig. 3.29

(vii) The electric field inside a uniformly charged hollow cylinder is

(a) zero   (b) infinite

(c) finite

(d) depends on the distance of the point of observation   (H.P.U., 1993)

(viii) The outward pull per unit area of a charged conductor is

(a) $\varepsilon_0 \sigma^2$ (b) σ^2/ε_0

(c) $\sigma^2/2\varepsilon_0$ (d) $2\varepsilon_0 \sigma^2$

Ans.   (i) d   (ii) b   (iii) c   (iv) a

        (v) a   (vi) b   (vii) a   (viii) c

EXERCISE

1. A point charge q is located at the centre of a cube of side a. Find the electric flux through one face of the cube. $\left[\text{Ans.} \dfrac{1}{6} \dfrac{q}{\varepsilon_0} \right]$

2. In a region in space electric field $\vec{E} = 5\,\hat{x} + 2\,\hat{y} + \hat{z}$. Calculate the electric flux through a surface $\vec{S} = 200\,\hat{y}$. [Ans. 400 N m^2 C^{-1}]

3. A point charge 0.1×10^{-6} C is kept at the centre of a cube of side 10 cm. Calculate the electric flux through one face. (G.N.D.U., 1991; P.U., 1991) [Ans. 0.19×10^5 N m^2 C^{-1}]

4. Electric field in a certain region of space is $\vec{E} = 4\,\hat{i} + 3\,\hat{j} - 2\,\hat{k}$. Calculate the electric flux through a surface having area $\vec{S} = 50\,\hat{k}$. (G.N.D.U., 1997) [Ans. 100 Nm^2 C^{-1}]

5. Electric field in a given region of space $\vec{E} = 5x\,\hat{i} + 6y\,\hat{j} + 5z\,\hat{k}$, find the volume charge density. (G.N.D.U. 1991) [Ans 141·6 $\times$ 10^{-12} C/m^3]

4

Electric Potential

Q. 4.1. Prove that the line integral of the electric field due to a point charge between two points is path independent. *(H.P.U., 2003, 2000, 1995, 1993; P.U., 2007, 1991)*

Ans. Line integral of electric field is path independent. The electric field is a *conservative field*. In other words, when a charge moves from one point to another in an electric field, the work done is independent of the path taken by it.

To prove this, consider the electric field due to a point charge Q, lying at O, the origin of the co-ordinate system and let A and B be two points in the field having vector distances $\vec{r_1}$ and $\vec{r_2}$ respectively from the origin. Join A to B by any path say ACB. Let P be a point on the path at a vector distance $\vec{r}$ and having co-ordinates x, y and z, then

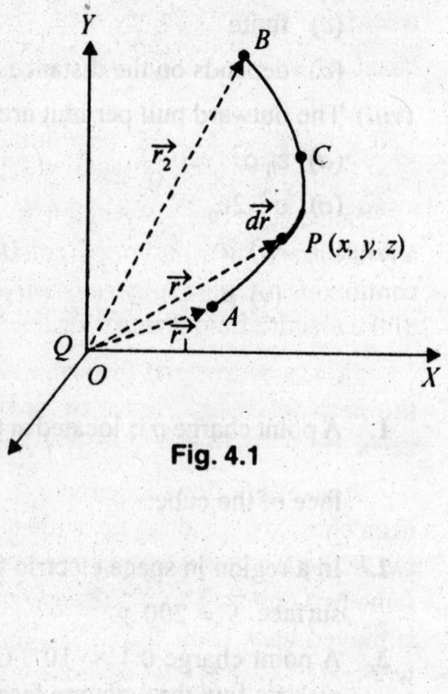

$$\vec{r} = x\,\hat{i} + y\,\hat{j} + z\,\hat{k}$$

and $\quad |r^2| = x^2 + y^2 + z^2$

Fig. 4.1

Differentiating, we have

$$2r\,dr = 2x\,dx + 2y\,dy + 2z\,dz$$

or $\qquad r\,dr = x\,dx + y\,dy + z\,dz$

The electric field at P, $\qquad \vec{E} = \dfrac{1}{4\pi\varepsilon_0}\dfrac{Q}{r^2}\,\hat{r} = \dfrac{1}{4\pi\varepsilon_0}\dfrac{Q}{r^3}\,\vec{r}$

$$= \dfrac{1}{4\pi\varepsilon_0}\dfrac{Q}{r^3}[x\,\hat{i} + y\,\hat{j} + z\,\hat{k}]$$

Take a small elementary displacement $d\vec{r}$ from the point P along the path, then

$$d\vec{r} = dx\,\hat{i} + dy\,\hat{j} + dz\,\hat{k}$$

∴ Work done when a unit positive charge at P moves through a vector distance $d\vec{r}$

$$= \vec{E} \cdot d\vec{r}$$

Hence total work done when a unit positive charge moves from A to B due to the electric field

$$= \int_A^B \vec{E} \cdot d\vec{r} = \frac{1}{4\pi \varepsilon_0} \int_A^B \frac{Q}{r^3} (x\,\hat{i} + y\,\hat{j} + z\,\hat{k}) \cdot (dx\,\hat{i} + dy\,\hat{j} + dz\,\hat{k})$$

$$= \frac{1}{4\pi \varepsilon_0} \int_A^B \frac{Q}{r^3} (x\,dx + y\,dy + z\,dz) = \frac{1}{4\pi \varepsilon_0} \int_A^B \frac{Q}{r^3} r\,dr$$

$$= \frac{1}{4\pi \varepsilon_0} \int_A^B \frac{Q}{r^2}\,dr = \frac{1}{4\pi \varepsilon_0} \left[-\frac{Q}{r} \right]_A^B = \frac{Q}{4\pi \varepsilon_0} \left[\frac{1}{r_1} - \frac{1}{r_2} \right]$$

Thus the line integral of the electric field due to a point charge depends only on the initial and final positions of the field and is independent of the actual path along which the charge moves.

Line integral due to a continuous charge distribution. Applying the principle of superposition, we find that the resultant electric field $\vec{E}$ due to a number of charges $Q_1, Q_2 \ldots Q_n$ etc., is given by

$$\vec{E} = \vec{E}_1 + \vec{E}_2 + \ldots + \vec{E}_n$$

where $\vec{E} = \vec{E}_1, \vec{E}_2, \ldots, \vec{E}_n$ is the electric field due to $Q_1, Q_2, \ldots Q_n$ respectively. Since work is a scalar quantity the total work done when a unit positive charge moves from A to B is given by

$$\therefore \qquad \int_A^B \vec{E}_1 \cdot d\vec{r} + \ldots \int_A^B \vec{E}_i \cdot d\vec{r} + \ldots \int_A^B \vec{E}_n \cdot d\vec{r} = \int_A^B \vec{E} \cdot d\vec{r}$$

Since each line integral due to a point charge is independent of the path, the line integral due to any arbitrary distribution of point charges is also path independent. If the charge distribution is continuous it can be supposed to be made up of a number of point charges and hence the line integral of the electirc field due to it is also path independent.

Q. 4.2. Show that the work done in moving a charge in an electric field is independent of the path followed. Hence show that the line integral of an electric field over a closed path is zero.   *(H.P.U., 1995)*

Ans. Work done is independent of the path. Suppose a small test charge q_0 moves from A to B in an electric field along the path ACB in a *quasi-static manner* and W_1 is the work done **by** the field. Let W_2 be the work done by the field when the same charge moves along the path ADB between the same two points. This also means that when the same charge is moved back from B to A by the path BCA an amount of work W_1 will have to be done **against** the electric field. Similarly if the test charge is moved back along the path BDA an amount of work W_2 will have to be done **against** the field. If W_1 and W_2 are not equal, let W_1 be greater than W_2. Let the charge q_0 go along the path ACB and return by the path BDA. In this way a net *positive* amount of work $(W_1 - W_2)$ is done by the electric field during a process which leaves the test charge q_0 in its original position at A. According to the principle of conservation of energy this is not possible unless an amount of energy $(W_1 - W_2)$ is made to enter the system from outside. This doen not happen in the case of an electric

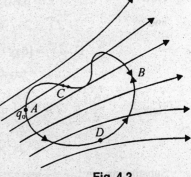

Fig. 4.2

field because magnitude and positions of all the charges remains unchanged during the process. Thus no work can be obtained by moving a charge away from the point A and back to it again.

Hence $\qquad W_1 - W_2 = 0 \quad$ or $\quad W_1 = W_2$

Thus equal and same amount of work is done on a charge along all possible paths joining A and B. In other words, *the work done when a charge moves from one point to another in an electric field, is independent of the path.*

Line integral of an electric field over a closed path is zero. The work done in taking a unit positive charge from A to B in an electric field $\vec{E}$ is given by $\int_A^B \vec{E} \cdot d\vec{r}$ where $d\vec{r}$ is a small element of the path.

$\therefore$ Work done in moving a unit positive charge from A to B via the path ACB by the electric field

$$= W_1 = \int_A^B \vec{E} \cdot d\vec{r}$$

and work done in moving a unit positive charge from B to A via the path BDA **against** the field

$$= W_2 = \int_B^A \vec{E} \cdot d\vec{r} = - \int_A^B \vec{E} \cdot d\vec{r}$$

$\therefore$ Total work done in taking a unit positive charge from A to B and back again to A over the closed path $ACBDA$ is given by

$$\oint \vec{E} \cdot d\vec{l} = \int_A^B \vec{E} \cdot d\vec{r} - \int_A^B \vec{E} \cdot d\vec{r} = 0$$

Hence the line integral of an electric field over a closed path is zero.

Q. 4.3. The intensity of the electric field at a point is given by $\vec{E} = 6xy\,\hat{i} + (3x^2 - 3y^2)\,\hat{j} + 4z\,\hat{k}$ **Newton/Coulomb. Calculate the amount of work done by the field in taking a unit positive charge from the origin to the point** (x_1, y_1, z_1).

If $x_1, y_1, z_1 = 1, 1, 1$ **find the work done for a charge of 1 coulomb.**

Ans. The work done by the field in taking a unit positive charge from the origin $(0, 0, 0)$ to the point (x_1, y_1, z_1) is given by

$$\int_{000}^{x_1 y_1 z_1} \vec{E} \cdot d\vec{r}$$

Now $\qquad \vec{E} = 6xy\,\hat{i} + (3x^2 - 3y^2)\,\hat{j} + 4z\,\hat{k}$

and $\qquad d\vec{r} = dx\,\hat{i} + dy\,\hat{j} + dz\,\hat{k}$

$\therefore \qquad \vec{E} \cdot d\vec{r} = [6xy\,\hat{i} + (3x^2 - 3y^2)\,\hat{j} + 4z\,\hat{k}] \cdot [dx\,\hat{i} + dy\,\hat{j} + dz\,\hat{k}]$

$$= 6xy\,dx + (3x^2 - 3y^2)\,dy + 4z\,dz$$

Hence $\qquad \int_{000}^{x_1 y_1 z_1} \vec{E} \cdot d\vec{r} = \int_{000}^{x_1 y_1 z_1} [6xy\,dx + (3x^2 - 3y^2)\,dy + 4z\,dz]$

$$= \left[3x^2 y + 3x^2 y - y^3 + 2z^2 \right]_{000}^{x_1 y_1 z_1} = 6x_1^2 y_1 - y_1^3 + 2z_1^2$$

Substituting $x = 1, y = 1$ and $z = 1$ in the above relation, work done for a charge of 1 coulomb $= 6 - 1 + 2 = 7$ Joules.

Q. 4.4. (a) Prove that in an electrostatic field $\vec{E}$, **the potential difference between two points** A **and** B **is given by**

$$V_B - V_A = - \int_A^B \vec{E} \cdot d\vec{r}$$

or Show that the potential difference between any two points is the line integral of the electric field between these points. (G.N.D.U. 2007)

(b) How will you define potential difference and potential at a point from this relation ?

(H.P.U., 2001, 2000, 1999, 1992; P.U., 2000; Gharwal U., 1999; G.N.D.U., 2002)

(c) Is the potential difference more basic or potential?   (H.P.U. 2007)

Ans. Potential difference between two points. The work done by the static electric field $\vec{E}$ when a test charge q_0 move through a small vector distance $d\vec{r}$ is given by

$$dW = q_0 \vec{E} \cdot d\vec{r}$$

∴ The work done in taking a test charge q_0 through a vector distance $d\vec{r}$ against the electric field is given by

$$dW = -q_0 \vec{E} \cdot d\vec{r}$$

This work is stored in the test charge as its potential energy dU.

∴ $$dU = -q_0 \vec{E} \cdot d\vec{r}$$

As the electrostatic field is a conservative field, the potential energy only depends upon the initial and final positions of the test charge and is independent of the path along which the test charge travels.

If the charge is moved *quasi-statically* through a finite distance say from a point A to a point B *against* the electrical forces, the change in potential energy

$$U_B - U_A = - \int_A^B q_0 \vec{E} \cdot d\vec{r}$$

Thus the properties of an electric field can be described by a scalar quantity which is equivalent to the amount of work necessary to move a unit charge quasi-statically between any two points in space and is called the *potential difference* between the two points.

∴ Potential difference between two points an infinitesimally small vector distance $d\vec{r}$ apart is given by

$$dV = - \frac{dU}{q_0} = - \vec{E} \cdot d\vec{r} \qquad ...(i)$$

For two points A and B a finite distance apart

$$V_B - V_A = \frac{U_B - U_A}{q_0} = - \int_A^B \vec{E} \cdot d\vec{r} \qquad ...(ii)$$

The quantity $\int_A^B \vec{E} \cdot d\vec{r}$ is known as the *line integral of the electric field* between the points A and B.

(b) Potential difference. *The difference of electric potential between two points A and B in an electric field is defined as the work done in taking a unit positive charge from A to B against electric forces or it may be defined as the negative of the line integral of the electric field from A to B.*

A point at infinity *i.e.*, far removed from all other charges is said have zero potential.

Potential at a point. *The electric potential at a point in an electric field is defined as the work done in taking a unit positive charge from infinity to that point against the electric forces.*

(c) The potential difference is more basic. Even the potential at a point is the potential difference between, the given point and a point at infinity.

Q. 4.5. What is the significance of negative sign in the equation $dU_p = -q_0 \vec{E} . d\vec{r}$ **?**

(H.P.U., 2003)

Ans. The work done in taking a test charge q_0 through a vector distance $d\vec{r}$ *against* the electric field $\vec{E}$ is given by

$$dW = -q_0 \vec{E} . d\vec{r}$$

This work is stored in the test charge as its potential energy dU_p

$$\therefore \qquad dU_p = -q_0 \vec{E} . d\vec{r}$$

Thus the negative sign signifies that the potential energy stored in the test charge is due to the work done against the electric field.

Q. 4.6. How is potential difference between two points related to work? (P.U., 2003)

Ans. Relation between potential difference and work. *The potential difference between two points A and B in an electric field is equal to the work done is taking a unit positive charge from A to B against the electrical forces.*

The work done in taking a unit positive charge from A to B against the force of an electric field $\vec{E}$

$$W = -\int_A^B \vec{E} . d\vec{r} \qquad \therefore \qquad V_B - V_A = -\int_A^B \vec{E} . d\vec{r}$$

Q. 4.7. Define electric potential and give its C.G.S and S.I units. Explain the difference between a volt and stat-volt. Establish relationship between them.

(Kerala U., 2001; H.P.U., 2000, 1996; Pbi.U., 2002; G.N.D.U., 1997)

Ans. Electric potential. See **Q. 4.4 (b)**

Unit of electric potential. The potential difference between two points an infinitesimally small vector distance $d\vec{r}$ apart is given by

$$dV = -\frac{dU}{q_0}$$

where dU is the work stored in the test charge q_0 as its potential energy.

$\therefore$ Unit of potential (or potential difference)

$$= \frac{\text{unit of } U}{\text{unit of } q_0} = \frac{\text{erg}}{\text{stat–coulomb}} \text{ in C.G.S. units}$$

$$= \frac{\text{Joule}}{\text{Coulomb}} \text{ in S.I. units}$$

Stat-volt. The C.G.S. Gaussian unit of potential is a *stat-volt*.

The potential at a point is one stat-volt if one erg of work is done in taking a positive charge of one stat-coulomb from infinity to that point against the electrical forces.

Volt. The S.I. unit of potential is a *volt*.

The potential at a point is said to be one volt if one joule of work is done in taking a positive charge of one coulomb from infinity to that point against the electrical forces.

Relation. $\quad$ 1 volt $= \dfrac{\text{Joule}}{\text{Coulomb}} = \dfrac{10^7 \text{ erg}}{3 \times 10^9 \text{ stat-coulomb}} = \dfrac{1}{300}$ stat-volt

or $\quad$ 1 stat-volt $= 300$ volts.

Q. 4.8. (a) **Determine the energy gained by an α-particle when it is accelerated through a potential difference of 1000 volts.** $\hfill$ (*P.U., 1995*)

(b) **In an electron gun electrons of charge e and mass m are accelerated through a potential difference V. Find the maximum speed attained by electrons.** $\hfill$ (*Luck.U., 1996*)

Ans. (a) The difference of potential between two points A and B is given by

$$V_B - V_A = \frac{U_B - U_A}{q}$$

where $U_B - U_A$ is the energy gained by the charge q in moving through a potential difference $V_B - V_A (V_B > V_A)$.

If $\qquad V_B - V_A = V$ and $U_B - U_A = U$, then

$$U = qV$$

i.e., the energy gained by a particle of charge q coulomb when accelerated through a potential difference of V volts $= qV$ Joules

$\qquad$ Charge on the α-particle $q = 2 \times 1.6 \times 10^{-19}$ C

$\qquad$ Potential difference $V = 1000$ V

$\therefore \qquad$ Energy gained $= 2 \times 1.6 \times 10^{-19} \times 1000 = 3.2 \times 10^{-16}$ J

(b) Let v be the maximum velocity gained by the electron, then

$\qquad$ Kinetic energy gained by the electron $= \dfrac{1}{2} mv^2$

Work done on the electron when it is accelerated through a potential difference $V = eV$

$\therefore \qquad \dfrac{1}{2} mv^2 = eV$

or $\qquad V = \sqrt{\dfrac{2eV}{m}}$

Q. 4.9. (a) **Find the electric potential difference between two points located at position vectors $\vec{r_1}$ and $\vec{r_2}$ due to a point charge q at the origin.**

(b) **A point charge 5×10^{-9} C is situated at the origin of the co-ordinates. Find the potential difference between the points A (1, 2, 2) and B ($\sqrt{5}, 2, 4$).** $\hfill$ (*M.D.U., 2001*)

Ans. (a) **Potential difference between two points due to a point charge.** The difference of electric potential between two points A and B in an electric field is given by

$$V_B - V_A = - \int_A^B \vec{E} \cdot d\vec{r} \qquad \qquad ...(i)$$

where $\int_A^B \vec{E} \cdot d\vec{r}$ is the line integral of the electric field between the two points.

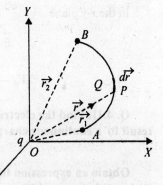

Fig. 4.3

If a charge q lies at the origin of co-ordinate system and the radial distances of the points A and B are $\vec{r_1}$ and $\vec{r_2}$ respectively, as shown then, the electric field at a point P at a radial distance $\vec{r}$ due to a point charge q lying at the origin is given by

$$\overrightarrow{E} = \frac{1}{4\pi\varepsilon_0} \frac{q}{|\overrightarrow{r}|^3} \overrightarrow{r}$$

Substituting this value of $\overrightarrow{E}$ in relation (i), we get

$$V_B - V_A = -\int_A^B \overrightarrow{E}.d\overrightarrow{r} = -\frac{1}{4\pi\varepsilon_0} \int_{r_1}^{r_2} \frac{q}{|\overrightarrow{r}|^3} \overrightarrow{r}.d\overrightarrow{r}$$

Now
$$\overrightarrow{r}.d\overrightarrow{r} = \frac{1}{2}d(r^2) = \frac{1}{2} 2r\, dr = r\, dr$$

$$\therefore \qquad V_B - V_A = -\frac{1}{4\pi\varepsilon_0} \int_{r_1}^{r_2} \frac{q}{r^2} dr$$

$$= \frac{q}{4\pi\varepsilon_0}\left[\frac{1}{r}\right]_{r_1}^{r_2} = \frac{q}{4\pi\varepsilon_0}\left[\frac{1}{r_2} - \frac{1}{r_1}\right]$$

(b) Co-ordinates of points A; $x = 1, y = 2, z = 2$

$\therefore$ Radial distance of A, $\quad r_1 = \sqrt{x^2 + y^2 + z^2} = \sqrt{1+4+4} = 3$

Co-ordinates of point B; $\quad x = \sqrt{5}, y = 2, z = 4$

$\therefore$ Radial distance of B, $\quad r_2 = \sqrt{5+4+16} = 5$

Now
$$V_B - V_A = \frac{q}{4\pi\varepsilon_0}\left[\frac{1}{r_2} - \frac{1}{r_1}\right] = 5\times10^9 \times 9\times10^9 \times \left[\frac{1}{5} - \frac{1}{3}\right]$$

$$= -6 \text{ volt}$$

or
$$V_A - V_B = 6 \text{ volt}.$$

Q. 4.10. The electric field in the xy plane is given by $\overrightarrow{E} = (y\hat{i} + x\hat{j})$, find the potential difference between two points A to B having co-ordinates $(0, 0)$ and $(2, 2)$ respectively.

Ans.
$$V_B - V_A = -\int_A^B \overrightarrow{E}.d\overrightarrow{r}$$

In the x-y plane
$$d\overrightarrow{r} = dx\,\hat{i} + dy\,\hat{j} \text{ and } \overrightarrow{E} = y\hat{i} + x\hat{j}$$

$$\therefore \qquad \overrightarrow{E}.d\overrightarrow{r} = (y\hat{i} + x\hat{j}).(dx\,\hat{i} + dy\,\hat{j}) = y\,dx + x\,dy$$

$$\therefore \qquad V_B - V_A = -\int_A^B [y\,dx + x\,dy] = [2xy]_{0,0}^{2,2} = 8 \text{ units.}$$

Q. 4.11. Find the electric potential at a point distance r from a point charge q. Extend the result to a continuous charge distribution (*C.C.D*).   (*Meerut U.*, 2002)

OR

Obtain an expression for electrical potential due to a point charge (*a*) located at the origin (*b*) located at any arbitrary points.   (*G.N.D.U.*, 2003)

Ans. Electric potential due to a point charge. (*i*) *When charge lies at the origin.* The electric potential at a point in an electric field is defined as the work done in taking a unit positive charge from infinity to that point against the electrical forces.

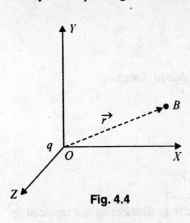

Fig. 4.4

It is given by $V = - \int_{\infty}^{r} \vec{E} \cdot d\vec{r}$

where $\vec{r}$ is the position vector of the point and $\vec{E}$ the electric field.

Consider a charge q lying at the origin O and a point B at a position vector $\vec{r}$, then

Electric potential at B, $V_B = - \int_{\infty}^{r} \vec{E} \cdot d\vec{r}$ ...(*i*)

The electric field at B due to the charge q at the origin

$$\vec{E} = \frac{1}{4\pi\varepsilon_0} \cdot \frac{q}{|\vec{r}|^3} \vec{r}$$

Substituting in Eq. (*i*), we have

$$V_B = - \frac{q}{4\pi\varepsilon_0} \int_{\infty}^{r} \frac{\vec{r} \cdot d\vec{r}}{|\vec{r}|^3} = - \frac{1}{4\pi\varepsilon_0} \int_{\infty}^{r} \frac{r\,dr}{r^3} = - \frac{q}{4\pi\varepsilon_0} \int_{\infty}^{r} \frac{dr}{r^2}$$

$$= \frac{1}{4\pi\varepsilon_0} \left[\frac{1}{r} \right]_{\infty}^{r} = \frac{1}{4\pi\varepsilon_0} \frac{q}{r}$$

Hence in general for a point lying at a distance r from a charge q, electric potential $V = \frac{1}{4\pi\varepsilon_0} \frac{q}{r}$.

(*ii*) **When charge is located at an arbitrary point.** Suppose the charge q lies at A at the position vector $\vec{r'}$.

Let the position vector of the observation point B be $\vec{r}$, then

$$\vec{r} = \vec{r'} + \vec{r_0}$$

where $\vec{r_0}$ is the vector distance of B from the point charge q.

$\therefore \quad \vec{r_0} = \vec{r} - \vec{r'}$

and $\quad |\vec{r_0}| = |\vec{r} - \vec{r'}|$

Hence electric potential at B due to the point charge q

$$= V_B = \frac{1}{4\pi\varepsilon_0} \frac{q}{r_0} = \frac{1}{4\pi\varepsilon_0} \frac{q}{|\vec{r} - \vec{r'}|}$$

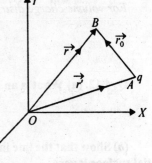

Fig. 4.5

Note that $\vec{r}$ is the position vector of the observation point and $\vec{r'}$ the position vector of the source charge q.

Potential due to number of point charges. Potential is a scalar quantity. Therefore, for a number of point charges $q_1, q_2, q_3 .... q_n$ located at position vectors $\vec{r_1}, \vec{r_2}, \vec{r_3} .... \vec{r_n}$ etc. respectively, the net potential at the observation point at the position vector $\vec{r}$ is given by

$$V = \frac{1}{4\pi\varepsilon_0}\frac{q_1}{|\vec{r}-\vec{r_1}|} + \frac{1}{4\pi\varepsilon_0}\frac{q_2}{|\vec{r}-\vec{r_2}|} + ... + \frac{1}{4\pi\varepsilon_0}\frac{q_n}{|\vec{r}-\vec{r_n}|}$$

$$= \frac{1}{4\pi\varepsilon_0}\sum_{i=1}^{n}\frac{q_i}{|\vec{r}-\vec{r_i}|}$$

Now $\dfrac{1}{4\pi\varepsilon_0}\dfrac{q_1}{|\vec{r}-\vec{r_1}|} = V_1$ potential at the observation point due to charge q_1

Similarly $\dfrac{1}{4\pi\varepsilon_0}\dfrac{q_2}{|\vec{r}-\vec{r_2}|} = V_2$ and so on.

$$\therefore \qquad\qquad V = V_1 + V_2 + V_3 + ... + V_n = \sum_{i=1}^{n}V_i$$

Continuous charge distribution. In the case of continuous charge distribution q is replaced by elementary charge dq, its vector distance from the origin by $\vec{r_i}$ the summation sign being replaced by the integral.

$$\therefore \qquad\qquad V = \frac{1}{4\pi\varepsilon_0}\int\frac{dq}{|\vec{r}-\vec{r_i}|}$$

For a line charge distribution

$$V = \frac{1}{4\pi\varepsilon_0}\int\frac{\lambda\,dl}{|\vec{r}-\vec{r_i}|}$$

For surface charge distribution

$$V = \frac{1}{4\pi\varepsilon_0}\int\frac{\sigma\,ds}{|\vec{r}-\vec{r_i}|}$$

For volume charge distribution

$$V = \frac{1}{4\pi\varepsilon_0}\int\frac{\rho\,dv}{|\vec{r}-\vec{r_i}|}$$

Q. 4.12. (*a*) **What is an equipotential surface? Can two equipotential surfaces intersect?**

(*H.P.U., 2006, 2002, 2001, 1999, 1991;*

G.N.D.U., 2000; Kerala U., 2001; Pbi.U., 2007, 2002; P.U., 1992)

(*b*) **Show that the line integral of the electric field between any two points on an equipotential surface is zero.** (*Pbi.U. 2007; H.P.U., 2002, 1999*)

(*c*) **Prove that the electric field on the surface of a charged conductor is perpendicular to the surface at any point.** (*G.N.D.U., 2006, 2002; Pbi.U., 2000; P.U., 2000*)

Ans. (*a*) **Equipotential surface.** *The locus of all the points which have the same potential is called an equipotential surface.*

For a point charge, the equipotential surfaces are a family of concentric spheres. Similarly, for a spherical charge the equipotential surfaces are also concentric spheres due to symmetry considerations. For a uniform electric field, the equipotential surfaces are planes perpendicular to the field.

Two equipotential surfaces cannot intersect. Two equipotential surfaces cannot intersect. If they intersect the point of intersection will have two different values of potential which is not possible.

(b) **Line integral of electric field on equipotential surface is zero.** The potential difference between two points A and B in an electric field is given by

$$V_B - V_A = -\int_A^B \vec{E} \cdot \vec{dr}$$

For an equipotential surface $V_B = V_A$ or $V_B - V_A = 0$

$$\therefore \qquad \int_A^B \vec{E} \cdot \vec{dr} = 0$$

Hence the line integral of the electric field between any two points or an equipotential surface is zero.

(c) **Electric field perpendicular to surface of charged conductor.** The surface of a charged conductor is an equipotential surface. The equipotential surfaces are always at right angles to the lines of electric force and to the direction of electric field $\vec{E}$. If electric field $\vec{E}$ were not at right angles to the equipotential surface it would have a component lying in that surface. Then work would have to be done in moving a test charge from one point to the other on the equipotential surface. But no work is done to move a test charge between any two points on an equipotential surface because there is no difference of potential.

Therefore, $\vec{E}$ is always at right angles to an equipotential surface and no work is done in moving a charge from one point to the other on an equipotential surface.

Q. 4.13. Define equipotential surface and prove that electric field is always perpendicular to equipotential surface.   (*P.U., 2003*)

Ans. Equipotential surface See Q. 4.12. (*a*)

Electric field perpendicular to equipotential surface. Consider an equipotential surface S as shown in Fig. 4.6. Let A and B be two *very close* points on the surface S.

Position vector of $\qquad A = \vec{r_A}$

Position vector of $\qquad B = \vec{r_B}$

$$\therefore \qquad \vec{AB} = \vec{OB} - \vec{OA}$$

or $\qquad \vec{dr} = \vec{r_B} - \vec{r_A}$ $\qquad$ ...(*i*)

The potential difference between the points A and B,

$$V_B - V_A = -\int_A^B \vec{E} \cdot \vec{dr} \qquad ...(ii)$$

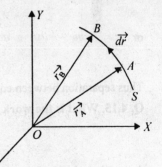

Fig. 4.6

where $\vec{E}$ is the electric field at any point between A and B. Since the points A and B are very close, the electric field $\vec{E}$ has approximately the same value everywhere along the displacement from A to B. Taking $\vec{E}$ to be a constant, Eq. (*ii*) becomes

$$V_B - V_A = - \vec{E} . \int_A^B d\vec{r} = - \vec{E} . [\vec{r}]_A^B = - \vec{E} . \left(\vec{r_B} - \vec{r_A} \right)$$

or $$V_B - V_A = \vec{E} . \vec{AB} \qquad\qquad \left[\because \vec{r_B} - \vec{r_A} = \vec{AB} \text{ by Eq. (i)} \right]$$

But the points A and B lie on the equipotential surface S i.e., $V_A = V_B$ or $V_B - V_A = 0$

$\therefore \qquad\qquad\qquad - \vec{E} . \vec{AB} = 0 \qquad\qquad\qquad\qquad\qquad\qquad\qquad\qquad ...(iii)$

Eq. (iii) shows that electric field $\vec{E}$ is perpendicular to $\vec{AB}$ as the scalar product of the vectors $\vec{E}$ and $\vec{AB}$ is zero.

Thus we find that electric field is always perpendicular (or normal) to the equipotential surface.

Q. 4.14. A thin infinite charged sheet has a surface charge density σ = 10^{-7} C/m². Find the separation between equipotential surfaces which differ in potential by 5 V. (M.D.U., 2002)

Ans. The magnitude of electric field near an infinite charged sheet having surface charge density σ

$$E = \frac{\sigma}{2\varepsilon_0}$$

The direction of $\vec{E}$ is perpendicular to the charged plane and is a constant being independent of the distance from the charged sheet.

Let x be the distance between two equipotential surface which differ in potential by 5V, then

$$5V = \frac{\sigma}{2\varepsilon_0} x$$

or $$5 = \frac{10^{-7} x}{2 \times 8.85 \times 10^{-12}}$$

or $$x = \frac{5 \times 2 \times 8.85 \times 10^{-12}}{10^{-7}} = 8.85 \times 10^{-4} \text{ m}$$

$$= 0.885 \text{ m.m}$$

Thus separation between equipotential surfaces which differ in potential by 5V is 0.885 mm.

Q. 4.15. What is the work done in moving a charge 2C on the equipotential surface?

(H.P.U., 1995)

OR

A positive charge is transferred from one point to another point on an equipotential surface. Find out the work done by it. (Vid. S.U., 1991)

Ans. The difference of electric potential between two points A and B in an electric field is defined as the work done in taking a unit positive charge from A to B against the electrical forces. The potential at every point on an equipotential surface is the same. Therefore if the two points A and B lie on an equipotential surface the work done in taking a unit positive charge from A to B on the equipotential surface is zero.

Hence the work done in moving a charge 2C on the equipotential surface is zero.

Q. 4.16. Consider a point charge $q = 1.5 \times 10^{-6}$ C. What is the radius of the equipotential surface having potential 30 V ?   (*G.N.D.U., 1991*)

Ans. Let r be the radius of the equipotential surface having potential $30V$, then

$$30 = \frac{1}{4\pi\varepsilon_0}\frac{q}{r} = \frac{9 \times 10^9 \times 1.5 \times 10^{-6}}{r}$$

or

$$r = \frac{9 \times 10^9 \times 1.5 \times 10^{-6}}{30} = 450 \, \text{m}.$$

Q. 4.17. (a) (*i*) Can the potential at a point be zero if the field strength there is non-zero? (*ii*) If the electric field at a point is zero, should the potential be zero? Explain.

(*P.U. 2009; Kerala U., 2001; G.N.D.U., 2004, 1992*)

(*b*) Give an example of a charge distribution for which (*i*) electric potential is zero at a given point but the electric field is finite (*ii*) electric field is zero but potential is finite.

(*H.P.U., 1994*)

Ans. (*a*) (*i*) **Yes.** The potential at a point can be zero if the field strength there is non-zero. This is because potential is a scalar quantity whereas field strength is a vector.

(*ii*) The converse is also true *i.e.* the field strength at a point can be zero, even if the potential there is non-zero. For explanation see part (*b*)

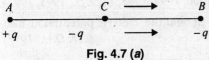

Fig. 4.7 (a)

(*b*) (*i*) Consider two charges $+q$ and $-q$ lying at the points A and B respectively, then for a point C midway between them. (Fig. 4.7 (*a*))

The electric potential is given by

$$+\frac{1}{4\pi\varepsilon_0}\frac{q}{AC} - \frac{1}{4\pi\varepsilon_0}\frac{q}{BC} = 0 \qquad [\because AC = BC]$$

But the electric field at C due to the charge $+q$

$$= \frac{1}{4\pi\varepsilon_0}\frac{q}{AC^2} \text{ along } AC \text{ produced.}$$

and electric field at C due to the charge $-q$

$$= \frac{1}{4\pi\varepsilon_0}\frac{q}{BC^2} \text{ along } AC \text{ produced}$$

$\therefore$ Total electric field $= \frac{1}{4\pi\varepsilon_0}\left[\frac{q}{AC^2} + \frac{q}{BC^2}\right] \neq 0$

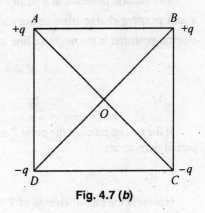

Fig. 4.7 (b)

even when $AC = BC$. The field acts along AC produced.

Similarly if charges $+q$ each are placed at the corners A and B of a square and charges $-q$ each at the corners C and D, then potential at O, the point of intersection of two diagonals is zero but the field is non-zero.

(*ii*) If, on the other hand in the first case both the charges are positive, the electric field at C the mid-point of AB is zero since the field at C due to the charge of $+q$ at A and a charge $+q$ at B are equal and opposite and hence net field is zero. But the net electric potential is not zero because potential due to the two charges $+q$ at A and $+q$ at B are both positive and add up.

Similarly in the second case if all the four charges are positive, the net electric field at O is zero but the net electric potential is non-zero.

Q. 4.18. Is it possible for a body to have a charge and still be at zero potential? Explain with an example. *(G.N.D.U., 2003)*

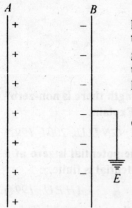

Fig. 4.8

Ans. Yes. It is possible for a body to have a charge and still be at zero potential. As an example consider a charged parallel plate capacitor having two plates A and B as shown. The plate B is earthed. When the plate A is given a positive charge it induces an equivalent (bound) negative charge on the plate B and the (free) positive charge flows to the earth. Thus the plate B has a charge but no potential or zero potential.

Q. 4.19. (a) Show that the intensity of the electric field at a point equals the negative gradient of potential at that point.

(P.U., 2001, 2000; K.U., 2001; Kerala U., 2001; M.D.U., 1999; H.P.U., 1997)

OR

Show that $\vec{E} = -\vec{\nabla} V$ where symbols have their usual meanings. What is the significance of negative sign here ? *(M.D.U., 2008;*
Pbi.U. 2006; Nagpur U., 2002, 2001; Meerut.U., 2001; P.U., 2001; H.P.U., 2001;
Gharwal U.,1999; G.N.D.U., 2009, 2008, 2006, 1999, 1995; Luck.U., 1995, 1992)

(b) Electric field in a certain region of space is zero. Should the electric potential be also zero? Explain. *(G.N.D.U., 1997)*

Ans. (a) Electric field as gradient of potential. The expression $\vec{E} = -\vec{\nabla} V$ means that the electric field at a point is the negative gradient of potential at that point.

The electric potential at a point P in an electric field $\vec{E}$ is defined as the work done in bringing a unit positive charge from infinity to that point *against* the electrical forces. In other words, the electric potential is the negative line integral of the electric field.

$$\therefore \qquad V = -\int_{\infty}^{P} \vec{E} \cdot d\vec{r}$$

or $\qquad\qquad dV = -\vec{E} \cdot d\vec{r}$ ...(i)

If the co-ordinates of the point P are x, y, z, then $V(x, y, z)$ is a function of these co-ordinates. The partial derivatives

$$\frac{\partial V}{\partial x}, \frac{\partial V}{\partial y} \text{ and } \frac{\partial V}{\partial z}$$

represent the rate of change of V with x, y and z respectively.

$$\therefore \qquad dV = \frac{\partial V}{\partial x} dx + \frac{\partial V}{\partial y} dy + \frac{\partial V}{\partial z} dz$$

$$= \left(\frac{\partial V}{\partial x} \hat{i} + \frac{\partial V}{\partial y} \hat{j} + \frac{\partial V}{\partial z} \hat{k} \right) \cdot (dx\, \hat{i} + dy\, \hat{j} + dz\, \hat{k})$$

But $dx\, \hat{i} + dy\, \hat{j} + dz\, \hat{k} = d\vec{r}$ where dx, dy and dz are components of the displacement vector $d\vec{r}$ along x, y and z directions respectively. Also

$$\left(\frac{\partial V}{\partial x}\hat{i} + \frac{\partial V}{\partial y}\hat{j} + \frac{\partial V}{\partial z}\hat{k}\right) = \left(\frac{\partial}{\partial x}\hat{i} + \frac{\partial}{\partial y}\hat{j} + \frac{\partial}{\partial z}\hat{k}\right)V = \vec{\nabla}V$$

$$= grad\ V$$

$$\therefore \qquad\qquad dV = \vec{\nabla}V.d\vec{r} \qquad\qquad\qquad\qquad ...(ii)$$

From (i) and (ii) we have

$$-\vec{E}.d\vec{r} = \vec{\nabla}V.d\vec{r}$$

or $$\qquad\qquad \vec{E} = -\vec{\nabla}V = -\ grad\ V \qquad\qquad ...(iii)$$

Relation (iii) may be written in the form

$$\vec{E}(x,y,z) = \frac{\partial V(xyz)}{\partial x}\hat{i} + \frac{\partial V(xyz)}{\partial y}\hat{j} + \frac{\partial V(xyz)}{\partial z}\hat{k}$$

Hence the electric field intensity has a magnitude which is equal to the maximum rate of change of electric potential and its direction is the same as the direction along which rate of change of potential is maximum.

Significance of negative sign. The negative sign implies that the electric intensity $\vec{E}$ points in the direction of decreasing V.

(b) The electric field at a point is the negative of the gradient of electric potential at that point i.e., $\vec{E} = -\vec{\nabla}V$. If in a certain region of space the electric field $\vec{E} = 0$ it means $-\vec{\nabla}V = 0$ or $V = a$ constant.

Thus the electric potential has a constant value not necessarily zero.

For example, in the case of a uniformly charged spherical shell the electric field is zero inside but the electric potential has a constant value everywhere in the shell.

Q. 4.20. The electric potential in space is given by

$$V = 3x + 4y - 7z.$$

Obtain the expression for potential gradient and electric intensity. (H.P.U., 2002, 1996)

Ans. $\qquad\qquad V = 3x + 4y - 7z$

Potential gradient $= \vec{\nabla}V = \frac{\partial V}{\partial x}\hat{i} + \frac{\partial V}{\partial y}\hat{j} + \frac{\partial V}{\partial z}\hat{k}$

Now $\qquad\qquad \frac{\partial V}{\partial x} = 3;\ \frac{\partial V}{\partial y} = 4;\ \frac{\partial V}{\partial z} = -7$

$\therefore \qquad\qquad \vec{\nabla}V = 3\hat{i} + 4\hat{j} - 7\hat{k}$

Electric intensity $\qquad \vec{E} = -\vec{\nabla}V = -[3\hat{i} + 4\hat{j} - 7\hat{k}]$

Exercise. The potential function at a point is given by $V = (3y^2 - x^2 + z)$

Find the components of the electric field at that point. (M.D.U., 2008)

Ans. $E_x = 2x\hat{i};\ E_y = -6y\hat{j};\ E_z = 1\hat{k}$

Q. 4.21. The electric potential at any point in x, y plane is given by

$$\phi = 5x\,(x^2 + y^2)^{1/2} + y\,(x^2 + y^2)^{-1/2}.$$

(P.U., 1991)

Find the components of the electric field at that point.

Ans. Given $\qquad\qquad \phi = 5x\,(x^2 + y^2)^{1/2} + y\,(x^2 + y^2)^{-1/2}$

Now electric field $\qquad\qquad \vec{E} = -\vec{\nabla}\,\phi$

$$= -\left[\frac{\partial\phi}{\partial x}\hat{i} + \frac{\partial\phi}{\partial y}\hat{j} + \frac{\partial\phi}{\partial z}\hat{k}\right] = E_x\,\hat{i} + E_y\,\hat{j} + E_z\,\hat{k}$$

$$\therefore \qquad\qquad E_x = -\frac{\partial\phi}{\partial x}$$

and $\quad \dfrac{\partial\phi}{\partial x} = 5x\left[\dfrac{1}{2}\,(x^2 + y^2)^{-1/2}\,2x\right] + 5\,(x^2 + y^2)^{1/2} + y\left[-\dfrac{1}{2}\,(x^2 + y^2)^{-3/2}\,2x\right] + 0$

$$= \frac{5x^2}{(x^2 + y^2)^{1/2}} + 5\,(x^2 + y^2)^{1/2} - \frac{xy}{(x^2 + y^2)^{3/2}}$$

$$\therefore \quad E_x = -\left[\frac{5x^2}{(x^2 + y^2)^{1/2}} + 5\,(x^2 + y^2)^{1/2} - \frac{xy}{(x^2 + y^2)^{3/2}}\right]$$

$$\frac{\partial\phi}{\partial y} = 5x\left[\frac{1}{2}\,(x^2 + y^2)^{-1/2}\,2y\right] + y\left[-\frac{1}{2}\,(x^2 + y^2)^{-3/2}\,2y\right] + (x^2 + y^2)^{-1/2}$$

$$= \frac{5xy}{(x^2 + y^2)^{1/2}} - \frac{y^2}{(x^2 + y^2)^{3/2}} + \frac{1}{(x^2 + y^2)^{1/2}}$$

$$\therefore \quad E_y = -\left[\frac{5xy}{(x^2 + y^2)^{1/2}} - \frac{y^2}{(x^2 + y^2)^{3/2}} + \frac{1}{(x^2 + y^2)^{1/2}}\right]$$

$$E_z = 0$$

Q. 4.22. The potential V at a point (x, y, z) is given by

$$V = \frac{2x^2 y}{(x^2 + y^2)} + 5z$$

Determine the rectangular components of the electric field at that point. (P.U., 1992)

Ans. $\qquad\qquad V = \dfrac{2x^2 y}{x^2 + y^2} + 5z$

$$\vec{E}\,(x, y, z) = -\vec{\nabla}V\,(x, y, z)$$

$$= -\left[\frac{\partial V\,(x, y, z)}{\partial x}\hat{i} + \frac{\partial V\,(x, y, z)}{\partial y}\hat{j} + \frac{\partial V\,(x, y, z)}{\partial z}\hat{k}\right]$$

Now $\qquad\qquad \dfrac{\partial V}{\partial x} = 2x^2 y\left[-(x^2 + y^2)^{-2}\,2x\right] + \dfrac{4xy}{(x^2 + y^2)}$

$$= \frac{-4x^3y}{(x^2+y^2)^2} + \frac{4xy}{(x^2+y^2)} = \frac{-4x^3y + 4x^3y + 4xy^3}{(x^2+y^2)^2}$$

$$= \frac{4xy^3}{(x^2+y^2)^2}$$

$$\therefore \qquad E_x = \frac{-4xy^3}{(x^2+y^2)^2}$$

Again $\qquad \dfrac{\partial V}{\partial y} = 2x^2y\left[-(x^2+y^2)^{-2}\,2y\right] + \dfrac{2x^2}{(x^2+y^2)}$

$$= \frac{-4x^2y^2}{(x^2+y^2)^2} + \frac{2x^2}{(x^2+y^2)}$$

$$= \frac{-4x^2y^2 + 2x^4 + 2x^2y^2}{(x^2+y^2)^2} = \frac{2x^2(x^2-y^2)}{(x^2+y^2)^2}$$

$$\therefore \qquad E_y = \frac{-2x^2(x^2-y^2)}{(x^2+y^2)^2}$$

Also $\qquad \dfrac{\partial V}{\partial z} = 5 \qquad \therefore \qquad E_z = -5\hat{k}$

Hence $\qquad \vec{E} = -\left\{\left[\dfrac{4xy^3}{(x^2+y^2)^2}\right]\hat{i} + \left[\dfrac{2x^2(x^2-y^2)}{(x^2+y^2)^2}\right]\hat{j} + 5\hat{k}\right\}$

Q. 4.23. (*a*) **Electric potential at a point is given by $V = x^2y + 2z$. What are the components of electric field at that point? Find the electric field at a point (2, 1, 2).**

(*Pbi. U. 2006; H.P.U., 1999; G.N.D.U., 1997, 1996*)

(*b*) **Calculate the force acting on the charge 2×10^{-10} Coulomb located at the point (2, 0, –3) in the field region in terms of $\hat{i}, \hat{j}, \hat{k}$ when the electric potential at any point in the region is given by**

$$V(x, y, z) = (20 + 6x^2 - 5xy + 4y^2 + 3z^2).$$ (*Luck.U., 1992*)

Ans. (*a*) Electric potential $V = x^2y + 2z$

Now electric field intensity $\vec{E} = -\vec{\nabla}V = -\left[\dfrac{\partial V}{\partial x}\hat{i} + \dfrac{\partial V}{\partial y}\hat{j} + \dfrac{\partial V}{\partial z}\hat{k}\right] = E_x\hat{i} + E_y\hat{j} + E_z\hat{k}$

$$\frac{\partial V}{\partial x} = 2xy \qquad \therefore \quad E_x = -\frac{\partial V}{\partial x}\hat{i} = -2xy\,\hat{i}$$

$$\frac{\partial V}{\partial y} = x^2 \qquad \therefore \quad E_y = -\frac{\partial V}{\partial y}\hat{j} = -x^2\,\hat{j}$$

$$\frac{\partial V}{\partial z} = 2 \qquad \therefore \quad E_z = -\frac{\partial V}{\partial y}\hat{k} = -2\hat{k}$$

At the point (2, 1, 2)

$$E_x = 4\hat{i}; E_y = 4\hat{j}; E_z = -2\hat{k}$$

$\therefore$ $\qquad\qquad\qquad\qquad \vec{E} = 4\hat{i} + 4\hat{j} - 2\hat{k}$

and magnitude of $\qquad \vec{E} = |\vec{E}| = \sqrt{4^2 + 4^2 + (-2)^2} = \sqrt{36} = 6$ units

(b) Here $\qquad\qquad\qquad V = 20 + 6x^2 - 5xy + 4y^2 + 3z^2$

Now $\qquad\qquad\qquad \vec{E} = -\vec{\nabla}V = -\left(\dfrac{\partial V}{\partial x}\hat{i} + \dfrac{\partial V}{\partial y}\hat{j} + \dfrac{\partial V}{\partial z}\hat{k}\right)$

$\qquad\qquad \dfrac{\partial V}{\partial x} = 12x - 5y; \dfrac{\partial V}{\partial y} = -5x + 8y; \dfrac{\partial V}{\partial z} = 6z$

$\therefore$ $\qquad\qquad\qquad \vec{E} = -[(12x - 5y)\hat{i} + (-5x + 8y)\hat{j} + (6z)\hat{k}]$

At the point 2, 0, –3,

$\qquad\qquad\qquad\qquad \vec{E} = -[24\hat{i} - 10\hat{j} - 18\hat{k}] = -24\hat{i} + 10\hat{j} + 18\hat{k}$

Force on a charge 2×10^{-10} C at (2, 0, –3)

$\qquad\qquad\qquad\qquad = 2 \times 10^{-10}(-24\hat{i} + 10\hat{j} + 18\hat{k})$

Exercise. *Electric potential in a region is given by V (x, y, z) = $4x^2 - 3y^2 - 9z^2$. Find electric field at P (3, 4, 5).* $\qquad\qquad\qquad\qquad\qquad\qquad\qquad$ (G.N.D.U. 2008; Pbi.U., 2001)

Ans. $\qquad\qquad\qquad \vec{E} = -8x\hat{i} + 6y\hat{j} + 18z\hat{k}$

At P (3, 4, 5), $\qquad\qquad \vec{E} = -24\hat{i} + 24\hat{j} + 90\hat{k}$

Q. 4.24. The potential function at a point is given by $V(x, y, z) = 10(x^2 + y^2 + z^2)^{-1/2}$. Find electric field intensity at point (2, 4, 4). $\qquad\qquad\qquad\qquad\qquad\qquad$ (Pbi.U., 1993)

Ans. $\qquad\qquad\qquad V(x, y, z) = 10(x^2 + y^2 + z^2)^{-1/2}$

Now electric field $\qquad\qquad \vec{E} = -\vec{\nabla}V$

$\qquad\qquad\qquad\qquad = -\left[\hat{i}\dfrac{\partial}{\partial x} + \hat{j}\dfrac{\partial}{\partial y} + \hat{k}\dfrac{\partial}{\partial z}\right]\left[10(x^2 + y^2 + z^2)^{-\frac{1}{2}}\right]$

$\qquad\qquad\qquad\qquad = \left[\dfrac{1}{2} \times 10(x^2 + y^2 + z^2)^{-3/2} 2x\right]\hat{i} + \left[\dfrac{1}{2} \times 10(x^2 + y^2 + z^2)^{-3/2} 2y\right]\hat{j}$

$\qquad\qquad\qquad\qquad\qquad + \left[\dfrac{1}{2} \times 10(x^2 + y^2 + z^2)^{-3/2} 2z\right]\hat{k}$

$\therefore$ $\quad \vec{E} = \dfrac{10x}{(x^2 + y^2 + z^2)^{3/2}}\hat{i} + \dfrac{10y}{(x^2 + y^2 + z^2)^{3/2}}\hat{j} + \dfrac{10z}{(x^2 + y^2 + z^2)^{3/2}}\hat{k}$

At the point 2, 4, 4

$\qquad\qquad (x^2 + y^2 + z^2)^{3/2} = (2^2 + 4^2 + 4^2)^{3/2} = 216$

$\therefore$ $\qquad\qquad\qquad \vec{E} = \dfrac{20}{216}\hat{i} + \dfrac{40}{216}\hat{j} + \dfrac{40}{216}\hat{k}$

$\qquad\qquad\qquad\qquad = \dfrac{5}{54}\hat{i} + \dfrac{5}{27}\hat{j} + \dfrac{5}{27}\hat{k}$

Exercise. *The potential due to a certain charge distribution is given by* $V = \dfrac{1}{\sqrt{x^2 + y^2}}$. *Find the electric field intensity.*

(P.U., 2007, 2005)

Hint. The problem is similar to the one solved above. Proceeding as above, we get

$$\vec{E} = \frac{x}{(x^2 + y^2)^{\frac{3}{2}}}\, \hat{i} + \frac{y}{(x^2 + y^2)^{\frac{3}{2}}}\, \hat{j}$$

Q. 4.25. (*a*) **The electric potential in space is given by** $3x + 4y - z$. **Show that the electric field intensity is uniform everywhere.**

(*H.P.U., 1991*)

(*b*) **If electric potential is constant in a certain region of space, what inference can be drawn about the electric field?**

(*Luck.U., 1996*)

Ans. (*a*) Given $\qquad\qquad \phi = 3x + 4y - z$

Now electric field intensity $\quad \vec{E} = -\vec{\nabla}\,\phi$

$$= -\left[\frac{\partial \phi}{\partial x}\,\hat{i} + \frac{\partial \phi}{\partial y}\,\hat{j} + \frac{\partial \phi}{\partial z}\,\hat{k}\right] = -[3\hat{i} + 4\hat{j} - \hat{k}]$$

As the electric field does not depend upon the space co-ordinates (x, y, z) it is constant and uniform everywhere.

(*b*) If the electric potential is constant in a certain region of space, the electric field is zero. The electric field is the *negative of the gradient* of electric potential *i.e.*,

$$\vec{E} = -\vec{\nabla} V$$

As V = a constant, $\vec{\nabla} V = 0 \qquad \therefore \ \vec{E} = -\vec{\nabla} V = 0$

Q. 4.26. (*a*) **Show that the electric field satisfies the equation**

$$\vec{\nabla}\cdot\vec{E} = \frac{\rho}{\varepsilon_0},\ \vec{\nabla}\times\vec{E} = 0$$

(*b*) **Electric potential in a region of space is given by**

$$V(x, y, z) = 50x^2 - 75y\ (V\text{ in volts})\ x, y, z \text{ in metres. Find}$$

(*i*) **Magnitude of electric field at point (1, 1, 0)** (*ii*) **Charge density** (*iii*) **Show that electric field is not uniform.**

(*G.N.D.U., 2002; Pbi.U., 2000, 1999; H.P.U., 1993*)

Ans. (*a*) For proof of $\vec{\nabla}\cdot\vec{E} = \dfrac{\rho}{\varepsilon_0}$ See. Q. 3.31 relation (*iii*).

Now $\vec{E} = -\vec{\nabla} V = -grad\ V$ where V is the electric potential [For proof See **Q. 4.19** Eq. (*iii*)]

$\therefore \qquad\qquad \vec{\nabla}\times\vec{E} = -\vec{\nabla}\times\vec{\nabla} V = 0$

since $\vec{\nabla}\times\vec{\nabla} = 0$ being the vector product of two equal vectors.

(*b*) (*i*) $\qquad\qquad V = 50x^2 - 75y$

Electric field $\qquad\qquad \vec{E} = -\vec{\nabla} V$

$$= -\left[\frac{\partial}{\partial x}\,\hat{i} + \frac{\partial}{\partial y}\,\hat{j} + \frac{\partial}{\partial z}\,\hat{k}\right](50x^2 - 75y)$$

$$= -[100 x \hat{i} + 75 \hat{j}]$$

or
$$\vec{E} = -100 x \hat{i} + 75 \hat{j}$$

Magnitude of $\vec{E}$ at 1, 1, 0 $\vec{E} = -100 \hat{i} + 75 \hat{j}$

$\therefore$
$$|\vec{E}| = \sqrt{100^2 + 75^2} = 125 \text{ Vm}^{-1}$$

(ii) Now
$$\vec{\nabla} . \vec{E} = \frac{\rho}{\varepsilon_0}$$

$$\vec{\nabla} . \vec{E} = \left(\hat{i} \frac{\partial}{\partial x} + \hat{j} \frac{\partial}{\partial y} + \hat{k} \frac{\partial}{\partial z} \right) . (-100 x \hat{i} + 75 \hat{j}) = -100$$

$\therefore$
$$\rho = -100 \varepsilon_0 = -100 \times 8.85 \times 10^{-12} = -8.85 \times 10^{-10} \text{ C m}^{-3}$$

(iii) Electric field
$$\vec{E} = 100 x \hat{i} + 75 \hat{j}$$

The y-component of $\vec{E}$ is constant but the x-component of $\vec{E}$ varies with x. Hence the resultant electric field $\vec{E}$ is not uniform.

Q. 4.27. (a) **Calculate the electric potential at any point due to an infinite line charge having line charge density λ. Hence show that the potential due to infinite charged wire is infinite.**

(b) **Show that** (i) **the potential difference between two points distance r_1 and r_2 from an infinitely long line charge of line charge density λ is given by** $\nabla V = \dfrac{\lambda}{2 \pi \varepsilon_0} \log_e \dfrac{r_2}{r_1}.$

(ii) **The potential at a point distance r_1 and r_2 respectively from the centre of a long parallel pair of wires of negligible cross-section and having equal and opposite charge density λ is given**

by $V = \dfrac{\lambda}{2 \pi \varepsilon_0} \log_e \dfrac{r_2}{r_1}$

(c) **Hence calculate the electric field intensity due to an infinitely long uniformly charged line wire.**   (*G.N.D.U., 2006, 2001, 2000; P.U., 2001, 1991; H.P.U., 2006, 1991*)

Ans. (a) **Potential due to a line charge.** Consider a straight line charge placed along the X-axis and extending from $x = a$ to $x = b$.

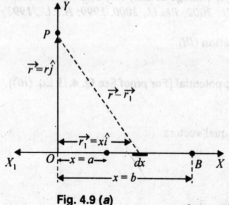

Fig. 4.9 (a)

Let P be a point on the Y-axis at a distance $\vec{r}$ from the origin O, then position vector of the point P,
$$\vec{r} = r \hat{j}$$

Take a small element of length dx at a distance x from O, then position vector of the charge element,
$$\vec{r_1} = x \hat{i}$$

If λ is the line charge density, then the charge on the element $dx = dq = \lambda dx$.

The potential at P due to this charge element dq is

$$dV = \frac{1}{4 \pi \varepsilon_0} \frac{dq}{|\vec{r} - \vec{r_1}|} = \frac{1}{4 \pi \varepsilon_0} \frac{\lambda dx}{|r \hat{j} - x \hat{i}|} = \frac{1}{4 \pi \varepsilon_0} \frac{\lambda dx}{\sqrt{r^2 + x^2}} \qquad ...(i)$$

because $\qquad |r\hat{j} - x\hat{i}| = \sqrt{r^2 + x^2}$

$\therefore$ Potential at P due to the whole line charge

$$V = \int_a^b dV = \frac{\lambda}{4\pi\varepsilon_0} \int_a^b \frac{dx}{\sqrt{r^2 + x^2}}$$

Now $\qquad \int \frac{dx}{\sqrt{r^2 + x^2}} = \log_e (x + \sqrt{r^2 + x^2})$

Hence $\qquad V = \frac{\lambda}{4\pi\varepsilon_0} \left[\log_e (x + \sqrt{r^2 + x^2}) \right]_a^b$

$$= \frac{\lambda}{4\pi\varepsilon_0} \left[\log_e (b + \sqrt{r^2 + b^2}) - \log_e (a + \sqrt{r^2 + a^2}) \right]$$

$$= \frac{\lambda}{4\pi\varepsilon_0} \log_e \frac{b + \sqrt{r^2 + b^2}}{a + \sqrt{r^2 + a^2}} \qquad \qquad ...(ii)$$

If the line charge extends on both sides of the origin say from $x = -a$ to $x = +b$, then the potential at P = Potential of the portion from $-a$ to the origin + potential of the portion from the origin to $+b$ as potential is a scalar quantity.

$$\therefore \qquad V = \frac{\lambda}{4\pi\varepsilon_0} \left[\int_{-a}^0 \frac{dx}{\sqrt{r^2 + x^2}} + \int_0^b \frac{dx}{\sqrt{r^2 + x^2}} \right]$$

$$= \frac{\lambda}{4\pi\varepsilon_0} \left[\int_0^a \frac{dx}{\sqrt{r^2 + x^2}} + \int_0^b \frac{dx}{\sqrt{r^2 + x^2}} \right]$$

$$= \frac{\lambda}{4\pi\varepsilon_0} \left\{ \left[\log_e (x + \sqrt{r^2 + x^2}) \right]_0^a + \left[\log_e (x + \sqrt{r^2 + x^2}) \right]_0^b \right\}$$

$$= \frac{\lambda}{4\pi\varepsilon_0} \left\{ \left[\log_e (a + \sqrt{r^2 + a^2}) - \log_e r \right] + \left[\log_e (b + \sqrt{r^2 + b^2}) - \log_e r \right] \right\}$$

$$= \frac{\lambda}{4\pi\varepsilon_0} \left[\log_e \frac{a + \sqrt{r^2 + a^2}}{r} + \log_e \frac{b + \sqrt{r^2 + b^2}}{r} \right]$$

$$= \frac{\lambda}{4\pi\varepsilon_0} \left\{ \log_e \left[\frac{a}{r} + \frac{\sqrt{r^2 + a^2}}{r} \right] + \log_e \left[\frac{b}{r} + \frac{\sqrt{r^2 + b^2}}{r} \right] \right\}$$

If $a \neq b$ i.e., the line charge extends from $-b$ to $+b$, we have

$$V = \frac{2\lambda}{4\pi\varepsilon_0} \log_e \left[\frac{b}{r} + \frac{\sqrt{r^2 + b^2}}{r} \right] = \frac{\lambda}{2\pi\varepsilon_0} \log_e \left[\frac{b}{r} + \frac{\sqrt{r^2 + b^2}}{r} \right] \qquad ...(iii)$$

Potential due to an infinitely long line charge. If $b = \infty$, $V = \dfrac{\lambda}{2\pi\varepsilon_0} \log_e \infty = \infty$. This shows that electric potential due to infinite charged wire is infinite. Hence, if the line charge extends from $-\infty$ to $+\infty$ the result becomes, indeterminate. However, if b is very large as compared to r so that r^2 can be neglected as compared to b^2, then

$$V = \frac{\lambda}{2\pi\varepsilon_0} \log_e \frac{2b}{r} \qquad \qquad \qquad ...(iv)$$

(b) (i) Potential difference. The difference of potential between two points at distances r_1 and r_2 from a *very long* line charge according to Eq. *(iv)* is thus given by

$$V_1 - V_2 = \frac{\lambda}{2\pi\varepsilon_0} \log_e \frac{2b}{r_1} - \frac{\lambda}{2\pi\varepsilon_0} \log_e \frac{2b}{r_2}$$

$$= \frac{\lambda}{2\pi\varepsilon_0} \log_e \frac{2b/r_1}{2b/r_2}$$

$$= \frac{\lambda}{2\pi\varepsilon_0} \log_e \frac{r_2}{r_1}$$

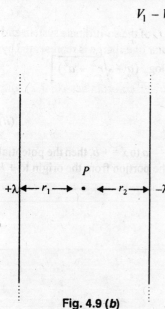

Fig. 4.9 (b)

(ii) Electric Potential due to a parallel pair of wires. Consider a point P between infinitely long parallel pairs of wires of length b ($b \to \infty$) and negligible cross-section, one having line charge density $+\lambda$ and the other $-\lambda$. The distance of point P from the wire of charge density $+\lambda$ is r_1 and from the wire of charge density $-\lambda$ is r_2 as shown in Fig. 4.9. (b).

Potential at P due to wire of charge density $+\lambda$

$$V_1 = \frac{\lambda}{2\pi\varepsilon_0} \log_e \frac{2b}{r_1}$$

and potential at P due to wire of charge density $-\lambda$

$$V_2 = -\frac{\lambda}{2\pi\varepsilon_0} \log_e \frac{2b}{r_2}$$

$\therefore$ Net potential at P,

$$V = V_1 - V_2 = \frac{\lambda}{2\pi\varepsilon_0} \log_e \frac{2b}{r_1} - \frac{\lambda}{2\pi\varepsilon_0} \log_e \frac{2b}{r_2}$$

$$= \frac{\lambda}{2\pi\varepsilon_0} \log_e \frac{r_2}{r_1}$$

(c) Electric field due to an infinitely long line charge. The *electric field intensity* in case of an infinitely long line charge is obtained from relation *(iv)* as given below.

$$\vec{E} = -\vec{\nabla}V = -\left[\frac{\partial V}{\partial x}\hat{i} + \frac{\partial V}{\partial y}\hat{j} + \frac{\partial V}{\partial z}\hat{k} \right]$$

Since r is along the Y-axis.

$$\frac{\partial V}{\partial x} = 0 \text{ and } \frac{\partial V}{\partial z} = 0$$

$$\therefore \qquad \vec{E} = -\frac{\partial V}{\partial y}\hat{j} = -\frac{\partial V}{\partial r}\hat{j} = \frac{\lambda}{2\pi\varepsilon_0} \frac{r}{2b} \cdot \frac{2b}{r^2}\hat{j} = \frac{1}{2\pi\varepsilon_0} \frac{\lambda}{r}\hat{j}$$

In other words the magnitude of the field is $\dfrac{1}{2\pi\varepsilon_0}\dfrac{\lambda}{r}$ and its direction is perpendicular to the line charge at any point *i.e.*, it is a *radial field*.

Q. 4.28. Find the electric potential due to a circular line charge (or ring of small cross-section) at a point on its axis. Hence find the electric field intensity.

(Gharwal U., 1999; H.P.U., 1994)

Ans. Potential due to a uniform circular line charge. Consider a circular line charge (or ring of small cross-section) of radius a and having a total charge q, then

Line charge density $\qquad \lambda = \dfrac{q}{2\pi a}$

Let the centre of the circular line charge (or ring) be at the origin O of the co-ordinate system and the circular line charge lie in the X-Y plane so that the axis of the circular line charge is represented by the Z-axis.

Let P be the point where the electric potential is to be calculated with co-ordinates $(0, 0, z)$, and having position vector $\vec{r}$, then

$$\vec{OP} = \vec{r} = z\,\hat{k}$$

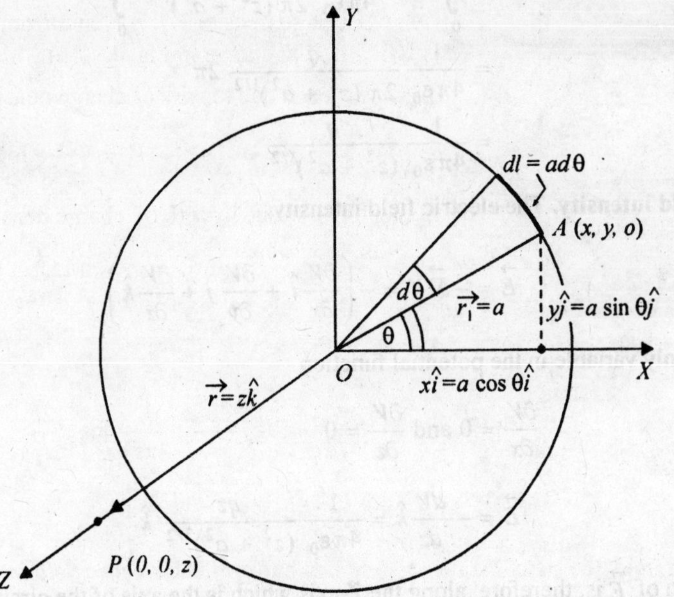

Fig. 4.10

Consider a small element of length dl at A having co-ordinates $(x, y, 0)$ and position vector $\vec{r_1}$ so that $|\vec{r_1}| = a$, making angles θ and $\theta + d\theta$ with the X-axis. Then

$$dl = a\,d\theta$$

and charge on the small element

$$= dq = \lambda\,dl = \dfrac{q}{2\pi a}\,a\,d\theta = \dfrac{q}{2\pi}\,d\theta$$

The position vector of the charge element

$$\vec{r_1} = x\hat{i} + y\hat{j} = a\cos\theta\,\hat{i} + a\sin\theta\,\hat{j}$$

Potential at P due to this charge element

$$dV = \frac{1}{4\pi\varepsilon_0}\frac{dq}{|\vec{r} - \vec{r_1}|}$$

Now

$$|\vec{r} - \vec{r_1}| = |z\hat{k} - a\cos\theta\,\hat{i} - a\sin\theta\,\hat{j}|$$

$$= \sqrt{z^2 + a^2\cos^2\theta + a^2\sin^2\theta}$$

$$= \sqrt{z^2 + a^2}$$

$\therefore$

$$dV = \frac{1}{4\pi\varepsilon_0}\frac{dq}{(z^2 + a^2)^{1/2}} = \frac{1}{4\pi\varepsilon_0}\frac{q}{2\pi(z^2 + a^2)^{1/2}}d\theta \qquad ...(i)$$

The total electric potential at P due to the whole circular line charge (or ring)

$$V = \int_0^{2\pi} dV = \frac{1}{4\pi\varepsilon_0}\frac{q}{2\pi(z^2 + a^2)^{1/2}}\int_0^{2\pi}d\theta$$

$$= \frac{1}{4\pi\varepsilon_0}\frac{q}{2\pi(z^2 + a^2)^{1/2}}2\pi$$

$$= \frac{1}{4\pi\varepsilon_0}\frac{q}{(z^2 + a^2)^{1/2}} \qquad ...(ii)$$

Electric field intensity. The electric field intensity

$$\vec{E} = -\vec{\nabla}V = -\left(\frac{\partial V}{\partial x}\hat{i} + \frac{\partial V}{\partial y}\hat{j} + \frac{\partial V}{\partial z}\hat{k}\right)$$

As z is the only variable in the potential function

$$\frac{\partial V}{\partial x} = 0 \text{ and } \frac{\partial V}{\partial z} = 0$$

$$\vec{E} = -\frac{dV}{dz}\hat{k} = \frac{1}{4\pi\varepsilon_0}\frac{qz}{(z^2 + a^2)^{3/2}}\hat{k} \qquad ...(iii)$$

The direction of $\vec{E}$ is, therefore, along the Z-axis which is the axis of the circular line charge.

Q. 4.29. Find the electric potential at a point on the axis of a uniformly charged thin circular disc. Also find its value at the centre and edges of the disc. Hence find the electric field intensity and discuss the variation of V and $\vec{E}$ with distance from the centre of the disc for positive as well as negative values.

(*Pbi.U.*, 2001; *P.U.*, 2007, 2006, 1995; *G.N.D.U.*, 2004, 2001,1999, 1995)

Ans. Potential on the axis of a uniformly charged circular disc. Suppose we have a circular non-conducting charged disc of radius R in the XY plane as shown (for convenience). Consider a ring of radius a and thickness da of this disc, then surface area of the ring

$$= 2\pi\, a\, da$$

If σ is the surface charge density, then charge on the ring

$$dq = \sigma\, 2\pi\, a\, da$$

Let P be a point on the axis of the disc perpendicular to its surface and passing through its centre O, then OP represents the Z-axis.

Let $OP = z$, then position vector of the point $P = z\hat{k}$

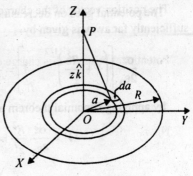

Fig. 4.11 (a)

∴ Electric potential at P due to the circular element of radius a and thickness da is given by (According to **Eq. (ii) Q. 4.28**)

$$dV = \frac{1}{4\pi\varepsilon_0}\frac{dq}{(z^2 + a^2)^{1/2}} = \frac{1}{4\pi\varepsilon_0}\frac{\sigma 2\pi a\, da}{(z^2 + a^2)^{1/2}} = \frac{\sigma}{2\varepsilon_0}\frac{a\, da}{(z^2 + a^2)^{1/2}}$$

Hence electric potential at P due to the whole disc

$$V = \frac{\sigma}{2\varepsilon_0}\int_0^R \frac{a\, da}{(z^2 + a^2)^{1/2}}$$

$$= \frac{\sigma}{2\varepsilon_0}\left[(z^2 + a^2)^{1/2}\right]_0^R$$

$$= \frac{\sigma}{2\varepsilon_0}[\sqrt{z^2 + R^2} - \sqrt{z^2}] = \frac{\sigma}{2\varepsilon_0}[\sqrt{z^2 + R^2} - z]$$

(*i*) For a point on the $+ Z$ axis *i.e.*, $z > 0$

$$V = \frac{\sigma}{2\varepsilon_0}[\sqrt{z^2 + R^2} - z]$$

(*ii*) For a point on the $- Z$ axis *i.e.*, $z < 0$

$$V = \frac{\sigma}{2\varepsilon_0}[\sqrt{z^2 + R^2} + z]$$

where z is the positive or absolute value of $\sqrt{z^2}$.

Hence

$$V = \frac{\sigma}{2\varepsilon_0}[\sqrt{z^2 + R^2} \mp z]$$

according at the point lies on the $+ Z$ or $- Z$ axis.

The symmetry of the problem requires V to be the same for points at the same distance from the disc along the positive as well as the negative Z-axis. When $R = \infty$ *i.e.*, the circular disc is an infinite charged sheet [For infinite size of the sheet there is no shape] $V = \infty$. Thus the potential due to an infinite sheet does not have a finite value.

Discussion. Potential at the centre. The electrical potential at the **centre** of the disc

$$z = 0 \text{ is given by } (0, 0, 0) = \frac{\sigma}{2\varepsilon_0}R. \qquad\qquad ...(i)$$

The potential goes on decreasing when we move away from the centre of the disc and at a point sufficiently far away is given by

$$\frac{\sigma z}{2\varepsilon_0}\left[\left(1+\frac{R^2}{z^2}\right)^{1/2}-1\right] = \frac{\sigma z}{2\varepsilon_0}\left[1+\frac{1}{2}\frac{R^2}{z^2}-1\right]$$

by applying Binomial theorem and neglecting higher power terms

$$\therefore \qquad V = \frac{\sigma z}{4\varepsilon_0}\frac{R^2}{z^2} = \frac{1}{4\pi\varepsilon_0}\frac{\pi\sigma R^2}{z} \qquad\qquad ...(ii)$$

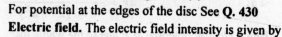

Relation (*ii*) is the same as for potential at a distance z from a point charge $\pi R^2 \sigma$, the total charge on the disc.

Thus for points very far away the whole charge on the disc can be supposed to be concentrated at its centre. A graph between V and z is shown in Fig. 4.11. (*b*).

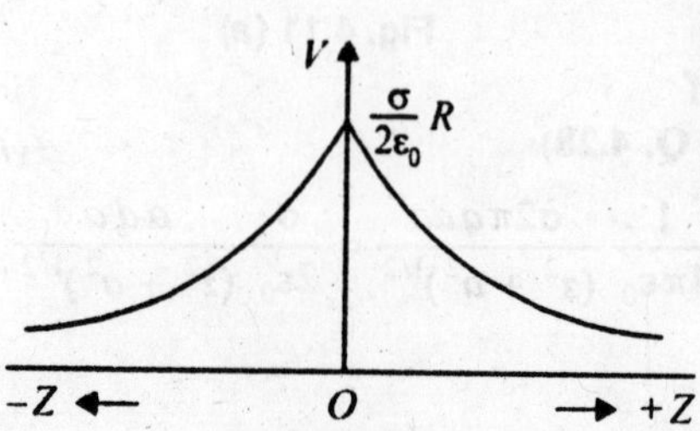

For potential at the edges of the disc See **Q. 430**

Electric field. The electric field intensity is given by

$$\vec{E} = -\vec{\nabla}V = -\left(\frac{\partial V}{\partial x}\hat{i}+\frac{\partial V}{\partial y}\hat{j}+\frac{\partial V}{\partial z}\hat{k}\right)$$

$$= -\frac{\partial V}{\partial z}\hat{k}$$

Fig. 4.11 (b)

because the point P lies on the Z-axis and hence

$$\frac{\partial V}{\partial x} = 0 \text{ and } \frac{\partial V}{\partial z} = 0$$

$\therefore$ The electric field intensity is directed along the Z-axis and its magnitude for a point on the $+Z$ axis ($z > 0$) is given by

$$E = -\frac{\partial}{\partial z}\left[\frac{\sigma}{2\varepsilon_0}\left(\sqrt{z^2+R^2}-z\right)\right]$$

$$= -\frac{\sigma}{2\varepsilon_0}\left[\frac{z}{\sqrt{z^2+R^2}}-1\right]$$

$$= \frac{\sigma}{2\varepsilon_0}\left[1-\frac{z}{\sqrt{z^2+R^2}}\right] \qquad\qquad ...(iii)$$

For a point on the $-Z$ axis ($z < 0$), the magnitude of

$$E = -\frac{\partial}{\partial z}\left[\frac{\sigma}{2\varepsilon_0}\left(\sqrt{z^2+R^2}+z\right)\right]$$

$$= -\frac{\sigma}{2\varepsilon_0}\left[\frac{z}{\sqrt{z^2+R^2}}+1\right]$$

$$= -\frac{\sigma}{2\varepsilon_0}\left[1 + \frac{z}{\sqrt{z^2 + R^2}}\right] \qquad \qquad ...(iv)$$

If we proceed towards the centre of the circular disc from positive side the magnitude of $\vec{E}$ decreases and for $z = 0$ is given by

$$E = \frac{\sigma}{2\varepsilon_0} \qquad \qquad ...(v)$$

Similarly if we proceed towards the centre from the negative side the magnitude of $\vec{E}$ decreases and for $-z = 0$ it is given by

$$E = -\frac{\sigma}{2\varepsilon_0} \qquad \qquad ...(vi)$$

For a point far away from the disc

$$E = \frac{\sigma}{2\varepsilon_0}\left[1 - \frac{z}{z\left(1 + \dfrac{R^2}{z^2}\right)^{1/2}}\right] = \frac{\sigma}{2\varepsilon_0}\left[1 - 1 + \frac{1}{2}\frac{R^2}{z^2}\right]$$

$$= \frac{\sigma}{2\varepsilon_0}\frac{1}{2}\frac{R^2}{z^2} = \frac{1}{4\pi\varepsilon_0}\frac{\pi R^2 \sigma}{z^2} \qquad \qquad ...(vii)$$

$\therefore$ For a point far removed from the disc the whole charge $\pi R^2 \sigma$ behaves as if concentrated at the centre as is evident from relation (vii). A graph showing the variation of E with z (+ or −) is shown in Fig. 4.12.

Thus the value of E suddenly changes from $+ \sigma/2 \varepsilon_0$ [Eq. (v)] to $- \sigma/2 \varepsilon_0$ [Eq. (vi)] as we cross the disc.

Points of discontinuity. The points at which a function shows sudden discontinuity (as at $z = 0$ above) are called *points of discontinuity*. The difference in the limiting values of the function immediately to the right and left of the point of discontinuity is known as the magnitude of discontinuity.

Hence in the above example, the magnitude of discontinuity in the limit $z \to 0$ is given by

$$\frac{\sigma}{2\varepsilon_0} - \left(-\frac{\sigma}{2\varepsilon_0}\right) = \frac{\sigma}{\varepsilon_0}$$

Fig. 4.12

Q. 4.30. Derive an expression for the electric potential at a point on (a) axis and (b) the edge of a uniformly charged insulating disc. Show that the uniformly charged insulating disc is not an equipotential surface and the potential at the centre is higher than at points on the circumference of the disc. Also discuss the case of conducting disc.

(G.N.D.U., 1999; Gharwal U., 1999)

Ans. (*a*) **Electric potential at a point on the axis of a uniformly charged disc.** See **Q. 4.29.**

(*b*) **Electric potential on the edge of a uniformly charged disc.** Consider a point P just on the edge of a charged disc in the X-Y plane having a uniform surface charge density σ. Imagine the segment of a ring charge between radii r and $r + dr$ with P as centre.

The area of segment $= 2r\,\theta\,dr$

$\therefore$ Charge on the segment $dq = 2r\,\theta\,dr\,\sigma$

Potential at P due to the charge on this arc segment

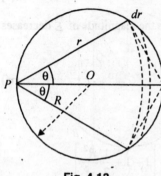

Fig. 4.13

$$dV = \frac{1}{4\pi\varepsilon_0}\,\frac{dq}{(z^2 + a^2)^{1/2}} \qquad\text{[Eq. (\textit{i}) Q. 4.28]}$$

Here $z = 0$ as the point P lies on the disc which is in the X-Y plane and $a =$ radius of the circular line charge $= r$

$\therefore \quad dV = \dfrac{1}{4\pi\varepsilon_0}\,\dfrac{dq}{r} = \dfrac{1}{4\pi\varepsilon_0}\,\dfrac{2r\,\theta\,dr\,\sigma}{r} = \dfrac{1}{4\pi\varepsilon_0}\,2\sigma\,\theta\,dr$

But $\qquad r = 2R\cos\theta$

$\therefore \qquad dr = -2R\sin\theta\,d\theta$

Hence $\quad dV = -\dfrac{1}{4\pi\varepsilon_0}\,4\sigma\,R\,\theta\sin\theta\,d\theta$

$\therefore$ Total potential V due to the entire charge on the disc is given by

$$V = -\frac{1}{4\pi\varepsilon_0}\,4\sigma R \int_{\pi/2}^{0}\theta\sin\theta\,d\theta = \frac{1}{4\pi\varepsilon_0}\,4\sigma R \int_{0}^{\pi/2}\theta\sin\theta\,d\theta$$

$$= \frac{1}{4\pi\varepsilon_0}\,4\sigma R\left[-\theta\cos\theta + \sin\theta\right]_{0}^{\pi/2}$$

$$= \frac{1}{4\pi\varepsilon_0}\,4\sigma R = \frac{1}{\pi\varepsilon_0}\,\sigma R$$

The potential at the centre $\quad = \dfrac{1}{2\varepsilon_0}\,\sigma R \qquad\qquad$ [See **Q. 4.29** Eq. (*i*)]

Therefore potential at a point on the edge is less than that at the centre. *Thus a uniformly charged disc is not an equipotential surface.* The potential is higher at the centre than at the rim and hence the electric field will have a component in the plane of the disc pointing radially outward.

Conducting disc. A charge given to a *conducting* disc will be uniformly distributed over its surface because under *static* conditions a conductor forms an *equipotential surface.* Hence the charged conducting disc will have a higher charge density near the edge than that near the centre.

Q. 4.31. (*a*) **Obtain an expression for the potential due to a uniformly charged thin spherical shell at (*i*) an external and (*ii*) an internal point. Show that the electric potential at any point inside it is equal to the potential on the surface and find the potential inside a spherical shell of radius 0.1 m when it has a charge of 100 μC uniformly distributed over it.**

(*H.P.U., 2001, 1996; Kerala U., 2001*)

(*b*) **Hence show that the electric field intensity at an external points is the same as if the whole charge were concentrated at the centre and intensity at an internal point is zero.**

Ans. (*a*) **Potential due to a uniformly charged spherical shell.** Consider a spherical shell of radius R with centre O (for convenience, the origin of the co-ordinate system). Let q be the charge uniformly distributed over its surface, then

Surface density of charge $\sigma = \dfrac{q}{4\pi R^2}$

(i) For an external point. Let P be a point outside the spherical shell at a distance r from its centre lying on the X-axis as shown in Fig. 4.14. To find the potential at P draw two parallel planes AB and CD very close to each other. The two planes will cut out a *ring* the area of the curved surface of which is given by

$$2\pi \cdot AE \cdot AC \qquad \qquad ...(i)$$

Join OA and OC. Let the angle AOE be θ and AOC be $d\theta$, then

$$AC = R\,d\theta$$

and $\quad AE = OA \sin\theta = R \sin\theta$

Substituting in (i), we have

Area of the curved surface of the ring

$$= 2\pi R \sin\theta \, R\,d\theta = 2\pi R^2 \sin\theta \, d\theta$$

$\therefore$ Charge on the ring $= 2\pi R^2 \sin\theta \, d\theta \, \sigma$

$$= \frac{2\pi R^2 \sin\theta \, d\theta \, q}{4\pi R^2} = \frac{q}{2} \sin\theta \, d\theta$$

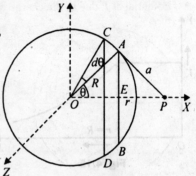

Fig. 4.14

Now the point P lies on the axis of the sliced ring. If the distance of a point on the circumference of the ring from $P = a$, then

Potential at P due to the ring is given by

$$dV = \frac{1}{4\pi\varepsilon_0} \frac{q}{2} \frac{\sin\theta \, d\theta}{a} \qquad \qquad ...(ii)$$

Now $\qquad a^2 = R^2 + r^2 - 2Rr \cos\theta$

Differentiating both sides, we have

$$2a\,da = 2Rr \sin\theta \, d\theta$$

$$\therefore \qquad \frac{\sin\theta \, d\theta}{a} = \frac{da}{Rr}$$

Substituting in (ii), we have

Potential at P due to the ring $dV = \dfrac{1}{4\pi\varepsilon_0} \dfrac{q}{2} \dfrac{da}{Rr}$

$\therefore$ Potential due to the whole shell

$$\int dV = V = \frac{1}{4\pi\varepsilon_0} \int\limits_{r-R}^{r+R} \frac{q}{2Rr} \, da = \frac{1}{4\pi\varepsilon_0} \frac{q}{2Rr} \left[a\right]_{R-r}^{R+r} = \frac{1}{4\pi\varepsilon_0} \frac{q}{r}$$

Hence potential at an external point is the same as if the whole charge were concentrated at the centre.

(ii) For an internal point. When the point P lies inside the charged spherical shell the limits of integration are $(R - r)$ to $(R + r)$.

∴ Potential at an internal point due to the whole shell

$$= \frac{1}{4\pi\varepsilon_0} \int\limits_{R-r}^{R+r} \frac{q}{2Rr} \, da = \frac{1}{4\pi\varepsilon_0} \frac{q}{2Rr} \left[a\right]_{R-r}^{R+r} = \frac{1}{4\pi\varepsilon_0} \frac{q}{R}$$

Hence the potential at an internal point is everywhere the same and is equal to the potential on the surface of the shell.

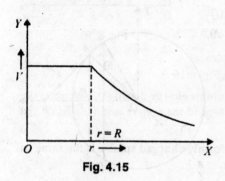

Fig. 4.15

A graph between potential V and distance r from the origin (centre of the shell is shown in Fig. 4.15).

Problem. Charge on the surface of the shell $q = 100$ $\mu C = 100 \times 10^{-6}$ C

Radius $R = 0.1$ m

∴ Electric potential inside the spherical shell

$= $ Potential on the surface of the shell $= \dfrac{1}{4\pi\varepsilon_0} \dfrac{q}{R}$

$$= \frac{9 \times 10^9 \times 100 \times 10^{-6}}{0.1}$$

$$= 9 \times 10^6 \text{ Volt.}$$

(b) Electric field intensity. The electric field intensity at a point is given by the negative gradient of potential at that point.

∴

$$\vec{E} = -\vec{\nabla}V$$

$$= -\left(\frac{\partial V}{\partial x}\hat{i} + \frac{\partial V}{\partial y}\hat{j} + \frac{\partial V}{\partial z}\hat{k}\right)$$

As P lies on the X-axis

$$\frac{\partial V}{\partial y} = 0 \text{ and } \frac{\partial V}{\partial z} = 0$$

∴ The magnitude of electric field intensity

$$= -\frac{\partial V}{\partial x} = -\frac{\partial V}{\partial r}$$

(i) For an external point. For an external point, the potential

$$V = \frac{1}{4\pi\varepsilon_0} \frac{q}{r}$$

∴ Magnitude of $\vec{E}$

$$|\vec{E}| = -\frac{d}{dr}\left[\frac{1}{4\pi\varepsilon_0} \frac{q}{r}\right] = \frac{1}{4\pi\varepsilon_0} \frac{q}{r^2}$$

∴

$$\vec{E} = \frac{1}{4\pi\varepsilon_0} \frac{q}{r^2}\hat{i}$$

Hence the electric intensity at an external point is the same as if the whole charge were concentrated at its centre.

(ii) For an internal point. For an internal point the potential

$$V = \frac{1}{4\pi\varepsilon_0} \frac{q}{R}$$

∴ Magnitude of $\vec{E}$

$$|\vec{E}| = -\frac{d}{dr}\left[\frac{1}{4\pi\varepsilon_0}\frac{q}{R}\right] = 0$$

Hence the electric field intensity inside a charged hollow spherical shell is zero.

The variation of electric intensity with distance $|\vec{r}|$ from the centre of a hollow spherical shell of radius R is shown in Fig. 4.16.

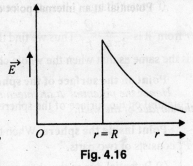

Fig. 4.16

Q. 4.32. (*a*) **A solid sphere of radius R has a uniform volume charge density ρ. Calculate the potential at a point (*i*) outside the sphere (*ii*) on the surface of the sphere and (*iii*) inside the sphere at a distance r from it.**   (*G.N.D.U., 2002*)

Show that the potential at any point outside the uniformly charged sphere is the same as that when the whole charge is concentrated at the centre.

From the values of potential calculate the electric intensity at these points.
                                                        (*Gauhati U., 2000; H.P.U., 2002, 1999*)

(*b*) **Find the electric potential on the surface of a nucleus having mass number 64, atomic number 30. Take charge on proton 1.6×10^{-19} C and radius of proton 1.2×10^{15}m**
                                                                    (*Kerala U., 2001*)

Ans. Potential at a point outside the sphere. Consider a sphere of radius R with its centre at O. Draw a concentric spherical shell of radius x and thickness dx in the sphere of charge.

The volume of the shell $= 4\pi x^2\, dx$

Charge in the shell $= 4\pi x^2\, dx\, \rho$

For a point P_1 at a distance r from the centre ($r > R$), the electric potential due to the shell

$$dV = \frac{1}{4\pi\varepsilon_0} \frac{4\pi x^2\, dx\, \rho}{r}$$

∴ Total electric potential at P_1

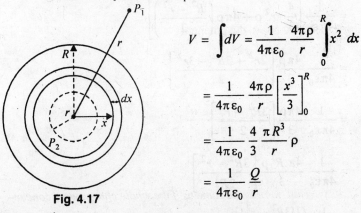

$$V = \int dV = \frac{1}{4\pi\varepsilon_0} \frac{4\pi\rho}{r} \int_0^R x^2\, dx$$

$$= \frac{1}{4\pi\varepsilon_0} \frac{4\pi\rho}{r}\left[\frac{x^3}{3}\right]_0^R$$

$$= \frac{1}{4\pi\varepsilon_0} \frac{4}{3} \frac{\pi R^3}{r} \rho$$

$$= \frac{1}{4\pi\varepsilon_0} \frac{Q}{r}$$

Fig. 4.17

because $\dfrac{4}{3}\pi R^3\, \rho = Q$ = the total charge in the sphere.

If a total charge Q lies at the centre O of the sphere, then also the electric potential at a distance r from it is $\dfrac{1}{4\pi\varepsilon_0}\dfrac{Q}{r}$. Thus we find that the potential at any point outside a uniformly charged sphere is the same as that when the whole charge is concentrated at the centre of the sphere.

Point on the surface of the sphere. When the point P lies on the surface of the sphere $r = R$ and

Potential on the surface of the sphere $= \dfrac{1}{4\pi\varepsilon_0}\dfrac{Q}{R}$

Point inside the sphere. When the point P_2 lies inside the sphere, then total electric potential at P_2 consists of two parts.

(*i*) Potential due to the charge within the sphere of radius r

$$V_1 = \frac{1}{4\pi\varepsilon_0}\frac{4}{3}\frac{\pi r^3 \rho}{r} = \frac{1}{4\pi\varepsilon_0}\frac{4}{3}\pi r^2 \rho$$

because the point P_2 lies on the surface of the sphere of charge of radius r.

(*ii*) Potential at P_2 due to the spherical shell of inner radius r and outer radius R. Let it be V_2.

Potential at P_2 due to the charge $4\pi x^2 dx \rho$ contained in the elementary shell of radius x and thickness dx

$$dV = \frac{1}{4\pi\varepsilon_0}\frac{4\pi x^2 \, dx \, \rho}{x} = \frac{1}{4\pi\varepsilon_0}4\pi\rho x \, dx$$

because potential at a point inside the shell is the same as on its surface.

$$\therefore \quad V_2 = \int_r^R dV = \frac{1}{4\pi\varepsilon_0}4\pi\rho\int_r^R x \, dx$$

$$= \frac{1}{4\pi\varepsilon_0}4\pi\rho\left[\frac{x^2}{2}\right]_r^R$$

$$= \frac{1}{4\pi\varepsilon_0}4\pi\rho\left[\frac{R^2 - r^2}{2}\right]$$

Total potential $\quad V = V_1 + V_2$

$$= \frac{1}{4\pi\varepsilon_0}\left[\frac{4}{3}\pi r^2 \rho + 4\pi\rho\left(\frac{R^2 - r^2}{2}\right)\right]$$

$$= \frac{1}{4\pi\varepsilon_0}\frac{4\pi\rho}{3}\left[\frac{2r^2 + 3R^2 - 3r^2}{2}\right]$$

$$= \frac{1}{4\pi\varepsilon_0}\frac{4\pi\rho}{3}\left[\frac{3R^2 - r^2}{2}\right]$$

$$= \frac{1}{4\pi\varepsilon_0}\frac{4\pi R^3 \rho}{3}\left[\frac{3R^2 - r^2}{2R^3}\right]$$

$$= \frac{1}{4\pi\varepsilon_0}\frac{Q[3R^2 - r^2]}{2R^3}$$

where
$$Q = \frac{4}{3} \pi R^3 \rho = \text{Total charge in the sphere}$$

Electric field. (*i*) **Point lying outside the sphere.** For a point outside the sphere, the potential

$$V = \frac{1}{4\pi\varepsilon_0} \frac{Q}{r}$$

∴ Electric field
$$\vec{E} = -\vec{\nabla}V = -\frac{Q}{4\pi\varepsilon_0} \vec{\nabla}\left(\frac{1}{r}\right)$$

$$= \frac{1}{4\pi\varepsilon_0} \frac{Q}{r^2} \hat{r} \qquad \left[\text{For the value of } \vec{\nabla}\left(\frac{1}{r}\right) \text{See Q. 1.12. Ex. } (iii)\right]$$

(*i*) **Point inside the sphere.** For a point inside the sphere, the potential

$$V = \frac{1}{4\pi\varepsilon_0} \frac{4\pi\rho}{3} \left[\frac{3R^2 - r^2}{2}\right]$$

∴
$$\vec{E} = -\vec{\nabla}V = -\frac{1}{4\pi\varepsilon_0} \frac{4\pi\rho}{3} \vec{\nabla}\left[\frac{3R^2 - r^2}{2}\right]$$

Now
$$\vec{\nabla}\left[\frac{3R^2 - r^2}{2}\right] = \vec{\nabla}\frac{3R^2}{2} - \vec{\nabla}\frac{r^2}{2}$$

$$= \frac{3}{2}\vec{\nabla}R^2 - \frac{1}{2}\vec{\nabla}r^2$$

But $\vec{\nabla}R^2 = 0$ since $R = $ a constant

Now $r^2 = x^2 + y^2 + z^2$ where x, y, z are the co-ordinates of the point P_2.

∴
$$\frac{1}{2}\vec{\nabla}r^2 = \frac{1}{2}\left(\hat{i}\frac{\partial}{\partial x} + \hat{j}\frac{\partial}{\partial y} + \hat{k}\frac{\partial}{\partial z}\right)(x^2 + y^2 + z^2)$$

$$= \frac{1}{2}(2x\hat{i} + 2y\hat{j} + 2z\hat{k}) = (x\hat{i} + y\hat{j} + z\hat{k}) = \vec{r}$$

∴
$$\vec{\nabla}\left[\frac{3R^2 - r^2}{2}\right] = 0 - \vec{r} = -\vec{r}$$

Hence
$$\vec{E} = -\frac{1}{4\pi\varepsilon_0} \frac{4\pi\rho}{3} (-\vec{r})$$

$$= \frac{1}{4\pi\varepsilon_0} \frac{4\pi\rho}{3} \vec{r}$$

(*b*) Mass number of the nucleus $A = 64$

Atomic number Z $= 30 = $ Number of protons in the nucleus

∴ Charge in the nucleus Q $= Ze = 30 \times 1.6 \times 10^{-19} = 4.8 \times 10^{-18}$ C

Radius of the proton r_0 $= 1.2 \times 10^{-15}$ m

$\therefore$ Radius of the nucleus R $= r_0 A^{1/3} = 1.2 \times 10^{-15} \times (64)^{1/3} = 4 \times 1.2 \times 10^{-15}$

$$= 4.8 \times 10^{-15} \text{ m}$$

Potential on the surface of the nucleus $V = \dfrac{1}{4\pi\varepsilon_0} \dfrac{Q}{R}$

$$= \frac{9 \times 10^9 \times 4.8 \times 10^{-18}}{4.8 \times 10^{-15}} = 9 \times 10^6 \text{ volt}$$

Q. 4.33. (*a*) **What is an electric dipole? Show that the potential V due to an electric dipole of dipole moment $\overrightarrow{P}$ and located at the origin is given by**

$$\frac{1}{4\pi\varepsilon_0} \frac{\overrightarrow{p} \cdot \overrightarrow{r}}{r^3} = -\frac{1}{4\pi\varepsilon_0} \overrightarrow{p} \cdot \overrightarrow{\nabla}\left(\frac{1}{r}\right).$$

How does potential vary with distance?

(*G.N.D.U.* 2009, 2007; *Pbi.U.*, 2008, 2002; *H.P.U.*, 2002; *Gauhati U.*, 2000; *P.U.*, 2006, 2000; *H.P.U.*, 2000; *Gharwal U.*, 2000, *Luck.U.*, 1996, 1995)

(*b*) **What is the value of potential at a point (*i*) on the axis of the dipole (*ii*) on the normal to the axis?**

Ans. (*a*) **For electric dipole and dipole moment see Q. 2.27, chapter 2.**

Electric potential due to a dipole. Consider a dipole consisting of charges $+q$ and $-q$ separated by a *small* distance $2\overrightarrow{l}$, lying along the X-axis with its centre at the origin, then

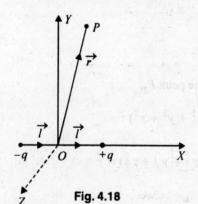

Fig. 4.18

Dipole moment of the electric dipole $\overrightarrow{p} = 2q\overrightarrow{l}$

Consider a point P having a position vector r, then

Potential at P due to the charge $+qz$

$$V_+ = \frac{1}{4\pi\varepsilon_0} \frac{q}{|\overrightarrow{r} - \overrightarrow{l}|}$$

and potential at P due to the charge $-q$

$$V_- = -\frac{1}{4\pi\varepsilon_0} \frac{q}{|\overrightarrow{r} + \overrightarrow{l}|}$$

$\therefore$ Net potential at P due to the electric dipole

$$V = V_+ + V_-$$

$$= \frac{q}{4\pi\varepsilon_0} \left[\frac{1}{|\overrightarrow{r} - \overrightarrow{l}|} - \frac{1}{|\overrightarrow{r} + \overrightarrow{l}|} \right] \qquad \ldots(i)$$

To find the value of $|\overrightarrow{r} - \overrightarrow{l}|$, consider the term

$$|\overrightarrow{r} - \overrightarrow{l}|^2 = (\overrightarrow{r} - \overrightarrow{l}) \cdot (\overrightarrow{r} - \overrightarrow{l})$$

$$= r^2 + l^2 - 2\overrightarrow{r} \cdot \overrightarrow{l}$$

$$= r^2 \left[1 + \frac{l^2}{r^2} - 2\frac{\overrightarrow{r} \cdot \overrightarrow{l}}{r^2} \right]$$

$\therefore$

$$|\vec{r} - \vec{l}| = r\left[1 + \frac{l^2}{r^2} - \frac{2\vec{r}.\vec{l}}{r^2}\right]^{1/2}$$

or

$$\frac{1}{|\vec{r} - \vec{l}|} = \frac{1}{r}\left[1 + \frac{l^2}{r^2} - \frac{2\vec{r}.\vec{l}}{r^2}\right]^{-1/2}$$

When P is at a *far off* point from O or the dipole is a *point* or *short dipole* i.e., $r > l$, $\dfrac{l^2}{r^2}$ can be neglected as compared to 1. Hence

$$\frac{1}{|\vec{r} - \vec{l}|} = \frac{1}{r}\left[1 - \frac{2\vec{r}.\vec{l}}{r^2}\right]^{-1/2}$$

Expanding the term on the right hand side and neglecting terms containing $\dfrac{l^2}{r^2}$ and higher powers we get

$$\frac{1}{|\vec{r} - \vec{l}|} = \frac{1}{r}\left[1 + \frac{\vec{r}.\vec{l}}{r^2}\right] = \frac{1}{r} + \frac{\vec{r}.\vec{l}}{r^3}$$

Similarly

$$\frac{1}{|\vec{r} + \vec{l}|} = \frac{1}{r} - \frac{\vec{r}.\vec{l}}{r^3}$$

Substituting these values of $\dfrac{1}{|\vec{r} - \vec{l}|}$ and $\dfrac{1}{|\vec{r} + \vec{l}|}$ in relation (i) we get

$$V = \frac{2q}{4\pi\varepsilon_0}\frac{\vec{r}.\vec{l}}{r^3} = \frac{\vec{r}.2q\vec{l}}{4\pi\varepsilon_0\, r^3} = \frac{\vec{r}.\vec{p}}{4\pi\varepsilon_0\, r^3} = \frac{\vec{p}.\vec{r}}{4\pi\varepsilon_0\, r^3} = \frac{1}{4\pi\varepsilon_0}\,\vec{p}.\left[\frac{\vec{r}}{r^3}\right] = -\frac{1}{4\pi\varepsilon_0}\,\vec{p}.\vec{\nabla}\left(\frac{1}{r}\right)$$

as $\quad \vec{\nabla}\left(\dfrac{1}{r}\right) = -\dfrac{\vec{r}}{r^3}$ [See Q. 1.12 Ex. (iii)]

Also

$$\frac{\vec{p}.\vec{r}}{4\pi\varepsilon_0\, r^3} = \frac{\vec{p}.\hat{r}}{4\pi\varepsilon_0\, r^2} \qquad \qquad ...(ii)$$

where $\hat{r}$ is a unit vector in the direction of $\vec{r}$. If θ is the angle between $\vec{p}$ and $\vec{r}$, then

$$V = \frac{pr\cos\theta}{4\pi\varepsilon_0\, r^3} = \frac{p\cos\theta}{4\pi\varepsilon_0\, r^2} \qquad \qquad ...(iii)$$

Thus we find that *potential at a point due to a point dipole varies inversely as the square of the distance.*

(*i*) **Potential on the axial line.** When the point P lies on the axis of the dipole (or axial line), the vectors $\vec{p}$ and $\vec{r}$ are in the same direction (or $\theta = 0$ and $\cos\theta = 1$) *i.e.*, along the X-axis

$\therefore \qquad\qquad \vec{p}.\vec{r} = pr$

Substituting in (ii), we have

$$V = \frac{pr}{4\pi\varepsilon_0\, r^3} = \frac{p}{4\pi\varepsilon_0\, r^2}$$

Note. When the point P lies on the axial line of the dipole in a direction opposite to that of $\vec{p}$; $\theta = \pi$ and $\cos \theta = -1$.

$$\therefore \qquad V = -\frac{p}{4\pi \varepsilon_0 \, r^2}$$

(ii) **Potential on the normal to the axis (Equatorial line).** When the point P lies on the normal to the axis $\vec{p}$ and $\vec{r}$ are at right angles to each other ($\vec{p}$ along X-axis and $\vec{r}$ along Y-axis) or $\theta = \pi/2$ and $\cos \theta = 0$

$$\therefore \qquad \vec{p} \cdot \vec{r} = 0$$

Substituting in *(ii)*, we have

$$V = 0$$

Thus the electric potential at a point on the equatorial line of a dipole is zero.

Q. 4.34. *(a)* **Prove that** $\vec{\nabla} \dfrac{(\vec{p} \cdot \vec{r})}{r^3} = \dfrac{\vec{p}}{r^3} - \dfrac{3(\vec{p} \cdot \vec{r}) \, \vec{r}}{r^5}$ $\qquad\qquad$ *(G.N.D.U., 1990)*

(b) **Hence find the electric field at any point due to a dipole if the potential is** $\dfrac{1}{4\pi \varepsilon_0} \dfrac{\vec{p} \cdot \vec{r}}{r^3}$.

What is the value of electric field on the *(i)* **axial line and** *(ii)* **on the line normal to the axis of the dipole ?** *(G.N.D.U. 2009, 2007, 2006; Pbi. U. 2007; Gauhati U., 2000; Luck. U., 1996, 1992)*

Ans. *(a)* If u and v are two scalar functions, then

$$\vec{\nabla}(uv) = u \, \vec{\nabla} v + v \, \vec{\nabla} u$$

The product $\vec{p} \cdot \vec{r}$ is a scalar quantity. We shall, therefore take

$$\therefore \qquad \vec{\nabla}\left(\frac{\vec{p} \cdot \vec{r}}{r^3}\right) = \frac{1}{r^3} \vec{\nabla}(\vec{p} \cdot \vec{r}) + (\vec{p} \cdot \vec{r}) \vec{\nabla}\left(\frac{1}{r^3}\right) \qquad \dots(i)$$

But $\qquad \vec{\nabla}(\vec{p} \cdot \vec{r}) = \vec{\nabla}\{(p_x \hat{i} + p_y \hat{j} + p_z \hat{k}) \cdot (x\hat{i} + y\hat{j} + z\hat{k})\}$

$$= \vec{\nabla}\{p_x x + p_y y + p_z z\}$$

$$= \left(\hat{i}\frac{\partial}{\partial x} + \hat{j}\frac{\partial}{\partial y} + \hat{k}\frac{\partial}{\partial z}\right)(p_x x + p_y y + p_z z)$$

$$= p_x \hat{i} + p_y \hat{j} + p_z \hat{k} = \vec{p} \qquad\qquad \dots(ii)$$

$$\vec{\nabla}\left(\frac{1}{r^3}\right) = \left(\hat{i}\frac{\partial}{\partial x} + \hat{j}\frac{\partial}{\partial y} + \hat{k}\frac{\partial}{\partial z}\right)(x^2 + y^2 + z^2)^{-3/2}$$

$$= -\left\{\hat{i}\frac{3}{2}(x^2 + y^2 + z^2)^{-5/2} 2x + \hat{j}\frac{3}{2}(x^2 + y^2 + z^2)^{-5/2} 2y + \hat{k}\frac{3}{2}(x^2 + y^2 + z^2)^{-5/2} 2z\right\}$$

$$= \frac{-3(x\hat{i} + y\hat{j} + z\hat{k})}{(x^2 + y^2 + z^2)^{+5/2}} = \frac{-3\vec{r}}{r^5} \qquad\qquad \dots(iii)$$

Substituting the value of $\vec{\nabla}(\vec{p} \cdot \vec{r}) = \vec{p}$ from *(ii)* and $\vec{\nabla}\left(\dfrac{1}{r^3}\right) = \dfrac{-3\vec{r}}{r^5}$ from *(iii)* in Eq. *(i)*, we have

$$\vec{\nabla}\left(\frac{\vec{p}.\vec{r}}{r^3}\right) = \frac{\vec{p}}{r^3} - \frac{3(\vec{p}.\vec{r})\vec{r}}{r^5} \qquad ...(iv)$$

(b) Electric field at any point due to a dipole. The potential at any point due to a dipole is given by

$$V = \frac{1}{4\pi\varepsilon_0}\frac{\vec{p}.\vec{r}}{r^3}$$

The electric field at a point is the negative gradient of the potential at that point

$$\therefore \qquad \vec{E} = -\vec{\nabla}V = -\vec{\nabla}\left(\frac{\vec{p}.\vec{r}}{4\pi\varepsilon_0\,r^3}\right) = -\frac{1}{4\pi\varepsilon_0}\vec{\nabla}\left(\frac{\vec{p}.\vec{r}}{r^3}\right)$$

But according to Eq. (iv)

$$\vec{\nabla}\left(\frac{\vec{p}.\vec{r}}{r^3}\right) = \frac{\vec{p}}{r^3} - \frac{3(\vec{p}.\vec{r})\vec{r}}{r^5}$$

Substituting, we get

$$\vec{E} = \frac{1}{4\pi\varepsilon_0}\left[\frac{3(\vec{p}.\vec{r})\vec{r}}{r^5} - \frac{\vec{p}}{r^3}\right] \qquad ...(v)$$

$$= \frac{1}{4\pi\varepsilon_0}\left[\frac{3(\vec{p}.\vec{r})\vec{r}}{r^5} - \frac{\vec{p}r^2}{r^5}\right]$$

From relation (v), we find that the electric field at a point due to a dipole varies inversely as the cube of the distance.

(i) Electric field on the axis of a dipole. When the point P lies on the axis of the dipole, the vectors $\vec{P}$ and $\vec{r}$ are in the same direction i.e., along the X-axis.

$$\therefore \qquad \vec{p}.\vec{r} = pr \qquad \vec{r} = r\hat{r} = r\hat{i} \text{ or } \hat{r} = \hat{i}$$
$$\vec{p} = p\hat{p} = p\hat{r} = p\hat{i}$$

Substituting in (v), we have

$$\vec{E} = \frac{1}{4\pi\varepsilon_0}\left[\frac{3pr^2\hat{r} - pr^2\hat{r}}{r^5}\right]$$

$$= \frac{1}{4\pi\varepsilon_0}\frac{2p}{r^3}\hat{r} = \frac{1}{4\pi\varepsilon_0}\frac{2p}{r^3}\hat{i}$$

i.e., $\vec{E}$ acts along the $+ X$-axis.

(ii) Electric field on the normal to the axis. When the point P lies on the normal to the axis $\vec{P}$ and $\vec{r}$ are at right angles to each other and $\vec{P}$ is directed along the X-axis.

$$\therefore \qquad \vec{p}.\vec{r} = 0 \text{ and } \vec{p} = p\hat{i}$$

Substituting in (v), we have

$$E = - \frac{1}{4\pi\varepsilon_0} \frac{p}{r^3} \hat{i} \qquad \qquad i.e., \ \vec{E} \text{ acts along the } -X\text{-axis.}$$

Q. 4.35. How do electric field and electric potential due to an electric dipole vary with respect to distance ?   (*G.N.D.U., 2003*)

Ans. Potential due to an electric dipole. The potential V due to an electric dipole of dipole moment $\vec{p}$ and located at the origin at a distance $\vec{r}$ is given by

$$V = \frac{\vec{p} \cdot \hat{r}}{4\pi\varepsilon_0 \, r^2} = \frac{1}{4\pi\varepsilon_0} \cdot \frac{p\cos\theta}{r^2}$$

or

$$V \propto \frac{1}{r^2}$$

For a point on the axial line $V = - \dfrac{1}{4\pi\varepsilon_0} \dfrac{p}{r^2}$ and for a point on the equatorial line $V = 0$.

Thus we find that *potential at any point due to a point dipole varies inversely as the square of the distance.*

Electric field due to a dipole. The electric field $\vec{E}$ at the same point is given by

$$\vec{E} = \frac{1}{4\pi\varepsilon_0} \left[\frac{3\,(\vec{p} \cdot \vec{r})\,\vec{r}}{r^5} - \frac{\vec{p}}{r^3} \right]$$

$$= \frac{1}{4\pi\varepsilon_0} \left[\frac{3\,p\cos\theta}{r^3} - \frac{p}{r^3} \right] \qquad \qquad \text{(Taking magnitudes only)}$$

or

$$E \propto \frac{1}{r^3}$$

For a point on the axial line $E = \dfrac{1}{4\pi\,\varepsilon_0} \dfrac{2p}{r^3}$ and for a point on the equatorial line $E = - \dfrac{1}{4\pi\varepsilon_0} \dfrac{p}{r^3}$

Thus we find that *electric field at any point due to a point dipole varies inversely as the cube of the distance.*

Q. 4.36. (a) Calculate the force and torque on a dipole in an external field.

(*Kan.U., 1995; Luck.U., 1995*)

(b) Derive an expression for the potential energy of an electric dipole placed in a uniform electric field. When is the energy of dipole minimum?   (*Luck.U., 1995, P.U., 1994*)

Note. *In this question we shall denote the length of the dipole by 2dl instead of 2l to indicate that the length of the dipole is infinitessimally small.*

Ans. (a) Force on a dipole. Consider an electric dipole consisting of charges $+q$ and $-q$ separated by a distance $2\,d\vec{l}$ apart, then dipole moment $\vec{p} = 2qd\vec{l}$

Uniform field. When such a dipole is placed in a uniform electric field $\vec{E}$ with its axis making an angle θ with the direction of $\vec{E}$ as shown, then

Force on the charge $+ q = + qE$

i.e., in the direction of the field

Force on the charge $-q = -qE$

i.e., this force is equal and opposite to the force on the charge $+q$.

∴ Net force $= 0$

Hence the net translatory force on a dipole in a uniform electric field is zero.

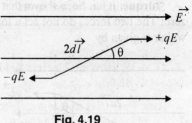

Fig. 4.19

Non-uniform field. When the field is non-uniform let it be $\vec{E}$ at the charge $-q$ lying at the position vector $\vec{r} = \hat{i}\,x + \hat{j}\,y + \hat{k}\,z$ and $\vec{E'}$ at the charge $+q$ lying at the position vector $\vec{r'} = \hat{i}\,(x + dx) + \hat{j}\,(y + dy) + \hat{k}\,(z + dz)$. Let E_x, E_y, E_z be the components of $\vec{E}$ and E_x', E_y', E_z' those of $\vec{E'}$. As the charge $+q$ is displaced from the charge $-q$ by a vector distance

$$\vec{r'} - \vec{r} = 2\,\vec{dl} = \hat{i}\,dx + \hat{j}\,dy + \hat{k}\,dz$$

the dipole moment

$$\vec{p} = 2q\,\vec{dl} = q(\hat{i}\,dx + \hat{j}\,dy + \hat{k}\,dz)$$

Further

$$E_x' = E_x + \left(\frac{\partial E_x}{\partial x}\right) dx + \left(\frac{\partial E_x}{\partial y}\right) dy + \left(\frac{\partial E_x}{\partial z}\right) dz$$

∴ Net force on the dipole in the X-direction

$$F_x = q\,E_x' - q\,E_x = q\left[\left(\frac{\partial E_x}{\partial x}\right) dx + \left(\frac{\partial E_x}{\partial y}\right) dy + \left(\frac{\partial E_x}{\partial z}\right) dz\right]$$

$$= q\,(\hat{i}\,dx + \hat{j}\,dy + \hat{k}\,dz) \cdot \left(\frac{\partial E_x}{\partial x} + \frac{\partial E_x}{\partial y} + \frac{\partial E_x}{\partial z}\right)$$

$$= q\,2\,\vec{dl} \cdot \vec{\nabla}\,E_x = \vec{p} \cdot \vec{\nabla}\,E_x$$

Similarly net force on the dipole along the Y and Z direction is given by

$$F_y = \vec{p} \cdot \vec{\nabla}\,E_y$$

and

$$F_z = \vec{p} \cdot \vec{\nabla}\,E_z$$

∴ Total force on the dipole

$$\vec{F} = F_x\,\hat{i} + F_y\,\hat{j} + F_z\,\hat{k}$$

$$= (\vec{p} \cdot \vec{\nabla})\,(E_x\,\hat{i} + E_y\,\hat{j} + E_z\,\hat{k})$$

$$= (\vec{p} \cdot \vec{\nabla})\,\vec{E}$$

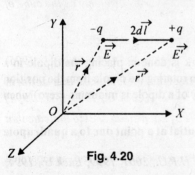

Fig. 4.20

$(\vec{p} \cdot \vec{\nabla})$ is a scalar differential operator given by

$$\left(p_x\frac{\partial}{\partial x} + p_y\frac{\partial}{\partial y} + p_z\frac{\partial}{\partial z}\right)$$

Torque. It has been shown that the net translatory force on a dipole in a uniform electric field is zero. The two forces do not act a long the same straight line and constitute a couple, the moment of which is given by

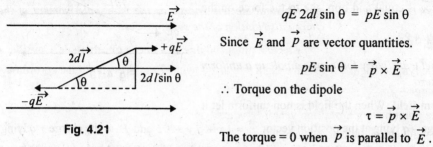

$$qE \, 2dl \sin \theta = pE \sin \theta$$

Since $\vec{E}$ and $\vec{P}$ are vector quantities.

$$pE \sin \theta = \vec{p} \times \vec{E}$$

∴ Torque on the dipole

$$\tau = \vec{p} \times \vec{E}$$

Fig. 4.21

The torque = 0 when $\vec{P}$ is parallel to $\vec{E}$.

(*b*) **Energy of a dipole.** *The potential energy of a dipole in an electric field is defined as the amount of work done against the electric field in bringing the dipole from infinity and placing it in the desired orientation in the field.*

When the dipole is placed perpendicular to the direction of the electric field the work done = 0. The equipotential lines are always at right angles to the lines of electric field, therefore the work done in bringing the charge + q and the charge – q to the same potential being equal and opposite cancel each other. Work is, therefore, only done in rotating the dipole from the position perpendicular to the field to any other position.

Let the dipole make an angle θ with the field $\vec{E}$, then the magnitude of the couple (torque) acting on it = $pE \sin \theta$. Work done in turning the dipole from the position making an angle θ with the field to the position making an angle $\theta + d\theta$ is given by

$$dW = pE \sin \theta \, d\theta$$

∴ Potential energy of the dipole in the orientation θ

$$U = \int_{\theta = \frac{\pi}{2}}^{\theta = \theta} dW = \int_{\theta = \frac{\pi}{2}}^{\theta = \theta} pE \sin \theta \, d\theta = [- pE \cos \theta]_{\theta = \frac{\pi}{2}}^{\theta = \theta}$$

$$= - pE \cos \theta = \vec{p} \cdot \vec{E}$$

as $\vec{p}$ and $\vec{E}$ are vector quantities.

Minimum energy of dipole. As explained above no work is done in placing the dipole in a direction perpendicular to the electric field. Work is only done in rotating the dipole from the position perpendicular to the field to any other position. Thus the energy of a dipole is minimum (zero) when placed at right angles to the direction of electric field.

Q. 4.37. What is a quadrupole ? Prove that electric potential at a point due to a quadrupole varies as $\dfrac{1}{r^3}$.

(*Pbi. U., 2008; H.P.U., 2001, 1999; Luck. U., 1994; Kan. U., 1996, 1995, 1992; P.U., 2002, 2001, 2000, 1996*)

Ans. Electric quadrupole. *A linear electric quadrupole consists of two electric dipoles placed end to end along the same line.*

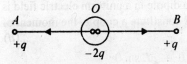

Fig. 4.22

As shown in Fig. 4.22, OA is one dipole having a charge $-q$ at O and $+q$ at A and OB is the second dipole having a charge $-q$ at O and $+q$ at B. *Thus the total charge at O is $-2q$ and the total electric charge or the monopole moment of the charge distribution of the system is zero.*

Electric potential due to a linear quadrupole. Consider a linear quadrupole lying along the X-axis having a length $2\vec{l}$ with O as the origin of the co-ordinate system at the charge $-2q$.

Let P be the point having a position vector $\vec{r}$ where potential due to the quadrupole is to be calculated.

The position vector of the charge $+q$ at B, $\vec{r_B} = +\vec{l}$

$\therefore$ Potential at P due to charge $+q$ at B

$$V_B = \frac{1}{4\pi\varepsilon_0}\frac{q}{|\vec{r}-\vec{r_B}|} = \frac{1}{4\pi\varepsilon_0}\frac{q}{|\vec{r}-\vec{l}|}$$

The position vector of the charge $+q$ at A, $\vec{r_A} = -\vec{l}$

$\therefore$ Potential at P due to charge $+q$ at A

$$V_A = \frac{q}{4\pi\varepsilon_0}\frac{q}{|\vec{r}-\vec{r_A}|} = \frac{1}{4\pi\varepsilon_0}\frac{q}{|\vec{r}+\vec{l}|}$$

The position vector of the charge $-2q$ at O, $\vec{r_0} = 0$

$\therefore$ Potential at P due to charge $-2q$ at O

$$V_0 = -\frac{1}{4\pi\varepsilon_0}\frac{2q}{|\vec{r}|}$$

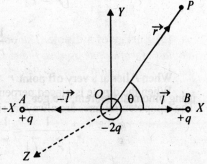

Fig. 4.23

Hence total potential at P due to the linear quadrupole

$$V = V_B + V_A + V_0 = \frac{q}{4\pi\varepsilon_0}\left[\frac{1}{|\vec{r}-\vec{l}|} + \frac{1}{|\vec{r}+\vec{l}|} - \frac{2}{r}\right] \qquad ...(i)$$

To find the value of $|\vec{r}-\vec{l}|$, we find that

$$|\vec{r}-\vec{l}|^2 = (\vec{r}-\vec{l}).(\vec{r}-\vec{l})$$

$$= r^2 + l^2 - 2\vec{r}.\vec{l}$$

$$= r^2\left(1 + \frac{l^2}{r^2} - 2\frac{\vec{r}.\vec{l}}{r^2}\right)$$

or

$$|\vec{r}-\vec{l}| = r\left(1 + \frac{l^2}{r^2} - 2\frac{\vec{r}.\vec{l}}{r^2}\right)^{1/2}$$

and

$$\frac{1}{|\vec{r} - \vec{l}|} = \frac{1}{r}\left(1 + \frac{l^2}{r^2} - 2\frac{\vec{r} \cdot \vec{l}}{r^2}\right)^{-1/2} \qquad \text{...(ii)}$$

If θ is the angle between $\vec{r}$ and $\vec{R}$, then $\vec{r} \cdot \vec{l} = rl \cos \theta$

Substituting $\vec{r} \cdot \vec{l} = rl \cos \theta$ in relation (ii) we have

$$\frac{1}{|\vec{r} - \vec{l}|} = \frac{1}{r}\left(1 + \frac{l^2}{r^2} - \frac{2rl \cos \theta}{r^2}\right)^{-1/2}$$

$$= \frac{1}{r}\left(1 + \frac{l^2}{r^2} - \frac{2l \cos \theta}{r}\right)^{-1/2} \qquad \text{...(iii)}$$

When P lies at a very off point $r > l$ and $\dfrac{l}{r} < 1$. Therefore, expanding right hand side of Eq. (iii) using binomial theorem, we get

$$\frac{1}{|\vec{r} - \vec{l}|} = \frac{1}{r}\left[1 - \frac{1}{2}\left(\frac{l^2}{r^2} - \frac{2l \cos \theta}{r}\right) + \frac{3}{8}\left(\frac{l^2}{r^2} - \frac{2l \cos \theta}{r}\right)^2 + \dots\dots\right]$$

Neglecting terms containing powers of $\dfrac{l}{r}$ higher than $\dfrac{l^2}{r^2}$, we get

$$\frac{1}{|\vec{r} - \vec{l}|} = \frac{1}{r}\left[1 - \frac{l^2}{2r^2} + \frac{l \cos \theta}{r} + \frac{3}{8}\frac{4l^2 \cos^2 \theta}{r^2}\right]$$

$$= \frac{1}{r} - \frac{l^2}{2r^3} + \frac{l \cos \theta}{r^2} + \frac{3}{2}\frac{l^2 \cos^2 \theta}{r^3}$$

Similarly

$$\frac{1}{|\vec{r} + \vec{l}|} = \frac{1}{r} - \frac{l^2}{2r^3} - \frac{l \cos \theta}{r^2} + \frac{3}{2}\frac{l^2 \cos^2 \theta}{r^3}$$

Substituting the values of $\dfrac{1}{|\vec{r} - \vec{l}|}$ and $\dfrac{1}{|\vec{r} + \vec{l}|}$ in Eq. (i), we get

$$V = \frac{q}{4\pi\varepsilon_0}\left[\frac{1}{r} - \frac{l^2}{2r^3} + \frac{l \cos \theta}{r^2} + \frac{3}{2}\frac{l^2 \cos^2 \theta}{r^3} + \frac{1}{r} - \frac{l^2}{2r^3} - \frac{l \cos \theta}{r^2} + \frac{3}{2}\frac{l^2 \cos^2 \theta}{r^3} - \frac{2}{r}\right]$$

$$= \frac{q}{4\pi\varepsilon_0}\left[-\frac{l^2}{r^3} + \frac{3l^2 \cos^2 \theta}{r^3}\right]$$

$$= \frac{ql^2}{4\pi\varepsilon_0 r^3}[3 \cos^2 \theta - 1] \qquad \text{...(iv)}$$

Equation (iv) shows that *the electric potential due to a quadrupole varies inversely as the cube of the distance.*

Q. 4.38. The potential at a far off point having position vector $\vec{r}$ due to linear quadrupole is given by

$$V = \frac{ql^2}{4\pi\varepsilon_0\, r^3}\, (3\cos^2\theta - 1)$$

where $+q$ is the charge at the two ends; $-2q$ at the centre of the quadrupole of length $2l$ and θ the angle between $\vec{r}$ and axis of the quadrupole.

Hence find the electric field.   *(Kan.U., 1996, 1995, 1992)*

Ans. Potential due to the linear quadrupole

$$V = \frac{ql^2}{4\pi\varepsilon_0\, r^3}\, (3\cos^2\theta - 1)$$

As θ is the angle between position vector $\vec{r}$ and the vector $\vec{l}$ representing half the length of the quadrupole

$$\vec{r}\cdot\vec{l} = rl\cos\theta$$

$\therefore$

$$\cos\theta = \frac{\vec{r}\cdot\vec{l}}{rl} \quad \text{or} \quad \cos^2\theta = \frac{(\vec{r}\cdot\vec{l})^2}{r^2 l^2}$$

Substituting this value of $\cos^2\theta$ in the expression for potential, we get

$$V = \frac{q}{4\pi\varepsilon_0}\left[\frac{3(\vec{r}\cdot\vec{l})^2}{r^5} - \frac{l^2}{r^3}\right] \qquad \qquad ...(i)$$

Suppose the quadrupole lies along the X-axis.

$\therefore$

$$\vec{l} = l\,\hat{i}$$

If the co-ordinates of the point having position vector $\vec{r}$ are x, y, z, then

$$\vec{r} = x\,\hat{i} + y\,\hat{j} + z\,\hat{k}$$

$\therefore$

$$\vec{r}\cdot\vec{l} = lx$$

and

$$r = (x^2 + y^2 + z^2)^{1/2}$$

Substituting in Eq. (i), we get

$$V = \frac{q}{4\pi\varepsilon_0}\left[\frac{3l^2\, x^2}{(x^2 + y^2 + z^2)^{5/2}} - \frac{l^2}{(x^2 + y^2 + z^2)^{3/2}}\right]$$

$$= \frac{ql^2}{4\pi\varepsilon_0}\left[\frac{3x^2}{(x^2 + y^2 + z^2)^{5/2}} - \frac{1}{(x^2 + y^2 + z^2)^{3/2}}\right]$$

The electric field is the negative of the gradient of electric potential.

$\therefore$

$$\vec{E} = -\vec{\nabla}V$$

$$= \frac{-ql^2}{4\pi\varepsilon_0}\,\vec{\nabla}\left[\frac{3x^2}{(x^2 + y^2 + z^2)^{5/2}} - \frac{1}{(x^2 + y^2 + z^2)^{3/2}}\right]$$

$$= \frac{-ql^2}{4\pi\varepsilon_0}\left[\vec{\nabla}\frac{3x^2}{(x^2 + y^2 + z^2)^{5/2}} - \vec{\nabla}\frac{1}{(x^2 + y^2 + z^2)^{3/2}}\right] \qquad ...(ii)$$

Now $\vec{\nabla} \dfrac{3x^2}{(x^2 + y^2 + z^2)^{5/2}} = 3\vec{\nabla} \, x^2 \, (x^2 + y^2 + z^2)^{-5/2}$

$= 3\left[\hat{i}\dfrac{\partial}{\partial x}\{x^2(x^2 + y^2 + z^2)^{-5/2}\} + \hat{j}\dfrac{\partial}{\partial y}\{x^2(x^2 + y^2 + z^2)^{-5/2}\} + \hat{k}\dfrac{\partial}{\partial z}\{x^2(x^2 + y^2 + z^2)^{-5/2}\} \right]$

$= 3\,\hat{i}\left\{ x^2 \times \dfrac{-5}{2}(x^2 + y^2 + z^2)^{-7/2}\,2x + 2x\,(x^2 + y^2 + z^2)^{-5/2} \right\}$

$+ \hat{j}\left\{ x^2 \times \dfrac{-5}{2}(x^2 + y^2 + z^2)^{-7/2}\,2y \right\} + \hat{k}\left\{ x^2 \times \dfrac{-5}{2}(x^2 + y^2 + z^2)^{-7/2}\,2z \right\}$

$= \dfrac{6x\hat{i}}{(x^2 + y^2 + z^2)^{5/2}} - \dfrac{15x^3\,\hat{i}}{(x^2 + y^2 + z^2)^{7/2}} - \dfrac{15x^2\,y\hat{j}}{(x^2 + y^2 + z^2)^{7/2}} - \dfrac{15x^2\,z\hat{k}}{(x^2 + y^2 \, z^2)^{7/2}}$

$= \dfrac{6x\hat{i}}{r^5} - \dfrac{15x^2(x\hat{i} + y\hat{j} + z\hat{k})}{r^7}$

$= \dfrac{6x\hat{i}}{r^5} - \dfrac{15x^2\,\vec{r}}{r^7}$

and $\quad \vec{\nabla}\left[\dfrac{1}{(x^2 + y^2 + z^2)^{3/2}} \right] = \hat{i}\dfrac{\partial}{\partial x}(x^2 + y^2 + z^2)^{-3/2}$

$+ \hat{j}\dfrac{\partial}{\partial y}(x^2 + y^2 + z^2)^{-3/2} + \hat{k}\dfrac{\partial}{\partial z}(x^2 + y^2 + z^2)^{-3/2}$

$= -\dfrac{3}{2}(x^2 + y^2 + z^2)^{-5/2}\,2x\hat{i} - \dfrac{3}{2}(x^2 + y^2 + z^2)^{-5/2}\,2y\hat{j} - \dfrac{3}{2}(x^2 + y^2 + z^2)^{-5/2}\,2z\hat{k}$

$= -\dfrac{3(x\hat{i} + y\hat{j} + z\hat{k})}{(x^2 + y^2 + z^2)^{5/2}}$

$= -\dfrac{3\vec{r}}{r^5}$

Substituting these values in Eq. (ii), we have

$$\vec{E} = -\dfrac{ql^2}{4\pi\varepsilon_0}\left[\dfrac{6x\hat{i}}{r^5} - \dfrac{15x^2\,\vec{r}}{r^7} + \dfrac{3\vec{r}}{r^5} \right]$$

$$= \dfrac{-q}{4\pi\varepsilon_0}\left[\dfrac{6l^2\,x\hat{i}}{r^5} - \dfrac{15l^2\,x^2\,\vec{r}}{r^7} + \dfrac{3l^2\,\vec{r}}{r^5} \right]$$

Now $lx = \vec{r}\cdot\vec{l}$ and $l\hat{i} = \vec{l}$

$\therefore \qquad\qquad \vec{E} = \dfrac{-q}{4\pi\varepsilon_0}\left[\dfrac{6\,(\vec{r}\cdot\vec{l})\,\vec{l}}{r^5} - \dfrac{15\,(\vec{r}\cdot\vec{l})^2\,\vec{r}}{r^7} + \dfrac{3l^2\,\vec{r}}{r^5} \right]$

Q. 4.39. (*a*) **A conductor is placed in an electric field. Show that**

(*i*) **The electric field inside the conductor is zero and there is no volume charge density.**

(*ii*) **The electric potential is constant throughout the body of the conductor and on the surface.** (*G.N.D.U., 2002*)

(*b*) **Find the net charge in a region where electric field is uniform.** (*G.N.D.U., 2004*)

Ans. (*a*) **Conductor in an electric field.** Suppose an electrically neutral conductor AB is placed in an external electric field E_{ext} directed from A to B. This field will exert forces on the positively charged ions and negatively charged free electrons which constitute the conducting material. The positive ions being massive remain almost fixed in their respective position and the free electrons move under the influence of the external field from B to A in a direction opposite to that of the field. The electrons, therefore, collect at the end A thereby inducing a negative charge at this end because of the collection of electrons and a positive charge at the end B because of a deficiency of free electrons there. Although the conductor, on the whole is still neutral, it appears to be charged with negative charge at one end and positive charge at the other end. The charge distribution which develops on the surface of a conductor when it is placed in an external electric field is

Fig. 4.24

called *induced charge distribution*. This induced charge distribution sets up an electric field E_{int} in a direction opposite to external electric field. The process will stop and an equilibrium stage will be reached when $E_{int} = E_{ext}$. At this stage *the net electric field inside the conductor E = 0*.

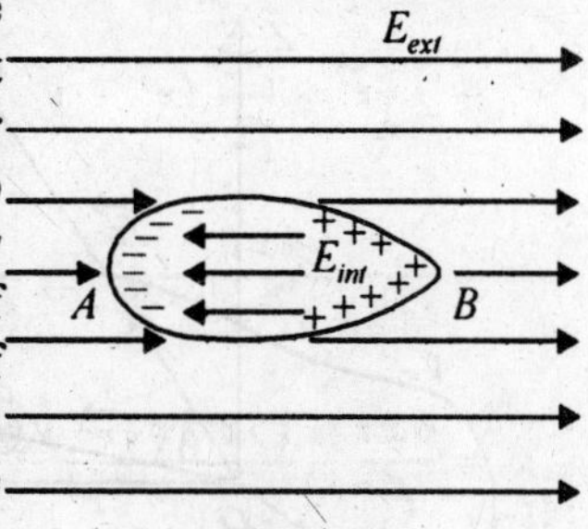

(*i*) According to differential from of Gauss's theorem

$$\vec{\nabla}.\vec{E} = \frac{\rho}{\varepsilon_0}$$

As $\qquad\qquad\qquad \vec{E} = 0, \vec{\nabla}.\vec{E} = 0$

∴ Within the conductor $\dfrac{\rho}{\varepsilon_0} = 0$ or $\rho = 0$

Hence *there is no volume charge density inside the conductor*. In other words, the induced charge distribution is only a surface charge distribution.

(*ii*) Further, electric field $\vec{E} = -\vec{\nabla}\phi$ where ϕ is the electric potential.

Hence $-\vec{\nabla}\phi = 0$ or $\phi = $ a constant

Thus *the potential is a constant throughout the body and on the surface of the conductor i.e.,* the surface of a conductor is an *equipotential surface*.

(*b*) According to differential form of Gauss's theorm $\vec{\nabla}.\vec{E} = \dfrac{\rho}{\varepsilon_0}$, where ρ is the charge density.

When electric field is uniform, $\vec{E}$ is a constant. Therefore $\vec{\nabla}.\vec{E} = 0$, and hence $\rho = 0$. Thus the net charge in a region where electric field is uniform, is zero.

Q. 4.40. Prove that the electric potential due to an arbitrary charge distribution is given by

$$\frac{1}{4\pi\varepsilon_0}\left[\frac{K_1}{r} + \frac{K_2}{r^2} + \frac{K_3}{r^3} + ...\right]$$

where r is the distance of the observation point, K_1, K_2, K_3 ..... are the moments of monopole, dipole, quadrupole ..... respectively. Show that potential due to quadrupole varies inversely as cube of the distance.

    Hence define electric multipole. (multipole moments)

                                       (Pbi. U., 2007, 2006; Meerut. U., 2007; P.U., 2009, 2001, 2000;

                                   H.P.U., 2007, 2001; G.N.D.U., 2008, 2007, 1994; Luck. U., 1993)

    Ans. Potential due to a continuous charge distribution. In the study of Physics we come across

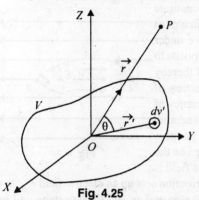

atoms and molecules which consist of some electric charges occupying a *small* volume (1 cubic angstrom $= 10^{-30}$ m^3). To find the electric potential due to such a charge distribution at a far off point consider a point P at a *large* distance from the origin O having a position vector $\vec{r}$. Let a localised charge distribution extend to a small volume V around the origin. Now consider a very small element of volume dv' at a vector distance $\vec{r'}$ from the origin and let $\rho\,(x', y', z')$ represent the charge density in the element dv'.

Fig. 4.25

    ∴ Charge in the volume element $dv' = dq = \rho\,dv'$

Potential at P due to the charge in the elementary volume dv'

$$= \frac{1}{4\pi\varepsilon_0}\frac{dq}{|\vec{r}-\vec{r'}|} = \frac{1}{4\pi\varepsilon_0}\frac{\rho(x',y',z')\,dv'}{|\vec{r}-\vec{r'}|}$$

where $|\vec{r}-\vec{r'}|$ is the magnitude of the distance of the point P from the element of volume dv'. Hence potential at P due to the whole charge distribution

$$\phi = \frac{1}{4\pi\varepsilon_0}\iiint_V \frac{\rho\,(x',y',z')}{|\vec{r}-\vec{r'}|}\,dv' \qquad\qquad ...(i)$$

But $|\vec{r}-\vec{r'}|^2 = (\vec{r}-\vec{r'}) \cdot (\vec{r}-\vec{r'}) = r^2 + r'^2 - 2\vec{r}\cdot\vec{r'}$

and $\vec{r}\cdot\vec{r'} = r\,r'\cos\theta$ where θ is the angle between $\vec{r}$ and $\vec{r'}$

∴ $|\vec{r}-\vec{r'}| = (r^2 + r'^2 - 2r\,r'\cos\theta)^{1/2}$

Denoting $\rho\,(x', y', z')$ by ρ only, we have from (i)

$$\phi = \frac{1}{4\pi\varepsilon_0}\iiint_V \rho\,dv'\,[r^2 + r'^2 - 2\,r\,r'\cos\theta]^{-1/2}$$

$$= \frac{1}{4\pi\varepsilon_0}\iiint_V \rho\,dv'\left[1 + \frac{r'^2}{r^2} - \frac{2r'}{r}\cos\theta\right]^{-1/2}$$

    For a very far off point $r' < r$

∴ $\dfrac{r'}{r} < 1$

∴ Using the expression

$$(1 + \delta)^{-1/2} = 1 - \frac{1}{2}\delta + \frac{3}{8}\delta^2 + \ldots\ldots, \text{ we have}$$

$$\left[1 + \left(\frac{r'^2}{r^2} - \frac{2r'}{r}\cos\theta\right)\right]^{-1/2} = 1 - \frac{1}{2}\left(\frac{r'}{r}\right)^2 + \frac{r'}{r}\cos\theta + \frac{3}{8}\left(\frac{2r'}{r}\right)^2\cos^2\theta + \text{terms containing}$$

higher powers of $\left(\frac{r'}{r}\right)$

$$= 1 + \frac{r'}{r}\cos\theta + \left(\frac{r'}{r}\right)^2 \cdot \frac{3\cos^2\theta - 1}{2} + \ldots\ldots$$

$$\therefore \quad \phi = \frac{1}{4\pi\varepsilon_0 r}\iiint_V \rho\, dv' + \frac{1}{4\pi\varepsilon_0 r^2}\iiint_V r'\cos\theta\, \rho\, dv'$$

$$+ \frac{1}{4\pi\varepsilon_0 r^3}\iiint_V r'^2 \frac{3\cos^2\theta - 1}{2}\rho\, dv' + \ldots \quad \ldots(ii)$$

or
$$\phi = \frac{K_1}{4\pi\varepsilon_0 r} + \frac{K_2}{4\pi\varepsilon_0 r^2} + \frac{K_3}{4\pi\varepsilon_0 r^3} + \ldots\ldots$$

$$= \phi_1 + \phi_2 + \phi_3 + \ldots\ldots \quad \ldots(iii)$$

where
$$K_1 = \iiint_V \rho\, dv'$$

$$K_2 = \iiint_V r'\,\rho\, dv'\cos\theta$$

$$K_3 = \iiint_V r'^2\,\rho\, dv'\frac{(3\cos^2\theta - 1)}{2}$$

Monopole moment. The first term of equation (iii) $\phi_1 = \frac{1}{4\pi\varepsilon_0}\frac{K_1}{r}$

where $K_1 = \iiint_V \rho\, dv' = q = $ The total charge of the distribution.

$$\therefore \quad \phi_1 = \frac{1}{4\pi\varepsilon_0}\frac{q}{r} \quad \ldots(iv)$$

This is the potential which would result if the entire charge of the distribution were concentrated at the origin. The quantity $\iiint_V \rho\, dv' = q$ the net charge is known as the *monopole moment* of the charge distribution. The potential which varies as $\frac{1}{r}$ is known as *monopole potential*. If we have equal amounts of positive and negative charges as in a *neutral* molecule $q = 0$. Whenever q is not equal to zero, as in a singly ionised molecule, the first term is the most dominant term and at sufficiently large distances, the potential (and field) are the same as due to a *point* charge at the origin.

Dipole moment. When $q = 0$ there is no contribution to potential and field by the first term. The second term in Eq. (*iii*),

$$\phi_2 = \frac{1}{4\pi\varepsilon_0} \frac{K_2}{r^2}$$

or

$$\phi_2 = \frac{1}{4\pi\varepsilon_0 r^2} \iiint_V r' \cos\theta \, \rho \, dv'$$

$$= \frac{1}{4\pi\varepsilon_0 r^2} \iiint_V \frac{\vec{r}.\vec{r'}}{r} \rho \, dv'$$

$$= \frac{1}{4\pi\varepsilon_0 r^3} \iiint_V \vec{r}.\vec{r'} \, \rho \, dv' \qquad \qquad ...(v)$$

The electric potential at any point having position vector $\vec{r}$ due to a dipole of dipole moment $\vec{P}$ is given by

$$\phi = \frac{1}{4\pi\varepsilon_0} \frac{\vec{r}.\vec{p}}{r^3} \qquad \qquad ...(vi)$$

Comparing Eq. (*vi*) and Eq. (*v*), we have

$$\iiint_V \vec{r'} \, \rho \, dv' = \vec{p}$$

and

$$\phi_2 = \frac{1}{4\pi\varepsilon_0} \frac{\vec{r}.\vec{p}}{r^3}$$

$$= \frac{1}{4\pi\varepsilon_0} \frac{\hat{r}.\vec{p}}{r^2} \qquad \qquad \left(\text{where } \hat{r} = \frac{\vec{r}}{r} \right)$$

The quantity $\iiint_V \vec{r'} \, \rho \, dv = \vec{p}$ is known as the *dipole moment* of the charge distribution. It is a *vector* quantity and has the dimensions of charge × displacement. The potential due to the second term is known as *dipole potential*. It varies as $\frac{1}{r^2}$ and is given by

$$\phi_2 = \frac{1}{4\pi\varepsilon_0} \frac{\hat{r}.\vec{p}}{r^2} = \frac{1}{4\pi\varepsilon_0} \frac{\vec{r}.\vec{p}}{r^3}$$

As $\vec{p} = \iiint_V \rho \, dv'$ the value of *dipole moment* depends upon the distribution of charge in the volume V and origin of the co-ordinate system.

Quadrupole moment. The third term in Eq. (*iii*) is

$$\phi_3 = \frac{1}{4\pi\varepsilon_0} \frac{K_3}{r^3}$$

where

$$K_3 = \iiint_V r'^2 \, \rho \, dv' \frac{(3\cos^2\theta - 1)}{2}$$

$$\therefore \qquad \phi_3 = \frac{1}{4\pi\varepsilon_0 \, r^3} \iiint_V r'^2 \, \rho \, dv' \frac{(3 \cos^2\theta - 1)}{2}$$

The quantity within the integrals is called *quadrupole moment*. The potential due to quadrupole moment varies as $\frac{1}{r^3}$ and is known as *quadrupole potential i.e.*, the potential due to a quadrupole moment varies inversely as the cube of the distance.

Thus it follows from Eq. (*iii*) that *the potential at any point due to an arbitrary charge distribution is the sum of the potentials due to monopole, dipole, quadrupole and so on moments all assumed to be placed at the origin.*

Multipole moment. We have seen that the terms K_1, K_2, K_3 .... etc. in equation (*iii*) are known as monopole, dipole, and quadrupole etc. moments of the continuous charge distribution. All these taken together are known as *multipole* moments of the charge distribution.

Q. 4.41. Show that the dipole moment of an arbitrary charge distribution is independent of the choice of the origin if monopole moment of the charge distribution vanishes.

Ans. Dipole moment is independent of the choice of origin when monopole moment vanishes.

When the monopole moment of a charge distribution vanishes *i.e.*, $\iiint_V \rho \, dv' = 0$ the value of

dipole moment is independent of the position of the origin as proved below.

The dipole moment of an arbitrary charge distribution having its origin at O is given by

$$\vec{p} = \iiint_V \vec{r'} \, \rho \, dv'$$

where ρ is the charge density in a small volume element dv' situated at the position vector $\vec{r'}$.

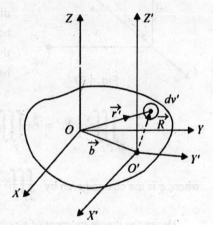

Consider a new co-ordinate system with origin O' at position vector $\vec{b}$ with respect to O. Let $\vec{R}$ be the position vector of the charge element $\rho \, dv'$ with respect to O' then

$$\vec{b} + \vec{R} = \vec{r'} \quad \text{or} \quad \vec{R} = \vec{r'} - \vec{b}$$

Fig. 4.26

The dipole moment of the charge distribution with respect to O' is given by $\vec{p'} = \iiint_V \vec{R} \, \rho \, dv'$

$$\therefore \qquad \vec{p'} = \iiint_V (\vec{r'} - \vec{b}) \, \rho \, dv' = \iiint_V \vec{r'} \, \rho \, dv' - \vec{b} \iiint_V \rho \, dv'$$

$$= \vec{p} - \vec{b} \, K_1$$

where $K_1 = \iiint_V \rho \, dv'$ is the *monopole moment* of the charge distribution.

Thus the value of dipole moment depends upon the choice of the origin O.

When the total charge in the distribution is zero. The monopole moment of the charge distribution vanishes. Thus

$$\iiint_V \rho \, dv' = K_1 = 0 \text{ and}$$

$$\therefore \qquad \vec{p}' = \vec{p}$$

i.e., the dipole moment of charge distribution is independent of the origin of the co-ordinate system if the monopole moment vanishes or total charge in the distribution is zero.

Q. 4.42. (a) Find the dipole moment of a point charge.

(b) Three charges + 1.5 q, + 1.5 q and – 3 q are placed at the vertices of an equilateral triangle of side b. Find the dipole moment of the charge distribution.   (G.N.D.U., 1999)

Ans. (a) Dipole moment of a point charge. The dipole moment of a small charge distribution in a volume V about the origin is given by

$$p = \iiint_V \vec{r}' \rho \, dv'$$

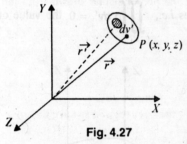

Fig. 4.27

where ρ is the charge density at a point having a radial distance $\vec{r}'$ within an infinitesimally small volume dv'. As the charge distribution becomes smaller and smaller, the charge density becomes larger and larger if the total charge is kept constant. In the limit when the total charge is concentrated on a point say P having a distance $\vec{r}$ from the origin, then $\vec{r}$ can be taken to be a constant and

$$\vec{p} = \iiint_V \vec{r}' \rho \, dv' = \vec{r} \iiint_V \rho \, dv' = \vec{r} q$$

where q is the charge given by $\iiint_V \rho \, dv'$

Hence the dipole moment of a point charge q at a radial distance $\vec{r}$ is given by

$$\vec{p} = r q$$

If the cartesian co-ordinates of the point P are x, y, z, then the dipole moment vector will have components p_x, p_y, p_z along X, Y, and Z-axis respectively, given by

$$\vec{p_x} = xq \, \hat{i}, \ \vec{p_y} = yq \, \hat{j} \text{ and } \vec{p_z} = zq \, \hat{k}.$$

(b) Let the charges + 1.5 q, + 1.5 q and – 3 q be placed at the corners of an equilateral triangle ABC as shown. From A draw AO perpendicular to BC and let O be the origin of the co-ordinate system so that OC represents the + X axis, and OB the – X axis and OA the + Y axis.

Since each side of the triangle is b, $OC = \dfrac{b}{2}$, $OB = \dfrac{b}{2}$

and $OA = b \sin 60° = \dfrac{b}{2} \sqrt{3}$

The co-ordinates of the points A, B, C, therefore are $\left(0, \dfrac{\sqrt{3}}{2}b\right)\left(-\dfrac{b}{2}, 0\right)$ and $\left(+\dfrac{b}{2}, 0\right)$ respectively.

As the algebraic sum of all the charges is zero, the monopole moment = 0.

To find the dipole moment $\vec{p}$ we shall calculate the x and y components $\vec{P_x}$ and $\vec{P_y}$ separately.

$$\therefore \qquad \vec{P_x} = \left[+1.5q\left(\frac{b}{2}\right) + 1.5q\left(-\frac{b}{2}\right) - 3q\,(0)\right]\hat{i} = 0$$

and
$$\vec{P_y} = \left[+1.5q\,(0) + 1.5q\,(0) - 3q\left(\frac{\sqrt{3}}{2}b\right)\right]\hat{j}$$

$$= -3\,\frac{\sqrt{3}}{2}\,qb\,\hat{j}$$

$$\therefore \qquad \vec{P} = \vec{P_y} = -\frac{3\sqrt{3}}{2}\,qb\,\hat{j}$$

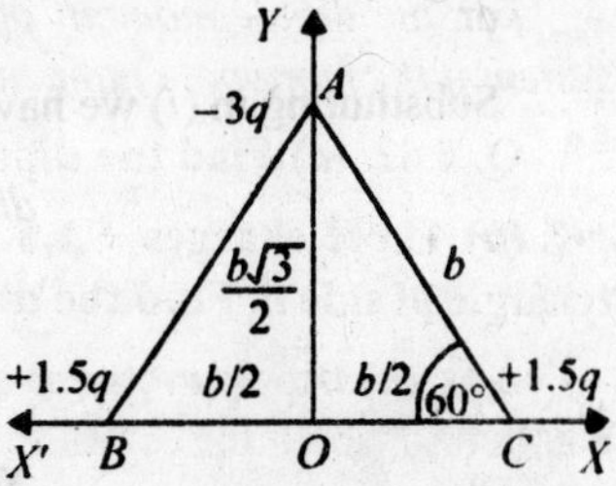

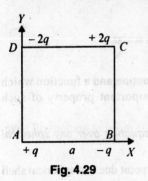

Fig. 4.28

i.e., the dipole moment acts away from the point A along the perpendicular drawn from the charge $-3q$ on the line joining the charges $+1.5q$ and $+1.5\,q$.

Exercise. *Electric charges, q, q, and 2q are placed at the corners of an equilateral triangle ABC of side 1. Find the resultant electric dipole moment of the system.*   (P.U. 2008)

Ans.
$$\vec{P} = \sqrt{3}\,q\,\hat{j}$$

Q. 4.43. Four charges $+q, -q, +2q$ and $-2q$ are located at the corners of a square of side a. Find (*i*) Monopole moment (*ii*) Electric dipole moment of charge distribution.   (P.U., 2002)

Ans. Let the charges $+q, -q, +2q$ and $-2q$ be placed at the corners A, B, C and D of the square. Let A be the origin of the co-ordinate system, AB the X-axis and AD the Y-axis. As the algebraic sum of all the charges is zero, the monopole moment = 0.

To find the dipole moment $\vec{P}$ we shall calculate the x and y components $\vec{P_x}$ and $\vec{P_y}$ separately. The co-ordinates of the points A, B, C, D are $[0, 0]$, $[a, 0]$, $[a, a]$ and $[0, a]$ respectively.

$$\therefore \qquad \vec{P_x} = +q \times 0 + (-q \times a) + 2q \times a + (-2q \times 0)$$

$$= q\,a$$

and
$$\vec{P_y} = +q \times 0 + (-q \times 0) + 2q \times a + (-2q \times a)$$

$$= 0$$

$$\therefore \qquad \vec{P} = \vec{P_x} = qa\,\hat{i}$$

Fig. 4.29

i.e., the dipole moment acts along the $+X$ axis.

Q. 4.44. (*a*) **From the differential form of Gauss's law develop the Poisson's and Laplace's equation and define Laplacian operator.**

(*b*) **What is the value of $\nabla^2\phi$ at a point in empty space? What is the significance of Laplace's equation?**

(*Pbi.U.*, 2003, 2002, 2001, 2000, 1999; *H.P.U.*, 2007, 2003, 2001, 2000, 1999, 1997; *P.U.*, 2007, 2006, 2003, 2002, 2000, 1995; *G.N.D.U.*, 2007, 2004, 2003, 1999, 1997; *M.D.U.*, 1999; *Kerala U.*, 2001; *K.U.*, 2001, 1996; *Nagpur U.*, 2001)

Ans. (*a*) **Poisson's equation.** The differential form of Gauss's law states

$$\vec{\nabla} . \vec{E} = \frac{\rho}{\varepsilon_0}$$

(In S.I. units)

where $\vec{E}$ is the electric field intensity and ρ the volume density of charge.

The electric field at a point is given by the negative gradient of electric potential ϕ.

or

$$\vec{E} = -\ grad\ \phi = -\vec{\nabla}\phi$$

Substituting in (*i*) we have

$$div\ \vec{E} = \vec{\nabla} . \vec{E} = \vec{\nabla} . (-\vec{\nabla}\phi)$$

$$= -\nabla^2\phi = \frac{\rho}{\varepsilon_0}$$

or

$$\nabla^2\phi = -\frac{\rho}{\varepsilon_0}$$

or

$$\left(\frac{\partial^2\phi}{\partial x^2} + \frac{\partial^2\phi}{\partial y^2} + \frac{\partial^2\phi}{\partial z^2}\right) = -\frac{\rho}{\varepsilon_0}$$

This is Poisson's equation which holds good for each point in space.

Laplace's equation. When the enclosed charge density is zero, *i.e.*, the point of observation is in empty space $\rho = 0$ and we get

$$\nabla^2\phi = 0$$

or

$$\frac{\partial^2\phi}{\partial x^2} + \frac{\partial^2\phi}{\partial y^2} + \frac{\partial^2\phi}{\partial z^2} = 0$$

This is Laplace's equation.

Laplacian operator. The operator $div\ grad = \nabla^2$ is known as Laplacian operator.

Thus $div\ grad\ \phi = \vec{\nabla} . \vec{\nabla}\phi = \nabla^2\phi$

where ϕ is a scalar function, $grad\ \phi$ is a vector but $div\ grad\ \phi$ is again a scalar.

(*b*) The value of $\nabla^2\phi$ in empty space $(\rho = 0) = 0$.

Significance. Laplace's equation is an important differential equation and a function which satisfies this equation is known as *spherical harmonic*. A very important property of such function is

"*The average value of a function ϕ (x y z) satisfying Laplace's equation over any spherical surface is equal to its value at the centre of the spherical surface*".

We have already seen that the electric potential and intensity at any point due to a spherical shell of charge is the same as if the whole charge were concentrated at its centre.

Exercise. *Derive and name the equation* $\nabla^2 V = -\dfrac{\rho}{\varepsilon_0}$ (*Pbi. U.*, 2006)

Hint. For derivation of $\nabla^2 V = -\dfrac{\rho}{\varepsilon_0}$ see part (*a*) where ϕ has been used for V. This is Poisson's equation.

Q. 4.45. Write Laplace's equation in Cartesian co-ordinates and find its solution.

Ans. Laplace's equation in Cartesian co-ordinates

Laplace's equation in Cartesian co-ordinates is

$$\nabla^2\phi = \frac{\partial^2\phi}{\partial x^2} + \frac{\partial^2\phi}{\partial y^2} + \frac{\partial^2\phi}{\partial z^2} = 0 \qquad \ldots (i)$$

From this equation we find that the potential function ϕ is a function of x, y and z co-ordinates. Therefore, we can put

$$\phi = X(x)\, Y(y)\, Z(z) = XYZ$$

where $X(x)$ or X is a function of only x co-ordinate $Y(y)$ or Y a function of only y co-ordinate and $Z(z)$ or Z a function of only z co-ordinate.

$$\therefore \qquad \phi = XYZ$$

From this equation we get

$$\frac{\partial\phi}{\partial x} = YZ\frac{\partial X}{\partial x}$$

and

$$\frac{\partial^2\phi}{\partial x^2} = YZ\frac{\partial^2 X}{\partial x^2}$$

Similarly $\dfrac{\partial\phi}{\partial y} = XZ\dfrac{\partial Y}{\partial y}$ and $\dfrac{\partial^2\phi}{\partial y^2} = XZ\dfrac{\partial^2 Y}{\partial y^2}$ and $\dfrac{\partial\phi}{\partial z} = XY\dfrac{\partial Z}{\partial y}$ and $\dfrac{\partial^2\phi}{\partial z^2} = XY\dfrac{\partial^2 Z}{\partial y^2}$

Substituting these values of $\dfrac{\partial^2\phi}{\partial x^2}, \dfrac{\partial^2\phi}{\partial y^2}$ and $\dfrac{\partial^2\phi}{\partial z^2}$ in Eq. (*i*), we get

$$YZ\frac{\partial^2 X}{\partial x^2} + XZ\frac{\partial^2 Y}{\partial y^2} + XY\frac{\partial^2 Z}{\partial z^2} = 0$$

Dividing by XYZ, we get

$$\frac{1}{X}\frac{\partial^2 X}{\partial x^2} + \frac{1}{Y}\frac{\partial^2 Y}{\partial y^2} + \frac{1}{Z}\frac{\partial^2 Z}{\partial z^2} = 0 \qquad \ldots (ii)$$

In equation (*ii*), the first term is only a function of x, the second term only a function of y and the last term only a function of z.

Therefore, each term should be equal to a constant quantity. Suppose

$$\frac{1}{X}\frac{\partial^2 X}{\partial x^2} = -k_1^2 \qquad \text{or} \qquad \frac{\partial^2 X}{\partial x^2} + k_1^2 X = 0 \qquad \ldots (iii)$$

$$\frac{1}{Y}\frac{\partial^2 Y}{\partial y^2} = -k_2^2 \qquad \text{or} \qquad \frac{\partial^2 Y}{\partial y^2} + k_2^2 Y = 0 \qquad \ldots (iv)$$

and

$$\frac{1}{Z}\frac{\partial^2 Z}{\partial z^2} = -k_3^2 \qquad \text{or} \qquad \frac{\partial^2 Z}{\partial z^2} + k_3^2 Z = 0 \qquad \ldots (v)$$

From Eq. (*iii*)

$$X = e^{\pm i k_1 x}$$

From Eq. (*iv*) $Y = e^{\pm i k_2 y}$

and from Eq. (*v*) $Z = e^{\pm i k_3 z}$

Hence the complete solution of equation (*i*) would be

$$\phi = \text{a constant} \left[X(x)Y(y)Z(z) \right]$$

$$= CXYZ \text{ where } C \text{ is the constant}$$

$$= C\, e^{\pm i k_1 x} \, e^{\pm i k_2 y} \, e^{\pm i k_3 z}$$

$$= C\, e^{\pm i (k_1 x + k_2 y + k_3 z)}$$

Q. 4.46. State Laplace's equation in spherical co-ordinates and find its complete solution.

Ans. Laplace's equation in spherical co-ordinates. Laplace's equation in spherical co-ordinates is

$$\frac{1}{r^2}\frac{\partial}{\partial r}\left(r^2\frac{\partial V}{\partial r}\right) + \frac{1}{r^2 \sin\theta}\frac{\partial}{\partial\theta}\left(\sin\theta\frac{\partial V}{\partial\theta}\right) + \frac{1}{r^2 \sin^2\theta}\frac{\partial^2 V}{\partial\phi^2} = 0 \qquad \ldots (i)$$

Note : In spherical co-ordinates, since ϕ is one of the co-ordinates of the system, the potential function ϕ is replaced by potential function V.

From this equation, we find that potential function V is a function of r, θ and ϕ co-ordinates. Therefore, we can put

$$V = R\,(r)\,\textcircled{H}(\theta)\ \Phi\,(\phi) = R\textcircled{H}\Phi$$

where $R(r)$ or R is a function of only co-ordinate r, $\textcircled{H}$ (θ) or $\textcircled{H}$ a function of only co-ordinate θ and Φ (ϕ) or ϕ a function of only co-ordinate ϕ.

$$\therefore \qquad V = R\,\textcircled{H}\,\Phi$$

From this equation, we get

$$\frac{\partial V}{\partial r} = \textcircled{H}\,\Phi\,\frac{\partial R}{\partial r}$$

$$\frac{\partial V}{\partial\theta} = R\,\Phi\,\frac{\partial\textcircled{H}}{\partial\theta}$$

$$\frac{\partial V}{\partial\phi} = R\textcircled{H}\,\frac{\partial\Phi}{\partial\phi}$$

and $$\frac{\partial^2 V}{\partial\phi^2} = R\textcircled{H}\,\frac{\partial_2\Phi}{\partial\phi^2}$$

Substituting these values in Eq. (*i*), we get

$$\frac{1}{r^2}\frac{\partial}{\partial r}\left(r^2\textcircled{H}\,\Phi\,\frac{\partial R}{\partial r}\right) + \frac{1}{r^2 \sin\theta}\frac{\partial}{\partial\theta}\left(\sin\theta R\Phi\,\frac{\partial\textcircled{H}}{\partial\theta}\right) + \frac{1}{r^2 \sin^2\theta}\left(R\textcircled{H}\,\frac{\partial^2\Phi}{\partial\phi^2}\right) = 0$$

Multiplying by $\dfrac{r^2 \sin^2 \theta}{R \, \textcircled{H} \, \Phi}$, we get

$$\frac{\sin^2 \theta}{R} \frac{\partial}{\partial r}\left(r^2 \frac{\partial R}{\partial r}\right) + \frac{\sin \theta}{\textcircled{H}} \frac{\partial}{\partial \theta}\left(\sin \Theta \frac{\partial \textcircled{H}}{\partial \theta}\right) + \frac{1}{\Phi} \frac{\partial^2 \Phi}{\partial \phi^2} = 0 \qquad \ldots (ii)$$

The last part of Eq. (ii) is only a function of ϕ. To solve this equation, put

$$\frac{1}{\Phi} \frac{\partial^2 \Phi}{\partial \phi^2} = \text{a constant} = -m^2$$

$\therefore$

$$\frac{\partial^2 \Phi}{\partial \phi^2} + m^2 \Phi = 0$$

The general solution of this equation is

$$\Phi = \text{a constant } e^{\pm im\phi} = C_1 \, e^{\pm im\phi} \qquad \ldots (iii)$$

Substituting the value of $\quad \dfrac{1}{\Phi} \dfrac{\partial^2 \Phi}{\partial \phi^2} = -m^2$ in Eq. (ii), we get

$$\frac{\sin^2 \theta}{R} \frac{\partial}{\partial r}\left(r^2 \frac{\partial R}{dr}\right) + \frac{\sin \theta}{\textcircled{H}} \frac{\partial}{\partial \theta}\left(\sin \theta \frac{\partial \textcircled{H}}{\partial \theta}\right) - m^2 = 0 \qquad \ldots (iv)$$

Dividing by $\sin^2\theta$, we get

$$\frac{1}{R} \frac{\partial}{\partial r}\left(r^2 \frac{\partial R}{\partial r}\right) + \frac{1}{\sin \theta \, \textcircled{H}} \frac{\partial}{\partial \theta}\left(\sin \theta \frac{\partial \textcircled{H}}{\partial \theta}\right) - \frac{1}{\sin^2 \theta} m^2 = 0 \qquad \ldots (v)$$

Now, put

$$\frac{1}{R} \frac{\partial}{\partial r}\left(r^2 \frac{\partial R}{\partial r}\right) = n(n+1)$$

Then Eq. (v) becomes

$$n(n+1) + \frac{1}{\sin \theta \, \textcircled{H}} \frac{\partial}{\partial \theta}\left(\sin \theta \frac{\partial \textcircled{H}}{\partial \theta}\right) - \frac{1}{\sin^2 \theta} m^2 = 0$$

Multiplying by $\textcircled{H}$ and rearranging, we get

$$\frac{1}{\sin \theta} \frac{\partial}{\partial \theta}\left(\sin \theta \frac{\partial \textcircled{H}}{\partial \theta}\right) + \left[n(n+1) - \frac{m^2}{\sin^2 \theta}\right]\textcircled{H} = 0 \qquad \ldots (vi)$$

To solve Eq. (vi), put $\cos \theta = x$

Then

$$-\sin \theta = \frac{\partial x}{\partial \theta}$$

or
$$-\frac{\partial}{\partial x}\sin\theta = \frac{\partial}{\partial x}\frac{\partial x}{\partial\theta} = \frac{\partial}{\partial\theta}$$

Substituting this value of $\frac{\partial}{\partial\theta}$ in Eq. (vi), we get

$$\frac{1}{\sin\theta}\left(-\frac{\partial}{\partial x}\sin^2\theta\right)\frac{\partial H}{\partial\theta} + \left[n(n+1) - \frac{m^2}{1-x^2}\right]H = 0$$

or
$$\frac{1}{\sin\theta}\left\{\left[-\frac{\partial}{\partial x}\sin^2\theta\right]\left[-\frac{\partial H}{\partial x}\sin\Theta\right]\right\} + \left[n(n+1) - \frac{m^2}{1-x^2}\right]H = 0$$

or
$$\left[\frac{\partial}{\partial x}(1-x^2)\frac{\partial H}{\partial x}\right] + \left[n(n+1) - \frac{m^2}{1-x^2}\right]H = 0 \qquad \text{... (vii)}$$

This equation is associated Legendre's equation of which the solution is

$$H = (1-x^2)^{m/2}\frac{d^m[P_n(x)]}{dx^m} \qquad \text{... (viii)}$$

where $P_n(x)$ is Legendre's polynomial defined by the relation

$$P_n(x) = \frac{1}{2^n n!}\left(\frac{d}{dx}\right)^n (x^2-1)^n$$

Legendre's polynomials for $n = 0, 1, 2, 3$ etc are given below

$n = 0$ $\qquad\qquad\qquad\qquad$ $P_0(x) = 1$

$n = 1;$ $\qquad\qquad\qquad\qquad$ $P_1(x) = x$

$n = 2;$ $\qquad\qquad\qquad\qquad$ $P_2(x) = (3x^2 - 1)/2$

$n = 3;$ $\qquad\qquad\qquad\qquad$ $P_3(x) = (5x^3 - 3x)/2$

$n = 4;$ $\qquad\qquad\qquad\qquad$ $P_4(x) = (35x^4 - 30x^2 + 3)/8$

Substituting $x = \cos\theta$ in Eq. (viii), we get

$$H = (\sin^2\theta)^{m/2}\frac{d^m[P_n(\cos\theta)]}{d(\cos\theta)^m}$$

or
$$H = \sin^m\theta\frac{d^m[P_n(\cos\theta)]}{d(\cos\theta)^m} \qquad \text{... (ix)}$$

Now consider the equation

$$\frac{1}{R}\frac{\partial}{\partial r}\left(r^2\frac{\partial R}{\partial r}\right) = n(n+1)$$

or
$$\frac{\partial}{\partial r}\left(r^2\frac{\partial R}{\partial r}\right) - n(n+1)R = 0$$

or $\quad\quad\quad r^2\,\dfrac{\partial^2 R}{\partial r^2}+2r\,\dfrac{\partial R}{\partial r}-n(n+1)\,R\ =\ 0$ ... (x)

Put $\quad\quad\quad\quad r=e^z$ then $\quad\dfrac{\partial r}{\partial z}=e^z$

and

$$\dfrac{\partial R}{\partial r}=\dfrac{\partial R}{\partial z}\dfrac{\partial z}{\partial r}=\dfrac{\partial R}{\partial z}\,e^{-z}$$

$$=\dfrac{\partial R}{\partial z}\dfrac{1}{r}=\dfrac{1}{r}\dfrac{\partial R}{\partial z}$$

$\therefore\quad\quad\quad\quad r\,\dfrac{\partial R}{\partial r}=\dfrac{\partial R}{\partial z}$ ... (xi)

Also

$$\dfrac{\partial^2 R}{\partial r^2}=\dfrac{\partial}{\partial r}\left(\dfrac{\partial R}{\partial r}\right)=\dfrac{\partial}{\partial z}\dfrac{\partial z}{\partial r}\left(e^{-z}\dfrac{\partial R}{\partial z}\right)$$

$$=\dfrac{\partial}{\partial z}\left(e^{-z}\dfrac{\partial R}{\partial z}\right)\dfrac{\partial z}{\partial r}$$

$$=\left(e^{-z}\dfrac{\partial^2 R}{\partial z^2}-\dfrac{\partial R}{\partial z}e^{-z}\right)\dfrac{\partial z}{\partial r}$$

$$=\dfrac{1}{r}\left[\dfrac{\partial^2 R}{\partial z^2}-\dfrac{\partial R}{\partial z}\right]\dfrac{\partial z}{\partial r}$$

$$=\dfrac{1}{r}\left[\dfrac{\partial^2 R}{\partial z^2}-\dfrac{\partial R}{\partial z}\right]\dfrac{1}{r}$$

$$=\dfrac{1}{r^2}\left[\dfrac{\partial^2 R}{\partial z^2}-\dfrac{\partial R}{\partial z}\right]$$

$\therefore\quad\quad\quad\quad r^2\,\dfrac{\partial^2 R}{\partial z^2}=\dfrac{\partial^2 R}{\partial z^2}-\dfrac{\partial R}{\partial z}$ ... (xii)

Substituting the value of $r^2\,\dfrac{\partial^2 R}{\partial r^2}$ and $r\,\dfrac{\partial R}{\partial r}$ from Equation (xii) and (xi) in Eq. (x), we get

$$\dfrac{\partial^2 R}{\partial z^2}-\dfrac{\partial R}{\partial z}+2\dfrac{\partial R}{\partial z}-n(n+1)R\ =\ 0$$

or $\quad\quad\quad\dfrac{\partial^2 R}{\partial z^2}+\dfrac{\partial R}{\partial z}-n(n+1)R\ =\ 0$ ... $(xiii)$

The solution of Eq. $(xiii)$ is given by

$$R=\ A_n\ e^{nz}+B_n\ e^{-(n+1)\,z}$$

or $\quad\quad\quad\quad R=\ A_n\ r^n+B_n\ r^{-(n+1)}$ ... (xiv)

The complete solution will be

$$V(r, \theta, \phi) = R\textcircled{H}\,\Phi$$

$$= \left(C_1,\ e^{\pm im\phi}\right)\frac{\left\{\sin^m\theta\, d^m\left[P_n(\cos\theta)\right]\right\}}{d\,(\cos\theta)^m}\left[A_n r^n + B_n r^{-(n+1)}\right] \qquad \ldots (xv)$$

The separation of variables yields an infinite set of solutions; one for each value of n. The general solution is the linear combination of separate solutions.

$$\therefore \qquad V(r, \theta, \phi) = \sum_{n=0}^{\infty}\left(C_1 e^{\pm im\phi}\right)\left[A_n r^n B_n r^{-(n+1)}\right]\left[\frac{\sin^m\theta\, d^m P_n(\cos\theta)}{d(\cos\theta)^m}\right]$$

In case of azimuthal symmetry, V is independent of ϕ i.e., $m = 0$ and

$$V(r, \theta) = \sum_{n=0}^{\infty}A_n r^n\, B_n r^{-(n+1)}\right]P_n(\cos\theta)$$

Q. 4.47. (a) What are the conditions under which potential in a conductor satisfies Laplace's equation?   *(G.N.D.U., 2004)*

(b) What is charge density in a region of space where electrostatic potential is given by

$$V = a - b\,(x^2 + y^2) - c\log(x^2 + y^2)\ ? \qquad \textit{(G.N.D.U., 1995)}$$

Ans. (a) According to Laplace's equation $\nabla^2\phi = 0$. The potential in a conductor satisfies this equation when charge density $\rho = 0$ i.e., it is a charge free or empty space.

(b) Accordint to Poisson's equation

$$\nabla^2 V = -\frac{\rho}{\varepsilon_0}$$

where V is the electrostatic potential (a scalar function) and ρ the volume charge density.

or $\vec{\nabla}\cdot(-\vec{\nabla}V) = \dfrac{\rho}{\varepsilon_0}$

Now $V = a - b\,(x^2 + y^2) - c\log(x^2 + y^2)$

and $\vec{\nabla} = \dfrac{\partial}{\partial x}\,\hat{i} + \dfrac{\partial}{\partial y}\,\hat{j} + \dfrac{\partial}{\partial z}\,\hat{k}$

$\therefore$ $\vec{\nabla}V = \dfrac{\partial V}{\partial x}\,\hat{i} + \dfrac{\partial V}{\partial y}\,\hat{j} + \dfrac{\partial V}{\partial z}\,\hat{k}$

Again $\dfrac{\partial V}{\partial x} = -\,2bx - \dfrac{2cx}{x^2 + y^2}$

$$\dfrac{\partial V}{\partial y} = -\,2by - \dfrac{2cy}{x^2 + y^2}$$

$$\dfrac{\partial V}{\partial z} = 0$$

$$\therefore \qquad -\vec{\nabla} V = \left(2bx + \frac{2cx}{x^2 + y^2}\right)\hat{i} + \left(2by + \frac{2cy}{x^2 + y^2}\right)\hat{j}$$

Hence
$$\vec{\nabla} . (-\vec{\nabla} V) = \left(\frac{\partial}{\partial x}\hat{i} + \frac{\partial}{\partial y}\hat{j} + \frac{\partial}{\partial z}\hat{k}\right).$$

$$\left[\left(2bx + \frac{2cx}{x^2 + y^2}\right)\hat{i} + \left(2by + \frac{2cy}{x^2 + y^2}\right)\hat{j}\right]$$

$$= \frac{\partial}{\partial x}\left(2bx + \frac{2cx}{x^2 + y^2}\right) + \frac{\partial}{\partial y}\left(2by + \frac{2cy}{x^2 + y^2}\right)$$

Also
$$\frac{\partial}{\partial x}(2bx) = 2b; \quad \frac{\partial}{\partial x}\left(\frac{2cx}{x^2 + y^2}\right) = \frac{2c}{x^2 + y^2} - \frac{4cx^2}{(x^2 + y^2)^2}$$

and
$$\frac{\partial}{\partial y}(2by) = 2b; \quad \frac{\partial}{\partial y}\left(\frac{2cy}{x^2 + y^2}\right) = \frac{2c}{x^2 + y^2} - \frac{4cy^2}{(x^2 + y^2)^2}$$

$$\therefore \qquad \vec{\nabla} . (-\vec{\nabla} V) = 4b + \frac{4c}{x^2 + y^2} - \frac{4c\,(x^2 + y^2)}{(x^2 + y^2)^2} = 4b$$

Hence
$$\frac{\rho}{\varepsilon_0} = 4b \text{ or } \rho = 4\varepsilon_0\, b$$

Q. 4.48. (*a*) **Evaluate $\nabla^2 \vec{r}$ where $\vec{r}$ is position vector.**   (*K.U., 2001*)

(*b*) **Prove that div. grad $r^m = \nabla^2 r^m = m\,(m+1)\,r^{m-2}$.**   (*Kan.U., 1997*)

Hence evaluate $\nabla^2 r$ where $r = \sqrt{x^2 + y^2 + z^2}$.   (*K.U., 1992*)

Ans. (*a*) Here
$$\vec{r} = x\hat{i} + y\hat{j} + z\hat{k}$$

$$\therefore \qquad |\vec{r}| = r = (x^2 + y^2 + z^2)^{1/2}$$

and

$$\nabla^2 \vec{r} = \nabla^2 r = \frac{\partial^2}{\partial x^2}(x^2 + y^2 + z^2)^{1/2} + \frac{\partial^2}{\partial y^2}(x^2 + y^2 + z^2)^{1/2} + \frac{\partial^2}{\partial z^2}(x^2 + y^2 + z^2)^{1/2}$$

Now

$$\frac{\partial^2}{\partial x^2}(x^2 + y^2 + z^2)^{1/2} = \frac{\partial}{\partial x}\left[\frac{\partial}{\partial x}(x^2 + y^2 + z^2)^{1/2}\right] = \frac{\partial}{\partial x}\left[\frac{1}{2}(x^2 + y^2 + z^2)^{-1/2}\,2x\right]$$

$$= \frac{\partial}{\partial x}\left[x\,(x^2 + y^2 + z^2)^{-1/2}\right] = x \times \frac{-1}{2}(x^2 + y^2 + z^2)^{-3/2}\,2x + (x^2 + y^2 + z^2)^{-1/2}$$

$$= -x^2\,(x^2 + y^2 + z^2)^{-3/2} + (x^2 + y^2 + z^2)^{-1/2}$$

Similarly $\dfrac{\partial^2}{\partial y^2}(x^2 + y^2 + z^2)^{1/2} = -y^2\,(x^2 + y^2 + z^2)^{-3/2} + (x^2 + y^2 + z^2)^{-1/2}$

and $\dfrac{\partial^2}{\partial z^2}(x^2 + y^2 + z^2)^{1/2} = -z^2\,(x^2 + y^2 + z^2)^{-3/2} + (x^2 + y^2 + z^2)^{-1/2}$

$$\therefore \qquad \nabla^2 r = -(x^2 + y^2 + z^2)(x^2 + y^2 + z^2)^{-3/2} + 3(x^2 + y^2 + z^2)^{-1/2}$$

$$= -(x^2 + y^2 + z^2)^{-1/2} + 3(x^2 + y^2 + z^2)^{-1/2}$$

$$= -\frac{1}{r} + \frac{3}{r} = \frac{2}{r}$$

(b) $div.\ grad\ r^m = \vec{\nabla}.\vec{\nabla}\ r^m = \nabla^2 r^m = \dfrac{\partial^2}{\partial x^2} r^m + \dfrac{\partial^2}{\partial y^2} r^m + \dfrac{\partial^2}{\partial z^2} r^m$

$$= \frac{\partial^2}{\partial x^2}(x^2 + y^2 + z^2)^{m/2} + \frac{\partial^2}{\partial y^2}(x^2 + y^2 + z^2)^{m/2} + \frac{\partial^2}{\partial z^2}(x^2 + y^2 + z^2)^{m/2}$$

Now $\qquad \dfrac{\partial^2}{\partial x^2}(x^2 + y^2 + z^2)^{m/2} = \dfrac{\partial}{\partial x}\left[\dfrac{\partial}{\partial x}(x^2 + y^2 + z^2)^{m/2}\right]$

and $\qquad \dfrac{\partial}{\partial x}(x^2 + y^2 + z^2)^{m/2} = \dfrac{m}{2}(x^2 + y^2 + z^2)^{m/2-1}\ 2x$

$$= mx\,(x^2 + y^2 + z^2)^{m/2-1}$$

Hence $\quad \dfrac{\partial^2}{\partial x^2}(x^2 + y^2 + z^2)^{m/2} = \dfrac{\partial}{\partial x}[mx\,(x^2 + y^2 + z^2)^{m/2-1}]$

$$= mx\left(\frac{m}{2} - 1\right)(x^2 + y^2 + z^2)^{m/2-2}\ 2x + m\,(x^2 + y^2 + z^2)^{m/2-1}$$

$$= mx^2\,(m-2)(x^2 + y^2 + z^2)^{m/2-2} + m\,(x^2 + y^2 + z^2)^{m/2-1}$$

Similarly $\dfrac{\partial^2}{\partial y^2}(x^2 + y^2 + z^2)^{m/2}$

$$= my^2\,(m-2)(x^2 + y^2 + z^2)^{m/2-2} + m\,(x^2 + y^2 + z^2)^{m/2-1}$$

and $\qquad \dfrac{\partial^2}{\partial z^2}(x^2 + y^2 + z^2)^{m/2}$

$$= mz^2\,(m-2)(x^2 + y^2 + z^2)^{m/2-2} + m\,(x^2 + y^2 + z^2)^{m/2-1}$$

$\therefore\ \nabla^2 r^m = m\,(m-2)(x^2 + y^2 + z^2)(x^2 + y^2 + z^2)^{m/2-2} + 3m\,(x^2 + y^2 + z^2)^{m/2-1}$

$$= m\,(m-2)(x^2 + y^2 + z^2)^{m/2-1} + 3m\,(x^2 + y^2 + z^2)^{m/2-1}$$

$$= m\,(m+1)\,r^{m-2} \qquad\qquad\qquad\qquad\qquad ...(i)$$

Put $m = 1$ in relation (i) and we get

$$\nabla^2 r = 2r^{-1} = \frac{2}{r}$$

Note. The same relation can be obtained directly as in part (a) of this question.

Q. 4.49. Evaluate $\nabla^2 \left(\dfrac{1}{r}\right)$ where $r = \sqrt{x^2 + y^2 + z^2}$ and show that $\phi = q\,(x^2 + y^2 + z^2)^{-1/2}$

satisfies Laplace's equation. $\qquad$ *(P.U., 2006; Meerut U. 2003; M.D.U., 2000; H.P.U., 1995)*

Ans. $\nabla^2\left(\dfrac{1}{r}\right) = \vec{\nabla}\cdot\vec{\nabla}\left(\dfrac{1}{r}\right)$

$$\vec{\nabla}\left(\frac{1}{r}\right) = \left(\hat{i}\frac{\partial}{\partial x} + \hat{j}\frac{\partial}{\partial y} + \hat{k}\frac{\partial}{\partial z}\right)(x^2 + y^2 + z^2)^{-1/2}$$

$$= \hat{i}\frac{\partial}{\partial x}(x^2 + y^2 + z^2)^{-1/2} + \hat{j}\frac{\partial}{\partial y}(x^2 + y^2 + z^2)^{-1/2} + \hat{k}\frac{\partial}{\partial z}(x^2 + y^2 + z^2)^{-1/2}$$

The first term $= \hat{i}[-1/2\,(x^2 + y^2 + z^2)^{-3/2}\,2x] = -\hat{i}\,x\,(x^2 + y^2 + z^2)^{-3/2}$

Similarly second term $= -\hat{j}\,y\,(x^2 + y^2 + z^2)^{-3/2}$

and third term $= -\hat{k}\,z\,(x^2 + y^2 + z^2)^{-3/2}$

$$\therefore \quad \vec{\nabla}\left(\frac{1}{r}\right) = -\left[\frac{\hat{i}\,x + \hat{j}\,y + \hat{k}\,z}{(x^2 + y^2 + z^2)^{3/2}}\right] = -\frac{\vec{r}}{r^3}$$

Again $\quad \vec{\nabla}\cdot\vec{\nabla}\left(\dfrac{1}{r}\right) = -\left(\hat{i}\dfrac{\partial}{\partial x} + \hat{j}\dfrac{\partial}{\partial y} + \hat{k}\dfrac{\partial}{\partial z}\right)\cdot(\hat{i}\,x + \hat{j}\,y + \hat{k}\,z)(x^2 + y^2 + z^2)^{-3/2}$

$$= -\left\{\frac{\partial}{\partial x}[x\,(x^2 + y^2 + z^2)^{-3/2}] + \frac{\partial}{\partial y}[y\,(x^2 + y^2 + z^2)^{-3/2}] + \frac{\partial}{\partial z}[z\,(x^2 + y^2 + z^2)]^{-3/2}\right\}$$

The first term $= x\,[-3/2\,(x^2 + y^2 + z^2)^{-5/2}\,2x] + (x^2 + y^2 + z^2)^{-3/2}$

$$= \frac{-3x^2}{(x^2 + y^2 + z^2)^{5/2}} + \frac{1}{(x^2 + y^2 + z^2)^{3/2}}$$

$$= \frac{-3x^2}{(x^2 + y^2 + z^2)^{5/2}} + \frac{x^2 + y^2 + z^2}{(x^2 + y^2 + z^2)^{5/2}}$$

$$= \frac{-2x^2 + y^2 + z^2}{(x^2 + y^2 + z^2)^{5/2}}$$

Similarly second term $= \dfrac{x^2 - 2y^2 + z^2}{(x^2 + y^2 + z^2)^{5/2}}$

and third term $= \dfrac{x^2 + y^2 - 2z^2}{(x^2 + y^2 + z^2)^{5/2}}$

$$\therefore \quad \nabla^2\left(\frac{1}{r}\right) = \vec{\nabla}\cdot\vec{\nabla}\left(\frac{1}{r}\right)$$

$$= -\left\{\frac{-2x^2 + y^2 + z^2 + x^2 - 2y^2 + z^2 + x^2 + y^2 - 2z^2}{(x^2 + y^2 + z^2)^{5/2}}\right\} = 0$$

Hence $\phi = q(x^2 + y^2 + z^2)^{-1/2}$ satisfies Laplace's equation $\nabla^2 \phi = 0$, because $(x^2 + y^2 + z^2)^{-1/2} = \dfrac{1}{r}$

and $\nabla^2 \left(\dfrac{1}{r}\right) = 0$ as proved above.

Remember as a general rule $\nabla^2 (r^m)$

$$= m(m+1) r^{m-2} \quad \text{[as proved in } \textbf{Q. 4.48} \text{ Eq. } (i)]$$

Thus
$$\nabla^2 r = 1 \times 2 \times r^{1-2} = \frac{2}{r}$$

$$\nabla^2 \frac{1}{r} = -1 \times 0 \times r^{-1-2} = 0$$

Q. 4.50. Write down Laplace's equation and show if the functions

$$f(xy) = x^2 - y^2$$

and
$$g(xy) = x^2 + y^2$$

satisfy the two dimensional Laplace's equation.   (*H.P.U., 1994, 1993*)

Ans. Laplace's equation states $\nabla^2 \phi = 0$

Now
$$\nabla^2 \phi = \vec{\nabla} \cdot \vec{\nabla} \phi = \left(\hat{i}\frac{\partial}{\partial x} + \hat{j}\frac{\partial}{\partial y} + \hat{k}\frac{\partial}{\partial z}\right) \cdot \left(\hat{i}\frac{\partial \phi}{\partial x} + \hat{j}\frac{\partial \phi}{\partial y} + \hat{k}\frac{\partial \phi}{\partial z}\right)$$

$$= \frac{\partial^2 \phi}{\partial x^2} + \frac{\partial^2 \phi}{\partial y^2} + \frac{\partial^2 \phi}{\partial z^2}$$

In two dimensions
$$\nabla^2 \phi = \frac{\partial^2 \phi}{\partial x^2} + \frac{\partial^2 \phi}{\partial y^2}$$

(*i*) For
$$\phi = f(xy) = x^2 - y^2$$

$$\frac{\partial \phi}{\partial x} = 2x \text{ and } \frac{\partial^2 \phi}{\partial x^2} = -2$$

Similarly
$$\frac{\partial \phi}{\partial y} = -2y \text{ and } \frac{\partial^2 \phi}{\partial y^2} = -2$$

$\therefore$
$$\nabla^2 \phi = +2 - 2 = 0$$

Hence $f(x, y) = x^2 - y^2$ satisfies two dimensional Laplace's equation.

(*ii*) For
$$\phi = g(xy) = x^2 + y^2$$

$$\frac{\partial \phi}{\partial x} = 2x \text{ and } \frac{\partial^2 \phi}{\partial x^2} = 2$$

Similarly
$$\frac{\partial \phi}{\partial y} = 2y \text{ and } \frac{\partial^2 \phi}{\partial y^2} = 2$$

$\therefore$
$$\nabla^2 \phi = +2 + 2 = +4$$

As
$$\nabla^2 \phi \neq 0$$

Function $g(xy) = x^2 + y^2$ does not satisfy two dimensional Laplace's equation.

Q. 4.51. (*a*) **Show that the potential function**

$$V = x^2 + y^2 - 2z^2 \text{ satisfies the Laplace equation.}$$

(*H.P.U., 2003; Pbi.U., 2002; G.N.D.U., 1990*)

(*b*) **Show that the potential function** $x^2 - y^2 + z$ **satisfies the Laplace's equation.**

(*G.N.D.U., 2006, 2004; P.U., 2007, 2006, 2002, 2000; Pbi.U., 2003, 2000; H.P.U., 1999, 1997*)

Ans. Laplace's equation states $\nabla^2 V = 0$.

Now

$$\nabla^2 V = \frac{\partial^2 V}{\partial x^2} + \frac{\partial^2 V}{\partial y^2} + \frac{\partial^2 V}{\partial z^2}$$

and

$$\frac{\partial V}{\partial x} = 2x \quad \frac{\partial^2 V}{\partial x^2} = 2$$

$$\frac{\partial V}{\partial y} = 2y \quad \frac{\partial^2 V}{\partial y^2} = 2$$

$$\frac{\partial V}{\partial z} = -4z \quad \frac{\partial^2 V}{\partial z^2} = -4$$

$$\therefore \quad \frac{\partial^2 V}{\partial x^2} + \frac{\partial^2 V}{\partial y^2} + \frac{\partial^2 V}{\partial z^2} = 2 + 2 - 4 = 0$$

Hence the potential function $V = x^2 + y^2 - 2z^2$ satisfies the Laplacian equation.

(*b*) Laplace's equation states $\nabla^2 V = 0$

Now

$$\nabla^2 V = \frac{\partial^2 V}{\partial x^2} + \frac{\partial^2 V}{\partial y^2} + \frac{\partial^2 V}{\partial z^2}$$

and

$$\frac{\partial V}{\partial x} = \frac{\partial}{\partial x} (x^2 - y^2 + z) = 2x \text{ and } \frac{\partial^2 V}{\partial x^2} = 2$$

$$\frac{\partial V}{\partial y} = \frac{\partial}{\partial y} (x^2 - y^2 + z) = -2y \text{ and } \frac{\partial^2 V}{\partial y^2} = -2$$

$$\frac{\partial V}{\partial z} = \frac{\partial}{\partial z} (x^2 - y^2 + z) = 1 \text{ and } \frac{\partial^2 V}{\partial z^2} = 0$$

$$\therefore \quad \frac{\partial^2 V}{\partial x^2} + \frac{\partial^2 V}{\partial y^2} + \frac{\partial^2 V}{\partial z^2} = 2 - 2 + 0 = 0$$

This shows that the potential function $V = x^2 - y^2 + z$ satisfies Laplace's equation.

Exercise. *Show that* $U = 2x^2 - 2y^2 + 4z$ *satisfies Laplace's equation.* (*P.U., 2001, 2000*)

Hint. $\nabla^2 U = 4 - 4 + 0 = 0$

Exercise. *Show that electric potential derived from electric field* $x\hat{i} - y\hat{j} + 2\hat{k}$ *satisfy Laplace's equation.*

(*P.U., 2007*)

Hint. Given

$$\vec{E} = x\hat{i} - y\hat{j} + 2\hat{k}$$

Now

$$\vec{E} = -\vec{\nabla} V \text{ where } V \text{ is electric potential}$$

$$\therefore \quad -\vec{\nabla} V = x\hat{i} - y\hat{j} + 2\hat{k} \text{ or } \vec{\nabla} V = -\left(x\hat{i} - y\hat{j} + 2\hat{k} \right)$$

This will satisfy Laplace's equation if $\nabla^2 V = 0$ or $\vec{\nabla}.\vec{\nabla} V = 0$

Now
$$\vec{\nabla}.\vec{\nabla} V = \vec{\nabla}.\left[-\left(x\hat{i} - y\hat{j} + 2\hat{k}\right)\right]$$

$$= -\left(\frac{\partial}{\partial x}\hat{i} + \frac{\partial}{\partial y}\hat{j} + \frac{\partial}{\partial z}\hat{k}\right).\left(x\hat{i} - y\hat{j} + 2\hat{k}\right)$$

$$= -[1 - 1 + 0] = 0$$

As $\nabla^2 V = 0$, this satisfies Laplace's equation.

Q. 4.52. (*a*) **Write the basic differential equation of the electrostatic field and potential.**

(*b*) **Given a region in space in which there exists an electrostatic field in *z*-direction. Show that the field is independent of *x* and *y* co-ordinates.**

(*c*) **Show that if there is no charge in the region, the field is also independent of *z* co-ordinate.**   (*G.N.D.U., 2002*)

Ans. (*a*) **Basic equation of field.** The basic differential equations of electrostatic field are

1. $$\vec{\nabla}.\vec{E} = \frac{\rho}{\varepsilon_0}$$ ...(*i*)

This is the differential form of Gauss's law.

2. $$\vec{\nabla} \times \vec{E} = 0 \text{ or } Curl\ \vec{E} = 0$$ ...(*ii*)

To derive equation (*ii*) we have

$$\vec{E} = -\ grad\ \phi = -\vec{\nabla}\ \phi$$

where ϕ is the electric potential.

$$\therefore \qquad\qquad \vec{\nabla} \times \vec{E} = -\vec{\nabla} \times (\vec{\nabla}\ \phi) = 0 \qquad\qquad \text{(For proof see Q. 4.26)}$$

Basic equations of potential. The basic differential equations of potential are

(*i*) **Poisson's equation.** According to this equation

$$\nabla^2 \phi = -\frac{\rho}{\varepsilon_0}$$

(*ii*) **Laplace's equation.** According to this equation

$$\nabla^2 \phi = 0 \qquad\qquad\qquad\qquad \text{(For proof see Q. 4.44)}$$

(*b*) As the electrostatic field is in the Z-direction it has only a Z-component. If E is the magnitude of the field then it can be represented vectorially as

$$\vec{E} = E\hat{k}$$

The electrostatic field being a conservative field

$$curl\ \vec{E} = \vec{\nabla} \times \vec{E} = 0$$

i.e.,
$$\begin{vmatrix} \hat{i} & \hat{j} & \hat{k} \\ \dfrac{\partial}{\partial x} & \dfrac{\partial}{\partial y} & \dfrac{\partial}{\partial z} \\ 0 & 0 & E \end{vmatrix} = 0$$

or
$$\hat{i}\,\frac{\partial E}{\partial y} - \hat{j}\,\frac{\partial E}{\partial x} = 0$$

When a vector = 0, its components are individually = 0

$$\therefore \qquad \frac{\partial E}{\partial y} = 0 \text{ and } \frac{\partial E}{\partial x} = 0$$

In other words the field does not vary with x or y *i.e.*, it is independent of x and y co-ordinates.

(*c*) An electric field must satisfy Gauss's law in differential form $\vec{\nabla} . \vec{E} = \dfrac{\rho}{\varepsilon_0}$.

If there is no charge in the region
$$\rho = 0$$

$$\therefore \qquad \vec{\nabla} . \vec{E} = 0$$

Now
$$\vec{\nabla} . \vec{E} = \frac{\partial E}{\partial x} + \frac{\partial E}{\partial y} + \frac{\partial E}{\partial z} = 0$$

As proved above
$$\frac{\partial E}{\partial x} = 0 \text{ and } \frac{\partial E}{\partial y} = 0$$

$$\therefore \qquad \frac{\partial E}{\partial z} = 0$$

Thus the field does not vary with Z *i.e.*, it is independent of Z-co-ordinate. The field is, therefore, completely uniform.

Q. 4.53. (*a*) **Prove that there is a discontinuity in the normal component of electric field at a charged layer having a magnitude $\dfrac{\sigma}{\varepsilon_0}$ in S.I. units where σ is the local surface charge density.**

Also show that the tangential component of electric field is continuous. (*Kerala U.,* 2001)
(*b*) **Write a short note on boundary conditions for electric field.** (*G.N.D.U.,* 2002)

Ans. (*a*) **Discontinuity in the normal component.**
Consider a charged surface *AB*. Imagine a cylindrical Gaussian surface enclosing a small element of area ΔS of the surface *AB*. If σ is the *average surface* charge density, then the charge enclosed within the closed surface

$$= \sigma \, \Delta S$$

The Gaussian surface has three parts S_1, S_2 and S_3 as shown.

$\therefore$ According to Gauss's theorem

$$\iint\limits_{S_1} \vec{E} . \, \vec{dS} + \iint\limits_{S_2} \vec{E} . \, \vec{dS} + \iint\limits_{S_3} \vec{E} . \, \vec{dS} = \frac{\sigma \Delta S}{\varepsilon_0} \qquad ...(i)$$

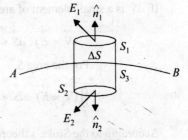

Fig. 4.30

As the surfaces S_1 and S_2 approach the element ΔS, the surface S_3 goes on becoming smaller and smaller and in the limit $S_3 \rightarrow 0$. In such a case S_1 and S_2 coincide with ΔS and the unit normals $\hat{n_1}$ and

$\hat{n}_2$ are equal and opposite. In the limit

$$\iint_{S_3} \vec{E} \cdot \vec{dS} = 0$$

$$\iint_{S_1} \vec{E} \cdot \vec{dS} = \vec{E}_1 \cdot \hat{n}_1 \, \Delta S$$

and

$$\iint_{S_2} \vec{E} \cdot \vec{dS} = \vec{E}_2 \cdot \hat{n}_2 \, \Delta S = -\vec{E}_2 \cdot \hat{n}_1 \, \Delta S$$

Substituting in (i), we have

$$(\vec{E}_1 - \vec{E}_2) \cdot \hat{n}_1 \, \Delta S = \sigma \frac{\Delta S}{\varepsilon_0}$$

or

$$(\vec{E}_1 - \vec{E}_2) \cdot \hat{n}_1 = \frac{\sigma}{\varepsilon_0}$$

Now $\vec{E}_1 \cdot \hat{n}_1 - \vec{E}_2 \cdot \hat{n}_1$ is the discontinuity in the normal component of $\vec{E}$ at the charged surface.

Hence *"The magnitude of discontinuity in the normal component of electric field at a point on a charged surface is equal to* $\dfrac{1}{\varepsilon_0}$ *times the local surface charge density."*

Tangential component of electric field is continuous. The electric field at a point is given by

$$\vec{E} = -\vec{\nabla} V$$

where V is the electric potential at that point.

$$\therefore \qquad \vec{\nabla} \times \vec{E} = \vec{\nabla} \times \vec{\nabla} V = 0$$

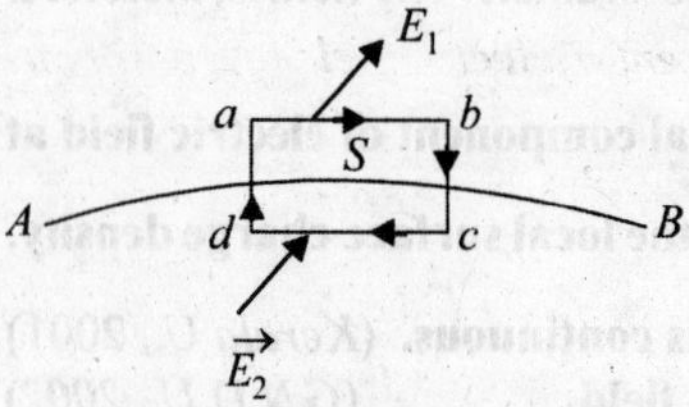

Fig. 4.31

Now consider a rectangular loop *abcd* across the charged surface and let S be the surface bounded by the loop, then for a point on the bounding surface having an electric field intensity $\vec{E}$

$$\vec{\nabla} \times \vec{E} = 0$$

If $\vec{dS}$ is a small element of area surrounding the point, then

$$(\vec{\nabla} \times \vec{E}) \cdot \vec{dS} = 0$$

$\therefore$ For the area S,

$$\iint_S (\vec{\nabla} \times \vec{E}) \cdot \vec{dS} = 0$$

According to the Stoke's theorem in vector analysis, we have.

"The line integral of vector field $\vec{A}$ *for a closed path is equal to the surface integral of the curl of the vector field over the surface bounded by the path"* i.e.,

$$\oint \vec{A} \cdot \vec{dr} = \int (\vec{\nabla} \times \vec{A}) \cdot \vec{dS}$$

$\therefore$ For the closed path $a\,b\,c\,d$ $\oint\limits_{abcd} \vec{E} . \vec{dr} = 0$

But $\qquad \oint\limits_{abcd} \vec{E} . \vec{dr} = \int\limits_{ab} \vec{E} . \vec{dr} + \int\limits_{bc} \vec{E} . \vec{dr} + \int\limits_{cd} \vec{E} . \vec{dr} + \int\limits_{da} \vec{E} . \vec{dr}$

In the limit as elements ab and cd approach the boundary

$$bc \to 0 \text{ and } da \to 0$$

and if $\vec{E_1}$ and $\vec{E_2}$ are the values of the electric field on the two sides respectively, then

$$\int\limits_{ab} \vec{E_1} . \vec{dr} + \int\limits_{cd} \vec{E_2} . \vec{dr} = 0$$

If E_{1t} is the tangential component of E_1 and E_{2t} that of E_2, then

$$\int\limits_{ab} E_{1t}\, dr + \int\limits_{cd} E_{2t}\, dr = 0$$

or $\qquad\qquad\qquad \int\limits_{ab} E_{1t}\, dr = \int\limits_{dc} E_{2t}\, dr$

$\therefore \qquad\qquad\qquad\qquad E_{1t} = E_{2t}$

i.e., the tangential components of electric field are continuous.

(b) Boundary conditions for electric field. From the above discussion, we conclude that

(i) The discontinuity in the normal component of electric field $\vec{E}$ at the charged surface

$$\vec{E_1} . \hat{n_1} - \vec{E_2} . \hat{n_1} = \frac{\sigma}{\varepsilon_0}$$

Hence '*The magnitude of discontinuity in the normal component of electric field at a point on a charged surface is equal to $\dfrac{1}{\varepsilon_0}$ times the local surface charge density*'.

(ii) The tangential components $E_{1t} = E_{2t}$

Hence '*The tangential components of the electric field are continuous*'.

Q. 4.54. (a) Explain the method of electrical images.

(G.N.D.U., 2002, 2001, 2000; Pbi.U., 1999, 1995; H.P.U., 2000)

(b) A charge is situated at a distance d from an infinite conducting sheet at zero potential in the X-Y plane. The source charge lies in the region $Z > 0$. Using the method of electrical images find the value of electric potential and field at any point in the region $Z > 0$. Show that the sum of the potentials due to source charge and image charge is zero. What is the value of the field when the point lies on the conducting sheet ?

(G.N.D.U., 2009, 2007, 2006, 2002, 2000, 1995; K.U., 1996;

H.P.U., 2007, 2000; Pbi. U., 2008, 2007; A.U., 1994, 1993; Patna U., 1991)

Ans. (a) Electrical image. *An electric image is defined as a point charge or a set of point charges on one side of a conducting surface which produces on the other side of the surface the same electrical effects (potential, field etc.) as is produced by the actual electrification of the surface.*

In calculating the field and potential by the method of electrical images, the actual electrification of the conducting surface is, therefore, ignored and only the image charge is used for the purpose.

This method is based on '*uniqueness theorem*' according to which the electric potential (and hence the field) in a region bounded by a set of conductors is uniquely defined *i.e.*, there is one and only one value of potential or field. In other words, if one of the conductors of such a system is removed and replaced by a point charge or a set of point charges within the boundary occupied by the removed conductor so that this charge or set of charges produce the same potential at the boundary as that of the removed conductor, then the electrical effects of these charges outside the boundary will also be the same as those of the original conductor.

Magnitude and position of image charge. Consider an earthed conducting plane sheet of infinite extent in the *X-Y* plane. Let a (point) source charge of magnitude +*q* be placed at *A* at a perpendicular distance $OA = d$ along the + *Z* axis, then the co-ordinates of *A* are $(0, 0, d)$ and the position vector of the charge + *q*

$$\vec{d} = d\,\hat{k}$$

The plane conducting sheet divides the space into two regions; one in which the charge +*q* lies and in which $Z > 0$ everywhere and the other in which $Z < 0$ everywhere.

The source charge + *q* will set up an induced charge distribution on the conducting sheet the value of which is not known.

The conducting sheet is earthed and the potential at every point on it is zero.

∴   At $z = 0$, Potential $V = 0$.

Let *C* be a point on the sheet having position vector $\vec{r}$ and co-ordinates $(x, y, 0)$, then

$$\vec{r} = x\,\hat{i} + y\,\hat{j}$$

The potential at *C* due to the source charge + *q*

$$V_s = \frac{1}{4\pi\varepsilon_0} \frac{q}{|\vec{r} - \vec{d}|} = \frac{1}{4\pi\varepsilon_0} \frac{q}{|\vec{r} - d\hat{k}|} = \frac{1}{4\pi\varepsilon_0} \frac{q}{|x\hat{i} + y\hat{j} - d\hat{k}|}$$

or $$V_s = \frac{1}{4\pi\varepsilon_0} \frac{q}{(x^2 + y^2 + d^2)^{1/2}} \qquad \qquad ...(i)$$

If the conducting sheet is removed and charge – *q* is placed in the region $Z < 0$ at a point *B* at a perpendicular distance $OB = -d$ along the – *Z* axis, then the co-ordinates of *B* are $(0, 0, -d)$ and the position vector of charge – *q*

$$\vec{d} = -d\,\hat{k}$$

This charge constitutes the *image charge*.

The potential at *C* due to the image charge – *q*.

$$V_i = -\frac{1}{4\pi\varepsilon_0} \frac{q}{|\vec{r} - \vec{d}|} = -\frac{1}{4\pi\varepsilon_0} \frac{q}{|\vec{r} + d\hat{k}|} = -\frac{1}{4\pi\varepsilon_0} \frac{q}{|x\hat{i} + y\hat{j} + d\hat{k}|}$$

or $$V_i = -\frac{1}{4\pi\varepsilon_0} \frac{q}{(x^2 + y^2 + d^2)^{1/2}} \qquad \qquad ...(ii)$$

From (*i*) and (*ii*), we have, the net potential at *C*,

$$V = V_s + V_i = \frac{1}{4\pi\varepsilon_0} \frac{q}{(x^2 + y^2 + d^2)^{1/2}} - \frac{1}{4\pi\varepsilon_0} \frac{q}{(x^2 + y^2 + d^2)^{1/2}} = 0$$

Thus, *the sum of the potentials due to source charge and image charge is zero.*

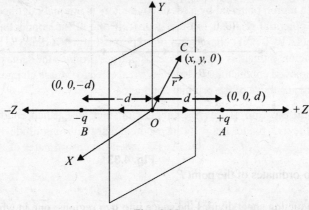

Fig. 4.32

i.e., the potential due to image charge neutralises the potential due to the source charge at all points on the sheet. This means that *a single charge of magnitude – q and located at (0, 0, –d) will cancel the potential due to the source charge at all points on the conducting sheet.* In other words the *image charge – q* located at (0, 0, – d) serves the purpose of the earthed conducting sheet.

(b) Potential at any point (region Z > 0). To find the potential at any point in the region $Z > 0$, consider a point P having position vector $\vec{r}$ given by $\vec{r} = x\hat{i} + y\hat{j} + z\hat{k}$ as shown in Fig. 4.33.

The conducting plane sheet lies in the X-Y plane with O as the origin of the co-ordinate system. The position vector of the source charge $+q = \overrightarrow{OA} = \vec{d}$ with co-ordinates $(0, 0, d)$ along the Z-axis so that $\vec{d} = d\hat{k}$.

The position vector of the image charge $– q = \overrightarrow{OB} = \vec{d}$ along $– Z$ axis with co-ordinates $(0, 0, -d)$ so that $\vec{d} = - d\hat{k}$

The potential at P due to the source charge $+ q$

$$V_s = \frac{1}{4\pi\varepsilon_0} \cdot \frac{q}{|\vec{r} - \vec{d}|} = \frac{1}{4\pi\varepsilon_0} \frac{q}{|\vec{r} - d\hat{k}|}$$

The potential at P due to the image charge $– q$

$$V_i = - \frac{1}{4\pi\varepsilon_0} \frac{q}{|\vec{r} - \vec{d}|} = -\frac{1}{4\pi\varepsilon_0} \frac{q}{|\vec{r} + d\hat{k}|}$$

∴   Net potential at P,

$$V = V_s + V_i = \frac{1}{4\pi\varepsilon_0} \left[\frac{q}{|\vec{r} - d\hat{k}|} - \frac{q}{|\vec{r} + d\hat{k}|} \right]$$

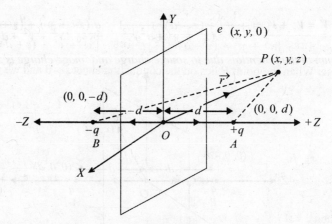

Fig. 4.33

In terms of co-ordinates of the point P

$$V = \frac{1}{4\pi\varepsilon_0}\left[\frac{q}{|x\hat{i} + y\hat{j} + z\hat{k} - d\hat{k}|} - \frac{q}{|x\hat{i} + y\hat{j} + z\hat{k} + d\hat{k}|}\right]$$

$$= \frac{1}{4\pi\varepsilon_0}\left[\frac{q}{|x\hat{i} + y\hat{j} + (z - d)\hat{k}|} - \frac{q}{|x\hat{i} + y\hat{j} + (z + d)\hat{k}|}\right]$$

or $$V = \frac{1}{4\pi\varepsilon_0}\left[\frac{q}{|x^2 + y^2 + (z - d)^2|^{1/2}} - \frac{q}{|x^2 + y^2 + (z + d)^2|^{1/2}}\right]$$

Electric field. The electric field at P due to the source charge $+ q$

$$\vec{E}_s = \frac{1}{4\pi\varepsilon_0}\frac{q\,(\vec{r} - \vec{d})}{|\vec{r} - \vec{d}|^3} = \frac{1}{4\pi\varepsilon_0}\frac{q\,(\vec{r} - d\hat{k})}{|\vec{r} - d\hat{k}|^3}$$

Electric field at P due to the image charge $- q$

$$\vec{E}_i = -\frac{1}{4\pi\varepsilon_0}\frac{q\,(\vec{r} - \vec{d})}{|\vec{r} - \vec{d}|^3} = \frac{1}{4\pi\varepsilon_0}\frac{q\,(\vec{r} + d\hat{k})}{|\vec{r} + d\hat{k}|^3}$$

$\therefore$ Resultant electric field at P

$$\vec{E} = \vec{E}_s + \vec{E}_i$$

$$= \frac{1}{4\pi\varepsilon_0}\frac{q\,(\vec{r} - d\hat{k})}{|\vec{r} - d\hat{k}|^3} - \frac{1}{4\pi\varepsilon_0}\frac{q\,(\vec{r} + d\hat{k})}{|\vec{r} + d\hat{k}|^3}$$

In terms of the co-ordinates of the point P

$$\vec{E} = \frac{1}{4\pi\varepsilon_0}\frac{q\,(x\hat{i} + y\hat{j} + z\hat{k} - d\hat{k})}{|x\hat{i} + y\hat{j} + z\hat{k} - d\hat{k}|^3} - \frac{1}{4\pi\varepsilon_0}\frac{q\,(x\hat{i} + y\hat{j} + z\hat{k} + d\hat{k})}{|x\hat{i} + y\hat{j} + z\hat{k} + d\hat{k}|^3}$$

$$= \frac{1}{4\pi\varepsilon_0}\frac{q\,(x\hat{i} + y\hat{j} + (z - d)\hat{k})}{|x\hat{i} + y\hat{j} + (z - d)\hat{k}|^3} - \frac{1}{4\pi\varepsilon_0}\frac{q\,(x\hat{i} + y\hat{j} + (z + d)\hat{k})}{|x\hat{i} + y\hat{j} + (z + d)\hat{k}|^3}$$

$$= \frac{1}{4\pi\varepsilon_0} \frac{q\,(x\hat{i} + y\hat{j} + (z-d)\hat{k})}{[x^2 + y^2 + (z-d)^2]^{3/2}} - \frac{1}{4\pi\varepsilon_0} \frac{q\,(x\hat{i} + y\hat{j} + (z+d)\hat{k})}{[x^2 + y^2 + (z+d)^2]^{3/2}}$$

Special case. When the point P lies on the conducting sheet $z = 0$ and we get

$$\vec{E} = \frac{1}{4\pi\varepsilon_0} \frac{q\,(x\hat{i} + y\hat{j} - d\hat{k})}{[x^2 + y^2 + d^2]^{3/2}} - \frac{1}{4\pi\varepsilon_0} \frac{q\,(x\hat{i} + y\hat{j} + d\hat{k})}{[x^2 + y^2 + d^2]^{3/2}}$$

$$= -\frac{1}{4\pi\varepsilon_0} \frac{q\,2d\hat{k}}{[x^2 + y^2 + d^2]^{3/2}} = -\frac{1}{4\pi\varepsilon_0} \frac{2qd\hat{k}}{|r^2 + d^2|^{3/2}}$$

because when $z = 0$; $\vec{r} = x\hat{i} + y\hat{j}$ and $|\vec{r}| = \sqrt{x^2 + y^2}$.

The electric field is, therefore normal to the plane of the conducting sheet and is directed into the plane.

Q. 4. 55. (*a*) **A point charge q is placed at a distance d from an infinite plane conductor held at zero potential. Using the method of images calculate**

(*i*) **Induced surface charge density**

(*ii*) **Total induced charge**

(*iii*) **Force of attraction between the charge and the conductor and**

(*iv*) **Work done in removing q to infinity.**(*P.U., 2006; Patna.U., 1993; G.N.D.U., 1993, 1992*)

(*b*) **A uniformly charged wire carrying 5000 e.s.u. per cm is situated at a height of 2 metres from an infinite conducting plane. Calculate the force per unit length experienced by the wire.**
(*G.N.D.U., 1999*)

Ans. (*i*) **Induced surface charge density.** When an earthed conducting plane of infinite extent lies in the X-Y plane and a point source charge $+q$ is placed at a perpendicular distance d along the $+Z$ axis, then the electric field at a point on the conducting sheet having a position vector $\vec{r} = x\hat{i} + y\hat{j}$

is given by
$$\vec{E} = -\frac{1}{4\pi\varepsilon_0} \frac{2qd}{|r^2 + d^2|^{3/2}} \hat{k}$$

As the electric field is directed normally towards the conducting sheet, the induced surface charge density must be *negative*.

The field outside the conductor having a surface charge density σ is given by

$$E = \frac{\sigma}{\varepsilon_0}$$

where E is the magnitude of $\vec{E}$

$$\therefore \qquad \sigma = \varepsilon_0 E = -\frac{\varepsilon_0}{4\pi\varepsilon_0} \frac{2qd}{|r^2 + d^2|^{3/2}} = -\frac{qd}{2\pi\,(r^2 + d^2)^{3/2}}$$

(*ii*) **Total induced charge.** To find the total induced charge, consider an annular ring of internal radius r and outer radius $r + dr$, then

The area of the ring $= 2\pi r\,dr$

Charge on the ring $= \sigma \, 2\pi r \, dr$

$$= -\frac{qdr\,dr}{(r^2 + d^2)^{3/2}}$$

$\therefore$ Total induced charge on the conducting *infinite sheet*.

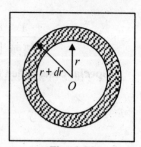

Fig. 4.34

$$= \int_0^\infty \frac{-q\,dr}{(r^2 + d^2)^{3/2}}\,dr = -\frac{qd}{2}\int_0^\infty \frac{2\,r\,dr}{(r^2 + d^2)^{3/2}}$$

If we put $\qquad\qquad r^2 + d^2 = u,$

then $\qquad\qquad 2r\,dr = du$ $\qquad\qquad\qquad\qquad$ [$\because d = a$ constant]

$$\therefore \quad \int_0^\infty \frac{2r\,dr}{(r^2 + d^2)^{3/2}} = \int_0^\infty \frac{du}{u^{3/2}}$$

$$= \left[\frac{u^{-1/2}}{-\dfrac{1}{2}}\right]_0^\infty = \left[\frac{(r^2 + d^2)^{-1/2}}{-\dfrac{1}{2}}\right]_0^\infty = \frac{2}{d}$$

$\therefore$ Total charge on the conducting plane

$$= -q\,\frac{d}{2}\cdot\frac{2}{d} = -q$$

Thus the total induced charge = the image charge.

(iii) Force of attraction between the charge and the conductor. The force $\vec{F}$ with which the conductor and the point charge $+q$ *attract* each other is equal to the force of attraction between the charge $+q$ and the image charge $-q$ and is given by

$$F = \frac{1}{4\pi\varepsilon_0}\frac{q^2}{4d^2} = \frac{q^2}{16\pi\,\varepsilon_0\,d^2}\ \text{(attraction)}$$

(iv) Work done in removing q to infinity. The force $\vec{F}$ calculated above is directed along the Z-axis towards the origin.

$$\therefore \qquad \vec{F} = -\frac{q^2}{16\pi\varepsilon_0\,d^2}\,\hat{k}$$

Hence at a point distance $+z$ from the origin

$$\vec{F} = -\frac{q^2}{16\pi\varepsilon_0\,z^2}\,\hat{k}$$

$\therefore$ Work done in removing the charge $+q$ from a point $z = +d$ to $z = \infty$ is given by

$$W = \int_{+d}^{+\infty} -\vec{F}\cdot\vec{dl} = \int_{+d}^{+\infty} F\,dz$$

$$= \frac{q^2}{16\pi\varepsilon_0}\int_{+d}^{+\infty}\frac{1}{z^2}\,dz$$

$$= \frac{q^2}{16\pi\varepsilon_0}\left[-\frac{1}{z}\right]_{+d}^{+\infty} = \frac{q^2}{16\pi\varepsilon_0\,d}$$

(b) Charge on the wire $\qquad = 5000$ e.s.u./cm

$$\therefore \qquad q = \frac{5000 \times 100}{3 \times 10^9} = \frac{5}{3 \times 10^4} \, Cm^{-1}$$

$$d = 2m$$

$\therefore$ Force of attraction per unit length

$$= \frac{1}{4\pi\varepsilon_0} \frac{q^2}{4d^2} = 9 \times 10^9 \times \frac{25}{9 \times 10^8 \times 4 \times 4}$$

$$= \frac{250}{16} = 15.625 \, Nm^{-1}$$

Q. 4.56. A point charge $+q$ is placed at a distance d from the centre of an earthed conducting sphere of radius R. Apply the method of electrical images to calculate

(*i*) Strength of the image charge and its position in the sphere

(*ii*) Field on the sphere

(*iii*) Surface density induced on the sphere

(*iv*) The force between the charge $+q$ and the induced charge on the sphere.

(*Magadh.U., 1996*)

Ans. (*i*) **Strength and position of image charge.** Consider a point charge $+q$ at a point A at a distance d from the centre O of an *earthed* conducting sphere of radius R, placed in free space (or vacuum). For convenience we shall suppose the line OA to represent the Z-axis.

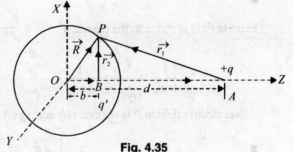

Fig. 4.35

Now take a point B on the line OA such that

$$OB \cdot OA = R^2$$

or

$$\frac{OB}{R} = \frac{R}{OA}$$

or

$$\frac{b}{R} = \frac{R}{d}$$

where

$$b = OB$$

If we take a point P on the surface of the sphere and consider triangles POB and POA, then

$$\frac{OB}{R} = \frac{R}{OA} \quad \text{or} \quad \frac{OB}{OP} = \frac{OP}{OA}$$

and

$$\angle POB = \angle POA$$

$\therefore \Delta S \, POB$ and POA are similar.

Hence

$$\frac{OB}{OP} = \frac{OP}{OA} = \frac{BP}{AP} \quad \text{or} \quad \frac{b}{R} = \frac{R}{d} = \frac{r_2}{r_1}$$

where

$$\overrightarrow{AP} = \vec{r_1} \text{ and } \overrightarrow{BP} = \vec{r_2}$$

Suppose we place a charge q' at B, then the potential at the position of the point P on the surface of the conducting sphere (when the sphere is removed) is given by

$$\frac{1}{4\pi\varepsilon_0}\frac{q}{|\vec{r_1}|} + \frac{1}{4\pi\varepsilon_0}\frac{q'}{|\vec{r_2}|}$$

In order that the point charge q' placed at B may be the *image charge*, the potential at $P = 0$

$$\therefore \qquad \frac{1}{4\pi\varepsilon_0}\frac{q}{|\vec{r_1}|} + \frac{1}{4\pi\varepsilon_0}\frac{q'}{|\vec{r_2}|} = 0$$

or $$q' = -q\frac{r_2}{r_1} = -q\frac{R}{d} \qquad\qquad \text{[where } r_2 = |\vec{r_2}| \text{ and } r_1 = |\vec{r_1}|\text{]}$$

$\therefore$ The image charge is negative and its strength $= q\dfrac{R}{d}$

The position of the point where the image charge is placed is given by

$$OB = b = \frac{R^2}{OA} = \frac{R^2}{d}$$

(ii) Electric field at P. Electric field at P due to the charge $+q$ at A

$$= \frac{1}{4\pi\varepsilon_0}\frac{q}{|\vec{r_1}|^2}\hat{r_1} = \frac{1}{4\pi\varepsilon_0}\frac{q}{|\vec{r_1}|^3}\vec{r_1} = \frac{q}{|\vec{r_1}|^3}(\vec{R} - \vec{d}) \qquad ...(i)$$

as $$\vec{r_1} = \vec{R} - \vec{d}$$

Electric field at P due to the charge $q' = -q\dfrac{R}{d}$ placed at B

$$= \frac{1}{4\pi\varepsilon_0}\frac{-q\dfrac{R}{d}}{|\vec{r_2}|^2} = \frac{1}{4\pi\varepsilon_0}\frac{-q\dfrac{R}{d}}{|\vec{r_2}|^3}\vec{r_2} = \frac{1}{4\pi\varepsilon_0}\frac{-q\dfrac{R}{d}}{|\vec{r_2}|^3}(\vec{R} - \vec{b}) \qquad ...(ii)$$

$\therefore$ Net electric field at P is obtained by adding (i) and (ii) and is

$$= \frac{1}{4\pi\varepsilon_0}\left[\frac{q\vec{R}}{|\vec{r_1}|^3} - \frac{q\dfrac{R}{d}\vec{R}}{|\vec{r_2}|^3} - \frac{q\vec{d}}{|\vec{r_1}|^3} + \frac{q\dfrac{R}{d}\vec{b}}{|\vec{r_2}|^3}\right]$$

The components of the field along $\vec{d}$ and $\vec{b}$ are along the same line and $b = \dfrac{R^2}{d}$

$\therefore$ Taking magnitudes only, we have

$$\frac{-qd}{r_1^3} + \frac{q\dfrac{R}{d}\dfrac{R^2}{d}}{r_2^3} = \frac{-qd}{r_1^3} + \frac{q}{d^2}\frac{R^3}{r_2^3}$$

$$= \frac{-qd}{r_1^3} + \frac{q}{d^2}\frac{d^3}{r_1^3} = 0$$

as $$\frac{R}{d} = \frac{r_2}{r_1} \text{ or } \frac{R}{r_2} = \frac{d}{r_1}$$

$\therefore$ Net field along $\vec{R}$

$$\vec{E} = \frac{1}{4\pi\varepsilon_0}\left[\frac{q\vec{R}}{r_1^3} - \frac{q\dfrac{R}{d}\vec{R}}{r_2^3}\right]$$

$$= \frac{1}{4\pi\varepsilon_0}\left[\frac{q}{r_1^3}\left(1 - \frac{R}{d}\cdot\frac{r_1^3}{r_2^3}\right)\vec{R}\right]$$

$$= \frac{1}{4\pi\varepsilon_0}\left[\frac{q}{r_1^3}\left(1 - \frac{R}{d}\cdot\frac{d^3}{R^3}\right)\vec{R}\right]$$

$$= \frac{1}{4\pi\varepsilon_0}\left[\frac{q}{r_1^3}\left(1 - \frac{d^2}{R^2}\right)\vec{R}\right]$$

$$= \frac{1}{4\pi\varepsilon_0}\left[\frac{q}{r_1^3}\left(\frac{R^2 - d^2}{R^2}\right)\vec{R}\right] = \frac{1}{4\pi\varepsilon_0}\frac{q}{r_1^3}\frac{R^2 - d^2}{R}\hat{R}$$

i.e., the field is *directed radially outward* and has a magnitude

$$|\vec{E}| = E = \frac{1}{4\pi\varepsilon_0}\frac{q}{r_1^3}\frac{R^2 - d^2}{R}$$

(iii) **Surface density of induced charge at P.** The electric field *just* outside the conductor

$$E = \frac{\sigma}{\varepsilon_0}$$

$$\therefore \qquad \frac{\sigma}{\varepsilon_0} = \frac{1}{4\pi\varepsilon_0}\frac{q}{r_1^3}\frac{R^2 - d^2}{R}$$

or $$\sigma = -\frac{1}{4\pi}\frac{q}{r_1^3}\frac{(d^2 - R^2)}{R}$$

(iv) **Force between charge + q and the induced charge.** This force is given by the *attraction* between the charge + q and its image charge − q.

∴ Force of attraction

$$= \frac{1}{4\pi\varepsilon_0}\frac{q\left(q\frac{R}{d}\right)}{(d - b)^2} = \frac{1}{4\pi\varepsilon_0}\frac{q^2 R}{d\left(d - \frac{R^2}{d}\right)^2} = \frac{1}{4\pi\varepsilon_0}\frac{q^2 R d}{(d^2 - R^2)^2}$$

Q. 4.57. Mark the correct choice

(i) A charge of 1 micro coulomb is moved in a circle of radius $\frac{20}{\pi}$ m about another charge of + 10 μ C at the centre. The work done in so doing is

(a) zero   (b) 4×10^{-9} J

(c) 4×10^{-6} J   (d) 4×10^{-5} J   (P.U., 1994)

[**Ans.** Zero. The equipotential lines due to a point charge are concentric circles with charge as its centre.]

(ii) The work done in displacing a charge 2 C through 0.5 m on an equipotential surface is

(a) zero   (b) 1 J

(c) 4 J   (d) none of these.   (G.N.D.U., 1990)

(iii) The relation between electric field and potential is

(a) $E = \vec{\nabla}V$ (b) $\vec{E} = -\vec{\nabla}V$

(c) $\vec{E} = \nabla^2 V$ (d) $\vec{E} = -\nabla^2 V$ (H.P.U., 2000, 1993) (*iv*) A charge of 10^{-4} C is placed at (0, 0) shown in the figure. The work done in moving a charge of 1 μC from B to C is

(*a*) – 3 J

(*b*) + 3 J

(*c*) + 3.9 J

(*d*) – 3.9 J

(*P.U., 1994*)

[**Ans.** The correct answer is + 3J.

$$AB = 6 \text{ cm}$$

∴ Potential at B

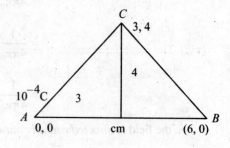

Fig. 4.36

$$V_B = \frac{1}{4\pi\varepsilon_0} \frac{10^{-4}}{6 \times 10^{-2}}$$

$$= \frac{9 \times 10^9 \times 10^{-4}}{6 \times 10^{-2}} = 15 \times 10^6 \text{ V}$$

$$AC = \sqrt{3^2 + 4^2} = 5 \text{ cm}$$

∴ Potential at C,

$$V_c = \frac{1}{4\pi\varepsilon_0} \frac{10^{-4}}{5 \times 10^{-2}} = 18 \times 10^6 \text{ V}$$

As the charge of 1 μC is moved from B to C *i.e.*, from a lower potential to a higher potential, work will have to be done *i.e.*, work done is *positive*.

Hence work done = $q\,(V_c - V_B) = 10^{-6}\,(18 - 15) \times 10^6 = +3$ J]

(*v*) A point charge Q is located at the origin. The amount of work done in bringing a unit positive charge from infinity to the origin is

(*a*) zero

(*b*) infinite

(*c*) finite

(*d*) unknown

(*H.P.U., 1994*)

[**Ans.** The correct answer is *infinite*.

Electric potential $V = \dfrac{1}{4\pi\varepsilon_0} \dfrac{Q}{|\vec{r} - \vec{r_1}|}$

At the origin $r = 0$. Also the charge Q is located at the origin.

Therefore $\vec{r_1} = 0$. Hence $V = \infty$

The work done in bringing a unit positive charge from infinity to the origin being equal to the potential at the origin is *infinite*.]

(*vi*) A proton, deutron and an α-particle are accelerated through the same potential difference, their kinetic energies will be in the ratio of

(*a*) 2 : 1 : 1

(*b*) 2 : 2 : 1

(*c*) 1 : 1 : 2

(*d*) 1 : 2 : 2

(*P.U., 1994*)

[**Ans.** The correct answer is 1 : 1 : 2.

Charge on the proton = + e, charge on the deutron = + e

Charge on the α-particle = + 2e

Energy gained $U = qV$

As the particles are accelerated through the same potential difference (V), the energy gained is proportional to q.

$\therefore$ Kinetic energies are in the ratio of $1 : 1 : 2$]

(vii) In a free space Poisson's equation is

(a) $\nabla^2 V = \varepsilon_0 / \rho$ (b) $\nabla^2 V = -\rho / \varepsilon_0$

(c) $\nabla^2 V = 0$.   (d) $\nabla^2 V = \infty$ (*H.P.U., 1996*)

(viii) The potential is constant in a certain region of space.

The value of $\vec{E}$ in that region is

(a) zero   (b) finite

(c) infinite   (d) depends on the location of the point.

(ix) Work done in carrying 2 C charge in a circular path of radius 3 m around a charge of 10 C is.

(a) zero   (b) 6.66 J

(c) 15 J   (d) 6 J   (*H.P.U., 2002, 2001*)

(x) $\vec{E} = -\vec{\nabla} U$. Here negative sign signifies that

(a) *E is opposite to U*   (b) *E is negative*

(c) *E increases when U decreases*   (d) *E is directed in the direction of decreasing U.*

(*H.P.U., 2003*)

Ans.   (i) *a*   (ii) *a*   (iii) *b*   (iv) *b*

         (v) *b*   (vi) *c*   (vii) *b*   (viii) *a*

         (ix) *a*   (x) *d*

EXERCISES

1. If the potential at a point is given by $V = y(x^2 - 2z)$, then calculate the field at 1, 2, 2.

(*H.P.U., 1995*)

[**Hint.** $E_x = 2xy\ \hat{i}$; $E_y = (x^2 - 2z)\ \hat{j}$; $E_z = -2y\ \hat{k}$

$\therefore$ $\vec{E} = -[2xy\ \hat{i} + (x^2 - 2z)\ \hat{j} - 2y\ \hat{k}]$

At the point 1, 2, 2 $\vec{E} = -4\hat{i} + 3\hat{j} + 4\hat{k}$]

2. The potential V in xy plane is given by

$$V = \frac{1}{\sqrt{x^2 + y^2}}.$$

Calculate the electric field at a point (3, 4) in xy plane.   (*H.P.U., 1992*)

[**Hint.** $E_x = -\dfrac{\partial}{\partial x}\left[(x^2 + y^2)^{-1/2}\right] = \dfrac{x}{(x^2 + y^2)^{3/2}}$; $E_y = -\dfrac{\partial}{\partial y}(x^2 + y^2)^{-1/2} = \dfrac{y}{(x^2 + y^2)^{3/2}}$; $E_z = 0$

$$\vec{E} = \frac{x}{(x^2 + y^2)^{3/2}}\hat{i} + \frac{y}{(x^2 + y^2)^{3/2}}\hat{j}$$

At the point, $(3, 4)$ $\vec{E} = \dfrac{3}{\sqrt{125}}\hat{i} + \dfrac{4}{\sqrt{125}}\hat{j}$]

3. Find the expression for electric field in a region where potential is given by
$$V = -k\,xy.$$
(G.N.D.U., 1994)

[**Hint.** $E_x = -\dfrac{\partial}{\partial x}(-kxy) = ky;\ E_y = -\dfrac{\partial}{\partial y}(-kxy) = kx$

$E_z = -\dfrac{\partial}{\partial z}(-kxy) = 0$ $\therefore\ \vec{E} = ky\,\hat{i} + kx\,\hat{j}$]

4. The potential at a point is given by $V = x\,(3y^2 - x^2 + z)$.

Find the components of the electric field at that point.   (*K.U.* 1991)

[**Hint.** $E_x = -\dfrac{\partial}{\partial x}[3xy^2 - x^3 + xz] = -[3y^2 - 3x^2 + z]\hat{i}$

$E_y = -\dfrac{\partial}{\partial y}[3xy^2 - x^3 + xz] = -6xy\,\hat{j}$

$E_z = -\dfrac{\partial}{\partial z}[3xy^2 - x^3 + xz] = -x\,\hat{k}$

5. If the electric potential in a region is $\phi = 4x + 3y - 2z$, find the electric field.

(G.N.D.U., 1992)

[**Hint.** $\vec{E} = -\vec{\nabla}\phi = -[4\hat{i} + 3\hat{j} - 2\hat{k}]$]

6. Electric potential in space is given by $V = 3x + 2y + 7z$. Show that electric field acting in space is uniform.

[**Hint.** $\vec{E} = -\vec{\nabla}V = -[3\hat{i} + 2\hat{j} + 7\hat{k}]$. It is independent of space co-ordinates.]

7. Show that the function $\phi = x^2 - y^2 + z^2$ satisfies Laplace's equation.   (*H.P.U.,* 1994)

[**Hint.** $\dfrac{\partial\phi}{\partial x} = 2x,\ \dfrac{\partial^2\phi}{\partial x^2} = 2;\ \dfrac{\partial\phi}{\partial y} = -2y,\ \dfrac{\partial^2\phi}{\partial y^2} = -2$

$\dfrac{\partial\phi}{\partial z} = 1,\ \dfrac{\partial^2\phi}{\partial z^2} = 0$ $\therefore\ \nabla^2\phi = 0$].

5 Electric Fields in Dielectrics

Q. 5.1 (a) Explain the terms conductors and insulators.

(b) What is a dielectric substance? Give examples. Discuss the importance of dielectrics.

(H.P.U., 1997; GNDU., 2006, 2000, 1990)

Ans. (a) Conductors and insulators. Matter is composed of molecules which in turn may consist of one or more atoms. An atom has a positively charged nucleus and revolving round it are one or more electrons so that the atom, on the whole, is neutral. These electrons revolve in more or less circular orbits having radii of the order of 10^{-10} metre and are, therefore, confined within a very small region. These are known as *bound electrons.*

Electrons revolving in orbits close to the nucleus are more strongly bound to it than the electrons moving in the outer orbits. The atoms in a solid are very closely packed, the inter atomic distance being of the order of 5×10^{-10} metre. The neighbouring atoms exert *inter-atomic* forces due to the interaction of charge distribution on them. In some of the atoms these forces are sufficiently strong and are able to detach the outermost electrons which is most loosely bound from the parent atom. These electrons move about freely within the boundaries of the material just like the molecules of a gas in a vessel and collide with each other as well as with the positively charged ions formed due to the detachement of the electron (negatively charged) from the neutral atom. These electrons are known as *free electrons.*

In a *good conductor* each atom on an average gives rise to one free electron. In a solid the number of atoms per c.c. is of the order of 10^{22}. We therefore, suppose that the number of free electrons is also the same *i.e.,* 10^{22} electrons/c.c. Metals like Ag, Cu, Al are typical examples of good conductors.

In an *insulator* or *bad conductor* the atoms do not lose their outermost electron due to inter atomic forces and there are practically no free electrons. The conductivity of such materials is hardly 10^{-20} times the conductivity of a good conductor. Substances like glass, ebonite and mica are typical examples of insulators. Such substances are also known as *dielectrics.* [See part (*b*)]

The interatomic forces in liquids are much weaker than those in solids because the interatomic distances are about 10 times larger. Hence liquids are mainly insulators. Mercury is an exception. The conductivity of electrolytes like $CuSO_4$ solution is due to the dissociation of the molecule into positively charged Cu^{++} and negatively charged SO_4^{--} ions which move about freely in the liquid like free electrons and when a potential difference is applied the positive ions move from positive to negative and negative ions from negative to positive electrode thereby giving rise to a conduction current.

In gases the inter atomic distances are again 10 times greater than that in the case of liquids. The interatomic forces are even weaker and there are practically no free electrons. Gases are, therefore, mostly *insulators*.

Semiconductors are such materials which have conductivity about half way between good conductors and insulators *i.e.*, their conductivity is about 10^{-10} times the conductivity of good conductors. These substances form a very useful class and find a number of applications in solid state electronic devices.

(*b*) **Dielectrics.** *A dielectric substance is a material which does not conduct electricity i.e.*, dielectrics are insulators. In such substances the electrons are firmly bound to the atoms of the material. These electrons can, therefore, move through very small distances of the order of atomic dimensions. There are practically no free electrons in dielectrics. Familiar examples are glass, mica, ebonite, paraffine wax and air.

Importance. The importance of dielectric, lies in the fact that dielectric materials are very good insulators. Electric current flows through high tension wires because air (as dielectric) is very good insulator. High voltage transformers are immersed in oil, a high insulator dielectric, to avoid leakage. Porcelain clamps are used at the top of electric poles to insulate the poles from earth. Dielectrics like rubber, plastic etc. are used as cover (sheaths) for underground and overhead cables. Dielectric like mica and paper are used in high quality capacitors employed in radio and television transmission and reception circuits.

Q. 5.2 What are polar and non-polar molecules? Discuss the effect of electric fields on polar dielectrics. What is meant by polarisation of a dielectric?

(*K.U.* 2001, 2000; *Kerala U.* 2001; *P.U.* 2001, 1995, 1992; *Nagpur U.* 2001;
Gauhati U. 2000; *Meerut. U.* 2002; *M.D.U.* 2002; *Gharwal U.* 1999; *Kan.U.*1997, 1995, 1995;
Agra U. 1995; *Pbi.U.* 1995, 1992; *H.P.U.* 2007, 1995; *G.N.D.U.* 2004, 1990)

Ans. Polar and non-polar molecules. All substances can be classified into two types as regards their behaviour in an electric field.

(*b*) *Conductors* in which there are a large number of free electrons, just behaving like gas molecules.

(*c*) *Insulators* or *dielectrics* which do not contain any free electrons.

According to the quantum theory *neutral* atoms in their *ground* state consist of a central *positively* charged nucleus surrounded by a *spherically symmetric cloud of equal negative* charge of smoothly varying charge density. The radius of this electron cloud constitutes the atomic radius and is of the order of 10^{-10} m. Thus for an atom, in its ground state, the *centre of gravity* of its negative charge lies exactly at its nucleus which is taken to be a *point* positive charge. The dipole moment of an atom is, therefore, zero.

For a molecule the positive charge is supposed to be concentrated, at the nuclear points and the negative charge forming a cloud of smoothly varying density around the constituent nuclei. Depending upon the shape of this cloud and variation of charge density inside it, the molecules of a dielectric can be classified into two types (*i*) *non-polar molecules* and (*ii*) *polar molecules*.

(*i*) **Non-polar molecules.** *The molecules in which the centre of gravity of positive charges exactly coincides with that of the negative charges* and *the net dipole moment is zero are called non-polar molecules.*

These molecules do not have any permanent dipole moment because the dipole length is zero. Familiar examples are H_2, O_2, N_2, CO_2, CCl_4 and CH_4.

(ii) Polar molecules. *The molecules in which the centre of gravity of positive charges does not coincide with that of the negative charges are known as polar molecules.* Such molecules, therefore, constitute a permanent dipole and have a permanent dipole moment. Familiar examples are H_2O, HCl and NH_3. These molecules consist of dissimilar atoms and their dipole moments are of the order of 10^{-29} coulomb metre which means a separation of 1 Å (10^{-10} m) between the centres of positive and negative charges of magnitude 1 electronic unit (1.6×10^{-19} C).

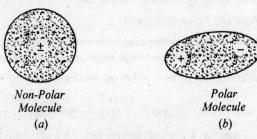

Non-Polar
Molecule
(a)

Polar
Molecule
(b)

Fig. 5.1

Polar molecules in the absence of electric field. In the absence of any external electric field, in any bulk material, the molecular dipoles are randomly oriented and their electric dipole moments

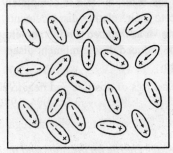

point in all possible directions cancelling out the effect of each other as shown in Fig. 5.2. Hence, if we take a *macroscopic* view the material will not show any dipole moment and the *net resultant dipole moment per unit volume is zero.* It should be noted that though the individual molecules have dipole moments, the dipole moment of the bulk dielectric sample is zero.

Polar molecules in the presence of electric field. When an electric field is applied the electric dipole moments tend to align themselves in the direction of external field.

Fig. 5.2

If $\vec{E_0}$ is the applied external field and $\vec{p}$ the molecular dipole moment, then

Torque experienced by each molecule $\vec{\tau} = \vec{p} \times \vec{E_0}$.

This torque tends to align the molceules in the direction of the applied electric field. This tendency of alignment is opposed by thermal agitation of the molecules. Thus the degree of alignment of the molecules depends upon

(a) The intensity of the applied electric field and

(b) The temperature of the dipole.

Greater the intensity of the electric field greater will be the separation between the centres of gravity of the positive and negative charges. The increase in dipole length will increase the dipole moment and thus the dipole moment per unit volume will increase. The net effect is a greater torque tending to align the molecules in the direction of the applied electric field.

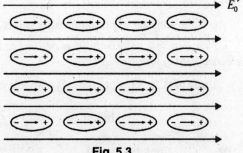

Lower the temperature lesser will be the thermal vibrations of the molecules and hence it

Fig. 5.3

will be easier for the molecular dipoles to align in the direction of the field.

Polarisation of a dielectric. As a result of alignment the dielectric material when placed in an electric field acquires a net dipole moment. This dipole moment being due to the applied electric field is known as *induced dipole moment.*

When the molecules of a dielectric are aligned completely or partially in the direction of the electric field, the dielectric is said to be polarised. A polarised dielectric is shown in Fig. 5.3.

Exercise. *Molecules consisting of dissimilar atoms are usually polar. Why?* (*P.U.*, 2005)

Hint. See under the head (*ii*) **Polar molecules.**

Q. 5.3 (*a*). **What happens when a non-polar molecule is placed in an electric field? Define atomic dipole moment and atomic polarisability. What are its dimensions? Give its S.I. Units.**

(*b*) **How long does polarisation of non-polar molecules last?**

(*P.U.* 2001, 2000; *H.P.U.* 2001, 1999, 1997, 1996; *G.N.D.U.* 2008, 2007, 2006, 2001, 1996; *Kerala U.* 2001)

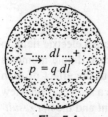

Fig. 5.4

Ans. (*a*) Effect of electric field on a non-polar dielectric. When a non-polar molecule is placed in an electric field, the centre of the positive charge moves in the direction of the field and the centre of the negative charge in an opposite direction. This separation of positive and negative charges continues till the force on either of them due to the external field is completely balanced by the internal forces arising due to their relative displacements. The molecule develops a dipole moment known as *induced dipole* moment. Such a molecule is said to be *polarised.* The induced dipole moment disappears as soon as the electric field is removed.

Atomic dipole moment. If $d\vec{l}$ is the separation between the centres of positive and negative charges and q is the positive or negative charge on the atom, then

Atomic dipole moment $\vec{p} = q\,d\,\vec{l}$

Thus atomic dipole moment is the product of the positive or negative charge on the atom and the distance between the centres of the positive and the negative charges in the direction of the applied electric field.

Atomic polarisability. The net induced electric dipole moment for an atom $\vec{p}$ is proportional to the strength of the applied electric field $\vec{E_0}$ and its direction is also parallel to that of $\vec{E_0}$

$$\vec{p} = \alpha\,\vec{E_0}$$

or

$$\alpha = \frac{\vec{p}}{\vec{E_0}}$$

α is the constant of proportionality and is known as the *atomic polarisability.*

Hence atomic polarisability is defined as the electric dipole moment induced in the atom by an electric field of unit strength.

Units of α. In S.I. units, the unit of dipole moment $\vec{p}$ Cm and the unit of electric field $\vec{E}$ is Vm^{-1}.

$$\therefore \qquad \text{Unit of } \alpha = \frac{Cm}{Vm^{-1}} = Cm^2 V^{-1}$$

As $\dfrac{C}{V} = \dfrac{\text{Coulomb}}{\text{volt}}$ = Farad, the unit of capacitance, the unit of atomic polarisability α may also be put as Farad m^2 (Fm^2).

Dimensions of α. The dimensions of dipole moment $\vec{p}$ are $[Q^1 L^1]$ and that of electric field $\vec{E}_0$

i.e. Force per unit charge $\quad = \dfrac{F}{Q} = \left[M^1 L^1 T^{-2} Q^{-1} \right]$

$\therefore$ Dimensions of $\quad \alpha = \dfrac{[Q^1 L^1]}{[M^1 L^1 T^{-2} Q^{-1}]} = [M^{-1} T^2 Q^2]$

Note. In S.I. units the atomic polarisability is some times defined as $\alpha = \dfrac{\vec{p}}{\varepsilon_0 \vec{E}}$. The dimensions

of $\varepsilon_0 \vec{E}$ = (Dimensions of ε_0) × (Dimension of $\vec{E}$) = $(C^2 N^{-1} m^{-2})(N^1 C^{-1})$ = Cm^{-2}.

$\therefore$ Dimensions of $\quad \alpha = \dfrac{Cm}{Cm^{-2}} = m^3$

i.e., the dimensions of α are those of volume $[L^3]$. We shall, however define $\alpha = \dfrac{\vec{p}}{\vec{E}}$ and take its
dimensions a $[C\, m^2\, V^{-1}]$

(*b*) The induced dipole moment *i.e.* polarisation in non-polar molecules lasts only for the time
the electric field is applied. It disappears as soon as the electric field is removed.

Exercise. *Show that unit of atomic polarisability is $F\, m^2$.* $\hfill$ (*P.U.*, 2007)

Hint. See **Q 5.3** under the head ('**units of α**')

**Q.5.4. What is atomic polarisability? Find a relation between dipole moment and atomic
polarisability.**

OR

Show that $\vec{p} = \alpha\, \vec{E}_0$

(*G.N.D.U.*, 2007; *P.U.*, 2006; *H.P.U.*, 1999, 1997; *Luck. U.*, 1992; *Pbi. U.*, 1995)

Ans. Atomic polarisability. *Atomic polarisability is defined as the electric dipole moment
induced in the atom by an electric field of unit strength.*

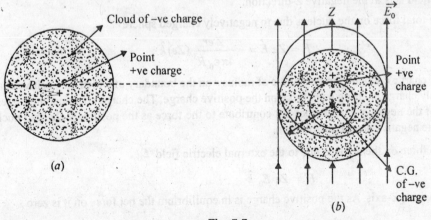

Fig. 5.5

If $\vec{p}$ is the dipole moment induced in an atom by an external electric field $\vec{E}_0$, then

Atomic polarisability $\quad \alpha = \dfrac{\vec{p}}{\vec{E}_0}$

Induced dipole moment. To calculate the value of induced atomic dipole moment, consider an atom of atomic number Z, then positive charge on the nucleus $= + Ze$.

As the atom is on the whole neutral, the charge carrried by all the electrons $= - Ze$.

It is assumed that the positive charge lies exactly at the centre of a sphere of radius R and the negative charge is distributed uniformly in the form of a spherical cloud so that the centre of gravity of the negative charge also lies exactly at the centre of the sphere and coincides with the centre of gravity of the positive charge as shown in Fig. 5.5 (a). In such a case the atom has zero dipole moment.

An electric field $\vec{E}_0$ is now applied in the Z-direction. The positive charge being firmly fixed in the nucleus is supposed to continue in its original position. On the other hand it is assumed that the negatively charged spherical cloud is not distorted in shape by the external electric field but is only bodily displaced in the negative Z-direction as shown in Fig. 5.5 (b).

In the equilibrium position let r be the separation between the positively charged nucleus and the centre of negative charge distribution, then

The magnitude of induced dipole moment of the atom $p = Ze\,r$ ...(i)

Assuming that the volume charge density ρ in the cloud of negative charge has a uniform value and R is the radius of the atom

$$\rho = \frac{-Ze}{\frac{4}{3}\pi R^3}$$

and charge within a radius of sphere r

$$= \frac{4}{3}\pi r^3 \rho = \frac{-Ze}{\frac{4}{3}\pi R^3}\frac{4}{3}\pi r^3 = -Ze\frac{r^3}{R^3}$$

The field at the nucleus due to negative charge within the sphere of radius r

$$\vec{E} = -Ze\frac{r^3}{R^3}\cdot\frac{1}{4\pi\varepsilon_0 r^2}\hat{k} = -\frac{Z\,er}{4\pi\varepsilon_0 R^3}\hat{k}$$

i.e., the field acts in the negative Z-direction.

The total force on the nucleus due to negatively charged sphere

$$\vec{F} = Ze\,\vec{E} = -\frac{Z\,er}{4\pi\varepsilon_0 R^3}(Ze)\hat{k}$$

The charge contained in the sphere of radius r on the boundary of which the positive charge lies is the only charge exerting a net force on the positive charge. The charge contained in the rest of the sphere of the negative charge does not contribute to the force as the positively charged nucleus lies within the negative charge distribution.

The force on the nucleus due to the external electric field $\vec{E}_0$

$$\vec{F'} = Ze\,E_0\,\hat{k}$$

along positive Z-axis. As the positive charge is in equilibrium the net force on it is zero

i.e., $\vec{F} + \vec{F'} = 0$

This is possible when

$$Ze\,E_0\,\hat{k} - \frac{Z\,er\,(Ze)}{4\pi\varepsilon_0 R^3}\hat{k} = 0.$$

or $$Zer = 4\pi\,\varepsilon_0\,R^3\,E_0 \qquad\qquad ...(ii)$$

Comparing (i) and (ii), we have

Magnitude of induced atomic dipole moment $p = Zer = 4\pi\varepsilon_0\,R^3\,E_0$ ...(iii)

Relation between dipole moment and atomic polarisability. The relation $p = 4\pi\,\varepsilon_0\,R^3\,E_0$ may be put in the form $p = \alpha\,E_0$ where $\alpha = 4\pi\,\varepsilon_0\,R^3$ is the induced atomic polarisability. It is defined as *atomic dipole moment per unit polarising electric field.*

The magnitude of dipole moment induced in the atom (or molecule)

p = charge × separation between the centres of positive and negative charges = $Z\,e\,r$

The direction of the dipole moment p is from the negative charge to positive charge *i.e.,* along the direction of electric field.

$$\therefore \qquad \frac{\vec{p}}{\vec{E}_0} = \alpha \quad \text{or} \quad \vec{p} = \alpha\,\vec{E}_0$$

Thus the induced dipole moment is proportional to the external electric field $\vec{E}_0$. As soon as $\vec{E}_0$ is removed $\vec{P}$ becomes zero.

Q. 5.5. Will an atom having a spherically symmetric charge distribution be polar or non-polar? Explain. *(H.P.U., 1997; G.N.D.U., 1991)*

Ans. Atoms with spherically symmetric charge distribution are non-polar and have zero dipole moment.

Consider an atom having atomic number Z. The positive charge on the atom is $+ Ze$. This charge is concentrated within the nucleus and can be supposed to act at the centre of the atom. The negative charge on the atom is also $- Ze$ as the atom is on the whole, neutral. In a spherically symmetric atom this charge is distributed uniformly over the volume of the atom *i.e.,* the electrons revolving round the nucleus behave as spherically symmetric cloud of negative charge with the centre of gravity of the cloud at the centre of the atom. Thus the centre of gravity of the positive as well as the negative charge will coincide.

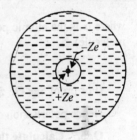

Fig. 5.6

The atom will, therefore, have zero dipole moment and hence will be *non-polar.*

Q. 5.6. Define polarisation density vector $\vec{P}$. Show that for a non-polar dielectric

$$\vec{P} = N\,\varepsilon_0\,(4\pi\,R^3)\,\vec{E}$$

where N is the number of molecules per unit volume, $\vec{E}$ the electric field and R the radius of the atom. *(M.D.U., 1999; H.P.U., 1995; P.U., 1991)*

Ans. Polarisation density vector $\vec{P}$. When a dielectric slab is placed in an electric field the molecular dipoles whether induced or permanent align themselves in the direction of the field. As a result of alignment the dielectric material acquires a net *dipole moment* known as *induced dipole moment* and the dielectric is said to be *polarised.*

If we consider any point inside the dielectric and $\Delta\vec{p}$ is the dipole moment of a small volume ΔV around this point then, the average dipole moment per unit volume $= \dfrac{\Delta\vec{p}}{\Delta V}$.

In the limit when $\Delta V \to 0$ i.e.,

$$\underset{\Delta V \to 0}{Lt} \frac{\Delta \vec{p}}{\Delta V} = \vec{P}$$

where $\vec{P}$ is the *polarisation density vector.*

Hence the polarisation $\vec{P}$ *(or density of polarisation or polarisation density vector) is defined as electric dipole moment per unit volume.*

In a region of *uniform* polarisation where all dipoles are pointing in the same direction the induced dipole density is given by the product of induced dipole moment and the number of dipoles (or atoms) in a unit volume. If N is the number of dipoles (or atoms) per unit volume, then

Dipole moment density $= N\vec{p} = \vec{P}$

The dimension of P are $\dfrac{\text{charge} \times \text{length}}{(\text{length})^3} = \dfrac{\text{charge}}{(\text{length})^2}$

In other words the dimensions of $\vec{P}$ are the same as those of $\varepsilon_0\,E$. The vector $\vec{p}$ and $\vec{P}$ are in the direction of relative displacement of positive charge *i.e.,* from negative to positive charge.

Value of $\vec{P}$. The induced electric dipole moment for a molecule (or atom) placed in an electric field $\vec{E}$ is given by

$$\vec{p} = \alpha \vec{E}$$

where α is the atomic polarisability and has a value $\alpha = 4\pi\,\varepsilon_0\,R^3$ (R being the radius of the atom/molecule).

$$\therefore \qquad \vec{p} = 4\pi\varepsilon_0\,R^3\,\vec{E}$$

(For proof See Q. 5.4 Eq. (*iii*))

Hence polarisation density vector (or polarisation) $\vec{P} = N\vec{p} = N\varepsilon_0\,(4\pi R^3)\vec{E}$

Q. 5.7. Calculate the induced dipole moment per unit volume of He gas if placed in a field of 6000 volts/cm. The atomic polarisability of He = 0.18 × 10⁻⁴⁰ farad m² and density of He is 2.6 × 10²⁵ atoms per m³. Also calculate the separation between the centres of positive and negative charges.

Ans. Electric field $\qquad \vec{E} = 6000$ volts/cm $= 6 \times 10^5$ volts/m

Atomic polarisability of *He,* $\quad \alpha = 0.18 \times 10^{-40}$ Farad m²

Number of atoms per m³ $\qquad N = 2.6 \times 10^{25}$

Dipole moment of He atom $\quad \vec{p} = \alpha \vec{E} = 0.18 \times 10^{-40} \times 6 \times 10^5 = 1.08 \times 10^{-35}$ C-m

Induced dipole moment per unit volume $\vec{P} = N\vec{p} = 2.6 \times 10^{25} \times 1.08 \times 10^{-35}$

$$= 2.81 \times 10^{-10} \text{ C/m}^2$$

Charge on *He* nucleus $\qquad q = 2e = 2 \times 1.6 \times 10^{-19}$ C

$$\therefore \qquad \vec{p} = qd\,\vec{l}$$

Separation between the positive and negative charges of the atom

$$d\,\vec{l} = \frac{\vec{p}}{q} = \frac{1.08 \times 10^{-40}}{2 \times 1.6 \times 10^{-19}} = 3.37 \times 10^{-17} \text{ m}$$

Q. 5.8. Show that the surface charge density at the surface of a uniformly polarised slab is $P \cos \theta = \vec{P}.\hat{n}$ where $\vec{P}$ is the polarisation density and θ the angle between the direction of polarisation and normal to the surface of the end. When is the polarisation density equal to induced surface charge density?

(*H.P.U.*, 2003; *Kerala U.* 2001; *M.D.U.* 1999; *Kan. U.*, 1995; *Luck. U.*, 1995, 1992; *G.N.D.U.*, 1994)

Ans. Relation between surface charge density and polarisation density. When a dielectric slab is placed in an electric field $\vec{E}_0$, the molecular dipoles whether induced or permanent align

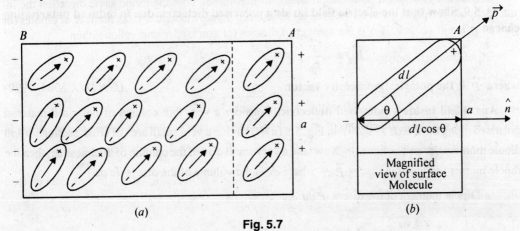

(*a*)   (*b*)

Fig. 5.7

themselves in the direction of the field so that the positive charge of one molecule lies just close to the negative charge of the succeeding molecule. Thus the positive charge on one molecule is neutralised due to an equal negative charge on the next molecule except the molecules at the extreme ends A and B of the slab. At the end A all the molecules have their positive charge free and thus give rise to a positive charge on the surface A. Similarly at the end B all the molecules have their negative charge free and thus give rise to a negative charge on the surface B. Thus the charge developed due to polarisation at the end A or B of the dielectric slab lies within a layer of molecular thickness. If dl is the diameter of the molecule *i.e.*, the distance between the centre of the negative charge and the centre of the positive charge and a, the surface area of the slab, then the volume of the molecular layer $= a \, dl \cos \theta$ where θ is the angle between the direction of the applied electric field or that of the molecular polarisation $\vec{P}$ and the outward drawn normal to the surface as shown in Fig. 5.7. (*b*).

If the number of molecules per unit volume $= N$, then the number of molecules in the layer $= N \, a \, dl \cos \theta$

$\therefore$ Positive charge induced at the end $A = N \, dl \cos \theta \, q$

where q is the positive charge on each molecule.

Hence induced surface charge density $\sigma_p = \dfrac{N a \, dl \cos \theta \, q}{a} = N \, dl \cos \theta \, q$

[σ_p is sometimes denoted as σ_i to indicate that it is the induced charge density or σ_{bound} to indicate that this charge density is bound to the dielectric and does not take part in electrical conduction].

Now $q \, dl = p =$ the electric dipole moment of the molecule and $q \, dl \cos \theta = p \cos \theta = \vec{P}.\hat{n}$ where $\hat{n}$ is the outward drawn unit vector normal to the surface as shown in Fig. 5.7 (*b*).

Induced surface charge density $\sigma_p = N p \cos \theta = P \cos \theta$

or   induced surface charge density $\sigma_p = N\vec{p}.\hat{n} = \vec{P}.\hat{n}$ ...(i)

i.e., σ_p = The normal component of $\vec{P}$ the dipole moment per unit volume or density of polarisation.

Special case. When the direction of applied electric field and the direction of molecular dipole moment is the same as the outward drawn normal, $\theta = 0$ and $\cos\theta = 1$

$\therefore$ $\sigma_p = P$ (or $\sigma_{bound} = P$)

i.e. Induced (or bound) surface charge density = polarisation per per unit volume or **polarisation density.**

Q. 5.9. Show that the electric field inside a polarised dielectric due to induced polarisation charge

$$\vec{E}_p = -\frac{\vec{P}}{\varepsilon_0}$$

where $\vec{P}$ is the polarisation density vector.   (G.N.D.U. 2004, 1999)

Ans. Field inside a polarised dielectric. Consider a very thin column of polarised material polarised along the Z-axis as shown in Fig. 5.8 (a) (i) having a very small area of cross-section da and dipole moment per unit volume $\vec{P}$. Now take a very small disc of the column of thickness dz, then the dipole moment of this thin disc = $\vec{P}\,dv$ where dv is the volume of the disc = $da\,dz$.

$\therefore$ Dipole moment of the disc = $\vec{P}\,da\,dz$.

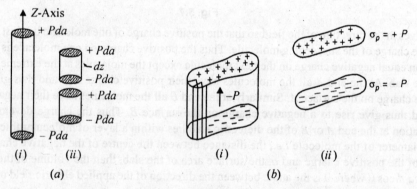

Fig. 5.8

As the column is very thin $da \to 0$ and the disc can be supposed to consist of a *point* charge $+ Pda$ at the top and a *point* charge $- Pda$ at its bottom so that the magnitude of the dipole moment = $Pda\,dz$. The whole column can be, therefore, supposed to be made up of a very large number of similar discs placed one above the other as shown in Fig. 5.8 (a) (ii). In such a case the positive charge on the top of one disc will be completely neutralised by the negative charge on the bottom of the disc placed on it. Proceeding in this way we build up the thin column. It will behave as a dipole consisting of a charge $+ Pda$ at the top and $- Pda$ at the top and $- Pda$ at the bottom. Hence a thin small layer of charge $+ Pda$ at the top and $- Pda$ at the bottom of a thin column will produce the same electrical effects as the whole polarised column of the dielectric material does.

Now we place a number of such columns side by side so as to make a slab of dielectric material uniformly polarised in a direction perpendicular to its parallel faces as shown in Fig. 5.8 (b) (i). This will behave as a pair of charged sheets having a surface charge density $\sigma_p = + P$ at the top and $\sigma_p = - P$ at the bottom as shown in Fig. 5.8 (b) (ii).

Now consider a thin slab of the dielectric having a very large surface area and very small thickness as shown in Fig. 5.9 (a). As proved above this can be considered to be equivalent to two infinitely large charged sheets having a charge $\sigma_p = + P$ at the top sheet and $\sigma_p = - P$ at the bottom sheet as shown in Fig. 5.9 (b).

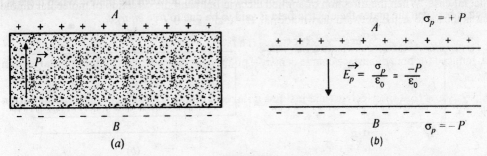

$$A \qquad \qquad \sigma_p = + P$$

$$\vec{E_p} = \frac{\sigma_p}{\varepsilon_0} = \frac{-P}{\varepsilon_0}$$

$$B \qquad \sigma_p = - P$$

(a) \qquad\qquad\qquad (b)

Fig. 5.9

∴ The electric field at a point well away from the edges within the space between the two charged surfaces $= \dfrac{\sigma_p}{\varepsilon_0}$.

Hence the average electric field $<\vec{E}>$ inside the thin polarised slab $= \dfrac{\sigma_p}{\varepsilon_0}$ acting from top to bottom i.e., in a direction opposite to the direction of polarisation $\vec{P}$

∴ $$<\vec{E}> = \frac{\sigma_p}{\varepsilon_0} = \frac{-\vec{P}}{\varepsilon_0} \qquad\qquad\qquad [\because \ \sigma_p = - P]$$

This average electric field $<\vec{E}>$ is the *spatial average* of the electric field at various points within the polarised slab and is given by

$$<\vec{E}> = \frac{1}{V} \iiint \vec{E}\, dv$$

The actual field $\vec{E}$ at different points being widely different due to the presence of displaced charges within the molecules of the dielectric, the average electric field is the *macroscopic* average field within the dielectric material due to the induced polarisation charge.

If we denote this field by $\vec{E_p}$, then

$$\vec{E_p} = -\frac{\vec{P}}{\varepsilon_0} \qquad\qquad\qquad\qquad\qquad\qquad ...(i)$$

Q. 5.10. Define and explain the three electric vectors $\vec{P}, \vec{E}$ and $\vec{D}$. Why electric field inside a dielectric decreases due to polarisation? Show that $D = \varepsilon_0 \vec{E} + \vec{P}$. Also give their units. *(Meerut. U., 2006; K.U. 2002; P.U. 2001, 2000; H.P.U. 2001, 2000,1996 Indore. U. 2001; M.D.U. 2001; Gharwal. U. 1999; Osm. U. 1997; Kan. U. 1997, 1996; G.N.D.U. 1999, 1991; Luck. U. 1995; Pbi.U. 2007, 1994)*

Ans. Polarisation density vector $\vec{P}$. For definition and explanation of $\vec{P}$ see Q. 5.6.

The electric field inside a polarised dielectric due to induced polarisation charge is given by

$$\vec{E_p} = -\frac{\vec{P}}{\varepsilon_0} \qquad\qquad\qquad\qquad\qquad\qquad ...(i)$$

For proof See **Q. 5.9.** Eq. (*i*)

Net electric field vector $\vec{E}$. To define and explain the net electric field vector $\vec{E}$, we shall calculate the electric field between the plates of a parallel plate capacitor when there is no dielectric between the plates and also when there is a dielectric medium between the plates. When there is no dielectric between the plates the electric field is said to be due to *free charge*.

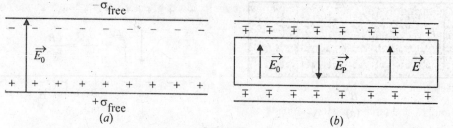

(*a*)   (*b*)

Fig. 5.10

Electric field between capacitor plates due to free charge. Consider a parallel plate capacitor having a positive charge of surface density $+\sigma_{free}$ at the lower plate and $-\sigma_{free}$ at the upper plate. We denote the charge density due to the external charge supplied to the capacitor as σ_{free} to distinguish it from the induced charge density developed due to polarisation which we call as bound or polarisation charge density and denote it as σ_{bound} or σ_p.

When there is no dielectric between the capacitor plates *i.e.*, it is free space or vacuum, electric field between the two plates is given by

$$\vec{E}_0 = \frac{\sigma_{free}}{\varepsilon_0} \qquad\qquad ...(ii)$$

Electric field between capacitor plates with dielectric. When the space between the capacitor plates is filled with the dielectric, polarisation charge develops, positive on the upper surface and negative on the lower surface. If $\vec{P}$ is the polarisation per unit volume, then for an isotropic dielectric, the polarisation vector $\vec{P}$ is parallel to $\vec{E}_0$ and the average (macroscopic) electric field due to polarisation

$$\vec{E}_p = -\frac{\vec{P}}{\varepsilon_0}$$

i.e., acting opposite to $\vec{E}_0$ within the capacitor and in the dielectric.

The net electric field is given by

$$\vec{E} = \vec{E}_0 + \vec{E}_p = \vec{E}_0 - \frac{\vec{P}}{\varepsilon_0} \qquad\qquad ...(iii)$$

Hence *net electric field $\vec{E}$ within the dielectric is defined as the vector sum of the electric field $\vec{E}_0$ due to free charge density σ_{free} and polarisation field $\vec{E}_p$ due to bound charge density σ_p.*

Why electric field inside a dielectric decreases? It is clear from equation (*iii*) that the electric field in the dielectric is reduced due to charges induced on its surface by the applied electric field $\vec{E}_0$ as the induced electric field due to dielectric polarisation $\vec{E}_p = -\frac{\vec{P}}{\varepsilon_0}$ acts in a direction opposite to that of $\vec{E}_0$.

Electric displacement vector D. Relation (iii) can be put as

$$\vec{E}_0 = \vec{E} + \frac{\vec{P}}{\varepsilon_0}$$

or

$$\varepsilon_0 \, \vec{E}_0 = \varepsilon_0 \vec{E} + \vec{P}$$

The quantity $\varepsilon_0 \, \vec{E}_0 = \varepsilon_0 \vec{E} + \vec{P}$ within the dielectric is given a special name, the *electric displacement vector* and is denoted by $\vec{D}$.

∴

$$\vec{D} = \varepsilon_0 \, \vec{E}_0 = \varepsilon_0 \vec{E} + \vec{P} \qquad \qquad ...(iv)$$

Relation between three electric vector $\vec{E}, \vec{P}$ and $\vec{D}$. Equation (iv) gives the relation between $\vec{E}, \vec{P}$ and $\vec{D}$, the three electric vectors as

$$\vec{D} = \varepsilon_0 \vec{E} + \vec{P}$$

In free space or vacuum, there is no polarisation $(\vec{P} = 0)$

∴

$$\vec{D} = \varepsilon_0 \vec{E}$$

As all the vectors in relation (iv) act in the same direction we consider their magnitudes and get

$$D = \varepsilon_0 E + P$$

Units. The units of D are the same as those of P or $\varepsilon_0 E$ i.e., Cm^{-2}.

Q. 5.11 (a). Define the terms dielectric constant k and electric susceptibility χ_e. Prove the relation $k = 1 + \chi_e$.

(*Pbi. U.*, 2006; *G.N.D.U.*, 2007)

OR

Derive a relation between dielectric constant and electric susceptibility.

(b) Find the relation between induced charge and free charge when a dielectric material of dielectric constant k is placed between the plates of a parallel plate capacitor.

(*P.U.* 2007, 2002, 2001, 2000; *Meerut U.* 2001, 1999; *Pbi. U.* 2003, 2002, 2001, 1999, 1995; *G.N.D.U.* 2004, 2002, 1997, 1996, 1995; *Kerala U.* 2001; *H.P.U.* 2002, 2000, 1999, 1996, 1995; *Gharwal. U.* 2000, 1999; *Osm. U.* 1997; *K. U.* 1994)

(c) Prove that induced charge varies within the dielectric as $k = \left[1 - \dfrac{\sigma_p}{\sigma_{free}} \right]^{-1}$ where σ_p and σ_{free} are the induced and free surface charge densities respectively. Hence show that for a metal dielectric $k = \infty$.

(*M.D.U.* 2002)

Ans. (a) Dielectric constant. If we consider a parallel plate capacitor having a surface charge density $+ \sigma_{free}$ at the lower plate and $- \sigma_{free}$ at the upper plate, then for free space or vacuum, the electric field between the two plates is given by

$$\vec{E}_0 = \frac{\sigma_{free}}{\varepsilon_0} \qquad \qquad ...(i)$$

acting upward as shown in Fig. 5.10 (a).

When the space between the capacitor plates is filled with a dielectric, polarisation charge develops, positive on the upper surface and negative on the lower surface giving rise to bound polarisation charge density σ_p and polarisation per unit volume $\vec{P}$.

The polarisation electric field $\vec{E}_p = \dfrac{\sigma_p}{\varepsilon_0} = -\dfrac{\vec{P}}{\varepsilon_0}$ ...(ii)

acting in a direction opposite to $\vec{E}_0$.

The net electric field within the dielectric

$$\vec{E} = \vec{E}_0 - \dfrac{P}{\varepsilon_0}$$

or $\qquad\qquad\qquad \varepsilon_0 \vec{E}_0 = \varepsilon_0 \vec{E} + \vec{P}$ ...(iii)

or $\qquad\qquad\qquad \vec{D} = \varepsilon_0 \vec{E} + \vec{P}$ ...(iv)

where $\vec{D}$ is the electric displacement vector.

As the vectors $\vec{D}, \vec{E}_0, \vec{E}$ and $\vec{P}$ all act along the same direction, we can take their magnitudes and get

$$\varepsilon_0 E_0 = \varepsilon_0 E + P$$ ...(v)

and $\qquad\qquad\qquad D = \varepsilon_0 E + P$ ...(vi)

(i) *The ratio of the electric field E_0 between the capacitor plates in vacuum or free space to the net electric field E when the space is filled with the dielectric is known as dielectric constant or specific inductive capacity of the medium and denoted by k. It is also known as relative permittivity and denoted by ε_r.*

∴ Dielectric constant $\qquad k = \dfrac{E_0}{E}$ ...(vii)

$$= \dfrac{\varepsilon_0 E_0}{\varepsilon_0 E} = \dfrac{D}{\varepsilon_0 E}$$ ...(viii)

(ii) *Hence dielectric constant may also be defined as the ratio of displacement D to the net electric field $\varepsilon_0 E$.*

Also $\qquad\qquad E_0 = \dfrac{\sigma_{free}}{\varepsilon_0}$ and $E = E_0 - \dfrac{P}{\varepsilon_0}$ where $P = \sigma_p$

∴ $\qquad\qquad E = \dfrac{\sigma_{free}}{\varepsilon_0} - \dfrac{\sigma_p}{\varepsilon_0} = \dfrac{\sigma_{free} - \sigma_p}{\varepsilon_0}$

Hence dielectric constant $\quad k = \dfrac{E_0}{E} = \dfrac{\sigma_{free}}{\varepsilon_0} \cdot \dfrac{\varepsilon_0}{\sigma_{free} - \sigma_p}$

$$= \dfrac{\sigma_{free}}{\sigma_{free} - \sigma_p}$$ ...(ix)

(iii) *Thus dielectric constant is the ratio of free charge density to the difference between free and bound (polarisation) charge density.*

The dielectric constant k (or relative permittivity ε_r) is a mere number *i.e.*, a *dimensionless constant.*

(i) **k for metals.** For a metallic dielectric between the capacitor plates $\sigma_p = \sigma_{free}$. Substituting in Eq. (ix), we get $k = \infty$.

(ii) **k for vacuum.** For vacuum or free space $\sigma_p = 0$

∴ $\qquad\qquad\qquad k = 1$

Thus dielectric constant for vacuum is **unity.**

(***iii***) As σ_p is less than σ_{free}, the dielectric constant k is always greater than unity for most of the dielectrics.

The dielectric constant k (or relative permittivity ε_r) may also be defined as the ratio of the capacitance of a capacitor with the given dielectric between the plates to the capacitance of the same capacitor with air or vacuum between the plates.

Electric susceptibility. *The ratio of polarisation per unit volume P to the net electric field $\varepsilon_0 E$ as modified by the induced charges on the surface of the dielectric is called electric susceptibility and is denoted by χ_e.*

$\therefore$ For uniform isotropic medium $\chi_e = \dfrac{P}{\varepsilon_0 E}$ ...(x)

Relation between dielectric constant k and electric susceptibility χ_e. According to relation (*v*)

$$\varepsilon_0 E_0 = \varepsilon_0 E + P$$

Dividing both sides by $\varepsilon_0 E$, we get

$$\frac{\varepsilon_0 E_0}{\varepsilon_0 E} = \frac{E_0}{E} = 1 + \frac{P}{\varepsilon_0 E}$$

But $\dfrac{E_0}{E} = k$ and $\dfrac{P}{\varepsilon_0 E} = \chi_e$

$\therefore$ $k = 1 + \chi_e$ ...(xi)

As $k = \varepsilon_r$, we have $\varepsilon_r = 1 + \chi_e$ ...(xi) (a)

Note. As proved in Eq. (*viii*) dielectric constant or relative permittivity

$$\varepsilon_r = \frac{E_0}{E} = \frac{D}{\varepsilon_0 E}$$

$$D = \varepsilon_0 \varepsilon_r E$$

or $D = \varepsilon E$

where $\varepsilon = \varepsilon_0 \varepsilon_r$, the permittivity of the dielectric.

(***b***) **Relation between induced charge and free charge.** According to relation (*ix*)

$$k = \frac{\sigma_f}{\sigma_f - \sigma_p}$$

where k is the dielectric constant of the dielectric material introduced between the plates of a parallel plate capacitor, σ_f the free charge density and σ_p the induced or (bound) charge density due to dielectric polarisation.

$\therefore$ $\sigma_f = k(\sigma_f - \sigma_p)$ or $k\sigma_p = k\sigma_f - \sigma_f$

Hence $\sigma_p = \sigma_f - \dfrac{\sigma_f}{k} = \sigma_f \left(1 - \dfrac{1}{k}\right)$

Multiplying both sides by area A of the capacitor plates we get

$$q_p = q_f \left(1 - \frac{1}{k}\right)$$

where $q_f = A\sigma_f$ and $q_p = A\sigma_p$, q_f being the free charge and q_p the induced charge.

(***c***) According to Eq. (*ix*),

$$k = \frac{\sigma_{free}}{\sigma_{free} - \sigma_p}$$

Dividing numerator and denominator by σ_{free}, we get

$$k = \frac{1}{1 - \frac{\sigma_p}{\sigma_{free}}} = \left[1 - \frac{\sigma_p}{\sigma_{free}} \right]^{-1}$$

For a metallic dielectric.

$$\sigma_p = \sigma_{free}$$

$$\therefore \qquad k = \infty$$

Q. 5.12. (*a*) **Two parallel plates have equal and opposite charges. When the space between them is evacuated the electric intensity is 3×10^5 volts/m and when the space is filled with dielectric the electric intensity is 1.0×10^5 volts/m. What is the induced charge density on the surface of the dielectric?**

(*G.N.D.U.*, 1991)

(*b*) **Two parallel plates having equal and opposite charges are separated by a slab 2 cm thick and having dielectric constant 3. If the electric field strength inside is 10^6 Vm^{-1} calculate the polarisation and displacement of vector.**

(*K.U.* 2000)

Ans. (*a*) Here $\qquad \vec{E_0} = 3 \times 10^5$ volts/m $\qquad\qquad \vec{E} = 1.0 \times 10^5$ volts/m

Now $\qquad\qquad\qquad \vec{D} = \varepsilon_0 \vec{E_0} = \varepsilon_0 \vec{E} + \vec{P}$

and $\qquad\qquad\qquad P = -\sigma_p$

Also $\qquad\qquad\qquad \varepsilon_0 = 8.85 \times 10^{-12}$ C^{2}N^{-1} m^{-2}

$$-\sigma_p = \varepsilon_0 (E_0 - E]$$

$$= 8.85 [3 \times 10^5 - 1 \times 10^5]$$

$$= 1.77 \times 10^{-6} \text{ Coul/m}^2$$

Note. $\qquad\qquad$ Volt/m $= \dfrac{\text{Newton m}}{\text{Coulomb m}} = \dfrac{\text{N}}{\text{C}}$

$$\therefore \qquad \varepsilon_0 \left[E_0 - E \right] = \frac{\text{Coulomb}^2}{\text{Newton m}^2} \times \frac{\text{Newton}}{\text{Coulomb}}$$

$$= \text{Coulomb/m}^2$$

(*b*) Electric field strength between the plates $E = 10^6$ Vm^{-1} = 10^6 NC^{-1}

Dielectric constant $k = 3$

Permittivity of free space $\varepsilon_0 = 8.85 \times 10^{-12}$ C^2 N^{-1} m^{-2}

$\therefore$ Displacement vector $\quad D = k \varepsilon_0 E = 3 \times 8.85 \times 10^{-12} \times 10^6 = 26.55 \times 10^{-6}$ Cm^{-2}

Again $\qquad\qquad\qquad D = \varepsilon_0 E + P$

or $\qquad P = D - \varepsilon_0 E = 3 \varepsilon_0 E - \varepsilon_0 E = 2 \varepsilon_0 E = 2 \times 8.85 \times 10^{-12} \times 10^6 = 17.70 \times 10^{-6}$ Cm^{-2}

Q. 5.13. (*a*) **Define polarisation $\vec{P}$ and dielectric susceptibility χ_e and establish the relation**

$$\vec{P} = \varepsilon_0 \chi_e \vec{E} = \varepsilon_0 (k-1) \vec{E}.$$

(*Kan. U.*, 1996; *K.U.*, 1996; *Pbi. U.*, 1991)

(*b*) **The dielectric constant of Argon at N.T.P. is 1.00538. Calculate the dipole moment induced in each atom of Argon when placed in an electric field of 60 K volt/metre.**

(*Luck. U.*, 1996. 1993)

Ans. Polarisation $\vec{P}$. **See Q. 5.6.**

Electric susceptibility χ_e. **See Q. 5.11.**

Relation. For a uniform isotropic medium $\chi_e = \dfrac{P}{\varepsilon_0\, E}$

or $\qquad\qquad\qquad\qquad P = \varepsilon_0\, \chi_e\, E$

As the vectors $\vec{P}$ and $\vec{E}$ act in the same direction.

$$\vec{P} = \varepsilon_0\, \chi_e\, \vec{E}$$

Now $\qquad\qquad\qquad k = 1 + \chi_e \qquad\qquad \therefore \chi_e = (k - 1)$

Hence $\qquad\qquad\qquad \vec{P} = \varepsilon_0\, \chi_e\, \vec{E} = \varepsilon_0\,(k - 1)\, \vec{E}$

(b) Dielectric constant of Argon at N.T.P = k = 1.00538

Now $\qquad\qquad\qquad \chi_e = (k - 1) = 1.00538 - 1 = 0.000538$

Polarisation $\qquad\qquad P = \varepsilon_0\, \chi_e\, E$

Suppose there are n Argon atoms per unit volume in the gas, then dipole moment induced in each

atom $p = \dfrac{P}{n} = \dfrac{\varepsilon_0\, \chi_e\, E}{n}$

Given $\qquad\qquad\qquad E = 60$ K Volt/metre $= 6 \times 10^4$ Vm^{-1}

Also $\qquad\qquad\qquad \varepsilon_0 = 8.85 \times 10^{-12}$

Number of atoms in one gm. atom of a gas at N.T.P.

$\qquad\qquad = 6.06 \times 10^{23}$ and volume $= 22.4$ litres $= 22.4 \times 10^{-3}$ m^3

$\therefore \qquad\qquad\qquad n = \dfrac{6.06 \times 10^{23}}{22.4 \times 10^{-3}} = 2.7 \times 10^{25}$ Atm/m^3

Hence $\qquad p = \dfrac{\varepsilon_0\, \chi_e\, E}{n} = \dfrac{8.85 \times 10^{-12} \times 0.000538 \times 6 \times 10^4}{2.7 \times 10^{25}} = 10.38 \times 10^{-38}$ Cm

Q. 5.14. (a) **The electric field between the plates of a parallel plate capacitor is** $\vec{E}_0$ **without dielectric. But if dielectric of relative permittivity** ε_r **is introduced between the plates what will the electric field be?** *(Pbi. U., 1990)*

(b) **Dielectric constant of a gas at N.T.P. is 1.00074. Calculate dipole moment of each atom of the gas when it is held in an external field of** 3×10^4 **Vm**$^{-1}$. *(G.N.D.U. 1995)*

Ans. (a) **Electric field.** Let the electric field between the plates of a parallel plate capacitor without dielectric be $\vec{E}_0$. When a dielectric is introduced between the plates of the parallel plate capacitor polarisation charge develops on the surface of the dielectric. The polarisation charge density is negative near the positive plate of the capacitor and positive near the negative plate of the capacitor. The induced surface charge density due to polarisation $\sigma_p = -P$ where P is the magnitude of the polarisation per unit volume and opposite in sign to σ_p. If $\vec{E}$ is the electric field in the dielectric and $\vec{P}$ is the polarisation charge density, then

$$\vec{E}_0 = \vec{E} + \frac{\vec{P}}{\varepsilon_0}$$

or
$$\frac{E_0}{E} = 1 + \frac{P}{\varepsilon_0 E} = 1 + \chi_e = \varepsilon_r$$

$$\therefore \qquad E = \frac{E_0}{\varepsilon_r} \quad \left(\text{or } E = \frac{E_0}{k} \right)$$

(b) Electric field $\qquad E = 3 \times 10^4$ volt/m

Dielectric constant = relative permittivity

$$\varepsilon_r = 1.000074$$

Now $\qquad \varepsilon_r = 1 + \chi_e$ where χ_e is the electric susceptibility.

$$\therefore \qquad \chi_e = \varepsilon_r - 1 = 1.000074 - 1 = 0.000074$$

If P is the induced dipole moment per unit volume, then $\chi_e = \dfrac{P}{\varepsilon_0 E}$

or $\qquad P = \chi_e \varepsilon_0 E$

where $\qquad \varepsilon_0 = 8.85 \times 10^{-12}$ $C^2 N^{-1} m^{-2}$

$$\therefore \qquad P = 0.000074 \times 8.85 \times 10^{-12} \times 3 \times 10^4$$

$$= 19.65 \times 10^{-12} \text{ Cm}$$

Number of gas atoms per gm atom $= 6.06 \times 10^{23}$

Volume per gm atom $= 22.4$ litre $= 22.4 \times 10^{-3}$ cubic metre

$\therefore$ Number of gas atoms per cubic metre

$$N = \frac{6.06 \times 10^{23}}{22.4 \times 10^{-3}} = 2.7 \times 10^{25}$$

$\therefore$ Dipole moment per atom $p = \dfrac{P}{N}$

or $\qquad p = \dfrac{19.65 \times 10^{-12}}{2.7 \times 10^{25}} = 7.28 \times 10^{-37}$ coulomb metre

Q. 5.15. What is the effect of temperature on the dielectric constant of a substance containing molecules of permanent dipole moment? (G.N.D.U. 2003)

Ans. The dielectric constant of a medium is defined as the ratio of free charge density σ_{free} to the difference between the free and bound (or polarisation) change density σ_p.

$$\therefore \qquad k = \frac{\sigma_{free}}{\sigma_{free} - \sigma_p}$$

As the temperature of the polar dielectric is increased the degree of alignment of molecules having permanent dipole moment decreases, thereby decreasing the bound (or polarisation) surface charge density σ_p. As σ_p decreases the ratio $\dfrac{\sigma_{free}}{\sigma_{free} - \sigma_p} = k$ i.e. the dieletric constant also decreases.

Q. 5.16 (a) Derive relationship between electric susceptibility and atomic polarisability on the basis of microscopic description of matter at atomic level.

(H.P.U. 2001; Meerut U. 2001; G.N.D.U. 1999)

(b) Derive Clausius Mossoti relation for non-polar dielectrics.

(Pbi. U. 2008; Meerut U. 2007, 2006, 2002, 2001; Kerala U. 2001; Gharwal U. 2000, 1999)

OR

Establish the relation between polarisability and dielectric constant. (*H.P.U.* 2003)

Ans. (*a*) **Local field in a dielectric.** When a dielectric material is placed in a uniform electric field $\vec{E}_0$ an induced electric field

$$\vec{E}_p = -\frac{\vec{P}}{\varepsilon_0}$$

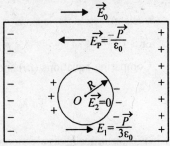

Fig. 5.11

is developed due to induced or bound charges on the surfaces of the dielectric normal to $\vec{E}_0$. $\vec{P}$ is called the *polarisation density vector.*

∴ Net field within the dielectric

$$\vec{E} = \vec{E}_0 - \frac{\vec{P}}{\varepsilon_0}$$

If we consider a molecule well within the dielectric at a point O, then the alignment of this molecule is due to a local electric field $\vec{E}$ acting on it. The local electric field is due to the combined effect of net electric field $\vec{E}$ in the dielectric and two more electric fields $\vec{E}_1$ and $\vec{E}_2$.

To evaluate these two fields draw an imaginary sphere of radius R with centre O – the site of the molecule. The value of R is such that the molecules outside the sphere behave like a continuum and produce an electric field $\vec{E}_1$ and those within it behave like individual molecules and produce an electric field $\vec{E}_2$.

It can be shown that $\vec{E}_1 = \frac{\vec{P}}{3\varepsilon_0}$ and $\vec{E}_2 = 0$ for perfectly symmetric as well as perfectly random distribution.

∴

$$\vec{E}_{Local} = \vec{E} + \frac{\vec{P}}{3\varepsilon_0}$$

Relation between electric susceptibility and atomic polarisability. The dipole moment $\vec{p}$ induced in the molecule is given by

$$\vec{p} = \alpha \vec{E} \qquad \qquad ...(i)$$

where α is the *atomic (or molecular) polarisability defined as dipole moment induced in the molecule (or atom) per unit polarising electric field.*

Taking the polarising electric field $= \vec{E}_{Local}$, we have from equation (*i*)

$$\vec{p} = \alpha \vec{E}_{Local}$$

If N is the number of molecules per unit volume, then

$$\vec{P} = N\vec{p} = N\alpha \vec{E}_{Local} = N\alpha \left(\vec{E} + \frac{\vec{P}}{3\varepsilon_0} \right) \qquad \qquad ...(ii)$$

or

$$\vec{P} - \frac{N\alpha \vec{P}}{3\varepsilon_0} = N\alpha \vec{E}$$

or

$$\vec{P} \left(1 - \frac{N\alpha}{3\varepsilon_0} \right) = N\alpha \vec{E}$$

$$\vec{P} = \frac{N\alpha}{\left(1 - \dfrac{N\alpha}{3\varepsilon_0}\right)} \vec{E}$$

...(iii)

For uniform isotropic medium, electric susceptibility

$$\chi_e = \frac{\vec{P}}{\varepsilon_0 \vec{E}}$$

or

$$\vec{P} = \varepsilon_0 \chi_e \vec{E}$$

...(iv)

Comparing equations (iii) and (iv) we have

$$\varepsilon_0 \chi_e \vec{E} = \frac{N\alpha}{\left(1 - \dfrac{N\alpha}{3\varepsilon_0}\right)} \vec{E}$$

or

$$\chi_e = \frac{1}{\varepsilon_0} \frac{N\alpha}{\left(1 - \dfrac{N\alpha}{3\varepsilon_0}\right)} = \frac{N\alpha}{\left(\varepsilon_0 - \dfrac{N\alpha}{3}\right)}$$

...(v)

Equation (v) gives the relation between electric susceptibility χ_e and atomic polarisation α.

(b) Clausius Mossoti equation. According to relation (ii)

$$\vec{P} = N\alpha \vec{E}_{Local}$$

...(vi)

where $\vec{E}_{Local} = \vec{E} + \dfrac{\vec{P}}{3\varepsilon_0}$, $\vec{E}$ being the *net* electric field within the dielectric. Taking magnitudes only

$$E_{Local} = E + \frac{P}{3\varepsilon_0}$$

...(vii)

Also, *displacement vector* $\vec{D} = \varepsilon_0 \vec{E} + \vec{P} = \varepsilon_r \varepsilon_0 \vec{E}$

or

$$\vec{P} = \varepsilon_r \varepsilon_0 \vec{E} - \varepsilon_0 \vec{E} = \varepsilon_0 \vec{E}(\varepsilon_r - 1)$$

Again, taking magnitudes only

$$P = \varepsilon_0 E (\varepsilon_r - 1)$$

...(viii)

Substituting the above value of P in equation (vii), we get

$$E_{Local} = E + \frac{\varepsilon_0 E(\varepsilon_r - 1)}{3\varepsilon_0} = \frac{E(\varepsilon_r + 2)}{3}$$

...(ix)

From Eq. (vi)

$$E_{Local} = \frac{P}{N\alpha} = \frac{\varepsilon_0 E(\varepsilon_r - 1)}{N\alpha}$$

...(x)

Comparing (ix) and (x), we get

$$\frac{E(\varepsilon_r + 2)}{3} = \frac{\varepsilon_0 E(\varepsilon_r - 1)}{N\alpha}$$

or

$$\frac{N\alpha}{3\varepsilon_0} = \frac{(\varepsilon_r - 1)}{(\varepsilon_r + 2)}$$

...(xi)

Eq. (xi) gives Clausius Mossoti equation in terms of α–the atomic polarisability and ε_r, the relative permittivity or dielectric constant k, (since $\varepsilon_r = k$).

In terms of electric susceptibility. In the above treatment we have defined atomic polarisability $\alpha = \dfrac{\vec{P}}{\vec{E}}$. If however, we define $\alpha = \dfrac{\vec{P}}{\varepsilon_0 \vec{E}}$.

so that α has dimensions of volume $[L^3]$ and its unit is m^3 as explained in **Q. 5.3**, Then relation (*xi*) becomes

$$\frac{N\alpha}{3} = \frac{(\varepsilon_r - 1)}{(\varepsilon_r + 2)} \qquad\qquad ...(xii)$$

Substituting $\varepsilon_r = 1 + \chi_e$ in relation (*xii*), we get

$$\frac{N\alpha}{3} = \frac{(1 + \chi_e - 1)}{(1 + \chi_e + 2)} = \frac{\chi_e}{\chi_e + 3}$$

The relation $\dfrac{N\alpha}{3} = \dfrac{\chi_e}{\chi_e + 3}$ gives Clausius Mossoti equation in terms of χ_e the electric susceptibility of the dielectric.

Q. 5.17. (*a*) **Define capacitance and the units to measure it. Derive an expression for the capacitance of a parallel plate capacitor.** (*G.N.D.U.* 2009; *Vid. S.U.* 1990)

(*b*) **A potential difference of 3000 volt is applied across the two plates of a parallel plate capacitor separated by a distance of 2 cm and area 4 m^2. The potential falls to 1000 Volt when a sheet of dielectric is introduced. Determine**

(*i*)   **Electric field with air as dielectric**

(*ii*) **Capacity with air as dielectric**

(*iii*) **Charge on the dielectric.** (*K.U.* 2001)

Ans. (*a*) **Capacitance.** *Capacitance of a conductor is defined as the ratio of charge on it to its potential*

Capacitance $\qquad\qquad C = \dfrac{Q}{V}$

If $\qquad\qquad\qquad V = 1, \ C = Q$

Hence capacitance may also be defined as the quantity of charge required to raise the potential of a conductor through unity.

The capacitance of a capacitor is the quantity of charge required to establish a unit potential difference between its two coatings.

Units. The unit of capacitance is a **Farad.** The capacitance of a conductor is one farad if its potential difference is raised by one volt when a charge of one coulomb is given to it.

A smaller unit known as a *microfarad* is also used

$$1 \text{ microfarad } (\mu F) = 10^{-6} \text{ farad.}$$

Capacitance of a parallel plate capacitor. A parallel plate capacitor consists of two plates placed parallel to one another separated by a small distance containing air or some other dielectric medium. One of the plates is earthed and a charge is given to the other as shown in Fig. 5.12. Let A be the area of each plate, $+ \sigma$ the *surface density of charge* on the plate A and $- \sigma$ that induced on the plate B, d the distance between the plates, then

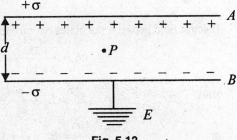

Fig. 5.12

Electric field near a charged conducting plane in air $= \dfrac{\sigma}{2\varepsilon_0}$

$\therefore$ Force experienced by a unit positive charge at a point P

(i) due to the upper plate $A = \dfrac{\sigma}{2\varepsilon_0}$ (repulsion)

and (ii) due to the lower plate $B = \dfrac{\sigma}{2\varepsilon_0}$ (attraction)

The two forces act in the same direction $i.e.$, downward

$\therefore$ Resultant force on a unit positive charge at P

$$= \dfrac{\sigma}{2\varepsilon_0} + \dfrac{\sigma}{2\varepsilon_0} = \dfrac{\sigma}{\varepsilon_0}$$

Hence the work done in moving a unit positive charge from plate B to a plate A against the electrical forces

$$= \dfrac{\sigma}{\varepsilon_0} d$$

because the field between the two plates is uniform and is in a direction perpendicular to the plates.

$\therefore$ Potential difference between the two plates $V_a - V_b = \dfrac{\sigma}{\varepsilon_0} d$

Charge on the plate A, $Q = A\sigma$

$\therefore$ $\qquad$ Capacitance $= \dfrac{Q}{V_a - V_b} = \dfrac{A\sigma}{\dfrac{\sigma}{\varepsilon_0} d} = \dfrac{\varepsilon_0 A}{d}$

(b) Potential difference between the plates of the parallel plate capacitor $V = 3000$ volt

Distance between the plates $d = 2$ cm $= 2 \times 10^{-2}$ m

(i) Electric field with air as dielectric

$$E_0 = \dfrac{V}{d} = \dfrac{3000}{2 \times 10^{-2}} = 1.5 \times 10^5 \text{ Vm}^{-1} \text{ (NC}^{-1}\text{)}$$

Area of each plate $A = 4$ m^2

$$\varepsilon_0 = 8.85 \times 10^{-12} \text{ C}^2 \text{ N}^{-1} \text{ m}^{-2}$$

(ii) Capacity with air as dielectric $C = \dfrac{\varepsilon_0 A}{d}$

$$= \dfrac{8.85 \times 10^{-12} \times 4}{2 \times 10^{-2}} = 17.7 \times 10^{-10} \text{ F}$$

Electric field between the plates on introducing a sheet of dielectric

$$E = \dfrac{1000}{2 \times 10^{-2}} = 0.5 \times 10^5 \text{ Vm}^{-1} \text{ (NC}^{-1}\text{)}$$

Now $\qquad\qquad E = E_0 - \dfrac{P}{\varepsilon_0}$ where P is the polarisation density vector

or $\qquad\qquad \dfrac{P}{\varepsilon_0} = E_0 - E = 1.5 \times 10^5 - 0.5 \times 10^5 = 10^5 \text{ Vm}^{-1}$

But $\qquad\qquad P = \sigma_{bound} = \sigma_p$

$\therefore$ $\qquad\qquad \sigma_p = P = \varepsilon_0 \times 10^5 = 8.85 \times 10^{-12} \times 10^5 = 8.85 \times 10^{-7} \text{ Cm}^{-2}$

(*iii*)   Charge on the dielectric $= \sigma_p \times A$

$$= 8.85 \times 10^{-7} \times 4 = 35.4 \times 10^{-7} \text{ C} = 3.54 \times 10^{-6} \text{ C}$$

$$= 3.54 \ \mu\text{C}.$$

Q. 5.18. (*a*) **Discuss the effect of introducing a dielectric between the plates of a capacitor. Show that the capacitance of a charged capacitor when a dielectric of dielectric constant *k* is introduced between the plates is given by** $k \ \varepsilon_0 \dfrac{A}{d}.$

(*G.N.D.U.*, 2009, 2008, 2007, 1997; *H.P.U.*, 1996; *P.U.*, 2007, 1991)

(*b*) **A capacitor has a capacity of 50 pico farads. Its capacity increases to 200 pico farads when it is filled with a dielectric. Calculate the dielectric constant of the dielectric.**

(*H.P.U.*, 2007)

Ans. Capacitance of a parallel plate capacitor with dielectric. The capacitance of a parallel plate capacitor with free space (or air, or vacuum) as dielectric is given by

$$C_a = \frac{Q}{E_0 d} = \frac{\sigma_{free} A}{\dfrac{\sigma_{free}}{\varepsilon_0} d} = \frac{\varepsilon_0 A}{d}$$

where A is the area of the plates, d the distance between the two plates, E_0 the magnitude of the electric field at a point within the plates, Q the total external charge and σ_{free} the external or free surface charge density $= \dfrac{Q}{A}$.

With the dielectric, the electric field within the dielectric

$$E = E_0 - \frac{P}{\varepsilon_0} = \frac{\sigma_{free}}{\varepsilon_0} - \chi_e E$$

where χ_e is the electric susceptibility of the dielectric.

or $$E (1 + \chi_e) = \frac{\sigma_{free}}{\varepsilon_0}$$

or $$E = \frac{\sigma_{free}}{\varepsilon_0 (1 + \chi_e)} = \frac{\sigma_{free}}{k \varepsilon_0} \qquad\qquad [\because 1 + \chi_e = k]$$

Hence the capacitance of the same capacitor with dielectric of dielectric constant k

$$C_d = \frac{Q}{E d} = \frac{\sigma_{free} A}{\dfrac{\sigma_{free}}{k \varepsilon_0} d} = \frac{k \varepsilon_0 A}{d} \qquad\qquad ...(ii)$$

The dielectric constant $k = \varepsilon_r$ the relative permittivity of the dielectric medium. Substituting $k = \varepsilon_r$ in (*ii*), we get

$$C_d = \frac{\varepsilon_r \varepsilon_0 A}{d} = \frac{\varepsilon A}{d} \qquad\qquad ...(iii)$$

where ε is the absolute permittivity.

Hence $$\frac{\text{The capacitance of a dielectric filled capacitor}}{\text{The capacitance of a vacuum filled capacitor}} = \frac{k \varepsilon_0 A / d}{\varepsilon_0 A / d}$$

or $\dfrac{C_d}{C_a} = k.$ The dielectric constant of the medium.

Hence dielectric constant of a dielectric medium is defined as the ratio of the capacitance of a capacitor with dielectric to the capacitance of the same capacitor with air or vacuum.

When the thickness of the dielectric is less than the distance between the plates. When a plate G of thickness t (less than d, the distance between the capacitor plates) and dielectric constant k (or relative permittivity ε_r) is introduced between the two plates of the air capacitor, then

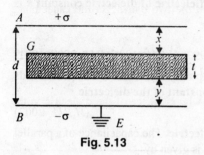

Fig. 5.13

Electric field in the dielectric medium $= \dfrac{\sigma}{\varepsilon_0 \varepsilon_r}$

and in the air space $= \dfrac{\sigma}{\varepsilon_0}$.

[We shall use σ in place of σ_{free}]

Suppose the thickness of air above the plate is x and below the plate is y, then

$$x + y = d - t$$

Hence work done in taking a unit positive charge from B to A against the electrical forces

$$= \frac{\sigma}{\varepsilon_0} y + \frac{\sigma}{\varepsilon_0 \varepsilon_r} t + \frac{\sigma}{\varepsilon_0} x = \frac{\sigma}{\varepsilon_0}\left(x + y + \frac{t}{\varepsilon_r} \right) = \frac{\sigma}{\varepsilon_0}\left(d - t + \frac{t}{\varepsilon_r} \right)$$

$\therefore$ Potential difference $V_A - V_B = \dfrac{\sigma}{\varepsilon_0}\left(d - t + \dfrac{t}{\varepsilon_r} \right)$

Hence capacitance

$$C = \frac{A\sigma}{\dfrac{\sigma}{\varepsilon_0}\left(d - t + \dfrac{t}{\varepsilon_r} \right)} = \frac{\varepsilon_0 A}{d - t + \dfrac{t}{\varepsilon_r}}$$

$$= \frac{\varepsilon_r \varepsilon_0 A}{\varepsilon_r d - t(\varepsilon_r - 1)}$$

In terms of k,

$$C = \frac{\varepsilon_0 A}{d - t + \dfrac{t}{k}} = \frac{k \varepsilon_0 A}{k d - t(k - 1)}$$

(*b*) Capacity with air $C_a = 50 \times 10^{-12}\ F$

Capacity with dielectric

$$C_d = 200 \times 10^{-12}\ F$$

$\therefore$ Dielectric constant

$$k = \frac{C_d}{C_a} = \frac{200 \times 10^{-12}}{50 \times 10^{-12}} = 4$$

Q. 5.19 (*a*). Explain why the introduction of a dielectric slab between the plates of a capacitor changes its capacitance. or the presence of dielectric in the capacitor enhances its capacity. Justify. *(G.N.D.U., 2001; P.U. 1991)*

(*b*) A parallel plate capacitor has air between its two plates which are of area A each and separated by a distance d. Calculate the change in its capacity if a very thin metallic sheet of area A is introduced between the two plates. *(G.N.D.U. 1999)*

Ans. (a) On the introduction of dielectric slab of dielectric constant k between the plates of a capacitor, the electric field intensity at a point between the two plates falls from $\dfrac{\sigma}{\varepsilon_0}$ to $\dfrac{\sigma}{k\varepsilon_0}$ where σ is the charge per unit area on the charged plate. Thus the potential difference between the two plates decreases from $\dfrac{\sigma d}{\varepsilon_0}$ to $\dfrac{\sigma d}{k\varepsilon_0}$ where d is the distance between the two plates. As the capacitance

$C = \dfrac{Q}{V}$, the capacitance increases from $\dfrac{A\sigma}{\dfrac{\sigma}{\varepsilon_0}d} = \dfrac{\varepsilon_0 A}{d}$ to $\dfrac{A\sigma}{\dfrac{\sigma}{k\varepsilon_0}d} = \dfrac{k\varepsilon_0 A}{d}$ i.e., it becomes k times the

capacitance before introduction of the dielectric slab. This is why presence of the dielectric in the capacitor enhances its capacity.

(b) Fig. 5.14 shows a very thin metallic sheet of area A introduced between the two plates of a parallel plate capacitor each of area A separated by a distance d. Let the distance of the thin metallic sheet from the upper plate be x and from the lower plate $(d - x)$.

A negative charge is induced on the upper face of the metal sheet and positive charge on the lower face thereby converting the single capacitor into two capacitors connected in series as the negative of the upper capacitor is connected to the positive of the lower capacitor.

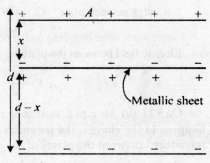

Fig. 5.14

The capacity of the upper capacitor $C_1 = \dfrac{\varepsilon_0 A}{x}$

The capacity of the lower capacitor $C_2 = \dfrac{\varepsilon_0 A}{d - x}$

If C is the combined capacity of C_1 and C_2 connected in series,

$$\frac{1}{C} = \frac{1}{C_1} + \frac{1}{C_2} = \frac{x}{\varepsilon_0 A} + \frac{d - x}{\varepsilon_0 A} = \frac{d}{\varepsilon_0 A}$$

or
$$C = \frac{\varepsilon_0 A}{d}$$

Before introducing the metal sheet, the capacity of the capacitor is also

$$C = \frac{\varepsilon_0 A}{d}$$

There is, therefore, no change in capacity on the introduction of a thin metallic sheet between the plates of a parallel plate capacitor.

Q. 5.20. A potential difference of 200 volts is applied across the two plates of a parallel plate capacitor. The area of each plate is $100\,\pi\ \text{cm}^2$ and separation between the plates is 1 mm. The space between the plates is filled with a mica sheet having $k = 6$. Calculate **(i)** Charge on each plate and **(ii)** Electric field intensity within the sheets.   (*P.U.*, 1995)

Ans. Area of capacitor plates $\quad A = 100\,\pi\ \text{cm}^2$

$$= 100\,\pi \times 10^{-4} = \pi \times 10^{-2}\ \text{m}^2$$

Separation between the plates $\quad d = 1 \text{ mm} = 10^{-3} \text{ m}$

Dielectric constant of the medium k = relative permittivity $\varepsilon_r = 6$

Capacitance $\qquad C = \dfrac{\varepsilon_0 \, \varepsilon_r \, A}{d} = \dfrac{\varepsilon_0 \, 6\pi \times 10^{-2}}{10^{-3}} = 60 \, \pi \, \varepsilon_0$ farad

Now $\qquad \dfrac{1}{4\pi\varepsilon_0} = 9 \times 10^9$

$\therefore \qquad\qquad \pi\varepsilon_0 = \dfrac{1}{4 \times 9 \times 10^9}$

Hence capacitance $\qquad C = 60 \; \pi\varepsilon_0 = \dfrac{60}{4 \times 9 \times 10^9} = \dfrac{1}{6} \times 10^{-8} = 1.67 \times 10^{-9}$ farad

Potential difference between the plates = 200 volts

$\therefore$ Charge on each plate $\quad Q = CV$

$\qquad\qquad\qquad = 200 \times 1.67 \times 10^{-9} = 3.34 \times 10^{-7}$ C

Electric field between the plates

$$E = \frac{V}{d} = \frac{200}{10^{-3}} = 2 \times 10^5 \text{ Volts/m}$$

Q. 5.21 (a) An e.m.f. source is connected to a capacitor and then disconnected. What happens to the charge, the potential difference and the capacitance when a dielectric slab is introduced between the plates of the capacitor? (*P.U.*, 1995)

(*b*) **A condenser with two horizontal metal plates separated by a distance of 4 mm is given a potential of 9.8 V. A particle of mass 0.01 g and charge (– q) is at rest at a point between the plates. Find the value of charge q.** (*Nag. U.* 2001)

Ans. (a) Charge. The charge on the plates of the capacitor *remains unchanged.*

Potential difference. On introducing the dielectric the net electric field between the plates of the capacitor decreases from E_0 to E where $E = E_0/\varepsilon_r$, ε_r being the relative permittivity (or dielectric constant k) of the medium. The potential difference between the plates, therefore, *decreases.*

Capacitance. The capacitance of a parallel plate capacitor with air as dielectric is $C_a = \dfrac{\varepsilon_0 \, A}{d}$

and with the given dielectric is $C_d = \dfrac{\varepsilon_0 \, \varepsilon_r \, A}{d}$ *i.e.*, with the introduction of the dielectric slab the capacitance *increase* ε_r times.

· (*b*) As the charged particle is at rest between the horizontal condenser plates, its downward weight is balanced by the upward electric force

or $\qquad\qquad mg = qE$

Now $\qquad\qquad E = \dfrac{V}{d} = \dfrac{9.8}{4 \times 10^{-3}} = 2.45 \times 10^3 \text{ Vm}^{-1} \text{ (NC}^{-1}\text{)}$

and $\qquad\qquad mg = 0.01 \times 10^{-3} \times 9.8 = 9.8 \times 10^{-5}$ N

$\therefore \qquad\qquad q \times 2.45 \times 10^3 = 9.8 \times 10^{-5}$

or $\qquad\qquad q = \dfrac{9.8 \times 10^{-5}}{2.45 \times 10^3} = 4 \times 10^{-8} \text{ C} = 0.04 \times 10^{-6} \text{ C}$

$\qquad\qquad\qquad = 0.04 \; \mu C.$

Q. 5.22. Can a capacitor store more or less charge with a dielectric than its does without dielectric, for a given potential difference? (P.U., 1992)

Ans. The capacitance of a parallel plate capacitor with vacuum (or free space) between the plates

$$C_a = \frac{\varepsilon_0 A}{d}$$

and with a dielectric of relative permittivity ε_r (or dielectric constant k) the capacitance of the same capacitor is

$$C_d = \frac{\varepsilon_0 \varepsilon_r A}{d}$$

$$\therefore \quad \frac{C_d}{C_a} = \varepsilon_r \quad \text{or} \quad C_d = \varepsilon_r C_a$$

For a given potential difference V, the charge on the air capacitor $Q_a = C_a V$ and the charge on the capacitor with dielectric $Q_d = C_d V$

$$\therefore \quad \frac{Q_d}{Q_a} = \frac{C_d V}{C_a V} = \frac{C_d}{C_a} = \varepsilon_r$$

As $\varepsilon_r > 1$, the capacitor will store more charge with a dielectric than it does without it.

Q. 5.23. Two parallel plates each of area A are separated by two insulating slabs of thickness t_1 and t_2 having dielectric constant k_1 and k_2 respectively. If charges $+ Q$ and $- Q$ are uniformly distributed on the plates, what is the

(i) Electric field within each insulator (ii) Potential difference across the plates (iii) capacitance of the capacitor?

Ans. (i) Electric field within each insulator. Surface density of charge on the plate P

$$= \sigma = +\frac{Q}{A}$$

Surface density of charge on the plate Q

$$= -\sigma = -\frac{Q}{A}$$

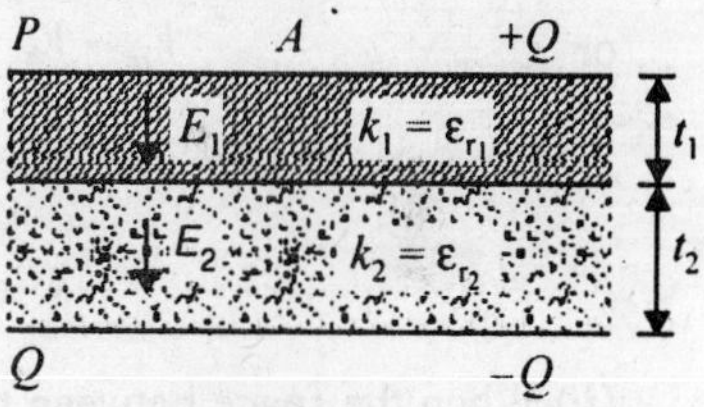

Electric field in the slab of dielectric constant k_1 = relative permittivity ε_{r_1}

Fig. 5.15

$$E_1 = \frac{\sigma}{\varepsilon_0 \varepsilon_{r_1}} \text{ from } P \text{ to } Q$$

Electric field in the slab of dielectric constant k_2 = relative permittivity ε_{r_2}

$$E_2 = \frac{\sigma}{\varepsilon_0 \varepsilon_{r_2}} \text{ from } P \text{ to } Q$$

(ii) Potential difference across the plates. Work done in taking a unit positive charge from plate Q to plate P

$$= \frac{\sigma}{\varepsilon_0 \varepsilon_{r_1}} t_1 + \frac{\sigma}{\varepsilon_0 \varepsilon_{r_2}} t_2$$

$$\therefore \quad \text{Potential difference} \quad V = V_P - V_Q = \frac{\sigma}{\varepsilon_0} \left[\frac{t_1}{\varepsilon_{r_1}} + \frac{t_2}{\varepsilon_{r_2}} \right]$$

(iii) Capacitance of the capacitor. Capacitance of the capacitor

$$C = \frac{A\sigma}{\dfrac{\sigma}{\varepsilon_0} \left[\dfrac{t_1}{\varepsilon_{r_1}} + \dfrac{t_2}{\varepsilon_{r_2}} \right]} = \frac{\varepsilon_0 A}{\dfrac{t_1}{\varepsilon_{r_1}} + \dfrac{t_2}{\varepsilon_{r_2}}}$$

Q. 5.24. Calculate the capacitance of a capacitor consisting of two concentric spheres of radius a and b respectively separated by (*i*) air and (*ii*) a dielectric of dielectric constant k (or relative permittivity ε_r).

(*a*) When the outer sphere is earthed and the inner sphere is charged and (*b*) when the inner sphere is earthed and the outer sphere is charged.

(*Gauhati. U. 2000 Burd. U.,* 1991; *Vid. S. U.,* 1990)

Ans. (*i*) **Capacitance of a spherical capacitor.** Let A and B be the two concentric spheres of radii a and b respectively separated by air. Let the *outer sphere be earthed and a positive charge q be given to the inner sphere.*

Consider a concentric shell of radius x and thickness dx as shown in Fig. 5.16

Electric field at a point distant x from the centre O.

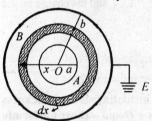

Fig. 5.16

$$E = \frac{1}{4\pi\varepsilon_0}\frac{q}{x^2}$$

The field acts radially outward.

Potential difference between the spheres A and B.

$$V_A - V_B = \int_b^a -\vec{E}.d\vec{r}$$

Since $\vec{E}$ and $d\vec{r}$ have the same direction say, along the X-axis

$$\therefore \quad \int_b^a -\vec{E}.d\vec{r} = \int_b^a -E\,dx = \frac{1}{4\pi\varepsilon_0}\int_b^a -\frac{q}{x^2}dx$$

or

$$V_a - V_b = \frac{q}{4\pi\varepsilon_0}\left[\frac{1}{x}\right]_b^a = \frac{q}{4\pi\varepsilon_0}\left[\frac{1}{a}-\frac{1}{b}\right] = \frac{q}{4\pi\varepsilon_0}\frac{b-a}{ab}$$

$\therefore$ Capacitance of the air capacitor

$$C = \frac{q.}{V_A - V_B} = 4\pi\varepsilon_0\frac{ab}{b-a}$$

(*ii*) When the space between the two spheres is completely filled with the dielectric of relative permittivity ε_r (or dielectric constant k), the value of E is reduced to $\dfrac{E}{\varepsilon_r}$ as the value of charge on the surface of the sphere A is reduced from q to $\dfrac{q}{\varepsilon_0}$ due to the polarisation of the dielectric

$$\therefore \quad V_A - V_B = \frac{q}{4\pi\varepsilon_0\,\varepsilon_r}\frac{b-a}{ab}$$

Hence

$$C = \frac{q}{V_A - V_B} = 4\pi\varepsilon_0\,\varepsilon_r\frac{ab}{b-a}$$

(*b*) **When the inner sphere is earthed and outer sphere is charged.** Suppose now a charge $+q$ is given to the outer sphere B and the inner sphere A is earthed as shown Fig. 5.17. The charge $+q$ will distribute over both the surfaces of the sphere B as there is the earth connected sphere A on its inner side and there is the earth and other earth connected objects surrounding it. Let $+q_1$ be the charge on the inner surface of B and $+q_2$ the remaining charge on the outer surface of B such that

$$q = q_1 + q_2$$

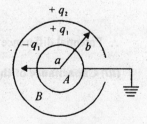

Fig. 5.17

The charge $+ q_1$ on the inner surface of B induces a charge $- q_1$ on the sphere A and $+ q_1$ flows to the earth. There are thus two capacitors

(*i*) between the sphere A and the inner surface of B. The capacity of this capacitor $= 4\pi\varepsilon_0 \dfrac{ab}{b-a}$, as proved above.

(*ii*) between the outer surface of B and the earth.

The capacity of this capacitor = The capacity of the spherical conductor of radius $b = 4\pi\varepsilon_0 b$

$\therefore$ Total capacity $\qquad C = 4\pi\varepsilon_0 \dfrac{ab}{b-a} + 4\pi\varepsilon_0 b$

$$= 4\pi\varepsilon_0 \left[\dfrac{ab}{b-a} + b\right] = 4\pi\varepsilon_0 \dfrac{b^2}{b-a}$$

Q. 5.25. Find the expression for the capacitance of a cylindrical capacitor.

(*Cal. U.*, 1992; *Burd. U.*, 1990)

Ans. Capacitance of a cylindrical capacitor. A cylindrical capacitor consists of two coaxial cylinders, the space between the cylinders contains air or some other dielectric. Let A and B represent the sections of two coaxial cylinders of radius a and b respectively. Let the cylinder B be earthed and a charge λ per unit length be given to the cylinder A.

Consider a point P within the two cylinders at a distance r from the axis, then magnitude of electric field intensity

$$E = \frac{1}{2\pi\varepsilon_0}\frac{\lambda}{r}$$

The field at every point is directed radially outward.

$\therefore$ The difference of potential between two cylinders

$$V_a - V_b = \int_b^a - \vec{E}.d\vec{r}$$

As the vectors $\vec{E}$ and $d\vec{r}$ are both in the same direction.

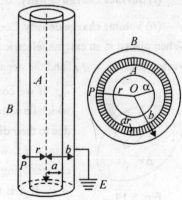

Fig. 5.18

$$V_a - V_b = -\int_b^a E\,dr = -\int_b^a \frac{\lambda}{2\pi\varepsilon_0}\frac{dr}{r}$$

$$= \frac{\lambda}{2\pi\varepsilon_0}\left[-\log_e r\right]_b^a = \frac{\lambda}{2\pi\varepsilon_0}\log_e \frac{b}{a}$$

Hence capacitance per unit length of the capacitor $C = \dfrac{\lambda}{\dfrac{\lambda}{2\pi\varepsilon_0}\log_e \dfrac{b}{a}} = \dfrac{2\pi\varepsilon_0}{\log_e \dfrac{b}{a}}$

The capacitance of a length l of the cylindrical capacitor $C_l = \dfrac{2\pi\varepsilon_0 l}{\log_e \dfrac{b}{a}}$

When the space between the two cylinders is filled with a medium of dielectric constant k or relative permittivity ε_r

$$E = \frac{1}{2\pi\varepsilon_0 \varepsilon_r}\frac{\lambda}{r}$$

and $\qquad C_d = \dfrac{2\pi\varepsilon_0\,\varepsilon_r}{\log_e \dfrac{b}{a}}$ Also C_l (with dielectric) $= \dfrac{2\pi\varepsilon_0\,\varepsilon_r\,l}{\log_e \dfrac{b}{a}}$

In terms of k, $C_d = \dfrac{2\pi\varepsilon_0\,k}{\log_e \dfrac{b}{a}}$ and C_l (with dielectric) $= \dfrac{2\pi\varepsilon_0\,k\,l}{\log_e \dfrac{b}{a}}$

Q. 5.26. Show that a volume distribution of dipole moments may be represented by an equivalent system of bound charge densities. **OR**

Prove that for a non-uniform polarisation of a dielectric

$$\vec{\nabla}.\vec{P} = -\,\rho_{bound}$$

where symbols have usual meanings. *(P.U. 2009; H.P.U. 2003, 2000;*

Luck. U., 1995, 1992; G.N.D.U., 1996)

Ans. From a macroscopic viewpoint a dielectric may be represented by a volume distribution of dipole moments. The electric field due to a volume distribution of dipole moments can be supposed to be due to a surface charge density $\sigma_p = \vec{P}.\hat{n}$ and a volume charge density $\rho_p = -\vec{\nabla}.\vec{P}$ where $\vec{P}$ is the macroscopic dipole moment per unit volume.

(i) **Surface charge density.** $\sigma_p = \vec{P}.\hat{n}$ [For proof See **Q. 5.8** Eq. *(i)*.]

(ii) **Volume charge density.** Consider a macroscopic volume ΔV having a surface S as its boundary. When placed in an external electric field let the positive charge in a molecule be displaced through a vector distance $+\,d\vec{l}$ and the negative charge through a vector distance $-\,d\vec{l}$.

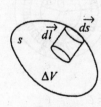

Fig. 5.19

If we consider a surface element of area $d\vec{s}$ then all positive charges which lie within a distance $+\,d\vec{l}$ from this element will cross the area element due to their displacement but positive charges lying at vector distances greater than $+\,d\vec{l}$ will not be able to reach the surface. In other words all the positive charges lying within a cylinder of volume $+\,d\vec{l}.d\vec{s}$ will leave the surface $d\vec{s}$. If N is the number density of positive charges and q the magnitude of positive charge on a molecule, the positive charge lost by the area $d\vec{s}$

$$= qN(+\,d\vec{l}).d\vec{s}$$

$\therefore$ The positive charge leaving the entire surface S of the volume ΔV

$$= \oiint_S \vec{q}\,N\,(+d\vec{l}).d\vec{s}$$

As the molecular dipoles are each made up of a pair of equal and opposite charges, the negative charge lost by the volume ΔV

$$= \oiint_S q\,N\,(-\vec{dl}).\vec{ds}$$

The negative charge lost by the volume ΔV results in a corresponding gain of positive charge.

$\therefore$ Net positive charge gained by the volume ΔV

$$\Delta Q = \oint_S Nq[(-\vec{dl}) - (+\vec{dl})].ds = -\oint_S Nq2d\,\vec{l}.d\vec{s}$$

Now molecular dipole moment $\vec{p}$ = Charge × distance of the centre of positive charge from the centre of negative charge

$\therefore$

$$\vec{p} = q[(+\vec{dl}) - (-\vec{dl})] = 2q\,\vec{dl}$$

Hence dipole moment density or dipole moment per unit volume

$$\vec{P} = N\vec{p} = N2qd\,\vec{l}$$

$\therefore$ Net positive charge gained by the volume ΔV

$$\Delta Q = -\oint_S \vec{P}.d\vec{s}$$

According to Gauss's divergence theorem in vector analysis

$$\oint_S \vec{P}.\vec{ds} = \iiint_V (\vec{\nabla}.\vec{P})\,dv$$

$\therefore$

$$\Delta Q = - \iiint_{\Delta V} (\vec{\nabla}.\vec{P})\,dv \qquad \qquad ...(i)$$

If ρ_p (or ρ_{bound}) is the volume charge density induced in the dielectric due to polarisation, then

Charge gained in volume ΔV, $\Delta Q = - \iiint_{\Delta V} \rho_p\,dv \qquad \qquad ...(ii)$

Equating (i) and (ii), we have

$$\iiint_{\Delta V} \rho_p\,dv = - \iiint_{\Delta V} \vec{\nabla}.\vec{P}\,dv$$

or $$\rho_p = -\vec{\nabla}.\vec{P} = -div\,\vec{P}$$

or $$\rho_{bound} = -\vec{\nabla}.\vec{P}$$

Thus a volume distribution of dipole moments may be represented by a *bound* volume charge density $\rho_p = \rho_{bound} = -\vec{\nabla}.\vec{P}$ and a bound surface charge density $\sigma_p = \sigma_{bound} = \vec{P}.\hat{n}$.

These charge densities ρ_p and σ_p are not due to any external charges. They are only due to the slight displacement of centres of positive and negative charges within the molecules and their rearrangement in the dielectric. As the dielectric on the whole remains neutral these charges cannot leave it and are therefore known as *bound* charges. They do not take part in electrical conduction.

Q. 5.27. Derive an expression for Gauss's law in the presence of dielectric. Prove that divergence of displacement vector is equal to density of free charge or $\vec{\nabla}.\vec{D} = \rho_{free}$. Also discuss integral form of Gauss's law. (*M.D.U.* 2002, 2000; *K.U.* 2001, 2000, 1996, 1995; *P.U.* 2009, 2006, 2002, 2001, 2000, 1992; *H.P.U.* 2001; *Pbi. U.* 2003, 1999, 1995; *G.N.D.U.* 2003, 2002, 1999, 1992; *Meerut U.* 2003, 2001)

Ans. Gauss's law for dielectrics. The differential form of Gauss's law is given by

$$\vec{\nabla} . \vec{E} = \frac{\rho}{\varepsilon_0} \qquad \qquad ...(i)$$

where ρ is the net volume charge density.

When the charge is present within a dielectric, in addition to *free* (external) charge density ρ_{free} (or ρ_f) an *induced* charge density ρ_{bound} (or ρ_p) is developed due to polarisation effect so that the *net* charge density ρ is the algebraic sum of ρ_{free} and ρ_{bound} *i.e.*,

$$\rho = \rho_f + \rho_p$$

$$\therefore \qquad \vec{\nabla} . \vec{E} = \frac{\rho_f}{\varepsilon_0} + \frac{\rho_p}{\varepsilon_0} \qquad \qquad ...(ii)$$

The volume charge density of polarisation ρ_p is given by

$$\rho_p = -\vec{\nabla} . \vec{P}$$

Substituting $\rho_p = -\vec{\nabla} . \vec{P}$ in Eq. (*ii*), we get

$$\vec{\nabla} . \vec{E} = \frac{\rho_f}{\varepsilon_0} - \frac{\vec{\nabla} . \vec{P}}{\varepsilon_0}$$

or $\qquad \vec{\nabla} . \vec{E} + \vec{\nabla} . \left(\frac{\vec{P}}{\varepsilon_0} \right) = \frac{\rho_f}{\varepsilon_0}$

or $\qquad \vec{\nabla} . \left[\frac{\varepsilon_0 \vec{E} + \vec{P}}{\varepsilon_0} \right] = \frac{\rho_f}{\varepsilon_0}$

or $\qquad \vec{\nabla} . [\varepsilon_0 \vec{E} + \vec{P}] = \rho_f$

The expression $\varepsilon_0 \vec{E} + \vec{P}$ is called the **electric displacement vector** and denoted as $\vec{D}$

Electric displacement vector $\vec{D}$ is, therefore, defined as the sum of two vectors (i) $\varepsilon_0 \vec{E}$ i.e. product of permittivity of free space and applied electric field and (ii) $\vec{P}$ the dipole moment per unit volume developed in the dielectric due to polarisation.

$$\therefore \qquad \vec{\nabla} . \vec{D} = \rho_f \qquad \qquad ...(iii)$$

Eq. (iii) shows that divergence of displacement vector is equal to density of free charge.

As $\qquad \vec{D} = \varepsilon_0 \varepsilon_r E = \varepsilon \vec{E}$

$$\vec{\nabla} . \vec{D} = \vec{\nabla} . \varepsilon \vec{E} = \rho_f$$

or $\qquad \vec{\nabla} . \vec{E} = \frac{\rho_f}{\varepsilon} \qquad \qquad ...(iv)$

This is known as the *differential form of Gauss's law for dielectrics.*

Compare Eq. (*iv*) with the statement of Gauss's law for free space or vacuum $\vec{\nabla} . \vec{E} = \frac{\rho}{\varepsilon_0}$.

Eq. (*iv*) may also be put in terms of dielectric constant k as

$$\vec{\nabla} \cdot \vec{E} = \frac{\rho_f}{\varepsilon_0 \varepsilon_r} = \frac{\rho_f}{\varepsilon_0 k}$$

Integral form of Gauss's law for dielectrics. The differential form of Gauss's law for dielectrics as given in Eq. (*iii*) is

$$\vec{\nabla} \cdot \vec{D} = \rho_f$$

Multiplying both sides by dv and integrating over the volume of the dielectric V, we get

$$\iiint_V \vec{\nabla} \cdot \vec{D} \, dv = \iiint_V \rho_f \, dv$$

Now $\iiint \rho_f \, dv = q_f$ gives the entire free charge inside the volume V.

$$\therefore \qquad \iiint_V \vec{\nabla} \cdot \vec{D} \, dv = q_f \qquad \qquad \text{...(v)}$$

According to Gauss's divergence theorem in vector calculus

$$\oiint_S \vec{D} \cdot d\vec{s} = \iiint_V \vec{\nabla} \cdot \vec{D} \, dv \qquad \qquad \text{...(vi)}$$

Comparing Eqs. (*v*) and (*vi*), we have

$$\oiint_S \vec{D} \cdot d\vec{s} = q_f \qquad \qquad \text{...(vii)}$$

This is known as *the integral form of Gauss's law for dielectrics.*

As
$$\vec{D} = \varepsilon_0 \varepsilon_r \vec{E} = \varepsilon \vec{E}, \quad \oiint_S \vec{D} \cdot \vec{ds} = \iint \varepsilon \vec{E} \cdot d\vec{s}$$

$$\therefore \qquad \oiint \varepsilon \vec{E} \cdot d\vec{s} = q_f$$

or
$$\oiint \vec{E} \cdot d\vec{s} = \frac{q_f}{\varepsilon} \qquad \qquad \text{...(viii)}$$

Compare Eq. (*viii*) with the integral form of statement of Gauss's law for free space or vacuum

$$\oiint \vec{E} \cdot d\vec{s} = \frac{q}{\varepsilon_0}.$$

Eq. (*viii*) may also be put in terms of dielectric constant k as

$$\oiint \vec{E} \cdot d\vec{s} = \frac{q}{\varepsilon_0 \varepsilon_r} = \frac{q}{\varepsilon_0 k}.$$

Q. 5.28. A thin dielectric rod of cross-section A extends along the Z-axis from $Z = 0$ to $Z = h$. The polarisation of the rod along Z-axis is given by

$$P_z = 3z^2 + 2$$

Find (*i*) the bound volume charge density.

(*ii*) the bound surface charge density.

(*iii*) the total bound charge.

Ans. Here $P_z = 3z^2 + 2$ along Z-axis

$\therefore$ $\vec{P} = (3z^2 + 2)\,\hat{k}$

(*i*) The bound volume charge density is given by

$$\vec{\nabla} . \vec{P} = -\rho_{bound}$$

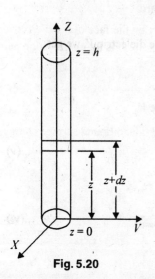

Fig. 5.20

$$\vec{\nabla}.\vec{P} = \left(\frac{\partial}{\partial x}\hat{i} + \frac{\partial}{\partial y}\hat{j} + \frac{\partial}{\partial z}\hat{k} \right) . (3z^2 + 2)\,\hat{k}$$

$$= \frac{\partial}{\partial z}(3z^2 + 2) = 6z$$

Hence $\rho_{bound} = -6z$

(*ii*) Polarisation at the surface $z = 0$

$$\vec{P}(z = 0) = 2\,\hat{k}$$

$\therefore$ σ_{bound} at the surface $z = 0$

$$\vec{P} . \hat{n} = 2\hat{k} . (-\hat{k}) = -2$$

Polarisation at the surface $z = h$

$$\vec{P}(z = h) = (3h^2 + 2)\,\hat{k}$$

$\therefore$ σ_{bound} at the surface $z = h$

$$\vec{P} . \hat{n} = (3h^2 + 2)\hat{k} . \hat{k} = 3h^2 + 2$$

σ_{bound} at the curved surface = 0 as the outward normal on the curved surface $\hat{n}$ is perpendicular to the direction of polarisation.

(*iii*) Total bound surface charge = $-2A + (3h^2 + 2)A = 3h^2 A$.

To find the total bound volume charge, consider a thin slice of the rod of thickness dz at a distance z from the origin.

Volume of the slice $= A\,dz$.

Volume charge in the slice $= A\,dz \times \rho_{bound} = -A\,6z\,dz$

$\therefore$ Total bound volume charge $= \displaystyle\int_0^h - A\,6z\,dz$

$$= -6A \left[\frac{z^2}{2} \right]_0^h = -3Ah^2$$

Hence total bound charge = Total bound surface charge + Total bound volume charge

$$= 3Ah^2 - 3Ah^2 = 0$$

Q. 5.29. A dielectric slab of dielectric constant k is placed so as to fill the space between the plates of a parallel plate capacitor originally carrying an electric field $\vec{E_0}$. Find the bound charge densities.

Ans. Bound volume charge density ρ_{bound}. When the space between the plates of a parallel plate capacitor is filled with dielectric slab of dielectric constant k = relative permittivity ε_r, the dielectric medium experiences a force due to the electric field $E_0 = \dfrac{\sigma_{free}}{\varepsilon_0}$ already existing between the plates and will get *polarised* in the direction of the field. This polarisation leads to appearance of bound charge densities. Since the polarisation is uniform, $\vec{P}$ is a constant vector. Hence $\vec{\nabla} . \vec{P} = 0$

As bound volume charge density $\rho_{bound} = -\vec{\nabla} . \vec{P}$

$$\therefore \qquad \rho_{bound} = 0$$

Thus the net charge within the whole volume of the dielectric is zero.

Bound surface charge density. The bound surface charge density on the face of the dielectric opposite to the positive plate of the capacitor is negative and vice-versa. If $\vec{P}$ is the polarisation per unit volume, then

$$\sigma_{bound} = \sigma_p = \vec{P} . \hat{n}$$

where $\hat{n}$ is a unit outward normal on the charged surface of the dielectric.

The vector $\vec{P}$ is opposite to $\vec{E_0}$ in direction and the electric field due to bound surface charge density $E_p = \dfrac{\sigma_{bound}}{\varepsilon_0}$.

$\therefore$ The net electric field in the dielectric

$$E = \frac{\sigma_{free}}{\varepsilon_0} - \frac{\sigma_{bound}}{\varepsilon_0} = \frac{1}{\varepsilon_0} [\sigma_{free} - \sigma_{bound}]$$

or $\qquad \dfrac{\sigma_{bound}}{\varepsilon_0} = \dfrac{\sigma_{free}}{\varepsilon_0} - E = E_0 - \dfrac{E_0}{E_r} = E_0 \left(1 - \dfrac{1}{\varepsilon_r}\right)$

or $\qquad \sigma_{bound} = \varepsilon_0 E_0 \left(1 - \dfrac{1}{\varepsilon_r}\right)$

In terms of k, $\qquad \sigma_{bound} = \varepsilon_0 E_0 \left[1 - \dfrac{1}{k}\right]$

Q. 5.30. A dielectric is placed in the field of a point charge. Will there be polarisation volume charge density? *(H.P.U., 1992)*

Ans. Polarisation volume charge density due to a point charge. The electric field produced by a point charge placed in a medium of dielectric constant (relative permittivity) ε_r is given by

$$\vec{E} = \frac{1}{4\pi\varepsilon_0\,\varepsilon_r}\frac{q}{r^2}\hat{r}$$

i.e., the value of $\vec{E}$ varies inversely as the square of the distance and its direction at any point is along the radius vector at that point. Thus the dielectric is polarised non-uniformly. In other words the polarisation vector $\vec{P}$ is not a constant.

As polarisation volume charge density $\rho_p = \vec{\nabla} . \vec{P}$ and $\vec{P}$ is a variable quantity ρ_p will have a *finite* value.

Q. 5.31. Show that the electric field at a distance r from a point charge q in a homogeneous medium of dielectric constant k is $E = \dfrac{1}{4\pi\varepsilon_0}\dfrac{q}{kr^2}$. Hence prove Gauss's theorem for a dielectric medium and prove the relation $\vec{\nabla} . \vec{D} = \rho_{free}$.

(Pbi. U. 2006; G.N.D.U. 1999; H.P.U, 2000, 1997; Luck. U., 1993)

Ans. Electric field in a dielectric. Consider a *free positive* charge q located at a *point O* inside a dielectric. This charge is in addition to the charges on the molecules constituting the dielectric. Due to the *radial* electric field produced by the point charge the dielectric is polarised *radially*. The centre of negative charge of the molecule is drawn towards the charge $+q$ and the centre of positive charge moves away from it thereby producing a dipole moment. Let the polarisation per unit volume be $\vec{P}$, then the magnitude of the density of polarisation $P = \sigma_p$ where σ_p is the surface charge density due to polarisation developed on any surface containing the charge $+q$.

To find the electric field at a distance r from the charge $+q$ within the dielectric draw a spherical Gaussian surface of radius r. Due to polarisation a net negative charge $= 4\pi r^2 P$ remains within the Gaussian surface and an equal positive charge stays out. In addition there is a charge $+q$ within the Gaussian surface.

∴ Net charge within the Gaussian surface $= q - 4\pi r^2 P$.

According to Gauss's theorem

$$\oiint \vec{E} \cdot d\vec{s} = \frac{1}{\varepsilon_0} [q - 4\pi r^2 P] \qquad \text{...(i)}$$

The electric field $\vec{E}$ at every point on the spherical surface has the same magnitude and is directed along the radius.

∴ $$\vec{E} \cdot d\vec{s} = E \, ds \text{ where } E \text{ is the magnitude of } \vec{E}.$$

Hence $$\oiint \vec{E} \cdot d\vec{s} = E \, ds = E \, 4\pi r^2$$

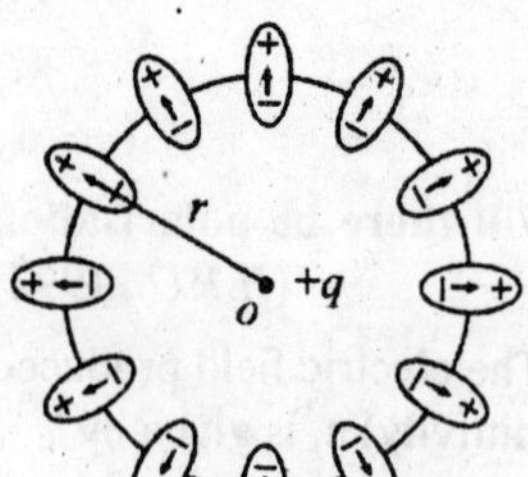

Substituting in (i), we have

$$E \, 4\pi r^2 = \frac{1}{\varepsilon_0} [q - 4\pi r^2 P]$$

Fig. 5.21

or $$E = \frac{1}{4\pi\varepsilon_0} \frac{q}{r^2} - \frac{P}{\varepsilon_0}$$

or $$E\left(1 + \frac{P}{\varepsilon_0 E}\right) = \frac{1}{4\pi\varepsilon_0} \frac{q}{r^2}$$

But $$\frac{P}{\varepsilon_0 E} = \chi_e \text{ and } 1 + \chi_e = \varepsilon_r = k$$

∴ $$E = \frac{1}{4\pi\varepsilon_0} \frac{q}{kr^2} \left[\text{or } E = \frac{1}{4\pi\varepsilon_0\varepsilon_r} \frac{q}{r^2} \right]$$

This means that the polarisation of the dielectric medium reduces the effective value of free charge from q to $\dfrac{q}{k}$ or $\dfrac{q}{\varepsilon_r}$ where k is the dielectric constant or ε_r is the relative permittivity of the medium.

In other words a free charge q kept in an isotropic homegeneous dielectric medium together with the consequent polarisation charge behaves as a total charge.

$$q_{total} = \frac{q}{k} = \frac{q}{\varepsilon_r} \text{ kept in vacuum.}$$

Thus a system of charges kept in a dielectric medium is equivalent to a system of charges kept in free space with each charge replaced by its equivalent charge $= \dfrac{q}{k} = \dfrac{q}{\varepsilon_r}$.

Gauss's theorem for dielectrics. Taking into considereation the polarisation effects in a dielectric, we replace a charge q by an equivalent charge $\dfrac{q}{\varepsilon_r}$. Gauss's law in a dielectric can, therefore, be stated as $\oint \vec{E} \cdot d\vec{s} = \dfrac{1}{\varepsilon_0} \dfrac{q}{\varepsilon_r}$ or $\varepsilon_0 \varepsilon_r \oint \vec{E} \cdot d\vec{s} = q$

If ρ_{free} is the free volume charge density, then the charge q contained in a volume V is given by

$$q = \iiint_V \rho_{free} \, dv$$

$$\therefore \quad \varepsilon_0 \varepsilon_r \oint \vec{E} \cdot d\vec{s} = \iiint_V \rho_{free} \, dv$$

$$\therefore \quad \oint \varepsilon_0 \varepsilon_r \vec{E} \cdot d\vec{s} = \iiint_V \rho_{free} \, dv \qquad \qquad ...(i)$$

Now $\qquad \qquad \varepsilon_0 \varepsilon_r E = \varepsilon \vec{E} = \vec{D}$

where $\vec{D}$ is the displacement vector.

Hence $\qquad \qquad \oint \vec{D} \cdot d\vec{s} = \iiint_V \rho_{free} \, dv$

This is **Gauss's theorem** for a dielectric medium in **integral form.**

Gauss's theorem in differential form. According to Gauss's divergence theorem in vector analysis

$$\oint \vec{E} \cdot d\vec{s} = \iiint_V (\vec{\nabla} \cdot \vec{E}) \, dv$$

$$\therefore \quad \oint \varepsilon_0 \varepsilon_r \vec{E} \cdot d\vec{s} = \iiint_V \varepsilon_0 \varepsilon_r (\vec{\nabla} \cdot \vec{E}) \, dv \qquad \qquad ...(ii)$$

From relations (i) and (ii), we have

$$\iiint_V \varepsilon_0 \varepsilon_r (\vec{\nabla} \cdot \vec{E}) \, dv = \iiint_V \rho_{free} \, dv$$

$$\therefore \quad \varepsilon_0 \varepsilon_r (\vec{\nabla} \cdot \vec{E}) = \rho_{free}$$

or $\qquad \vec{\nabla} \cdot \varepsilon_0 \varepsilon_r \vec{E} = (\vec{\nabla} \cdot \varepsilon \vec{E}) = \vec{\nabla} \cdot \vec{D} = \rho_{free} \qquad \qquad ...(iii)$

$\therefore$ Gauss's theorem in *differential* form for a dielectric medium states

$$\vec{\nabla} \cdot \varepsilon \vec{E} = \vec{\nabla} \cdot \vec{D} = \rho_{free}$$

Q. 5.32. Using Gauss's law in dielectric medium, show that

$$\vec{\nabla} \cdot \vec{D} = \rho_{free}$$

and $\qquad \qquad \vec{\nabla} \cdot \vec{P} = -\rho_{bound}$

where symbols have their usual meanings.

(Luck. U., 1993; H.P.U. 2000, 1991; P.U., 2001, 1991, Pbi. U, 1999)

Ans. (*i*) To prove $\vec{\nabla} \cdot \vec{D} = \rho_{free}$. See **Q. 5.31.** Eq. (*iii*)

(*ii*) **To prove** $\vec{\nabla} \cdot \vec{D} = -\rho_{bound}$. According to differential form of Gauss's theorem $\vec{\nabla} \cdot \vec{E} = \dfrac{\rho}{\varepsilon_0}$

where ρ is the net volume charge density. When the charge is present within a dielectric, in addition to the *free* (external) charge density ρ_{free} an induced charge density ρ_{bound} is developed due to polarisation effect so that the net charge density ρ is the algebraic sum of ρ_{free} and ρ_{bound}.

$$\therefore \qquad \vec{\nabla} \cdot \vec{E} = \frac{1}{\varepsilon_0} (\rho_{free} + \rho_{bound}) \quad \text{or} \quad \varepsilon_0 \vec{\nabla} \cdot \vec{E} = \rho_{free} + \rho_{bound}$$

Also in a dielectric $\qquad \varepsilon_0 \vec{E} = \vec{D} - \vec{P}$

where $\vec{E}$ is net electric field vector, $\vec{D}$ the displacement field vector and $\vec{P}$ the bound charge density due to polarisation.

$$\therefore \qquad \vec{\nabla} \cdot \varepsilon_0 \vec{E} = \vec{\nabla} \cdot (\vec{D} - \vec{P}) = \vec{\nabla} \cdot \vec{D} - \vec{\nabla} \cdot \vec{P}$$

As proved in (*i*) $\qquad \vec{\nabla} \cdot \vec{D} = \rho_{free}$

$$\therefore \qquad \rho_{free} + \rho_{bound} = \varepsilon_0 \vec{\nabla} \cdot \vec{E} = \vec{\nabla} \cdot \varepsilon_0 \vec{E} = \vec{\nabla} \cdot \vec{D} - \vec{\nabla} \cdot P = \rho_{free} - \vec{\nabla} \cdot \vec{P}$$

Hence $\qquad \rho_{bound} = -\vec{\nabla} \cdot \vec{P}$. or $\vec{\nabla} \cdot \vec{P} = -\rho_{bound}$

Q. 5.33. A charged spherical ball of radius b is placed in an infinite dielectric medium of dielectric constant k. Find the bound charge density in the spherical cavity cut by the ball if it has a total charge q uniformly distributed over the surface.

Ans. Suppose a charged spherical ball of radius b is placed in an infinite dielectric medium. The charge on the ball is q uniformly distributed over the surface. Therefore from symmetry consider-ations

(*i*) the electric field at a point outside the sphere will be in a direction radially outward from the centre of the sphere, and

(*ii*) it will depend upon the distance 'r' of the point from the centre of the sphere.

To find the value of electric field at a point at a distance r from the centre of the sphere, consider a concentic spherical Gaussian surface of radius r, then

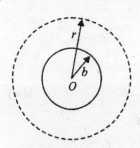

Fig. 5.22

Electric flux on the surface $= \oint \vec{E} \cdot d\vec{s} = \oint E \, ds$

$$= E \oint ds = 4\pi r^2 E$$

According to Gauss's theorem for a dielectric medium having relative permittivity ε_r,

$$\oint \vec{E} \cdot d\vec{s} = \frac{q}{\varepsilon_0 \varepsilon_r}$$

$$\therefore \qquad 4\pi \, r^2 \, E = \frac{q}{\varepsilon_0 \, \varepsilon_r}$$

or
$$E = \frac{1}{4\pi \, \varepsilon_0 \, \varepsilon_r} \, \frac{q}{r^2}$$

This show that the electric field in a dielectric is $\dfrac{1}{\varepsilon_r}$ times the value in vacuum.

The reduction or weakening of the electric field is due to the bound charge density developed on the surface of the spherical cavity cut into the dielectric by the ball as bound charge density appearing on the surface of the cavity neutralises some of the charge q on the surface of the sphere.

Magnitude of bound charge density. The electric field at a point outside the sphere at a distance r in a medium of relative permittivity ε_r is given by

$$\vec{E} = \frac{1}{4\pi \varepsilon_r \, \varepsilon_0} \, \frac{q}{r^2} \, \hat{r}$$

The field $\vec{E}$ acts *radially outward.*

$\therefore$ Displacement
$$\vec{D} = \varepsilon \vec{E} = \varepsilon_0 \, \varepsilon_r \, \vec{E} = \frac{1}{4\pi} \, \frac{q}{r^2} \, \hat{r}$$

where $\hat{r}$ is a unit vector in the radially outward direction.

But
$$\vec{D} = \varepsilon_0 \vec{E} + \vec{P}$$

$\therefore$ Polarisation
$$\vec{P} = \vec{D} - \varepsilon_0 \vec{E} = \frac{1}{4\pi} \, \frac{q}{r^2} \left[1 - \frac{1}{\varepsilon_r} \right] \hat{r}$$

$\therefore$ Polarisation at $r = b$ is given by

$$\vec{P} = \frac{1}{4\pi} \, \frac{q}{b^2} \left[1 - \frac{1}{\varepsilon_r} \right] \hat{r}$$

The bound surface charge density at the surface of the cavity

$$\sigma_{bound} = \vec{P} \cdot \hat{n}$$

The outward drawn normal on the inner surface of the cavity and on the surface of the sphere are oppositely directed.

$\therefore$
$$\hat{n} = - \hat{r}$$

$\therefore$
$$\sigma_{bound} = - P = - \frac{1}{4\pi} \, \frac{q}{b^2} \left[1 - \frac{1}{\varepsilon_r} \right] = \frac{1}{4\pi} \, \frac{q}{b^2} \left[\frac{1}{\varepsilon_r} - 1 \right]$$

Thus we again find that the effective charge on the sphere in the infinite dielectric is $\dfrac{q}{\varepsilon_r}$.

Q. 5.34. (*a*) **What do you mean by electric potential energy of charge? Define electric potential energy of a system of charges. Deduce its value for a system of three charges q_1, q_2 and q_3 located at $\vec{r}_1, \vec{r}_2,$ and $\vec{r}_3$ respectively and generalise the result for n charges.**   (*Pbi., U.* 2000; *H.P.U.* 2000)

(*b*) **Three charges q_1, q_2 and q_3 are placed at the corners of an equilateral triangle of side r. Calculate the electric potential energy of the system.**   (*G.N.D.U.,* 1996, 1993)

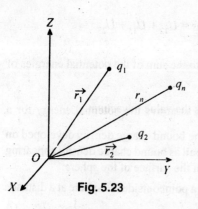

Fig. 5.23

Ans. (a) Potential energy of charge. Electric potential at a point in an electric field is defined as the work done in taking a unit positive charge from infinity to that point against the electrical forces.

If V is the electrical potential at a point, then work done in bringing a test charge q_0 from infinity to that point $= q_0 V$.

This work is stored in the test charge as its potential energy.

∴ Potential energy of a charge q_0 at a potential $V = q_0 V$.

Potential energy of a system of charges. *The potential energy of a system of charges is defined as the minimum external work done in assembling the system.*

Suppose we have a set of charges q_1 at $\vec{r_1}$, q_2 at $\vec{r_2}$ and so on q_n at r_n.

To begin with all the charges are at infinity and are also at infinite distance from one another so that there is no interaction between them. At this stage the configuration has zero potential energy.

Now we bring the charge q_1 from infinity to $\vec{r_1}$ infinitely slowly keeping the other charges q_2, q_3 .... q_n still at infinity. Since all other charges are at infinity the electric potential already existing at the position $\vec{r_1}$ is zero. Hence no work is done in bringing the charge q_1 from infinity to the position $\vec{r_1}$.

Potential energy of a system of two charges. Now keep the charge q_1 fixed at $\vec{r_1}$ and bring the charge q_2 from infinity to $\vec{r_2}$ keeping charges q_3, q_4 ... q_n still at infinity. There now exists a prior potential at $\vec{r_2}$ due to the charge q_1 at $\vec{r_1}$ given by

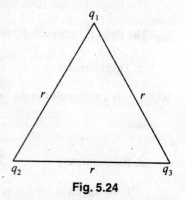

Fig. 5.24

$$\frac{1}{4\pi\varepsilon_0} \frac{q}{|\vec{r_2} - \vec{r_1}|}$$

Hence the work done in bringing the charge q_2 from infinity to $\vec{r_2}$

$$= U_{12} = \frac{1}{4\pi\varepsilon_0} \frac{q_1}{|\vec{r_2} - \vec{r_1}|} q_2$$

This gives the *potential energy of a system of two charges.*

Potential energy of a system of three charges. Now bring the charge q_3 from infinity to the position $\vec{r_3}$ keeping q_1 and q_2 fixed at $\vec{r_1}$ and $\vec{r_2}$. The electric potential at $\vec{r_3}$ due to the charges q_1 and q_2 at $\vec{r_1}$ and $\vec{r_2}$ respectively is given by

$$\frac{1}{4\pi\varepsilon_0} \frac{q_1}{|\vec{r_3} - \vec{r_1}|} + \frac{1}{4\pi\varepsilon_0} \frac{q_2}{|\vec{r_3} - \vec{r_2}|}$$

∴ The work done in bringing the charge q_3 from infinity to $\vec{r_3}$

$$= \frac{1}{4\pi\varepsilon_0} \frac{q_1 q_3}{|\vec{r_3} - \vec{r_1}|} + \frac{1}{4\pi\varepsilon_0} \frac{q_2 q_3}{|\vec{r_3} - \vec{r_2}|} = U_{13} + U_{23}$$

Thus the total potential energy of a *system of three charges* = $U_{12} + U_{13} + U_{23}$

$$= \frac{1}{4\pi\varepsilon_0} \left[\frac{q_1 q_2}{|\vec{r_2} - \vec{r_1}|} + \frac{q_1 q_3}{|\vec{r_3} - \vec{r_1}|} + \frac{q_2 q_3}{|\vec{r_3} - \vec{r_2}|} \right]$$ which is equal to the sum of the potential energies of

various pairs.

Potential energy of a system of *n*-charges. Proceeding as above the potential energy for a system of four charges

$$U = U_{12} + U_{13} + U_{14} + U_{23} + U_{24} + U_{34}$$

∴ For a system of a *n* charges, we have

$$U = \frac{1}{2} \sum_{i=1}^{n} \sum_{j=1}^{n} \frac{1}{4\pi\varepsilon_0} \frac{q_i\, q_j}{|\vec{r_i} - \vec{r_j}|} \qquad [i \neq j] \quad ...(i)$$

The factor 1/2 has been introduced because in the above summation we get a term U_{12} and another term U_{21}. The two are equal. But in the calculation of potential energy we have to count each pair only once.

Relation (*i*) can be put in the form

$$U = \frac{1}{2} \sum_{i=1}^{n} q_i \sum_{j=1}^{n} \frac{q_j}{|\vec{r_i} - \vec{r_j}|} \qquad [i \neq j]$$

Now $\qquad \displaystyle\sum_{\substack{j=1 \\ \neq i}}^{n} \frac{q_j}{|\vec{r_i} - \vec{r_j}|} = V_i$ the electric potential at the charge q_i due to all other charges.

Hence $\qquad\qquad\qquad U = \frac{1}{2} \sum_{i=1}^{n} q_i\, V_i.$

(*b*) Let q_1, q_2 and q_3 be the three charges placed at the corners of an equilateral triangle of side r as shown in Fig. 5.24.

The total electric potential energy of the system is the sum of the energies of each pair of charges.

∴ $\qquad\qquad\qquad U = U_{12} + U_{13} + U_{23}$

$$= \frac{1}{4\pi\varepsilon_0} \left[\frac{q_1 q_2}{r} + \frac{q_1 q_3}{r} + \frac{q_2 q_3}{r} \right]$$

$$= \frac{1}{4\pi\varepsilon_0} \left[q_1 q_2 + q_1 q_3 + q_2 q_3 \right]$$

Q. 5.35. Three charges $q_1 = 3\ \mu C$, $q_2 = -6\mu C$, $q_3 = 7\ \mu C$ are located at points (− 1, 1, 0) (1, 2, 0) and (3, − 1, 0) respectively. If the distances are measured in metres find the total configurational energy of the system. (*H.P.U.,* 1994)

Ans. Distance between q_1 and q_2

$$\sqrt{(-1 - 1)^2 + (1 - 2)^2}$$

∴ $\qquad\qquad\qquad |\vec{r_1} - \vec{r_2}| = \sqrt{5}$

Distance between q_2 and q_3

$$= \sqrt{\{(1 - 3)^2 + [2 - (-1)]^2\}}$$

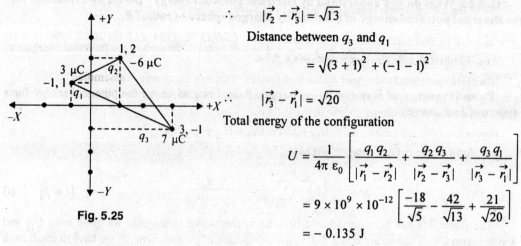

$$\therefore \quad |\vec{r_2} - \vec{r_3}| = \sqrt{13}$$

Distance between q_3 and q_1

$$= \sqrt{(3+1)^2 + (-1-1)^2}$$

$$\therefore \quad |\vec{r_3} - \vec{r_1}| = \sqrt{20}$$

Total energy of the configuration

$$U = \frac{1}{4\pi\,\varepsilon_0} \left[\frac{q_1\,q_2}{|\vec{r_1} - \vec{r_2}|} + \frac{q_2\,q_3}{|\vec{r_2} - \vec{r_3}|} + \frac{q_3\,q_1}{|\vec{r_3} - \vec{r_1}|} \right]$$

$$= 9 \times 10^9 \times 10^{-12} \left[\frac{-18}{\sqrt{5}} - \frac{42}{\sqrt{13}} + \frac{21}{\sqrt{20}} \right]$$

Fig. 5.25

$$= -0.135 \text{ J}$$

Q. 5.36. Two protons in thorium nucleus are 3×10^{-15} m apart. What is their mutual potential enrgy? *(P.U., 1995)*

Ans. The mutual potential energy of a system of two charges q_1 and q_2 a distance r apart is given by

$$U_{12} = \frac{1}{4\pi\,\varepsilon_0} \frac{q_1\,q_2}{r}$$

Now $q_1 = q_2 = 1.6 \times 10^{-19} \text{ C} \quad \frac{1}{4\pi\,\varepsilon_0} = 9 \times 10^9 \quad r = 3 \times 10^{-15} \text{ m}$

$\therefore$ Potential energy $= \dfrac{9 \times 10^9 \times 1.6 \times 10^{-19} \times 1.6 \times 10^{-19}}{3 \times 10^{-15}}$

$$= 7.68 \times 10^{-14} \text{ J.}$$

Q. 5.37. Find the potential energy of a charged spherical shell. *(P.U. 2002; H.P.U., 1992)*

Ans. Potential energy of a charged spherical shell. Let R be the radius of the shell and Q the charge on its surface.

Let this charge be brought from infinity to the surface of the shell in small instalments. If q is the charge concentrated on the surface at any instant, then

Electric potential at any point on the surface $= \dfrac{1}{4\pi\,\varepsilon_0} \dfrac{q}{R}$.

If another charge dq is now brought from infinity to the surface at any instant, then

Work done $dW = \dfrac{1}{4\pi\,\varepsilon_0} \dfrac{q}{R}\, dq$

$\therefore$ Total work done in bringing a charge Q from infinity to the surface of the shell

$$W = \int_0^Q dW = \frac{1}{4\pi\,\varepsilon_0\, R} \int_0^Q q\, dq$$

$$= \frac{1}{4\pi\,\varepsilon_0} \frac{Q^2}{2R}$$

This work is stored in the shell as its potential energy of charge.

Q. 5.38. What do you understand by electrical potential energy? Derive an expression for the electrical potential energy of a uniformly charged sphere of radius R.

(*G.N.D.U.*, 1994; *H.P.U.*, 2002, 2000, 1993)

Ans. Electrical potential energy. See Q. 5.34.

Electrical potential energy of a charged sphere. Suppose the charge is assembled bit by bit by bringing small instalments of charge dq each from infinity. Let x be the radius of the sphere of charge at any instant and ρ its volume charge density, then

Potential of the sphere of charge at a point on its surface

$$= \frac{1}{4\pi\,\varepsilon_0}\,\frac{4}{3}\,\frac{\pi x^3 \rho}{x}$$

$$= \frac{1}{4\pi\,\varepsilon_0}\,\frac{4}{3}\,\pi\rho x^2$$

where $\frac{4}{3}\pi x^3$ gives the volume of the sphere of radius x and $\frac{4}{3}\pi x^3\,\rho$ the total charge on the assembled sphere.

If we bring a further charge dq from infinity so that the radius of the sphere increases from x to $x + dx$, then the additional charge is contained in the shell of radius x and thickness dx (having charge density ρ), then

$$dq = 4\pi\,x^2\,dx\,\rho$$

Work done in bringing this charge dq

$$dW = \frac{1}{4\pi\varepsilon_0}\,\frac{4}{3}\,\pi x^2\,\rho\,.\,4\pi x^2\,dx\rho$$

$$= \frac{1}{4\pi\varepsilon_0}\,\frac{16}{3}\,\pi^2\,x^4\,\rho^2\,dx$$

$\therefore$ Total work done in assembling the sphere of charge of radius R

$$W = \int dW = \frac{1}{4\pi\varepsilon_0}\,\frac{16}{3}\,\pi^2\,\rho^2\,\int_0^R x^4\,dx$$

$$= \frac{1}{4\pi\,\varepsilon_0}\,\frac{16}{3}\,\pi^2\,\rho^2\,\left[\frac{x^5}{5}\right]_0^R$$

$$= \frac{1}{4\pi\,\varepsilon_0}\,\frac{16}{15}\,\pi^2\,\rho^2\,R^5$$

But $\frac{4}{3}\,\pi R^3\rho = Q$ the total charge in the sphere

$\therefore$

$$Q^2 = \frac{16}{9}\,\pi^2\,R^6\,\rho^2 \quad \text{and} \quad \frac{16}{15}\,\pi^2\,\rho^2\,R^5 = \frac{3}{5}\,\frac{Q^2}{R}$$

Hence

$$W = \frac{1}{4\pi\,\varepsilon_0}\,\frac{3}{5}\,\frac{Q^2}{R}$$

This work is stored in the sphere as its electrical potential energy. Hence

Electrical potential energy of the sphere

$$U = \frac{1}{4\pi\,\varepsilon_0}\,\frac{3}{5}\,\frac{Q^2}{R}$$

Q. 5. 39. Calculate the energy per unit volume associated with an electric field or Prove that energy stored per unit volume in an electric field is equal to $\frac{1}{2} k \varepsilon_0 E^2$ Jm^{-3}. Hence calculate the work done in assembling a conducting sphere (or shell) of radius a and having a total charge q. (*H.P.U.* 2003; *P.U.* 2003, 2001, 2000; *G.N.D.U.* 2000, 1999; *M.D.U.* 1999; *K.U.* 1996)

Ans. Energy per unit volume of an electric field. When a conductor is charged outward force per unit area of its surface $= \frac{\sigma^2}{2\varepsilon_0}$ where σ is the surface density of charge and the conductor lies in air or free space. Let us suppose that the conductor is spherical and has a radius r, then the total outward force acting normally on its surface $= \left(\frac{\sigma^2}{2\varepsilon_0}\right) (4\pi \ r^2)$.

Suppose we *shrink* the sphere from a radius r to a radius $r - dr$, then we have to apply an equal and opposite force through a distance dr.

$\therefore$ Work done on the system by these external forces $dW = \left(\frac{\sigma^2}{2\varepsilon_0}\right) (4\pi r^2) \ dr$.

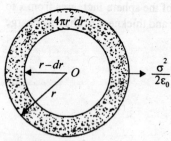

Fig. 5.26

But $4\pi \ r^2 \ dr$ gives the total decrease in volume. If we put $4\pi \ r^2 \ dr = dv$ then

$$dW = \frac{\sigma^2}{2\varepsilon_0} \ dv$$

The electric field at a point just outside the surface $E = \frac{\sigma}{\varepsilon_0}$ acting radially outward.

$\therefore$ $\sigma = \varepsilon_0 E$

Substituting in (*i*), we have

$$dW = \frac{\varepsilon_0^2 \ E^2}{2\varepsilon_0} \ dv = \frac{\varepsilon_0 \ E^2}{2} \ dv$$

As a result of shrinking the sphere an electric field $\frac{\sigma}{\varepsilon_0}$ has been created in the space between the radii r and $r - dr$ i.e., within the volume $dv = 4\pi r^2 \ dr$ at the cost of work dW. Therefore, dW gives the energy of the electric field in the volume dv.

$\therefore$ Energy stored per unit volume of the electric field

$$= \frac{dW}{dv} = \frac{1}{2} \ \varepsilon_0 E^2$$

In a medium of relative permittivity ε_r

$$E = \frac{\sigma}{\varepsilon_0 \varepsilon_r}$$

$\therefore$ Energy per unit volume $= \frac{\sigma^2}{2\varepsilon_0 \varepsilon_r} = \frac{1}{2} \ \varepsilon_0 \varepsilon_r E^2$ Jm$^{-3} = \frac{1}{2} \ \varepsilon_0 \ kE^2$ Jm^{-3} ...(*ii*)

Work done in assembling the spherical surface charge. The total energy stored in the field of a spherical surface charge of radius a and having a total charge q is given by the total work done in shrinking the radius of the sphere from ∞ to a.

$$\therefore \qquad \text{Total energy stored} = -\int_{\infty}^{a} \frac{\sigma^2}{2\varepsilon_0} 4\pi r^2 \, dr$$

$$= -\int_{\infty}^{a} \frac{1}{2\varepsilon_0} \frac{q^2}{(4\pi r^2)^2} 4\pi r^2 \, dr$$

$$= \frac{1}{4\pi \, \varepsilon_0} \frac{q^2}{2} \int_{\infty}^{a} -\frac{dr}{r^2} = \frac{1}{4\pi \, \varepsilon_0} \frac{q^2}{2a}$$

Q. 5.40. Show that the electrostatic energy stored per unit volume in a dielectric is $\frac{1}{2} \vec{D} \cdot \vec{E}$ where symbols have their usual meanings. *(H.P.U. 2007, 2003, 2002; P.U. 2007, 2002)*

Ans. Electrostatic energy per unit-volume in a dielectric. The capacitance C_d of a parallel plate capacitor filled with a dielectric of dielectric constant k is given by $C_d = k \, C_a$ where C_a is the capacitance of the same capacitor with air or vacuum.

Now $C_a = \dfrac{\varepsilon_0 \, A}{d}$ where A is the area of the plates, d the distance between them and ε_0 the permittivity of air or vacuum.

$$\therefore \qquad C_d = k \, \varepsilon_0 \, A/d$$

If $\vec{E}$ is the intensity of the electric field between the capacitor plates, the potential difference between the plates $V = Ed$

$\therefore$ The energy stored in the capacitor dielectric $= \dfrac{1}{2} C_d \, V^2$

$$= \frac{1}{2} \frac{k \, \varepsilon_0 \, A}{d} E^2 \, d^2 = \frac{1}{2} k \, \varepsilon_0 \, A d \, E^2$$

The volume of the capacitor $= Ad$

$\therefore$ Energy per unit volume stored in the dielectric

$$= \frac{1}{2} k \varepsilon_0 \, E^2 = \frac{1}{2} k \varepsilon_0 \, \vec{E} \cdot \vec{E} = \frac{1}{2} \vec{D} \cdot \vec{E}$$

because the electric displacement vector $\vec{D} = \varepsilon_r \, \varepsilon_0 \, \vec{E} = k \varepsilon_0 \, \vec{E}$.

Q. 5.41. Derive a relation for the energy of an electric field due to a continuous charge distribution and show that electric energy per unit volume in a dielectric is $\frac{1}{2} \vec{D} \cdot \vec{E}$ where symbols have their usual meanings. Hence calculate the energy of a charged spherical shell.

(Pbi. U. 2000; Luck. U., 1995; P.U. 2001, 1995; K.U., 1995; H.P.U. 2000, 1995; G.N.D.U., 1995, 1993, 1990)

Ans. Energy of a continuous charge distribution. Let V be a volume having continuous charge distribution. Consider a volume element dv at $\vec{r}$ of this continuous charge distribution.

If ρ is the volume charge density at the position $\vec{r}$ and ϕ the electric potential at $\vec{r}$ due to the whole charge distribution, then

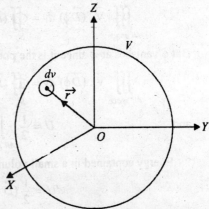

Fig. 5.27

Potential energy of the charge element = $\phi \rho \, dv$

The total potential energy of the whole of the continous charge distribution

$$U = \frac{1}{2} \iiint_V \phi \rho \, dv$$

where V is the volume of the entire charge distribution.

Let V' be the volume of the space which contains no charge, then for this charge distribution

$$\frac{1}{2} \iiint_{V'} \phi \rho \, dv = 0$$

as $\rho = 0$ at all points lying in the volume V'.

According to Gauss's theorem for dielectrics

$$\vec{\nabla} \cdot \vec{D} = \rho$$

where $\vec{D}$ is the displacement vector

$$\therefore \qquad U = \frac{1}{2} \iiint_{All\ space} (\vec{\nabla} \cdot \vec{D}) \, \phi \, dv \qquad\qquad ...(i)$$

Now $\qquad\qquad \vec{\nabla} \cdot (\vec{D}\phi) = (\vec{\nabla} \cdot \vec{D}) \, \phi + \vec{D} \cdot \vec{\nabla} \phi$

Also $\vec{\nabla} \phi = -\vec{E}$ where $\vec{E}$ is the electric field vector.

$$\therefore \qquad \vec{\nabla} \cdot (\vec{D}\phi) = (\vec{\nabla} \cdot \vec{D}) \, \phi - \vec{D} \cdot \vec{E} \quad \text{or} \quad (\vec{\nabla} \cdot \vec{D}) \, \phi = \vec{\nabla} \cdot (\vec{D}\phi) + \vec{D} \cdot \vec{E}$$

Substituting in (i), we get

$$U = \frac{1}{2} \iiint_{All\ space} \vec{\nabla} \cdot (D\phi) \, dv + \frac{1}{2} \iiint_{All\ space} (\vec{D} \cdot \vec{E}) \, dv$$

According to Gauss's divergence theorem of vector analysis, if S is the surface bounding volume V, then

$$\iiint_V \vec{\nabla} \cdot \vec{A} \, dv = \oiint_S \vec{A} \cdot \vec{ds}$$

If the volume V encloses all space, the surface S lies at infinity. If we denote this surface by S_∞, then

$$\iiint_{All\ space} \vec{\nabla} \cdot (\vec{D}\phi) \, dv = \oiint_{S_\infty} (D\phi) \cdot \vec{ds}$$

But ϕ vanishes at ∞ since it is the potential due to a finite charge distribution. Thus the integral

$$\iiint_{All\ space} \vec{\nabla} \cdot (\vec{D}\phi) \, dv = \oiint_{S_\infty} (\vec{D}\phi) \cdot \vec{ds} = 0$$

and $\qquad\qquad\qquad U = \frac{1}{2} \iiint_{All\ space} (\vec{D} \cdot \vec{E}) \, dv$

$\therefore$ Energy contained in a small volume dv is given by

$$dU = \frac{1}{2} (\vec{D} \cdot \vec{E}) \, dv$$

or energy per unit volume

$$\frac{dU}{dv} = \frac{1}{2}\vec{D}\cdot\vec{E} \qquad\qquad ...(ii)$$

Relation (ii) shows that electric energy per unit volume in a dielectric is $\frac{1}{2}\vec{D}\cdot\vec{E}$.

For vacuum or free space $\vec{D} = \varepsilon_0\,\vec{E}$ and

$\therefore$ Energy per unit volume $= \frac{1}{2}\varepsilon_0\,\vec{E}\cdot\vec{E} = \frac{1}{2}\varepsilon_0\,E^2$

For a medium of relative permittivity ε_r, $\vec{D} = \varepsilon_r\,\varepsilon_0\,\vec{E}$

and Energy per unit volume $= \frac{1}{2}\varepsilon_0\,\varepsilon_r\,E^2$

This relation shows that electric field contains energy.

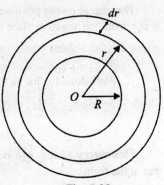

Fig. 5.28

Energy of a charged spherical shell. Suppose we have a spherical shell of radius R with centre O having a charge q uniformly distributed over its surface. There is no electric field inside the shell. So no electric field energy is contributed by the volume enclosed by the shell. Thus the region $r < R$ makes no contribution to the electric field energy.

Electric field at a point outside the shell at a distance r $(r > R)$ from the centre O.

$$E = \frac{1}{4\pi\,\varepsilon_0}\frac{q}{r^2}$$

Energy per unit volume at a distance $r = \frac{1}{2}\varepsilon_0\,\frac{1}{16\pi^2}\frac{q^2}{\varepsilon_0^2\,r^4}$

$$= \frac{1}{32\pi^2\,\varepsilon_0}\frac{q^2}{r^4}$$

Draw two spheres of radius r and $(r + dr)$ concentric with the shell.

The volume of the space contained between the spheres of radius r and $(r + dr) = 4\pi r^2\,dr$

$\therefore$ Electric field energy in this space $= \dfrac{1}{32\pi^2\,\varepsilon_0}\dfrac{q^2}{r^4}\,4\pi\,r^2\,dr$

$$= \frac{1}{8\pi\,\varepsilon_0}\frac{q^2}{r^2}\,dr$$

$\therefore$ Total potential energy of the charged shell

$$U = \frac{q^2}{8\pi\,\varepsilon_0}\int\limits_R^\infty \frac{1}{r^2}\,dr = \frac{q^2}{8\pi\,\varepsilon_0}\left[-\frac{1}{r}\right]_R^\infty = \frac{1}{4\pi\,\varepsilon_0}\frac{q^2}{2R}$$

Q. 5. 42. (a) **Find an expression for the energy stored in a capacitor.**

(Pbi. U. 2000; Osm. U. 1997)

(b) **A capacitor consists of two metallic discs each 1 metre in diameter placed parallel to each other at a distance of 4 mm. The potential difference between the plates is 10,000 volts. Calculate the energy stored by the capacitor.**

$$\varepsilon_0 = 8.85 \times 10^{-12}\ C^2/N\text{-}m^2$$

(Luck. U., 1996, 1993)

(c) **The space between the plates of a capacitor is filled with a medium of dielectric constant k. Find the energy density when** (i) **the potential is kept constant and** (ii) **the charge is kept constant. In what form energy is stored in a charged capacitor? Give formula in support of your answer.**

(G.N.D.U. 2003, 2000)

Ans. (a) Energy stored in a capacitor. Consider a capacitor of capacitance C having a potential difference V between the plates.

$\therefore$ Charge on the plate $Q = CV$

The charge on the positive plate $= + Q$ and that on the negative plate $= - Q$. If we take a charge $+ dQ$ from the negative plate to the positive plate the work done against the potential difference

$$dW = V \, dQ = \frac{Q}{C} \, dQ$$

$\therefore$ Work done to charge the capacitor to a charge Q from the uncharged state

$$= W = \int dW = \int_0^Q \frac{Q}{C} = \frac{1}{2} \frac{Q^2}{C}$$

This energy $U = \frac{1}{2} \frac{Q^2}{C}$ is stored in the capacitor as potential energy of charge. This may also be put in the form

$$U = \frac{1}{2} \frac{Q^2}{C} = \frac{1}{2} QV = \frac{1}{2} CV^2$$

(b) Area of each disc of the capacitor $A = \frac{\pi}{4} D^2 = \frac{\pi}{4} \times 1^2 = \frac{\pi}{4}$ m^2

Distance between the discs $d = 4$ mm $= 4 \times 10^{-3}$ m

Capacitance of the capacitor $C = \frac{\varepsilon_0 \, A}{d} = \frac{8.85 \times 10^{-12}}{4 \times 10^{-3}} \times \frac{\pi}{4} = \frac{8.85 \, \pi}{16} \times 10^{-9}$ Farad

Voltage applied $V = 10,000$ $V = 10^4$ V

Energy stored in the capacitor $= \frac{1}{2} CV^2 = \frac{1}{2} \times \frac{8.85 \, \pi}{16} \times 10^{-9} \times 10^8 = 0.87$ J

(c) **Energy density.** The energy stored in a capacitor is given by

$$U = \frac{1}{2} CV^2$$

If we have a parallel plate capacitor of capacitance C_a with air in between the plates each of area A separated by a distance d apart and introduce into it a dielectric slab of the same thickness d and dielectric constant k, or relative permittivity ε_r, then the new capacitance

$$C_d = k \, C_a = \varepsilon_r \, C_a$$

(i) **Keeping E or V constant.** If we keep the potential difference between the plates constant *by adding more charge to the capacitor* then the energy of the capacitor with dielectric

$$U_d = \frac{1}{2} C_d \, V^2$$

and with air

$$U_a = \frac{1}{2} C_d \, V^2$$

As V is a constant

$$\frac{U_d}{U_a} = \frac{C_d}{C_a} = k = \varepsilon_r$$

Thus the energy stored in the capacitor with the medium of dielectric constant k (or relative permittivity ε_r) between the plates is k (or ε_r) times the energy when the medium is air or vacuum.

The energy stored in the parallel plate capacitor with air or vacuum

$$U_a = \frac{1}{2} C_a V^2 = \frac{1}{2} \frac{\varepsilon_0 A}{d} \cdot (Ed)^2 = \frac{1}{2} \varepsilon_0 E^2 Ad \qquad ...(i)$$

where E is the electric intensity between the plates of the capacitor. But Ad is the volume of the capacitor.

For an air capacitor

Energy density = Energy stored per unit volume

$$= \frac{\frac{1}{2} \varepsilon_0 E^2 Ad}{Ad} = \frac{1}{2} \varepsilon_0 E^2 \qquad ...(ii)$$

For a capacitor with a medium of (dielectric constant k) relative permittivity ε_r

$$U_d = \frac{1}{2} C_d V^2 = \frac{1}{2} \frac{\varepsilon_0 \varepsilon_r A}{d} (Ed)^2$$

$$= \frac{1}{2} \varepsilon_0 \varepsilon_r E^2 Ad$$

∴ Energy density $= \frac{1}{2} \varepsilon_0 \varepsilon_r E^2 = \frac{1}{2} \varepsilon_0 \varepsilon_r \vec{E} \cdot \vec{E} = \frac{1}{2} \vec{D} \cdot \vec{E}$ ...(iii)

where $$\vec{D} = \varepsilon_r \varepsilon_0 \vec{E} = \varepsilon \vec{E}$$

Thus when the value of the potential difference V between the plates of a capacitor (or E) is kept constant, the energy increases k (or ε_r) times when a medium of dielectric constant k (or relative permittivity ε_r) is introduced between the plates. This energy is drawn from the source (or battery) which keeps V constant.

(ii) **Keeping Q constant. See Q. 5.43**

In what form energy is stored? Energy is stored in the capacitor in the form of electric field energy of the charged capacitor. It resides in the dielectric medium between the capacitor plates and is given by $\frac{1}{2} \varepsilon_0 \varepsilon_r E^2$ per unit volume [See Eq. *(iii)*].

Q. 5.43. An isolated air gap parallel plate capacitor C_a has a charge Q. A dielectric having constant k is inserted between the plates in such a way that charge on the capacitor is not changed. Find the change in energy stored in the capacitor. (*G.N.D.U.* 2003; *P.U.* 2003)

Ans. Change in energy- Q constant. The energy stored in a capacitor is given by

$$U = \frac{1}{2} \frac{Q^2}{C}$$

where Q is the charge on the capacitor and C its capacity.

If we have a parallel plate capacitor of capacitance C_a with air in between the plates each of area A separated by a distance d apart and introduce into it a dielectric of the same thickness d and dielectric constant k (or relative permittivity ε_r) then the new capacitance

$$C_d = k C_a = \varepsilon_r C_a$$

The energy stored in the capacitor with air in the gap between the capacitor plates

$$U_a = \frac{1}{2} \frac{Q^2}{C_a}$$

If the charge Q on the capacitor is kept constant and a plate having dielectic constant k (or relative permittivity ε_r) is introduced, the energy

$$U_d = \frac{1}{2} \frac{Q^2}{C_d} = \frac{1}{2} \frac{Q^2}{\varepsilon_r C_a} = \frac{1}{\varepsilon_r} U_a$$

i.e. the energy is reduced to $\dfrac{1}{\varepsilon_r}$ $\left(\text{or } \dfrac{1}{k}\right)$ of its original value.

The decrease in energy equal to $U_a\left(1 - \dfrac{1}{k}\right)$ is due to the fact that a part of the energy is now used up in inducing the polarisation charge in the dielectric which in turn reduces the value of E or V.

Q. 5.44. The voltage between parallel plates of a capacitor is V_1. The plates are isolated electrically. A dielectric slab of dielectric constant k is inserted between the plates and completely fills the volume between them. Find the new potential V_2. Compare the total stored energy before and after inserting the slab. Also state whether electrostatic force pulls the slab into the space between the plates or pushes it away.

Ans. New potential. When a dielectric slab is introduced within the plates of a parallel plate capacitor the electric field between the plates is reduced from E_1 to a value E_2 given by

$$E_2 = \frac{E_1}{k} \quad \text{or} \quad \frac{E_1}{E_2} = k$$

If d is the distance between the plates, then

$$V_1 = E_1 d \text{ and } V_2 = E_2 d$$

$$\therefore \quad \frac{V_2}{V_1} = \frac{E_2}{E_1} = \frac{1}{k} \quad \text{or} \quad V_2 = \frac{V_1}{k}$$

i.e., the new potential $\quad V_2 = \dfrac{1}{k}$ times V_1.

If instead of dielectric constant k, relative permittivity ε_r is given, then $V_2 = \dfrac{V_1}{\varepsilon_r}$

Stored energy. As the plates are isolated electrically, the *charge is kept constant*.

$\therefore$ Stored energy with dielectric $= \dfrac{1}{k} = \dfrac{1}{\varepsilon_r}$ of stored energy with air.

[For proof See **Q. 5.43**]

Pull on the slab. The electrostatic force pulls the slab into the space between the plates.

[For proof See **Q. 5.45**]

Q. 5.45. Derive an expression for the total force experienced by a dielectric slab when it is introduced in an electric field.   (*P.U.*, 2006, 2005)

Ans. Force on a dielectric slab. When a slab of a dielectric is being introduced into a capacitor a force acts on it. To calculate the force consider a parallel plate capacitor. The length of each plate $= l$ and the breadth $= b$.

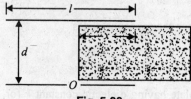

Fig. 5.29

$\therefore$ Area of the plate $A = bl$

Distance between the plates $= d$

Let a slab of length l and thickness d be introduced into the capacitor and consider the position when a length x of the slab is within the capacitor, then capacitance of the capacitor

$$= \frac{\varepsilon_r \, \varepsilon_0 \, xb}{d} + \frac{\varepsilon_0 \, (l - x)b}{d}$$

If V is the difference of potential between the plates the total charge

$$Q = \frac{\varepsilon_0 \, bV}{d} \, (\varepsilon_r \, x + l - x)$$

If the slab moves into the capacitor through a further distance dx, the capacitance of the capacitor will increase and more charge will be drawn from the source to keep the potential constant.

$\therefore$
$$Q + dQ = \frac{\varepsilon_0 \, bV}{d} \left[\varepsilon_r \, (x + dx) + l - (x + dx) \right]$$

or
$$dQ = \frac{\varepsilon_0 \, bV}{d} \, (\varepsilon_r - 1) \, dx$$

As the charge dQ is drawn into the capacitor at a constant potential V.

Energy drawn by the capacitor = $V \, dQ$

A part of this energy is used up in drawing the slab into the capacitor and the rest in raising the energy of the charge of the capacitor.

If F is the force acting on the slab drawing it inwards, then

Work done when it moves inward through a distance $dx = F \, dx$

The energy of the capacitor with charge $Q = U = \dfrac{1}{2} \, QV$

and with charge $\quad Q + dQ = U + dU = \dfrac{1}{2} \, (Q + dQ) \, V$

$\therefore$ Increase in energy $\quad dU = \dfrac{1}{2} \, dQV = \dfrac{1}{2} \, \dfrac{\varepsilon_0 \, bV^2}{d} \, (\varepsilon_r - 1) \, dx$

Hence $\qquad F \, dx + \dfrac{1}{2} \, dQV = V dQ$

or $\qquad\qquad F \, dx = \dfrac{1}{2} \, V dQ = \dfrac{1}{2} \, \dfrac{\varepsilon_0 \, bV^2}{d} \, (\varepsilon_r - 1) \, dx$

$\therefore$ $\qquad\qquad F = \dfrac{1}{2} \, \dfrac{\varepsilon_0 \, bV^2}{d} \, (\varepsilon_r - 1)$

Since F is positive it is in the direction of increasing x. Hence the slab is pulled into the capacitor due to electric forces. Half the energy drawn from the source is used up to increase the stored energy and half appears as work pulling the dielectric slab into the space between the plates.

Q. 5.46. What is dielectric break down? What is dielectric strength of a material? In what units is it measured ? *(H.P.U. 1999; G.N.D.U., 1996)*

Ans. Dielectric strength. *Dielectric strength of a material is defined as the maximum electric field which the material can withstand without breaking down.*

It is found that every dielectric starts conducting if an external electric field above a certain value is applied to it. When the dielectric starts conducting it is said to have *broken down*. The dielectric strength depends upon the nature of the material. As a dielectric material is used between the coatings of a capacitor, the maximum voltage that can be applied to the capacitor depends upon the nature and thickness of the dielectric. This voltage is marked on the capacitor. If the voltage is exceeded the dielectric is likely to breakdown.

The value of dielectric strength for alternating voltages is different from that of direct voltages.

Units. As electric field is measured in volts per metre, the dielectric strength is measured in Kilovolts per mm (kV/mm). For example, the dielectric strength of air is 0.8 kV/mm and that of mica 160 kV/mm.

Q. 5.47. A 10μF capacitor charged to 100 V is connected in parallel to an uncharged capacitor. After making the connection the common voltage on the capacitor is found to be 30 V. What is the capacity of the second capacitor? Also calculate net loss of energy during the process of connection.

(G.N.D.U. 1999)

Ans.   Capacity of first capacitor $C_1 = 10\ \mu F = 10 \times 10^{-6}$ F

Potential $V_1 = 100$ V

Let capacity of second capacitor $= C_2$

Common potential after connection $V_2 = 30$ V

Now, as the total charge is conserved

$$C_1 V_1 = (C_1 + C_2)\, V_2$$

or

$$C_2 = \frac{C_1 V_1}{V_2} - C_1 = \frac{10 \times 10^{-6} \times 100}{30} - 10 \times 10^{-6}$$

$$= \frac{70}{3} \times 10^{-6}\ F = 23.3\ \mu F$$

Energy before connection $= \dfrac{1}{2}\, C_1 V_1^2 = \dfrac{1}{2} \times 10 \times 10^{-6} \times 100 \times 100$

$$= 50 \times 10^{-3}\ J$$

Energy after connection $= \dfrac{1}{2}\, C_1 V_2^2 + \dfrac{1}{2}\, C_2 V_2^2$

$$= \frac{1}{2} \times 10 \times 10^{-6} \times 30 \times 30 + \frac{1}{2} \times \frac{70}{3} \times 10^{-6} \times 30 \times 30$$

$$= 4.5 \times 10^{-3} + 10.5 \times 10^{-3} = 15 \times 10^{-3}\ J$$

∴   Loss of energy $= 50 \times 10^{-3} - 15 \times 10^{-3} = 35 \times 10^{-3}$ J

Q. 5.48. Mark the correct answer.

(*i*) The atomic polarisability has dimensions of

(*a*) $CV^{-1}\ m^2$ (*b*) CVm   (*c*) Cm^{-2} (*d*) none

(P.U., 1994)

(*ii*) The net charge inside a polarised dielectric is

(*a*) positive   (*b*) negative

(*c*) zero   (*d*) Either positive or negative

(*iii*) Electric susceptibility for vacuum is

(*a*) 1   (*b*) Zero   (*c*) −1

(*d*) less than 1 but positive

(*iv*) The S.I. unit of electric displacement vector is

(*a*) C-m   (*b*) C/m

(*c*) C-m²

 (*d*) Cm⁺²

(*v*) The potential energy of the given charge configuration is

(*a*) positive   (*b*) negative

(*c*) zero   (*d*) infinite   (P.U. 1994)

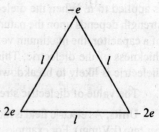

Fig. 5.30

[Hint. Negative.
$$U = \frac{1}{4\pi\,\varepsilon_0}\left[-\frac{2e^2}{l} + \frac{2e^2}{l} - \frac{4e^2}{l}\right]$$

$$= \frac{1}{4\pi\,\varepsilon_0}\left[-\frac{4e^2}{l}\right].$$

(*vi*) A capacitor is charged to a potential V_0. A dielectric slab of relative permittivity ε_r is introduced between the plates. Its energy stored will

    (*a*) increase by a factor ε_r (*b*) decrease by a factor ε_r

    (*c*) remain unchanged

    (*d*) may increase or decrease depending upon the nature of the dielectric.   (*P.U.*, 1994)

[Hint. The value of energy stored in a capacitor on the introduction of a dielectric slab depends upon whether the potential difference is kept constant or the charge on the capacitor plates is kept constant. When the *potential difference is kept constant at* V_0 the energy stored in the capacitor *increases* ε_r times on introducing the dielectric slab.

When the *charge is kept constant* the energy stored in the capacitor is reduced to $\dfrac{1}{\varepsilon_r}$ times on introducing the dielectric slab.]

The students may assume that V_0 is kept constant and therefore the energy will increase by a factor ε_r.

(*vii*) A dielectric slab is placed in an electric field. Mark the correct statement (s).

    (*a*) All its atoms get polarised.

    (*b*) Polarisation charge appears on its faces.

    (*c*) Gauss's law can be applied to polarisation charge.

    (*d*) The electric field strength gets altered inside the dielectric.   (*P.U.*, 1994)

(*viii*) The dielectric constant of a metal is always

    (*a*) more than 1   (*b*) less than 1   (*c*) zero   (*d*) infinity.

                                                                (*H.P.U.*, 2000)

Ans.   (*i*) *a*   (*ii*) *c*   (*iii*) *b*   (*iv*) *d*

          (*v*) *b*   (*vi*) *a*   (*vii*) All   (*viii*) *d*

EXERCISES

1. Calculate the magnitude of dipole moment of the charge distribution shown in the figure. What is the direction of dipole moment vector $\vec{p}$.

    [Hint] $p_x = [q\,(l/2) + q\,(-l/2) - 2q\,(0)]\,\hat{i} = 0$

$$p_y = \left[q \times 0 + q \times 0 - 2q\left(d^2 - \frac{l^2}{4}\right)\right]\hat{j} = -q\sqrt{4d^2 - l^2}\,\hat{j}$$

assuming the origin of the co-ordinate system at O where O is the base of the perpendicular drawn from the point having charge $-2q$ on the line joinning the charges q each a distance l apart.

∴ Dipole moment $\vec{p} = \vec{p}_y = -q\sqrt{4d^2 - l^2}\,\hat{j}$ *i.e.*, it acts along $-Y$ direction as shown.

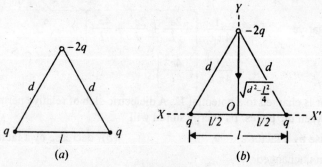

Fig. 5.31

2. A potential difference of 100 volts is applied across the parallel plates of a parallel plate capacitor. Each of these plates are of area 0.01 m² and are separated by a distance of 1 mm. If the space between the plates is filled with a medium of dielectric constant $k = 5$, evaluate the charge on each plate.   (*P.U.*, 1994) **[Ans. 4.425 × 10⁻⁸ C]**

3. An electric field 600 volt/cm is applied to a sample of neon gas at N.T.P. Find the dipole moment induced in each atom. Given that the dielectric constant of neon at N.T.P. = 1.000134 and Avogadro's number is 6.06 × 10²³.   **[Ans. 2.64 × 10⁻³⁶ Cm]**

6

Electric Current

Q. 6.1. (*a*) **Define the terms drift velocity, current and current density vector** $\vec{J}$. **Differentiate between electric current and current density.** (*P.U.* 2009, 2001; *Kerala U.* 2001;

Pbi. U. 2007, 2000, 1999; *H.P.U.* 2003, 1999, 1997; *G.N.D.U.* 2008, 2006, 1996; *K.U.* 1994)

(*b*) **Is current a scalar or a vector quantity?** (*P.U.*, 2007)

(*c*) **A current of 10 Amp. exists in a 10 ohm resistance for 4 minutes. Find (*i*) how many coulombs and (*ii*) how many electrons pass through any cross-section of the resistance in this time?** (*M.D.U.* 2000)

Ans. Drift velocity. Consider a conductor AB the two ends of which are connected to a battery. A *steady* electric field $\vec{E}$ is thus established in the conductor in the direction A to B. Before the field is applied the free electrons in the conductor move in all random directions like the molecules of a gas confined to a vessel, but as soon as the electric field is established the free electrons at the end B experience a force $-\vec{E}e$ from B to A in a direction opposite to that of the field $\vec{E}$. The electrons are, therefore, accelerated in this direction. In the process, the electrons collide with each other and with the positive ions in the conductor. At each collision the momentum gained in the direction of the force acting on the charge carrier due to the electric field is lost and the electron is accelerated afresh after each collision. Thus, due to collisions, a *backward* force acts on the electrons. The force is known as *collision drag*. The overall effect of the these collisions is that the electrons *slowly drift* with a *constant average drift velocity* in the direction of $-\vec{E}$. The organised transport of charge by the electrons over distances very large as compared to atomic distances constitutes an electric current.

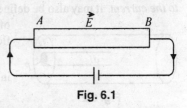
Fig. 6.1

The vector average velocity with which the charge carriers move under the effect of the electric field is known as drift velocity, the average being macroscopic i.e., taken over a volume large as compared to molecular volume.

Consider the case of free electrons as charge carriers in a conductor and let a number n_1 have a velocity v_1, n_2 a velocity v_2 ..., n_i a velocity v_i and so on, then

$$\text{Average velocity } v = \frac{1}{N} \sum_{i=1}^{i=N} n_i v_i$$

where $N = n_1 + n_2 + ... n_i + ...$ = total number of electrons.

Current. *The conventional current is defined as the rate of flow of positive charge through any cross-sectional area of a conductor.*

If a net charge q passes through any cross-section of a conductor in a time t, then

$$\text{current } I = \frac{q}{t}$$

When q is in *coulombs* and t in *seconds*, the current I is measured in *amperes*.

If the rate of flow of charge is not constant, the current varies with time and the instantaneous value represented as i is given by

$$i = \frac{dq}{dt}$$

The current I is characteristic of a particular conductor and is a *macroscopic quantity*.

The direction of conventional current is taken as the direction of flow of positive charge. Current is a *scalar* quantity.

Units. The S.I. unit of current is an *ampere*.

A current of one ampere is said to flow through a conductor if one coulomb of charge passes through any cross-sectional area of the conductor in 1 second.

The C.G.S. unit of current is a stat-ampere.

As 1 Coulomb $= 3 \times 10^9$ stat-coulomb

$$1\,\text{Ampere} = 3 \times 10^9 \frac{\text{stat-coulomb}}{\text{second}} = 3 \times 10^9 \text{ stat-ampere.}$$

Current density. *The current density at a point in a conductor carrying current is defined as the current per unit area of cross-section of the conductor the area being taken in a direction normal to the current.* It may also be defined as the quantity of charge passing per second through a unit area of cross-section of the conductor taken normal to the direction of flow of charge.

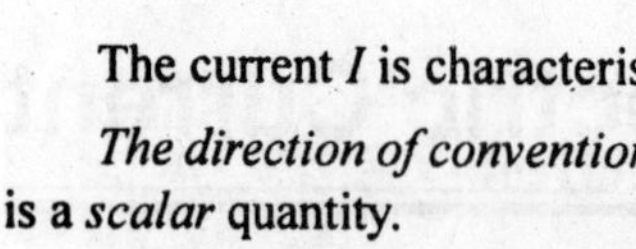

Fig. 6.2

If dl is the current through a small area ds containing a point P in a direction normal to that of the current, then

$$\text{Current density at } P, \ J = \frac{dI}{ds}$$

Current density-a vector. Current density at a point is a *vector* quantity and its direction is that in which a positive charge carrier would move at that point. It is denoted as $\vec{J}$.

Dimensions. The current density has dimensions of

$$\frac{\text{current}}{\text{area}} = \frac{\text{amp}}{\text{met}^2} = \frac{\text{coulomb}}{\text{met}^2 \text{ sec}} \qquad \text{[in S.I. units]}$$

and

$$\frac{\text{stat-Amp}}{\text{cm}^2} = \frac{\text{stat-coulomb}}{\text{cm}^2 \text{ sec}} \qquad \text{[in C.G.S. units]}$$

Distinction between current and current density. (*i*) Current density is the current per unit area normal to the direction of drift velocity of the electrons.

(*ii*) Current density is a vector quantity whereas current is a scalar quantity.

(*iii*) Current I is the scalar product of current density vector $\vec{J}$ and area vector $\vec{ds}$ at a point

$$I = \vec{J} \cdot \vec{ds}$$

(*iv*) The unit of current density is current per unit area. The S.I. unit is Amp per m^2.

(b) **Current-Scalar or vector.** Current I is a scalar quantity. It is the scalar product of current density vector $\vec{J}$ and area vector $\vec{ds}$ i.e., $I = \vec{J}.\vec{ds}$

(c) Current $I = 10$ Amp;   time $t = 4$ min $= 4 \times 60$ s.

Charge $Q = It = 10 \times 4 \times 60 = 2400$ Coulombs.

Charge on the electron $e = 1.6 \times 10^{-19}$ C

∴ Number of electrons passing through any cross-section of the resistance in 4 min

$$= \frac{Q}{e} = \frac{2400}{1.6 \times 10^{-19}} = 1.5 \times 10^{22} \text{ electrons}$$

Q. 6.2. (a) Derive a relation between (i) current density and current $\left(I = \iint\limits_S \vec{J} \cdot \vec{ds} \right)$.

(ii) Current density and drift velocity $(\vec{J} = ne\vec{v})$.

(G.N.D.U. 2006, 2004; P.U. 2001, 2000; H.P.U. 2002, 1999)

(iii) Current and drift velocity $\left(I = \iint\limits_S Ne\vec{v} \cdot \vec{ds} \right)$.   (M.D.U. 2002, 2001)

Ans. (i) Current density and current. If dI is the current through a small area ds containing a point P in a direction normal to that of the current then current density at P

$$J = \frac{dI}{ds} \quad \text{or} \quad dI = J\, ds$$

but when the cross-sectional area ds is not normal to the direction of the current at that point, then

$$dI = J\, ds \cos\theta = \vec{J} \cdot \vec{ds}$$

where θ is the angle between direction of current or the vector $\vec{J}$ and the outward drawn normal to the area element $\vec{ds}$.

∴ Flux of the vector $\vec{J}$ over the whole are $S =$ current through

the conductor $I = \iint\limits_S \vec{J} \cdot \vec{ds}$

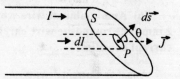

Fig. 6.3

(ii) Current density and drift velocity. Consider a medium through which a macroscopic electric current is flowing. We suppose that this current is only due to one type of charge carriers. The average of the random thermal velocities of these particles will be zero and they will posses an average drift velocity say $\vec{v}$ in the direction of the applied electric field. To find the value of $\vec{J}$ at a point P consider a small vector area $\vec{ds}$ surrounding the point, then all the charge carriers lying in a cylinder of length v will pass through the area in one second.

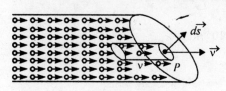

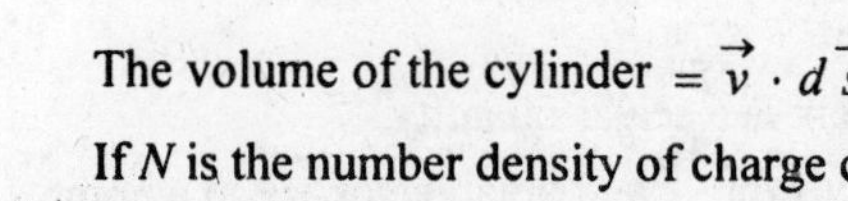

Fig. 6.4

The volume of the cylinder $= \vec{v} \cdot \vec{ds}$

If N is the number density of charge carriers i.e., the number of charge carriers per unit volume, then

Number passing through the area $\vec{ds}$ in one second $= N\vec{v} \cdot \vec{ds}$.

If e is the charge per carrier, then

Charge passing through the area $\vec{ds}$ in one second $= dq = Ne\vec{v} \cdot \vec{ds}$

The charge dq passing per second through the area $d\vec{s}$ measures the current dI through it

$$\therefore \qquad dI = Ne\,\vec{v} \cdot d\vec{s} = \vec{J} \cdot d\vec{s} \qquad \qquad ...(i)$$

where $\vec{J} = ne\vec{v}$ is called the *current density vector.*

$$\therefore \qquad \vec{J} = ne\vec{v} \qquad \qquad ...(ii)$$

The direction of current density vector is along the direction of drift velocity $\vec{v}$.

(*iii*) **Current and drift velocity.** According to relation (*i*) $dI = \vec{J} \cdot d\vec{s} = Ne\vec{v} \cdot d\vec{s}$

$$\therefore \qquad \text{Current } I = \iint_S dI = \iint_S Ne\vec{v} \cdot d\vec{s}$$

Q. 6.3. In the absence of any external electric field the free electrons in a metallic conductor do not contribute anything towards current density. Explain. *(H.P.U. 2003, 1997, 1992)*

Ans. No current density in absence of external electric field. A metallic conductor can be supposed to be a *lattice* of atoms in fixed positions and a large number of free electrons known as *conduction* electrons. These electrons come from the atoms of the metal leaving the atoms as positively charged ions. The conduction electrons move in all random directions like the molecules of a gas confined to a vessel. The random motion arises because of collisions between the electrons and the ions of the metal lattice. In the absence of an electric field the average of these random thermal velocities is zero and they do not have an organised motion in any particular direction. Hence they do not contribute anything towards current density.

Q. 6.4. (*a*) **A copper wire is carrying a current of 2A and is having an area of cross-section equal to 10^{-6} m². If the number of electrons per m³ be 8×10^{28}, calculate the current density and average drift velocity. The charge on the electron is 1.6×10^{-19} C.** *(K.U., 1995)*

(*b*) **An aluminium wire whose radius is 1 mm is welded to a copper wire whose radius is 2 mm. The composite wire carries a steady current of 5 Amp. What would be the ratio of their current densities?** *(Gharwal U. 2000)*

Ans. (*a*) Current density $\vec{J} = \dfrac{\text{current}}{\text{area}} = \dfrac{2A}{10^{-6}\text{ m}^2}$

$$= 2 \times 10^6 \text{ A/m}^2 = 2 \times 10^6 \text{ C/m}^2\text{ s}$$

Now $\vec{J} = Ne\vec{v}$ where $\vec{v}$ is the average drift velocity, N the number of electrons per m³ and e the electronic charge.

$$\therefore \qquad v = \frac{J}{Ne} = \frac{2 \times 10^6}{8 \times 10^{28} \times 1.6 \times 10^{-19}} = 15.6 \times 10^{-5} \text{ m/sec.}$$

(*b*) Radius of Al wire $r_{Al} = 1$ mm $= 1 \times 10^{-3}$ m

Radius of Cu wire $r_{cu} = 2$ mm $= 2 \times 10^{-3}$ m

Current $I = 5$ Amp.

Current density in Al wire $J_{Al} = \dfrac{I}{\pi r_{Al}^2} = \dfrac{5}{\pi(1 \times 10^{-3})^2} = \dfrac{5}{\pi \times 10^{-6}}$

Current density in Cu wire $J_{cu} = \dfrac{I}{\pi r_{cu}^2} = \dfrac{5}{\pi(2 \times 10^{-3})^2} = \dfrac{5}{4\pi \times 10^{-6}}$

$$\therefore \qquad \frac{J_{Al}}{J_{cu}} = \frac{5}{\pi \times 10^{-6}} \times \frac{4\pi \times 10^{-6}}{5} = 4$$

Q. 6.5. In a certain region of space 20% of the electrons have a drift velocity 2 cm/sec along the negative direction of Y-axis and the rest 80% are moving along the positive direction of Y-axis with a drift velocity of 3 cm per second. Calculate the current density vector $\vec{J}$ in the region assuming 5×10^{22} electrons per c.c. present in the region. *(G.N.D.U., 1995)*

Ans. Electrons moving along the negative direction of Y-axis produce a current density along the + Y direction and *vice-versa* as each electron carries a *negative* charge = 1.6×10^{-19} coulomb.

$\therefore$ Current density along + Y direction

$$\vec{J} + = N e \vec{v} = \frac{20}{100} \times 5 \times 10^{22} \times 1.6 \times 10^{-19} \times 2 = 3.2 \times 10^{3} \text{ amp/cm}^2$$

Current density along – Y direction

$$\vec{J} - = \frac{80}{100} \times 5 \times 10^{22} \times 1.6 \times 10^{-19} \times 3 = 19.2 \times 10^{3} \text{ amp/cm}^2$$

$\therefore$ Net current density along – Y direction

$$\vec{J} = (19.2 - 3.2) \, 10^{3} = 1.6 \times 10^{4} \text{ amp/cm}^2.$$

Q. 6.6. In a region of space 5×10^{11} electrons per c.c. are moving due north-west at a speed 2×10^{9} cm/sec. In the same region there are 6×10^{10} electrons per c.c. moving due south-west at a speed of 10^{9} cm/sec. Determine $\vec{J}$.

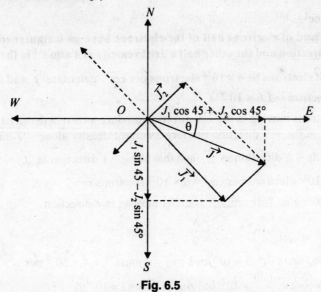

Fig. 6.5

Ans. Current density in *SE* direction due to electrons moving *NW*

$$= N e \vec{v} = J_1 = 5 \times 10^{11} \times 1.6 \times 10^{-19} \times 2 \times 10^{9} = 160 \text{ amp/cm}^2$$

Component of J_1 towards East = $J_1 \cos 45° = \frac{1}{\sqrt{2}} \times 160 = 80\sqrt{2} \text{ amp/cm}^2$

Component of J_1 towards South $= J_1 \sin 45° = \dfrac{1}{\sqrt{2}} \times 160 = 80\sqrt{2}$ amp/cm^2

Current density in NE direction due to electrons moving SW

$$= J_2 = 6 \times 10^{10} \times 1.6 \times 10^{-19} \times 10^9 = 9.6 \text{ amp/sec}^2$$

Component of J_2 towards East $= J_2 \cos 45° = \dfrac{1}{\sqrt{2}} \, 9.6 = 4.8\sqrt{2}$ amp/cm^2

Component of J_2 towards North

$$= J_2 \sin 45° = \dfrac{1}{\sqrt{2}} \times 9.6 = 4.8\sqrt{2} \text{ amp/cm}^2$$

Total current density towards East $= J_1 \cos 45° + J_2 \cos 45°$

$$= 80\sqrt{2} + 4.8\sqrt{2} = 84.8\sqrt{2} \text{ amp/cm}^2$$

Total current density towards South $= J_1 \sin 45° - J_2 \sin 45°$

$$= 80\sqrt{2} - 4.8\sqrt{2} = 75.2\sqrt{2} \text{ amp/cm}^2$$

∴ Magnitude of net current density

$$J = \sqrt{(84.8\sqrt{2})^2 + (75.2\sqrt{2})^2} = 160.3 \text{ amp/cm}^2$$

Let the direction of J make an angle θ with the Eastward direction, then

$$\tan\theta = \dfrac{75.2\sqrt{2}}{84.8\sqrt{2}} = 0.8868$$

∴ $\theta = 41°34'$

Q. 6.7. In a cloud of electrons half of the electrons have an instantaneous drift velocity 3 mm s^{-1} in the X-direction and the other half a drift velocity of 4 mm s^{-1} in the Y-direction. If the number density of electrons be 6×10^{23} electrons per cm^3, calculate $\vec{J}$ and also its magnitude. Charge on the electron $= 1.6 \times 10^{-19}$ C.   (*H.P.U.* 2003)

Ans. The electrons moving in the $+ X$-direction produce a current density along $- X$ directions and those moving in the $+ Y$ direction produce a current density along $- Y$ direction. We denote current density along $- X$ direction as $\vec{J}_x$ and that along $- Y$ direction as $\vec{J}_y$.

Now $N = 6 \times 10^{23}$ electrons per cm$^3 = 6 \times 10^{29}$ electrons/m^3

∴ Number moving in X-direction = Number moving in Y direction

$$= \dfrac{N}{2}$$

$$\vec{v}_x = 3\,\text{mm s}^{-1} = 3 \times 10^{-3} \text{ m/s} \; ; \; \vec{v}_y = 4\,\text{mm s}^{-1} = 4 \times 10^{-3} \text{ m/s}$$

∴ $\vec{J}_x = \dfrac{N}{2} e \vec{v}_x = \dfrac{6}{2} \times 10^{23} \times 1.6 \times 10^{-19} \times (3 \times 10^{-3}\,\hat{i})$

$$= 4.8 \times 10^7 \times (3\hat{i})$$

$$\vec{J}_y = \dfrac{N}{2} e \vec{v}_y = \dfrac{6}{2} \times 10^{29} \times 1.6 \times 10^{-19} \times (4 \times 10^{-3}\,\hat{j})$$

$$= 4.8 \times 10^7 \times (4\hat{j})$$

$$\therefore \qquad \vec{J} = \vec{J}_x + \vec{J}_y = 4.8 \times 10^7 \, (3\hat{i} + 4\hat{j})$$

Magnitude of $\vec{J} = \sqrt{\vec{J}_x^2 + \vec{J}_y^2} = 4.8 \times 10^7 \sqrt{(3^2 + 4^2)}$

$$= 2.4 \times 10^6 \text{ A/sq metre}$$

Q. 6.8. A copper wire having area of cross-section 10^{-2} m^2 is carrying a current of 1.6 A. Given that the current is due to the flow of electrons ($e = 1.6 \times 10^{-19}$ C) and that number density of electrons is 10^{23} electrons per cm^3, calculate the average drift velocity.

(Pbi. U. 2002)

Ans. Given $I = 1.6$ A; $\quad a = 10^{-2}$ m^2; $\quad N = 10^{23}$ electrons per cm^3 $= 10^{29}$ electrons per m^3

Average drift velocity $|\vec{v}| = \dfrac{|\vec{J}|}{Ne} = \dfrac{I}{a \, Ne}$

$$= \frac{1.6}{10^{-2} \times 10^{29} \times 1.6 \times 10^{-19}} = 10^{-8} \text{ ms}^{-1}$$

Q. 6.9. A current of 10 Amp. flows through a conductor of cross-section 1 mm^2. If density of the charge carrier be 10^{21} cm^{-3}, calculate the drift velocity of the electrons. Charge on an electron $= 1.6 \times 10^{-19}$ C.

(H.P.U. 2001, 1999; G.N.D.U 1990)

Ans. $I = 10$ A $\qquad\qquad a = 1$ mm$^2 = 10^{-6}$ m^2

Now $I = Ja \qquad \therefore \quad J = \dfrac{I}{a} = \dfrac{10}{10^{-6}} = 10^7$ A/m^3

Now $\vec{J} = Ne\vec{v}$ and $\quad N = 10^{21}$ cm$^{-3} = 10^{27}$ m^{-3}, $e = 1.6 \times 10^{-19}$ C

$$\therefore \qquad \vec{v} = \frac{\vec{J}}{Ne} = \frac{10^7}{10^{27} \times 1.6 \times 10^{-19}} = \frac{1}{16} \text{ms}^{-1} = 0.0625 \text{ ms}^{-1}$$

Q. 6.10. Differentiate between microscopic and macroscopic currents. Is current density vector a macroscopic or microscopic concept? *(P.U. 2006, 2001, 1995)*

Ans. Microscopic current. *Microscopic currents are those currents which are confined within the boundaries of the atoms.*

The most familiar example is that of an electron revolving round the nucleus in an orbit. This orbital motion of the electron is equivalent to a current. The current being localised within the volume of the atom is a microscopic current. This microscopic current is also responsible for the magnetic properties of atoms.

Macroscopic current. *Macroscopic currents are those in which there is an organised motion of electric charge over distances large as compared to atomic dimensions.*

The current passing through a conductor connected to a battery is an example of macroscopic current.

Current density vector. The current density vector is *not* microscopic. The current density vector $\vec{J} = Ne\vec{v}$ where $\vec{v}$ is the drift velocity of the electron. The drift velocity of an electron is the average of the microscopic velocities of all electrons over a volume large compared to the molecular size. The drift velocity is therefore, a macroscopic quantity.

Hence the current density vector is also a macroscopic concept.

Q. 6.11. A wire is carrying current. Is it charged? *(Pbi. U. 2003)*

Ans. No. It is not charged. When a wire is carrying current, electrons flow in the wire from one end to the other. The number of electrons entering per second at one end is equal to the number of electrons leaving at the other end. As there is no accumulation of charge at any point, the wire remains neutral.

Q. 6.12. Derive and discuss the continuity equation

$$\vec{\nabla} \cdot \vec{J} + \frac{\partial \rho}{\partial t} = 0$$

where $\vec{J}$ **is the current density vector and** ρ **is the charge density.**

(K.U. 2001, 1995, 1994; P.U. 2009, 2006, 2002, 2001, 1994;
H.P.U. 2001, 1996, 1993; Indore U. 2001; Kerala U. 2001,G.N.D.U. 2008,
2007, 2001, 2000, 1993; Pbi U. 2007, 2003, 2002, 2000, 1999; M.D.U. 2002, 2000)

Ans. Equation of continuity. Consider a small area elements $d\vec{s}$ of a closed surface S.

If P is a point on the area element $d\vec{s}$ and $\vec{J}$ the current density vector at P, then the charge flowing out of the area $d\vec{s}$ per second

$$dI = \vec{J} \cdot d\vec{s}$$

∴ The total charge crossing the closed surface S outward per unit time

$$I = \oint_S \vec{J} \cdot d\vec{s}$$

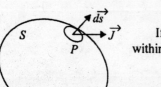

Fig. 6.6

If ρ is the volume density of charge at any point, then total charge within the volume V enclosed by the surface S

$$q = \iiint_V \rho \, dv$$

Since the current is flowing outward the charge within the enclosed surface is decreasing with time. The time rate of *decrease* of charge is given by

$$-\frac{dq}{dt} = I = \frac{-\partial}{\partial t} \iiint_V \rho \, dv$$

According to the principle of conservation of charge,

Total charge crossing the closed surface S per second

= Rate of decrease of charge in the enclosed volume

or

$$\oint_S \vec{J} \cdot d\vec{s} = -\frac{\partial}{\partial t} \iiint_V \rho \, dv$$

$$= -\iiint_V \frac{\partial \rho}{\partial t} \, dv \qquad \qquad ...(i)$$

But according to Gauss's divergence theorem

$$\oint_S \vec{J} \cdot d\vec{s} = \iiint_V (\vec{\nabla} \cdot \vec{J}) \, dv \qquad \qquad ...(ii)$$

From (*i*) and (*ii*) we have

$$-\iiint_S \frac{\partial \rho}{\partial t} \, dv = \iiint_V (\vec{\nabla} \cdot \vec{J}) \, dv$$

or $$-\frac{\partial \rho}{\partial t} = \vec{\nabla} \cdot \vec{J}$$

$\therefore$ $$\vec{\nabla} \cdot \vec{J} + \frac{\partial \rho}{\partial t} = 0 \qquad \qquad \qquad ...(iii)$$

This equation is known as *equation of continuity and holds at each point of space and time.*

It gives the relation between current density vector $\vec{J}$ and volume charge density ρ.

Discussion. The term $\vec{\nabla} \cdot \vec{J}$ represent the limiting value of net outward flow of electric current per unit area while the term $\frac{\partial \rho}{\partial t}$ gives the rate of change of charge per unit volume.

According to the equation of continuity the two terms are equal and opposite and their sum is zero.

Q. 6.13. Show that the equation $\vec{\nabla} \cdot \vec{J} + \frac{\partial \rho}{\partial t} = 0$ implies conservation of charge in space.

(*G.N.D.U.* 2001, *P.U.* 2001, *K.U.* 2001; *H.P.U.* 2003, 1992)

Ans. Conservation of charge in space. The equation

$$\vec{\nabla} \cdot \vec{J} + \frac{\partial \rho}{\partial t} = 0$$

can be put in the form

$$\vec{\nabla} \cdot \vec{J} = -\frac{\partial \rho}{\partial t}$$

$\therefore$ $$(\vec{\nabla} \cdot \vec{J}) dv = -\frac{\partial \rho}{\partial t} dv$$

Integrating both sides over the whole volume V, we have

$$\iiint_V (\vec{\nabla} \cdot \vec{J}) dv = - \iiint_V \frac{\partial \rho}{\partial t} dv \qquad \qquad ...(i)$$

According to Gauss's divergence theorem

$$\iiint_V (\vec{\nabla} \cdot \vec{J}) dv = \oiint_S \vec{J} \cdot d\vec{s} \qquad \qquad ...(ii)$$

Comparing (*i*) and (*ii*), we gave

$$\oiint_S \vec{J} \cdot d\vec{s} = - \iiint_V \frac{\partial \rho}{\partial t} dv = -\frac{\partial}{\partial t} \iiint_V \rho \, dv = -\frac{\partial q}{\partial t}$$

where q is the total charge in the volume V.

$$\oiint_S \vec{J} \cdot d\vec{s} = I$$ the rate of flow of charge out of the volume V through the closed surface S.

Hence the rate of flow of charge out of a volume V through the closed surface S = rate of decrease of charge in the volume V.

In other words *the total charge in space remains constant and is therefore conserved.*

Q. 6.14. (*a*) What do you understand by steady current? Show analytically that for stationary current div $\vec{J} = 0$. (*Pbi. U.* 1993; *G.N.D.U.* 2001, 1992; *P.U.* 1992; *K.U.* 2001, 1992)

(*b*) What physical fact is represented by continuity equation? Find the equation for steady current. (*P.U.,* 2006)

Ans. (a) Steady current. A current flowing through a conductor is said to be stationary or steady if the current passing through any two sections of the conductor say A and B is the same. In other words, the total charge entering the volume V through the section at A = the total charge leaving the volume V through the section at B. Thus, the charge density ρ in any volume V of the conductor remains constant.

or
$$\frac{\partial \rho}{\partial t} = 0$$

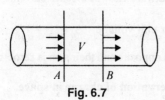

Fig. 6.7

Substituting in the equation of continuity $\vec{\nabla} \cdot \vec{J} + \dfrac{\partial \rho}{\partial t} = 0$, we have

$$\vec{\nabla} \cdot \vec{J} = 0$$

∴ For stationary current $\vec{\nabla} \cdot \vec{J} = div\ J = 0$

This is the *basic* equation or *continuity* equation for *steady* or *stationary* current. *This equation also expresses the conservation of charge in space.*

(b) *The physical fact represented by continuity equation* $\vec{\nabla} \cdot \vec{J} + \dfrac{\partial \rho}{\partial t} = 0$ *is 'Total charge is space remains constant and is, therefore, conserved.* **See Q 6.13** for details. The equation for steady current is $\vec{\nabla} \cdot \vec{J} = 0$. **For proof see Q 6.14 (a).**

Q. 6.15. What is vector form of Ohm's law? Starting from the vector form of Ohm's law $\vec{J} = \sigma \vec{E}$ derive the conventional form of the law $V = IR$.   (*Pbi. U.* 2008; *G.N.D.U.* 2006;

H.P.U. 2001, 1999, 1995, 1994; *P.U.* 2000; *M.D.U.* 2002, 2000)

OR

Write the relation between current density-vector $\vec{J}$ conductivity σ and electric field intensity $\vec{E}$. Using this equation derive the conventional form of Ohm's law. (*G.N.D.U.,* 2007)

Ans. Vector form of Ohm's law. For a very large number of solid homogeneous materials known as ohmic media *the current density vector $\vec{J}$ at any point is proportional to the electric field strength so long as the field is low.*

∴
$$\vec{J} \propto E$$

or
$$\vec{J} = \sigma \vec{E}$$

The statement $\vec{J} = \sigma \vec{E}$ is known as the vector form of Ohm's law. σ is a constant characteristic of the medium and is known as its *conductivity.*

Fig. 6.8

Derivation of conventional form of Ohm's law. To derive the conventional form of Ohm's law from the vector form consider a conductor AB to which a steady electric field $\vec{E}$ is applied as shown in the direction from A to B. The current density vector $\vec{J}$ will have the same value at each point and also the same direction *i.e.*, from A to B. Let a be the area of cross-section of the conductor and $d\vec{s}$ a small vector element of this area.

Electric current I. The electric current flowing through the conductor

$$I = \iint_a \vec{J} \cdot d\vec{s}$$

As $\vec{J}$ and $d\vec{s}$ have the same direction, $\vec{J} \cdot d\vec{s} = J\,ds$

$$\therefore \qquad I = \iint_a J\,ds = J\iint_a ds = Ja \qquad\qquad ...(i)$$

as J = a constant.

As $\quad J = nev \quad$ according to Eq. (ii) Q. 6.2.

$$I = Ja = naev \qquad\qquad\qquad ...(i)\,(a)$$

Potential difference V. If V represents the potential difference between the point A and B and $d\vec{r}$ a small vector element of its length, then

$$V = \int_A^B \vec{E} \cdot d\vec{r}$$

Again the vectors $\vec{E}$ and $d\vec{r}$ have the same direction

$$\therefore \qquad\qquad \vec{E} \cdot d\vec{r} = Edr$$

and

$$V = \int_A^B Edr = E\int_0^l dr = El$$

or

$$E = \frac{V}{l} \qquad\qquad\qquad ...(ii)$$

as E = a constant and $AB = l$

According to vector form of Ohm's law $\vec{J} = \sigma \vec{E}$

Taking magnitudes only when $\vec{J}$ and $\vec{E}$ are in the same direction, we have

$$J = \sigma E$$

Substituting in (i), we have

$$I = \sigma Ea = V\frac{\sigma a}{l}$$

or

$$\frac{V}{I} = \frac{l}{\sigma a} = R\,(a\ \text{constant}) \qquad\qquad ...(iii)$$

Thus starting from the vector form of Ohm's law $\vec{J} = \sigma \vec{E}$ we obtain the conventional form of Ohm's law $\dfrac{V}{I} = R$ or $V = RI$

The relation $V = RI$ shows that *the potential difference between two ends of a conductor is directly proportional to the current flowing through it.* The constant of proportionally $R = \dfrac{l}{\sigma a}$ is called the resistance of the conductor.

The relation $I = \sigma Ea$ can be put in the form $I = -\sigma a\,\dfrac{dV}{dl}$.

as $\quad E = -\dfrac{dV}{dl}$ the potential gradient.

Q. 6.16. A wire of 4×10^{-3} m radius carries a current of 7.84 A. If the average number of electrons crossing per cm of wire is 1.4×10^{21} find the drift velocity of the electrons.

(H.P.U., 1992)

Ans. Given $I = 7.84$ A $\quad e = 1.6 \times 10^{-19}$ C

Number of electrons per cm of wire $= 1.4 \times 10^{21}$

$\therefore$ Number of electrons per metre of wire $= 1.4 \times 10^{23}$

Now current density $J = \dfrac{I}{a} \qquad \therefore I = Ja$

and $\qquad\qquad\qquad \vec{J} = Ne\vec{v}$

where N = number of electrons per m^3 and $\vec{v}$ = Average drift velocity

$\therefore \qquad\qquad\qquad |\vec{v}| = \dfrac{|\vec{J}|}{Ne} = \dfrac{I}{aNe}$

Also number of electrons per m^3, $N = \dfrac{\text{Number of electrons per m}}{\text{volume of 1 metre length}}$

$$= \frac{1.4 \times 10^{23}}{\pi r^2 \times 1} = \frac{1.4 \times 10^{23}}{a}$$

where $a = \pi r^2$ = area of cross-section of the wire.

Hence $\qquad\qquad v = \dfrac{7.84}{a \times \dfrac{1.4 \times 10^{23}}{a} \times 1.6 \times 10^{-19}} = \dfrac{7.84}{1.4 \times 10^{23} \times 1.6 \times 10^{-19}}$

$$= 3.5 \times 10^{-4} \text{ ms}^{-1}$$

Q. 6.17. (a) Define the terms electrical conductivity (σ) and resistivity (ρ). Express conductivity in terms of $|\vec{E}|$ and $|\vec{J}|$. Establish a relation between the two states and define the S.I. unit of electrical conductivity and resistivity.

(H.P.U. 2002; Pbi.U. 2002; M.D.U. 2001; P.U., 1991; Pbi. U., 1991)

(b) How does electrical conductivity depend upon temperature of conductor?

(G.N.D.U., 1997)

Ans. Electrical conductivity. *Electrical conductivity σ is defined as the ratio of current density vector $\vec{J}$ to the electric field vector $\vec{E}$.*

or $\qquad\qquad\qquad \sigma = \dfrac{\vec{J}}{\vec{E}} = \dfrac{|\vec{J}|}{|\vec{E}|}$

Units. The practical C.G.S. unit of $\sigma = \dfrac{\text{ampere/cm}^2}{\text{volt/cm}} = (\text{ohm cm})^{-1}$ known as 'reciprocal Ohm cm' and the S.I. unit is (ohm met.)$^{-1}$ or Siemens per metre (Sm^{-1}).

Resistivity. According to the conventional form of Ohm's law the ratio of the potential difference V applied to the ends of a conductor to the current I flowing through it is a constant.

or $\qquad\qquad\qquad \dfrac{V}{I} = R$

where R is a constant known as the resistance of the conductor.

Thus resistance of a conductor is defined as the ratio of the potential difference applied at the ends of a conductor to the current flowing through it.

The unit of resistance is an *Ohm. It is the resistance of a conductor through which a current of 1 ampere flows when a potential difference of 1 volt is applied across it.* Its value depends upon the length of the conductor l, the area of cross-section a and the volume resistivity or specific resistance ρ and

$$R = \rho \frac{l}{a}$$

or

$$\rho = R \frac{a}{l}$$

In C.G.S. units. *Resistivity* is, therefore, *defined as the resistance of a cm cube of the material or the resistance of a conductor of length 1cm and area of cross-section 1 sq cm.*

The unit of resistivity is ohm cm.

In S.I. units *the resistivity is the resistance of a metre cube of the material* or the resistance of a conductor of length 1 metre and area of cross-section one square metre.

The unit of resistivity in S.I. is ohm-metre.

Relation. According to Eq. (*i*) $R = \rho \dfrac{l}{a}$ and according to relation (*iii*) Q. **6.15** $R = \dfrac{l}{\sigma a}$

$\therefore$
$$\frac{l}{\sigma a} = \rho \frac{l}{a} \quad \text{or} \quad \sigma = \frac{1}{\rho}$$

Thus conductivity is the reciprocal of resistivity.

$\therefore$
$$\rho = \frac{|\vec{E}|}{|\vec{J}|}$$

Its dimensions are $\dfrac{\text{charge}}{\text{distance}^2} \Big/ \dfrac{\text{charge}}{\text{sec.distance}^2} = \text{sec.}$

Thus resistivity has dimensions of time.

(b) **Variation of conductivity with temperature.** Conductivity σ is the reciprocal of resistivity ρ *i.e.*, $\sigma = \dfrac{1}{\rho}$. It has been explained in Q. **6.27** that resistivity of a good conductor increases with temperature. This therefore, means that conductivity decreases with temperature. It is for this reason that the conductivity becomes very large at very low temperatures. At temperatures near the absolute zero, the conductor becomes *super conducting.*

Q. 6.18. Derive the equation $\vec{J} = \sigma \vec{E}$ **from the relation** $V = IR$ **i.e., Ohm's law.**

(*Pbi. U.* 2000; *G.N.D.U.,* 2009, 2007, 1994; *P.U.,* 2007, 2000, 1991)

Ans. In Q. 6. 15 we have derived the conventional form of Ohm's law from its vector form. This is the converse of the same.

Proceeding as in Q. **6.15**, we have

$$I = Ja \qquad \qquad \qquad ...(i)$$

and

$$E = \frac{V}{l} \quad \text{or} \quad V = El \qquad \qquad ...(ii)$$

The conventional form of Ohm's law states that

$$V = IR \text{ where } R = \rho\frac{l}{a}$$

Substituting the value of $V = El$ and $I = Ja$, we have

$$El = Ja\,R = Ja\rho\frac{l}{a} = J\rho l$$

or

$$E = J\rho$$

$$\therefore \qquad\qquad \frac{J}{E} = \frac{1}{\rho} = \sigma$$

Hence

$$\vec{J} = \sigma\vec{E}$$

which is the vector form of Ohm's law.

Q. 6.19. $\vec{J} = \sigma\vec{E}$ **is one form Ohm's law. Another form of the same law is** $V = IR$**. Show that each form can be derived from the other and that they convey the same information. Which form is applicable for practical problems?**   *(G.N.D.U., 1994)*

Ans. For derivation of the relation $V = IR$ from the relation $\vec{J} = \sigma\vec{E}$ See **Q. 6.15.**

For derivation of relation $\vec{J} = \sigma\vec{E}$ from the relation $V = IR$ See **Q. 6.18.**

Both the forms of Ohm's law $\vec{J} = \sigma\vec{E}$ and $V = IR$ convey the same information. The relation

$\vec{J} = \sigma\vec{E}$ is a point equation. It gives the relation between current density $\vec{J}$ and electric field $\vec{E}$ at every point on the conductor. The relation $V = IR$ gives the relation between total current I and potential difference V through a conductor of resistance R. Both the equations lead to the same result.

For practical problems the form $V = IR$ is applicable.

Q. 6.20. In a conductor of radius r_0 the current density $\vec{J}$ varies with radius according to $\vec{J} = \vec{J_0}\,r$**. Calculate the total current through the conductor.**   *(G.N.D.U., 1992)*

Ans. Radius of the conductor $= r_0$.

Consider a ring of radius r and thickness dr, then the area of the annular ring like element ds $= 2\pi r\,dr$.

Now $\vec{J} = \vec{J_0}\,r$

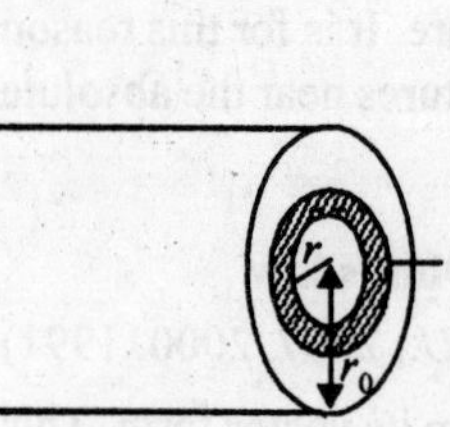

Taking magnitudes only, current through the annular ring

$$dI = \vec{J} \cdot d\vec{s} = J_0\,r\,2\pi r\,dr$$
$$= 2\pi J_0\,r^2\,dr$$

Fig. 6.9

$\therefore$ Current through the conductor $I = \int dI$

$$= \iint \vec{J} \cdot d\vec{s} = \int_0^{r_0} 2\pi J_0\,r^2\,dr = 2\pi J_0\left[\frac{r^3}{3}\right]_0^{r_0} = \frac{2\pi}{3}\,r_0^3\,J_0$$

Q. 6.21. A current of 10 amp is flowing through a copper conductor of area 1 cm^2. Find out the

(*i*) **electric field in the conductor**

(*ii*) **potential drop across its one km length. Resistivity of copper 1.7×10^{-6} ohm cm.**

(*Pbi. U.* 2003; *H.P.U.* 2002)

Ans.   Current density $\vec{J}$ = 10 amp/sq cm.

Resistivity ρ = 1.7×10^{-6} ohm cm.

Now $\vec{J} = \sigma \vec{E}$

$\therefore$ $\vec{E} = \dfrac{\vec{J}}{\sigma} = \vec{J}\rho = 10 \times 1.7 \times 10^{-6} = 1.7 \times 10^{-5}$ volt/cm

(*ii*) **Potential difference** $V = \int_l \vec{E} \cdot \vec{dl} = El$

$l = 1$ km $= 10^5$ cm

$\therefore$ $V = 1.7 \times 10^{-5} \times 10^5 = 1.7$ volt.

Exercise. *An electric current of 1 Ampere is flowing in a wire of copper 0.01 cm^2 cross-sectional area. What is the electric field in the wire? Take resistivity of copper = 1.6×10^{-8} ohm metre.*

(*K.U.*, 2002)

Hint. $a = 0.01$ cm$^2 = 10^{-2}$ cm$^2 = 10^{-6}$ m^2

$$\vec{J} = \frac{I}{a} = \frac{1}{10^{-6}} = 10^6 \text{ A/m}^2;$$

$$\rho = 1.6 \times 10^{-8} \text{ ohm metre}$$

$\therefore$ $\sigma = \dfrac{1}{\rho} = \dfrac{1}{1.6 \times 10^{-8}} = \dfrac{10^8}{1.6}$ (ohm m)$^{-1}$

$$\vec{E} = \frac{\vec{J}}{\sigma} = \frac{10^6 \times 1.6}{10^8} = 1.6 \times 10^{-2} = 0.16 \times 10^{-3} \text{ volt/m}$$

Q. 6.22. An electric field of intensity 0.01 Vm^{-1} exists between two points on a conductor of cross-sectional area 10^{-6} m^2. Calculate the current density and current if resistivity of the material of conductor is 1.75×10^{-8} ohm. m.   (*H.P.U.* 2000; *M.D.U.* 2002; *K.U.* 1996)

Ans. Here $\vec{E}$ = 0.01 Vm^{-1} $\rho = 1.75 \times 10^{-8}$ ohm–m; $a = 10^{-6}$ m^2

Now $\vec{J} = \sigma \vec{E} = \dfrac{\vec{E}}{\rho}$ $\left[\because \sigma = \dfrac{1}{\rho} \right]$

$$= \frac{0.01}{1.75 \times 10^{-8}} = 0.571 \times 10^6 \text{ Amp/m}^2$$

$$= 57.1 \times 10^4 \text{ Amp/m}^2$$

Also $I = Ja = 0.571 \times 10^6 \times 10^{-6} = 0.571$ Amp.

Q. 6.23. (*a*) **A current of 10 A flows through a conductor of cross-sectional area 10 cm^2 and conductivity 6×10^7 mho–m^{-1}. Calculate the electric field within the conductor.** (*G.N.D.U.*, 1993)

(*b*) **A conductor of uniform cross-sectional area is 150 cm long. It has a voltage drop of 1.3 volt and a current density of 4.65×10^5 Am^{-2}. What is the conductivity of its material?**

(*H.P.U.* 2000; *G.N.D.U.*, 1997)

Ans.   Electric current $I = 10$ A

Area of cross-section $a = 10\,\text{cm}^2 = \dfrac{10}{10^4} = 10^{-3}\,\text{m}^2$

$\therefore$ Current density $J = \dfrac{I}{a} = \dfrac{10}{10^{-3}} = 10^4\,\text{Am}^2$

Conductivity $\sigma = 6 \times 10^7$ mho m^{-1}

Now $\vec{J} = \sigma\vec{E}$

or $\vec{E} = \dfrac{\vec{J}}{\sigma} = \dfrac{10^4}{6 \times 10^7} = 0.16 \times 10^{-3}$ volt/m

(b)   Voltage drop $V = 1.3$ Volt; Length of conductor $l = 150$ cm $= 1.5$ m

$\therefore$ Electric field $\vec{E} = \dfrac{V}{l} = \dfrac{1.3}{1.5}\,\text{Vm}^{-1}$

Electric current density $\vec{J} = 4.65 \times 10^5\,\text{Am}^{-2}$

According to vector form of Ohm's law, $\vec{J} = \sigma\vec{E}$

$\therefore$ Conductivity $\sigma = \dfrac{\vec{J}}{\vec{E}} = \dfrac{4.65 \times 10^5 \times 1.5}{1.3} = 5.36 \times 10^5\,(\text{ohm–m})^{-1}$

Q. 6.24. (a) **Discuss the validity of Ohm's law from atomic viewpoint and derive the microscopic form of Ohm's law $\vec{J} = \sigma\vec{E}$ from consideration of motion of free electrons in a conductor.**

(b) **Give its limitations and discuss the situation where Ohm's law fails.**

(Pbi.U., 2006, 1995; H.P.U., 2007, 2002, 2000, 1994, 1993; K.U., 2000, 1995, 1994, 1991; G.N.D.U., 2001, 1993; P.U., 2006, 2003, 2001, 1991)

Ans. (a) **Atomic view of Ohm's law.** The vector form of Ohm's law states that $\vec{J} = \sigma\vec{E}$. If there are only *one* type of charge carriers, N their number density, e the charge on each and $\vec{v}$ the average drift velocity, then according to atomic view $\vec{J} = N e \vec{v}$.

Average drift velocity. In the absence of the electric field the charge carriers have velocities in all possible directions and their average value taken over a sufficient time is zero. When the electric field $\vec{E}$ is applied a force $\vec{E}e$ acts on each charge carrier. If m is the mass of a charge carrier, then

acceleration $= \dfrac{\vec{E}e}{m}$.

If T is the *mean free time* between collisions, then the *additional* momentum (or impulse) acquired by the particle

$$= \text{Force} \times \text{time} = \vec{E}eT$$

This is an *ordered* contribution and is the same for each particle. As the charge carriers have random velocities and are moving about in all possible directions, they suffer collisions in the process. At each collision the momentum gained by the charge carrier gets altered. If, however, we take an average over a *large* number of collisions the additional ordered momentum gained by the charge carriers due to the electric field gets completely destroyed by the collisions. We can, therefore, suppose that just after a collision the velocity of a charge carrier is zero and it has a constant acceleration $\dfrac{Ee}{m}$ and, therefore, its velocity after a time T is given by

$$\vec{v_r} = 0 + \dfrac{\vec{E}eT}{m} = \dfrac{\vec{E}eT}{m}$$

∴   Average drift velocity during the mean free time

$$\vec{v} = \dfrac{0 + \vec{E}e\dfrac{T}{m}}{2} = \dfrac{1}{2}\dfrac{\vec{E}eT}{m}$$

Ohm's law. $\vec{J} = \sigma\vec{E}$. If we consider the charge carriers to be free electrons, then since an electron carries a negative charge.

Average drift velocity $\vec{v} = -\dfrac{1}{2}\dfrac{\vec{E}eT}{m}$ ...(i)

The current density vector corresponding to the flow of electrons

$$\vec{J} = -Ne\vec{v}$$ ...(ii)

Substituting the value of $\vec{v}$ from (i) in (ii), we have

$$\vec{J} = \dfrac{Ne^2T}{2m}\vec{E}$$

or $\vec{J} = \sigma\vec{E}$ ...(iii)

where $\sigma = \dfrac{Ne^2T}{2m}$

Now, N, e and m are constant quantities independent of $\vec{E}$. If T is also a constant, then

$$\sigma = \dfrac{\vec{J}}{\vec{E}} = \text{a constant}$$ ...(iv)

More than one charge carrier. If we have more than one type of charge carriers and N_i, e_i, m_i and T_i represents the number density, charge, mass and mean free time for one type (say ith) then current density due to this type.

$$\vec{J_i} = \dfrac{N_i e_i^2 T_i}{2m_i}\vec{E}$$

The total current density $\vec{J}$ is given by the summation of current densities due to all types of particles

$$\vec{J} = \sum \dfrac{N_i e_i^2 T_i}{2m_i}\vec{E} = \sigma\vec{E}$$

(b) **Limitation and failure of Ohm's law.** Ohm's law in vector form states that $\vec{J} = \sigma\vec{E}$ where σ is the electrical conductivity of the medium and is given by $\sigma = \dfrac{Ne^2T}{2m}$.

A medium will obey Ohm's law as long as σ is a constant *i.e.*, independent of $\vec{E}$. N, e and m are constant which do not depend upon $\vec{E}$. Therefore, *if T becomes a function of $\vec{E}$, then σ no longer remains constant and Ohm's law breaks down.*

Suppose λ is the mean free path of the electron, then λ gives the distance travelled by the electron between two collisions.

$\therefore$ Average time between two collisions $T = \dfrac{\lambda}{v + u}$

where v is the drift velocity and u the thermal velocity of the electron. We shall now discuss the validity of Ohm's law for low as well as high electric fields.

Low electric fields. For small values of $\vec{E}$ say 100 volt/metre the drift speed of free electrons in metals is about 0.08 metres/sec. which is very low as compared to their thermal velocities of the order of 10^5 metres/sec. T is then determined only by the thermal velocities, the average value of which for a metal remains constant at a given temperature.

$\therefore$ T is a constant and $\sigma = \dfrac{Ne^2T}{2m} = $ a constant

Hence Ohm's law is obeyed.

High electric fields. For large values of $\vec{E}$ of the order of 10^8 V/m the drift velocity becomes 0.8×10^5 m/s which is comparable to the thermal velocity. This changes the time between collisions. The mean free time will not, therefore, be a constant but will now be a function of $\vec{E}$. The current density $\vec{J}$ will no longer be proportional to $\vec{E}$.

Hence Ohm's law breaks down.

The failure of Ohm's law occurs at electric fields of the order of 10^8 V/m.

Q. 6.25. Calculate the average time between collisions for an electron of electron gas colliding with positive ions of copper wire having 10^{29} electrons per m^3. Given resistivity of copper is 1.7×10^{-8} Ωm.   (*Pbi.U.* 2000, 1999; *H.P.U.* 1993)

Ans. Here number of electrons per m^3, $N = 10^{29}$

Resistivity of copper $\rho = 1.7 \times 10^{-8}$ Ωm

$\therefore$ Conductivity $\sigma = \dfrac{1}{1.7 \times 10^{-8}} (\Omega m)^{-1}$

Now   conductivity $\sigma = \dfrac{Ne^2T}{2m}$

or $T = \dfrac{2m\sigma}{Ne^2}$ ...(i)

Also $m = 9 \times 10^{-31}$ kg $e = 1.6 \times 10^{-19}$ C

$\therefore$ $T = \dfrac{2 \times 9 \times 10^{-31}}{1.7 \times 10^{-8} \times 10^{29} \times (1.6 \times 10^{-19})^2} = \dfrac{18}{1.7 \times 1.6 \times 1.6} \times 10^{-14}$

or $T = 4.13 \times 10^{-14}$ S.

Q. 6.26. (a) Explain drift velocity of electrons. Does it depend upon field intensity within the material?   (*P.U.*, 1992)

(b) Give a comparison of thermal and drift speeds of electrons in conductors at room temperature for low and high $\vec{E}$ fields.   (*H.P.U.*, 1994)

Ans. (a) Drift velocity of electrons. See Q. 6.1

The average drift velocity of electron is given by

$$\vec{v} = -\frac{eT}{2m}\vec{E}$$

For low values of electric field T is independent of $\vec{E}$ and hence $\dfrac{eT}{2m}$ = a constant.

$$\therefore \quad \vec{v} \propto \vec{E}$$

Thus drift velocity of electrons depends upon field intensity $\vec{E}$ within the material.

(b) **Thermal speed.** Suppose the room temperature is T. At this temperature each free electron has

a thermal energy $\dfrac{3}{2}KT$. If v_t is the thermal speed of the electron at temperature T, then

$$\frac{1}{2}mv_t^2 = \frac{3}{2}KT$$

or

$$v_t = \sqrt{\frac{3KT}{m}}$$

Taking the room temperature to be 27°C (for convenience),

$$k = 1.38 \times 10^{-23} \text{ J/K and } m = 9 \times 10^{-31} \text{ kg, we have}$$

$$v_t = \sqrt{\frac{3 \times 1.38 \times 10^{-23} \times 300}{9 \times 10^{-31}}} = 1.17 \times 10^5 \text{ m/s}$$

$$= 10^5 \text{ m/s (say)}$$

Drift speed. The drift speed of an electron is given by

$$v_d = \frac{eT}{2m}E$$

Taking the average time between two successive collisions as 10^{-14} sec. we have

$$v_d = \frac{1.6 \times 10^{-19} \times 10^{-14}}{2 \times 9 \times 10^{-31}} E = 0.88 \times 10^{-3} E \text{ m/s}$$

$$= 0.8 \times 10^{-3} E \text{ m/s}$$

At low electric fields. At low electric fields of the order of 100 V/m the drift speed

$$v_d = 0.8 \times 10^{-3} \times 100 = 0.08 \text{ m/s}$$

This drift speed is very small as compared to thermal speed.

Thus for low electric fields the drift speed is very small as compared to thermal speed.

At high electric fields. At high electric fields of the order of 10^8 V/m the drift speed

$$v_d = 0.8 \times 10^{-3} \times 10^8 = 0.8 \times 10^5 \text{ m/s}$$

This drift speed is comparable to thermal speed.

Thus for high electric fields the drift speed becomes comparable to thermal speed.

Q. 6.27. (a) Define resistivity of a conductor. How does it depend upon temperature? Why does resistivity of a good conductor increase with increase in temperature ?

(G.N.D.U., 1996; P.U., 1992, 1991; H.P.U., 1991)

(b) What are ohmic and non-ohmic resistances?

(G.N.D.U., 2008; H.P.U., 2007)

Ans. (a) Resistivity. See Q. 6.17

Variation of resistance with temperature. The resistance of pure metals increases as the temperature is raised. If R_0 is the resistance at 0° C and R_t the resistance at $t°$ C, then

$$R_t = R_0 (1 + \alpha t)$$

where α is called the *temperature coefficient of resistance.*

or
$$\alpha = \frac{R_t - R_0}{R_0\, t}$$

This temperature coefficient of resistance is thus defined as the increase in resistance per unit resistance per degree rise of temperature.

Alloys do not increase in resistance by the same amount as pure metals do. Some alloys like *constantan* and *manganin* have a negligible temperature coefficient. Carbon, electrolytes and insulators decrease in resistance when heated. A resistor with a high negative temperature coefficient is called a **thermistor.**

Why resistivity of good conductor increases with temperature. The explanation of the increase in resistance with temperature on the electronic theory is roughly as follows:

The electric current consists of the flow of 'free' electrons through the spaces or avenues between the positively charged nuclei of the atoms of the conductor. As the atoms of the substance are vibrating about their mean position the electrons collide with them and thus their motion is opposed. This is the cause of electrical resistance.

As the temperature is raised the atoms of the substance vibrate about their mean positions with greater and greater amplitude. The space between the atoms through which the electrons forming the current move is then less clearly defined. The electrons are impeded in their motion by their collision with the atoms and the resistance of the metal increases. When the temperature is lowered, the space is more clearly defined, the electrons suffer a lesser number of collisions and their motion is free. The resistance thus decreases.

At a temperature near the absolute zero the resistance decreases rapidly and the substances become *super-conducting.* For example, a current in a ring of lead may be kept flowing for several days without the help of any external arrangement at a temperature near the absolute zero.

(b) (i) Ohmic resistances. The metallic conductors like copper, aluminium, silver etc. obey Ohm's law provided the temperature remains constant. Such conductors are called *ohmic conductors* or *ohmic resistances.* The resistance of such conductors is known as *ohmic resistance.* For such materials graph between potential difference V across the conductor and I the current through it is a straight line.

(ii) Non-ohmic resistances. Materials which offer resistance but do not obey Ohm's law are called *non-ohmic resistances.* For example, in a diode valve I is not proportional to V but obeys Child's law $I \propto V^{\frac{3}{2}}$. Similarly in liquid electrolytes V is not proportional to I and the graph between V and I is not a straight line.

Q. 6.28. Prove that for steady current $\vec{\nabla} \cdot \vec{E} = 0$ and also in the absence of a source of e.m.f. $\nabla^2 V = 0$ where V is electric potential.

Ans. Steady current. Consider a circuit in which a steady current is maintained. As the current is steady there is no *source* or *sink* of charge in the circuit. Hence the rate of change of charge (or charge density) with time is zero everywhere.

$$\therefore \qquad \frac{\partial \rho}{\partial t} = 0$$

According to the equation of continuity

$$\vec{\nabla} \cdot \vec{J} = -\frac{\partial \rho}{\partial t}$$

where $\vec{J}$ is the current density vector

When $\quad \dfrac{\partial \rho}{\partial t} = 0 \qquad \vec{\nabla} \cdot \vec{J} = 0$

But $\vec{J} = \sigma \vec{E}$ where $\vec{E}$ is the electric field vector and σ the conductivity. For a homogeneous conductor σ is constant everywhere.

$$\therefore \qquad \vec{\nabla} \cdot \vec{J} = \vec{\nabla} \cdot (\sigma \vec{E}) = 0$$

or $\qquad \sigma \vec{\nabla} \cdot \vec{E} = 0 \quad$ or $\quad \vec{\nabla} \cdot \vec{E} = 0 \qquad \qquad \qquad ...(i)$

Absence of source of e.m.f. The electric field $\vec{E}$ is given by

$$\vec{E} = \vec{E}_s + \vec{E}_b$$

where $\vec{E}_s$ is the electrostatic component of the electric field and $\vec{E}_b$ the electric field generated by the source of e.m.f. (battery). Substituting in (i), we get

$$\vec{\nabla} \cdot (\vec{E}_s + \vec{E}_b) = 0 \quad \text{or} \quad \vec{\nabla} \cdot \vec{E}_s + \vec{\nabla} \cdot \vec{E}_b = 0$$

In the absence of a source of e.m.f. $\vec{E}_b = 0$

$$\therefore \qquad \qquad \vec{\nabla} \cdot \vec{E}_s = 0$$

The electrostatic field is given by $\vec{E}_s = -\vec{\nabla} V$ where V is the electric potential

Hence $\qquad \qquad \vec{\nabla} \cdot (-\vec{\nabla} V) = 0$

or $\qquad \qquad \qquad \nabla^2 V = 0 \qquad \qquad \qquad \qquad ...(ii)$

Eq. (ii) is known as *Laplace's equation*. It shows that electric potential can be defined at points in a conducting medium carrying current but without any source of e.m.f.

Q. 6.29. (*a*) **Define electromotive force. What are its units ?**

(*b*) **Show that e.m.f. of a cell in an open circuit is equal to the potential difference between the open ends.** *(G.N.D.U.* 2003, 2001)

Ans. (*a*) **Electromotive force.** *The electromotive force of a cell is defined as the amount of work done by the non-conservative electric field E_n in taking a unit positive charge from the negative pole B of the cell to the positive pole A through the inside of the cell.*

$$\therefore \qquad \qquad e = \int_B^A \vec{E}_n \cdot \vec{dr}$$

The source of the non-conservative electric field $\vec{E}_n$ is the chemical reaction taking place in the cell. The unit of e.m.f. is the same as that of potential. The S.I. unit is a *volt*.

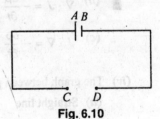
Fig. 6.10

e.m.f. in open circuit. Consider a circuit *ACDBA* as shown. As there is a gap between C and D no current flows in the circuit. Such a circuit is known as *open circuit*.

By definition, the *e.m.f.* in the circuit

$$e = \oint \vec{E} \cdot \vec{dr}$$

which can be split into two integrals as under

$$\therefore \qquad e = \int_C^D \vec{E} \cdot \vec{dr} + \int_{DBAC} \vec{E} \cdot \vec{dr} \qquad \qquad ...(i)$$

The total electric field at any point in the circuit

$$\vec{E} = \vec{E}_c + \vec{E}_n .$$

where $\vec{E}_n$ is the non-conservative field which exists only within the cell. Therefore, for the path CD, $E_n = 0$ and hence for this path $\vec{E} = \vec{E}_c$

Eq. (*i*) can, therefore, be written as

$$e = \int_C^D \vec{E}_c \cdot \vec{dr} + \int_{DBAC} \vec{E} \cdot \vec{dr}$$

The cell and the connecting wires constitute an *ohmic path* and obey Ohm's law $\vec{J} = \sigma \vec{E}$ for all points along the path *DBAC*.

$$\therefore \qquad e = \int_C^D \vec{E}_c \cdot \vec{dr} + \int_{DBAC} \frac{\vec{J}}{\sigma} \cdot \vec{dr}$$

As no current flows through the path $\vec{J} = 0$ and we get

$$e = \int_C^D \vec{E}_c \cdot \vec{dr}$$

The line integral of a conservative field between two points is equal to the difference of potential between the points.

$$\therefore \qquad \int_C^D \vec{E}_c \cdot \vec{dr} = V_C - V_D$$

Hence $e = V_C - V_D$

This result shows that electromotive force in an open circuit is equal to the potential difference between the open ends.

Q. 6.30. Mark the correct answer.

(*i*) The relation between current density vector $\vec{J}$ and average drift velocity of electrons is

(*a*) $\vec{J} = ne\vec{v}$ (*b*) $\vec{J} = -ne\vec{v}$ (*c*) $\vec{J} = e\vec{v}$ (*d*) $\vec{J} = -e\vec{v}$

(*ii*) The equation of continuity is

(*a*) $div\ \vec{J} = -\dfrac{\partial \rho}{\partial t}$ (*b*) $div\ \vec{J} = -\dfrac{\rho}{\varepsilon_0}$ (*c*) $div\ \vec{J} = \dfrac{\rho}{\varepsilon_0}$ (*d*) $div\ \vec{J} = \dfrac{\partial \rho}{\partial t}$

(*P.U.*, 1994)

(*iii*) The differential equation of conservation of charge is

(*a*) $\vec{\nabla} \cdot \vec{J} = -\dfrac{\partial \rho}{\partial t}$ (*b*) $\vec{\nabla} \cdot \vec{J} = \dfrac{\partial \rho}{\partial t}$

(*c*) $\vec{J} \cdot \vec{\nabla} = -\dfrac{\partial \rho}{\partial t}$ (*d*) $\vec{J} \cdot \vec{\nabla} = \dfrac{\partial \rho}{\partial t}$

(*H.P.U.*, 2000, 1994)

(*iv*) The graph between potential difference and current for ohmic conductor will be

(*a*) Straight line   (*b*) circle   (*c*) ellipse   (*d*) parabola

(*H.P.U.*, 1993)

(*v*) The unit of electrical conductivity is

(*a*) $\Omega\,m$ (*b*) $\Omega\,m^{-1}$ (*c*) $\Omega^{-1}\,m^{-1}$ (*d*) $m\,\Omega^{-1}$

Ans. (*i*) *b*   (*ii*) *a*   (*iii*) *a*   (*iv*) *a*

      (*v*) *c.*

EXERCISES

1. A copper wire having a cross-section 1 cm^2 carries a current of 1.5 ampere. Assuming that each copper atom contributes one free electron, calculate the drift velocity of free electrons. Given that atomic weight and density of copper are 63 and 9 gms/cc respectively.

    Hint. current density $\vec{J} = \dfrac{1.5\,A}{10^{-4}\,m^2} = 1.5 \times 10^4\ A/m^2 = 1.5 \times 10^4\ C/m^2\,s$

    Number of atoms per c.c. $= \dfrac{6.02 \times 10^{23}}{7}$

    as gm atomic volume $= \dfrac{63}{9}$ c.c.

    Number of atoms per $m^3 = N = \dfrac{6.02 \times 10^{23} \times 10^6}{7}$

    $e = 1.6 \times 10^{19}\ C$

    $\therefore\ \vec{v} = \dfrac{\vec{J}}{Ne} = \dfrac{7 \times 1.5 \times 10^4}{6.02 \times 10^{23} \times 10^6 \times 1.6 \times 10^{-19}} = 10.9 \times 10^{-5}\ ms^{-1}$

2. A current of 100 A is flowing through a copper conductor of area of cross-section 1 cm^2. Given that conductivity of copper is $6 \times 10^7\ \Omega^{-1}\ m^{-1}$, calculate the electric field in the conductor. **[Ans. 0.0166 Vm^{-1}]**

7

Fields of Charges in Motion

Q. 7.1. (a) What is meant by invariance of charge? Give evidence in support of it.

(*P.U.* 2009, 2001; *G.N.D.U.* 2006, 2001, 1997, 1996, 1995, 1990; *Pbi. U.* 2008, 2000, 1999; *H.P.U.*, 1996, 1994, 1992, 1991)

(b) *e/m* for an electron is constant or variable quantity? Justify. (*Pbi. U.* 1999)

(c) Is volume charge density invariant under motion? Explain in brief. (*P.U.*, 2009)

Ans. (a) Invariance of charge. It is found that the magnitude of a physical quantity may or may not depend upon its state of motion. For example, the mass of a body in motion is different from the mass of the same body at rest. Similarly, length and time are not invariant under motion. A physical quantity is said to be invariant if it has the same value for all observers in uniform motion with respect to one another.

It has been found from experiments that total amount of charge in a body is the same for all observers in different inertial frames. In other words *electric charge is invariant.*

The invariance of electric charge implies that total charge in a system does not change due to the motion of the charge carriers.

Evidence in support. A hydrogen molecule consists of two electrons and two protons. The electrons are moving at very high speeds around the protons, but this motion makes no change in the charge on an electron. This is why the hydrogen molecule remains neutral. A helium atom also consists of two protons and two electrons but their motion is quite different. In hydrogen molecule the two protons 0.7 Å units apart revolve slowly but in Helium atom they are tightly bound into the nucleus where they move with kinetic energies of the order of millions of electron volts. If motion had any effect on the amount of charge exact neutralisation of charge both in hydrogen molecule and the helium atom would not have been possible.

There is a marked difference in the motion of protons within the nucleus of the isotopes of the same element *i.e.*, atoms having different nuclear masses but the same nominal nuclear charge. The spectral lines of two different isotopes do not show any discrepancy which may be due to even a slight difference in total nuclear charge.

(b) *e/m* not constant. *e/m* for an electron is not a constant but varies with the velocity of the electron.

The value of charge e is *invariant* but the value of mass m varies with velocity according to the

relation $m = \dfrac{m_0}{\sqrt{1 - \dfrac{v^2}{c^2}}}$ where m_0 is the rest mass of the electron and m the mass when it is moving

with velocity v. As $m > m_0$, e/m for an electron decreases as the velocity increases.

(c) The volume charge density ρ of a body having a charge Q in a stationary frame S is given by

$\rho = \dfrac{Q}{V}$ where V is the volume of the body. The charge Q is invariant, but the volume in moving frame

S' will appear to be contracted due to relativity phenomenon of length contraction. So the volume charge density ρ' in the moving frame S' will be more than ρ— the volume charge density in the stationary frame S. Hence *the volume charge density is not invariant.*

Q. 7.2. Why a charge in motion cannot be measured directly by Coulomb's law? Explain how can we apply Gauss's law to measure a moving charge.

(H.P.U., 1994; Pbi.U., 2001, 2000, 1993, 1991; G.N.D.U., 1992)

Ans. Charge in motion cannot be measured by Coulomb's law. Coulomb's law of electric force is strictly applicable to charges at rest. When a charge is in motion forces other than electric forces come into play and Coulomb's law cannot be used to measure the charges in motion.

Measurement of charge at rest. Let us first see how a charge at rest is measured.

Consider an unknown charge Q located at O the origin of the co-ordinate system. A test charge q_0 is placed at a distance r from it. If F is the magnitude of the force experienced by the test charge, then according to Coulomb's law

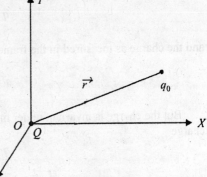

Fig. 7.1

$$F = \frac{1}{4\pi \varepsilon_0} \frac{Q q_0}{r^2}$$

or

$$Q = 4\pi \varepsilon_0 r^2 \frac{F}{q_0}$$

Now $\dfrac{F}{q_0}$ is the magnitude of the electric field E produced by the charge Q at q_0.

$\therefore$ $\qquad\qquad Q = 4\pi \varepsilon_0 r^2 E$

If $r = 1$ metre, then $Q = 4\pi \varepsilon_0 E$

From Eq. (i) we find that the charge Q can be measured by finding the electric field E at a point 1 metre away from it.

Measurement of charge in motion. If the charge Q is in motion, it will produce electric field of different magnitudes even at points equidistant from it. In other words the electric field E at a distance of 1 metre from the charge Q will not have a single unique value. Thus it is not possible to find the exact value of charge by using relation (i).

Hence Coulomb's law cannot be used to measure directly the charge in motion.

Measurement of moving charge by Gauss's law. To measure a moving charge we use Gauss's law. Gauss's law states that

$$\oiint_S \vec{E} \cdot d\vec{s} = \frac{1}{\varepsilon_0} Q.$$

The charge Q within the closed Gaussian surface may be at rest or in motion. It may be a single charge or the algebraic sum of a number of charges so long as all the charges at rest, or in motion are included inside the Gaussian surface.

$\therefore$ Unknown charge $\qquad Q = \varepsilon_0 \oiint_S \vec{E} \cdot d\vec{s} = \varepsilon_0 \phi$

where ϕ is the electric flux through the closed surface S. By evaluating the flux ϕ through the surface the value of a moving charge can be measured.

$\therefore$ Moving charge $\qquad\qquad Q = \varepsilon_0 \phi$.

Q. 7.3. Show that the surface integral of the electric field is independent of the frame of reference.

(*P.U. 2009; H.P.U., 1996*)

Ans. Surface integral of electric field independent of reference frame. Suppose an inertial frame F' is in motion with respect to another inertial frame F. If S is a closed surface in the frame F containing some charged particles at a time t and S' is a closed surface in the frame F' containing the **same** charged particles at a time t', then the charge as measured in the frame F

$$q = \varepsilon_0 \oiint_{S(t)} \vec{E} \cdot d\vec{s}$$

and the charge as measured in the frame F'

$$q' = \varepsilon_0 \oiint_{S(t')} \vec{E}' \, d\vec{s}'$$

But the charge is invariant under motion. Therefore, according to the principle of invariance of charge

$$q = q'$$

or $\qquad\qquad \varepsilon_0 \oiint_{S(t)} \vec{E} \cdot d\vec{s} = \varepsilon_0 \oiint_{S(t')} \vec{E}' \cdot d\vec{s}'$

Hence, in general, in any system of units, according to the principle of invariance of charge

$$\oiint_{S(t)} \vec{E} \cdot d\vec{s} = \oiint_{S(t')} \vec{E}' \cdot d\vec{s}' \qquad\qquad ...(i)$$

where $\oiint_{S(t)}$ means integral over the closed surface S at a time t and $\oiint_{S'(t')}$ means integral over the closed surface S' at a time t'. Further, the field $\vec{E}$ is measured by the force on a test charge at rest in the frame F' just as the field $\vec{E}$ is measured by the force on a test charge at rest in the frame F. Each integral is to be evaluated at *one* time in its own frame. The times t and t' could be different but these should be such that at the instances considered the charged particles within the respective surfaces S and S' must be the same.

Relation (*i*) shows that *the surface integral of the electric field is independent of the frame of reference.*

Q. 7.4. What do you understand by conservation of charge? State the equation which expresses the conservation of charge. Point out the difference between charge invariance and charge conservation. (P.U. 2000; H.P.U., 1997; G.N.D.U., 1997)

Ans. Conservation of charge. Suppose we have a box which contains charges $q_1, q_2 \ldots q_n$ as shown in Fig. 7.2, then the total charge in the box is the algebraic sum of all the charges as charges add like scalar quantities. Thus the law of conservation of charge states that 'The total electric charge in an isolated system i.e., the algebraic sum of the positive and negative charges present at any time, never changes'.

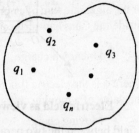

Fig. 7.2

An isolated system is defined as that system the boundary of which is not crossed by any matter. This principle is not violated if we allow light to pass into or out of an isolated system as the photons carry no charge. However, if we use gamma rays, a high energy photon may give rise to a pair-a negative electron and a positive electron or positron. This will also not violate the principle of conservation of charge because net charge produced is zero.

Thus the total charge in the system does not change

(i) due to mutual interaction of charges and

(ii) due to interaction of charges with electromagnetic radiation inside or outside the system.

Equation of conservation of charge. If ρ is the volume charge density in a closed surface which decreases at the rate of $\dfrac{\partial \rho}{\partial t}$ and gives rise to a current density $\vec{J}$, then the principle of conservation of charge can be stated as

$$ div\,\vec{J} = -\frac{\partial \rho}{\partial t} $$

This is the equation which mathematically represents the principle of conservation of charge.

Charge in variance. See Q. 7.1.

Difference. The principle of conservation of charge implies that the total charge in an isolated system does not change with time.

The invariance of charge implies that charge is also relativistic invariant i.e., charge is a scalar quantity and the number representing its measure is an invariant under Lorentz transformations.

Q. 7.5. Show that the transformation laws for transforming electric field from one inertial frame to another are given by

$$ E_{\|}{}' = E_{\|} $$
$$ E_{\perp}' = \gamma\,E_{\perp} = \frac{E_{\perp}}{\sqrt{1 - \dfrac{v^2}{c^2}}} $$

where the symbols have their usual meanings.

(G.N.D.U., 2007, 2006, 2004, 2001, 1999, 1997, 1996, 1993; H.P.U., 2007, 2002, 2000, 1997, 1996, 1995; P.U., 2007, 2006, 2000, 1991; Pbi.U. 2008, 2000, 1999, 1991)

Ans. Transformation of electric field from one inertial frame to another. Consider two plane parallel stationary sheets having a uniform surface charge density $+\sigma$ and $-\sigma$ separated by a very small distance apart in the $X - Z$ plane with their sides parallel to the X and Z axes in inertial frame F as shown in Fig. 7.3 (a). The length and breadth of each side is say b i.e., these are square sheets. The distance between the sheets is so small as compared to the surface area that electric field at any point in between the sheets may be taken to be constant.

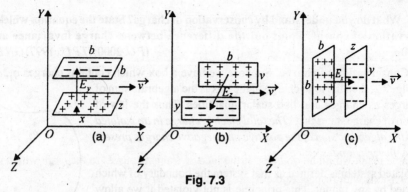

Fig. 7.3

Electric field as viewed by an observer in frame F. For an observer in the frame F, the electric field between the two parallel plate is $\dfrac{\sigma}{\varepsilon_0}$ along the Y-axis.

$$\therefore \qquad E_y = \frac{\sigma}{\varepsilon_0} \qquad\qquad\qquad ...(i)$$

Electric field as viewed by an observer in frame F'. Now consider another inertial frame F' the co-ordinate axes $O'X'$, $O'Y'$, $O'Z'$ of which are parallel to the respective axes of F. Let the inertial frame F' move towards the left *i.e.*, along the $-X$ axis with a velocity $\vec{v}$. To an observer in F' the inertial frame F appears to be moving towards the right along $+X$ axis with the same velocity $\vec{v}$. Therefore, to the observer in F' the length of the plate parallel to the X-axis appears to have contracted from b to $b\sqrt{1 - \dfrac{v^2}{c^2}}$.

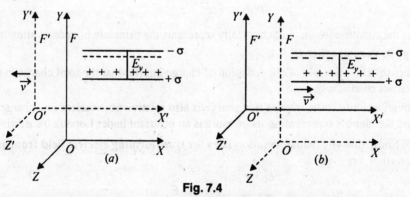

Fig. 7.4

According to the theory of relativity the contraction in length takes place along the direction of motion. There is no change in length in a direction perpendicular to the direction of motion. Thus to the observer in F' the plate appears to be a rectangle of side b parallel to Z-axis and side $b\sqrt{1 - \dfrac{v^2}{c^2}}$ parallel to X-axis. As the total charge is invariant, the charge density measured by an observer in the frame F' is given by

$$\sigma' = \frac{\sigma b^2}{b^2\sqrt{1 - \dfrac{v^2}{c^2}}} = \frac{\sigma}{\sqrt{1 - \dfrac{v^2}{c^2}}} \qquad\qquad ...(ii)$$

So an observer in F' measures the field between the two plates not as $\dfrac{\sigma}{\varepsilon_0}$ but as $\dfrac{\sigma'}{\varepsilon_0}$.

$$\therefore \qquad E'_y = \frac{\sigma'}{\varepsilon_0} = \frac{\sigma}{\varepsilon_0 \sqrt{1 - \dfrac{v^2}{c^2}}} = \gamma E_y$$

where
$$\gamma = \frac{1}{\sqrt{1 - \dfrac{v^2}{c^2}}}$$

or
$$E'_y = \gamma E_y \qquad\qquad ...(iii)$$

The same result would be obtained if the inertial frame F moves to the *right* with a velocity $\vec{v}$ along the $+X$-axis with respect to the frame F' as shown in Fig. 7.4 (*b*).

Plates in X-Y plane. If the two charged plates are placed in the X-Y plane with their sides parallel to the X and Y-axis then the electric field E_z between the plates will point along the Z-axis as shown in Fig. 7.3 (*b*) and is given by

$$E_z = \frac{\sigma}{\varepsilon_0}.$$

to an observer in the frame F.

When the inertial frame F' moves to the left with a velocity $\vec{v}$ along the $-X$ axis [which is equivalent to the frame F moving to the right with a velocity $\vec{v}$ along the $+X$ axis the length of the plate along X-axis appears to the observer in the frame F' to have contracted to $b\sqrt{1 - \dfrac{v^2}{c^2}}$, the length along the Y-axis remaining constant as b.

Hence again the surface density of charge

$$\sigma' = \frac{\sigma}{\sqrt{1 - \dfrac{v^2}{c^2}}} = \gamma \sigma$$

$\therefore$ Electric field measured by the observer in F',

$$E'_z = \frac{\sigma'}{\varepsilon_0} = \frac{\sigma}{\varepsilon_0 \sqrt{1 - \dfrac{v^2}{c^2}}} = \gamma \frac{\sigma}{\varepsilon_0} = \gamma E_z$$

or
$$E'_z = \gamma E_z \qquad\qquad ...(iv)$$

Plates in the Y-Z plane. If now the two charged plates are placed in the Y-Z plane parallel to Y and Z axes, the electric field E_x between them will point along the X-axis as shown in Fig. 7.3 (*c*) and is given by

$$E_x = \frac{\sigma}{\varepsilon_0}$$

When the inertial frame F' moves to the left with a velocity $\vec{v}$ along the $-X$-axis there is no apparent change in the length or breadth of the plate as these are along the Y and Z axes respectively perpendicular to the X-axis along which the motion takes place. The distance between the two plates will, of course, appear to contract but this will not effect the electric field between the plates as the electric field is independent of the distance between the charged plates so long as the plates have an area very large as compared to the distance apart.

$$\therefore \qquad E'_x = E_x \qquad\qquad ...(v)$$

From relation (*iii*), (*iv*) and (*v*) we find that the *apparent* value of the electric field in an inertial frame moving with a velocity $\vec{v}$ is γ times the value with respect to the stationary inertial frame when the direction of the field is perpendicular to the direction of motion. In other words, when the inertial frame moves along the X-axis the field along the Y-axis and Z-axis will be modified, the field in the direction of motion remaining uncharged.

Plates in any position. When the parallel plates have an arbitrary orientation the electric field $\vec{E}$ has all the three components E_x, E_y and E_z. If the inertial frame F has a velocity $\vec{v}$ along the X-axis with respect to the inertial frame F', then an observer in F' will measure the values of these component fields as E_x', E_y' and E_z' given by

$$E_x' = E_x; \; E_y'; = \gamma E_y; \; E_z' = \gamma E_z \qquad \qquad ...(vi)$$

The same result may also be stated in terms of *longitudinal* and *transverse* components where longitudinal component means a component *parallel* to the direction of motion (E_x) and denoted by $E_\parallel$ and transverse component means a component in either direction *perpendicular* to the direction of motion (E_y and E_z) and denoted by $E_\perp$.

$$\therefore \qquad \qquad E_\parallel' = E_\parallel$$

and $$E'_\perp = \gamma E_\perp$$

The equations $$E_x' = E_x$$

$$E_y' = \gamma E_y = \frac{E_y}{\sqrt{1 - \dfrac{v^2}{c^2}}}$$

and $$E_z' = \gamma E_z = \frac{E_z}{\sqrt{1 - \dfrac{v^2}{c^2}}}$$

are known as *Lorentz transformation equations* for the components of electric field.

If E_x', E_y' and E_z' are the components of electric field measured by an observer in the frame F' and E_x, E_y and E_z are the corresponding values measured by an observer in frame F, then

$$E_x = E_x'$$
$$E_y = \gamma E_y'$$
$$E_z = \gamma E_z'$$

The same result in terms of *longitudinal* and *transverse* components can be stated as

$$E_\parallel = E_\parallel'$$
$$E_\perp = \gamma E_\perp'$$

Q. 7.6. (a) In a stationary frame of reference the electric field is $\vec{E} = \left(5\hat{i} - 6\hat{j}\right) \times 10^4$ N/C. Find its value in a frame moving with velocity 0.6c with respect to it along X-axis.

(G.N.D.U.,2007)

(b) In the Lab. system an electric field $\vec{E} = (2\hat{i} + 3\hat{j})$ Vm^{-1}. Calculate the electric field as measured in a frame of reference moving with a velocity of $4(3\hat{i} + 4\hat{j}) \times 10^7$ ms^{-1} relative to the lab. system.

(H.P.U., 1995)

Ans. (a) Given $$\vec{E} = \left(5\hat{i} - 6\hat{j}\right) \times 10^4 \text{ NC}^{-1}$$

$$v = 0.6c = \frac{3}{5}c$$

The components of the electric field in the stationary frame S are
$$E_x = 5 \times 10^4 \; ; \; E_y = -6 \times 10^4$$

The components of the electric field in the moving frame S' are
$$E'_x = E_x = 5 \times 10^4 \, NC^{-1}$$

$$E'_y = \gamma E_y = -\gamma \times 6 \times 10^4 = -\frac{6 \times 10^4}{\sqrt{1 - \frac{v^2}{c^2}}} = -\frac{6 \times 10^4}{\sqrt{1 - \frac{9}{25}}}$$

$$= \frac{-6 \times 10^4 \times 5}{4} = -7.5 \times 10^4 \, NC^{-1}$$

Thus the electric field vector in the moving frame S'

$$E' = E'_x \, \hat{i} + E'_y \, \hat{j} = 5 \times 10^4 \, \hat{i} - 7.5 \times 10^4 \, \hat{j}$$

$$= \left(5 \hat{i} - 7.5 \hat{j} \right) \times 10^4 \, NC^{-1}$$

(b) Velocity $\vec{v} = 4(3\hat{i} + 4\hat{j}) \times 10^7 \, ms^{-1}$

$\therefore$ Magnitude of velocity $|\vec{v}| = 4\sqrt{(3^2 + 4^2)} \times 10^7 = 20 \times 10^7 = 2 \times 10^8 \, ms^{-1}$

Unit vector along $\vec{v}, \hat{v} = \dfrac{\vec{v}}{|\vec{v}|} = \dfrac{4(3\hat{i} + 4\hat{j}) \times 10^7}{20 \times 10^7} = 0.6\hat{i} + 0.8\hat{j}$

The component of $\vec{E}$ along $\vec{v} = |\vec{E}_{\parallel}| = \vec{E} . \hat{v}$

$$= (2\hat{i} + 3\hat{j}).(0.6\hat{i} + 0.8\hat{j}) = 1.2 + 2.4 = 3.6 \, NC^{-1}$$

$\therefore \qquad \vec{E}_{\parallel} = |\vec{E}_{\parallel}|\hat{v} = 3.6(0.6\hat{i} + 0.8\hat{j}) = (2.16\hat{i} + 2.88\hat{j})$

Now $\qquad \vec{E} = \vec{E}_{\parallel} + \vec{E}_{\perp}$

$\therefore \qquad \vec{E}_{\perp} = \vec{E} - \vec{E}_{\parallel} = (2\hat{i} + 3\hat{j}) - (2.16\hat{i} + 2.88\hat{j}) = (-0.16\hat{i} + 0.12\hat{j}) \, NC^{-1}$

Again $\qquad \gamma = \dfrac{1}{\sqrt{1 - \dfrac{v^2}{c^2}}} = \dfrac{1}{\sqrt{1 - \dfrac{(2 \times 10^8)^2}{(3 \times 10^8)^2}}} = \dfrac{1}{\sqrt{\dfrac{5}{9}}} = 1.34$

Now $\qquad \vec{E}'_{\parallel} = \vec{E}_{\parallel} = 2.16\,\hat{i} + 2.88\,\hat{j}$

$\qquad\qquad \vec{E}'_{\perp} = \gamma \vec{E}_{\perp} = 1.34(-0.16\hat{i} + 0.12\hat{j}) = (-0.21\hat{i} + 0.16\hat{j})$

$\therefore \qquad \vec{E}' = \vec{E}'_{\parallel} + \vec{E}'_{\perp} = (2.16\hat{i} + 2.88\hat{j}) + (-0.21\hat{i} + 0.16\hat{j})$

$$= (1.95\hat{i} + 3.04\,\hat{j}) \, NC^{-1}$$

(b) **NOTE.** In this problem the motion of the frame S' is not along the X-axis. So this problem cannot be solved by the method used in part (a)

Q. 7.7. An electric field measured in Lab. frame is given by $\vec{E} = (3\hat{i} + 4\hat{j})\,Vm^{-1}$. Calculate the field in a frame of reference moving with a velocity $\vec{v} = (2\hat{i} + 1.5\hat{j})\ 10^8\ ms^{-1}$ relative to lab. frame.

(*H.P.U.*, 1996)

Ans. Velocity $\vec{v} = (2\hat{i} + 1.5\hat{j}) \times 10^8\ ms^{-1}$

$\therefore$ Magnitude of velocity $|\vec{v}| = \sqrt{2^2 + 1.5^2} \times 10^8 = 2.5 \times 10^8\ ms^{-1}$

Unit vector along $\vec{v}, \hat{v} = \dfrac{\vec{v}}{|\vec{v}|} = \dfrac{(2\hat{i} + 1.5\hat{j}) \times 10^8}{2.5 \times 10^8} = 0.8\hat{i} + 0.6\hat{j}$

The component of $\vec{E}$ along $\vec{v} = |\vec{E}_{\parallel}| = \vec{E}\cdot\hat{v}$

$\qquad\qquad = (3\hat{i} + 4\hat{j})(0.8\hat{i} + 0.6\hat{j}) = 4.8\,NC^{-1}$

$\therefore\qquad\qquad \vec{E}_{\parallel} = |\vec{E}_{\parallel}|\hat{v} = 4.8\,(0.8\hat{i} + 0.6\hat{j})$

Now $\qquad\qquad \vec{E} = \vec{E}_{\parallel} + \vec{E}_{\perp}$

$\therefore\qquad \vec{E}_{\perp} = \vec{E} - \vec{E}_{\parallel} = (3\hat{i} + 4\hat{j}) - 4.8(0.8\hat{i} + 0.6\hat{j})$

$\qquad\qquad = (3 - 3.84)\hat{i} + (4 - 2.88)\hat{j} = (-0.84\hat{i} + 1.12\hat{j})NC^{-1}$

Again $\qquad\qquad \gamma = \dfrac{1}{\sqrt{1 - \dfrac{v^2}{c^2}}} = \dfrac{1}{\sqrt{1 - \dfrac{(2.5 \times 10^8)^2}{(3 \times 10^8)^2}}} = 1.8$

Now $\qquad \vec{E}_{\parallel}' = \vec{E}_{\parallel} = 4.8(0.8\hat{i} + 0.6\hat{j})NC^{-1}$

$\qquad \vec{E}_{\perp}' = \gamma\vec{E}_{\perp} = 1.8(-0.84\hat{i} + 1.12\hat{j})NC^{-1}$

$\therefore\qquad \vec{E}' = \vec{E}_{\parallel}' + \vec{E}_{\perp}' = (3.84\hat{i} + 2.88\hat{j}) + (-1.51\hat{i} + 2.02\hat{j})$

$\qquad\qquad = (2.33\hat{i} + 4.90\hat{j})NC^{-1}$

Q. 7.8. (*a*) **A parallel plate capacitor lying in the X–Y plane of frame S had a surface charge density σ. Find the speed with which the frame S' should move so that the charge density measured is three lines the value in frame S'.** (*P.U.*, 2007)

(*b*) **In a stationary frame of reference a uniform electric field of 10 Vm^{-1} is acting. The same field as observed from a varying frame moving at right angles is 20 Vm^{-1}. What is the speed of the moving frame?** (*G.N.D.U.*, 2000)

Ans. (*a*) If σ' is the charge density as measured by the moving frame S', then

$$\sigma' = \frac{\sigma}{\sqrt{1 - \dfrac{v^2}{c^2}}}$$

where v is the velocity of the moving frame S'

But $\qquad \sigma' = 3\sigma\ ;\ \therefore\ 3\sigma = \dfrac{\sigma}{\sqrt{1 - \dfrac{v^2}{c^2}}}$

or $\quad 3 = \dfrac{1}{\sqrt{1-\dfrac{v^2}{c^2}}}\quad$ or $9 = \dfrac{1}{1-\dfrac{v^2}{c^2}}\quad$ or $1-\dfrac{v^2}{c^2} = \dfrac{1}{9}\quad$ or $\dfrac{v^2}{c^2} = 1-\dfrac{1}{9} = \dfrac{8}{9}$

$\therefore \qquad \dfrac{v}{c} = \dfrac{\sqrt{8}}{3}\quad$ or $v = \dfrac{\sqrt{8}}{3}\ c = 0.943\ C$

(b) Let $E_y = 10\ \text{Vm}^{-1}$ be the electric field in stationary frame of reference acting along the Y-axis. If v is the speed of the moving frame in a direction at right angles say along X-axis and $E_y' = 20\ \text{Vm}^{-1}$ is the value of the field as observed from the moving frame, then

$$E_y' = \gamma E_y = \dfrac{E_y}{\sqrt{1-v^2/c^2}}$$

or $\qquad 20 = \dfrac{10}{\sqrt{1-v^2/c^2}}\qquad$ or $\dfrac{1}{2} = \sqrt{1-v^2/c^2}$

$\therefore \qquad \dfrac{1}{4} = 1 - \dfrac{v^2}{c^2}\qquad$ or $\dfrac{v^2}{c^2} = \dfrac{3}{4}$

Hence $\qquad v = \dfrac{\sqrt{3}}{2}\,c = 0.866\,c$

where c is the velocity of light.

Q. 7.9. (a) Find an expression for the field of a point charge moving with uniform velocity. How does it differ from the field due to a stationary charge. Show that the field is not spherically symmetric. Will the field be conservative?

(H.P.U. 1999; Kan. U., 1996, 1995; G.N.D.U., 1995; P.U., 1995, 1994; Pbi. U. 2003, 1991)

(b) Prove that the electric field of a moving charge is γ^3 times stronger in a direction perpendicular to its motion than the field at the same distance along the direction of motion where

$$\gamma = \dfrac{1}{\sqrt{1-\dfrac{v^2}{c^2}}} \qquad\qquad\qquad (P.U., 2006)$$

Ans. (a) Electric field due to moving charge. Consider a point charge q at rest at the origin of an inertial frame F. The electric field $\vec{E}$ at a point P at a vector distance $\vec{r}$ is given by $\vec{E} = \dfrac{1}{4\pi\varepsilon_0}\dfrac{q}{r^3}\vec{r}$ and is directed radially outward.

Let the co-ordinates of the point P in the frame F be x, y, z, then

$$\vec{r} = x\hat{i} + y\hat{j} + z\hat{k}$$

and $\quad |\vec{r}| = r = (x^2 + y^2 + z^2)^{1/2}$

$\therefore \qquad \vec{E} = \dfrac{1}{4\pi\varepsilon_0}\dfrac{q}{r^3}(x\hat{i} + y\hat{j} + z\hat{k}) \quad ...(i)$

The X-component of $\vec{E}$

$$E_x = \vec{E}.\hat{i} = \dfrac{1}{4\pi\varepsilon_0}\dfrac{q}{r^3}x \quad ...(ii)$$

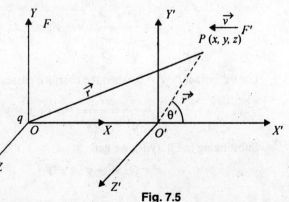

Fig. 7.5

Similarly Y and Z-components of $\vec{E}$ are

$$E_y = \frac{1}{4\pi\varepsilon_0}\frac{q}{r^3}y$$ ...(iii)

and $$E_z = \frac{1}{4\pi\varepsilon_0}\frac{q}{r^3}z$$ ...(iv)

Now consider the inertial frame F' having its co-ordinate axes parallel to the respective axes of the frame F and let the frame F' move in the direction of $-X$ axis with a velocity $\vec{v}$.

If there is an observer in the frame F', then with respect to him the frame F and hence the charge q is moving along the $+X$ direction with a velocity $\vec{v}$. The values of E_x', E_y' and E_z' i.e., the X, Y and Z components of $\vec{E}$ the electric field due to the charge q as observed by the observer in the frame F' can be obtained by

(i) Applying the field transformation equations and (ii) substituting the values of x, y and z terms of x', y' and z' in accordance with Lorentz transformation equations.

According to rule (i) $E_x' = E_x$

$$E_y' = \gamma E_y$$

$$E_z' = \gamma E_z$$

where $$\gamma = \frac{1}{\sqrt{1 - v^2/c^2}}$$

Now $$E' = E_x'\hat{i} + E_y'\hat{j} + E_z'\hat{k}$$ ...(v)

The unit vector $\hat{i}, \hat{j}$ and $\hat{k}$ in the inertial frame F and F' are the same as the co-ordinate axes of both the frames are parallel.

Substituting the value of $E_x' = E_x$, $E_y' = \gamma E_y$ and $E_z' = \gamma E_z$ in Eq. (v), we get

$$E' = E_x\hat{i} + \gamma E_y\hat{j} + \gamma E_z\hat{k}$$ ...(vi)

$$= \frac{1}{4\pi\varepsilon_0}\frac{q}{r^3}(x\hat{i} + \gamma y\hat{j} + \gamma z\hat{k})$$ ...(vii)

Now $$r = (x^2 + y^2 + z^2)^{1/2}$$

$$\therefore \quad r^3 = (x^2 + y^2 + z^2)^{3/2}$$ ...(viii)

According to Lorentz transformation equations, as the inertial frame F has been considered to be moving with a velocity $+\vec{v}$ in the $+X$ direction with respect to the inertial frame F', we have

$$x = \frac{x' - vt'}{\sqrt{1 - \frac{v^2}{c^2}}}; \quad y = y'; \quad z = z'; \quad t = \frac{t' - v/c^2}{\sqrt{1 - v^2/c^2}}$$

For the instant $t = t' = 0$, when the charge q passes the origin O' in the frame F' we have

$$x = \frac{x'}{\sqrt{1 - v^2/c^2}} = \gamma x'; \quad y = y'; \quad z = z'; \quad t = t' = 0$$

Substituting in Eq. (viii), we get

$$r^3 = (\gamma^2 x'^2 + y'^2 + z'^2)^{3/2}$$

$$= \gamma^3 \left[x'^2 + \frac{(y'^2 + z'^2)}{\gamma^2} \right]^{3/2}$$

Now $\quad \dfrac{1}{\gamma^2} = 1 - \dfrac{v^2}{c^2} = 1 - \beta^2$ where $\beta = \dfrac{v}{c}$

$$\therefore \quad r^3 = \gamma^3 \left[x'^2 + (1 - \beta^2)(y'^2 + z'^2) \right]^{3/2}$$

$$= \gamma^3 \left[x'^2 + y'^2 + z'^2 - \beta^2 (y'^2 + z'^2) \right]^{3/2}$$

$$= \gamma^3 \left[r'^2 - \beta^2 (y'^2 + z'^2) \right]^{3/2}$$

$$= \gamma^3 r'^3 \left[1 - \beta^2 \frac{(y'^2 + z'^2)}{r'^2} \right]^{3/2} \qquad \qquad \qquad \qquad ...(ix)$$

and $\quad (x\hat{i} + \gamma y \hat{j} + \gamma z \hat{k}) = (\gamma x' \hat{i} + \gamma y' \hat{j} + \gamma z' \hat{k})$

$$= \gamma (x'\hat{i} + y'\hat{j} + z'\hat{k}) = \gamma \vec{r}' \qquad \qquad \qquad \qquad ...(x)$$

Substituting the values of r^3 from Eq. (ix) and $(x\hat{i} + \gamma y \hat{j} + \gamma z \hat{k})$ from Eq. (x) in Eq. (vii), we get

$$E' = \frac{1}{4\pi\varepsilon_0} \frac{q}{\gamma^3 r'^3 \left[1 - \beta^2 \frac{(y'^2 + z'^2)}{r'^2} \right]^{3/2}} \gamma \vec{r}'$$

$$= \frac{1}{4\pi\varepsilon_0} \frac{q \vec{r}'}{\gamma^2 r'^3 \left[1 - \beta^2 \frac{(y'^2 + z'^2)}{r'^2} \right]^{3/2}}$$

or $\qquad \vec{E}' = \frac{1}{4\pi\varepsilon_0} \frac{q(1 - \beta^2)}{r'^3 \left[1 - \beta^2 \frac{(y'^2 + z'^2)}{r'^2} \right]^{3/2}} \vec{r}' \qquad ...(xi) \quad \left[\because \frac{1}{\gamma^2} = (1 - \beta^2) \right]$

Special case. When the point P lies in the X-Y plane (or $X' - Y'$ plane), then for the observation point P, $z' = 0$.

$$\therefore \qquad \vec{E}' = \frac{1}{4\pi\varepsilon_0} \frac{q(1 - \beta^2)}{r'^3} \frac{1}{\left[1 - \beta^2 \frac{y'^2}{r'^2} \right]^{3/2}} \vec{r}' \qquad \qquad ...(xii)$$

Also $\vec{r}' = x'\hat{i} + y'\hat{j}$ and $r'^2 = x'^2 + y'^2$

$$\therefore \qquad \vec{E}' = \frac{1}{4\pi\varepsilon_0} \frac{q(1 - \beta^2)}{[x'^2 + (1 - \beta^2)y'^2]^{3/2}} (x'\hat{i} + y'\hat{j})$$

$\therefore$ X and Y components of the field E', E_x' and E_y' are

$$E_x' = \frac{1}{4\pi\varepsilon_0} \frac{(1 - \beta^2)qx'}{[x'^2 + (1 - \beta^2)y'^2]^{3/2}}$$

and $\qquad E_y' = \frac{1}{4\pi\varepsilon_0} \frac{(1 - \beta^2)qy'}{[x'^2 + (1 - \beta^2)y'^2]^{3/2}}$

$$\therefore \qquad \frac{E_y'}{E_x'} = \frac{y'}{x'} \qquad \qquad \qquad \qquad ...(xiii)$$

Thus we find that the vector $\vec{E'}$ given by the resultant of vectors E_y' and E_x' makes the same angle with X' axis as does the vector $\vec{r'}$ given by the resultant of x' and y'. Hence $\vec{E'}$ points radially outward along a line drawn from the instantaneous position of q, i.e., at O.

The magnitude of $\vec{E'}$ from Eq. (xii) is given as

$$E' = \frac{1}{4\pi\varepsilon_0}\frac{q}{r'^2}\frac{1-\beta^2}{\left[1-\beta^2\dfrac{y'^2}{r'^2}\right]^{3/2}}$$

$$= \frac{1}{4\pi\varepsilon_0}\frac{q}{r'^2}\frac{1-\beta^2}{[1-\beta^2\sin^2\theta']^{3/2}} \qquad \ldots(xiv)$$

where θ' is the angle that $\vec{O'P}$ or $\vec{r'}$ makes with X-axis and $\dfrac{y'}{r'} = \sin\theta'$

Hence we find that

(i) The electric field of a charge in uniform motion, at a given instant of time, is directed radially from the *instantaneous* position of charge.

(ii) Its magnitude is given by relation (xiv) where θ' is the angle between the direction of motion of the charge and the radius vector r' from the instantaneous position of the charge to the point of observation.

When $v \ll c$. When the velocity v is very small as compared to c, $\beta = \dfrac{v}{c}$ is negligible, and

$$E' = \frac{1}{4\pi\varepsilon_0}\frac{q}{r'^2}$$

In other words, the field is the same as due to a point charge at rest in the frame F'.

Difference between field due to a stationary and a moving charge. When v is comparable to c, $\beta = \dfrac{v}{c}$ is not negligible. In such a case, the field E' will be of varying magnitudes in different directions. For example

For $\theta' = 0$ $E_0' = E_\parallel' = \dfrac{1}{4\pi\varepsilon_0}\dfrac{q}{r'^2}(1-\beta^2)$ $\ldots(xv)$

For $\theta' = \dfrac{\pi}{2}$ $E_{\pi/2}' = E_\perp' = \dfrac{1}{4\pi\varepsilon_0}\dfrac{q}{r'^2}\dfrac{1}{(1-\beta^2)^{1/2}}$ $\ldots(xvi)$

$\therefore$ $\dfrac{E_{\pi/2}'}{E_0'} = \dfrac{E_\perp'}{E_\parallel'} = \dfrac{1}{(1-\beta^2)^{3/2}}$

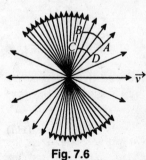

As β is less than 1, $E_{\pi/2}' > E_0'$. Hence the strength of the field increases as θ' varies from 0 to $\pi/2$. The field is symmetrical with respect to the line of motion of the charge as also if θ' is changed from θ' to $\pi - \theta'$. As a result the field lines tend to concentrate along the Y (and in a three dimensional case Y and Z) direction prependicular to the X-direction of motion of the charge because the field is stronger at right angles to the motion than in the direction of motion at the same distance from the charge. The field is as shown in Fig. 7.6. It is **not spherically symmetrical**. The assymmetry is all the more marked for large values of $\beta = v/c$. Such a field cannot be produced by any stationary charge distribution.

Fig. 7.6

Field is non-conservative. The line integral of the field $E' = \oint \vec{E'} \cdot \vec{dl} = \text{curl } \vec{E'}$ is *not zero* around every closed path. The reason is quite evident if we consider a closed path $ABCD$. The circular arcs AB and CD being perpendicular to the field do not contribute anything to the line integral. The line integral along BC is greater than that along AD because the field is stronger along BC than along DA. Thus it is different from the field due to stationary charge or electrostatic field. Hence the field is **not conservative**.

(b) It has been proved in part (a) of this question that when $\theta' = 0$ i.e., the electric field is measured along the direction of motion of the moving charge q, the field due to the moving charge

$$E'_0 = \frac{1}{4\pi\varepsilon_0} \frac{q}{r'^2} (1-\beta^2) \qquad \ldots[\text{Eq. } (xv)]$$

$$= \frac{1}{4\pi\varepsilon_0} \frac{q}{r'^2} \left(1-\frac{v^2}{c^2}\right) \qquad \left[\therefore b = \frac{v}{c}\right]$$

$$= \frac{1}{4\pi\varepsilon_0} \frac{q}{r'^2} \frac{1}{\gamma^2} \qquad \left[\therefore \gamma = \frac{1}{\sqrt{1-\dfrac{v^2}{c^2}}}\right]$$

and when $\theta' = \dfrac{\pi}{2}$ i.e., the field is measured in a direction perpendicular to the direction of motion of the charge q, the field due to the moving change

$$E'_{\pi/2} = \frac{1}{4\pi\varepsilon_0} \frac{q}{r'^2} \frac{1}{\left(1-\beta^2\right)^{1/2}} \qquad \ldots[\text{Eq. } (xvi)]$$

$$= \frac{1}{4\pi\varepsilon_0} \frac{q}{r'^2} \gamma$$

Therefore, the ratio of the electric field due to the moving charge at a distance (r') in a direction perpendicular to the direction of motion $(E'_{\pi/2})$ to the electric field at the same distance in a direction parallel to the motion of the moving charge (E'_0) is

$$\frac{E'_{\pi/2}}{E'_0} = \gamma \times \gamma^2 = \gamma^3$$

Hence the electric field due to a moving charge is γ^3 times stronger in a direction perpendicular to its motion than the field at the same distance along the direction of motion.

Q. 7.10. Is the electric field due to a moving charge conservative? If not, what is the source of e.m.f. ? (H.P.U. 2002)

Ans. The electric field due to a moving charge is not conservative. For explanation.

See **Q. 7.9** under the head 'Field is non-conservative'.

The source of this non-conservative field is the varying magnetic field produced by the moving charge.

Q. 7.11. Describe qualitatively with figures the electric field produced by (i) stationary charge (ii) a positive charge initially at rest is suddenly accelerated and moves with constant velocity thereafter and (iii) a moving charge that suddenly stops. (H.P.U., 1995; G.N.D.U., 1994; P.U., 1991)

Ans. (i) **Stationary charge.** Consider a positively charged particle at rest at the origin of the co-ordinate system. The electric field due to it varies inversely as the square of the distance from the point charge. The value of the field at a particular distance from the charge will be the same at every point lying on the surface of a sphere with the point charge as its centre. If, however, we consider the situation only in the X-Y plane the field all along a circle with the charge as the centre will be the same *i.e.,* the equipotential lines will be circular and the direction of the field as well as the lines of force will be *radial outward* as shown in Fig. 7.7.

(*ii*) **Charge suddenly starts moving.** Suppose the charged particle suddenly starts moving along the X-axis and acquires a uniform velocity v in a very small time Δt. As soon as the charge starts moving the *information* about its movement will spread out with the velocity of light c. After a time t this *information* will arrive at all the points on a sphere (circle in the plane X-Y) of radius ct drawn with the origin of the co-ordinate system as centre. Outside the sphere (circle in the plane X-Y) the lines of force will be radial and directed away from the origin of the co-ordinate system as the *information* about the movement of the charge has not yet reached beyond the sphere (circle in the plane X-Y) of radius ct. Within the sphere the lines of force will be directed away from the instantaneous position of the charge.

Thus we find that outside the sphere of radius ct the lines of electric force appear to be originating from the origin of the co-ordinate system and within the sphere these appear to originate from the instantaneous location of the charge.

Let us now try to look at the situation within the spherical envelop of thickness $c\,\Delta t$ where Δt is the *very very* small time during which the charge is accelerated from rest to the constant velocity v. Taking the envelop to be a Gaussian surface, the number of lines of force entering it must be equal to the number of lines leaving it. In other words, the field lines within the envelop will be as shown by the dotted portion connecting the field lines within the sphere to the field lines just outside the spherical surface (Fig. 7.8.)

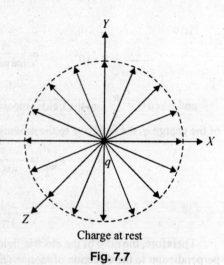

Charge at rest

Fig. 7.7

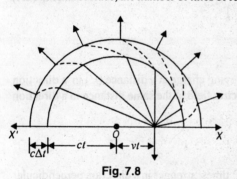

Fig. 7.8

(*iii*) **Moving charge suddenly stops.** Let us now consider the case of a charged particle moving with a constant velocity v, which suddenly stops in a very very small time Δt. In such a case the lines of force outside the sphere (circle in the plane X-Y) of radius ct will be as if these were originating from q' the position of the charge which it would have occupied if it had continued to move with a constant velocity v. Within the sphere (circle in the plane X-Y) the lines of force will be originating from the position of rest of the particle which has been taken to be the origin of the co-ordinate system.

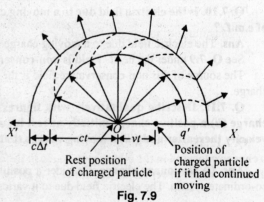

Rest position of charged particle

Position of charged particle if it had continued moving

Fig. 7.9

Therefore, within the envelop of radius $c\Delta t$ where Δt is the time taken by the charged particle to decelerate from a velocity v to rest, the lines of force will be as shown by dotted portion connecting the field lines within the sphere to the field lines just outside the spherical surface (Fig. 7.9).

Q. 7.12. (a) **A proton moves in a straight line with constant speed of 2.4×10^8 ms^{-1}. Find the electric field due to it along a line perpendicular to the direction of motion at a point 15 cm from it.**   (G.N.D.U., 2007 similar; H.P.U., 1992)

(b) **An electron is moving with velocity 0.6 c. Calculate the magnitude of maximum and minimum field produced by it at a distance of 2m. Given charge on the electron is 1.6×10^{-19} C.**   (P.U., 2000)

Ans. (a) Suppose the proton moves along the X-axis, then the electric field due to it at any point at a distance r in a direction prependicular to its direction of motion is given by

$$E_{\pi/2} = \frac{1}{4\pi\varepsilon_0} \frac{q}{r^2} \frac{1}{(1 - \beta^2)^{1/2}}$$

Here $r = 15 \text{ cm} = 0.15 \text{ m};$ $\beta = \dfrac{v}{c} = \dfrac{2.4 \times 10^8}{3 \times 10^8} = 0.8$

$\dfrac{1}{4\pi\varepsilon_0} = 9 \times 10^9$ Charge on the proton $= 1.6 \times 10^{-19}$ C

$\therefore$ $E_{\pi/2} = \dfrac{9 \times 10^9 \times 1.6 \times 10^{-19}}{(0.15)^2 (1 - 0.64)^{1/2}} = 1.06 \times 10^{-7}$ NC^{-1}

(b) The magnitude of the electric field due to a moving charge is given by

$$E' = \frac{1}{4\pi\varepsilon_0} \frac{q(1 - \beta^2)}{r^2 (1 - \beta^2 \sin^2\theta)^{3/2}}$$

For $\theta = 0;$ $E' = \dfrac{q(1 - \beta^2)}{4\pi\varepsilon_0 r^2}$ *i.e.* has a minimum value

$\therefore$ Magnitude of minimum field $E'_{min} = \dfrac{q(1 - \beta^2)}{4\pi\varepsilon_0 r^2}$

$= \dfrac{9 \times 10^9 \times 1.6 \times 10^{-19} (1 - 0.36)}{4} = 9 \times 10^9 \times 1.6 \times 10^{-19} \times \dfrac{0.64}{4}$

$= 2.304 \times 10^{-10}$ NC^{-1}

For $\theta = \pi/2;$ $E' = \dfrac{q}{4\pi\varepsilon_0 r^2} \dfrac{(1 - \beta^2)}{(1 - \beta^2)^{3/2}} = \dfrac{q}{4\pi\varepsilon_0 r^2} \dfrac{1}{(1 - \beta^2)^{1/2}}$

i.e., has a maximum value.

$\therefore$ Magnitude of maximum field $E'_{max} = \dfrac{q}{4\pi\varepsilon_0 r^2} \dfrac{1}{(1 - \beta^2)^{1/2}}$

$= 9 \times 10^9 \times 1.6 \times 10^{-19} \times \dfrac{1}{4 \times (1 - 0.36)^{1/2}}$

$= \dfrac{9 \times 10^9 \times 1.6 \times 10^{-19}}{4 \times 0.8} = 4.5 \times 10^{-10}$ NC^{-1}

Q. 7.13. Given that the magnitude of the electric field as measured in the moving frame due to charge q located in the laboratory frame in the direction making an angle θ with the direction of motion of the observer at a distance r' is given by

$$E' = \frac{1}{4\pi\varepsilon_0} \frac{q(1-\beta^2)}{r'^2(1-\beta^2\sin^2\theta)^{3/2}}$$

where $\beta = v/c$, v being the velocity of the observer as measured in the laboratory frame. Prove that Gauss's law is true for moving charges as well.

(*Pbi.U.* 2001, 2000; *P.U.* 2002; *G.N.D.U.* 2002, 1990)

Ans. Validity of Gauss's law for moving charges. The charge q is located in the laboratory frame F and the observer in the moving frame F' measures the magnitude of the electric field due to the charge q at a distance r' from it in a direction making an angle θ with the direction of motion of the observer to be

$$E' = \frac{1}{4\pi\varepsilon_0} \frac{q(1-\beta^2)}{r'^2(1-\beta^2\sin^2\theta)^{3/2}}$$

where $\beta = v/c$, v the velocity of the observer as measured in the laboratory frame F.

Consider a spherical Gaussian surface in the moving frame F' having a radius r', then the surface area of an elementary ring of radius $r'\sin\theta$ and thickness $r'\,d\theta$ is given by

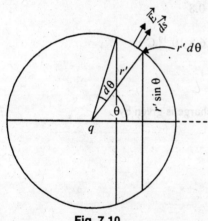

Fig. 7.10

$$ds = 2\pi\, r'\sin\theta\, r'\, d\theta$$
$$= 2\pi\, r'^2\sin\theta\, d\theta$$

Electric flux through the elementary ring $d\phi = E'\, ds$

Since E' and ds act along the same direction *i.e.*, the outward drawn normal to the area ds.

$$\therefore\quad d\phi = \frac{1}{4\pi\varepsilon_0} \frac{q(1-\beta^2)}{r'^2(1-\beta^2\sin^2\theta)^{3/2}} 2\pi r'^2\sin\theta\, d\theta$$

$$= \frac{q(1-\beta^2)}{2\varepsilon_0} \frac{\sin\theta\, d\theta}{(1-\beta^2\sin^2\theta)^{3/2}}$$

Hence total flux through the sphere $\phi = \int\limits_0^{2\pi} d\phi$

or

$$\phi = \frac{q(1-\beta^2)}{2\varepsilon_0} \int\limits_0^{2\pi} \frac{\sin\theta\, d\theta}{(1-\beta^2\sin^2\theta)^{3/2}}$$

$$\phi = \frac{q(1-\beta^2)}{2\varepsilon_0} \int\limits_0^{2\pi} \frac{\sin\theta\, d\theta}{[(1-\beta^2)+\beta^2\cos^2\theta]^{3/2}}$$

$$= \frac{q(1-\beta^2)}{2\varepsilon_0} \int\limits_0^{2\pi} \frac{\sin\theta\, d\theta}{(1-\beta^2)^{3/2}\left[1+\left(\dfrac{\beta\cos\theta}{\sqrt{1-\beta^2}}\right)^2\right]^{3/2}}$$

or

$$\phi = \frac{q}{2\varepsilon_0(1-\beta^2)^{1/2}} \int\limits_0^{2\pi} \frac{\sin\theta\, d\theta}{\left[1+\left(\dfrac{\beta\cos\theta}{\sqrt{1-\beta^2}}\right)^2\right]^{3/2}} \qquad \ldots(i)$$

To evaluate the integral in Eq. (*i*), put $\dfrac{\beta\cos\theta}{\sqrt{1-\beta^2}} = \tan\alpha$

$$\therefore \quad \frac{-\beta}{\sqrt{1-\beta^2}} \sin\theta \, d\theta = \sec^2\alpha \, d\alpha$$

or

$$\sin\theta \, d\theta = -\frac{\sqrt{1-\beta^2}}{\beta} \sec^2\alpha \, d\alpha$$

Hence

$$\int \frac{\sin\theta \, d\theta}{\left[1 + \left(\frac{\beta\cos\theta}{\sqrt{1-\beta^2}}\right)^2\right]^{3/2}} = \int \frac{-\frac{\sqrt{1-\beta^2}}{\beta} \sec^2\alpha \, d\alpha}{[1 + \tan^2\alpha]^{3/2}}$$

$$= -\frac{\sqrt{1-\beta^2}}{\beta} \int \frac{\sec^2\alpha \, d\alpha}{\sec^3\alpha} = -\frac{\sqrt{1-\beta^2}}{\beta} \int \cos\alpha \, d\alpha$$

$$= -\frac{\sqrt{1-\beta^2}}{\beta} \sin\alpha$$

But

$$\sin\alpha = \frac{\sin\alpha}{\cos\alpha}\cos\alpha = \frac{\tan\alpha}{\sec\alpha} = \frac{\tan\alpha}{[1 + \tan^2\alpha]^{1/2}}$$

$$= \frac{\frac{\beta}{\sqrt{1-\beta^2}}\cos\theta}{\left[1 + \frac{\beta^2}{1-\beta^2}\cos^2\theta\right]^{1/2}} = \frac{\beta\cos\theta}{[1 - \beta^2 + \beta^2\cos^2\theta]^{1/2}} = \frac{\beta\cos\theta}{[1 - \beta^2\sin^2\theta]^{1/2}}$$

$$\therefore \quad \int \frac{\sin\theta \, d\theta}{\left[1 + \left(\frac{\beta\cos\theta}{1-\beta^2}\right)^2\right]^{3/2}} = -\frac{\sqrt{1-\beta^2}}{\beta} \frac{\beta\cos\theta}{[1 - \beta^2\sin^2\theta]^{1/2}} = \frac{-\sqrt{1-\beta^2}\cos\theta}{[1 - \beta^2\sin^2\theta]^{1/2}}$$

Substituting in Eq. (*i*), we have

$$\phi = -\frac{q}{2\varepsilon_0(1-\beta^2)^{1/2}} \left[\frac{(1-\beta^2)^{1/2}\cos\theta}{[1-\beta^2\sin^2\theta]^{1/2}}\right]_0^\pi$$

$$= \frac{-q}{2\varepsilon_0}\left[\frac{\cos\theta}{(1-\beta^2\sin^2\theta)^{1/2}}\right]_0^\pi = +\frac{q}{2\varepsilon_0}[1+1] = \frac{q}{\varepsilon_0}$$

Thus the flux due to the moving charge is the same as due to a stationary charge. Hence we conclude that '*Gauss's law is valid even for moving charges*'.

Q. 7.14. Show that the electrostatic force acting on a charged particle in motion is independent of the velocity of the particle. *(Pbi.U., 2006; Kan.U., 1994)*

Ans. Force on a moving charge. Consider a charged particle carrying a charge q moving through an electric field $\vec{E}$ with a velocity $\vec{v}$ along the $+X$-axis in an inertial frame S. Let an inertial frame S' also move with the same velocity $\vec{v}$ along the $+X$-axis so that the charged particle is *momentarily at rest* in the frame S'. Let the electric field as observed in the frame S' be $\vec{E}$ and its component $E'_\parallel$

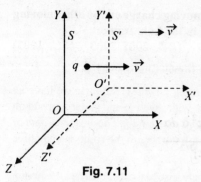

Fig. 7.11

and $E'_\perp$ respectively parallel and perpendicular to the direction of motion. If $E_\parallel$ and $E_\perp$ are the corresponding components of the field $\vec{E}$ in the frame S, then according to the electric field transformation equations,

$$E'_\parallel = E_\parallel$$
$$E'_\perp = \gamma E_\perp$$

The Lorentz transformation equations for force are

$$F'_x = F_x; F'_y = \frac{F_y}{\sqrt{1 - \frac{v^2}{c^2}}} = \gamma F_y$$

and

$$F'_z = \frac{F_z}{\sqrt{1 - \frac{v^2}{c^2}}} = \gamma F_z$$

[For proof see Chapter **'Relativity'** in **'Mechanics and Properties of Matter'** portion by the same author]

As the charged particle is moving along the $+X$ axis, the component of force F_x is parallel to it and components of force F_y and F_z are perpendicular to its direction of motion.

In the $\parallel$ and $\perp$ notation the force transformation equations can be stated as

$$F'_\parallel = F_\parallel \qquad \qquad ...(i)$$
$$F'_\perp = \gamma F_\perp \qquad \qquad ...(ii)$$

Force experienced by the moving charge q in the frame S due to the field component $E_\parallel$

$$= F_\parallel = qE_\parallel.$$

Force experienced by the moving charge q, in the frame S' due to the field component $E'_\parallel$

$$= F'_\parallel = qE'_\parallel = qE_\parallel \qquad \qquad [\because E'_\parallel = E_\parallel] ...(iii)$$

Therefore, transforming the force back to the frame S, and comparing equations (i) and (iii) we have

$$F_\parallel = qE_\parallel$$

Force experienced by the moving charge q in the frame S' due to the field component $E'_\perp$

$$= F'_\perp = qE'_\perp = \gamma qE_\perp \qquad \qquad [\because E'_\perp = \gamma E_\perp] ...(iv)$$

Therefore, transforming the force back to the frame S, and comparing equations (ii) and (iv), we have

$$\gamma F_\perp = \gamma qE_\perp$$

or

$$F_\perp = qE_\perp$$

Hence the force acting on a charged particle carrying a charge q in motion through a stationary electric field $\vec{E}$ in an inertial frame $S = qE$ and is strictly independent of velocity of the particle. In other words, the force on a charge moving through a stationary electric field remains the same as the force applied by the field $\vec{E}$ on a stationary charge.

Q. 7.15. (a) Discuss mathematically the interaction of a moving charge on the other moving charges and obtain an expression for the force as measured in the Lab. frame.

(*P.U.*, 2005, 2003; *Pbi.U.*, 1995)

(b) Using the above expression derived for force define the magnetic field $\vec{B}$.

Ans. (a) Interaction of a moving charge with other moving charges. Suppose we have an infinitely long procession of *positive* charges moving to the *right* with speed v_0 and superimposed on it a procession of *negative* charges moving to the *left* with the *same* speed in the *Laboratory frame* of reference *S*. We can imagine a '*wire*' along which positive ions are moving to the right and negative ions to the left.

The charges are supposed to be so large in number and so closely spaced that the charge distribution along the *line* can be taken to be continuous. Let the density of positive charge along the line be λ as measured in the *Lab. frame S,* and density of negative charge also be the *same*. In such a case, the *net* density of charge on the line in the *Lab. frame* = 0.

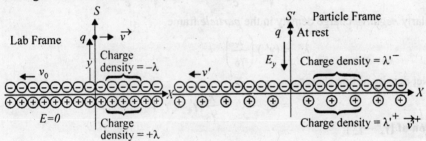

Fig. 7.12

$\therefore$ In the *Lab. frame S* the electric field $\vec{E} = 0$.

Hence a *stationary test charge q* placed at some distance say *y* from the wire will experience *no force.*

Suppose the test charge *q* is now set in motion to the *right* with a speed *v* in the *Lab frame.* If we have another frame of reference which is also moving to the *right* with the speed *v*, then the test charge *q* is at *rest* in this frame. Let this frame be known as *particle frame S'.*

Speed of positive and negative charges in frame S'. The speed of the *positive* charges and that of the *negative* charges in this new *particle frame* of reference S' is given by Lorentz velocity transformations. If we denote, the speed of *positive* charges in the *particle frame* as v'_+ and that of *negative* charges as v'_-, then

$$v'_+ = \frac{v_0 - v}{1 - \dfrac{v_0 v}{c^2}} \text{ and } v'_- = \frac{v_0 + v}{1 + \dfrac{v_0 v}{c^2}}$$

Charge density in frame S'. Now consider a reference frame moving to the right with a speed v_0, then in this frame the *positive* charges are at *rest.* As seen from this *positive's own rest frame* the *lab frame* is moving to the left with speed v_0.

$\therefore$ To an observer in *positive's own rest frame* each unit length of the wire appears to have contracted and $= \sqrt{1 - \dfrac{v_0^2}{c^2}}$.

Hence charge density in *positive's own rest frame*

$$= \lambda \sqrt{1 - \frac{v_0^2}{c^2}}$$

In the particle frame the speed of positive charges $= v_+'$.

There will, therefore, be a length contraction and each unit length will appear $= \sqrt{1 - \frac{(v_+')^2}{c^2}}$.

The line charge density will therefore, increase.

Hence *positive* charge density in the *particle frame S'*

$$\lambda_+' = \frac{\lambda \sqrt{1 - \frac{v_0^2}{c^2}}}{\sqrt{1 - \frac{(v_+')^2}{c^2}}} = (\gamma_+') \left(\frac{\lambda}{\gamma_0}\right)$$

where $\gamma_+' = \dfrac{1}{\sqrt{1 - \dfrac{(v_+')^2}{c^2}}}$ and $\gamma_0 = \dfrac{1}{\sqrt{1 - \dfrac{v_0^2}{c^2}}}$

Similarly *negative* charge density in the *particle* frame

$$\lambda_-' = (\gamma_-') \left(\frac{\lambda}{\gamma_0}\right)$$

$\therefore$ Net density of line charge

$$= \lambda_+' - \lambda_-' = \frac{\lambda}{\gamma_0}[\gamma_+' - \gamma_-'] \qquad\qquad \text{...(i)}$$

Evaluation of $[\gamma_+' - \gamma_-']$

To find the value of $[\gamma_+' - \gamma_-']$, we have

$$v_+' = \frac{v_0 - v}{1 - \frac{v_0 v}{c^2}}$$

or

$$\frac{v_+'}{c} = \frac{\frac{v_0}{c} - \frac{v}{c}}{1 - \frac{v_0}{c}\frac{v}{c}}$$

or

$$\beta_+' = \frac{\beta_0 - \beta}{1 - \beta_0 \beta}$$

where

$$\beta_+' = \frac{v_+'}{c}, \; \beta_0 = \frac{v_0}{c} \text{ and } \beta = \frac{v}{c}$$

Now

$$\gamma_+' = \frac{1}{\sqrt{1 - \frac{(v_+')^2}{c^2}}} = \frac{1}{\sqrt{1 - (\beta_+')^2}}$$

$$= \frac{1}{\sqrt{1 - \left(\frac{\beta_0 - \beta}{1 - \beta_0 \beta}\right)^2}}$$

$$= \frac{1 - \beta_0 \beta}{\sqrt{1 + \beta_0^2 \beta^2 - \beta_0^2 - \beta^2}} = \frac{1 - \beta_0 \beta}{\sqrt{(1 - \beta_0^2)(1 - \beta^2)}} = \gamma_0 \gamma (1 - \beta_0 \beta)$$

Similarly

$$\beta_-' = \frac{\beta_0 + \beta}{1 + \beta_0 \beta} \text{ and } \gamma_-' = \gamma_0 \gamma (1 + \beta_0 \beta)$$

$$\therefore \qquad (\gamma'_+ - \gamma'_-) = \gamma_0 \gamma [1 - \beta_0 \beta - 1 - \beta_0 \beta]$$

$$= -2 \gamma_0 \gamma \beta_0 \beta \qquad \qquad ...(ii)$$

Evaluation of $(\lambda'_+ - \lambda'_-)$. Substituting the value of $[\gamma'_+ - \gamma'_-)$ from Eq. (ii) in Eq. (i), we have

$$\frac{\lambda}{\gamma_0}[\gamma'_+ - \gamma'_-] = -\frac{\lambda}{\gamma_0} 2 \gamma_0 \gamma \beta_0 \beta = -\frac{2 \lambda \gamma v_0 v}{c^2}$$

$\therefore$ Net density of line charge

$$\lambda'_+ - \lambda'_- = -\frac{2 \lambda \gamma v_0 v}{c^2} \qquad \qquad ...(iii)$$

Electric field and force on the charge q **in lab. frame** S''. Applying Gauss's law to a cylinder of radius y enclosing the line charge, we have

Electric field in the *particle frame* S', $E'_y = \dfrac{1}{2\pi\varepsilon_0} \dfrac{(\lambda'_+ - \lambda'_-)}{y}$

Substituting the value of $(\lambda'_+ - \lambda'_-)$ from Eq. (iii), we have the magnitude of the electric field

$$E'_y = -\frac{1}{2\pi\varepsilon_0} \frac{2 \lambda \gamma v_0 v}{c^2 y} \qquad \qquad ...(iv)$$

But according to electromagnetic theory $c^2 = \dfrac{1}{\mu_0 \varepsilon_0}$

Substituting in Eq. (iv), we get

$$E'_y = -\frac{\mu_0}{4\pi} \frac{4 \lambda \gamma v_0 v}{y}$$

$\therefore$ Magnitude of the force on a positive charge q in the *particle frame* S'

$$F'_y = -\frac{\mu_0}{4\pi} \frac{4 q \lambda \gamma v_0 v}{y}$$

The field is radial and the force is directed radially *inward towards* the line charge *i.e.*, in the $-Y$ direction. In other words this is a *transverse* force acting in a direction perpendicular to the direction of motion of the test charge. If F_y is the magnitude of this force as observed in the *lab. frame* S, then according to Lorentz force transformations

$$F'_y = \gamma F_y$$

Hence on the basis of the theory of relativity and Gauss's theorem, we find the magnitude of the force on a charge q moving with a speed v along the $+X$ axis, parallel to the 'wire' carrying a line charge λ per unit length, in the *lab. frame* S.

$$F_y = \frac{F'_y}{\gamma} = -\frac{\mu_0}{4\pi} \frac{4 q \lambda v_0 v}{y} \qquad \qquad ...(v)$$

and its direction is along $-Y$ direction.

$$\therefore \qquad \vec{F}_y = -\frac{\mu_0}{4\pi} \frac{4 q \lambda v_0 v}{y} \hat{j} \qquad \qquad ...(vi)$$

and

$$\vec{E}_y = -\frac{\mu_0}{4\pi} \frac{4 \lambda v_0 v}{y} \hat{j} \qquad \qquad ...(vii)$$

The magnitude of $\qquad \vec{E}_y = -\dfrac{\mu_0}{4\pi} \dfrac{4 \lambda v_0 v}{y} \qquad \qquad ...(viii)$

Now, λv_0 is the rate of flow of positive charge to the right in the 'wire' and λv_0 is also the rate of flow of negative charge to left. Both these give rise to a conventional current to the right, of magnitude

$$I = (\lambda v_0) - (-\lambda v_0) = 2 \lambda v_0$$

Substituting in (v), we have, the magnitude of the force on the charge q moving with a velocity v is given by

$$F_y = -\frac{\mu_0}{4\pi}\frac{2qvI}{y}$$

Also

$$\vec{F}_y = -\frac{\mu_0}{4\pi}\frac{2qvI}{y}\hat{j} \qquad \qquad ...(viii)\ (a)$$

and magnitude of electric field $E_y = -\frac{\mu_0}{4\pi}\frac{2vI}{y}$

Also

$$\vec{E}_y = -\frac{\mu_0}{4\pi}\frac{2vI}{y}\hat{j}$$

(b) **Magnetic field.** From the above discussion, we conclude that when the test charge is at rest in the lab. frame, there is no force on it due to the line charge when the positive as well as the negative charges of the line charge are at rest or when the positive charge is moving in one direction with a velocity $\vec{v}_0$ and the negative charges are moving in the opposite direction with the same velocity $\vec{v}_0$ giving rise to a current $I = 2\lambda\, v_0$ where λ is the line charge density. Similarly, if there is a steady current flowing through a conductor, the electrons move from one end to the other, keeping the body of the conductor electrically neutral, there is no electric force on a stationary test charge.

But we find that a force

$$F_y = -\frac{\mu_0}{4\pi}\frac{4q\lambda v_0 v}{y} = -\frac{\mu_0}{4\pi}\frac{2qvI}{y} \qquad \qquad ...(ix)$$

acts on the test charge in a direction perpendicular to its instantaneous velocity when it is set in motion.

This force which is experienced by a moving charge in the field of other moving charges is known as the *magnetic force* and is said to arise due to the *magnetic induction field produced by moving charges*.

It has been proved from experiments that the magnetic force $\vec{F}_m$ acting on a charge q moving with a velocity $\vec{v}$ is given by

$$\vec{F}_m = q\vec{v} \times \vec{B}$$

where $\vec{B}$ is the magnetic induction field vector.

The force F_y given by Eq. (ix) acts along $-Y$ direction

$$\therefore \qquad \vec{F}_y = -\frac{\mu_0}{4\pi}\frac{2qvI}{y}\hat{j} \qquad \qquad ...(x)$$

The charge q moves in the $+X$ direction.

$$\therefore \qquad \vec{v} = v\hat{i}$$

In order that $\vec{F}_y = \vec{F}_m$, the vector $\vec{v} \times \vec{B}$ must be directed along $-\hat{j}$. Hence $\vec{B}$ must be in the direction of $+Z$ axis so that

$$\vec{B} = B\hat{k}$$

and

$$\vec{v} \times \vec{B} = v\hat{i} \times B\hat{k} = -vB\hat{j}$$

Hence

$$\vec{F}_m = q\vec{v} \times \vec{B} = -qvB\hat{j} \qquad \qquad ...(xi)$$

When

$$\vec{F}_y = \vec{F}_m, \text{ we have from Eq. } (x) \text{ and } (xi),$$

$$-qvB\hat{j} = -\frac{\mu_0}{4\pi}\frac{2qvI}{y}\hat{j}$$

or $$B = \frac{\mu_0}{4\pi} \frac{2I}{y}$$

∴ $$\vec{B} = \frac{\mu_0}{4\pi} \frac{2I}{y} \hat{k}$$

Thus we find that when a charge moves in the $+ X$ direction in a magnetic field acting in the $+ Z$ direction the force on it acts in the $- Y$ direction.

Hence the electric field $\vec{E}$ and the magnetic field $\vec{B}$ are the parts of a general field known as the electromagnetic field.

Q. 7.16. Find the force per unit length on a straight wire carrying a current of I_1 ampere when it is placed at a distance 'y' from a parallel wire carrying current I_2. Hence show that (i) two parallel wires carrying current in the same direction attract and (ii) two parallel wires carrying current in opposite direction repel each other.

(Meerut U., 2002; Keerala. U., 2001; G.N.D.U., 1994, 1942)

Ans. Force per unit length on a current carrying wire. Using Gauss's law and theory of relativity it can be proved that the force acting on a charge q moving with a velocity $\vec{v}$ in a direction parallel to the direction of current I in straight conductor is given by

$$\vec{F}_y = - \frac{\mu_0}{4\pi} \frac{2qvI}{y} \hat{j}$$ (For proof See Q. 7.15)[(Eq. (*viii*) (*a*)]

i.e., when the conventional current flows along the $+ X$-direction and a charge $+ q$ also moves in the same direction the force is directed towards the conductor.

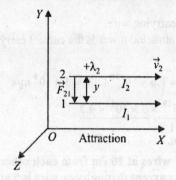

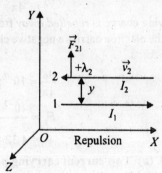

Fig. 7.13

Let a straight conductor 1 carry a current I_1 ampere in the $+ X$ direction as shown. Suppose another conductor 2 lies at a distance $+ y$ from it and carries a positive charge $+ \lambda_2$ per unit length moving along the $+ X$-direction with a velocity $\vec{v}_2$, then force experienced by a unit length of conductor 2 is given by

$$\vec{F}_{21} = - \frac{\mu_0}{4\pi} \frac{2\lambda_2 v_2 I_1}{y} \hat{j}$$

i.e, the force is directed along $- Y$ direction towards conductor 1. Now if I_2 is the current in conductor 2, then

$$I_2 = \lambda_2 v_2$$

Hence force per unit length of conductor 2 carrying current I_2 due to current I_1 in conductor 1 is given by

∴ $$\vec{F}_{21} = - \frac{\mu_0}{4\pi} \frac{2I_1 I_2}{y} \hat{j}$$

As the force is directed towards conductor 1, *conductor 2 is attracted by conductor 1*. The force, however is mutual.

(*i*) *Therefore, two conductors carrying currents flowing in the same direction i.e., two parallel currents attract each other.*

If the charge $+ \lambda_2$ on conductor 2 moves along the $- X$ axis, then v_2 is negative and

$$\vec{F}_{21} = - \frac{\mu_0}{4\pi} \frac{2\lambda_2 (- v_2) I_1}{y} \hat{j} = + \frac{\mu_0}{4\pi} \frac{2\lambda_2 v_2 I_1}{y} \hat{j} = + \frac{\mu_0}{4\pi} \frac{2 I_1 I_2}{y} \hat{j}$$

The force is directed along $+ Y$ direction *i.e.*, *away* from conductor 1.

As the force is directed away from *conductor 1, conductor 2 is repelled by conductor 1*. The force of *repulsion* is mutual.

(*ii*) *Therefore, two conductor carrying currents flowing in opposite directions i.e., two anti-parallel currents repel each other.*

Q. 7.17. An infinite straight wire lies along the X-axis. A steady current of 4.5 amperes flows through the wire along positive X-axis. An electron travels parallel to the X-axis in a direction opposite to the current and at a distance of 10 cm from the wire with a velocity of 3×10^6 cms/sec. Find the force experienced by the electron due to the magnetic field of the current in the wire.

Ans. The force acting on a charge q moving with velocity v along $- X$-axis due to the magnetic field of a current I flowing in an infinite straight wire in the $+ X$ direction at a distance y in the $+ Y$ direction is given by

$$\vec{F}_y = \frac{\mu_0}{4\pi} \frac{2qvI}{y} \hat{j}$$

i.e., the moving charge is *repelled away* from the current carrying wire.

But as the electron carries a negative charge it will be attracted towards the current carrying wire by the same force.

Now $\qquad \frac{\mu_0}{4\pi} = 10^{-7}; y = 0.1 \, \text{m}; q = 1.6 \times 10^{-19} \, \text{C}; v = 3 \times 10^4 \, \text{m/s}$

$$\therefore \qquad F_y = \frac{10^{-7} \times 2 \times 1.6 \times 10^{-19} \times 3 \times 10^4 \times 4.5}{0.1}$$

$$= 4.32 \times 10^{-20} \, \text{Newton.}$$

Q. 7.18. (*a*) Two current carrying parallel copper wires at 10 cm from each other exert a force of 2×10^{-4} Newton per metre on each other. If the current through one wire is 5 amp, find the current through the second wire.

(*b*) **Two parallel wires separated by a distance of 10 cm are each carrying a current of 5A. Calculate the force between them, if the current in both is in the same direction.**

(*G.N.D.U.*, 2009; *P.U.*, 2003; *H.P.U.*, 1997)

Ans. (*a*) The magnitude of the force between two current carrying wires per unit length is given by

$$F_{21} = \frac{\mu_0}{4\pi} \frac{2 I_1 I_2}{y}$$

Here $I_1 = 5$ amp; $y = 10 \, \text{cm} = 0.1 \, \text{m}$; $\frac{\mu_0}{4\pi} = 10^{-7}$; $I_2 = ?$; $F_{21} = 2 \times 10^{-4}$ Newton

$$\therefore \qquad 2 \times 10^{-4} = \frac{10^{-7} \times 2 \times 5 \times I_2}{0.1}$$

or $\qquad I_2 = \frac{2 \times 10^{-4} \times 0.1}{10^{-7} \times 2 \times 5} = 20 \, \text{Amp.}$

(b) The magnitude of the force between two current carrying wires per unit length is given by

$$F_{21} = \frac{\mu_0}{4\pi} \frac{2 I_1 I_2}{y}$$

Here $I_1 = 5A$; $I_2 = 5A$; $y = 10$ cm $= 0.1$ m; $\dfrac{\mu_0}{4\pi} = 10^{-7}$

$$\therefore \qquad F_{21} = \frac{10^{-7} \times 2 \times 5 \times 5}{0.1} = 50 \times 10^{-6} = 5 \times 10^{-5} \text{ Nm}^{-1}$$

As the current in the two wires is in the same direction, the force is of *attraction*.

Exercise. *What is the force per unit length between two parallel conductors each carrying current of 3 Amps. placed at a distance of 2 m?*

(*P.U.*, 2007)

Hint. $F_{21} = \dfrac{\mu_0}{4\pi} \dfrac{I_1 I_2}{y} = \dfrac{10^{-7} \times 3 \times 3}{2} = 4.5 \times 10^{-7} \text{ Nm}^{-1}$

Q. 7.19. Define an ampere and show that 1 coulomb is equal to 3×10^9 e.s.u. of charge.

(*G.N.D.U.*, 1992)

Ans. Ampere. *An ampere is the strength of that current which flowing through two very thin parallel, straight and very long conductors placed in vacuum at a distance of 1 metre from each other exert a mutual force of 2×10^{-7} Newton per metre length of the conductor.*

In C.G.S. system the unit of current is said to be 1 C.G.S. unit if 1 C.G.S. unit of charge flows in one second.

It is known as *e.s.u.* of current or *stat-ampere* if the charge is measured in *e.s.u.* or stat-coulomb.

It is known as *e.m.u.* of current or *ab-ampere* if the charge is measured in *e.m. units* or *ab-coulomb.*

$$\text{or} \quad \left. \begin{array}{ll} 1 & e.m.u. \text{ of current} \\ 1 & ab\text{-}ampere \end{array} \right] = 3 \times 10^{10} \left[\begin{array}{ll} & e.s.u. \text{ of current} \\ \text{or} & stat\text{-}ampere \end{array} \right.$$

Relation between ampere and e.s.u. of current. If F is the magnitude of the force experienced by a length l of a straight, thin line conductor when a current I_1 flows through it and a current I_2 flows through a similar neighbouring parallel conductor at a perpendicular distance r from it, then the force per unit length of the conductor

$$\frac{F}{l} = \frac{\mu_0}{4\pi} \frac{2 I_1 I_2}{r} \qquad \text{in S.I. units}$$

and

$$\frac{F}{l} = \frac{1}{c^2} \frac{2 I_1 I_2}{r} \qquad \text{in C.G.S. units}$$

If $I_1 = I_2 = I$ (say), then

$$\frac{F}{l} = \frac{\mu_0}{4\pi} \frac{2 I^2}{r} = 2 \times 10^{-7} \frac{I^2}{r} \qquad \text{in S.I. units} \quad ...(i)$$

and

$$\frac{F}{l} = \frac{1}{c^2} \frac{2 I^2}{r} = \frac{2 \times 10^{-20}}{9} \frac{I^2}{r} \qquad \text{in C.G.S. units} ...(ii)$$

If $I = 1$ Amp, $r = 1$ m and $l = 1$ m, then from (i)

$$F = 2 \times 10^{-7} \text{ Newton} \qquad ...(iii)$$

If $I = 1$ e.s.u., $r = 1$ cm and $l = 1$ cm, then from (ii)

$$F = \frac{2}{9} \times 10^{-20} \text{ dyne} \qquad ...(iv)$$

The e.s.u. of current is a much smaller unit and $F \propto I^2$

$$\therefore \quad \frac{F\,(\text{S.I.})}{F\,(\text{C.G.S.})} = \frac{(1\,\text{amp})^2}{(1\,\text{e.s.u.})^2} = \frac{2 \times 10^{-7}\,\text{Newton}}{\dfrac{2}{9} \times 10^{-20}\,\text{dyne}}$$

$$= \frac{2 \times 10^{-7} \times 10^5\,\text{dyne}}{\dfrac{2}{9} \times 10^{-20}\,\text{dyne}}$$

$$= 9 \times 10^{18}$$

or 1 Amp $= 3 \times 10^9$ e.s.u. of current (stat-ampere)

In S.I. ampere is the basic unit and the unit of charge *i.e.*, coulomb is defined as that much charge which passes through any cross-section of a conductor in one second when a current of 1 amp flows through it.

$\therefore$ 1 coulomb $= 3 \times 10^9$ e.s.u. of charge (or stat-coulomb).

Q. 7.20. Mark the correct answer.

(*i*) Which quantity is invariant under Lorentz transformation?

  (*a*) charge   (*b*) electric field intensity

  (*c*) magnetic induction   (*d*) Lorentz force   (*P.U.*, 1994)

(*ii*) The electric field in stationary frame S is found to be in the y-direction and has a magnitude E_y. The electric field as measured in moving frame S' will be

  (*a*) zero   (*b*) E_y/γ (*c*) γE_y (*d*) E_y

(*iii*) The electric field produced by a moving charge depends upon

  (*a*) value of charge   (*b*) velocity of charge

  (*c*) location of charge   (*d*) all of these   (*H.P.U.*, 1993)

(*iv*) Two parallel wires carrying currents flowing in opposite directions will

  (*a*) attract each other   (*b*) repel each other

  (*c*) neither attract nor repel

(*v*) The electric field produced by a uniformly moving charge is

  (*a*) conservative   (*b*) non-conservative

  (*c*) anything depending upon velocity

  (*d*) some time conservative, some time non-conservative.   (*H.P.U.*, 2000, 1996, 1994)

(*vi*) A body has charge q in stationary frame S. The value of charge measured in frame S' moving with velocity v relative to S is

  (*a*) $\dfrac{q}{\sqrt{1 - v^2/c^2}}$ (*b*) $\dfrac{q}{\sqrt{1 - \dfrac{v^2}{c^2}}}$ (*c*) zero   (*d*) q (*H.P.U.*, 1999)

Ans. (*i*) *a*   (*ii*) *c*   (*iii*) *d*   (*iv*) *b*   (*v*) *b*   (*vi*) *d*

EXERCISES

1. In the observer's frame $\vec{E} = 4\hat{i} + 7\hat{j}$. Calculate the electric field in a reference frame moving with a velocity $(6\hat{i} + 8\hat{j}) \times 10^7$ ms^{-1} relative to the observer.

$$[\text{Ans. } (3.952\hat{i} + 7.036\hat{j}) \text{ NC}^{-1}]$$

2. Find the speed with which the charge should move in order that electric field due to it at any point in front of it in its line of motion is one fourth of the electric field due to stationary charge at that point.

   [Hint. The magnitude of the electric field due to a moving charge at a point in the direction of motion $(\theta = 0)$ is given by

$$E_0 = \frac{q(1 - \beta^2)}{4\pi\varepsilon_0 \, r^2}$$

   For stationary charge $E = \dfrac{q}{4\pi\varepsilon_0 \, r^2}$

   $\therefore \quad \dfrac{E_0}{E} = 1 - \beta^2 = 1 - \dfrac{v^2}{c^2} = \dfrac{1}{4}$

   $\therefore \quad \dfrac{v^2}{c^2} = \dfrac{3}{4} \quad$ or $\quad v = \dfrac{\sqrt{3}}{2}c = 0.866c]$

3. A current of 20 Amp. flows through each of the two parallel long wires which are 4 cms apart. Compute the force exerted per unit length of each wire.   (*Meerut U.,* 2001)

   Hint. $F_{21} = \dfrac{\mu_0}{4\pi} \dfrac{2I_1 I_2}{y} = 10^{-7} \times 2 \times \dfrac{20 \times 20}{4 \times 10^{-2}} = 2 \times 10^{-3}$ Nm^{-1}

8

The Magnetic Field

Q. 8.1. Define magnetic induction field without the concept of magnetic poles. What are the C.G.S. and M.K.S. units of magnetic field and how are they related?

OR

Derive the relation between Tesla and Gauss.

(M.D.U., 2001; Pbi. U., 2007, 2002; Luck. U., 1995)

Ans. Magnetic induction field $\vec{B}$. The electric field vector $\vec{E}$ is defined as the force per unit positive stationary test charge. The direction of the electric field is the same as the direction of the force acting on the test charge. A test charge q at rest in the electric field $\vec{E}$ experiences a force $\vec{F_s}$ given by

$$\vec{F_s} = q\,\vec{E}$$

Suppose the test charge begins to move with a velocity $\vec{v}$ through a point P and experiences an additional force $\vec{F_m}$ (neglecting the force of gravity) which changes with magnitude as well as direction of $\vec{v}$ then a magnetic induction field $\vec{B}$ is said to exist at P.

If we vary the direction of $\vec{v}$ through the point P, keeping the magnitude of $\vec{v}$ constant, then in general, the magnitude of the force $\vec{F_m}$ changes but the direction always remains perpendicular to the direction of $\vec{v}$. For a particular direction of $\vec{v}$ as also for the opposite direction $-\vec{v}$ the force $\vec{F_m}$ = 0. This direction gives the direction of $\vec{B}$.

If now the direction of $\vec{v}$ is taken at right angles to this direction the force $\vec{F_m}$ is a maximum. The magnitude of the force depends upon the angle θ that the direction of $\vec{v}$ makes with the direction of $\vec{B}$, the charge q and the velocity v. It is given by

$$|\vec{F_m}| = qvB\sin\theta$$

Evidently for $\theta = 0$ (or π) *i.e.*, when the direction of $\vec{v}$ is the same as that of $\vec{B}$ (or opposite to it) $F_m = 0$ and for $\theta = \pi/2$ ($\sin\theta = 1$) F_m has a maximum value given by

$$(F_m)_{max} = qvB$$

The magnitude of $\vec{B}$ is, therefore, given by

$$B = \frac{(F_m)_{max}}{qv}$$

In the vector form the force $\vec{F_m}$ acting on a test charge q moving with velocity $\vec{v}$ in a magnetic inducting field $\vec{B}$ is given, in magnitude and direction by

$$\vec{F_m} = q\,\vec{v} \times \vec{B}$$

Hence a magnetic induction field is defined as that field in which a moving charge experiences a velocity dependent force given by

$$\vec{F_m} = q\,\vec{v} \times \vec{B}$$

Units. The magnitude of the force on a charge q moving with a velocity $\vec{v}$ in a direction perpendicular to the magnetic induction field $\vec{B}$ is given by

$$F = qvB$$

or

$$B = \frac{F}{qv}$$

when $F = 1$ Newton; $q = 1$ coulomb; $v = 1$ met/sec; $B = 1$.

The S.I. (or M.K.S.) unit of magnetic induction is known as a Tesla or Weber per metre^2.

Tesla. *A magnetic induction field has a strength of 1 Tesla if it exerts a force of 1 newton on a charge of 1 coulomb moving with a velocity of 1 metre per second in a direction perpendicular to that of the field.*

The C.G.S. unit of magnetic induction field is a *Gauss*.

Gauss. *A magnetic induction field has a strength of 1 Gauss if it exerts a force of 1 dyne on a charge of one ab-coulomb (or e.m.u.) moving with a velocity 1 cm per second in a direction perpendicular to that of the field.*

Relation

$$\text{Tesla} = \frac{\text{Newton}}{\text{coulomb} \times \text{metre sec}^{-1}}$$

$$\text{Gauss} = \frac{\text{dyne}}{\text{ab-coulomb} \times \text{cm sec}^{-1}}$$

∴

$$\frac{\text{Tesla}}{\text{Gauss}} = \frac{\text{Newton/dyne}}{(\text{coulomb/ab-coulomb}) \times (\text{metre}/\text{cm})} = \frac{10^5}{\dfrac{1}{10} \times 100} = 10^4$$

∴   1 Tesla $= 10^4$ Gauss

Q. 8.2. (*a*) What is Lorentz force in magnetostatics ? A test charge q moves with a velocity $\vec{v}$ through a region in which both electric field $\vec{E}$ and magnetic field $\vec{B}$ are present. What is the force experienced by the charge? (*G.N.D.U., 2008; Meerut. U., 2003, 2001; Pbi. U., 1991*)

(*b*) $\vec{F} = q\,(\vec{v} \times \vec{B}) = 0$. What does this indicate? (*Pbi. U., 1993*)

(*c*) Is any work done by a magnetic field on a moving charge? Give reasons.

(*G.N.D.U., 1991*)

OR

Show that no work is done by a magnetic field on a charged particle moving in it and that the magnetic force acting on a moving charged particle cannot increase its kinetic energy.

(*P.U., 2001; Kerala U., 2001*)

Ans. (a) Lorentz force law. The force on a test charge q when it moves with a velocity $\vec{v}$ through a region in which both electric field $\vec{E}$ and magnetic field $\vec{B}$ are present, is given by

$$\vec{F} = q\,\vec{E} + q\,(\vec{v} \times \vec{B})$$

This relation is known as *Lorentz force law* and the force $\vec{F}$ is known as *Lorentz force*.

When $\vec{E} = 0$, *i.e.*, only a magnetic field $\vec{B}$ is present, then

$$\vec{F} = q\,(\vec{v} \times \vec{B})$$

This equation gives the experimental law of interaction between the magnetic induction field $\vec{B}$ and the moving charge q.

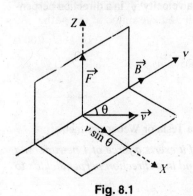

Fig. 8.1

The directions of vectors $\vec{F}$, $\vec{v}$ and $\vec{B}$ are shown in Fig. 8.1. It is clear that the direction of $\vec{F}$ is perpendicular to the plane containing the magnetic field vector $\vec{B}$ and the velocity vector $\vec{v}$. The magnitude of $\vec{F}$ is given by

$$F = qvB \sin \theta$$

where $v \sin \theta$ is the component of $\vec{v}$ normal to $\vec{B}$.

When $\theta = 0$, $F = 0$ and when $\theta = \pi/2$,

$$F = qvB$$

(b) $\vec{F} = q\,(\vec{v} \times \vec{B}) = 0$, if

(a) $q = 0$ *i.e.*, there is no charge in the magnetic field

(b) $(\vec{v} \times \vec{B}) = 0$. Now $(\vec{v} \times \vec{B}) = 0$ if

    (i) $\vec{v} = 0$ *i.e.*, the *charge is at rest*. A charge experiences a force in a magnetic field only when it is in motion.

    (ii) $\vec{B} = 0$ *i.e.*, there is no magnetic field.

    (iii) $\vec{v} \times \vec{B} = vB \sin \theta$ where θ is the angle between the direction of $\vec{B}$ and $\vec{v}$.

If $\theta = 0$ or π ; $\sin \theta = 0$, $v B \sin \theta = 0$ or $\vec{v} \times \vec{B} = 0$

Hence $\vec{F} = q\,\vec{v} \times \vec{B} = 0$ when the charge q moves in a direction parallel to that of the magnetic field.

To sum up $\vec{F} = q\vec{v} \times \vec{B} = 0$ indicates that $q = 0$, or $\vec{B} = 0$ or the direction of $\vec{v}$ is parallel to that of $\vec{B}$.

(c) Work done by a magnetic field on a moving charge. From the relation $\vec{F} = q\,(\vec{v} \times \vec{B})$ we find that when the charge moves in a steady magnetic field the magnetic force $\vec{F}$ is always at right angles to the velocity vector $\vec{v}$ as well as the field vector $\vec{B}$.

The work done by the force $\vec{F} = \vec{F}.d\vec{s} = \vec{F}.\vec{v}\,dt = 0$ as $\vec{F}.\vec{v} = 0$ because $\vec{F}$ is always perpendicular to $\vec{v}$

No work is, therefore, done by a static magnetic field on a moving charge or a moving charged particle.

Hence kinetic energy of a moving charge remains unchanged in a static magnetic field. Thus an applied magnetic field can only alter the direction of the velocity vector but it cannot change the speed of the charged particle and therefore cannot increase its kinetic energy.

Q. 8.3. (*a*) **What is the force experienced by a stationary charge in an electric field and a magnetic field?**   (*H.P.U.*, 2002; *P.U.*,1995, 1992)

(*b*) (*i*) **What is the force experienced by a charged particle moving along the direction of magnetic field? Give reasons for your answer.**   (*G.N.D.U.*, 2002; *P.U.*, 2000)

(*ii*) **What force will act on a proton moving parallel to magnetic field?**   (*H.P.U.*, 2001)

(*c*) **A proton is moving with velocity 10^8 m/s in a magnetic field of 6 Tesla making angle 30° with the direction of the field. Find the force experienced by it and the shape of the path.**

(*G.N.D.U.*, 2007)

Ans. (*a*) **Electric field.** When a stationary charge q is placed in an electric field $\vec{E}$ it experiences a force $\vec{F} = \vec{E} q$ in the direction of the field.

Magnetic field. A stationary charge experiences no force in a magnetic field. The force $\vec{F}$ acting on a charge q moving with a velocity $\vec{v}$ in a magnetic induction field $\vec{B}$ is given by

$$\vec{F} = q \, (\vec{v} \times \vec{B})$$

If $\vec{v} = 0 \quad \vec{F} = 0$

(*b*) (*i*) When a charged particle having a charge q moves with a velocity $\vec{v}$ in a magnetic field $\vec{B}$, the force $\vec{F}$ acting on it is given by

$$\vec{F} = q \, (\vec{v} \times \vec{B})$$

When the charged particle moves along the direction of magnetic field. $\vec{v} \times \vec{B} = 0$. Hence there is no force acting on the charged particle.

(*ii*) For the same reason there is no force acting on a proton moving parallel to the magnetic field.

(*c*) The force experienced by a charge q moving with a velocity $\vec{v}$ making an angle θ with the direction of the magnetic field $\vec{B}$ is given by

$$\vec{F} = q \left(\vec{v} \times \vec{B} \right) \text{ or } F = q \, v \, B \sin \theta$$

where $v \sin \theta$ is the component of $\vec{v}$ at right angles to $\vec{B}$

Given charge on the proton $q = 1.6 \times 10^{-19} C$; $v = 10^8$ m/s; $\theta = 30°$

∴ $F = 1.6 \times 10^{-19} \times 10^8 \times 6 \times \sin 30 = 1.6 \times 10^{-19} \times 10^8 \times 6 \times 0.5$

$$= 4.8 \times 10^{-11} \text{ N}$$

This force acts at right angles to the direction of motion of the proton, which, therefore, moves along a circular path. But the proton is also having a velocity component $v \cos \theta$ along the direction of the magnetic field. The proton will, therefore, also continue to move along its original path in this direction. Under the combined effect of the two motions, the path of the proton will be spiral in shape.

Q. 8.4. (*a*) **When a charged particle of charge q and mass m moving with velocity v is subjected to a magnetic field B in a direction perpendicular to v, show that the particle will describe a circular path and its angular frequency is given by**

$$\omega = B\,q/m$$

(*b*) (*i*) **An electron moving along X-axis is acted upon by a magnetic field along Y-axis. What is the direction of force on it?** (*G.N.D.U.*, 1995)

(*ii*) **State Fleming's left hand rule.** (*Kerala U.*, 2001)

(*c*) **An electron is not deflected while moving through a certain region of space. Can you say with certainty that there is no magnetic field in the region? Explain.** (*H.P.U.*, 1996)

Ans. (*a*) The force acting on a particle of charge q moving with a velocity v in a direction perpendicular to a magnetic induction field B is given by

$$F = q\,v\,B$$

This force always acts at right angles, to the direction of motion of the particle. The particle, therefore, moves along a circlar path of radius r so that the centripetal force $mr\omega^2$ is equal to qvB

∴ $mr\omega^2 = qvB = qr\omega B$ ($\because v = r\omega$)

or $\omega = B\,q/m$

(*b*) (*i*) The force acting on a positive charge q moving with a velocity $\vec{v}$ in a magnetic field $\vec{B}$ is given by $\vec{F} = q\,(\vec{v} \times \vec{B})$. The direction of the force $\vec{F}$ is given by the *right hand screw rule* for vector cross product or *Fleming's left hand rule* as stated in (*b*) (*ii*).

Thus if $\vec{v}$ acts along the $+ X$ axis, $\vec{B}$ along $+ Y$ axis, then according to the rule for vector cross product $\vec{F}$ will act along $+ Z$ axis as shown in Fig. 8.1 for a positive charge.

As the electron carries a negative charge, the direction of the force on it is along $- Z$ axis.

(*ii*) **Fleming's left hand rule.** *If we stretch the first finger, the middle finger and the thumb of left hand mutually perpendicular to each other such that the first finger points in the direction of magnetic field. The middle finger in the direction of motion of positive charge (or direction of electric current) then the thumb represents the direction of force experienced by the charged particle.*

(*c*) The force acting on a charged particle moving with a velocity v through a magnetic field $\vec{B}$ is given by

$$\vec{F} = q\,(\vec{v} \times \vec{B}) = qvB \sin \theta$$

where θ is the angle between the direction of $\vec{v}$ and that of $\vec{B}$.

When the electron is not deflected while moving through a certain region of space, there can be two reasons

(*i*) Magnetic field $B = 0$

(*ii*) $\sin \theta = 0$ or π *i.e.*, the electron moves in a direction parallel (or antiparallel) to that of the magnetic field.

Therefore, it cannot be said with certainty that the magnetic field $B = 0$.

Q. 8.5. A particle goes undeflected through a region of space containing a magnetic field. Can you say anything definitely about the charge on the particle?

(*Pbi. U.*, 2008, 2007; *H.P.U.*, 2002)

Ans. No. The force acting on a particle having a charge q moving with a velocity $\vec{v}$ in a magnetic field of intensity $\vec{B}$ is given by

$$\vec{F} = q\,(\vec{v} \times \vec{B}) = qvB \sin \theta$$

where θ is the angle between the directions of $\vec{v}$ and $\vec{B}$. A particle will go undeflected through a region of space containing a magnetic field if there is no force acting on it due to the field. This is possible if

(*i*) The particle carries no charge, $q = 0$

(*ii*) As the particle is moving through the magnetic field, $\vec{v} \neq 0$, $\vec{B} \neq 0$. Hence the only other reason is $\sin \theta = 0$ or $\theta = 0$ *i.e.*, the particle moves in a direction parallel to the magnetic field.

Thus we cannot say anything definitely about the charge on the particle.

Q. 8.6. (*a*) **A proton and a deutron have equal kinetic energies. Compare the radii of their paths when a magnetic field is applied normal to their orbits.** (*P.U.*, 1994)

(*b*) **An electron is accelerated by a potential difference of 5 KV and then enters a uniform magnetic field of 4×10^{-2} T perpendicular to its direction of motion. Determine the radius of the path taken by the electron in the magnetic field.** $e = 1.6 \times 10^{-19}$C, and $m = 9.1 \times 10^{-31}$ kg.

(*Nagpur U.*, 2002)

Ans. (*a*) Let mass of the proton $= m$

$\therefore$ Mass of the deutron $= 2m$ [Supposing mass of proton = mass of neutron]

                Velocity of the proton $= v_p$

                Velocity of the deutron $= v_d$

As their kinetic energies are equal; $\dfrac{1}{2} m v_p^2 = \dfrac{1}{2} 2m\, v_d^2$

or $v_p^2 = 2 v_d^2$ or $v_p = \sqrt{2}\, v_d$ $\therefore \dfrac{v_d}{v_p} = \dfrac{1}{\sqrt{2}}$

            Charge on the proton $=$ charge on the deutron $= e$

                 Magnetic field $= \vec{B}$

$\therefore$ Force on the proton due to magnetic field $= e\, \vec{v}_p \times \vec{B}$

                         $= e\, v_p\, B$ $[\because \vec{B}$ is normal to $\vec{v}$]

     Force on the deutron $= e\, v_d\, B$

     Radius of the circular orbit of proton $= r_p$

     Radius of the circular orbit of deutron $= r_d$

$\therefore$ $e\, v_p\, B = \dfrac{m\, v_p^2}{r_p}$

or $r_p = \dfrac{m\, v_p}{eB}$

and $e\, v_d\, B = \dfrac{2\, m\, v_d^2}{r_d}$

or $r_d = \dfrac{2\, m\, v_d}{eB}$

Hence $\dfrac{r_d}{r_p} = \dfrac{2\, v_d}{v_p} = \dfrac{2}{\sqrt{2}} = \sqrt{2}$

or $\qquad r_d = \sqrt{2}\; r_p.$

(b) Accelerating potential $V = 5\ KV = 5 \times 10^3$ volt

$$e = 1.6 \times 10^{-19}\ C\; ;\; m = 9.1 \times 10^{-31}\ kg\; ;\; B = 4 \times 10^{-2}\ T$$

If v is the velocity gained by the electron on being accelerated through a potential difference V, then

$$\frac{1}{2}\, m\, v^2 = e\, V$$

or $\qquad v = \sqrt{\dfrac{2\, eV}{m}} = \sqrt{\dfrac{2 \times 1.6 \times 10^{-19} \times 5 \times 10^3}{9.1 \times 10^{-31}}} = \sqrt{\dfrac{1.6}{9.1.}} \times 10^8$

$$= 0.42 \times 10^8 = 4.2 \times 10^7\ ms^{-1}$$

When it enters a uniform magnetic field B, perpendicular to the direction of motion of the electron,

Force on the electron $\vec{F} = e\,(\vec{v} \times \vec{B})$

or $\qquad F = e\, v\, B$

This force will act at right angles to $\vec{v}$, the electron will therefore, move in a circular path of radius r given by $\qquad F = \dfrac{mv^2}{r}$

$\therefore \qquad e\, v\, B = \dfrac{mv^2}{r}$

or $\qquad r = \dfrac{mv}{eB} = \dfrac{9.1 \times 10^{-31} \times 4.2 \times 10^7}{1.6 \times 10^{-19} \times 4 \times 10^{-2}} = 5.97 \times 10^{-3}\ m$

$$= 5.97\ mm.$$

Exercise. *An electron is moving in a field of magnetic induction of 0.5 Weber/met^2 with a velocity of 3×10^7 ms^{-1} along a circle. Find the radius of the circle and energy of motion. $m = 9.1 \times 10^{-31}$ kg ; $e = 1.6 \times 10^{-19}$ C.* (*Meerut U.*, 2000)

Hint. $\qquad r = \dfrac{mv}{eB} = \dfrac{9.1 \times 10^{-31} \times 3 \times 10^7}{1.6 \times 10^{-19} \times 0.5} = 3.4125 \times 10^{-4}\ m$

Energy of motion = kinetic energy $= \dfrac{1}{2}\, mv^2 = \dfrac{1}{2} \times 9.1 \times 10^{-31} \times 3 \times 10^7 \times 3 \times 10^7$

$$= 4.095 \times 10^{-16}\ J$$

Q. 8.7. A test charge $q = 3.2 \times 10^{-19}\ C$ is moving with a linear velocity $\vec{v} = (2\ \hat{i} + 2\ \hat{j})\ ms^{-1}$ in a combined electric and magnetic field of intensity $\vec{E} = (3\ \hat{i} + 6\ \hat{j} + \hat{k})\ NC^{-1}$ and $\vec{B} = (2\ \hat{j} + 3\ \hat{k})\ T$ respectively. Calculate the force experienced by the test charge.

(*Pbi. U.*, 2001)

Ans. Here $\qquad q = 3.2 \times 10^{-19}\ C\; ;\; \vec{v} = (2\ \hat{i} + 2\ \hat{j})\ ms^{-1}\; ;$

$$\vec{E} = (3\ \hat{i} + 6\ \hat{j} + \hat{k})\ NC^{-1}\; ;\; \vec{B} = (2\ \hat{j} + 3\ \hat{k})\ T$$

The force experienced by the test charge q moving with velocity $\vec{v}$ in a combined electric and magnetic field $\vec{E}$ and $\vec{B}$ respectively is given by

$$\vec{F} = q\,\vec{E} + q\,(\vec{v} \times \vec{B})$$

$\therefore \qquad \vec{F} = 3.2 \times 10^{-19}\,(3\ \hat{i} + 6\ \hat{j} + \hat{k}) + 3.2 \times 10^{-19}\,[(2\,\hat{i} + 2\,\hat{j}) \times (2\ \vec{j} + 3\ \vec{k})]$

$$= 3.2 \times 10^{-19} [(3\,\hat{i} + 6\,\hat{j} + \hat{k}) + (4\,\hat{k} - 6\,\hat{j} + 6\,\hat{i})]$$

$$= 3.2 \times 10^{-19} (9\,\hat{i} + 5\,\hat{k})\ N$$

Exercise. *A particle of charge 5 μC having velocity* $8 \times 10^6\ \hat{i}$ *enters a combined electric field* $10^6\ \hat{j}$ *and magnetic field* $0.2\ \hat{k}$. *What is the force acting on it?*   (*Kerala U.*, 2001)

Hint. $\vec{F} = q\,\vec{E} + q\,(\vec{v} \times \vec{B}) = 5 \times 10^{-6}\ (10^6\ \hat{j}) + 5 \times 10^{-6}\ (8 \times 10^6\ \hat{i} \times 0.2\ \hat{k})$

$$= 5\,\hat{j} - 8\,\hat{j} = -3\,\hat{j}\ \text{ i.e., a force of 3 N will act along } (-Y) \text{ direction.}$$

Q. 8.8. (*a*) **Explain the term magnetic flux and give its units in S.I.**   (*K.U.*, 1994)

(*b*) **Can magnetic flux linked with a coil placed in a uniform magnetic field be zero? Explain.**   (*G.N.D.U.*, 1996)

Ans. Magnetic flux. *Magnetic flux through a surface is defined as the total number of lines of magnetic induction passing through the surface.*

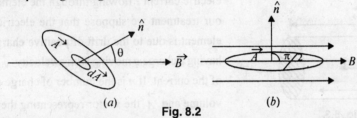

$$(a) \qquad\qquad\qquad\qquad (b)$$

Fig. 8.2

Consider an element of surface area $d\vec{A}$ of a surface area $\vec{A}$. Let $\hat{n}$ be a unit vector normal to the area element $d\vec{A}$, then $\hat{n}$ represents the direction of the area vector $d\vec{A}$ as shown in Fig. 8.2(*a*). The number of lines of magnetic induction over the area *i.e.*, the magnetic flux over area $d\vec{A}$ is given by

$$d\,\phi_B = \vec{B} \cdot d\vec{A} = \vec{B} \cdot \hat{n}\ dA \qquad\qquad \text{...(i)}$$

$\therefore$ Magnetic flux over the whole surface area $\vec{A} = \phi_B = \int_A \vec{B} \cdot \hat{n}\ dA$

If $\hat{n}$ makes an angle θ with $\vec{B}$, then $\vec{B} \cdot \hat{n} = B \cos\theta$

$$\therefore \qquad\qquad \phi_B = \int_A B \cos\theta\ dA$$

If $\vec{B}$ is uniform over the area $\vec{A}$, then

$$\phi_B = B \cos\theta \int_A dA = B \cos\theta\ A = BA \cos\theta \qquad\qquad \text{...(ii)}$$

or magnetic flux $\phi_B = \vec{B} \cdot \vec{A}$ ...(iii)

When $\theta = 0,\ \vec{B} \cdot \hat{n} = B \cos\theta = B$

and $d\phi_B = \vec{B} \cdot \hat{n}\ dA = B\ dA$

$$\therefore \qquad\qquad B = \frac{d\,\phi_B}{dA}$$

B is thus known as *magnetic flux density* and is defined as magnetic flux per unit area.

Units. The S.I. unit of magnetic induction B is *Tesla* and that of area dA metre^2.

The units of magnetic flux is, therefore, *Tesla metre²*. It is also known as Weber

1 Weber = Tesla metre²

(*b*) When $\theta = \dfrac{\pi}{2}$, cos $\theta = 0$. In such a case, according to relation (*ii*) $\phi_B = 0$.

The magnetic flux linked with a coil placed in a uniform magnetic induction field can, therefore, be zero when $\theta = \dfrac{\pi}{2}$ *i.e.*, when the unit normal to the area makes an angle $\pi/2$ with the field vector $\vec{B}$. In such a case no line of magnetic induction cuts through the area, as shown in Fig. 8.2(*b*).

Q. 8.9. Derive an expression for the force acting on a small current element placed in a uniform magnetic field. Hence find the force on a long straight conductor carrying current and on a current loop.

Ans. Force on a current element. Consider a current element of length $d\vec{l}$ in the direction of electric current I flowing through the element. To simplify our treatment we suppose that the electric current in the element is due to the drift of positive charge carriers each having a charge q moving with a velocity $\vec{v}$ in the direction of the current. If n is the number of charge carriers per unit volume and $\vec{A}$ the vector representing the cross-sectional area, then

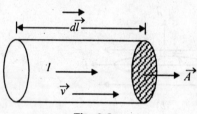

Fig. 8.3

$$I = nq\,(\vec{A}\cdot\vec{v})$$

When a magnetic induction field $\vec{B}$ is applied, each charge carrier experiences a force given by

$$\vec{F} = q\,(\vec{v}\times\vec{B})$$

The number of charge carriers in the element of length $\vec{dl}$

$$= n\,(\vec{A}\cdot\vec{dl})$$

where $\vec{A}\cdot\vec{dl}$ gives the volume of the element.

∴ Force on the current element $\vec{dF} = qn\,(\vec{A}\cdot\vec{dl})\,(\vec{v}\times\vec{B})$

If the charge carrier travels the vector distance $\vec{dl}$ in a time dt, then

$$\vec{v} = \dfrac{\vec{dl}}{dt}$$

∴

$$d\vec{F} = qn\,(\vec{A}\cdot\vec{dl})\left(\dfrac{\vec{dl}}{dt}\times\vec{B}\right)$$

$$= qn\left(\vec{A}\cdot\dfrac{\vec{dl}}{dt}\right)(\vec{dl}\times\vec{B})$$

$$= qn\,(\vec{A}\cdot\vec{v})\,(\vec{dl}\times\vec{B})$$

$$= I\,\vec{dl}\times\vec{B} \qquad\qquad ...(i)$$

Thus the magnetic force $d\vec{F}$ on a *current element* $I\,\vec{dl}$ placed in a magnetic induction field $\vec{B}$ is given by

$$d\vec{F} = I\,\vec{dl} \times \vec{B}$$

The magnitude of this force $dF = Idl\,B\sin\theta$ where θ is the angle between the vectors $\vec{dl}$ and $\vec{B}$. If $\theta = \pi/2$

$$dF = I\,dl\,B$$

Force acting on a straight conductor. The force experienced by a straight conductor of length $\vec{l}$ placed in a *uniform* magnetic induction field $\vec{B}$ is given by

$$\vec{F} = \int_l I\,d\vec{l} \times \vec{B}$$

$$= I\left(\int_l \vec{dl}\right) \times \vec{B} = I\,\vec{l} \times \vec{B}$$

as $\vec{B}$ is uniform throughout the length of the wire the element $\vec{dl}$ will have the same direction at every point of the length $\vec{l}$

The magnitude of this force is given by

$$F = I\,l\,B\sin\theta$$

where θ is the angle between the vectors $\vec{l}$ and $\vec{B}$. When $\theta = 0$, $F = 0$ and when $\theta = \dfrac{\pi}{2}$;

$F = I\,l\,B$ and is a maximum.

The direction of the force $\vec{F}$ is perpendicular to the plane containing the vectors $\vec{l}$ and $\vec{B}$ given by right hand screw rule for vector products.

Force on a current loop. Suppose a closed loop carrying current I is placed in a uniform external magnetic field $\vec{B}$ as shown in Fig. 8.4. To find the force acting on it, let $\vec{dl}$ be a small element of the loop. The magnetic force acting on this element is given by

$$d\vec{F} = I\,\vec{dl} \times \vec{B}$$

$\therefore$ Total force on the loop $\vec{F} = \oint I\,d\vec{l} \times \vec{B}$

As $\vec{B}$ is uniform $\qquad \vec{F} = I\left(\oint \vec{dl}\right) \times \vec{B}$

Now $\oint \vec{dl}$ is the vector sum of the elements of the loop from the beginning to the end and according to the polygon law of vectors it is given by the vector drawn from the initial to the final point. But for a closed loop the initial and the final points are the same.

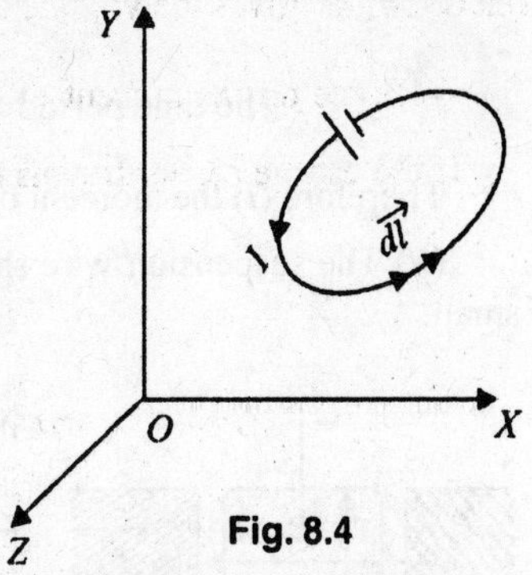

$\therefore \qquad\qquad \oint \vec{dl} = 0$

Hence $\qquad\qquad \vec{F} = I\left(\oint \vec{dl}\right) \times \vec{B} = 0$

Fig. 8.4

In other words *a closed steady current loop does not experience any magnetic force when placed in a uniform steady magnetic field.*

However, if the magnetic field is non-uniform over the dimensions of the loop, there will be a net magnetic force on the loop.

Q. 8.10. A one metre long wire carrying a current of 5 Amp. is placed at an angle of 30° with the direction of a uniform magnetic field of one Tesla. Find the magnitude and direction of the force on the wire.

(*Luck. U.*, 1995)

Ans. The force experienced by a straight conductor of length $\vec{l}$ placed in a uniform magnetic induction field $\vec{B}$ is given by

$$\vec{F} = I\,\vec{l} \times \vec{B}$$

The magnitude of the force $F = I\,l\,B \sin\theta$ where θ is the angle between the vectors $\vec{l}$ and $\vec{B}$.

Here $I = 5$ Amp; $l = 1$ metre; $B = 1$ Tesla ; $\theta = 30°$

$\therefore$
$$F = 5 \times 1 \times 1 \times \sin 30 = 5 \times \frac{1}{2} = 2.5 \text{ Newton}$$

The direction of force is perpendicular to the plane containing $\vec{l}$ and $\vec{B}$ given by the right hand screw rule for cross product of vectors.

Q. 8.11. (*a*) **What is the difference between dead beat and ballistic galvanometer? State conditions under which the galvanometer acts as a ballistic galvanometer. Give the theory of a moving coil ballistic galvanometer and deduce the relation** $q = k_b\,\theta$ **for the charge flowing through it.**

(*Nagpur U.*, 2002, 2001; *Meerut U.*, 2007, 2002; *Kerala U.*, 2001; *Gauhati U.*, 2000; *Magadh U.*, 1996; *A.U.*, 1995, 1994; *Luck. U.*, 1993; *K.U.*, 1992; *Cal. U.*, 1992; *G.N.D.U.*, 1991)

(*b*) **If the charge sensitivity is equal to current sensitivity of a ballistic galvanometer, what is the periodic time?** (*Nagpur U.*, 2002)

Ans. (*a*) **Dead beat and ballistic galvanometer.** An ordinary galvanometer is used to *measure steady current.* It is called a *dead beat galvanometer.*

A ballistic galvanometer is used to measure the total charge that passes through it in a given time not as steady current but as a sudden discharge. Such sudden discharges are met with in the discharging of a capacitor and in electromagnetic induction.

Conditions for a galvanometer to be ballistic. A ballistic galvanometer should have the following special features.

1. The moving system should not move appreciably from its position of rest during the time the discharge passes through it. To achieve this its time period should be large.

The time period $T = 2\pi\sqrt{\dfrac{I}{c}}$

Therefore (*i*) the moment of inertia I of the moving system must be large and

(*ii*) The suspension wire should be long and fine so that the couple per unit angular twist c is small.

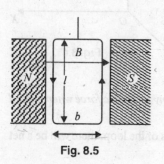

2. As the moving system suffers a deflection due to the impulse of the whole charge it receives a kick, and hence it is the first throw which is proportional to the charge. Therefore, in such instruments damping must be very small. In order to reduce this damping in a moving coil type ballistic galvanometer:

(*i*) The coil is wound over a non-conducting frame of ivory, or ebonite, etc. to avoid eddy currents and consequent damping.

(*ii*) The soft iron core which damps the motion of the coil is not used.

Fig. 8.5

The construction of the moving coil ballistic galvanometer is similar to the ordinary moving coil galvanometer except for the modification given above.

Theory of ballistic galvanometer. Let n be the number of turns in the coil; l the length of its vertical side, b its breadth and B the magnetic field in which it is suspended.

Let there be a current i at any instant, then

Force on each vertical wire $= i\,l\,B$

$\therefore$ Force on each vertical side $= n\,i\,l\,B$

If this current remains constant for a very small time dt, then

Impulse of force $= n\,l\,B\,i\,dt$

$\therefore$ Total change in momentum during the time the whole charge q passes through it.

$$= \int n\,l\,B\,i\,dt = nl\,B\int i\,dt = n\,l\,B\,q$$

This change in momentum causes a rotation of the coil about the axis of suspension producing an angular momentum given by

Angular momentum $= nl\,Bq\,b = n\,BA\,q$

where $\qquad\qquad\qquad A =$ area of the coil $= lb$

The angular momentum $= I\omega$ where I is the moment of inertia and ω the angular velocity

$$I\omega = n\,BA\,q \qquad\qquad\qquad\qquad ...(i)$$

Due to the angular velocity the coil possesses a kinetic energy $\dfrac{1}{2}I\,\omega^2$ and is brought to rest by performing work in twisting the suspension wire. If c is the restoring couple per unit angular twist, then

Couple for a twist $\theta = c\theta$

and work done for a further small deflection $d\theta$

$$= c\theta \cdot d\theta$$

$\therefore$ Total work done in twisting the suspension wire from 0 to θ.

$$= \int_0^\theta c\theta \cdot d\theta = \frac{1}{2}c\theta^2$$

where θ is the deflection of the coil when whole of the kinetic energy has been used up in producing the twist.

$\therefore \qquad\qquad\qquad \dfrac{1}{2}I\omega^2 = \dfrac{1}{2}c\theta^2$

or $\qquad\qquad\qquad I\omega^2 = c\theta^2 \qquad\qquad\qquad\qquad ...(ii)$

If T is the time period of torsional vibrations of the coil when no current passes through it, then

$$T = 2\pi\sqrt{\frac{I}{c}}$$

or $\qquad\qquad\qquad I = \dfrac{T^2 c}{4\pi^2} \qquad\qquad\qquad\qquad ...(iii)$

Multiplying (ii) and (iii), we have

$$I^2\omega^2 = \frac{c^2 T^2\theta^2}{4\pi^2}$$

or $I\omega = \dfrac{cT\theta}{2\pi}$ ...(iv)

Comparing (i) and (iv), we have

$$nABq = \dfrac{cT\theta}{2\pi}$$

or $q = \dfrac{cT}{2\pi n\,AB}\,\theta = \dfrac{T}{2\pi}\,\dfrac{c}{nAB}\,\theta = k_b\,\theta$

The quantity $\dfrac{c}{nAB}$ is known as the *current sensitivity* and the quantity $\dfrac{T}{2\pi}\cdot\dfrac{c}{nAB}$ is known as the *charge sensitivity* of the ballistic galvanometer.

$\therefore$ Charge sensitivity $= \dfrac{T}{2\pi}$ current sensitivity.

The charge sensitivity of a ballistic galvanometer is also denoted as k_b and is called the *constant of the ballistic galvanometer*.

(b) Charge sensitivity $= \dfrac{T}{2\pi} \times$ current sensitivity.

When charge sensitivity is equal to current sensitivity, $\dfrac{T}{2\pi} = 1$ or Periodic time (Time period)

$T = 2\pi$ sec.

Q. 8.12. What is the function of iron core in a moving coil galvanometer? (*Pbi. U.*, 2003)

Ans. In a moving coil *dead beat* galvanometer the current carrying coil moves around a soft iron core, thereby inducing an eddy current in it. This induced current opposes the motion of the coil thereby causing damping and making the galvanometer dead beat.

No such iron core is used in a ballistic galvanometer.

Q. 8.13. (a) Define current sensitivity of a moving coil galvanometer? (*Meerut U.*, 2003)

(b) When 0.1 C of charge is passed through a moving coil ballistic galvanometer a deflection of 30 mm is observed on a scale 1 metre away. Time period of the coil is 12 s. Find current sensitivity of the galvanometer. (*K.U.*, 1991)

Ans. (a) **Current sensitivity.** For an ordinary moving coil galvanometer, the current

$$i = \dfrac{c}{nAB}\,\theta$$

when c, n, A, B and θ have their usual meanings.

$\therefore$ $\dfrac{i}{\theta} = \dfrac{c}{nAB}$ ...(i)

This measures the *current sensitivity* and is defined as the current required to produce a unit deflection. (*i.e.* $\theta = 1$ radian)

For a moving coil ballistic galvanometer, the charge

$$q = \dfrac{cT}{(2\pi nAB)}\,\theta = \dfrac{T}{2\pi}\,\dfrac{c}{nAB}\,\theta$$

$\therefore$ $\dfrac{q}{\theta} = \dfrac{T}{2\pi}\,\dfrac{c}{nAB}$ ...(ii)

This measures the *charge sensitivity* and is defined as the charge required to produce a unit deflection (*i.e.* $\theta = 1$ radian)

According to Eq. (*i*) $\dfrac{c}{nAB}$ = current sensitivity. Therefore, Eq. (*ii*) can be put as

Charge sensitivity $\qquad = \dfrac{T}{2\pi}$ current sensitivity

(*b*) Here Charge $\qquad q = 0.1$ C

Deflection $\qquad \theta = \tan\theta = \dfrac{30 \text{ mm}}{1 \text{ metre}} = 0.03 \qquad$ [As θ is small $\tan\theta = \theta$ (radian)]

Time period $\qquad T = 12$ s

$\therefore\quad$ Charge sensitivity $\dfrac{q}{\theta} = \dfrac{0.1}{.03} = \dfrac{10}{3}$ coulomb/unit angular deflection

But charge sensitivity $= \dfrac{T}{2\pi}$ current sensitivity

$\therefore\quad$ Current sensitivity $= \dfrac{2\pi}{T}$ charge sensitivity

$\qquad\qquad = \dfrac{2\pi}{12} \times \dfrac{10}{3} = 1.75$ Amp/unit angular deflection.

Exerice. *A 0.2 µF capacitor is charged to 4 volt. It gives a deflection of 10 cm. when discharged through a ballistic galvanometer. If the time period of the galvanometer is 10 sec. Calculate the current sensitivity.* (*Gharwal U.*, 2000)

Hint. $\qquad\qquad q = CV = 0.2 \times 10^{-6} \times 4 = 0.8 \times 10^{-6}$ C ; $\theta = 10$ cm $= 0.1$ m

$\therefore\qquad$ Charge sensitivity $= \dfrac{q}{\theta} = \dfrac{0.8 \times 10^{-6}}{0.1} = 8 \times 10^{-6}$ C/m

$\qquad$ Current sensitivity $= \dfrac{2\pi}{T}$ charge sensitivity

$\qquad\qquad = \dfrac{2 \times 3.14 \times 8 \times 10^{-6}}{10} = 5 \times 10^{-6}$ A/m $= 5$ µA/m.

Q. 8.14. (*a*) **Show mathematically how the observed throw can be corrected for damping in a ballistic galvanometer.** (*Nagpur U.*, 2001; *Kerala U.*, 2001)

(*b*) (*i*) **The first and eleventh throw of a ballistic galvanometer are 15 cm and 12 cm respectively. Calculate the value of logarithmic decrement.** (*K.U.*, 1992; *A.U.*, 1994)

(*ii*) **The observed first throw is a ballistic galvanometer is 10 cm. If logarithmic decrement is 0.5, what is the corrected throw?** (*Nagpur. U.*, 2001)

Ans. (*a*) **Damping.** In the theory of the ballistic galvanometer it has been supposed that the whole of the kinetic energy of the moving system is used up in twisting the suspension fibre.In practice, however, the motion of the coil is opposed by (*i*) resistance of air, and (*ii*) induced *e.m.f.* in the coil. The amplitude of successive oscillations goes on decreasing and this effect is known as *damping*.

Need for damping correction. The first throw of the ballistic galvanometer is always smaller than what it would have been in the ideal case when there is no damping and a correction must be applied to it to get the correct value.

When successive values of θ are observed to the left and right as the coil oscillates, it is found that

$$\frac{\theta_1}{\theta_2} = \frac{\theta_2}{\theta_3} = \frac{\theta_3}{\theta_4} = \dots\dots = d$$

where the constant d is called the *decrement* of the swing and is defined as the ratio of two successive deflections, one to the right and the other to the left.

If $d = e^\lambda$

then $\lambda = \log_e d$

Here λ is known as the **logarithmic decrement**.

Damping correction. When there is no damping, the motion of the coil is simple harmonic and can be represented by the projection of a point P moving in a circle on a fixed straight line, say AB.

In this case the amplitude of successive oscillations will be

$$OA, OB, OA, \text{ etc.}$$

When there is damping, the amplitude of successive oscillations goes on decreasing at a constant rate. It is clear from Fig. 8.6 that the shrinkage (decrease in amplitude) from θ_1 to θ_2 takes place in half of a vibration or one oscillation. Since the impulse is given to the moving system when it was in the mean position, the shrinkage that actually takes place before the first throw θ_1 is observed, is in a quarter vibration or half an oscillation.

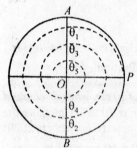

Fig. 8.6

Now for one oscillation, the shrinkage is given by the relation

$$\frac{\theta_1}{\theta_2} = \frac{\theta_2}{\theta_3} = \frac{\theta_3}{\theta_4} = e^\lambda$$

∴ For two oscillations the shrinkage is

$$\frac{\theta_1}{\theta_3} = \frac{\theta_1}{\theta_2} \times \frac{\theta_2}{\theta_3} = e^\lambda \times e^\lambda = e^{2\lambda}$$

Hence for half an oscillation the shrinkage is $e^{\lambda/2}$

If θ_0 is the corrected throw, then

$$\frac{\theta_0}{\theta_1} = e^{\lambda/2}$$

or
$$\theta_0 = \theta_1\, e^{\lambda/2} = \theta_1 \left(1 + \frac{\lambda}{2} + \frac{\lambda^2}{4\,(2\,!)} + ...\right)$$

$$= \theta_1 \left(1 + \frac{\lambda}{2}\right)$$

as λ is small and its squares and higher powers can be neglected.

Hence the corrected formula for the moving coil ballistic galvanometer is

$$q = \frac{cT}{2\pi nAB}\, \theta \left(1 + \frac{\lambda}{2}\right)$$

In practice the value of λ is found by observing θ_{11} and θ_1, i.e., the first throw and the throw after 10 oscillations. Then

$$\frac{\theta_1}{\theta_{11}} = e^{10\lambda}$$

or
$$\lambda = \frac{1}{10} \log_e \frac{\theta_1}{\theta_{11}}$$

(b) (i)   First throw $\theta_1 = 15$ cm

Eleventh throw $\theta_{11} = 12$ cm

$\therefore$ Logarithmic decrement $\lambda = \dfrac{1}{10} \log_e \dfrac{\theta_1}{\theta_{11}} = \dfrac{1}{10} \log_e \dfrac{15}{12} = \dfrac{1}{10} \times 0.2231 = 0.0223$

(*ii*) First throw $\theta_1 = 10$ cm ; logarithmic decrement $\lambda = 0.5$

Using the relation $\theta_0 = \theta_1\, e^{\lambda/2}$

$$\theta_0 = 10 \times e^{0.5/2} = 10 \times e^{0.25}$$

or $\qquad\qquad\qquad In\ \theta_0 = In\ 10 + 0.25 = 2.3026 + 0.25 = 2.5526$

$\therefore$ $\qquad\qquad\qquad \theta_0 = 12.84$ cm

Using approximate formula $\theta_0 = \theta_1\left(1 + \dfrac{\lambda}{2}\right)$

$$\theta_0 = 10\left(1 + \dfrac{0.5}{2}\right) = 10 \times 1.25 = 12.5 \text{ cm.}$$

Q. 8.15. (*a*) **A capacitor charged to 2 volts is discharged through a ballistic galvanometer. Calculate the capacitance of the capacitor using the data.**

Galvanometer scale distance = 1 metre; θ_1 = 60 mm, θ_{11} = 40 mm; mass of the coil = 0.007 kg, mean length of the coil = 0.06 m, mean breadth = 0.017 m, number of turns = 600, period = 5 sec and magnetic field = 2 × 10^{-7} Tesla.

(*b*) **A capacitor charged to 2 volts is discharged through a ballistic galvanometer. The corrected first throw is 9.6 cm and figure of merit of the galvanometer is 2.2 × 10^{-8} A/cm, periodic time 12 sec. Find the capacity of the capacitor.** (*Nagpur U.*, 2002, 2001)

Ans. First throw $\theta_1 = 60$ mm Eleventh throw $\theta_{11} = 40$ mm

$\therefore$ Logarithmic decrement $\lambda = \dfrac{1}{10} \log_e \dfrac{\theta_1}{\theta_{11}} = \dfrac{1}{10} \log_e \dfrac{60}{40} = 0.04055$

Distance of the scale $= 1$ m

$\therefore$ Corrected throw $\theta_0 = \dfrac{0.06}{1}\left(1 + \dfrac{\lambda}{2}\right) = 0.06\ (1 + 0.02028) = 0.06122$ radian

Mean length of the coil $l = 0.06$ m; breadth $b = 0.017$ m; mass $m = 0.007$ kg

$\therefore$ Moment of inertia $I = \dfrac{mb^2}{12} = \dfrac{0.007 \times 0.017 \times 0.017}{12}$ kg m^2

Time period $T = 2\pi\sqrt{\dfrac{I}{c}}$ or $c = \dfrac{4\pi^2 I}{T^2}$

Charge flowing through the ballistic galvanometer

$$q = \dfrac{cT}{2\pi nAB}\ \theta\left(1 + \dfrac{\lambda}{2}\right) = \dfrac{4\pi^2 I}{T^2}\ \dfrac{T}{2\pi nAB}\ \theta\left(1 + \dfrac{\lambda}{2}\right) = \dfrac{2\pi}{T}\ \dfrac{I}{nAB}\ \theta_0$$

$$= \dfrac{2 \times \pi}{5}\ \dfrac{0.007 \times 0.017 \times 0.017}{12 \times 600 \times 0.06 \times 0.017 \times 2 \times 10^{-2}} \times 0.06122$$

$$= 1.06 \times 10^{-6} \text{ coulomb.}$$

Capacitance $C = \dfrac{q}{V} = \dfrac{1.06 \times 10^{-6}}{2} = 0.53 \times 10^{-6}$ Farad $= 0.53$ microfarad.

(b)   Figure of merit = Current sensitivity = 2.2×10^{-8} A/cm

$\therefore$ Charge sensitivity $k_B = \dfrac{T}{2\pi} \times$ current sensitivity

$$= \frac{12 \times 7 \times 2.2 \times 10^{-8}}{2 \times 22} = 4.2 \times 10^{-8} \text{ C/cm.}$$

Deflection $\theta = 9.6$ cm

$\therefore$ Charge on the capacitor $q = k_B\,\theta = 9.6 \times 4.2 \times 10^{-8}$ C

Voltage applied V = 2 volt = 4.032×10^{-7} C

$\therefore$ Capacity of the capacitor $C = \dfrac{q}{V} = \dfrac{4.032 \times 10^{-7}}{2}$

$$= 2.016 \times 10^{-7} \text{ F} = 0.2 \ \mu F \text{ (Approx.)}$$

Q. 8.16. (*a*) **State and prove Ampere's circuital law of magnetic field. Deduce Ampere's law in the form $\oint \vec{B}.d\,\vec{l} = \mu_0\,I$ where the symbols have usual meaning.**

(*b*) **Show that the line integral of the magnetic field over a closed path is independent of the shape of the path.**   *Nagpur U.*, 2002; *G.N.D.U.*, 2006, 2004, 2001, 2000, 1997, 1995

Meerut U., 2006, 2001, 1994; *Pbi. U.*, 2007, 2006, 2001; *H.P.U.* 2007,

2001, 1997, 1995; *P.U.*, 1995, 1994; *Luck. U.*, 1995; *A.U.*, 1995, 1994)

Ans. Ampere's circuital law. Ampere's circuital law states that '*The line integral of a magnetic induction field vector along any closed path is equal to* μ_0 *times the net current enclosing the path*'.

If a magnetic field $\vec{B}$ encloses a current I flowing through a straight conducting wire in a direction perpendicular to the plane of the closed path and $\vec{dl}$ a vector element of the path, then

$$\oint \vec{B} \cdot \vec{dl} = \mu_0\ I$$

where $\oint \vec{B} \cdot \vec{dl}$ is the line integral of the magnetic field for the closed path.

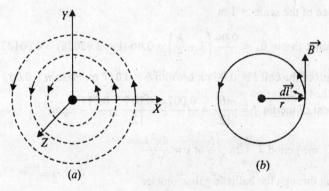

(a)   (b)

Fig. 8.7

Ampere's line integral theorem. The magnetic induction field $\vec{B}$ due to an infinitely long straight conductor carrying a current I at a point lying at a perpendicular distance r from it is given by

$\dfrac{\mu_0}{4\pi}\,\dfrac{2I}{r}$. For proof see **Q. 8.25** Eq. (*iii*). The direction of the field is everywhere perpendicular to a plane containing the wire and the point. The sense of the direction of $\vec{B}$ is given by the right hand screw rule.

Consider a straight wire carrying a current I perpendicular to the plane of the paper flowing towards the reader *i.e.*, along the $+ Z$ direction. The magnetic lines of force lie in the X-Y plane and are counter clockwise as shown in Fig. 8.7(*a*). If we draw circle with the point where the wire leaves the paper as centre and radius r, then the circumference of the circle is a line of constant magnetic induc-

tion $B = \dfrac{\mu_0}{4\pi} \dfrac{2I}{r}$ and its direction is along the tangent to the circle in the plane of the paper counter clockwise as shown in Fig. 8.7 (*b*).

A small element $d\vec{l}$ of the circular line of constant magnetic induction is also tangential to the circle so that the vectors $\vec{B}$ and $d\vec{l}$ are parallel

$\therefore$ $$\vec{B} \cdot \vec{dl} = B \, dl \cos\theta = B \, dl$$

The value of the line integral for the whole closed path is given by

$$\oint \vec{B} \cdot \vec{dl} = B \oint dl = B \, 2\pi r$$

Since B is constant. Substituting the value of $B = \dfrac{\mu_0}{4\pi} \dfrac{2I}{r}$, we have

$$\oint \vec{B} \cdot \vec{dl} = \dfrac{\mu_0}{4\pi} \dfrac{2I}{r} 2\pi r = \mu_0 \, I \qquad \qquad ...(i)$$

The line integral of the magnetic field is independent of the radius of the path. This means that the value of line integral of the magnetic field along all circular paths of any radius would be the same and equal to $\mu_0 I$.

(*b*) Ampere's law independent of the shape of the path. The relation $\oint \vec{B} \cdot \vec{dl} = \mu_0 \, I$ holds

not only for a circular path but for any arbitrary closed path which encircles the wire carrying current as shown in Fig. 8.8. As the wire carries a steady current in the $+ Z$ direction, the magnetic field due to it lies entirely in XY plane. We shall, therefore, consider the closed path to also lie in the XY plane

$\therefore$ $$\vec{B} \cdot \vec{dl} = B \, dl \cos\theta$$

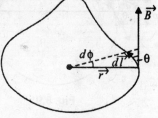

Fig. 8.8

where $dl \cos\theta$ is the component of the line element $\vec{dl}$ along the direction of $\vec{B}$, θ being the angle between the vector $\vec{dl}$ and the vector $\vec{B}$ which has a direction perpendicular to the radius vector $\vec{r}$. Thus $dl \cos\theta$ is perpendicular to $\vec{r}$ and if $\vec{dl}$ subtends an angle $d\phi$ at the wire, then

$$d\phi = \dfrac{dl \cos\theta}{r}$$

$\therefore$ $$\vec{B} \cdot \vec{dl} = B \, dl \cos\theta = Br \, d\phi = \dfrac{\mu_0}{4\pi} \dfrac{2I}{r} r \, d\phi = \dfrac{\mu_0}{4\pi} 2I \, d\phi \qquad ...(ii)$$

Hence $$\oint \vec{B} \cdot \vec{dl} = \dfrac{\mu_0}{4\pi} 2I \oint d\phi = \dfrac{\mu_0}{4\pi} 2I \cdot 2\pi = \mu_0 \, I \qquad ...(iii)$$

as $\oint d\phi$, the angle subtended by a closed path at a point inside it is 2π.

The relation $\oint \vec{B} \cdot d\vec{l} = \mu_0 \, I$ is known as *Ampere's line integral theorem or Ampere's circuital law*. It is similar to Gauss's law in electrostatics.

It is clear from the expression $\oint \vec{B} \cdot d\vec{l} = \mu_0 \, I$ that the line integral only depends upon the value of the current and is *independent of the shape of the path.*

If the path goes round the current carrying conductor N times, then $\oint \vec{B} . d\vec{l} = N \mu_0 I$.

Ampere's law in terms of current density. If the current I is constituted by a current distribution given by the current density function $\vec{J}$, then

$$I = \iint \vec{J} . ds$$

and Equation (i) or (ii) can be written as

$$\oint \vec{B} . d\vec{l} = \mu_0 \iint \vec{J} . ds$$

Q. 8.17. (a) Show that the line integral of the magnetic field around any path that does not enclose a current carrying wire is always zero. (G.N.D.U., 1994)

(b) Using Ampere's law obtain an expression for the magnetic field due to a current carrying straight conductor of infinite length. (P.U., 2007, Meerut. U., 2006, 2001; Kan. U., 1996)

(c) A long wire carries a current of 5 m A. Find the line integral of $\vec{B}$ around the path (of radius 10 cm) enclosing the wire. $\mu_0/4\pi = 10^{-7}$ S.I. units. (Pbi. U., 1999)

Ans. (a) Line integral when the closed path does not enclose current. Consider a closed path lying entirely outside the current which flows towards the reader out of the plane of the paper at a point P.

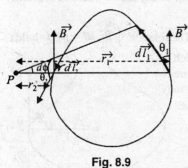

Fig. 8.9

Select a pair of line elements $d\vec{l_1}$ and $d\vec{l_2}$ which subtend the same angle $d\phi$ at the current carrying wire and let their vector distances from P be $\vec{r_1}$ and $\vec{r_2}$ respectively, then the angle θ_1 between $d\vec{l_1}$ and $\vec{B}$ is acute ($< 90°$) and the angle θ_2 between $d\vec{l_2}$ and $\vec{B}$ is obtuse ($> 90°$).

$$\therefore \quad \frac{dl_1 \cos \theta_1}{r_1^2} = + d\phi \text{ as } \cos \theta_1 \text{ is } + \text{ve}$$

and

$$\frac{dl_2 \cos \theta_2}{r_2^2} = - d\phi \text{ as } \cos \theta_2 \text{ is } - \text{ve}$$

But

$$\vec{B} . d\vec{l} = \frac{\mu_0}{4\pi} . 2Id\phi = \frac{\mu_0}{2\pi} Id\phi \qquad \text{For proof see } \mathbf{Q. 8.16.} \text{ Eq. (ii).}$$

$$\therefore \qquad \vec{B_1} . d\vec{l_1} + \vec{B_2} . d\vec{l_2} .$$

$$= \frac{\mu_0}{2\pi} Id\phi - \frac{\mu_0}{2\pi} Id\phi = 0$$

The entire closed path can be divided into such pairs of line elements and for each pair $\vec{B_1} . d\vec{l_1} + \vec{B_2} . d\vec{l_2} = 0$. It, therefore, means that $\int \vec{B} . d\vec{l} = 0$.

∴ When the closed path does not enclose the current $\int \vec{B} . d\vec{l} = 0$.

Hence the line integral of the magnetic field around any closed path that does not enclose a current carrying wire is always zero.

(b) Magnetic field due to current in a straight conductor of infinite length. Consider an infinitely long wire along the Y-axis through which a current I is flowing.

The lines of magnetic induction will consist of concentric circles with the perpendicular distance r from the wire.

According to Ampere's law, the line integral of the magnetic field for a closed path

$$\oint \vec{B} . d\vec{l} = \mu_0 I$$

From symmetry the magnitude of B is the same at all points lying at a distance r from the wire *i.e.*, on a circle of radius r

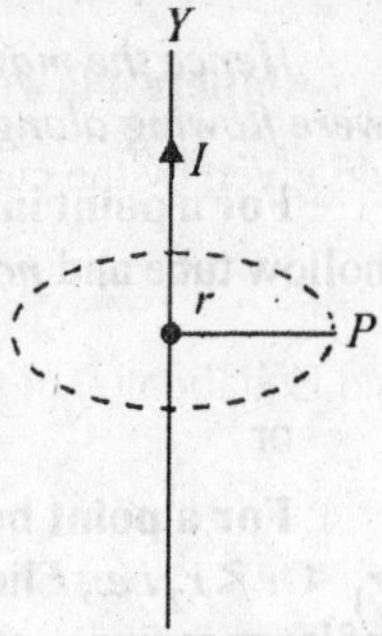

∴ $$\oint \vec{B} . d\vec{l} = B\, 2\pi r = 2\pi\, Br$$

or $$2\pi Br = \mu_0 I$$

and $$B = \frac{\mu_0}{2\pi} \frac{I}{r} \quad \text{or} \quad B = \frac{\mu_0}{4\pi} \frac{2I}{r}$$

Fig. 8.9(a)

(c)   Current $I = 5 \text{ mA} = 5 \times 10^{-3} \text{A}$; $\dfrac{\mu_0}{4\pi} = 10^{-7}$ S.I. units

∴ $\mu_0 = 4\pi \times 10^{-7}$ S.I. units.

According to Ampere's law the line integral of a magnetic field along any closed path is equal to μ_0 times the net current enclosing the path

or $$\oint \vec{B} . \vec{dl} = \mu_0 I = 4\pi \times 10^{-7} \times 5 \times 10^{-3} = 62.9 \times 10^{-10} \text{ Tesla metre}$$

Q. 8.18. (*a*) **Using Ampere's circuital law, calculate the magnetic induction field due to an infinite hollow tube carrying a steady current at points inside and outside the tube.**

(*b*) **A long straight cylindrical hollow pipe has inner and outer radii 1.0 cm and 2.0 cm respectively. Calculate the magnetic field at a distance of 0.5 cm, 1.5 cm, 4.0 cm from the axis of the pipe. The pipe carries a current of 100 A.**   (*G.N.D.U.*, 1992)

Ans. Magnetic field due to a current in a hollow tube. Consider an infinitely long hollow cylindrical tube of internal radius r_1, and external radius r_2 with its axis along the Y-axis. A uniform current I is flowing in it along the periphery of the tube in $+Y$ direction. From symmetry we find that the lines of magnetic induction are concentric circles round the axis of the tube, in the counter clockwise direction.

For a point outside the tube. Let P be a point *outside* the tube at a distance r from the axis of the tube $(r > r_2)$, then it lies on a line of force which is a circle of radius r.

∴ According to Ampere's law, the line integral of the magnetic field

$$\oint \vec{B} . \vec{dl} = \mu_0 I$$

But $$\oint \vec{B} . \vec{dl} = B\, 2\pi r = 2\pi\, Br$$

∴ $$2\pi Br = \mu_0 I$$

or $$B = \frac{\mu_0}{2\pi} \frac{I}{r} = \frac{\mu_0}{4\pi} \frac{2I}{r}$$

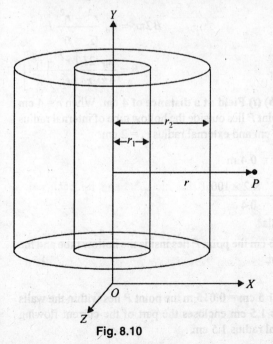

Fig. 8.10

This result is the same as for the magnetic field due to an infinitely long straight wire carrying current I as proved in **Q. 8.25** Eq. (*iii*) and **Q. 8.17** (*b*).

Hence the magnetic field at a point outside the cylindrical tube is the same as if all the current were flowing along the axis.

For a point inside the tube. If we take a point P at a distance r ($r < r_1$) then P lies inside the inner hollow tube and *no* current is enclosed by a circular path of radius r around the axis of the tube.

$$\therefore \qquad I = 0 \quad \text{and} \quad B\, 2\pi r = 0$$

$$\text{or} \qquad B = 0$$

For a point between the inner and outer tube. Consider a point P at a distance r such that $r_1 < r < r_2$ *i.e.*, r lies between r_1 and r_2. In such a case only the part of the current flowing in the tube of inner radius r_1 and outer radius r will be effective in producing the magnetic field at this point. The current flowing in the tube of inner radius r and outer radius r_2 will not produce any magnetic field at a point inside it.

The area of the annular face of the whole tube $= \pi r_2^2 - \pi r_1^2 = \pi\,(r_2^2 - r_1^2)$

The area of the annular face of the tube of internal radius r_1 and external radius r

$$= \pi r^2 - \pi r_1^2 = \pi\,(r^2 - r_1^2)$$

$\therefore$ Part of the current flowing through the annular face of this tube

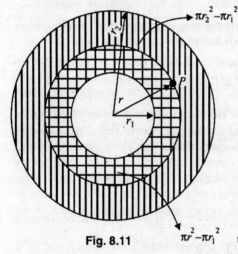

$$= \frac{\pi\,(r^2 - r_1^2)}{\pi\,(r_2^2 - r_1^2)}\, I = \frac{r^2 - r_1^2}{r_2^2 - r_1^2}\, I$$

$\therefore$ According to Ampere's law

$$\oint \vec{B} \cdot \vec{dl} = \mu_0\, \frac{r^2 - r_1^2}{r_2^2 - r_1^2}\, I$$

But $\qquad \oint \vec{B} \cdot \vec{dl} = B\, 2\pi r$

$$\therefore \qquad B\, 2\pi r = \mu_0\, \frac{r^2 - r_1^2}{r_2^2 - r_1^2}\, I$$

or $\qquad B = \frac{\mu_0}{4\pi}\, \frac{2I}{r}\left[\frac{r^2 - r_1^2}{r_2^2 - r_1^2}\right]$

Fig. 8.11

(b) (i) Field at a distance of 4 cm. When $r = 4$ cm the point P lies outside the hollow tube of internal radius $r_1 = 1$ cm and external radius $r_2 = 2$ cm.

Now $\dfrac{\mu_0}{4\pi} = 10^{-7}$ N/A^2; $I = 100$ A; $r = 4$ cm $= 0.4$ m

$\therefore \qquad$ Magnetic field at $P = \dfrac{\mu_0}{4\pi} \cdot \dfrac{2I}{r} = \dfrac{10^{-7} \times 2 \times 100}{0.4}$

$\therefore \qquad B = 0.5 \times 10^{-4}$ Tesla

(ii) Field at a distance of 0.5 cm. When $r = 0.5$ cm the point P lies inside the hollow tube and the circular path of radius 0.5 cm encloses *zero* current.

$$\therefore \qquad B = 0$$

(iii) Field at a distance of 1.5 cm. When $r = 1.5$ cm $= 0.015$ m the point P lies within the walls of the hollow tube and the circular path of radius 1.5 cm encloses the part of the current flowing within this tube of internal radius 1 cm and external radius 1.5 cm

$$\therefore \qquad \text{Magnetic field at } P = \frac{\mu_0}{4\pi} \frac{2I}{r} \left[\frac{r^2 - r_1^2}{r_2^2 - r_1^2} \right]$$

$$= 10^{-7} \times \frac{2 \times 100}{0.015} \left[\frac{1.5^2 - 1^2}{2^2 - 1^2} \right] = 5.5 \times 10^{-4} \text{ Tesla.}$$

Q. 8.19. Using Ampere's law calculate the magnetic field at a point inside a long current carrying solenoid. *(Kan. U.*, 1993; *Luck. U.*, 1995; *A.U.*, 1994; *Meerut U.*, 1994)

Ans. Magnetic field inside an infinite solenoid. Consider a solenoid infinitely long placed along the Z-axis of a co-ordinate system and extending from $Z = -\infty$ to $Z = +\infty$ having n turns per unit length.

Take a closed rectangular path *ABCD* in the counter clockwise direction such that the length *AB* lies inside the solenoid and the length *CD* lies outside the solenoid.

If $AB = L$ (in length), then number of turns contained in the rectangular path $ABCD = nL$.

If I is the current through the solenoid, then each turn of the solenoid which passes through the path *ABCD* contributes a current I. The total current through the path *ABCD* is, therefore, equal to the product of the number of turns passing through the area *ABCD* and current I.

Or the total current through the closed rectangular path $I_{total} = nLI$

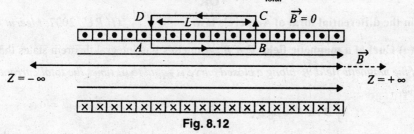

Fig. 8.12

The line integral of the magnetic field $\vec{B}$ around the path *ABCD* is $\oint\limits_{ABCDA} \vec{B}.\vec{dl}$

$$\text{Now} \quad \oint\limits_{ABCDA} \vec{B}.\vec{dl} = \int\limits_{AB} \vec{B}.\vec{dl} + \int\limits_{BC} \vec{B}.\vec{dl} + \int\limits_{CD} \vec{B}.\vec{dl} + \int\limits_{DA} \vec{B}.\vec{dl}$$

The magnetic field inside the solenoid is uniform and parallel to the axis. Magnetic field outside the solenoid is zero.

The magnetic field $\vec{B}$ along the path *AB* is parallel to $\vec{dl}$

$$\therefore \qquad \int\limits_{AB} \vec{B}.\vec{dl} = \int\limits_{AB} B\,dl = B \int\limits_{AB} dl = BL$$

because inside the solenoid B is uniform and has a constant value and $\int\limits_{AB} dl = L$

The path *BC* is perpendicular to the field $\vec{B}$

$$\therefore \qquad \int\limits_{BC} \vec{B}.\vec{dl} = \int\limits_{BC} B\,dl \cos\frac{\pi}{2} = 0$$

The path *CD* lies outside the solenoid where $\vec{B} = 0$

$$\therefore \qquad \int\limits_{CD} \vec{B}.\vec{dl} = 0$$

The path *DA* is again perpendicular to the field $\vec{B}$

$$\therefore \qquad \int_{DA} \vec{B} . d\vec{l} = \int_{DA} B\,dl \cos\frac{\pi}{2} = 0$$

$$\therefore \qquad \oint_{ABCDA} \vec{B} \cdot d\vec{l} = \int_{AB} \vec{B} . d\vec{l} + \int_{BC} \vec{B} . d\vec{l} + \int_{CD} \vec{B} . d\vec{l} + \int_{DA} \vec{B} . d\vec{l} = BL \qquad ...(i)$$

According to the Ampere's law

$$\oint_{ABCDA} \vec{B} . d\vec{l} = \mu_0\, I_{total} = \mu_0\, n L I \qquad ...(ii)$$

Equating (*i*) and (*ii*), we have

$$BL = \mu_0\, n L I$$
$$B = \mu_0\, n I$$

Q. 8.20. Prove that if the magnetic induction field $\vec{B}$ is not a function of time

$$\text{Curl } \vec{B} = \vec{\nabla} \times \vec{B} = \mu_0\, \vec{J}$$

where symbols have usual meaning.

(*G.N.D.U.*, 2009, 2008, 2007, 2001, 2000, 1995; *M.D.U.*, 2007, 2001, 2000; *P.U.*, 2009, 2002, 2001, 1992; *K.U.*, 2002, 2000; *Pbi. U.*, 2006, 2002, 1999; *A.U.*, 1995, 1993; *Luck. U.*, 1993)

OR

Obtain the differential form of Ampere's law.   (*H.P.U.*, 2007, *Meerut U.*, 1994)

Ans. (*a*) Curl of a magnetic field $\vec{\nabla} \times \vec{B}$. Ampere's line integral theorem states that *the line integral of the magnetic field $\vec{B}$ along a closed curve is equal to μ_0 times the total current enclosed by the curve.*

$$\oint \vec{B} . d\vec{l} = \mu_0\, I \qquad ...(i)$$

If $\vec{J}$ is the current density which varies from place to place but is *constant in time*, then

$$I = \iint_S \vec{J} . d\vec{s}$$

where $d\vec{s}$ is a small vector element of surface area and S is the whole surface bounded by a closed path C.

Substituting in (*i*), we have

$$\oint \vec{B} . d\vec{l} = \mu_0 \iint_S \vec{J} . d\vec{s} \qquad ...(ii)$$

But according to Stoke's teorem in vector analysis

$$\oint \vec{B} . d\vec{l} = \iint_S (Curl\ \vec{B}) . d\vec{s}$$

$$\iint_S (\vec{\nabla} \times \vec{B}) . d\vec{s} \qquad ...(iii)$$

Fig. 8.13   or

From (*ii*) and (*iii*), we have

$$\iint_S (\vec{\nabla} \times \vec{B}) . d\vec{s} = \mu_0 \iint_S \vec{J} . d\vec{s}$$

$$\vec{\nabla} \times \vec{B} = \mu_0\, \vec{J} \qquad ...(iv)$$

The equation $\vec{\nabla} \times \vec{B} = \mu_0 \vec{J}$ *is known as Ampere's law in differential form.* It is a point equation and gives the relation between magnetic field at a point and the current density at the same point in space.

Q. 8.21. Show that the divergence of magnetic field vector is zero everywhere.

What does the equation div $\vec{B} = 0$ indicate about the existence of magnetic poles? Explain why an isolated monopole does not exist. Hence bring out the significance of $\oiint \vec{B} \cdot \vec{ds} = 0$ in magnetism. (*Pbi. U.*, 2007, 2001, 2000, 1999; *Gauhati U.*, 2000; *H.P.U.*, 1999, 1997, 1994; *M.D.U.*, 2007; *K.U.*, 2002, 1996, 1994; *A.U.*, 1995; *G.N.D.U.*, 2007, 2004, 1999, 1993, 1992)

Ans. Divergence of a magnetic field $\vec{\nabla} \cdot \vec{B}$. According to the definition of divergence of a vector field.

$$Div \ \vec{B} = \frac{\text{Flux of } \vec{B} \text{ through a surface } S \text{ enclosing volume } v}{\text{volume } v \text{ in the limit } v \to 0}$$

$$= \frac{1}{v} \lim_{v \to 0} \iint_S \vec{B} \cdot \vec{ds}$$

In the case of an electric field, the lines of electric force originate from a positive charge and terminate on a negative charge. But magnetic lines of force have no such source or sink but are continuous and join back on themselves *i.e.*, the magnetic lines of force form loops without a beginning or an end. If, therefore, we consider a closed surface S in a magnetic field, we always have as many lines of the magnetic field entering into the surface as leaving it. Thus the magnetic flux of $\vec{B}$ over any surface is zero.

or $$\iint \vec{B} \cdot d\vec{s} = 0$$

$\therefore$ $$Div \ \vec{B} = \vec{\nabla} \cdot \vec{B} = 0$$

In other words, $\vec{\nabla} \cdot \vec{B} = 0$ whether the point lies outside or inside the current loop. *Thus the divergence of magnetic field vector is zero everywhere.*

Isolated magnetic poles do not exist. The relation

$$\text{Magnetic flux } \phi_B = \oiint \vec{B} \cdot d\vec{s} = 0 \qquad\qquad ...(i)$$

through any closed *gaussian surface* is known as Gauss's law in magnetism. Gauss's law in electrostatics in S.I. units states that

$$\varepsilon_0 \oiint \vec{E} \cdot d\vec{s} = q \qquad\qquad ...(ii)$$

Comparing relations (*i*) and (*ii*) we find that in magnetism there is no counter part to the free charge q in electricity which in other words means that '*isolated magnetic (poles or monoples) do not exist*'. or *Magnetic poles always exist in pairs.*

Q.8.22. Explain why the relation $\vec{\nabla} \times \vec{B} = \mu_0 \vec{J}$ and $\vec{\nabla} \cdot \vec{B} = 0$ is not sufficient to determine $\vec{B}$ at a point even if $\vec{J}$ is known at this point.

Ans. The equation $\vec{\nabla} \cdot \vec{B} = 0$ for a magnetic induction field has a simple solution $\vec{B} = \vec{\nabla} \times \vec{A}$ because $\vec{\nabla} \cdot \vec{\nabla} \times \vec{A} = 0$. It is, therefore possible to write the magnetic induction field $\vec{B}$ in terms of curl of another vector field $\vec{A}$. But the field $\vec{A}$ is not *uniquely* defined by the equation $\vec{\nabla} \times \vec{A} = 0$ because if we add to $\vec{A}$ another term $\vec{\nabla} \phi$ and call it $\vec{A}'$ then $\vec{\nabla} \times \vec{A}' = \vec{\nabla} \times (\vec{A} + \vec{\nabla} \phi) = \vec{\nabla} \times \vec{A}$. Thus $\vec{A}$ and $\vec{A}'$ are equivalent and give rise to the same magnetic field. For the same reason from the relation $\vec{\nabla} \times \vec{B} = \mu_0 \vec{J}$ it is not possible to uniquely define $\vec{B}$ even if the value of $\vec{J}$ at a particular point is known.

Q. 8.23. What is the value of $\vec{\nabla} . \vec{B}$ and $\vec{\nabla} \times \vec{B}$ for points inside and outside a current loop?   (*G.N.D.U.*, 2002, 2000, 1999, 1997, 1996)

Ans. The divergence of magnetic field is always zero at all points whether inside or outside the current loop.

The equation $\vec{\nabla} . \vec{B} = 0$ indicates that isolated magnetic poles do not exist *i.e.*, there are no free north and south poles in nature.

According to differential form of Ampere's law

$$\vec{\nabla} \times \vec{B} = \mu_0 \vec{J}$$

Since $\vec{J} = 0$ for all points inside the current loop

$$\vec{\nabla} \times \vec{B} = 0$$

Hence for points inside a current loop $\vec{\nabla} . \vec{B} = 0$ as well as $\vec{\nabla} \times \vec{B} = 0$.

However, for points outside a current loop. $\vec{\nabla} \times \vec{B} = \mu_0 \vec{J}$ and $\vec{\nabla} . \vec{B} = 0$.

Q. 8.24. State and explain Biot and Savart's law in vector form in S.I. and C.G.S. units.

(*G.N.D.U.*, 2008, 2007, 2004, 2003, 2000, 1996; *Kerala U.*, 2001; *M.D.U.*, 2001, 2000; *Meerut U.*, 2001, 1995; *H.P.U.*, 2006; *Pbi. U.*, 1995; *Osm. U.*, 1997; *Luck. U.*, 1996; *A.U.*, 1994; *H.P.U.*, 1994; *P.U.*, 2006, 1991; *K.U.*, 1991)

Ans. Biot's and Savart's law. The magnetic field due to a current distribution can be calculated with the help of Ampere's law

$$\oint \vec{B} . d\vec{l} = \mu_0 I$$

The law is easily applicable for highly symmetrical cases, but it is difficult to apply in cases which do not have a high symmetry.

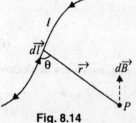

Fig. 8.14

In such a case, we divide the current circuit into a large number of *small* current elements and calculate the field at any point due to these elements. The vector sum of the contributions due to these elements gives the magnetic field due to the current circuit.

As a result of his experimental studies on forces between current carrying conductors Ampere observed that "The force on a current element $I_1 \, \vec{dl_1}$ *i.e.*, a conductor of length $\vec{dl_1}$ carrying a current I_1 due to another current element $I_2 \, \vec{dl_2}$ separated by a distance $|\vec{r_{12}}| = |\vec{r_{21}}|$ is given by (in S.I. units)

$$\vec{dF_{21}} = \frac{\mu_0}{4\pi} \frac{I_1 I_2}{r_{21}^3} [\vec{dl_1} \times (\vec{dl_2} \times \vec{r_{21}})] \qquad \qquad ...(i)$$

On the other hand, the force on a current element $I\,d\vec{l}$ in a magnetic induction field $d\vec{B}$ is given by

$$d\vec{F} = I\,d\vec{l} \times d\vec{B}$$

Using the above notation we can put it in the form

$$d\vec{F}_{21} = I_1\,d\vec{l}_1 \times d\vec{B} \qquad \qquad ...(ii)$$

Comparing (i) and (ii), we have

$$d\vec{B} = \frac{\mu_0}{4\pi}\,\frac{I_2}{r_{21}^3}\,(d\vec{l}_2 \times \vec{r}_{21})$$

If we drop the suffixes, we have a general relation

$$d\vec{B} = \frac{\mu_0}{4\pi}\,\frac{I}{r^3}\,(d\vec{l} \times \vec{r})$$

$$= \frac{\mu_0}{4\pi}\,\frac{I}{r^2}\,(d\vec{l} \times \hat{r}) \qquad \qquad ...(iii)$$

Acccording to relation (iii) the magnetic field $d\vec{B}$ at a point P, due to a small element $d\vec{l}$ of current I is given by

$$d\vec{B} = \frac{\mu_0}{4\pi}\,\frac{I}{r^2}\,(d\vec{l} \times \hat{r})$$

where $\vec{r}$ is a vector drawn from the location of $d\vec{l}$ to the point P and $\hat{r}$ a unit vector in the direction or $\vec{r}$.

The above relation is a mathematical statement of *Biot's* and *Savart's law* and is a modification of Ampere's law. According to this law the magnitude of $d\vec{B}$ is given by

$$dB = |d\vec{B}| = \frac{\mu_0}{4\pi}\,\frac{Idl}{r^2}\,\sin\theta \qquad \qquad ...(iv)$$

where θ is the angle between the direction of $d\vec{l}$ and $\vec{r}$ and the direction of the field is perpendicular to the plane containing $d\vec{l}$ and $\vec{r}$ given by the right hand screw rule for cross-product of vectors.

Some times Biot and Savart's law is used in the form

$$d\vec{B} = \frac{\mu_0}{4\pi}\,\frac{I}{r^3}\,(d\vec{l} \times \vec{r}) \qquad \qquad ...(v)$$

[Note. In C.G.S. units relation (iii) becomes $d\vec{B} = \dfrac{I}{r^2}\,(d\vec{l} \times \hat{r})$, and relation (iv) becomes $|d\vec{B}| = \dfrac{Idl}{r^2}\,\sin\theta$ whereas relation (v) becomes $d\vec{B} = \dfrac{I}{r}\,(d\vec{l} \times \vec{r})$]

Thus according to Biot and Savart's law given by Eq. (iv), the magnetic field due to a current element at a point P is

(i) directly proportional to the magnitude of the current element

$$dB \propto Idl$$

(ii) inversely proportional to the square of the distance of the point P from the current element

$$dB \propto \frac{1}{r^2}$$

(iii) directly proportional to the sine of the angle between the direction of current element $(Id\,\vec{l}\,)$ and vector $\vec{r}$

$$dB \propto \sin\theta$$

The constant of proportionality in S.I. units is $\dfrac{\mu_0}{4\pi}$ and in C.G.S. units it is *unity* or 1

General vector form. If the current element $I\,\vec{dl}$ lies at the position vector $\vec{r'}$ and observation point P at $\vec{r}$, then the position of the point P from the current element is given by

$$(\vec{r} - \vec{r'})$$

Then replacing $\vec{r}$ by $(\vec{r} - \vec{r'})$ and r^3 by $|\vec{r} - \vec{r'}|^3$ Biot and Savart's law can be put in the *general vector form*

$$d\,\vec{B} = \frac{\mu_0}{4\pi}\frac{I\,d\,\vec{l} \times (\vec{r} - \vec{r'})}{|\vec{r} - \vec{r'}|^3} \qquad ...(vi)$$

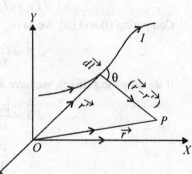

Fig. 8.15

When the current element is located at the origin $\vec{r'} = 0$ and we have

$$\vec{dB} = \frac{\mu_0}{4\pi}\frac{I\,dl \times \vec{r}}{|\vec{r}|^3}$$

which is the same as equation (*v*).

Q. 8.25. Using Biot and Savart's law find the magnetic field due to an infinite straight wire carrying current. (*H.P.U.*, 2006, 2003; *Meerut U.*, 2001, 2000, *M.D.U.*, 2001; *Gauhati U.*, 2000; *Osm. U.*, 1997; *Luck. U.*, 1995; *A.U.*, 1995; *K.U.*, 1997; *P.U.*, 1997)

Ans. Magnetic field due to a straight wire carrying current. Let AB be a straight conductor carrying a current I as shown in Fig. 8.16. The conductor is taken along the Y-axis and the current is supposed to flow along $-Y$ direction. Consider a point P at a perpendicular distance $x = OP$ from the conductor where O represents the origin and OP produced represents the X-axis.

Let $d\,\vec{l} = -\,\hat{j}\,dy$ be a small current element at a distance y from the origin O and let the vector distance of P from the centre of the element be $\vec{r}$, then

$$\vec{r} = -\,\hat{j}\,y + \hat{i}\,x$$

The magnetic field at P due to the current element $\vec{dl}$ is given by Biot and Savart's law

$$d\,\vec{B} = \frac{\mu_0}{4\pi}\frac{I\,d\,\vec{l} \times \vec{r}}{r^3} = \frac{\mu_0 I}{4\pi}\frac{(-\,\hat{j}\,dy) \times (-\,\hat{j}\,y + \hat{i}\,x)}{r^3}$$

$$= \frac{\mu_0 I}{4\pi}\frac{x\,dy}{r^3}\,\hat{k}$$

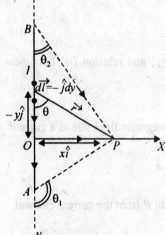

Fig. 8.16

i.e., the magnetic induction field $\overrightarrow{dB}$ is along the $+Z$ axis perpendicular to the plane containing the conductor AB and the point P.

∴ Total magnetic field at P due to whole length of the wire AB

$$\overrightarrow{B} = \frac{\mu_0 I}{4\pi} \int_A^B \frac{x\, dy}{r^3}\, \hat{k} \qquad ...(i)$$

If θ is the angle between the direction of current element $I\,d\overrightarrow{l}$ and vector $\overrightarrow{r}$, then

$$x = r\sin\theta \quad \text{or} \quad r = x\, \mathrm{cosec}\, \theta$$
$$y = r\cot\theta$$

∴
$$dy = -x\, \mathrm{cosec}^2\, \theta\, d\theta$$

Substituting in (i) we have $\overrightarrow{B} = \dfrac{\mu_0 I}{4\pi} \displaystyle\int_{\theta_1}^{\theta_2} \dfrac{-x^2\, \mathrm{cosec}^2\, \theta\, d\theta}{x^3\, \mathrm{cosec}^3\, \theta}\, \hat{k}$

where θ_1 is the value of θ at the end A and θ_2 that at the end B.

∴
$$\overrightarrow{B} = \frac{\mu_0 I}{4\pi x} \int_{\theta_1}^{\theta_2} -\frac{d\theta}{\mathrm{cosec}\,\theta}\, \hat{k}$$

$$= \frac{\mu_0}{4\pi}\frac{I}{x} \int_{\theta_1}^{\theta_2} -\sin\theta\, d\theta\, \hat{k} = \frac{\mu_0 I}{x}\, [\cos]_{\theta_1}^{\theta_2}\, \hat{k}$$

or
$$\overrightarrow{B} = \frac{\mu_0}{4\pi}\frac{I}{x}(\cos\theta_2 - \cos\theta_1)\, \hat{k} \qquad ...(ii)$$

Infinitely long conductor. If the conductor is infinitely long

$$\theta_1 = \pi \quad \text{and} \quad \theta_2 = 0$$
∴
$$\cos\theta_2 = 1 \quad \text{and} \cos\theta_1 = -1$$

Hence
$$\overrightarrow{B} = \frac{\mu_0}{4\pi}\frac{2I}{x}\, \hat{k} \qquad ...(iii)$$

Q. 8.26. A long wire carries a current of 2 A. An electron travels with a velocity of 4×10^4 ms^{-1} parallel to the wire 0.1 m from it in a direction opposite to the current. What force does the magnetic field of current exert on the moving electron? *(G.N.D.U., 2001)*

Ans. Let the wire be along Y-axis and current flow through it along $-Y$ direction as shown in Fig. 8.16., then the magnetic field $\overrightarrow{B}$ at a distance x from it in the $+X$ direction is given by

$$\overrightarrow{B} = \frac{\mu_0}{4\pi}\frac{2I}{x}\, \hat{k}$$

i.e., the field $\overrightarrow{B}$ acts along the $+Z$ direction.

Distance of the moving electron from the long wire $x = 0.1$ m

$$I = 2\, A \quad \text{and} \quad \frac{\mu_0}{4\pi} = 10^{-7}\ \text{S.I. units}$$

∴
$$\overrightarrow{B} = 10^{-7} \times \frac{2 \times 2}{0.1} = 4 \times 10^{-6}\, \hat{k}\ \text{Tesla}$$

Velocity of the electron $= 4 \times 10^4$ ms^{-1}

As the electron traves in a direction opposite to the current, its direction of motion is along $+ Y$ direction and

$$\vec{v} = 4 \times 10^4 \, \hat{j}$$

Charge on the electron $q = - 1.6 \times 10^{-19}$ C

$\therefore$ Force on the moving electron

$$= q \, (\vec{v} \times \vec{B})$$

$$= - 1.6 \times 10^{-19} \, (4 \times 10^4 \, \hat{j} \times 4 \times 10^{-6} \, \hat{k})$$

$$= - 2.56 \times 10^{-20} \hat{i} = 2.56 \times 10^{-20} \text{ N along } - X \text{ direction}$$

The electron is, therefore, attracted towards the current carrying wire.

Q. 8.27. (a) Calculate the magnitude of the magnetic field due to a long thin wire carrying current of 15 Amp at distance of 1 cm from the wire, given $\mu_0 = 4\pi \times 10^{-7}$ N/A². (H.P.U., 1993)

(b) Calculate the magnetic field at a distance of 5m from an infinite straight conductor carrying current of 100 A.   (*P.U.*, 2002; *H.P.U.*, 1997)

Ans. (a) Current $I = 15$ Amp; Distance $x = 1$ cm $= 0.01$ m

Magnitude of magnetic field $|\vec{B}| = \dfrac{\mu_0}{4\pi} \dfrac{2I}{x} = 10^{-7} \dfrac{2 \times 15}{0.01}$

$$= 3 \times 10^{-4} \text{ Tesla}$$

(b) Current $I = 100$ A; Distance $x = 5$ cm

Magnitude of the magnetic field $|\vec{B}| = \dfrac{\mu_0}{4\pi} \dfrac{2I}{x} = 10^{-7} \dfrac{2 \times 100}{5} = 4 \times 10^{-6}$ Tesla

Q. 8.28. Two parallel straight wires are placed at 2 cm and 6 cm mark at right angles to the metre scale. The currents in them are 1 A and 3 A respectively. Find the mark at which they will produce zero magnetic field.   (*Pbi. U.*, 1991)

Ans. Suppose the two wires are A and B and current flows through them in $- Y$ direction as shown.

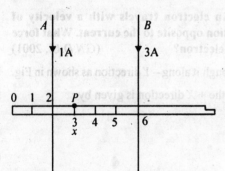

Let P be the point at the mark x at which the two currents produce zero magnetic field.

For wire A kept at 2 cm $= 0.02$ m mark the point P lies in the $+ X$ direction. Hence

Magnetic field at $P = \dfrac{\mu_0}{4\pi} \dfrac{2I}{r} \hat{k}$

$$= \dfrac{\mu_0}{4\pi} \dfrac{2 \times 1}{x - 0.02} \hat{k}$$

(The field acts in $+ Z$ direction)

For wire B kept at 6 cm $= 0.06$ m mark the point P lies in the $-X$ direction. Hence

Fig. 8.17

Magnetic field at $P = \dfrac{\mu_0}{4\pi} \dfrac{2 \times 3}{0.06 - x} (- \hat{k})$ (The field acts in $- Z$ direction)

As the field at $P = 0$

$$\frac{\mu_0}{4\pi} \frac{2 \times 1}{(x - 0.02)} \hat{k} + \frac{\mu_0}{4\pi} \frac{2 \times 3}{(0.06 - x)} (-\hat{k}) = 0$$

or
$$\frac{\mu_0}{4\pi} \frac{2}{x - 0.02} - \frac{\mu_0}{4\pi} \frac{6}{(0.06 - x)} = 0$$

∴
$$\frac{2}{x - 0.02} = \frac{6}{0.06 - x}$$

or
$$0.12 - 2x = 6x - 0.12$$

or
$$8x = 0.24 \text{ m} \qquad\qquad \therefore \quad x = 0.03 \text{ m} = 3 \text{ cm}$$

∴ At the mark 3 cm the magnetic field is zero.

Q. 8.29. An infinite straight wire lying along the Y-axis carries a current of 100 amps in the + Y direction. A uniform magnetic field $B_0 = 10^{-3}$ Tesla points towards + X axis. Find the resultant magnetic field at the following points.

(*i*) $x = 0$; $z = 2$ cm   (*ii*) $x = 2$ cms; $z = 0$.

Ans. For the point $x = 0$; $z = 2$ cm = 0.02 m

As the current flows along the + Y direction the perpendicular distance of the point from the infinite straight wire $z = 2$ cm = .02 m as $x = 0$.

∴ The magnitude of the magnetic field $B_1 = \dfrac{\mu_0}{4\pi} \dfrac{2I}{x} = \dfrac{10^{-7} \times 2 \times 100}{0.02} = 10^{-3}$ Tesla

Direction. The direction of the field can be deduced from the relation $d\vec{B} = \dfrac{\mu_0}{4\pi} \dfrac{Id\vec{l} \times \vec{r}}{r^3}$.

In this case $d\vec{l} = \hat{j} \, dy$, $\vec{r} = \hat{k}$ as the current flows along + Y direction and the observation point lies on the Z-axis.

∴
$$d\vec{l} \times \vec{r} = \hat{j} \, dy \times \hat{k} z = dy \, z \hat{i}$$

i.e., the field acts along the + X direction. The field B_0 also acts along + X-axis.

∴   Resultant field $\vec{B} = \vec{B_1} + \vec{B_0} = 10^{-3} \hat{i} + 10^{-3} \hat{i} = 2 \times 10^{-3} \hat{i}$ Tesla

i.e., the resultant field has a magnitude 2×10^{-3} Tesla and acts along the + X direction as shown in Fig. 8.18 (a).

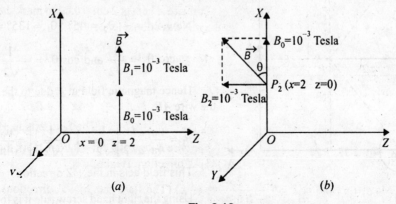

(a)   (b)

Fig. 8.18

(*ii*) *For the point.* $x = 2$ cm = 0.02 m; $z = 0$

The magnitude of the magnetic field $B_2 = \dfrac{\mu_0}{4\pi} \dfrac{2I}{x} = \dfrac{10^{-7} \times 2 \times 100}{0.02} = 10^{-3}$ Tesla

In this case $d\vec{l} = \hat{j}\,dy$ and $\vec{r} = \hat{i}x$

$\therefore \qquad d\vec{l} \times \vec{r} = \hat{j}\,dy \times \hat{i}\,x = dy\,x\,(-\hat{k})$

i.e., the field acts along $-Z$ direction. The field $\vec{B_0}$ acts along $+X$-axis

$\therefore \qquad$ Resultant field $\vec{B} = \vec{B_2} + \vec{B_0} = -10^{-3}\,\hat{k} + 10^{-3}\,\hat{i}$

$\therefore \qquad$ Magnitude of $B = \sqrt{(10^{-3})^2 + (10^{-3})^2} = \sqrt{2} \times 10^{-3}$ Tesla

Direction of $\vec{B}$ is given by $\tan\theta = \dfrac{-10^{-3}}{10^{-3}} = -1$ or $\theta = -45°$

i.e., the resultant field makes an angle of $-45°$ with $+X$ axis in the X-Z plane as shown in Fig. 8.18 (b).

Q. 8.30. A square loop of wire of edge a carries a current I. Show that the value of $\vec{B}$ at the centre is given by $2\sqrt{2}\,\mu_0\,\dfrac{I}{\pi\,a}$ in usual notation.   (*Luck. U.*, 1993; *G.N.D.U.*, 1991)

OR

Find the magnetic field at the centre of a square carrying a current I in the counter clock-wise direction.   (*G.N.D.U.*, 2003)

Ans. Suppose $ABCD$ is a square of each side a and P the observation point at the centre of the square, then the point P is at a perpendicular distance $\dfrac{a}{2}$ from each side.

When a current I flows in a straight conducting wire in the $-Y$ direction and the observation point P lies at a perpendicular distance r from it in the $+X$ direction, then

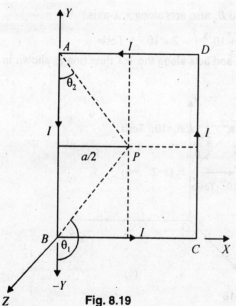

Fig. 8.19

Magnetic field at $P = \dfrac{\mu_0}{4\pi} \dfrac{I}{r} (\cos\theta_2 - \cos\theta_1)\,\hat{k}$

where θ_1 and θ_2 are the angles subtended at the ends of the conductor. The unit vector $\hat{k}$ indicates that the magnetic field acts in the $+Z$ direction

Now $r = \dfrac{a}{2}$; $\theta_2 = 45°$; $\theta_1 = 135° = (\pi - 45°)$

$\therefore \cos\theta_2 = \dfrac{1}{\sqrt{2}}$ and $\cos\theta_1 = -\dfrac{1}{\sqrt{2}}$

Hence magnetic field at P due to the current I in the wire AB,

$\vec{B_1} = \dfrac{\mu_0}{4\pi} \dfrac{I}{a/2}\left[\dfrac{1}{\sqrt{2}} - \left(-\dfrac{1}{\sqrt{2}}\right)\right] = \dfrac{\mu_0}{4\pi} \dfrac{I}{a} 2\sqrt{2}\,\hat{k}$

This field acts in the $+Z$ direction.

Using the right hand screw rule it is found that the magnetic field at P due to all the four sides of the square is in the same $+Z$ direction i.e., along the vector $\hat{k}$.

$\therefore$ Total magnetic field

$$\vec{B} = 4\,\vec{B_1} = 4 \times \frac{\mu_0}{4\pi}\, 2\,\sqrt{2}\,\frac{I}{a}\,\hat{k} = 2\,\sqrt{2}\,\frac{\mu_0}{\pi}\,\frac{I}{a}\,\hat{k}$$

Q. 8.31. A wire of square shape of each side 10 cm long is carrying a current of 2 A in the anti-clockwise direction. Calculate the magnetic field at its centre. *(P.U., 1991)*

Ans. Magnetic field at the centre of the square $\vec{B} = \dfrac{\mu_0}{\pi}\,\dfrac{I}{a}\,2\sqrt{2}\,\hat{k}$

[For proof See **Q. 8.30**.]

Substituting $I = 2\text{A}$, $a = 10$ cm $= 0.1$ m; $\dfrac{\mu_0}{4\pi} = 10^{-7}\ \text{T m A}^{-1}$, we have

$$|\vec{B}| = 4 \times \frac{\mu_0}{4\pi}\,\frac{I}{a}\,2\sqrt{2}\,\hat{k} = 4 \times 2\sqrt{2} \times 10^{-7} \times \frac{2}{0.1} = 22.62 \times 10^{-6} = 2.262 \times 10^{-5}\ \text{T}$$

As the current is anticlockwise as shown in Fig. 8.19, **Q. 8.30**, the direction of $\vec{B}$ is along $\hat{k}$ the $+Z$ direction.

Exercise. *A conductor of length 64 cm is bent into a square and a current of 4 A is passed through it. Find the magnetic field at the centre of the square.* *(Kerala U., 2001)*

Hint. Each side of square $a = \dfrac{64}{4} = 16$ cm $= 0.16$ m

$$\therefore \quad \vec{B} = \frac{\mu_0}{\pi}\,\frac{I}{a}\,2\sqrt{2} = 4 \times 10^{-7} \times 2\sqrt{2} \times \frac{4}{0.16} = 2.82 \times 10^{-5}\ \text{T}$$

Q. 8.32. A wire shaped to regular hexagon of side 2 cm carries a current of 2 amp. Find the magnetic induction at the centre of the hexagon. *(P.U., 1992)*

Ans. Let $ABCDEF$ be a regular hexagon of side 2 cm. The point O where the lines AD, BE and CF cut is the centre of the hexagon.

Then each triangle formed with O as vertex and any side of the hexagon as base is an equilateral triangle

$\therefore \qquad AO = BO = CO = DO = EO = FO = 2$ cm

The perpendicular distance of the observation point O from each side is the same $= ON$ from the side AB.

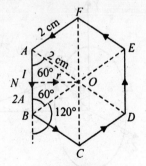

Fig. 8.20

Let $ON = r$, then $r = 2 \sin 60 = \dfrac{2\sqrt{3}}{2} = \sqrt{3}$ cm $= \sqrt{3} \times 10^{-2}$ m

Magnetic field at O due to a current I flowing in the wire AB

$$\vec{B_1} = \frac{\mu_0}{4\pi}\,\frac{I}{r}\,(\cos\theta_2 - \cos\theta_1)\,\hat{k}$$

Now $\qquad\qquad \theta_2 = 60° \text{ and } \theta_1 = 120° = (\pi - 60°)$

$$\therefore \quad \vec{B_1} = \frac{\mu_0}{4\pi}\,\frac{2}{\sqrt{3}\times 10^{-2}}\,(\cos 60° - \cos 120°) = 10^{-7} \times \frac{2}{\sqrt{3}\times 10^{-2}}\left[\frac{1}{2} - \left(-\frac{1}{2}\right)\right]$$

$$= \frac{2}{\sqrt{3}} \times 10^{-5}\,\hat{k}\ \text{Tesla}$$

As the current flows in AB along $-Y$ direction and the point O lies along $+X$ direction, the magnetic field acts in the $+Z$ direction according to right hand screw rule. Similarly the magnetic field due to all the six sides has the same magnitude and acts in the same direction.

$$\therefore \quad \text{Total magnetic field } \vec{B} = 6\, \vec{B_1} = 6 \times \frac{2}{\sqrt{3}} \times 10^{-5}\, \hat{k} \text{ Tesla}$$

$$= 4\sqrt{3} \times 10^{-5}\, \vec{k} = 6.93 \times 10^{-5}\, \vec{k} \text{ Tesla}$$

Exercise. *A wire shaped to a regular hexagon of side 8 cm. carries a current of 10A. Find the magnetic field at the centre of the hexagon.* (P.U., 2007)

Ans. $$B = \frac{6 \times 10^{-4}}{4\sqrt{3}} = 8.66 \times 10^{-5}\, T$$

Q. 8.33. (*a*) **Using Biot and Savart's law find an expression for the intensity of magnetic induction field at a point on the axis of a circular coil carrying a steady current. Will this field be uniform? Show graphically the variation of the field with distance from the centre.**

(*b*) **From the result so obtained calculate the field at the centre of a circular coil having *n* turns.**   (*G.N.D.U.*, 2008, 2003, 2001, 1996; *Nagpur U.*, 2000; *Kerala U.*, 2001;

Meerut U., 2003, 1995, 1994; *H.P.U.*, 1994; *K.U.*, 1992; *Pbi. U.*, 1991; *P.U.*, 2006, 1991)

Ans. (*a*) **Magnetic field on the axis of a circular coil.** Consider a circular coil of radius *a* carrying a current *I* lying in the *YZ* plane with its centre at the origin *O*. The axis of the coil coincides with the *X*-axis.

Let *P* be a point on the axis of the coil at a distance $\vec{x}$ from *O*, then

$$\vec{x} = \hat{i}\, x$$

Let the direction of the current in the coil be anti-clockwise as seen from *P*. Now consider a small element *AB* of length $d\vec{l}$ (in the *Y-Z* plane) and let the co-ordinates of *A* be $(0, y, z)$ and that of B $(0, y + dy, z + dz)$, then

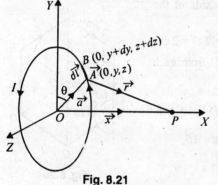

Fig. 8.21

$$\vec{OA} = \vec{a} = y\hat{j} + z\hat{k} \text{ and}$$

$$d\vec{l} = (y + dy)\,\hat{j} + (z + dz)\,\hat{k} - y\hat{j} - z\hat{k}$$

$$= dy\,\hat{j} + dz\,\hat{k}$$

Let the vector distance of the point *P* from the element be $\vec{r}$, then

$$\vec{a} + \vec{r} = \vec{x} \text{ or } \vec{r} = \vec{x} - \vec{a}$$

$$= \hat{i}\,x - y\hat{j} - z\hat{k}$$

If θ is the angle that *OA* makes with the *Y*-axis, then

$$y = a \cos\theta\, ; z = a \sin\theta$$

and $$dy = -a \sin\theta\, d\theta\, ; dz = a \cos\theta\, d\theta$$

$$\therefore \quad \vec{a} = a \cos\theta\, \hat{j} + a \sin\theta\, \hat{k}$$

Hence $d\vec{l} \times \vec{r} = (dy \, \hat{j} + dz \, \hat{k}) \times (x \, \hat{i} - y \, \hat{j} - z \, \hat{k})$

$$= \begin{bmatrix} \hat{i} & \hat{j} & \hat{k} \\ 0 & dy & dz \\ x & -y & -z \end{bmatrix}$$

$$= \hat{i} \, (- dyz + dzy) + \hat{j} \, (dzx) + \hat{k} \, (- xdy)$$

$$= \hat{i} \, (a^2 \sin^2 \theta \, d\theta + a^2 \cos^2 \theta \, d\theta) + \hat{j} \, (ax \cos \theta \, d\theta) + \hat{k} \, (ax \sin \theta \, d\theta)$$

$$= \hat{i} \, a^2 \, d\theta + \hat{j} \, ax \cos \theta \, d\theta + \hat{k} \, ax \sin \theta \, d\theta$$

The magnetic field at P due to the element $d\vec{l}$

$$= d\vec{B} = \frac{\mu_0 \, I}{4\pi} \frac{d\vec{l} \times \vec{r}}{r^3}$$

$$= \frac{\mu_0}{4\pi} \frac{I}{r^3} \, [\hat{i} \, a^2 \, d\theta + \hat{j} \, ax \cos \theta \, d\theta + \hat{k} \, ax \sin \theta \, d\theta]$$

The field due to the whole circular coil

$$\vec{B} = \frac{\mu_0}{4\pi} \frac{Ia}{r^3} \left[\hat{i} \int_0^{2\pi} a \, d\theta + \hat{j} \int_0^{2\pi} x \cos \theta \, d\theta + \hat{k} \int_0^{2\pi} x \sin \theta \, d\theta \right]$$

Now $\qquad \int_0^{2\pi} a \, d\theta = 2\pi a; \quad \int_0^{2\pi} \cos \theta \, d\theta = 0 \quad \text{and} \quad \int_0^{2\pi} \sin \theta \, d\theta = 0$

$$\therefore \qquad \vec{B} = \frac{\mu_0}{4\pi} \frac{Ia}{r^3} \cdot 2\pi a \, \hat{i} = \frac{\mu_0 \, Ia^2}{2r^3} \, \hat{i}$$

But $\qquad \vec{r} = \vec{x} - \vec{a} \quad \therefore \quad r^2 = x^2 + a^2$ $\hspace{2cm}$ or

$$r^3 = (x^2 + a^2)^{3/2}$$

Hence $\qquad \vec{B} = \frac{\mu_0 \, Ia^2}{2 \, (x^2 + a^2)^{3/2}} \, \hat{i}$ $\hspace{3cm}$ ...(i)

Hence when the current carrying coil lies in the YZ plane and its axis coincides with the X-axis, the magnetic field is along the $+ X$ direction for an anti-clockwise current.

If there are n turns in the coil, then

$$\vec{B} = \frac{\mu_0 \, n \, I \, a^2}{2 \, (a^2 + x^2)^{3/2}} \, \hat{i}$$ $\hspace{3cm}$ ...(ii)

Will the field be uniform? The field decreases as we move away from the centre of the coil along its axis. Hence it is *not uniform*. It is maximum at the centre and decreases symmetrically on both sides along $+ X$ as well as $-X$ direction. The variation of magnetic field $\vec{B}$ with distance x from the centre of the coil along its axis is shown graphically in Fig. 8.22.

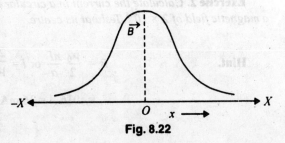

Fig. 8.22

(b) **Field at the centre of the coil.** At the centre of the coil

$$x = 0$$

$$\therefore \qquad \vec{B} = \frac{\mu_0 \, Ia^2}{2a^3} \, \hat{i} = \frac{\mu_0 I}{2a} \, \hat{i} \qquad \qquad ...(iii)$$

For n turns $\qquad \vec{B} = \frac{\mu_0}{2} \frac{nI}{a} \, \hat{i} \qquad \qquad ...(iv)$

The field is thus perpendicular to the plane of the coil.

Q. 8.34. A current of 1 Amp. is passed through a coil of radius 31.4 cm and number of turns 50. Calculate the magnetic field at the centre of the coil and 5 cm away from the centre. Given that $\mu_0 = 4\pi \times 10^{-7}$ Wb/A–m. *(Nagpur U., 2002)*

Ans. Current $I = 1$ Amp; Radius of coil $a = 31.4$ cm $= 0.314$ m

Number of turns $n = 50$; $\mu_0 = 4\pi \times 10^{-7}$ Wb/A–m

Field at the centre of the coil $B = \dfrac{\mu_0}{2} \dfrac{nI}{a}$

$$= \frac{4\pi \times 10^{-7}}{2} \times \frac{50 \times 1}{0.314} = \frac{4 \times 3.14 \times 10^{-7} \times 50}{2 \times 0.314} = 10^{-4} \, T$$

For a point 5cm away from the centre $x = 5$ cm $= 0.05$ m

Field at a point on the axis, x metre away

$$B = \frac{\mu_0}{2} \, nI \, \frac{a^2}{(a^2 + x^2)^{3/2}}$$

$$= \frac{4\pi \times 10^{-7} \times 50 \times 1}{2} \qquad \frac{(0.314)^2}{[(0.314)^2 + (0.05)^2]^{3/2}}$$

$$= \frac{4 \times 3.14 \times 10^{-7} \times 50 \times 0.0986}{2 \times 0.03216} = 9.63 \times 10^{-5} \, T$$

$$= 0.963 \times 10^{-4} \, T$$

Exercise 1. *Find the magnetic field due to a circular coil of radius 0.1 m and having 200 turns at the centre of the coil when circulating current is 500 mA.* *(M.D.U., 2001)*

Hint. $\qquad B = \dfrac{\mu_0}{2} \dfrac{nI}{a} = \dfrac{4\pi \times 10^{-7}}{2} \times \dfrac{200 \times 0.5}{0.1}$

$$= 2\pi \times 10^{-4} = 6.28 \times 10^{-4} \, T$$

Exercise 2. *Calculate the current in a circular coil of radius 5 cm having 100 turns to produce a magnetic field of 2×10^{-5} Tesla at its centre.* *(G.N.D.U., 2007)*

Hint. $\qquad B = \dfrac{\mu_0}{2} \dfrac{nI}{a} \text{ or } I = \dfrac{2Ba}{\mu_0 N} = \dfrac{2 \times 2 \times 10^{-5} \times 5 \times 10^{-2}}{4\pi \times 10^{-7} \times 100}$

$$= .016 \, A = 16 \, mA$$

Q. 8.35. In the Bohr model of the hydrogen atom, the electron circulates around the nucleus in a path of radius 5.1×10^{-11} metre at a frequency of 6.8×10^{15} rev/sec.

(a) What value of B is set up at the centre of the orbit?

(b) What is the equivalent magnetic dipole moment?

(G.N.D.U., 2000; Luck. U., 1992; A.U., 1993; Pbi. U., 1991)

Ans.   Current I = rate at which the charge passes any point on the orbit

$$= \frac{\text{Charge}}{\text{time}} = \text{charge} \times \text{frequency} = ev$$

Now $e = 1.6 \times 10^{-19}$ C $v = 6.8 \times 10^{15}$ rev/sec

∴ $I = 1.6 \times 10^{-19} \times 6.8 \times 10^{15} = 10.88 \times 10^{-4}$ Amp.

(a) Magnetic field at the centre of the orbit $B = \dfrac{\mu_0 I}{2a}$

Now $\dfrac{\mu_0}{4\pi} = 10^{-7}$ Weber/A–m or $\mu_0 = 4\pi \times 10^{-7}$ Weber/A–m

$a = 5.1 \times 10^{-11}$ m

∴ $B = \dfrac{4\pi \times 10^{-7} \times 10.88 \times 10^{-4}}{2 \times 5.1 \times 10^{-11}} = 13.4$ Weber/m^2 = 13.4 Tesla

(b) Magnetic dipole moment $M = IA = I\pi r^2$

$$= 10.88 \times 10^{-4} \times \pi \times (5.1 \times 10^{-11})^2$$

$$= 8.89 \times 10^{-24} \text{ Am}^2$$

Q. 8.36. Describe with necessary theory the construction and working of a Helmholtz galvanometer. Discuss its superiority over an ordinary tangent galvanometer.

(Nagpur U., 2001; Gharwal U., 1999; Luck. U., 1995, 1991; A.U., 1995; Meerut U., 1992)

Ans. Helmholtz tangent galvanometer. It consists of two circular coils of the same radius and having the same number of turns placed co-axially at a distance equal to the radius of either. The magnetic needle is pivoted or suspended at a point *mid-way* between the coils because *the field about this point is practically uniform over a large region*. The coils are connected to each other *in series* so that the current passing through each is in the same direction and the resultant field at a point mid-way between them is twice that due to one coil.

Uniform field with two coils. To make the field uniform over a large region about a point, the rate of decrease of the magnetic field due to one coil must be equal to the rate of increase of the field at the same point and in the same direction due to the other coil.

The magnitude of the field at a point on the axis at a distance x from the centre of the coil of radius a and n turns is given by

$$B = \frac{\mu_0}{2} \frac{nI \, a^2}{(a^2 + x^2)^{3/2}}$$

The rate of change of the field with distance x is given by

$$\frac{dB}{dx} = \frac{\mu_0 \, n \, Ia^2}{2} \frac{d}{dx} (a^2 + x^2)^{-3/2}$$

$$= \frac{\mu_0 \, nI \, a^2}{2} \left[-\frac{3}{2} (a^2 + x^2)^{-5/2} \, 2x \right]$$

$$= \frac{\mu_0 \, n I a^2}{2} \, [- 3x \, (a^2 + x^2)^{-5/2}]$$

In order that the rate of decrease of the field due to one coil may be the same as the rate of increase due to the other, $\dfrac{dB}{dx}$ *must be a constant.*

Hence
$$\frac{d^2 B}{dx^2} = 0$$

But
$$\frac{d^2 B}{dx^2} = \frac{\mu_0 \, n I a^2}{2} \, \frac{d}{dx} \, [- 3x \, (a^2 + x^2)^{-5/2}]$$

$$= \frac{\mu_0 \, n I a^2}{2} \left[- 3 \, (a^2 + x^2)^{-5/2} + 3x \times \frac{5}{2} \, (a^2 + x^2)^{-7/2} \, 2x \right]$$

$$= \frac{3}{2} \, \mu_0 \, n \, I a^2 \, (a^2 + x^2)^{-7/2} \, [- (a^2 + x^2) + 5x^2]$$

$$= \frac{3}{2} \, \mu_0 \, n I a^2 \, (a^2 + x^2)^{-7/2} \, (4x^2 - a^2)$$

This is zero if $\quad 4x^2 - a^2 = 0$ or $4x^2 = a^2$

or
$$x = \pm \frac{a}{2}$$

Point of inflexion. A point lying at a distance $\pm \dfrac{a}{2}$ from the centre of a coil at which the rate of change of magnetic field is constant is known as the *point of inflexion.*

Resultant field midway between the two coils. Hence at a point

lying at a distance $\dfrac{a}{2}$ from the plane of the coil, the rate of change of

field along the axis is constant and the decrease in field due to one coil is balanced by the increase in field due to the other. This is shown in Fig. 8.23 were ABC represents the field due to one coil and DBE due to other coil. The dotted line represents the resultant field in the space between the two coils and the straight portion indicates that it is uniform over a fairly large distance on either side of B.

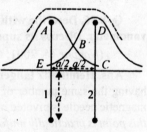

Fig. 8.23

The resultant field midway between the two coils.

$$B = 2 \times \frac{\mu_0}{2} \, \frac{n I a^2}{\left[a^2 + \left(\dfrac{a}{2} \right)^2 \right]^{3/2}} = \frac{8\mu_0}{\sqrt{125}} \, \frac{n I}{a}$$

If the planes of the coils are in the magnetic meridian and B_H is the field due to the earth, then
$$B = B_H \tan \theta$$

where θ is the deflection of the needle.

Hence $\dfrac{8\mu_0 \, n \, I}{\sqrt{125} \, a} = B_H \, \tan \theta$

or
$$I = \frac{\sqrt{125} \, a \, B_H \, \tan \theta}{8\mu_0 n} = \frac{5\sqrt{5} \, a \, B_H \, \tan \theta}{8 \quad \mu_0 n}$$

Superiority over a tangent galvanometer. (*i*) It is more sensitive. The intensities of magnetic field due to the two coils reinforce each other and the field at the centre is much greater than that in a tangent galvanometer.

(*ii*) The rate of variation of the magnetic field due to the two coils being constant, equal and opposite over a fairly large region, the resultant field at the centre is uniform over a considerable distance. Hence it is not necessary to use a very small magnetic needle.

Q. 8.37. (*a*) **A Helmholtz galvanometer has coils of radius 11 cm and the number of turns $70\sqrt{5}$. Calculate the current through the coil which produces a deflection of 45°.**

$$H = \frac{0.32}{4\pi \times 10^{-3}} \text{ Amp. turns/m.}$$ (*Gharwal U.*, 2000)

(*b*) **Two similar coils of wire having a radius of 7 cm and 60 turns have a common axis and are 18 cm apart. Find the strength of the magnetic field at a point midway between them on their common axis, when a current of 0.1 Amp is passed through them.**   (*G.N.D.U.*, 2002)

Ans. (*a*) Here $a = 11$ cm $= 0.11$ m ; $n = 70\sqrt{5}$, $\theta = 45°$

$$H = B_H = \frac{0.32}{4\pi \times 10^{-3}} \text{ Amp. turns/m} = \frac{0.32 \times 4\pi \times 10^{-7}}{4\pi \times 10^{-3}} = 0.32 \times 10^{-4} \text{ T}$$

$$I = \frac{5\sqrt{5}\ a\ B_H\ \tan\theta}{8\ \mu_0\ n} = \frac{5\sqrt{5} \times 0.11 \times 0.32 \times 10^{-4} \times 1}{8 \times 4\pi \times 10^{-7} \times 70\sqrt{5}}$$

$$= \frac{5\sqrt{5} \times 0.11 \times 0.32 \times 10^{-4} \times 1 \times 7}{8 \times 4 \times 22 \times 10^{-7} \times 70\sqrt{5}} = 25 \times 10^{-3} \text{ A} = 25 \text{ mA}$$

(*b*)   Here $n = 60$ $a = 7$ cm $= 0.07$ m ; $x = 9$ cm $= 0.09$ m

Current $I = 0.1$ Amp $\mu_0 = 4\pi \times 10^{-7}$

Field due to either coil $= \dfrac{\mu_0}{2} \dfrac{nIa^2}{(a^2 + x^2)^{3/2}}$

$$= \frac{1}{2} \times 4\pi \times \frac{10^{-7} \times 60 \times 0.1 \times (0.07)^2}{(0.09^2 + 0.07^2)^{3/2}}$$

$$= 0.01247 \times 10^{-4} \text{ Tesla}$$

∴ Field due to the two coils midway between them

$$= 0.1247 \times 10^{-4} \times 2 = 0.2494 \times 10^{-4} \text{ Tesla.}$$

Q. 8.38. Use Biot and Savart's law to find an expression for magnetic field at a point on the axis of a current carrying solenoid. Hence prove that the magnetic field at the end is half the magnetic field at the centre of a very long solenoid.

(*P.U.*, 2009, 2003, 2001; *G.N.D.U.*, 2007, 2000; *Luck. U.*, 1993; *A.U.*, 1993; *H.P.U.*, 1991)

Ans. Magnetic field at a point on the axis of a circular coil. Using Biot and Savart's law, the magnetic field at a point on the axis (taken along the *X*-axis) of a circular coil of *n* turns of radius *a* distant *x* from the centre of the coil is given by

$$\vec{B} = \frac{\mu_0}{2} \frac{nIa^2}{(a^2 + x^2)^{3/2}} \hat{i}$$

i.e., the field acts along the $+X$ axis.

For proof See **Q. 8.33** Eq, (*ii*).

Intensity of magnetic field inside a solenoid. A solenoid is a long cylindrical coil having a large number of circular turns as shown in Fig. 8.24. Consider a long closely wound solenoid having n turns per unit length, each of radius a, through which a current I is flowing in the anti-clockwise direction, as seen from

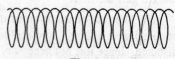

Fig. 8.24

P, a point on the axis of the solenoid well inside it. Consider a small portion AB of the solenoid having a length dx at distance x from the origin O of the co-ordinate system.

The number of turns in $AB = n\,dx$

Let P be a point on the axis of the solenoid at a distance x_0 from O, then,

The magnetic induction field at P due to ndx turns

$$d\vec{B} = \frac{\mu_0}{2} \frac{ndx\, Ia^2}{[a^2 + (x_0 - x)^2]^{3/2}} \hat{i}$$

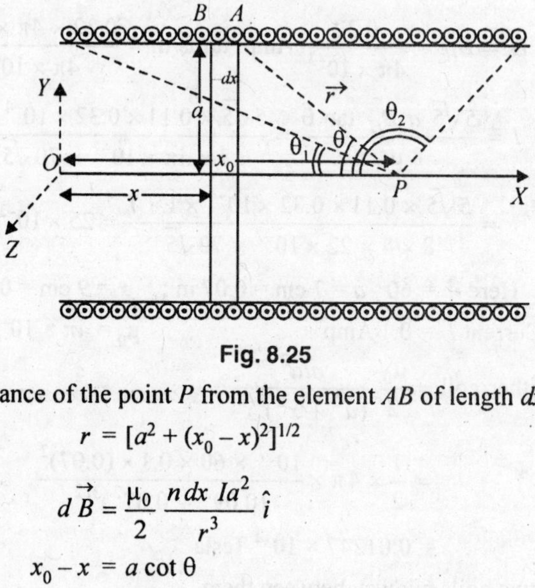

Fig. 8.25

If $r = PA$ is the distance of the point P from the element AB of length dx of the solenoid, then

$$r = [a^2 + (x_0 - x)^2]^{1/2}$$

Hence $$d\vec{B} = \frac{\mu_0}{2} \frac{ndx\, Ia^2}{r^3} \hat{i} \qquad \qquad \qquad ...(i)$$

Now $$x_0 - x = a \cot \theta$$

$\therefore$ $$-dx = -a\, \mathrm{cosec}^2\,\theta\, d\theta \text{ or } dx = a\, \mathrm{cosec}^2\,\theta\, d\theta$$

Also $$\frac{a}{r} = \sin\theta \text{ or } r = \frac{a}{\sin\theta} = a\, \mathrm{cosec}\,\theta$$

Substituting in (*i*), we have

$$d\vec{B} = \frac{\mu_0}{2}\, nI\, \frac{a^3\, \mathrm{cosec}^2\,\theta\, d\theta}{a^3\, \mathrm{cosec}^3\,\theta} \hat{i}$$

$$= \frac{\mu_0}{2}\, nI\, \frac{1}{\mathrm{cosec}\,\theta}\, d\theta\, \hat{i} = \frac{\mu_0}{2}\, nI \sin\theta\, d\theta\, \hat{i} \qquad \qquad ...(ii)$$

The field $\vec{B}$ due to the whole length of the solenoid is obtained by integrating (*ii*) between the limits $\theta = \theta_1$ and $\theta = \theta_2$ where θ_1 and θ_2 are the angles subtended at P by the two ends of the solenoid respectively.

$$\therefore \quad \vec{B} = \hat{i} \int_{\theta_1}^{\theta_2} \frac{\mu_0}{2} \, nI \, \sin\theta \, d\theta = \frac{\mu_0}{2} \, nI \, [-\cos\theta]_{\theta_1}^{\theta_2} \, \hat{i}$$

$$= \frac{\mu_0}{2} \, nI \, [\cos\theta_1 - \cos\theta_2] \, \hat{i} \qquad \qquad ...(iii)$$

Infinitely long solenoid. For an infinitely long solenoid, when the point P lies well inside it and far removed from either of the ends

$$\theta_1 = 0 \text{ and } \theta_2 = \pi$$

$$\therefore \qquad \vec{B} = \frac{\mu_0}{2} \, nI \, [1 + 1] \, \hat{i} = \mu_0 \, nI \, \hat{i} \qquad \qquad ...(iv)$$

Thus the magnitude of the field $\vec{B}$ is $B = \mu_0 nI$ and it acts along the axis of the solenoid from O to P i.e., in the $+X$ direction.

Field at the end. When the point P lies near one end of the solenoid $\theta_1 = 0$ and $\theta_2 = \pi/2$

$$\therefore \qquad B = \frac{\mu_0}{2} \, nI \, [1 - 0] = \frac{\mu_0}{2} \, nI \qquad \qquad ...(v)$$

Comparing (iv) and (v) we find that the magnitude of the field $\vec{B}$ at a point lying at one end of the solenoid is one half of that at its centre.

The magnetic field inside a long solenoid is uniform and the lines of magnetic induction are parallel to the axis of the solenoid.

For a point outside the solenoid the magnetic field is zero.

Q. 8.39. What is a toroid? What is the value of the magnetic field inside, outside and within the core of the toroid. (G.N.D.U., 2006; H.P.U., 2007; Meerut.U., 2006)

Ans. What is a toroid ? *A solenoid bent into a circular form and whose ends are put together, is called an endless solenoid or* **toroid.** It behaves like an infinitely long solenoid as regards magnetic field for a point within the solenoid. The magnitude of the magnetic field is given by

$$B = \mu_0 \, n \, I$$

A toroid which is tightly wound and has uniform spacing between its turns is known as an *ideal toroid.*

The lines of magnetic induction are endless circles concentric with the toroid as shown in Fig. 8.26 (a). The direction of the magnetic field $\vec{B}$ will be tangent to the circle at every point.

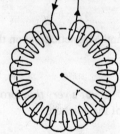

Fig. 8.26 (a)

Magnetic field due to a toroid. If we consider a toroid having inner radius r_1, outer radius r_2 with centre O and total number of turns N as shown in Fig. 8.26 (b), the magnetic field due to the toroid will depend upon the location of the observation point. Three cases arise :–

(i) *The observation point P_i lies at a distance r_i less than r_1.* To find the magnetic field at P_i draw a circle with radius r_i and centre O. It is clear from the figure that no turn of the current carrying wire of the toroid passes through the area enclosed by the path i.e., $I = 0$

According to Ampere's circuital law the line integral of the magnetic field along the closed path i.e.,

$$\oint \vec{B} . \, d\vec{r} = 2\pi r_i \, B = \mu_0 \, N I = 0 \qquad \qquad [\because I = 0]$$

$$\therefore \qquad B = 0$$

Thus the magnetic field is zero inside the ideal toroid.

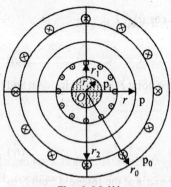

Fig. 8.26 (b)

(ii) The observation point P_0 lies at a distance r_0 greater than r_2. To find the magnetic field at P_0 draw a circle with radius r_0 and centre O. It is clear from the figure that as many turns of the current carrying wire emerge out of the outer boundary of the toroid (shown as $\otimes$) as enter into its inner boundary (shown as $\odot$) *i.e.* the net current I linked with the whole area enclosed by the path is zero or $I = 0$

The line integral of the magnetic field along the closed path *i.e.*

$$\oint \vec{B} . \, d\vec{r} = 2\pi r_0 \, B = \mu_0 \, N \, I = 0 \qquad (\because I = 0)$$

Thus the magnetic field is zero outside the ideal toroid.

(iii) The observation point P lies at a distance r where r > r_1 but r < r_2. To find the magnetic field at P draw a circle with radius r and centre O. It is clear from the figure that all the N turns of the current carrying wire enter into its boundary (shown as $\odot$) *i.e.* the current linked with the whole area enclosed by the path = $N I$.

The line integral of the magnetic field along the closed path *i.e.*

$$\oint \vec{B} . \, d\vec{r} = 2\pi r \, B = \mu_0 \, N \, I$$

or
$$B = \frac{\mu_0 \, N \, I}{2\pi r}$$

As r varies from r_1 to r_2 as we move from the inner edge to the outer edge of the toroid *the magnetic field inside the core of the ideal toroid is non-uniform*

Magnetic field on the inner edge of the toroid of radius r_1

$$B_1 = \frac{\mu_0 \, N \, I}{2\pi r_1}$$

and Magnetic field on the outer edge of toroid of radius r_2

$$B_2 = \frac{\mu_0 \, N \, I}{2\pi r_2}$$

For a *very thin* toroid $r_1 = r_2 = r$. In such a case $2\pi r$ = circumference of the toroid = mean length of the solenoid

$$\therefore \qquad B = \frac{\mu_0 \, N \, I}{2\pi r} = \mu_0 \, n I$$

where n is the number of turns per unit length of the solenoid (or toroid)

For a toroid of small cross-sectional area having inner radius r_1 and out radius r_2, the mean radius

$$r = \frac{r_1 + r_2}{2} \qquad \text{and}$$

$$B = \frac{\mu_0 \, N \, I}{2\pi r}$$

Q. 8.40. A toroid of small cross-sectional area has 10^4 turns and outer radius of 9 cm and inner radius of 5 cm. The current in the toroid winding is 0.14 A. Find the magnetic field inside the toroid. *(P.U., 2003)*

Ans. Total number of turns on the toroid $N = 10^4$

Mean radius of the toroid (of small cross-sectional area)

$$r = \frac{r_1 + r_2}{2} = \frac{5 + 9}{2} = 7\,cm = 7 \times 10^{-2}\,m$$

$$\text{Current } I = 0.14\,A.$$

Magnetic field inside the toroid $B = \dfrac{\mu_0\,NI}{2\pi r}$

$$= \frac{\mu_0}{4\pi} \cdot \frac{2NI}{r} = \frac{10^{-7} \times 2 \times 10^4 \times 0.14}{7 \times 10^{-2}}$$

$$= 4 \times 10^{-3}\,T$$

Q. 8.41. A solenoid has length 2 metres and mean diameter 0.05 metre. It has 4 layers of 1000 turns each. Calculate flux density at its centre when a current of 2.5 amperes flows through it. (*G.N.D.U.*, 1995)

Ans. Number of turns per metre $n = \dfrac{4 \times 1000}{2} = 2 \times 1000$

Current $I = 2.5\,Amp.$

$$\frac{\mu_0}{4\pi} = 10^{-7}\,Wb\,m^{-2} \text{ or } \mu_0 = 4\pi \times 10^{-7}\,Wb\,m^{-2}$$

Flux density $= $ Magnetic induction field $B = \mu_0\,nI$

$$= 4\pi \times 10^{-7} \times 2 \times 1000 \times 2.5$$

$$= 6.3 \times 10^{-3}\,Wb/m^2 = 6.3 \times 10^{-3}\,Tesla$$

Exercise. *In the above question calculate the magnetic flux for a cross-section of the solenoid at its centre.*

Hint. Mean diameter of the solenoid $D = 0.05$ metre

$\therefore$ Mean radius $r = 0.025\,m$

Effective cross-sectional area $A = \pi r^2 = \dfrac{22}{7} \times 0.025 \times 0.025$

$$= 19.64 \times 10^{-4}\,sqm$$

$\therefore$ Magnetic flux $\phi_B = BA = 6.3 \times 10^{-3} \times 19.64 \times 10^{-4} = 12.7 \times 10^{-5}\,Wb$

Q. 8.42. A solenoid 4 m long and mean diameter 8 cm has 10^4 turns. If a current of 5A is flowing through it, calculate the magnetic field at its centre.

(*H.P.U.*, 1991; *P.U.*, 1991; *G.N.D.U.*, 1990)

Ans. As the solenoid has a length 100 times its radius, it may be taken to be a solenoid of infinite length.

Number of turns $= 10^4;$ Length $= 4\,m$

$\therefore$ Number of turns per metre $n = \dfrac{10^4}{4} = 2.5 \times 10^3$

Current $I = 5A$

$\therefore$ Magnetic field at the centre of the solenoid $B = \mu_0\,nI$

$$= 4\pi \times 10^{-7} \times 2.5 \times 10^3 \times 5 = 15.7 \times 10^{-3}\,Tesla.$$

Q. 8.43. A solenoid of 1200 turns is wound uniformly in single layer on a glass tube 24 cms long and 10 cms in diameter. Find the strength of the field (a) at the centre and (b) at the end when 0.1 ampere current flows through it.

Ans. Length of the solenoid $= 24\,cms = 0.24\,m$

Total number of turns $= 1200$

Number of turns per metre $n = \dfrac{1200}{0.24} = 5000$

Current through the solenoid $I = 0.1$ amp

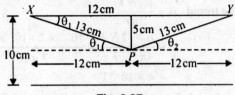

Fig. 8.27

Let θ_1 and θ_2 be the angles subtended at P by the ends X and Y, then

$$\cos\theta_2 = \cos(180 - \theta_1) = -\cos\theta_1 = \frac{12}{13}$$

(a) Magnitude of magnetic field at any point P inside the solenoid

$$B = \frac{\mu_0}{2} nI (\cos\theta_1 - \cos\theta_2) = \mu_0 nI \cos\theta_1 \qquad [\because \cos\theta_2 = -\cos\theta_1]$$

$$= 4\pi \times 10^{-7} \times 5000 \times 0.1 \times \frac{12}{13} = 5.8 \times 10^{-4} \text{ Tesla}$$

(b) If the point P lies at the end Y of the solenoid, then let $\theta_1 = \theta$ be the angle *subtended* by X at P, then

$$PX = \sqrt{24^2 + 5^2} = \sqrt{601} \qquad \therefore \quad \cos\theta = \frac{24}{\sqrt{601}}$$

The angle θ_2 subtended by Y at $P = \pi/2$ $\therefore \cos\theta_2 = 0$

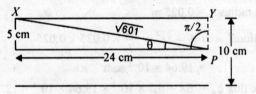

Fig. 8.28 (a)

Magnitude of the field at P; $B = \dfrac{\mu_0}{2} nI (\cos\theta_1 - \cos\theta_2)$

$$= \frac{\mu_0}{2} nI \cos\theta = \frac{1}{2} \times 4\pi \times 10^{-7} \times 5000 \times 0.1 \times \frac{24}{\sqrt{601}}$$

$$= 3.075 \times 10^{-4} \text{ Tesla.}$$

Exercise. *A solenoid has 800 turns over a length of 0.5 m when the current is 8 Amp. What will be its magnetic moment and magnetic field at the ends ? Area of cross-section 0.2 m^2*

(*Kerala U. 2001*)

Hint. Taking the solenoid to be infinitely long, we have magnetic field at the ends

$$B = \frac{\mu_0}{2} nI$$

$$= \frac{4\pi \times 10^{-7}}{2} \times \frac{800}{0.5} \times 8 = 8.04 \times 10^{-3} \text{ Tesla}$$

Magnetic moment $\qquad \vec{P}_m = NIA = 800 \times 8 \times 0.2 = 1280 \text{ Am}^2 \text{ (or J/Tesla)}$

Q. 8.44. A Solenoid of length 20 cm and radius 2 cm is closely wound with 200 turns. Calculate the magnetic field intensity at the centre of an end of the solenoid. The current in the solenoid is 5 amp.

(Meerut U. 2002)

Ans. Length of the solenoid = 20 cm = 0.2 m

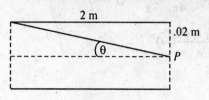

Fig. 8.28 (b)

Total number of turns = 200

∴ Number of turns per metre $n = \dfrac{200}{0.2} = 1000$

Current through the solenoid $I = 5A$.

Magnetic field at

$$P = \frac{\mu_0}{2} n I \cos\theta$$

Now

$$\cos\theta = \frac{.2}{\sqrt{.2^2 + .02^2}}$$

$$= \frac{0.2}{0.201} = 0.995$$

∴   Field at $P = \dfrac{\mu_0}{2} \times 1000 \times 5 \times 0.995$

$$= \frac{1}{2} \times 4\pi \times 10^{-7} \times 5 \times 995$$

$$= \pi \times 995 \times 10^{-6}$$

$$= 3126 \times 10^{-6} = 3.126 \times 10^{-3} \text{ T}$$

Q. 8.45 (a) Calculate the force between two long straight wires carrying currents (*i*) in the same direction and (*ii*) in the opposite directions using Biot's and Savart's law. Also find the force between two co-axial circular coils.

(P.U., 2001; Luck.U., 1996)

(b) Two parallel wires of copper are separated by a distance of 10 cm. Each of these wires carries a current of 10 amp in opposite directions. Calculate the force per unit length acting on each wire and indicate direction of force also.

(Pbi.U. 1993)

Ans. **(a)** **(i)** **Force between two straight conductors.** Let AB and CD be two *long* straight conductors carrying currents I_1 and I_2 respectively and lying parallel to each other along the Y-axis at a distance x. The current in both is flowing along the $-Y$ direction. Then according to Biot's and Savart's law the intensity of the magnetic field $\vec{B}$ at a point on the wire CD due to the current I_1 in AB is given by

$$\vec{B} = \frac{\mu_0}{4\pi} \frac{2I_1}{x} \hat{k} \qquad ...(i)$$

The direction of magnetic field $\vec{B}$ is along the $+Z$ direction.

Force experienced by a length $\vec{dl}$ of the wire CD due to the field $\vec{B}$

$$= I_2 \vec{dl} \times \vec{B} = I_2 (-dl\,\hat{j}) \times (B\hat{k}) \qquad ...(ii)$$

As the current flows in CD along $-Y$ direction, the current element is taken as $-I_2\, dl\,\hat{j}$

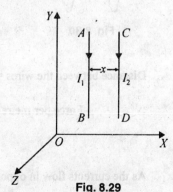

Fig. 8.29

Substituting the value of $\vec{B}$ from (i) in (ii), we have

Force on a length dl of CD

$$= I_2(-dl\,\hat{j}) \times \left(\frac{\mu_0}{4\pi}\frac{2I_1}{x}\right)\hat{k} = -\frac{\mu_0}{4\pi}\frac{2I_1 I_2}{x}\frac{dl}{x}(\hat{j} \times \hat{k})$$

$$= -\frac{\mu_0}{4\pi}\frac{2I_1'I_2}{x}\frac{dl}{}\hat{i} = \frac{\mu_0}{4\pi}\frac{2I_1 I_2}{x}\frac{dl}{}(-\hat{i})$$

$\therefore$ Force on a length

$$l = \frac{\mu_0}{4\pi}\frac{2I_1 I_2}{x}(-\hat{i})\int_0^l dl$$

$$= \frac{\mu_0}{4\pi}\frac{2I_1 I_2}{x}\frac{l}{}(-\hat{i})$$

Hence force on a unit length $= \dfrac{\mu_0}{4\pi}\dfrac{2I_1 I_2}{x}(-\hat{i}) = \dfrac{\mu_0}{2\pi}\dfrac{I_1 I_2}{x}(-\hat{i})$

Thus the force due to the current in AB on the conductor CD acts along $-X$ direction $i.e.$, it is a force of *attraction* and its magnitude is $\dfrac{\mu_0}{2\pi}\dfrac{I_1 I_2}{x}$.

(ii) The force is mutual $i.e.$, the force on a unit length of AB due to the current in CD is also same. This is in according with Newton's third law of motion. Two conductors *attract* each other if the current flows in the *same direction* and they *repel* each other if the currents flow in *opposite directions*.

Force between two equal parallel co-axial coils. Let A and B be two co-axial circular coils of one turn each of radius a with their centres a small distance x apart. Let I_1 be the current in the coil A and I_2 that in B. As x is small as compated to a the magnitude of the force on unit length of B due to A

$$= \frac{\mu_0}{4\pi}\frac{2I_1 I_2}{x}$$

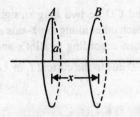

Fig. 8.30

The total force on B is the product of force per unit length and the circumference.

$\therefore$ Total force $= \dfrac{\mu_0}{4\pi}\dfrac{2I_1 I_2}{x} 2\pi a$

$$= \mu_0\frac{I_1 I_2\, a}{x}$$

(b) Current in each wire $= 10$ Amp

$\therefore$ $I_1 = I_2 = 10$ Amp

Distance between the wires $= 10$ cm $= 0.1$ m; $\dfrac{\mu_0}{4\pi} = 10^{-7}$ N/A^2

$\therefore$ Force per metre $= \dfrac{\mu_0}{4\pi}\dfrac{2I_1 I_2}{x}$

$$= 10^{-7}\frac{2\times 10\times 10}{0.1} = 2\times 10^{-4}\ \text{N/m}$$

As the currents flow in opposite directions the two wires **repel** each other.

Q. 8.46. Two straight wires each 10 cms long are parallel to one another and separated by a distance of 2 cms. They carry currents of 30 amps and 40 amps respectively. Calculate the force experienced by either of the wires.

Ans.   Length of each wire $= 10$ cms $= 0.1$ metre

Distance between the wires $x = 2$ cm $= 0.2$ metre

Current in one wire $I_1 = 30$ amps

Current in the other wire $I_2 = 40$ amps.

Force per metre of the wire $= \dfrac{\mu_0}{4\pi} \dfrac{2 I_1 I_2}{x}$

$$= \dfrac{10^{-7} \times 2 \times 30 \times 40}{.02} = 12 \times 10^{-3} \text{ Newton}$$

Hence force on either of the conductors of 0.1 metre length

$$= 12 \times 10^{-3} \times 0.1 = 12 \times 10^{-4} \text{ Newton.}$$

Q. 8.47. Two straight wires are kept in air 2 m apart carrying currents of 80 A and 30 A in the same direction. Calculate the force between them and specify its nature.   *(H.P.U. 1991)*

Ans. Force per metre of each wire $= \dfrac{\mu_0}{4\pi} \dfrac{2 I_1 I_2}{x}$

$$= 10^{-7} \times \dfrac{2 \times 80 \times 30}{2} = 2.4 \times 10^{-4} \text{ Newton}$$

As the currents are in the same direction the two wires attract each other.

Q. 8.48. A current is sent through a hanging coiled spring. What changes do you expect and why?   *(H.P.U., 1994; Luck.U., 1996)*

Ans. The coiled spring will contract in length as soon as a current is passed through it. The coiled spring carrying current is equivalent to series of wires carrying parallel currents in the same direction. As the two parallel wires carrying currents in the same direction attract each other, the coils of the spring come close together. So the spring contracts in length.

Q. 8.49. Differentiate between the terms scalar and vector potentials as applied in magnetism. Derive the expression $\vec{A} = \dfrac{\mu_0}{4\pi} \iiint \dfrac{\vec{J}\, dv}{r}$ **for the vector potential and show that** $\vec{B} = \vec{\nabla} \times \vec{A}$ **where** $\vec{B}$ **is the magnetic induction and** $\vec{A}$ **the magnetic vector potential.**   *(G.N.D.U., 2009,*
2007, 2006, 2001, 2000, 1999, 1996; K.U., 2001, 1996, 1994;
M.D.U., 2001, 1999; Pbi. U., 2008, 2001, 2000, 1999; P.U., 2001, 1995;
Kerala U., 2001; H.P.U., 2007, 2003, 2002,1999; Luck. U., 1996; Kan. U., 1995, 1994)

Ans. Magnetic scalar potential. In the case of an electric field, we have

$$\vec{E} = - \, grad. \, V = - \vec{\nabla} V_E$$

where $\vec{E}$ is the electric field intensity and V_E the electric potential, which is a *scalar* quantity. The electric field is a *conservative* field and hence

$$\vec{\nabla} \times \vec{E} = 0 \quad \text{or} \quad \vec{\nabla} \times \vec{\nabla} V_E = 0$$

But *curl* $\vec{B} = \vec{\nabla} \times \vec{B} = 0$ only in the special case when the line integral $\oint \vec{B} \cdot dl = 0$ *i.e.*, when the line integral does not enclose a current. When the line integral encloses a current of current density $\vec{j}$ then $\vec{\nabla} \times \vec{B} = \mu_0 \vec{J}$

In a *current free space* $\vec{J} = 0$ and therefore $\vec{\nabla} \times \vec{B} = 0$

Thus for a *current free space* we can write

$$\vec{B} = -\vec{\nabla} V_m$$

where V_m is a scalar function called *magnetic scalar potential.*

$\vec{B}$ is the negative gradient of scalar potential only in current free space. $\vec{B}$ is not, in general, the negative gradient of a scalar potential.

The condition for a magnetic scalar potential to exist is that the current density vector $\vec{J} = 0$ *i.e.*, it is a *current free space.*

Magnetic vector potential. The divergence of a magnetic induction field $\vec{\nabla} \cdot B$ is always zero.

$\therefore$

$$\vec{\nabla} \cdot \vec{B} = 0$$

If $\vec{A}$ is another vector such that $\vec{B} = \vec{\nabla} \times \vec{A}$, then

$$\vec{\nabla} \cdot \vec{B} = \vec{\nabla} \cdot \vec{\nabla} \times \vec{A} \text{ is always equal to zero.}$$

The vector $\vec{A}$ is called *magnetic vector potential.*

Hence magnetic vector potential is defined as a vector function the curl of which is equal to $\vec{B}$ the magnetic induction field.

Vector potential due to an arbitrary current element (or current loop). Consider an arbitrary current distribution (or current loop) through which a current I is flowing. Let $d\vec{r}'$ be a small current element (of the loop) at the position vector $\vec{r}'$ as shown. If P is a point at the position vector $\vec{r}$, then

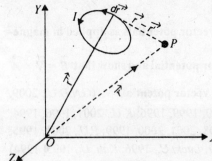

the vector drawn from the location of $d\vec{r}'$ to the point

$$P = \vec{r} - \vec{r}'$$

Let $d\vec{B}(\vec{r})$ be the magnetic induction field at P due to the current element $I d\vec{r}'$, then according to Biot and Savart's law

$$d\vec{B}(\vec{r}) = \frac{\mu_0}{4\pi} \frac{I(d\vec{r}') \times (\vec{r} - \vec{r}')}{|\vec{r} - \vec{r}'|^3} \qquad ...(i)$$

Fig. 8.31

The direction of $d\vec{B}(\vec{r})$ is perpendicular to the plane containing $d\vec{r}'$ and $(\vec{r} - \vec{r}')$. The total magnetic field due to the whole current distribution (or loop) is

$$\vec{B}(\vec{r}) = \int d\vec{B}(\vec{r}) = \frac{\mu_0 I}{4\pi} \int \frac{d\vec{r}' \times (\vec{r} - \vec{r}')}{|\vec{r} - \vec{r}'|^3} \qquad ...(i)\,(a)$$

If S is the area of cross-section of the current element $I d\vec{r}'$, dv' its volume and $\vec{J}$ the current density, then

$$I d\vec{r}' = \frac{I}{S} S d\vec{r}' = JS d\vec{r}' = \vec{J}S dr' = \vec{J} dv' \qquad \ldots(ii)$$

because the direction of $\vec{J}$ is the same as that of $d\vec{r}'$ and $Sdr' = dv'$.

Relation (i) can now be put in the form

$$d\vec{B}(\vec{r}) = \frac{\mu_0}{4\pi} \frac{\vec{J}(dv') \times (\vec{r} - \vec{r}')}{|\vec{r} - \vec{r}'|^3}$$

This is the statement of Biot's and Savart's law in terms of current density vector $\vec{J}$ and volume element dv' i.e., in terms of *volume currents element* $(\vec{J} dv')$ located at the position vector $\vec{r}'$.

Also

$$\frac{(\vec{r} - \vec{r}')}{|\vec{r} - \vec{r}'|^3} = -\vec{\nabla} \left[\frac{1}{|\vec{r} - \vec{r}'|} \right] \qquad \ldots(iii)$$

Substituting the values obtained in (ii) and (iii) in the relation (i) (a)

$$\vec{B}(\vec{r}) = -\frac{\mu_0}{4\pi} \iiint \vec{J} dv' \times \vec{\nabla} \left[\frac{1}{|\vec{r} - \vec{r}'|} \right]$$

$$= \frac{\mu_0}{4\pi} \iiint \vec{\nabla} \left[\frac{1}{|\vec{r} - \vec{r}'|} \right] \times \vec{J} dv' \qquad \ldots(iv)$$

But

$$\vec{\nabla} \times \frac{\vec{J}}{|\vec{r} - \vec{r}'|} = (\vec{\nabla} \times \vec{J}) \frac{1}{|\vec{r} - \vec{r}'|} + \vec{\nabla} \frac{1}{|\vec{r} - \vec{r}'|} \times \vec{J}$$

and for steady current $\vec{\nabla} \times \vec{J} = 0$

$$\therefore \quad \vec{\nabla} \times \frac{\vec{J}}{|\vec{r} - \vec{r}'|} = \vec{\nabla} \frac{1}{|\vec{r} - \vec{r}'|} \times \vec{J} \qquad \ldots(v)$$

From (iv) and (v), we get

$$\vec{B}(\vec{r}) = \frac{\mu_0}{4\pi} \iiint \vec{\nabla} \left[\frac{1}{|\vec{r} - \vec{r}'|} \right] \times \vec{J} dv' = \vec{\nabla} \times \frac{\mu_0}{4\pi} \iiint \frac{\vec{J} dv'}{|\vec{r} - \vec{r}'|}$$

But $\vec{B}(\vec{r}) = curl \, \vec{A}(\vec{r}) = \vec{\nabla} \times \vec{A}(\vec{r})$ where $\vec{A}(\vec{r})$ is the magnetic vector potential at the position vector $\vec{r}$.

$$\therefore \quad \vec{\nabla} \times \vec{A}(\vec{r}) = \vec{\nabla} \times \frac{\mu_0}{4\pi} \iiint \frac{\vec{J}}{\vec{r} - \vec{r}'} dv'$$

or

$$\vec{A}(\vec{r}) = \frac{\mu_0}{4\pi} \iiint \frac{\vec{J} dv'}{|\vec{r} - \vec{r}'|} \qquad \ldots(vi)$$

If $\vec{r}$ is the vector distance of the point P from the current element taken to be of a small vector length $d\vec{r}$, then replacing $\vec{r} - \vec{r}'$ by $|\vec{r}|$ and $dv' = S\,dr'$ by $S\,dr = dv$, we get

$$\vec{A} = \frac{\mu_0}{4\pi} \iiint \frac{\vec{J}}{r}\,dv \qquad \qquad \text{...}(vii)$$

Q. 8.50. (*a*) **Show that for a finite current distribution divergence of magnetic vector poten-, tial** *i.e.,* $\vec{\nabla} \cdot \vec{A} = 0$ (*H.P.U.* 2002)

(*b*) **State the condition under which magnetic scalar potential exists ?**

(*G.N.D.U.* 2004, 2003; *H.P.U.* 1993)

Ans. (*a*) **Divergence of magnetic vector potential** $\vec{A}$. The magnetic vector potential $\vec{A}$ due to an arbitrary current distribution is given by

$$\vec{A}(\vec{r}) = \frac{\mu_0}{4\pi} \iiint \frac{\vec{J}\,dv'}{|\vec{r} - \vec{r}'|}$$

If $\vec{r}$ is the vector distance of a point P from the current element taken to be of a small vector length $d\vec{r}$, then replacing $|\vec{r} - \vec{r}'|$ by $|\vec{r}| = r$ and $dv' = S\,dr'$ by $S\,dr = dv$

we get $$\vec{A} = \frac{\mu_0}{4\pi} \iiint \frac{\vec{J}}{r}\,dv$$

$\therefore$ Divergence of magnetic vector potential

$$\vec{\nabla} \cdot \vec{A} = \frac{\mu_0}{4\pi} \iiint \vec{\nabla} \cdot \frac{\vec{J}}{r}\,dv$$

But according to Gauss's divergence theorem

$$\iiint \vec{\nabla} \cdot \frac{\vec{J}}{r}\,dv = \oiint \frac{\vec{J}}{r} \cdot d\vec{S}$$

or $$\vec{\nabla} \cdot \vec{A} = \frac{\mu_0}{4\pi} \oiint \frac{\vec{J}}{r} \cdot d\vec{S}$$

As the volume integral is over the whole space, the surface integral may also be considered over the whole surface extending upto infinity. For any finite current distribution, the current density vector $\vec{J}$ vanishes at infinity. Hence $\vec{J} = 0$

or $$\oiint_S \frac{\vec{J}}{r} \cdot d\vec{S} = 0$$

$\therefore$ $$\vec{\nabla} \cdot \vec{A} = 0$$

(*b*) The differential form of Ampere's law states that $\vec{\nabla} \times \vec{B} = \mu_0 \vec{J}$. Thus the magnetic scalar potential will exist only if the curl of magnetic field is zero. This condition is satisfied only when $\vec{J} = 0$ *i.e.,* magnetic scalar potential will exist only in a current free space. (Also see **Q 8.49** under **'Magnetic scalar poltential'**

Q. 8.51. Show that $\nabla^2 \vec{A} = -\mu_0 \vec{J}$ **where** $\vec{A}$ **is the magnetic vector potential and** $\vec{J}$ **is the current density.** *(P.U., 1994; K.U., 1994; Pbi. U., 1993)*

Ans. Magnetic vector potential is defined as the vector function, the curl of which is equal to the magnetic induction field

or
$$\vec{B} = curl\ \vec{A} = \vec{\nabla} \times \vec{A}$$

Now
$$Curl\ \vec{B} = \vec{\nabla} \times \vec{B} = \mu_0 \vec{J}$$

$\therefore$
$$Curl\ (Curl\ \vec{A}) = \vec{\nabla} \times (\vec{\nabla} \times \vec{A}) = \vec{\nabla} \times \vec{B} = \mu_0 \vec{J} \qquad ...(i)$$

Now
$$\vec{B} = \vec{\nabla} \times \vec{A} = \begin{vmatrix} \hat{i} & \hat{j} & \hat{k} \\ \dfrac{\partial}{\partial x} & \dfrac{\partial}{\partial y} & \dfrac{\partial}{\partial z} \\ A_x & A_y & A_z \end{vmatrix}$$

$$= \hat{i}\left(\frac{\partial A_z}{\partial y} - \frac{\partial A_y}{\partial z}\right) + \hat{j}\left(\frac{\partial A_x}{\partial z} - \frac{\partial A_z}{\partial x}\right) + \hat{k}\left(\frac{\partial A_y}{\partial x} - \frac{\partial A_x}{\partial y}\right)$$

$$= \hat{i}\,B_x + \hat{j}\,B_y + \hat{k}\,B_z$$

and
$$\vec{\nabla} \times \vec{B} = \begin{vmatrix} \hat{i} & \hat{j} & \hat{k} \\ \dfrac{\partial}{\partial x} & \dfrac{\partial}{\partial y} & \dfrac{\partial}{\partial z} \\ B_x & B_y & B_z \end{vmatrix}$$

$$= \hat{i}\left(\frac{\partial B_z}{\partial y} - \frac{\partial B_y}{\partial z}\right) + \hat{j}\left(\frac{\partial B_x}{\partial z} - \frac{\partial B_z}{\partial x}\right) + \hat{k}\left(\frac{\partial B_y}{\partial x} - \frac{\partial B_x}{\partial y}\right)$$

$\therefore$ *X*-component of $\vec{\nabla} \times \vec{B} = (\vec{\nabla} \times \vec{B})_x$

$$= X\text{-component of } \vec{\nabla} \times (\vec{\nabla} \times \vec{A}) = [\vec{\nabla} \times (\vec{\nabla} \times \vec{A})]_x$$

$$= (\vec{\nabla} \times \vec{B})_x = \frac{\partial B_z}{\partial y} - \frac{\partial B_y}{\partial z}$$

$$= \frac{\partial}{\partial y}\left(\frac{\partial A_y}{\partial x} - \frac{\partial A_x}{\partial y}\right) - \frac{\partial}{\partial z}\left(\frac{\partial A_x}{\partial z} - \frac{\partial A_z}{\partial x}\right)$$

$$= -\frac{\partial^2 A_x}{\partial y^2} - \frac{\partial^2 A_x}{\partial z^2} + \frac{\partial^2 A_y}{\partial y \partial x} + \frac{\partial^2 A_z}{\partial z \partial x}$$

Adding and subtracting $\dfrac{\partial^2 A_x}{\partial x^2}$ and rearranging the above expression, we get

$$(\vec{\nabla} \times \vec{B})_x = -\left(\frac{\partial^2 A_x}{\partial x^2} + \frac{\partial^2 A_x}{\partial y^2} + \frac{\partial^2 A_x}{\partial z^2}\right) + \frac{\partial}{\partial x}\left(\frac{\partial A_x}{\partial x} + \frac{\partial A_x}{\partial y} + \frac{\partial A_x}{\partial z}\right)$$

$$= \mu_0 J_x \qquad ...(ii)$$

The expression $\dfrac{\partial A_x}{\partial x} + \dfrac{\partial A_y}{\partial y} + \dfrac{\partial A_z}{\partial z} = \vec{\nabla} . \vec{A}$. As the vector potential $\vec{A}$ has been defined as the

vector the curl of which *i.e.*, $\vec{\nabla} \times \vec{A} = \vec{B}$, there is no other condition to be satisfied by the vector. In

other words $div\ \vec{A} = \vec{\nabla} . \vec{A}$ may have any value. We, therefore, substitute $\vec{\nabla} . \vec{A} = 0$. This means that,

of all the functions which satisfy the equation $Curl\ \vec{A} = \vec{B}$, we select only the function for which

$div\ \vec{A} = 0$.

Substituting $\vec{\nabla} . \vec{A} = 0$ equation (*ii*) becomes

$$\frac{\partial^2 A_x}{\partial x^2} + \frac{\partial^2 A_y}{\partial y^2} + \frac{\partial^2 A_z}{\partial z^2} = \nabla^2 A_x = -\mu_0 J_x$$

Similarly $\nabla^2 A_y = -\mu_0 J_y$ and $\nabla^2 A_z = -\mu_0 J_z$

$$\therefore \quad \nabla^2 (\hat{i} A_x + \hat{j} A_y + \hat{k} A_z) = -\mu_0 (\hat{i} J_x + \hat{j} J_y + \hat{k} J_z)$$

or $$\nabla^2 \vec{A} = -\mu_0 \vec{J} \qquad \qquad \qquad ...(iii)$$

This is vector Poisson's equation for magnetic vector potential $\vec{A}$ corresponding to scalar Poisson's

equation $\nabla^2 \phi = -\dfrac{\rho}{\varepsilon_0}$ for electric scalar potential ϕ.

For a current free space $\vec{J} = 0$ and we have

$$\nabla^2 \vec{A} = 0 \qquad \qquad \qquad ...(iv)$$

which is Laplace's equation for magnetic vector potential.

Note. The relation obtained in (*iii*) above can also be proved from equation (*i*)

$$\vec{\nabla} \times (\vec{\nabla} \times \vec{A}) = \vec{\nabla} \times \vec{B} = \mu_0 \vec{J}$$

using the vector identity

$$\vec{A} \times (\vec{B} \times \vec{C}) = (\vec{A} . \vec{C}) \vec{B} - (\vec{A} . \vec{B}) \vec{C}$$

We, therefore have

$$\nabla \times (\vec{\nabla} \times \vec{A}) = (\vec{\nabla} . \vec{A}) \vec{\nabla} - (\vec{\nabla} . \vec{\nabla}) \vec{A}$$

For magnetic vector potential $\vec{\nabla} . \vec{A} = 0$

Also $$\vec{\nabla} . \vec{\nabla} = \nabla^2$$

$$\therefore \quad \vec{\nabla} \times (\vec{\nabla} \times \vec{A}) = -\nabla^2 \vec{A}$$

Hence $$\nabla^2 \vec{A} = -\mu_0 \vec{J}$$

Q. 8.52. (a) Explain the term vector potential. Using the concept of vector potential deduce Biot and Savart's law. (*P.U.*, 2003, 2000; *H.P.U.*, 1996)

OR

Given that $\vec{A} = \dfrac{\mu_0}{4\pi} \iiint \dfrac{\vec{J}\ dv}{r}$ **derive the mathematical expression for Biot and Savart's law.** (*Pbi.U.*, 2006; *P.U.*, 2002)

(b) Compare and contrast Biot's Savart's law and coulomb's law. (*P.U.*, 2003, 2000)

Ans. Vector potential. For definition of magnetic vector potential **See Q. 8.49**

If $\vec{r}$ is the vector distance of the observation point P from a current element having a small vector length $\vec{dl}$ and volume $dv = adl$ where a is the area of cross-section of the current element and $\vec{J}$ the current density vector, then vector potential at P, $\vec{A} = \dfrac{\mu_0}{4\pi} \iiint \dfrac{\vec{J}\,dv}{r}$ [Eq (*vii*) Q. 8.49]

Biot and Savart's law. Consider a current element of vector length $\vec{dl}$ having an area of cross-section a through which a current I is flowing such that the vector $\vec{dl}$ points in the direction of positive current, then, volume of the current element $= dv = \vec{a} \cdot \vec{dl} = a\,dl$. If $\vec{J}$ is the current density, then its magnitude

$$J = \frac{I}{a}$$

$$J\,dv = \frac{I}{a}\,a\,dl = I\,dl$$

since $\vec{J}$ and $d\vec{l}$ have the same direction

$$\vec{J}\,dv = I\,\vec{dl}$$

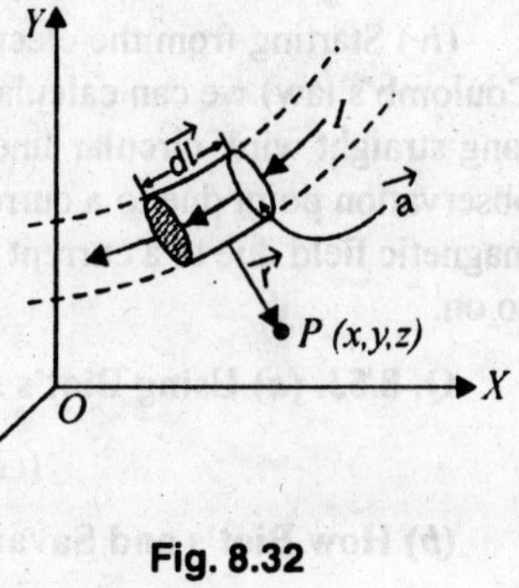

Now vector potential $\vec{A} = \dfrac{\mu_0}{4\pi} \iiint \dfrac{\vec{J}\,dv}{r}$

or

$$d\vec{A} = \frac{\mu_0}{4\pi}\frac{\vec{J}\,dv}{r} = \frac{\mu_0}{4\pi}\frac{I\,\vec{dl}}{r}$$

Fig. 8.32

where r is the magnitude of the vector $\vec{r}$ drawn from the location of $d\vec{l}$ to the point P where the value of $\vec{A}$ is to be determined.

Further

$$\vec{B} = \vec{\nabla} \times \vec{A}$$

$\therefore$

$$d\vec{B} = \vec{\nabla} \times d\vec{A} = \vec{\nabla} \times \frac{\mu_0}{4\pi}\frac{I\,\vec{dl}}{r} = \frac{\mu_0 I}{4\pi}(\vec{\nabla} \times d\vec{l})\frac{1}{r}$$

$$= -\frac{\mu_0 I}{4\pi}(d\vec{l} \times \vec{\nabla})\frac{1}{r} = -\frac{\mu_0 I}{4\pi}d\vec{l} \times \vec{\nabla}\frac{1}{r}$$

$$= -\frac{\mu_0 I}{4\pi}d\vec{l} \times \left(-\frac{\vec{r}}{r^3}\right) = \frac{\mu_0 I}{4\pi}\frac{\vec{dl} \times \vec{r}}{r^3} \qquad \left[\because \vec{\nabla}\frac{1}{r} = -\frac{\vec{r}}{r^3}\right]$$

or

$$d\vec{B} = \frac{\mu_0}{4\pi}\frac{I\,\vec{dl} \times \vec{r}}{r^3}$$

This is Biot and Savart' law.

The magnitude of $d\vec{B} = \dfrac{\mu_0}{4\pi}\dfrac{Idl}{r^2}\sin\theta$ where θ is the angle between the direction of $d\vec{l}$ and $\vec{r}$.

The direction of magnetic induction vector $d\vec{B}$ is perpendicular to the plane containing $d\vec{l}$ and $\vec{r}$ as given by right hand screw rule for cross product of two vectors.

(b) Biot and Savart's law – Comparison and contrast

(i) Coulomb's law is used to find the *electric field* due to a *stationary charge* whereas Biot's and Savart's law is used to calculate the *magnetic field* due to a *current element*.

(ii) The direction of the electric field due to a point charge given by Coulomb's law acts along the line joining the charge to the point of observation.

The magnetic field due to a current element given by Biot's and Savart's law always acts in a direction perpendicular to the line joining the current elements to the point of observation.

(iii) The electric field due to a point charge (according to Coulomb's law) as well as the magnetic field due to a current element (according to Biot and Savart's law) both vary inversely as the square of the distance of the observation point from the point charge or the current element as the case may be.

(iv) Starting from the electric field at the observation point due to a point charge (according to Coulomb's law) we can calculate the total electric field due to an electric dipole, uniformly charged long straight wire, circular line charge and so on. Similarly starting from the magnetic field at the observation point due to a current element (according to Biot and Savart law) we can calculated the magnetic field due to a current carrying straight wire, circular coil, long closely wound solenoid and so on.

Q. 8.53. (a) **Using Biot's and Savart's law prove that** $\vec{\nabla} \cdot \vec{B} = 0$

(G.N.D.U., 2008, 2007; P.U., 2007; Pbi. U., 2006, 2001; H.P.U., 1999)

(b) **How Biot's and Savart's law is used to prove that no free magnetic poles exist?**

(G.N.D.U. 2002, 2001; Gauhati U., 2000)

Ans. Divergence of magnetic field. According to Biot and Savart's law the magnetic field due to a current element $I\,\vec{dl}$ located at the origin is given by

$$d\vec{B} = \frac{\mu_0 I}{4\pi} \frac{\vec{dl} \times \vec{r}}{r^3}$$

where $\vec{r}$ is the position vector of the observation point P.

For simplicity, we shall denote $d\vec{B}$ by $\vec{B}$ so that

$$\vec{B} = \frac{\mu_0}{4\pi} \frac{I\,\vec{dl} \times \vec{r}}{r^3}$$

$$\vec{\nabla} \cdot \vec{B} = \vec{\nabla} \cdot \left(\frac{\mu_0}{4\pi} \frac{I\,\vec{dl} \times \vec{r}}{r^3} \right)$$

$$= \frac{\mu_0}{4\pi} I \vec{\nabla} \cdot \left(\frac{\vec{dl} \times \vec{r}}{r^3} \right) \qquad ...(i)$$

The divergence of the cross product of two vectors $\vec{A}$ and $\vec{B}$ is given by the identity

$$\nabla \cdot (\vec{A} \times \vec{B}) = \vec{B} \cdot (\nabla \times \vec{A}) - \vec{A} \cdot (\nabla \times \vec{B})$$

Substituting $\vec{A} = \vec{dl}$ and $\vec{B} = \dfrac{\vec{r}}{r^3}$, we get

$$\vec{\nabla} \cdot \left(\vec{dl} \times \dfrac{\vec{r}}{r^3} \right) = \dfrac{\vec{r}}{r^3} \cdot (\vec{\nabla} \times \vec{dl}) - \vec{dl} \cdot \left(\vec{\nabla} \times \dfrac{\vec{r}}{r^3} \right)$$

Now
$$\vec{\nabla} \times \vec{dl} = 0$$

$\therefore$
$$\vec{\nabla} \cdot \left(\vec{dl} \times \dfrac{\vec{r}}{r^3} \right) = - \vec{dl} \cdot \left(\vec{\nabla} \times \dfrac{\vec{r}}{r^3} \right)$$

Substituting in Eq. (i), we get

$$\vec{\nabla} \cdot \vec{B} = - \dfrac{\mu_0 I}{4\pi} \vec{dl} \cdot \vec{\nabla} \times \left(\dfrac{\vec{r}}{r^3} \right) \qquad \qquad ...(ii)$$

But
$$\vec{\nabla} \times \dfrac{\vec{r}}{r^3} = \begin{vmatrix} \hat{i} & \hat{j} & \hat{k} \\ \dfrac{\partial}{\partial x} & \dfrac{\partial}{\partial y} & \dfrac{\partial}{\partial z} \\ \dfrac{x}{r^3} & \dfrac{y}{r^3} & \dfrac{z}{r^3} \end{vmatrix}$$

$$= \hat{i} \left[\dfrac{\partial}{\partial y} \left(\dfrac{z}{r^3} \right) - \dfrac{\partial}{\partial z} \left(\dfrac{y}{r^3} \right) \right] + \hat{j} \left[\dfrac{\partial}{\partial z} \left(\dfrac{x}{r^3} \right) - \dfrac{\partial}{\partial x} \left(\dfrac{z}{r^3} \right) \right] + \hat{k} \left[\dfrac{\partial}{\partial x} \left(\dfrac{y}{r^3} \right) - \dfrac{\partial}{\partial y} \left(\dfrac{x}{r^3} \right) \right]$$

$$= \hat{i} \left(\dfrac{-3zy}{r^5} + \dfrac{3zy}{r^5} \right) + \hat{j} \left(- \dfrac{3zx}{r^5} + \dfrac{3zx}{r^5} \right) + \hat{k} \left(- \dfrac{3xy}{r^5} + \dfrac{3xy}{r^5} \right) = 0$$

Substituting $\vec{\nabla} \times \dfrac{\vec{r}}{r^3} = 0$ in Eq. (ii), we get

$$\vec{\nabla} \cdot \vec{B} = 0$$

Thus the divergence of magnetic field due to a *current element* is zero. The magnetic field due to the entire current circuit is the vector sum of fields due to current elements into which the whole circuit can be divided. So divergence of the total magnetic field is also zero.

(b) Comparing the relation $\vec{\nabla} \cdot \vec{B} = 0$ with the corresponding electrostatic field equation

$\vec{\nabla} \cdot \vec{E} = \dfrac{\rho}{\varepsilon_0}$ we conclude that magnetic charge density is zero. This means there do not exist isolated single magnetic poles. In other words free north and south poles do not exist in nature.

Q. 8.54. (a) If at any position vector potential $\vec{A} = 5(x^2 + y^2 + z^2) \hat{i}$ evaluate the magnetic field at that position.

(b) Compare the electrostatic field and magnetic field.   (G.N.D.U., 2002; H.P.U., 1997)

Ans. (a) Vector potential $\vec{A} = 5(x^2 + y^2 + z^2) \hat{i}$

$\therefore$ Magnetic field $\vec{B} = curl \, \vec{A} = \vec{\nabla} \times \vec{A}$

$$= \begin{vmatrix} \hat{i} & \hat{j} & \hat{k} \\ \dfrac{\partial}{\partial x} & \dfrac{\partial}{\partial y} & \dfrac{\partial}{\partial z} \\ 5(x^2 + y^2 + z^2) & 0 & 0 \end{vmatrix}$$

$$= \hat{j}\frac{\partial}{\partial z}[5(x^2 + y^2 + z^2)] - \hat{k}\frac{\partial}{\partial y}[5(x^2 + y^2 + z^2)]$$

or $$\vec{B} = \hat{j}10z - \hat{k}\,10y = 10(\hat{j}\,z - \hat{k}\,y)$$

(b) **Comparison between electrostatic field and magnetic field.**

	Electrostatic field $\vec{E}$	Magnetic field $\vec{B}$
1	The source of electrostatic field is the *charge*, stationary or in motion.	The source of magnetic field is a steady current or a moving charge.
2	The electrostatic field is *conservative* because $\vec{\nabla} \times \vec{E} = 0$. In other words electric field is the gradient (negative) of electric potential (a scalar quantity) $\vec{E} = -\vec{\nabla}V$	The magnetic field is *non-conservative* because $\vec{\nabla} \cdot \vec{B} = \mu_0 \vec{J}$ where $\vec{J}$ is the electric current density. In general $\vec{\nabla} \times \vec{B}$ is not equal to zero *i.e.*, the magnetic field cannot be expressed as the gradient of a scalar potential at points where electric current exists.
3	The lines of force of electrostatic field originate on positive charges and terminate on negative charges. Thus positive and negative charges can exist separately and independently. For this reason $\vec{\nabla} \cdot \vec{E} = \rho/\varepsilon_0$ where ρ is the volume charge density.	The lines of force of a magnetic field form closed curves because isolated magnetic poles do not exist. For this reason $\vec{\nabla} \times \vec{B} = 0$ (Always)

Q. 8.55. Explain the term surface current density and calculate the change in magnetic field at a current sheet. (*K.U.*, 2001; *G.N.D.U.*, 1993; *P.U.*, 1991)

Ans. Surface current density. Consider a conducting sheet of infinite extent (length and breadth) and finite thickness t lying in the $X - Y$ plane carrying a current I in the X-direction.

Let $\vec{J}$ be the current density inside the sheet. As the current I is in the X-direction

$$J_x = J;\ J_y = 0,\ J_z = 0$$

The area of cross-section of the sheet of length l (along Y-axis) and thickness t (along Z-axis) = $l \times t$

$\therefore \qquad J = \dfrac{I}{lt} \quad$ or $\quad \dfrac{I}{l} = Jt$

$\dfrac{I}{l}$ gives the current flowing per unit length of the sheet taken in a direction perpendicular to the direction of flow of current. It is represented by J_s and is called *surface current density*

$$\therefore \qquad J_s = \dfrac{I}{l} = Jt$$

The unit of J_s is Ampere/metre.

The concept of surface current density is helpful in describing the change in magnetic field in going from one side of the sheet to the other.

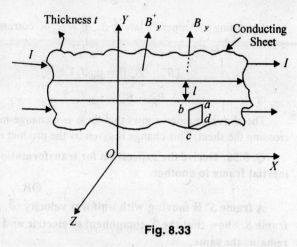

Fig. 8.33

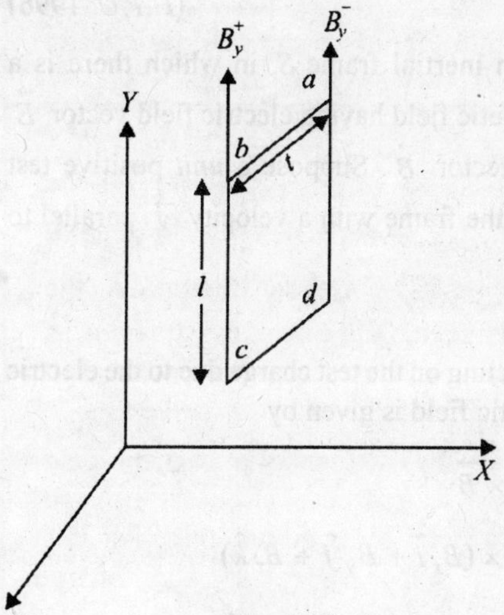

Change in magnetic field at a current sheet.

Suppose the components of the magnetic field on the two sides of the sheet are B_y^+ and B_y^- as shown and the sheet is very thin $(t \to 0)$. B_y^+ and B_y^- may include the magnetic fields due to sources other than the current in the sheet.

Consider a rectangular loop *abcd* parallel to Y-Z plane cutting the current sheet such that *da* lies on one side of the sheet and the segment *bc* lies on other side of the sheet. The loop is shown magnified in Fig. 8.34.

The line integral of the magnetic field around a closed path is given by

$$\oint \vec{B} \cdot \vec{dl} = \mu_0 \times \text{Current enclosed by the path}$$

For the path *abcda*, we have

$$\oint_{abcda} \vec{B} \cdot \vec{dl} = \int_{ab} \vec{B} \cdot \vec{dl} + \int_{bc} \vec{B} \cdot \vec{dl} + \int_{cd} \vec{B} \cdot \vec{dl} + \int_{da} \vec{B} \cdot \vec{dl}$$

Fig. 8.34

On the path *ab* and *cd* only the Z-components will enter into the integral. Even if B_z^+ and B_z^- have a finite value the fact that the sheet is very thin *i.e.*, $t \to 0$

$$\int_{ab} \vec{B} \cdot \vec{dl} = \int_{cd} \vec{B} \cdot \vec{dl} = B_z t = B_z \times 0 = 0$$

Therefore, we have

$$\oint \vec{B} \cdot \vec{dl} = \int_{bc} \vec{B} \cdot \vec{dl} + \int_{da} \vec{B} \cdot \vec{dl} = -B_y^+ l + B_y^- l$$

$$= [B_y^- - B_y^+]l$$

Current enclosed by the loop $= I = J_s l$

According to Ampere's law $\oint \vec{B} \cdot \vec{dl} = \mu_0 \times$ current enclosed

$$= \mu_0 J_s \, l$$

$$\therefore \qquad [B_y^- - B_y^+] l = \mu_0 J_s \, l$$

or $\qquad B_y^- - B_y^+ = \mu_0 J_s$

The above equation shows that there is a change in tangential component of magnetic field on crossing the sheet. This change is given by the product of μ_0 and surface current density J_s.

Q. 8.56. Derive the expression for transformation of electric and magnetic fields from one inertial frame to another. (*G.N.D.U.*, 1994)

OR

A frame S' is moving with uniform velocity $\vec{v}$ along X-direction as seen from reference frame S. Show that the X-component of electric and magnetic field as observed in two frames remains the same. (*H.P.U.* 1996)

Ans. Transformation of electric fields. Consider an inertial frame S, in which there is a constant electromagnetic field having electric field vector $\vec{E}$ and magnetic field vector $\vec{B}$. Suppose a *unit* positive test change is moving in the frame with a velocity $\vec{v}$ parallel to the X-axis, then

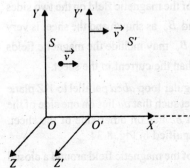

Fig. 8.35

$$\vec{v} = v\,\hat{i}$$

The total force acting on the test charge due to the electric as well as the magnetic field is given by

$$\vec{F} = \vec{E} + \vec{v} \times \vec{B}$$

$$= \vec{E} + v\hat{i} \times (B_x \hat{i} + B_y \hat{j} + B_z \hat{k})$$

$$= \vec{E} + v B_y \hat{k} - v B_z \hat{j}$$

$$[\because \hat{i} \times \hat{i} = 0, \hat{i} \times \hat{j} = \hat{k} \text{ and } \hat{i} \times \hat{k} = -\hat{j}]$$

$$= E_x \hat{i} + E_y \hat{j} + E_z \hat{k} + v B_y \hat{k} - v B_z \hat{j}$$

$$= E_x \hat{i} + (E_y - v B_z)\hat{j} + (E_z + v B_y)\hat{k}$$

$$\therefore \qquad F_x = E_x; F_y = E_y - v B_z; F_z = E_z + v B_y \qquad \qquad ...(i)$$

Moving frames S'. Now consider another inertial frame S' with its axes respectively parallel to those of S and let it move with a velocity v in the $+ X$ direction with respect to the frame S. To an observer in S', the test charge will appear to be *stationary*. Hence in the frame S' there will be no force on the test charge due to the magnetic field *i.e.*, the *only force acting on it will be that due to the electric field.* Let this force be $\vec{F}$ having components F'_x, F'_y and F'_z

Now, according to Lorentz transformation equation for force

$$F'_x = F_x - \frac{v/c^2}{1 - \dfrac{vu_x}{c^2}} (u_y F_y - u_z F_z)$$

$$F_y' = F_y \frac{\sqrt{\left(1 - \dfrac{v^2}{c^2}\right)}}{1 - \dfrac{vu_x}{c^2}} \; ; \quad F_z' = \frac{F_z \sqrt{1 - \dfrac{v^2}{c^2}}}{1 - \dfrac{vu_x}{c^2}}$$

where F_x, F_y and F_z are the components of the force $\vec{F}$ in the frame S, F_x', F_y', F_z' components of $\vec{F}$ in the frame S' acting on a particle moving with a velocity $\vec{u}$ having components u_x, u_y and u_z when the frame S' is moving with a velocity $\vec{v}$ along the $+X$ direction.

In this case $u_x = v$, $u_y = 0$ and $u_z = 0$

Lorentz transformation equations for force, therefore, become

$$F_x' = F_x, F_y' = \frac{F_y}{\sqrt{1 - \dfrac{v^2}{c^2}}} \quad \text{and} \quad F_z' = \frac{F_z}{\sqrt{1 - \dfrac{v^2}{c^2}}} \qquad \text{...(ii)}$$

Comparing (i) and (ii), we have

$$F_x' = E_x, F_y' = \frac{E_y - v B_z}{\sqrt{1 - \dfrac{v^2}{c^2}}} \quad \text{and} \quad F_z' = \frac{E_z + v B_y}{\sqrt{1 - \dfrac{v^2}{c^2}}} \qquad \text{...(iii)}$$

But F_x', F_y' and F_z' represent only the components of the force $\vec{F}$ due to the electric field, in the frame S',

$\therefore \qquad\qquad F_x' = E_x', F_y' = E_y', F_z' = E_z' \qquad\qquad\qquad \text{...(iv)}$

From (iii) and (iv), we have

$$E_x' = E_x \qquad\qquad\qquad \text{...(v) (a)}$$

$$E_y' = \frac{E_y - v B_z}{\sqrt{1 - \dfrac{v^2}{c^2}}} = \gamma \left(E_y - v B_z \right) \qquad\qquad \text{...(v) (b)}$$

$$E_z' = \frac{E_z - v B_y}{\sqrt{1 - \dfrac{v^2}{c^2}}} = \gamma \left(E_z - v B_y \right) \qquad\qquad \text{...(v) (c)}$$

Equations (v) (a), (v) (b) and (v) (c) give the required transformation equations for the electric field in two inertial frames which are in uniform relative motion.

The inverse transformation equations are obtained by changing dashed to undashed and undashed to dashed quantities and v to $-v$. Thus the *inverse transformation relations are*

$$E_x = E_x', E_y = \gamma(E_y' + v B_z'), E_z = \gamma(E_z' - v B_y')$$

Transformation of Magnetic field. Now suppose that the unit positive test charge is stationary with respect to the frame S. The test charge will, therefore, not experience any force due to the magnetic field in the frame S. It will only experience a force $\vec{F}$ due to the pure electric field

$\therefore \qquad\qquad\qquad \vec{F} = \vec{E}$

or $\qquad\qquad\qquad F_x = E_x, F_y = E_y, F_z = E_z \qquad\qquad\qquad\qquad \text{...(vi)}$

If $\vec{F}'$ is the force on the test charge as observed in the frame S', then the various components of $\vec{F}'$ can be obtained in terms of $\vec{F}$ by substituting $u_x = u_y = u_z = 0$ in Lorentz equation for transformation of force; and we get

$$F_x' = F_x \,;\, F_y' = \sqrt{1 - \frac{v^2}{c^2}}\, F_y\,;\ F_z' = \sqrt{1 - \frac{v^2}{c^2}}\, F_z \qquad \text{...(vii)}$$

From (vi) and (vii), we have

$$F_x' = E_x \,;\, F_y' = \sqrt{1 - \frac{v^2}{c^2}}\, E_y\,;\, F_z' = \sqrt{1 - \frac{v^2}{c^2}}\, E_z \qquad \text{...(viii)}$$

The total force $\vec{F}$ in the frame S' is partly electric and partly magnetic as the test charge appears to be moving with a velocity $\vec{v}$ along the $-X$ axis with respect to the frame S'

i.e., $\vec{v} = - v\,\hat{i}$

If $\vec{F_m'}$ is the magnetic force on the (unit) test charge in the frame S' then it is given by

$$\vec{F_m'} = \vec{F'} - \vec{E'}$$

where $\vec{E'}$ is the electric force on the test charge in the frame S'.

Now, from relation (v) and (viii), we have

$$(F_m')_x = F_x' - E_x' = E_x - E_x = 0$$

$$(F_m')_y = F_y' - E_y' = \sqrt{1 - \frac{v^2}{c^2}}\, E_y - \frac{E_y - v B_z}{\sqrt{1 - \frac{v^2}{c^2}}}$$

$$= \frac{v B_z - \frac{v^2}{c^2} E_y}{\sqrt{1 - \frac{v^2}{c^2}}} = \gamma v \left(B_z - \frac{v}{c^2} E_y \right)$$

$$(F_m')_z = F_z' - E_z' = \sqrt{1 - \frac{v^2}{c^2}}\, E_z - \frac{E_z + v B_y}{\sqrt{1 - \frac{v^2}{c^2}}}$$

$$= \frac{-v B_y - \frac{v^2}{c^2} E_z}{\sqrt{1 - \frac{v^2}{c^2}}} = \gamma v \left(- B_y - \frac{v}{c^2} E_z \right)$$

$\therefore$ The magnetic force vector on the test charge in the frame S' is given by

$$\vec{F_m'} = \gamma v \left\{ \left(B_z - \frac{v}{c^2} E_y \right)\hat{j} + \left(- B_y - \frac{v}{c^2} E_z \right)\hat{k} \right\} \qquad \text{...(ix)}$$

If $\vec{B'}$ is the magnetic field in S', then the force on the unit positive test charge moving with a velocity $\vec{v} = - v\,\hat{i}$ in this field is given by

$$\vec{F_m'} = - v\,\hat{i} \times \vec{B'} = - v\,\hat{i} \times (B_x'\,\hat{i} + B_y'\,\hat{j} + B_z'\,\hat{k})$$

$$= v[-B_y'\,\hat{k} + B_z'\,\hat{j}] \qquad \text{...(x)}$$

Comparing (*ix*) and (*x*), we get

$$B_y' = \gamma\left(B_y + \frac{v}{c^2}E_z\right) \quad \text{and} \quad B_z' = \gamma\left(B_z - \frac{v}{c^2}E_y\right) \qquad ...(xi)$$

Transformation of X-component of magnetic field. The above procedure does not give the transformation equation for the X-component of the magnetic field.

To obtain the transformation equations of B_x' in terms of B_x consider a pure magnetic field B_x in the X-direction in the frame S and let the test charge have a velocity $\vec{u}$ in the Y-direction

i.e.,
$$\vec{u} = u\hat{j}$$

∴ Force on the unit test charge

$$= u\hat{j} \times B_x\hat{i} = -u\,B_x\,\hat{k} = F_z$$

i.e., there is a force only in the Z-direction and the force along the X and Y direction is zero. According to Lorentz transformation equation for velocity, the velocity of the test charge as measured by an observer in S', is given by

$$\vec{u}' = u\sqrt{1 - \frac{v^2}{c^2}}\,\hat{j}$$

Further, substituting $F_x = 0$, $F_y = 0$, $u_z = 0$ in Lorentz transformation equations for force, we have

$$F_x' = 0\ \ F_y' = 0;\ F_z' = F_z\sqrt{1 - \frac{v^2}{c^2}}$$

or
$$F_z' = -u\sqrt{1 - \frac{v^2}{c^2}}\,B_x \qquad ...(xii)$$

As there is no electric field in the frame S, there will be no electric field in the frame S'. If $\vec{B}$ is the pure magnetic field in S', and $\vec{u}$ is the velocity of the test charge measured in the frame S', then

Force on the unit test charge

$$\vec{F}_m' = \vec{u}' \times \vec{B}' = u\sqrt{1 - \frac{v^2}{c^2}}\,\hat{j} \times \vec{B}'$$

But $\vec{F}_m'$ is in the $-Z$ direction, therefore $\vec{B}'$ must be in the $+X$ direction

i.e.,
$$\vec{B}' = B_x'\hat{i}$$

Hence
$$\vec{F}_m' = u\sqrt{1 - \frac{v^2}{c^2}}\,\hat{j} \times B_x'\hat{i} = -u\sqrt{1 - \frac{v^2}{c^2}}\,B_x'\,\hat{k}$$

As $\vec{F}_m'$ is the only force acting on the test charge as observed in the frame S' and it acts along the Z-axis

∴
$$F_m' = F_z' \quad \text{or} \quad F_z' = -u\sqrt{1 - \frac{v^2}{c^2}}\,B_x' \qquad ...(xiii)$$

From (*xii*) and (*xiii*), we have

$$B_x' = B_x \qquad ...(xiii)\,(a)$$

Hence the transformation equations for Electric and Magnetic fields are

$$E_x' = E_x;\ \ E_y' = \gamma\,(E_y - vB_z);\ \ E_z' = \gamma\,(E_z + vB_y) \qquad ...(xiv)$$

$$B'_x = B_x; \ B'_y = \gamma\left(B_y + \frac{v}{c^2}E_z\right); B'_z = \gamma\left(B_z - \frac{v}{c^2}E_y\right) \qquad ...(xv)$$

Special cases. The results given in Eqs. (xiv) and (xv) are highly symmetrical. This fact can be further brought out by considering two special cases.

(i) *When the magnetic field $\vec{B}$ is zero, everywhere in the frame S*

$$E'_x = E_x; \ E'_y = \gamma E_y; E'_z = \gamma E_z \qquad ...(xvi)$$

$$B'_x = 0; \ B'_y = \gamma\frac{v}{c^2} E_z; \ B'_z = -\gamma\frac{v}{c^2} E_y \qquad ...(xvii)$$

From (xvi) and (xvii), we further get

$$B'_x = 0; \ B'_y = \frac{v}{c^2} E'_z; \ B'_z = -\frac{v}{c^2} E'_y$$

The above three relations can be combined into a general vector form

$$\vec{B} = \left(-\frac{\vec{v}}{c^2}\right) \times \vec{E} \qquad \text{[If } \vec{B} = 0 \text{ everywhere in some frame] } ...(xviii)$$

(ii) *When the electric field $\vec{E}$ is zero, everywhere in the frame S'*

$$E'_x = 0; \ E'_y = -\gamma v B_z; \ E'_z = \gamma v B_y \qquad (xix)$$

$$B'_x = B_x; \ B'_y = \gamma B_y; \ B'_z = \gamma B_z \qquad (xx)$$

From (xix) and (xx), we further get

$$E'_x = 0; \ E'_y = -v B'_z; \ E'_z = v B'_y$$

The above relation can be combined into a general vector form

$$\vec{E} = \vec{v} \times \vec{B} \qquad \text{[If } \vec{E} = 0 \text{ everywhere in some frame] } ...(xxi)$$

The conditions for equations (xviii) and (xxi) are very difficult to satisfy because generally there in *no* frame for which $\vec{B}$ is zero *everywhere* and similarly there is no frame for which electric charge density and hence $\vec{E}$ is zero *everywhere*.

Q. 8.57. Explain the phenomenon of Hall effect. How does the Hall effect decide that current in a metallic conductor is due to negatively charged particles? Derive the value of Hall voltage and show that Hall co-efficient $R_H = \dfrac{1}{ne}$, and Hall mobility $= \sigma R_H$. Mention the applications of Hall effect. (G.N.D.U., 2008, 2006, 2004, 2001, 2000, 1995; P.U., 2007, 2006, 2003, 2001, 1995; Meerut U., 2007, 2003, 2002; Pbi. U., 2006, 2002, 2001, 1995; H.P.U., 2002, 2000, 1997, 1996, 1994; M.D.U. 2007; Nagpur U., 2002; Kerala U., 2001; Osm. U., 1997)

Ans. Hall effect. *When a metal plate carrying a current is placed in a magnetic field acting perpendicular to the direction of current, then an electric field is developed in a direction perpendicular to both the current as well as the magnetic field. This phenomenon is known as Hall effect.*

Negative charge carriers. Consider a metallic plate ABCDEFGH carrying a current I in the $+X$ direction. A magnetic field $\vec{B}$ is applied to the plate in the $+Z$ direction, then

$$\vec{B} = B \hat{k}$$

Suppose the charge carriers are electrons. As the current is flowing in the $+X$ direction the free electrons are drifting in the $-X$ direction. If $\vec{v}$ is the *drift velocity* of electrons, then

Magnetic force on each electron $\vec{F}_m = -e\,\vec{v} \times \vec{B} = -e\,(-v\,\hat{i} \times B\,\hat{k})$

or $$\vec{F}_m = -ev\,B\,\hat{j}$$

The force $\vec{F}_m$ acts in the $-Y$ direction. This causes the electron to bend downward towards the face $ABCD$ of the plate. The electrons accumulate on the lower surface producing a net negative charge on the face $ABCD$. As a result a net positive charge is developed on the opposite upper surface $EFGH$ of the plate. The negative charge on the lower face $ABCD$ and positive charge on the upper face $EFGH$ set up on *electric field in the downward* $-Y$ *direction*. This electric field is known as *Hall electric field* and is denoted by E_H.

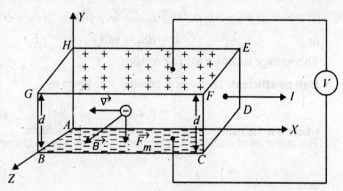

Fig. 8.36

$$\therefore \qquad \vec{E}_H = -E_H\,\hat{j}$$

The flow of electrons towards the lower face will stop when the force on the electron due to the Hall field $\vec{F}_e$ balances the force due to the magnetic field *i.e.*,

$$\vec{F}_e + \vec{F}_m = 0$$

Now $$\vec{F}_e = -e\,\vec{E}_H = eE_H\,\hat{j}$$

and $$\vec{F}_m = -ev\,B\,\hat{j}$$

$$\therefore \qquad eE_H\,\hat{j} - ev\,B\,\hat{j} = 0$$

or $$E_H = vB \qquad\qquad\qquad ...(i)$$

Positive charge carriers. Now suppose that the electric current is due to positively charged particles. The positively charged particles move in the direction of the current

$$\therefore \qquad \vec{v} = v\,\hat{i}$$

If q is charge on each positive charge carrier, then

Magnetic force on each positive carrier $\vec{F}_m = q\,\vec{v} \times \vec{B} = q\,v\,\hat{i} \times B\,\hat{k} = -q\,v\,B\,\hat{j}$

This equation shows that positive charge carriers will also experience a force in the $-Y$ direction.

As the positive charge carriers are deflected towards the lower face $ABCD$, this face gets positively charged. As a result the upper face is negatively charged. This gives rise to an electric field in the $+Y$ direction. Hence Hall field

$$\vec{E}_H = E_H\,\hat{j}$$

Thus the direction of Hall field now is opposite to that of the Hall field due to negative charge carrier.

The direction of Hall electric field is an indication of the kind of charge carriers responsible for the current in the conductor.

If the Hall electric field is in the − Y direction when the current flows along + X direction and magnetic field acts along + Z direction, the charge carriers are negatively charged electrons.

Hall voltage. If V is the voltage developed between the two faces $EFGH$ and $ABCD$ and d is the distance between the two faces, then

$$E_H = \frac{V}{d} = vB$$

or $$V = dE_H = vdB \qquad \qquad \qquad ...(ii)$$

This voltage is known as *Hall voltage.*

Hall co-efficient. The current density $\vec{J}$ is given by

$$\vec{J} = n e \vec{v}$$

where n is the number of charge carriers per unit volume.

$\therefore$ $$J = nev$$

or $$v = \frac{J}{ne} \qquad \qquad \qquad ...(iii)$$

From Eq. (i) $$v = \frac{E_H}{B} \qquad \qquad \qquad ...(iv)$$

Comparing (iii) and (iv), we get

$$\frac{J}{ne} = \frac{E_H}{B}$$

or $$E_H = \frac{JB}{ne}$$

$\therefore$ $$\frac{E_H}{JB} = \frac{1}{ne}$$

The quantity $\frac{E_H}{JB}$ i.e., *the Hall electric field per unit current density per unit magnetic field is called Hall co-efficient (or Hall constant) and denoted by* R_H

$\therefore$ $$R_H = \frac{1}{ne}$$

The value of R_H depends upon the number density of charge carriers. The Hall co-efficient is negative if the charge carriers are negatively charged particles and it is positive if the charge carriers are positively charged particles. Hence the sign of R_H decides the type of charge carriers in a conductor.

Hall mobility. If a steady electric field E is maintained in a conductor (by applying an external voltage across it) the current carriers in the conductor acquire a drift velocity v.

The drift velocity acquired per unit electric field is called mobility of the carrier and denoted as μ.

$\therefore$ Mobility $\mu = \frac{v}{E}$

Also current density $J = n e v$

and $$J = \sigma E$$

where σ is electrical conductivity

$$\therefore \qquad\qquad n\,e\,v = \sigma\,E$$

or $\qquad\qquad \mu = \dfrac{v}{E} = \sigma\,\dfrac{1}{ne} = \sigma\,R_H$

Hence Hall mobility is equal to the product of electrical conductivity and Hall co-efficient.

Applications. Hall effect can be used to determine

(i) The nature of charge carriers carrying current through a conductor.

(ii) Number density of charge carriers. The value of n determined by Hall effect agrees very closely with the value calculated on the assumption that each atom contributes one free electron for metals like Na, K, Li, Cu etc.

(iii) Measure the value of magnetic induction field.

(iv) Determine the value of mobility of charge carrier

(v) To find whether the given specimen is a metal, semi conductor or insulator.

Q. 8.58. Calculate the Hall voltage developed in Germanium crystal of thickness 0.5×10^{-3} m when a magnetic field of 0.7 T is applied. Current density is 250 Am^{-2} and electron density 2×10^{23} m^{-3}. *(Bang. U., 2001, P.U., 2000)*

Ans. Here thickness of the crystal $d = 0.5 \times 10^{-3}$ m

Applied magnetic field $B = 0.7$ T; Current density $J = 250$ Am^{-2} and electron density $n = 2 \times 10^{23}$ m^{-3}. Charge on the electron $e = 1.6 \times 10^{-19}$ C

Hall voltage $V = d\,E_H$.

and Hall field $\qquad\qquad E_H = \dfrac{JB}{ne}$

$$\therefore \qquad V = \dfrac{d\,JB}{ne} = \dfrac{0.5 \times 10^{-3} \times 250 \times 0.7}{2 \times 10^{23} \times 1.6 \times 10^{-19}}$$

$$= 273 \times 10^{-6} \text{ volt.}$$

Q. 8.59. Mark the correct answer.

(i) The force experienced by a charged particle moving in a magnetic field is independent of

(a) velocity of the particle   (b) charge on the particle

(c) strength of the field   (d) mass of the particle   *(H.P.U., 1993)*

(ii) The S.I. unit of magnetic induction field is

(a) Gauss   (b) Oersted

(c) Tesla   (d) Weber

(iii) The force on a current element due to a magnetic field is zero if the angle between the current element and magnetic field is

(a) zero   (b) $\dfrac{\pi}{4}$

(c) $\dfrac{\pi}{2}$ (d) $\dfrac{3\pi}{4}$

(iv) The magnetic field at the centre of a current loop is proportional to

(a) R (b) R^{-1}

(c) R^2 (d) R^{-2} *(H.P.U., 2003; G.N.D.U., 1990)*

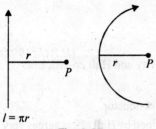

$l = \pi r$

Fig. 8.37

(v) A current I passes through a straight conductor of length $= \pi r$. The magnetic induction at a point P (shown in the figure) distant 'r' from the conductor is say B_1. The same conductor is now bent in the form of a semicircular arc of the same radius r and centre P. The new magnetic induction is B_2. The ratio of B_1 and B_2 is

(a) $1 : \dfrac{2}{\sqrt{\pi^2 + 4}}$ 　　　　 (b) $\dfrac{2}{\sqrt{\pi^2 + 4}} : 1$

(c) $1 : 1$ 　　　　 (d) none of these

Hint. $B_1 = \dfrac{\mu_0}{4\pi} \dfrac{I}{r} (\cos \theta_2 - \cos \theta_1)$

$$\cos \theta_2 = \frac{\dfrac{\pi r}{2}}{\sqrt{\dfrac{\pi^2 r^2}{4} + r^2}} = \frac{\dfrac{\pi r}{2}}{\dfrac{r}{2}\sqrt{\pi^2 + 4}} = \frac{\pi}{\sqrt{\pi^2 + 4}} \qquad \text{(Fig. 8.38)}$$

$$\cos \theta_1 = \cos(\pi - \theta_2) = -\cos \theta_2 = -\frac{\pi}{\sqrt{\pi^2 + 4}}$$

$$\therefore \qquad \cos \theta_2 - \cos \theta_1 = \frac{\pi}{\sqrt{\pi^2 + 4}} + \frac{\pi}{\sqrt{\pi^2 + 4}} = \frac{2\pi}{\sqrt{\pi^2 + 4}}$$

$$B_1 = \frac{\mu_0}{4\pi} \frac{I}{r} \frac{2\pi}{\sqrt{\pi^2 + 4}} = \frac{\mu_0 I}{2r} \frac{1}{\sqrt{\pi^2 + 4}}$$

$$B_2 = \frac{1}{2} \frac{\mu_0 I}{2r} = \frac{\mu_0 I}{2r} \frac{1}{2}$$

$$\frac{B_1}{B_2} = \frac{1}{\dfrac{\sqrt{\pi^2 + 4}}{1/2}} = \frac{2}{\sqrt{\pi^2 + 4}}$$

or

$$B_1 : B_2 :: \frac{2}{\sqrt{\pi^2 + 4}} : 1$$

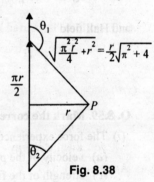

$\sqrt{\dfrac{\pi^2 r^2}{4} + r^2} = \dfrac{r}{2}\sqrt{\pi^2 + 4}$

$\dfrac{\pi r}{2}$

Fig. 8.38

(vi) A straight long wire ABC carrying current I would create magnetic field B_1 at P. If the wire is bent in the form $ABC'DE$ such that $BC'D$ forms a semi-circle with P as centre and DE parallel to AB, the magnetic field at P would be B_2 then $B_2 : B_1$ as

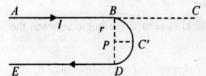

Fig. 8.39

(a) $1 : 1$ 　　　　 (b) $1 : (\pi + 1)$

(c) $1 : (\pi - 1)$ 　　　　 (d) None of these but.....

(P.U., 1994)

(vii) A current I is passing through the wire shaped as shown in Fig. 8.40. The magnetic field at the point P is

(a) $\dfrac{\mu_0 I}{4\pi r}$ 　　　　 (b) $\dfrac{\mu_0 I}{2r}$

(c) $\dfrac{\mu_0 I}{4r}$ 　　　　 (d) $\dfrac{\mu_0 I}{r}$ 　　 (P.U., 1994)

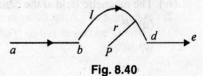

Fig. 8.40

(*viii*) The magnetic field outside the infinite solenoid is

(*a*) zero

(*b*) $\mu_0\, n\, I$

(*c*) $\mu_0\, \dfrac{nI}{2}$

(*d*) infinite   (*H.P.U.*, 1992)

(*ix*) Mark the statement which is correct in all circumstances

(*a*) $\vec{\nabla} \times \vec{E} = 0$

(*b*) $\vec{\nabla} \cdot \vec{E} = 0$

(*c*) $\vec{\nabla} \times \vec{B} = 0$

(*d*) $\vec{\nabla} \cdot \vec{B} = 0$

where $\vec{E}$ and $\vec{B}$ are electric field intensity and magnetic field intensity respectively.

(*P.U.*, 1994)

(*x*) An isolated magnetic pole does not exist. This is equivalent to saying   (*H.P.U.*, 1994)

(*a*) $\vec{\nabla} \times \vec{A} = 0$ where A is any vector potential

(*b*) $\vec{\nabla} \cdot \vec{B} = 0$ where B is magnetic field intensity

(*c*) $\vec{\nabla} \times \vec{B} = \mu_0\, \vec{j}$ where $\vec{j}$ is current density

(*d*) $\vec{\nabla} \cdot \vec{B} = \mu_0\, \vec{j}$

(*xi*) The differential form of Ampere's law in current free space is

(*a*) $\vec{\nabla} \times \vec{B} = \mu_0\, \vec{j}$

(*b*) $\vec{\nabla} \cdot \vec{B} = 0$

(*c*) $\vec{\nabla} \times \vec{B} = 0$

(*d*) $\vec{\nabla} \times \vec{B} = \mu_0\, I$ (*H.P.U.*, 1997)

(*xii*) No force is exerted by a magnetic field on a charge

(*a*) Moving with constant velocity

(*b*) moving in a circle

(*c*) at rest

(*d*) moving along a curved path. (*H.P.U.*, 2001)

(*xiii*) Motion of a charged particle is in a direction perpendicular to the magnetic field. What will change

(*a*) its speed

(*b*). direction of motion

(*c*) kinetic energy

(*d*) momentum?   (*P.U.*, 2000)

Ans.   (*i*) *d*   (*ii*) *c*   (*iii*) *a*   (*iv*) *b*

(*v*) *b*   (*vi*) *b*   (*vii*) *c*   (*viii*) *a*

(*ix*) *d*   (*x*) *b*   (*xi*) *b*   (*xii*) *c*

(*xiii*) *b*

EXERCISES

1. A one metre long wire carrying 10 A current is placed perpendicular to a magnetic field of 15 Tesla. Find the magnitude of the force on the wire.

   [**Hint.** In S.I. units, when the conductor is perpendicular to magnetic field,

   Force $F = IlB = 10 \times 1 \times 15 = 150$ Newton]

2. A current of 1 Amp flows in one thousand turns of an insulated flat coil of length one metre of inner and outer radius 5 cm and 10 cm respectively. Find the magnetic field at the centre of the coil.   (*G.N.D.U.*, 1994)

   [**Ans.** 12.42×10^{-4} Tesla]

[**Hint.** Take average radius = 7.5 cm, then as shown

$$\cos \theta_1 = \frac{50}{\sqrt{50^2 + (7.5)^2}} = 0.989$$

and $\cos \theta_1 - \cos \theta_2 = 1.978$

∴ $B = \dfrac{\mu_0}{2} \, nI \, (\cos \theta_1 - \cos \theta_2)$

$$= \frac{1}{2} \times 4\pi \times 10^{-7} \times 1000 \times 1 \times 1.978$$

$$= 12.42 \times 10^{-4} \text{ Tesla]}$$

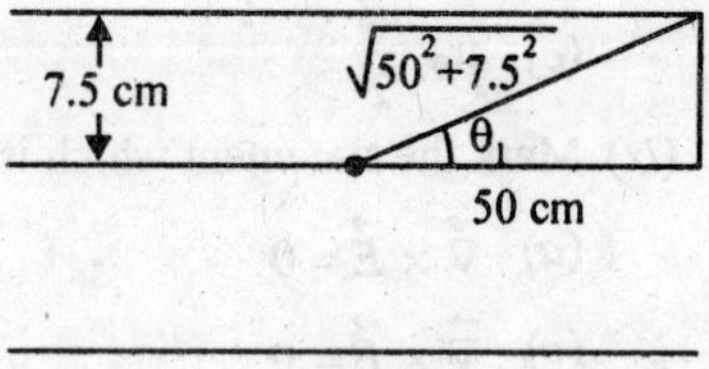

7.5 cm

$\sqrt{50^2 + 7.5^2}$ 7.5

θ_1

50 cm

1 metre

Fig. 8.41

3. A solenoid 50 cm long and mean diameter 8 cm has one thousand turns. If a current of 4.0 A is flowing through it, calculate the magnetic field at the centre.   (*G.N.D.U.*, 1993)

[**Ans.** 99.26 × 10⁻⁴ Tesla]

[**Hint.** $\cos \theta_1 = \dfrac{25}{\sqrt{25^2 + 4^2}} = 0.987$

∴ $\cos \theta_1 - \cos \theta_2 = 1.974$]

4. A solenoid 200 cm long and mean diameter 10 cm has ten layers of 500 turns each. If a current of 10 Amp flows through its windings, calculate the magnetic field at the mid centre.

(*Kan. U.*, 1992)

[**Ans.** π/10 Tesla]

9

Magnetism in Matter

Q. 9.1 (a) Calculate the energy stored in an inductor or (long solenoid). *(K.U. 2000)*

Or

Show that the energy required to build up a current I in a circuit of self inductance L is $\frac{1}{2} L I^2$. *(M.D.U.1999)*

(b) Show that the energy stored in a magnetic field per unit volume is $= \frac{B^2}{2\mu_0}$.

(Pbi.U., 2007; P.U. 2002, 2000 ; A.U., 1995)

Ans. (a) Energy stored in an inductor. The inductance of a circuit resists any change in current through it and, therefore any change in magnetic flux linked with it. Hence work has to be done in increasing the current from zero to a particular value say I against the *e.m.f.* induced in the inductance. This work done by the current is stored in the inductor as *magnetic energy* of the field surrounding it.

If e is the self-induced *e.m.f.* at any instant in the circuit when the current established in the circuit is i and it changes at the rate $\frac{di}{dt}$, then

$$e = - L \frac{di}{dt}$$

where L is the co-efficient of self inductance of the circuit.

If the current i remains unchanged for a small time dt, then

Work done in time $\qquad dt = - e\, i\, dt$

$\therefore$ Total work done W in establishing a current I in a time t is given by

$$W = \int_0^I - e\, i\, dt = \int_0^I L \frac{di}{dt} i\, dt = \int_0^I Li\, di$$

$$= \left[\frac{1}{2} Li^2 \right]_0^I = \frac{1}{2} LI^2$$

This work is stored up in the inductor as energy of the magnetic field. In other words, the energy required to build up a current I in a circuit of self inductance $L = \frac{1}{2} L I^2$.

381

(b) **Energy stored in a magnetic field.** When a current flows through an inductor in the form of a solenoid, the work done in establishing the current is stored as energy of the magnetic field linked with the solenoid. If the solenoid has a length l, total number of turns n, and a current I flows through it, then magnetic field within the solenoid

$$= B = \mu_0 \frac{nl}{l} \qquad \qquad ...(i)$$

If a is the area of cross-section of the solenoid, then co-efficient of self-induction

$$L = \frac{\mu_0 \, n^2 \, a}{l} \qquad \qquad ...(ii)$$

$\because$ Energy stored in the magnetic field $W = \frac{1}{2} LI^2$

But from (i) $I = \dfrac{Bl}{\mu_0 \, n}$

$\therefore$ $W = \dfrac{1}{2} \dfrac{\mu_0 \, n^2 \, a}{l} \dfrac{B^2 \, l^2}{\mu_0^2 \, n^2} = \dfrac{1}{2} \dfrac{B^2}{\mu_0} \, al$

$\therefore$ Energy per unit volume $= \dfrac{1}{2} \dfrac{B^2}{\mu_0}$ ...(iii)

$$[\because \; al = \text{volume of the magnetic field in the solenoid}]$$

Further $\vec{B} = \mu_0 \vec{H}$ or $\vec{H} = \dfrac{\vec{B}}{\mu_0}$ where $\vec{H}$ is known as magnetic field vector.

$\therefore$ Energy stored per unit volume $= \dfrac{1}{2} \dfrac{B^2}{\mu_0} = \dfrac{1}{2} \vec{B} \cdot \dfrac{\vec{B}}{\mu_0} = \dfrac{1}{2} \vec{B} \cdot \vec{H}$ ...(iv)

This is a general expression and holds even when the magnetic field is not constant at all points in space. In such a case

Total magnetic energy of the field $W = \displaystyle\iiint \dfrac{B^2}{2\mu_0} \, dv.$

Q. 9.2. Show that the energy stored in the magnetic field of a coil of 1000 turns, length 100 cm, area of cross-section 7 sq. cm. and wound over a core of magnetic permeability 1000 is nearly 0.44 Joule when 1 Amp current is passed through it.   *(K.U., 1994)*

Ans. Magnetic field at a point on the axis of a long coil (solenoid) $= \mu_0 \, nI$ where n is the number of turns per metre and the core is air. For a core of relative permeability μ_r

Magnetic field $B = \mu_r \, \mu_0 \, nI$

In such a case energy per unit volume $= \dfrac{B^2}{2\mu_r \, \mu_0}$ instead of $\dfrac{B^2}{2\mu_0}$

Now $B = \mu_r \, \mu_0 \, nI = \mu_0 \times 1000 \times 1000 \times 1 = 10^6 \, \mu_0$ Tesla

$\therefore$ Energy per unit volume $= \dfrac{B^2}{2\mu_r \, \mu_0} = \dfrac{\mu_0^2 \times 10^{12}}{2 \times 1000 \times \mu_0} = \dfrac{\mu_0}{2} \times 10^9$ Joule

Now $\dfrac{\mu_0}{4\pi} = 10^{-7}$ $\therefore \mu_0 = 4\pi \times 10^{-7}$

$\therefore$ Energy per unit volume $= \dfrac{4\pi \times 10^{-7}}{2} \times 10^9 = 2\pi \times 10^2$ Joule

Volume of the solenoid $= 7 \times 10^{-4} \times 1 = 7 \times 10^{-4}$ cubic metre

$\therefore$ Total energy stored $= 2\pi \times 10^2 \times 7 \times 10^{-4} = 44 \times 10^{-2} = 0.44$ Joule

Q.9.3. (*a*) **Calculate the torque on a current loop in a steady magnetic induction field.** Hence obtain the expression for the torque on a rectangular current loop suspended in a uniform magnetic field. (*Gauhati. U.* 2000)

(*b*) **How will you explain that a current carrying loop is equivalent to a magnet ? Hence define the magnetic moment of a current loop. Also find the *S.I.* unit of pole strength.**

(*Pbi.U.* 2002; 2001, *Gauhati. U.* 2000; *K.U.* 1994)

Ans. Torque on a current loop. Consider a current element $I\,dl$ of a current loop at the position vector $\vec{r}$ placed in a uniform magnetic induction field $\vec{B}$.

The magnetic force on the element

$$d\vec{F} = I\,d\vec{l} \times \vec{B}$$

Torque on the element

$$d\vec{\tau} = \vec{r} \times d\vec{F} = I\,\vec{r} \times (d\vec{l} \times \vec{B})$$

∴ Total torque on whole of the loop

$$\vec{\tau} = \int I\,\vec{r} \times (d\vec{l} \times \vec{B})$$

$$= I \int \vec{r} \times (d\vec{l} \times \vec{B})$$

Now

$$d\vec{l} \times \vec{B} = (\hat{i}\,dx + \hat{j}\,dy + \hat{k}\,dz) \times (\hat{i}B_x + \hat{j}\,B_y + \hat{k}\,B_z)$$

$$= \begin{vmatrix} \hat{i} & \hat{j} & \hat{k} \\ dx & dy & dz \\ B_x & B_y & B_z \end{vmatrix}$$

$$= \hat{i}\,(dy\,B_z - dz\,B_y) + \hat{j}\,(dz\,B_x - dx\,B_z) + \hat{k}\,(dx\,B_y - dy\,B_x)$$

∴

$$\vec{r} \times (d\vec{l} \times \vec{B}) = (\hat{i}x + \hat{j}y + \hat{k}z) \times \{\hat{i}\,(dy\,B_z - dz\,B_y)$$

$$+ \hat{j}\,(dz\,B_x - dx\,B_z) + \hat{k}\,(dx\,B_y - dy\,B_x)\}$$

$$= \begin{vmatrix} \hat{i} & \hat{j} & \hat{k} \\ x & y & z \\ (dy\,B_z - dz\,B_y) & (dz\,B_x - dx\,B_z) & (dx\,B_y - dy\,B_x) \end{vmatrix}$$

Hence the *X*-component $[\vec{r} \times (d\vec{l} \times \vec{B})]_x$

$$= \hat{i}\,(ydxB_y - ydyB_x - zdzB_x + zdxB_z)$$

∴

$$\oint \{\vec{r} \times (d\vec{l} \times \vec{B})\}_x = \oint ydxB_y - \oint ydyB_x - \oint zdzB_x + \oint zdxB_z$$

Now $\oint ydy = 0$ *and* $\oint zdz = 0$, for it we plot a curve of y against y or z against z it is a straight line and the area included by it for a complete cycle is zero, $\oint y\,dx$ gives the component of the vector area $\vec{A}$ of the loop in the xy plane taken in the clockwise direction *i.e.*, the area is directed along the $-Z$ axis

∴

$$\oint y\,dx = -A_z$$

Similarly $\oint z\,dx$ gives the component of the area in the zx, plane taken in the anticlockwise direction *i.e.*, the area is directed along the $+Y$ axis.

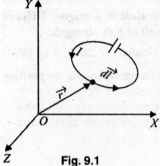

Fig. 9.1

$$\therefore \qquad \oint z\,dx = A_y$$

Since $\vec{B}$ is uniform, its components B_x, B_y and B_z are constant.

$$\therefore \qquad \oint \{\vec{r} \times (d\vec{l} \times \vec{B})\}_x = -A_z\,B_y + A_y\,B_z = [\vec{A} \times \vec{B}]_x$$

Similarly

$$\oint \{\vec{r} \times (d\vec{l} \times \vec{B})\}_y = [\vec{A} \times \vec{B}]_y$$

and

$$\oint \{\vec{r} \times (d\vec{l} \times \vec{B})\}_z = [\vec{A} \times \vec{B}]_z$$

Combining, we get

$$\oint \vec{r} \times (d\vec{l} \times \vec{B}) = \vec{A} \times \vec{B}$$

$$\therefore \qquad \text{Torque } \vec{\tau} = I\,(\vec{A} \times \vec{B})$$

Thus the torque on a current loop depends only on the area of the loop. It does not depend upon the shape of the loop. The magnitude of the torque $= IAB \sin \theta$ where θ is the angle between the area vector $\vec{A}$ and field vector $\vec{B}$.

Current loop of n turns. If the loop has n turns, each turn experiences the same torque.

$$\therefore \quad \text{Torque on whole coil of } n \text{ turns} = n\,I\left(\vec{A} \times \vec{B}\right)$$

Rectangular current loop. For a rectangular current loop of length a and breadth b, the magnitude of the area vector $|\vec{A}| = A = ab$ and the magnitude of the torque $|\vec{\tau}| = |I\,(\vec{A} \times \vec{B})| = IAB \sin \theta = I\,ab\,B \sin \theta$

For $\theta = 90° = \pi/2$, $\tau = I\,a\,b\,B$

(b) Magnetic moment of a current loop. The torque on a current loop of area $\vec{A}$ through which a current I flows is given by

$$\vec{\tau} = I\,\vec{A} \times \vec{B} \qquad\qquad \ldots(i)$$

where $\vec{B}$ is the magnetic induction field.

The torque acting on an electric dipole having electric dipole moment $\vec{p}$ in an electric field $\vec{E}$ is given by

$$\vec{\tau} = \vec{p} \times \vec{E} \qquad\qquad \ldots(ii)$$

Comparing (i) and (ii), we find that *the current loop in a uniform magnetic field behaves similar to an electric dipole in a uniform electric field i.e.* a small current loop has the properties of a *magnetic dipole.*

The vector $I\,\vec{A} = \vec{p_m}$ is called the magnetic moment of the current loop. Hence if a current loop of magnetic moment $\vec{p_m}$ is placed in a uniform magnetic field $\vec{B}$, the torque acting on it is given by

$$\tau = \vec{p_m} \times \vec{B}.$$

In otherwords, a current carrying loop of wire behaves as a *magnetic dipole* of magnetic moment $\vec{p_m} = I\,\vec{A}$ where I is the current and $\vec{A}$ the area of the loop.

Unit of magnetic moment. The unit of magnetic moment of a current loop, $\vec{p_m}$ is $IA = Amp\ m^2$

$= \dfrac{Coulumb}{sec}\ m^2 = Cs^{-1}\ m^2$. Also torque $\vec{\tau} = \vec{P_m} \times \vec{B}$. The unit of torque is $(\vec{\tau} = \vec{r} \times \vec{F})$ that of work.

$$\therefore \text{Unit of } p_m = \frac{work}{B} = \text{Joule per Tesla (J T}^{-1})$$

Pole strength. In the study of magnetism, the magnetic moment of a magnetic dipole (say a bar magnet) is defined as the product of the pole strength m and the distance between two opposite poles (one north pole and the other south), the distance between the two poles being known as magnetic *length* and denoted as $2\,\vec{l}$.

$$\therefore \text{ Magnetic moment } \quad \vec{p_m} = m \times 2\vec{l}$$

Unit of pole strength. The unit of pole strength $m = \dfrac{\text{Unit of } \vec{p_m}}{\text{Unit of length}} = \dfrac{Amp\ m^2}{m} = Amp\ m$

Direction of magnetic moment of a current loop. The magnitude of the magnetic moment of current loop is the product of the current and the area of the loop. The direction of the dipole moment is given by the following rule.

Let the fingers of the right hand curl round the loop in the direction of the current, the extended right thumb will then point in the direction of magnetic dipole moment vector.

Q.9.4. A current of 10 Amp is flowing through a coil of radius 0.5 m and 10 turns. Calculate the magnetic moment of the coil.   (*Meerut. U.* 2003, 2001)

Ans.   Area of the coil $A = \pi\,r^2 = \dfrac{22}{7} \times 0.5 \times 0.5 = 0.7857$ sq. mt.

Current through the coil $I = 10$ Amp

Number of turns $n = 10$

$\therefore$ Magnetic moment of the current loop $p_m = n\,I\,A$

$$= 10 \times 10 \times 0.7857 = 78.57\ Am^2$$

Q.9.5. (*a*) Calculate the force on a current loop placed in a non-uniform external magnetic field and hence derive an expression for the force on a dipole.   (*P.U.*, 1995)

(*b*) In liquid oxygen, the spins of the two electrons per O$_2$ molecule contribute towards paramagnetism. The spin magnetic moment of the electron is 0.93×10^{-20} erg/ Gauss. Calculate the force on one gm of liquid oxygen placed in a field with a gradient of 1700 Gauss/cm.

(*G.N.D.U.* 1999)

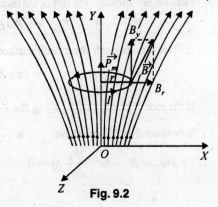

Fig. 9.2

Ans. (*a*) Force on a current loop in a non-uniform magnetic field. Consider a small circular loop of radius r carrying a current I with its axis coinciding with the Y-axis, placed in a *non-uniform* external magnetic field. The magnetic field acts generally in the Y-direction but it is not a uniform field. The magnitude of the field goes on decreasing as we proceed along the positive direction of Y-axis. This is shown by the *fanning out* of the lines of force. We further assume, for the sake of simplicity, that the field is symmetrical about the axis of the current loop *i.e.*, the Y-axis. The external field does not include the field due to the current loop. It is also not necessary to take it into consideration because the magnetic field due to the current loop itself does not produce any net force on it.

The magnetic field $\vec{B}$ at any point of the ring can be resolved into two components

(i) B_y along the Y-direction and

(ii) B_r in the plane of the loop and directed radially outward.

The force due to the component B_y acts radially outward on every small element dl of the loop. Due to the circular symmetry around the axis of the loop, the resultant of all the forces acting at various points of the loop due to the component B_y is zero as shown in Fig. 9.3 (a).

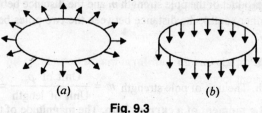

(a)   (b)

Fig. 9.3

The magnitude of the force due to the component B_r on an element of length $dl = I\, dl\, B_r$. This force acts downwards at every point of the loop along the $-Y$ direction as shown in Fig. 9.3 (b).

∴ Net downward force on the loop

$$\vec{F} = -2\pi r\, I\, B_r\, \hat{j} \qquad \qquad ...(i)$$

Let us now consider a closed surface of the shape of cylindrical box of base area πr^2 and height

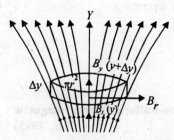

Fig. 9.4

Δy with its axis, along the Y-axis. The net outward magnetic flux over any closed surface is zero as $div.\,\vec{B} = 0$

Flux of $\vec{B}$ through the *curved* surface of the cylinder

$$= 2\pi r\, \Delta y\, B_r$$

Let $(B_y)_y$ be the value of B_y at the *lower* surface of the box and $(B_y)_{y+\Delta y}$ at the upper surface, then

Flux of $\vec{B}$ through the lower surface of the cylinder

$$= -\pi r^2 (B_y)_y$$

The negative sign indicates that B_y acts in the $+Y$ direction and the outward drawn normal to the surface is directed along $-Y$ direction.

Flux of $\vec{B}$ through the upper surface of the cylinder

$$= \pi r^2 (B_y)_{y+\Delta y}$$

∴ Net flux through the closed surface $= \displaystyle\iint \vec{B}.d\vec{s}$

$$= 2\pi r\, \Delta y\, B_r + \pi r^2 [(B_y)_{y+\Delta y} - (B_y)_y] = 0 \qquad ...(ii)$$

If the rate of change of B_y along the Y-axis is $\dfrac{\partial B_y}{\partial y}$, then $[(B_y)_{y+\Delta y} - (B_y)_y] = \dfrac{\partial B_y}{\partial y} \Delta y$

Substituting in (ii), we have

$$2\pi r\, \Delta y\, B_r + \pi r^2 \frac{\partial B_y}{\partial y} \Delta y = 0$$

or $\quad \pi r \; \Delta y \left(2Br + r \; \dfrac{\partial B_y}{\partial y} \right) = 0$

or $\qquad\qquad\qquad\qquad B_r = -\dfrac{r}{2} \dfrac{\partial B_y}{\partial y}$

But $\dfrac{\partial B_y}{\partial y}$ is itself a negative quantity.

$\therefore \qquad\qquad\qquad\qquad B_r = \dfrac{r}{2} \dfrac{\partial B_y}{\partial y}$

Force acting on the loop is obtained by substituting the value of B_r in (i) and we get

$$\vec{F} = \pi r^2 \; I \; \dfrac{\partial B_y}{\partial y} \; \hat{j} \qquad\qquad\qquad\qquad ...(iii)$$

Force on a magnetic dipole in a non-uniform magnetic field. In Eq. (iii) $\pi r^2 I = $ The magnetic dipole moment of the current loop $\vec{P_m}$.

$\therefore$ Magnitude of the force acting on the loop

$$= F_y = P_m \; \dfrac{\partial B_y}{\partial y} \qquad\qquad\qquad\qquad ...(iv)$$

In general, the dipole moment $\vec{P_m}$ may not be parallel to $\vec{B}$ and the spatial variation in X, Y, Z components of $\vec{B}$ may be different in different directions.

Let us suppose that the X, Y, Z components of $\vec{B}$ vary according to the relations given below

$$dB_x = \dfrac{\partial B_x}{\partial x} \; dx + \dfrac{\partial B_x}{\partial y} \; dy + \dfrac{\partial B_x}{\partial z} \; dz$$

$$dB_y = \dfrac{\partial B_y}{\partial x} \; dx + \dfrac{\partial B_y}{\partial y} \; dy + \dfrac{\partial B_y}{\partial z} \; dz$$

$$dB_z = \dfrac{\partial B_z}{\partial x} \; dx + \dfrac{\partial B_z}{\partial y} \; dy + \dfrac{\partial B_z}{\partial z} \; dz$$

and the X, Y, Z components of $\vec{P_m}$ are $(p_m)_x$, $(p_m)_y$ and $(p_m)_z$.

The components of $\vec{B}$ along the Y-axis is B_y and it varies with x, y and z. All the three variations give rise to a force in the Y-direction given by

$$F_{y1} = (p_m)_x \; \dfrac{\partial B_y}{\partial x}$$

$$F_{y2} = (p_m)_y \; \dfrac{\partial B_y}{\partial y}$$

$$F_{y3} = (p_m)_z \; \dfrac{\partial B_y}{\partial z}$$

$\therefore \qquad F_y = F_{y1} + F_{y2} + F_{y3} = (p_m)_x \; \dfrac{\partial B_y}{\partial x} + (p_m)_y \; \dfrac{\partial B_y}{\partial y} + (p_m)_z \; \dfrac{\partial B_y}{\partial z}$

$$= \vec{P_m} \cdot \vec{\nabla} \; B_y = (\vec{P_m} \cdot \vec{\nabla}) \; B_y$$

Similarly $\qquad\qquad F_x = (\vec{P_m} \cdot \vec{\nabla}) \; B_x$

$$F_z = (\vec{P_m} \cdot \vec{\nabla}) \; B_z$$

Hence
$$\vec{F} = \hat{i}\, F_x + \hat{j}\, F_y + \hat{k}\, F_z$$
$$= (\vec{p_m} \cdot \vec{\nabla})\,(\hat{i}\, B_x + \hat{j}\, B_y + \hat{k}\, B_z)$$
$$= (\vec{p_m} \cdot \vec{\nabla})\, \vec{B} \qquad\qquad\qquad ...(v)$$

Eq. (v) gives the general expression for the force on a dipole in a non-uniform magnetic field.

(b) Spin magnetic moment of an electron = 0.93×10^{-20} erg/ Gauss .

Number of electrons contributing their spin magnetic moment per O_2 molecule = 2.

∴ Total magnetic moment of an O_2 molecule = $2 \times 0.93 \times 10^{-20}$ erg/ Gauss

Number of molecules per gm. molecule = Avogadro's number = 6.023×10^{23}.

Molecular weight of Oxygen = 32.

∴ Number of O_2 molecules in one $gm = \dfrac{6.023 \times 10^{23}}{32}$

Hence total magnetic moment of 1 gm of liquid oxygen
$$= \vec{P_m} = \frac{6.023 \times 10^{23} \times 2 \times 0.93 \times 10^{-20}}{32} \text{ erg/gauss.}$$

Field gradient $\dfrac{\partial B_y}{\partial y} = 1700$ gauss/cm

Magnitude of the force acting on 1 gm of liquid oxygen
$$= P_m \frac{\partial B_y}{\partial y} = \frac{6.023 \times 10^{23} \times 2 \times 0.93 \times 10^{-20}}{32} \times 1700$$
$$= 5.95 \times 10^5 \text{ dynes} = 5.95 \text{ Newton}$$

Q. 9.6 (a) Calculate the energy of a dipole in a steady magnetic field.

(b) A magnetic dipole is subjected to an external magnetic field. What direction will it prefer and why ?
                                                                        (H.P.U., 1994)

Ans. (a) Energy of a dipole in a magnetic field. Consider a current loop representing a magnetic dipole of magnetic moment $\vec{P_m}$ placed in a uniform magentic field $\vec{B}$. If the plane of the current loop is parallel to the field, then the force acting on the loop is perpendicular to the plane of the loop. Hence, if the field acts in the Y-direction and the current loop is placed with its plane in the Y-Z plane, the force on the loop will be in the X direction i.e., in the direction of the magnetic dipole equivalent to the current loop. If now the loop is moved parallel to its plane say from infinity where $B = 0$ to a point in the field of strength $\vec{B}$, then since the loop is being displaced in a direction perpendicular to the force acting on the loop, no work is done. In other words, the potential energy of the current loop is zero when its plane is parallel to the magnetic field $\vec{B}$. This further means that the potential energy of a dipole is zero when it is placed so that the direction of the dipole magnetic moment $\vec{P_m}$ is perpendicular to $\vec{B}$ i.e., the vector $\vec{P_m}$ makes an angle $\dfrac{\pi}{2}$ with the vector $\vec{B}$.

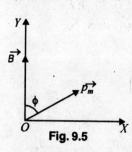

Fig. 9.5

Torque on a dipole. Now consider a magnetic dipole in an orientation making an angle ϕ with respect to the direction of $\vec{B}$. The torque acting on the dipole is given by

$$\vec{\tau} = \vec{P_m} \times \vec{B}$$

Now
$$\vec{P_m} = p_m \sin \phi \, \hat{i} + p_m \cos \phi \, \hat{j}$$
$$\vec{B} = B\hat{j}$$
∴
$$\vec{P_m} \times \vec{B} = p_m \, B \sin \phi \, \hat{k}$$

Hence magnitude of the torque $= p_m \, B \sin \phi$ and it acts in the $+ Z$ direction.

Potential energy of the dipole. Under the action of the external field $\vec{B}$ the dipole will have a tendency to orient the direction of its dipole magnetic moment $\vec{P_m}$ parallel to the magnetic field $\vec{B}$ and an equal and opposite external torque will have to be applied to keep the dipole in position.

Thus the magnitude of the external torque $= - p_m \, B \sin \phi$

∴ Work done by the external field in changing the orientation of the dipole from ϕ to $(\phi - d\phi)$

$$= p_m \, B \sin \phi \, d\phi$$

This work is stored in the dipole and gives its potential energy du.

∴
$$du = p_m \, B \sin \phi \, d\phi$$

∴ Total potential energy of the dipole at an orientation ϕ with respect to the field $\vec{B}$

$$u = \int du = \int_{\pi/2}^{\phi} p_m \, B \sin \phi \, d\phi$$

$$= [- p_m \, B \cos \phi]_{\pi/2}^{\phi} = - p_m \, B \cos \phi \qquad ...(i)$$

$$= - \vec{P_m} \cdot \vec{B}$$

The integration is taken between the limits $\dfrac{\pi}{2}$ to ϕ as the potential energy of the dipole in the orientation $\phi = \dfrac{\pi}{2}$ is zero.

(b) When a magnetic dipole of dipole moment $\vec{P_m}$ is placed in a magnetic field $\vec{B}$, it experiences a torque $\vec{\tau} = \vec{P_m} \times \vec{B}$. The magnitude of the torque $\tau = p_m \, B \sin \phi$ where ϕ is the angle that the vector $\vec{P_m}$ makes with the vector $\vec{B}$. The dipole will, therefore, have a tendency to orient the direction of its dipole magnetic moment $\vec{P_m}$ parallel to the magnetic field $\vec{B}$ so that $\phi = 0$ and there is no torque on the dipole.

Q. 9.7. What do understand by the term magnetisation? (*K.U.* 2000; *H.P.U.* 1996)

Ans. Magnetisation. Magnetisation is also known as *intensity of magnetisation*.

If we consider a small volume ΔV of a magnetic material around a point P having a position vector $\vec{r}$ and $\Delta \vec{P_m}$ is the magnetic dipole moment of this small volume, then

Average magnetic moment per unit volume $= \dfrac{\Delta \vec{P_m}}{\Delta V}$

In the limit as $\Delta V \to 0$ the above relation gives the magnetisation $\vec{P_m}$ at the point P

∴
$$\vec{P_m} = \underset{\Delta V \to 0}{Lt} \dfrac{\Delta \vec{P_m}}{\Delta V}$$

$\vec{P_m}$ generally varies from point to point in the magnetic material. But if the sample is magnetised uniformly, $\vec{P_m}$ is constant vector and independent of position vector $\vec{r}$. In such

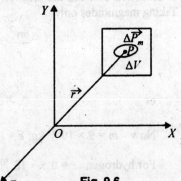

Fig. 9.6

a case *magnetisation or intensity of magnetisation is defined as the magnetic dipole moment per unit volume.*

Q. 9.8. Calculate the magnetic moment of an atomic dipole. *(P.U. 2003)*

Ans. Magnetic moment of an atomic dipole. An atomic dipole consists of an electron of charge $-e$ and mass m revolving around an atomic nucleus with a linear velocity v in an orbit of radius r. The revolving electron is equivalent to a current $I = -\dfrac{e}{2\pi r/v} = -\dfrac{ev}{2\pi r}$

The magnitude of the dipole magnetic moment of a current loop of area A carrying a current I is given by

$$P_m = IA$$

$\therefore$ Magnetic moment of the atomic dipole $= -\dfrac{ev}{2\pi r} \times \pi r^2$

$$= -\frac{1}{2} evr = -\frac{1}{2}\frac{e}{m} mvr = -\frac{1}{2}\frac{e}{m} L$$

where $L = mvr = $ the magnitude of the angular momentum of the electron revolving around the nucleus.

Q. 9.9 (a) Prove that the magnetic moment of an electron is given by $\vec{P_m} = -\dfrac{e}{2m}\vec{L}$ **where** e = **charge on the electron,** m = **electron mass and** $\vec{L}$ = **orbital angular momentum due to orbital motion. Hence show that magnetic moment due to orbital motion of an electron must be an integral multiple of** $\dfrac{e\hbar}{2m}$. **How do you define a Bohr magneton ? Give its numerical value.**

(P.U. 2006, 2000; G. N. D.U. 2000, 1999; Gauhati U. 2000; H.P.U. 2001, 2000, 1996, 1994; Pbi. U. 2003, 2002, 2001, 1995; M.D.U. 2002)

(b) What is orbital gyromagnetic ratio? *(Pbi. U. 2006, 2001; P.U. 2000)*

Ans. (a) Orbital magnetic moment of an electron. All substances are composed of atoms and an atom consists of a central positively charged nucleus where the whole mass of the atom is supposed to be concentrated, with suitable number of electrons revolving round it in more or less circular orbits. An electron carries a *negative* charge of 1.6×10^{-19} coulomb. The revolution of an electron in a clockwise direction is equivalent to a conventional current in the anticlockwise direction and the electronic orbit behaves like a *magnetic dipole.*

Consider the simplest atom of hydrogen. It consists of one proton in the nucleus and one electron revolving round it. If m is the mass of the electron, $-e$ the the charge on it, v its vleocity of revolution and r the radius of the orbit, then the electron is maintained in the orbit due to the electrostatic force of attraction between the electron and the nucleus which provides the necessary centripetal force. Taking magnitudes only

$$\therefore \qquad \frac{mv^2}{r} = \frac{1}{4\pi\varepsilon_0}\frac{e \cdot e}{r^2} = \frac{1}{4\pi\varepsilon_0}\frac{e^2}{r^2}$$

or $\qquad\qquad v = \left[\dfrac{1}{4\pi\varepsilon_0}\dfrac{e^2}{mr}\right]^{1/2}$

Now $\quad m \doteq 9 \times 10^{-31}$ kg; $e = 1.6 \times 10^{-19}\,C$

For hydrogen $\quad r = 0.5 \times 10^{-10}\,m;\ \dfrac{1}{4\pi\varepsilon_0} = 9 \times 10^9\ Nm^2\ C^{-2}$

$$\therefore \qquad v = \left[\frac{9 \times 10^9 \times 1.6 \times 1.6 \times 10^{-38}}{9 \times 10^{-31} \times 0.5 \times 10^{-10}} \right]^{1/2} = 2.262 \times 10^6 \text{ m/sec}$$

and time taken by the electron to complete one revolution

$$= \frac{2\pi r}{v} = \frac{2\pi \times 0.5 \times 10^{-10}}{2.262 \times 10^6} = 1.39 \times 10^{-16} \text{ sec}$$

Current in the orbit. From the above calculations we find that the time taken by the electron to complete one orbit is *very very small* and hence the electron will go round the nucleus millions of times during the time of observation. In other words, the electron going round the orbit will not behave as an isolated particle but will appear to be a current loop carrying a current I given by

$$I = \frac{\text{Charge}}{\text{Time taken to complete the orbit}} = \frac{e}{2\pi r / v} = \frac{ev}{2\pi r}$$

Orbital magnetic moment. The magnitude of the dipole magnetic moment of the current loop is given by

$$P_m = IA = \frac{ev}{2\pi r} \pi r^2 = \frac{1}{2} evr$$

The magnitude of the angular momentum of the electron revolving round the nucleus

$$L = mvr$$

$$\therefore \qquad P_m = \frac{1}{2} \frac{e}{m} L \qquad\qquad\qquad ...(i)$$

As $\vec{P_m}$ and $\vec{L}$ are both vector quantities and electron charge e is negative, relation (i) can be put as

$$\vec{P_m} = - \frac{e}{2m} \vec{L} \qquad\qquad\qquad ...(i)\,(a)$$

Orbital magnetic moment integral multiple of $\dfrac{e\hbar}{2m}$. According to Bohr's theory, an electron can only revolve in an orbit in which its total angular momentum is an integral multiple of $\dfrac{h}{2\pi}$ where h is Planck's constant.

$$\therefore \qquad L = n \frac{h}{2\pi}$$

where n is an integer.

Substituting the value of L in (i), we have

$$P_m = \frac{1}{2} \frac{e}{m} \frac{nh}{2\pi} = \frac{neh}{4\pi m}$$

$$= \frac{ne\hbar}{2m} \qquad\qquad ...(ii) \left[\text{where } \hbar = \frac{h}{2\pi} \right]$$

From relation (ii) we find that the magnetic moment due to orbital motion of an electron must be an integral multiple of $\dfrac{e\hbar}{2m}$.

Bohr magneton. The smallest value of orbital magnetic moment of the electron for $n = 1$ is given by

$$P_m = \frac{e\hbar}{2m} = \frac{eh}{4\pi m} \qquad\qquad\qquad ...(iii)$$

This is the unit of magnetic moment and is known as a *Bohr Magneton*. It is denoted by μ_B.

Numerical value of Bohr magneton. Now $e = 1.6 \times 10^{-19}$ coul.

$$h = 6.6 \times 10^{-24} \text{ Joule sec}; \ m = 9 \times 10^{-31} \text{ kg}$$

Substituting these values in Eq. (*iii*), we get

$$\mu_B = \frac{eh}{4\pi m} = \frac{1.6 \times 10^{-19} \text{ coul} \times 6.6 \times 10^{-34} \text{ Joule sec}}{4\pi \times 9 \times 10^{-31} \text{ kg}}$$

$$= 9.27 \times 10^{-24} \text{ Joule } \frac{\text{coul met sec}^{-1}}{\text{kg met sec}^{-2}}$$

$$= 9.27 \times 10^{-24} \text{ Joule } \frac{\text{coul met sec}^{-1}}{\text{Newton}}$$

$$= 9.27 \times 10^{-24} \frac{\text{Joule}}{\text{Tesla}} = 9.27 \times 10^{-24} \text{ Joule/Tesla}$$

[The unit of Bohr magneton is also the same as that of p_m. As $p_m = IA$, the unit of Bohr magneton is also . m²]

Bohr magneton is used as a unit of measurement of atomic magnetic moments.

Orbital gyromagnetic ratio. It is defined as *the ratio of magnetic moment of the atomic dipole to its angular momentum.*

From relation (*i*) we have,

Orbital gyromagentic ratio $= \dfrac{P_m}{L} = \dfrac{e}{2m}$.

Q.9.10. In hydrogen atom an electron revolves around a nucleus in an orbit of radius 0.53Å. If the frequency of revolution of electron is 6.6×10^{15} Hz. Find the magnetic moment of orbiting electron.   (*H.P.U.* 2000)

Ans. Radius of the electronic orbit $r = 0.53$ Å $= 0.53 \times 10^{-10}$ m

Frequency of revolution of the electron $= 6.6 \times 10^{15}$ Hz

$\therefore$ Time taken to complete the electronic orbit $T = \dfrac{1}{6.6 \times 10^{15}} s$

Charge on the electron $q = 1.6 \times 10^{-19} C$

$\therefore$ Equivalent current $\quad I = \dfrac{q}{T} = 1.6 \times 10^{-19} \times 6.6 \times 10^{15} A$

Area of the electronic orbit $A = \pi r^2 = \pi (0.53 \times 10^{-10})^2$ m²

$\therefore$ Magnetic moment of the orbiting electron $p_m = IA$

$$= 1.6 \times 10^{-19} \times 6.6 \times 10^{15} \times \pi \times 0.53 \times 0.53 \times 10^{-20} \text{ Am}^2$$

$$= 9.31 \times 10^{-24} \text{ Am}^2$$

Q. 9.11. (a) Show that when a magnetic field is applied on a diamagnetic substance the change in magnetic moment of an orbiting electron is given by $\dfrac{- Be^2 r^2}{4m}$ **where the symbols have their usual meanings.**

Prove that the change is the same whether the electron is orbiting around the nucleus in clockwise or anticlockwise direction. Hence prove that magnetic dipole moment per unit volume is given by $P_m = \dfrac{- NZ^2 e^2 r^2 \mu_0 H}{4m}$ **and diamagnetic susceptibility** $\chi_m = \dfrac{- NZ^2 e^2 r^2 \mu_0}{4m}$

(b) Discuss Langevin's theory of diamagnetism.   (*G.N.D.U.* 2009, 2004; *Nagpur.U.* 2002;
K.U. 2002, 2001, 1994; *P.U.,* 2009; *Gharwal. U.* 2000, 1999;
Pbi.U. 1999, 1991; *M.D.U.* 2008, 2003, 1999; *Kan.U.* 1997, 1994; *H.P.U.* 1999)

Ans. (a) Induced diamagnetic moment in an electron. An electron revolving in a circular orbit around the nucleus in an atom is equivalent to a current loop. If $-e$ is the charge on the electron and ω its angular velocity in the orbit, then the equivalent current

$$I = \frac{\text{Charge}}{\text{Time taken to complete the orbit}} = \frac{-e}{2\pi/\omega} = \frac{-e\omega}{2\pi}$$

Electron revolving in counter clockwise direction. Suppose the electron revolves in a circular orbit of radius r in a counter clockwise direction in the $X-Y$ plane, with the nucleus at the origin, then the magnetic moment of the electron

$$\vec{P}_m = I\,\vec{a} = \frac{-e\omega}{2\pi}\,\pi r^2\,\hat{k} \qquad [\because \text{Area vector } \vec{a} \text{ is along } +Z \text{ axis}]$$

$$= \frac{-e\omega r^2\,\hat{k}}{2}$$

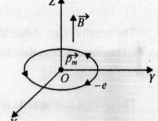

Fig. 9.7

The direction of dipole magnetic moment $\vec{P}_m$ is along the $-Z$ axis.

As the electron is moving in a circular orbit, the centripetal force acting on it

$$F = m\,\omega^2 r \qquad\qquad ...(i)$$

where m is the mass of the electron. The direction of this force is *radially* inward and it is provided by the *electrostatic force of attraction* between the nucleus and the electron.

If an external magnetic field $\vec{B}$ is now applied perpendicular to the plane of the orbit of this single electron *i.e.*, in the $+Z$ direction, then an additional magnetic force ΔF will act on it, given by

$$\Delta \vec{F} = e\,\vec{v} \times \vec{B}$$

Since $\vec{B}$ is perpendicular to $\vec{v}$, the magnitude of the force

$$\Delta F = evB = er\omega B = Ber\omega \qquad\qquad ...(ii)$$

This force will also act *radially inward* on the electron at right angles to both the orbit and the magnetic field. Thus the force on the electron due to the external magnetic field and the electrostatic force acting on it due to the nucleus both act in the same direction.

$\therefore$ Net force acting on the electron in the magentic field

$$= -(m\omega^2 r + Ber\omega)$$

Under the effect of this increased force the electron can either move in an orbit of smaller radius or have a greater velocity in the same orbit or both. But according to the laws of quantum mechanics which are applicable to the electronic orbits, the electron can move only in specific orbits of fixed radii governed by quantum laws. Hence the only alternative for the electron is to increase its angular velocity in the original orbit. If $\omega + \Delta\omega$ is the angular velocity of the electron after the application of the magnetic field, the new magnetic moment of the electron

$$\vec{P}_m + \Delta \vec{P}_m = -\frac{er^2}{2}\,(\omega + \Delta\omega)\,\hat{k}$$

$\therefore$ Change in the magnetic moment

$$\Delta \vec{P}_m = -\left[\frac{er^2}{2}\,(\omega + \Delta\omega) - er^2\,\omega\right]\hat{k}$$

$$= -\frac{er^2}{2}\Delta\omega\,\hat{k} \qquad \qquad ...(iii)$$

According to relation (i) $F = m\omega^2 r$

$$\therefore \qquad\qquad \Delta F = 2mr\omega\,\Delta\,\omega \qquad\qquad ...(iv)$$

From relation (ii) $\Delta F = Ber\omega$

$$\therefore \qquad\qquad 2mr\omega\Delta\omega = Ber\omega$$

or $$\Delta\omega = \frac{e}{2m}\,B$$

Substituting the value of $\Delta\omega$ in (iii), we have

$$\Delta\,\vec{p}_m = \frac{-e^2 r^2}{4m}\,B\,\hat{k}$$

$$= \frac{-e^2 r^2}{4m}\,\vec{B} \qquad\qquad ...(v)$$

The negative sign shows that the change in magnetic moment takes place in a direction opposite to $\vec{B}$. Thus the electron develops an induced magnetic moment $\Delta\,\vec{p}_m$ in a direction opposite to the external magnetic field.

The change in magnetic moment of the orbiting electron is $\dfrac{-e^2 r^2}{4m}\,\vec{B}$.

Electron revolving in clockwise direction. If we consider the electron as moving in the *clockwise* direction, the area vector of the current loop

$$\vec{a} = -\pi r^2\,\hat{k}$$

and the magnetic moment of the electron before the application of the magnetic field is

$$\vec{p}_m = \left(-\frac{e\omega}{2\pi}\right)\left(-\pi r^2\,\hat{k}\right) = \frac{e\omega r^2}{2}\,\hat{k}$$

The directon of $\vec{p}_m$ is, therefore, along $+ Z$ axis.

As in this case the direction of the velocity vector has also changed, the force due to the external magnetic field will now act on the electron in the *radially outward* direction *i.e.*, opposite to that of the electrostatic force. The net force on the electron will decrease and the electron will move in the same orbit with a smaller angular velocity $(\omega - \Delta\omega)$. The change in the magnetic moment will, therefore be given by

$$\Delta\,\vec{p}_m = \left[\frac{er^2}{2}\,(\omega - \Delta\omega) - \frac{er^2}{2}\,\omega\right]\hat{k}$$

$$= -\frac{er^2}{2}\,\Delta\,\omega\,\hat{k}\ ...(v)\,(a)$$

which on substituting the value of $\Delta\omega = \dfrac{e}{2m}\,B$ gives

$$\Delta\vec{p}_m = \frac{-e^2 r^2}{4m}\,\vec{B} \qquad\qquad ...(v)\,(a)$$

Thus the value of $\Delta\,\vec{p}_m$ is the same in direction as well as in magnitude whether the electron is moving in the clockwise or anticlockwise direction.

If N is the number of electrons per unit volume and Z the atomic number, then

$$\vec{P}_m = \frac{-NZe^2r^2}{4m}\vec{B} = \frac{-NZe^2r^2\mu_0}{4m}\vec{H}$$

and susceptibility $\qquad \chi_m = \chi_m = \frac{\vec{P}_m}{\vec{H}} = \frac{-NZe^2r^2\mu_0}{4m}$

(b) **Langevin's theory of diamagnetism.** In the expression, (v) (a) if the electronic orbit is not perpendicular to the applied field. then r is replaced by r_1, the projection of the radius r of the orbit on the plane perpendicular to the magnetic field i.e., in the $X-Y$ plane.

If x, y, z are the co-ordinates of the radius r of the orbit, then

$$r^2 = x^2 + y^2 + z^2$$

and $\qquad\qquad r_1^2 = x^2 + y^2$

If the radii are arranged in all possible directions, then the average value of

$$r^2 = x^2 + y^2 + z^2 = 3x^2$$

and $\qquad\qquad r_1^2 = x^2 + y^2 = 2x^2 = \frac{2}{3}r^2$

If we denote the average value of r^2 as $<r^2>$, we have relation (v) as

$$\Delta\vec{P}_m = \frac{-e^2}{4m}\cdot\frac{2}{3}<r^2>\vec{B}$$

$$= \frac{-e^2}{6m}<r^2>\vec{B}$$

If N is the number of electrons per unit volume and Z the atomic number, then the diamagnetic dipole moment per unit volume

$$\vec{P}_m = \frac{-NZe^2}{6m}<r^2>\vec{B} = \frac{-NZe^2}{6m}<r^2>\mu_0\vec{H}$$

$$= \chi_d\vec{H} \qquad\qquad\qquad\qquad ...(vi)$$

where χ_d is the diamagnetic susceptibility of the material.

$$\therefore \qquad\qquad \chi_d = -\frac{NZe^2\mu_0}{6m}<r^2> \qquad\qquad ...(vii)$$

According to the laws of atomic structure, the electrons in an atom have a tendency to exist in pairs with their angular momentum vectors pointing in opposite directions. Thus for most of the atoms which have an even number of electrons, the total angular momentum is zero. Such atoms have zero magnetic dipole moment and are *diamagnetic.*

If we consider an atom having two electrons moving in the same orbit but in opposite directions, the net magnetic dipole moment of such an atom will be zero as the dipole moment due to one electron will be equal and opposite to that of the other. When an external magnetic field is applied; as explained in Eq (v) (a) above both the electrons will acquire a magnetic moment

$$\Delta \vec{p}_m = \frac{-e^2 r^2}{4m} \vec{B}$$

irrespective of the fact whether the motion of the electron is clockwise or anticlockwise. The induced dipole magnetic moment will act in a direction opposite to that of the applied field and hence the atom will experience a force in the direction of decreasing B and the material is *repelled*.

From the above discussion we note the following points :

(*i*)   The diamagnetic dipole moment per unit volume $\vec{P}_m$ is proportional to the magnetic field $\vec{B}$ (or $\vec{H}$).

(*ii*) The direction of $\vec{P}_m$ is opposite to that of $\vec{B}$ (or $\vec{H}$).

(*iii*) The diamagnetic susceptibility χ_d is always negative and almost independent of temperature.

Q. 9.12 (*a*) Using electron theory of magnetism show that a diamagnetic substance is feebly repelled by a magnet.   (*H.P.U.* 1999; *Kan.U.*, 1994; *K.U.*, 1995)

(*b*) **Show that diamagnetic susceptibility is independent of temperature.**

(*M.D.U.* 2007, 2000; *Kan.U.*, 1997, 1993)

Ans. Repulsion of a diamagnetic material. Let *SN* be a strong bar magnet which produces a magnetic field B along the *X*-axis. The field is non-uniform and goes on decreasing as we move away from the magnet in $+X$ direction.

$\therefore$ Rate of change of magnetic field along *X*-axis $= -\dfrac{\partial B}{\partial x}$ *i.e.*, $\dfrac{\partial B}{\partial x}$ acting along $-X$ direction.

If we place a slab of diamagnetic material of unit volume at a position where the average magnetic field is B, then the magnetic dipole moment per unit volume produced in the slab,

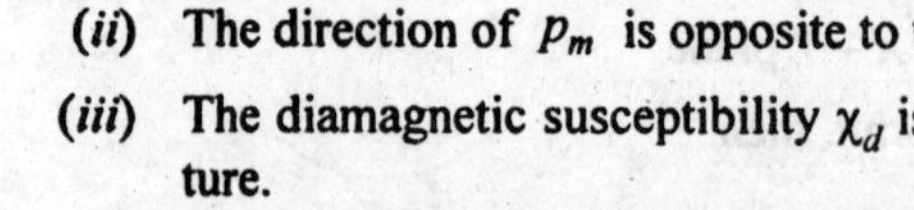

Diamagnetic

Fig. 9.8

$$\vec{P}_m = -\frac{Ne^2}{6m} <r^2> \vec{B} = \chi_d \vec{B}$$

[For proof see **Q. 9.11** Eq. (*vi*)]

where χ_d is the diamagnetic susceptibility and has a negative value.

The magnitude of the force acting on a dipole of magnetic moment $\vec{P}_m$ when placed in a non-uniform magnetic field varying at the rate $\dfrac{\partial B}{\partial x} = P_m \dfrac{\partial B}{\partial x}$.

But $\dfrac{\partial B}{\partial x}$ as well as p_m are both negative. Therefore the force acting on the material is $+ \chi_d \vec{B} \dfrac{\partial B}{\partial x}$. *i.e.*, it acts along the $+X$ direction and hence the substance is *repelled* away from the magnet.

(*b*) **Diamagnetic susceptibility independent of temperature.** The diamagnetic susceptibility $\chi_d = -\dfrac{Ne^2}{6m} <r^2>$ where N is the number of electrons per unit volume, e and m the charge and mass of the electron respectively and $<r^2>$ is the average value of r^2 (r being the radius of the electronic orbit. [For proof see **Q. 9.11** Eq. (*vii*)]

None of these factors depends upon temperature. Hence the susceptibility of diamagnetic materials is independent of temperature.

Q. 9.13. Explain the term spin angular momentum and spin magnetic moment of an electron. (*P.U.*, 1994; *G.N.D.U.*, 1990)

Ans. Spin angular momentum. An electron in an atom revolves round the nucleus in a more or less circular orbit and possessses an orbital angular momentum which is an integral miultiple of $\frac{h}{2\pi}$ where h is Planck's constant. In addtion, the electron possesses an angular momentum which according to classical theory is supposed to arise due to the rotation of the electron about an axis passing through its centre. This property is called *spin* and the electron is said to possess a spin angular momentum equal to $\frac{1}{2}\frac{h}{2\pi} = \frac{1}{2}\hbar$.

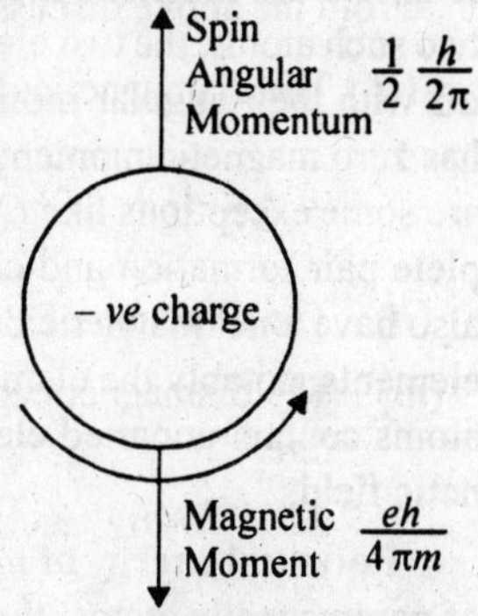

Spin magnetic moment. Electron spin is a quantum phenomenon and in accordance with quantum laws, there is an *intrinsic magnetic moment* attached to the spin angular momentum of *constant magnitude* equal to one Bohr magneton. Its value $\frac{eh}{4\pi m} = \frac{e\hbar}{2m} = 9.27 \times 10^{-24}$ Joule/Tesla

Spin Angular Momentum $\frac{1}{2}\frac{h}{2\pi}$

$-ve$ charge

Magnetic Moment $\frac{eh}{4\pi m}$

Fig. 9.9

The magnetic moment vector points *antiparallel* to the spin angular momentum vector. This is in accordance with the fact that the electron can be considered as a small sphere of negative charge spinning around its axis.

[**Note.** The orbital magnetic moment of the electron

$$\vec{P_m} = -\frac{e}{2m}\vec{L_0} \text{ where } \vec{L_0} \text{ is the orbital angular momentum.}$$

Similarly, according to the classical theory the spin magnetic moment of the electron should be given by $(\vec{P_m})_{spin} = -\frac{e}{2m}\vec{L_s}$

where $\vec{L_s}$ is the spin angular momentum $= \frac{1}{2}\frac{h}{2\pi}$

$$\therefore \qquad (\vec{P_m})_{spin} = -\frac{e}{2m}\frac{1}{2}\frac{h}{2\pi} = -\frac{1}{2}\frac{eh}{4\pi m}$$

This value of spin magnetic moment of the electron is half the value given above. But this derivation is based on laws of classical Physics whereas the spin motion of the electron obeys quantum laws according to which the spin magnetic moment of the electron is given by

$$(\vec{P_m})_{spin} = 2\left(-\frac{e}{2m}\right)\vec{L_s}$$

$$= 2\left(-\frac{e}{2m}\right) \times \frac{1}{2}\frac{h}{2\pi} = -\frac{eh}{4\pi m} = -\frac{e\hbar}{2m}]$$

Q.9.14 (a) Give Langevin's electronic theory of paramagnetism and hence prove that susceptibility χ_p of paramagnetic substances is inversely proportional to absolute temperature. What is Curie's law?

(*H.P.U.* 2003, 2001, 1999; *Pbi. U.* 2006, 2001, 2000, 1995; *G.N.D.U.* 2003, 1999, 1993; *M.D.U.* 1999; *Kan. U.* 1996, 1992; *K.U.* 1996, 1995, 1994; *P.U.* 1995)

(b) Why are some substances diamagnetic while others are paramagnetic? Explain.

(*G.N.D.U.* 1999)

Ans. Langevin's theory of paramagnetism. According to the laws of atomic structure the electrons in an atom have a tendency to exist in pairs with their angular momentum vectors pointing in opposite directions. Thus for most of the atoms which have an *even* number of electrons the total angular momentum is zero. Such atoms have zero net magnetic dipole moment and are dimagnetic. Atoms with an *odd* number of electrons have at least one electron which is *unpaired*. Such atoms tend to have a net magnetic moment and are *paramagnetic* . In a molecule consisting of two such atoms, the two electrons which are originallly unpaired in the atom will pair off with their angular momenta pointing in opposite directions. The molecule thus has zero magnetic moment and behaves as a diamagnetic molecule. However, there are some exceptions like O_2 whose electronic structure is such as not to favour complete pair formation and cancellation of spin angular momentum. Such substances also have a net magnetic dipole moment and are paramagnetic. In certain groups of elements, notably the elements around gadolinium and iron in the periodic table the atoms contain unparied electron spin which are relatively free to orient in the magnetic field.

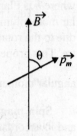

Fig. 9.10

Potential energy of an atomic dipole. If we have a bulk sample containing a very large number of paramagnetic atoms, their dipole moments will normally be oriented in random direction so that the net magnetic moment of the sample as a whole on the macroscopic scale is zero. When such a sample is placed in an external magnetic field, an atomic dipole of magnetic moment $\overrightarrow{p_m}$ lying in a direction making an angle θ with the direction of the magnetic field will tend to align itself in the direction of the field and the *magnitude* of the corresponding torque.

$$= p_m B \sin \theta$$

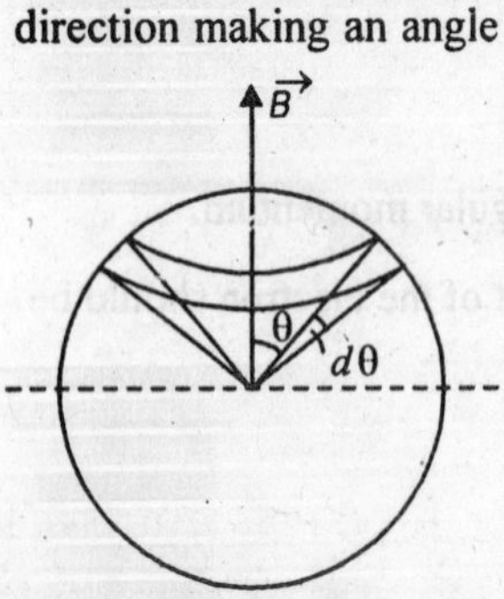

If an external force displaces it through an angle $d\theta$, the work done by the force

$$= p_m B \sin \theta \, d\theta$$

Hence the total work done in displacing the atomic dipole to the position making an angle θ with the direction of $\overrightarrow{B}$

$$= \int_0^\theta p_m B \sin \theta \, d\theta = - p_m B \cos \theta$$

Fig. 9.11

This work is stored in the atomic dipole as its potential energy.

$\therefore$ Potential energy of atomic dipole $U = -p_m B \cos \theta$ \hfill [Also See **Q. 9.6** Eq. (*i*)]

Average dipole moment induced in the atom. If we consider a spherical volume having a very large number of atomic dipoles, the number of those possessing an energy $U = p_m B \cos \theta$ will be proportional to the solid angle enclosed between two cones with semi-vertical angle θ and $\theta + d\theta$ *i.e.*, within a solid angle

$$2\pi \sin \theta \, d\theta$$

Further, the tendency of the magnetic dipoles to align themselves parallel to the applied magnetic field is opposed by their thermal agitation. Hence the probability that an atomic dipole will lie in the position making an angle θ with the direction of the magnetic field $\overrightarrow{B}$, according to the laws of probability is $e^{-U/kT}$ where k is Boltzmann constant and T the absolute temperature *i.e.*, the number of such atoms will be proportional to $e^{-U/kt}$.

If dN is the number of such atoms, then

$$dN \propto e^{-U/kT} 2\pi \sin \theta \, d\theta$$

$$= C e^{-U/kT} 2\pi \sin \theta \, d\theta$$

where C is the constant of proportionality.

The total number of atoms

$$= C \int_0^\pi e^{-U/kT} \, 2\pi \sin \theta \, d\theta \qquad \qquad ...(i)$$

The magnetic moment contributed by each atomic dipole in the direction of field $\vec{B} = p_m \cos \theta$.

$\therefore$ Total magnetic moment contributed by the atomic dipoles

$$= C \int_0^\pi p_m \cos \theta \, e^{-U/kT} \, 2\pi \sin \theta \, d\theta \qquad \qquad ...(ii)$$

But $\qquad\qquad U = -p_m B \cos \theta$

$\therefore \qquad\qquad e^{-u/kT} = e^{p_m B \cos \theta/kT}$

Now $\dfrac{p_m B}{kT}$ is of the order of 10^{-2} and $\ll 1$

$\therefore \qquad\qquad e^{p_m B \cos \theta/kT} = 1 + \dfrac{p_m B \cos \theta}{kT}$

Substituting the value of

$$e^{-U/kT} = 1 + \dfrac{p_m B \cos \theta}{kT}$$

in (i) and (ii), we have

Average magnetic moment per atom in the direction of the field

$$<p_m> = \frac{C \int_0^\pi p_m \cos \theta \left(1 + \dfrac{p_m B \cos \theta}{kT}\right) 2\pi \sin \theta \, d\theta}{C \int_0^\pi \left(1 + \dfrac{p_m B \cos \theta}{kT}\right) 2\pi \sin \theta \, d\theta}$$

Now $\displaystyle\int_0^\pi \cos \theta \sin \theta \, d\theta = 0; \displaystyle\int_0^\pi \cos^2 \theta \sin \theta \, d\theta = \left[\dfrac{-\cos^3 \theta}{3}\right]_0^\pi = \dfrac{2}{3}$ and $\displaystyle\int_0^\pi \sin \theta \, d\theta = 2$

$\therefore \qquad\qquad <p_m> = \dfrac{\dfrac{2}{3} \dfrac{2\pi p_m^2 B}{kT}}{4\pi} = \dfrac{p_m^2 B}{3kT} \qquad \qquad ...(iii)$

This gives the average magnetic moment induced in each atom by the external magnetic field.

Magnetic dipole moment per unit volume. If N is the total number of magnetic dipoles (atomic or molecular), per unit volume, then the magnetic dipole moment per unit volume or intensity of magnetisation is given by

$$\vec{P_m} = \frac{N \, p_m^2 \, \vec{B}}{3kT} = \chi_p \, \vec{B} \qquad \qquad ...(iv)$$

where χ_p is the paramagnetic susceptibility.

Now $\qquad\qquad \vec{B} = \mu_0 (\vec{H} + \vec{P_m})$

where $\vec{H}$ is the *magnetic field vector*. But for paramagnetic materials $\vec{P_m}$ is very small.

$\therefore \qquad\qquad \vec{B} = \mu_0 \vec{H}$

Hence $\qquad\qquad \vec{P_m} = \dfrac{N \, p_m^2 \, \mu_0 \, \vec{H}}{3kT} = \chi_p \, \vec{H} \qquad \qquad ...(v)$

where
$$\chi_p = \frac{\vec{P_m}}{\vec{H}} = \frac{\mu_0 \ N \ p_m^2}{3kT} \qquad \qquad \ldots(vi)$$

is the magnetic susceptibility for a paramagentic material.

Equation (v) shows that the *paramagnetic sample acquires magnetisation in the direction of the magnetic field.*

Thus (i) The magnetisation $\vec{P_m}$ induced in the paramagnetic material is proportional to $\vec{H}$.

(ii) The direction of $\vec{P_m}$ is the same as the direction of magnetic field.

(iii) The susceptibility of a paramagnetic substace χ_p is always positive.

Curie law. The susceptibility of a paramagnetic substance is given by

$$\chi_p = \frac{\mu_0 \ N \ p_m^2}{3kT} \quad \text{or} \quad \chi_p \propto \frac{1}{T}$$

as $\dfrac{\mu_0 \ N \ p_m^2}{3k}$ is a constant. The relation $\chi_p \propto \dfrac{1}{T}$ is known as *Curie's law*. Hence Curie's law states that

'*The susceptibility of a paramagnetic substance varies inversely as the absolute temperature*'.

(b) **Diamagnetism and paramagnetism.** To explain why some substances are diamagnetic while others are paramagnetic see part (a) under '*Langevin's theory of paramagnetism*'.

Q. 9.15. Explain why a paramagnetic material is attracted by a bar magnet.

(H.P.U., 1992)

OR

Why does a sample of paramagnetic substance placed in a non-uniform magnetic field move from weaker to stronger part of the field?

(G.N.D.U. 2004)

Ans. Attraction of a paramagnetic material. Let SN be a strong magnet which produces a magnetic field B along the X-axis. The field is non-uniform and goes on decreasing as we move away from the magnet in the $+X$ direction.

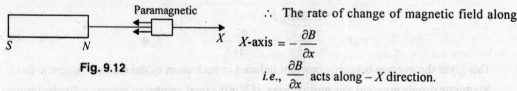

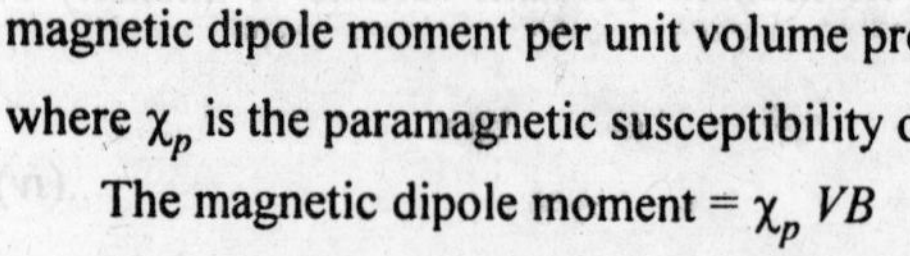

∴ The rate of change of magnetic field along

Fig. 9.12

X-axis $= -\dfrac{\partial B}{\partial x}$

$i.e.,$ $\dfrac{\partial B}{\partial x}$ acts along $-X$ direction.

Place a slab of paramagnetic material at a position where the average magnetic field is B, then the magnetic dipole moment per unit volume produced in the slab $\vec{P_m} = \chi_p B$, [Eq. (iv) **Q. 9.14**] where χ_p is the paramagnetic susceptibility of the material. If V is the volume of the slab, then

The magnetic dipole moment $= \chi_p VB$

The magnitude of the force acting on a dipole of magnetic moment $\vec{P_m}$ when placed in a non-uniform magnetic field varying at the rate $\dfrac{\partial B}{\partial x} = \vec{P_m} \dfrac{\partial B}{\partial x}.$

∴ Force on the paramagnetic slab $F = \chi_p \ V B \dfrac{\partial B}{\partial x}.$

But $\dfrac{\partial B}{\partial x}$ acts along the $-X$ direction. It means that the force on the paramagnetic substance acts in the $-X$ direction and hence the substance is *attracted* towards the magnet. In other words, a sample of paramagnetic substance placed in a non-uniform magnetic field moves from weaker to stronger parts of the field.

Q. 9.16. Why is the magnetic susceptibility of diamagnetic substances negative?

(*H.P.U.*, 1991)

Ans. Diamagnetic susceptibility is given by

$$\chi_d = -\frac{Ne^2}{6m} <r^2>$$

As N and m are always positive and e^2 and $<r^2>$ being squares are also always positive χ_d is *negative*.

Q. 9.17 (a) (i) Can a free electron have a magnetic moment?   (*H.P.U.* 1992)

(ii) Can a free electron show diamagnetism? Explain.   (*Pbi.U.*, 2008)

(b) A hydrogen atom is paramagnetic. Will a hydrogen molecule be paramagnetic? Why?

(*H.P.U.* 1994, 1992)

Ans. (a) (i) Yes, A free electron possesses *spin angular momentum*, the value of which is $\frac{1}{2}\hbar = \frac{h}{4\pi}$. where h is Planck's constant. The electron also has a charge. A spinning charged particle has a magnetic moment. Hence a free electron has a magnetic moment because of its charge and spin.

The value of spin magnetic moment of the electron $= \frac{eh}{4\pi m} = 9.27 \times 10^{-24}$ Joule/Tesla.

(ii) No. Diamagnetism arises due to orbital motion of the electron. Since a free electron possesses only spin angular momentum (and no orbital angular momentum), so it will not show any diamagnetic effect. Also see **Q. 9.13.**

(b) A hydrogen molecule consists of two hydrogen atoms. When a hydrogen molecule is formed the electrons of the two hydrogen atoms get *paired with their angular momentum vectors pointing in* opposite directions and thus cancelling each other. The molecule, therefore, has zero dipole moment and is *diamagnetic*.

The hydrogen molecule is not *paramagnetic*.

Q. 9.18. What is ferromagnetism? Explain ferromagnetism on the basis of domain theory. Why does a piece of iron ordinarily not behave as a magnet?

(*Meerut U.* 2002; *H.P.U.* 2007, 2002, 1999, 1997, 1995, 1993, 1992, 1991; *G.N.D.U.*, 1997, 1995, 1990; *P.U.* 2001, 2000, 1994, 1992; *Pbi. U.*, 1995; *M.D.U.* 2002)

Ans. Ferromagnetism. *Ferromagnetic substances are those which can be magnetised and retain magnetism even when the external magnetising field has been removed.* Familiar examples are *Fe, Co, Ni, Gd, Dy* and their alloys. The magnetic dipole moment per unit volume or the intensity of magnetisation $\vec{P}_m$ produced in such substances is very high. It is also not proportional to the magnetising force $\vec{H}$ i.e., The susceptibility χ_m is not a constant but a function of $\vec{H}$ as well as of absolute temperature T. The susceptibility decreases with temperature and above a certain temperature known as the *Curie point* the substance loses its ferromagnetic character and behaves as a paramagnetic material.

Domain theory. Ferromagnetism like paramagnetism is caused by the spin magnetic moment of the electron. Thus individually each atom of a ferromagnetic substance is paramagnetic and has a permanent magnetic dipole moment due to *unpaired electron spins*. In a paramagnetic substance, in the unmagnetised state the atomic or molecular dipoles are themselves arranged at random so that the net resultant magnetic dipole moment of the substance is zero. But in ferromagnetic substances adjacent atomic dipoles are locked in rigid parallelism as each atomic or molecular dipole is very strongly coupled to the neighbouring atom by a typical quantum mechanical interaction known as *exchange interaction* with the result that a large number of atomic dipoles are aligned in the same direction. This group of atomic dipoles is known as a *ferromagnetic domain*. A domain contains about 10^{16} or more atoms and has a volume between 10^{-8} to 10^{-12} cubic metre. All the atoms in a domain are lined up in the same direction and hence it is magnetised to the saturation stage. *Thus domains are local regions within which there is essentially perfect alignment of atomic dipoles.*

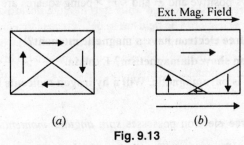

(a) (b)

Fig. 9.13

The direction of magnetisation of each domain in a ferromagnetic material depends upon the crystalline state of the substance. In the case of single crystal domains magnetisation is along the *axes of symmetry or easy directions*. For examples, a single crystal of iron has three axes of symmetry perpendicular to one another and if we denote them as X, Y, Z, the domain magnetisation will be along the $\pm X$, $\pm Y$, and $\pm Z$ direction. There is not a sudden transition from one domain to the other. The domain wall, knwon as '*Block wall*' has a finite thickness extending over a number of atoms whose spins change gradually in direction as we proceed through the wall and in an extreme case may change from $0°$ to $180°$.

Thus we find that ferromagnetic substances are intrinsically magnetised even in the absence of an external magnetic field due to the presence of these domains.

Why a piece of iron ordinarily does not behave as a magnet. Every piece of iron does not ordinarily behave as a magnet because the magnetic domains within the material are, so arranged as to form closed chains and cancel the magnetic effect of one another with the result that the material is on the whole neutral (unmagnetised). A possible arrangement of domains forming closed chains is shown in Fig. 9.13 (*a*). Here all the domains are of the same size and their direction of magnetisation is shown by arrow heads. These are so arranged that the net magnetic moment of the sample is zero as shown in Fig. 9.13 (*a*).

Magnetisation. When a *small* external magnetic field is applied in a particular direction two effects take place.

(*i*) The size of the domains within the material which have their magnetic orientation in the direction of the applied magnetic field increases at the expense of those that are not favourably oriented, and

(*ii*) More and more atomic dipoles within a domain become parallel to the magnetising field.

As a result of both these effect the size of domains oriented in unfavoured directions decreases as shown in Fig. 9.13 (*b*). The material, therefore, acquires a net magnetic dipole moment.

Saturation stage. As the strength of the magnetising field is increased further a stage is reached when all the dipoles are oriented parallel to the magnetising field in a single domain. On further increasing the magnetising field, there is no increase in magnetism. This stage is known as *saturation stage.*

Hysteresis. When an external magnetic field is applied, the domain walls of the favourably oriented domains expand and start moving out. If the field is extremely small the process is reversible *i.e.*, as soon as the field is removed the material gets demagnetised and domains regain their original size and orientation. It is observed that when the magnetic field is increased the imperfections in the crystalline structure of the material offer obstruction to the outward movement of the domain walls and the impurities resist the favourable orientation of the atomic dipoles. However, when the magnetising field is sufficiently increased the domain walls snap past these imperfections with a *sudden jerk.* Thereafter, the movement of the domain wall is again quite smooth and rapid till the next imperfection is reached.

If the field is now *decreased* the domain walls start moving inward and there is an obstruction again in moving past an imperfection. The field has to be decreased to a much lower value in order to overcome the obstruction and some energy is lost in the process. Even when the magnetising field is reduced to zero, some magnetism may still be present in the material. This explains *residual magnetism.* In order to reduce the residual magnetism to zero a field in the reverse direction has to be applied. This measures the *coercive foce.* As the magnetisation always lags behind the magnetising force the phenomenon is known as *hysteresis* and the energy lost in the process as stated above is the loss of energy due to hysteresis.

Q. 9.19. Why ferromagnetism is found in solids only and not in fluids?

(*Pbi., U.,* 1995; *H.P.U.* 2000, 1994)

Ans. Ferromagnetism in solids only. Ferromagnetism is found in solids only because ferromagnetism is due to the formation of *domains* consisting of a group of atomic dipoles. In solids each atomic (or molecular) dipole is very strongly coupled to the neighbouring atoms by a quantum mechanical interaction known as *exchange interaction.* This interaction occurs only between those atoms which are very close to each other as in solids.

No ferromagnetism in fluids. In fluids (liquids and gases) the average distance between the atoms or molecules is very large as compared to that in solids. The exchange interaction is, therefore, absent and formation of domains cannot take place. This is why ferromagnetism does not occur in liquids and gases.

Q. 9.20. Is it meaningful to say that atom is ferromagnetic?   (*Pbi. U.,* 1993)

Ans. It is not meaningful to say that an atom is ferromagnetic. Ferromagnetism is a macroscopic phenomenon due to the formation of domains which consist of a group of large numbr of atomic dipoles held together by forces of *exchange interaction.* Thus a single atom cannot be ferromagnetic. It can only be paramagnetic or diamagnetic.

Q. 9.21. What are the characteristics of diamagnetic, paramagnetic and ferro-magnetic substance? Illustrate by simple experiments.

(*P.U.,* 2007; *H.P.U.* 1997, 1996; *Pbi. U.* 2003, 1995;
G.N.D.U. 2004, 2003, 2002,1990; *M.D.U.* 2001; *Meerut U.* 2003;
2002, 2001; *Gauhati.U.* 2000; *Luck. U.* 1993; *Kan.U.,* 1997, 1996, 1995)

Ans. Paramagnetic substances. *Paramagnetic substances are those which are attracted by magnets and when placed in a non-uniform magnetic field move from weaker to stronger parts of the field.* Familiar examples are aluminium, manganese, platinum, rare earth elements like *Gd,* crown glass solutions of salts of iron and oxygen.

Properties. (*i*) If a bar of paramagnetic material is suspended in between the pole pieces of an electromagnet, it sets itself parallel to the lines of forces as shown in Fig. 9.14 showing thereby that the lines of force try to have their longest path through the paramagnetic materials.

Fig. 9.14

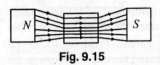

Fig. 9.15

(*ii*) When a bar of paramagnetic material is placed in a magnetic field, the lines of force tend to accumulate in it as shown in Fig. 9.15.

(*iii*) When a paramagnetic material is placed in a non-uniform magnetic field it moves from weaker to stronger parts of the field.

If a paramagnetic liquid is placed in a watch glass on the pole pieces (not more than 2 to 3 mm apart) of an electromagnet then it accumulates in the middle as shown in Fig. 9.16. It is because in the central region the field is the strongest. If the pole pieces are not close together the field is *strongest near the poles* and the liquid moves away from the centre giving an almost opposite effect.

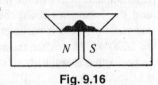

Fig. 9.16

(*iv*) If one end of a narrow *U*-tube containing a paramagnetic liquid is placed within the pole pieces of an electromagnet in such a manner that the level of the liquid is in line with the field, then on applying the field, the level of the liquid rises. The rise is proportional to the susceptibility of the liquid. This is shown in Fig. 9.17.

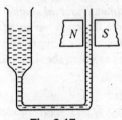

(*v*) When a paramagnetic gas rendered visible by traces of ammonia and hydrogen chloride is allowed to ascend between the pole pieces of an electromagnet it spreads along the direction of the field.

Fig. 9.17

(*vi*) The susceptibility of the paramagnetic material is positive though it has a small value (< 1). The permeability is slightly greater than one. For example, for platinum χ_p = 1.71 × 10^{-6} and permeability μ = 1.00002.

(*vii*) When paramagnetic substances are subjected to a magnetic field these are feebly magnetised in the direction of the field.

The magnetisation (or magnetic dipole moment per unit volume) P_m is proportional to the magnetising force. Therefore, susceptibility and hence permeability remains constant for varying values of the field.

(*viii*) The susceptibility for a given magnetising force is inversely proportional to the absolute temperature and thus obeys *Curie's law* $\chi_p \propto \dfrac{1}{T}$. If, therefore, the temperature is increased the susceptibility decreases and at some high temperature it even becomes negative *i.e.* the substance becomes diamagnetic.

Diamagnetic substances. *Diamagnetic substances are those which are repelled by magnets and when placed in a non-uniform magnetic field move from stronger to weaker part of the field.* Familiar examples of these are bismuth, phosphorous, antimony, copper, water, alcohol and hydrogen.

Properties. (*i*) When a diamagnetic substance is placed in a magnetic field it sets itself at right angles to the direction of the lines of force as shown in Fig. 9.18. This indicates that the lines of force tend to have minimum path through the diamagnetic substances.

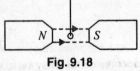

Fig. 9.18

(*ii*) When a diamagnetic material is placed within a magnetic field the lines of force tend to go away from the material as shown in Fig. 9.19.

(*iii*) When a diamagnetic material is placed in a non-uniform magnetic field it moves from stronger to weaker parts of the field.

Fig. 9.19

When a diamagnetic liquid is placed in a watch glass on the pole pieces of a magnet the liquid accumulates on the sides causing a depression at the centre which is the strongest part of the field as shown in Fig. 9.20. When the distance between the pole pieces is large, the effect is reversed.

(*iv*) A diamagnetic liquid in a *U*-tube placed in a magnetic field shows a depression.

Fig. 9.20

(*v*) When a diamagnetic gas is allowed to ascend between the pole pieces of an electromagnet it spreads across the field.

(*vi*) The susceptibility of diamagnetic material is negative and has a small value. For example, for bismuth $\chi_d = -1.4 \times 10^{-8}$. The permeability is less than one but can never be negative.

(*vii*) The susceptibility neither changes with the strength of the field nor with temperature.

Ferromagnetic substances. *Ferromagnetic substances are those which are attracted by the magnets and can also be magnetised. Familiar examples are iron, nickel, cobalt and their alloys.*

Properties. (*i*) Ferromagnetic substances show all the properties of a paramagnetic substance to a much greater degree.

(*ii*) The susceptibility has a positive value and the permeability is also very large.

(*iii*) The magnetisation (or magnetic dipole moment per unit volume) $\vec{P_m}$ is proportional to the magnetising field $\vec{H}$ for small values as shown by part *OA* of the curve in Fig. 9.21 (*a*). For moderate values of *H*, P_m increases rapidly as shown by the part *AB* and for very large values of *H*, P_m almost remains constant due to the approach of saturation stage as shown by the part *BC* of the same curve.

(*iv*) The susceptibility χ_m remains constant for very small values of the magnetising field, increases with the medium values of the field and begins to decreases for very large values of the field as shown by the parts *PQ*, *QR* and *RS* respectively in the curve between χ_m and *H* in Fig. 9.21 (*a*).

(*v*) The susceptibility decreases with temperature and obeys **Curie's law**, which is expressed as

$$\chi_m \propto \frac{1}{T} \quad \text{or} \quad \chi_m T = \text{constant}$$

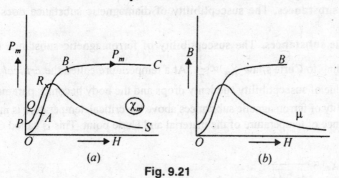

(*a*) (*b*)

Fig. 9.21

At a temperature called the critical temperature or **Curie point** the value of susceptibility drops suddenly and the body becomes paramagnetic.

The Curie point for steel is 770°C, for cobalt 1100°C and for nickel 400°C. The susceptibility of a ferromagnetic substance above its Curie point is proportional to the difference of temperature of the material and Curie point. This is called **Curie-Wiess law.**

The magnetic induction *B* varies nearly in the same manner with *H* as P_m does except that the value of *B* does not become constant for large values of *H*. This is shown in Fig. 9.21 (*b*). The permeability μ varies with *H* in a similar manner as susceptibility does.

Q. 9.22. What is Curie point or Curie temperature? Magnetic behaviour of magnetic substances decreases with increasing temperature. Comment.

(Pbi.U. 2003, 2002; H.P.U., 1995; P.U. 1993)

Ans. Curie point. *Curie point is that temperature above which a ferromagnetic substance becomes paramagnetic.*

The susceptibility of a magnetic material decreases with temperature and according to Curie's law

$$\chi_m \propto \frac{1}{T}$$

As the temperature increases χ_m decreases. A substance which is ferromagnetic slowly loses it ferromagnetic character as the temperature is raised and at the critical temperature known as Curie point the susceptibility becomes so small that the substance becomes paramagnetic.

On further raising the temperature the paramagnetic susceptibility also goes on decreasing and at a still higher temperature becomes zero and then negative. As χ_m becomes negative the magnetic substance loses its paramagnetic character and becomes diamagnetic.

Thus the magnetic behaviour of magnetic substances decreases with temperature.

Q. 9.23. Explain the temperature dependence of behaviour of paramagnetic, diamagnetic and ferromagnetic substances. *(K.U. 2002)*

Ans. Paramagnetic substances. The susceptibility of a paramagnetic substance is given by

$$\chi_p = \frac{\mu_0 \, N \, p_m^2}{3kT} \quad \text{or} \quad \chi_p \propto \frac{1}{T}$$

where $\frac{\mu_0 \, N \, p_m^2}{3k}$ is a constant called *Curie constant.*

The relation $\chi_p \propto \frac{1}{T}$ is known as *Curie's law.* Hence Curie's law states that '*The susceptibility of a paramagnetic substance varies inversely as the absolute temperature*'.

As the temperature is increased the paramagnetic susceptibility decreases and at some high temperature it even becomes negative *i.e.* the substance becomes diamagnetic.

Diamagnetic substances. The susceptibility of diamagnetic substance does not vary with temperature.

Ferromagnetic substances. The susceptibility of ferromagnetic substance decreases with temperature according to Curie's law $\chi_m \propto \frac{1}{T}$. At a temperature called the *critical temperature* or *Curie point* the value of susceptibility suddenly drops and the body becomes paramagnetic.

The susceptibility of ferromagnetic substances above the critical temperature is inversely proportional to the difference of temperature of the material and Curie point. This is called *Curie Wiess law* and is stated as.

$$\chi_m \propto \frac{1}{T - T_c}$$

where T_c is the critical temperature

Q. 9.24. Calculate the magnetic dipole moment of a uniformly charged spherical shell rotating about an axis passing through its centre with constant angular speed.

(P.U., 2006; Pbi. U. 2001)

Ans. Magnetic dipole moment of rotating charged spherical shell. Consider a spherical shell of radius R having origin O at its centre. Let σ be the surface charge density of the shell. Then

$$\sigma = \frac{Q}{4\pi \, R^2}$$

where Q is the total charge on the spherical shell. Divide the shell into a series of rings and consider one such ring of radius $R \sin \theta$ and thickness $R\, d\theta$ as shown in Fig. 9.22.

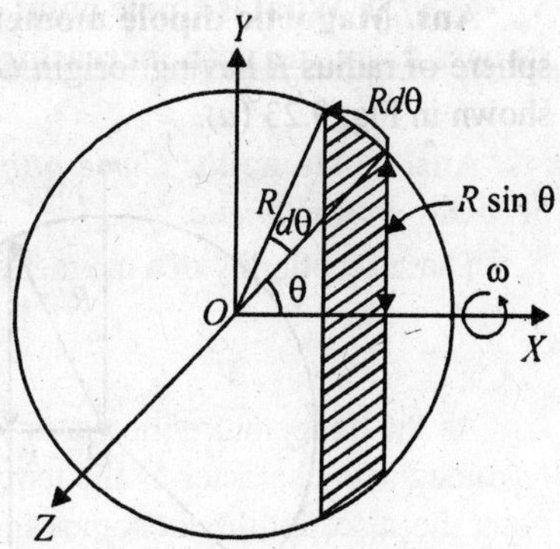

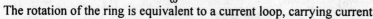

Magnetic moment of the ring. Surface area of this ring

$$dS = 2\pi R \sin \theta .\, Rd\, \theta = 2\pi R^2 \sin \theta\, d\theta$$

Charge on the ring $dq = \sigma\, dS = 2\pi R^2 \sin \theta\, d\theta \times \dfrac{Q}{4\pi R^2}$

or

$$dq = \frac{1}{2} Q \sin \theta\, d\theta$$

When the spherical shell rotates about its axis (say X-axis) with angular velocity ω, the ring also rotates with it. Let T be the time-period of rotation, then

Fig. 9.22

$$T = \frac{2\pi}{\omega}$$

The rotation of the ring is equivalent to a current loop, carrying current

$$I = \frac{dq}{T} = \frac{Q \sin \theta\, d\theta\, \omega}{2 \times 2\pi} = \frac{Q\, \omega \sin \theta\, d\theta}{4\pi}$$

The area of the ring (loop) $A = \pi\, (R \sin \theta)^2 = \pi R^2 \sin^2 \theta$

∴ Magnetic moment of the ring $dp_m = IA$

$$= \frac{Q\, \omega \sin \theta\, d\theta}{4\pi} \times \pi R^2 \sin^2 \theta = \frac{\omega Q R^2 \sin^2 \theta \sin \theta\, d\theta}{4}$$

Magnetic moment of the spherical shell. The magnetic moment of the whole spherical shell

$$P_m = \frac{\omega Q R^2}{4} \int\limits_0^\pi \sin^2 \theta \sin \theta\, d\theta$$

To find the value of the integral put $\cos \theta = Z$

∴ $\qquad - \sin \theta\, d\theta = dZ$ and $\sin^2 \theta = 1 - \cos^2 \theta = 1 - Z^2$

When $\qquad\qquad \theta = 0, Z = + 1$ and when $\theta = \pi, Z = - 1.$

∴ $\qquad P_m = \frac{\omega Q R^2}{4} \int\limits_{+1}^{-1} - (1 - Z^2)\, dZ = \frac{\omega Q R^2}{4} \int\limits_{-1}^{+1} (1 - Z^2)\, dZ$

or, $\qquad P_m = \frac{\omega Q R^2}{4} \left[\int\limits_{-1}^{+1} dZ - \int\limits_{-1}^{+1} Z^2\, dZ \right]$

$$= \frac{\omega Q R^2}{4} \left[[Z]_{-1}^{+1} - \left[\frac{Z^3}{3} \right]_{-1}^{+1} \right]$$

$$= \frac{\omega Q R^2}{4} \left[2 - \frac{2}{3} \right] = \frac{\omega Q R^2}{4} \times \frac{4}{3}$$

or $\qquad P_m = \frac{\omega Q R^2}{3}$

Q. 9.25. Calculate the magnetic dipole moment of a uniformly charged solid sphere rotating about an axis passing through its centre with constant angular velocity. (*P.U.*2001)

Ans. Magnetic dipole moment of rotating charged solid sphere. Consider a charged solid sphere of radius R having origin O at its centre rotating about X-axis with an angular velocity ω as shown in Fig. 9.23 (a).

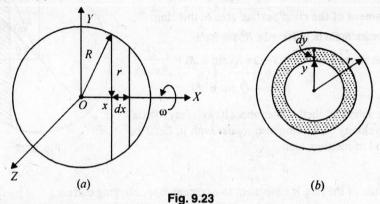

Fig. 9.23

Divide the sphere into a series of discs and consider one such disc of radius r, thickness dx lying perpendicular to the axis of rotation and cutting the X-axis at a distance x from the origin. The disc is further divided into a large number of concentric rings as shown in Fig. 9.23 (b).

Consider one such ring at a distance y from the centre of the disc and of thickness dy.

Magnetic moment of the ring. The surface area of the ring $= 2\pi\, y\, dy$

The thickness of the ring being dx,

Volume of the ring $= 2\pi\, y\, dy\, dx$

$\therefore$ Charge on the ring $\Delta q = 2\pi\, y\, dy\, dx\, \rho$

where ρ is the volume charge density.

Angular velocity of rotation of the ring $= \omega$

$\therefore$ Time period of rotation $T = \dfrac{2\pi}{\omega}$

and current through the ring $I = \dfrac{\Delta q}{T} = \dfrac{2\pi\, y\, dy\, dx\, \rho \times \omega}{2\pi}$

$= \rho\, \omega\, dx\, y\, dy$

Area of the ring $A = \pi\, y^2$

$\therefore$ Magnetic moment of the ring $\Delta p_m = I \times A$

$= \rho\, \omega\, dx\, y\, dy\, (\pi\, y^2)$

$= \pi\, \rho\, \omega\, dx\, y^3\, dy$ ...(i)

Magnetic moment of the disc. The magnetic moment of the disc of radius r can be obtained by integrating relation (i) between the limits 0 and r i.e.

$$dp_m = \int_0^r \pi\rho\omega\, dx\, y^3\, dy$$

In the above integral the variable is y (dx the thickness of the disc being constant)

$\therefore$ $dp_m = \pi\, \rho\, \omega\, dx \left[\dfrac{y^4}{4}\right]_0^r = \dfrac{\pi\, \rho\, \omega\, dx\, r^4}{4}$ ...(ii)

Magnetic moment of the solid sphere. From Fig. 9.23 (*a*), we have $r^2 = R^2 - x^2$. Substituting in (*ii*), we have

$$dp_m = \frac{\pi \rho \omega}{4} (R^2 - x^2)^2 \, dx$$

∴ Magnetic moment of the whole sphere

$$P_m = \frac{\pi \rho \omega}{4} \int_{-R}^{+R} (R^2 - x^2)^2 \, dx$$

$$= \frac{\pi \rho \omega}{4} \int_{-R}^{+R} (R^4 - 2 R^2 x^2 + x^4) \, dx$$

$$= \frac{\pi \rho \omega}{4} \left[R^4 x - \frac{2 R^3}{3} x^2 + \frac{x^5}{5} \right]_{-R}^{+R}$$

$$= \frac{\pi \rho \omega}{4} \left[2 R^5 - \frac{4 R^5}{3} + \frac{2 R^5}{5} \right]$$

$$= \frac{\pi \rho \omega}{4} \times \frac{16 R^5}{15} = \frac{4 \pi \rho \omega R^5}{15} \qquad \qquad ...(iii)$$

If Q is the total charge on the sphere,

$$\rho = \frac{Q}{\frac{4}{3} \pi R^3}$$

Substituting in Eq. (*iii*), we get

$$P_m = \frac{\omega Q R^2}{5}$$

Q. 9.26. (*a*) What do you understand by free and bound currents? Establish the relations

(*i*) Curl $\vec{M} = \vec{\nabla} \times \vec{M} = \vec{J}_{bound}$

(*ii*) Curl $\vec{H} = \vec{\nabla} \times \vec{H} = \vec{J}_{free}$

(P.U. 2000, 1995; H.P.U. 2007, 2003, 2002, 1993;
Pbi.U. 2008, 2007, 2006, 1993; G.N.D.U., 2009, 1992)

OR

Obtain differential form of Ampere's law for magnetic materials.   (*P.U.*, 2007)

(*b*) A magnetic material is non-uniformly magnetised. The magnetisation at any point in the material is given by $x z^2 \hat{i} + x y \hat{j}$. Find the equivalent current density.   (*P.U.*, 2006)

[**Note.** In this question we shell use $\vec{M}$ for $\vec{P}_m$ and $\vec{m}$ for $\vec{P}_m$]

Ans. (*a*) Free and bound currents. Ordinary conduction currents which arise because of the presence of batteries or other sources of *e.m.f.* in electrical circuits and actually involve motion of electrons in a macroscopic path are called *free currents*. Such currents can be started or stopped with a switch and measured with the help of an ammeter.

The currents associated with molecular or atomic magnetic dipole moments are known as *bound currents*. These arise due to orbital or the spin motion of the electrons within the atom.

Uniformly magnetised matter. The electron in an atom have a magnetic dipole moment due to their orbital motion around the nucleus as well as due to their spin. Due to this fact certain atoms and molecules have a *net* magnetic dipole moment. As a result when a substance is magnetised all its magnetic dipoles are oriented in the same direction. A block of material is said to be *uniformly magnetised* if it contains a large number of atomic dipoles all pointing in the same direction evenly distributed throughout its volume. If the dipole moment of each atomic dipole is $\vec{m}$ and the number of such dipoles per unit volume is n, then

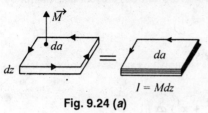

Fig. 9.24 (*a*)

Magnetic moment per unit volume $\vec{M} = \vec{m}\,n$

The magnetic moment per unit volume is known as magnetic polarisation or intensity of magnetisation or simply magnetisation.

Consider a small rectangular piece of uniformly magnetised material of magnetisation $\vec{M}$ having surface area da and thickness dz, then its

Magnetic moment $= \vec{M}\, da\, dz$

Now a current loop has a magnetic moment $I \times$ area of the loop $= Ida$

$\therefore$ $I = M\,dz$

Hence a magnetic dipole of moment $\vec{M}\, da\, dz$ is equivalent to a loop of area da through the boundary of which is flowing a current Mdz in the *anticlockwise* direction as shown in Fig.9.24 (*a*).

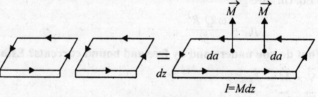

Fig. 9.24 (*b*)

Now, place two identical pieces side by side so that the rim currents in the boundary where they touch each other are *equal and opposite* and thus *cancel out*. The two pieces are thus equivalent to a single slab of area $2\, da$ through the boundary of which current $I = Mdz$ is flowing.

In this way, we can have any number of pieces and construct a slab of an arbitrary shape of thickness dz and area $A = \Sigma\, da$ and uniform magnetisation $\vec{M}$ which is equivalent to a current circuit of area A through the boundary of which a current $I = Mdz$ is flowing.

By placing a number of slabs each of thickness dz one above the other we can have a magnetised material of any shape and thickness with an equivalent boundary current $I = \Sigma\, M\,dz$. Conversely a material of any thickness or shape can be divided into slabs each of thickness dz and each slab can be further subdivided into rectangular pieces of area da. The result derived by placing two such pieces in contact with a common boundary can be generalised for the whole material.

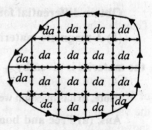

Fig. 9.25 (*a*)

This is the situation when the magnetisation is uniform so that the currents cancel out at the common boundary of the two pieces of the slab and the magnetisation is only due to the current in the outermost boundary or rim of the slab.

The equivalent current is purely theoretical concept and it is a fictitious current that cannot be measured.

As M is uniform, $\qquad I = \Sigma M \, dz = M \Sigma \, dz = Mz$

Now $\dfrac{I}{z}$ = current through unit length is denoted by J_z. It is known as *surface current density.*

$\therefore$ $\qquad\qquad\qquad J_z = M$

Non-uniformly magnetised matter. Now, consider the case when the magnetisation of the material is *non-uniform.* Let a rectangular piece A of thickness dz be placed along the Y-axis and have a magnetisation in the Z-direction denoted by $M_z \, \hat{k}$ and a similar rectangular piece B be placed so that they have a common boundary along the X-axis, and a magnetisation $(M_z + d\,M_z) \, \hat{k}$. If the length of each piece in the Y-direction is dy, the distance between the centres of two pieces is

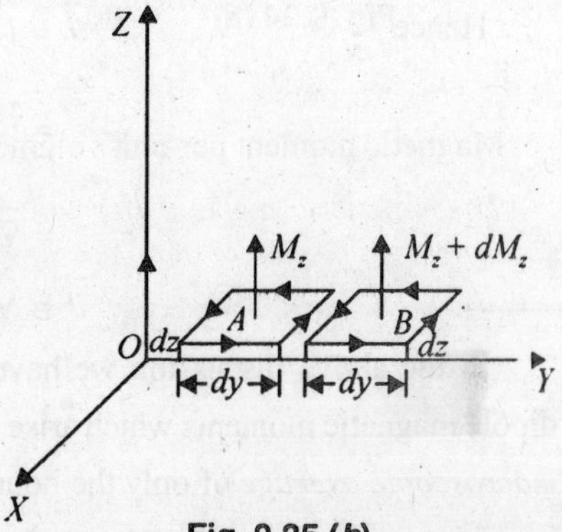

Fig. 9.25 (b)

$$\frac{dy}{2} + \frac{dy}{2} = dy$$

The equivalent rim (boundary) current which produces a magnetisation $M_z \, \hat{k}$ in the piece A is given by $M_z \, dz$. Similarly the equivalent rim boundary current which produces a magnetisation $M_z + d\,M_z$ in the piece B is given by $(M_z + dM_z)\, dz$. Thus exact cancellation of currents does not now take place on the common boundary of the two pieces. On the other hand, a net current dI flows in the $+X$ direction, given by

$$dI = (M_z + dM_z)\, dz - M_z \, dz = dM_z \, dz$$

If $\dfrac{\partial M_z}{\partial y}$ is the rate of change of magnetisation along the Y-axis, then

$$dM_z = \frac{\partial M_z}{\partial y} \, dy$$

$\therefore$
$$dI = dz \frac{\partial M_z}{\partial y} \, dy$$

This is the net current flowing in the $+X$ direction per piece. The face area of each piece $= dy\,dz$. Thus the current dI flows through an area $dy \, dz$ in the $+X$ direction.

$\therefore$ Current density (along X) $J_{x1} = \dfrac{dI}{dy\,dz} = \dfrac{\partial M_z}{\partial y}$

Current density along X-axis due to variation of M_y with Z. We have considered the variation of M_z along the Y-axis and obtained a current density J_{x1} in the X-direction. Similarly, if we consider the variation of M_y along the Z-axis, we obtain current density J_{x2} in the negative X-direction as shown in Fig. 9.26 given by

$$J_{x2} = -\frac{\partial M_y}{\partial z}$$

Magnetisation current density vector. Hence total contribution to current density vector in X-direction

$$J_x = J_{x1} + J_{x2}$$

$$= \left(\frac{\partial M_z}{\partial y} - \frac{\partial M_y}{\partial z} \right)$$

In general, the value of J_y and J_z will also be involved and given by

$$J_y = \left(\frac{\partial M_x}{\partial z} - \frac{\partial M_z}{\partial x} \right) \quad \text{and} \quad J_z = \left(\frac{\partial M_y}{\partial x} - \frac{\partial M_x}{\partial y} \right)$$

Hence

$$\vec{J} = \hat{i} J_x + \hat{j} J_y + \hat{k} J_z$$

$$= \hat{i} \left(\frac{\partial M_z}{\partial y} - \frac{\partial M_y}{\partial z} \right) + \hat{j} \left(\frac{\partial M_x}{\partial z} - \frac{\partial M_z}{\partial x} \right) + \hat{k} \left(\frac{\partial M_y}{\partial x} - \frac{\partial M_x}{\partial y} \right)$$

$$= \vec{\nabla} \times \vec{M} = Curl \ \vec{M}$$

$$\therefore \qquad \vec{J} = \vec{\nabla} \times \vec{M} \qquad \qquad \qquad ...(i)$$

In the above discussion we have considered the magnetisation due to atomic and molecular dipole magnetic moments which arise due to bound currents. The current density vector $\vec{J}$ is thus the *macroscopic average* of only the bound currents and we denote it by J_{bound}.

$$\therefore \qquad Curl \ \vec{M} = \vec{\nabla} \times \vec{M} = \vec{J}_{bound} \qquad \qquad ...(ii)$$

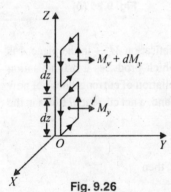

Fig. 9.26

If the material is magnetised uniformly, then $\vec{M}$ is a constant vector and hence $\vec{\nabla} \times \vec{M} = 0$.

$$\therefore \qquad \vec{J}_{bound} = 0$$

(*i*) The relation $Curl \ \vec{B} = \vec{\nabla} \times \vec{B} = \mu_0 \vec{J}$ [For proof of differential form of Ampere's law **See Q. 8.20.** Eq. (*iv*)] can be modified in the light of free and bound current densities. In producing the magnetic induction vector $\vec{B}$, in general, both the currents are involved and $\vec{J}$ is given by total current density denoted as

$$\vec{J}_{total} = \vec{J}_{free} + \vec{J}_{bound}$$

Hence $\qquad Curl \ \vec{B} = \vec{\nabla} \times \vec{B} = \mu_0 \vec{J}_{total} = \mu_0 (\vec{J}_{free} + \vec{J}_{bound}) \qquad ...(iii)$

Substituting the value of $\vec{J}_{bound}$ from Eq. (*ii*) in Eq. (*iii*), we have

$$\vec{\nabla} \times \vec{B} = \mu_0 \vec{J}_{free} + \mu_0 (\vec{\nabla} \times \vec{M})$$

or $\qquad \vec{\nabla} \times (\vec{B} - \mu_0 \vec{M}) = \mu_0 \vec{J}_{free}$

or $\qquad \vec{\nabla} \times \left(\frac{\vec{B}}{\mu_0} - \vec{M} \right) = \vec{J}_{free} \qquad \qquad \qquad ...(iv)$

The quantity $\left(\dfrac{\vec{B}}{\mu_0} - \vec{M} \right)$ is a new macroscopic field vector $\vec{H}$ given by

$$\vec{H} = \frac{\vec{B}}{\mu_0} - \vec{M}$$

It is called *magnetic field vector* to distinguish it from *magnetic induction vector* $\vec{B}$. Equation (*iv*) can be further written as

$$\vec{\nabla} \times \vec{H} = \vec{J}_{free} \qquad ...(v)$$

Thus the vector $\vec{H}$ is determined only by free currents and not by the magnetisation of the material. $\vec{H}$, therefore, represents the *magnetising field*. The vector $\vec{B}$ is due to the total current and represents the total field or *induction field*

$$\vec{B} = \mu_0 \, (\vec{H} + \vec{M})$$

The relation $\vec{\nabla} \times \vec{H} = \vec{J}_{free}$ is known as *differential form of Ampere's law in the presence of magnetic material.*

[**Note.** The readers have used $\vec{M}$ as the magnetic moment of a magnet (magnetic dipole) in the earlier classes, whereas in the above question we have used $\vec{M}$ for intensity of magnetisation *i.e.* magnetic dipole moment per unit volume. In order to avoid confusion, in some earlier questions and in further questions, we shall use $\vec{P}_m$ to denote magnetisation or magnetic dipole moment per unit volume by analogy with electric case where we used $\vec{P}$ for electric polarisation or electric dipole moment per unit volume and further we shell use p_m for *m*.]

(*b*) Here $\vec{M} = xz^2 \, \hat{i} + xy \, \hat{j}$

The equivalent value of current density $\vec{J}$ is given by the relation $\vec{J} = \vec{\nabla} \times \vec{M}$

$$\therefore \quad \vec{J} = \vec{\nabla} \times \vec{M} = \begin{vmatrix} \hat{i} & \hat{j} & \hat{k} \\ \dfrac{\partial}{\partial x} & \dfrac{\partial}{\partial y} & \dfrac{\partial}{\partial z} \\ xz^2 & xy & 0 \end{vmatrix}$$

$$= \hat{i} \left[0 - \frac{\partial}{\partial z} xy \right] + \hat{j} \left[\frac{\partial}{\partial z} xz^2 - 0 \right] + \hat{k} \left[\frac{\partial}{\partial x} xy - \frac{\partial}{\partial y} xz^2 \right]$$

$$= \hat{j} \, (2xz) + \hat{k} \, (y - 0) = 2xz \, \hat{j} + y \, \hat{k}$$

$$\therefore \quad \vec{J} = 2xz \, \hat{j} + y \, \hat{k}$$

Q. 9.27. Define $\vec{M}$ and $\vec{H}$ and find their relations with free and bound currents.

(*H.P.U.*, 1997; *Luck. U.*, 1994; *G.N.D.U.*, 2008, 1994, 1993)

Ans. Intensity of magnetisation. $\vec{M}$ is known as *intensity of magnetisation, magnetic polarisation or simply magnetisation.*

It is defined as magnetic dipole moment per unit volume of the magnetised material.

Magnetising field. $\vec{H}$ is known as *magnetic field* vector or the *magnetising field.*

The field $\vec{H}$ is due to the free or conduction currents I_{free} and is equal to the field $\vec{B}$ in vacuum produced by the same current.

$$\vec{H} = \frac{\vec{B}}{\mu_0} - \vec{M}$$

Relation between $\vec{M}$ and bound current. This relation is

$$\vec{\nabla} \times \vec{M} = \vec{J}_{bound} \qquad\qquad \text{[For proof see Eq. } (ii) \text{ Q.9.26.]}$$

where $\vec{J}_{bound}$ is the bound current density.

Relation between $\vec{H}$ and free current. This relation is

$$\vec{\nabla} \times \vec{H} = \vec{J}_{free}$$

where $\vec{J}_{free}$ is the free current density.

For proof See **Q. 9.26 Eq. (v).**

Q. 9.28. Establish the relation $\vec{B} = \mu_0 \, (\vec{H} + \vec{P}_m)$ where $\vec{B}$ is the magnetic induction vector, $\vec{H}$ the magnetic field vector and $\vec{P}_m$ the intensity of magnetisation. Hence define $\vec{B}, \vec{H}$ and $\vec{P}_m$. Explain the difference between $\vec{B}$ and $\vec{H}$ as applied to magnetism.

(M.D.U. 2001, 1999; K.U. 2000, 1994; Pbi. U. 2000; Nagpur. U. 2000; Luck. U. 1996, 1994; H.P.U. 1995; P.U. 1994, 1992)

Ans. Relation between $\vec{B}, \vec{H}$ and $\vec{P}_m$. Consider a toroidal solenoid through which a current i_{free} (i_f) is flowing. In vacuum the magnetic induction B_{vac} in the toroid is given by

$$B_{vac} = \frac{\mu_0 \, n i_f}{l}$$

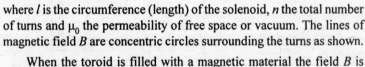

where l is the circumference (length) of the solenoid, n the total number of turns and μ_0 the permeability of free space or vacuum. The lines of magnetic field B are concentric circles surrounding the turns as shown.

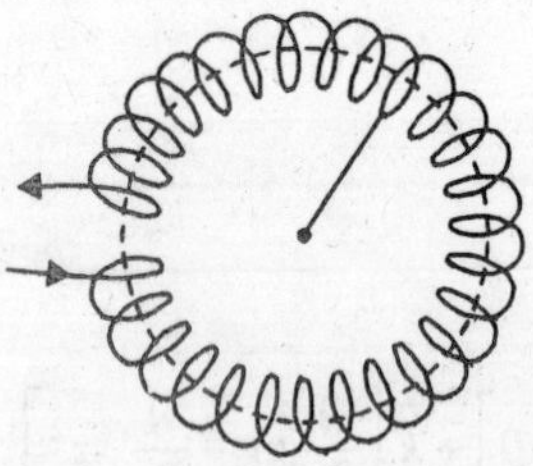

When the toroid is filled with a magnetic material the field B is modified due to the presence of the material. Due to the current the magnetic material is *uniformly* magnetised. For paramagnetic specimens B is increased and for diamagnetic specimens B is decreased. A uniformly magnetised substance behaves as if a *bound* current is flowing through the material. If we represent the *bound* current by i_{bound} (i_b) and replace the magnetic material by vacuum again, then in order to have the same value of B as with the material the total current magnetising the solenoid will have to be increased to $(i_f + i_b)$.

Fig. 9.27

The existence of bound current will produce additional lines of magnetic field which will also be concentric circles around the turns of the toroid. Thus the introduction of the magnetic material will increase the density of the lines of magnetic force.

If $\vec{B}$ is the total field due to both free and bound currents then $\vec{B} = \vec{B}_{free} + \vec{B}_{bound}$.

Now $\qquad \vec{B}_{free} = \mu_0 \, \vec{H} \quad \text{where} \quad \vec{H} = \frac{n i_f}{l}$

$\qquad\qquad\qquad\qquad$. = current in Amps × number of turns per metre

$\qquad\qquad\qquad\qquad$ = Ampere turns per metre

If $\vec{P}_m$ is the intensity of magnetisation *i.e.* magnetic dipole moment per unit volume of the magnetic material, then

$$\vec{B}_{bound} = \mu_0 \, \vec{P}_m$$

$\therefore \qquad\qquad \vec{B} = \vec{B}_{free} + \vec{B}_{bound} = \mu_0 \, \vec{H} + \mu_0 \, \vec{P}_m$

$$\vec{B} = \mu_0 \, [\vec{H} + \vec{P_m}] \qquad \ldots(i)$$

Magnetic induction vector field $\vec{B}$. Magnetic field $\vec{B}$ is the total magnetic field within the magnetic material. It is the sum of the magnetising field $\mu_0 \vec{H}$ due to the free (conduction) current and the field $\mu_0 \vec{P_m}$ due to magnetisation of the material having dipole magnetic moment per unit volume $\vec{P_m}$

$$\therefore \qquad \vec{B} = \mu_0 \vec{H} + \mu_0 \vec{P_m} = \mu_0 \, (\vec{H} + \vec{P_m})$$

Thus $\vec{B}$ consists of two parts.

(*i*) **The magnetising field $\vec{H}$.** This field is also known as *magnetic field* and is due to the free (or conduction) current i_f and is equal to the field $\vec{B}$ in vacuum produced by the same current. The field $\vec{H}$ is responsible for magnetising the specimen and is, therefore, known as *magnetising field.*

$$\vec{H} = \frac{n \, i_f}{l} = \text{Ampere turns per metre}$$

Also

$$\vec{H} = \frac{\vec{B}}{\mu_0} - \vec{P_m}$$

(*ii*) **Intensity of magnetisation P_m.** Due to the magnetising field $\vec{H}$ the material acquires a magnetic dipole moment $\vec{P_m}$ per unit volume. $\vec{P_m}$ is called intensity of magnetisation or simply magnetisation.

It is defined as the magnetic dipole moment per unit volume of the magnetised material.

The field due to magnetisation $= \mu_0 \vec{P_m}$

Units. The magnetic induction $\vec{B}$ and magnetic field $\vec{H}$ are different fields. They are, therefore, measured in different units.

The units of $\vec{B}$ is a Tesla.

$$1 \; \text{Tesla} \; (T) = 1 \; Wb/m^2$$

As $\vec{B} = \mu_0 \, (\vec{H} + \vec{P_m})$, the unit of $\vec{H}$ and $\vec{P_m}$ is the same as that of $\dfrac{\vec{B}}{\mu_0}$. The unit of $\vec{P_m}$ is Ampere turns per metre. The unit of $\vec{H}$ is also Ampere turns per metre.

Q. 9.29 (a) Define magnetic susceptibility and permeability. Establish a relation between them and prove that $\mu_r = 1 + \chi_m$ and hence show that $\vec{B} = \mu_0 \, (1 + \chi_m) \, \vec{H}$.

(b) How can you classify magnetic materials on the basis of these properties?

(c) State the difference between permittivity and permeability.

(*Pbi. U.* 2003, 2002; *Nagpur. U.* 2002; *M.D.U.* 2001, 1999; *Meerut. U.* 2006, 2002, 2001, 2000; *P.U.* 2006, 2001, 1994; *G.N.D.U.* 2008, 2006, 2003, 2001, 1995; *Gharwal. U.* 2000, 1999; *Gauhati. U.* 2000; *H.P.U.* 1997, 1995; *K.U.* 2002, 1994)

Ans. (a) Magnetic susceptibility. *The ratio of the magnitude of magnetic dipole moment per unit volume $\vec{P_m}$ and the magnitude of the magnetising field $\vec{H}$ is known as magnetic susceptibility χ_m.*

$$\therefore \qquad \chi_m = \frac{\left| \vec{P_m} \right|}{\left| \vec{H} \right|} = \frac{P_m}{H} \qquad \ldots(i)$$

The magnetic susceptibility of vacuum (or free space) is zero. Magnetic susceptibility is a pure number as the units P_m and H are the same.

Permeability. *The ratio of magnitude of magnetic induction field $\vec{B}$ inside the material and the magnitude of magnetising field $\vec{H}$ is known as magnetic permeability* μ.

$$\therefore \qquad \mu = \frac{|\vec{B}|}{|\vec{H}|} = \frac{B}{H} \qquad \qquad \dots(ii)$$

Units of μ. unit of $\mu = \dfrac{\text{Unit of } B}{\text{Unit of } H} = \dfrac{\text{Tesla}}{A/m}$

But $\qquad\qquad \text{Tesla} = \dfrac{\text{Newton}}{\text{Amp metre}} = \dfrac{N}{Am}$

$$\therefore \qquad \mu = \frac{N}{Am \; A/m} = \frac{N}{A^2}$$

Relation. All the three vectors $\vec{B}$, $\vec{H}$ and $\vec{P}_m$ are in the same direction.

$\therefore$ From Eq. (*i*) $\qquad\qquad \vec{P}_m = \chi_m \, \vec{H}$

and From Eq. (*ii*) $\qquad\qquad \vec{B} = \mu \, \vec{H}$

But $\qquad\qquad\qquad \vec{B} = \mu_0 \, (\vec{H} + \vec{P}_m)$ $\qquad\qquad$ [For proof See **Q. 9.28 Eq. (*i*)**]

Substituting the values of $\vec{B}$ and $\vec{P}_m$ in terms of $\vec{H}$, we have

$$\vec{B} = \mu \vec{H} = \mu_0 \, (\vec{H} + \chi_m \vec{H}) = \mu_0 \, (1 + \chi_m) \, \vec{H}$$

or $\qquad\qquad\qquad \mu = \mu_0 \, (1 + \chi_m)$

$$\therefore \qquad\qquad \frac{\mu}{\mu_0} = \mu_r = (1 + \chi_m) \qquad\qquad \dots(iii)$$

The constant μ_r is called *relative permeability.*

Relative permeability. *It is the ratio of the permeability* μ *of the material to that of vacuum* μ_0. Relative permeability is a mere number being the ratio of μ/μ_0.

As $\qquad\qquad\qquad \mu_r = 1 + \chi_m$

or $\qquad\qquad\qquad \chi_m = \mu_r - 1$

$$\therefore \qquad\qquad \vec{P}_m = \chi_m \, \vec{H} = (\mu_r - 1) \, \vec{H}$$
$$\vec{B} = \mu \, \vec{H} = \mu_r \, \mu_0 \, \vec{H} \qquad\qquad \dots(iv)$$

Relation. $\vec{B} = \mu_0 \, (1 + \chi_m) \, \vec{H}$. Substituting the value of $\mu_r = (1 + \chi_m)$ from Eq. (*iii*) in Eq. (*iv*), we get,

$$\vec{B} = \mu_0 \, (1 + \chi_m) \, \vec{H} \qquad\qquad \dots(v)$$

(*b*) **Classification of magnetic materials.** Magnetic materials have been classified into *diamagnetic, paramagnetic* and *ferromagnetic* on the basis of their permeability and susceptibility.

The susceptibility of *diamagnetic* materials is *negative* and has a small value (between 0 and – 1). For example, for Bismuth $\qquad \chi_d = -1.4 \times 10^{-8}$

The susceptibility of *paramagnetic* materials is *positive* and has a small value (between 0 and + 1) For example, for Platinum $\chi_p = +1.71 \times 10^{-6}$

The susceptibility of ferromagnetic materials is *positive* and has a *very large value.*

The permeability of *diamagnetic* materials is *less than 1* (but > 0) *i.e.* it cannot be *negative.*

The permeability of *paramagnetic* materials is *slightly greater than one* and that of *ferromagnetic* materials is *very large.*

(c) **Difference between permittivity and permeability.** Permittivity ε is the electrical property of a medium.

It is defined as the ratio of electric displacement vector $\vec{D}$ in a dielectric medium to the electric field vector $\vec{E}$ in vacuum (or air).

or
$$\varepsilon = \frac{\vec{D}}{\vec{E}}$$

Relative permittivity ε_r is defined as the ratio of the absolute permittivity of a medium ε to the permittivity of air (or free space) ε_0

$\therefore$
$$\varepsilon_r = \frac{\varepsilon}{\varepsilon_0}$$

$$\varepsilon_r = 1 + \chi_e$$

where χ_e is the electric susceptibility. Further

$$\varepsilon = \varepsilon_0 \, \varepsilon_r = \varepsilon_0 \, (1 + \chi_e).$$

For permeability μ, relative permeability μ_r and the relation $\mu_r = (1 + \chi_m)$ or $\mu = \mu_0 (1 + \chi_m)$ see part (a) of the question.

Q. 9.30. Find the percentage increase in magnetic induction when the space within a current carrying toroid is filled with magnesium. Given χ_m for magnesium 1.2×10^{-5}

(*P.U.* 2001, *M.D.U.*2000)

Ans. Magnetic induction $B = \mu_0 H$

When the space within the current carrying toroid is filled with magnesium of relative permeability μ_r, the new value of magnetic induction

$$B' = \mu_r \, \mu_0 \, H$$

But $\qquad \mu_r = (1 + \chi_m)$ where χ_m is the magnetic susceptibility.

$\therefore \qquad B' = \mu_0 (1 + \chi_m) H = (1 + \chi_m) B$

and percentage increase in magnetic induction

$$= \frac{B' - B}{B} \times 100 = \frac{(1 + \chi_m) B - B}{B} \times 100 = \chi_m \times 100$$

$$= 1.2 \times 10^{-5} \times 100 = 1.2 \times 10^{-3} = 0.0012\%.$$

Q. 9.31. A current in a solenoid produces a magnetising field of 167 Amp met^{-1}. What is the magnetic induction inside it if it has an iron core of magnetic susceptibility 5000?

(*P.U.*, 2007; *G.N.D.U.* 1997, 1996)

Ans. Magnetising field $H = 167 \text{ Am}^{-1}$

Susceptibility $\chi_m = 5000$

Permeability $\mu = \mu_0 (1 + \chi_m) = 4\pi \times 10^{-7} (1 + 5000) \ N/A^2$

Now $\frac{B}{H} = \mu$

$\therefore$ $B = \mu H = 167 \times 4\pi \times 10^{-7} \times 5001 \; N/Am = 1.05 \; N/Am = 1.05 \; Tesla.$

Q. 9.32. The magnetic susceptibility of a medium is 940×10^{-4}. Calculate its absolute and relative permeability.   (*P.U.* 2000; *K.U.* 1996)

Ans. Susceptibility $\chi_m = 940 \times 10^{-4} = 0.094$

Relative permeability $\mu_r = \frac{\mu}{\mu_0} = 1 + \chi_m$

$\therefore$ $\mu_r = 1.094$

and $\mu = \mu_r \, \mu_0 = 1.094 \times 4\pi \times 10^{-7} = 13.75 \times 10^{-7} \; N/A^2$

Exercise. *Magnetic susceptibility of aluminium is 2.3×10^{-5}. Find its permeability and relative permeability.*   (*M.D.U.* 2003)

Hint. $\mu_r = 1 + \chi_m = 1 + 2.3 \times 10^{-5} = 1.000023$

$\mu = \mu_0 \, \mu_r = 4\pi \times 10^{-7} \times 1.000023 = 12.57 \times 10^{-12} \; N/A^2$

Q. 9.33. A sample of iron develops a magnetic moment of 8000 Am^2. If the area of cross-section of the sample is 16 sq. cm, and its length is 5 cm, calculate.

(*i*) Intensity of magnetisation (*ii*) Magnetic induction

(*iii*) permeability and (*iv*) susceptibility of the sample when the magnetising field intensity is $2 \times 10^7 \; Am^{-1}$.   (*K.U.* 2002)

Ans.   Magnetic moment $= 8000 \; Am^2$

Area of cross-section $= 16 \; Sq. \; cm = 16 \times 10^{-4} \; m^2$

Length $= 5 \; cm = 5 \times 10^{-2} \; m$

$\therefore$ Volume of the sample $= 16 \times 10^{-4} \times 5 \times 10^{-2} = 80 \times 10^{-6} \; m^3$

Intensity of magnetisation $P_m = \dfrac{\text{Magnetic moment}}{\text{Volume}}$

$= \dfrac{8000}{80 \times 10^{-6}} = 10^8 \; Am^{-1}$

Magnetising field $H = 2 \times 10^7 \; Am^{-1}$

$\therefore$ Susceptibility $\chi_m = \dfrac{P_m}{H} = \dfrac{10^8}{2 \times 10^7} = 5$

Permeability $\mu = \mu_0 (1 + \chi_m) = 4\pi \times 10^{-7} (1 + 5)$

$= 24 \pi \times 10^{-7} = 75.4 \times 10^{-7} \; N/A^2$

Magnetic induction $B = \mu H = 24 \pi \times 10^{-7} \times 2 \times 10^7$

$= 48 \pi = 150.8 \; Tesla.$

Q. 9.34. The maximum value of permeability of a material is 0.126 N/A^2. What is relative permeability and magnetic susceptibility?   (*P.U.* 2003)

Ans. $\mu = 0.126 \; N/A^2, \; \mu_0 = 4\pi \times 10^{-7} \; N/A^2$

$\therefore$ Relative permeability $\mu_r = \dfrac{\mu}{\mu_0} = \dfrac{0.126}{4\pi \times 10^{-7}} = 10^5$

Susceptibility χ_m is given by

$$\mu_r = 1 + \chi_m$$

$$\therefore \qquad \chi_m = \mu_r - 1 = 10^5 - 1 = 99999$$

Q. 9.35. An iron rod of 50 cm length and 2 mm^2 area of cross-section is placed in a long solenoid of 25 turns per cm carrying a current of 2 Amp. Assuming the relative permeability of iron to be 6000, find the magnetic moment of the bar. *(P.U.* 2007, 2002)

Ans. Here n = 25 turns/cm

$\therefore$ Number of turns per metre

$$N = 25 \times 100 = 2500$$

Now magnetising field $\vec{H} = \dfrac{n\, i_f}{l} = N\, i_f$

Given current in the coil = free current $i_f = 2$ A

$\therefore \qquad \vec{H} = N\, i_f = 2500 \times 2 = 5000$ Amp turns/metre

The magnetic induction field

$$\vec{B} = \mu \vec{H} = \mu_0\, \mu_r\, \vec{H}$$

Here $\mu_r = 6000$ and $\mu_0 = 4\pi \times 10^{-7}$

$\therefore \qquad \vec{B} = \mu_0\, \mu_r\, H = 4\pi \times 10^{-7} \times 6000 \times 5000 = 12\pi\ T$

Also $\qquad \vec{B} = \mu_0\, (\vec{H} + \vec{P_m})$

where $\vec{P_m}$ is the induced magnetic moment per unit volume.

$$\therefore \qquad \vec{P_m} = \frac{\vec{B}}{\mu_0} - \vec{H} = \frac{12\pi}{4\pi \times 10^{-7}} - 5000$$

$$= 3 \times 10^7 - 5000 = 29995 \times 10^3\ \text{A/m}$$

Length of the bar l = 50 cm = 0.5 m

Area of cross-section a = 2 mm^2 = 2×10^{-6} m^2

$\therefore \qquad$ Volume of the bar = $0.5 \times 2 \times 10^{-6}$ m^3 = 10^{-6} m^3

Hence Magnetic moment of the bar = $\vec{P_m} \times V$

or $\qquad \vec{M} = 29995 \times 10^{+3} \times 10^{-6} = 29995 \times 10^{-3}$ A/m^2

$$= 29.995\ \text{A/m}^2$$

Q. 9.36. An iron rod of length 1m and cross-section 4 sq cm is in the form of a closed ring. If the permeability of iron is 50×10^{-4} Hm^{-1}, show that the number of ampere turns required to produce a magnetic flux of 4×10^{-4} Wb through the closed ring is 200.

(M.D.U. 2001; *K.U.* 1994)

Ans. Magnetic flux $\phi = 4 \times 10^{-4}$ Wb

Area of cross-section A = 4 sq cm = 4×10^{-4} sq m

$\therefore \qquad$ Flux density $B = \dfrac{\phi}{A} = \dfrac{4 \times 10^{-4}}{4 \times 10^{-4}} = 1$ Wb/sq m

Now $\qquad B = \mu\, nI$

where nI is the Ampere turns required.

$$\therefore \qquad nI = \frac{B}{\mu} = \frac{1}{50 \times 10^{-4}} = \frac{10^4}{50} = 200\ \text{Am}^{-1}$$

Exercise. *The mean length of an iron ring having 200 turns of wire upon it is 0.5 m and its cross-section is 4×10^{-4} m². What current through the winding should be sent to produce a flux of 4×10^{-4} Wb in the ring. Permeability of iron is 65×10^{-4} Wb/Amp met.* (M.D.U. 1999)

Hint. $B = \dfrac{\phi}{A} = \dfrac{4 \times 10^{-4}}{4 \times 10^{-4}} = 1$ Wb/m² ; $B = \mu n I$ where n is the number of turns

per metre $= \dfrac{200}{0.5} = 400$

∴ $$I = \frac{B}{\mu n} = \frac{1}{65 \times 10^{-4} \times 400} = 0.385 \text{ Amp.}$$

Q. 9.37. A magnetic field of 1.6×10^3 MKS units produces a flux of 2.4×10^{-5} Wb in a bar of iron of cross-section 0.2 cm². Derive the permeability and susceptibility of the specimen.

(P.U., 1994)

Ans.   Magnetic field $H = 1.6 \times 10^3$ MKS units $= 1.6 \times 10^3$ Am^{-1}

Flux $\phi = 2.4 \times 10^{-5}$ Wb

Area of cross-section $A = 0.2$ cm² $= 0.2 \times 10^{-4}$ m² $= 2 \times 10^{-5}$ m²

∴   Flux density = magnetic induction $B = \dfrac{\phi}{A} = \dfrac{2.4 \times 10^{-5}}{2 \times 10^{-5}} = 1.2$ Wb/m²

Permeability $\mu = \dfrac{B}{H} = \dfrac{1.2}{1.6 \times 10^3} = 0.75 \times 10^{-3} = 7.5 \times 10^{-4}$

Now $\dfrac{\mu}{\mu_0} = 1 + \chi_m$

or $\chi_m = \dfrac{\mu}{\mu_0} - 1 = \dfrac{7.5 \times 10^{-4}}{4\pi \times 10^{-7}} - 1 = 597 - 1 = 596$

Exercise. *A magnetising field of 1000 A/m produces a magnetic flux 2×10^{-5} Weber in a bar of iron of cross-section 0.2 cm². Calculate permeability and susceptibility of the bar.* (M.D.U. 2002)

Hint. $H = 1000$ A/m; $\phi = 2 \times 10^{-5}$ Wb; $A = 0.2$ cm² $= 2 \times 10^{-5}$ m²

∴ $$B = \frac{\phi}{A} = \frac{2 \times 10^{-5}}{2 \times 10^{-5}} = 1 \text{ Wb/m}^2; \quad \mu = \frac{B}{H} = \frac{1}{1000} = 10^{-3}$$

$$\chi_m = \frac{\mu}{\mu_0} - 1 = \frac{10^{-3}}{4\pi \times 10^{-7}} = 796 - 1 = 795$$

Q. 9.38. An iron rod 80 cm long and 3 mm² cross-section is placed in a long solenoid of 30 turns cm^{-1} carrying a current of 2.5 Amp. The rod gains a magnetisation of 12×10^5 Am^{-1}. Determine the magnetic moment, susceptibility and the magnetic field. (P.U., 1994, 1991)

Ans.   Length of the rod $= 80$ cm $= 0.8$ m

Area of cross-section $= 3$ mm² $= 3 \times 10^{-6}$ m²

Number of turns per metre $n = 30 \times 100 = 3 \times 10^3$ turns/m

Magnetisation $P_m = 12 \times 10^5$ Am^{-1}

Volume of the rod $V = 0.8 \times 3 \times 10^{-6} = 2.4 \times 10^{-6}$ m³

∴   Magnetic moment $= P_m \times V = 12 \times 10^5 \times 2.4 \times 10^{-6} = 28.8 \times 10^{-1} = 2.88$ Am²

Susceptibility $\chi_m = \dfrac{P_m}{H}$

Now magnetic field $H = nI = 3 \times 10^3 \times 2.5 = 7.5 \times 10^3$ Am^{-1}

$$\therefore \quad \chi_m = \frac{12 \times 10^5}{7.5 \times 10^3} = 160$$

Q. 9.39. The magnetic susceptibility of He at N.T.P. $= -1.1 \times 10^{-9}$. Find the average magnetic dipole moment induced in an atom of helium when it is subjected to a field of 400 $\hat{k}$ A/m.

(*H.P.U.*, 1994)

Ans. Magnetic field applied $\vec{H} = 400 \, \hat{k}$ A/m

Susceptibility of *He* at N.T.P. $\chi_m = -1.1 \times 10^{-9}$

Let $\vec{P}_m$ be the magnetisation produced in *He*, then

$$\vec{P}_m = \chi_m \vec{H} = -1.1 \times 10^{-9} \times 400 \, \hat{k} \, A/m = -4.4 \times 10^{-7} \, \hat{k} \, A/m$$

Suppose $\vec{p}_m$ is the magnetic moment induced in each atom and N the number of atoms per unit volume, then

$$\vec{P}_m = N \, \vec{p}_m$$

or

$$\vec{p}_m = \frac{\vec{P}_m}{N}$$

Number of atoms in one mole of gas at N.T.P. $= 6.06 \times 10^{23}$

Volume of one mole of gas at N.T.P. $= 22.4$ litres $= 22.4 \times 10^{-3}$ m^3

$$\therefore \text{ Number of atoms per } \text{m}^3 = \frac{6.06 \times 10^{23}}{22.4 \times 10^{-3}} = 2.7 \times 10^{25} \text{ atoms/m}^3$$

$$\therefore \quad \vec{P}_m = -\frac{4.4 \times 10^{-7}}{2.7 \times 10^{25}} = -1.63 \times 10^{-32} \, \hat{k} \, Am^2$$

The negative sign indicates that the atomic dipole points in a direction opposite to $\vec{H}$.

Q. 9.40. Explain what you understand by Hysteresis, remanence (retentivity) and coercivity. What is hysteresis loop? How will you determine the value of remanence and coercivity from a loop? (*Meerut. U.* 2008, 2003, 2002, 2001; *Pbi. U.* 1999; *K.U.* 1996, 1995, 1994; *G.N.D.U.* 2009, 2008, 2007, 1995, 1992, 1990; *P.U.* 2002, 2001, 1992; *A.U.*, 1994, 1993; *H.P.U.*, 1995, 1992; *Luck.U.*, 1996, 1995; *Kan. U.*, 1997, 1995)

Ans. (*i*) **Hysteresis.** A speciment of iron can be magnetised by placing it in a solenoid and passing a current through it. If the value of current is gradually increased the magnitude of the magnetising field H increases and the magnitude of the intensity of magnetisation P_m developed in the specimen also increases. A graph between P_m and H is shown in Fig. 9.28. At O when H is zero P_m is also zero. When H increases P_m also increases but not very uniformly till we reach A. Beyond A if H is further increased P_m remains constant. The substance in this condition is said to be *saturated*.

(*ii*) If H is now decreased the value of P_m decreases but at a much lower rate and when H is zero the value of P_m is not zero but has finite value represented by OB.

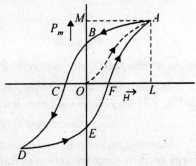

Fig. 9.28

(*iii*) If the value of H is now increased in the opposite direction the value of P_m further decreases and becomes zero when the value of the magnetising field H is equal to OC.

(*iv*) If the value of H is further increased again the saturation stage is reached in the opposite direction and the curve CD is obtained.

(*v*) On decreasing the value of H to zero, we get the portion DE of the curve. It is clear from the curve that P_m has a value given by OE even when H is zero.

(*vi*) On increasing the value of H in the positive direction the part EFA of the cycle is repeated till we again reach the saturation stage at A. This completes the cycle of magnetisation.

The graph between magnetic induction B and the magnetising field H as shown in Fig. 9.29 is almost similar in shape as that between P_m and H but is bigger in size. Since at the saturation stage, increase in B does not stop but is equal to the increase in H, this part of the B–H curve slopes very slightly upwards and unlike the P_m– H curve is not parallel to the H-axis.

In the above experiment it is seen that the intensity of magnetisation or magnetic induction does not become zero although the magnetising field is brought down to zero, *i.e.,* the value of P_m or B aways lags behind H. This shows that the magnetic conditions of iron tend to persist or oppose any change.

This lagging of magnetic induction or intensity of magnetisation behind the magnetising force producing it when a specimen of iron is taken through a cycle of magnetisation is called **hysteresis.**

Hysteresis loop. *The graph showing how P_m or B increases with H from zero to a maximum in one direction and then taken through zero to a maximum in the opposite direction and finally back again through zero to the first maximum is called a* **hysteresis loop.**

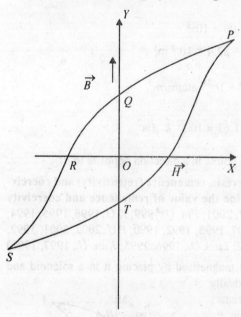

Fig. 9.29

Remanence (or retentivity). *The value of magnetic induction B which remains after the material has been magnetised and the magnetising force i.e., H has been reduced to zero is known as* **remanent induction.**

The value of remanent induction depends upon the degree of magnetisation of the specimen before making H zero. *If the magnetic induction B reaches the saturation value before H is reduced to zero, the limiting value of remanent induction is known as* **remanence** *or* **retentivity**. Thus in Fig. 9.29 the magnetic induction left behind when H is reduced to zero after the specimen has reached the saturation state is represented by OQ.

∴ Remanence = OQ.

Coercivity. *The coercive force is the magnitude of the reverse field required to reduce the remanent induction to zero.*

The limiting value of coercive force required to reduce remanence to zero is known as **coercivity.** In Fig. 9.29 the reverse field required to make remanence zero is OR.

∴   Coercivity = OR

Magnetic materials having a **small** coercive force are known as **soft** whereas those possessing a **large** coercive force are known as **hard.**

Q. 9.41. Show that the loss of energy due to hysteresis per unit volume of the material per cycle of magnetisation is given by (i) μ_0 × area of $P_m - H$ loop and (ii) area of $B-H$ loop. What happens to this energy?   (*M.D.U.* 2007, 2001; *Gauhati.U.* 2000; *H.P.U.* 2007, 1999; *A.U.* 1994, 1993, 1992; *K.U.* 2000, 1995, 1994; *G.N.D.U.* 2006, 2001, 1997, 1995; *P.U.* 2001, 2000, 1992; *Pbi.U.* 2002, 2001, 1993; *Luck. U.*, 1996, 1993; *Kan.U.*, 1997, 1995,1993)

Ans. Dissipation of energy due to Hysteresis. Consider a unit volume *a b c d* of a material placed in a magnetising field of strength $\vec{H}$. Let $\vec{P_m}$ be the magnetic moment of one of the molecular or atomic magnets of the specimen and let θ be the angle between the direction of magnetic dipole moment of this molecule and the direction of the magnetising field $\vec{H}$.

The component of $\vec{P_m}$ parallel to the field $\vec{H} = p_m \cos \theta$ and component of $\vec{P_m}$ perpendicular to the field $\vec{H} = p_m \sin \theta$

∴ The total magnetic moment parallel to the field $= \Sigma p_m \cos \theta$ and total magnetic moment perpendicular to the field $= \Sigma p_m \sin \theta$ where Σ denotes the sum of the components of the magnetic moment due to all the molecular magnets in a particular direction.

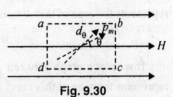

Fig. 9.30

Now $\Sigma p_m \cos \theta = P_m$

where P_m denotes the density of magnetisation, *i.e.*, magnetic moment per unit volume.

Since there is no magnetisation perpendicular to $\vec{H}$, the sum of all the magnetic moments in a direction perpendicular to the field = 0 or

$$\Sigma p_m \sin \theta = 0$$

When P_m is increased by a very small amount dP_m, it is given by

$$dP_m = d \Sigma p_m \cos \theta = - \Sigma p_m \sin \theta \, d \theta \qquad \text{...(i)}$$

The negative sign simply indicates that P_m decreases as θ increases.

The torque acting on a dipole of magnetic moment $\vec{P_m}$ in a magnetic induction field $\vec{B}$

$$= \vec{\tau} = \vec{P_m} \times \vec{B} = p_m \, B \sin \theta$$

If now the angle is *decreased* by a small amount $d\theta$, then

Work done in rotating the dipole through $(-d\theta)$

$$= \tau \, (- d \theta) = - B \, p_m \sin \theta \, d \theta$$

∴ Work done in rotating all the molecular magnets in a unit volume

$$dW = - \sum B \, p_m \sin \theta \, d \theta = - B \sum p_m \sin \theta \, d\theta \qquad \text{...(ii)}$$

Substituting $- \sum p_m \sin \theta \, d \theta = dP_m$ from Eq. (*i*) in Eq. (*ii*), we have

$$dW = B \, dP_m$$

or the work done in changing the value of P_m from P_{m_1}, to P_{m_2}

$$= \int_{P_{m_1}}^{P_{m_2}} B \, dP_m.$$

The total work done in taking the sample through a complete cycle of magnetisation

$$W = \oint B \, dP_m$$

But $\vec{B} = \mu_0\,(\vec{H} + \vec{P}_m)$

As $\vec{B},\vec{H}$ and $\vec{P}_m$ act in the same direction

$$B = \mu_0\,(H + P_m) = \mu_0\,H + \mu_0\,P_m$$

Multiplying both sides by dP_m and integrating over a complete cycle, we have

$$\oint B\;dP_m = \mu_0\;\oint H dP_m + \mu_0\;\oint P_m\;dP_m$$

$$= \mu_0\;\oint H\;dP_m$$

as $\oint P_m\;dP_m = 0$ for if we plot a curve for P_m against P_m, it is a straight line and $\oint P_m\;d\,P_m$ which represents the area of this closed curve for a complete cycle is zero.

$$\therefore \qquad\qquad W = \oint B\,d\,P_m = \mu_0\;\oint H\,d\,P_m \qquad\qquad\qquad ...(iii)$$

If we plot a graph between $\vec{H}$ and $\vec{P}_m$ for a complete cycle we get a closed curve. $\oint H\;d\,P_m$ represents the area of this curvs as proved below.

(i) Loss of energy per cycle. Consider a complete cycle of magnetisation *ABCDEFA*. Let *pq* be the small step in the process of magnetisation in which $\vec{P}_m$ increases by a small amount $d\,\vec{P}_m$.

$\therefore$ Work done per unit volume

$$= \mu_0\;HdP_m = \mu_0 \times \text{area } pqrs$$

where H is the magnitude of the magnetising field $\vec{H}$ and dP_m that of change in intensity of magnetisation $\vec{P}_m$.

(*i*) When the magnetising force H is increased from 0 to *OL*, the intensity of magnetisation changes from *OE* (in the negative direction) to *OM* (in the positive direction).

$\therefore$ Work done on the specimen per unit volume in increasing $\vec{P}_m$ from the value $- OE$ to $+ OM$

$$= \mu_0 \int_E^M H\;dP_m = \mu_0 \times \text{area } EFAMBOE$$

(*ii*) When H is decreased from *OL* to zero P_m decreases from *OM* to *OB*.

Work done by the specimen per unit volume

$$= \mu_0 \int_M^B H\;dP_m = \mu_0 \times \text{area } AMBA$$

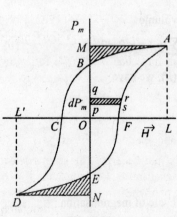

Fig. 9.31

(*iii*) When H is increased in the opposite direction from zero to *OL'*, P_m changes from $+ OB$ to $- ON$

$\therefore$ Work done **on** the specimen per unit volume

$$= \mu_0 \int_B^N H\;dP_m = \mu_0 \times \text{area } BCDNEOB$$

(*iv*) When H is again decreased to zero and the cycle is completed P_m decreases from $- ON$ to $-OE$.

$\therefore$ Work done **by** the specimen per unit volume

$$= \mu_0 \int_N^E H\;dP_m = \mu_0 \times \text{area } DNED$$

It is seen that when the specimen is taken through a complete cycle of magnetisation more work is done **on** the material than is recovered **from** it.

Thus there is a net loss of energy in each cycle of hysteresis which is given by

Loss of energy per cycle per unit volume

$$= \mu_0 \,(\text{area } EFAMBOE + \text{area } BCDNEOB) - \mu_0 \,(\text{area } AMBA + \text{area } DNED)$$

$$= \mu_0 \times \text{ area of the hysteresis loop } ABCDEFA$$

Hence the loss of energy per unit volume per cycle due to hysteresis is equal to $\mu_0 \times$ area of $P_m H$ hysteresis loop.

(*ii*) **Hysteresis loss from B-H cycle.** We know that

$$B = \mu_0 \,(H + P_m)$$

$\therefore$
$$dB = \mu_0 \,(dH + dP_m) = \mu_0 \, dH + \mu_0 \, dP_m$$

Multiplying both sides by H and integrating over a complete cycle we have

$$\oint H dB = \mu_0 \oint H dH + \mu_0 \oint H d P_m = \mu_0 \oint H d P_m$$

as $\oint H dH = 0$ for if we plot a curve of H against H, it is a straight line and the area included by it for a complete cycle is zero.

But $\mu_0 \oint H dP_m$ gives the loss of energy per unit volume per cycle of hysteresis and $\oint H dB$ the area of *B-H* hysteresis loop.

Hence loss of energy per unit volume per cycle of hysteresis is equal to $\oint H dB = $ *Area of B-H loop*.

What happens to this energy? This energy appears as heat in the ferromagnetic material and raises its temperature.

Exercise. *What does the area of B-H loop represent?* (*Pbi. U.* 2006, 2003)

Ans. The area of a *B-H* loop represents the loss of energy per unit volume of the magnetic material per cycle of hysteresis.

Q. 9.42. What type of material should be used for making (*a*) permanent magnets (*b*) electromagnets? (or Cores of transformers and chokes)

(*P.U.* 2007, 2001, 2000, 1995, 1992, 1991;
Pbi. U., 2007; *G.N.D.U.,* 1993; *H.P.U.* 2002, 2000, 1996, 1991; *M.D.U.* 2002, 2000)

Ans. Permanent magnets. The material for a permanent magnet should have the following properties :

1. *High residual magnetism* even in the presence of the mechanical disturbances.

2. *Large coercivity* so that the magnetisation is not wiped out by stray external fields.

3. It should be able to withstand mechanical ill-treatment and temperature changes.

4. Large hysteresis loss, so that the energy stored in the material may be large. This is not a defect as permanent magnets are never subjected to cyclic changes of magnetisation. Looking at the $P_m - H$ curves for iron and steel we find that steel is better suited for making permanent magnets as it possesses all the properties except that it has a small residual magnetism. In actual practice, however, **tungsten steel** having about 5% of tungsten and **cobalt steel** having a coercivity of 240 oersteds are used for

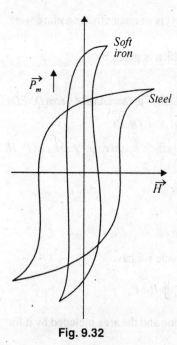

Fig. 9.32

the purpose. There are other alloys like **Alni** (57.6% *Fe* + 29% *Ni* 13.4% *Al*) and **Alnico** (18% *Ni*, 13% *Al*, 12% *Co*, 3% *Cu* and 54% *Fe*) which have very high coercive force.

Very recently a new magnetic alloy **vicalloy** has been developed. It contains iron, cobalt and vanadium and has the highest value of coercive force so far obtained. It can be made into the form of a wire or ribbon (tape) and is used in magnetic recording of sound.

(*ii*) **Electromagnets (or cores of transformers and chokes).** The material for the electromagnet should have the following properties.

1. Large value of P_m with comparatively small magnetising field.

2. High susceptibility for low fields and high permeability.

3. Low hysteresis loss because the material is subjected to cyclic changes of magnetisation.

All these properties are possessed by soft iron which is thus the best suited material for the purpose.

Also see Q. 9.45.

Q. 9.43. The volume of the core of a transformer is 1000 cm³. It is fed with A.C of 50 Hz. If the loss of energy due to hysteresis per hour is 36 Joules calculate the area of B-H loop.

(*P.U.* 2000; *H.P.U.* 2003; *Pbi. U.* 2007, 2002)

Ans. Loss of energy due to hysteresis per second

$$= \frac{36}{60 \times 60} = 10^{-2} \text{ J/s}$$

∴ Loss of energy per cycle $= \dfrac{10^{-2}}{50} = 2 \times 10^{-4}$ J/s/cycle

Volume of transformer core $= 1000 \text{ cm}^3 = \dfrac{1000}{10^6} = 10^{-3} \text{ m}^3$

∴ Loss of energy per cycle per unit volume $= \dfrac{2 \times 10^{-4}}{10^{-3}}$

$$= 2 \times 10^{-1} = 0.2 \text{ Jm}^{-3}$$

$$= \text{area of } B\text{-}H \text{ loop}$$

Q. 9.44 (a) Hysteresis loss per cubic metre for soft iron is 10³ Joules. Taking the density 7.5 gm per c.c. and specific heat 100 cal k gm⁻¹°C⁻¹ calculate the rise of temperature per minute when the specimen is subjected to an alternating magnetic field of frequency 50 cycles/second.

(*b*) **The hysteresis loop of a transformer has area 2500 ergs cm⁻³. Calculate the loss of energy per hour at 50 Hz frequency. Density of iron is 7.5 gm cm⁻³ and weight is 10 kg.**

(*Kan. U.*, 1995, 1991)

Ans. (*a*) Loss of energy per unit volume per cycle $= 10^3$ Joules

∴ Energy lost per minute per cubic metre $= 10^3 \times 50 \times 60$ Joule

Heat generated per minute $= \dfrac{10^3 \times 50 \times 60}{4.2}$ cals

Mass of iron per cc = 7.5 gm

Mass of iron per cubic metre in kg $= \dfrac{7.5 \times 10^6}{10^3} = 7.5 \times 10^3$

If θ is the rise in temperature then

$$7.5 \times 10^3 \times 100 \times \theta = \dfrac{10^3 \times 50 \times 60}{4.2}$$

$\therefore \qquad\qquad \theta = 0.95°C$

(b) Loss of energy per unit volume per cycle = 2500 ergs cm^{-3}

$\therefore$ Loss of energy per unit volume per hour = $50 \times 60 \times 60 \times 2500$ ergs cm^{-2}

Volume of iron $= \dfrac{10 \times 1000}{7.5}$ c.c.

$\therefore$ Total loss of energy per hour $= \dfrac{50 \times 60 \times 60 \times 2500 \times 10 \times 1000}{7.5} = 6 \times 10^{11}$ ergs

$\qquad\qquad\qquad\qquad = 6 \times 10^4$ Joules

Q. 9.45. Explain the use of Hysteresis curve. What type of magnetic material is suitable for transformer cores, telephone diaphragm and chokes?

(P.U., 2006; K.U. 2001; Pbi.U. 2007, 2006, 2000; H.P.U. 2003, 2001, 1997; Luck.U. 1993)

Ans. Use of hysteresis curve. The loss of energy per unit volume per cycle of hysteresis is equal to the area of a B-H loop. Therefore, in electrical and magnetic applications where alternating currents are used particularly of high frequency the hysteresis loss has to be kept a minimum. Transformer cores, telephone diaphragms and chokes are usually subjected to cyclic changes. Therefore the magnetic material suitable for these must have the following essential properties.

(i) *High initial permeability* so that the material acquires a high flux density even for low magnetising fields.

(ii) *Low hysteresis loss* so that there is a small dissipation of energy. This will avoid heating and reduce the possibility of breakdown of the insulation of the windings.

(iii) *High specific resistance* to reduce the eddy current losses.

Taking into consideration these requirements, *soft iron is better than steel* for these appliances.

Transformer steel is an alloy of soft iron containing 4% silicon. **Mumetal** is an alloy having high initial permeability. It contains 76% Ni, 5% Cu, 17% Fe and 1.5% Cr.

Q. 9.46. Explain what is meant by a magnetic circuit. What is its practical significance ? Explain the terms magnetomotive force and reluctance. In what ways magnetic circuit differs from electric circuit? (M.D.U. 2002, 2001, 2000; K.U. 2001, 1996, 1994, 1991)

Ans. Magnetic circuit. The lines of magnetic force start from a north pole and end on a south pole, but they continue within the magnet as lines of induction. If we take a ring of iron and magnetise it by passing electric current through a solenoid wound round it then the lines of induction remain only within the material. There is no magnetic field in the space outside the solenoid. The magnetic flux thus flows within the material in the form of a closed circuit. By analogy with the electric current circuit, such a closed magnetic field is known as **magnetic circuit.**

A magnetic circuit simply refers to the path of magnetic flux. There is no flow of any kind and no energy is required for maintaining the flux in the circuit.

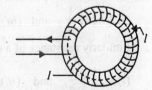

Fig. 9.33

Consider a ring of iron magnetised by passing a current I amperes through the solenoid having a total number of n turns. The intensity of magnetic field B along the axis of the ring is given by

$$B = \mu_0 \, \mu_r \, n \frac{I}{l} \text{ Wb m}^{-2}$$

Where l is the mean circumference of the ring, μ_0 the permeability of free space and μ_r the relative permeability of the material of the ring.

If a is the area of cross-section of the ring, then

$$\text{Magnetic flux } \phi = Ba = \mu_0 \, \mu_r \, a \frac{nI}{l} = \frac{nI}{l / \mu_0 \mu_r \, a} = \frac{M}{R} \text{ Wb}$$

where M stands for nI and R for $\dfrac{l}{\mu_0 \mu_r \, a}$

M is called the **magnetomotive force** and R the **reluctance** by comparison with similar relation in current electricity

$$\text{Current} = \frac{\text{Electromotive force}}{\text{Resistance}} \quad \text{or} \quad I = \frac{E}{R}$$

Magnetomotive force. The magnetomotive force drives or tends to drive flux through a magnetic circuit and corresponds to electromotive in an electrical circuit.

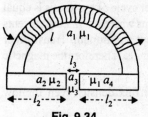

Fig. 9.34

The magnetomotive force in any magnetic circuit is defined as the work done in Joules in carrying a unit magnetic pole once round the magnetic circuit.

The unit of magnetomotive force is *Ampere turns*. It is the product of the number of turns and the current in Amperes in the coil.

$M = nI$ where n is the total number of turns

In an electrical circuit the eletromotive force is defined in a similar way and is responsible for maintainting the flow of current.

Reluctance. It is the name given to the property of a material which opposes the creation of magnetic flux in it.

$$\text{Reluctance} \qquad R = \frac{l}{\mu_0 \, \mu_r \, a} = \frac{l}{\mu a} \text{ where } \mu = \mu_0 \, \mu_r$$

As Magnetic flux $\phi = \dfrac{M}{R}$, the unit of reluctance R is

$$\frac{\text{Unit of } M}{\text{Unit of } \phi} = \frac{\text{Amp turns}}{\text{Weber}} = \text{Amp Turns/Weber}$$

Reluctance in magnetic circuit is similar to resistance in electrical circuit as is clear from the following :

Reluctance in a magnetic circuit is proportional to

(i) l (ii) $\dfrac{1}{a}$ and   (iii) $\dfrac{1}{\mu}$

Similarly resistance of a conductor in an electrical circuit is proportional to

(i) l (ii) $\dfrac{1}{a}$ and   (iii) ρ

where ρ is the specific resistance.

Thus in a magnetic circuit the reciprocal of permeability $\left(\dfrac{1}{\mu}\right)$ behaves in the same way as the specific reisistance ρ in an electrical circuit.

The quantity $\dfrac{1}{\mu}$ *is sometimes called the* **reluctivity** *and is defined as the magnetic resistance offered to the passage of magnetic flux between two opposite faces of a metre cube of the substance.*

When a magnetic circuit consists of a number of parts of different materials of different dimensions, the total reluctance is the sum of reluctances of the various parts. If $l_1, a_1, \mu_1; l_2, a_2, \mu_2 \ldots$ etc. represent the length, area of cross-section and permeability of various parts of the circuit as shown in Fig. 9.34, then

Total reluctance

$$R = \frac{l_1}{a_1\,\mu_1} + \frac{l_2}{a_2\,\mu_2} + \frac{l_3}{a_3\,\mu_3} + \ldots$$

$$= \frac{l_1}{\mu_0\mu_{r_1}\,a_1} + \frac{l_2}{\mu_0\mu_{r_2}\,a_2} + \frac{l_3}{\mu_0\mu_{r_3}\,a_3} + \ldots$$

Difference between magnetic and electric circuits

(*i*) The quantity $\dfrac{1}{\mu}$ in a magnetic circuit corresponds to specific resistance ρ in electrical circuit so that μ apparently corresponds to specific conductivity. Actually permeability in magnetism corresponds to permittivity (dielectric constant) in an electric phenomenon.

(*ii*) The resistance of a conductor is independent of current strength at a given temperature, but reluctance of a magnetic circuit varies considerably with magnetic flux because μ depends upon intensity of magnetisation.

(*iii*) The electric circuit involves the expenditure of energy as long as the current flows but in magnetic circuit energy is required only to establish the flux.

Practical significance. Many electrical machines and other applicanes *e.g.*, the dynamo and the galvanometer make use of almost closed magnetic circuit for producing the magnetic flux. The idea of magnetic circuit enables us to find the value of flux whatever the material and dimensions of its different parts may be, and whether the windings of the solenoid are uniformly distributed or not.

Q. 9.47. An iron ring of mean length 50 cm has an air gap of 1 mm and a winding of 200 turns. If the permeability of iron is 300, find the flux density when a current of 1 Amp flows through it.

Ans.   Length of the ring l_1 = 50 cm = 0.5 m ; Relative permeability μ_r = 300

Length of the air gap l_2 = 1 mm = 0.001 m

Let a be the area of cross-section of the ring, then

$$\text{Reluctance of the air gap} = \frac{l_2}{\mu_0\mu_r a} = \frac{l_2}{\mu_0\, a} = \frac{0.001}{\mu_0 a}$$

$$\text{Reluctance of iron ring} = \frac{l_1}{\mu_0\mu_r a} = \frac{0.5}{300\,\mu_0 a}$$

$$\text{Total reluctance }\; R = \frac{l_1}{\mu_0\mu_r a} + \frac{l_2}{\mu_0\mu_r a} = \left[0.001 + \frac{0.5}{300}\right]\frac{1}{\mu_0 a} = \frac{8\times 10^{-3}}{3\mu_0\, a}$$

Magnetomotive force $M = nI = 200 \times 1 = 200$ Amp. turns

$$\text{Magnetic flux } \phi = \frac{M}{R} = \frac{200 \times 3\mu_0 \, a \times 10^3}{8}$$

$$\therefore \text{ Magnetic flux density } B = \frac{\phi}{a} = \frac{200 \times 3 \times \mu_0 \times 10^3}{8}$$

$$= \frac{200 \times 3 \times 4\pi \times 10^{-7} \times 10^3}{8} = 9.4 \times 10^{-2} = 0.94 \text{ Wb/m}^2$$

Q. 9.48. What are ferrites? How do ferrites differ from ferromagnetic substances? Why do we use ferrite material in radios and other communication equipment? Discuss their other applications.

(G.N.D.U. 2000, 1999, 1997, 1995, 1994, 1993; H.P.U. 2002, 2000, 1993, 1992; P.U. 2002, 2001, 1993, 1991; Pbi.U. 2008, 2003, 2002)

Ans. Ferrites. In addition to the diamagnetic, paramagnetic and ferromagnetic materials, there are some other material having extra ordinary magnetic properties. Some of these are '*Antiferromagnetic*' and '*Ferrimagnetic*'.

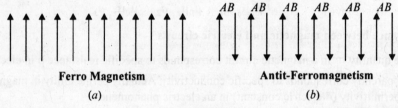

Ferro Magnetism   **Antit-Ferromagnetism**

(*a*)   (*b*)

Fig. 9.35

The *ferrites* belong to the category of *ferrimagnetic* substances. We shall first give a brief introduction of antiferromagnetism.

Antiferromagnetism. According to the domain theory ferromagnetism is due to the exchange interaction or exchange field which arises when the wave functions of two atoms overlap. This gives rise to an **exchange energy**. The **exchange energy** is positive when neighbouring spins are parallel [Fig. 9.35 (*a*)] and the material is ferromagnetic.

When the neighbouring spins are antiparallel [(Fig. 9.35 (*b*)] and hence there is co-operative alternating alignment, the situation leads to a *ground state*.

In these crystals the alternate atoms have their spins parallel but not the adjacent atoms. Such crystals can be considered to be composed of two interpenetrating sub lattices A and B -one with atoms having their spin moments oriented in one direction and the other with atoms having their spin moments oriented in the other direction. Thus one sub-lattice gets aligned in one direction whereas the second gets aligned in the other. Such substances are known as *antiferromagnetics*. In the absence of an external magnetic field the net magnetic moment is zero.

Ferrimagnetism. Ferrimagnetism is a special case of antiferromagnetism in which opposing magnetic moments of the two sets of atoms in the sub-lattices are of different magnitudes giving rise to a large net magnetisation (Fig. 9.36.). This important class of crystals is known as *ferrimagnets* or *ferrites*.

The ferrimagnetic crystals are magnetic compounds consisting of two or more different kinds of atoms. The usual chemical formula for ferrimagnetic crystals or ferrites is MO Fe$_2$O$_3$

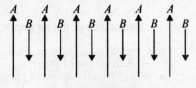

Ferrimagnetism

Fig. 9.36

where M is a divalent metal like Mn^{2+}, Co^{2+}, Ni^{2+}, Fe^{2+}, Zn^{2+}, Cd^{2+}, or Mg^{2+} and Fe^{3+} is the trivalent ferric ion.

Ferrites are ferrimagnetic materials having negligible conductivity (resistivity 10^9 times that of ferromagnetics).

Difference between ferrites and ferromagnetic materials. Ferrites differ from ferromagnetic materials in following respects :

(*i*)   Ferrites have a negligible electrical conductivity.

(*ii*) Magnetic induction of ferrites is much less than that of ferromagnetics.

(*iii*) Ferrites have a higher permeability and lower hysteresis loss as compared to ferromagnetics.

Use of ferrite material in radios and communication equipment. Ferrites have a very low electrical conductivity. They are, therefore, used as the cores of *a.c.* inductors and transformers in radios and communication devices operating with high frequency currents. Because of poor conductivity, negligible eddy currents are set up in them and loss of energy due to Joule heating and hysteresis is very small.

Ferrites can be obtained by replacing the magnesium and aluminium atoms from $MgAl_2O_4$ (Magnesium Aluminium oxide or spinel) by iron, zinc, nickel, cobalt, manganese etc. *i.e.*, some of non-magnetic atoms (magnesium and aluminium) are substituted by magnetic atoms like iron, zinc, manganese etc. This can be achieved by mixing ferric oxide or the oxide of manganese zinc etc. wih magnesium aluminium oxide.

Other uses. (*i*) Ferrites can be used for making permanent magnets. Barium ferrite is as good as alnico magnet. The properties of a ferrite depend upon its composition. For example, the coercivity of Nickel zinc ferrite is 1 A/m and that of cobalt ferrite is $2 \times 10^5 \, Am^{-1}$.

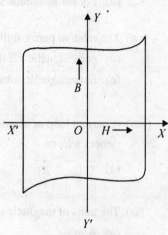

Fig. 9.37

(*ii*) The hysteresis loop of magnesium manganese ferrite is nearly rectangular in shape (Fig. 9.37). Such materials can be magnetised only in one direction or the other. The reversal of the magnetic field can remagnetise the material in the reverse direction almost instantaneously and to the same strength as before. This makes such material very useful in computers and in memory circuits.

Q. 9.49. Mark the correct answer.

(*i*) Dipole moment of a current loop does not depend upon

(*a*) Current in the loop   (*b*) Area of the loop

(*c*) Number of turns in the loop   (*d*) Shape of the loop   (*H.P.U.*, 1994)

(*ii*) Diamagnetism is explained in terms of

(*a*) spin motion of the electron   (*b*) orbital motion of electron

(*c*) both orbtial and spin motion   (*d*) spin motion of the nucleus

                                                                    (*P.U.*, 1994)

(*iii*) The magnetic moment of an atom is due to

(*a*) orbital motion of electron only   (*b*) spin motion of electron

(*c*) both orbtial and spin motion   (*d*) none of these   (*H.P.U.*, 1992)

(*iv*) The unit of Bohr magneton is

(*a*) JT   (*b*) $J^{-1} T$ (*c*) JT^{-1} (*d*) JT^{-2}

                                                                    (*H.P.U.*, 1995)

(v) Susceptibility of a diamagnetic material is

    (a) very large   (b) small but positive

    (c) small but negative   (d) zero   (H.P.U., 1992)

(vi) Which of the following statements are true about magnetic susceptibility χ_m?

    (a) χ_m may be positive or negative

    (b) χ_m for paramagnetic material has values close to 1

    (c) At a given temperature the values of χ_m increases with increasing magnetic field.

    (d) For paramagnetic substances χ_m is inversely proportional to absolute temperature of the same.   (P.U., 1994)

(vii) The relative permeability of a material is 0.99. It will essentially be

    (a) paramagnetic substance   (b) Diamagnetic substance

    (c) ferromagnetic substance   (d) none of these.

                                                  (H.P.U. 1999; P.U. 1994)

(viii) A current loop of magnetic moment $\vec{p_m}$ when placed in a non-uniform magnetic field experiences a force

    (a) $\vec{\nabla}\,(\vec{p_m}\cdot\vec{B})$ (b) $(\vec{\nabla}\cdot\vec{B})$ (c) $\vec{\nabla}\cdot\vec{p_m}\,\vec{B}$ (d) $(\vec{p_m}\cdot\vec{\nabla})\,\vec{B}$

                                                  (P.U., 1994)

(ix) The units of magnetic susceptibility are

    (a) A/m   (b) A/m^2 (c) Am^2 (d) no units

(x) Ferrites are

    (a) Ferrimagnetic having large electrical conductivity

    (b) Ferrimagentic having negligible electrical conductivity

    (c) Diamagnetic having large electical conductivity

    (d) Ferromagnetic having negligible electrical conductivity   (G.N.D.U., 1990)

(xi) Which of the following substance can have positive permeability and negative susceptibility ?

    (a) Ferromagnetic   (b) paramagnetic   (c) diamagnetic   (d) none

                                                  (H.P.U. 2001)

Ans.	(i) d	(ii) b	(iii) c	(iv) c
	(v) c	(vi) All	(vii) b	(viii) d
	(ix) d	(x) b	(xi) c	

EXERCISES

1. Calculate the current that should flow in a single turn circular wire loop of radius 7 m to produce a magnetic dipole moment of 11 A.m².   [Ans. 0.07 A]

2. The volume of the core of a transformer is 10^{-3} m³. If the loss of energy per unit volume per cycle of hysteresis is 0.2 Jm⁻³, calculate the loss of energy per hour when it is fed with A.C. of 50 Hz.   [Ans. 36 J]

10

Electromagnetic Induction

Q. 10.1. Define magnetic flux. Give the units in which it is measured.

Ans. Magnetic flux. *The magnetic flux through an area is defined as the number of lines of magnetic induction crossing the area normally.*

If $\vec{B}$ is the magnetic induction field at a point and $\vec{ds}$ a small area surrounding the point, then the magnetic flux $d\phi$ through the small area element is given by

$$d\phi = \vec{B}.\vec{ds}$$

If $\vec{B}$ is perpendicular to $\vec{ds}$ then

$$\vec{B}.\vec{ds} = B\,ds$$

and

$$d\phi = B\,ds \qquad \qquad ...(i)$$

If the area element $\vec{ds}$ is a part of the surface S, then magnetic flux ϕ through the surface S is given by

$$\phi = \int d\phi = \iint_S \vec{B}.\vec{ds} \qquad \qquad ...(ii)$$

Units. In C.G.S. system B is measured in *Gauss* and ds in *centimetres square*. The unit of magnetic flux is known as a *Maxwell*

and

$$\text{Maxwell} = \text{Gauss cm}^2$$

In S.I. units B is measured in *Tesla* and ds in metres-square. Then unit of magnetic flux is known as a *Weber* and

$$\text{Weber} = \text{Tesla metre}^2$$

As

$$1 \text{ Tesla} = 10^4 \text{ Gauss}$$

$\therefore$

$$1 \text{ Weber} = 10^4 \text{ Gauss} \times 10^4 \text{ cm}^2 = 10^8 \text{ Gauss cm}^2 = 10^8 \text{ Maxwells}$$

Magnetic flux density. From relation (*i*) we have

$$B = \frac{d\phi}{ds}$$

B is known as magnetic flux density and is defined as *the magnetic flux per unit area.*

Q. 10.2. (a) What is electromagnetic induction ? State and explain Faraday's and Lenz's law of electromagnetic induction. Prove that $e = -\vec{B}\dfrac{\vec{ds}}{dt}$. *(Kerala.U., 2001; Meerut U., 2002; 2001; Pbi. U., 2003, 2000, 1995; Osm. U., 1997; A.U., 1995, 1994; H.P.U., 1995, 1992; P.U., 1995)*

433

(*b*) **The magnetic flux associated with a coil moving in a magnetic field changes according to the following equation**

$$\phi = \frac{t^3}{3} + \frac{t^2}{2} + 4t$$

where value of ϕ is in milli-weber and t in seconds. Find the induced e.m.f in the coil when $t = 2$ sec. (*M.D.U., 2001*)

Ans. Electromagnetic induction. Whenever the number of lines of magnetic induction or *magnetic flux* through a conducting circuit changes, an induced *e.m.f.* is produced in it. If the circuit is closed a current flows. The *e.m.f.* or current lasts only for the time the change in magnetic flux continues. The magnitude of the induced *e.m.f.* or current is proportional to the rate at which the magnetic flux changes. The magnetic flux through a circuit can be changed by any of the following methods:

(*i*) By motion of a magnet near a circuit or away from it or the motion of a circuit towards or away from a magnet.

(*ii*) By rotation of a coil in a magnetic field.

(*iii*) By starting, stopping or changing the current in a neighbouring circuit (Mutual induction).

(*iv*) By starting, stopping or changing the current in the circuit itself (self induction).

Laws of electromagnetic induction. The laws of electromagnetic induction are

(*i*) Faraday's law of electromagnetic induction

(*ii*) Lenz's law

Faraday's law of electromagnetic induction. *Whenever the number of magnetic lines of induction or magnetic flux through a circuit changes, an induced e.m.f. is produced in the circuit. The magnitude of induced e.m.f. is proportional to the rate of change of magnetic flux and lasts so long as the change continues.*

Lenz's law. *The direction of the induced e.m.f. or current is such that it tends to stop the movement which produces it.*

Induced e.m.f. If $d\phi$ is the change in magnetic flux in a time dt, then according to Faraday's law the induced *e.m.f.*

$$e \propto \frac{d\phi}{dt}$$

But according to Lenz's law, it opposes the cause that produces it. As the cause of induced *e.m.f.* is change in flux $d\phi$, the two have opposite signs

$$\therefore \qquad e \propto -\frac{d\phi}{dt}$$

or $$e = -k\frac{d\phi}{dt}$$

where k is the constant of proportionality.

In S.I. units $k = 1$ and

$$e = -\frac{d\phi}{dt}$$

But $$d\phi = \vec{B}.d\vec{s}$$

where $\vec{B}$ is the magnetic flux density (or magnetic induction field) and $d\vec{s}$ a small area surrounding the point where magnetic flux density is $\vec{B}$.

$$\therefore \qquad e = -\frac{d\phi}{dt} = -\vec{B}\frac{d\vec{s}}{dt}$$

(b) Here

$$\phi = \frac{t^3}{3} + \frac{t^2}{2} + 4t$$

$$\therefore \qquad e = -\frac{d\phi}{dt} = -\left[\frac{3t^2}{3} + \frac{2t}{2} + 4\right] = -\left[t^2 + t + 4\right]$$

When

$$t = 2 \text{ and } \phi \text{ in milli Weber}$$

$$e = (4 + 2 + 4) \text{ Milli Weber/Sec.} = 10 \times 10^{-3} \text{ Weber / Sec}$$

$$= 10^{-2} \text{ Wb/sec} = 10^{-2} \text{ Volt.}$$

Exercise. *The magnetic flux through a circular loop is given by* $0.02 \ t^3 Wb$. *What is the induced e.m.f. in the loop at* $t = 1$ *millisecond?* (*P.U., 2002*)

Hint.

$$e = -\frac{d\phi}{dt} = -0.02 \times 3t^2. \qquad \text{At } t = 1 \text{ millisecond} = 10^{-3} \text{ sec}$$

$$e = 0.06 \times 10^{-6} \text{ Volt} = 6 \times 10^{-8} \text{ Volt.}$$

Q. 10.3. Explain the fact that Lenz's law is in accordance with the law of conservation of energy. (*M.D.U., 2002, 2001; H.P.U., 1995*)

Ans. Lenz's law is in accordance with the law of conservation of energy. Connect the terminals of a coil of wire through a galvanometer as shown in Fig. 10.1. Introduce the north pole of a bar magnet, into the coil and note that there is a deflection showing thereby that an induced *e.m.f.* (or current) has been set up. If we withdraw the magnet the galvanometer again shows a deflection in the opposite direction indicating thereby that the induced *e.m.f.* (or current) is now in the opposite direction.

When the north pole of a magnet is brought near a coil, the upper face of the coil should acquire a north polarity due to the induced *e.m.f.* or current because it will then be able to oppose the movement of the magnet. Similarly when the north pole of the magnet is taken away, the upper face should acquire a south polarity so that it again opposes the movement of the magnet by attracting the north pole. This is in accordance with the law of conservation of energy. When the north pole of the magnet is brought near the coil, the upper face,

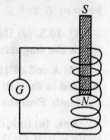

Fig. 10.1

which acquires a north polarity due to the induced current in it, exerts a force of repulsion. Work is done in moving the magnet into the coil against the force of repulsion. It is this mechanical work which is converted into electrical energy.

Similarly on taking away the north pole, the upper face becomes a south pole and work has to be done in moving the magnet away from the coil against the force of attraction.

Thus we find that Lenz's law is in accordance with the law of conservation of energy.

Q. 10.4. (*a*) **A coil of 100 turns is pulled in 0.04 sec from between the poles of a magnet where its area includes a flux of** 40×10^{-6} **Wb. Calculate the induced e.m.f. in the coil.**

(*P.U., 1991*)

(*b*) **A closed loop is rotated in its own plane in a magnetic field** B **with angular velocity** ω**. What is the induced e.m.f. in the coil?**

(*P.U., 2009*)

Ans. (*a*) Number of turns in the coil = 100

Magnetic flux included in the coil area = 40×10^{-6} Wb

∴ Total magnetic flux linked with the coil $\phi = 100 \times 40 \times 10^{-6} = 4 \times 10^{-3}$ Wb

Time in which flux is removed $t = 0.04$ sec

∴ Induced *e.m.f.* $e = -\dfrac{d\phi}{dt} = -\dfrac{\text{Change in magnetic flux}}{\text{Time}}$

$$= \frac{4 \times 10^{-3}}{0.04} = 0.1 \text{ volt.}$$

(*b*) Suppose the closed loop of area $\vec{S}$ lies in a direction perpendicular to the magnetic field $\vec{B}$, then the magnetic flux linked with the loop

$$\phi = \vec{B} \cdot \vec{S} = B S \cos \theta = B S$$

as the field vector and area vector are parallel $\theta = 0$ and $\cos \theta = 1$. When the closed loop or coil is rotated *in its own plane* there is no change in magnetic flux as neither $\vec{B}$ nor $\vec{S}$ nor the angle θ between $\vec{B}$ and $\vec{S}$ changes. As

Induced e.m.f. $e = \dfrac{-d\phi}{dt}$ the e.m.f induced in the closed loop (or coil) is zero.

The same is true even when the magnetic field makes an angle with the area vector because so long as the coil (or loop) rotates in its *own plane*. There is no change in $\vec{B}$ or $\vec{S}$ or the angle θ between $\vec{B}$ and $\vec{S}$.

Q. 10.5. (*a*) **Derive an expression for the quantity of electricity induced in a coil through which the magnetic flux is varying.**

(*b*) **A coil of 100 turns of area 3.0 cm² is jerked out of a magnetic field. The charge thus induced in the coil which is connected to a circuit with a total resistance of 600 ohm is 5×10^{-5} Coulomb. Find the flux density of the field** (*Meerut U., 2001*)

Ans. (*a*) **Induced charge.** When the magnetic flux linked with a coil varies, an induced *e.m.f.* is set up in it. If *e* is the induced *e.m.f.* in volts at an instant and *R* the resistance of the circuit, in ohms (*S.I. units*), then

$$e = -\frac{d\phi}{dt}$$

and current in amperes in the circuit at that time, $i = \dfrac{e}{R} = -\dfrac{1}{R} \dfrac{d\phi}{dt}$.

If the current remains constant for a very small time *dt*, then

Charge *dq* passing through the circuit $= -\dfrac{1}{R} \dfrac{d\phi}{dt} \cdot dt = -\dfrac{d\phi}{R}$

∴ Total charge through the circuit, if the flux increases from ϕ_1 to ϕ_2 is given by

$$q = \int_{\phi_1}^{\phi_2} -\frac{d\phi}{R}$$

$$= \frac{1}{R}[-\phi]_{\phi_1}^{\phi_2} = \frac{\phi_1 - \phi_2}{R}$$

It is thus seen that the total charge is independent of the time during which the change in magnetic flux takes place.

$$\therefore \quad \text{Charge in coulombs} = \frac{\text{Change in magnetic flux in webers}}{\text{Resistance in ohms}}$$

(b) Number of turns $\quad n = 100$; Area $A = 3$ cm^2 $= 3 \times 10^{-4}$ m^2

Mag flux $\quad \phi = nAB = 100 \times 3 \times 10^{-4} \times B$

where B is the flux density.

Change in magnetic flux when the coil is jerked out of the magnetic field $= \phi_1 - \phi_2 = \phi$

Charge induced $\quad q = 5 \times 10^{-5}$ C; $R = 600 \, \Omega$

Now $\quad q = \frac{\phi_1 - \phi_2}{R} = \frac{\phi}{R}$

or $\quad 5 \times 10^{-5} = \frac{100 \times 3 \times 10^{-4} \times B}{600}$

$\therefore \quad B = \frac{5 \times 600 \times 10^{-5}}{100 \times 3 \times 10^{-4}} = 1 \, \text{Tesla}$

Q. 10.6. A field of 0.02 Tesla acts at right angles to a coil of area 0.01 sq. metre with 50 turns. The coil is removed from the field in 1/10th of a second. Find the average e.m.f. produced in it.

Ans. Strength of the field $B = 0.02$ Tesla

Area of the coil $S = 0.01$ sq. metre; Number of turns $n = 50$

As the coil is at right angles to the field, the direction of the area vector and field vector is the same and the angle between them is zero.

$\therefore$ Magnetic flux linked with the coil, when placed in the magnetic field

$$\phi = n \iint_S \vec{B}.d\vec{s} = nBS = 50 \times 0.02 \times 0.01 \, \text{Weber}$$

Time during which the flux is removed $= 0.1$ sec

$$\therefore \quad \frac{d\phi}{dt} = \frac{50 \times 0.02 \times 0.01}{0.1} = 0.1$$

Hence induced e.m.f. $\quad e = -\frac{d\phi}{dt} = -0.1$ volt

The negative sign only indicates the direction of induced e.m.f.

Q. 10.7. A loop of wire of area A and resistance R is kept perpendicular to a uniform magnetic induction B. If the loop is rotated uniformly through 180° in a time t, find the amount of charge which flows through the loop in this time. (G. N.D.U., 2003)

Ans. Magnetic flux linked with the wire loop $\phi = BA$

Change in magnetic flux, when rotated through 180° $= +\phi - (-\phi) = 2\phi = 2BA$

Charge which flows through the loop

$$= \frac{\text{Change in magnetic flux}}{R} = \frac{2BA}{R}$$

Q. 10.8. What are the various methods of changing magnetic field linked with a coil?

(G.N.D.U., 2003)

Ans. The magnetic flux through an area $\vec{S}$ bounded by a coil is given by

$$\phi_m = \iint_S \vec{B}.d\vec{S} = \iint_S B\, dS \cos\theta$$

where θ is the angle between the magnetic field vector $\vec{B}$ and area vector $\vec{S}$.

The magnetic flux linked with the coil can be changed by

1. Varying the magnetic field B. This can be done as under

(*i*) By the motion of a magnet towards or away from the coil or by moving the coil towards or away from a magnet.

(*ii*) By starting, stopping or changing current in a neighbouring coil (mutual induction).

(*iii*) By starting, stopping or changing current in the coil itself (self induction)

2. Varying the area S cut by the magnetic field

3. By varying the angle θ between $\vec{B}$ and area vector $\vec{S}$. This can be done by rotating the coil in a magnetic field.

Q. 10.9. What is a search coil? How does it help in measuring a magnetic field ?

(Luck. U., 1993)

Ans. Search coil. A search coil is a small coil of about 50 turns of fine insulated copper wire having a face area of about 1 sq. cm. The arrangement of the apparatus for finding the intensity of a magnetic field with the help of a search coil and a ballistic galvanometer is shown in Fig. 10.2.

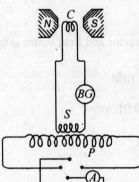

The primary coil P is connected through a reversing key to a battery, a rheostat and an ammeter. The secondary coil is connected in series with the ballistic galvanometer and the search coil C which is placed within the pole pieces of a magnet so that maximum magnetic flux passes through it.

(*i*) Let n be the *total* number of turns, a the face area of the search coil and B the intensity of the magnetic field in which it is placed, then

Magnetic flux linked with the search coil = nBa

When the search coil is suddenly removed from the field the magnetic flux is reduced to zero and the ballistic galvanometer gives a throw θ_1 due to charge q_1 sent through it by the induced *e.m.f.* The charge passing through the galvanometer

Fig. 10.2

$$q_1 = \frac{\text{Total change in magnetic flux}}{R}$$

$$= \frac{nBa}{R}$$

where R is the resistance of the secondary circuit containing the search coil, the secondary coil and the ballistic galvanometer,

$$\therefore \qquad q_1 = \frac{nBa}{R} = k\theta_1$$

where k is the constant of the ballistic galvanometer.

(*ii*) A steady current I is now passed through the primary circuit.

If n_1 is the *number of turns per centimetre* of the primary coil and A its area of cross-section, then

Intensity of field on the axis of primary coil = $\mu_0 n_1 I$

Magnetic flux linked with *each* turn of the primary = $\mu_0 n_1 IA$

As the secondary coil is wound on the central part of the primary coil,

$\therefore$ Magnetic flux linked with each turn of secondary = $\mu_0 n_1 IA$

If the *total number* of turns in the secondary is n_2, then

Magnetic flux linked with n_2 turns of secondary = $\mu_0 n_1 IA \times n_2$

If the current in the primary circuit is reversed the total flux in the secondary changes from $+ \mu_0 n_1 n_2 IA$ to $- \mu_0 n_1 n_2 IA$. The ballistic galvanometer now gives a throw θ_2 due to the charge q_2 through it by the induced *e.m.f.* Hence the charge passing through the ballistic galvanometer

$$q_2 = \frac{2\mu_0 n_1 n_2 IA}{R} = k\theta_2 \qquad\qquad ...(ii)$$

Dividing (*i*) by (*ii*), we have

$$\frac{nBa}{2\mu_0 n_1 n_2 IA} = \frac{\theta_1}{\theta_2}$$

$$\therefore \qquad B = \frac{2\mu_0 n_1 n_2 IA}{na} \times \frac{\theta_1}{\theta_2}$$

Q. 10.10. Describe an earth inductor and give its theory. How is the value of earth's horizontal induction field B_H determined with it?   (*Meerut U., 1992*)

Ans. Earth inductor. It consists of a coil C of a rectangular or a circular shape of known face area having about 5000 turns of insulated copper wire. It is capable of rotation about an axis along its diameter. By means of two stops the rotation is confined to exactly 180°. When the coil is held between the two stops it can be released by pressing the push button P. The position of the coil and its axis of

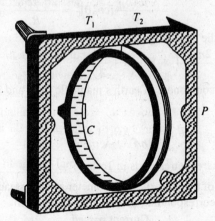

Fig. 10.3

rotation can be adjusted. The ends of the coil are connected to two segments of a commutator. Small pieces of brass strips connected to two terminals, T_1 and T_2 press against the two halves of the commutator. This arrangement enables to draw the current from the earth inductor when it is rotated in a magnetic field. It is used to find the horizontal component of the earth's field and the value of dip at a place.

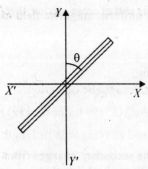

Fig. 10.4

Theory. Let n be the number of turns and A the face area of the coil C of the earth inductor capable of rotation in air in a uniform magnetic field of intensity B_H. When the coil is vertical with its plane along YY' the magnetic flux through it $= nAB_H$. When it is rotated through an angle θ from its original position as shown in Fig. 10.4 the *effective* area of the coil is $A \cos \theta$ and the magnetic flux through it is

$$\phi = nAB_H \cos \theta$$

As the coil is rotated, the magnetic flux through it continuously changes and an induced *e.m.f.* is set up in it. In S.I. units it is given by

$$e = -\frac{d\phi}{dt}$$

$$= -\frac{d}{dt}[nAB_H \cos \theta] \qquad \qquad ...(i)$$

Determination of horizontal component of earth's magnetic field. The earth inductor is connected to a ballistic galvanometer and the plane of the coil is adjusted to be exactly vertical and at right angles to the magnetic meridian. When the coil is rotated through 180°, a charge flows through the ballistic galvanometer which gives a deflection θ_1. The quantity of charge produced as the coil is rotated from 0 to π is given by

$$q = \int_0^\pi i \cdot dt = \int_0^\pi \frac{e}{R} \cdot dt$$

where R is the combined resistance of the earth inductor and the ballistic galvanometer. Substituting the value of e from (i), we have

$$q = \int_0^\pi -\frac{d}{dt}\left[\frac{nAB_H \cos \theta}{R}\right] dt$$

$$= \frac{-nAB_H}{R}[\cos \theta]_0^\pi = \frac{2n\,AB_H}{R}$$

If K is the constant of the ballistic galvanometer, then

$$\frac{2nAB_H}{R} = K\theta_1\left(1 + \frac{\lambda}{2}\right)$$

where B_H is the horizontal component of earth's magnetic field and λ the logarithmic decrement of the ballistic galvanometer.

$$\therefore \qquad B_H = \frac{R}{2nA} K\theta_1\left(1 + \frac{\lambda}{2}\right) \qquad \qquad ...(ii)$$

If R is in ohm, A in square metres B_H is in Tesla.

To find the constant K of the ballistic galvanometer a small steady current is passed through the ballistic galvanometer and corresponding deflection is noted, then

$$\text{Current sensitivity } i = \frac{\text{Current passed}}{\text{Steady deflection}}$$

If T is the time period of the ballistic galvanometer coil, then

$$K = i\frac{T}{2\pi}$$

The value of λ is calculated by noting the first throw and subsequent throws. As all the constants of equation (ii) are known the value of B_H can be calculated.

Q. 10.11. If a conducting rod is moving with a velocity $\vec{v}$ in a uniform magnetic field of induction $\vec{B}$, prove that (*i*) The electric field inside the rod

$$\vec{E} = -(\vec{v} \times \vec{B})$$

and (*ii*) induced e.m.f. $e = -\dfrac{d\phi}{dt}$. Hence state Faraday's law of electromagnetic induction.

(*P.U.*, 2001; *Luck U.*, 1996, 1993; *G.N.D.U.*, 1994; *Pbi.U.*, 1991)

Ans. (*i*) **Induced electric field.** Consider a straight conducting rod *ab* lying with its length along the Z-axis in a uniform magnetic field $\vec{B}$ directed along the Y-axis and moving with a velocity $\vec{v}$ along + X-axis.

According to Lorentz force equation a charged particle in the conductor carrying a charge *q* will experience a force $\vec{F}$ given by

$$\vec{F} = q(\vec{v} \times \vec{B})$$

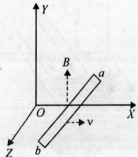

Fig. 10.5

Thus if *q* is *positive*, the force is in + Z direction and if *q* is *negative*, it is in − Z direction. A positive charge in the conductor will, therefore, move from *a* to *b* under the effect of this force.

An observer in the laboratory frame with respect to which the conductor is moving, will find as if the charge in the conductor is moving under the influence of an electric field given by

$$\frac{\vec{F}}{q} = \vec{v} \times \vec{B}$$

In the case of a conductor, it is the negatively charged electrons which are free to move, the positive charges remaining at rest. Thus the electrons in the rod move from *b* to *a* under the effect of the force leaving *b* positively charged and making *a* negatively charged. The motion of the positively charged particles will be from *a* to *b*, thereby also making *b* positively charged and leaving *a* negatively charged. In other words, the effect is the same whether it is the negatively charged particles that move or the positively charged particles or both.

The motion of the charged particles will continue till the electric field due to the accumulation of the charged particles at the ends of the conductor is equal and opposite to the electric field produced due to the motion of the conductor. This is known as the *induced electric field*.

∴ Induced electric field $E = -(\vec{v} \times \vec{B})$ ...(*i*)

(*ii*) **Induced electromotive force.** The induced *e.m.f.* across the ends of the conductor due to the electric field is given by

$$e = \int_{a}^{b} \vec{E}.d\,\vec{l} = \int_{a}^{b} (\vec{v} \times \vec{B}).d\,\vec{l}$$

[where $d\,\vec{l}$ is a small element of conductor *ab*]

$$= \int_{a}^{b} -\vec{B}.(\vec{v} \times d\,\vec{l})$$

$[\because (\vec{A} \times \vec{B}).\vec{C} = -\vec{B}.(\vec{A} \times \vec{C})]$

or
$$e = -\vec{B}.\left[\int_a^b \vec{v} \times d\vec{l}\right] \qquad ..(i)(a)$$

$[\because \vec{B}$ is a uniform field$]$

The conductor ab moves through a distance $\vec{v}\, dt$ along the X-axis in a time dt and in this time the area swept by the element $d\vec{l}$ is

$$\vec{v}\, dt \times d\vec{l}$$

$\therefore$ Total area $d\vec{s}$ swept by the conductor ab in time dt is given by

$$d\vec{s} = \int_a^b \vec{v}\, dt \times d\vec{l}$$

or

$$\frac{d\vec{s}}{dt} = \int_a^b \vec{v} \times d\vec{l}$$

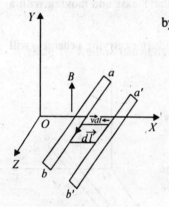

Fig. 10.6

Substituting in $(i)(a)$, we have

$$e = -\vec{B}.\left[\frac{d\vec{s}}{dt}\right] = -\frac{\vec{B}.d\vec{s}}{dt}$$

But

$$\vec{B}.d\vec{s} = d\phi$$

$\therefore$

$$e = -\frac{d\phi}{dt} \qquad ...(ii)$$

If $d\phi = 1$ Weber $= 1$ Tesla met^2 and $dt = 1$ sec, then $e = 1$ volt

$$1 \text{ volt} = \frac{\text{Tesla met}^2}{\text{sec}}$$

Faraday's law of electromagnetic induction. The relation proved in Eq. (ii) *is the mathematical form of Faraday's law of electromagnetic induction.* It states that

The induced electromotive force set up in a conductor is the negative rate of change of magnetic flux linked with it with time.

Q. 10.12. (a) **A wire of length 200 cms held perpendicular to XY plane is moved with a velocity $\vec{v} = 2\hat{i} + 3\hat{j} + \hat{k}$ metres/sec through a region of uniform induction $\vec{B} = \hat{i} + 2\hat{k}$ Weber/metre^2. Calculate the electric field $\vec{E}$ developed in the wire and potential difference between its ends.**

(Pbi. U., 1992)

(b) **An aeroplane is flying with a speed of 1000 km/hour. Calculate the e.m.f. generated between the tips of the wings of the plane if the length of each wing is 20 metres and vertical component of earth's magnetic field is 3.1×10^{-5} Weber/m^2.**

(Luck. U., 1996)

Ans. (a) The electric field $\vec{E}$ developed in the wire is independent of its length and is given by

$$\vec{E} = -(\vec{v} \times \vec{B}) \qquad \text{[in S.I. units]}$$

where $\vec{E}$ is in coulombs/metre^2, $\vec{v}$ is in metres/sec and $\vec{B}$ in webers/metre^2.

$$\therefore \quad \vec{E} = \vec{v} \times \vec{B} \begin{vmatrix} \hat{i} & \hat{j} & \hat{k} \\ 2 & 3 & 1 \\ 1 & 0 & 2 \end{vmatrix}$$

$$= \hat{i}(6-0) + \hat{j}(1-4) + \hat{k}(0-3)$$

$$= 6\hat{i} - 3\hat{j} - 3\hat{k} = 3(2\hat{i} - \hat{j} - \hat{k})$$

Now potential difference between the ends of the wire is equal to the *e.m.f.* induced in it

or
$$e = \int_a^b \vec{E}.d\vec{l} = \int_0^l (\vec{E}.\hat{k}) \, dl$$

where *l* is the length of the wire and $d\vec{l} = \hat{k} \, dl$ as the wire is perpendicular to the $X - Y$ plane, *l* is along the *Z*-axis and its small vector element $d\vec{l} = \hat{k}.dl$.

$$\therefore \quad e = \int_0^l (6\hat{i} - 3\hat{j} - 3\hat{k}).\hat{k} \, dl = \int_0^l -3 \, dl = -3[l]_0^l = -3l$$

Since $l = 200$ cm $= 2$ met

$$\therefore \quad e = -6 \text{ volt}$$

The negative sign indicates that the *e.m.f.* acts along the $-Z$ direction.

(b) Let the aeroplane fly along the *X*-axis.

$\therefore$ Velocity of the aeroplane $= v\hat{i} = 1000 \text{ km/hr} = \dfrac{1000 \times 10^3}{60 \times 60} = \dfrac{10^4}{36} \text{ ms}^{-1}$

Then, the wings of the aeroplane will be along the *Y*-axis.

Length of each wing $= 20$ metres

$\therefore$ Distance between the tips of the wing $= l\hat{j} = 2 \times 20 = 40$ m

Vertical component of earth's magnetic field, therefore, acts along the Z-axis

$$= B\hat{k} = 3.1 \times 10^{-5} \text{ Weber/m}^2$$

Induced *e.m.f.*, $e = -\vec{B}.\left[\displaystyle\int_a^b \vec{v} \times d\vec{l}\right]$

As $\vec{v}$ is a constant, $\displaystyle\int_a^b \vec{v} \times d\vec{l} = \vec{v} \times \int_a^b d\vec{l} = \vec{v} \times \vec{l}$ $\left[\because \displaystyle\int_a^b d\vec{l} = l\right]$

Now $\vec{v} \times \vec{l} = v\hat{i} \times l\hat{j} = vl\,\hat{k} = \dfrac{10^4 \times 40}{36} = 1.11 \times 10^4 \, \hat{k}$

Hence $e = -\vec{B}.\left[\displaystyle\int_a^b \vec{v} \times d\vec{l}\right] = -B\hat{k} \times 1.11 \times 10^4 \, \hat{k}$

$$= -3.1 \times 10^{-5} \times 1.11 \times 10^4 = -0.344 \text{ volt}$$

Q. 10.13. Establish Faraday's law $e = -\dfrac{d\phi}{dt}$, when a conducting loop moves with a velocity $\vec{v}$ in a non-uniform magnetic field.   (*P.U., 1991; Pbi. U., 2001, 1991; G.N.D.U., 1990*)

Ans. Faraday's law of electromagnetic induction. Consider a wire loop or frame of any shape which occupies the position C_1 at time t. It is moving with a velocity $\vec{v}$ so that it occupies the position C_2 at time $t + dt$.

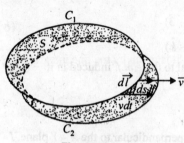

An elementary length $d\vec{l}$ of the loop is displaced through a distance $\vec{v}\,dt$ in time dt, then the area $d\vec{s}$ swept by the element $d\vec{l}$ is given by

$$d\vec{s} = (\vec{v}\,dt \times d\vec{l}) \qquad \ldots(i)$$

If $\vec{B}$ is the magnetic field at any point on this area, then the magnetic flux through the area $d\vec{s}$

$$= \vec{B}.d\vec{s}$$

Fig. 10.7

Hence the total magnetic flux crossing the ribbon shaped surface S spanned by the boundary of the loop

$$= \iint_S \vec{B}.d\vec{s}$$

The integral $\iint \vec{B}.d\vec{s}$, therefore, represents the change in magnetic flux crossing the wire loop, as it moves from the position C_1 to the position C_2 in a time dt.

Hence it is denoted by $d\phi$.

$$\therefore \qquad d\phi = \iint_S \vec{B}.d\vec{s}$$

Substituting the value of $d\vec{s}$ from (i), we have

$$d\phi = \iint_S \vec{B}.(\vec{v}\,dt \times d\vec{l})$$

Since dt is constant for the integration, it can be taken out of the integral sign.

$$\therefore \qquad \frac{d\phi}{dt} = \iint_S \vec{B}.(\vec{v} \times d\vec{l})$$

Now, according to the vector identity

$$\vec{A}.(\vec{B} \times \vec{C}) = -(\vec{B} \times \vec{A}).\vec{C}$$

$$\vec{B}.(\vec{v} \times d\vec{l}) = -(\vec{v} \times \vec{B}).d\vec{l}$$

$$\therefore \qquad \frac{d\phi}{dt} = -\oint(\vec{v} \times \vec{B}).d\vec{l} \qquad \ldots(ii)$$

or

$$-\frac{d\phi}{dt} = \oint(\vec{v} \times \vec{B}).d\vec{l} \qquad \ldots(iii)$$

As the integration is now with respect to $d\vec{l}$ which is a line element and the integration is to be carried out over the boundary of the loop, the surface integral $\iint_S$ has been changed to line integral $\oint$.

If $\vec{E}$ is the electric field associated with the elementary length $d\vec{l}$ when it is moving with a velocity v, then

$$\vec{E} = (\vec{v} \times \vec{B})$$

[Q. 10.11 Eq. (i)]

Substituting the value of $\vec{E}$ in (iii), we have

$$-\frac{d\phi}{dt} = \oint \vec{E}.d\vec{l} \qquad \qquad ...(iv)$$

If e is the electromotive force generated in the circuit, then it is given by the line integral of $\vec{E}$ over the circuit and therefore

$$e = \int \vec{E}.d\vec{l} \qquad \qquad ...(v)$$

From (iv) and (v), we have

$$e = -\frac{d\phi}{dt} \qquad \qquad ....(vi)$$

(i) When ϕ is in Tesla met^2 and t in sec, e is in volts

(ii) If the current loop consists of only one turn

$$\phi = \iint_S \vec{B}.d\vec{s}$$

but if the current loop consists of n turns each of area S, then

$$\phi = n \iint_S \vec{B}.d\vec{s}$$

Q. 10.14. State Faraday's law of electromagnetic induction and give the integral form of the law.

(b) Prove that Faraday's law of electromagnetic induction can be expressed in the differential form curl $\vec{E} = \vec{\nabla} \times \vec{E} = -\frac{\partial \vec{B}}{\partial t}$ and give the physical meaning of the equation.

(H.P.U.. 2001, 1999, 1996, 1995; K.U., 2001, 1996; P.U., 2007, 2006, 2003, 2002, 2000, 1995; Meerut U., 2000; G N. D.U., 2009, 2000, 1997, 1996; Pbi.U., 2008, 2003, 1999, 1991; A.U. 1994, 1993; Luck. U., 1993, 1992)

Ans. Faraday's law of electromagnetic induction. Faraday's law of electromagnetic induction states:

"Whenever the magnetic flux linked with a circuit changes, an induced electromotive force is set up in the circuit, the magnitude of the e.m.f. is proportional to the rate of change of magnetic flux and its direction is such as to oppose the cause producing a change in magnetic flux."

Integral form of Faraday's law. Consider a circuit C placed in a magnetic field $\vec{B}$. If S is the surface bounded by the current circuit, then the magnetic flux ϕ linked with the circuit is given by

$$\phi = \iint_S \vec{B}.d\vec{s}$$

If the magnetic field changes and $\frac{\partial B}{\partial t}$ is the *time rate* of the change of the field, then

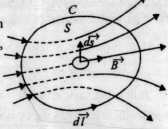

Fig. 10.8

$$\frac{d\phi}{dt} = \iint_S \frac{\partial \vec{B}}{\partial t} . d\vec{s}$$

[Note. The magnetic field $\vec{B}$ may be a function of both space and time co-ordinates and may also have a space rate of variation. This is why a partial differential with respect to t has been used.]

The e.m.f. induced in the circuit due to the changing magnetic flux is given by

$$e = -\frac{d\phi}{dt} = -\iint_S \frac{\partial \vec{B}}{\partial t} . d\vec{s} \qquad \qquad ...(i)$$

This is *integral form of Faraday's law.*

Differential form of Faraday's law. Now, e.m.f. is defined as the work done in taking a unit positive charge completely round the circuit *i.e.*, it is the line integral of the electric field $\vec{E}$ over the circuit, given by

$$e = \oint \vec{E} . d\vec{l} \qquad \qquad ...(ii)$$

Comparing (*i*) and (*ii*), we have

$$\oint \vec{E} . d\vec{l} = -\iint_S \frac{\partial \vec{B}}{\partial t} . d\vec{s}$$

But according to Stoke's law in vector analysis

$$\oint \vec{E} . d\vec{l} = \iint_S \vec{\nabla} \times \vec{E} . d\vec{s}$$

Hence $\qquad \iint_S \vec{\nabla} \times \vec{E} . d\vec{s} = -\iint_S \frac{\partial \vec{B}}{\partial t} . d\vec{s}$

$$\therefore \qquad \vec{\nabla} \times \vec{E} = -\frac{\partial \vec{B}}{\partial t} \qquad \text{or} \qquad Curl \ \vec{E} = -\frac{\partial \vec{B}}{\partial t} \qquad \qquad ...(iii)$$

In other words the above statement is equivalent to Faraday's law of electromagnetic induction. Eq. (*iii*) is known as *differential form of Faraday's law.*

Physical meaning and difference between electric field due to stationary charge and changing magnetic field. The differential form of Faraday's law of electromagnetic induction indicates that the changing magnetic field produces an electric field. The electric and magnetic vector fields in Eq. (*iii*) are, in general, functions of space co-ordinates and time.

If $\vec{B}$ is constant with time, we have $\dfrac{\partial B}{\partial t} = 0$

$$\therefore \qquad \vec{\nabla} \times \vec{E} = 0$$

This is the basic equation of electrostatics and Eq. (*iii*) is the generalisation of the equation $\vec{\nabla} \times \vec{E} = 0$ to time varying electric and magnetic fields.

The electric field due to a *stationary charge* statisfies the equation $\vec{\nabla} \times \vec{E} = 0$ *i.e.*, the electric field due to a stationary charge is *conservative.*

The *curl* of the induced electric field is given by the relation $\vec{\nabla} \times \vec{E} = -\dfrac{\partial \vec{B}}{\partial t}$ and is *not zero i.e.,* the induced electric field is *non-conservative.* It cannot, therefore, be the negative gradient of a scalar function (potential).

In other words, the induced electric field has a nature different from the electric field due to a stationary charge and has a different source — the changing magnetic field.

Q. 10.15. (*a*) **What is mutual induction? Define co-efficient of mutual induction between two coils. Give the units in which it is measured.**

(*Nagpur U., 2001; Kerala U., 2001; Meerut U., 2003, 2001; Pbi. U. 2001, 1994; M.D.U. 2001, 1999; K.U. 2000, 1996, 1995; Pbi.U. 1995; A.U. 1992*)

(*b*) **Calculate the co-efficient of mutual induction of a pair if two coils if a current of 10 Amp. in one coil produces a flux of 10^{-4} Wb per turn in the second coil of 1000 turns.**

(*M.D.U., 2001*)

Ans. Mutual induction. Consider two coils A and B placed close to each other. When a current flows in A, a magnetic flux is set up in B. If the current in A changes, the magnetic flux in B changes and an induced *e.m.f.* is set up in it. The phenomenon is mutual *i.e.,* if the current flows in B a magnetic flux is set up in A and if the current in B changes, the magnetic flux in A changes and an induced *e.m.f.* is set up in A. The coil in which the current flows or is changed is called the *primary* and the coil in which the magnetic flux or an induced *e.m.f.* is set up is called the *secondary.*

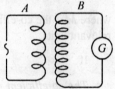

Fig. 10.9

The setting up of magnetic flux in a circuit due to a current flowing in a neighbouring circuit or the phenomenon of producing an induced e.m.f. in a circuit due to variation of current in a neighbouring circuit is called mutual induction.

Co-efficient of mutual induction. Consider two coils or circuits or loops C_1 and C_2 as shown. Suppose a current I_1 is made to flow through the coil C_1 and let $\vec{B_1}$ be the magnetic field produced at a point on the surface S_2 enclosed by the coil C_2, then

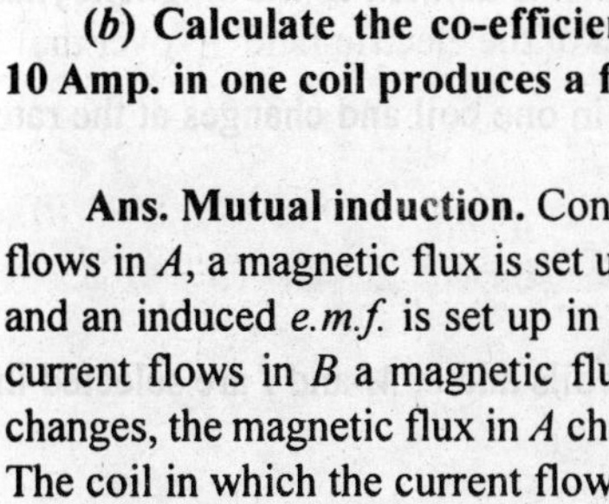

Magnetic flux of B_1 through the circuit C_2

$$\phi_{21} = \iint_S \vec{B_1} . \vec{ds_2}$$

Fig. 10.10

where $\vec{ds_2}$ is a small vector area element of the surface S_2. If the shape and relative position of the two circuits is fixed, then the magnetic flux ϕ_{21} is proportional to the current I_1.

$$\therefore \quad \phi_{21} = \text{constant } I_1 = M_{21}\, I_1 \qquad \qquad ...(i)$$

Suppose the current in C_1 changes very slowly so that ϕ_{21} remains proportional to I_1, then an electromotive force e_{21} will be induced in the circuit C_2 given by

$$e_{21} = -\frac{d\phi_{21}}{dt} = -M_{21}\frac{dI_1}{dt} \qquad \qquad ...(ii)$$

where M_{21} is a constant known as *co-efficient of mutual induction of coil C_2 with respect to the coil C_1.* Conversely if a current I_2 is made to flow in coil C_2 instead of current I_1 in the coil C_1 then

$$\phi_{12} = \text{constant } I_2 = M_{12}\, I_2 \qquad \qquad ...(iii)$$

If the current in C_2 changes at the rate $\dfrac{dI_2}{dt}$, then *e.m.f.* induced in the coil C_1 is given by

$$e_{12} = -\frac{d\phi_{12}}{dt} = -M_{12}\frac{dI_2}{dt} \qquad \qquad ...(iv)$$

where M_{12} is the co-efficient of mutual induction of coil C_1 with respect to the coil C_2.

But $M_{12} = M_{21}$ [For proof See Q. 10.16]

∴ From relations (i) and (iii), we have that if a current I flows in one coil the magnetic flux ϕ linked with the other is given by

$$\phi = MI$$

where M is the co-efficient of mutual induction between the two circuits.

If $I = 1, M = \phi$

Hence the co-efficient of mutual induction between two circuits is defined as the magnetic flux linked with one due to a unit current flowing through the other.

From relations (ii) and (iv), we have that if a current I flows in one coil and changes at the rate $\frac{dI}{dt}$ then e.m.f. induced in the other coil ·

$$e = -M\frac{dI}{dt}$$

where M is the co-efficient of mutual induction between the two coils and e, M and I are selected in relevant units.

If $\frac{dI}{dt} = 1$, then $M = -e$

The co-efficient of mutual induction of two circuits is thus numerically equal to the induced e.m.f. in one circuit due to a unit rate of change of current in the other.

Units. The S.I. units of mutual inductance is called **henry** (H).

If $e = 1$ volt, $\frac{dI}{dt} = 1$ Amp/sec, then $M = 1$ henry

Thus two circuits have a mutual inductance of one henry when current changing in one at the rate of one ampere per second produces an induced e.m.f. of one volt in the other.

∴ $\text{Henry} = \dfrac{\text{Volt}}{\text{ampere/sec}} = \dfrac{\text{Volt}}{\text{coulomb/sec}^2}$

The circuit or coil in which the current changes is known as the *primary* coil and the circuit or coil in which an induced *e.m.f.* is set up is known as the *secondary* coil.

The unit of mutual induction '*Henry*' may also be defined as under

Two circuits have a mutual inductance of one henry when a current of one ampere flowing in one produces a magnetic flux of one Weber in the other.

∴ $\text{Henry} = \dfrac{\text{Weber}}{\text{Amp}} = \dfrac{\text{Volt sec}}{\text{Amp}} = \dfrac{\text{Volt}}{\text{Amp/sec}}$

(b) Magnetic flux per turn = 10^{-4} Wb

∴ Total magnetic flux linked with 1000 turns $\phi = 1000 \times 10^{-4} = \dfrac{1}{10}$ Wb

Current $I = 10$ A

∴ Co-efficient of mutual induction $M = \dfrac{\phi}{I} = \dfrac{10}{10} = 1$ Wb/Amp $= 1$ Henry.

Q. 10.16. (*a*) **Prove that** $M_{21} = M_{12}$ **and show that the co-efficient of mutual induction is the same whether one or the other coil is taken as primary.**

OR

State and prove Reciprocity Theorem in mutual induction.

(*H.P.U., 2007, 2001, 1999, 1995, 1992; M.D.U., 2001; P.U., 2006, 1992;*
G.N.D.U., 1996. 1992; Pbi. U., 2008, 2006, 2000, 1995, 1993; A.U., 1994)

(*b*) **How will the mutual inductance respond to the following?** (*i*) **Change in size of one or both circuits** (*ii*) **Change in current through one or both** (*iii*) **Change in distance between the two circuits** (*iv*) **Any non magnetic material in the neighbour hood of the two circuits.**

(*P.U., 2006; H.P.U., 1997*)

Ans. (*a*) **Reciprocity theorem.** The magnetic vector potential A is related to magnetic induction field $\vec{B}$ by the vector relation

$$\vec{B} = curl\ \vec{A} = \vec{\nabla} \times \vec{A}$$

According to Stoke's theorem, in vector analysis

$$\oint_C \vec{A}.d\vec{l} = \iint_S curl\ \vec{A}.d\vec{s} = \iint_S (\vec{\nabla} \times \vec{A}).d\vec{s}$$

$$\therefore \quad \oint_C \vec{A}.d\vec{l} = \iint_S \vec{B}.d\vec{s} = \phi$$

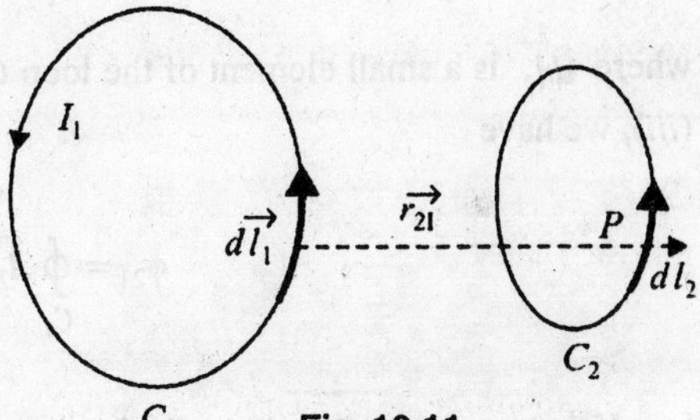

Fig. 10.11

In other words, the line integral of the magnetic vector potential around a loop is equal to the flux of $\vec{B}$ through the surface S enclosed by the loop.

The magnetic vector potential is given by

$$\vec{A} = \frac{\mu_0}{4\pi} \iiint \frac{\vec{J}\ dv}{r} \qquad \qquad ...(i)$$

where $\vec{J}$ is the current density vector, dv a very small volume element and r, the magnitude of the vector distance $\vec{r}$ of the observation point from the current element.

If the current element has a small length $d\vec{l}$, area of cross-section $\vec{a}$ and a current I flows through it, then

$$I = \vec{J}.\vec{a} \text{ and } dv = \vec{a}.d\vec{l}$$

$$\therefore \qquad I\vec{a}.d\vec{l} = \vec{J}.\vec{a}\ dv$$

or $$\qquad I\ d\vec{l}.\vec{a} = \vec{J}\ dv.\vec{a}$$

or $$\qquad I\ d\vec{l} = \vec{J}\ dv$$

Substituting in Eq. (*i*), we have

$$\vec{A} = \frac{\mu_0}{4\pi} \oint \frac{I\ d\vec{l}}{r} = \frac{\mu_0 I}{4\pi} \oint \frac{d\vec{l}}{r} \qquad \qquad ...(ii)$$

If a current I_1 is flowing through a circuit C_1, then the vector potential $\vec{A}_{21}$ at a point P is given by [according to Eq. (ii)]

$$\vec{A}_{21} = \frac{\mu_0}{4\pi} I_1 \oint_{C_1} \frac{d\vec{l}_1}{r_{21}} \qquad \qquad ...(iii)$$

where $d\vec{l}_1$ is a small element of the current loop C_1 and r_{21} is the magnitude of the distance from this current element to the point P.

If P is a point on the boundary of another loop C_2, then the flux through the surface enclosed by the loop C_2, due to the current I_1 in C_1 is given by

$$\phi_{21} = \oint_{C_2} \vec{A}_{21} . d\vec{l}_2 \qquad \qquad ...(iv)$$

where $d\vec{l}_2$ is a small element of the loop C_2 about the point P. Substituting the value of $\vec{A}_{21}$ from (iii), we have

$$\phi_{21} = \oint_{C_2} \vec{A}_{21} . d\vec{l}_2 = \oint_{C_2} d\vec{l}_2 . \vec{A}_{21} = \oint_{C_2} d\vec{l}_2 . \frac{\mu_0}{4\pi} I_1 \oint_{C_1} \frac{d\vec{l}_1}{r_{21}}$$

If the current I_1 in the loop C_1 changes at the rate $\dfrac{dI_1}{dt}$, then the magnetic flux ϕ_{21} through C_2 will also change and the rate of change is given by

$$\frac{d\phi_{21}}{dt} = \frac{\mu_0}{4\pi} \frac{dI_1}{dt} \oint_{C_2} d\vec{l}_2 . \oint_{C_1} \frac{d\vec{l}_1}{r_{21}} \qquad \qquad ...(v)$$

An induced e.m.f. e_{21} will, therefore, be set up in the coil C_2 given by

$$e_{21} = -\frac{d\phi_{21}}{dt} = -M_{21} \frac{dI_1}{dt} \qquad \qquad ...(vi)$$

where M_{21} is the co-efficient of mutual induction of the circuit C_2 with respect to circuit C_1.

∴ Relation (vi) can be put as

$$e_{21} = -\frac{d\phi_{21}}{dt} = -\frac{\mu_0}{4\pi} \frac{dI_1}{dt} \oint_{C_2} d\vec{l}_2 . \oint_{C_1} \frac{d\vec{l}_1}{r_{21}}$$

$$= -M_{21} \frac{dI_1}{dt}$$

∴

$$M_{21} = \frac{\mu_0}{4\pi} \oint_{C_2} d\vec{l}_2 . \oint_{C_1} \frac{d\vec{l}_1}{r_{21}} = \frac{\mu_0}{4\pi} \oint_{C_2} \oint_{C_1} \frac{d\vec{l}_2 . d\vec{l}_1}{r_{21}} \qquad ...(vii)$$

This equation shows that mutual inductance M_{21} depends not only on the sizes or shapes of the two circuits but also on their relative positions and orientations.

Similarly if a current I_2 is flowing in loop C_2, then magnetic flux through the loop C_1 is given by

$$\phi_{12} = \oint_{C_1} d\vec{l_1} \cdot \frac{\mu_0}{4\pi} I_2 \oint_{C_2} \frac{d\vec{l_2}}{r_{12}}$$

and

$$M_{12} = \frac{\mu_0}{4\pi} \oint_{C_1} \oint_{C_2} \frac{d\vec{l_1} \cdot d\vec{l_2}}{r_{12}} \qquad \qquad \text{...(viii)}$$

where M_{12} is the mutual inductance of circuit C_1 with respect to circuit C_2

Now $\qquad\qquad\qquad r_{12} = r_{21}$

because these are the magnitudes of the distances and not vectors.

$$\therefore \quad \frac{\mu_0}{4\pi} \oint_{C_2} \oint_{C_1} \frac{d\vec{l_2} \cdot d\vec{l_1}}{r_{12}} = \frac{\mu_0}{4\pi} \oint_{C_1} \oint_{C_2} \frac{d\vec{l_1} \cdot d\vec{l_2}}{r_{12}} \qquad \left[\because d\vec{l_2} \cdot d\vec{l_1} = d\vec{l_1} \cdot d\vec{l_2} \right]$$

or $\qquad\qquad\qquad M_{21} = M_{12} \qquad\qquad\qquad\qquad\qquad\qquad$ ...(ix)

We, therefore denote the mutual inductance between two circuits as M.

The loop or coil or circuit in which the current changes is called the *primary* and the one in which induced e.m.f. (or current) is set up the *secondary* of the mutual inductance. From relation (*ix*) we find that the co-efficient of mutual inductance is the same whether one or the other coil is taken as primary.

The result $M_{21} = M_{12}$ is often nown as '*Reciprocity theorem*' in mutual induction.

(*b*) From Eq. (*vii*) and Eq. (*viii*) it is clear that

(*i*) Mutual inductance between two circuits depends upon the size and shape of the circuits. Therefore, co-efficient of mutual induction between two circuits will change if there is a change in size of one or both.

(*ii*) Mutual inductance does not depend upon the change in current in one or both the circuits. Hence a change in current in one or both the circuits produces no change in co-efficient of mutual inductance.

(*iii*) Change in distance between the two circuits changes the mutual induction between them.

(*iv*) Presence of any non-magnetic material in the neighbourhood of two circuits produces no charge in mutual induction.

Q. 10.17. Calculate the co-efficient of mutual induction between two coplanar concentric rings of radius R_1 and R_2 when current flows through the ring of radius R_1 and $R_1 \geq R_2$.

(*P.U.*, 2009; *G.N.D.U.*, 1999)

Ans. Let C_1 and C_2 be two coplanar concentric rings of radius R_1 and R_2. Suppose a current I_1 flows through the ring C_1 of larger radius $R_1 \geq R_2$ then the magnetic field at its centre is given by

$$B_1 = \frac{\mu_0}{2} \frac{I_1}{R_1}$$

As $R_2 \ll R_1$, the field within the ring C_2 can be taken to be uniform.

∴ Magnetic flux linked with C_2

$$\phi_{21} = \frac{\mu_0}{2} \frac{I_1}{R_1} (\pi R_2^2)$$

If the current I_1, changes at the rate $\dfrac{dI_1}{dt}$, then the induced *e.m.f.* set up in C_2 is given by

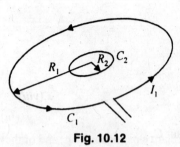

$$e_{21} = -\frac{d\phi_{21}}{dt} = -\frac{\mu_0}{2}\frac{\pi R_2^2}{R_1}\frac{dI_1}{dt}$$

$$= -M_{21}\frac{dI_1}{dt}$$

where M_{21} is the co-efficient of mutual induction of coil C_2 with respect to coil C_1.

Fig. 10.12

$$\therefore\ M_{21} = \frac{\mu_0}{2}\frac{\pi R_2^2}{R_1}\ \text{henry}\quad\text{[in S.I. units]}$$

Q. 10.18. (*a*) **Calculate the co-efficient of mutual induction of two solenoids when the secondary coil is wound on a small central part of the primary.**

(*M.D.U., 2000, 1999; K.U., 2000 1995, 1994; Pbi. U., 1993;*
H.P.U., 1993; G.N.D.U., 1993; P.U., 2001, 1991)

(*b*) **Give a laboratory method of measuring mutual induction of two solenoids.**

(*Luck. U., 1996*)

Ans. (*a*) **Co-efficient of mutual induction of two solenoids.**
Consider the secondary coil S wound on the central part of the primary coil P having an air core, as shown in Fig. 10.13 (*a*). Let n_1 be the total number of turns in the primary, l its length and a its area of cross-section. Let n_2 be the total number of turns in the secondary. When a current i flows through the primary,

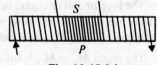

Fig. 10.13 (a)

Intensity of magnetic field on the axis of the solenoid

$$B = \frac{\mu_0 n_1 i}{l}$$

$\therefore$ Magnetic flux through each turn of primary

$$= \frac{\mu_0 n_1 i a}{l}$$

Since the secondary is wound over the central part of the primary, the same flux is also linked with *each turn* of the secondary.

$\therefore$ Magnetic flux linked with n_2 turns of the secondary $= \dfrac{\mu_0 n_1 i a}{l} \times n_2$

or $\qquad\qquad\qquad\qquad \phi = \dfrac{\mu_0 n_1 n_2 a i}{l}$ ...(*i*)

If M is the co-efficient of mutual induction between the two coils, then

$$\phi = Mi \qquad\qquad\qquad\qquad\qquad ...(ii)$$

From (*i*) and (*ii*), we have

$$M = \frac{\mu_0 n_1 n_2 a}{l}$$

The co-efficient of mutual induction may also be calculated from the *e.m.f.* induced in the secondary from the rate of change of current in the primary.

When the current in the primary changes at a rate $\dfrac{di}{dt}$, the induced electromotive force e in the secondary is given by

$$e = -M\frac{di}{dt} = -\frac{d\phi}{dt}$$

$$\therefore \qquad M\frac{di}{dt} = \frac{\mu_0\, n_1\, n_2\, a}{l}\frac{di}{dt}$$

or $\qquad\qquad M = \dfrac{\mu_0\, n_1\, n_2\, a}{l}$ ...(iii)

If the primary is closely wound on the iron core of constant relative permeability μ_r and of the same area of cross-section, then

$$M = \frac{\mu_0\, \mu_r\, n_1\, n_2\, a}{l}$$ ...(iv)

(b) Determination of mutual inductance. The principle of the method of measuring the mutual induction of two coils P and S is shown in Fig. 10.13 (b).

(i) The points A and B are connected together so that the secondary circuit is completed through the ballistic galvanometer. The points C and D are connected so that the resistance r is short-circuited and is not in the primary circuit. When the key K is pressed, the ballistic galvanometer gives a sudden kick. As the key K is pressed the current in the primary circuit slowly grows and an induced e.m.f. $e = -M\dfrac{di}{dt}$ is set up in the secondary circuit, where M is the coefficient of mutual induction between the two coils and $\dfrac{di}{dt}$ is the rate of change of current in the primary.

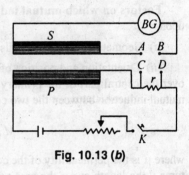

Fig. 10.13 (b)

The instantaneous current through the secondary

$$i = \frac{e}{R} = \frac{M}{R}\frac{di}{dt}$$

where R is the total resistance of the secondary circuit.

∴ The charge dq through the ballistic galvanometer in the time dt is given by

$$dq = idt = \frac{M}{R}\frac{di}{dt}dt$$

or $\qquad\qquad dq = \dfrac{M}{R}di$

If the current takes a time t to attain its value I in the primary circuit the charge q passing through the ballistic galvanometer is given by

$$q = \int_0^I \frac{M}{R}di$$

$$= \frac{MI}{R} = \frac{cT}{2\pi nAH}\,\theta_1\left(1+\frac{\lambda}{2}\right)$$ ...(v)

where c, T, n, A, and H have their usual meaning for a moving coil ballistic galvanometer, θ_1 the first throw and λ the logarithmic decrement.

(ii) The contact between A and B and between C and D is now broken. The contact between A and C and between B and D is established. The resistance r is thus introduced in the primary circuit but its value is so small that the steady current I is not altered. The potential difference Ir across the resistance r sends a steady deflection θ_2 given by

$$\frac{Ir}{R} = \frac{c}{nAH}\theta_2 \qquad\qquad ...(vi)$$

Dividing (v) by (vi), we have

$$\frac{M}{r} = \frac{T}{2\pi}\frac{\theta_1}{\theta_2}\left(1 + \frac{\lambda}{2}\right)$$

or

$$M = \frac{rT}{2\pi}\frac{\theta_1}{\theta_2}\left(1 + \frac{\lambda}{2}\right)$$

When r is in ohms M is in henries.

Q. 10.19. What do you mean by mutual induction and on what factors it depends?

(Pbi. U., 2006; G.N.D.U., 2003, 2002; P.U., 2002)

Ans. Mutual induction See Q. 10.15

Factors on which mutual inductance depends. The mutual inductance of two coils depends upon

(i) Geometries of the two coils and

(ii) Orientation and position of two coils. When the secondary of a mutual inductance is wound over the central part of the primary so that there is no leakage of magnetic flux, the co-efficient of mutual induction between the two coils is given by

$$M = \frac{\mu\, n_1\, n_2\, a}{l}$$

where μ is the permeability of the core material on which the two coils are wound, n_1 the number of turns, l the length and a the area of cross-section of the primary and n_2 the number of turns in the secondary.

In such a case the co-efficient of mutual induction between the two coils is *directly proportional to* μ, n_1, n_2 and a and inversely proportional to l.

Q. 10.20. A solenoid 16 cms long has 1,280 turns and its cross-section is 10 sq. cms. There is another coil of 1,000 turns closely wound on the central part of the solenoid. Find the mutual inductance of the coil in henries.   *(P.U., 2007)*

Ans. Length of the primary solenoid $l = 16$ cm $= 16 \times 10^{-2}$ m

Total number of turns in the primary $n_1 = 1280$

Area of cross-section $a = 10$sq cm $= 10 \times 10^{-4}$ sq m

Number of turns in secondary solenoid $n_2 = 1000$

Now

$$M = \frac{\mu_0\, n_1\, n_2\, a}{l} = 4\pi \times 10^{-7} \times \frac{1280}{16 \times 10^{-2}} \times 1000 \times 10 \times 10^{-4}$$

$$= 32\,\pi \times 10^{-4} = 0.01 \text{ Henry}$$

Q. 10.21. A straight solenoid has 50 turns per cm in primary and 200 turns in secondary. If the area of cross-section of solenoid in 4 sq cm, then show that mutual induction is nearly 50.27×10^{-5} henry.   *(K.U., 1994)*

Ans. Number of turns in primary $n_1 = 50$

Length of the primary $l = 1$ cm $= 10^{-2}$ m

Area of cross-section $a = 4$ sq cm $= 4 \times 10^{-4}$ sq m

Number of turns in secondary $n_2 = 200$

Co-efficient of mutual induction $M = \dfrac{\mu_0\, n_1\, n_2\, a}{l}$

$$= 4\pi \times 10^{-7} \times \frac{50}{10^{-2}} \times 200 \times 4 \times 10^{-4} = 50.27 \times 10^{-5} \text{ henry}$$

Q. 10.22. (*a*) **Mutual induction of two coils is 5 mH. If the current in one coil changes from 3 Amp to 1 Amp. in 0.1 sec. find the e.m. f. induced in the second coil.**   (*Luck. U., 1995*)

(*b*) **Coils A and B have respectively 200 and 800 turns. A current of 2 amperes in A produces a magnetic flux of 1.8×10^{-4} Wb in each turn of B. Compute**

(*i*) **The co-efficient of mutual inductance;**

(*ii*) **The magnetic flux through A, when there is a current of 4 amperes in B; and**

(*iii*) **The e.m.f. induced in B when the current in A changes from 3 amps to 1 amp in 0.3 sec.**

Ans. (*a*) Rate of change of current in one coil $\dfrac{dI}{dt} = \dfrac{3-1}{0.1} = 20$ amp/sec.

$\therefore$ *e.m.f.* induced in the second coil

$$e = -\frac{M\,dI}{dt} = -5 \times 10^{-3} \times 20 = 10^{-2} \text{ volt} = 0.01 \text{ volt}$$

(*b*) Current in coil A, $I_a = 2$ amps; Number of turns in $B = 800$

Magnetic flux per turn of $B = 1.8 \times 10^{-4}$ Wb.

$\therefore$ Total magnetic flux linked with B

$$\phi_b = 1.8 \times 10^{-4} \times 800 = 14.4 \times 10^{-2} \text{ Wb}$$

(*i*) Let M be the co-efficient of mutual inductance, then

$$\phi_b = MI_a$$

$\therefore$ Coefficient of mutual inductance $M = \dfrac{\phi_b}{I_a}$

$$= \frac{14.4 \times 10^{-2}}{2} = 7.2 \times 10^{-2} = 0.072 \text{ Henry}$$

(*ii*) Total magnetic flux linked with A when current in B is 4 amps

$$\phi_a = MI_b = 0.072 \times 4 = 0.288 \text{ Wb}$$

(*iii*) Rate of change of current in A.

$$\frac{dI}{dt} = \frac{3-1}{0.3} = \frac{20}{3} \text{ amp/sec}$$

$\therefore$ e.m.f. induced in $B = -M\dfrac{dI}{dt}$

$$= -.072 \times \frac{20}{3} = -0.48 \text{ volt.}$$

Q. 10.23. Does the mutual inductance of two coils depend upon their relative orientation? Explain.
                                                                      (*G.N.D.U., 1993*)

Ans. Yes. The mutual inductance of two coils depends upon their relative orientation.

If $d\vec{l_1}$ is a small vector element of length of coil C_1, $d\vec{l_2}$ a small vector element of length of a coil C_2 and r_{21} the magnitude of the vector distance $\vec{r_{21}}$ between the two elements, then co-efficient of mutual induction between the two coils is given by

$$M_{21} = \frac{\mu_0}{4\pi} \oint_{C_2} \oint_{C_1} \frac{d\vec{l_2} \cdot d\vec{l_1}}{r_{21}}$$

[For proof See **Q 10.16 Eq.** (*vii*)]

where $\oint_{C_1}$ and $\oint_{C_2}$ represent integration over the whole of the coil C_1 and C_2 respectively. This equation shows that mutual induction M_{21} (or M_{12}) depends not only on the shape and size of the two coils but also on their *relative positions and orientation.*

Q. 10.24. **What is self-induction? Define co-efficient of self-induction. State the units in which it is measured. Define practical unit of co-efficient of self induction and find its dimensiona. formula.**

(*P.U., 2006; Meerut U, 2003, 2001; K.U., 2001, 1996; G.N.D.U., 2000, 1997, 1995;
M.D.U., 2000, 1999; H.P.U., 2000, 1991; Kan. U., 1997; A.U., 1995; P.U., 1994*)

Ans. Self-induction. When a current flows through a coil of wire, it sets up a magnetic field which threads the coil that produces it. As the current rises from zero to a steady value, there is a change in magnetic flux linked with the coil. An *e.m.f.* is, therefore, induced in the coil acting in the *opposite* direction according to Lenz's law. *The effect of this is that the current takes rather a longer time to attain its full value.*

Similarly when the current is stopped, the magnetic flux linked with the coil decreases and an induced *e.m.f.* is set up in the *same* direction as the primary current. *The effect of this is that the current in the circuit does not stop suddenly.*

The property of an electric circuit by virtue of which it opposes a change in strength of the current flowing through the circuit by inducing an e.m.f. (or current) on itself is called self-induction.

Co-efficient of self-induction. When a current flows through a coil, it sets up a magnetic flux or a flow of magnetic induction through it. The flux is proportional to the current when the permeability of the medium remains constant. If ϕ is the magnetic flux linked with a circuit through which a current I flows, then

$$\phi \propto I$$
$$\phi = LI \qquad \qquad \text{...(i)}$$

where L is a constant known as *co-efficient of self-induction of the coil.*

If $\qquad\qquad I = 1, \phi = L$

The co-efficient of self-induction of a circuit is defined as the magnetic flux linked with the circuit when a unit current flows through it.

Suppose the current in the coil changes very slowly so that ϕ remains proportional to I, then an electromotive force e will be induced in the coil itself, given by

$$e = -\frac{d\phi}{dt} = -L\frac{dI}{dt} \qquad \qquad \text{...(ii)}$$

where the constant L is known as the *co-efficient of self-induction* of the coil.

If $\qquad\qquad \dfrac{dI}{dt} = 1$ then $L = -e$

The co-efficient of self-induction of a circuit is thus numerically equal to the induced e.m.f. in the circuit due to a unit rate of change of current in it.

Units. The practical as well as S.I. unit of self inductance is called a *henry*.

In relation (*ii*), if $e = 1$ volt, $\dfrac{dI}{dt} = 1$ Amp/sec $\;L = 1$

Henry. *A circuit has a self-inductance of one henry when a current increasing at the rate of one ampere per second produces an opposing e.m.f. of one volt.*

$$\text{One henry} = \frac{1\,\text{volt}}{1\,\text{amp/sec}} = \frac{\text{volt}}{\text{Coulomb sec}^{-2}}$$

Dimensional formula. $\text{Henry} = \dfrac{\text{Volt}}{\text{coulomb sec}^{-2}}$

But $\qquad\qquad \text{Volt} = \dfrac{\text{Joule}}{\text{Coulomb}} \qquad \therefore \qquad \text{Henry} = \dfrac{\text{Joule}}{\text{Coulomb}^2\,\text{sec}^{-2}}$

In dimensional form

[Inductance] $\qquad\qquad = \dfrac{M^1 L^2 T^{-2}}{C^2\,T^{-2}} = [M^1\,L^2\,C^{-2}]$

Q. 10.25. What is the difference between self induction and mutual induction? (*H.P.U., 2003*)

Ans. The property of an electrical circuit to set up a magnetic flux in itself due to a current flowing in it or the property of the circuit by virtue of which it opposes a change in strength of current flowing through the circuit itself by inducing an *e.m.f.* or current on itself is known as self induction.

On the other hand, the setting up of magnetic flux in a circuit due to current flowing in a neighbouring circuit or the property of producing an induced *e.m.f.* in a circuit due to variation of current in a neighbouring circuit is known as mutual induction.

Q. 10.26. Derive an expression for the co-efficient of self-induction of a current loop.

Ans. Co-efficient of self-induction of a current loop. Let C be the current loop through which a current i is flowing. Consider two small elements of length $d\vec{l_1}$ and $d\vec{l_2}$ separated by a vector distance $\vec{r}$, then magnetic field produced by the element $d\vec{l_1}$ at a point on the element $d\vec{l_2}$ according to Biot and Savart's law is given by

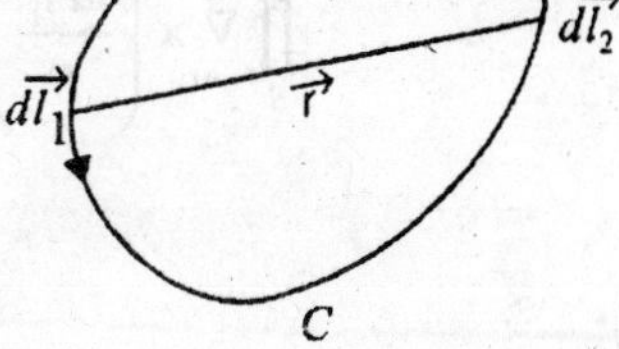

Fig. 10.14

$$B = \frac{\mu_0}{4\pi} \oint \frac{i\,d\vec{l_1} \times \hat{r}}{r^2} = \frac{\mu_0}{4\pi} \oint \frac{i\,d\vec{l_1} \times \vec{r}}{r^3}$$

But $\qquad\qquad \dfrac{\vec{r}}{r^3} = -\vec{\nabla}\dfrac{1}{r}$

$$\therefore \quad \oint \frac{i\,d\vec{l_1} \times \vec{r}}{r^3} = -\oint i\,d\vec{l_1} \times \vec{\nabla}\frac{1}{r} = \oint \vec{\nabla}\frac{1}{r} \times i\,d\vec{l_1}$$

Since $i\,d\vec{l_1}$ is not a function of position co-ordinates, we have $\vec{\nabla} \times i\,d\vec{l_1} = 0$

or $\qquad\qquad \dfrac{1}{r}\vec{\nabla} \times i\,d\vec{l_1} = 0$

We can therefore, put

$$\frac{\mu_0}{4\pi} \oint \frac{id\vec{l_1} \times \vec{r}}{r^3} = \frac{\mu_0}{4\pi} \left[\oint \vec{\nabla} \frac{1}{r} \times id\vec{l_1} + \oint \frac{1}{r} \vec{\nabla} \times id\vec{l_1} \right]$$

$$= \frac{\mu_0}{4\pi} \oint \vec{\nabla} \times \frac{id\vec{l_1}}{r}$$

Hence

$$\vec{B} = \frac{\mu_0}{4\pi} \oint \vec{\nabla} \times \frac{id\vec{l_1}}{r} \qquad \qquad ...(i)$$

The magnetic flux linked with the current loop

$$\phi = \iint_S \vec{B}.d\vec{s} = \iint_S d\vec{s}.\vec{B} \qquad \qquad ...(ii)$$

$$[\because \vec{A} . \vec{B} = \vec{B} . \vec{A}]$$

where $\vec{S}$ is the area of the surface bounded by the current loop and $d\vec{s}$ a small element of this area.

Substituting the value of $\vec{B}$ from (i) in (ii), we have

$$\phi = \iint_S d\vec{s} . \frac{\mu_0}{4\pi} \oint \vec{\nabla} \times \left(\frac{id\vec{l_1}}{r} \right)$$

$$= \frac{\mu_0}{4\pi} \oint \iint_S \vec{\nabla} \times \left(\frac{id\vec{l_1}}{r} \right).d\vec{s}$$

According to Stoke's theorem in vector analysis

$$\iint_S \vec{\nabla} \times \left(\frac{id\vec{l_1}}{r} \right).d\vec{s} = \oint \left(\frac{id\vec{l_1}}{r} \right).d\vec{l_2}$$

$$\therefore \qquad \qquad \phi = \frac{\mu_0}{4\pi} \oiint \frac{id\vec{l_1}}{r}.d\vec{l_2}$$

If the magnetic flux ϕ changes due to changes in current i, then the induced $e.m.f.$

$$e = -\frac{d\phi}{dt} = -L\frac{di}{dt}$$

where L is the co-efficient of self-inductance of the current loop.

$$\therefore \qquad \qquad L\frac{di}{dt} = \frac{\mu_0}{4\pi} \oiint \frac{di}{dt} \frac{d\vec{l_1}.d\vec{l_2}}{r}$$

or
$$L = \frac{\mu_0}{4\pi} \oiint \frac{d\vec{l_1} \cdot d\vec{l_2}}{r} \qquad \qquad \text{...(iii)}$$

Eq. (iii) gives the expression for self-inductance of a loop. It is known as *Neumann's formula*.

Q. 10.27. Calculate the co-efficient of self-induction of a coil of 1000 turns when a current of 2.5 Amp produces a magnetic flux of 0.5 micro-Weber.   (*G.N.D.U., 1991*)

Ans. Magnetic flux = 0.5×10^{-6} Weber

Number of turns = 1000

∴ Total magnetic flux linked with the coil $\phi = 1000 \times .5 \times 10^{-6}$ Weber

Now $\phi = LI$

and $I = 2.5$ Amp

∴ $L = \dfrac{\phi}{I} = \dfrac{1000 \times 0.5 \times 10^{-6}}{2.5} = 2 \times 10^{-4}$ Henry .

Q. 10.28. (a) Two closely wound coils have self-inductance L_1 and L_2 and placed so that practically the entire field set up by either coils links with all the turns of the other, compute the mutual inductance M of the coil and show that $M = \sqrt{L_1 L_2}$.

(*Luck. U., 1995, 1993; Osm. U., 1997*)

(b) What is co-efficient of coupling? State its value for no coupling and perfect coupling.
(*G.N.D.U., 2009, 2008, 2006; Pbi. U. 2002, 2001; Luck. U., 1996; P.U., 1991*)

Ans. Relation between self-inductance of two coils and mutual inductance. Let the two coils C_1 and C_2 consist of n_1 and n_2 turns respectively. Suppose ϕ_1 is the magnetic flux linked with each turn of coil C_1, when a current I flows through it, then the total magnetic flux linked with coil C_1 is given by

$$n_1\phi_1 = L_1 I_1 \text{ or } L_1 = \frac{n_1 \phi_1}{I_1}$$

where L_1 is the coefficient of self-induction of the coil C_1.

Similarly when a current I_2 flows through the coil C_2, the total magnetic flux linked with coil C_2 is given by

$$n_2 \phi_2 = L_2 I_2 \text{ or } L_2 = \frac{n_2 \phi_2}{I_2}$$

where L_2 is the co-efficient of self induction of the coil C_2.

Suppose ϕ_{21} is the magnetic flux linked with each turn of coil C_2 when a current I_1 passes through the coil C_1, then the total flux linked with n_2 turns of coil C_2 is given by

$$n_2 \phi_{21} = M_{21} I_1$$

or $M_{21} = \dfrac{n_2 \phi_{21}}{I_1}$

where M_{21} is the co-efficient of mutual induction of coil C_2, with respect to coil C_1.

Similarly when a current I_2 passes through the coil C_2 the total magnetic flux linked with coil C_1 is given by

$$n_1 \phi_{12} = M_{12} I_2$$

or
$$M_{12} = \frac{n_1\, \phi_{12}}{I_2}$$

where M_{12} is the co-efficient of mutual induction of coil C_1 with respect to coil C_2.

Now flux linked with each turn of coil C_1 due to current I_2 in $C_2 = \phi_2$ and flux linked with each turn of coil C_1 due to current I_2 in $C_2 = \phi_1$.

If all the flux due to the field set up by the current in coil C_2 is linked with the coil C_1, then

$$\phi_2 = \phi_{12}$$

Similarly
$$\phi_1 = \phi_{21}$$

Now
$$L_1\, L_2 = \frac{n_1\, n_2\, \phi_1\, \phi_2}{I_1\, I_2}$$

and
$$M_{12} \times M_{21} = \frac{n_1\, n_2\, \phi_{12}\, \phi_{21}}{I_1\, I_2} = \frac{n_1\, n_2\, \phi_1\, \phi_2}{I_1\, I_2}$$

But
$$M_{12} = M_{21} = M\ \text{(say)}$$

∴
$$M^2 = L_1\, L_2$$

or
$$M = \sqrt{L_1\, L_2}$$

(b) Co-efficient of coupling. In the above case we have supposed that the entire flux due to either coil links with all the turns of the other *i.e.*, there is no *leakage* of flux. When this condition is satisfied the coils are said to have a *perfect coupling*. In general, there is some leakage of flux and the co-efficient of mutual inductance is

$$M = k \sqrt{L_1\, L_2}$$

where k is the *coefficient of coupling*.

∴ Coefficient of coupling $k = \dfrac{M}{\sqrt{L_1\, L_2}}$

The value of k lies between 1 and zero. When $k = 1$, the *coupling is perfect* and the mutual inductance between the coils is a maximum.

When $k = 0$ there is *no coupling* and $M = 0$ (or minimum).

No coupling means that the flux produced by one coil is not at all linked with the other.

Q. 10.29. What is a solenoid ? Derive an expression for the co-efficient of self-inductance of a long uniformly wound solenoid. Hence find the co-efficient of self-induction of a toroidal solenoid of radius r.

(K.U., 2001, 1996, 1994; G.N.D.U., 2008, 2007, 2000, 1995; P.U., 2003, 1994; Pbi. U.,1991; H.P.U., 2000, 1991; M.D.U., 2000; Luck. U., 1996, 1993, 1992; OSm. U., 1997; A.U.,1995)

Ans. Solenoid. *A long wire wound in the form of a cylinder is called a solenoid.* Thus a solenoid consists of a number of co-axial circular loops of wire of the same radius.

When the wires are closely wound and solenoid is very long, it is known as an *ideal* or *long solenoid.*

Self-inductance of a solenoid. Consider a long closely wound solenoid of length l, *total number of turns n* and area of cross-section a placed in air. If a current I passes through it, then

Magnetic field B on the axis of the solenoid $= \dfrac{\mu_0\, nI}{l}$

∴ Magnetic flux through each turn $= \dfrac{\mu_0\, nIa}{l}$

Hence total flux linked with all the turns of the solenoid $= \dfrac{\mu_0\, nIa}{l} \times n$

or $\qquad\qquad\qquad\qquad \phi = \dfrac{\mu_0\, n^2\, Ia}{l}$

When the current in the solenoid changes at the rate $\dfrac{dI}{dt}$, the induced *e.m.f.* is given by

$$e = -L\dfrac{dI}{dt} = -\dfrac{d\phi}{dt}$$

∴ $\qquad\qquad\qquad\qquad L\dfrac{dI}{dt} = \dfrac{\mu_0\, n^2\, a}{l}\dfrac{dI}{dt}$

or $\qquad\qquad\qquad\qquad L = \dfrac{\mu_0\, n^2\, a}{l}$ ...(i)

When the solenoid is wound over a material of constant relative permeability μ_r, then

$$L = \dfrac{\mu_0\, \mu_r\, n^2\, a}{l}$$ ...(ii)

Self-induction of a toroidal solenoid. If the solenoid is in the form of a toroid of mean radius r as shown, then

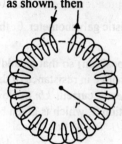

$$l = 2\,\pi\, r$$

For an air core

$$L = \dfrac{\mu_0\, n^2\, a}{2\pi r}$$

When the toroid is wound over a ring of the same area of cross-section and of constant relative permeability μ_r

Fig. 10.15 $\qquad\qquad L = \dfrac{\mu_0\, \mu_r\, n^2\, a}{2\pi r}$

Q. 10.30. Draw circuit diagram of Rayleigh's bridge and describe with necessary theory a method of measuring co-efficient of self induction. *(Kerala U., 2001, Luck U., 1994, 1992)*

Ans. Self inductance by Rayleigh's method. Lord Rayleigh used the principle of Wheatstone bridge method for measuring the self-inductance of a coil. The arrangement of apparatus known as Rayleigh's bridge is shown in Fig. 10.15 (a). Instead of an ordinary dead beat galvanometer a moving coil ballistic galvanometer is used. The arm CD contains an unknown inductance L in series with a small standard resistance r which does not appreciably affect the steady current in the circuit. This resistance is short circuited by a key K.

To start with the key K is closed so that the resistance r is not in circuit. The battery key K_1 and then the galvanometer key K_2 are pressed and an exact balance point is obtained for a *steady current* by adjusting the value of R in the usual

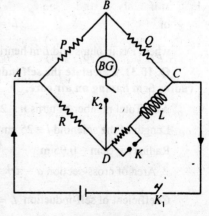

Fig. 10.15 (a)

manner. If now the galvanometer key is pressed **first** and **then** the battery key the ballistic galvanometer gives a sudden kick. It is because when the battery key is pressed (galvanometer key already being closed) the current slowly *grows* through the inductance and an induced *e.m.f.* $L\dfrac{di}{dt}$ is set up in the arm CD, where L is the coefficient of self-induction and $\dfrac{di}{dt}$ the rate of change of current.

The presence of the induced *e.m.f.* makes a proportional current to flow through the ballistic galvanometer. Hence the instantaneous current through the galvanometer is given by

$$kL\frac{di}{dt}$$

where k is the constant of proportionality.

Charge dq through the ballistic galvanometer *B.G.* in time dt

$$= kL\frac{di}{dt}.dt$$

or $$dq = kL\,di$$

If the current takes a time t to attain its constant value I in the arm CD the charge q passing through the ballistic galvanometer is given by

$$q = \int_0^I kL\,di$$

$$= kLI = \frac{cT}{2\pi nAB}\,\theta_1\left(1+\frac{\lambda}{2}\right) \qquad\qquad ...(i)$$

where c, T, A, n and B have their usual meanings for a moving coil ballistic galvanometer, θ_1 the first throw and λ the logarithmic decrement.

The key K is now removed (K_1 and K_2 being pressed in the balanced position) so that an additional small resistance of the order of 0.01 or 0.1 ohm is introduced. This change in resistance of the arm CD causes a small change in *e.m.f. Ir* and makes a proportionate steady current kIr to flow through the ballistic galvanometer. The galvanometer gives a steady deflection θ_2 which is given by

$$kIr = \frac{c}{nAB}\theta_2 \qquad\qquad ...(ii)$$

Dividing (*i*) by (*ii*), we have

$$\frac{L}{r} = \frac{T}{2\pi}\frac{\theta_1}{\theta_2}\left(1+\frac{\lambda}{2}\right)$$

or $$L = \frac{rT}{2\pi}\frac{\theta_1}{\theta_2}\left(1+\frac{\lambda}{2}\right)$$

where r is in ohms and L in henries.

Q. 10.31. Calculate the self inductance of a solenoid of 200 turns and length 25 cm, radius 5cm having an air core.   *(Pbi. U., 2003)*

Ans. Total number of turns $n = 200$

Length of the solenoid $l = 25$ cm $= 0.25$ m

Radius $r = 5$cm $= 0.05$ m

$\therefore$ Area of cross-section $a = \pi r^2 = \pi \times 0.05 \times 0.05$ sq m

Coefficient of self-induction $L = \dfrac{\mu_0 n^2 a}{l}$

$$= \frac{4\pi \times 10^{-7} \times 200 \times 200 \times \pi \times 0.05 \times 0.05}{0.25} = 1.58 \times 10^{-3} \text{ Henry}$$

Exercise 1. *Calculate the self-inductance of a solenoid of 100 turns and length 25 cm, radius 4 cm having an air core.* (*Pbi.U. 2000; P.U., 2000*)

Ans. 25.23×10^{-5} Henry

Exercise 2. *Calculate the coefficient of self-induction of a 1 metre solenoid of 500 turns and 5cm diameter.* (*Meerut U. 2003, 2002*)

Ans. 0.617×10^{-3} Henry

Exercise 3. *A wire is wound as a solenoid of 350 turns, a diameter of 4 cms and a length of 30 cms. Find the self inductance.* (*P.U., 2006*)

Ans. 64.5×10^{-5} Henry

Q. 10.32. A solenoid has a length of 50 cms and a radius of 1 cm. If the number of turns in the solenoid is 500, relative permeability of the material on which the turns are wound is 800, calculate the coefficient of self-inductance.

Ans. Number of turns $n = 500$

Length of the solenoid $l = 500$ cm $= 0.5$m

Radius $= 1$ cm $= 0.01$ m

$\therefore$ Area of cross-section $a = \pi \times .01 \times .01$ sq.m

Relative permeability $\mu_r = 800$

Co-efficient of self-induction $L = \dfrac{\mu_0 \mu_r \, n^2 a}{l}$

$$= \frac{4\pi \times 10^{-7} \times 800 \times 500 \times 500 \times \pi \times 0.01 \times 0.01}{0.5}$$

$$= 0.158 \text{ Henry.}$$

Q. 10.33. A solenoid having a core of 8 cm² cross-section, half air ($\mu_r = 1$) half iron ($\mu_r = 500$) is 50 cm long. If the number of turns on it is 2000, calculate the self-inductance. (*G.N.D.U., 1994*)

Ans. Number of turns $n = 2000$

Length of the solenoid $l = 50$cm $= 0.5$ m

Area of cross-section $= 8$ cm²

$\therefore$ Area of cross-section of air core $= 4$ cm² $= 4 \times 10^{-4}$ m²

Area of cross-section of iron core $= 4$ cm² $= 4 \times 10^{-4}$ m²

Inductance of air core part $L_a = \dfrac{\mu_0 \, n^2 a}{l}$

$$= \frac{4\pi \times 10^{-7} \times 2000 \times 2000 \times 4 \times 10^{-4}}{0.5} = 0.00402 \text{ Henry}$$

Inductance of iron core part L_i

$$= \frac{4\pi \times 10^{-7} \times 500 \times 2000 \times 2000 \times 4 \times 10^{-4}}{0.5} = 2.01 \text{ Henry}$$

Total inductance $L = L_a + L_i = 2.01 + 0.00402 = 2.01402$ Henry.

Q. 10.34. (*a*) **Show that the energy required to build up a current** *I* **in a circuit of self-inductance** *L* **is** $\frac{1}{2}LI^2$. **Obtain an expression for energy stored in an inductor.**

(*P.U.*, 2007; *M.D.U.*, 1999; *G.N.D.U.*, 2004)

(*b*) **Calculate the work done in establishing a current** *I* **in a circuit with self inductance** *L*. **Hence prove that co-efficient of self induction is numerically twice the work done in establishing a unit current in an inductor.**

(*Kerala U.*, 2001; *G.N.D.U.*, 1996; *A.U.*, 1996; *K.U.*, 1996, 1992, 1991).

Ans. (*a*) **Energy to build up a current in an inductor.** The inductance of a circuit resists any change in current through it and, therefore, any change in magnetic flux linked with it. Hence work has to be done in increasing the current from zero to a particular value say *I* against the *e.m.f.* induced in the inductance *i.e.*, energy is required to build up a current in an inductor.

If *e* is the self-induced *e.m.f.* at any instant in the circuit when the current established in the circuit is *i* and it changes at the rate $\frac{di}{dt}$, then

$$e = -L\frac{di}{dt}$$

where *L* is the co-efficient of self-inductance of the circuit.

If the current *i* remains unchanged for a small time *dt*, then

Work done in time *dt* = – *e i dt*

∴ Total work done *W* in establishing a current *I* in a time *t* or total energy required is given by

$$W = \int_0^t -ei\,dt = \int_0^t L\frac{di}{dt}i\,dt = \int_0^I Li\,di$$

$$= \left[\frac{1}{2}Li^2\right]_0^I = \frac{1}{2}LI^2 \qquad ...(i)$$

This expression gives the energy required to build up a current *I* in the inductor of inductance *L*.

Energy stored in the inductor. This energy is stored in the inductor in the form of magnetic energy.

∴   Energy stored $= \frac{1}{2}LI^2$

(*b*) It has been proved in part (*a*) that the work done in establishing a current *I* in a circuit with self-inductance $L = \frac{1}{2}LI^2$ ...(*ii*)

If *I* = 1, then equation (*ii*) becomes

$$W = \frac{1}{2}L \quad \text{or} \quad L = 2W$$

Thus the coefficient of self-induction is numerically equal to twice the work done in establishing a unit current in an inductor.

Q. 10.35. (*a*) **Why inductance is called electrical inertia?**   (*H.P.U.*, 2000, 1996)

(*b*) **An e.m.f. of 200 V is applied to an inductance of 10 H. It has a resistance of 40 Ω. If the current attains the maximum value, then find the energy stored in the inductance.** (*K.U.*, 2001)

Ans. Inductance is electrical inertia. Self-inductance is called *electrical inertia* because self inductance plays the same role in an electrical circuit as inertia (or mass) does in mechanical motion. The purpose of both is to slow down the change. At make of an electrical circuit self-inductance induces an *opposing e.m.f.* in the circuit and thus slows down the growth of current. At *break* it sets up an *e.m.f.* in the same direction as the original current and thus slows down the decay of the current.

Similarly, the moment of inertia slows down the motion of a body at start and prevents its stoppage when the body tends to stop. The energy associated with an inductance is $\frac{1}{2}Li^2$ and the energy due to linear motion is $\frac{1}{2}mv^2$ and in rotational motion is $\frac{1}{2}I\omega^2$. The magnetic flux ϕ linked with inductance is Li and it corresponds to linear momentum mv and angular momentum $I\omega$. The induced e.m.f. $L\frac{di}{dt}$ corresponds to force $m\frac{dv}{dt}$ or torque $I\frac{d\omega}{dt}$.

(b) When the current attains a maximum *steady* value there is no effect of inductance.

$\therefore$ Maximum steady current $\quad I = \dfrac{E}{R} = \dfrac{200}{40} = 5A$

Energy stored in establishing a current I, in an inductance L,

$$W = \frac{1}{2}LI^2 = \frac{1}{2} \times 10 \times (5)^2 = 125 \text{ Joule.}$$

Q. 10.36. Derive Helmholtz's equations for the growth and decay of an electric current in a circuit with resistance and self-inductance. What is meant by the time constant of the circuit?

(*Nag. U., 2001; Kerala U., 2001; Gauhati U., 2000; M.D.U., 1999; Luck. U., 1994, 1993; Meerut U., 2006, 1995; A.U., 1995*)

Ans. (a) Growth of current. Consider a circuit having an inductance L and a resistance R placed in series with a battery of *e.m.f.* E. When the key K is pressed the current slowly increases from zero to a maximum value I_m after some time. During the time the current is growing there is a back *e.m.f.* in the inductance. Let I be the value of the current at any instant during the variable state and $\frac{dI}{dt}$ be the rate at which the current grows, then

Fall of potential across the resistance $= RI$

Back *e.m.f.* in the inductance $= -L\dfrac{dI}{dt}$

This back *e.m.f.* opposes the *e.m.f.* E due to the battery.

Hence $\quad E - L\dfrac{dI}{dt} = RI$

Dividing both sides by R, we have

$$\frac{E}{R} - \frac{L}{R}\frac{dI}{dt} = I$$

$\therefore \qquad \dfrac{E}{R} - I = \dfrac{L}{R}\dfrac{dI}{dt}$

Dividing both sides by dI and taking the reciprocals, we have

$$\frac{dI}{E/R - I} = \frac{R}{L}dt$$

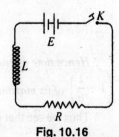

Fig. 10.16

$$\frac{-dI}{\dfrac{E}{R} - I} = -\frac{R}{L} \, dt$$

or

Integrating both sides, we have

$$\log_e \left(\frac{E}{R} - I \right) = -\frac{R}{L} t + C \qquad \ldots(i)$$

where C is constant of integration.

When $t = 0$, $I = 0$. Substituting these values in (i), we have

$$\log_e \left(\frac{E}{R} \right) = C$$

$\therefore$

$$\log_e \left(\frac{E}{R} - I \right) = \log_e \left(\frac{E}{R} \right) - \frac{R}{L} t$$

or

$$\log_e \frac{E/R - I}{E/R} = -\frac{R}{L} t$$

$\therefore$

$$\frac{E/R - 1}{E/R} = e^{-R/Lt}$$

or

$$\frac{E}{R} - I = \frac{E}{R} e^{-R/Lt}$$

or

$$I = \frac{E}{R}(1 - e^{-R/Lt})$$

Now I is the current at the end of time t from the instant of closing this circuit and E/R is the final steady value of the current. Denoting these by I_t and I_m respectively, we have

$$I_t = I_m \left(1 - e^{-\frac{R}{L} t} \right) \qquad \ldots(ii)$$

Time constant. The fraction $\dfrac{L}{R}$ is called the time constant of the circuit.

If $t = L/R$, then

$$I_t = I_m (1 - e^{-1}) = I_m \left(1 - \frac{1}{e} \right)$$

$$= I_m \left(\frac{e - 1}{e} \right) = I_m \left(\frac{1.718}{2.718} \right) = 0.6321 I_m$$

Hence time constant of a circuit is defined as the time during which the current rises to 0.6321 $\left(1 - \dfrac{1}{e} \right)$ *of its maximum value.*

Thus we see that during the time L/R, current rises to 0.6321 of its maximum value. Similarly it can be shown that when t is equal to $\dfrac{2L}{R}, \dfrac{3L}{R}$ ...etc. The ratio of the actual value of current to the maximum value attainable is given by $(1 - 1/e^2)$, $(1 - 1/e^3)$ ... etc., *i.e.*, at the end of the time $\dfrac{2L}{R}, \dfrac{3L}{R}$ ... etc. the current value will be 0.8647, 0.9502... etc. of the final attainable value. Thus we see that the current will attain maximum value I_m if $t = \infty$. In actual practice the time is small and for all practical purposes the current reaches almost to the maximum value (0.9953) in $\dfrac{5L}{R}$ seconds. The growth curve is shown in Fig. 10.18.

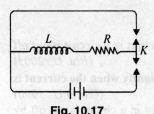

Decay of current. When the circuit is broken there is no *e.m.f.* and hence the current slowly decreases to zero. It is supposed that breaking of the circuit does not change its resistance R *i.e.*, a special key is used for the purpose as shown in Fig. 10.17 so that as soon as the battery is cut off contact is established on the other side thereby again completing the circuit. During the time the current is decreasing there is an *e.m.f.*

Fig. 10.17 induced in the inductance having a value $e = -L\dfrac{dI}{dt}$.

This *e.m.f.* causes a fall of potential RI across the resistance.

$$\therefore \qquad -L\frac{dI}{dt} = RI$$

or
$$\frac{dI}{I} = -\frac{R}{L}dt$$

Integrating both sides, we have

$$\log_e I = -\frac{R}{L}t + C \qquad\qquad ...(iii)$$

where C is the constant of integration.

When $t = 0$, $I = I_m$ and suppose $I = I_t$ after t seconds. Substituting these values in (*iii*), we have

$$\log_e I_m = C$$

$$\therefore \qquad \log_e I_t = -\frac{R}{L}t + \log_e I_m$$

or
$$\log_e \frac{I_t}{I_m} = -\frac{R}{L}t$$

or
$$\frac{I_t}{I_m} = e^{-\frac{R}{L}t}$$

$$\therefore \qquad I_t = I_m e^{-\frac{R}{L}t} \qquad\qquad ...(iv)$$

It is clear from Eq. (*iv*) that in time $\dfrac{L}{R}, \dfrac{2L}{R}, \dfrac{3L}{R}$ ..... etc. the current falls to $\dfrac{1}{e}, \dfrac{1}{e^2}, \dfrac{1}{e^3}$ .... etc. of the initial maximum value *i.e.*, to 0.3679, 0.1353, 0.0498 ... etc. of the initial value.

The decay of current is also shown graphically in Fig. 10.18. *The time constant of a circuit may also be defined as the time during which the current falls to 0.3679 or* $\left(\dfrac{1}{e}\right)$ *of its maximum value.*

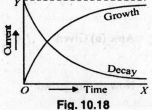

Fig. 10.18

Time constant has dimensions of time. The time constant of an LR circuit $= \dfrac{L}{R}$.

The dimensions of L are $\dfrac{\text{Volt}}{\text{Amp/sec}} = \dfrac{\text{Volt Sec}}{\text{Amp}}$.

The dimensions of R are $\dfrac{\text{volt}}{\text{Amp}}$.

$\therefore$ Dimensions of $\dfrac{L}{R} = \dfrac{\text{volt sec}}{\text{Amp}} \times \dfrac{\text{Amp}}{\text{volt}} = \sec = [\text{T}]$

Q. 10.37. (*a*) **Why is the self induced e.m.f. stronger when the current in a circuit is cut off than when it is started?**   (*Pbi. U., 2003*)

(*b*) **A lamp connected in parallel with a large inductor glows brilliantly when the current is swiched off. Explain.**   (*G.N.D.U., 1990*)

Ans. (*a*) **Self-induced e.m.f. at make and break.** When the current in a circuit is cut off by breaking the circuit, the total resistance of the circuit become very high due to the introduction of the air gap. If we denote the resistane of the circuit when the current is started (make) by R_m and when the current is cut off (break) by R_b, we have

Time constant at make $= \dfrac{L}{R_m}$

and time constant at break $= \dfrac{L}{R_b}$

Hence $\dfrac{L}{R_m}$ is greater than $\dfrac{L}{R_b}$. In other words, time taken by current to grow is greater than the time taken by it to decay. The total change in current at make and at break is the same. Therefore the rate of *growth of* current is very slow and the rate of *decay* is very rapid. Thus the rate of change of magnetic flux at make is slow and at break is rapid. The induced *e.m.f.* being proportional to the rate of change of magnetic flux, it is stronger at break than at make.

(*b*) **Brilliance of a lamp on switching off.**

The time constant of decay of an *LR* circuit is given by $\dfrac{L}{R}$. When the current is switched off the total resistance of the circuit becomes very high due to the introduction of the air gap. Hence $\dfrac{L}{R_{break}}$ is very small *i.e.*, the current takes a very small time to decay. The rate of change of magnetic flux at break is thus very high. The induced *e.m.f.* being proportional to the rate of change of magnetic flux is also very high. This is why the lamp glows brilliantly when the current is switched off.

Q. 10.38. (*a*) **In an *LR* circuit the current attains one third of its final steady value in 5 sec. What is the time constant of the circuit?**   (*Nagpur U., 2002, 2001; M.D.U., 1999*)

(*b*) **A relay having an inductance of 4H and resistane 200 Ω operates at a current of 2 mA. After applying a potential difference of 1 volt how long will the relay take to operate?**   (*Kerala U., 2001*)

Ans. (*a*) Given $I_t = \dfrac{1}{3} I_m$; $t = 5$ sec.

Now during growth $I_t = I_m \left(1 - e^{-\frac{R}{L}t} \right)$

or $\dfrac{1}{3} = \left(1 - e^{-\frac{R}{L}5} \right)$

$$\therefore \quad 1 - \frac{1}{3} = e^{-\frac{R}{L}5} \quad \text{or} \quad \frac{3}{2} = e^{\frac{R}{L}5}$$

or
$$\frac{5R}{L} = ln\frac{3}{2} = ln\,1.5 = 0.4055$$

or
$$\frac{R}{L} = \frac{0.4055}{5}$$

$$\therefore \quad \text{Time constant } \frac{L}{R} = \frac{5}{0.4055} = 12.33\,\text{sec}.$$

(b) Current required to operate the relay $I_t = 2\text{mA} = 2 \times 10^{-3}\text{A}$

Time constant of the circuit $\dfrac{L}{R} = \dfrac{4}{200} = \dfrac{1}{50}\text{sec}.$

Maximum steady current $I_m = \dfrac{E}{R} = \dfrac{1}{200} = 5 \times 10^{-3}$ A

Now
$$I_t = I_m\left(1 - e^{-\frac{R}{L}t}\right)$$

or
$$2 \times 10^{-3} = 5 \times 10^{-3}\left(1 - e^{-50t}\right)$$

or
$$\frac{2}{5} = 1 - e^{-50t} \quad \text{or} \quad 1 - \frac{2}{5} = e^{-50t}$$

$$\therefore \qquad \frac{5}{3} = e^{50t}$$

or
$$ln\,\frac{5}{3} = 50t \qquad \text{or} \qquad 50\,t = 0.511$$

$$\therefore \qquad t = \frac{0.511}{50} = 0.01\text{ sec}.$$

Q. 10.39. A solenoid has inductance of 30 H and a resistance of 30 Ω. If it is connected to a 60 volt battery how long will it take for current to reach one half its final value?

(*M.D.U., 2003*)

Ans. When the current attains its final steady value, there is no effect of inductance and the final maximum value of current $I_m = \dfrac{E}{R} = \dfrac{60V}{30\Omega} = 2$A

$\therefore$ One half of final value $I = 1$ A.

During the time the current is growing $I = I_m\left(1 - e^{-\frac{R}{L}t}\right)$

Here
$$\frac{R}{L} = \frac{30}{30} = 1$$

$\therefore$
$$1 = 2\left(1 - e^{-t}\right) \quad \text{or} \quad \frac{1}{2} = 1 - e^{-t}$$

or
$$e^{-t} = 1 - \frac{1}{2} = \frac{1}{2} \qquad \text{or} \qquad e^t = 2$$

$\therefore$
$$t = ln\,2 = 0.693\text{ sec}.$$

Q. 10.40. (*a*) An *LR* circuit having inductance 4.0 H and $R = 1.0\ \Omega$ and applied D.C. e.m.f. of 6 volt is switched at $t = 0$. Find the power dissipated in Joule heat in the circuit at $t = 4.0$ sec.

(Meerut U., 1995)

(*b*) The time constant of a coil is 2.5 mili-sec. On connecting 80 ohms in series the time constant is 0.5 milli-second. Calculate the self inductane and resistance of the coil.

(Osm.U., 1997)

Ans. (*a*) Inductance $L = 4.0$ H; Resistance $R = 1.0\ \Omega$

Applied voltage = 6 volts

$\therefore$ Maximum current $I_m = \dfrac{E}{R} = \dfrac{6}{1} = 6\ \text{Amp}$.

Current after a time t, $I_t = I_m\left(1 - e^{-\frac{R}{L}t}\right)$

$\therefore$ Current after 4 sec, $I_t = 6(1 - e^{-\frac{1}{4} \times 4} = 6\left(1 - \dfrac{1}{e}\right) = 6 \times 0.6321 = 3.7926$ Amp.

$\therefore$ Power dissipated $= I_t^2\ R = (3.7926)^2 \times 1 = 14.4$ Joule/ sec.

(*b*) Time constant $= \dfrac{L}{R}$

Ist case. $\dfrac{L}{R} = 2.5 \times 10^{-3}$ sec. or $L = 2.5 \times 10^{-3}\ R$ ...(*i*)

2nd case . $\dfrac{L}{R + 80} = 0.5 \times 10^{-3}$ sec or $L = 0.5 \times 10^{-3}\ R + 40 \times 10^{-3}$ ...(*ii*)

From (*i*) and (*ii*), we have

$0.5 \times 10^{-3}\ R + 40 \times 10^{-3} = 2.5 \times 10^{-3}\ R$

or $\hspace{6em} R = 20$ ohm

Substituting in (*i*), we have

$L = 2.5 \times 10^{-3} \times 20 = 50 \times 10^{-3}\ H = 50$ mH

Q. 10.41. A constant e.m.f. is applied to a circuit containing capacitance and resistance in series. Obtain an expression for the charge on capacitor plates and current during charging. Depict the variation of charge and current with time by a graph. Define capacitative time constant of the circuit.

(Nag, U., 2002, 2001; M.D.U., 2000; K.U., 2000, 1995; Gharwal U., 2000, 1999; Osm.U., 1997; Luck U., 1994)

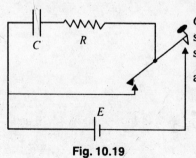

Fig. 10.19

Ans. Charge of a capacitor. A circuit containing a capacitor C, a resistor R connected to a source of *e.m.f.* through a key is shown in Fig. 10.19. When the current is switched on the capacitor starts getting charged. Let q be the charge on the capacitor plates after a time t from start and let the charge grow at the rate $\dfrac{dq}{dt}$, then

Potential difference across the capacitor plates $= \dfrac{q}{C}$

Potential difference across the resistor $Ri = R\dfrac{dq}{dt}$

If E is the applied *e.m.f.*, then

$$R\frac{dq}{dt} + \frac{q}{C} = E \qquad \text{...(i)}$$

The capacitor plates continue to get the charge from the source and when the potential difference across the capacitor plates is E, the e.m.f. of the source the charge is maximum and constant $= q_0$.

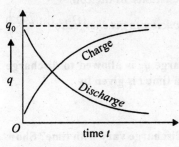

Fig. 10.20

$$\therefore \qquad E = \frac{q_0}{C}$$

Substituting in (i), we have

$$R\frac{dq}{dt} + \frac{q}{C} = \frac{q_0}{C}$$

or $\qquad q_0 - q = CR\frac{dq}{dt}$

or $\qquad \dfrac{dq}{q_0 - q} = \dfrac{1}{CR}dt$

Integrating, $\qquad \displaystyle\int \frac{dq}{q_0 - q} = \frac{1}{CR}\int dt$

or $\qquad -\log_e(q_0 - q) = \dfrac{t}{CR} + A \qquad \text{...(ii)}$

where A is the constant of integration.

When $t = 0$ $\qquad\qquad q = 0$

$\therefore \qquad\qquad -\log_e q_0 = A$

Substituting the value of A in (ii), we get

$$-\log_e(q_0 - q) = \frac{t}{CR} - \log_e q_0$$

or $\qquad \log_e\left(\dfrac{q_0 - q}{q_0}\right) = -\dfrac{t}{CR}$

or $\qquad \dfrac{q_0 - q}{q_0} = e^{-\frac{t}{CR}}$

or $\qquad q_0 - q = q_0\, e^{-\frac{t}{CR}}$

$\therefore \qquad q = q_0(1 - e^{-t/CR}) \qquad \text{...(iii)}$

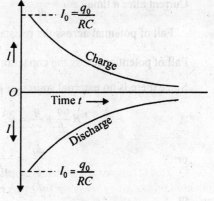

Fig. 10.21

Current $\qquad I = \dfrac{dq}{dt} = \dfrac{d}{dt}\Big[q_0(1 - e^{-t/CR})\Big]$

or $\qquad I = \dfrac{q_0}{RC}e^{-t/CR}$

The steady (maximum) current $I_0 = \dfrac{E}{R} = \dfrac{q_0}{RC}$

$\therefore \qquad I = I_0\, e^{-t/RC}$

The variation of charge with time and current with time at growth is shown in Fig. 35.20 and Fig. 10.21 respectively in curves marked *charge*.

Time constant. The time constant $= CR$ is known as *capacitative* time constant. Taking $CR = t$;

$$\frac{t}{CR} = 1$$

$$\therefore \qquad q = q_0 (1 - e^{-1}) = q_0 \left(1 - \frac{1}{e}\right) = 0.6321 \, q_0$$

Hence time constant (CR) is defined as the time taken by the capacitor to get charged to $\left(1 - \dfrac{1}{e}\right)$
or (0.6321) of the maximum value of charge.

Q. 10.42. A capacitor of capacitance C with an initial charge q_0 is allowed to discharge through a resistance R. Show that the charge remaining after a time t is given by

$$q = q_0 \, e^{-\frac{t}{RC}}$$

Hence define time constant. How does the current during discharge vary with time? Show that the sum of the currents at any time during charging and discharging of the capacitor is zero. (*Nag. U., 2001; Kerala U. 2001; M.D.U., 2000; A.U., 1995*)

Ans. Discharge of a capacitor. Let a capacitor of capacitance C, having a charge q_0 be connected to a resistance R. A current flows through the resistance. Let the charge left after a time t be q and let it decreases at the rate $\dfrac{dq}{dt}$, then

Current after a time $t = i = \dfrac{dq}{dt}$

$\therefore$ Fall of potential across the resistance $= Ri = R\dfrac{dq}{dt}$

Fall of potential across the capacitor $= \dfrac{q}{C}$

Since there is no external source of *e.m.f.*

$$\therefore \qquad R\frac{dq}{dt} + \frac{q}{C} = 0$$

or $$\frac{dq}{dt} = -\frac{q}{RC}$$

or $$\frac{dq}{q} = -\frac{1}{RC}.dt$$

Integrating both sides, we have

$$\log_e q = -\frac{1}{RC}t + A \qquad\qquad ...(i)$$

where A is a constant of integration.

When $t = 0$ $\qquad\qquad\qquad q = q_0$

$\therefore$ $\qquad\qquad\qquad\qquad A = \log_e q_0$

Substituting in (*i*) we get

$$\log_e q - \log_e q_0 = -\frac{1}{RC}t$$

or $$\frac{q}{q_0} = e^{-\frac{t}{RC}}$$

$$\therefore \qquad q = q_0 \, e^{-\frac{t}{RC}}$$

Time Constant. The time constant $= CR$

Taking $\qquad\qquad CR = t, \; \dfrac{t}{CR} = 1$

$$\therefore \qquad q = q_0 \, e^{-1} = \frac{q_0}{e} = 0.3679 q_0$$

Therefore, *the time constant of a CR circuit may also be defined as the time during which the charge on the capacitor falls to $\dfrac{1}{e}$ or (0.3679) of its maximum value of charge.*

Current $\qquad I = \dfrac{dq}{dt} = \dfrac{d}{dt}\left(q_0 \, e^{-t/RC}\right) = \dfrac{-q_0}{RC} \, e^{-t/RC}$

$$= - I_0 \, e^{-t/RC}$$

where $\qquad\qquad I_0 = \dfrac{q_0}{RC} = \text{The maximum current.}$

The variation of charge and current during discharging of a capacitor with time is shown in Fig. 10.20 and 10.21 *respectively in the curves marked discharge.*

Sum of the currents during charging and discharging. At any time t, the current during charging of a capacitor

$$I = \frac{q_0}{RC} \, e^{-\frac{t}{RC}}$$

and during discharging

$$I' = -\frac{q_0}{RC} \, e^{-t/RC}$$

$\therefore$ Sum of the currents $\quad I + I' = \dfrac{q_0}{RC} \, e^{-t/RC} - \dfrac{q_0}{RC} \, e^{-t/RC} = 0$

Q. 10.43. A capacitor charged by a D.C. source through a resistance of 2 mega ohm takes 0.5 sec to charge to $\dfrac{3}{4}$ of its final value. Show that the capacitance of the capacitor is nearby 0.18 microfarad. *(Gauhati U., 2000; K.U., 2002, 1994)*

Ans. When the capacitor is being charged,

$$q = q_0 \left(1 - e^{-t/RC}\right)$$

$$\therefore \qquad \frac{q}{q_0} = 1 - e^{-t/RC}$$

or $\qquad\qquad 1 - \dfrac{q}{q_0} = e^{-t/RC}$

or $\qquad\qquad \log_e\left(1 - \dfrac{q}{q_0}\right) = -\dfrac{t}{RC}$

Now $\qquad\qquad \dfrac{q}{q_0} = \dfrac{3}{4}, \; R = 2 \times 10^6 \text{ ohm}, \; t = 0.5 \text{ sec}$

$$\therefore \qquad \log_e\left(1 - \frac{3}{4}\right) = \frac{-0.5}{2 \times 10^6 \, C}$$

or $$\qquad \log_e \frac{1}{4} = -\frac{0.25 \times 10^{-6}}{C}$$

or $$\qquad -1.386 \, C = -0.25 \times 10^{-6}$$

$$\therefore \qquad C = \frac{0.25}{1.386} \times 10^{-6} = 0.18 \times 10^{-6} \text{ farad} = 0.18 \text{ microfarad}$$

Exercise *Find the capacitance of a capacitor which is charged by a. D.C. source through a resistance of 0.5 Mega ohm if the potential difference across it reaches 50% of its final value in half a second.*

(*M.D.U.*, 2007)

Hint $$\qquad \log_e\left[1 - \frac{q}{q_0}\right] = \frac{-t}{RC}$$

$$\therefore \qquad \log_e\left[1 - \frac{1}{2}\right] = \frac{-0.5}{0.5 \times 10^6 \, C}$$

$$-0.6931 = \frac{-10^{-6}}{C}$$

$$\therefore \qquad C = \frac{1}{0.6931} \times 10^{-6} \text{ Farad}$$

$$= 1.44 \times 10^{-6} \text{ Farad}$$

$$= 1.44 \text{ μfd}$$

Q. 10.44. (*a*) **Show that the discharge of a capacitor through an inductance is oscillatory. Calculate the natural frequency of oscillations.**

(*M.D.U.*, 2007, 2003, 2002, 2001; *Gauhati U.*, 2000; *K.U.*, 1996)

(*b*) **A capacitor of capacitance 1μf is connected to a conductor of 10 mH. Calculate the natural frequency of discharge of the capacitor.**

(*K.U.*, 1995)

Ans. Discharge of capacitor through inductance. Suppose a capacitor having a charge q_0 at time $t = 0$ is allowed to discharge through a pure inductance L. Let q be the charge on the capacitor after a time t and $I = \dfrac{dq}{dt}$, the current through the inductance. This current is changing at the rate $\dfrac{dI}{dt} = \dfrac{d^2q}{dt^2}$.

$\therefore$ Potential difference across the capacitor $= \dfrac{q}{C}$

and Back *e.m.f.* through the inductance $= -L\dfrac{dI}{dt} = -L\dfrac{d^2q}{dt^2}$

As there is no source of *e.m.f.* in the circuit

$$\frac{q}{C} = -L\frac{d^2q}{dt^2}$$

or
$$L\frac{d^2q}{dt^2} + \frac{q}{C} = 0$$

or
$$\frac{d^2q}{dt^2} + \frac{1}{LC}q = 0$$

Substituting $\dfrac{1}{LC} = \omega^2$, we have

$$\frac{d^2q}{dt^2} + \omega^2 q = 0$$

This is the differential equation of simple harmonic motion.
A general solution of this equation is

$$q = A \sin(\omega t + \theta)$$

At $\qquad t = 0 \qquad q = q_0 \qquad$ If $\theta = \pi/2$, then $q_0 = A$

Hence $\qquad q = q_0 \sin(\omega t + \pi/2)$

The discharge of the capacitor is, therefore, oscillatory. The circuit is of great importance in wireless, radio, television and radio-communication.

Frequency of oscillations. If f is the frequency of oscillations, then

$$\omega = 2\pi f = \frac{1}{\sqrt{LC}}$$

or
$$f = \frac{1}{2\pi\sqrt{LC}}$$

(*b*) Given $L = 10$ mH $= 10 \times 10^{-3}$ H $= 10^{-2}$ H

$$C = 1\ \mu f = 10^{-6}\ F$$

Now natural frequency $= \dfrac{1}{2\pi\sqrt{LC}} = \dfrac{1}{2\pi\sqrt{10^{-2} \times 10^{-6}}} = \dfrac{10^4}{2\pi} = 1.6 \times 10^3$ Hz

Q. 10.45. An experiment had a coil of 3 mH. Find the value of capacitor in order to use a resonant frequency of 10^3 K cycles per second. *(M.D.U., 2002)*

Ans. Given $L = 3$m H $= 3 \times 10^{-3}$ H; $C = ?$ $\qquad \Bigg[$ Resonant frequency $f = 10^3$k cycles per second $= 10^6$ cycles/sec.

Now
$$f = \frac{1}{2\pi\sqrt{LC}}$$

or $\qquad f^2 = \dfrac{1}{4\pi^2 LC} \qquad$ or $\qquad C = \dfrac{1}{4\pi^2 Lf^2}$

or $\qquad C = \dfrac{1}{4\pi^2 \times 3 \times 10^{-3} \times 10^6 \times 10^6} = 8.44 \times 10^{-12}$ Farad.

Q. 10.46. (*a*) A charged capacitor is discharged through an inductor of 0.2 H. The discharge is oscillatory with frequency 5000 Hz. Find the capacitance of the capacitor. *(Nagpur U., 2001)*

(*b*) The tuning circuit of a radio receiver has an inductance of 0.2 mH. Find the range of variable capacitor to get all the radio stations having frequency between 800 kHz and 1200 kHz. *(Kerala U., 2001)*

Ans. (*a*) Given $L = 0.2$ H; $f = 5000$ Hz.

Now
$$f = \frac{1}{2\pi\ \sqrt{LC}}$$

$\therefore$
$$5000 = \frac{1}{2\pi\sqrt{0.2\,C}}$$

or
$$5000 \times 5000 = \frac{1}{4\pi^2 \times 0.2\,C}$$

$\therefore$
$$C = \frac{1}{4\pi^2 \times 0.2 \times 5000 \times 5000} = \frac{10^{-7}}{2\pi^2}$$

$$= 5 \times 10^{-9} \text{ F}$$

(b)
$$L = 0.2 \times 10^{-3} \text{ H} = 2 \times 10^{-4} \text{ H}, f = 800 \times 10^3 \text{ Hz}$$

Now
$$f = \frac{1}{2\pi\sqrt{LC}} \text{ or } f^2 = \frac{1}{4\pi^2 LC}$$

or
$$C = \frac{1}{4\pi^2 L f^2}$$

For
$$f = 800 \times 10^3 \text{ Hz}$$

$$C = \frac{1}{4\pi^2 \times 2 \times 10^{-4} \times 800 \times 800 \times 10^6} = 1.98 \times 10^{-10} \text{ F}$$

For
$$f = 1200 \times 10^3 \text{ Hz}$$

$$C = \frac{1}{4\pi^2 \times 2 \times 10^{-4} \times 1200 \times 1200 \times 10^6} = 0.88 \times 10^{-10} \text{ F}$$

$\therefore$ The range of variable capacitor should be 0.88×10^{-10} F to 1.98×10^{-10} F.

Q. 10.47. Derive an expression for the charge on a capacitor at any time t when the capacitor is charged through a resistance and inductance. Hence find the current and frequency when the charge is oscillatory.

(*Meerut U., 2003, 2001; Cal. U., 1992; Luck. U., 1996, 1992; K.U., 1994, 1991*)

Ans. Charging a capacitor through resistance and inductance. Consider a circuit containing an inductance L, a resistance R and a capacitance C in series connected to a battery of e.m.f. E, through a key. As soon as the key is pressed the capacitance starts getting charged through the inductance L and resistance R.

Let q be the charge on the capacitor after a time t. The charge on the capacitor slowly grows due to which there is current $i = \dfrac{dq}{dt}$ at any instant. The current changes at the rate $\dfrac{di}{dt} = \dfrac{d^2q}{dt^2}$.

$\therefore$ Potential difference across the capacitor $C = \dfrac{q}{C}$

Potential difference across the resistance

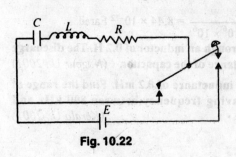

Fig. 10.22

$$R = Ri = R\frac{dq}{dt}$$

Back e.m.f. in the inductance

$$L = -L\frac{di}{dt} = -L\frac{d^2q}{dt^2}$$

As the applied e.m.f. is E, we have

$$\frac{q}{C} + R\frac{dq}{dt} = E - L\frac{d^2q}{dt^2}$$

or
$$L\frac{d^2q}{dt^2} + R\frac{dq}{dt} + \left(\frac{q}{C} - E\right) = 0$$

or
$$\frac{d^2q}{dt^2} + \frac{R}{L}\frac{dq}{dt} + \left(\frac{q}{LC} - \frac{E}{L}\right) = 0$$

Put
$$\frac{R}{L} = 2b \quad \text{and} \quad \frac{1}{LC} = k^2$$

$$\therefore \qquad \frac{d^2q}{dt^2} + 2b\frac{dq}{dt} + \left(k^2q - \frac{E}{L}\right) = 0$$

or
$$\frac{d^2q}{dt^2} + 2b\frac{dq}{dt} + k^2\left(q - \frac{E}{k^2 L}\right) = 0 \qquad ...(i)$$

Again put $q - \dfrac{E}{k^2 L} = x$ so that $\dfrac{dx}{dt} = \dfrac{dq}{dt}$ and $\dfrac{d^2x}{dt^2} = \dfrac{d^2q}{dt^2}$.

Substituting in (i), we have

$$\frac{d^2x}{dt^2} + 2b\frac{dx}{dt} + k^2 x = 0 \qquad ...(ii)$$

Let a trial solution of this differential equation be $x = e^{\alpha t}$, then

$$\frac{dx}{dt} = \alpha e^{\alpha t} \quad \text{and} \quad \frac{d^2x}{dt^2} = \alpha^2 e^{\alpha t}$$

Substituting in Eq. (ii), we have

$$\alpha^2 e^{\alpha t} + 2b\alpha e^{\alpha t} + k^2 e^{\alpha t} = 0$$

or
$$\alpha^2 + 2b\alpha + k^2 = 0$$

This is a quadratic equation in α. Its roots are

$$\alpha = -b \pm \sqrt{b^2 - k^2}$$

As there are two values of α, the general solution of differential equation (ii) is

$$x = A e^{(-b + \sqrt{b^2 - k^2})t} + B e^{(-b - \sqrt{b^2 - k^2})t} \qquad ...(iii)$$

where A and B are arbitrary constants, the values of which can be determined from boundary conditions.

Now
$$x = q - \frac{E}{k^2 L} = q - EC$$

$$\therefore \qquad q = x + EC = EC + A e^{(-b + \sqrt{b^2 - k^2})t} + B e^{(-b - \sqrt{b^2 - k^2})t}$$

$EC = q_0$ the steady charge on the capacitor

$$\therefore \qquad q = q_0 + A e^{(-b + \sqrt{b^2 - k^2})t} + B e^{(-b - \sqrt{b^2 - k^2})t} \qquad ...(iv)$$

At
$$t = 0 \qquad q = 0$$

$$\therefore \qquad q_0 + A + B = 0 \quad \text{or} \quad A + B = -q_0$$

Differentiating Eq. (iv), we have $I = \dfrac{dq}{dt}$

$$= A(-b + \sqrt{b^2 - k^2}) e^{(-b + \sqrt{b^2 - k^2})t} + B(-b \sqrt{b^2 - k^2}) e^{(-b - \sqrt{b^2 - k^2})t} \qquad ...(v)$$

At $\quad\quad\quad\quad t = 0 \quad\quad I = 0$

$\therefore \quad\quad\quad 0 = A(-b + \sqrt{b^2 - k^2}) + B(-b - \sqrt{b^2 - k^2})$

$\quad\quad = -b(A + B) + (A - B)\sqrt{b^2 - k^2} = bq_0 + (A - B)\sqrt{b^2 - k^2}$

$\therefore \quad\quad\quad A - B = -\dfrac{bq_0}{\sqrt{b^2 - k^2}} \quad$ Also $\quad A + B = -q_0$

$\therefore \quad\quad\quad A = \dfrac{-q_0}{2}\left(1 + \dfrac{b}{\sqrt{b^2 - k^2}}\right)$

and $\quad\quad\quad B = \dfrac{-q_0}{2}\left(1 - \dfrac{b}{\sqrt{b^2 - k^2}}\right)$

Hence $q = q_0 - \dfrac{q_0}{2}\left(1 + \dfrac{b}{\sqrt{b^2 - k^2}}\right)e^{(-b + \sqrt{b^2 - k^2})t} - \dfrac{q_0}{2}\left(1 - \dfrac{b}{\sqrt{b^2 - k^2}}\right)e^{(-b - \sqrt{b^2 - k^2})t}$ ...(vi)

Discussion. (i) When $b^2 > k^2$ i.e., $\dfrac{R^2}{4L^2} > \dfrac{1}{LC}$ the quantity under the root sign is *positive* and therefore, co-efficient of t is *real*. The charge goes on increasing till it acquires the steady value q_0 [Fig. 10.23 (i)]. The charge is *dead beat i.e.,* highly damped.

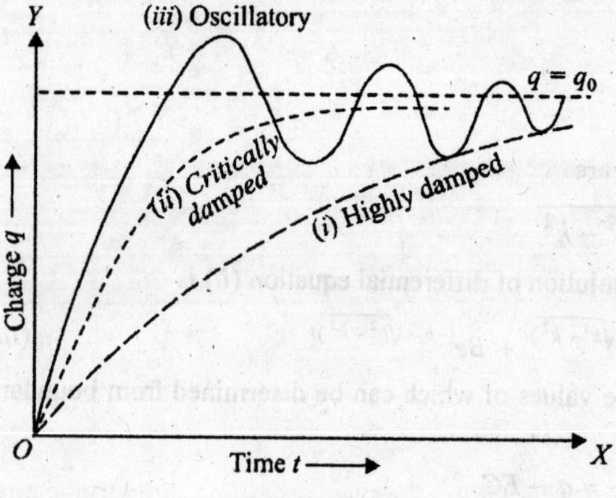

Fig. 10.23

(ii) When $b^2 = k^2$, $\dfrac{R^2}{4L^2} = \dfrac{1}{LC}$ the quantity under the root sign is *zero*. The charge is *critical one*, neither dead beat nor oscillatory. [Fig. 10.23 (ii)] i.e., it is critically damped.

(iii) When $b^2 < k^2$ i.e., $\dfrac{R^2}{4L^2}$, the quantity under the root sign is *negative* and $\sqrt{b^2 - k^2}$ is an imaginary quantity. Let it be equal to $j\omega$ where $j = \sqrt{-1}$ and $\omega = \sqrt{k^2 - b^2}$

Substituting in Eq. (vi), we have

$q = q_0 - \dfrac{q_0}{2}\left(1 + \dfrac{b}{j\omega}\right)e^{(-b + j\omega)t} - \dfrac{q_0}{2}\left(1 - \dfrac{b}{j\omega}\right)e^{(-b - j\omega)t}$

$= q_0\left[1 - e^{-bt}\left(\dfrac{e^{j\omega t} - e^{-j\omega t}}{2}\right) + \dfrac{b}{j\omega}e^{-bt}\left(\dfrac{e^{j\omega t} + e^{-j\omega t}}{2}\right)\right]$

$= q_0 - q_0 e^{-bt}\left[\cos \omega t + \dfrac{b}{\omega}\sin \omega t\right]$

$= q_0 - q_0 e^{-bt}\dfrac{k}{\omega}\left[\dfrac{\omega}{k}\cos \omega t + \dfrac{b}{k}\sin \omega t\right]$

Put $\dfrac{b}{k} = \sin\theta$ and $\dfrac{\omega}{k} = \cos\theta$ so that $\dfrac{b}{\omega} = \tan\theta$, then

$$q = q_0 - q_0\, e^{-bt}\, \frac{k}{\omega}[\cos(\omega t - \theta)] \qquad\qquad ...(vii)$$

Eq. (vii) represents a damped oscillatory charge, the charge being alternately greater and less than q_0 before settling down to the steady value q_0. [Fig. 10.23 (iii)]. The amplitude of vibration is

$$\frac{k}{\omega}e^{-bt} = \frac{k}{\sqrt{k^2 - b^2}}e^{-bt} = \frac{k}{\sqrt{k^2 - b^2}}\,e^{-\frac{R}{2L}t}$$

In circuits for which R is small the amplitude will die slowly. For $R = 0$, the amplitude is constant and the oscillations become simple harmonic. The maximum charge is much greater than the steady value q_0. It is possible that the maximum charge may raise the potential of the capacitor so high that the insulation may breakdown.

Current. The current in the circuit at any instant is obtained by differentiating the expression for charge, obtained in Eq. (vii).

$$I = \frac{dq}{dt} = q_0\, ke^{-bt}\sin(\omega t - \theta) + q_0\,\frac{kb}{\omega}e^{-bt}\cos(\omega t - \theta)$$

$$= q_0\, e^{-bt}\,\frac{k^2}{\omega}\left[\frac{\omega}{k}\sin(\omega t - \theta) + \frac{b}{k}\cos(\omega t - \theta)\right]$$

$$= q_0\, e^{-bt}\,\frac{k^2}{\omega}\left[\sin(\omega t - \theta)\cos\theta + \cos(\omega t - \theta)\sin\theta\right]$$

$$= q_0\, e^{-bt}\,\frac{k^2}{\omega}\sin\omega t$$

Period of oscillation. The time period of oscillation is given by

$$T = \frac{2\pi}{\omega} = \frac{2\pi}{\sqrt{k^2 - b^2}} = \frac{2\pi}{\sqrt{\dfrac{1}{LC} - \dfrac{R^2}{4L^2}}}$$

If R is negligible, then $T = 2\pi\sqrt{LC}$

and then frequency $n = \dfrac{1}{T} = \dfrac{1}{2\pi\sqrt{LC}}$

Q. 10.48. (a) **A charged capacitor discharges through a circuit containing inductance and resistance. Under what conditions the discharge will be oscillatory in character. Find an expression for the frequency of the oscillations.**

(b) **Point out its importance in wireless telegraphy.** (Magadh U., 1996; Luck. U., 1991)

(K.U., 2002, 1995, 1994, 1992; A.U., 1995, 1994; Meerut U., 1994, 1992)

Ans. (a) **Circuit containing resistance, capacitance and inductance.** In order that the discharge of a capacitor may be oscillatory in character an inductance L is placed in series with it. The circuit also possesses some resistance shown by R in Fig. 10.24.

When the key K is pressed downwards the capacitor C is charged. Let q_0 be the charge on it. When the key K is released the capacitor circuit is completed through the inductance and the resistance. The capacitor slowly loses its charge due to which there is a current I at any instant. The current varies at the rate $\dfrac{dI}{dt}$. If q is the charge on the capacitor some time later, then

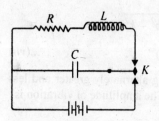

Fig. 10.24

Potential difference across the capacitor $= \dfrac{q}{C}$

Potential difference across the resistance $= RI$

Back *e.m.f.* in the inductance $= -L\dfrac{dI}{dt}$

As there is no source of *e.m.f.* in the circuit

$$\therefore \qquad \frac{q}{C} + RI = -L\frac{dI}{dt}$$

or $\qquad \dfrac{q}{C} + RI + L\dfrac{dI}{dt} = 0$

But as $\qquad I = \dfrac{dq}{dt}$ and $\dfrac{dI}{dt} = \dfrac{d^2q}{dt^2}$

$\therefore \qquad L\dfrac{d^2q}{dt^2} + R\dfrac{dq}{dt} + \dfrac{q}{C} = 0$

or $\qquad \dfrac{d^2q}{dt^2} + \dfrac{R}{L}\dfrac{dq}{dt} + \dfrac{1}{LC}q = 0$ $\qquad$ ...(i)

Put $\qquad \dfrac{R}{L} = 2b$ and $\dfrac{1}{LC} = k^2$, then

$$\frac{d^2q}{dt^2} + 2b\frac{dq}{dt} + k^2q = 0 \qquad ...(ii)$$

Let a trial solution of differential equation be

$$q = e^{\alpha t}$$

Then $\qquad \dfrac{dq}{dt} = \alpha e^{\alpha t}$ $\qquad$ and $\qquad \dfrac{d^2q}{dt^2} = \alpha^2 e^{\alpha t}$

Substituting the values in (ii) we have

$$\alpha^2 e^{\alpha t} + 2b\alpha e^{\alpha t} + k^2 e^{\alpha t} = 0$$

or $\qquad \alpha^2 + 2b\alpha + k^2 = 0$

This is a quadratic equation in α. Hence its roots are

$$a = -b \pm \sqrt{b^2 - k^2}$$

As there are two values of α, the general solution of the differential equation (ii) is

$$q = A e^{(-b + \sqrt{b^2 - k^2})t} + B e^{(-b - \sqrt{b^2 - k^2})t} = 0 \qquad ...(iii)$$

where A and B are arbitrary constants, the value of which can be determined from boundary conditions.

Now at $\qquad\qquad t = 0 \qquad q = q_0$

Substituting in (iii) we have

$$q_0 = A + B \qquad ...(iv)$$

The value of current i at any time is obtained by differentiating equation (iii) and we have

$$i = \frac{dq}{dt} = A(-b + \sqrt{b^2 - k^2})\, e^{\sqrt{(b^2 - k^2)}\,t} + B(-b - \sqrt{b^2 - k^2})\, e^{(-b - \sqrt{b^2 - k^2})t}$$

Again at $\qquad\qquad t = 0 \qquad i = 0$

$$\therefore \qquad 0 = A(-b + \sqrt{b^2 - k^2}) + B(-b - \sqrt{b^2 - k^2})$$

$$= -b(A + B) + \sqrt{b^2 - k^2}\ (A - B)$$

$$= -bq_0 + \sqrt{b^2 - k^2}\ (A - B)$$

or
$$A - B = \frac{bq_0}{\sqrt{b^2 - k^2}} \qquad \qquad ...(v)$$

Adding (iv) and (v), we get

$$2A = q_0\left(1 + \frac{b}{\sqrt{b^2 - k^2}}\right)$$

or
$$A = \frac{1}{2}q_0\left(1 + \frac{b}{\sqrt{b^2 - k^2}}\right)$$

Subtracting (v) from (iv) we get

$$2B = q_0\left(1 - \frac{b}{\sqrt{b^2 - k^2}}\right)$$

or
$$B = \frac{1}{2}q_0\left(1 - \frac{b}{\sqrt{b^2 - k^2}}\right)$$

Substituting the values of A and B in (iii), we have

$$q = \frac{1}{2}q_0\left[\left(1 + \frac{b}{\sqrt{b^2 - k^2}}\right)e^{(-b + \sqrt{b^2 - k^2})t} + \left(1 - \frac{b}{\sqrt{b^2 - k^2}}\right)e^{(-b - \sqrt{b^2 - k^2})t}\right] \qquad ...(vi)$$

Substituting the values of b and k we have

$$q = \frac{1}{2}q_0\left[1 + \frac{\dfrac{R}{2L}}{\sqrt{\dfrac{R^2}{4L^2} - \dfrac{1}{LC}}}\right]e^{\left(-\frac{R}{2L} + \sqrt{\frac{R^2}{4L^2} - \frac{1}{LC}}\right)t}$$

$$+ \left[1 - \frac{\dfrac{R}{2L}}{\sqrt{\dfrac{R^2}{4L^2} - \dfrac{1}{LC}}}\right]e^{\left(-\frac{R}{2L} - \sqrt{\frac{R^2}{4L^2} - \frac{1}{LC}}\right)t} \qquad ...(vii)$$

The exponential factor $e^{-\frac{Rt}{2L}}$ gives us a charge decaying exponentially with time. Superimposed upon this is the effect due to the factor under the root sign. This factor has three possible cases.

(i) When $\dfrac{R^2}{4L^2} > \dfrac{1}{LC}$

The quantity under the root sign is *positive* and, therefore coefficient of t is *real*. The charge decreases rapidly with time. The discharge is known as *aperiodic, deadbeat* or *non-oscillatory* as shown in Fig. 10.25, (curve 1).

(ii) When $\dfrac{R^2}{4L^2} = \dfrac{1}{LC}$

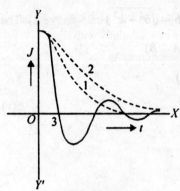

Fig. 10.25

The quantity under the root sign is zero and

$$q = q_0 e^{-\frac{R}{2L}}$$

This represents a *critically damped* discharge which is neither oscillatory nor non-oscillatory as shown in Fig. 10.25 (curve 2).

(*iii*)   When $\dfrac{R^2}{4L} < \dfrac{1}{LC}$

The quantity under the root sign $\dfrac{R^2}{4L^2} - \dfrac{1}{LC} = b^2 - k^2$ is imaginary.

Let it be equal to $j\omega$ where $j = \sqrt{-1}$ and $\omega = \sqrt{k^2 - b^2}$.

Substituting in equation (*vi*), we have

$$q = \frac{1}{2}q_0 \left[\left(1 + \frac{b}{j\omega}\right) e^{(-b+j\omega)t} + \left(1 - \frac{b}{j\omega}\right) e^{(-b-j\omega)t} \right]$$

$$= q_0 e^{-bt} \left[\frac{e^{j\omega t} + e^{-j\omega t}}{2} + \frac{b}{\omega} \frac{e^{j\omega t} e^{-j\omega t}}{2j} \right]$$

$$= q_0 e^{-bt} \left[\cos\omega t + \frac{b}{\omega} \sin\omega t \right]$$

or

$$q = q_0 \frac{e^{-bt}}{\omega} \left[\omega \cos\omega t + b\sin\omega t \right]$$

Put

$$\frac{b}{\omega} = \tan\theta$$

$\therefore$

$$\sin\theta = \frac{b}{\sqrt{\omega^2 + b^2}}$$

$$= \frac{b}{\sqrt{k^2 - b^2 + b^2}} = \frac{b}{k}$$

or

$$b = k \sin\theta$$

and

$$\cos\theta = \frac{\omega}{\sqrt{\omega^2 + b^2}} = \frac{\omega}{k}$$

or

$$\omega = k \cos\theta$$

Substituting, we have

$$q = q_0 e^{-bt} \frac{k}{\omega} \left[\frac{\omega}{k} \cos\omega t + \frac{b}{k} \sin\omega t \right]$$

$$= q_0 e^{-bt} \frac{k}{\omega} \left[\cos\omega t \cos\theta + \sin\theta \sin\omega t \right]$$

$$= q_0 \frac{k}{\omega} e^{-bt} \left[\cos(\omega t - \theta) \right]$$

$$= q_0 \frac{k}{\sqrt{k^2 - b^2}} e^{-bt} \cos[(\sqrt{k^2 - b^2})t - \theta]$$

This is the equation of a damped oscillatory discharge as shown in Fig. 10.25 (curve 3). The amplitude of the successive oscillations in the discharge decreases exponentially with time.

Hence the condition that the discharge of a capacitor may be oscillatory is

$$\frac{R^2}{4L^2} < \frac{1}{LC} \qquad \text{or} \qquad R < 2\sqrt{\frac{L}{C}}$$

Time period. The time period of the oscillations is given by

$$T = \frac{2\pi}{\omega} = \frac{2\pi}{\sqrt{k^2 - b^2}} = \frac{2\pi}{\sqrt{\dfrac{1}{LC} - \dfrac{R^2}{4L^2}}}$$

Frequency. The frequency

$$n = \frac{1}{T} = \frac{1}{2\pi}\sqrt{\frac{1}{LC} - \frac{R^2}{4L^2}}$$

If R is negligible, then

$$T = 2\pi\sqrt{LC}$$

and

$$n = \frac{1}{2\pi\sqrt{LC}}$$

(*b*) **Importance in wireless telegraphy.** The discharge of a capacitor through an inductance is oscillatory if the resistance of the circuit is small. When the capacitor is charged there is an electric field between the plates of the capacitor and the whole of the energy is electrostatic. During discharge a current flows thrugh the inductance coil for a very small time. This sets up a magnetic field within the coil and the whole of the energy is magnetic. When the oscillations are set up the energy continuously varies between electrostatic and magnetic forms. When the resistance is low a number of oscillations take place and changes in electric and magnetic fields give rise to an electromagnetic radiation which is propagated through space with the velocity of light. These electromagnetic waves form the basis of wireless telegraphy and with the help of a code enable the transmission of messages from one place to the other.

Q. 10.49. A capacitor of capacitance 1 microfarad is allowed to discharge through an inductance of 0.2 henry and a resistance of 800 ohm connected in series. Prove that the discharge is oscillatory. (*Gauhati U., 2000; K.U., 1996*)

Ans. $C = 1$ microfarad; $L = 0.2$ henry; $R = 800$ ohm

$$\frac{R^2}{4L^2} = \frac{800 \times 800}{4 \times 0.2 \times 0.2} = 4 \times 10^6$$

$$\frac{1}{LC} = \frac{1}{0.2 \times 1 \times 10^{-6}} = 5 \times 10^6$$

$$\therefore \qquad \frac{R^2}{4L^2} < \frac{1}{LC}; \text{ the discharge is oscillatory.}$$

Q. 10.50. Find whether the discharge of capacitor in the following cases is oscillatory or not. If so calculate the frequency.

(*i*) $C = 0.1\ \mu F$; $L = 10$ mH; $R = 1$ kΩ. (*K.U., 2000*)

(*ii*) $C = 0.1\ \mu F$; $L = 10$ mH; $R = 200\ \Omega$ (*Luck.U., 1996*)

Ans. (i) $C = 0.1 \ \mu F = 10^{-7} \ F; L = 10 \ mH = 10^{-2} \ H; R = 1 \ k\Omega = 10^3 \ \Omega$

$$\therefore \qquad \frac{R^2}{4L^2} = \frac{10^3 \times 10^3}{4 \times 10^{-4}} = 0.25 \times 10^{10}; \frac{1}{LC} = \frac{1}{10^{-2} \times 10^{-7}} = 10^9 = 0.1 \times 10^{10}$$

As $\dfrac{R^2}{4L^2} > \dfrac{1}{LC}$, the discharge is non-oscillatory.

(ii) $C = 0.1 \ \mu F = 10^{-7} \ F; L = 10 \ mH = 10^{-2} \ H; R = 200 \ \Omega$

$$\therefore \qquad \frac{R^2}{4L^2} = \frac{200 \times 200}{4 \times 10^{-4}} = 10^8; \frac{1}{LC} = \frac{1}{10^{-2} \times 10^{-7}} = 10^9 = 10 \times 10^8$$

As $\dfrac{R^2}{4L^2} < \dfrac{1}{LC}$ the discharge is oscillatory.

Frequency. $n = \dfrac{1}{2\pi} \sqrt{\dfrac{1}{LC} - \dfrac{R^2}{4L^2}} = \dfrac{1}{2\pi} \sqrt{\dfrac{1}{10^{-2} \times 10^{-7}} - \dfrac{200 \times 200}{4 \times 10^{-2} \times 10^{-2}}}$

$$= \frac{1}{2\pi} \sqrt{10^9 - 10^8} = \frac{10^4}{2\pi} \sqrt{10 - 1} = \frac{3}{2\pi} \times 10^4 = 4774 \ Hz.$$

Q. 10.51. In an oscillatory circuit $L = 0.2$ henry, $C = 0.0012$ microfarad. What is the maximum value of the resistance so that the circuit may oscillate? *(Nagpur U., 2002)*

Ans. Here inductance $L = 0.2$ henry

Capacitance $C = 0.0012$ microfarad $= 12 \times 10^{-10}$ farad

Let R be the maximum value of the resistance so that the discharge is oscillatory.

$$\therefore \qquad \frac{R^2}{4L^2} \text{ is less than } \frac{1}{LC}.$$

Hence, in order that the circuit may oscillate the *maximum* resistance is given by

$$\frac{R^2}{4L^2} = \frac{1}{LC}$$

or $\qquad R^2 = \dfrac{4L^2}{LC} = \dfrac{4L}{C}$

or $\qquad R = 2\sqrt{\dfrac{L}{C}} = 2\sqrt{\dfrac{0.2}{12 \times 10^{-10}}} = 25820 \ ohm.$

Q. 10.52. Discuss the reasons which lead Maxwell to modify Ampere's law for steady currents Curl $\vec{B} = \mu_0 \vec{J}$ by introducing the concept of displacement current. Hence derive the new relationship. Show that vacuum displacement current density $\vec{J_d} = \dfrac{\partial \vec{D}}{\partial t}$ and has dimensions of current density. Is the displacement current something fictitious?

(G.N.D.U., 2001, 2000, 1999, 1995, 1994; Pbi. U., 2001, 2000, 1999; Nag. U., 2002; Kerala U., 2001; Indore U., 2001; K.U., 2001, 2000; M.D.U., 1999)

OR

According to the equation of continuity div. $\vec{J} = -\dfrac{\partial P}{\partial t}$ which gives div $\vec{J} \neq 0$ for charge density varying in time but curl $\vec{B} = \mu_0 \vec{J}$ leads to div. $\vec{J} = $ div $(1/\mu_0 \ curl \ \vec{B}) = 0$. Explain the contradiction. *(H.P.U., 2003)*

Ans. Reasons for modification of Ampere's law. The differential form of Coulomb's law in electrostatics states

$$div \, \vec{E} = \vec{\nabla} . \vec{E} = \frac{\rho}{\varepsilon_0}$$

where $\vec{E}$ is the electric field and ρ the electric charge density. This equation is true for *stationary as well as moving charges.*

Electric charge in motion is equivalent to an electric current. As charge is never created or destroyed, the flow of current density or divergence $\vec{J}$ is equal and opposite to the rate of change of charge density.

or
$$div . \, \vec{J} = \vec{\nabla}.\vec{J} = -\frac{\partial \rho}{\partial t} \qquad \qquad ...(ii)$$

or
$$\vec{\nabla}.\vec{J} + \frac{\partial \rho}{\partial t} = 0 \qquad \qquad ...(iii)$$

This is known as the *equation of continuity* and is true for varying currents.

A steady current produces a magnetic field, given by

$$Curl \, \vec{B} = \vec{\nabla} \times \vec{B} = \mu_0 \, \vec{J} \qquad \qquad ...(iv)$$

This is the differential form of Ampere's law for steady currents.

Inconsistency with time varying fields From relation (*iv*), we have

$$\mu_0 \, \vec{\nabla}.\vec{J} = \vec{\nabla}.\vec{\nabla} \times \vec{B} = 0 \qquad \qquad ....(v)$$

Since the divergence of the curl of a vector is identically zero.

Thus the equation of continuity gives $\vec{\nabla}.\vec{J} = -\dfrac{\partial \rho}{\partial t}$ and from differential form of Ampere's law equation (*v*) we have $\vec{\nabla}.\vec{J} = 0$

Thus the equation of continuity (equation (*ii*)] $\vec{\nabla}.\vec{J} = -\dfrac{\partial \rho}{\partial t}$ gives $\vec{\nabla}.\vec{J} \neq 0$ for charge density varying in time. On the other hand the equation *curl* $\vec{B} = \vec{\nabla} \times \vec{B} = \mu_0 \, \vec{J}$ leads to $\vec{\nabla}.\vec{J} = 0$ [Equation (*v*)].

There is, therefore, an *apparent contradiction* between relation (*ii*) and (*iv*) which means relation (*iv*) needs to be modified for varying currents and should be written as

$$\vec{\nabla} \times \vec{B} = \mu_0 \, \vec{J} + \text{an additional term}$$

We shall discuss it in detail.

Concept of displacement current. Consider a parallel plate capacitor *ab* and a resistance *R* as shown in Fig. 10.26 (*a*).

If the plate *a* of the capacitor carries a positive charge and the plate *b* an equal negative charge, then the capacitor will discharge itself through the resistance *R* and a *varying* current will flow through the circuit when the key *K* is closed.

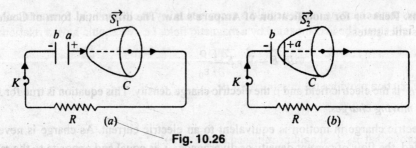

Fig. 10.26

Let i be the electric current at any instant of time during the discharging of the capacitor and $\vec{B}$ the magnetic field at a point on the surface $\vec{S_1}$ sufficiently far away from the capacitor plates. A current i flows through the surface S_1. If $\vec{J}$ is the corresponding current density, then

$$Curl\ \vec{B} = \vec{\nabla} \times \vec{B} = \mu_0 \vec{J}$$

Accoding to Stoke's theorem in vector analysis, if C is the linear boundary enclosing the surface, then

$$\oint_C \vec{B}.\vec{dl} = \iint_S Curl\ \vec{B}.\vec{ds}$$

$$\therefore \qquad \oint_C \vec{B}.\vec{dl} = \mu_0 \iint_S \vec{J}.\vec{ds} = \mu_0 i \qquad [\because i = \iint_S \vec{J}.\vec{ds}]$$

Now consider a surface $\vec{S_2}$ as shown in Fig. 10.26 (b). No current is flowing through the surface $\vec{S_2}$ but it is enclosed by the *same linear boundary C.*

$\therefore$ For the surface S_2

$$\oint_C \vec{B}.\vec{dl} = \mu_0 \iint_{S_2} \vec{J}.\vec{ds} = \mu_0 i = 0$$

[$\because$ no current flows through S_2]

The surface S_1 and S_2 are both bounded by the same linear boundary C and whereas $\oint_C \vec{B}.\vec{dl}$ for the surface S_1 has a value $\mu_0 i$. $\oint_C \vec{B}.\vec{dl}$ for the surface $S_2 = 0$. This is not possible.

In other words in the equation

$$Curl\ \vec{B} = \vec{\nabla} \times \vec{B} = \mu_0 \vec{J}$$

something is missing and it should in fact be of the form

$$Curl\ \vec{B} = \vec{\nabla} \times \vec{B} = \mu_0 \vec{J} + (an\ additional\ term)$$

Faraday's law of electromagnetic induction in the differential form

$$\vec{\nabla} \times \vec{E} = -\frac{\partial \vec{B}}{\partial t}$$

shows that a changing magnetic field is accompanied by an electric field. Symmetrically a changing electric field should be accompanied by a magnetic field, *i.e.*, we should have a relation of the type

$$\vec{\nabla} \times \vec{B} = \mu_0 \, \varepsilon_0 \, \frac{\partial \vec{E}}{\partial t}$$

The relation provides the missing term *i.e.*,

$$Curl \, \vec{B} = \vec{\nabla} \times \vec{B} = \mu_0 \left(\vec{J} + \varepsilon_0 \, \frac{\partial E}{\partial t} \right)$$

To prove that $\mu_0 \, \vec{J}$ should be replaced by the term

$$\mu_0 \left(\vec{J} + \varepsilon_0 \, \frac{\partial E}{\partial t} \right)$$

in relation (*iv*) we combine Coulomb's law and the equation of continuity.

Modification of Ampere's law. [*For varying currents*] According to differential form of Coulomb's law

$$div \, \vec{E} = \vec{\nabla} . \vec{E} = \frac{\rho}{\varepsilon_0}$$

or

$$\rho = \varepsilon_0 \, \vec{\nabla} . \vec{E}$$

$$\therefore \qquad \frac{\partial \rho}{\partial t} = \varepsilon_0 \vec{\nabla} . \frac{\partial \vec{E}}{\partial t}$$

Substituting this value of $\frac{\partial \rho}{\partial t}$ in continuity equation

$$\vec{\nabla} . \vec{J} + \frac{\partial \rho}{\partial t} = 0$$

We have

$$\vec{\nabla} . \vec{J} + \varepsilon_0 \, \vec{\nabla} . \frac{\partial \vec{E}}{\partial t} = 0$$

or

$$\vec{\nabla} . \left(\vec{J} + \varepsilon_0 \, \frac{\partial \vec{E}}{\partial t} \right) = 0$$

Thus for varying curents $\vec{\nabla} . \vec{J}$ is not equal to zero, but it is

$$\vec{\nabla} . \left(\vec{J} + \varepsilon_0 \, \frac{\partial \vec{E}}{\partial t} \right) = 0$$

Maxwell, therefore, replaced $\vec{J}$ in differential form of Ampere's law by $\vec{J} + \varepsilon_0 \, \frac{\partial \vec{E}}{\partial t}$ and stated it as

$$Curl \, \vec{B} = \vec{\nabla} \times \vec{B} = \mu_0 \left[\vec{J} + \varepsilon_0 \, \frac{\partial \vec{E}}{\partial t} \right] \qquad ...(v)(a)$$

The quantity $\varepsilon_0 \, \frac{\partial \vec{E}}{\partial t} = \frac{\partial \vec{D}}{\partial t}$ where $\vec{D}$ is the *electric displacement field vector*, is known as *vacuum displacement current density.* It has dimensions of current per unit area and is denoted by J_d to distinguish it from *conduction current density* $\vec{J}$.

$$\therefore \qquad \vec{\nabla} \times \vec{B} = \mu_0 \left[\vec{J} + \vec{J}_d \right] \qquad ...(vi)$$

Special case. In empty space where there are no currents

$$\vec{J} = 0$$

and equation (vi) becomes

$$\vec{\nabla} \times \vec{B} = \mu_0\, J_d = \mu_0\, \varepsilon_0\, \frac{\partial \vec{E}}{\partial t}$$

The term $\dfrac{\partial \vec{E}}{\partial t}$ is the rate at which electric field is changing between the plates of the capacitor. This equation shows that a varying electric field between the capacitor plates gives rise to a magnetic field. Hence varying electric field is also a source of magnetic field.

Dimensions of $\dfrac{\partial \vec{D}}{\partial t}$ $\dfrac{\partial \vec{D}}{\partial t} = \varepsilon_0\, \dfrac{\partial \vec{E}}{\partial t}$

The dimensions of ε_0 are Coulomb^2 / Newton m^2 = $[C^2\, N^{-1}\, m^{-2}]$

The dimensions of E are Newton/Coulomb = $[NC^{-1}]$

$\therefore$ Dimensions of $D = \varepsilon_0\, E$ are $[C^2\, N^{-1} m^{-2}]\,[N\, C^{-1}] = [Cm^{-2}]$

and   dimensions of $\dfrac{\partial D}{\partial t} = [Cm^{-2}]\,[S^{-1}] = [CS^{-1}\, m^{-2}] = \text{Amp} / m^2$

= Dimensions of current per unit area or current density

Displacement current density. When a capacitor is charged, there exists an electric field between the plates of the capacitor. In a parallel plate capacitor the magnitude of the electric field $\vec{E}$ is given by

$$E = \frac{\sigma}{\varepsilon_0} = \frac{1}{\varepsilon_0}\frac{q}{A}$$

where σ is the surface charge density, q is the charge on the plates and A its area. When the plates of the capacitor are connected through a resistance, the charge slowly flows from the positive to the negative plate in the outside circuit and the current i is given by

$$i = \frac{dq}{dt} = \varepsilon_0\, A\, \frac{dE}{dt}$$

or vacuum displacement current density $J_d = \dfrac{i}{A} = \varepsilon_0\, \dfrac{dE}{dt}$ ...(vii)

Displacement current is not fictitious. From Eq. (vii), we find that when the plates of a capacitor are connected through a high resistance, a current i flows from positive to the negative plate giving rise to a displacement current density J_d. A magnetic compass or a device to detect the magnetic field, placed near the leads will show the presence of the magnetic field. If sufficiently delicate experiment is performed it will be observed that a magnetic field is also set up in the region between the capacitor plates due to the changing electric field although no conduction current is flowing. Thus a changing electric field gives rise to a current known as displacement current. The displacement current is not involved in the actual transport of charge. The concept of displacement current is *real* and necessary as current is continuous. The conduction current is itself not continuous across the capacitor gap as no charge is transported across the gap. The continuity is maintained by the displacement current i_d which is exactly equal to the conduction current.

Q. 10.53. Define displacement current and derive an expression for it.

(*Pbi. U.,* 2002; *G.N.D.U.,* 2004; *Meerut U.,* 2003)

Ans. Displacement current. The vacuum displacement current density $\vec{J_d}$ is given by

$$\vec{J_d} = \varepsilon_0 \frac{\partial \vec{E}}{\partial t}$$

The displacement current through any surface area $\vec{S}$ is defined as

$$I_d = \iint\limits_S \vec{J_d}.d\vec{s} = \iint\limits_S \varepsilon_0 \frac{\partial \vec{E}}{\partial t}.d\vec{s} = \varepsilon_0 \iint\limits_S \frac{\partial \vec{E}}{\partial t}.d\vec{s}$$

where $d\vec{s}$ is a small area element on which electric field is $\vec{E}$.

$$\therefore \qquad I_d = \varepsilon_0 \frac{\partial}{\partial t} \iint\limits_S \vec{E}.d\vec{s} = \varepsilon_0 \frac{d\phi}{dt}$$

since $\iint\limits_S \vec{E}.ds = \phi$ the total electric flux through the surface S.

Hence displacement current $I_d = \varepsilon_0 \dfrac{d\phi}{dt}$. ..(i)

Q. 10.54. Show that Ampere's law for varying currents may be written as

$$\oint\limits_C \vec{B}.\vec{dl} = \mu_0 I + \mu_0 \varepsilon_0 \frac{d\phi}{dt}.$$

(*G.N.D.U.*, 2002)

Ans. The differential form of Ampere's law for varying currents is given by

$$\vec{\nabla} \times \vec{B} = \mu_0 \vec{J} + \mu_0 \varepsilon_0 \frac{\partial \vec{E}}{\partial t}$$

[For proof See **Q. 10.52** Eq. (*v*) (*a*)]

Taking the dot product of both sides with $d\vec{s}$ where $d\vec{s}$ is a small area element, we have

$$\vec{\nabla} \times \vec{B}.d\vec{s} = \mu_0 \vec{J}.d\vec{s} + \mu_0 \varepsilon_0 \frac{\partial \vec{E}}{\partial t}.d\vec{s}$$

Integrating both sides over the open surface S of which C is the boundary, we get

$$\iint\limits_S \vec{\nabla} \times \vec{B}.d\vec{s} = \iint\limits_S \mu_0 \vec{J}.d\vec{s} + \iint\limits_S \mu_0 \varepsilon_0 \frac{\partial \vec{E}}{\partial t}.d\vec{s} \qquad ...(i)$$

But $\iint\limits_S \mu_0 \vec{J}.d\vec{s} = \mu_0 I$ because $\iint\limits_S \vec{J}.d\vec{s} = I$

Applying Stokes theorem to left hand side of Eq. (*i*), we get

$$\iint\limits_S \vec{\nabla} \times \vec{B}.d\vec{s} = \oint\limits_C \vec{B}.\vec{dl}$$

Eq. (*i*), can now be put in the form

$$\oint\limits_C \vec{B}.\vec{dl} = \mu_0 I + \mu_0 \varepsilon_0 \iint\limits_S \frac{\partial \vec{E}}{\partial t}.d\vec{s}$$

$$= \mu_0 I + \mu_0 \varepsilon_0 \frac{\partial}{\partial t} \iint\limits_S \vec{E}.d\vec{s}$$

$$= \mu_0 I + \mu_0 \varepsilon_0 \frac{d\phi}{dt}$$

where $\phi = \iint\limits_S \vec{E}.d\vec{s}$ is the electric flux over the whole surface S of which C is the boundary.

Q. 10.55. Distinguish between conduction and displacement current.   (*G.N.D.U., 2003*)

Ans. Conduction current. Conduction current obeys ohm's law which in vector form is given by

$$\vec{J} = \sigma \vec{E}$$

where $\vec{J}$ is the conduction current density and $\vec{E}$ is the electric field.

A steady electric field thus gives rise to conduction current. The conduction current is involved in the actual flow of charge.

The equation of continuity for conduction current is given by $\vec{\nabla}.\vec{J} + \frac{\partial \rho}{\partial t} = 0$ where $\frac{\partial \rho}{\partial t}$ is the

time rate of change of volume charge density. For steady conduction current $\frac{\partial \rho}{\partial t} = 0$ and $\vec{\nabla}.\vec{J} = 0$.

Displacement current. Vacuum displacement current density is given by

$$\vec{J}_D = \varepsilon_0 \frac{\partial \vec{E}}{\partial t}$$

and   displacement current $I_d = \varepsilon_0 \frac{d\phi}{dt}$

where $\phi = \iint\limits_S \vec{E}.d\vec{s}$ is the total electric flux through the surface S.

Thus, a changing electric flux gives rise to displacement current. The displacement current is not involved in the actual transport of charge. The equation of continuity combining both conduction and displacement current densities is given by

$$\vec{\nabla}.\left(\vec{J} + \varepsilon_0 \frac{\partial \vec{E}}{\partial t} \right) = 0.$$

Q. 10.56. A conducting wire carries an alternating current given by $I = I_0 \sin \omega t$, calculate the displacement current in the wire.   (*G. N.D.U., 2003; P.U., 2003*)

Ans. The displacement current is given by

$$I_d = \varepsilon_0 \frac{d\phi}{dt} \qquad \text{...(}i\text{) [For proof see Eq. (}i\text{) Q. 10.53]}$$

where $\phi = \iint\limits_S \vec{E}.d\vec{s}$ ...(*ii*)

Assuming that the conducting wire obeys Ohm's law which in the vector form is given by

$$\vec{J} = \sigma \vec{E}$$

where σ is the conductivity of the wire, we have

$$\vec{E} = \frac{\vec{J}}{\sigma}$$

Substituting this value of $\vec{E}$ in Eq (ii), we get

$$\phi = \iint_S \frac{\vec{J}.\vec{ds}}{\sigma} = \frac{1}{\sigma}\iint_S \vec{J}.\vec{ds} = \frac{I}{\sigma}$$

as $\qquad \iint_S \vec{J}.\vec{ds} = I$

The alternating current is given by $I = I_0 \sin \omega t$

$$\therefore \qquad \phi = \frac{I}{\sigma} = \frac{I_0 \sin \omega t}{\sigma}$$

Substituting this value of ϕ in Eq. (i), we have

$$I_d = \varepsilon_0 \frac{d}{dt}\left[\frac{I_0 \sin \omega t}{\sigma}\right]$$

or displacement current $\qquad I_d = \frac{\varepsilon_0 I_0 \omega}{\sigma}\cos\omega t$

Q. 10.57. State Maxwell's equations for electro-magnetic field. Discuss each equation critically. *(Meerut U., 2003, 2001, 2000, 1994; Pbi. U., 2001, 2000, 1993; G.N.D.U., 2001, 1993; K.U., 2000; P.U., 1991)*

Note. *In order to meet the needs of readers using the C.G.S. (Gaussian) system and S.I. Units, we shall state these equations in both these systems for a dielectric medium as well as for free space. Students are advised to select only the relevant equations in accordance with the question.*

Ans. Maxwell's equations. The static electric charges produce electric fields, but moving charges also produce magnetic fields in addition to the electric fields. Whenever electric field at a point varies with respect to time a magnetic induction field is produced and similarly whenever a magnetic field at a point varies with respect to time an electric field (or *e.m.f.*) is produced.

The electro magnetic theory can be developed with the help of four vector differential relations based on the above phenomena and known as Maxwell's equations. Two of the relations are independent of time and are known as *steady state equations*. The other two relations depend upon time and are, therefore, known as *time varying equations*.

Steady state equations

(1) Maxwell's *first steady state* equation is given by

(C.G.S.)

$$div.\vec{D} = \vec{\nabla}.\vec{D} = 4\pi\rho$$

(S.I.)

$$div.\vec{D} = \vec{\nabla}.\vec{D} = \rho$$

where $\vec{D}$ is the electric displacement and ρ the volume charge density.

(C.G.S.)

Now $\vec{D} = \varepsilon\vec{E}$ for an isotropic linear medium where ε is the dielectric constant or permittivity of the medium.

For vacuum $\varepsilon = 1$

∴ For vacuum or free space

$$\vec{D} = \vec{E}$$

(S.I.)

Now $\vec{D} = \varepsilon_0\vec{E}$ for free space or vacuum where ε_0 is the permittivity of free space and $\vec{D} = \varepsilon\vec{E}$ for any isotropic linear medium where ε is the permittivity of the medium.

Hence for any medium.

$$\vec{\nabla}.\vec{D} = \vec{\nabla}.\varepsilon\vec{E} = \varepsilon\vec{\nabla}.\vec{E} = \rho$$

Hence for any medium

$$\vec{\nabla}.\vec{D} = \vec{\nabla}.\varepsilon\vec{E} = \varepsilon\vec{\nabla}.\vec{E} = 4\pi\rho$$

and for vacuum

$$\vec{\nabla}.\vec{E} = 4\pi\rho.$$

and for vacuum or free space

$$\vec{\nabla}.\vec{D} = \vec{\nabla}.\varepsilon_0\vec{E} = \varepsilon_0\vec{\nabla}.\vec{E} = \rho$$

or $$\vec{\nabla}.\vec{E} = \frac{\rho}{\varepsilon_0}$$

(2) Maxwell's *second steady state* equation is given by

(C.G.S.)

$$div.\vec{B} = \vec{\nabla}.\vec{B} = 0 \text{ where } \vec{B} \text{ is the magnetic}$$
induction field.

Now $\vec{B} = \mu\vec{H}$ where μ is the permeability
of the medium and $\vec{H}$ the magnetic field vector.

For vacuum $\mu = 1$ and hence

$$\vec{B} = \vec{H}$$

∴ For any medium

$$\vec{\nabla}.\vec{B} = \vec{\nabla}.\mu\vec{H} = \mu\vec{\nabla}.\vec{H} = 0$$

or $$\vec{\nabla}.\vec{H} = 0$$

and for vacuum

$$\vec{\nabla}.\vec{B} = \vec{\nabla}.\vec{H} = 0$$

(S.I.)

$$div.\vec{B} = \vec{\nabla}.\vec{B} = 0$$

Now $\vec{B} = \mu\vec{H}$ where μ is the permeability of the medium. For vacuum $\mu = \mu_0$
and hence $\vec{B} = \mu_0\vec{H}$

∴ For any medium

$$\vec{\nabla}.\vec{B} = \vec{\nabla}.\mu\vec{H} = \mu\vec{\nabla}.\vec{H} = 0$$

or $$\vec{\nabla}.\vec{H} = 0$$

and for vacuum or free space

$$\vec{\nabla}.\vec{B} = \vec{\nabla}.\mu_0\vec{H} = \mu_0\vec{\nabla}.\vec{H} = 0$$

or $$\vec{\nabla}.\vec{H} = 0$$

Time varying equations (1) Maxwells *first time varying* equation is given by

(C.G.S.)

$$Curl\ \vec{E} = \vec{\nabla} \times \vec{E} = -\frac{1}{c}\frac{\partial\vec{B}}{\partial t}$$

For any isotropic linear magnetic medium of
permeability μ

$$\vec{\nabla} \times \vec{E} = -\frac{1}{c}\frac{\partial\vec{B}}{\partial t} = -\frac{\mu}{c}\frac{\partial\vec{H}}{\partial t}$$

and for vacuum $\mu = 1$

$$\vec{\nabla} \times \vec{E} = -\frac{1}{c}\frac{\partial\vec{B}}{\partial t} = -\frac{1}{c}\frac{\partial\vec{H}}{\partial t}$$

(S.I.)

$$Curl\ \vec{E} = \vec{\nabla} \times \vec{E} = -\frac{\partial\vec{B}}{\partial t}$$

For any isotropic linear magnetic medium of permeability μ

$$\vec{\nabla} \times \vec{E} = -\frac{\partial\vec{B}}{\partial t} = -\mu\frac{\partial\vec{H}}{\partial t}$$

and for vacuum $\mu = \mu_0$

$$\vec{\nabla} \times \vec{E} = -\frac{\partial\vec{B}}{\partial t} = -\mu_0\frac{\partial\vec{H}}{\partial t}$$

(2) Maxwell's *second time varying* equation is given by

(C.G.S.)

$$Curl\ \vec{H} = \vec{\nabla} \times \vec{H} = \frac{4\pi}{c}\vec{J} + \frac{1}{c}\frac{\partial\vec{D}}{\partial t}$$

where $\vec{J}$ is the current density. For any isotropic linear medium

$$\mu\vec{\nabla} \times \vec{H} = \vec{\nabla} \times \mu\vec{H} = \vec{\nabla} \times \vec{B}$$

(S.I.)

$$Curl\ \vec{H} = \vec{\nabla} \times \vec{H} = \vec{J} + \frac{\partial\vec{D}}{\partial t}$$

where $\vec{J}$ is the current density vector. For any isotropic linear medium

$$\mu\vec{\nabla} \times \vec{H} = \vec{\nabla} \times \mu\vec{H} = \vec{\nabla} \times \vec{B}$$

$$\therefore \ \vec{\nabla} \times \vec{B} = \mu \left[\frac{4\pi}{c} \vec{J} + \frac{\varepsilon}{c} \frac{\partial \vec{E}}{\partial t} \right]$$

For vacuum $\mu = 1$, $\varepsilon = 1$

$$\therefore \ \vec{\nabla} \times \vec{H} = \frac{4\pi}{c} \vec{J} + \frac{1}{c} \frac{\partial \vec{E}}{\partial t}$$

For vacuum, if $\rho = 0$ and $\vec{J} = 0$, we have these equations as

$$\therefore \ \vec{\nabla} \times \vec{B} = \mu \left[\vec{J} + \varepsilon \frac{\partial \vec{E}}{\partial t} \right]$$

and for vacuum $\mu = \mu_0$; $\varepsilon = \varepsilon_0$

$$\vec{\nabla} \times \mu_0 \vec{H} = \mu_0 \left[\vec{J} + \varepsilon_0 \frac{\partial \vec{E}}{\partial t} \right]$$

or $\vec{\nabla} \times \vec{H} = \vec{J} + \varepsilon_0 \dfrac{\partial \vec{E}}{\partial t}$

(C.G.S.)	(S.I.)
(i) $\vec{\nabla} \cdot \vec{E} = 0$	(i) $\vec{\nabla} \cdot \vec{E} = 0$
(ii) $\vec{\nabla} \cdot \vec{B} = 0$	(ii) $\vec{\nabla} \cdot \vec{B} = 0$
(iii) $\vec{\nabla} \times \vec{E} = -\dfrac{1}{c} \dfrac{\partial \vec{H}}{\partial t}$	(iii) $\vec{\nabla} \times \vec{E} = -\dfrac{\partial \vec{B}}{\partial t} = -\mu_0 \dfrac{\partial \vec{H}}{\partial t}$
(iv) $\vec{\nabla} \times \vec{H} = \dfrac{1}{c} \dfrac{\partial \vec{E}}{\partial t}$	(iv) $\vec{\nabla} \times \vec{H} = \varepsilon_0 \dfrac{\partial \vec{E}}{\partial t} = \dfrac{\partial \vec{D}}{\partial t}$

For further details see chapter on **Electromagnetic waves** in the **Waves, vibration and E.M. Theory,** which forms **Section II** of this book

Q. 10.58. Give the physical significance of Maxwell's equations.

(*K.U., 2000; Pbi. U., 2003, 2000; P.U., 1995; G.N.D.U., 1994; Meerut U., 1994*)

Ans. Physical significance of Maxwell's equations. (1) Maxwell's **first** steady state equation gives $\vec{\nabla} \cdot \vec{D} = \rho$.

The physical significance of this equation is

(*i*) It is a steady state equation independent of time.

(*ii*) According to this equation the flux lines of electric force depend upon charge density ρ.

(*iii*) As $\rho = \vec{\nabla} \cdot \vec{D}$, it signifies that ρ the charge density is a scalar quantity.

(*iv*) The *positive* charge acts as a *source* and *negative* charge as a *sink* for electric lines of force.

2. Maxwell's **second** steady state equation gives $\vec{\nabla} \cdot \vec{B} = 0$.

The physical significance of this equation is

(*i*) It is steady state equation independent of time.

(*ii*) According to this equation '*isolated magnetic poles do not exist.*'

(*iii*) As $\vec{\nabla} \cdot \vec{B} = 0$, equal number of lines of magnetic force enter and leave a given volume.

(*iv*) Lines of magnetic force are endless *i.e.*, there is no source or sink for lines of magnetic force.

(3) Maxwell's **first** time varying equation is $\vec{\nabla} \times \vec{E} = -\dfrac{\partial \vec{E}}{\partial t}$.

The physical significance of this equation is

(*i*) It is a time dependent equation varying with time.

(*ii*) It relates the space variation of $\vec{E}$ with time variation of $\vec{B}$.

(*iii*) It gives the relation between electric field vector $\vec{E}$ and magnetic field vector $\vec{B}$.

(*iv*) It is statement of Faraday's and Lenz's law of electromagnetic induction.

(4) Maxwell's **second** time varying equation is $\vec{\nabla} \times \vec{B} = \mu_0 \left[\vec{J} + \varepsilon_0 \dfrac{\partial \vec{E}}{\partial t} \right] = \mu_0 \left[\vec{J} + \dfrac{\partial \vec{D}}{\partial t} \right]$.

The physical significance of this equation is

(*i*) It is time dependent equation and relates the space variation of $\vec{B}$ with time variation of $\vec{D}$ or $\vec{E}$.

(*ii*) It relates the magnetic field vector $\vec{B}$ with electric displacement vector $\vec{D}$ and current density vector $\vec{J}$.

(*iii*) It is a statement of Ampere's law.

(*iv*) According to this equation magnetic field vector $\vec{B}$ can be generated by current density vector $\vec{J}$ and time variation of $\vec{D}$ (or $\vec{E}$) jointly as well as separately.

Q.10.59. Write down Maxwell's equations. What is the Physics associated with them?

(G.N.D.U., 2002, 1991; P.U., 1991)

Ans. Maxwell's equations. See Q. 10.57.

All the phenomenon in electricity and magnetism are governed by the four Maxwell's equation which represent the laws of physics noted against each. The equations for vacuum are

(*i*) $\vec{\nabla} . \vec{E} = \dfrac{\rho}{\varepsilon_0}$

This equation represents the differential form of Gauss's law in electrostatics.

(*ii*) $\vec{\nabla} . \vec{B} = 0$

This equation represents the differential form of Gauss's law in magnetism.

(*iii*) $\vec{\nabla} \times \vec{E} = -\dfrac{\partial \vec{B}}{\partial t}$

This equation represents the differential form of Faraday's law of electromagnetic induction.

(*iv*) $\vec{\nabla} \times \vec{B} = \mu_0 \left[\vec{J} + \varepsilon_0 \dfrac{\partial \vec{E}}{\partial t} \right]$

This equation represents the differential form of Ampere's law for steady as well as varying currents.

Q.10.60. (*a*) **Prove that** $\vec{E} = \cos(y - t)\,\hat{k},\ \vec{B} = \cos(y - t)\,\hat{i}$ **constitute a possible electromagnetic field.**

(P.U., 2006, G.N.D.U., 2001)

**(b) Show that the following constitute a possible electromagnetic field $\vec{E} = \cos(x - ct)\,\hat{j}$;
$\vec{B} = \cos(x - ct)\,\hat{k}$;**   (*P.U.*, 2005)

Ans. (*a*) $\vec{\nabla} \times \vec{E} = \vec{\nabla} \times \cos(y - t)\,\hat{k}$

$$= \left(\frac{\partial}{\partial x}\,\hat{i} + \frac{\partial}{\partial y}\,\hat{j} + \frac{\partial}{\partial z}\,\hat{k} \right) \times [\cos(y - t)\,\hat{k}]$$

$$= \begin{vmatrix} \hat{i} & \hat{j} & \hat{k} \\ \dfrac{\partial}{\partial x} & \dfrac{\partial}{\partial y} & \dfrac{\partial}{\partial z} \\ 0 & 0 & \cos(y - t) \end{vmatrix}$$

$$= \hat{i}\,\frac{\partial}{\partial y}\cos(y - t) - \hat{j}\,\frac{\partial}{\partial x}(\cos y - t)$$

$$= -\sin(y - t)\,\hat{i}$$

Also $$\frac{\partial \vec{B}}{\partial t} = \frac{\partial}{\partial t}(\cos y - t)\,\hat{i} = \sin(y - t)\,\hat{i}$$

Hence $$\vec{\nabla} \times E = -\frac{\partial \vec{B}}{\partial t}$$

The field, therefore, satisfies Maxwell's first time varying equation and hence constitutes a possible electromagnetic field.

(*b*) $$\vec{\nabla} \times \vec{E} = \vec{\nabla} \times \cos(x - ct)\,\hat{j}$$

$$= \begin{vmatrix} \hat{i} & \hat{j} & \hat{k} \\ \dfrac{\partial}{\partial x} & \dfrac{\partial}{\partial y} & \dfrac{\partial}{\partial z} \\ 0 & \cos(x - ct) & 0 \end{vmatrix}$$

$$= \hat{i}\left[0 - \frac{\partial}{\partial z}(x - ct)\right] + \hat{j}\,[0 - 0] + \hat{k}\left[\frac{\partial}{\partial x}\cos(x - ct) - 0\right]$$

$$= \hat{k}\left[\frac{\partial}{\partial x}\cos(x - ct)\right] = -\hat{k}\sin(x - ct)$$

$$\frac{\partial \vec{B}}{\partial t} = \frac{\partial}{\partial t}\cos(x - ct)\,\hat{k} = c\sin(x - ct)\,\hat{k}$$

$\therefore$ $$\vec{\nabla} \times \vec{E} = -\frac{1}{c}\frac{\partial B}{\partial t}$$

Thus Maxwell's first time varying equation in C.G.S. units for vacuum is satisfied.

Therefore the given equations constitute a possible electro-magnetic field.

NOTE. For a more detailed treatment of '*Maxwell's Equations for Electromagnetic field*' see **chapter 8** '*Electromagnetic Waves*' in section **II** '*Waves' Vibrations and E.M. Theory*' of this book.

Q.10.61. Mark the correct answer.

(*i*) The direction of induced *e.m.f.* in a circuit is given by

(*a*) Faraday's law   (*b*) Fleming's left hand rule

(*c*) Lenz's law   (*d*) none of these   (*H.P.U., 1996*)

(*ii*) A cylindrical bar magnet is kept along the axis of a circular coil. On rotating the magnet about its axis the coil will have induced in it

(*a*) Alternating current   (*b*) direct current

(*c*) no current   (*d*) only *e.m.f.*   (*P.U., 1994*)

(*iii*) Which of the following does not have dimensions of time?

(*a*) CR (*b*) $\dfrac{L}{R}$

(*c*) $\sqrt{LC}$ (*d*) LC (*P.U., 1994*)

(*iv*) The dimentions of inductance are

(*a*) $\mu_0^{-1}\, L^{-1}\, T^{-2}$ (*b*) $\mu_0\, LT^{-1}$

(*c*) $\mu_0\, L$ (*d*) $\mu_0^{1/2}\, M^{1/2}\, L^{3/2}\, T^{-2}$ (*P.U., 1994*)

(*v*) In which of the following cases is mutual inductance maximum?   (*Pbi. U., 1991*)

(*vi*) The displacement current through a circuit is given by

(*a*) $\varepsilon_0\, \dfrac{\partial \vec{E}}{\partial t}$ (*b*) $\mu_0\, \varepsilon_0\, \dfrac{\partial \vec{E}}{\partial t}$

(*c*) $\varepsilon_0\, \dfrac{\partial \phi}{\partial t}$ (*d*) $\mu_0 \varepsilon_0\, \dfrac{\partial \phi}{\partial t}$ (*H.P.U., 1993*)

(*vii*) An electromagnetic field satisfies

(*a*) Gauss law   (*b*) Faraday's law

(*c*) Ampere's law   (*d*) All of them

(*viii*) A magnet is moved towards a coil (*x*) quickly (*y*) slowly, then the induced *e.m.f.* is

(*a*) larger in case (*x*)   (*b*) smaller in case (*x*)

(*c*) equal in both the cases   (*d*) Larger or smaller depending upon the radius of the coil.   (*H.P.U., 1997*)

(*ix*) The displacement current is due to

(*a*) variation of magnetic field   (*b*) variation of electric field

(*c*) flow of steady current   (*d*) Magnetic flux linked with the circuit.

                                                      (*H.P.U., 2002, 1999*)

(*x*) The equation $\vec{\nabla} \times \vec{E} = -\dfrac{\partial \vec{B}}{\partial t}$ represents

    (*a*) Gauss's law   (*b*) Coulomb's law

    (*c*) Ampere's law   (*d*) Faraday's law   (*H.P.U.*, *2003, 2002*)

Ans.   (*i*) *c*   (*ii*) *c*   (*iii*) *d*   (*iv*) *c*

            (*v*) *c*   (*vi*) *a*   (*vii*) *d*   (*viii*) *a*

           (*ix*) *b*   (*x*) *d*

EXERCISES

1. Show that the discharge of a capacitor through the inductive circuit is oscillatroy when there is a capacitance of 10^{-6} μ*f*, inductance 0.0125 henry and resistance 100 ohms.

    Ans. $\dfrac{R^2}{4L^2} = 16 \times 10^6$; $\dfrac{1}{LC} = 8 \times 10^{13}$; $\dfrac{R^2}{4L^2} < \dfrac{1}{LC}$ The discharge is oscillatory.

2. A coil has 600 turns and a self inductance of 100 mH. What will be self inductance of a similar coil with 500 turns?

    Hint. $L = \dfrac{\mu_0 n^2 a}{l}$ ∴ $\dfrac{L_1}{L_2} = \dfrac{500^2}{600^2}$ or $L_2 = 100 \times \dfrac{500^2}{600^2} = 69.4$ mH.

3. A capacitor is charged to a certain potential by a battery through a resistance of 3 mega ohm. If it reaches 2/3 of its final potential in 0.6 sec; calculate its capacitance.   (*A.U.*, *1992*)

                                                             [Ans. 0.18 microfarad.]

11

Alternating Currents

[**Note 1.** In earlier chapters we have used E to denote Electric field. In this chapter we shall use E to denote alternating *e.m.f.* or voltage.

2. We shall use j to denote the imaginary quantity $\sqrt{-1}$ as in this chapter we shall use i to denote instantaneous value of current.]

Q. 11.1. (*a*) **Distinguish between the mean value and root mean square value of an alternating current. Deduce expressions for the true mean value and the root mean square value of an alternating current represented by the equation** $i = I_0 \sin \omega t$. (*Meerut U.* 2003, 2002, 2001)

(*b*) **Calculate the time required by an A.C. of frequency 50 Hz to reach the value** $\dfrac{1}{\sqrt{2}}$ **of its peak value.** (*Gauhati U.* 2000)

Ans. (*a*) **Mean value of alternating current.** *It is that steady current which sends the same charge through a circuit in the same time as the alternating current does in half its time period.*

Root mean square value of an alternating current. *It is that steady current which produces the same heating effect in a resistance in a given time as the alternating current does in the same resistance in the same time.*

The strength of an alternating current is not constant. To find the heating effect we take a large number of instantaneous values for a half cycle of *A.C.*, square them, find their mean and then take the square root. Hence the name root mean square (*r.m.s.*) value. It is also known as the *virtual value* or the *effective value* of an alternating current.

Expression for mean value. The alternating current is represented by

$$i = I_0 \sin \omega t$$

where i is the instantaneous value of the current at a time t, I_0 the maximum value and $\omega = 2\pi n$, n being the frequency of the alternating current. Suppose the value of the current remains constant for a very small time dt, then

Charge passing in time $dt = i \, dt$

Hence charge passing in time T

$$= \int_0^T i \, dt = \int_0^T I_0 \sin \omega t \, dt$$

where T is half the time period of the alternating current.

If I denotes the mean value of the current, the charge passing in time T

$$= IT$$

or

$$IT = \int_0^T I_0 \sin \omega t \; dt$$

or Mean value of current $I = \dfrac{I_0}{\omega T}[-\cos \omega t]_0^T = \dfrac{I_0}{\pi}[1 - (-1)] = \dfrac{2I_0}{\pi}$ $[\because \omega T = \pi]$

Therefore *the average or mean value of an alternating current is* $\dfrac{2}{\pi}$ or 0.637 times the maximum value of the current. It should be noted that the mean value for a complete cycle is zero as the current changes direction after half the period.

Expression for root mean square (r.m.s.) value. Let an alternating current given by $i = I_0 \sin \omega t$ flow through a resistance of one ohm.

Heat produced in time $dt = i^2 \; dt$

$\therefore$ Heat produced in time T

$$= \int_0^T i^2 \; dt = \int_0^T I_0^2 \sin^2 \omega t \; dt$$

where T is half the time period of the alternating current.

If I_v is the **root mean square** (or virtual) value of the $A.C.$, then heating effect in a resistance of one ohm in T seconds.

$$\therefore \quad I_v^2 T = \int_0^T I_0^2 \sin^2 \omega t \; dt = I_0^2 \int_0^T \frac{1 - \cos 2\omega t}{2} dt$$

$$= \frac{I_0^2}{2}\left[\int_0^T dt - \int_0^T \cos 2 \; \omega t \; dt \right] \qquad \left[\because \int_0^T \cos 2\omega t \; dt = 0 \right]$$

$$= \frac{I_0^2 T}{2}$$

$$\therefore \qquad I_v^2 = \frac{I_0^2}{2}$$

or

$$I_v = \frac{I_0}{\sqrt{2}} = 0.707 \; I_0$$

Hence the *root mean square value* of the current is $\dfrac{1}{\sqrt{2}}$ or 0.707 times the maximum value of the current.

(b) Here $i = \dfrac{I_0}{\sqrt{2}};$ $\omega = 2\pi n = 2\pi \times 50 = 100 \; \pi$

Now $i = I_0 \sin \omega t$

$$\therefore \qquad \frac{I_0}{\sqrt{2}} = I_0 \sin 100 \pi t \quad \text{or} \quad \sin 100 \; \pi t = \frac{1}{\sqrt{2}}$$

$$\therefore \qquad 100 \pi t = \frac{\pi}{4} \qquad\qquad\qquad \left[\because \sin \frac{\pi}{4} = \frac{1}{\sqrt{2}} \right]$$

or

$$t = \frac{1}{400} \; \text{sec}$$

Q. 11.2. (*a*) **Obtain an expression between current and voltage in an alternating current circuit consisting of resistance** R **and inductance** L**. Show that current lags behind voltage by** $\tan^{-1}\dfrac{L\omega}{R}$.

(M.D.U. 2001; K.U. 2001; Luck.U. 1996, 1995, 1993)

(*b*) **Define and explain reactance and impedance of an alternating current circuit.**

(K.U., 1991)

Ans. (*a*) **A.C. circuit with resistance and inductance.** Consider an *A.C.* circuit having non-inductive resistance R and an inductance (without resistance) L. Let the alternating current at any instant be represented by $i = I_0 \sin \omega t$ where i is the instantaneous value of the current at a time t, I_0 the maximum value and $\omega = 2\pi n$, n being the frequency of the alternating current.

The potential difference across the resistance $R = Ri$.

As the current is varying at a rate $\dfrac{di}{dt}$ a back *e.m.f.* $e = -L\dfrac{di}{dt}$ is induced in the inductance. The applied *e.m.f.* E must produce a potential difference Ri across the resistance and should overcome the back *e.m.f.* $-L\dfrac{di}{dt}$ due to the inductance. Hence

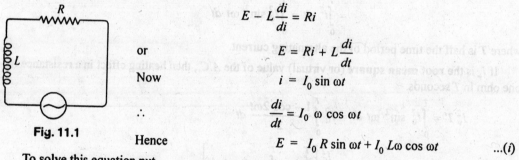

$$E - L\frac{di}{di} = Ri$$

or

$$E = Ri + L\frac{di}{dt}$$

Now

$$i = I_0 \sin \omega t$$

$$\therefore \quad \frac{di}{dt} = I_0\, \omega \cos \omega t$$

Hence

$$E = I_0\, R \sin \omega t + I_0\, L\omega \cos \omega t \qquad \qquad ...(i)$$

Fig. 11.1

To solve this equation put

$$R = a \cos \phi \text{ and } L\omega = a \sin \phi$$

$$\therefore \qquad a = \sqrt{R^2 + L^2 \omega^2}$$

and

$$\tan \phi = \frac{L\omega}{R}$$

Substituting the values of R and $L\omega$ in (*i*), we have

$$E = I_0\, (a \cos \phi \sin \omega t + a \sin \phi \cos \omega t)$$

or

$$E = I_0\, (a \sin (\omega t + \phi) = I_0 \sqrt{R^2 + L^2 \omega^2}\, \sin (\omega t + \phi)$$

$$= E_0 \sin (\omega t + \phi) \qquad \qquad ...(ii)$$

where $E_0 = I_0 \sqrt{R^2 + L^2\omega^2}$ and represents the maximum value of the *e.m.f.* when $\sin (\omega t + \phi) = 1$.

Current lags e.m.f. It is clear from Eq. (*ii*) that *e.m.f.* and current differ in phase by an angle

$$\phi = \tan^{-1}\left(\frac{L\omega}{R}\right).$$

When the current is represented by $I = I_0 \sin \omega t$, the *e.m.f.* is given by $E = E_0 \sin (\omega t + \phi)$. If we start with the relation $E = E_0 \sin \omega t$, then current is given by $I = I_0 \sin (\omega t - \phi)$ *i.e.*, the current lags the *e.m.f.* by a phase angle $\phi = \tan^{-1}\dfrac{L\omega}{R}$.

The current is shown by a full line curve in Fig. 11.2 (a) and the potential difference in the circuit is shown by the dotted curve. The current curve crosses the axis at A after attaining a maximum value in the positive direction and the e.m.f. curve crosses at B after attaining the maximum positive value. The angle between AB gives the value by which the current lags behind the e.m.f. and is known as **Phase lag**. If the circuit contains a pure inductance having no resistance, then

$$\tan \phi = \infty$$

and the angle of lag will be equal to 90°.

The e.m.f. leads the current or in other words, the *current lags*.

If the e.m.f. is represented by the relation

$$e = E_0 \sin \omega t$$

the current is given by the relation

$$\therefore \qquad i = I_0 \sin (\omega t - \phi)$$

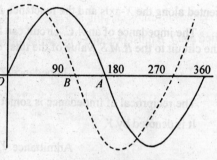

Fig. 11.2 (a)

$$\therefore \qquad E_0 = I_0 \sqrt{R^2 + L^2 \omega^2}$$

$$\text{or} \qquad I_0 = \frac{E_0}{\sqrt{R^2 + L^2 \omega^2}}$$

Multiplying both sides by $\frac{1}{\sqrt{2}}$, we have

$$\frac{I_0}{\sqrt{2}} = \frac{E_0 / \sqrt{2}}{\sqrt{R^2 + L^2 \omega^2}}$$

$$\text{or} \qquad I_v = \frac{E_v}{\sqrt{R^2 + L^2 \omega^2}} = \frac{E_v}{Z}$$

where I_v and E_v represent the root mean square or virtual values of the current and voltage respectively and Z is known as the **impedance** or effectively resistance of the A.C. circuit.

(b) **Inductive Reactance.** An inductance offers no resistance in a steady current circuit, but when the current is varying as in an A.C. circuit a back e.m.f. is set up in the inductance. This reduces the current and thus is equivalent to a resistance.

The resistance due to inductance in an A.C. circuit is called its reactance and is expressed in ohms. It is denoted by X_L.

Inductive reactance $= X_L = \omega L = 2\pi nL$

Thus reactance is not a constant quantity but it is directly proportional to the frequency of the applied e.m.f.

*The **reactance** due to an inductance can be defined as the ratio of the R.M.S. value of alternating e.m.f. across the inductance to the R.M.S. value of the corresponding current through it.*

The reciprocal of reactance is sometimes called **susceptance** and is denoted by Y_L.

$$\therefore \qquad Y_L = \frac{1}{X_L}$$

Impedance. *Impedance in an A.C. circuit is the effective resistance.* In a circuit containing a resistance R and an inductance L,

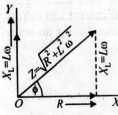

Fig. 11.2 (b)

$$I_v = \frac{E_v}{\sqrt{R^2 + L^2 \omega^2}} = \frac{E_v}{Z}$$

Hence by comparison with Ohm's law the effective resistance or impedance

$$Z = \sqrt{R^2 + L^2 \omega^2} = \sqrt{R^2 + X_L^2}$$

$$= \sqrt{(\text{resistance})^2 + (\text{reactance})^2}$$

Thus the resistance R and the reactance $L\omega$ act at right angle to each other and their resulting impedance can be determined by the vector diagram method as shown in Fig. 36.2 (b) where the resistance R is represented along the X-axis and the reactance $L\omega$ along the Y-axis.

The impedance of an *A.C.* circuit can be defined as the ratio of the *R.M.S.* value of total *e.m.f.* in the circuit to the *R.M.S.* value of the total current.

$$\text{Impedance } Z = \frac{E_v}{I_v}$$

The reciprocal of impedance is sometimes known as **admittance**.

It is denoted by Y.

$$\therefore \qquad \text{Admittance } Y = \frac{1}{Z}$$

Note. In stead of assuming the current to be of the form $I = I_0 \sin \omega t$ we could assume the current to be $= I_0 \cos \omega t$ and get

$$E = E_0 \cos (\omega + \phi)$$

Q. 11.3. (a) An alternating e.m.f. $E = E_0 \sin \omega t$ is applied to the ends of a coil having a resistance R and a self-inductance L. Calculate the current in the circuit.   *(Meerut U. 2002)*

(b) A circuit has inductance $\frac{1}{\pi}$ henry and resistance 200 ohm. A supply of 50 cycle per second A.C. is applied to it. Calculate the reactance and impedance offered by the circuit.

(K.U., 1991)

(c) A long solenoid connected to a 12 volt d.c. source passes a steady current of 2 A. When the solenoid is connected to an A.C. source of 12 V at 50 Hz the current flowing is 1A. Calculate the inductance of the solenoid.   *(M.D.U., 2007)*

Ans. Consider an *A.C.* circuit having a non-inductive resistance R and inductance (without resistance) L as shown in Fig. 11.1. Let the alternating *e.m.f.* represented by $E = E_0 \sin \omega t$ be applied to the circuit, so that at any instant, i is the current in the circuit and $\dfrac{di}{dt}$ the rate at which the current varies. The applied *e.m.f.* E must produce a potential difference Ri across the resistance and overcome the back *e.m.f.* $-L\dfrac{di}{dt}$ due to the inductance.

Hence $$E - L\frac{di}{dt} = Ri$$

or $$E_0 \sin \omega t = Ri + L\frac{di}{dt} \qquad\qquad ...(i)$$

The current in the circuit will also vary harmonically but will have a different amplitude and will differ in phase by an angle, say ϕ. Let the current in the circuit be represented by

$$i = I_0 \sin (\omega t - \phi)$$

Then $$\frac{di}{dt} = I_0 \, \omega \cos(\omega t - \phi)$$

Substituting these values in (i), we have

$$E_0 \sin \omega t = RI_0 \sin(\omega t - \phi) + L \, \omega I_0 \cos(\omega t - \phi) \qquad \text{...(ii)}$$

To solve this equation put $R = a \cos \phi$ and $L\omega = a \sin \phi$

$$\therefore \qquad a = \sqrt{R^2 + L^2 \omega^2}$$

and $$\tan \phi = \frac{L\omega}{R}$$

Substituting the value of R and $L\omega$ in (ii), we have

$$E_0 \sin \omega t = I_0 \, a \, [\cos \phi \sin(\omega t - \phi) + \sin \phi \cos(\omega t - \phi)]$$
$$= I_0 \, a \sin(\omega t - \phi + \phi).$$
$$= I_0 \sqrt{R^2 + L^2 \omega^2} \, \sin \omega t$$

$$\therefore \qquad E_0 = I_0 \sqrt{R^2 + L^2 \omega^2}$$

Hence $$I_0 = \frac{E_0}{\sqrt{R^2 + L^2 \omega^2}}$$

or $$I_v = \frac{E_v}{\sqrt{R^2 + L^2 \omega^2}}$$

Note. In Q. 11.2 the relation $I_v = \dfrac{E_v}{\sqrt{R^2 + L^2 \omega^2}}$ has been derived when the current in the circuit

is represented by $i = I_0 \sin \omega t$. The e.m.f. was then represented by $E = E_0 \sin(\omega t + \phi)$.

In this equation it is given that $E = E_0 \sin \omega t$ and it has been assumed that the current will have a form $i = I_0 \sin(\omega t - \phi)$. The students must carefully read the question and proceed accordingly.

(b) Inductance $L = \dfrac{1}{\pi}$ Henry; $R = 100 \ \Omega$; Frequency $n = 50$ c.p.s.

Reactance $X_L = L\omega = 2\pi n L = 2\pi \times 50 \times \dfrac{1}{\pi} = 100 \ ohm$

Impedance $Z = \sqrt{R^2 + X_L^2} = \sqrt{200^2 + 100^2} = 223.6 \ ohm$

(c) D.C. voltage = 12 V; D.C. current = $2A$

$\therefore$ Resistance $R = \dfrac{12}{2} = 6\Omega$

Supposing that the values of A.C. voltage and current given are R.M.S. values, we have

$$I_v = \frac{E_v}{\sqrt{R^2 + L^2 \omega^2}}$$

A.C. voltage $E_v = 12$ volt; A.C. current $I_v = 1$ Amp

Frequency = 50 c.p.s $\therefore \omega = 2\pi \times 50 = 100 \ \pi$

$$1 = \frac{12}{\sqrt{6^2 + (100\pi\, L)^2}}$$

or $\qquad 6^2 + 100^2\, \pi^2\, L^2 = 144$ or $100^2\, \pi^2\, L^2 = 144 - 36 = 108$

or $\qquad 100\, \pi\, L = \sqrt{108} = 10.39$

$\therefore \qquad\qquad L = \dfrac{10.39}{100\, \pi} = 0.033\, H$

Q. 11.4. (*a*) **An alternating e.m.f is applied to a circuit containing a resistance and a capacitance in series. Find the current in the circuit and the impedance of the circuit. Show that the current leads the e.m.f by an angle** $\phi = \tan^{-1} \dfrac{1}{\omega CR}$. $\qquad$ (*M.D.U.*, 2003; *Luck.U.*, 1993)

(*b*) **An alternating e.m.f of 200 volts and 50 c.p.s. is applied in series with a capacitor and a lamp. If the power of the lamp is 10 W and it operates on 40 V d.c., find the capacitance of the capacitor.**

Ans. (*a*) Consider an *A.C.* circuit having a non-inductive resistance R and a capacitance C in series. Let an alternating *e.m.f.* represented by $E = E_0 \sin \omega t$ be applied to the circuit so that at any instant i is the current in the circuit and q is the charge on the capacitor, then the applied *e.m.f.* E must produce a potential difference Ri across the resistance and a potential difference q/C across the capacitor.

$\therefore \qquad\qquad E = Ri + \dfrac{q}{C}$

or $\qquad\qquad E_0 \sin \omega t = Ri + \dfrac{q}{C}$

The current in the circuit will also vary harmonically but will have a different amplitude and will differ in phase by an angle, say ϕ. Let the current in the circuit be represented by

$$i = I_0 \sin (\omega t + \phi)$$

$\therefore \qquad q = \int i\, dt = \int I_0 \sin (\omega t + \phi)\, dt = -\dfrac{I_0}{\omega} \cos (\omega t + \phi)$

$\therefore \qquad E_0 \sin \omega t = RI_0 \sin (\omega t + \phi) - \dfrac{I_0}{C\omega} \cos (\omega t + \phi) \qquad \ldots(i)$

To solve the above equation

Let $\qquad\qquad\qquad R = a \cos \phi$

and $\qquad\qquad\qquad \dfrac{1}{C\omega} = a \sin \phi$

$\therefore \qquad\qquad\qquad a = \sqrt{R^2 + \dfrac{1}{C^2\omega^2}}$

and $\qquad\qquad\qquad \tan \phi = \dfrac{1}{RC\omega}$

Substituting the values of R and $\dfrac{1}{C\omega}$ in (*i*), we have

$E_0 \sin \omega t = I_0\, a\, [\cos \phi \sin (\omega t + \phi) - \sin \phi \cos (\omega t + \phi)]$

$\qquad\qquad\quad = I_0\, a \sin \omega t$

$$= I_0 \sqrt{R^2 + \frac{1}{C^2 \omega^2}} \sin \omega t$$

or

$$I_0 = \frac{E_0}{\sqrt{R^2 + \frac{1}{C^2 \omega^2}}}$$

∴

$$I_v = \frac{E_v}{\sqrt{R^2 + \frac{1}{C^2 \omega^2}}}$$

The quantity $\frac{1}{C\omega}$ is known as **reactance** due to capacitance or **capacitative reactance** and denoted as X_c.

Current leads e.m.f. The *e.m.f.* is represented by $E = E_0 \sin \omega t$ and the current by $I = I_0 \sin (\omega t + \phi)$ where $\tan \phi = \frac{1}{RC\omega}$. Hence the current leads the *e.m.f.* by a phase angle given by $\tan^{-1} \frac{1}{RC\omega}$. The presence of the capacitance thus makes the current lead which in other words means that the *e.m.f.* **lags** behind the current in a capacitative circuit.

(*b*) Current taken by the lamp

$$I_v = \frac{\text{Watts}}{\text{Volts}} = \frac{10}{40} = \frac{1}{4} \text{amp.}$$

Resistance of the lamp $R = \dfrac{\text{Volts}}{\text{Current}} = \dfrac{40}{\dfrac{1}{4}} = 160 \, \text{ohms.}$

While working on 220 volts, total impedance required

$$Z = \frac{E_v}{I_v} = \frac{200}{1/4} = 800 \, \text{ohms}$$

Let C be the capacitance of the capacitor, then

$$Z = \sqrt{R^2 + \frac{1}{C^2 \omega^2}}$$

or

$$800^2 = 160^2 + \frac{1}{4\pi^2 \, 50^2 \, C^2}$$

∴

$$\frac{1}{C^2} = (800^2 - 160^2) 4\pi^2 \, 50^2$$

or

$$C = \left[\frac{1}{960 \times 640 \times 4\pi^2 \times 50^2} \right]^{1/2}$$

$$C = 4.06 \times 10^{-6} \text{ Farad} = 4.06 \, \mu\text{Fd.}$$

Q. 11.5. An *A.C.* voltage $E = E_0 \, e^{j\omega t}$ is applied to a circuit having (*i*) an inductance L and a resistance R and (*ii*) a capacitance C and a resistance R in series. Derive an expression for the current that flows in the circuit. Also determine the impedance and phase difference between current and *e.m.f.* using j–operator. (*K.U.* 2002, *M.D.U.*, 2002)

Ans. (*i*) A.C. circuit with inductance and resistance. Let the A.C. circuit contain a pure resistance R and a pure inductance L to which a complex E.M.F. $E = E_0 \, e^{j\omega t}$ is applied as shown in Fig. 11.3 (*a*). If I is the instantaneous current through the circuit, then

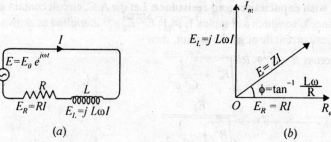

Fig. 11.3

Potential drop across $R = E_R = RI$

The current in R is in phase with E.M.F.

Potential drop across $L = E_L = jL\omega I$

where $L\omega$ is the reactance due to inductance X_L. Multiplication by j implies that E_L leads the current by a phase angle $\pi/2$. Hence we can represent $E_R = RI$ along the real axis and $E_L = jL\omega I$ along the imaginary axis of the complex plane as in Fig.11.3 (b).

$$\therefore \qquad E = E_R + E_L = RI + jL\omega I = I(R + jL\omega)$$

or
$$I = \frac{E}{R + jL\omega} = \frac{E_0\, e^{j\omega t}}{R + jL\omega} \qquad\qquad ...(i)$$

Put $R = Z\cos\phi$ and $L\omega = Z\sin\phi$, then

$$\tan\phi = \frac{L\omega}{R} \text{ and } Z = \sqrt{R^2 + L^2\omega^2}$$

$$\therefore \qquad R + jL\omega = Z\cos\phi + jZ\sin\phi = Ze^{j\phi}$$

Substituting in (i), we have

$$I = \frac{E_0\, e^{j\omega t}}{Z\, e^{j\phi}} = \frac{E_0}{Z} e^{j(\omega t - \phi)} = I_0\, e^{j(\omega t - \phi)}$$

where
$$I_0 = \frac{E_0}{Z}$$

Phase difference. When an alternating E.M.F. $E = E_0\, e^{j\omega t}$ is applied to a circuit containing a resistor and an inductor in series, the current through the circuit is given by

$$I = I_0\, e^{j(\omega t - \phi)}$$

The current, therefore, *lags* with respect to the E.M.F. On the other hand if a current $I = I_0\, e^{j\omega t}$ flows through an LR circuit, the E.M.F. is given by

$$E = E_0\, e^{j(\omega t + \phi)}$$

i.e., the E.M.F. leads the current which is the same thing as the current lags.

Impedance. The complex impedance of the A.C. circuit

$$Z = R + jL\omega = R + jX_L$$

$\sqrt{R^2 + X_L^2}$ gives the *modulus* of Z and

$$\phi = \tan^{-1}\frac{L\omega}{R} = \tan^{-1}\frac{X_L}{R} \text{ gives the } argument \text{ of } Z.$$

(*ii*) **A.C. circuit with capacitance and resistance.** Let the A.C. circuit contain a pure resistance R and a pure capacitance C to which a complex E.M.F. $E = E_0 e^{j\omega t}$ is applied as shown in Fig. 11.4 (*a*). If I is the instantaneous current through the circuit, then

Potential drop across $R = E_R = RI$

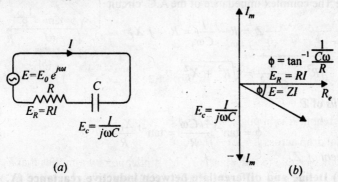

(*a*)   (*b*)

Fig. 11.4

The current in R is in phase with E.M.F.

Potential drop across $C = E_C = \dfrac{1}{j\omega C} I$

where $\dfrac{1}{\omega C}$ is the reactance due to capacitance X_C.

Multiplication by $\dfrac{1}{j}$ implies that E_C lags with respect to the current by a phase angle $\pi/2$. Hence we can represent $E_R = RI$ along the real axis and $E_C = \dfrac{1}{j\omega C} I = -\dfrac{j}{\omega C} I$ along the negative direction of the imaginary axis of the complex plane as in Fig. 11.4 (*b*)

$$\therefore \quad E = E_R + E_C = RI - \frac{jI}{C\omega} = I\left(R - \frac{j}{C\omega}\right)$$

or

$$I = \frac{E}{R - j/C\omega} = \frac{E_0 e^{j\omega t}}{R - j/C\omega} \qquad \text{...(ii)}$$

Put $R = Z \cos\phi$ and $\dfrac{1}{C\omega} = Z \sin\phi$, then

$$\tan\phi = \frac{1/C\omega}{R} \quad \text{and} \quad Z = \sqrt{R^2 + \frac{1}{C^2\omega^2}}$$

$$\therefore \qquad R - \frac{j}{C\omega} = Z \cos\phi - jZ \sin\phi = Z e^{-j\phi}$$

Substituting in (*ii*), we have

$$I = \frac{E_0 e^{j\omega t}}{Z e^{-j\phi}} = \frac{E_0}{Z} e^{j(\omega t + \phi)} = I_0 e^{j(\omega t + \phi)}$$

where

$$I_0 = \frac{E_0}{Z}$$

Phase difference. When an alternating E.M.F. $E = E_0 e^{j\omega t}$ is applied to a circuit containing a resistor and a capacitor in series, the current through the circuit is given by $I = I_0 e^{j(\omega t + \phi)}$

The current, therefore, *Leads* the E.M.F.

On the other hand if a current $I = I_0\, e^{j\omega t}$ flows through an RC circuit, the E.M.F. is given by

$$E = E_0\, e^{j\,(\omega t - \phi)}$$

i.e., the E.M.F. *lags* with respect to the current which is the same thing as the current leads.

Impedance The complex impedance of the A.C. circuit

$$Z = R - \frac{j}{C\omega} = R - j\,X_C$$

$$\sqrt{R^2 + \frac{1}{C^2\omega^2}} = \sqrt{R^2 + X_C^2}$$

gives the *modulus* of Z

and

$$\phi = \tan^{-1}\frac{1/C\omega}{R} = \tan^{-1}\frac{X_C}{R}$$

gives the *argument* of Z.

Q. 11.6. (a) Define and differentiate between inductive reactance (X_L) and capacitative reactance (X_C). Draw the graph of variation of X_L and X_C with frequency.

(*M.D.U.* 2001; *Nag. U.* 2001)

(b) Find the reactance of a capacitor of capacity 1μF at 1 KHZ frequency. (*Nag. U.* 2001)

Ans. (a) Inductive reactance. See **Q. 11.2 (b)**

As inductive reactance $X_L = \omega L = 2\pi n L$, clearly

$$X_L \propto n$$

As n increases X_L increases. A graph showing variation of X_L with frequency n is given in Fig. 11.5 (a).

Capacitative reactance. A capacitor offers infinite resistance to *direct current* (*D.C.*) and blocks its flow. However, it only offers a finite resistance to *alternating current* (*A.C.*).

The resistance due to capacitance in an A.C. circuit is called its capacitative reactance and is also expressed in *ohms*.

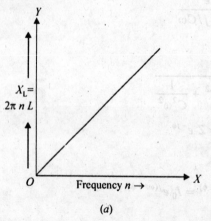

(a)

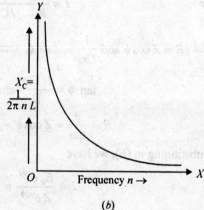

(b)

Fig. 11.5

It is denoted by X_C and is given by

$$X_C = \frac{1}{C\omega} = \frac{1}{2\pi n C}$$

where $\omega = 2\pi n$, n being the frequency of alternating current. (For proof **See Q. 11.4**)

The reactance due to capacitance can be defined as the ratio of the R.M.S. value of the alternating e.m.f. across the capacitor to the R.M.S. value of the corresponding current through it.

As capacitative reactance $X_C = \dfrac{1}{\omega C} = \dfrac{1}{2\pi n C}$ it is not a constant quantity but is inversely proportional to the frequency of the applied e.m.f. or current. As n increases X_C decreases. A graph showing the variation of X_C with frequency n is given in Fig. 11.5 (b).

(b) Here $n = 1000$ Hz; $C = 1\mu F = 10^{-6}$ F

$\therefore$ Reactance of capacitor $X_C = \dfrac{1}{\omega C} = \dfrac{1}{2\pi n C}$

$$= \dfrac{1}{2\pi \times 1000 \times 10^{-6}} = \dfrac{500}{\pi} = 159.2 \text{ ohm.}$$

Q. 11.7. (a) **A resistance of 8 ohms is in series with a pure inductance of 0.01 henry. If a potential difference of 220 volts is applied, calculate the current, the voltage across resistance, the voltage across inductance and phase. Take the frequency of the applied voltage 50 cycles per second.** (*A.U.* 1993)

(b) **An e.m.f. of 230 volts r.m.s. at 50 Hz is applied to a circuit containing a capacitance of 5 µF in series with a resistance of 1000 ohm. Find the rate at which energy is dissipated in the circuit.** (*Gauhati U.* 2000)

Ans. (a) Here $L = 0.01$ henry; $R = 8$ ohm; $E_v = 220$ volts; $n = 50$ Hz

$\therefore$ Reactance $X_L = L\omega = 2\pi n L = 2\pi \times 50 \times 0.1 = 3.142$ ohm

Impedance $Z = \sqrt{R^2 + X_L^2} = \sqrt{8^2 + (3.142)^2} = 8.6$ ohm.

Current $I_v = \dfrac{E_v}{Z} = \dfrac{220}{8.6} = 25.6\,A$

Potential difference or voltage across $R = I_v\,R = 8 \times 25.6 = 204.8$ volt

Potential difference or voltage across $L = I_v\,X_L = 25.6 \times 3.142 = 80.44$ volt

Angle of lag $\phi = \tan^{-1}\dfrac{L\omega}{R} = \tan^{-1}\dfrac{X_L}{R}$

or $\qquad \tan\phi = \dfrac{X_L}{R} = \dfrac{3.142}{8} = .393$ or $\phi = 21.45°$

(b) Here $E_v = 230\ V$; $n = 50$ Hz; $C = 5\mu F$; $R = 1000$ ohm.

$\therefore$ Reactance due to capacitance $X_C = \dfrac{1}{\omega C} = \dfrac{1}{2\pi n C} = \dfrac{1}{2\pi \times 50 \times 5 \times 10^{-6}} = 637\,\Omega$

$\therefore$ Impedence $Z = \sqrt{R^2 + X_C^2} = \sqrt{1000^2 + 637^2}$

$$= 1186 \text{ ohm.}$$

$$I_v = \dfrac{E_v}{Z} = \dfrac{230}{1186} = 0.194\,A$$

$\cos\phi$ (Power factor) $= \dfrac{R}{Z} = \dfrac{1000}{1186} = 0.8432$

Power (or Rate of dissipation of energy) $= E_v\,I_v \cos\phi$

$= 230 \times 0.194 \times 0.8432 = 37.6$ Watt.

Exercise *What is reactance? What are its units? Write expressions for inductive and capacitative reactance.*

(G.N.D.U., 2007)

Hint. Reactance The resistance due to inductance or capacitance in an *A.C.* circuit is called *reactance*. The unit of reactance is an *ohm*

Inductive reactance $= \omega L = 2\pi n L$ and

Capacitative reactance $= \dfrac{1}{C\omega} = \dfrac{1}{2\pi n C}$

where $\omega = 2\pi n$, n being the frequency of alternating current.

Q. 11.8. An alternating e.m.f. $E_0 \sin \omega t$ is applied to the ends of a circuit containing resistance R, self-inductance L and capacitance C. Calculate the impedance of the circuit, phase angle and the current at any instant. (*G.N.D.U.* 2009, 2007, 2006, 2003, 1999, 1997, 1996; *Nag. U.*, 2002; *P.U.*, 2008, 2007; *Meerut U.* 2003, 2000, 1995, 1994, 1992; *A.U.* 1995; *K.U.* 1992)

Ans. Consider an *A.C.* circuit having a resistance R, an inductance L and a capacitance C connected in *series* as shown in Fig. 11.6. Let an alternating *e.m.f.* $E = E_0 \sin \omega t$ be applied to the circuit, so that at any instant, q is the charge on the capacitor, i is the current in the

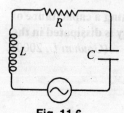

Fig. 11.6

circuit and $\dfrac{di}{dt}$ the rate at which the current varies. The applied *e.m.f.* E must produce a potential difference Ri across the resistance, a potential difference $\dfrac{q}{C}$ across the capacitor and should overcome a back *e.m.f.* $-L\dfrac{di}{dt}$ due to the inductance.

$$\therefore \quad E - L\dfrac{di}{dt} = Ri + \dfrac{q}{C}$$

or $$E_0 \sin \omega t = L\dfrac{di}{dt} + Ri + \dfrac{q}{C} \qquad ...(i)$$

The current in the circuit will vary harmonically but will have a different amplitude and will differ in phase by an angle, say ϕ. Let the current in the circuit be represented by

$$i = I_0 \sin(\omega t - \phi)$$

then $$\dfrac{di}{dt} = I_0 \omega \cos(\omega t - \phi)$$

and $$q = \int i\, dt = \int I_0 \sin(\omega t - \phi)\, dt$$

$$= -\dfrac{I_0}{\omega} \cos(\omega t - \phi)$$

Substituting these values in (i), we have

$$E_0 \sin \omega t = L\omega I_0 (\cos \omega t - \phi) + RI_0 \sin(\omega t - \phi) - \dfrac{I_0}{C\omega} \cos(\omega t - \phi)$$

or $$E_0 \sin \omega t = I_0\left[R\sin(\omega t - \phi) + \left(L\omega - \dfrac{1}{C\omega}\right)\cos(\omega t - \phi)\right] \qquad ...(ii)$$

To solve this equation put $R = a\cos\phi$

and $$\left(L\omega - \dfrac{1}{C\omega}\right) = a\sin\phi$$

$$a = \sqrt{R^2 + \left(L\omega - \frac{1}{C\omega}\right)^2}$$

and

$$\tan\phi = \frac{\left(L\omega - \frac{1}{C\omega}\right)}{R}$$

Substituting the values of R and $\left(L\omega - \frac{1}{C\omega}\right)$ in (ii), we have

$$E_0 \sin\omega t = I_0 \, a \, [\cos\phi \sin(\omega t - \phi) + \sin\phi \cos(\omega t - \phi)]$$

$$= I_0 \, a \sin(\omega t - \phi + \phi) = I_0 \, a \sin\omega t$$

$$= I_0 \sqrt{R^2 + \left(L\omega - \frac{1}{C\omega}\right)^2} \sin\omega t$$

$$\therefore \qquad E_0 = I_0 \sqrt{R^2 + \left(L\omega - \frac{1}{C\omega}\right)^2}$$

or

$$I_0 = \frac{E_0}{\sqrt{R^2 + \left(L\omega - \frac{1}{C\omega}\right)^2}}$$

$$\therefore \qquad I_v = \frac{E_v}{\sqrt{R^2 + \left(L\omega - \frac{1}{C\omega}\right)^2}} \qquad \qquad \ldots (iii)$$

The current at any instant is given by

$$i = \frac{E_0}{\sqrt{R^2 + \left(L\omega - \frac{1}{C\omega}\right)^2}} \sin(\omega t - \phi)$$

Phase angle. The phase angle

$$\phi = \tan^{-1} \frac{\left(L\omega - \frac{1}{C\omega}\right)}{R}$$

Impedance. The quantity $\sqrt{R^2 + \left(L\omega - \frac{1}{C\omega}\right)^2}$ is known as the effective resistance of the *A.C.*
circuit containing resistance, inductance and capacitance. It is called *impedance* and is denoted by *Z*.
$L\omega$ is the reactance due to inductance and is denoted by X_L and $\frac{1}{C\omega}$ is the reactance due to capacitance. It is denote by X_C.

$$\therefore \qquad Z = \sqrt{R^2 + (X_L - X_C)^2}$$

The *e.m.f.* and current have a phase difference of ϕ given by the relation

$$\phi = \tan^{-1} \frac{\left(L\omega - \frac{1}{C\omega}\right)}{R} = \tan^{-1} \frac{X_L - X_C}{R}$$

The presence of the inductance makes the *e.m.f.* lead whereas the presence of the capacitance makes the *e.m.f.* lag behind the current. When both the inductance and the capacitance are present in a circuit, the lag or lead depends upon the relative values of L and C.

Q. 11.9. (*a*) A series *LCR* circuit contains a coil with $L = 2.25$ H, a capacitor having $C = \dfrac{50}{\pi}\,\mu f$ and a resistor with $R = 50\ \Omega$. Calculate (*i*) the impedance and (*ii*) phase difference between current and voltage. (Take frequency of current 50 c.p.s.)   (*P.U.*, 1995)

(*b*) A coil of inductance 0.5 *H* and resistance 500 ohm is connected in series with a capacitance of 1 μF and an alternating *e.m.f.* 10 sin 2000 π *t*. Find the current and phase difference between *e.m.f.* and current.   (*Kerala U.*, 2001)

Ans. $L = 2.25\,H$; $C = \dfrac{50}{\pi} \times 10^{-6}$ Farad ; $R = 50\ \Omega$;   frequency $n = 50$ c.p.s.

∴ Reactance due to inductance $X_L = L\omega = 2\pi n L$

$$= 2\pi \times 2.25 \times 50 = 707 \text{ ohm.}$$

Reactance due to capacitance $X_C = \dfrac{1}{C\omega} = \dfrac{10^6}{\dfrac{50}{\pi} \times 2\pi \times 50} = 200\,\text{ohm}$

Impedance $Z = \sqrt{R^2 + (X_L - X_C)^2} = \sqrt{50^2 + (707 - 200)^2}$

$$= 509.5 \text{ ohm.}$$

Phase difference $\phi = \tan^{-1}\dfrac{X_L - X_C}{R} = \dfrac{707 - 200}{50} = \tan^{-1} 10.1$

$$\phi = 84.35°$$

(*b*) Here *e.m.f.*, $E = 10 \sin 2000\,\pi t$. Comparing with *e.m.f.* equation $E = E_0 \sin \omega t = E_0 \sin 2\pi\, nt$, we have $E_0 = 10$; and $\omega = 2000\,\pi$ or $n = 1000$

Also $L = 0.5\,\text{H}$; $R = 500\ \Omega$; $C = 1\mu F = 10^{-6}\,F$

∴ Reactance due to inductance $X_L = L\omega = 2\,\pi n\,L$

$$= 2000\,\pi \times 0.5 = 1000\,\pi = 3142\ \Omega$$

Reactance due to capacitance $X_C = -\dfrac{1}{C\omega} = \dfrac{1}{2\pi n C}$

$$= \dfrac{1}{2000\,\pi \times 10^{-6}} = \dfrac{500}{\pi} = 159\ \Omega$$

and Impedance $Z = \sqrt{R^2 + (X_L - X_C)^2} = \sqrt{500^2 + (3142 - 159)^2}$

$$= 3025\ \Omega$$

R.M.S. value of current $I_v = \dfrac{E_v}{Z} = \dfrac{E_0}{\sqrt{2}\,Z} = \dfrac{.707\,E_0}{Z}$

$$\dfrac{7.07}{3025} = 2.34 \times 10^{-3}\,\text{A.}$$

$$= 2.34 \text{ mA}$$

Phase difference between e.m.f. and current

$$\phi = \tan^{-1}\dfrac{X_L - X_C}{R} = \dfrac{3142 - 159}{500} = \tan^{-1} 5.966$$

or $\phi = 80.48°$

Q. 11.10. A coil of resistance 100 ohms and inductance 0.16 henry is connected with a capacitor of 16 microfarads capacitance across a 50 cycles 180 volts supply. Calculate the reactance due to inductance, reactance due to capacitance, impendance, current and the phase angle. Find the potential difference across the resistance, inductance and capacitance. How do you explain the fact that the voltage across the capacitor is greater than the applied voltage?

What capacitance would be required to bring the current into phase with the supply voltage and what would be the current under these conditions?

Ans. Here resistance $R = 100$ ohms

$$\text{Inductance } L = 0.16 \text{ henry}$$

$$\text{Capacitance } C = 16 \text{ microfarads} = 16 \times 10^{-6} \text{ farad}$$

$$\text{Frequency } n = 50 \text{ cycle/sec}$$

$$\text{Applied voltage } E_v = 180 \text{ volts}$$

Reactance due to inductance

$$X_L = L\omega = 2\pi nL = 2\pi \times 50 \times 0.16$$

$$= 50.27 = 50 \text{ ohms app.}$$

Reactance due to capacitance

$$X_C = \frac{1}{C\omega} = \frac{1}{2\pi nC} = \frac{1}{2\pi \times 50 \times 16 \times 10^{-6}}$$

$$= 198.9 = 200 \text{ ohms app.}$$

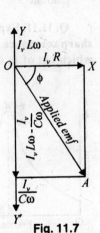

Fig. 11.7

Impedance $Z = \sqrt{R^2 + \left(L\omega - \dfrac{1}{C\omega}\right)^2}$

$$= \sqrt{100^2 + (50 - 200)^2}$$

$$= 180.3 \text{ ohm}$$

$$= 180 \text{ ohms app.}$$

Current $I_v = \dfrac{E_v}{\sqrt{R^2 + \left(L\omega - \dfrac{1}{C\omega}\right)^2}} = \dfrac{E_v}{Z}$

$$\frac{180}{180} = 1.0 \text{ amp.}$$

Phase angle $\phi = \tan^{-1}\left(L\omega - \dfrac{1}{C\omega}\right) = \dfrac{X_L - X_C}{R}$

$$= \tan^{-1}\frac{-150}{100}$$

or $\tan\phi = -1.5$

$$\phi = 56° 18' \text{ (numerically)}$$

The negative sign indicates that the voltage lags behind the current or in other words the current leads the voltage. This is always the case when the reactance due to the capacitance is greater than the reactance due to the inductance.

Potential difference across the resistance R

$$= I_v R = 1 \times 100 = 100 \text{ volts}$$

Potential difference across the inductance

$$I_v X_L = I_v L\omega = 1 \times 50 = 50 \text{ volts}$$

Potential difference across the capacitor

$$I_v X_c = \frac{I_v}{C\omega} = 1 \times 200 = 200 \text{ volts.}$$

The potential difference across the capacitor is greater than the applied voltage. This is because potential difference across the capacitor, potential difference across the inductance and potential difference across the resistance are not in phase. The potential difference across the inductance is 90° ahead of the potential difference across the resistance and the potential difference across the capacitor is 90° behind as shown in Fig. 11.7. The effective voltage acting along OA

$$= \sqrt{(200 - 50)^2 + 100^2} = 180 \text{ volts}$$

which is the applied voltage.

The capacitance C' required to bring the current in phase with the supply voltage, i.e., to make $\phi = 0$ or $\tan \phi = 0$ is given by

$$L\omega - \frac{1}{C'\omega} = 0$$

$$C' = \frac{1}{L\omega^2} = \frac{1}{50 \times 2\pi \times 50 \times 2\pi \times 50} = 0.2 \times 10^{-6} \text{ farad}$$

$$= 0.2 \text{ micro-farad}$$

Current $\qquad \dfrac{E_v}{R} = \dfrac{180}{100} = 1.8 \text{ amps.}$

Q. 11.11. Explain the term resonance as applied to electrical circuits. Find the condition for sharp resonance in case of a series LCR resonant circuit. In series LCR circuit at resonance, which out of L, C and R control the flow of current ? Write a suitable formula. What is the phase angle between current and applied e.m.f. when current is maximum?

(*Nag. U.*, 2001; *G.N.D.U.*, 2006, 2000; *Pbi. U.* 2002, 2000; *P.U.*, 2009, 2006; *Luck.U.* 1996; *Meerut U.*, 1994)

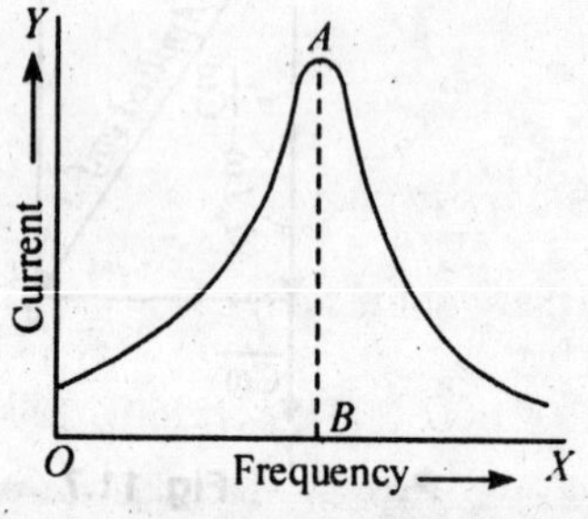

Ans. Resonance. The variation of current with frequency in an electric circuit containing resistance, inductance and capacitance in series is shown in Fig. 11.8.

Fig. 11.8

When the frequency of the applied e.m.f. equals the natural frequency of the electrical circuit the current reaches a maximum value and the circuit is said to be in resonance with applied e.m.f. This is given by AB.

Condition for sharp resonance. In an *A.C.* circuit containing a resistance R, inductance L, capacitance C to which an applied e.m.f. of value E_v having an angular frequency ω is applied, the current I_v is given by

$$I_v = \frac{E_v}{\sqrt{R^2 + \left(L\omega - \dfrac{1}{C\omega}\right)^2}}$$

For the current in the circuit to be maximum $R^2 + \left(L\omega - \dfrac{1}{C\omega}\right)^2$ must have a minimum value.

This is so when

$$L\omega - \frac{1}{C\omega} = 0$$

or

$$L\omega = \frac{1}{C\omega}$$

or

$$\omega = \sqrt{\frac{1}{LC}}$$

$$\therefore \qquad n = \frac{1}{2\pi\sqrt{LC}}$$

Hence *sharp resonance* takes place when the reactance due to capacitance $\frac{1}{C\omega}$ is equal to the reactance due to inductance $L\omega$. For resonance the frequency of the applied *e.m.f.* must be given by

$$n = \frac{1}{2\pi\sqrt{LC}}$$

i.e., the frequency of the applied *e.m.f.* must be equal to the natural frequency of the circuit.

Current At resonance $L\omega - \frac{1}{C\omega} = 0$

$$\therefore \qquad \text{Current} \qquad I_v = \frac{E_v}{\sqrt{R^2 + \left(L\omega - \frac{1}{C\omega}\right)^2}} = \frac{E_v}{R}$$

This is the *maximum* value of current in the circuit.

Hence, at resonance, out of L, C and R it is the resistance R which controls the current.

Phase angle At resonance $L\omega - \frac{1}{C\omega} = 0$. As the phase angle ϕ between current and applied *e.m.f.* is given by

$$\phi = \tan^{-1}\frac{L\omega - \frac{1}{C\omega}}{R}, \quad \phi = 0$$

Thus at resonance the current is maximum and *e.m.f. and current are in phase.*

Q. 11.12. (*a*) **What is quality factor for an A.C. circuit? Prove that quality factor** $Q = \frac{1}{R}\sqrt{\frac{L}{C}}$.

(*Nag. U.* 2001; *Kerala U.* 2001)

(*b*) **What is meant by electrical resonance in a series *LCR* circuit. Explain the term sharpness of resonance. How can it be achieved in the circuit? Explain the effect of resistance.**

(*Nag. U.*, 2002; *Meerut U.*, 2002; *Luck. U.* 1996)

Ans. Quality factor. In a series *RLC* circuit at *resonance*

$$L\omega = \frac{1}{C\omega}$$

As the same current flows through each circuit element the drop of potential across the inductance is *equal* in magnitude but *opposite* in phase to the drop of potential across the capacitance.

The ratio of the potential drop across the inductance or capacitance to the potential drop across the resistance (or the applied voltage) is called the Quality factor or Q of the circuit.

If I is the current in the circuit, then

$$Q = \frac{\text{Potential drop across } L}{\text{Potential drop across } R} = \frac{I\,L\omega}{IR} = \frac{L\omega}{R}$$

As at resonance $L\omega = \dfrac{1}{C\omega}$, $\omega = \dfrac{1}{\sqrt{LC}}$

$$\therefore \quad Q = \frac{L\omega}{R} = \frac{L}{R}\cdot\frac{1}{\sqrt{LC}} = \frac{1}{R}\sqrt{\frac{L}{C}}$$

In general, the ohmic resistance R in a series RLC circuit is *small* as compared to the inductive or the capacitative reactance. There is a very high potential drop across the inductance or capacitance as compared to the potential drop across the resistance. This potential drop at resonance can be much greater than the applied voltage.

Resonance. In a series LCR circuit, the current is given by

$$I_v = \frac{E_0}{\sqrt{R^2 + \left(L\omega - \dfrac{1}{C\omega}\right)^2}}$$

The current has a maximum value when the impedance of the circuit

$$\sqrt{R^2 + \left(L\omega - \frac{1}{C\omega}\right)^2}$$

is a minimum. The value of the impedance is the least when

$$L\omega - \frac{1}{C\omega} = 0$$

or
$$L\omega = \frac{1}{C\omega}$$

or
$$\omega = \sqrt{\frac{1}{LC}}$$

or   Frequency
$$n = \frac{1}{2\pi\sqrt{LC}}$$

In other words, when the frequency of the applied *e.m.f.* is equal to the *natural frequency* of the LC circuit, the current is a maximum and *resonance* is said to take place. Such a circuit is known as *series resonant* circuit and the corresponding frequency is known as *resonant frequency*. In series resonance the voltage across the inductance is equal to the voltage across the capacitance but these have a phase difference of 180° between them.

The maximum amplitude of current at resonance is given by

$$(I_0)_{res} = \frac{E_0}{R}$$

because at resonance $X_L - X_C = L\omega - \dfrac{1}{C\omega} = 0$, the impedance $Z = R$ and is purely *resistive*. The phase difference between current and voltage

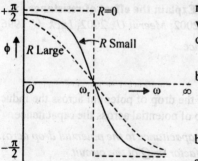

Fig. 11.9 (a)

$$(\phi)_{res} = \tan^{-1}\left[\frac{L\omega - \dfrac{1}{C\omega}}{R}\right]_{res} = 0$$

Thus the current is in phase with applied voltage at resonance frequency $\omega = \omega_r = \dfrac{1}{\sqrt{LC}}$. If $R = 0$, then for all values of $\omega < \omega_r$, the current leads the voltage by a phase angle $\dfrac{\pi}{2}$ and for all values of $\omega > \omega_r$ the current lags behind the voltage by $\dfrac{\pi}{2}$. For finite values of R the angle ϕ by which the current leads for values of $\omega < \omega_r$ and lags for values of $\omega > \omega_r$ with respect to the voltage, slowly increases from 0 to $+\dfrac{\pi}{2}$ as ω decreases from ω_r to zero and from 0 to $-\dfrac{\pi}{2}$ as ω increases from ω_r to infinity as shown in Fig. 11.9 (a).

Sharpness of Resonance (Effect of resistance) The amplitude of the current at resonance $(I_0)_{res} = \dfrac{E_0}{R}$. Thus smaller the value of R, larger is the value of $(I_0)_{res}$. If $R = 0$; $(I_0)_{res} = \infty$. A graph showing the variation of I with frequency ω of the applied voltage for $R = 0$, R very low and R large

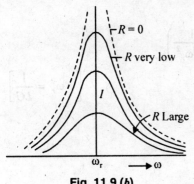

is shown in Fig. 11.9 (b). It is seen from the graph that smaller the value of R sharper is the resonance peak. The resonance is said to be sharp if the current amplitude at resonance falls off quickly for a small change in frequency on either side of the resonant frequency ω_r. Quantitatively, '*The sharpness of resonance for a series resonant circuit is defined as the ratio of the resonant frequency to the difference in frequencies taken on both sides of the resonant frequency for which the power dissipation in the circuit becomes half the value at resonance frequency.*' The two points on the resonance curve for which the power dissipation is half of its value at resonance are called *half power points.*

Fig. 11.9 (b)

As electric power $= I^2R$, for power to fall to half its value the current amplitude will become $\dfrac{1}{\sqrt{2}}$ the amplitude at resonance. Therefore, *sharpness of resonance may also be defined as the ratio of the resonance frequency to the difference of frequencies on both sides of the resonance frequency at which the current in the circuit falls to $\dfrac{1}{\sqrt{2}}$ of its value at resonance.*

Let the corresponding values of the frequencies be

$$\omega_r - \Delta\omega \text{ and } \omega_r + \Delta\omega.$$

If $(I_0)_{res}$ is the current at resonance, the current at a frequency $\omega_r \pm \Delta\omega$

$$= \frac{1}{\sqrt{2}}(I_0)_{res} = \frac{1}{\sqrt{2}}\frac{E_0}{R}$$

$$= \frac{E_0}{\sqrt{R^2 + \left[(\omega_r \pm \Delta\omega)\,L - \dfrac{1}{C(\omega_r \pm \Delta\omega)}\right]^2}}$$

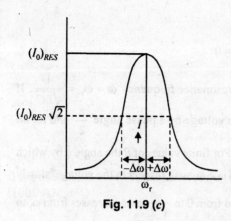

Fig. 11.9 (c)

Squaring both sides we have

$$\frac{1}{2}\frac{E_0^2}{R^2} = \frac{E_0^2}{R^2 + \left[(\omega_r \pm \Delta\omega)\,L - \dfrac{1}{C(\omega_r \pm \Delta\omega)}\right]^2}$$

or

$$2R^2 = R^2 + \left[(\omega_r \pm \Delta\omega)\,L - \frac{1}{C(\omega_r \pm \Delta\omega)}\right]^2$$

$$\therefore \qquad R = (\omega_r \pm \Delta\omega)\,L - \frac{1}{C(\omega_r + \Delta\omega)}$$

Now $\dfrac{\Delta\omega}{\omega_r} \ll 1$

$$\therefore \qquad R = \omega_r L \pm \Delta\omega L - \frac{1}{C\omega_r}\left(1 \pm \frac{\Delta\omega}{\omega_r}\right)^{-1}$$

$$= \omega_r\, L \pm \Delta\omega L - \frac{1}{C\omega_r} \pm \frac{\Delta\omega}{C\omega_r^2}$$

As $\qquad \omega_r\, L = \dfrac{1}{C\omega_r}$, we have

$$R = \Delta\omega L + \frac{\Delta\omega}{C\omega_r^2} = \Delta\omega L\left(1 + \frac{1}{LC\omega_r^2}\right)$$

$$= 2\,\Delta\omega L \qquad\qquad \left[\because \omega_r^2 = \frac{1}{LC}\right]$$

or $\qquad\qquad 2\Delta\omega = \dfrac{R}{L}$

$\therefore$ Sharpness of resonance $\dfrac{\omega_r}{2\Delta\omega} = \dfrac{L\omega_r}{R} = Q$ factor.

Thus larger the value of Q, sharper is the resonance.

As $\qquad\qquad \omega_r = \dfrac{1}{\sqrt{LC}}, \dfrac{L\omega_r}{R} = \dfrac{\sqrt{\dfrac{L}{C}}}{R}$

$\therefore$ For sharper resonance

(i) R must be small and (ii) Ratio of $\dfrac{L}{C}$ must be large.

Q. 11.13. An A.C. circuit has $L = 10$ mH, $C = 10$ μF, $R = 10$ ohm, calculate (i) Natural frequency (ii) resonant frequency (iii) impedance of the circuit at resonance (iv) Q-factor.

(A.U., 1995)

Ans. (i) Natural frequency $n = \dfrac{1}{2\pi\sqrt{LC}}$

$$= \frac{1}{2\pi\sqrt{10 \times 10^{-3} \times 10 \times 10^{-6}}} = \frac{10^3 \times \sqrt{10}}{2\pi}$$

$$= 0.502 \times 10^3 = 502 \text{ Hz}$$

(ii) Resonant frequency = natural frequency = **502 Hz**

(iii) Impedance $Z = \sqrt{R^2 + \left(L\omega - \dfrac{1}{C\omega}\right)^2}$

At resonance $L\omega = \dfrac{1}{C\omega}$ or $L\omega - \dfrac{1}{C\omega} = 0$

$\therefore$ Impedance at resonance $= R = 10$ ohm.

(iv) Q-factor $= \dfrac{L\omega_r}{R} = \dfrac{10 \times 10^{-3} \times 502 \times 2\pi}{10} = 3.154.$

Exercise. *A resistance of 10 ohm, is joined in series with an inductance of 0.5 H. What capacity should be kept in series with the combination to get maximum current ? The current is supplied at 50 Hz.* (Nag. U., 2001)

Hint. Current is maximum at resonance when $n = \dfrac{1}{2\pi\sqrt{LC}}$ or $50 = \dfrac{1}{2\pi\sqrt{0.5 \times C}}$

or $\quad C = \dfrac{1}{4\pi^2 \times 50 \times 50 \times 0.5} = 20.25 \times 10^{-6}\, F = 20.25\,\mu F$

Q. 11.14. A circuit has $R = 10$ ohm, $L = 0.05$ H and $C = 20$ μF. An alternating potential difference of 100 V (R.M.S.) is applied across it, calculate (a) resonant frequency (b) current at resonance (c) Q-value of the circuit. (A.U., 1994)

Ans. (a) Resonant frequency $n = \dfrac{1}{2\pi\sqrt{LC}} = \dfrac{1}{2\pi\sqrt{0.05 \times 20 \times 10^{-6}}} = 159$

Impedance $Z = \sqrt{R^2 + \left(L\omega - \dfrac{1}{C\omega}\right)^2}$

At resonance $L\omega - \dfrac{1}{C\omega} = 0 \qquad \therefore\ Z = R$

(b) $\quad$ Current at resonance $= \dfrac{E_{R.M.S.}}{R} = \dfrac{100}{10} = 10$ Amp.

(c) $\quad$ Q-value of the circuit $= \dfrac{L\omega_r}{R} = \dfrac{0.05 \times 2\pi \times 159}{10} = 4.997$

Exercise. *A series LCR circuit has $L = 500$ μH, $C = 200$ μF, and $R = 32$ ohm. The supply voltage is 5 Volt. Calculate the resonant frequency and current at resonance.* (Gharwal U. 1999)

Hint. Resonant frequency $n = \dfrac{1}{2\pi\sqrt{LC}} = \dfrac{1}{2 \times 3.142 \times \sqrt{500 \times 10^{-6} \times 200 \times 10^{-6}}} = 500\, Hz$

Current at resonance $I_v = \dfrac{E_v}{R} = \dfrac{5}{32}$ Amp.

Q. 11.15. (a) What is (i) a series resonant circuit and (ii) a parallel resonant circuit ? Distinguish between the two. Why a series resonant circuit is known as an acceptor circuit and parallel resonant circuit as rejector circuit ? What are their practical applications ? Discuss the resonance condition in parallel LCR circuit. Why the current is maximum at resonance frequency in series resonant circuit and minimum in parallel resonant circuit.

(P.U. 2009, 2006, 2002; M.D.U. 2007, 2002, 2001;
G.N.D.U. 2000; Gharwal. U. 2000; Luck. U. 1993)

(*b*) Find the natural frequency of a circuit containing inductance 50 micro-henry and a capacity of 0.005 micro farad. Find the wavelength to which this corresponds.

(G.N.D.U. 1996; K.U. 1991)

Ans. (*a*) Series resonant circuit. The impedance of an *A.C.* circuit containing resistance, inductance and capacity in series is given by

$$Z = \sqrt{R^2 + \left(L\omega - \frac{1}{C\omega}\right)^2}$$

The value of the impedance is the least when $\left(L\omega - \frac{1}{C\omega}\right)$ is zero, *i.e.*, when the reactance due to inductance is equal to the reactance due to capacitance.

or $$L\omega = \frac{1}{C\omega}$$

or $$\omega = \sqrt{\frac{1}{LC}}$$

$$\therefore \quad \text{Frequency } n = \frac{1}{2\pi\sqrt{LC}}$$

In other words when the frequency of the applied *e.m.f.* is equal to the natural frequency of the *LC* circuit, current is a maximum and resonance is said to take place. Such a circuit is known as a **series resonant** circuit and the corresponding frequency is called a resonant frequency. If *L* is in henry and *C* in farads, the resonant frequency is in cycles per second or Hertz. In series resonance the voltage across the inductance is equal to the voltage across the capacitance but these have phase difference of 180° between them. The ratio of the voltage across the inductance (or capacitance) to the applied voltage or the voltage across the resistance at resonance is called **voltage amplification factor *Q* of the series circuit.**

Acceptor circuit. As the current in a series resonant circuit is very high, it is called an **acceptor circuit.** The circuit accepts or responds to the incoming signals of the frequency which is equal to its natural frequency.

Applications. Series resonant circuit is, therefore, used as a *tuning circuit* in radio and television receivers. Signals of several frequencies from different transmitting stations are received by the set. The receiver picks up the signal of the desired frequency which matches with the natural frequency of the *LC* unit in the set.

Parallel resonant circuit. A parallel circuit consists of an inductance *L* having a low ohmic resistance and a capacitor *C* placed in parallel as shown in Fig. 11.10.

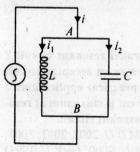

Let i_1 be the current through the inductance and i_2 through the capacitance, then the current through the circuit.

$$i = i_1 + i_2$$

If $E_0 \sin \omega t$ represents the applied *e.m.f.* then

Current through the inductance

$$i_1 = \frac{E_0}{L\omega} \sin\left(\omega t - \frac{\pi}{2}\right)$$

and current through the capacitance

Fig. 11.10

$$i_2 = \frac{E_0}{\dfrac{1}{C\omega}} \sin\left(\omega t + \frac{\pi}{2}\right)$$

$$\therefore \quad i = \frac{E_0}{L\omega} \sin\left(\omega t - \frac{\pi}{2}\right) + E_0 \, C\omega \sin\left(\omega t + \frac{\pi}{2}\right)$$

$$= E_0\left(C\omega - \frac{1}{L\omega}\right)\cos \omega t$$

If $C\omega = \dfrac{1}{L\omega}$ the current in the circuit will be zero.

This will happen when

$$\omega = \sqrt{\frac{1}{LC}} = \frac{1}{2\pi\sqrt{LC}}$$

i.e., the frequency of the A.C. supply is equal to the natural frequency of the LC circuit.

Resonance is again said to take place and such a circuit is known as **parallel resonant circuit.** The corresponding frequency is called resonant frequency.

Rejector circuit. As the current in a parallel resonant circuit at resonant frequency is minimum and has almost zero value (Impedance being maximum) such a circuit is known as **rejector circuit.** The circuit does not accept i.e rejects the incoming signals of the frequency which is equal to its natural frequency.

Applications. Parallel resonant circuits produce oscillations and are used as *transmitting circuits.*

In such a circuit the current through the inductance is equal to the current through the capacitance but these have a phase difference of 180° between them. Such circuits, therefore, reject (or cut off) the currents corresponding to parallel resonant frequencies and allow other frequencies to pass through. These are, therefore known as **filter circuits** or *rejector circuits.* Sometimes these are also called *anti-resonant circuits.*

Distinction why current is maximum at series resonance and minimum at parallel resonance (*i*) In series resonant circuit impedance is minimum at resonance whereas in a parallel resonant circuit it is maximum.

(*ii*) This is why in a series resonant circuit the current through the circuit is maximum whereas in a parallel resonant circuit maximum voltage is set up across A and B, the two ends of the circuit having L and C in parallel, and hence the current is minimum and has almost zero value.

(*b*) Here inductance $L = 50 \times 10^{-6}$ henry

Capacitance $C = 0.0005$ microfarad $= 5 \times 10^{-10}$ farad

Natural frequency of the circuit

$$n = \frac{1}{2\pi\sqrt{LC}} = \frac{1}{2\pi\sqrt{50 \times 10^{-6} \times 5 \times 10^{-10}}}$$

$$= \frac{10^8}{10\pi\sqrt{10}} = 1007000 \text{ cycles/sec.}$$

Corresponding wavelength

$$\lambda = \frac{3 \times 10^8}{1007000} = 298.1 \text{ metres.}$$

Exercise. *A capacitor of 50 μF and inductance of 0.2025 H are connected in series. If the resistance of the circuit is negligible find the frequency at which resonance occurs.* (*Nag. U.*, 2002)

Hint. Resonant frequency $n = \dfrac{1}{2\pi\sqrt{LC}} = \dfrac{1}{2 \times 3.142 \times \sqrt{0.2025 \times 50 \times 10^{-6}}}$

$$= 50 \text{ Hz}$$

Q. 11.16. (*a*) **Find a general expression for the power consumed in an** *A.C.* **circuit containing** *LCR* **and hence define power factor and wattless current. How the value of power factor can be found from impedance triangle?**

(*G.N.D.U.*, 2009, 2008, *P.U.*, 2007; *Gauhati U.* 2000; *Meerut U.*, 2003, 1993; *K. U.* 1991)

(*b*) **Explain why a capacitor of large value is connected across an electric motor?**

(*Gauhati U.*, 2000; *Nag. U.*, 2001)

Ans. (*a*) **Power in an A.C. circuit.** In an *A.C.* circuit, in general the applied *e.m.f.* and the current are not in phase. Let the applied *e.m.f.* and the current be represented by

$$E = E_0 \sin \omega t$$

or

$$i = I_0 \sin(\omega t - \phi)$$

where ϕ is the angle of lag or lead.

The power Ei at any instant is given by

$$Ei = E_0 I_0 \sin \omega t \sin(\omega t - \phi)$$

∴ Work done in a very small time dt

$$Ei\,dt = E_0 I_0 \sin \omega t \sin(\omega t - \phi)\,dt$$

Hence the total work done in time T, equal to half the time period

$$= \int_0^T E_0 I_0 \sin \omega t \sin(\omega t - \phi)\,dt$$

$$= \frac{E_0 I_0}{2}\int_0^T \cos\phi\,dt - \frac{E_0 I_0}{2}\int_0^T \cos(2\omega t - \phi)\,dt$$

∵ $\sin A \sin B = \dfrac{1}{2}\{\cos(A-B) - \cos(A+B)\}$

Now $\int_0^T \cos(2\omega t - \phi)\,dt = 0$ and $\int_0^T \cos\phi\,dt = \cos\phi\,T$

∴ Work done in time $T = \dfrac{E_0 I_0}{2}\cos\phi \times T$

∴ Average power $= \dfrac{E_0 I_0 \cos\phi}{2 \times T} \times T = \dfrac{E_0 I_0}{2}\cos\phi$

$$= \frac{E_0}{\sqrt{2}}\frac{I_0}{\sqrt{2}}\cos\phi$$

$$= E_v I_v \cos\phi \qquad\qquad ...(i)$$

Power factor. From Eq. (*i*) we find that

Average power = virtual current × virtual *e.m.f.* × cosine of the angle of lag (or lead)

The factor $\cos\phi$ is called the *power factor* and $E_v I_v \cos\phi$ is called the *true power*.

Hence true power = apparent power × power factor.

For a circuit containing resistance, inductance and capacitance in series, the value of ϕ is given by

$$\tan \phi = \frac{X_L - X_C}{R}$$

where X_L is the reactance due to inductance, X_C the reactance due to capacitance and R the ohmic resistance. The value of the power factor $\cos \phi$ as shown in Fig. 11.11 is given by

$$\cos \phi = \frac{R}{\sqrt{R^2 + (X_L - X_C)^2}} = \frac{R}{Z}$$

$$= \frac{\text{Resistance}}{\text{Impedance}}$$

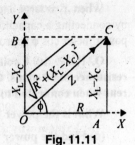

Fig. 11.11

This relation holds good for a circuit containing only resistance and inductance, only resistance and capacitance as well as for a circuit containing resistance, inductance and capacitance.

For circuits having only resistance and inductance

$$\cos \phi = \frac{R}{\sqrt{R^2 + X_L^2}}$$

For circuits having only resistance and capacitance

$$\cos \phi = \frac{R}{\sqrt{R^2 + X_C^2}}$$

Wattless current. *Current is said to be wattless when the power factor $\cos \phi = 0$ and the circuit does not consume any power.*

Therefore the condition for the current to be wattless is that

$$\cos \phi = 0$$

or

$$\phi = \frac{\pi}{2}$$

i.e., the phase difference between the current and the voltage should be $\frac{\pi}{2} = 90°$.

Impedance triangle. In Fig 11.11 OA taken along $+ X$ axis represents the ohmic resistance $R = OA$. $OB = AC$ taken along $+ Y$ axis represents the net reactance due to inductance and capacitance $= X_L - X_c$. The impedance Z is given by $OC = \sqrt{R^2 + (X_L - X_c)^2}$. The angle ϕ that the direction of Z (OC) makes with the direction of R (OA) gives the angle of lead or lag. The triangle OAC is the *impedance triangle.*

Determination of power factor. Power factor $= \frac{R}{Z} = \cos \phi = \frac{OA}{OC}$

(*b*) **Why a capacitor is connected across an electric motor?** A capacitor of large value is connected across an electric motor to improve the power factor. The armature and the field magnets of an electric motor consist of a large number of windings of copper wire wound over a magnetic core and therefore, have a *large inductance.* The power factor in an A.C. circuit is given by

$$\cos \phi = \frac{R}{\sqrt{R^2 + (X_L - X_C)^2}}$$

When X_L is large and X_C is small (or negligible) cos ϕ has a *low* value. But when X_C is increased by connecting a capacitor of large value across the motor $(X_L - X_C)$ has a very small value and the power factor cos ϕ approaches nearly *unity* thereby giving a high useful power.

Q. 11.17. (*a*) **A coil of self-inductance 0.7 henry is joined in series with a non-inductive resistance of 50 ohms. Calculate the Wattless and power components as well as the total current when connected to a supply of 200 V at 50 Hz.**

What is the power factor ?

(*b*) **Find the power factor in an LR circuit if $X_L = \sqrt{3}\,R$.**   (*Nag. U.* 2002)

Ans. (*a*) Reactance due to inductance $X_L = 2\pi n L = 2 \times \dfrac{22}{7} \times 50 \times 0.7 = 220 \, \Omega$

Resistance $R = 50 \, \Omega$

Impedance $Z = \sqrt{X_L^2 + R^2} = \sqrt{220^2 + 50^2} = 225.6 \, \Omega$

Total current $I_v = \dfrac{E_v}{Z} = \dfrac{200}{225.6} = 0.8865 \, A$

The power through the inductance is wattless as the voltage and the current in it have a phase difference of $\dfrac{\pi}{2}$.

∴ Wattless component of power = $I_v \times$ potential drop across the inductance

$$= I_v \times I_v \times X_L$$

$$= I_v^2 \times X_L = (0.8865)^2 \times 220$$

$$= 172.9 \text{ watt}$$

Power component is the power through the resistance in which the current and voltage are in phase.

∴ Power component = $I_v \times$ potential drop across R

$$= I_v^2 \, R = (0.8865)^2 \times 50$$

$$= 39.29 \text{ watt}$$

Power factor $= \cos \phi = \dfrac{R}{Z} = \dfrac{50}{225.6} = 0.2216.$

Note. In the above question true power $= E_v \, I_v \cos \phi$

$$= 200 \times 0.8863 \times 0.2216 = 39.29 \text{ watt}$$

which is the same as the power component across R showing thereby that the power component across the inductance does not contribute towards the power in the circuit *i.e.*, it is wattless.

(*b*) Here $X_L = \sqrt{3}\,R$

∴   Power factor $\cos \phi = \dfrac{R}{\sqrt{R^2 + X_L^2}} = \dfrac{R}{\sqrt{R^2 + 3R^2}} = \dfrac{1}{2}$

Q. 11.18. (*a*) **Explain with necessary theory the principle of a choke coil. Why is the choke considered superior both to rheostat and a transformer ?**

                                      (*Meerut U.*, 2003, 2002; *A.U.*, 1993; *K.U.*, 1992, 1991)

(*b*) **Core of a low frequency choke is made of soft iron. Why ?**   (*Pbi. U.*, 2001)

Ans. For many purposes it is required to reduce the current in a given circuit when the supply voltage is constant. In a direct current circuit this is done by using a rheostat but in this case there is a loss of power equal to $i^2 R$. Thus actually we deliberately allow a part of the available power to be wasted across an idle resistance and maintain the useful power in the apparatus within the desired limit.

Choke coil. In an alternating current circuit a **choke coil** is used for this purpose. It consists of an inductance which is made by having a large number of turns of an insulated copper wire wound over a closed soft iron laminated core. The presence of an inductance in an $A.C.$ circuit reduces the current which is given by the relation

$$I_v = \frac{E_v}{\sqrt{R^2 + L^2 \omega^2}}$$

The power in an $A.C.$ circuit is given by $E_v I_v \cos \phi$. The controlling action of the choke coil is due to the presence of the power factor

$$\cos \phi = \frac{R}{\sqrt{R^2 + L^2 \omega^2}}$$

As the inductance L is increased the value of $\cos \phi$ decreases and the circuit draws a lesser power from the source. Since the ohmic resistance of the inductance is small the loss of power across the choke coil is negligible the only loss being due to hysteresis. Choke coils used on low frequency have an iron core and are known as low frequency or audio frequency ($A.F.$) chokes whereas chokes used on high frequency have air cores and are known as high frequency or radio frequency ($R.F.$) chokes.

Reason. The core of low frequency choke (or $A.F.$ choke) is made of soft iron to increase its inductance. The co-efficient of self induction of a coil is given by $L = \mu_r \, \mu_0 \, N^2 a / l$ when N is the total number of turns in the choke, l its length, a the area of cross-section, μ_0 the permeability of air or free space and μ_r the relative permeability of the material of the core. As μ_r for soft iron is very high, a choke with soft iron core has an inductance μ_r times the inductance of the same choke with air core. As reactance due to inductance $X_L = L\omega = 2\pi n L$, X_L also becomes very large for a choke with soft iron.

A soft iron core is not required for high frequency ($R.F.$) chokes as the frequency and hence ω being very large the reactance is very high even with an air core.

Superiority of choke coil. A choke coil is considered superior to a rheostat and a transformer because in it the only wastage of energy is due to hysteresis loss in the iron core which is much less than the wastage of energy in the resistance that would reduce the current to the same extent. A choke coil draws nearly the same energy from the source as is required in the circuit by changing the power factor of the circuit. Whereas in a rheostat the energy drawn from the source remains unchanged–the rheostat wasting more energy if the circuit requires less. On the other hand in a transformer in addition to the hysteresis loss there are many other losses, the most important being the loss due to leakage of magnetic flux. Moreover the primary circuit consumes energy due to its ohmic resistance even when the secondary circuit is open.

Q. 11.19. (*a*) **Find the inductance of a choke coil which is needed to run an arc lamp with an alternating current supply of 100 volts and 50 cycles per second. The arc runs at 10 amperes and has an effective resistance of 4 ohms.**

(*b*) **If the same arc is worked on 100 volts D.C. find the additional resistance required. Compare the power losses in the two cases and bring out the superiority of the choke coil.**

(*Luck. U.,* 1995)

Ans. (a) A.C. supply voltage $E = 100$ volts; Frequency $n = 50$ cycles/sec.; Current $I_v = 10$ amps; Resistance $R = 4$ ohms.

Let L be the inductance required to work the arc, then

$$I_v = \frac{E}{\sqrt{R^2 + L^2 \omega^2}}$$

$$10 = \frac{100}{\sqrt{4^2 + L^2 (2\pi \times 50)^2}}$$

or $4^2 + 100^2 \pi^2 L^2 = 100$

or $L^2 = \dfrac{100 - 16}{100^2 \pi^2}$

$\therefore$ $L = \dfrac{\sqrt{84}}{100\pi} = 0.0292 \, \text{henry}$

(b) When the arc is worked on 100 volts D.C. let the additional resistance required by R_1, then

$$10 = \frac{100}{R_1 + 4}$$

$\therefore$ $R_1 = 6$ ohms.

Comparison of power losses. (i) *Worked on A.C.*

$$Z = \sqrt{R^2 + L^2 \omega^2} = \frac{E_v}{I_v} = \frac{100}{10} = 10 \, \text{ohms.}$$

$\therefore$ Power factor $\cos \phi = \dfrac{R}{\sqrt{R^2 + L^2 \omega^2}} = \dfrac{4}{10} = 0.4$

$\therefore$ Power consumed by the circuit $= E_v I_v \cos \phi$

$$= 100 \times 10 \times 0.4 = 400 \text{ watts}$$

Power consumed by the arc lamp $= I^2 R$

$$= 10^2 \times 4 = 400 \text{ watts}$$

Thus in the extreme case when the ohmic resistance of the choke coil is negligible whole of the power supplied to the circuit is used for doing useful work.

(ii) *Worked on D.C.*

Power consumed by the circuit $= EI = 100 \times 10 = 1000$ watts

Power consumed by the arc $= I^2 R = 10^2 \times 4 = 400$ watts

Power lost $= 1000 - 400 = 600$ watts.

Hence when worked on D.C. we find that 60% of the power supplied to the circuit is wasted. This shows the superiority of the choke coil where there is no loss of power.

Exercise. *A 20 volt, 5 Watt lamp is to be used on A.C. source of 200 volt, 50 Hz. Calculate the inductance of the choke coil required to be put in series to run the lamp. How much pure resistance should be used in place of the choke so that the lamp may run on its rated voltage ?*

(*Meerut U.* 2000)

Hint. Current required by the lamp $I = \dfrac{W}{E} = \dfrac{5}{20} = 0.25 \, \text{A.}$

Resistance of the lamp $R = \dfrac{E}{I} = \dfrac{20}{0.25} = 80 \, \text{ohm.}$

If L is the inductance of the choke required to work the lamp on 200 volt 50 Hz, *A.C.*, then

$$I = \frac{E_v}{\sqrt{R^2 + (2\pi n L)^2}} \quad \text{or} \quad 0.25 = \frac{200}{\sqrt{80^2 + 100\pi^2 L^2}} \quad \text{or} \quad \sqrt{80^2 + 100\pi^2 L^2} = \frac{200}{0.25} = 800$$

$$\therefore \ 100\pi L = \sqrt{800^2 - 80^2} \quad \text{or} \quad L = \frac{796}{100 \times 3.142} = 2.53 \, \text{H}.$$

Pure resistance X required is given by $I = \dfrac{E}{R + X} = \dfrac{200}{80 + X}$ or $80 + X = 800$

or $\qquad X = 720$ ohm.

Q. 11.20. An average voltage of 20 volts and 100 c.p.s. is supplied to a 5 H choke of resistance 200 Ω. Find the power factor of the coil and power consumed. *(K.U., 1991)*

Ans. Reactance of the choke $X_L = 2\pi n L = 2\pi \times 100 \times 5 = 3142 \, \Omega$

Resistance $R = 200 \, \Omega$

$\therefore$ Impedance of the choke $Z = \sqrt{R^2 + X_L^2} = \sqrt{200^2 + (3142)^2} = 3148 \Omega$

Power factor $\cos\phi = \dfrac{R}{\sqrt{R^2 + (X_L)^2}} = \dfrac{R}{Z} = \dfrac{200}{3148} = 0.0635$

Power consumed $= E_v \, I_v \cos\phi = E_v \dfrac{E_v}{Z} \cos\phi$

$$= \frac{20 \times 20 \times 0.0635}{3148} = 0.008 \, \text{watt}$$

Exercise. *A 25 watt 100 volt lamp is to be run on 250 V (r.m.s) 50 Hz mains supply. Calculate the power factor.* *(Nag. U. 2001)*

Hint. Current taken by the lamp $I_v = \dfrac{25}{100} = 0.25 \, \text{A}.$

When working on 250 V (*r.m.s*), 50 Hz, Power $= E_v I_v \cos\phi$

$\therefore \ 25 = 250 \times 0.25 \times \cos\phi$ or Power factor $\cos\phi = \dfrac{25}{250 \times 0.25} = 0.4$

Q. 11.21. Derive the relation for impedance of an *LCR* parallel circuit. *(G.N.D.U., 2006)*

Ans. *LCR* parallel circuit. A circuit containing inductance L, capacitance C and resistance R all connected in parallel with an A.C. source of e.m.f. $E = E_0 \sin \omega t$ is shown in Fig. 11.12.

Let I be the total current in the circuit and I_R, I_C and I_L the currents through R, C and L respectively, then

$$I = I_R + I_C + I_L \qquad\qquad ...(i)$$

Current through R (I_R). $I_R = \dfrac{E}{R} = \dfrac{E_0 \sin \omega t}{R}$

Current through C (I_C). The charge on the capacitor when E is the *P.D.* across it, $Q = EC = CE_0 \sin \omega t$ and current through the capacitor $I_c = \dfrac{dQ}{dt} = C E \omega \cos \omega t$

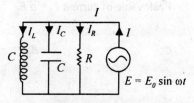

Fig. 11.12

Current through L (I_L). when the current through inductance L varies at the rate $\dfrac{dI_L}{dt}$, potential

difference across $L = E_L = L\dfrac{dI_L}{dt} = E_0 \sin \omega t$

$\therefore$ $\qquad\qquad\qquad\qquad L\dfrac{dI_L}{dt} = E_0 \sin \omega t$ or $\dfrac{dI_L}{dt} = \dfrac{E_0}{L}\sin \omega t$

or $\qquad\qquad\qquad d I_L = \dfrac{E_0}{L}\sin \omega t\, dt$ $\quad\therefore I_L = \int d I_L = \int \dfrac{E_0}{L}\sin \omega t\, dt$

or $\qquad\qquad\qquad I_L = \dfrac{E_0}{R}\left(-\dfrac{\cos \omega t}{\omega}\right) = -\dfrac{E_0}{L\omega}\cos \omega t$

Substituting the values of I_R, I_C and I_L in relation (i), we get

$$I = \dfrac{E_0}{R}\sin \omega t + E_0\,(C\omega)\cos \omega t - \dfrac{E_0}{L\omega}\cos \omega t$$

$$= E_0\left[\dfrac{\sin \omega t}{R} + \left(C\omega - \dfrac{1}{L\omega}\right)\cos \omega t\right]$$

If we put $\dfrac{1}{R} = a \cos\theta$ and $\left(C\omega - \dfrac{1}{L\omega}\right) = a \sin\theta$, we get

$$I = E_0\,[\,a \sin \omega t \cos\theta + a \cos \omega t \sin\theta\,]$$

$$= a\,E_0 \sin(\omega t + \theta) = I_0 \sin(\omega t + \theta)$$

where $\qquad\qquad\qquad I_0 = a\,E_0$ the *peak value* of current through the circuit.

Thus when the e.m.f is $E = E_0 \sin \omega t$, the current is given by $I = I_0 \sin(\omega t + \theta)$ where θ is the *phase difference* between current and e.m.f in a parallel *LCR* circuit.

The value of θ is given by the relation

$$\tan\theta = \dfrac{a \sin\theta}{a \cos\theta}\, R\left(C\omega - \dfrac{1}{L\omega}\right)$$

The value of a is given by the relation

$$a^2 = a^2 \cos^2\theta + a^2 \sin^2\theta = \dfrac{1}{R^2} + \left(C\omega - \dfrac{1}{L\omega}\right)^2$$

or $\qquad\qquad\qquad a = \sqrt{\dfrac{1}{R^2} + \left(C\omega - \dfrac{1}{L\omega}\right)^2}$

Peak value of current $I_0 = a\,E_0$ $\qquad\qquad \therefore E_0\sqrt{\dfrac{1}{R^2} + \left(C\omega - \dfrac{1}{L\omega}\right)^2}$

or $\qquad\qquad\qquad E_0 = \dfrac{I_0}{\sqrt{\dfrac{1}{R^2} + \left(C\omega - \dfrac{1}{L\omega}\right)^2}}$

Impedance If Z is the impedance of the parallel *LCR* circuit, then $I_0 = \dfrac{E_0}{Z}$

or   Impedance $Z = \dfrac{E_0}{I_0} = \dfrac{1}{\sqrt{\dfrac{1}{R^2} + \left(C\omega - \dfrac{1}{L\omega}\right)^2}}$

Resonance in parallel LCR circuit. When $C\omega - \dfrac{1}{L\omega} = 0$

or $\omega^2 = \dfrac{1}{LC}$ or $\omega = \dfrac{1}{\sqrt{LC}}$, $Z = R$ and $(I_0)_{minimum} = \dfrac{E_0}{R}$

Thus at resonance, the impendance is maximum and, therefore, the amplitude of current in the circuit is minimum. This is in contrast with the case of series resonance where at resonance the impedance is minimum and amplitude of current in the circuit maximum.

Q. 11.22. (*a*) **What is skin effect?**   (*Pbi. U.* 2003, 2002, 2001)

(*b*) **Explain the existence of eddy currents. To what practical purpose have eddy currents been applied.**

Ans. (*a*) **Skin effect.** When a steady current flows in a wire, it uniformly distributes itself throughout the cross-section of the wire and the current density is uniform. But when an alternating current flows through a wire it does not distribute itself uniformly there being a concentration of current on the outer surface of the conductor. The effect increases as the frequency of the current increases. For very high frequency the current is almost wholly confined to the surface layer. The phenomenon is known as **skin effect**.

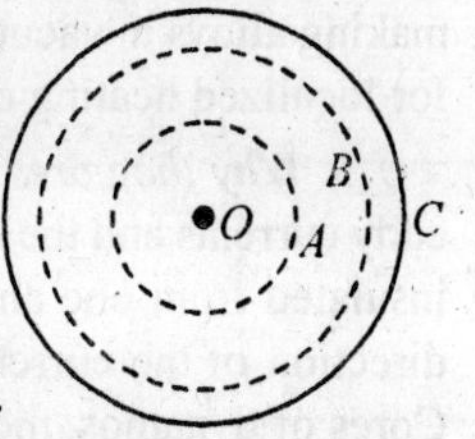

Fig. 11.13 (*a*)

The effective resistance of a conductor for alternating current is, therefore, greater than for a steady current *e.g.*, in the case of bare copper wire of diameter 0.03149 cm. the *A.C.* resistance for a frequency of 1.08×10^6 is 1.45 times that for a steady current.

(*b*) **Explanation.** Consider a cylindrical conductor *C* carrying an alternating current. The magnetic field due to a cylindrical shell at a point outside it is the same as if the currents were concentrated along the axis of the conductor and for points inside the shell the field is zero. Thus for a given current the magnetic flux is less when the current flows in the surface layers of the wire than when it flows in the layers near the axis. The self inductance and hence the impedance of the inner part *A* will be greater than that of an outer shell *B* of equal area. Hence more current will flow through *B* than through *A*.

Due to skin effect the conductors which are required to carry *A.C.* specially of high frequency do not consist of single thick wire but are made of a large number of strands of fine wire insulated from each other. This increases the surface area and hence decreases the resistance. Tubular conductors are used to carry alternating currents as the central part of a thick wire is practically useless.

Eddy currents. When a solid mass of metal is moved in a magnetic field induced currents are set up in closed paths within the body of the metal. These induced currents are called **Focault** or **eddy currents.** The direction of these currents is given by *Lenz's law* or *Fleming's right-hand rule*.

If a copper cylinder is placed with its axis at right angles to a uniform magnetic field acting in the plane of the paper and rotated about its axis as indicated (in the clockwise direction), then eddy currents will flow parallel to the axis of rotation in the upward direction in the right half of the cylinder and in the downward direction in the left half as shown in Fig. 11.13(*b*).

Practical applications. 1. *Induction motor.* When a metallic cylinder is placed in a rotating magnetic field and is capable of rotation about its axis *eddy currents* are set up in it. According to Lenz's law the direction of these currents is such as to stop the relative motion between the cylinder and the field. The cylinder, therefore, begins to rotate in the direction of rotation of the field. This is the principle of an induction motor.

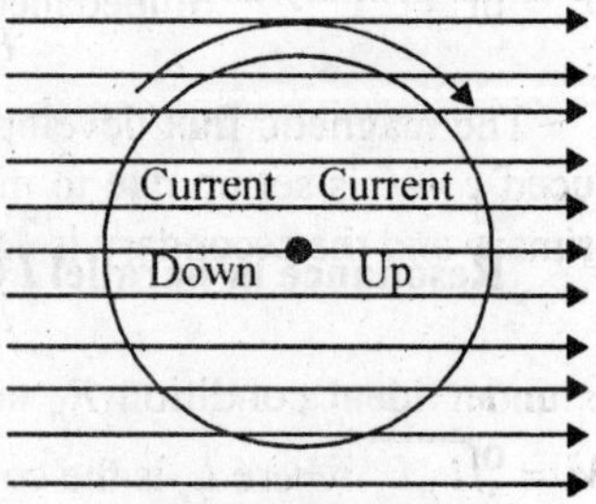

2. *Electric brake.* If in the previous case a stationary magnetic field is suddenly applied to a rotating cylinder or a disc the eddy currents set up in them exert a couple which tends to stop the motion of the disc. This principle is used in stopping an electric train.

Fig. 11.13 (b)

3. *Damping.* If a metal plate is made to oscillate between the poles of a powerful electromagnet its amplitude decreases rapidly when the field is applied until it stops. An important application of this electromagnetic damping is met with in the case of the moving coil type *dead beat* galvanometer. The eddy currents set up in the metallic frame on which the coil is wound and in the soft iron core when the coil oscillates tend to stop the oscillations and make it dead beat. The oscillations of a moving coil ballistic galvanometer can be stopped by short-circuiting it.

4. *Induction furnaces.* The eddy currents set up in the metallic masses produce a heating effect. This is used in induction furnaces in which the conducting substance to be heated is placed in a rapidly changing magnetic field. The heat generated melts the substance. This method is used for making alloys in vacuum to prevent oxidation. The heating effect of eddy currents has been also used for localized heating of the tissues of the body and is known as *inducto-thermy.*

5. *Why the cores of dynamos and motors are laminated* ? To reduce the heating effect due to eddy currents and the resultant loss of energy the metallic conductor is made in thin sheets or laminas insulated from one another by a coat of varnish, etc. The laminas are placed at right angles to the direction of the current. The insulating layer reduces the current and decreases the loss of energy. Cores of dynamos, motors and transformes are laminated on that account.

Q. 11.23. (*a*) **Explain in detail the construction, theory and uses of a transformer. What are energy losses and how are they reduced to a minimum?**

(*b*) **Why should alternating currents be used instead of direct for long distance power transmission?** (*Nag. U.*, 2002; *Meerut U.,* 2003, 2002, 2001; *Kerala U.* 2001; *Magadh U.* 1996)

Ans. (*a*) Transformer. A transformer is a device for converting alternating current at low voltages to high voltages and *vice-versa.* The transformer which converts low potentials to high potentials is called a **step-up transformer,** whereas the one which converts high potentials to low potentials is called a **step-down transformer.** A step up transformer is shown in Fig. 11.14.

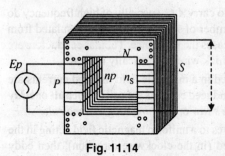

Fig. 11.14

Construction. A transformer usually consists of a rectangular (or circular) core of soft iron in the form of laminas insulated from one another. The *primary* and the *secondary* coils are wound up on the iron core so as to avoid leakage of magnetic flux and are well insulated from one another.

In the step-up transformer the number of turns in the secondary coil is greater than the number of turns in the primary coil while opposite is the case in a step-down transformer.

Principle. Let L_p and R_p be the inductance and resistance of the primary coil and L_S and R_S the corresponding values of the secondary coil. When an alternating *e.m.f.* E_p is applied to the primary a current I_p flows in it. This develops a magnetic flux in the core due to which an induced *E.M.F.* is set up in the primary and

$$E_p = R_p I_p + j\omega L_p I_p \qquad ...(i)$$

The magnetic flux developed in the primary is also linked with the secondary in which an induced *e.m.f.* is set up due to mutual induction. If the co-efficient of mutual induction between the primary and the secondary is M, then if the secondary circuit is *open*, we have

$$E_s = j\,\omega M I_p \qquad ...(ii)$$

as under ideal condition R_p may be assumed to be zero. Further if there is no leakage of flux $M = \sqrt{L_p L_s}$ where L_s is the co-efficient of self induction of the secondary. Thus we have

$$\frac{E_s}{E_p} = \frac{M}{L_p} = \frac{\sqrt{L_p L_s}}{L_p} = \sqrt{\frac{L_s}{L_p}}$$

If the primary coil is assumed to be infinite solenoid, then its inductance

$$L_p = \frac{\mu_0 \mu_r n_p^2 a}{l}$$

where n_p is the total number of turns in the primary, l its length, a the area of cross-section, μ_0 the permeability of free space and μ_r the relative permeability of the material of the core. Similarly the self inductance L_S of the secondary is given by

$$L_s = \frac{\mu_0 \mu_r n_s^2 a}{l}$$

assuming that the secondary has n_S turns and is wound over the primary *i.e.*, it has the same length and area of cross-section

$$\therefore \qquad \frac{L_s}{L_p} = \frac{n_s^2}{n_p^2}$$

Hence

$$\frac{E_s}{E_p} = \sqrt{\frac{L_s}{L_p}} = \frac{n_s}{n_p} = k$$

k is called the *transformation ratio* The secondary *e.m.f.*, however differs in phase from the primary *e.m.f.* by an angle π *i.e.*, it is opposite in phase.

It is further seen that whatever is gained in voltage is lost in current. Assuming that the power losses in the transformer are negligible, we have

Power in secondary = Power in primary

or

$$E_s I_s = E_p I_p$$

or

$$\frac{I_s}{I_p} = \frac{E_p}{E_s} = \frac{n_p}{n_s}$$

When the secondary circuit is open no current passes through it and there is very small current in the primary for magnetising the iron core. When the secondary circuit is closed a current flows in it in a direction opposite to that of primary current. This demagnetises the iron core which decreases the back *e.m.f.* in the primary circuit. The current in it increases till magnetic flux regains its original value. The transformer thus works automatically. It draws more current and hence consumes more energy in the primary when the load in the secondary circuit is increased. If the secondary circuit is open a negligible amount of energy is consumed.

The terminal voltage across the secondary also falls as the current in the secondary circuit increases. This can be shown as follows :

Let V_p be the voltage applied to the primary, then

$$V_p - E_p = I_p R_p$$

where R_p is the resistance of the primary circuit, I_p the current in it and E_p the back *e.m.f.*

$$\therefore \qquad\qquad E_p = V_p - I_p R_p \qquad\qquad\qquad ...(iii)$$

If V_S is the terminal voltage in the secondary, then

$$V_s = E_s - I_s R_s$$

where R_S is the resistance of the secondary circuit, I_s the current in it and E_s the induced *e.m.f.*

Hence $\qquad\qquad E_s = V_s + I_s R_s \qquad\qquad\qquad ...(iv)$

Dividing (*iv*) by (*iii*), we have

$$\frac{E_s}{E_p} = \frac{V_s + I_s R_s}{V_p - I_p V_p} = k$$

or $\qquad\qquad V_s + I_s R_s = k\,(V_p - I_p R_p)$

or $\qquad\qquad V_s = k V_p - I_s R_s - I_p R_p k$

But $\qquad\qquad I_p = k I_S$

$\therefore \qquad\qquad V_s = k V_p - I_s\,(R_s + k^2 R_p)$

Hence as I_s increases V_s decreases.

Uses. (*i*) A transformer is used to step-up or step down the *A.C.* voltage. If it raises the voltage, the current is automatically lowered in the same ratio. Such a transformer is called a *step-up transformer.* If it lowers the voltage, the current automatically rises. Such a transformer is called a *step down transformer* and is used in welding.

(*ii*) It is used to convert a variable audio-frequency current from lower voltage to high voltage as in telephone or in radio communication.

(*iii*) It is used to change the range of *A.C.* measuring instruments. Such transformers are known as instrument transformers.

(*iv*) In addition to these uses there are some special purpose transformers:

(*a*) *Impedance transformer.* It is used to match the impedance of two independent circuits.

(*b*) *Constant voltage transformer.* It is designed to give a constant output voltage even when the input voltage varies considerably.

(*c*) *Constant current transformer.* It is designed to give a constant output current.

Losses in a transformer. Although a transformer is a very efficient machine as there are no moving parts in it, yet it suffers from a number of losses.

(*i*) **Copper losses.** As the current flows through the primary and the secondary coil which generally consist of **copper** wires and have some resistance, heat is produced. The heat produced is given by $I^2 R$ and brings about a loss of energy.

(*ii*) **Iron losses.** Induced currents are also produced in the **iron** core of the transformer and utilise a part of energy. This loss is reduced by making the core of laminated sheets of soft iron insulated from each other.

(*iii*) **Magnetic leakage.** The entire magnetic flux produced by the primary does not flow through the secondary, thereby allowing a certain amount of energy supplied to the primary to go waste.

(*iv*) **Hysteresis loss.** The core of the transformer is taken through a cycle of magnetisation as many times per second as the frequency of the *A.C.* supply. In each cycle a loss of energy equal to the area of the P_mH loop takes place per unit volume of the core. This loss can be reduced by selecting a core for which the P_mH loop has a very small area.

(*b*) **Advantage of A.C. in long distance transmission.** When electrical energy is to be transmitted over a long distance the following disadvantages may be experienced :

(*i*) The line wire being very long has an appreciable resistance. A large amount of energy is dissipated in the wire in the form of heat.

(*ii*) There is a large fall of potential along the line wire so that the voltage at the receiving station is much below the voltage at the generating station.

(*iii*) In order to keep the line resistance low and to carry large currents thick wires have to be used which have a high initial cost. Thick wires being heavy require stronger poles to support them.

In *A.C.* transmission the use of a transformer removes all these disadvantages. The efficiency of a transformer is very high and there are practically no losses except for slight loss of energy due to *magnetic leakage, eddy currents* and *hysteresis*. The following example will make it clear :

Suppose we require 100 amperes current at 220 volts at the receiving station. The voltage at the generating station is stepped up, say to 22,000 volts and supplied at one ampere. The same is stepped down to 220 volts and 100 amperes at the receiving station. If we compare the heat losses in the line wire we find that in the first case the loss of energy being proportional to I^2 is 10,000 times that in the second case. Moreover, as the conductors have to carry only one ampere current thinner wires at a low initial cost can be used. This cannot be done in *D.C.* transmission. Hence *A.C.* transmission is preferred to *D.C.* transmission.

Q. 11.24. What is rotating magnetic field? Explain how a rotating magnetic field is established. Describe how it is used in the working of a single phase motor.   (*Magadh U.*, 1996)

Ans. Rotating magnetic field. A rotating magnetic field is that in which the magnitude of the magnetic field remains constant but the direction continuously rotates round a fixed axis with a uniform angular velocity. Such a field can be produced by a system of stationary coils supplied with single, two or three-phase *A.C.* An arrangement with two-phase alternating current is shown in Fig. 11.15.

How is it established. Let *AB* and *CD* be two pairs of poles supplied with alternating current. The pair *AB* is supplied current from one phase and the current through it is represented by

$$i_1 = I_0 \sin \omega t$$

The pair *CD* is supplied current from the other phase and the current through it differs in phase from the first by an angle $\pi/2$ and is represented by

$$i_2 = I_0 \sin \left(\omega t + \frac{\pi}{2} \right)$$

The magnetic field produced by these two currents are at *right angles to each other* as shown in Fig. 11.16 and their strengths at any instant are proportional to the current.

When the current is maximum, *i.e.*, I_0 the field is also maximum say H_0. The magnetic fields H_1 and H_2 along *AB* and *CD* respectively, are then represented by

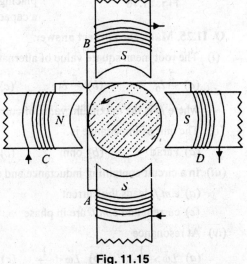

Fig. 11.15

$$H_1 = H_0 \sin \omega t$$

and
$$H_2 = H_0 \sin\left(\omega t + \frac{\pi}{2}\right)$$

$$= H_0 \cos \omega t$$

The magnitude of the resultant of the two fields.

$$= \sqrt{H_1^2 + H_2^2}$$

$$= \sqrt{(H_0 \sin \omega t)^2 + (H_0 \cos \omega t)^2}$$

$$= H_0$$

The direction of this resultant is given by

$$\tan \theta = \frac{H_0 \sin \omega t}{H_0 \cos \omega t} = \tan \omega t$$

$$\therefore \qquad \theta = \omega t$$

Hence the resultant field has constant value H_0 and rotates with a constant angular velocity ω in the anti-clockwise direction.

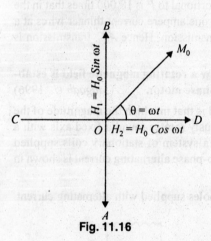

Fig. 11.16

If the field H_1 leads the field H_2 by an angle $\frac{\pi}{2}$, then the resultant field will rotate in the opposite direction with the same angular velocity. If now a conductor or a coil is placed within the magnetic field as shown in Fig. 11.15 an induced *e.m.f.* will be set up in the conductor due to the rotation of the magnetic field. According to Lenz's law, the conductor will also begin to rotate in the same direction so as to reduce the relative velocity between the resultant field and itself.

Single phase motor. The above theory is used in the construction of induction type *A.C.* motors. For single phase *A.C.* supply the phase difference of 90° ($\pi/2$) is produced by placing an inductance in the circuit of one pair of poles and a capacitance in the circuit of the other pair.

Q. 11.25. Mark the correct answer.

(*i*) The root mean square value of alternating current is

(*a*) $\frac{2}{\pi} I_0$ (*b*) $\frac{\pi}{2} I_0$ (*c*) $\frac{I_0}{\sqrt{2}}$ (*d*) $\sqrt{2} I_0$

where I_0 is the maximum value of current.

(*ii*) The unit of impedance is

(*a*) Farad   (*b*) ohm   (*c*) henry   (*d*) all these

(*iii*) In a circuit containing inductance and resistance

(*a*) *e.m.f.* leads the current   (*b*) current leads the *e.m.f.*

(*c*) current and *e.m.f.* are in phase   (*d*) anything

(*iv*) At resonance

(*a*) $L\omega > \frac{1}{C\omega}$ (*b*) $L\omega < \frac{1}{C\omega}$ (*c*) $L\omega = \frac{1}{C\omega}$ (*d*) $L\omega = C\omega$

(v) Current in a circuit is wattless when the phase difference between current and voltage is

    (a) zero   (b) $\dfrac{\pi}{2}$ (c) $+\pi$ (d) $-\pi$

Ans. (i) c   (ii) b   (iii) a   (iv) c   (v) b

EXERCISES

1. To a circuit containing an inductance of 10 milli-henry a capacitor of 1 microfarad and a resistance of 10 ohms in series an R.M.S. voltage of 100 volts is applied. Calculate the frequency at which the circuit will be in resonance with current of the same frequency and find the value of current.   **[Ans.** $n = 1592$; $I_v = 10$ Amp**]**

2. A series circuit has resistance of 75 ohms and an impedance of 150 ohms. What power is consumed in the circuit when an effective voltage 120 volts is applied to it?

                                                        [Ans. 48 Watts]

3. An inductance coil takes 10 Amp and dissipates 1000 watts when connected to A.C. supply of 250 volts 25 cycles. Find (a) the power factor (b) angle of lag.

                                              [Ans. (a) 0.4 (b) 66° 23′**]**

4. When a choke and 20 ohm resistance are connected in series with 110 volt 50 Hz alternating e.m.f., power consumption is 5 W. Find the inductance of choke.   *(Kerala U., 2001)*

Hint. $I_v = \dfrac{E_v}{\sqrt{R^2 + X_L^2}}$; $\cos\phi = \dfrac{R}{\sqrt{R^2 + X_L^2}}$

Power consumed $= E_v\, I_v \cos\phi = E_v \times \dfrac{E_v}{\sqrt{R^2 + X_L^2}} \times \dfrac{R}{\sqrt{R^2 + X_L^2}}$

$$= \dfrac{E_v^2 \times R}{R^2 + X_L^2} = 5$$

or $\dfrac{110 \times 110 \times 20}{400 + X_L^2} = 5$ or $X_L^2 = \dfrac{110 \times 110 \times 20}{5} - 400$

$$= 48000$$

or $X_L = \sqrt{48000} = 219$

or $2\pi n L = 219$ $\therefore\ L = \dfrac{219}{2 \times 3.14 \times 50} = 0.7\,H$